A COMPREHENSIVE TREATISE ON
INORGANIC AND THEORETICAL CHEMISTRY

VOLUME VII
Ti, Zr, Hf, Th, Ge, Sn, Pb, Inert Gases

The complete work

A COMPREHENSIVE TREATISE ON
INORGANIC AND THEORETICAL CHEMISTRY
In Sixteen Volumes.   With Diagrams.

Vol. I.	H, O.
Vol. II.	F, Cl, Br, I, Li, Na, K, Rb, Cs.
Vol. III.	Cu, Ag, Au, Ca, Sr, Ba.
Vol. IV.	Ra and Ac Families, Be, Mg, Zn, Cd, Hg.
Vol. V.	B, Al, Ga, In, Tl, Sc, Ce, and Rare Earth Metals, C (Part I).
Vol. VI.	C (Part II), Si, Silicates.
Vol. VII.	Ti, Zr, Hf, Th, Ge, Sn, Pb, Inert Gases.
Vol. VIII.	N, P.
Vol. IX.	As, Sb, Bi, V, Cb, Ta.
Vol. X.	S, Se.
Vol. XI.	Te, Cr, Mo, W.
Vol. XII.	U, Mn, Ma and Re, Fe (Part I).
Vol. XIII.	Fe (Part II).
Vol. XIV.	Fe (Part III), Co.
Vol. XV.	Ni, Ru, Rh, Pd, Os, Ir.
Vol. XVI.	Pt and General Index, completing the work.

SUPPLEMENT TO MELLOR'S COMPREHENSIVE
TREATISE ON INORGANIC AND THEORETICAL CHEMISTRY

Vol. II, Supplement I:	F, Cl, Br, I, At.
Vol. II, Supplement II:	Li, Na.
Vol. II, Supplement III:	K, Rb, Cs, Fr.
Vol. VIII, Supplement I:	N.

Other volumes in preparation.

By the same author
MODERN INORGANIC CHEMISTRY

A COMPREHENSIVE TREATISE ON

INORGANIC
AND THEORETICAL
CHEMISTRY

BY

J. W. MELLOR, D.Sc., F.R.S.

VOLUME VII

WITH 255 DIAGRAMS

1724

LONGMANS

LONGMANS, GREEN AND CO LTD
48 Grosvenor Street, London W.1

Associated companies, branches and representatives
throughout the world

New Impression 1963

Made and Printed in Great Britain by
William Clowes and Sons Ltd, London and Beccles

CONTENTS

CHAPTER XLI

TITANIUM

§ 1. The Discovery of Titanium (1); § 2. The Occurrence of Titanium (2); § 3. The Extraction of Titania (6); § 4. The Preparation of Titanium (8); § 5. The Physical Properties of Titanium (14); § 6. The Chemical Properties of Titanium (18); § 7. The Titanium Oxides and Hydroxides (27); § 8. The Titanates (50); § 9. The Higher Oxides of Titanium—Pertitanates and Hypertitanates (63); § 10. Titanium Fluorides (66); § 11. Hydrofluotitanic Acid, and the Fluotitanates (69); § 12. Titanium Chlorides (74); § 13. Titanium Bromides (87); § 14. Titanium Iodides (89); § 15. The Titanium Sulphides (90); § 16. The Titanium Sulphates (91); § 17. Titanium Carbonates, Nitrates, and Phosphates (96).

CHAPTER XLII

ZIRCONIUM

§ 1. History of Zirconium (98); § 2. The Occurrence of Zirconium (99); § 3. The Extraction of Zirconia from the Minerals (101); § 4. The Preparation of Zirconium (106); § 5. The Physical Properties of Zirconium (110); § 6. The Chemical Properties of Zirconium (114); § 7. The Zirconium Oxides (123); § 8. The Zirconates (134); § 9. Zirconium Fluoride, and the Fluozirconates (137); § 10. Zirconium Chlorides and Chlorozirconates (143); § 11. Zirconium Bromides and Iodides (149); § 12. Zirconium Sulphides and Sulphates (152); § 13. Zirconium Carbonates (160); § 14. Zirconium Nitrates (161); § 15. Zirconium Phosphates (163).

CHAPTER XLIII

HAFNIUM

§ 1. The History of Hafnium and Celtium (166); § 2. The Occurrence of Hafnium (166); § 3. The Extraction of Hafnia (167); § 4. Hafnium and its Properties (170); § 5. The Salts of Hafnium (170).

CHAPTER XLIV

THORIUM

§ 1. The History and Occurrence of Thorium (174); § 2. The Extraction of Thoria (178); § 3. The Radioactivity of Thorium (184); § 4. The Preparation and Properties of Thorium (203); § 5. The Incandescent Mantle (213); § 6. Thorium Oxides and

Hydroxides (220); § 7. Thorium Fluorides (227); § 8. Thorium Chlorides (228); § 9. Thorium Bromides (236); § 10. Thorium Iodi es (238); § 11. Thorium Sulphides (239); § 12. Thorium Sulphates (240); § 13. Thorium Carbonates (248); § 14. Thorium Nitrates (249); § 15. Thorium Phosphates (252).

CHAPTER XLV

GERMANIUM

§ 1. The Discovery and Occurrence of Germanium (254); § 2. The Extraction and Preparation of Germanium (256); § 3. The Properties of Germanium (258); § 4. Germanium Hydrides (263); § 5. The Germanium Oxides and Hydroxides (265); § 6. The Germanium Fluorides (268); § 7. The Germanium Chlorides (269); § 8. Germanium Bromide and Iodides (271); § 9. The Germanium Sulphides (273).

CHAPTER XLVI

TIN

§ 1. The History of Tin (276); § 2. The Occurrence of Tin (280); § 3. The Extraction and Purification of Tin (286); § 4. The Physical Properties of Tin (295); § 5. The Chemical Properties of Tin (323); § 6. The Alloys of Tin with the Alkali Metals (344); § 7. The Alloys of Tin and Copper (347); § 8. Alloys of Tin with Silver and Gold (368); § 9. Alloys of Tin with the Metals of the Alkaline Earths, and of the Zinc Family (372); § 10. Alloys of Tin with Aluminium, Indium, Thallium, and Cerium (383); § 11. Stannous Oxide and Hydroxide (386); § 12. Stannic Oxide (394); § 13. The Stannic Hydroxides; and the Stannic and Perstannic Acids (404); § 14. The Stannates (414); § 15. The Fluorides of Tin and the Fluostannates (422); § 16. The Stannous Chlorides (424); § 17. The Stannic Chlorides (436); § 18. The Stannous Bromides (452); § 19. The Stannic Bromides (454); § 20. The Stannous Iodides (457); § 21. The Stannic Iodides (462); § 22. Stannous Sulphides (465); § 23. Stannic Sulphide (469); § 24. The Sulphostannates or Thiostannates (473); § 25. The Tin Sulphates (477); § 26. Tin Carbonates (480); § 27. Tin Nitrates (480); § 28. The Tin Phosphates (481).

CHAPTER XLVII

LEAD

§ 1. The History of Lead (484); § 2. The Occurrence of Lead (487); § 3. The Extraction of Lead (495); § 4. The Physical Properties of Lead (515); § 5. The Chemical Properties of Lead (561); § 6. The Valency and Atomic Weight of Lead (600); § 7. The Alloys of Lead with the Alkali Metals (606); § 8. The Alloys of Lead with Copper, Silver, and Gold (609); § 9. Alloys of Lead with the Metals of the Alkaline Earths, and of the Magnesium-Zinc Family (613); § 10. Alloys of Lead with Aluminium, Indium, Thallium, and Tin (624); § 11. Lead Suboxide, or Hemioxide (636); § 12. Lead Monoxide (638); § 13. The Physical Properties of Lead Monoxide (644); § 14. The Chemical Properties of Lead Monoxide (650); § 15. Lead Hydroxides (661); § 16. The Plumbites (665); § 17. The Higher Oxides of Lead (669); § 18. Red-lead, or Minium (672); § 19. Lead Dioxide (681); § 20. The Plumbates (695); § 21. Lead Fluorides (701); § 22. Lead Chlorides (706); § 23. Complex Salts with the Lead Chlorides — Chloroplumbites (725); § 24. Chloroplumbates (734); § 25. Lead Oxychlorides (736); § 26. Lead Bromides (745);

§ 27. Lead Iodide (757); § 28. The Complex Salts of Lead Iodide (771); § 29. Lead Sulphide (779); § 30. Lead Sulphates (803); § 31. Lead Carbonates (828); § 32. White-Lead (841); § 33. Complex Salts of Lead Carbonates (852); § 34. Lead Nitrates (856); § 35. Lead Phosphates (875).

CHAPTER XLVIII

INERT GASES

§ 1. The History of the Inert Gases (889); § 2. The Occurrence of the Inert Gases (892); § 3. The Preparation of the Rare Gases (902); § 4. The Physical Properties of the Inert Gases (906); § 5. The Chemical Properties of the Inert Gases (941); § 6. The Atomic and Molecular Weights of the Inert Gases (947).

INDEX 953

ABBREVIATIONS

aq. = aqueous

atm. = atmospheric or atmosphere(s)

at. vol. = atomic volume(s)

at. wt. = atomic weight(s)

$T°$ or $°K$ = absolute degrees of temperature

b.p. = boiling point(s)

$θ°$ = centigrade degrees of temperature

coeff. = coefficient

conc. = concentrated or concentration

dil. = dilute

eq. = equivalent(s)

f.p. = freezing point(s)

m.p. = melting point(s)

$mol(s) = \begin{cases} \text{gram-molecule(s)} \\ \text{gram-molecular} \end{cases}$

$mol(s). = \begin{cases} \text{molecule(s)} \\ \text{molecular} \end{cases}$

mol. ht. = molecular heat(s)

mol. vol. = molecular volume(s)

mol. wt. = molecular weight(s)

press. = pressure(s)

sat. = saturated

soln. = solution(s)

sp. gr. = specific gravity (gravities)

sp. ht. = specific heat(s)

sp. vol. = specific volume(s)

temp. = temperature(s)

vap. = vapour

In the **cross references** the first number in clarendon type is the number of the volume; the second number refers to the chapter; and the succeeding number refers to the "§," section. Thus **5**. 38, 24 refers to § 24, chapter 38, volume 5.

The oxides, hydrides, halides, sulphides, sulphates, carbonates, nitrates, and phosphates are considered with the basic elements; the other compounds are taken in connection with the acidic element. The double or complex salts in connection with a given element include those associated with elements previously discussed. The carbides, silicides, titanides, phosphides, arsenides, etc., are considered in connection with carbon, silicon, titanium, etc. The intermetallic compounds of a given element include those associated with elements previously considered.

The use of **triangular diagrams** for representing the properties of three-component systems was suggested by G. G. Stokes (*Proc. Roy. Soc.*, **49**. 174, 1891). The method was immediately taken up in many directions and it has proved of great value. With practice it becomes as useful for representing the properties of ternary mixtures as squared paper is for binary mixtures. The principle of triangular diagrams is based on the fact that in an equilateral triangle the sum of the perpendicular distances of any point from the three sides is a constant. Given any three substances *A*, *B*, and *C*, the composition of any possible combination of these can be represented by a point in or on the triangle. The apices of the triangle represent the single components A, B, and C, the sides of the triangle represent binary mixtures of A and B, B and C, or C and A; and points within the triangle ternary mixture. The compositions of the mixtures can be represented in percentages, or referred to unity, 10, etc. In Fig. 1, pure A will be represented by a point at the apex marked A. If 100 be the

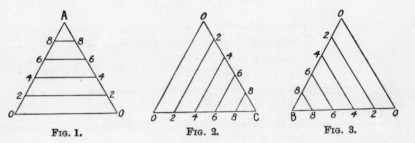

FIG. 1.   FIG. 2.   FIG. 3.

standard of reference, the point A represents 100 per cent. of A and nothing else; mixtures containing 80 per cent. of A are represented by a point on the line 88, 60 per cent. of A by a point on the line 66, etc. Similarly with B and C—Figs. 3 and 2 respectively. Combine Figs. 1, 2, and 3 into one diagram by superposition, and Fig. 4 results. Any point in this

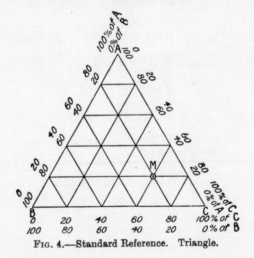

FIG. 4.—Standard Reference. Triangle.

diagram, Fig. 4, thus represents a ternary mixture. For instance, the point M represents a mixture containing 20 per cent. of A, 20 per cent. of B, and 60 per cent. of C.

CHAPTER XLI

TITANIUM

§ 1. The Discovery of Titanium

In 1791, W. Gregor [1] studied the black sands of Menacan, near Falmouth, Cornwall, and found some greyish-black granules which were attracted by a magnet. He digested 100 grains of the mineral with hydrochloric acid and obtained an insoluble grey powder, and a soln. which, when treated with aq. ammonia, furnished a precipitate which, on calcination, gave $46\frac{9}{16}$ grains of magnetic oxide of iron with traces of manganese oxide. When the grey powder was digested for a long time with hot sulphuric acid, an insoluble residue was obtained, which, after calcination, contained $3\frac{1}{2}$ grains of silica. When the yellow sulphuric acid soln. was treated with potash-lye, a white precipitate was obtained which gave on calcination 45 grains of a brownish calx. W. Gregor's analysis of the black sand is therefore

Magnetite	Silica.	Brownish calx.	Loss.
$46\frac{9}{16}$	$3\frac{1}{2}$	45	$4\frac{15}{16}$ per cent.

The yellow sulphuric acid soln. was changed to an amethyst or purple colour by the action of metallic zinc, tin, or iron ; and to yellow, by tincture of galls. The precipitate itself, in contact with dil. acid, is also coloured purple by contact with zinc ; and a reddish-purple slag is obtained when an intimate mixture of the powdered mineral and coal-dust is fused in a crucible. Hence, said W. Gregor :

The extraordinary properties of the sand have led me to believe that it contains a new metallic substance. In order to distinguish this substance from others, I have ventured to suggest a name derived from the neighbourhood—Menacan, Cornwall—where it was found, and therefore I propose to call the metal *menacanite.*

Three years later, M. H. Klaproth [2] analyzed a specimen of a mineral from Boinik, called *Hungarian red schörl*. He found this product to be a natural metallic oxide which possessed peculiar properties, and hence, he inferred it to be the calx of a new metal which he called *titanium*. The name was borrowed from mythology —the Titans, " the first sons of the earth "—because, " in order to avoid giving rise to erroneous ideas, it is best to choose a name which means nothing in itself, whenever no name can be found which indicates the peculiar and characteristic properties of a substance." About the same time, 1794, M. H. Klaproth also found that a brown mineral from Passau contained about 33 per cent. of titanium oxide, 33 per cent. of lime, and 33 per cent. of silica, with a trace of manganese. He called this · mineral *titanite.* About 1797, the same observer analyzed the black magnetic sand from Menacan, and found it to contain iron oxide, 51 per cent. ; titanium oxide, 42·25 per cent. ; silica, 3·5 per cent. ; and manganese oxide, 0·25 per cent. He accordingly suggested that the suspected new element in W. Gregor's mineral— *kein anderer sei, als eben der, welcher den hungarischen roten Schorl bildet ; namlich Titankalk*, so that W. Gregor's new metallic substance is identical with M. H. Klaproth's titanium. M. H. Klaproth's results were confirmed by W. A. Lampadius,[3] J. T. Lowitz, and L. N. Vauquelin, but the systematic investigation of purified titanic oxide was made by H. Rose, about 1824. The impure metal was isolated by J. J. Berzelius in 1825, and by F. Wöhler, in 1849 ; but it was not until comparatively recent times that a metal of even a moderate degree of purity was obtained.

A. Scott [4] reported a new element from the black titaniferous sands of Maketu, New Zealand. The properties of its compounds were those characteristic of the titanium-uranium family ; its at. wt. was stated to be 144 ; and it was said to form a cinnamon-coloured oxide very resistant to chemical agents. He proposed calling the new element *oceanium*—from Oceanus, one of the Titans. D. Coster and G. Hevesy's examination of A. Scott's preparation showed no X-ray spectral lines characteristic of a new element ; and C. J. Smithells and F. S. Goucher failed to establish the existence of a new element in the Maketu sands. A. Scott showed later that the oxide of the supposed new element was nothing more than titanium oxide associated with silica, and postulated that part of the titanium was replaced by silicon. The colour was due to the presence of a little iron oxide.

REFERENCES.

[1] W. Gregor, *Crell's Ann.*, i, 40, 103, 1791 ; ii, 55, 1791 ; *Journ. Phys.*, **72.** 152, 1791.
[2] M. H. Klaproth, *Beiträge zur chemischen Kenntniss der Mineralkörper*, Berlin, **1.** 233, 245, 1795 ; **2.** 222, 226, 1797 ; **4.** 153, 1801 ; **5.** 208, 1810 ; *Journ. Mines,* **2.** 45, 1795 ; **3.** 1, 1796.
[3] W. A. Lampadius, *Sammlung praktisch-chemischen Abhandlungen*, Dresden, **2.** 124, 1797 ; *Crell's Ann.*, **25.** 1, 230, 259, 1797 ; J. T. Lowitz. *ib.*, **31.** 1, 183, 1799 ; L. N. Vauquelin, *Journ. Phys.*, **66.** 345, 1805 ; L. N. Vauquelin and L. Hecht *Journ. Mines*, **3.** 15, 1796 ; R. Chenevix, *Phil. Trans.*. **92.** 327, 1802 ; *Nicholson's Journ.*, **5.** 132, 1802 ; J. J. Berzelius, *Pogg. Ann.*, **4.** 1, 1825 ; F. Wöhler, *Liebig's Ann.*, **73.** 34, 1849 ; **74.** 212, 1849 ; H. Rose, *Gilbert's Ann.*, **73.** 7, 129, 1821 : *Pogg. Ann.*, **1.** 76, 1824 ; **3.** 13, 1825 ; **12.** 479, 1828 ; **15.** 145, 1829 ; **16.** 57, 18 9 ; **24.** 141, 1832 ; **42.** 527, 1837 ; E. J. Hallock, *Index to the Literature of Titanium, 1783-1876*, Washington, 1879 ; *Ann. New York Acad.*, **1.** 53, 1879 ; G. A. Koenig, *Proc. Phil. Acad. Science*, 42, 1876.
[4] A. Scott, *Journ. Chem. Soc.*, **123.** 311, 1923 ; *Nature*, **111.** 463, 598, 1923 ; C. J. Smithells and F. S. Goucher, *ib.*, **111.** 397, 463, 881, 1923 ; D. Coster and G. Hevesy, *ib.*, **111.** 252, 1923.

§ 2. The Occurrence of Titanium

The metal does not occur free in nature. Its compounds are very widely diffused in small quantities ; indeed, although titanium is often grouped with the scarce metals, it appears to be more abundant than copper, lead, zinc, or any of the common metals except iron. Titanium, however, is rarely found with any considerable quantity located in one spot. Concentrated deposits are scarce. Titanium is nearly always a constituent of igneous rocks, and of sediments derived therefrom. According to F. W. Clarke,[1] out of 800 rocks analyzed in the United States, 784 contained titanium. J. H. L. Vogt, J. F. Kemp, A. Harker, and H. S. Washington also made confirmatory reports. From J. Joly's and F. W. Clarke's estimates 0·46 per cent. of the earth's crust is titanium, 27·7 per cent. silicon, and thorium 0·002 per cent. F. W. Clarke and H. S. Washington gave 0·46 per cent. of titanium ; and J. H. L. Vogt, 0·33 per cent. According to A. J. Angström,[2] F. Cornu, G. Salet, R. Thalén, H. L. Cortie, J. N. Lockyer and F. E. Baxandall, H. Deslandres, W. M. Mitchell, M. N. Saha, F. W. Dyson, and W. S. Adams, titanium is present, probably in the gaseous state, in the atm. of the sun. A. Fowler observed it in the spectra of stars. A. Daubrée, C. F. Rammelsberg, G. P. Merrill and H. N. Stokes, and E. E. Howell and co-workers found titanium in various meteorites.

The most important mineral sources of titanium are rutile and ilmenite ; perowskite and sphene are of less importance. These minerals are discussed elsewhere. **Rutile** contains 90–100 per cent. TiO_2 (*q.v.*), and varieties are represented by the minerals *crispite, davidite, dicksbergite, ilmenorutile, nigrine, sagenite,* and *strüverite.* Another tetragonal form of rutile is **anatase** or *octahedrite ;* and the rhombic form is **brookite,** with its varieties *arkansite* and *jurinite.* The **titanates** are represented by **ilmenite,** a ferrous titanate, $FeTiO_3$. This mineral has 3 to 59 per cent. TiO_2, and varieties are called *crichtonite, hystatite, iserine, kibdelophane, picroilmenite, titanoferrite, washingtonite,* and *titaniferous iron ore.* The ferric orthotitanate, $Fe_4(TiO_4)_3$, is represented by **pseudobrookite,** and ferric meta-titanate, $Fe_2(TiO_3)_3$, by **arizonite ;** calcium metatitanate, $CaTiO_3$, by **perowskite ;**

hydrotitanite is an altered perowskite; and *knopite* is a related variety. Magnesium metatitanate, $MgTiO_3$, is represented by **geikielite** ; manganese metatitanate, $MnTiO_3$, by **pyrophanite** ; a mixed mesodititanate $(Fe,Mn,Pb)TiO_3$, by *senaite*. *Astrophyllite* is a titanium silicate ; and *lamprophyllite* is a related variety. The **titanosilicates** are represented by **sphene** or *titanite*, $CaTiSiO_5$, and *guarinite*, $CaTiSiO_1$. As varieties appear *alshedite, aspidelite, eucolite-titanite, greenovite, grothite, lederite, ligurite, menacanite, pictite, spinthere;* and *yttrotitanite;* with the alteration products *leucoxene, titanomorphite,* and *xanthitane.* A barium titanosilicate, $BaTiSi_3O_9$, is represented by *benitoite.* A titaniferous garnet is called *schlorlomite,* and the variety *ivaarite; œnigmatite* and the variety *cossyrite* are iron and columbium titanosilicates ; *neptunite* is a titanosilicate of alkalies and iron ; *keilhauite,* of calcium, aluminium, iron, and yttrium ; *narsarsukite,* iron and sodium ; *lorenzenite,* of sodium and zirconium ; *leucosphenite,* sodium, barium, and zirconium ; *tscheffkinite,* of calcium, iron, aluminium, cerium, and yttrium ; and *molengraaffite* and *rhonite* are still more complex. The **boro.itanates** are represented by *warwickite;* and the **titanoantimonites** by *lewisite, mauzelite,* and *derbylite—vide* antimonites.

J. C. G. de Marignac [3] showed that a number of columbates and tantalates may be regarded as titanium minerals, although they are separately discussed with the elements columbium and tantalum. For example, *œschynite* (21 per cent. TiO_2), *blomstrandine* (21–23 per cent. TiO_2), *blomstrandite* (10–11 per cent. TiO_2), *chalcolamprite* are related to *pyrochlore, dysanalyte* (40–60 per cent. TiO_2), *epistolite* (7–8 per cent. TiO_2), *euxenite* (20–24 per cent. TiO_2), *marignacite* and *pyrochlore* (5·14 per cent. TiO_2), *polycrase* (25–30 per cent. TiO_2), *polymignite* (18–19 per cent. TiO_2), *risörite* (6–7 per cent. TiO_2), and *wilkite* (23–24 per cent. TiO_2). Similar remarks apply to the cerium minerals *johnstrupite* (7–8 per cent. TiO_2), *mosandrite* (5–10 per cent. TiO_2), *rinkite* (13–14 per cent. TiO_2) ; the yttrium minerals *delorenzite* (55–70 per cent. TiO_2), and *yttrocrasite* (40–50 per cent. TiO_2) ; and the zirconium minerals *hainite* (28–32 per cent. TiO_2), *rosenbuschite* (20 per cent. TiO_2), and *zirkelite* (14–15 per cent. TiO_2). The occurrence of titanium in the spinel *hoegbomite* was discussed by T. L. Watson.[4] Many observations,[5] in addition to those cited above, have been made on the occurrence of titanium in minerals.

E. Cohen,[6] M. F. Heddle, E. Jackson, P. Jannasch and J. H. Kloos, F. Knapp, E. Riley, H. Rose, A. Sauer, T. Scheerer, A. Stelzner, G. Vogt, and L. van Werweke have emphasized the almost ubiquitous occurrence of titanium in silicate rocks. R. Apjohn, and V. Roussel found it in basalt and trap rocks. A. F. de Fourcroy and L. N. Vauquelin found titanium in the ferruginous gangue of the platinum deposits ; and A. Damour, J. J. Berzelius and co-workers, and A. des Cloizeaux, in auriferous and platiniferous sands. T. Thomson, and R. D. Silva reported it in various sands ; H. St. C. Deville, in bauxite ; and J. Peschier, H. Rose, and L. N. Vauquelin, in many micas. L. Dieulafait reported it in various primordial rocks ; and A. B. Griffiths found 0·68 per cent. TiO_2 in the volcanic ash of Mt. Pelée ; and P. A. Dufrénoy, in volcanic iron. It occurs in biotite (up to 5 per cent.), lepidomelane (up to 5 per cent.), titanolivine (up to 6 per cent.), pyroxenes (up to 5 per cent.), andradite (up to 10 per cent.), and in amphiboles (up to 9 per cent.). It has been found in felspars, dolomitic marble, nepheline, etc. Analyses have been reported by F. P. Dunnington, W. P. Jorissen, A. Harker, F. W. Clarke, H. S. Washington, W. M. Thornton, etc. It is a very common constituent of clays, and was noted in various clays by C. M. Kersten, W. F. Salm-Horstmar, E. Riley, G. Vogt, C. Bischof, W. Aleksiejeff, F. P. Dunnington, etc. R. H. Brett and G. Bird found titanium in Hessian crucibles, but F. Wöhler and A. Schwarzenberg, O. L. Erdmann, and J. E. Herberger could not confirm this. Titanium was found in most soils examined by W. F. Salm-Horstmar, E. Jackson, F. P. Dunnington, G. F. McCaleb, E. Odernheimer, etc. W. O. Robinson and W. J. McCaughey found it in the soils of Chinese tea plantations. W. Biltz and

E. Marcus detected it in the clay of the Stassfurt salt beds. C. Baskerville found it in peat ; E. Jackson, in coal ash ; C. E. Wait, in bituminous coal (0·69–0·95 per cent.), and anthracite (up to 2·59 per cent.). L. Franck found some diamonds coloured with titanium ; but H. Moissan did not find any in the ash of diamonds. This element is found in beds of hæmatite and magnetite, forming titaniferous magnetites. J. T. Singewald,[7] C. U. Slocum, A. Vogel and C. Reischauer, etc., have discussed this subject. The occurrence of titanium in iron ores has been reported by A. Terreil, J. H. L. Vogt, E. Riley, H. Rose, R. Mushet, J. J. Nöggerath, T. Virlet d'Aoust, C. F. Rammelsberg, R. Thalén, G. W. Maynard, R. Akerman, E. J. Chapman, P. W. Shimer, A. Tamm, T. König and O. F. von der Pfordten, T. W. Hogg, A. Ledebur, J. F. Kemp, T. H. Cope, L. de Launey, N. P. Hulst, F. W. Clarke, P. Berthier, H. S. Washington, H. le Chatelier, etc. P. C. Grignon, and W. H. Wollaston found crystals of titanium, or rather titanium carbonitride, in the iron slags of Merthyr Tydvil, Wales ; and they have been remarked by many others—C. Reinhardt, E. Franck, J. J. Nöggerath, B. Osann, H. von Fehling, M. Meyer, F. L. Hünefeld, T. W. Hogg, J. W. Döbereiner, G. F. Comstock, C. M. Kersten, etc. The crystals have also been observed in blast-furnace iron by F. A. Walchner, H. E. F. G. Sandberger, E. Emmons and W. R. Johnson, J. K. L. Zincken, A. Laugier, R. Akerman, C. F. B. Karsten, J. Nöggerath, L. Franck, J. L. Bell, H. Blumenau, H. D. Rogers, W. H. Harris and J. Stenson, J. Percy, B. Kerl, A. J. Rossi, C. F. Rammelsberg, D. Forbes, T. S. Hunt, G. W. Maynard, C. U. Slocum, J. Hörnhager, F. Kick and W. F. Gintl, W. Bettel, and E. Riley ; and described in various treatises on the manufacture of iron and steel. The element has been reported in various iron alloys and in steel, by A. J. Rossi and co-workers, J. A. Paris, R. Mushet, E. Riley, O. Bauer, E. Bahlsen, J. H. Pratt, R. A. Hadfield, L. Guillet, C. U. Slocum, W. Venator, F. A. Fitzgerald, L. Treuheit, E. von Maltitz, P. H. Dudley, G. B. Waterhouse, A. E. Nordenskjöld, E. L. Gruner, A. Nies, A. Carnot and E. Goutal, etc. C. H. Pfaff reported titanium in a sample of commercial sulphuric acid. M. Mazade, and O. Henry found titanium in the mineral water of Nérac. E. Jackson, and C. E. Wait found this element in the ashes of many plants—the former found it in cotton-seed cake, sawdust, and in the seeds of French beans ; the latter found apple- and pear-tree ash contained 0·21 per cent. TiO_2 ; oak-wood ash, 0·31 per cent. ; apples, 0·11 per cent. ; cow-peas ash, 0·01 per cent. ; cotton-seed cake, 0·02 per cent. ; and F. Traetta-Mosca found it spectroscopically in tobacco. E. O. von Lippmann found 0·12 per cent. of titanium in vinasse. G. O. Rees found titanium in human blood and in the suprarenal glands, but R. L. Marchand contradicted this ; however, C. Baskerville found 0·0195 per cent. titanium in beefbone ; 0·013 per cent. in beef flesh ; 0·0325 per cent. in human flesh ; and a trace in human bone.

REFERENCES.

[1] F. W. Clarke, Chem. News, **61**. 31, 1890 ; Bull. U.S. Geol. Sur., 419, 1910 ; The Data of Geochemistry, Washington, 1914 ; T. L. Watson and S. Taber, Bull. Virginia Geol. Sur., **111**. 10, 1913 ; J. Joly, Phil. Mag., (6), **17**. 760, 1909 ; (6), **18**. 140, 1909 ; (5), 20. 125, 353, 1910 ; A. Harker, Geol. Mag., (4), **6**. 220, 1899 ; H. S. Washington, Prof. Paper U.S. Geol. Sur., **14**. 106, 1903 ; Amer. Journ. Science, (4), **24**. 217, 1907 ; F. W. Clarke and G. Steiger, Journ. Washington Acad., **4**. 57, 1914 ; F. W. Clarke and H. S. Washington, Proc. Nat. Acad. Sciences, **8**. 108, 1922 ; The Composition of the Earth's Crust, Washington, 1924 ; J. H. L. Vogt, Zeit. prakt. Geol., **6**. 225, 314, 377, 413, 1898 ; **7**. 10, 274, 1899 ; J. F. Kemp, Econ. Geol., **1**. 207, 1905 ; L. Moser, Œster. Chem. Ztg., **26**. 67, 1923.

[2] A. Fowler, Proc. Roy. Soc., **79** A, 509, 1907 ; J. N. Lockyer and F. E. Baxandall, ib., **74**. 255, 1905 ; H. L. Cortie, Astrophys. Journ., **20**. 253, 1904 ; W. S. Adams, ib., **30**. 86, 1909 ; W. M. Mitchell, ib., **22**. 4, 1905 ; F. W. Dyson, Phil. Trans., **206**. A, 493, 1906 ; A. J. Angström, Recherches sur le spectre normal du soleil, Upsala, 1868 ; G. P. Merrill and H. N. Stokes, Proc. Washington Acad., **2**. 41, 1900 ; E. E. Howell, W. F. Hillebrand, and G. P. Merrill, Amer. Journ. Science, (3), **47**. 430, 1894 ; F. Cornu, Ann. Scient. École Norm. Sup., (2), **9**. 21, 1880 ; Compt. Rend., **86**. 101, 315, 530, 983, 1878 ; A. Daubrée, ib., **72**. 200. 1866 ; H. Deslandres, ib., **141**.

409, 1905; R. Thalén, *Ann. Chim. Phys.*, (4), **18**. 202, 1869; G. Salet, *ib.*, (4), **18**. 222, 1869; C. F. Rammelsberg, *Pogg. Ann.*, **73**. 585, 1848; M. N. Saha, *Phil. Mag.*, (6), **40**. 472, 1920.
³ J. C. G. de Marignac, *Bibl. Univ. Genève*, **26**. 89, 1866.
⁴ T. L. Watson, *Amer. Min.*, **10**. 1, 1925.
⁵ J. T. Lowitz, *Crell's Ann.*, i, 183, 1799; *Scherer's Journ.*, **2**. 210, 1799; P. C. Abildgaard, *ib.*, **2**. 502, 1799; A. G. Ekeberg, *ib.*, **14**. 348, 1805; M. H. Klaproth, *Leonhard's Taschenbuch*, **5**. 163, 1811; L. Pansner, *ib.*, **11**. 309, 1817; A. Breithaupt, *Scherer's Ann.*, **7**. 200, 1821; G. Ulrich, *Berg. Hütt. Ztg.*, **12**. 254, 1853; Anon., *Bull. Imp. Inst.*, **9**. 134, 1911; H. Thürach, *Über das Vorkommen mikroskopischer Zirkone und Titan-Mineralien in den Gesteinen*, Würzburg, 1884; P. Holland, *Chem. News*, **59**. 27, 1889; W. A. Noyes, *Journ. Anal. App. Chem.*, **5**. 39; C. U. Slocum, *Min. World*, **36**. 123, 1912; Anon., *Bull. Imp. Inst.*, **15**. 82, 1917.
⁶ T. Scheerer, *Liebig's Ann.*, **92**. 178, 1854; *Chem. News*, **1**. 143, 1860; E. Jackson, *ib.*, **47**. 157, 1883; R. Apjohn, *ib.*, **26**. 183, 1872; A. B. Griffiths, *ib.*, **88**. 231, 1903; *Bull. Soc. Chim.*, (3), **29**. 1117, 1903; E. Riley, *ib.*, **8**. 233, 1863; *Journ. Chem. Soc.*, **12**. 13, 1860; H. Rose, *Gilbert's Ann.*, **70**. 315, 1822; *Pogg. Ann.*, **1**. 76, 1824; *Ann. Chim. Phys.*, (2), **28**. 105, 1825; A. Sauer, *Zeit. deut. geol. Ges.*, **37**. 445, 1884; *Neues Jahrb. Min.*, 569, 1879; L. van Werweke, *ib.*, ii, 275, 1880; A. Stelzner, *ib.*, i, 229, 1882; G. Vogt, *ib.*, i, 97, 1889; E. Cohen, *ib.*, ii, 23, 1880; *Neues Jahrb. Min. B.B.*, **2**. 369, 1882; M. F. Heddle, *Trans. Roy. Soc. Edin.*, **30**. 427, 1883; *Proc. Roy. Soc. Edin.*, **11**. 549, 1882; T. Thomson, *ib.*, **6**. 253, 1807; *Phil. Mag.*, **35**. 100, 1807; P. Jannasch and J. H. Kloos, *Tschermak's Mitt.*, (2), **3**. 97, 1880; F. Knapp, *Neues Jahrb. Min.*, ii, 381, 1881; *Die doleritischen Gesteine des Frauenberges bei Schlüchtern in Hessen*, Würzburg, 1880; V. Roussel, *Compt. Rend.*, **77**. 1103, 1873; H. Moissan, *ib.*, **116**. 460, 1893; L. Dieulafait, *ib.*, **93**. 804, 1881; R. D. Silva, *ib.*, **65**. 207, 1867; C. M. Kersten, *Pogg. Ann.*, **3**. 175, 1825; **49**. 229, 1840; *Journ. prakt. Chem.*, (1), **1**. 363, 1834; (1), **20**. 373, 1840; F. P. Dunnington, *Amer. Journ. Science*, (3), **42**. 491, 1891; *Chem. News*, **65**. 65, 1892; **76**. 221, 1897; *Zeit. anorg. Chem.*, **1**. 387, 1892; *Journ. Amer. Chem. Soc.*, **13**. 210, 1892; *Neues Jahrb. Min.*, i, 97, 1889; *Zeit. angew. Chem.*, **16**. 595, 1903; *La Cer.*, **6**. 68, 1903; W. Aleksiejeff, *Zapisky Imp. Russ. Tech. Obschtsch.*, **30**. 6, 7, 1896; C. Bischof, *Dingler's Journ.*, **248**. 167, 1883; W. P. Jorissen, *Bull. Acad. Belg.*, 902, 1903; R. H. Brett and G. Bird, *Phil. Mag.*, (3), **6**. 113, 1835; F. Wöhler and A. Schwarzenberg, *ib.*, **35**. 507, 527, 1835; O. L. Erdmann, *Journ. prakt. Chem.*, (1), 4. 496, 1835; W. F. Salm-Horstmar, *ib.*, (1), **54**. 129, 1851; J. E. Herberger, *Repert. Pharm.*, **55**. 62, 1836; J. J. Berzelius, G. H. Frick, and F. Wöhler, *Pogg. Ann.*, **31**. 674, 1834; G. F. McCaleb, *Amer. Chem. Journ.*, **10**. 36, 1888; C. E. Wait, *Journ. Amer. Chem. Soc.*, **18**. 402, 1896; C. Baskerville, *ib.*, **21**. 706, 1099, 1899; L. Franck, *Stahl Eisen*, **17**. 449, 1897; W. M. Thornton, *Amer. Journ. Science*, (4), **31**. 218, 1911; H. S. Washington, *ib.*, (4), **24**. 217, 1907; *Prof. Paper U.S. Geol. Sur.*, **14**. 106, 1903; F. W. Clarke, *Bull. U.S. Geol. Sur.*, 419, 1910; A. Harker, *Geol. Mag.*, (4), **6**. 220, 1899; E. Odernheimer, *Tonind. Ztg.*, **27**. 1475, 1903; W. Biltz and E. Marcus, *Zeit. anorg. Chem.*, **68**. 91, 1910; W. O. Robinson and W. J. McCaughey, *Journ. Ind. Eng. Chem.*, **2**. 462, 1910; A. F. de Fourcroy and L. N. Vauquelin, *Ann. Chim. Phys.*, (1), **49**. 188, 1804; L. N. Vauquelin, *ib.*, (2), **27**. 67, 1824; H. St. C. Deville, *ib.*, (3), **61**. 311, 1861; A. Damour and A. des Cloizeaux, *ib.*, (3), **51**. 445, 1857; J. Peschier, *ib.*, (2), **21**. 203, 1822; P. A. Dufrénoy, *ib.*, (2), **67**. 251, 1837.
⁷ A. Terreil, *Compt. Rend.*, **84**. 407, 1877; A. Carnot and E. Goutal, *ib.*, **125**. 213, 1897; C. U. Slocum, *Min. Journ.*, **35**. 1260, 1911; **36**. 123, 1912; J. T. Singewald, *The Titaniferous Iron Ores in the United States*, Washington, 1913; E. Riley, *Journ. Chem. Soc.*, **12**. 13, 1860; **16**. 387, 1863; *Chem. News*, **8**. 233, 1863; W. Bettel, *ib.*, **28**. 93, 1873; W. H. Harris and J. Stenson, *ib.*, **1**. 274, 1859; A. A. and S. D. Hayes, *ib.*, **19**. 163, 1869; J. H. L. Vogt, *Zeit. prakt. Geol.*, **8**. 233, 370, 1900; **9**. 9, 180, 1901; *Ber. Intern. Cong. App. Chem.*, **1**. 741, 1904; J. Hörnhager, *Œster. Zeit. Berg. Hütt.*, **52**. 571, 1904; A. J. Rossi, *Journ. Amer. Chem. Soc.*, **12**. 91, 1890; *Journ. Franklin Inst.*, **154**. 241, 1903; *Trans. Amer. Inst. Min. Eng.*, **22**. 570, 1901; A. Vogel and C. Reischauer, *Anz. Gelehrte München*, **42**. 7, 1856; A. Nies, *Versl. deut. Nat. Aerzte*, **46**. 122, 1873; O. Bauer, *Stahl Eisen*, **24**. 1058, 1904; H. Rose, *Ann. Mines*, (1), **12**. 300, 1826; (4), **8**. 701, 1845; P. Berthier, *ib.*, (3), **3**. 41, 1833; J. J. Nöggerath, *Sitzber. Ver. Rheinl. Westphalen*, **18**. 77, 1861; *Ann. Mines*, (6), **8**. 247, 1865; L. de Launey, *ib.*, (10), **3**. 86, 1903; J. W. Döbereiner, *ib.*, (3), **9**. 350, 1836; H. von Fehling, *Württemburg. Jahresh.*, **2**. 255, 1847; T. Virlet d'Aoust, *Compt. Rend.*, **22**. 505, 1846; *Bull. Geol. Soc.*, (1), **3**. 425, 1846; R. Thalén, *Ann. Chim. Phys.*, (4), **18**. 222, 1869; R. Akerman, *Jern-Kontorets Ann.*, **32**. 79, 1877; *Iron*, **6**. 450, 1875; A. Tamm, *ib.*, **41**. 127, 1886; E. J. Chapman, *Trans. Roy. Soc. Canada*, **2**. 159, 1884; *Journ. Iron Steel Inst.*, **26**. ii, 613, 1884; T. H. Cope, *ib.*, **61**. i, 426, 1902; *Journ. Liverpool Geol. Soc.*, **9**. 208, 1902; P. W. Shimer, *Trans. Amer. Inst. Min. Eng.*, **15**. 455, 1886; H. S. Washington, *ib.*, **39**. 735, 1908; T König and O. F. von der Pfordten, *Ber.*, **22**. 1485, 1889; T. W. Hogg, *B.A. Rep.*, 721, 1893; A. Ledebur, *Stahl Eisen*, **14**. 810, 1894; E. Bahlsen, *ib.*, **22**. 326, 1902; W. Venator, *ib.*, **28**. 259, 1908; **30**. 650, 1910; L. Treuheit, *ib.*, **29**. 1023, 1909; E. von Maltitz, *ib.*, **29**. 1593, 1909; J. F. Kemp, *Ann. Rep. U.S. Geol. Sur.*, **19**. iii, 371, 1887; *School Mines Quart.*, **21**. 1, 1899; N. P. Hulst, *Iron Trade Rev.*, **37**. 92, 1904; F. W. Clarke, *Data of Geochemistry*, Washington, 1920; H. le Chatelier, *Rev. Mét.*, **8**. 367, 1911; L. Guillet, *ib.*, **1**. 506, 1904; Anon., *Bull. Imp. Inst.*, **9**. 134, 1911; C. Reinhardt, *Zeit. angew. Chem.*, **1**. 124, 1888; E. Emmons and W. R. Johnson, *Report of the State Geologist of New York*, New York, 1840; C. F. B. Karsten, *Eisenhüttenkunde*, **1**. 533, 1841; **2**. 55, 1841; *Pogg. Ann.*, **27**. 160, 1841; J. L. Bell, *B.A. Rep.*, 730, 1863; *Principles of the Manufacture of Iron and Steel*,

London, 157, 167, 1884; J. H. Pratt, *Mineral Resources U.S.A.*, 309, 1903; R. A. Hadfield, *Iron Steel Met.*, 7. 3, 1904; F. A. Fitzgerald, *Trans. Amer. Electrochem. Soc.*, 12. 165, 1907; *Elektrochem. Met. Ind.*, 6. 494, 1908; 7. 129, 1909; *Iron Age*, 88. 1284, 1909; G. B. Waterhouse, *ib.*, 20. 265, 1911; *Proc. Amer. Soc. Testing Materials*, 10. 201. 1910; *Iron Age*, 80. 1306, 1901; P. H. Dudley, *Mech. Eng.*, 27. 463, 1910; A. J. Rossi, J. MacNaughton, and W. D. Edmonds, *Brit. Pat. No.* 3582. 1901; J. A. Paris, *Trans. Cornwall Geol. Soc.*, 1. 226, 1818; *Gilbert's Ann.*, 59. 226, 1818; R. Mushet, *Chem. News*, 1. 231, 276, 1860; 4. 11, 1861; *Brit. Pat. Nos.* 703, 1115, 1150, 1151, 1859; 3045, 1860; 2609, 1861; *Dingler's Journ.*, 155. 317, 1860; 156. 76. 1860; 164. 74, 1862; 166. 156, 1862; E. L. Gruner, *ib.*, 195. 336, 1870; *Deut. Ind. Ztg.*, 14. 97, 1873; *Ann. Mines*, (6), 17. 346, 1870; *Compt. Rend.*, 70. 571, 1870; *Chem. News*, 27. 71, 1873; *Bull. Soc. Nat. Ind.*, (2), 20. 84, 1873; A. E. Nordenskjöld, *Pogg. Ann.*, 122. 615, 1864; C. M. Kersten, *ib.*, 3. 175, 1825; 49. 229, 1840; *Journ. prakt. Chem.*, (1), 1. 636, 1834; (1), 20. 373, 1840; C. H. Pfaff, *Schweigger's Journ.*, 18. 283, 1816; F. A. Walchner, *Pogg. Ann.*, 3. 176, 1825; *Schweigger's Journ.*, 41. 80, 1824; 44. 47, 1825; F. L. Hünefeld, *Ann. Mines*, (2), 5. 316, 1829; *Phil. Mag.*, (2), 3. 121, 1828; *Schweigger's Journ.*, 50. 332, 1827; J. J. Nöggerath, *ib.*, 65. 385, 1832; *Karsten's Arch.*, 4. 351, 1825; M. Meyer, *ib.*. 13. 272, 1828; J. K. L. Zincken, *Pogg. Ann.*, 3. 175, 1825; H. E. F. G. Sandberger, *ib.*, 83. 596, 1851; *Jahrb. Nass. Ver. Nat.*, 131, 1851; D. Forbes, *Journ. Iron Steel Inst.*, 4. i, 158, 1872; A. Laugier, *Soc. Philomath.*, 102, 1825; *Trommsdorff's Journ. Pharm.*, 12. 253, 1826; H. Blumenau, *Liebig's Ann.*, 67. 122, 1848; F. Kick and W. F. Gintl, *Deut. Ind. Ztg.*, 13. 346, 1872; W. H. Wollaston, *Phil. Trans.*, 113. 17, 400, 1823; *Edin. Phil. Journ.*, 9. 403, 1823; P. C. Grignon, *Mémoires de physique sur l'art de fabriquer le fer*, Paris, 1775; W. F. Salm-Horstmar, *Journ. prakt. Chem.*, (1), 54. 129, 1851; C. U. Slocum, *Electrochem. Met. Ind.*, 7. 128, 1909; *Iron Trade Rev.*, 44. 408, 1909; *Iron Age*, 86. 1393, 1907; *Chem. Met. Ind.*, 7. 128, 1909; *Min. World*, 35. 1260, 1911; *Trans. Amer. Electrochem. Soc.*, 20. 265, 1911; L. Franck, *Chem. Ztg.*, 21. 520, 1897; *Stahl Eisen*, 17. 449, 1897; T. S. Hunt, *Eng. Min. Journ.*, 13. 148, 1872; G. W. Maynard, *ib.*, 13. 275, 1872; *Journ. Iron Steel Inst.*, 7. 109, 1874; B. Osann, *Stahl Eisen*, 41. 1487, 1921; G. F. Comstock, *Chem. Met. Engg.*, 26. 165, 1922; H. D. Rogers, *ib.*, (4), 8. 700, 1845; *Instit.*, 60, 1844; R. Kerl, *Handbuch der metallurgischen Hüttenkunde*, Freiberg, 1. 795, 1861; C. F. Rammelsberg, *Lehrbuch der chemischen Metallurgie*, Berlin, 140, 1865; *Pogg. Ann.*, 104. 497, 1860; J. Percy, *Metallurgy of Iron and Steel*, London, 164, 551, 570, 1864; M. Mazade, *Compt. Rend.*, 34. 952, 1852; O. Henry, *Journ. Pharm. Chim.*, (3), 24. 305, 1853; *Phil. Mag.*, (4), 7. 149, 1853; G. O. Rees, *ib.*, (3), 5. 398, 1834; (3), 6. 201, 1835; C. E. Wait, *Journ. Amer. Chem. Soc.*, 18. 402, 1896; C. Baskerville, *ib.*, 21. 1099, 1899; E. O. von Lippmann, *Ber.*, 30. 3037, 1897; R. L. Marchand, *Journ. prakt. Chem.*, (1), 16. 372, 1839; *Liebig's Ann.*, 32. 324, 1839; E. Jackson, *Chem. News*, 47. 157, 1883; F. Traetta-Mosca, *Gazz. Chim. Ital.*, 43. ii, 437, 1913.

§ 3. The Extraction of Titania

In an old process used by H. Rose [1] for extracting titanium dioxide or titania from rutile or titaniferous iron-ore, the mineral was heated to redness in a stream of hydrogen sulphide, and the iron sulphide removed by extraction with conc. hydrochloric acid, and the hydrated titania well washed. To remove all the iron, a repetition of the process is necessary. He also converted the iron into soluble sulphide by fusing the powdered mineral with sulphur, extracted the mass with hydrochloric acid, and treated the washed product with hydrogen sulphide as just indicated. H. Rose extracted rutile or titaniferous iron ore with hydrochloric acid and fused it with over three times its weight of potassium carbonate, or better, according to A. Laugier, with twice its weight of potassium hydroxide. The cold mass was washed with water until the acid potassium titanate began to pass through the filter-paper. The washed residue contained ferric oxide and potassium titanate. C. Friedel and J. Guérin volatilized the iron as chloride by heating the mixed precipitate in a current of hydrogen chloride and chlorine. To obtain titanium dioxide of a very high degree of purity, A. Stähler, and O. F. von der Pfordten recommended converting the oxide to the chloride—*vide infra*; treating the aq. soln. with ammonia; and igniting the washed precipitate.

There are many ways of separating the iron and titanium oxides from the soln. of the residue in cold conc. hydrochloric acid. If this soln. be boiled, the titanium chloride is hydroly ed and titanium hydroxide is precipitated. According to H. Rose, the hydrolysis is facilitated by the addition of sulphuric acid—*vide infra*, action of sulphuric acid on titanium dioxide. The precipitate is still contaminated with iron. If, however, the iron be reduced to the ferrous condition before the hydrolysis, it will not be precipitated with the titanium. P. Berthier recommended sulphur dioxide or ammonium sulphide as a reducing agent; V. Merz, and O. F. von der Pfordten, hydrogen sulphide; and F. Stromeyer, sodium thiosulphate. H. Rose treated the soln. with ammonia, and digested the precipitate with ammonium sulphide to convert the iron and manganese oxides into the bivalent sulphides, which were removed by hydrochloric acid. H. Rose also found that the iron can be kept in soln. by adding enough tartaric acid before the treatment with ammonia. G. Streit and B. Franz recommended acetic acid in place of tartaric, although other organic acids will do as well. A. Laugier, for example, used oxalic acid or ammonium oxalate. C. Dreher applied these principles to extract titanium dioxide from substances (such as bauxite residues) containing titanic acid associated with iron, aluminium, and other metals; the mineral is treated with sulphuric or other acid, and the iron is reduced to the bivalent condition by producing nascent hydrogen in the soln. by electrolysis or other means. The acids are nearly neutralized by an alkaline earth or corresponding carbonate; or substances, such as sulphites, acetates, or formates, may be added to bind the acid employed, without dissolving the titanous oxide which is precipitated.

P. Berthier fused the mineral with a mixture of sodium carbonate and sulphur added in small portions at a time to the hot crucible; and afterwards dissolved the mass in cold dil. sulphuric acid. The soln. was treated with sodium carbonate, the ferrous iron remained in soln., and the titanic acid was precipitated. R. Weber opened the mineral by fusion with twice its weight of fluorspar, and digested the cold mass with dil. sulphuric acid. The liquid was filtered from the calcium sulphate, reduced with sulphur dioxide, and boiled to precipitate the titanic oxide. J. C. G. de Marignac brought the mineral into soln. by fusion with potassium hydrosulphate; the cold cake was dissolved in water; the liquid diluted so that it contained 1 vol. of sulphuric acid to 6 vols. of water; and the soln. boiled to precipitate the titanic oxide. G. W. Sears and L. Quill studied the opening of titanium ores with alkali pyrosulphates, and found the sodium salt to be rather more efficient than the potassium salt. At least 12·5 parts of sodium pyrosulphate should be employed for one part of ore. F. Wöhler fused the finely powdered mineral with three times its weight of potassium carbonate, and digested the powdered cake with dil. hydrofluoric acid. The sparingly soluble potassium fluotitanate was boiled with sufficient water to dissolve all the salt; the soln. filtered while hot; and, on cooling, the potassium fluotitanate was obtained as lustrous, scaly crystals. The salt was washed with cold water, and purified by recrystallization from boiling water. The hot soln. can be treated with ammonia, and the washed precipitate ignited for titanium dioxide of a high degree of purity. V. Merz, and also L. Weiss and H. Kaiser, used a modification of this process. G. Streit and B. Franz found that much titanium dioxide remained in soln. with the ferric salt. F. Erban recommended the following process:

The ore is melted with sodium hydroxide, lixiviated with water, and the residue washed to free it from alkali. The product is dissolved in hydrochloric acid, and the soln. treated with alkali to precipitate the titanium as hydroxide. Iron is removed by adding sodium sulphide, washing the precipitate, and treating it with sulphurous acid. It is then converted into the double oxalate of titanium and ammonium by treatment with oxalic acid and ammonium oxalate. Thirty parts of rutile containing 80–90 per cent. of titanic acid gave 120 parts of " oxalate." The ignited precipitate furnished titanium dioxide.

F. Bayer prepared titanic acid from ferrotitanium by heating the alloy with calcium oxide or carbonate, and extracting the product with acids. P. H. Monk and C. Whittemore, and E. E. and P. C. Dutt discussed the extraction of titanic oxide from bauxites, etc. G. Siebert and E. Korten treated the raw material with halogens in the presence of carbon at a high temp. G. Carteret and M. Devaux described the following process:

The ore is heated in a retort at 800° for 1 or 2 hrs. in the presence of a slow current of reducing gas or mixed with carbon. Dry chlorine is passed through the furnace heated to 350°. At this temp., the iron only is attacked, and the ferric chloride formed passes out and is collected. The direction of the chlorine current is then reversed, and the temp. raised to 550°–600°. The titanium is attacked, and the titanium chloride, contaminated with traces of iron, silicon, etc., passes out through another opening. The titanium chloride is purified by distillation, and may be used for the preparation of titanium sulphate and oxide.

J. Blumenfeld opened the mineral by digestion with sulphuric acid; and J. Blumenfeld and C. Weizmann extracted titanic acid from ilmenite by the following process :

The mineral was heated with sulphuric acid of 70–90 per cent. conc. at 150°–180° for 1½ hrs. or for some time after the mass had become a dry powder. This was cooled to 50°, a limited quantity of water (such that only about 15–20 per cent. of the iron dissolves) added, and the whole stirred with spongy iron to reduce any ferric sulphate. The bulk of the ferrous sulphate remained undissolved and was filtered off. The titanium contained in the filtrate was precipitated as hydroxide and the latter washed with acidified water containing a small quantity of salts of trivalent titanium until free from iron. The hydroxide was calcined under oxidizing conditions, and yielded titanic acid of a colour suitable for use as a white pigment. T. Matsubaka said that the calcining temp. should not exceed 400°, and that an excess of acid reduces the yield of titanic oxide.

REFERENCES.

[1] H. Rose, *Pogg. Ann.*, **12.** 479, 1828 ; *Gilbert's Ann.*, **73.** 67, 1823 ; *Akad. Handl. Stockholm*, 231, 1821 ; J. C. G. de Marignac, *Ann. Chim. Phys.*, (4), **3.** 5, 1864 ; P. Berthier, *ib.*, (2), **50.** 362, 1832 ; (3), **7.** 85, 1843 ; A. Laugier, *ib.*, (2), **89.** 306, 1814 ; G. W. Sears and L. Quill, *Journ. Amer. Chem. Soc.*, **47.** 922, 1925 ; G. Streit and B. Franz, *Journ. prakt. Chem.*, (1), **108.** 65, 1869 ; V. Merz, *ib.*, (1), **99.** 157, 1866 ; *Zeit. Chem.*, (2), **3.** 122, 1867 ; *Untersuchungen über das Titan, Silicium, und Boron*, Zürich, 9, 1864 ; C. Friedel and J. Guérin, *Bull. Soc. Chim.*, (2), **23.** 289, 1875 ; *Ann. Chim. Phys.*, (5), **8.** 24, 1876 ; *Compt. Rend.*, **82.** 509, 1876 ; F. Wöhler, *Die Mineralanalyse in Beispielen*, Göttingen, 137, 1861 ; London, 130, 1854 ; *Liebin's Ann.*, **74.** 212, 1849 ; O. F. von der Pfordten, *ib.*, **237.** 207, 1886 ; F. Stromeyer, *ib.*, **113.** 127, 1859 ; G. Carteret and M. Devaux, *Brit. Pat. Nos.* 184132, 184948, 185374, 1921 ; E. E. and P C. Dutt, *ib.*, 189700, 1922 ; R. Weber, *Pogg. Ann.*, **120.** 287, 1863 ; *Sitzber. Akad. Berlin*, 358, 1863 ; *Journ. prakt. Chem.*, (1), **90.** 212, 1863 ; F. Erban, *Chem. Ztg.*, **30.** 145, 1906 ; A. Stähler, *Ber.*, **38.** 2619, 1905 ; C. Dreher, *Brit. Pat. No.* 1835, 1903 ; *French Pat. No.* 328855, 1903 ; *German Pat.*, *D.R.P.* 152257, 1904 ; F. Bayer, *ib.*, 396695, 1921 ; G. Siebert and E. Korten, *ib.*, 355485, 1920 ; L. Weiss and H. Kaiser, *Zeit. anorg. Chem.*, **65.** 345, 1910 ; W. B. Llewellyn and H. and P. Spence, *Brit. Pat. No.* 200848, 1922 ; H. Spence, W. B. Llewellyn, and S. F. W. Crudall, *ib.*, 230877, 1923 ; H Wrigley, H. Spence and P. Spence, *ib.*, 133336, 1917 ; F. Sommer and J. d'Ans, *ib.*, 214483, 1923 ; C. A. Doremus, *ib.*, 206809, 1923 ; T. Matsubaka, *Bull. Osaka Ind. Lab.*, **4.** 13, 1923 ; L. E. Barton, *U.S. Pat. No.* 1348843, 1920 ; H. N. McCoy, *ib.*, 1559113, 1925 ; J. Blumenfeld, *ib.*, 1504669, 1504670, 1504671, 1504672, 1924 ; J. Blumenfeld and C. Weizmann, *Brit. Pat. Nos.* 203352, 225593, 1923 ; Deutsche Gasglühlicht Auer Ges., *German Pat.*, *D.R.P.* 411723, 1921 ; A. L. Mond, *Brit. Pat. Nos.* 232680, 234518, 1924 ; Spencer, Chapman and Messel Ltd. and J. B. Liebert, *ib.*, 236087, 1924 ; P. H. Monk and C. Whittemore, *Canadian Chem. Met.*, **9.** 153, 1925.

§ 4. The Preparation of Titanium

In 1825, J. J. Berzelius [1] prepared what he called *amorphes Titan* by reducing potassium fluotitanate, K_2TiF_6, with sodium ; the black powder gave metallic streaks when rubbed with a polishing tool, and it was said to be " insoluble in hydrofluoric acid," whereas it is now known that the element readily dissolves in that menstruum. When M. A. Hunter repeated J. J. Berzelius' experiment, in vacuo, his best product contained but 73·2 per cent. of titanium. W. A. Lampadius [2] then heated a mixture of titaniferous earth and carbon in a clay crucible and obtained a dark brown metal which detonated when mixed with saltpetre and heated. A. Laugier likewise heated a mixture of the earth with oil, and obtained yellow crystals resembling some curious crystals found in blast-furnace slags—*Hochöfenkrystallen.* As indicated above, W. H. Wollaston mistook these crystals for the crystalline form of the metal itself. F. Wöhler isolated the impure metal in 1849, and showed that the product obtained by the high temp. reduction of the oxide by carbon was not the metal, but rather a mixture of the nitride and carbide—titanium carbonitride or cyanide. Thus, by heating W. H. Wollaston's " metal " in chlorine gas, F. Wöhler showed that it contained :

	Titanium.	Nitrogen.	Carbon.
W. H. Wollaston's product	77·26	18·30	4·56
Calculated for $Ti_{10}C_2N_8$	78·00	18·11	3·89

On account of the high m.p. of the metal, and the ease with which it unites with oxygen, carbon, nitrogen, silicon, and the other elements, it is doubtful if anything but a very impure form of the metal was really obtained by J. J. Berzelius, and F. Wöhler. The metallic appearance of the titanium nitrides also led to their being confused with the metal. Thus, H. Rose's dark blue or black powder obtained by heating titanium tetramminotetrachloride, $TiCl_4.4NH_3$, alone or with sodium, is now known to be a nitride. Accordingly, the early reports of the isolation of the metal are quite unreliable, and many early records of the properties of titanium are confused, and contradictory, and therefore erroneous.

(1) *Reduction of the halogen salts with the alkali metals.*—J. J. Berzelius,[3] and F. Wöhler reduced potassium fluotitanate with potassium or sodium, with or without a layer of sodium chloride above to protect the mass from oxidation; but A. Schüller and V. Wartha showed that the product always contained a relatively large proportion of titanium nitride; E. A. Schneider, oxygen and hydrogen; and V. Merz, that it contained sodium, and that in removing the alkali fluorides by washing with water, the latter reacts with the finely-divided titanium, forming titanium oxide. F. Wöhler and H. St. C. Deville heated a boat of the alkali fluotitanate and a boat of sodium in a stream of hydrogen, when the vapour of sodium passing over the fluotitanate effected the reduction. The metal was obtained by washing the product. E. Glatzel used a similar process. Instead of using glass or porcelain, L. Lévy said that enamelled iron can be employed as the containing vessel. He also used a copper vessel. V. Merz tried to obtain the titanium in a crystalline state by adding zinc to the mixture, but the results were nugatory. The product obtained by H. St. C. Deville must have contained carbonitride. V. Merz, and A. Polis tried to obtain the amorphous titanium in a crystalline state by addition of zinc, but the results were not satisfactory.

In 1876, S. Kern[4] passed the vapour of titanium tetrachloride over molten sodium and obtained a product resembling J. J. Berzelius' amorphous titanium, contaminated, according to L. F. Nilson and O. Pettersson, with oxygen; and, according to C. Winkler, with titanium monoxide. F. C. Robinson and C. C. Hutchins said that the reaction commences at about 150°, but O. F. von der Pfordten could not confirm this. M. Billy claimed to have made 100 per cent. titanium by the action of the vapour of purified titanium tetrachloride on sodium hydride at 400°; the product is heated to 400° in a stream of carbon dioxide, and then to 800° to decompose any solid titanium hydride which is produced simultaneously. L. F. Nilson and O. Pettersson reduced the tetrachloride by heating it in an air-tight steel bomb at a red heat, but the results were disappointing because the yellow scales so obtained only contained 94·73 per cent. of titanium; the chief impurity, oxygen, was probably combined as titanium monoxide, TiO_2, and, if so, the product could have contained only 78·97 per cent. of free titanium. In fact, all the specimens obtained by the above process were contaminated with much oxide which may have been produced by the action of water during the leaching of the product of the reaction from the amorphous metal. M. A. Hunter, however, heated a mixture of highly purified titanium tetrachloride and sodium in a steel bomb capable of withstanding an internal press. of 40,000 kilograms. The temp. was raised to a dull red heat so as to start the reaction, which was over in a few moments. On leaching the product with water, a grey powder, mixed with small, rounded grains of the fused metal, was obtained. The fused metal contained 99·9 per cent. of titanium, and there was a 71 per cent. yield. E. Podszus obtained 99·7 per cent. titanium by heating sodium and titanium tetrachloride in a steel bomb sealed with lead. M. A. Hunter and A. Jones studied the reaction. A. E. van Arkel and H. de Boer made the metal by passing the vapour of the tetra-iodide over a heated tungsten filament. L. Weiss and H. Kaiser purified the metal obtained by reducing the fluotitanate with sodium or aluminium by pressing the mixture into pencils and using the pencils as electrodes in a vacuum arc-furnace.

The arc-furnace employed by L. Weiss and E. Neumann is illustrated by Fig. 1. The mixture of potassium fluotitanate and aluminium was squeezed into rods or pencils 6 4 cm. long, 1·0 cm. broad, and 0 5 cm. thick. These were used as electrodes in an arc-furnace, Fig. 1, which enabled them to be heated in vacuo or in an atm. of any desired gas under reduced press. As in W. von Bolton's furnace the electrode holders were cooled by a current of cold water. The walls of the furnace were also cooled in a similar way. The distance of the electrodes apart was regulated by a rack-and-pinion arrangement. The window in the furnace enabled the arc to be kept in view during the experiment. The lower electrode, the negative pole, was insulated from the upper vessel. The rods conduct electricity well, and when the electrodes were about 2 or 3 mm. apart, with a current between 60 and 70 amps., at 20 to 25 volts, globules or stalagmites of titanium metal were formed about the lower electrode. The m.p. of the metal is so high that the chief impurity—aluminium—is volatilized. J. W. Marden and M. N. Rich have described other suitable furnaces. The metal separated in fused globules near the ends of the electrodes, and these were detached when the apparatus had cooled.

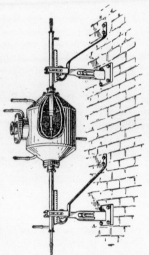

FIG. 1.—L. Weiss and E. Neumann's Vacuum Arc-Furnace.

(2) *Reduction of the halogen salts or the oxide by calcium, magnesium, or aluminium.*—W. Huppertz,[5] and A. Burger heated a mixture of calcium and titania in a porcelain tube evacuated at about 600°, and raised the temp. to 1050°. The titanium was isolated by washing with a soln. of ammonium chloride, and drying at 100°. The process was recommended by H. Kuzel and E. Wedekind. C. Winkler, and E. A. Schneider showed that the product obtained by the action of magnesium on titanic oxide largely consists of titanium monoxide. It is, however, probable that the reduction proceeds further than the monoxide since magnesium reduces both silica and zirconia to their elements. O. Ruff and H. Brintzinger obtained 82·8 per cent. titanium by reducing titanium dioxide with a sodium-calcium alloy. In H. Goldschmidt's process,[6] titanic oxide is mixed with aluminium, and the mixture ignited with a suitable fuse, when the reaction $3TiO_2+4Al=3Ti+2Al_2O_3$ occurs. The product is contaminated with 5 or 6 per cent. of aluminium which readily alloys with titanium. A. Stavenhagen and E. Schuchard obtained unsatisfactory results. The reaction was studied by W. Huppertz, W. Prandtl and B. Blayer, etc. According to K. A. Kühne, the reaction proceeds more quickly and at a higher temp. if barium or sodium peroxide, or potassium chlorate or perchlorate, is mixed with the initial products : $TiO_2 +2Al+BaO_2=BaO+Al_2O_3+Ti$. The consumption of aluminium is, however, augmented.

(3) *Reduction of the oxide by carbon.*—The early attempts by W. A. Lampadius,[7] L. N. Vauquelin, A. Laugier, and P. Berthier to reduce titanium oxide by carbon in a metallurgical furnace yielded a product consisting largely of the nitride. T. S. Hunt, L. Burgess, and E. H. and A. H. Cowles and C. F. Mabery attempted to make titanium by heating a mixture of rutile or titaniferous iron ore and coarsely granular carbon in an electric furnace. In 1895, H. Moissan obtained a sample contaminated with about 5 per cent. of carbon, by heating a mixture of titanic oxide and carbon in an electric arc furnace. The uppermost layer contained the metal or the carbide, the middle layer was crystalline nitride, and the lowest layer was largely contaminated with oxide. By fusing the top layer with an excess of titanic oxide, the proportion of carbon was reduced from 1·91 to 3·81 per cent., and the product was free from nitride and silicon, but it contained some oxide. The carbon was probably present as graphite. The metal was very brittle and possessed a brilliant white fracture. A few years later, H. Moissan distilled titanium in an electric furnace, and condensed the distillate in small crystals. M. A. Hunter heated an intimate mixture of powdered titanic oxide with lamp-

black in vacuo in an Asem electric furnace, and the best results were obtained with a tungsten crucible at 2400°, but even then the product was largely contaminated with oxide and carbide. A. Sternberg and A. Deutsch also patented the preparation of titanium by heating alkali or alkaline earth titanates with carbon between 1000° and 1400°.

(4) *Reduction of the oxide or halogen salts by other reducing agents.*—In attempts by B. Neumann [8] to reduce rutile with silicon, the produ ct contained 2·99 per cent. of iron and 20·37 per cent. of silicon, but no nitrogen. L. Lévy said that he prepared pure crystalline titanium by the action of the vapour of titanium tetrachloride on boron or silicon, but the product was later shown to be a boride or silicide; D. Gardner and L. Taverner used calcium silicide, ferrosilicon, or other silicide as reducing agent. According to E. Wehrlin and E. Giraud, titanium oxide can be reduced to the metal by heating potassium fluotitanate with metallic iron at a bright red heat and removing the iron by treating the cold mass with hydrochloric acid—but this is doubtful. F. Auer prepared titanium by reducing the oxide at a white heat by a mixture of hydrogen and ammonia gases ; and J. Schilling reduced ammonium titanate in an atm. of hydrogen or nitrogen. J. J. Ebelmen reduced titanium chloride with hydrogen. L. Lévy said that titanium tetrachloride can be advantageously reduced by mercury ethide in an atm. of carbon dioxide at 180°. Titanium di-iodide, TiI_2, at a bright red-heat, was found by E. Defacqz and H. Copaux to be reduced to amorphous titanium by hydrogen. A. Stahler and F. Bachran found that there is a kind of autoreduction of titanium dichloride when it is heated in a current of hydrogen at 1100° : $2TiCl_2 \rightleftharpoons TiCl_4 + Ti$. H. Fischvoigt and F. Koref obtained ductile titanium by passing the vapour of hydrogen and titanium tetrahalide over a heated tungsten filament. A. E. van Arkel and J. H. de Boer proceeded as follows : The filament is fitted by thicker tungsten electrodes into a glass globe. The tetraiodide is introduced, and the filament brought to incandescence. The whole globe is heated so as to vaporize the iodide and a layer of titanium is deposited on the filament as a lustrous coherent coating. In a few hours rods 2 to 4 mm. thick can be obtained. When the rod is over 3 mm. thick, the current heating the filament rises from 0·5 to 100 amps. The fine core of tungsten now remains as a negligibly small impurity.

(5) *The electrodeposition of titanium.*—J. de Bussy [9] claimed to have obtained silver-white titanium with a bright metallic lustre by the electrolysis of a soln. of potassium titanate, sodium sulphate, and sulphuric acid, but the claim is doubtful. A. C. Becquerel also electrolyzed a conc. hydrochloric acid soln. of titanium and iron chlorides with platinum electrodes ; the metal obtained was possibly an iron-titanium alloy, since no deposit is obtained if the iron chloride be excluded. W. Borchers and W. Huppertz electrolyzed molten calcium chloride in which titanic oxide was suspended. The calcium reduced the titanic oxide to titanium, which was separated in the form of a black powder by leaching away the soluble salts with water and hydrochloric acid. J. Königsberger and J. Schilling also obtained compact titanium by electrolyzing molten rutile with carbon electrodes ; and H. List, by electrolyzing soln. of rutile in molten potassium chloride.

The **smelting of titaniferous magnetites** in the blast furnace has not been satisfactorily solved. Some difficulties are encountered. These are discussed by B. J. Harrington,[10] D. Forbes, W. M. Bowron, J. T. Singewald, etc. If titaniferous iron ores be treated in a blast furnace in the ordinary way, for instance, the slag is viscid and does not run well ; the fuel consumption is high ; and titanium nitride and carbonitride form aggregations in the furnace. A. J. Rossi has claimed that the objections owing to the infusibility of the slags do not hold if the ores with up to about 50 per cent. titanium dioxide be properly fluxed. According to G. Gin, and A. Stansfield, direct smelting of the ore in electric furnaces has given very promising results. Two types of ferro-titanium are used as master-alloys in iron and steel metallurgy—*ferro-carbon-titanium* and *ferro-titanium*. In

A. J. Rossi's process for ferro-titanium, almost carbon-free aluminium is first melted in an electric furnace, pig or scrap-iron is then added to the charge, and rutile is introduced ; the temp. is then raised to the point necessary to start the reduction of the rutile by the aluminium. The reduced rutile alloys with the iron, and the practical product is carbon-free. Alloys with from 10 to 75 per cent. of titanium and 0·12 to 0·75 per cent. of carbon have been made in this way. With ilmenite or titaniferous iron ore in place of rutile, the consumption of aluminium is increased because it is then used in reducing the ferric oxide contained in these minerals. The alloy is also made by H. Goldschmidt's thermite process. When the alloy is made by reduction with carbon in an electric furnace the product contains 5 to 9 per cent. of carbon mainly in the form of graphite. In order to keep down the losses through the volatilization of titanium, A. J. Rossi used lime along with the furnace charge : $TiO_2 + CaO + 5C = Ti + CaC_2 + 3CO$. Analyses by R. J. Anderson of commercial alloys are :

	Si	Ti	C	Mn	Al	P	S
Ferro-carbon-titanium . .	1·41	15·79	7·46	0·11	0·80	0·05	0·08
Ferro-titanium (Goldschmidt) .	1·0–1·5	25	nil	nil	5·0–6·0	0·05	0·01

A. Sinding-Larsen's process is as follows :

The crushed and dressed ore is heated, in a horizontal revolving retort, to a temp. below that of fusion, and then reduced by some such agent as hydrogen, volatile hydrocarbons or carbon monoxide. As the reduction proceeds, the spongy product, containing the whole of its iron and a portion of its titanium as metal, is passed into a second retort which is heated to about 130°. It is there exposed to a current of carbon monoxide ; the iron carbonyl which is formed is conducted to decomposition chambers and decomposed at a temp. of 200° or more, the carbon monoxide being passed back into the second retort. In this way, by suitably shaping the decomposition chambers, it is possible to obtain mouldings of any form, which, however, must subsequently be carbonized since the deposited metal is too pure for technical purposes. The residue in the second retort, consisting of titanium oxide and a certain proportion of titanium, may be heated to a high temperature by means of an electric furnace, subjected to the action of reducing gases, and finally treated with nitrogen, the nitrides obtained being employed as a manure after any unreduced oxides, such as vanadium oxide, have been extracted by means of chlorine or acid.

The variable reports of the effects produced by the addition of titanium to iron and steel possibly depend on whether the titanium is present as a metal alloy or as nitride. Alloys with from 20 to 75 per cent. of silicon and 5 to 70 per cent. of titanium, are called *silico-titanium*, and they are made by reducing a mixture of rutile or titanium dioxide, sand, and carbon in an electric arc-furnace ; *ferro-silico-titanium* is made by adding scrap-iron and a certain amount of hæmatite to the charge. *Cupro-silico-titanium* is made by adding copper to the furnace charge. *Cupro-titanium* is manufactured by A. J. Rossi's process with copper in place of iron in the bath of aluminium ; and *mangano-titanium* is made by H. Goldschmidt's process with 30 to 35 per cent. of titanium.

REFERENCES.

1 J. J. Berzelius, *Pogg. Ann.*, 4. 1, 1825 ; 14. 57, 1837 ; F. Wöhler, *Liebig's Ann.*, 73. 34, 1849 ; 74. 212, 1849 ; *Compt. Rend.*, 29. 505, 1849 ; F. Wöhler and H. St. C. Deville, *ib.*, 45. 480, 1857 ; M. A. Hunter, *Journ. Amer. Chem. Soc.*, 32. 330, 1910.
2 W. A. Lampadius, *Sammlung praktisch-chemischer Abhandlungen*, Dresden, 2. 124, 1797 ; *Phil. Mag.*, 17. 95, 1803 ; *Crell's Ann.*, 25. 1, 230, 259, 1796 ; J. T. Lowitz, *ib.*, 31. 1, 183, 1798 ; L. N. Vauquelin, *Ann. Musée Hist. Nat.*, 6. 93, 1805 ; L. N. Vauquelin and L. Decht, *Journ. Mines*, 3. 15, 1796 ; A. Laugier, *Schweigger's Journ.*, 19. 60, 1817 ; *Ann. Chim. Phys.*, (1), 89. 306, 1814 ; P. Berthier, *ib.*, (2), 50. 362, 1833 ; J. J. Ebelmen, *ib.*, (3), 20. 385, 1827 ; J. von Liebig, *Pogg. Ann.*, 21. 159, 1831 ; J. J. Berzelius, *ib.*, 4. 1, 1825 ; 14. 57, 1837 ; F. Wöhler, *Liebig's Ann.*, 73. 34, 1849 ; 74. 212, 1849 ; *Compt. Rend.*, 29. 505, 1849 ; W. H. Wollaston, *Phil. Trans.*, 113. 400, 1823 ; *Gilbert's Ann.*, 75. 330, 1823 ; H. Rose, *Pogg. Ann.*, 16. 57, 1829 ; 24. 141, 1832 ; *Liebig's Ann.*, 40. 240, 1841.
3 A. Schüller and V. Wartha, *Ber.*, 8. 1011, 1875 ; V. Merz, *ib.*, 8. 1294, 1875 ; *Untersuchungen über das Titan, Silicium, und Boron*, Zürich, 1864 ; *Zeit. Chem.*, (2), 3. 122, 1867 ; M. A. Hunter and A. Jones, *Trans. Amer. Electrochem. Soc.*, 44. 23, 1923 ; F. Wöhler and H. St. C. Deville, *Compt. Rend.*, 45 480, 1857 ; *Gött. Nachr.*, 237, 1857 ; *Ann Chim. Phys.*, (3), 52. 92, 1857 ; *Chem.*

Gaz., **14.** 449, 1857 ; E. A. Schneider, *Zeit. anorg. Chem.*, **8.** 81, 1895 ; E. Podszus, *ib.*, **99.** 123, 1917 ; L. Lévy, *Contribution à l'étude du titane*, Paris, 1891 ; *Ann. Chim. Phys.*, (6), **25.** 449, 1892 ; C. Winkler, *Ber.*, **23.** 2657, 1890 ; A. Polis, *Chem. Ztg.*, **14.** 1003, 1890 ; J. J. Berzelius, *Pogg. Ann.*, **4.** 1, 1825 ; F. Wöhler, *Liebig's Ann.*, **73.** 34, 1849 ; **74.** 212, 1849 ; E. Glatzel, *Ber.*, **9.** 1831, 1876.

[4] S. Kern, *Chem. News*, **33.** 57, 1876 ; F. C. Robinson and C. C. Hutchins, *Amer. Chem. Journ.*, **6.** 74, 1884 ; O. F. von der Pfordten, *Liebig's Ann.*, **237.** 223, 1886 ; E. Podszus, *Zeit. anorg. Chem.*, **99.** 123, 1917 ; M. Billy *Ann. Chim. Phys.*, (9), **16.** 5, 1921 ; L. F. Nilson and O. Pettersson, *Zeit. phys. Chem.*, **1.** 27, 1887 ; L. Weiss and H. Kaiser, *Zeit. anorg. Chem.*, **65.** 345, 1910 ; L. Weiss and E. Neumann, *ib.*, **65.** 248, 1910 ; W. von Bolton, *Zeit Elektrochem.*, **11.** 5, 1905 ; J. W. Marden and M. N. Rich, *Investigations of Zirconium with especial Reference to the Metal and the Oxide*, Washington, 1921 ; *Journ. Ind. Eng. Chem.*, **12.** 651, 1920 ; M. A. Hunter, *Journ. Amer. Chem. Soc.*, **32.** 330, 1910 ; M. A. Hunter and A. Jones, *Trans. Amer. Electrochem. Soc.*, **44.** 23, 1923 ; L. Lévy, *Contribution à l'étude du titane*, Paris, 1891 ; *Ann. Chim. Phys.*, (6), **25.** 433, 1892 ; *Compt. Rend.*, **110.** 1368, 1890 ; **121.** 1148, 1895 ; H. St. C. Deville, *ib.*, **40.** 1034, 1855 ; C. Winkler, *Ber.*, **23.** 2657, 1890 ; A. E. van Arkel and H. de Boer, *Zeit. anorg. Chem.*, **148.** 345, 1925.

[5] W. Borchers and W. Huppertz, *German Pat.*, *D.R.P.* 150557, 1904 ; O. Ruff and H. Brintzinger, *Zeit. anorg. Chem.*, **129.** 267, 1923 ; W. Huppertz, *Versuch über die Herstellung von Titan und Titanlegierungen aus Rutil und Titanaten im elektrischen Oefen*, Aachen, 1904 ; A. Burger, *Reduction durch Calcium*, Basel, 1907 ; H. Kuzel and E. Wedekind, *Met. Chem. Engg.*, **12.** 260, 1914 ; E. A. Schneider, *Zeit anorg. Chem.*, **8.** 83, 1895 ; C. Winkler, *Ber.*, **23.** 2661, 1890 ; O. F. von Pfordten, *Liebig's Ann.*, **234.** 257, 1886 ; **237.** 201, 1887 ; T. König and O. F. von Pfordten, *Ber.*, **22.** 1485, 1889.

[6] H. Goldschmidt, *Liebig's Ann.*, **301.** 19, 1898 ; *Electrochem. Ind.*, **1.** 527, 1903 ; **2.** 145, 1904 ; **3.** 168, 226, 1905 ; H. Goldschmidt and C. Vanton, *Journ. Soc. Chem. Ind.*, **17.** 543, 1898 ; A. Stavenhagen and F. Schuchard, *Ber.*, **35.** 909, 1902 ; E. Wehrlin and E. Giraud, *Compt. Rend.*, **85.** 289, 1877 ; W. Huppertz, *Met.*, **1.** 362, 382, 404, 458, 901, 1904 ; K. A. Kühne, *Electrochem. Met. Ind.*, **7.** 127, 1909 ; *German Pat.*, *D.R.P.* 179403, 1904 ; *U.S. Pat. No.* 910396, 1909 ; W. Prandtl and B. Blayer, *Zeit. anorg. Chem.*, **64.** 223, 1909.

[7] W. A. Lampadius, *Sammlung praktisch-chemischen Abhandlungen*, Dresden, **2.** 124, 1797 ; *Crell's Ann.*, **25.** 1, 230, 259, 1796 ; L. N. Vauquelin, *Ann. Musée Hist. Nat.*, **6.** 93, 1905 ; A. Laugier, *Ann. Chim. Phys.*, (1), **89.** 306, 317, 1814 ; P. Berthier, *ib.*, (3), **20.** 385, 1847 ; L. Burgess, *U.S. Pat. No.* 1512271, 1924 ; E. H. and A. H. Cowles and C. F. Mabery, *Amer. Journ. Science*, (3), **30.** 308, 1885 ; T. S. Hunt, *Chem. News*, **53.** 64, 1886 ; H. Moissan, *Ann. Chim. Phys.*, (7), **9.** 229, 1896 ; *Compt. Rend.*, **120.** 290, 1895 ; **142.** 673, 1906 ; A. Sternberg and A. Deutsch, *German Pat.*, *D.R.P.* 69704, 1890 ; M. A. Hunter, *Journ. Amer. Chem. Soc.*, **32.** 330, 1910.

[8] B. Neumann, *Zeit. Elektrochem.*, **14.** 169, 1908 ; F. Auer, *ib.*, **17.** 482, 1911 ; J. Schilling, *Zeit. angew. Chem.*, **24.** 910, 1911 ; J. J. Ebelmen, *Ann. Chim. Phys.*, (3), **20.** 385, 1847 ; E. Defacqz and H. Copaux, *Compt. Rend.*, **147.** 65, 1908 ; L. Lévy, *ib.*, **110.** 1368, 1890 ; *Ann. Chim. Phys.*, (6), **25.** 433, 1892 ; *Contribution à l'étude du titane*, Paris, 1891 ; E. Wehrlin and E. Giraud, *Compt. Rend.*, **85.** 288, 1877 ; A. Stahler and F. Bachran, *Ber.*, **44.** 2906, 1911 ; D. Gardner and L. Taverner, *Brit. Pat. No.* 207247, 1922 ; A. E. van Arkel and J. H. de Boer, *Zeit. anorg. Chem.*, **148.** 345, 1925 ; A. E. von Arkel, *Chem. Weekbl.*, **22.** 248, 1925 ; *Physica*, **3.** 76, 1923 ; **4.** 286, 1924 ; H. F. Fischvoigt and F. Koref, *Zeit. tech. Phys.*, **6.** 296, 1925.

[9] J. de Bussy, *Compt. R nd.*, **36.** 540, 1853 ; A. C. Becquerel, *Ann. Chim. Phys.*, (2), **48.** 344, 1832 ; J. Königsberger and J. Schilling, *Phys. Zeit.*, **9.** 347, 1908 ; W. Borchers and W. Huppertz, *Chem. Z g.*, **28.** 484, 1904 ; W. Huppertz, *Met.*, **1.** 362. 382, 458, 1904 ; H. List, *Edelerden Erze*, **4. 53.** 1923.

[10] A. J. Rossi, *Journ. Amer. Chem. Soc.*, **12.** 90, 1890 ; *Trans. Amer. Inst. Min. Eng.*, **21.** 832, 1893 ; **33.** 170, 1903 ; *Min. Ind.*, **9.** 715, 1900 ; *Journ. Franklin Inst.*, **154.** 241, 1903 ; A. J. Rossi, *U.S. Pat. Nos.* 609466, 609467, 1898 ; 648439, 1900 ; 668266, 1901 ; 1019528, 1912 ; *French Pat. No.* 407858, 1909 ; G. H. Stanley, *Proc. Chem. Met. Mining Soc. South Africa*, **10.** 162, 1909 ; B. J. Harrington, *Rep. Geol. Sur. Canada*, 249, 1874 ; D. Forbes, *Chem. News*, **18.** 275, 1868 ; J. T. Singewald, *The Titaniferous Iron Ores in the United States : their Composition and Economic Value*, Washington, 1913 ; G. Stähler, *Stahl Eisen*, **29.** 1325, 1909 ; W. Borchers, *ib.*, **31** 706, 1911 ; B. Stoughton, *Ferrum*, **9.** 12, 1914 ; *Min. Ind.*, **19.** 655, 1910 ; M. A. Hunter, *Journ. Amer. Chem. Soc.*, **32.** 330, 1910 ; L. P. Hamilton and E. F. Smith, *ib.*, **23.** 151, 1901 ; A. Sternberg and A. Deutsch, *Brit. Pat. No.* 13117, 1893 ; *Iron Age*, **1.** 354, 464, 1896 ; *Electrochem. Met. Ind.*, **1.** 523, 1903 ; W. M. Bowron, *Trans. Amer. Inst. Min. Eng.*, **11.** 159, 1882 ; G. Gin, *Trans. Amer. Electrochem. Soc.*, **11.** 291, 1907 ; A. Lodyguine, *ib.*, **7.** 157, 1905 ; A. Stansfield, *Canadian Min. Journ.*, **33.** 448, 1912 ; H. Goldschmidt, *Electrochem. Met. Ind.*, **3.** 226, 1905 ; *U.S. Pat. No.* 1136670, 1915 ; A. Sinding-Larsen, *ib.*, 17632, 1910 ; *Brit. Pat. No.* 17632, 1909 ; R. J. Anderson, *Journ. Franklin Inst.*, **184.** 469, 637, 885, 1917 ; E. Schiemann, *Zeit. Ver. deut. Ing.*, **46.** 1791, 1902 ; P. Longmuir, *Journ. Iron Steel Inst.*, **61.** i, 457, 1903 ; A. M. Portevin, *Journ. Iron Steel Inst. Carnegie Mem.*, **1.** 355, 1909 ; R. Moldenke, *Trans. Amer. Foundry Assoc.*, **17.** 57, 1908 ; C. H. Gale, *ib.*, **20.** 271, 1911 ; B. Felse, *Stahl Eisen*, **28.** 697, 1908 ; L. Treuheit, *ib.*, **30.** 1192, 1910 ; O. D. West, *Trans. Amer. Soc. Mech. Eng.*, **34.** 235, 273, 1912 ; B. Stroughton, *Ferrum*, **9.** 12, 1914.

§ 5. The Physical Properties of Titanium

The titanium prepared by J. J. Berzelius,[1] and F Wöhler was impure, and in the form of a grey powder having the appearance of iron reduced by hydrogen at a low temp. The powder acquires a metallic lustre under the burnishing tool. Analyses of titanium were quoted by H. Rose, E. A. Schneider, M. A. Hunter, H. Moissan, and L. Weiss and H. Kaiser. H. Kuzel prepared **colloidal titanium** by the process indicated in connection with colloidal silicon. The **crystals** of the metal reported by many of the early workers—W. H. Wollaston, F. A. Walchner, J. J. Nöggerath, R. J. Haüy—were those of a nitride (J. von Liebig), or carbonitride (W. H. Wollaston), and not of the element at all. Accordingly, as already indicated, many properties attributed to the element do not refer to titanium, but to the carbonitride. The so-called amorphous variety is produced when the halogen salts or oxide are reduced at a low temp., and possibly represent the colloidal metal. V. Merz, and A. Polis tried to crystallize the amorphous form by melting it with zinc or aluminium, but with no definite result on account of the accumulation of titanium in the slag, and the formation of alloys. When cooled from the molten state, titanium gives a crystalline mass resembling polished steel, and, according to L. Lévy, titanium crystallizes in the cubic system ; and, according to J. Königsberger, the crystals are isomorphous with those of silicon and zirconium. L. Lévy's metal was probably titanium silicide. A. W. Hull found that titanium crystallizes in the hexagonal system with the axial ratio $a : c = 1 : 1.59$; the

X-radiogram by A. W. Hull, and R. A. Patterson corresponds with a close packed hexagonal lattice with unit cell having $a=2.97$ A., and $c=4.72$ A., Fig. 2. Each atom of the centred cube is surrounded by eight others. The subject was discussed by M. L. Huggins, G. Greenwood, and L. Vegard. R. A. Patterson observed no change in the space lattice with titanium which had been dipped in liquid air, or heated to 850°.

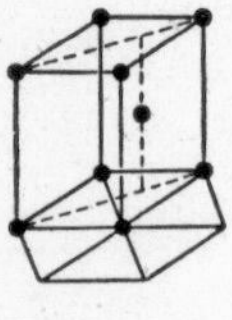

Fig. 2.— Space Lattice of Titanium, Zirconium, and Cerium.

The **specific gravity** of amorphous titanium given by K. B. Hofmann varied from 3.4973 to 3.5888, and he believed the latter value to be the more probable. L. Weiss and H. Kaiser gave 3.392 to 3.952 at 19° to 20°. C. J. B. Karsten made observations on the sp. gr. of titanium. M. A. Hunter gave 4.50 for the sp. gr. of crystalline titanium ; H. Moissan gave for crystals with 2 per cent. of carbon, 4.87 ; and L. Weiss and H. Kaiser, for metal with 0.3 per cent. of carbon and 1.56 per cent. of hydrogen, 5.174 at 19°. W. G. Mixter gave 4.49 to 4.51 at 18°. The sp. gr. 5.28, reported by C. M. Kersten, and 5.3 by W. H. Wollaston, refer to the carbonitride. L. Weiss and H. Kaiser gave for the **atomic volume** of the crystalline element, 9.3 ; and K. B. Hofmann, for the amorphous element, 13.4. W. L. Bragg estimated the **atomic radius** to be 1.40 A. R. Gross also discussed this subject. For the value of b of J. D. van der Waals' equation J. J. van Laar estimated $b_c=0.00180$; and for the valency attraction $\sqrt{A}=35$. According to H. Moissan, the **hardness** of crystalline titanium enables it to scratch quartz and steel, but the metal is so brittle that it can be pulverized in an agate mortar. M. A. Hunter found that although so hard and brittle when cold, titanium at a low red heat may be forged like red-hot iron ; but attempts to produce wire by passing the heated metal through a draw-plate were not successful. A. E. van Arkel and J. H. de Boer made ductile titanium by their process of preparation.

H. St. C. Deville stated that titanium is so refractory that it can be heated in an alumina crucible at the temp. of the vaporization of platinum without melting; and H. Moissan said that fused titanium is the most refractory body we have as yet prepared in the electric furnace ; it is more infusible than vanadium, and leaves far behind such metals as chromium, tungsten, molybdenum, and zirconium. As a matter of fact, said M. A. Hunter, the metal is not by any means as refractory a substance as was formerly believed, for its **melting point** is comparatively low, being within a hundred degrees of that of platinum. M. A. Hunter gave 1800°–1850° for the m.p.; L. Weiss and H. Kaiser, 2200°–2400°; W. Guertler and M. Pirani, 2000°; and G. K. Burgess and R. G. Waltenberg, 1795° ± 15°. O. Ruff found that titanium with about 5 per cent. of carbon melted at 2700° in an electric vacuum furnace. W. Guertler and M. Pirani adopted 2000° as the best representative value. J. K. L. Zincken, and C. Despretz observed the **volatility** of titanium. H. Moissan distilled the metal in an electric arc furnace, and said that its **boiling point** is very high; L. Weiss and H. Kaiser also volatilized the metal when an arc was struck between titanium electrodes. W. R. Mott estimated the b.p. of titanium to be 3400°; and calculated 2800° from J. J. van Laar's data, and the formula $T_c/T_b = 1 \cdot 60$, where T_c denotes the absolute critical temp., and T_b the absolute b.p. The **critical temperature** is 4490°, and the **critical pressure** 1120 atm. L. F. Nilson and O. Pettersson gave for the **specific heat** and the **atomic heat** of amorphous titanium containing 94·73 per cent. Ti:

	0°–100°	0°–211°	0°–301·5°	0°–440°
Sp. ht.	0·1125	0·1288	0·1485	0·1620
At. ht.	5·40	6·18	7·13	7·77

J. Dewar gave 0·0205 for the sp. ht. between −253° and −196°. L. Weiss and H. Kaiser gave 0·1394 to 0·1437—mean 0·1418 for the sp. ht. of titanium, and 6·830 for the at. ht. M. A. Hunter gave for the sp. ht. 0·1462 from 0° to 100°; 0·1503 from 0° to 187·5°; 0·1516 from 0° to 254°; and 0·1563 from 0° to 333°. P. Nordmeyer and A. L. Bernoulli found the sp. ht. between −185° and 20° to be 0·0824. G. N. Lewis and co-workers gave 6·5 Cals. per degree for the atomic **entropy** of titanium at 25°; and E. D. Eastman, 6·3 Cals. per degree. The **refraction equivalent** of titanium for red light as found by A. Schrauf [2] is 0·12782 when that of hydrogen as unit is 0·00405; J. H. Gladstone gave for the **atomic refraction** 24·6, and for the sp. refraction, 0·510. C. P. Smyth discussed the relation between the refraction and the electronic structure. R. Thalén [3] gave a drawing and some measurements of the **spark spectrum** of titanium, and observations were made by R. Capron, W. F. Meggers and co-workers, R. J. Lang, A. de Gramont, B. Hasselberg, E. Haschek, H. Gieseler and W. Grotrian, O. Lohse, N. A. Kent, A. Hagenbach and H. Konen, F. Exner and E. Haschek, H. Konen and H. Finger, E. Carter, H. Kayser, C. Keller, A. M. Kilby, F. L. Brown, J. H. Pollok, P. Fiebig, and J. M. Eder and E. Valenta. The more intense lines have the wave-lengths: 2516·10, 3349·20*, 3361·40*, 3372·92*, 3383·87, 3505·10, 3510·99, 3685·37*, 3759·40*, 3761·5*, 3900·81, 3913·72, 4163·90, 4395·20, 4549·90, 4572·27. The six marked with an asterisk were shown by J. H. Pollok to be the most persistent. The **arc spectrum** of titanium was studied by R. Capron, W. F. Meggers and co-workers, J. N. Lockyer, G. D. Liveing and J. Dewar, R. Thalén, H. A. Rowland, A. Hagenbach and H. Konen, R. E. Loving, E. J. Evans, A. M. Kilby, A. S. King, P. Fiebig, M. A. Catalan, C. C. and H. K. Kiess, H. Crew, K. Behner, J. M. Eder and E. Valenta, and F. Exner and E. Haschek. The more persistent lines have the wave-lengths: 3948·87, 3989·94, 3998·80, 4306·09, 4533·40, 4536·16, 4981·93, 4991·24, 4999·68, 5007·35, 5014·39, 5193·12, 5210·59. C. C. and H. K. Kiess studied the regularities in the arc spectrum of titanium. The **flame spectrum** was studied by J. N. Lockyer; the **band spectrum,** by A. Fowler, G. E. Hale and co-workers, P. Fiebig, and J. M. Eder and E. Valenta; the **series spectrum,** by H. N. Russell, C. C. Kiess and W. F. Meggers, and P. G. Nutting; and the ultra-violet spectrum, by A. S. King, R. J. Lang, and F. Exner and E. Haschek. The *enhanced lines* were investigated by J. N. Lockyer, A. S. King, H. M. Reese, M. Kimura and G. Nakamura, and F. E. Baxandall; the effect of *pressure*, by W. J. Humphreys, A. S. King, and H. G. Gale and W. S. Adams; and the effect of a *magnetic field*—the **Zeeman effect**—by H. D. Babcock, H. M. Reese, J. E. Purvis, and A. S. King. H. Gieseler studied the absorption spectrum of the vapour at 2000°. The relations between the spectra of carbon, boron, silicon, titanium, and zirconium were studied by L. Troost and P. Hautefeuille. According to J. Formanek, titanium salt soln. have no **absorption spectrum,** but with an alcoholic soln. of alkanna, there is a marked absorption band about 6271, and fainter bands about 5782 and 5350. For the titanium lines in the solar spectrum, *vide* the occurrence of titanium. The high frequency or **X-ray spectrum** was studied by G. Wentzel, H. G. J. Moseley, D. Coster, and E. H. Kurth. B. Walter, A. E. Lindh, M. Levi, F. Hund, V. Dolejsek, H. Fricke, E. Hjalmar, M. Siegbahn, D. M Bose, K. Chamberlain, O. Stelling, H. H. Robinson, and N. Stensson found, in Angström or 10^{-8} cm. units, for the K-series, $a_2a'=2.74648$; $a_1a=2.74284$; a_3 and $a_4=2.7269$; $\beta_1\beta=2.50874$; and $\beta_2\gamma=2.49367$. N. K. Sur discussed the spectrum of ionized titanium, and estimated the **ionizing potential** to be 13 volts.

W. H. Wollaston's [4] observations on the **electrical conductivity** of titanium really refer to the carbonitride. L. Weiss and H. Kaiser found that the metal is a fair conductor; its sp. **electrical resistance** varied from 0.125 to 0.448 ohm. P. W. Bridgman found that the press. coeff. of the conductivity of titanium is very small; it is probably less than 10 per kgrm.; and probably increases with press. F. Streitz attributed the negative temp. coeff. of the resistance of titanium to the presence of minute cavities which close as the temp. rises. J. Königsberger

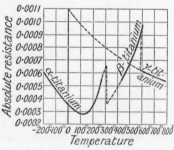

FIG. 3.—The Effect of Temperature on the Electrical Resistance of Titanium.

and J. Schilling showed that the absolute electrical resistance of titanium per c.c. changes from 0.000627 at −191° to a minimum of 0.00276 at 140°; this represents the absolute resistance of what they called α-titanium. Above this temp., there are changes possibly represented by the dotted lines, Fig. 3, between 275° and 435°, which are but slowly reversible; and above this temp. there appears to be another allotropic form of titanium called **β-titanium,** the electrical resistance of which rises from 0.000540 at 435° to 0.000815 at 560°. There is then a change to another form called γ-titanium. The change from γ to β is so slow that the dotted curve representing the resistance of γ-titanium has been realized down to 0.00109 at 15°. To summarize :

$$\alpha\text{-Ti} \overset{275°}{\rightleftharpoons} \beta\text{-Ti} \overset{560°}{\rightleftharpoons} \gamma\text{-Ti}$$

These allotropic forms of titanium have no relation with the allotropic forms reported by J. J. Berzelius. His α-titanium was obtained by the action of heat on tetramminotetra-chloride and was probably titanium nitride; his β-titanium was the ordinary amorphous form. The former readily burns when heated in air, the latter resists the action of heat; the former is readily attacked by boiling nitric acid and aqua regia, the latter resists the strong acids.

A. Thiel and W. Hammerschmidt found the overvoltage of titanium with $0.1N\text{-}H_2SO_4$ to be 0.570 volt. J. Keyrovsky studied the electrolytic soln. press. F. Fischer and G. Iliovici passed sparks between titanium electrodes under liquid argon, and found scarcely any disintegration of the metal. E. T. Wherry found artificial titanium to be a poor radio-detector. According to M. E. Verdet, the amorphous metal is paramagnetic; and, according to K. Honda, the **magnetic susceptibility** of the purest titanium available was 3.1×10^{-6} at 18°, and 3.5×10^{-6} at 1100°; S. Meyer gave 1.9×10^{-6} at ordinary temp. F. C. L. Elsner compared the magnetic properties of titanium with those of iron. I. Tamm, A. Duvillier, P. Weiss and P. Collet, and B. Cabrera studied the relation between the magnetic properties and the electronic structure of the atom.

REFERENCES.

W. H. Wollaston, *Phil. Trans.*, **113**. 17, 400, 1823 ; J. von Liebig, *Pogg. Ann.*, **21**. 259, 1831 : F. A. Walchner, *ib.*, **3**. 176, 1825 : *Schweigger's Journ.*, **41**. 80, 1824 : **44**. 47, 1825 ; J. J. Nöggerath, *ib.*, **65**. 385, 1832 ; *Karsten's Arch.*, **4**. 351, 1825 : R. J. Haüy, *Journ. Mines*, **3**. 28, 1796 ; A. Polis, *Chem. Ztg.*, **14**. 1003, 1890 ; V. Merz, *Untersuchungen über das Titan, Silicium, und Boron*, Zürich, 1864 ; *Zeit. Chem.*, (2), **3**. 122, 1867 ; *Journ. prakt. Chem.*, (1), **99**. 157, 1866 ; J. J. Berzelius, *Akad. Handl. Stockholm*, 1, 1843 ; *Taylor's Scientific Memoirs*, **4**. 240, 1846 ; *Pogg. Ann.*, **4**. 1, 1825 ; **14**. 57, 1837 ; **61**. 10, 1844 ; H. Rose. *ib.*, **15**. 145, 1829 ; C. M. Kersten, *ib.*, **3**. 175, 1825 ; J. K. L. Zincken, *ib.*, **3**. 175, 1825 ; **28**. 160, 1834 ; *Liebig's Ann.*, **12**. 222, 1834 ; F. Wöhler, *ib.*, **73**. 34, 1849 ; **74**. 212, 1849 ; *Compt. Rend.*, **29**. 505, 1849 ; H. St. C. Deville, *ib.*, **40**. 1034, 1855 ; C. Despretz, *ib.*, **29**. 545, 1849 ; H. Moissan, *ib.*, **120**. 290, 1896 ; **142**. 673, 1906 ; *Le four électrique*, Paris, 1897 ; London, 181, 1904 ; *Ann. Chim. Phys.*, (7), **9**. 229, 1896 ; L. Lévy, *ib.*. (6), **25**. 443, 1892 ; *Contribution à l'étude du titane*, Paris, 1891 ; *Compt. Rend.*, **121**. 1148, 1895 ; L. F. Nilson and O. Pettersson, *Zeit. phys. Chem.*, **1**. 27, 1887 ; W. Guertler and M. Pirani, *Zeit. Metallkunde*, **11**. 1, 1919 ; A. W. Hull, *Science*, (2), **52**. 227, 1920 ; *Phys. Rev.*, (2), **18**. 88, 1921 ; R. A. Patterson, *ib.*, (2), **26**. 56, 1925 ; H. Kuzel, *German Pat., D.R.P.* 197379, 1905 ; *Brit. Pat. No.* 25864, 1906 ; *French Pat. No.* 371799, 1906 ; C. J. B. Karsten, *Karsten's Arch.*, **4**. 362, 1832 ; *Sitzber. Akad. Berlin*, 229, 1831 ; M. A. Hunter, *Journ. Amer. Chem. Soc.*, **32**. 330, 1910 ; M. A. Hunter and E. C. Jones, *Reusselaer Polyt. Inst.*, **1**. 11, 1911 ; W. L. Bragg, *Phil. Mag.*, (6), **40**. 169, 1920 ; K. B. Hofmann, *Ber.*, **26**. 1025, 1893 ; O. Ruff, *ib.*, **43**. 1564, 1910 ; F. Fischer and G. Iliovici, *ib.*, **41**. 4449, 1908 ; E. A. Schneider, *Zeit. anorg. Chem.*, **8**. 81, 1895 ; L. Weiss and H. Kaiser, *ib.*, **65**. 345, 1910 ; G. K. Burgess and R. G. Waltenberg, *ib.*, **82**. 361, 1913 ; *Proc. Washington Acad.*, **3**. 371, 1913 ; *Brass World*, **9**. 349, 1913 ; J. Königsberger, *Centr. Min.*, 565, 1908 ; W. G. Mixter, *Amer. Journ. Science*, (4), **27**. 393, 1909 ; P. Nordmeyer and A. L. Bernoulli, *Ber. deut. phys. Ges.*, **9**. 175, 1907 ; W. R. Mott, *Trans. Amer. Electrochem. Soc.*, **34**. 255, 1918 ; J. J. van Laar, *Proc. Acad. Amsterdam*, **18**. 1220, 1916 ; **29**. 138, 492, 1918 ; *Die Zustandgleichung von Gasen und Flussigkeiten*, Leipzig, 1924 ; J. Dewar, *Proc. Roy. Soc.*, **89**. A, 158, 1913 ; G. N. Lewis, G. E. Nilson, and W. M. Latimer, *Journ. Amer. Chem. Soc.*, **44**. 1008, 1922 ; E. D. Eastman. *ib.*, **45**. 80, 1923 ; R. Gross, *Zeit. Elektrochem.*, **30**. 1, 1924 ; M. L. Huggins, *Phys. Rev.*, (2), **21**. 719, 1923 ; (2), **25**. 160, 1924 ; L. Vegard, *Phil. Mag.*, (6), **32**. 65, 1916 ; G. Greenwood, *ib.*, (6), **48**. 654, 1924 ; A. E. van Arkel and J. H. de Boer, *Zeit. anorg. Chem.*, **148**. 345, 1925.

[2] A. Schrauf, *Sitzber. Akad. Wien*, **52**. 176, 1865 ; *Pogg. Ann.*, **126**. 177, 1865 ; **127**. 175, 344, 1866 ; **133**. 479, 1868 ; *Zeit. Chem.*, (2), **2**. 167, 1866 ; J. H. Gladstone, *Proc. Roy. Soc.*, **18**. 49, 1869 ; *Phil. Trans.*, **159**. 13, 1869 ; C. P. Smyth, *Phil. Mag.*, (6), **50**. 361, 1925.

[3] R. Thalén, *Om Spectralanalys*, Upsala, 1866 ; *Acta Soc. Upsala*, (3), **6**. 9, 1863 ; (3), **12**. 1, 1884 ; *Ann. Chim. Phys.*, (4), **18**. 239, 1869 ; A. J. Angström, *Recherches sur le spectre normal du soleil*, Upsala, 1868 ; R. Capron, *Photographed Spectra*, London, 1877 ; F. Exner and E. Haschek, *Wellenlägentabellen für spectralanalytische Untersuchungen auf Grund der ultravioletten Funkenspectren der Elemente*, Leipzig, 1902 ; *Wellenlägentabellen für spectralanalytische Untersuchungen auf Grund der ultravioletten Bogenspectren der Elemente*, Leipzig, 1904 ; *Die Spectren der Elemente bei normalen Druck*, Leipzig, 1912 ; *Sitzber. Akad. Wien*, **107**. 792, 1898 ; E. Haschek, *ib.*, **110**, 181, 1901 ; *Astrophys. Journ.*, **14**. 181, 1901 ; H. M. Reese, *ib.*, **12**. 120, 1900 ; **19**. 322, 1904 ; E. Carter and A. S. King, *ib.*, **49**. 224, 1919 ; E. Carter, *ib.*, **55**. 162, 1922 ; N. A. Kent, *ib.*, **17**. 286, 1903 ; **22**. 182, 1905 ; *Proc. Amer. Acad.*, **41**. 281, 1905 ; *Phys. Rev.*, (1), **20**. 387, 1905 ; H. G. Gale and W. S. Adams, *ib.*, (1), **32**. 438, 1911 ; J. M. Eder and E. Valenta, *Atlas typischer Spectren*, Wien, 1911 ; *Sitzber. Akad. Wien*, **118**. 1077, 1909 ; **119**. 519, 1910 ; E. Néculcéa, *Recherches théoriques et expérimentales sur la constitution des spectres ultraviolettes d'étincelles oscillantes*, Paris, 1906 ; J. N. Lockyer, *Nature*, **19**. 197, 225, 1879 ; **61**. 263, 1899 ; *Proc. Roy. Soc.*, **28**. 157, 1878 ; **43**. 117, 1887 ; **65**. 451, 1899 ; J. N. Lockyer and F. E. Baxandall, *ib.*, **74**. 255, 1904 ; R. Rossi, *ib.*, **83**. A, 414, 1909 ; G. D. Liveing and J. Dewar, *ib.*, **32**. 402, 1881 ; W. N. Hartley and H. W. Moss, *ib.*, **87**. A, 38, 1912 ; G. Fowler, *ib.*, **73**. 219, 1904 ; **79**. A, 509, 1907 ; *Month. Notices Roy. Astron. Soc.*, **69**. 508, 1909 ; A. S. King, *Phys. Rev.*, (2), **22**. 200, 1923 ; H. D. Babcock, *ib.*, (2), **22**. 201, 1923 ; *Astrophys. Journ.*, **58**. 149, 1923 ; F. W. Dyson, *Phil. Trans.*, **206**. A, 493, 1906 ; C. C. and H. K. Kiess, *Journ. Washington Acad.*, **13**. 270, 1923 ; G. Wentzel, *Naturwiss.*, **10**. 464, 1922 ; L. Troost and P. Hautefeuille, *Compt. Rend.*, **73**. 620, 1871 ; A. de Gramont, *ib.*, **150**. 37, 1910 ; **166**. 94, 1918 ; *Bull. Soc. Min.*, **18**. 222, 1895 ; *Analyse spectrale directe des minéraux*, Paris, 1895 ; A. Hagenbach and H. Konen, *Atlas der Emissionsspectra*, Jena, 1905 ; H. A. Rowland, *Astron. Astrophys. Journ.*, **12**. 221, 1893 ; A. Cornu, *Ann. Scient. École Norm. Sup.*, (2), **9**. 21, 1880 ; B. Hasselberg, *Akad. Handl. Stockholm*, **28**. 1, 1895 ; **32**. 2, 1899 ; O. Lohse, *Publ. Astrophys. Obs. Potsdam*, **12**. 109, 1902 ; F. E. Baxandall, *Astrophys. Journ.*, **21**. 337, 1905 ; E. Carter, *ib.*, **55**. 162, 1922 ; F. L. Brown, *ib.*, **56**. 53, 1922 ; R. E. Loving, *ib.*, **22**. 285, 1905 ; W. M. Mitchell, *ib.*, **22**. 4, 1905 ; P. G. Nutting, *ib.*, **23**. 64, 1906 ; G. E. Hale, W. S. Adams, and H. G. Gale, *ib.*, **24**. 185, 1906 ; G. E. Hale and W S. Adams, *ib.*, **25**. 75, 1907 ; W. J. Humphreys, *ib.*, **6**. 169, 1897 ; **26**. 18, 1907 ; A. L. Cortie, *ib.*, **26**. 300, 1908 ; A. S. King, *ib.*, **29**. 76, 1909 ; **30**. 1, 1909 ; **31**. 433, 1910 ; **34**. 225, 1911 ; **62**. 238, 1925 ; E. J. Evans, *ib.*,

29. 160, 1909 ; W. S. Adams, *ib.*, 30. 86, 1909 ; A. M. Kilby, *ib.*, 30. 243, 1909 ; H. Kayser, *Handbuch der Spectroscopie*, Leipzig, 6. 655, 1912 ; *Zeit. wiss. Photochem.*, 3. 308, 1905 ; K. Behner, *ib.*, 23. 325, 1925 ; C. Keller, *ib.*, 4. 209, 1906 ; H. Finger, *ib.*, 7. 329, 369, 1909 ; P. Fiebig, *ib.*, 8. 73, 1910 ; J. E. Purvis, *Proc. Cambridge Phil. Soc.*, 14. 41, 1906 ; R. J. Lang, *Phil. Trans.*, 224. A, 371, 1924 ; A. H. Avery, *Proc. Amer. Acad.*, 43. 353, 1907 ; J. H. Pollok, *Proc. Roy. Soc. Dublin*, 9. 331, 1909 ; J. Formanek, *Die qualitative Spektralanalyse anorganischer und organischer Körper*, Berlin, 150, 1905 ; *Zeit. anal. Chem.*, 39. 406, 673, 679, 1900 ; H. Konen and H. Finger, *Zeit. Elektrochem.*, 15. 165, 1909 ; H G. J. Moseley, *Phil. Mag.*, (6), 26. 1024, 1913 ; (6), 27. 703, 1914 ; G. A. Hemsalech, *ib.*, (6), 39. 241, 1920 ; E. H. Kurth, *Phys. Rev.*, (2), 18. 461, 1921 ; V. Dolejsek, *Compt. Rend.*, 174. 441, 1922 ; H. Fricke, *Phys. Rev.*, (2), 16. 202, 1920 ; E. Hjalmar, *Zeit. Physik*, 1. 439, 1920 ; *Phil. Mag.*, (6), 41. 675, 1921 ; M. Siegbahn, *Jahrb. Rad. Elektron.*, 13. 296, 1916 ; N. Stensson, *Zeit. Physik*, 3. 60, 1920 ; D. Coster, *ib.*, 25. 83, 1924 ; H. Gieseler and W. Grotrian, *ib.*, 25. 362, 1924 ; H. Giesseler, *Naturwiss.*, 10. 438, 1924 ; M. A. Catalan, *Anal. Fis. Quim.*, 15. 487, 1917 ; 16. 513, 1918 ; C. C. Kiess and W. F. Meggers, *Bull. Bur. Standards*, 16. 51, 1920 ; C. C. and H. K. Kiess, *Journ. Amer. Opt. Soc.*, 8. 607, 1924 ; A. S. King, *Astrophys. Journ.*, 59. 155, 1924 ; H. Crew, *ib.*, 60. 108, 1924 ; H. N. Russell, *Science*, (2), 59. 512, 1924 ; N. K. Sur, *Nature*, 114. 611, 1924 ; B. Walter, *Zeit. Physik*, 30. 363, 1924 ; A. E. Lindh, *ib.*, 31. 210, 1925 ; F. Hund, *ib.*, 33. 345, 1925 ; W. F. Meggers, C. C. Kiess, and F. M. Walters, *Journ. Amer. Opt. Soc.*, 9. 355, 1924 ; A. S. King, *Phys. Rev.*, (2), 25. 237, 1925 ; M. Levi, *Trans. Roy. Soc. Canada*, (3), 18. 159, 1924 ; D. M. Bose, *Zeit. Physik*, 35. 213, 1925 ; K. Chamberlain, *Phys. Rev.*, (2), 26. 525, 1925 ; O. Stelling, *Zeit. phys. Chem.*, 117, 175, 1925 ; H H. Robinson, *Phil. Mag.*, (6), 50. 241, 1925 ; M. Kimura and G. Nakamura, *Science Papers Inst. Phys. Japan*, 3. 51, 1925.

⁴ J. Königsberger, *Zeit. Elektrochem.*, 15. 97, 1909 ; J. Königsberger and K. Schilling, *Ann. Physik*, (4), 32. 179, 1910 ; K. Honda, *ib.*, (4), 32. 1027, 1910 ; F. Streitz, *ib.*, (4), 44. 545, 1914 ; A. Thiel and W. Hammerschmidt, *Zeit. anorg. Chem.*, 132. 15, 1923 ; F. Fischer and G. Iliovici, *Ber.*, 41. 3802, 4449 1908 ; 42. 527, 1909 ; S. Meyer *ib.*, (4), 1. 664, 1900 ; *Wied. Ann.*, 68. 325, 1899 ; 69. 236, 1899 ; M. E. Verdet, *Ann. Chim. Phys.*, (3), 52. 156, 1858 ; A. Duvillier, *Compt. Rend.*, 176. 1802. 1923 ; B. Cabrera, *Ann. Fis. Quim.*, 20. 92, 1922 ; F. C. L. Elsner, *Dingler's Journ.*, 180. 326, 1866 ; *Chem. Tech. Mitt.*, 291, 1867 ; P. W. Bridgman, *Proc. Amer. Acad.*, 56. 61, 1921 ; L. Weiss and H. Kaiser, *Zeit. anorg. Chem.*, 65. 345, 1910 ; P. Weiss and P. Collet, *Compt. Rend.*, 178. 2146, 1924 ; J. J. Berzelius, *Akad. Handl. Stockholm*, 1, 1842 ; *Pogg. Ann.*, 61. 10, 1844 ; *Taylor's Scientific Memoirs*, 4. 240, 1846 ; W. H. Wollaston, *Phil. Trans.*, 113. 17, 400, 1823 ; E. T. Wherry, *Amer. Min.*, 10. 28, 1925 ; I. Tamm, *Zeit. Physik*, 32. 582, 1925 ; J. Keyrovsky, *Compt. Rend.*, 180. 1655, 1925.

§ 6. The Chemical Properties of Titanium

The whole of the properties of titanium, said H. Moissan,¹ bring it near to those of the metalloids, and more especially to those of silicon. J. B. van Mons made some observations on the affinity of titanium. E. A. Schneider said that amorphous titanium absorbs a large proportion of **hydrogen,** but it is uncertain whether the gas is merely absorbed, or chemically united with the metal. L. Weiss and H. Kaiser doubt if titanium free from occluded hydrogen has ever been made ; a metal melted in vacuo at 2000° still retained 1·56 per cent. of hydrogen. C. Renz passed chloroform vap. over finely divided, red-hot titanium dioxide, and obtained a colourless gas which furnished titanic acid when passed into water. It was assumed that **titanium hydride** was probably formed. It is, however, possible that very finely divided titanium dioxide was carried along with the gas. T. L. Phipson reported the formation of titanium hydride by the action of magnesium on titanic acid. A. Klauber did not make titanium hydride by the electrolysis of a 50 per cent. soln. of sulphuric acid, using a titanium cathode at 110 to 240 volts, and 0·1 to 4·0 amps. ; but by working with a discharge apparatus at 0·2 to 0·4 amp. and 240 volts, using titanium electrodes, and 0·1 to 0·2N-H_2SO_4, good yields of titanium hydride were obtained. It is said to be a colourless and odourless gas burning in air with a colourless flame like hydrogen, and forming titanium dioxide. The gas deposits titanium when passed through a heated glass tube. It gives a yellow soln. with hydrogen dioxide ; a blue soln. with zinc and hydrochloric acid ; and a reddish-orange colour is produced with a crystal of potassium iodide, and the colour disappears when exposed to ammonia. M. Billy claimed to have made a solid hydride, Ti_4H_5, as a dull black powder by the action of hydrogen and sodium hydride on titanium tetrachloride.

Titanium is stable in **air** at ordinary temp., and E. A. Schneider observed only a slight increase in weight after keeping the amorphous metal at 100°–120° for 15 hrs.; the increase was eq. to the formation of 0·06 per cent. TiO_2. M. A. Hunter found that titanium ignites in air at about 1200°; and H. Moissan that it burns in **oxygen** at 610° with incandescence, leaving a residue of amorphous titanium dioxide. W. G. Mixter gave for the heat of oxidation 218·4 Cals., while L. Weiss and H. Kaiser gave 97·772 Cals. F. Wöhler said that the brilliant combustion of titanium in air is attended by the formation of nitrogenous titanium dioxide, and when the powdered metal is strewn in the flame brilliant sparks appear. The affinity of oxygen for titanium, said C. Winkler, is very great, and many reducing agents furnish a lower oxide, but not the metal. F. Wöhler said that amorphous titanium begins to react with **water** at 100°, but S. Kern, L. Weiss and H. Kaiser, and E. A. Schneider showed that this action occurs only when the metal is contaminated with sodium. H. V. Regnault showed that titanium decomposes steam at a red heat, and H. Moissan found the reaction with pyrophoric titanium begins at 700°, but the decomposition is continuous until about 800°, when hydrogen is given off and titanium dioxide formed.

O. Ruff and R. Ipsen showed that **fluorine** reacts with warmed titanium, forming the tetrafluoride, and, according to F. Wöhler, **chlorine** does not attack titanium in the cold, but at a higher temp., the reaction is attended with incandescence. H. Moissan said the reaction begins at 350°, and that the tetrachloride is formed. He also found that the reaction with **bromine** begins at about 360°, forming, according to F. B. Duppa, the tetrabromide. The reaction with **iodine** begins at a higher temp. than is the case with bromine, there is no appreciable incandescence, and, according to R. Weber, the tetraiodide is formed. C. Willgerodt said that titanium does not act as *Halogenübertrager* for benzene. V. Merz, and L. Weiss and H. Kaiser found that **hydrofluoric acid** dissolves titanium quickly, forming, according to E. Glatzel, and O. Ruff and R. Ipsen, a soln. of the tetrafluoride; H. Moissan, and L. Weiss and H. Kaiser found that a mixture of nitric and hydrofluoric acids dissolves titanium with violent effervescence, and that the reaction is as energetic as with silicon. V. Merz found that with dry **hydrogen chloride,** titanium forms the tetrachloride. According to H. Moissan, and L. Weiss and H. Kaiser, boiling **hydrochloric acid** attacks titanium slowly with the evolution of hydrogen, and a violet soln. is formed. The nature of the product has been discussed by F. Wöhler, O. F. van der Pfordten, E. Glatzel, and E. A. Schneider— *vide* the titanium chlorides.

L. Lévy said that **sulphur** unites with titanium at a high temp.; and H. Moissan found that the attack is slow at the softening point of glass, and a dark-coloured substance is formed which is not attacked by cold hydrochloric acid, but gives off hydrogen sulphide with boiling conc. acid. For the action of **hydrogen sulphide** and **carbon disulphide,** *vide* the titanium sulphides. According to V. Merz, L. Weiss and H. Kaiser, and H. Moissan, cold dil. **sulphuric acid** readily dissolves titanium with the evolution of hydrogen, but heat is required for the continuous action; hot conc. sulphuric acid oxidizes titanium, forming sulphur dioxide, etc. According to H. Moissan, powdered titanium forms a nitride when heated to 800° in a stream of **nitrogen,** and the reaction is attended with vivid incandescence; according to F. Wöhler and H. St. C. Deville, if carbon is present, some carbonitride is formed. E. A. Schneider investigated the relative affinities of nitrogen for titanium, magnesium, and boron. F. Wöhler, and C. Friedel and J. Guérin also found that the nitride is formed when titanium is heated in a current of **ammonia.** V. Merz, L. Weiss and H. Kaiser, and H. Moissan found that dil **nitric acid** attacks titanium slowly in the cold, but dissolution is faster with the hot acid. Dissolution is also faster with aqua regia, but the coating of titanic acid which is formed soon stops the reaction. With nitric acid of sp. gr. 1·25, R. Weber found that there is formed much titanic oxide which does not dissolve. H. Moissan showed that titanium reacts with **phosphorus** vap. at about 1000°, forming a dark-coloured phosphide. The reaction is only superficial.

According to E. A. Schneider, and H. Moissan, **carbon** reacts with titanium at a high temp., forming a carbide; carbon also dissolves in molten titanium, forming a carbide, and on cooling, the excess of carbon crystallizes out as graphite. K. Nischk studied the affinity of titanium for carbon. V. Merz reported that cold **acetic acid** dissolves titanium slowly. L. Lévy found that titanium alone, or mixed with potassium or sodium, does not react with the **alkyl iodides ;** and that titanium does not react with **zinc, aluminium, or mercury ethides.** P. Schützenberger and A. Colson studied the absorption of **silicon** or **silicon nitrides** by titanium. According to H. Moissan, silicon unites with titanium in the electric furnace, forming a silicide which is as hard as the diamond. E. A. Schneider observed no reduction when titanium and silica are heated together. H. Moissan showed that titanium reacts with **boron,** forming a boride of adamantine hardness. For the reactions of titanium with the metals, *vide* the titanides. E. A. Schneider found that titanium does not react with **alumina** at a bright red heat.

According to H. Moissan, oxidizing agents readily attack titanium ; fused **potassium nitrate,** for instance, attacks it without any apparent evolution of heat, but if powdered titanium be thrown into **potassium chlorate** at its decomposition temp., there is a reaction attended by a vivid incandescence. The fused **alkali carbonates** attack titanium in the same way as does a mixture of potassium nitrate and carbonate. L. Weiss and H. Kaiser found that when a mixture with potassium chlorate or nitrate, or **potassium permanganate** is heated, an explosion ensues. F. Wöhler found that titanium reacts violently when heated with **cupric oxide** or **lead oxide** (red-lead). H. Moissan said that **silver fluoride** is reduced by powdered titanium at 320° with incandescence. L. Weiss and H. Kaiser found that molten **potassium hydrosulphate** dissolves titanium, forming a clear soln. M. G. Levi and co-workers found titanium dissolves slowly in a soln. of **potassium persulphate,** and still more slowly in one of **ammonium persulphate.**

The alloys of titanium with other metals have not been well investigated. E. A. Schneider heated a mixture of cuprous chloride, potassium fluotitanate, and sodium in an atm. of hydrogen, but failed to obtain a satisfactory alloy ; but by heating a mixture of potassium fluotitanate and sodium in the presence of strips of **copper** in an atm. of hydrogen, he found that the surface of the copper became very hard and was scarcely scratched by steel. By melting together the hardened parts, he obtained a hard and brittle **cupro-titanium** with 11·85 per cent. of titanium. K. Nischk made alloys of copper and titanium. The manufacture of cupro-titanium by A. J. Rossi's [2] process has been previously described. M. A. Hunter and J. W. Bacon measured the electrical resistance of these alloys. A. J. Rossi also made an **argento-titanium** by heating a mixture of silver, titanium dioxide, silver oxide, and aluminium turnings or carbon. C. Winkler, and L. Lévy did not succeed in making a *magnesium titanide ;* nor did L. Lévy make a *zinc titanide.*

Aluminium titanides are contained in the regulus obtained when rutile is reduced by aluminium in the alumino-thermite process. L. Guillet [3] prepared the titanides Al_3Ti_2 and Al_4Ti, and obtained mixtures corresponding with Al_2Ti, Al_3Ti, and Al_4Ti ; but there is as yet no satisfactory evidence as to what the actual compounds really are. J. Dewar and J. A. Fleming measured the electrical conductivity of some alumino-titanium alloys. E. van Erckelens studied the f.p. of alloys with up to 30 per cent. of titanium corresponding with $TiAl_4$, Fig. 4 ; and H. Schirmeister, the tensile strength. F. Wöhler prepared what he assumed, without analysis, to be an **aluminium ditritatitanide,** Al_3Ti_2, by melting together a mixture of titanic oxide, cryolite, salt. and aluminium for an hour ; it does not oxidize readily when heated in air ; it burns to titanium and aluminium chlorides when heated in chlorine or hydrogen chloride ; it dissolves in hydrochloric acid, forming a violet soln.; nitric acid vigorously attacks the product. L. Weiss and H. Kaiser, and L. Guillet made some observations on this alloy. W. Manchot and P. Richter prepared a regulus by melting 45·5 grms. of aluminium with 24 grms. of potassium titanofluoride, K_2TiF_6; and the excess of aluminium was removed by a warm normal soln. of sodium hydroxide. Analyses of the crystalline plates agree with **aluminium tritatitanide,** Al_3Ti. W. Manchot and A. Leber extended their study of this compound. The sp. gr. is 5·5; it is very hard and brittle. If it be covered with an acid, and allowed to stand in air, the soln. becomes yellow owing to the formation of hydrogen dioxide, and also of pertitanic acid. Boiling acids or alkali-lye dissolve the alloy rapidly; $\frac{1}{2}N$-H_2SO_4 dissolves. The product is oxidized when heated in air; and when heated with chlorine, the reaction is attended with incandescence. From the proportion of hydrogen evolved when the alloy is treated with acids, it was inferred that the titanium is tervalent, and that the constitution is Al_3Ti–$TiAl_3$. L. Lévy reported that he had prepared **aluminium tetritatitanide,** Al_4Ti, by melting sodium and potassium chloride in a crucible made of rutile and graphite; it was also made by reducing titanium dioxide with aluminium under a layer of molten sodium chloride; and by reducing titanium tetrachloride with aluminium. The product was treated with water and then with dil. acid, and a residue was obtained consisting of lustrous, steel-grey lamellæ, with angles of 90°, very brittle, and good conductors of heat; the sp. gr. at 16° is 3·11. The crystals do not alter in air or nitrogen oxides at the ordinary temp., but tarnish when heated, and burn if heated in oxygen. They are not attacked by vap. of sulphur, selenium, phosphorus, or arsenic, but burn in chlorine or in vap. of iodine or bromine, especially the former. Liquid bromine, however, is without action. Superheated steam and cold fuming nitric acid have no action, but hot nitric acid attacks the crystals slightly. Hydrochloric and sulphuric acids act somewhat in the cold and more readily when heated. The crystals burn when heated in hydrogen chloride, and dissolve readily in aqua regia, but are not dissolved by hydrobromic and hydriodic acids, or by mixtures of these acids with nitric acid. Sulphuric acid and calcium fluoride have little action, and potash only partially dissolves the crystals in the cold, but dissolution is complete on heating, with evolution of hydrogen. The crystals have a composition which agrees with the formula $(Ti : Si)Al_4$, and hence it is probable that they are mixtures of the isomorphous compounds, Al_4Ti, and Al_4Si. If zinc or magnesium is substituted for aluminium, no crystals are obtained. E. van Erckelens showed that the tetritatitanide, Fig. 4, forms neither eutectic nor solid soln. with aluminium, the solidus in the series being a straight line at 657°, the m.p. of aluminium. The liquidus rises very sharply with increase in the titanium content, in a smooth curve to a maximum at 1325° and 30·7 per cent. Ti. The alloy with only 2 per cent. Ti commences to solidify at about 1000°

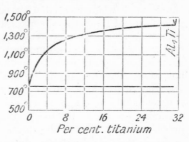

FIG. 4.—Freezing-point Curves of Aluminium-Titanium Alloys.

with the separation of Al_4Ti, followed by freezing of pure aluminium. The microstructure of the alloys shows needles of very hard Al_4Ti embedded in a soft ground-mass. The effect of up to about 1 per cent. titanium on the tensile properties of aluminium is to increase the ultimate strength; but further additions rapidly to reduce the strength. The hardness, specific electrical resistance, and resistance to corrosion are all increased with increase in the titanium content. The chief value of titanium in aluminium alloys depends on its great affinity for nitrogen and oxygen; for by the removal of these impurities the physical properties of the metal are greatly improved. E. Wedekind made some observations on this alloy. E. A. Schneider made an alloy of copper, aluminium, and zinc by

melting aluminium with titanium dioxide and copper under a layer of molten
sodium and potassium chlorides.

H. Moissan [4] found that titanium dissolves fairly quickly in molten lead, and
also in molten tin. A. Stavenhagen and E. Schuchardt also noted that tungsten
and molybdenum can be alloyed with titanium. A. W. Clement described an alloy
with chromium and iron. They also obtained an alloy with cobalt. M. A. Hunter
and T. W. Bacon measured the electrical resistance of the alloys of nickel and
titanium. Alloys of titanium and iron were made by F. Wöhler and H. St. C.
Deville, and C. J. B. Karsten. M. Faraday and J. Stodart, and J. Percy did not succeed in alloying the two metals. In 1859–1861, R. Mushet obtained a number of
patents for the preparation of alloys of iron and steel. H. Moissan found titanium
dissolves freely in molten iron ; and the alloy with iron, and the so-called ferro-
titanium, were studied by A. J. Rossi and co-workers, E. Piwowarsky, F. M. Becket.
H. W. Gillet and E. L. Mack, G. K. Burgess and G. W. Quick, R. Akerman,
E. W. Hopkins, L. Guillet, etc. The preparation of these alloys has been discussed
in connection with the smelting of titaniferous iron ores—*vide supra.* J. Lamont
studied the equilibrium diagram of alloys of iron with
up to 24 per cent. of titanium. Iron holds 6 per
cent. of titanium in solid soln., and there are indications of the existence of iron tritatitanide, Fe_3Ti,
Fig. 5. The magnetic properties of iron are lowered
in presence of titanium. Brinell's hardness for a 500
kgrms. load was raised from 96 for titanium-free
iron to 373 for iron having 8·92 per cent. Ti, and
to 484 for iron with 21·50 per cent. Ti. M. Wunder
and B. Jeanneret found ferro-titanium gives a clear
soln. when treated with hot phosphoric acid of sp. gr.
1·75 ; any carbon present remains undissolved. The
presence of titanium nitride and carbonitride can

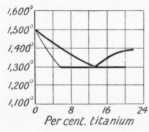

FIG. 5.—Freezing Points of the
Iron-Titanium Alloys.

usually be detected microscopically in ferro-titanium. J. Königsberger and
K. Schilling found that titanium begins to alloy with platinum at about 400°.

Some reactions of analytical importance.—Soln. of titanium disulphate or
of titanium dioxide in hydrochloric acid furnish in the cold a precipitate of orthotitanic acid when treated with potassium hydroxide, while hot soln. furnish a
precipitate of metatitanic acid ; the former is slightly soluble in an excess of the
reagent, and rapidly dissolves in mineral acids ; the latter dissolves very slowly
in these acids. Aq. ammonia, ammonium sulphide, and barium carbonate
likewise precipitate orthotitanic acid from cold soln., and metatitanic acid from
hot soln. The hydrolysis by water, with boiling soln. containing the minimum
quantity of free acid, furnishes a precipitate of metatitanic acid. When the soln.
is mixed with an alkali acetate and boiled, metatitanic acid is again precipitated ;
a similar result is obtained with sodium thiosulphate. A basic phosphate is
precipitated by sodium phosphate, and it is soluble in mineral acids but insoluble
in acetic acid. If hydrogen dioxide be added to a slightly acid soln. of titanium
sulphate, the soln. is coloured orange-red, and if but a trace of titanium is present,
the colour is yellow. Vanadic acid gives a rather browner coloration under similar
conditions. Reducing agents like tin or zinc and sulphuric or hydrochloric acid,
or sodium amalgam colour the soln. blue or violet. O. F. von der Pfordten [5] summarized the main distinguishing tests for bi-, ter-, and quadri-valent titanium salts
in Table I. Reactions with potassium cyanide, sodium nitroprusside, sodium
formate, citric acid, and tartaric acid were examined by H. Grossmann. The
production of a reddish-brown or yellow colour with dihydroxymaleic acid was
reported by H. J. H. Fenton ; with salicylic acid, by W. P. Jorissen ; and with
phenols, hydroquinone, and alkaloids like morphine or brucine, by L. Lévy
The coloration with salicylic acid is not produced by salts of cerium, iron,
aluminium, beryllium, lanthanum, didymium, thorium, zirconium, chromium, or

silicon. J. H. de Boer found that **alizarinsulphonic acid** gives a violet coloration with titanium salts—*vide* zirconium. I. Bellucci and G. Savoia found that **α-nitroso-β-naphthol** and **β-nitroso-α-naphthol** give coloured complex salts with titanium salts in neutral soln., but not in acid soln. F. Steidler observed that various shades of brown are produced by titanium salts on linen or artificial silk dyed with **turmeric.**

TABLE I.—REACTIONS OF SALTS OF BI-, TER-, AND QUADRI-VALENT TITANIUM SALTS.

Reagent.	TiO	Ti$_2$O$_3$	TiO$_2$
Aq. ammonia	black	bluish-black	white
Sod. phosphate	bluish-black	bluish-black	white
Sod. oxalate	greenish or brown	yellowish-brown	white
Sod. acetate	greenish or brown	—	white
Pot. ferrocyanide . . .	dark brown	reddish-brown	reddish-yellow
Pot. ferricyanide	reddish-brown	coffee-brown	yellow
Amm. molybdate	dark brown	greenish-black	white
Sodium succinate	greenish-black	greyish-blue	white
Tannin	reddish-brown	yellowish-brown	orange
Pot. thiocyanate and ether .	brown	—	—

The valency and atomic weight of titanium.—J. J. Berzelius,[6] in his early 1813 table of atomic weights, assigned to titanium a value corresponding with an atomic weight of 288·16, if oxygen be 16, but he could not have had much faith in this number since it was omitted from his 1818 table. In 1826, J. J. Berzelius adopted a number equivalent to 48·6, if oxygen be 16, based on the determinations of his pupil H. Rose, which were published in 1829. In these experiments, the amount of titanium dioxide which was formed when ammonia was added to an aq. soln. of titanium tetrachloride, to precipitate titanium hydroxide, and the amount of combined chlorine in the filtered soln. was determined as silver chloride. The earlier and inaccurate result, 61·59 (oxygen 16), obtained by H. Rose by roasting titanium sulphide to titanium dioxide was discarded. Several writers—J. Dalton, J. L. G. Meinecke, L. Gmelin, T. Thomson, L. J. Thénard, P. T. Meissner, O. B. Kühn, and P. F. Cauchy—assigned more or less inexact values to the at. wt. of titanium. In 1829, G. Mosander made some determinations of the amount of oxygen in titanium dioxide and obtained numbers equivalent to an at. wt. ranging from 46·38 to 48·34.

Between the time of J. Dalton's estimate, Ti=40 to 50 (O=7), and the appearance of H. Rose's memoir, there was some doubt whether the formula of titanium dioxide should be written TiO or TiO$_2$, and the tetrachloride TiCl$_2$ or TiCl$_4$. J. B. A. Dumas [7] measured the vapour density of the chloride, and assuming the formula to be TiCl$_2$, obtained a value equivalent to 30·6 if oxygen be 16 ; and very nearly equivalent to 48 if the formula be TiCl$_4$. This value for the at. wt. of titanium agrees with Avogadro's rule, the sp. ht. rule, the isomorphic law, and the periodic rule. If the value, 48, be accepted for the at. wt., then titanium must be quadrivalent in titanium dioxide, TiO$_2$, and titanium tetrachloride, TiCl$_4$. In addition, titanium must be bi- and ter-valent respectively in TiCl$_2$ and TiCl$_3$. The analogies between the titanium compounds and those of silicon, tin, and zirconium were emphasized by J. C. G. de Marignac, E. Glatzel, etc. The analogies of tervalent titanium compounds with those of tervalent iron, aluminium, manganese, and chromium were discussed by E. Glatzel, and C. Friedel and J. Guérin. The sexivalency of titanium was emphasized by P. Faber, and the bi-, ter-, quadri-, and sexi-valency of titanium corresponds with the other members of the family—zirconium, and cerium—in the fourth column of periodic table.

In 1847, J. I. Pierre determined the ratio TiCl$_4$: 4Ag, and found numbers in agreement with 49·91 if oxygen be 16 ; and two years later, A. Demoly, on the assumption that oxygen is 16, obtained 36·2 from the ratio TiCl$_4$: TiO$_2$; 56·4 from $TiCl_4 : 4AgCl$; and 43·93 from $TiO_2 : 4AgCl$. Between 1883 and 1885, T. E. Thorpe published a series of determinations of the at. wt. of titanium, and from the ratio $TiCl_4 : 4Ag$ obtained 48·04; from $TiCl_4 : 4AgCl$, 48·06; from $TiCl_4 : TiO_2$, 48·09; from $TiBr_4 : 4Ag$, 48·14; from $TiBr_4 : 4AgCl$, 48·13; and from $TiBr_4 : TiO_2$, 48·08, on the assumption that oxygen is 16. G. P. Baxter and C. J. Fertig obtained between 47·78 and 47·89 from the ratio $TiCl_4 : 4Ag$. From the work available in 1910, F. W. Clarke obtained 48·1, for the best representative value; and B. Brauner, 48·08. The International Table of Atomic Weights for 1925 gave 48·1 for the best representative value for the at. wt. The **atomic number** of titanium is 22. No **isotopes** have been found by F. W. Aston.[8] For the alleged degradation of titanium to carbon, *vide* thorium nitrate. E. Rutherford and J. Chadwick obtained no evidence of the emission of long-range particles when α-particles act on titanium. G. von Hevesy, N. V. Sidgwick, C. P. Smyth, and J. Beckenkamp discussed the **electronic structure** of the atom—*vide* hafnium. H. Petterson and G. Kirsch obtained evidence of **atomic disintegration** when the atoms are bombarded by α-rays.

The uses of titanium.—The pure element has not been used to any great extent, but metal alloys have been used a good deal in ferrous and non-ferrous metallurgy. The ferro-titanium alloys are used as deoxidizers or denitrogenizers in iron and steel metallurgy, and they are also said to impart desirable qualities— *e.g.* toughness to the steel for certain purposes.[9] According to H. Braune,[10] the effect of nitrogen in steel is to increase slightly the toughness, and reduce the ductility. Hard steel with 0·030 to 0·035 per cent. of nitrogen is brittle, and soft steel with 0·05 to 0·06 per cent. loses its ductility. The presence of nitrogen is also said to favour the segregation of phosphorus and sulphur causing cold shortness. Titanium is said to remove the greater portion of the deleterious nitrogen from steel, at about 800°, by forming titanium nitride. For example, some remarkable results have been reported on the improvement of steel rails effected by the use of titanium. Thus, the life of the rails in use is said to have been increased from 200 to 400 per cent. by the titanium treatment. Contradictory results have been reported on the effects produced by titanium in iron because its action depends on the nature and proportions of the various constituents of the sample of iron investigated. Titanium alone does not readily alloy with iron and steel since it floats on the surface of the molten metal, and is difficult to dissolve; *master alloys* are therefore made— ferro-titanium, or ferro-carbotitanium—which when added to molten steel enable any desired proportion of titanium to be added to the metal. Silico-titanium or ferro-silico-titanium has been recommended when it is desirable to add both elements to steel. According to A. J. Rossi,[11] the addition of 1 to 2 per cent. of titanium in molten copper by means of *cupro-titanium* as a master alloy eliminates oxide and absorbed gases and imparts a closer-grained structure than if titanium be absent, *mangano-titanium* is the master alloy which has been advertised as a deoxidizer in bronze manufacture. The effect of titanium on the magnetic properties of iron has been studied by K. P. Applegate—less than 1 per cent. of titanium in Swedish iron lessens the hysteresis losses; and increases the permeability whilst greater amounts increase the hysteresis losses.

Titanium and some of its compounds have been employed in the manufacture of incandescent media for illumination—arc lamp electrodes, filaments for glow lamps, and gas mantles. The use of the metal or of the compounds of titanium —rutile, ilmenite, titanium oxide, or carbide, etc.—for this purpose depends on their high fusion and vaporization temperatures and their high radiation efficiency.[12] Titanic oxide has been recommended in the manufacture of arc-lamp electrodes; and with rutile the results are said to be superior to those with carbon electrodes, particularly for street lighting. The positive electrode in the so-called *magnetite arc lamp* is made from a mixture of magnetite and chromite together with 15 to 25 per cent. of rutile or ilmenite, and it is operated on a direct, not alternating, current. It is claimed that this lamp gives a specially uniform distribution of light in a horizontal plane. It is also claimed that electrodes made wholly or partially of titanium carbide are comparatively free from the hissing of carbon electrodes, and that they give a steadier light and last longer. The use of titanium filaments for incandescent lamps has not been so successful on account of the rather greater efficiency of tungsten and tantalum filaments. Up to about 2 per cent. of titania in quartz-glass is said to improve the quality.

The salts of the lower oxides of titanium are used as dyes and mordants for producing brilliant stable colours on wool, cotton, and paper. Potassium titanyl oxalate, $TiO.C_2O_4.K_2C_2O_4.H_2O$, is used extensively for this purpose, although titanium trichloride, $TiCl_3$, titanium sesquisulphate, $Ti_2(SO_4)_3$, and the double sulphate of titanium and sodium, $Ti_2(SO_4)_3.Na_2SO_4.5H_2O$, are also employed. The salts are also used in dyeing leather because they do not embrittle the leather so much as iron salts.[13] Titanium trichloride or the corresponding sulphate is used for stripping or removing certain dyes from the goods to enable them to be re-dyed, and in laundries for removing iron stains. In his study of Hungarian red shörl, M. H. Klaproth stated that the purified white earth—titanic oxide—or the powdered native mineral, produces a straw-yellow colour when used as a colouring agent for porcelain glazes. Since that time, titanium oxide and rutile have been employed to a limited extent in pottery for producing ivory and cream colours to withstand high temperatures; and for colouring artificial teeth. These oxides are also used in the preparation of glazes to give crystalline and opalescent effects. Titanic oxide has been sold under the name T-siloxyd for use in quantities varying from 0·1 to 2·0 per cent. to improve fused silica ware. The use of ferruginous titanic oxide, roasted at different temp. and ground to an impalpable powder, has been patented as a pigment for paints.[14] The tints range from yellow to a brownish-red. Titanium trichloride is a powerful reducing agent, and it has been proposed [15] as a convenient reagent in volumetric analysis—thus, ferric salts can be titrated directly by a standard soln. of this chloride when ammonium thiocyanate is used as indicator. The titration is conducted in an atmosphere of carbon dioxide, to avoid atmospheric oxidation.

REFERENCES.

¹ H. Moissan, *Compt. Rend.*, 115. 1034, 1892; 120. 290, 1895; 142. 673, 1906; *Le four électrique*, Paris, 1897; London, 181, 1904; *Ann. Chim. Phys.*, (7), 9. 229, 1896; M. Billy, *ib.*, (9), 16. 5, 1921; H. V. Regnault, *ib.*, (3), 62. 235, 1837; L. Lévy, *ib.*, (6), 25. 477, 1892; *Contribution à l'étude du titane*, Paris, 1891; *Compt. Rend.*, 121. 1148, 1896; L. Guillet, *ib.*, 140. 1689, 1905; P. Schützenberger and A. Colson, *ib.*, 94. 1710, 1882; F. B. Duppa, *ib.*, 42. 352, 1856; *Ann. Chim. Phys.*, (3), 47. 164, 1856; J. B. van Mons, *ib.*, (1), 26. 91, 1798; C. Friedel and J. Guérin, *ib.*, (5) 8. 24, 1876; *Bull. Soc. Chim.*, (2), 24. 530, 1875; E. A. Schneider, *Zeit. anorg. Chem.*, 8. 94, 1895; L. Weiss and H. Kaiser, *ib.*, 65. 345, 1910; A. Klauber, *ib.*, 117. 243, 1921; K. Nischk, *Zeit. Elektrochem.*, 29. 373, 1923; C. Renz, *Ber.*, 39. 249, 1906; C. Winkler, *ib.*, 23. 2657, 1890; E. Glatzel, *ib.*, 9. 1829, 1876; O. Ruff and R. Ipsen, *ib.*, 36. 1777, 1903; R. Ipsen, *Ueber das Titanfluorid*, Berlin, 1904; R. Weber, *Pogg. Ann.*, 120. 291, 1863; T. L. Phipson, *Compt. Rend.*, 61. 745, 1865; *Chem. News*, 11. 144, 1865; S. Kern, *ib.*, 33. 57, 1876; R. L. Cousens, *ib.*, 92. 203, 213, 1905; C. Willgerodt, *Journ. prakt. Chem*, (2), 35. 391, 1887; V. Merz, *ib.*, (1), 99. 157, 1866; *Zeit. Chem.*, (2), 3. 122, 1867; *Untersuchungen über das Titan, Silicium, und Boron*, Zürich, 1864; O. F. von der Pfordten, *Liebig's Ann.*, 237. 223, 1866; F. Wöhler, *ib.*, 73. 34, 1849; F. Wöhler and H. St. C. Deville, *ib.*, 103. 230, 1857; *Nachr. Gött.*, 237, 1857; *Ann. Chim. Phys.*, (3), 52. 92, 1857; W. Ramsay and F. L. Usher, *Ber.*, 42. 2930, 1909; W. Ramsay, *Journ. Chem. Soc.*, 95. 624, 1909; M. A. Hunter, *Journ. Amer. Chem. Soc.*, 32. 330, 1910; M. G. Levi, E. Migliorini, and G. Ercolini, *Gazz. Chim. Ital.*, 38. i, 593, 1908; W. G. Mixter, *Amer. Journ. Science*, (4), 27. 229, 1908; (4), 33. 45, 1912.

² A. J. Rossi, *U.S. Pat. Ncs.* 802941, 812764, 1902; 1024476, 1912; L. Lévy, *Ann. Chim. Phys.*, (6), 25. 449, 1892; *Compt. Rend.*, 106. 66, 1888; *Contribution à l'étude du titane*, Paris, 1891; C. Winkler, *Ber.*, 23. 2661, 1890; E. A. Schneider, *Zeit. anorg. Chem.*, 8. 86, 1895; M. A. Hunter and J. W. Bacon, *Trans. Amer. Electrochem. Soc.*, 37. 515, 1920; F. Wöhler, *Liebig's Ann.*, 113. 248, 1860; K. Nischk, *Zeit. Elektrochem.*, 29. 373, 1923.

³ F. Wöhler, *Liebig's Ann.*, 113. 248, 1860; *Journ. prakt. Chem.*, (1), 80. 255, 1860; F. R. W. Michel and F. Wöhler, *ib.*, (1), 82. 237, 1860; *Liebig's Ann.*, 115. 102, 1860; W. Manchot and P. Richter, *ib.*, 357. 140, 1907; *Phil. Mag.*, (4), 20. 377, 1860; L. Lévy, *Compt. Rend.*, 106. 66, 1888; *Contribution à l'étude du titane*, Paris, 1891; *Ann. Chim. Phys.*, (6), 25. 449, 1892; E. Wedekind, *Chem. Ztg.*, 30. 223, 1906; L. Guillet, *Bull. Soc. Nat. Ind.*, 101. 244, 1902;

L. Weiss and H. Kaiser, *Zeit. anorg. Chem.*, **65**. 345, 1910; E. A. Schneider, *ib.*, **8**. 86, 1895; J. Dewar and J. A. Fleming, *Phil. Mag.*, (5), **36**. 298, 1893; J. W. Richards, *Proc. Amer. Soc. Testing Materials*, **3**. 233, 1903; E. van Erckelens, *Metall. Erz*, **20**. 206, 1923; C. Winkler, *Ber.*, **23**. 2661, 1890; H. Schirmeister, *Beiträge zur Kenntnis der binären Aluminiumlegierungen hinsichtlich ihrer technischen Eigenschaften*, Düsseldorf, 1914; W. Manchot and A. Leber, *Zeit. anorg. Chem.*, **150**. 26, 1925.

⁴ H. Moissan, *Ann. Chim. Phys.*, (7), **9**. 229, 1896; *Compt. Rend.*, **120**. 290, 1895; L. Guillet, *ib.*, **140**. 1689, 1905; A. Stavenhagen and E. Schuchardt, *Ber.*, **32**. 1513, 1899; **35**. 909, 1902; A. W. Clement, *U.S. Pat. No.* 1431720, 1922; R. Akerman, *Eng. Mag.*, **13**. 544. 1875; *Dingler's Journ.*, **219**. 86, 1876; *Jern-Kontorets Ann.*, **32**. 79, 1877; J. Königsberger and K. Schilling, *Ann. Physik*, (4), **32**. 181, 1910; E. W. Hopkins, *German Pat.*, *D.R.PP.* 138808, 1900; 161559, 1904; F. M. Becket, *Journ. Ind. Eng. Chem.*, **16**. 197, 1924; G. K. Burgess and G. W. Quick, *Tech. Papers Bur. Standards*, 241, 1923; A. J. Rossi, J. MacNaughton, and W. D. Edwards, *Brit. Pat. Nos* 3582, 1901; R. Mushet, *ib.*, 703, 1115, 1859; 2365, 3010, 3030, 3045, 3070, 1860; 163, 473, 2609, 2637, 2744, 3116, 1861; J. Percy, *The Metallurgy of Iron and Steel*, London, 165, 1864; M. Faraday and J. Stodart, *Quart. Journ. Science*, **9**. 329, 1820; *Phil. Trans.*, **112**. 266, 1822; *Phil. Mag.*, (1), **60**. 263, 1922; C. J. B. Karsten, *System der Metallurgie*, Berlin, **1**. 534, 1831; F. Wöhler and H. St. C. Deville, *Ann. Chim. Phys.*, (3), **52**. 91, 1858; F. Wöhler, *ib.*, (3), **29**. 166, 1850; A. J. Rossi, *U.S. Pat. Nos.* 609466, 609467, 1898; 648439, 1900; 668266, 1901; 1019528, 1912; *French Pat. No.* 407858, 1909; *Journ. Amer. Chem. Soc.*, **12**. 90, 1890; *Trans. Amer. Inst. Min. Eng.*, **21**. 832, 1893; **33**. 170, 1903; *Min. Ind.*, **9**. 715, 1900; *Journ. Franklin Inst.*, **154**. 241, 1903; *Iron Age*, **1**. 354, 464, 1896; *Electrochem. Met. Ind.*, **1**. 523, 1903; A. H. A. Robinson, *Chem. Trade Journ.*, **72**. 695, 1923; J. Lamont, *Ferrum*, **11**. 225, 1914; M. Wunder and B. Jeanneret, *Compt. Rend.*, **152**. 1770, 1911; M. A. Hunter and T. W. Bacon, *Trans. Amer. Electrochem. Soc.*, **37**. 513, 1923; H. W. Gillet and E. L. Mack, *ib.*, **37**. 231, 1923; E. Piwowarsky, *Stahl Eisen*, **43**. 1491, 1923.

⁵ O. F. von der Pfordten, *Liebig's Ann.*, **237**. 227, 1887; H. Grossmann, *Chem. Ztg.*, **30**. 907, 1906; W. P. Jorissen, *Bull. Acad. Belg.*, 902, 1903; L. Lévy, *Ann. Chim. Phys.*, (6), **25**. 504, 1892; *Compt. Rend.*, **103**. 1074, 1195, 1886; *Bull. Soc. Chim.*, (2), **47**. 460, 1886; *Chem. News*, **54**. 300, 1886; H. J. H. Fenton, *Journ. Chem. Soc.*, **93**. 1064, 1908; C. H. Pfaff, *Schweigger's Journ.*, **45**. 372, 1825; J. H. de Boer, *Chem. Weekbl.*, **21**. 404, 1924; I. Belluci and G. Savoia, *Atti Chim. Pure Appl.*, **483**, 1923; F. Steidler, *Microchemie*, **2**. 131, 1924.

⁶ J. J. Berzelius, *Pogg. Ann.*, **8**. 177, 1826; **26**. 320, 1832; *Lärbok i Kemien*, Stockholm, 1813 and 1818; H. Rose, *Gilbert's Ann.*, **73**. 141, 1823; *Pogg. Ann.*, **15**. 145, 1829; G. Mosander, *ib.*, **19**. 212, 1830; *Akad. Handl. Stockholm*, 210, 1829; J. Dalton, *A New System of Chemical Philosophy*, Manchester, **2**. 268, 1810; J. L. G. Meinecke, *Die chemische Messkunst*, Halle, 1817; T. Thomson, *A System of Chemistry*, Edinburgh, 1822; L. J. Thénard, *Traité de chimie élémentaire*, Paris, 1826; P. T. Meissner, *Chemische Aequivalenten-oder Atomenlehre*, Wien, 1834; O. B. Kühn, *Lehrbuch der Stöchiometrie*, Leipzig, 1837; P. F. Cauchy, *Principes généraux de chimie inorganique*, Bruxelles, 1838; L. Gmelin, *Handbuch der theoretischen Chemie*, Frankfurt-am-Main, 1827.

⁷ J. I. Pierre, *Ann. Chim. Phys.*, (3), **20**. 257, 1847; A. Demoly, *Recherches sur le titane et ses combinaisons*, Paris, 1849; *Compt. Rend. Trav. Chim.*, **5**. 325, 1849; *Liebig's Ann.*, **72**. 213, 1849; T. E. Thorpe, *Ber.*, **16**. 3014, 1883; *Chem. News*, **48**. 251, 1883; **51**. 260, 1885; *Proc. Roy. Soc.*, **36**. 43, 1884; *Journ. Chem. Soc.*, **47**. 108, 1885; *Proc. Roy. Soc.*, **36**. 43, 1884; *Journ. Chem. Soc.*, **47**. 108, 1885; J. B. A. Dumas, *Ann. Chim. Phys.*, (1), **33**. 388, 1826; G. P. Baxter and G. J. Fertig, *Journ. Amer. Chem. Soc.*, **45** 1228, 1923; A. W. Hofmann, *Sitzber. Akad. Berlin*, 154, 1856; *Pogg. Ann.*, **97**. 510, 1856; *Compt. Rend.*, **42**. 352, 1856; *Ann. Chim. Phys.*, (3), **47**. 164, 1856; H. Kopp, *ib.*, (3), **47**. 166, 1856; *Liebig's Ann.*, **98**. 265, 1856; *Phil. Mag.*, (4), **12**. 190, 1856; F. W. Clarke, *ib.*, (5), **12**. 101, 1881; *Amer. Chem. Journ.*, **3**. 263, 1881; *A Recalculation of the Atomic Weights*, Washington, 1910; J. C. G. de Marignac, *Ann. Mines*, (5), **15**. 235, 1859; *Arch. Sciences Genève*, (1), **32**. 231, 1856; C. Friedel and J. Guérin, *Compt. Rend.*, **82**. 509, 972, 1876; *Bull. Soc. Chim.*, (2), **24**. 530, 1875; *Ann. Chim. Phys.*, (5), **8**. 24. 1876; J. Persoz, *ib.*, (2), **60**. 113, 1835; E. Glatzel, *Ber.*, **9**. 1838, 1876; B. Brauner, *ib.*, **14**. 56, 1881; in R. Abegg, *Handbuch der anorganischen Chemie*, **3**. ii, 305, 1909; P. Faber, *Zeit. anal. Chem.*, **46**. 278, 1907; L. Meyer and K. Seubert, *Die Atomgewichte der Elemente*, Leipzig, 1883; D. I. Mendeléeff, *Liebig's Ann. Suppl.*, **8**. 133, 1871; *Zeit. Chem.*, (2), **5**. 405, 1869; *Journ. Russ. Phys. Chem. Soc.*, **1**. 60, 1869; **13**. 517, 1881.

⁸ R. L. Cousens, *Chem. News*, **92**. 203, 213, 1905; E. Rutherford and J. Chadwick, *Nature*, **107**. 41, 1921; F. W. Aston, *Nature*, **112**. 449, 1923; *Phil. Mag.*, (6), **47**. 385, 1924; (6), **49**. 1191, 1925; *Journ. Soc. Chem. Ind.—Chem. Ind.*, **42**. 935, 1923; N. V. Sidgwick, *ib.*, **42**. 1203, 1923; F. H. Loring, *Chem. News*, **126**. 385, 1923; J. Beckenkamp, *Zeit. anorg. Chem.*, **143**. 394, 1925; C. P. Smyth, *Phil. Mag.*, (6), **50**. 361, 1925; G. von Hevesy, *Zeit. anorg. Chem.*, **147**. 217, 1925· H. Pettersson and G. Kirsch, *Atomzertrummerung*, Leipzig, 104, 1926; *Sitzber. Akad. Wien*, **134**. 491, 1925.

⁹ W. Venator, *Stahl Eisen*, **28**. 41, 82, 149, 255, 1908; **30**. 650, 1910; L. Treuheit, *ib.*, **29**. 1410, 1909; E. von Maltitz, *ib.*, **29**. 1411, 1909; C. V. Slocum, *ib.*, **29**. 1171, 1909; F. M. Becket, *U.S. Pat. No.* 910894, 1909; R. J. Anderson, *Journ. Franklin Inst.*, **184**. 469, 637, 885, 1917; H. M Boylston, *Carnegie Scholarship Memoirs, Iron and Steel Inst.*, **7**. 102, 1916; L. Moser, *Œsterr. Chem. Ztg.*, **26**. 67, 1923; W. A. Lampadius and A. Breithaupt, *Journ. tech. ökon. Chem.*, **13**. 458, 1832.

[10] H. Braune, *Stahl Eisen*, **26**. 1357, 1431, 1496, 1906; E. von Maltitz, *ib.*, **29**. 1594, 1909; L. Treuheit, *ib.*, **30**. 1192, 1910; B. Stoughton, *Trans. Amer. Inst. Min. Eng.*, **42**. 1245, 1912; J. B. Waterhouse, *Proc. Amer. Soc. Testing Mat.*, **10**. 201, 1910; R. Moldenke, *Trans. Amer. Foundrymen's Assoc.*, **17**. 57, 1908; J. W. Richards, *Met. Chem. Eng.*, **15**. 26, 1916; G. F. Comstock, *Iron Age*, **114**. 1477, 1924.

[11] A. J. Rossi, *Electrochem. Ind.*, **1**. 523, 1903; **4**. 257, 286, 1908: *Min. Scient. Press*, **99**. 355, 1909—*vide* the smelting of titaniferous iron ores; K. P. Applegate, *Rensselaer Polyt. Inst.*, **5**, 1914; *Elect. World*, **64**. 141, 1914.

[12] W. S. Weedon, *Trans. Amer. Electrochem. Soc.*, **16**. 217, 1909; R. W. Hutchinson, *High Efficiency Electrical Illuminants*, New York, 1911; I. Ladorff, *Journ. Ind. Eng. Chem.*, **1**. 642, 1909; G. M. Little, *National Electric Light Assoc.*, 237, 1907.

[13] J. Barnes, *Journ. Soc. Chem. Ind.*, **15**. 420, 1896; **18**. 15, 1899; T. Erban, *Chem. Ztg.*, **30**. 145, 1906; C. Dreher, *Textile Colorist*, **25**. 4, 1903; *Leather Trades Rev.*, **46**. 183, 266, 1913; M. H. Klaproth, *Beiträge zur chemischen Kenntniss der Mineralkörper*, Berlin, **1**. 251, 1795.

[14] C. A. Klein and R. S. Brown, *Brit. Pat.* No. 243081, 1924; H. A. Leverin, *Canadian Chem. Met.*, **9**. 198, 1925.

[15] E. Knecht and E. Hibbert, *New Reduction Methods in Volumetric Analysis*, London, 1910.

§ 7. The Titanium Oxides and Hydroxides

Titanium forms fairly well-defined oxides, *titanium monoxide*, TiO, which is feebly basic; *titanium sesquioxide*, Ti_2O_3, which is basic, forming a series of characteristic salts; *titanic acid*, or *titanium dioxide*, TiO_2, which is amphoteric in that it has feebly basic properties and is also acidic in forming the titanates; and *pertitanic acid* or *titanium trioxide*, TiO_3. The titanosic oxide, $TiO.Ti_2O_3$, or Ti_3O_4, or $Ti(TiO_2)_2$, also called *titano-magnetite*, is not well established. The oxides, Ti_6O_{10}, or Ti_3O_5, and Ti_7O_{12}, have been reported, but the evidence of their chemical individuality is not unequivocal. Hydroxides corresponding with many of these oxides are known.

This is a case where a nomenclature analogous with that recommended by A. Werner [1] —1. 5, 13—is needed. The salts of titanium dioxide are called *titanic* salts; salts of bivalent and tervalent titanium are both called *titanous* salts. The monoxide derivatives are so little known that chance of confusion is very small. E. Knecht and E. Hibbert in their monograph on the application of titanium trichloride to volumetric analysis apply the term titanous chloride to salts of tervalent titanium, and this is probably the best expedient until a more satisfactory nomenclature has been adopted.

According to A. Laugier, when titanium dioxide is made into a paste with oil, and heated in a charcoal crucible to a high temp., the outside of the mass has a brown crust; within is a layer having many cavities and containing yellow particles; the central, denser mass consists of small, bluish, shining needles, probably of **titanium monoxide**, TiO. Analogous results were obtained by J. J. Berzelius, and P. Berthier. Titanium monoxide was made by H. Moissan in indigo-blue, prismatic crystals by heating titanium dioxide and carbon in the electric arc furnace. Titanium dioxide alone gave this oxide in the electric arc furnace; when the temp. was too high, titanium nitride was formed. E. Newbery and J. N. Pring found that under a press. of 150 atm. hydrogen reduces titanic oxide at 2000° to the monoxide. H. Rose made it by heating a mixture of titanium dioxide and an excess of zinc in a covered crucible until the zinc passed off as vapour. The mass was then digested with hydrochloric acid, and the titanium monoxide remained as a black powder. C. M. Kersten used an analogous process; and C. A. Winkler employed magnesium as the reducing agent. M. Billy also prepared this oxide in an analogous way. He said that when a mol of titanium dioxide and 2 gram-atoms of magnesium powder are heated to redness, in a current of hydrogen, reduction takes place with incandescence. The product must be allowed to cool in an atm. of hydrogen, as otherwise it readily catches fire in the air. After remaining for a night under glacial acetic acid, it is partially dried at a moderate heat, and then completely dried in a current of hydrogen at 150°. A brown powder is thus obtained, which contains no metallic titanium, but a lower oxide of the metal, mixed with magnesium in the form of magnesium titanate. From the quantity of oxygen taken up on heating the reduction product, it appears probable that the reaction takes place according to the equation $2TiO_2+Mg=TiO+MgTiO_3$. According to T. König and O. F. von der Pfordten, when the vapour of sodium is passed over heated titanium dioxide, the product is a mixture of titanium monoxide and sesquioxide.

F. Wöhler, V. Merz, and O. F. von der Pfordten consider that soln. of amorphous titanium in hydrochloric acid contain bivalent titanium, but E. Glatzel believed that a salt of tervalent titanium is present. A similar difference of opinion applies to the blue colour obtained by H. Rose, and P. Berthier by heating a soln. of a salt of titanium dioxide with zinc, tin, iron, or copper. It is probable that many reports in which the blue titanium colour is attributed to a compound of titanium monoxide should really be referred to the sesquioxide. Thus, C. M. Kersten observed that clays containing titanium dioxide may become blue when ignited with deoxidizing agents ; muffles made of such clays and used for the distillation of zinc may acquire in parts a rich violet colour ; the mixture of titaniferous marl and coke dust in the hearths of some Freiburg smelting furnaces exhibit a lavender blue colour ; when glass mixed with titanic oxide and zinc dust is fused, it acquires a violet colour; and when a mixture of silica, alumina, lime, 5 to 10 per cent. of titanic oxide and zinc is calcined, it acquires a fine blue colour. P. Berthier said that the blue colour of many slags is due to the presence of titanium monoxide ; but J. Fournet said the colour is an optical effect caused by the devitrification of the slag. This opinion was supported by C. Mène, and G. Bontemps.

Very little is known about titanium monoxide and that little is unsatisfactory. This oxide exhibits feebly basic properties, furnishing a chloride, iodide, and sulphate (*q.v.*). According to F. Wöhler, a black precipitate of **titanium dihydroxide,** $Ti(OH)_2$, is produced when ammonia is added to a soln. of titanium in hydrochloric acid ; and it is obtained by adding sodium amalgam to a soln. of titanium sesquioxide in hydrochloric acid. The precipitate is at first blue, and it finally passes into the white dioxide with the evolution of hydrogen. Raising the temp. favours the oxidation. According to O. F. von der Pfordten, the oxidation of the dihydroxide is slower than is the case with the trihydroxide.

C. A. Winkler prepared what he regarded as a hydroxide. Ti_3HO_4, by heating a mol of titanium dioxide and 4 gram-atoms of magnesium powder in a current of hydrogen. After cooling in the hydrogen atm., the product was covered with water in a flask, and hydrochloric acid passed in drop by drop, until present in excess, almost pure hydrogen being evolved. The compound in suspension was collected, washed with hydrochloric acid, alcohol, and ether, and dried over sulphuric acid in vacuo. It forms a black powder, which is not attacked by acids, and evolves hydrogen on treatment with potash-lye, but remains unchanged in appearance. When heated by itself, it also gives off hydrogen without change of appearance, and on ignition in air forms titanium dioxide ; the compound, however, still contains magnesium, probably as magnesium titanate. If in the numbers obtained on analysis the correction be made for a quantity of the latter compound corresponding with the magnesium found, the composition of the remainder is found to be Ti_3HO_4. The decomposition by heat would then be represented by the equation Ti_3HO_4 $=Ti_3O_4+H$.

G. Rose [2] claimed to have made **titanosic oxide,** Ti_3O_4, by melting a mixture of titanium dioxide and microcosmic salt in a loosely covered crucible. When the glassy product is heated, it becomes opaque owing to the development of octahedral crystals of this oxide—*vide infra*, R. Brauns. A. Piccini and L. Marino obtained cubic crystals of this oxide by the dry reduction of titanium dioxide. They regard it as a *titano-magnetite*, $TiO.Ti_2O_3$. By analogy with magnetite, it can also be represented as *titanium dititanite*, $Ti(TiO_2)_2$, *i.e.* O : Ti.O.Ti.O.TiO.

J. J. Ebelmen [3] heated titanium dioxide strongly in a current of hydrogen, and found it becomes black and loses weight corresponding with the formation of impure **titanium sesquioxide,** or **titanous oxide,** Ti_2O_3. A trace of moisture hindered the reduction. T. König and O. F. von der Pfordten consider that J. J. Ebelmen's observations do not prove that titanium dioxide is reduced to the sesquioxide when heated in a stream of hydrogen ; their product, *vide infra*, had a different composition. R. Brauns said that crystals of the sesquioxide are formed when titanium dioxide and microcosmic salt are heated in the reducing flame—*vide supra*, G. Rose. M. Billy made this oxide by the action of titanium tetrachloride on formic aldehyde followed by a decomposition of the addition product. According to C. Friedel and J. Guérin, this oxide is obtained in the form of minute, lustrous, red crystals together with titanium trichloride and oxychloride when a mixture of hydrogen and titanium tetrachloride is passed over white-hot titanium dioxide. T. König and O. F. von der Pfordten were unable to verify C. Friedel and J. Guérin's observation. J. J. Ebelmen's preparation was an amorphous black mass; and C. Friedel and J. Guérin's copper-red crystals were isomorphous with hæmatite from Elba, and with ferric oxide, and ferrous titanate, $FeTiO_3$. The titaniferous iron oxides are supposed to be mixtures of ferric oxide and ferrous titanate. The ditrigonal crystals have the axial ratio $a:c=1:1\cdot316$, and $a=87°\ 10'$. P. Groth said that alumina, ferric oxide, chromic oxide, and titanium sesquioxide form an isomorphous family, and that the salts of the different members of this family are also isomorphous. C. Friedel and J. Guérin gave 4·601 for the sp. gr. E. Friedrich and L. Sittig gave 2130° for the m.p., and 18,000 ohms for the electrical resistance at room temp. J. J. Ebelmen found the reoxidation of the sesquioxide is difficult and only proceeds at a very high temp. It is not acted upon by hydrochloric or nitric acid, but forms a violet-blue soln. with sulphuric acid. P. Sabatier and B. Senderens said that when the sesquioxide is heated in nitric oxide or in nitrogen peroxide, it passes into the dioxide with incandescence, without forming the nitrate.

E. Glatzel concluded that no salt of titanium monoxide is present in a soln. of the metal in hydrochloric acid, but a salt of the sesquioxide is formed. When a soln. of titanium tetrachloride is reduced by zinc, copper, or powdered silver obtained by reduction, and treated with ammonia or sodium amalgam, **titanium trihydroxide, titanous acid,** or **titanous hydroxide,** $Ti(OH)_3$, is deposited as a brownish-red precipitate. Observations in this connection were made by J. J. Ebelmen, J. N. von Fuchs, F. von Kobell, W. Manchot and P. Richter, C. F. Rammelsberg, O. F. von der Pfordten, C. Friedel and J. Guérin, and A. Piccini. According to E. Polidori, a soln. of titanium tetrachloride in 30 per cent. hydrochloric acid can be reduced by electrolysis, and when treated with sodium hydroxide gives a black precipitate of titanous hydroxide. T. König and O. F. von der Pfordten obtained titanous hydroxide by the decomposition of *sodium titanite*, Na_3TiO_3, by water. The last-named compound, $Ti(ONa)_3$, or Na_3TiO_3, was said to be formed among the products of the reduction of titanium dioxide by the vapour of sodium. It dissolves in dil. sulphuric acid, forming a violet soln., and it is readily decomposed by water, forming sodium hydroxide and titanous hydroxide; it is not so readily decomposed by alcohol.

Titanous hydroxide is oxidized with the development of hydrogen: $2Ti(OH)_3$ $=2TiO_2+2H_2O+H_2$, and at the same time the colour passes through various shades of brown, red, violet, and blue to white. W. Manchot and P. Richter found that when titanium sesquioxide is shaken with an aq. soln. of potassium hydroxide and oxygen, a considerably larger volume of oxygen is absorbed than corresponds with one eq. of oxygen. The hydrogen peroxide primarily formed is reduced partially by the titanium sesquioxide, the remainder of the peroxide oxidizing the titanium dioxide to pertitanic acid on acidification or possibly even in the alkaline soln. If a thick milk of lime or baryta-water is used in place of the potassium hydroxide, the hydrogen dioxide formed is not reduced by the titanium sesquioxide or dioxide, and the whole of the oxygen absorbed is found in the form of hydrogen dioxide. If the soln. of tervalent titanium in sulphuric acid is boiled with potassium hydroxide, it evolves a vol. of hydrogen equal to that of the oxygen absorbed on shaking the alkaline soln. with oxygen. The acid soln. also evolves hydrogen when boiled, but only extremely slowly. When shaken with oxygen, a soln. of tervalent titanium in sulphuric acid containing ferrous ammonium sulphate absorbs a still larger excess of the gas, and the soln. contains ferric oxide, whereas an acid soln. of ferrous ammonium sulphate alone does not absorb a measurable vol. of oxygen. When titanium sesquioxide is added to a soln. of chromic and hydriodic acids dissolved in the requisite amount of water, the liberated iodine may be estimated by thiosulphate. For the oxidation, 3 gram-atoms of oxygen were required for 1 gram-atom of titanium. The oxidation of titanium sesquioxide with permanganic acid in the presence of tartaric acid also led to a similar result. E. Knecht found that titanium sesquioxide or its hydroxide, prepared by precipitation from a soln. of the trichloride by sodium hydroxide is a powerful solid reducing agent; it converts alkaline nitrate soln. to ammonia; azobenzene to hydrazobenzene, etc. It is a convenient agent for reducing in neutral or ammoniacal soln. without a trace of the reducing agent passing into soln.

According to H. St. C. Deville, if a current of hydrogen chloride accompanied by a reducing agent, say hydrogen, be passed over titanium dioxide at a red heat, small rectangular crystals of deep indigo-blue colour and with the composition Ti_3O_5 are obtained. This may be regarded as $Ti_2O_3.TiO_2$, or **titanyl dititanite**. $TiO(TiO_2)_2$, *i.e.* $O : Ti.O(TiO).O.Ti : O$. The same compound was made by C. Friedel and J. Guérin. M. Billy obtained the oxide in a crystalline form when hydrogen chloride is present. It was assumed by C. F. Rammelsberg that this oxide is present among the products obtained by reducing a soln. of titanium tetrachloride with zinc—*vide supra*. O. F. von der Pfordten supposed that this oxide is formed when heated titanium dioxide is reduced in a current of hydrogen, but he later showed that the composition more nearly approximates to Ti_7O_{12}, or $2Ti_2O_3.3TiO_2$, or **titanous titanate**, $Ti_4'''(TiO_4)_4$.

J. B. L. Romé de l'Isle,[4] and S. R. I. Eques a Born referred to a *schorl rouge ou pourpre*, which, according to R. J. Haüy, is the same as A. L. Lavoisier's *spath adamantin brun-rougeâtre*. A. Estner described *schörlartiger granat;* and M. H. Klaproth a *rother schörl*. All these minerals are regarded as varieties of what R. Kirwan called *titanite*—not what is now known as titanite or sphene. H. B. de Saussure called a variety of *schörl rouge* from the Alps, *sagenite*—from σαγήνη, a net—in allusion to the interlacing and reticulation of the acicular crystals. J. C. Delamétherie called a variety from Crispalt, St. Gothard, *crispite*. A. G. Werner applied the term **rutile** to this mineral in allusion to its colour—*rutilus*, red. R. J. Haüy also called it *titane oxydé.*

W. E. Hidden called a variety from North Carolina *edisonite*—after T. A. Edison. D. L. G. Karsten applied the term *nigrine*—from *niger*, black—to a black ferruginous variety discussed by C. F. Rammelsberg, W. B. Smith, and A. von Lasaulx, and called by W. A. Lampadius, *schwarzer Granat.* H. Rose proved that rutile consists only of titanium dioxide associated with a small quantity of iron oxide. L. J. Igelström called a variety from Dicksberg, Sweden, *dicksbergite*, and M. Weibull and A. Upmark showed that it is rutile. A black mineral from Olary, South Australia, was called *davidite* by D. Mawson, and shown by E. H. Rennie and W. T. Cooke to have about 50 per cent. titanium dioxide, associated with iron rare earths, uranium, vanadium, and chromium; it approximates $FeO.Cb_2O_5 5TiO_2$. J. V. Janovsky found black grains of a mineral which he called *iserite* at Iserwiese, Bohemia; its composition corresponds with $FeTi_2O_5$. A black variety of rutile with over 10 per cent. of ferric oxide obtained by N. von Kokscharoff from the Ilmen Mts., Russia, was called *ilmenorutile.*

J. B. L. Romé de l'Isle referred to a *schorl bleu indigo ;* and J. L. Bournon, to a *schorl octaèdre rectangulaire*. Similar minerals were called *octaèdrite* by H. B. de Saussure ; *octahedrite*, by J. D. Dana ; *oisanite*—from the locality, Bourg d'Oisans, Dauphiné, where it occurred—by J. C. Delamétherie ; and *dauphinite*, by E. F. Glocker. R. J. Haüy first called the mineral octaèdrite, but later used the term **anatase**—from ἀνάτασις, erection—in allusion to the fact that c-axis is longer than that of rutile. L. N. Vauquelin showed that the chemical properties of anatase agree with those of rutile ; and H. Rose proved that powdered anatase has all the properties of calcined titanium dioxide.

A. Lévy found some rhombic crystals of a mineral from Snowdon, Wales, which he named **brookite**—after H. J. Brooke. W. Haidinger said that F. Soret had previously found a mineral like brookite accompanying the anatase at Bourg d'Oisans, Dauphiné, and P. A. Dufrénoy said that F. Soret called it *zurinite*—after L. Jurine of Genève. According to A. Lacroix, no publication by F. Soret on this subject has yet been traced. F. S. Beudant, indeed, in 1824 said that titanium oxide occurs in nature in two distinct forms, one being rutile, and the other occurs as *un prisme rhomboïdal*. H. Rose ן roved that brookite, anatase, and rutile consist of titanium dioxide associated with a little iron oxide.

C. U. Shepard called a mineral from Magnet Cove, Arkansas, *arkansite*, but the observations of A. Breithaupt, J. D. Whitney, W. H. Miller, A. des Cloizeaux and A. Damour, C. F. Rammelsberg, and R. Hermann showed that brookite and arkansite are crystallographically and chemically the same. Another mineral, called *eumanite* by C. U. Shepard, found at Chesterfield, Mass., is assumed by J. D. Dana to be related to brookite.

The main deposits of rutile [5] are in Amherst and Nelson counties in Virginia; Quebec (Canada); Carinthia; Transylvania; near Kragerö (Norway). Ilmenite is one of the chief constituents of the monazite sand of Ceylon and Travancore; Nigeria, Gold Coast, and Nyassaland (Africa); Mount Crawford (South Australia); Greenbushes (West Australia); Forth district (Tasmania); many places in Queensland; and in the Taranaki sands and various other places on the west coast of New Zealand. Many analyses of rutile have been reported.[6] In the analyses, the iron oxide is usually determined as ferric oxide, but in some cases the iron has been determined in the two states of oxidation:

	Iserite Iserwiese, Bohemia.	Yellowish-brown rutile.	Vannes black rutile.	Morbihan black rutile.	St. Peter's Dome, Colorado.
TiO_2	68·99	89·76	76·10	55·38	94·93
FeO	1·41	6·23	17·35	36·31	3·77
Fe_2O_3	28·57	3·88	5·41	8·25	0

Pure rutile does not seem to occur in nature, and it is thought that rutile is a solid soln. of titanic oxide, TiO_2, with ilmenite, $FeTiO_3$, and some ferric oxide. In the so-called ilmenorutile, iron tantalate and columbate, $FeO.(CbTa)_2O_5$, are present as well. The mineral is sometimes contaminated with a little oxide of vanadium, chromium, or tin. G. von Hevesy and V. T. Jantzen found no hafnia in the samples of rutile they examined. Samples from Brazil [7] have been reported with 2 to 4 per cent. of stannic oxide, SnO_2, and samples from Black's Hill, Dakota,[8] with 1·3 to 1·4 per cent. C. Friedel and T. Grandjean found 1·75 per cent. of stannic oxide in rutile from Vaux, Rhône. A. G. Ekeberg [9] found 3 per cent. of chromic oxide in a Swedish rutile. H. St. C. Deville reported 0·323 per cent. of vanadic acid, and 0·486 per cent. of molybdic acid in a sample from St. Yrieix; and, according to H. Rose, 2·0 per cent. of manganese oxide. B. Hasselberg observed vanadium and chromium in samples from many localities. R. J. Haüy called a grass-green variety *titane oxydé chromifère*—chromiferous rutile. Some silica and magnesia are usually present. R. H. Brett and G. Bird described some titanic oxide crystals in clay crucibles. Analyses of anatase were reported by H. Rose,[10] A. Damour, L. N. Vauquelin, J. P. O'Reilly, and E. Hussak; and of brookite by H. Rose, R. Hermann, A. Damour, K. Romanowsky, and K. Pfeil. All three minerals have the same ultimate composition, and are different crystalline forms of **titanium dioxide**, TiO_2, or **titanic acid.**

Rutile occurs in igneous, metamorphic, and sedimentary rocks; and it is probably of pyrogenetic origin. It is common in gneiss, mica-schist, and phyllites, and less common in granular limestone and dolomite. A. Bergeat [11] found it along with ilmenite and titanite. T. L. Watson and S. Taber found rutile associated with apatite. Rutile also occurs as a secondary mineral derived from ilmenite and titanite. The slight solubility of rutile in water and in soln. of sodium fluoride, and the crystallization of the mineral in such a soln. after 34 days at 145°, observed by C. Doelter, indicate that some secondary rutile may be derived from the dissolution of primary rutile, or of titanic oxide leached from other rocks. The occurrence of rutile has been discussed by F. Zirkel, E. Kalkowsky, A. Cathrein, H. Behrens, H. Gylling, G. A. Sauer, Comte de Limur, P. Mann, etc. Anatase and brookite appear only as secondary minerals. Anatase occurs in small amounts in rocks of all kinds as an alteration product of titaniferous minerals. The occurrence of anatase has been discussed by E. Hussak, R. Brauns,

A. Lacroix, G. Spezia, A. Schenk, F. Kollbeck, J. S. Diller, O. Mügge, B. Doss, J. B. Scrivenor, H. Rösler, C. Schmidt, K. von Chrustschoff, etc. H. Thürach mentioned the occurrence of brookite and anatase in a great variety of rocks. Brookite alters into rutile ; and rutile into ilmenite, and sphene. The occurrence of brookite has been discussed by A. Müller, J. R. Blum, A. Lacroix, etc.

The preparation of titanium dioxide.—Amorphous titanium dioxide was made by F. Wöhler,[12] and H. Rose by adding aq. ammonia to a soln. of titanium tetrachloride, washing and calcining the precipitate ; it is also made by the processes indicated in connection with the extraction of titanium—*vide supra*—namely, by fusing rutile or titanic iron ore with potassium carbonate, decomposing the mass with hydrofluoric acid ; separating and crystallizing the resulting potassium fluotitanate, and decomposing its hot soln. with aq. ammonia ; or by heating titanic iron ore in a stream of chlorine and hydrochloric acid—the iron is volatilized as chloride, and the titanium dioxide remains : $2FeTiO_3+4HCl+Cl_2=2FeCl_3+2TiO_2+2H_2O$. H. Geisow described the extraction of titanium dioxide from rutile, etc. ; and C. Winkler, and G. Cartaret and M. Devaux, the purification of commercial titanium dioxide. J. J. Ebelmen showed that if the amorphous titanium dioxide be heated with boric acid, or better, with microcosmic salt, in a pottery oven, golden yellow, acicular crystals of rutile were formed. According to G. Wunder, the crystals are sodium phosphotitanate, and not anatase as G. Rose assumed, or titanyl phosphate, $TiO(PO_3)_2$, as A. Knop supposed ; on the other hand, R. Brauns believed them to be titanium sesquioxide, and L. Ouvrard, rutile with titanyl phosphate and alkali titanophosphate. G. Rose, and A. Knop obtained fine crystals of rutile by heating for a long time amorphous titanium dioxide mixed with borax, or with borax and microcosmic salt. B. Doss used borax. J. J. Ebelmen also obtained rutile by heating the amorphous dioxide with potassium carbonate. H. St. C. Deville and H. Caron prepared rutile by heating to redness a mixture of amorphous titanium dioxide, silica, and stannic oxide. L. Bourgeois used barium chloride as a flux ; F. A. Genth, potassium hydrosulphate ; and P. Hautefeuille, sodium silicate, tungstate, or vanadate ; H. Cormimbœuf melted titanium dioxide with sodium carbonate, sodium tungstate, and as much tungstic oxide to make the composition of the fused tungstate that of the normal tungstate-crystals of rutile are formed ; with less tungstic acid, crystals of the alkali titanate are formed. H. Traube also used sodium tungstate as *agent minéralisateur*, and he was able to add to the rutile appreciable quantities of iron, manganese, and chromium which are present as impurities in the natural mineral. T. Scheerer observed crystals of rutile in the cracks of the brickwork of a blast-furnace ; and K. Endell, in pottery glazes containing 5 to 10 per cent. of rutile. H. E. Merwin and J. C. Hostetter obtained crystals of rutile by the action of chlorine on titaniferous clays at 1000°–1100°. F. Wöhler heated titanium nitride in air, and obtained crystals of what were thought to be rutile. L. Michel obtained a mixture of rutile and pyrrhotite by heating a mixture of ilmenite and pyrite. H. de Sénarmont heated amorphous titanium dioxide in the presence of carbon dioxide in a sealed tube at 200°. A. Daubrée decomposed titanium tetrachloride by steam at a red heat and obtained crystals of the dioxide ; and H. St. C. Deville passed hydrogen fluoride or chloride over red-hot titanium dioxide and obtained crystals of rutile ; if a reducing atm. be present, blue crystals of $TiO(TiO_2)_2$ were formed. Similar results were obtained by P. Hautefeuille and A. Perrey. The three forms of titanium dioxide were studied by P. Hautefeuille. A mixture of potassium titanate and potassium chloride heated to redness in a stream of dry air mixed with hydrogen chloride furnished crystals of rutile. Similar crystals were obtained by heating to redness a mixture of titanium dioxide and potassium fluoride or calcium fluoride, or a mixture of titanium dioxide and potassium fluosilicate in hydrogen chloride. In these experiments, if the temp. exceeded 1040°, rutile was formed ; between 800° and 1040°, brookite ; and below 800°, anatase. O. Lehmann discussed the transformation of one form into another. C. Friedel and J. Guérin heated to redness titanium chloride and ferrous oxide, and obtained ferrous chloride and crystals of titanium dioxide ; and by passing chlorine over titanium-iron at a red heat, ferric chloride is volatilized and crystals of rutile are formed. They proposed the reaction as a means of separating titanium from iron.

F. Wöhler heated titanium carbonitride in a current of steam and obtained crystals of anatase ; and H. Rose obtained anatase by heating amorphous titanium dioxide for a short time by means of a spirit-lamp. G. Rose found some crystals of anatase in the product obtained from a soln. of titanium dioxide in molten microcosmic salt. The process was examined by A. Knop, G. Wunder, B. Doss, and L. Ouvrard. F. A. Genth found that some anatase accompanied the rutile when titanium dioxide was fused with potassium hydrosulphate. B. Doss' attempts to make anatase with fused borax as *agent minéralisateur* were not successful, rutile was always formed. P. Hautefeuille obtained anatase by the decomposition of titanium tetrafluoride by aq. vapour, at or near 860° ; and also by heating titanium trifluoride in a current of air. P. Hautefeuille and A. Perrey found that hydrogen chloride has no action on titanium dioxide at a bright red heat, but under a press. of 3 atm., anatase is formed at a dull red heat ; at the same temp. and under ordinary atm. press., hydrogen chloride has a mineralizing effect on the carbonate, oxalate, or sulphate, but not on the oxide.

A. Daubrée made crystals of brookite by passing a mixture of the vapour of titanium tetrachloride, steam, and carbon dioxide through a red-hot tube ; and also when the vapour of titanium tetrachloride is decomposed by heated lime. P. Hautefeuille found that brookite is formed when potassium fluotitanate is heated in steam, and when hydrogen fluoride acts on titanium tetrachloride at a temp. not exceeding 1040°. A mixture of titanium dioxide, calcium fluoride, and potassium heated in a stream of hydrogen chloride, silicon tetrafluoride, and moist hydrogen, also furnished crystals of brookite, and a similar result was obtained when a mixture of titanium dioxide, silica, and potassium fluosilicate was heated in a current of hydrogen chloride alone. B. Doss obtained rutile, not brookite, from soln. of titanium dioxide in fused borax.

The physical properties of titanium dioxide.—Purified titanium dioxide is colourless ; the **colour** of the mineral forms is due to the presence of impurities, is usually reddish-brown passing into red, and sometimes yellowish, bluish, violet, black, and rarely, grass-green. In transmitted light the colour is yellow, various shades of red, and violet. Anatase may be various shades of yellow and brown ; and sometimes indigo-blue or black. In transmitted light, the same colours may appear, and they are sometimes distributed zonally or irregularly. Brookite may be yellowish- or reddish-brown or iron-black. In transmitted light the colour may be yellowish, reddish, brownish, or colourless, and rarely blue or bluish-green J. W. Retgers [13] said the colour of rutile is largely determined by the titanium dioxide and not by the ferric oxide. L. Wöhler and K. von Kraatz-Koschlau obtained colours ranging from bluish-black to greenish-black with titanium sesquioxide as the tinctorial agent. Red rutiles were obtained only with the ferric oxide ; vanadium oxide had no effect on the colour. H. Traube melted mixtures of rutile with ferric oxide and obtained a dark brown product with 1·98 per cent., and a black mass with 5·4 per cent. of ferric oxide ; manganese oxide gave a yellow tint, and the colour was bluish-black when 3 per cent. of this oxide was present. With chromic oxide, a green colour was obtained. R. F. Wagner said that the colour of titanium dioxide is determined by the treatment it has received. When moist orthotitanic acid is heated, there is a remarkable play of colours. The oxide becomes almost white when cold and citron-yellow when hot, and by continued heating the colour becomes more and more brownish.

O. Hahn [14] studied the surface area of the particles of different forms of precipitated titanic oxide in terms of adsorbed radioactive matter. The habit of the euhedral **crystals** of rutile is commonly prismatic with furrows or striations on the surface parallel to the c-axis. The crystals are often acicular, very slender, or hair-like. Transparent quartz is sometimes penetrated thickly with acicular or capillary crystals as illustrated by Fig. 6. This furnishes the so-called *sagenite* and *crispite* alluded to above ; and the *veneris crinis* of Pliny's *Historia Naturalis*

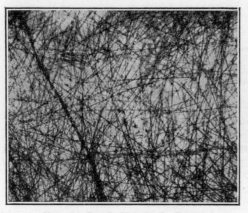

and the so-called *flêches d'amour* or *Venus' hair stone* are varieties of quartz penetrated with acicular rutile. Rutile occurs compact and massive, and in granules. Anatase is usually octahedral, in habit acute or obtuse, and also tabular. It is rarely prismatic. The habit of brookite crystals is varied. The euhedral crystals are often tabular parallel to the (100)-face ; with the (100)-face and the prismatic faces striated vertically. Sometimes the habit is prismatic with the (110)-face dominant, resembling rutile. According to R. J. Haüy, crystals of rutile belong to the tetragonal system ; and more exact measure-

FIG. 6.—Rutile Needles in Quartz.

ments were made by A. Breithaupt, G. A. Kenngott, and W. H. Miller. The last-named gave for the axial ratio $a : c = 1 : 0.644154$; H. Baumhauer, $1 : 0.6439$; and N. von Kokscharoff, $1 : 0.64418$. The optical anomalies of rutile led E. Mallard to assume that it does not belong to the tetragonal system ; and F. Wallerant regarded rutile as monoclinic. G. Friedel, and W. J. Sollas considered the space-lattice to be tetragonal. Observations on the crystals of rutile were made by H. Baumhauer, R. L. Parker, G. vom Rath, F. Hessenberg, C. O. Trechmann, F. Pisani, O. Lincio, H. Tertsch, A. von Lasaulx, W. C. Brögger, P. von Jeremejeff, G. Tschermak, F. Rinne, D. Brewster, O. Mügge, M. Bauer, L. Cahn, G. Rose, H. S. Washington and W. E. Hidden, etc. The crystals of anatase were examined by R. J. Haüy who placed them in the tetragonal system and the cognomen, as previously indicated, implied that the *c*-axis is longer than is the case with rutile. W. H. Miller gave for the axial ratio $a : c = 1 : 1.7771$. Observations were made by C. Klein, A. des Cloizeaux, O. Luedecke, C. Vrba, A. Frenzel, A. Stelzner, R. L. Parker, O. Pohl, F. Wiser, G. vom Rath, A. Brezina, G. Boeris, A. Lévy, H. Buttgenbach, J. Beckenkamp, G. Cesaro, R. W. Haare, O. C. Farrington and E. W. Tillotson, H. P. Whitlock, W. Prinz, J. Schetelig, S. L. Penfield, L. Colomba, A. Johnsen, H. Baumhauer, F. Millosevich, G. Seligmann, A. Sella, A. Streng, E. Bertrand, F. Hessenberg, C. Busz, A. E. Robinson, etc. The crystals of brookite, said F. S. Beudant, were *confondue pendant long-temps avec le rutile*. A. Lévy found that they belonged to the rhombic system. N. von Kokscharoff gave for the axial ratios $a : b : c = 0.84158 : 1 : 0.94439$. The crystals were measured by K. Romanowsky, W. H. Miller, and A. des Cloizeaux. A. Schrauf tried to show that the crystals of brookite are really monoclinic, but both N. von Kokscharoff and P. Groth showed that this is not a correct interpretation. Further observations were made by C. Vrba, G. Lechner, A. Wichmann, F. Wiser, C. Palache, A. Fornaro, L. Brugnatelli, G. vom Rath, C. Busz, G. Rose, P. von Jeremejeff, G. F. Kunz and S. L. Penfield, A. Breithaupt, E. S. Dana, etc. In addition to the three forms, rutile, anatase, and brookite, R. B. Riggs and J. S. Diller reported a fourth rhombohedral form occurring in thin iron-black scales as inclusions in the tourmaline of Hamberg, New Jersey, and De Kalb, New York. J. D. Dana, however, regarded it as a variety of ilmenite.

The **twinning** plane and composition plane (101) of rutile are often geniculated, and there are contact twins of very varied habit. There is also polysynthetic **twinning** in thin lamellæ parallel to (101), and the lamellæ are of various lengths, and distributed irregularly in the crystals. The **cleavage** of rutile parallel to (110) and (100) is distinct; and that parallel to (111) is in traces. This subject was studied by A. Breithaupt, G. A. Kenngott, W. H. Miller, etc. O. Mügge [15] reports a parting due to twinning parallel to (902). The cleavage of anatase parallel to (001) and (111) is perfect; and those of brookite parallel to (110) and (001) are indistinct and seldom observed in microscopic crystals. The **corrosion figures** of rutile with molten potassium fluoride, or hydrofluoride, were studied by H. Traube. Naturally etched crystals of anatase, and crystals etched with potash-lye were studied by H. Baumhauer; and the gliding planes of rutile, by A. Grühn and A. Johnsen. Observations on the **optic axial angle** of brookite were made by A. Beer,[16] W. H. Miller, J. Grailich and V. von Lang, etc. J. Grailich gave $2E = 65°$ for the red ray; and A. Schrauf gave:

λ	. .	691	670	661	592	589	555	534	532	486
$2E$	. .	58° 22′	55° 2½′	50° 45′	28° 56′	30° 16½′	0	33° 48′	38° 7′	c. 70°

A. des Cloizeaux measured the effect of temp., and found that by raising the temp. to redness, $2E$ changed from 42° to 47°; and U. Panichi changed $2E$ from 54° to 26° by cooling to $-190°$.

Anatase is isomeric but not isomorphous with rutile. The **X-radiogram** has been studied by L. Vegard,[17] H. Haga and F. M. Jäger, W. P. Davey, J. Beckenkamp, H. Tertsch, G. Greenwood, A. Johnsen, R. L. Parker, M. Born and O. F. Bollnow, and C. M. Williams. According to L. Vegard, in the space-lattice of zircon, $ZrSiO_4$, the oxygen atoms are arranged in pairs about the zirconium and silicon atoms, and he considers that the constitutional mol. formula of zircon is accordingly $ZrO_2.SiO_2$, not $ZrSiO_4$. The space-lattice of anatase can be derived from that of zircon by removing the zirconium atoms and their associated oxygen atoms, and substituting titanium atoms for the silicon atoms. The oxygen atoms are arranged in line with the titanium atoms with the lines parallel to the tetragonal axis. Hence, L. Vegard writes the mol. formula TiO_2. The estimated absolute dimensions of the space-lattices of rutile and anatase are given in Table II. C. M. Williams's data do not agree with those of L. Vegard, and he

TABLE II.—DIMENSIONS OF THE SPACE-LATTICES OF RUTILE AND ANATASE.

	Crystal axes in cm.			Volume in c.c.	Distance between the central Ti atom and the O atom cm.
	a	*c*	*a : c*		
Rutile, $(TiO_2)_2$ . .	9.05×10^{-8}	5.8×10^{-9}	1 : 0.644	4.77×10^{-22}	1.99
Anatase, TiO_2 . .	5.27×10^{-8}	9.37×10^{-8}	1 : 1.777	2.60×10^{-22}	1.95

assigns to the crystal unit a different structure. According to M. L. Huggins, in rutile and anatase, each titanium atom is surrounded by four equidistant oxygen atoms, and each oxygen atom by two equidistant titanium atoms, all at tetrahedron corners. F. Rinne represents the arrangement in the tetragonal unit by the drawing, Fig. 7. The observed data are not yet sufficient to establish the structures of anatase and rutile.

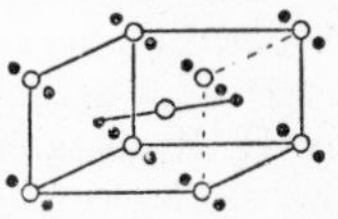

FIG. 7.—The Tetragonal Unit of Rutile—F. Rinne.

G. Rose [18] assumed that rutile, zircon, and cassiterite are isomorphous; and P. Groth wrote the formulæ $TiTiO_4$ and $SnSnO_4$, in order to emphasize their relationship to $ZrSiO_4$. He also considered brookite to be related to tridymite, and anatase to cristobalite. J. W. Retgers did not agree with the assumption that these minerals are isomorphous, and maintained that there is a chemical contrast between zirconium and silicon which is not characteristic of isomorphism; titanium and silicon dioxides, said he, *nicht die geringste Neigung zu inniger Mischung zeigen—*

this is illustrated by the rutile needles found in colourless crystals of quartz. **Further,** tin dioxide does not appear to be miscible with titanium or zirconium dioxide. Against J. W. Retgers' view, H. Traube found that the corrosion figures of rutile, zircon, and cassiterite show the holohedral tetragonal symmetry. Some crystallographic data for the minerals rutile, $TiTiO_4$; zircon, $ZrSiO_4$; cassiterite, $SnSnO_4$; thorite, $ThSiO_4$, polianite, $MnMnO_4$; and plattnerite, $PbPbO_4$, by S. Stevanovic, are shown in Table III. The mol. vol. axis ratios, and the topic axes increase with the

TABLE III.—CRYSTALLOGRAPHIC PROPERTIES OF THE ISOMORPHOUS DIOXIDES.

Mineral.	Mol. wt.	Sp. gr.	Mol. vol.	$a : c$	Topic parameters $\chi : \omega$
Rutile, TiO_2 . . .	80·1	4·24	18·85	1 : 0·6441	2·081 : 1·984
Polianite, MnO_2 . .	87·0	5·04	17·26	1 : 0·6647	2·960 : 1·969
Zircon, $(Zr,Si)O_2$ . .	91·50	4·70	19·48	1 : 0·6404	3·122 : 1·999
Cassiterite, SnO_2 . .	150·0	7·018	21·44	1 : 0·6726	3·608 : 2·136
Thorite, $(Th,Si)O_2$ . .	162·45	5·40	30·80	1 : 0·6402	3·176 : 2·310
Plattnerite, PbO_2 . .	238·0	8·50	28·11	1 : 8·6764	3·468 : 2·345

mol. wt. except in the case of polianite, which probably does not belong to the series, as is also the case with silica. H. Buttgenbach, V. Goldschmidt, A. Schrauf, G. Wunder, R. Ruer, G. Linck, W. T. Schaller, and M. Ladrey emphasized the crystallographic relationshp between the dioxides of tin, titanium, and zirconium. O. Lehmann discussed the transformation of **one** modification of titanium dioxide into the other.

M. H. Klaproth [19] gave 4·180 for the **specific gravity** of titanium dioxide and C. J. B. Karsten gave 3·9311. H. Rose found that when heated to 600°, the sp. gr. of the amorphous precipitate rose from 3·89 to 3·95 ; after exposure to a stronger source of heat for a longer time at 800°, 4·13 ; and after vigorous calcination at 1000°–1200°, 4·255. P. Hautefeuille found that after fusion and pulverization, the sp. gr. was 4·1. H. Fizeau said that artificially prepared rutile has the same sp. gr. as the mineral. For rutile, C. M. Kersten gave 4·242 ; A. Virlet, 4·325–4·246, and after fusion, 4·241 ; M. Weibull and A. Upmark, 4·2 ; R. Böttger, 4·249 ; T. Scheerer, 4·244–4·245 ; A. Breithaupt, 4·250–4·291 ; H. Kopp, 4·420 at 0° ; H. Müller, 4·56 ; A. von Lasaulx, 4·173–4·278. H. Geisow gave 4·21 for the sp. gr. of the strongly calcined oxide. For artificial rutile, J. J. Ebelmen found 4·260–4·283 ; and P. Hautefeuille, 4·3. A. des Cloizeaux and A. Damour found the sp. gr. of rutile rose from 4·273 to 4·365 when heated in a current of hydrogen. Rutile containing appreciable amounts of tin or iron oxides has a higher sp. gr. For instance, W. B. Smith found a sp. gr. 4·288 for a sample with 3·77 per cent. of ferrous oxide ; F. A. Genth, 4·249 for a sample with 6·68 per cent. of ferric oxide ; and W. P. Headden, 5·294 for samples with 7·92–8·10 per cent. ferrous oxide. L. N. Vauquelin gave for the sp. gr. of anatase, 3·857 ; N. von Kokscharoff, 3·815 ; E. Hussak, 3·794 ; F. Mohs, 3·826 ; A. Breithaupt, 3·750 ; C. Klein, 3·83–3·97 ; A. des Cloizeaux, 3·87 ; F. von Kobell, 3·82 ; H. Rose, 3·890–3·912 ; and A. Damour, 4·06. For artificial anatase, P. Hautefeuille gave 3·7–3·9. The sp. gr. of brookite by H. Rose ranged from 4·128 to 4·166, and on calcination, the sp. gr. became the same as that of rutile ; A. Breithaupt gave 3·952 ; C. F. Rammelsberg, 3·892–3·949 ; A. Damour, 4·030–4·083 ; J. D. Whitney, 4·085 ; W. von Beck, 4·200 ; M. Frodmann, 4·220 ; K. Romanowsky, 4·1–4·2 ; R. Hermann, 3·83 ; and N. von Kokscharoff, 4·1389–4·1410. P. Hautefeuille gave 4·1 for artificially prepared brookite.

J. D. Dana [20] tried to show that there is a simple relationship between the **molecular volume** and the crystallographic constants of minerals ; and he concluded that the relationship depended on mol. vol., and had nothing to do with chemical composition. G. T. Prior applied the theorem to estimate possible values for the mol. wt. of the three forms of titanium dioxide. In the case of rutile and zircon, the mol. vols. 19 and 39 respectively, are nearly equal when the mol. vol. of rutile is doubled. This would make the mol. wt. of rutile Ti_2O_4, or $TiTiO_4$. The close similarity of anatase with a mol. vol. 20, with calomel, mol. vol. 72, and matlockite, Pb_2OCl_2, mol. vol. 70, suggests that the mol. vol. of anatase is 80, in agreement with Ti_4O_8. Likewise with the series brookite, mol. vol. 19·6 ; tantalite, $FeTa_2O_6$, mol. vol. 62·32 ; and hübnerite, $MnWO_4$, mol. vol. 42·133, approximate equality is obtained by multiplying by these values respectively by 6, 2, and 3. This gives a mol. wt. for brookite in agreement with Ti_6O_{12}. A. Schrauf represented rutile by $Ti_{22}O_{44}$, anatase by $Ti_{40}O_{80}$, and brookite by $Ti_{43}O_{86}$; he considered anatase to be a titanyl compound $\{(TiO)O\}_{40}$. G. T. Prior also pointed out that the principle did not apply in the case of the homomorphous minerals, zincite, ZnO_2, greenockite, CdS, and iodyrite, AgI ; and in the case of scorodite, $FeAsO_4·2H_2O$, and gypsum, $CaSO_4·2H_2O$, and the case of pucherite, $BiVO_4$, and celestine, $SrSO_4$—*vide* anorthite. F. A. Henglein, and G. von Hevesy compared the mol. vol. of the titanium, zirconium, hafnium, thorium, and cerium oxides. The **hardness** of rutile, etc., on Mohs' scale is indicated in Table IV, in

TABLE IV.—THE POLYMORPHOUS TITANIUM DIOXIDES.

	Sp. gr. D	Hardness.	Crystal vol., v	vD	Ratios of $v : D$	Mean refractive index, μ	$\dfrac{\mu-1}{D}$	Optical character.
Anatase . .	3·840	5·5–6·0	0·7108	2·7496	2·73	2·5011	0·3909	Negative
Brookite . .	4·065	5·5–6·0	0·6667	2·7101	2·71	2·5872	0·3905	Positive
Rutile . .	4·239	6·0–6·5	0·6440	2·7300	2·73	2·6642	0·3926	Positive

which some properties of the polymorphous forms of titanium dioxide are compared. The hardness was discussed by A. Reis and L. Zimmermann. J. A. Deurs and P. E. Raaschou studied the viscosity of suspensions. E. Madelung and R. Fuchs found the **compressibility** of rutile to be $3·27 \times 10^{-12}$ dynes per sq. cm. P. W. Bridgman also measured the linear compressibility of rutile, and found at 30° $\delta l/l_0 = 1·038p - 0·70p^2$; and at 75° $\delta l/l_0 = 1·090p - 0·70p^2$ when taken parallel to the tetragonal axis ; p denotes press. ranging up to 12,000 kgrms. per sq. cm.

H. Kopp [21] gave for the coeff. of cubical **thermal expansion** of rutile, 0·000032 between 14° and 46° ; and H. Fizeau gave 0·0$_4$2347 at 40°, and for the coeff. of linear expansion of rutile parallel to the chief axis, $a = 0·0_5919$, and perpendicular to that axis, $a = 0·0_5714$; A. Schrauf gave respectively 0·0$_5$9943 and 0·0$_5$7192 for rutile at 17·5°. H. Fizeau gave 0·0$_5$819 in the direction of the axis of isotropy of anatase, and when perpendicular to that axis, 0·0$_5$468 at 40° ; and A. Schrauf gave respectively 0·0$_5$66724 and 0·0$_5$28801 at 17·5° ; the last-named also gave for the three axes of brookite, 0·0$_4$144938, 0·0$_4$192029, and 0·0$_4$220489. H. de Sénarmont found the principal axis of rutile to be the long axis of the isothermal ellipsoid, and, according to E. Jannetaz, the ratio of the square roots of the **thermal conductivity** in the direction of the principal axis and of the base is 0·826 for rutile, and 1·34 for anatase. F. E. Neumann gave 0·1724 for the **specific heat** of rutile between about 15° and 100° ; H. Kopp gave 0·157 for rutile between 16° and 47°, and 0·161 for brookite between 19° and 49°. H. V. Regnault gave 0·17164 for titanium dioxide between 16° and 98° ; and A. Schuller and V. Wartha, 0·1779–0·1785. L. F. Nilson and O. Petterson found 0·1784–0·1787 for rutile between 0° and 100° ; 0·1790–0·1792 between 0° and 211° ; 0·1841–0·1844 between 0° and 300° ; and 0·1906–0·1931 between 0° and 440°. The corresponding **molecular heats** were 14·25, 14·29, 14·70, and 15·30 respectively. Like stannic oxide, white titanium dioxide becomes yellow and then brown when heated, and E. D. Clarke fused titanium dioxide in the oxyhydrogen flame. F. Born estimated titanic oxide to be dissociated to the extent of 10^{-18} into oxygen and metal at 2000°. The **melting**

point of rutile found by R. Cusack was 1560° ; C. Doelter gave 1980° ; O. Ruff and co-workers, 1640° ; and A. L. Fletcher, 1610°. R. Cusack gave for brookite, 1610° ; R. Rieke gave for the m.p. of titanium dioxide, 1610°—*vide* titanium silicates. W. R. Mott showed the **boiling point** of titanium dioxide to be below 3000°. W. G. Mixter found for the **heat of formation** of amorphous titanium dioxide by heating the metal with sodium dioxide : $Ti+O_2=TiO_2+215\cdot6$ Cals. ; and for the heat of oxidation of the metal, 218·4 Cals. ; L. Weiss and H. Kaiser gave 97·772 Cals.

The **indices of refraction** of rutile were measured by K. Bärwald,[22] O. Mügge, and G. Lincio. According to P. Ites, for rutile :

	B-line.	C-line.	D-line.	E-line.	b-line.
ω	2·5469	2·5624	2·6030	2·6664	2·6795
ϵ	2·8186	2·8377	2·8899	2·9669	2·9838

Values for anatase were obtained by D. Brewster, C. Klein, O. Pohl, etc. E. A. Wülfing gave for Li-light, $a=2\cdot5183$, and $\omega=2\cdot4523$; for Na-light, $a=5618$, and $\omega=2\cdot4886$; and for Tl-light, $a=2\cdot6066$, and $\omega=2\cdot5262$. He also gave for brookite with Li-light, $a=2\cdot5408$, $\beta=2\cdot5418$, and $\gamma=2\cdot6444$; with Na-light, $a=2\cdot5832$, $\beta=2\cdot5856$, and $\gamma=2\cdot74114$; and with Tl-light, $a=2\cdot6265$. The **birefringence** of rutile is strong ; from P. Ites' data, $\gamma-a=0\cdot2864$. A. Ehringhaus and H. Rose compared the dispersion and double refraction of the dioxides of silicon, titanium (rutile and anatase), and tin with their mol. wts. The **optical character** of anatase is negative, and the optical characters of rutile, and brookite are positive. The crystals may show an **optical anomaly.** E. Mallard found rutile may appear abnormally biaxial, and, as indicated above, he assumed that the crystals are normally rhombic or monoclinic. The phenomenon with rutile was also studied by A. Madelung, and A. von Lasaulx ; and with anatase, by A. Madelung, E. Mallard, A. des Cloizeaux, and A. von Lasaulx. The **pleochroism** of the crystals of rutile was studied by H. Traube ; those of anatase by C. Klein, A. von Lasaulx, and E. Weinschenk ; and those of brookite, by H. Thürach, J. Grailich, A. Michel-Lévy and A. Lacroix, and L. Brugnatelli. J. Joly attributed pseudo-opaque patches in crystals of anatase to internal multi-reflections. According to J. Königsberger, the **ultra-violet absorption spectra** of rutile, anatase, and brookite have maxima at $0\cdot380\mu$; V. von Agafonoff found anatase to be transparent for ultra-violet light as far as the cadmium line, and rutile, as far as the line 3μ. P. Ites also studied the absorption and extinction coeff. of rutile. W. W. Coblentz found the **ultra-red transmission spectrum** of brookite showed no bands, but there was a depression in the curve at $3\cdot1\mu$; rutile was rather more opaque than brookite. The **ultra-red reflection spectrum** of rutile had maxima at $10\cdot1\mu$, $10\cdot6\mu$, 11μ, $11\cdot7\mu$, and $13\cdot6\mu$; and the **ultra-red emission spectrum** had maxima at $2\cdot4\mu$, $3\cdot2\mu$, $5\cdot5\mu$, and $7\cdot0\mu$ The mineral has a bright red colour at 1000°. T. Liebisch and H. Rubens studied the reflecting power of rutile for the long infra-red rays ; and H. R. Robinson, and D. Coster, the **X-ray spectrum.** A. de Gramont studied the **spark-spectrum** of rutile, anatase, and brookite. N. von Kokscharoff observed a **thermoluminescence** with a reddish-yellow glow, when anatase is heated. The **calorescence**—5. 33, 10—of titanium oxide was studied by J. J. Berzelius, L. Wöhler, M. E. Chevreul, G. Wagner, and H. Rose. J. Böhm showed by X-radiograms that the phenomenon is connected with the passage from the amorphous to the crystalline state. E. L. Nichols and co-workers studied the flame luminescence and spectrum of incandescent titanium dioxide as well as the luminescence in **ultra-violet light,** and in the **cathode rays**—ultra-violet light did not excite luminescence. H. J. Spanner studied the emission of electrically charged particles by heated titania. W. Crookes, and E. L. Nichols observed the luminescence of rutile when exposed to the cathode rays. C. Doelter found brookite to be more transparent than rutile to the **X-rays.**

According to F. Beijerinck,[23] the **electrical conductivity** of rutile, anatase, or brookite is inappreciable at ordinary temp., and C. Doelter said that this remark also applies to rutile below 950° : at 1150°, the sp. resistance of a plate of rutile is 950 ohms, and at high temp. the mineral conducts very well. W. Schmidt found the **dielectric constant** of rutile to be greater than that of any other mineral he examined, being 173 parallel to the principal axis; 89 perpendicular to that axis ; and 117 when in the powdered form. For brookite, W. Schmidt gave 78 ; and for powdered arkansite, 12. The Metal and Thermite Corporation, and S. J. Lubowsky prepared a conducting mixture by heating the dioxide in a reducing atm. E. T. Wherry found rutile showed no evidence of the rectification required by a radio-detector ; but octahedrite and brookite were fair radio-detectors. H. S. Roberts and L. H. Adams also discussed this subject. B. Bavink studied the **magnetic properties** of rutile.

The **hydrates of titanium dioxide.**—H. Rose,[24] and A. Knop obtained **colloidal titanium dioxide** in a gelatinous form during the separation of iron from titanium by adding tartaric acid to a hydrochloric acid soln. ; on the addition of aq. ammonia, the titanium oxide is precipitated as a gelatinous mass. This is washed with water. E. A. Schneider used a similar process and purified the gelatinous product by dialysis O. F. von der Pfordten melted a mixture of titanium dioxide and potassium carbonate, and digested the product with 36 per cent. hydrochloric acid without warming. The gelatinous residue was washed with cold water. T. Graham obtained the hydrosol of titanium dioxide by dialyzing a soln. of precipitated titanium dioxide in hydrochloric acid ; with conc. soln., a hydrogel is formed. He said :

Liquid titanic acid is prepared by dissolving gelatinous titanic acid in a small quantity of hydrochloric acid, without heat, and placing the liquid upon a dialyzer for several days. The liquid must not contain more than one per cent. of titanic acid, otherwise it gelatinizes spontaneously, but it appears more stable when dilute.

Titanium dioxide thus resembles silica very closely in its power of forming colloidal sol and gel. S. Klosky and C. Narzano obtained the best results in the preparation of the gel by coagulating a soln. of the composition $HCl + TiO_2.nH_2O$ with potassium, sodium, or ammonium carbonates. S. Glixelli studied the electrosmosis of titanic acid ; and K. van der Grinten, the cataphoresis. T. Graham also made *titanic alcogel, titanic etherogel, titanic sulphatogel,* and *titanic glycerogel* analogous to the corresponding compounds with silica. As in the analogous case of silica, it is believed that there exists an orthotitanic acid, H_4TiO_4, or $Ti(OH)_4$; a metatitanic acid, H_2TiO_3, or $TiO(OH)_2$; and possibly other condensed forms. What is here called orthotitanic acid was called by H. Rose *α-titanic acid ;* and metatitanic acid, *β-titanic acid.* As H. Geisow emphasized, the hydroxide has but a feeble acidic character, the basic character is marked. T. Carnelley and J. Walker found that the dehydration curves of silicic and titanic acids exhibit no breaks or evidence of the formation of definite hydrates. The titanates do not exhibit the degree of complexity characteristic of the silicates. A form of titanic acid analogous to the so-called β-stannic acid has not been prepared. A comparison of the stannic and titanic acids was made by H. Rose and R. Weber, and C. F. Rammelsberg.

According to H. Rose,[25] **orthotitanic acid,** $Ti(OH)_4$, or H_4TiO_4, is obtained as a voluminous white precipitate when ammonia, or an alkali hydroxide or carbonate is added to soln. of titanium dioxide in hydrochloric or sulphuric acid, prepared in the cold. It is also formed by decomposing potassium titanate with hydrochloric acid. The precipitate is washed with water and dried in the cold. If the temp. is raised, some metatitanic acid is formed. According to K. Bornemann and H. Schirmeister, orthotitanic acid may be precipitated from hot strongly acid soln. by the addition of ammonia without destroying its solubility in dil. acids. When metatitanic acid is dissolved in conc. sulphuric acid, boiling for more than a few minutes must be avoided, or an insoluble precipitate is formed. No difference in this respect is observed between ortho- and meta-titanic acids. G. Wagner also found that the ortho-acid gradually passes into the meta-acid if it is allowed to stand for long in contact with water. According to L. Weiss and M. Landecker, when orthotitanic acid is washed with water, the filtrate is very prone to turbidity, but not if the washing liquid be 0·5 per cent. aq. ammonia ; or about one per cent. acetic acid, not mineral acids. The ammonia is very difficult to wash away from the precipitate produced by that agent. G. Wagner made the ortho-acid by decomposing the tetrachloride with much water. The colour of the hydroxide is white, but if foreign oxides be present, the colour may be reddish, reddish-yellow, or yellow. If some nitric acid be added to the soln. of titanium tetrachloride before the aq. ammonia is added, the precipitate is white after calcination. The presence of ammonium nitrate, said O. F. von der Pfordten, prevents the formation of titanium nitride. H. Rose showed that while orthotitanic acid remains fully hydrated, it is soluble in dil. hydrochloric and sulphuric acids, and the stronger organic acids, forming the corresponding salts ; but when heated, it loses water, and forms complex, less soluble hydrates. A. Demoly said that when orthotitanic acid is dried in vacuo, it is insoluble in acids, and in that respect it resembles the meta-acid. When ignited, it forms titanium dioxide. According to V. Merz, when the hydrate has been dried 24 hrs. in air, it contains 35·43–35·70 per cent. of water ; and after drying 4–8 weeks, 29·83–31·11 per cent., thus corresponding with $Ti(OH)_4$. If the precipitate is dried 12 hrs. over conc. sulphuric acid, it contains 31·06–31·92 per cent. of water ; and a similar result was obtained by W. Delffs. After drying a week over conc. sulphuric acid, V. Merz found that the precipitate contained 28·0–28·37 per cent. of water ; after exposure for 4 weeks, 16·69 per cent. ; and after 10 weeks, 15·69 per cent. H. Rose found 12·53–16·05 per cent. water to be present after drying many weeks over sulphuric acid ; and after exposure to dry air to constant weight, A. Demoly found the composition corresponded with $3TiO_2.5H_2O$. H. Rose found that after drying in vacuo, over sulphuric acid, the composition approximated $2TiO_2.H_2O$; and J. Tuttscheff, $2TiO_2.3H_2O$. According to V. Merz, the hydrate dried at 60° corresponds with $4TiO_2.3H_2O$; and at 100°, with $2TiO_2.H_2O$. A. Demoly found 7·0 per cent. of water in the hydrate dried at 140°. T. Matsubara showed that when refined titanic acid is dehydrated at temp. exceeding 400°, it acquires a yellow tinge. C. Dreher found the ortho-acid forms lakes with some dyes, but the anhydrides, or the hydrates of the bi- or ter-valent oxides, do not form lakes. The ortho-acid gives an orange-yellow coloration with tannin.

H. Rose found that **metatitanic acid,** $TiO(OH)_2$, or H_2TiO_3, is precipitated from hot soln. Thus, boiling of an aq. soln. of titanium tetrachloride is attended by the partial precipitation of the meta-acid. When washed with water, it passes through the filter-paper as a turbid liquid, and at the same time clogs up its pores. This inconvenience does not occur if the water used for the washing is mixed with an acid, alkali, or salt. The precipitation occurs more readily in the presence of a sulphate or sulphuric acid, owing to the inferior stability of titanium sulphate. The hydrolysis which occurs on boiling a slightly acid soln. of titanium sulphate is utilized in quantitative analysis. The action was discussed by A. Demoly, E. Riley, K. Bornemann and H. Schirmeister, L. Weiss and M. Landecker, H. Pellet and C. Fribourg, P. Holland, D. Forbes, J. Brakes, C. Baskerville, A. Leclerc, etc. L. Lévy showed that on boiling for 6 hrs. soln. with n grms. of free H_2SO_4 per 100 c.c. (the first soln. had a slight excess of potassium hydroxide) :

nH_2SO_4	.	.	.	0·000	0·000	0·000	0·083	0·500	1·000	5·766
TiO_2 {Used	.	.	.	0·086	0·036	0·086	0·086	0·086	0·082	0·030
{Ppd	.	.	.	0·108	0·100	0·047	0·036	0·085	0·080	0·000

Hence, if too much sulphuric acid be present, the titanium dioxide will be imperfectly precipitated. The precipitate is washed with hot water. The last traces of sulphuric acid are difficult to remove. V. Merz washed with an ammoniacal soln., but H. Rose, and A. Demoly found the last traces of ammonia are then difficult to remove. H. Rose made the meta-acid by fusing a titaniferous mineral with potassium hydrosulphate, and boiling the aq. soln. of the cold mass. A. Demoly boiled a mixture of water, titanium tetrachloride, and barium carbonate, and obtained tabular crystals of the meta-acid; he also obtained the meta-acid by drying the ortho-acid in vacuo, or heating it to 140°; F. P. Dunnington made some observations on this subject. R. Weber obtained the meta-acid by the action of nitric acid, sp. gr. 1·25, on the metal. The meta-acid is a white powder which H. Rose found to be insoluble in water; almost insoluble in dil. acids; and soluble in hot conc. sulphuric acid. He observed no calorescence during the ignition of the meta-acid. V. Merz found that the meta-acid slowly loses water, and after many weeks' drying in air contained 18·48–19·22 per cent. of water; and after 24 hours' drying over conc. sulphuric acid, it contained water eq. to $TiO_2.H_2O$; and after 6 to 10 weeks' drying, $2TiO_2.H_2O$. After drying in vacuo, A. Demoly found water eq. to $3TiO_2.2H_2O$; he also found 12 per cent. of water present after drying at 140°; and J. Tuttscheff, 22·15–22·46 after drying at 120°; and 12·95 at 140°. V. Merz found that when dried at

	60°–70°	100°	120°	130°	150°	170°
Per cent. H_2O	9·45–10·91	6·83	5·17–5·46	5·05–5·53	4·22–4·46	4·17–4·53
Ratio $TiO_2 : H_2O$	—	3 : 1	4 : 1	—	—	5 : 1

C. H. Milligan and E. E. Reid found that titanic acid gel is about half as active as silica gel in promoting the esterification of alcohol. H. Rheinboldt and E. Wedekind studied the absorption of dyes by titanic acid; and A. M. Morley and J. K. Wood showed that the relatively greater surface of a-titanic acid, prepared with cold soln., gave it a greater absorptive capacity for dyes than β-titanic acid, prepared from boiling soln. Titanic acid prepared from alkaline soln. adsorbed basic but not acidic dyes; but titanic acid precipitated from slightly acid soln. adsorbs acidic but not basic dyes; while titanic acid, precipitated by calcium carbonate from soln. of titanic chloride, had a relatively low adsorptive power, but adsorbed both acidic and basic dyes. The difference in behaviour of titanic acid obtained from acid and alkaline soln., respectively, may be attributed to the amphoteric character of titanium hydroxide, resulting in the formation in the one case of a highly basic titanium salt, and in the other, of an alkali titanate; or it may be accounted for by the adsorption of hydrogen- or hydroxyl-ions, giving positively and negatively charged colloidal particles, respectively. Titanic acid, obtained by precipitation with calcium carbonate, would be neutral and have no preference for negative or positive ions of basic or acidic dyes.

The chemical properties of titanium dioxide.—O. F. von der Pfordten's [26] comparison of the properties of the three titanium oxides is shown in Table V,

TABLE V.—COMPARISON OF THE PROPERTIES OF THE TITANIUM OXIDES.

	TiO_2	Ti_2O_3	TiO
Ether reaction	—	—	Brown
Ammonia	White	Bluish-black	Black
Sod. phosphate	White	Bluish-white	Bluish-black
Sod. oxalate	White	Yellowish-brown	Greenish-brown
Sod. acetate	White	—	Greenish-black
Pot. ferrocyanide	Reddish-yellow	Brownish-red	Dark brown
Pot. ferricyanide	Yellow	Coffee-brown	Reddish-brown
Tannin	Orange	Brown	Reddish-brown

where TiO_2 is represented by a mixture of titanium chloride and alcohol diluted with water; Ti_2O_3, by the violet soln. of titanium trichloride, or the green soln. from potassium fluotitanate in hydrochloric acid; and TiO, by an aq. soln. of the dichloride. H. Rose said that **hydrogen** has **no action on** titanium dioxide at a

red heat.   H. von Wartenberg was unable to reduce titanic oxide to the metal
by hydrogen at 10 atm. press. at 2500°.   H. Gall and W. Manchot found that
quadrivalent titanium compounds form an equilibrium condition with tervalent
titanium when heated with hydrogen in the presence of platinum.   J. J. Ebelmen's
and O. F. von der Pfordten's observations on the reduction of heated titanium
dioxide by dry hydrogen have been discussed in connection with the lower oxides.
F. Bischoff and H. Adkins measured the adsorption of hydrogen by titania.
G. A. Kenngott found that powdered rutile moistened with **water** reacted alkaline.
C. Doelter found rutile to be slightly soluble in water, and more so in a soln. of sodium
fluoride ; after heating for 34 days to 145°, the mineral partially recrystallized.   For
the action of **hydrogen dioxide,** *vide* titanium trioxide.   L. Weiss and M. Landecker
noted the accelerating influence of hydrogen dioxide on the rate of dissolution of
titanium dioxide in acids, but O. Hahn and H. Gille could not confirm this ; they
found titanic acid is quite soluble in sulphuric acid soln. of hydrogen dioxide, and
becomes less soluble in the presence of tantalic acid ; they also found that the soln.
is, ultramicroscopically, a true soln.   According to L. Schönn, when titanium
dioxide is triturated with **barium dioxide,** a deep reddish-yellow colour appears
which becomes deep yellow when an acid is added.   The coloration disappears by
reduction with zinc, or with ferrous or stannous chloride.

According to C. Friedel and J. Guérin, when titanium dioxide is heated in a
stream of **chlorine,** some titanium tetrachloride is formed and oxygen evolved ;
if the dioxide is mixed with carbon, carbon monoxide and the tetrachloride are
formed.   The affinity of titanium dioxide for acids, said H. Rose, is very feeble.
The crystals of the mineral, and of the ignited oxide dissolve only in **hydrofluoric
acid.**   M. E. Pennington said that the ignited oxide dissolves in this acid very
slowly ; and if the oxide has been calcined to about 1000°, it is virtually insoluble
in hydrofluoric acid ; the oxide calcined at 700° soon dissolves in this acid.   Soln.
of titanium dioxide in various **acids** are obtained by using the hydrated oxide.
H. Rose added : The dissolution is effected slowly, but the action is faster if conc.
acids slightly warmed be employed than is the case with hot dil. acids.   The
hydrated titanium dioxide precipitated by ammonia, and washed with cold water,
dissolves the most readily ; that which has been washed with hot water less readily ;
and that obtained by boiling a dil. soln. in hydrochloric acid, least readily.   L. Weiss
and M. Landecker found the hydrated dioxide dissolves more quickly in **hydrochloric acid** than it does in nitric or sulphuric acid.   They also state that titanium
dioxide is insoluble in **perchloric acid.**   H. Traube studied the etching of rutile
with **potassium fluoride** or hydrofluoride.   According to E. Schulze, when titanium
dioxide is ignited with an **alkali chloride** in the presence of oxygen, there is a slight
decomposition ; and in the absence of oxygen titanium dioxide is without action
on **potassium iodide.**

For the action of **sulphur,** *vide* titanium sulphides.   According to H. Rose,
when strongly heated in a stream of **hydrogen sulphide,** titanium dioxide is blackened, but the colour is restored when the product is calcined in air.   E. F. Smith
found that when heated in the vapour of **sulphur chloride,** rutile forms titanium
tetrachloride.   G. Darzens and F. Bourion found that a mixture of chlorine and
SCl_2 vapour at a red heat forms $2TiCl_4.SCl_4$; and that with **thionyl chloride,** a
similar complex is produced.   According to H. Rose, when the vapour of **carbon
disulphide** is passed over heated titanium dioxide, carbon monoxide and dioxide,
and titanium sulphide are formed.   L. Wöhler and co-workers found titanium
dioxide acts as a catalytic agent in the oxidation of **sulphur dioxide** to the trioxide.
Titanium dioxide in its different forms is insoluble in **sulphuric acid** ; but the hot
acid slowly transforms the powdered dioxide into sulphate—*vide* hydrofluoric
acid.   K. Bornemann and H. Schirmeister said that titanium dioxide which has
been heated to 1000° is virtually insoluble in sulphuric acid ; but if the temp. of
ignition has not exceeded 700°, dissolution in conc. sulphuric acid occurs in 15 min.
R. D. Hall and E. F. Smith found that a mixture of 40 grms. of water and 70 grms.

of sulphuric acid of sp. gr. 1·145, dissolved 0·33 grm. titanium dioxide in 15 min. M. Blondel found that rutile readily dissolves in conc. sulphuric acid when heated to about 225°, but if the temp. of the acid exceeds 225°, a layer of sulphate forms on the surface, protecting the mineral from further attack by the acid. According to L. Weiss and M. Landecker, the speed of dissolution of ignited titanium dioxide in sulphuric acid is augmented by hydrogen dioxide; they also stated that the hydrated dioxide dissolves more slowly in sulphuric acid than it does in nitric or hydrochloric acid; and K. Bornemann and H. Schirmeister, less rapidly in sulphuric acid than in hydrofluoric acid. The fusion of titanium dioxide with **potassium hydrosulphate** readily brings about the complete soln. of titanium dioxide. K. Bornemann and H. Schirmeister add that it is not necessary to dissolve the product in cold water, for if dil. sulphuric acid be used, dissolution is complete, even if the liquid is boiled. P. Müller attempted to obtain titanium alloys free from sulphur, together with volatile titanium sulphides, by smelting a mixture of carbon, rutile, and nickel sulphide or iron sulphide in the electric arc furnace. The quantities were mixed according to the equations: $TiO_2+FeS+2C=TiS+Fe+2CO$ or $5TiO_2+3FeS+10C=Ti_2S_3+3(Fe,Ti)+10CO$, but it was found possible to obtain an iron-titanium alloy free from sulphur only by employing a double quantity of rutile and so large an excess of carbon that the iron and a portion of the titanium could form carbides. Similar results were obtained with nickel matte when a large excess of rutile was employed; in no case did the double carbide retain any appreciable amount of sulphur. The high current consumption is opposed to the economical application of the method, and the chief result of the investigation is to show that titanium, like silicon, acts at high temperatures as a desulphurizing agent.

According to F. Wöhler, the affinity of **nitrogen** for titanium is great enough for the two elements to unite at a high temp., forming the nitride (q.v.); but F. Wöhler and H. St. C. Deville observed that no nitride is formed at a bright red heat in a current of hydrogen and nitrogen, but the oxide assumes a greyish-black colour. F. Wöhler also found that with the dioxide at a red heat, **ammonia** forms water, hydrogen, and titanium nitride. H. Rose said that titanium dioxide is not changed when heated with ammonium chloride, but if the dioxide is associated with stannic oxide, some titanium tetrachloride is formed. For the action of **nitric acid**, *vide* hydrochloric acid. L. Weiss and M. Landecker found that the hydrated dioxide dissolves more slowly in nitric acid than it does in hydrochloric acid, and more quickly than in sulphuric acid. C. F. Rammelsberg found that molten **potassium nitrate** is without action on titanium dioxide. R. Weber observed that titanium dioxide is decomposed when heated in the vapour of **phosphorus pentachloride,** and J. Tuttscheff found that phosphoryl chloride and a compound, $TiCl_4.PCl_5$, is formed (q.v.). Titanium dioxide dissolves in molten **borax,** or microcosmic salt, and gives an amethyst blue in the reducing flame, and a pale blue in the oxidizing flame. The reaction was studied by J. J. Berzelius, R. Bunsen, E. Riley, G. Rose, E. J. Chapman, R. Brauns, etc. L. Weiss and M. Landecker found that a fused mixture of two parts of sodium carbonate and one of borax readily dissolves titanium dioxide.

H. Rose said that titanium dioxide is reduced to the metal by **carbon** at a white heat. According to F. Wöhler and H. St. C. Deville, when a mixture of carbon and titanium dioxide is heated in a carbon crucible, there is formed *Kohlenstoffstickstofftitan*—the nitrogen comes from the air. By heating titanium dioxide in an electric arc-furnace with carbon electrodes at 50–70 volts, and 100 amps., H. Moissan found that the blue oxide is formed; with 350 volts, the nitride is formed; with 1200 volts, the carbide is formed; with 1000 volts, the titanium has 15·3 per cent. of carbon; with 1200 volts, 11·2 per cent. of carbon. I. L. Bell found that when the dioxide is heated in a current of **carbon monoxide,** about 4·7 per cent. of oxygen was lost, and some carbon was formed. F. Göbel also studied the reaction; but H. Rose said that there is no action at a red heat. F. Bischoff and H. Adkins studied the adsorption of **carbon dioxide** by titania. According to E. A. Demarçay, and P. Camboulives, titanium dioxide heated to about 400°–430° in the vap. of **carbon tetrachloride,** furnishes titanium tetrachloride, but, according to L. Meyer, there is no reaction if the dioxide is heated to a very high temp. Fused **alkali carbonates** react with titanium dioxide, forming titanates (*q.v.*). K. Bornemann and H. Schirmeister found that after fusion with alkali carbonate, and dissolution in hydrochloric acid, the residue is difficult to wash, and readily passes through the filter-paper ; and that this is avoided by the use of sulphuric acid (1 : 2) in place of hydrochloric acid. H. Geisow said that no titanium is removed by washing with water the mass obtained by fusing alkali carbonate and titanium dioxide. The reactions of titanium dioxide and the alkali carbonates have been studied by D. P. Smith, T. Scheerer, and E. Mallard. C. F. Rammelsberg found that titanium dioxide is not attacked by **potassium cyanide.** A. Benrath found that titanium dioxide in the presence of **alcohol** or **oxalic acid** is reduced in light. P. Sabatier and A. Mailhe found that calcined titanium dioxide is reduced by the vapour of a primary alcohol at 350°–400° ; and they studied the catalytic influence of titanium dioxide on the formation of **ethers,** and on the decomposition of **formic acid.** C. N. Hinshelwood and B. Topley found the heat of activation of titanic oxide in the reaction $H.COOH = CO + H_2O$ to be much greater than is the case with glass. P. Sabatier and A. Mailhe, and F. Bischoff and H. Adkins studied the catalytic action of titanic oxide in the dehydration of alcohols, etc. F. Bischoff and H. Adkins also studied the adsorption of **ethylene** and **ethane** by titania. A. Kling also studied the catalytic effect of titanium dioxide on alcohol. Titanium dioxide alone is stable towards light, but C. Renz showed that it becomes markedly *photosensitive* in the presence of certain organic liquids and reducing soln., particularly glycerol. G. Tammann found that **silicon** reacts with titanium dioxide at a high temp., forming titanium sesquioxide, and silica. L. Bourgeois studied the action of **silica** on titanium dioxide—*vide* titanium silicates—and he found that when a mixture of **stannic oxide,** silica, titanium dioxide, and calcium chloride is fused, crystals containing the dioxide are formed. According to L. Troost and P. Hautefeuille, **silicon tetrachloride** does not attack red-hot titanium dioxide, but at 360°–370°, G. Rauter found that a little titanium tetrachloride is formed.

According to H. Rose, **sodium** or **potassium** at a red heat reduces titanium dioxide. The reaction is accompanied by a moderate incandescence ; and in addition to the alkali oxide, a black powder, not susceptible of metallic lustre, is formed, and the product is considered to be a mixture of the metal and its oxide. T. König and O. F. von der Pfordten observed the reduction of heated titanium dioxide by the vap. of sodium, forming TiO, Ti_2O_3, and Na_3TiO_3 (*q.v.*). A. Burger, and W. Huppertz found that titanium dioxide is reduced to the metal when heated with **calcium.** According to C. Winkler, and L. Gattermann, **magnesium** or **zinc** reacts with titanium dioxide with incandescence and partial reduction. For the reduction of the dioxide by **aluminium,** *vide* titanium. H. Baumhauer studied the etching of anatase with **potassium hydroxide ;** and found that after fusion with potassium or sodium hydroxide, the mineral is dissolved by acid. The fused alkali converts the titanium dioxide into a titanate (*q.v.*).

REFERENCES.

¹ A. Laugier, *Ann. Chim. Phys.*, (1), **89.** 306, 317, 1814 ; P. Berthier, *ib.*, (3), **7.** 84, **1843** ; J. Fournet, *ib.*, (3), **4.** 370, 1842 ; M. Billy, *ib.*, (9), **16.** 5, 1921 ; H. Moissan, *ib.*, (7), **4.** 136, 1895 ; (7), **9.** 229, 1896 ; *Bull. Soc. Chim.*, (3), **9.** 957, 1892 ; *Compt. Rend.*, **115.** 1034, 1892 ; **120.** 290, 1895 ; C. Mène, *ib.*, **63.** 608, 1866 ; J. J. Berzelius, *Pogg. Ann.*. **4.** 1, 1825 ; C. M. Kersten, *ib.*. **50.** 313, 1840 ; *Journ. prakt. Chem.*, (1), **20.** 373, 1840 ; C. A. Winkler, *Ber.*, **23.** 2657, 1890 ; V. Merz, *ib.*, **8.** 1294, 1875 ; E. Glatzel, *ib.*, **9.** 1829, 1876 ; T. König and O. F. von der Pfordten, *ib.*, **22.** 2072, 1889 ; O. F. von der Pfordten, *Liebig's Ann.*, **237.** 217, 1887 ; F. Wöhler, *ib.*, **73.** 49, 1850 ; G. Bontemps, *Phil. Mag.*, (3), **39.** 439, 1849 ; A. Werner, *Neuere Anschauungen auf dem Gebiete der anorganischen Chemie*, Braunschweig, 13, 1905 ; London, 75, 1911 ; E. Knecht

and E. Hibbert, *New Reduction Methods in Volumetric Analysis*, London, 1910 ; E. Newbery and J. N. Pring, *Proc. Roy. Soc.*, 92. A, 276, 1916; H. Rose, *Pogg. Ann.*, 61. 513, 1844.
² G. Rose, *Sitzber. Akad. Berlin*, 138, 1867 ; A. Piccini and L. Marino, *Zeit. anorg. Chem.*, 32. 70, 1902 ; R. Brauns, *Neues Jahrb. Min.*, ii, 237, 1892.
³ J. J. Ebelmen, *Ann. Chim. Phys.*, (3), 20. 392, 1847 ; M. Billy, *ib.*, (9), 16. 5, 1921 ; C. Friedel and J. Guérin, *ib.*, (5), 8. 38, 1876 ; *Bull. Soc. Chim.*, (2), 22. 482, 1876 ; *Compt. Rend.*, 81. 892, 1875 ; 82. 509, 972, 1876 ; P. Sabatier and B. Senderens, *ib.*, 114. 1429, 1892 ; 115. 236, 1892 ; *Bull. Soc. Chim.*, (3), 7. 505, 1892 ; (3), 9. 668, 1893 ; H. Moissan, *ib.*, (3), 13. 959, 1895 ; *Compt. Rend.*, 120. 290, 1895 ; H. St. C. Deville, *ib.*, 53. 163, 1861; J. N. von Fuchs, *Journ. prakt. Chem.*, (1), 18. 496, 1839 ; *Liebig's Ann.*, 46. 319, 1843 ; O. F. von der Pfordten, *ib.*, 237. 217, 1887 ; 238. 201, 1887 ; T. König and O. F. von der Pfordten, *Ber.*, 22. 1485, 2070, 1889 ; E. Glatzel, *Ber.*, 9. 1829, 1876 ; W. Manchot and P. Richter, *ib.*, 39. 320, 488, 1906 ; E. Knecht, *ib.*, 36. 166, 1903 ; H. Rose, *Gilbert's Ann.*, 73. 67, 1823 ; *Akad. Handl. Stockholm*, 231, 1821 ; *Quart. Journ. Science*, 26. 97, 107, 379, 381, 1823 ; *Ann. Phil.*, 6. 369, 1823 ; R. Brauns, *Neues Jahrb. Min.*, ii, 237, 1892 ; C. F. Rammelsberg, *Sitzber. Akad. Berlin*, 490, 1874 ; G. Rose, *ib.*, 138, 1867 ; P. Groth, *Tabellarische Uebersicht der Mineralien*, Braunschweig, 45, 1898 ; *Chemische Krystallographie*, Leipzig, 1. 103, 1906 ; F. von Kobell, *Pogg. Ann.*, 62. 599, 1844 ; E. Polidori, *Zeit. anorg. Chem.*, 19. 306, 1899 ; E. Friedrich and L. Sittig, *ib.*, 145. 127, 1925 ; A. Piccini, *Atti Accad. Lincei*, (4), 1. 682, 1885.
⁴ J. B. L. Romé de l'Isle, *Cristallographie*, Paris, 2. 406, 421, 1783 ; S. R. I. Eques a Born, *Catalogue méthodique et raisoné de la collection des fossiles de Mlle. Eleonore de Raab*, Wien, 1. 168, 1790 ; R. J. Haüy, *Traité de minéralogie*, Paris, 3. 129, 1801 ; 4. 296, 1801 ; 4. 333, 1822 ; *Journ. Mines*, 5. 273, 1799 ; A. L. Lavoisier, *Ann. Chim. Phys.*, (1), 2. 170, 1789 ; M. H. Klaproth, *Beiträge zur chemischen Kenntniss der Mineralkörper*, Berlin, 1. 233, 1795 ; 2. 235, 1797 ; J. C. Delamétherie, *Théorie de la terre*, Paris, 2. 269, 333, 1797 ; H. B. de Saussure, *Voyages dans les Alpes*, Neuchatel, 4. 74, 85, 1796 ; R. Kirwan, *Elements of Mineralogy*, London, 2. 329, 1796 ; A. Estner, *Versuch einer Mineralogie*, Wien, 2. 170, 1795 ; L. A. Emmerling, *Lehrbuch der Mineralogie*, Giessen, 3. 373, 1797 ; A. G. Werner, *Letztes Mineralsystem*, Freiberg, 1. 55, 1805 ; D. L. G. Karsten, *Mineralogische Tabellen*, Berlin, 56, 79, 1800 ; C. A. S. Hofmann, *Handbuch der Mineralogie*, Freiberg, 4. a, 259, 1817 ; C. F. Rammelsberg, *Handbuch der Mineralchemie*, Leipzig, 1008, 1860 ; *Pogg. Ann.*, 77. 586, 1849 ; A. von Lasaulx, *Zeit. Kryst.*, 8. 71, 1884 ; W. E. Hidden, *Amer. Journ. Science*, (3), 36. 272, 1888 ; N. von Kokscharoff, *Materialen zur Mineralogie Russlands*, St. Petersburg, 2. 352, 1854 ; 5. 193, 1869 ; R. Hermann, *Journ. prakt. Chem.*, (1), 50. 200, 1850 ; W. A. Lampadius, *Sammlung praktisch-chemischer Abhandlungen*, Dresden, 2. 119, 1797 ; J. L. Bournon, *Journ. Phys.*, 30. 386, 1787 ; J. D. Dana, *A System of Mineralogy*, New York, 240, 1892 ; *Amer. Journ. Science*, (3), 12. 211, 397, 1851 ; (3), 13. 117, 1851 ; H. Rose, *Pogg. Ann.*, 61. 513, 1844 ; A. Breithaupt, *ib.*, 77. 302, 1849 ; L. N. Vauquelin, *Ann. Chim. Phys.*, (1), 42. 72, 1802 ; *Journ. Mines*, 11. 425, 1802 ; 19. 478, 1806 ; *Mém. l'Inst.*, 159. 1807 ; *Journ. Phys.*, 66. 345, 1808 ; *Nicholson's Journ.*, 15. 322, 1806 ; T. L. Watson, *Amer. Min.*, 7. 185, 1922 : *Journ. Washington Acad.*, 12. 447, 1922 ; A. Lévy, *Ann. Phil.*, 9. 140, 1825 ; *Description d'une collection de minéraux formée par M. Henri Heuland*, Londres, 3. 349, 1837 ; W. Haidinger, *Treatise on Mineralogy*, Edinburgh, 3. 82, 1825 ; *Pogg. Ann.*, 5. 163, 1825 ; F. S. Beudant, *Traité élémentaire de minéralogie*, Paris, 492, 1824 ; 2. 641, 1832 ; P. A. Dufrénoy, *Traité de minéralogie*, Paris, 3. 809, 1847 ; A. Lacroix, *Minéralogie de la France et de ses colonies*, Paris, 3. 172, 1901 ; A. des Cloizeaux and A. Damour, *Ann. Mines*, (4), 15. 447, 1849 ; C. U. Shepard, *Amer. Journ. Science*, (2), 2. 250, 1846 ; (3), 12. 211, 1851 ; J. D. Whitney, *ib.*, (2), 7. 433, 1849 ; *Boston Journ. Nat. Hist.*, 8. 42, 1848 ; *Phil. Mag.*, (3), 35. 192, 1849 ; W. H. Miller, *ib.*, (3), 35. 75, 1849 ; L. J. Igelström, *Geol. För. Förh. Stockholm*, 18. 231, 1896 ; M. Weibull and A. Upmark, *ib.*, 18. 523, 1896 ; D. Mawson, *Trans. Roy. Soc. South Australia*, 30. 188, 1906 ; E. H. Rennie and W. T. Cooke, *ib.*, 30. 193, 1906 ; J. V. Janovsky, *Sitzber. Akad. Wien*, 80. 34, 1886 ; W. B. Smith, *Proc. Colorado Scient. Soc.*, 2. 175, 1887 ; E. F. Glocker, *Handbuch der Mineralogie*, Nürnberg, 541, 1831.
⁵ M. H. Klaproth, *Beiträge zur chemischen Kenntnis der Mineralkörper*, Berlin, 1. 233, 1795 ; 2. 235, 1797 ; A. G. Ekeberg, *Akad. Handl. Stockholm*, 46, 1803 ; C. M. Kersten, *Journ. prakt. Chem.*, (1), 37. 170, 1846 ; H. Müller, *ib.*, (1), 58. 183, 1853 ; C. F. Rammelsberg, *Handbuch der Mineralchemie*, Leipzig, 1008, 1860 ; J. V. Janovsky, *Sitzber. Akad. Wien*, 80. 34, 1886 ; K. Pfeil, *Centr. Min.*, 144, 1902 ; *Ueber die Aufschliessung der Silikate und anderer schwer zersetzbarer Mineralien mit Borsäureanhydrid*, Heidelberg, 1901 ; H. Rose, *Pogg. Ann.*, 3. 166, 1825 ; 61. 513, 1844 ; A. Damour, *Ann. Chim. Phys.*, (3), 10. 414, 1844 ; A. Virlet, *Bull. Soc. Géol.*, 3. 25, 1846 ; W. B. Smith, *Proc. Colorado Scient. Soc.*, 2. 175, 1887 ; F. A. Genth, *Amer. Journ. Science*, (3), 44. 384, 1892 ; W. P. Headden, *ib.*, (3), 41. 249, 1891 ; N. von Kokscharoff, *Materialen zur Mineralogie Russlands*, 2. 355, 1854 ; 5. 193, 1869 ; *Proc. Russ. Min. Soc.*, 3. 73, 1868 ; A. von Lasaulx, *Zeit. Kryst.*, 8. 69, 1884 ; L. Weiss and H. Kaiser, *Zeit. anorg. Chem.*, 65. 345, 1900 ; W. C. Brögger, *Die Mineralien der südnorwegischen Granitpegmatitgänge*, Kristiania, 46, 1906 ; G. T. Prior and F. Zambonini, *Min. Mag.*, 15. 86, 1907 ; G. von Hevesy and V. T. Jantzen, *Journ. Chem. Soc.*, 123. 328, 1923 ; T. L. Watson, *Journ. Washington Acad.*, 12. 447, 1922.
⁶ Anon., *Bull. Imp. Inst.*, 15. 82, 1917.
⁷ A. von Lasaulx, *Zeit. Kryst.*, 8. 69, 1884 ; J. V. Janovsky, *Sitzber. Akad. Wien*, 80. 34, 1886 ; L. G. Eakins and W. B. Smith, *Proc. Colorado Scientific Soc.*, 2. 175, 1887 ; W. P. Headden, *Amer. Chem. Journ.*, 41. 249, 1891.

⁹ L. Weiss and H. Kaiser, *Zeit. anorg. Chem.*, **65**. 345, 1909 ; W. P. Headden, *Amer. Chem. Journ.*, **41**. 249, 1891 ; G. Friedel and T. Grandjean, *Bull. Soc. Min.*, **32**. 52, 1909.

⁹ A. G. Ekeberg, *Akad. Handl. Stockholm*, **46**, 1803 ; R. H. Brett and G. Bird, *Phil. Mag.*, (3), **4**. 113, 1835 ; B. Hasselberg, *Bihang. Akad. Handl. Stockholm*, **22**. 7, 1896 ; **23**. 3, 1897 ; *Zeit. anorg. Chem.*, **18**. 85, 1898 ; *Astrophys. Journ.*, **6**. 22, 1897 ; **9**. 143, 1899 ; H. St. C. Deville, *Compt. Rend.*, **53**. 161, 1861 ; H. Rose, *Pogg. Ann.*, **3**. 166, 1825 ; **61**. 513, 1844 ; R. J. Haüy, *Traité de minéralogie*, Paris, **4**. 297, 1801 ; A. Arzruni, *Zeit. Kryst.*, **8**. 334, 1883.

¹⁰ H. Rose, *Pogg. Ann.*, **61**. 515, 1844 ; L. N. Vauquelin, *Ann. Chim. Phys.*, (1), **42**. 82, 1802 ; A. Damour, *ib.*, (3), **10**. 417, 1844 ; *Ann. Mines*, (4), **15**. 447, 1849 ; E. Hussak, *Tschermak's Mitt.*, (2), **18**. 334, 1899 ; J. P. O'Reilly, *Proc. Roy. Dublin Soc.*, **8**. 732, 1898 : R. Hermann, *Journ. prakt. Chem.*, (1), **46**. 404, 1849 ; (1), **50**. 200, 1850 ; H. Franke, *Centr. Min.*, 417, 1923 ; K. Pfeil, *ib.*, 144, 1902 ; *Ueber die Aufschliessung der Silikate und anderer schwer zersetzbarer Mineralien mit Borsäureanhydrid*, Heidelberg, 1901 ; K. Romanowsky, *Russ. Min. Journ.*, **1**. 256, 1852 ; *Berg. Hütt. Ztg.*, **12**. 444, 1853.

¹¹ A. Bergeat, *Neues Jahrb. Min.*, i, 232, 1895 ; G. A. Sauer, *ib.*, 575, 1879 ; i, 94, 1880 ; J. S. Diller, *ib.*, i, 187, 1883 ; E. Kalkowsky, *ib.*, 382, 1879 ; H. Gylling, *ib.*, i, 164, 1882 ; P. Mann, *ib.*, ii, 200, 1882 ; A. Müller, *ib.*, 820, 1858 ; A. Cathrein, *ib.*, i, 169, 1881 ; ii, 151, 1888 ; *Zeit. Kryst.*, **6**. 256, 1882 ; H. Behrens, *ib.*, **9**. 575, **1884** ; H. Rösler, *ib.*, **36**. 263, 1902 ; F. Zirkel, *Pogg. Ann.*, **144**. 319, 1871 ; F. Kollbeck, *Zeit. deut. geol. Ges.*, **35**. 478, 1883 ; J. R. Blum, *Die Pseudomorphosen des Mineralreichs*, Stuttgart, **3**. 17, 1863 ; T. L. Watson and S. Taber, *Bull. U.S. Geol. Sur.*, 430, 1910 ; W. S. Bayley, *Econ. Geol.*, **18**. 382, 1923 ; C. Doelter, *Tschermak's Mitt.*, (2), **11**. 325, 1890 ; E. Hussak, *ib.*, (2), **18**. 337, 1899 ; B. Doss, *ib.*, (2), **11**. 39, 1890 ; A. Lacroix, *Minéralogie de la France et de ses colonies*, Paris, **3**. 175, 1901 : *Bull. Soc. Min.*, **14**. 191, 1891 ; **24**. 425, 1901 ; Comte de Limur, *ib.*, **11**. 208, 1888 ; K. von Chrustschoff, *ib.*, **7**. 337, 1884 ; R. Brauns, *Chemische Mineralogie*, Leipzig, 294, 296, 409, 1896 ; G. Spezia, *Atti Accad. Torino*, **18**. 1, 1882 ; O. Mügge, *Neues Jahrb. Min. B.B.*, **8**. 559, 1893 ; C. Schmidt, *ib.*, **4**. 457, 1886 ; A. Schenk, *Verh. Ver. Rheinl. Bonn*, 73, 1884 ; J. B. Scrivenor, *Min. Mag.*, **13**. 348, 1903 ; H. Thürach, *Verh. Phys. Med. Ges. Würzburg*, **18**. 358, 1884 ; *Ueber das Vorkommen mikroskopischer Zirkone und Titan-Mineralien in den Gesteinen*, Würzburg, 1884.

¹² F. Wöhler, *Ann. Chim. Phys.*, (3), **28**. 382, 1850 ; (3), **29**. 166, 1850 ; *Sitzber. Akad. Berlin*, 244, 1849 ; *Compt. Rend.*, **29**. 505, 1849 ; *Pogg. Ann.*, **78**. 401, 1849 ; *Liebig's Ann.*, **73**. 44, 1850 ; A. Knop, *ib.*, **157**. 365, 1871 ; T. Scheerer, *ib.*, **112**. 179, 1860 ; *Berg. Hütt. Ztg.*, **21**. 98, 1862 ; H. Rose, *Gilbert's Ann.*, **73**. 67, 1823 ; *Akad. Handl. Stockholm*, 231, 1821 ; *Quart. Journ. Science*, **26**. 97, 107, 379, 381, 1823 ; *Ann. Phil.*, **6**. 369, 1823 ; *Pogg. Ann.*, **61**. 508, 1844 ; O. Lehmann, *Zeit. Kryst.*, **1**. 97, 1877 ; G. Rose, *Sitzber. Akad. Berlin*, 129, 1867 ; *Journ. prakt. Chem.*, (1), **101**. 217, 1867 ; (1), **102**. 385, 1867 ; *Pogg. Ann.*, **115**. 643, 1862 ; *Neues Jahrb. Min.*, 727, 1862 ; R. Brauns, *ib.*, ii, 237, 1892 ; J. J. Ebelmen, *Ann. Chim. Phys.*, (3), **33**. 34, 1851 ; *Bull. Soc. Chim.*, (2), **5**. 202, 1863 ; *Compt. Rend.*, **25**. 279, 661, 1847 ; **32**. 330, 710, 1851 ; **33**. 525, 1851 ; H. Cormimbœuf, *ib.*, **115**. 823, 1892 ; L. Ouvrard, *ib.*, **111**. 177, 1890 ; H. St. C. Deville and H. Caron, *ib.*, **46**. 290, 764, 1858 ; H. St. C. Deville, *ib.*, **53**. 161, 1861 ; L. Michel, *Bull. Soc. Chim.*, (3), **16**. 37, 1893 ; *Compt. Rend.*, **114**. 1020, 1893 ; A. Daubrée, *Ann. Mines*, (4), **16**. 129, 1849 ; *Phil. Mag.*, (4), **9**. 315, 1855 ; *Edin. Phil. Journ.*, **57**. 307, 1854 ; *Compt. Rend.*, **29**. 227, 1849 ; **30**. 383, 1850 ; **39**. 153, 1853 ; C. Friedel and J. Guérin, *ib.*, **82**. 509, 1876 ; *Ann. Chim. Phys.*, (5), **8**. 24, 1876 ; *Bull. Soc. Chim.*, (2), **23**. 289, 1875 ; P. Hautefeuille, *ib.*, (1), **5**. 588, 1863 ; *Compt. Rend.*, **57**. 148, 1863 ; **59**. 188, 1864 ; **90**. 868, 1880 ; *Ann. Chim. Phys.*, (4), **4**. 131, 1865 ; H. de Sénarmont, *ib.*, (3), **32**. 129, 1851 ; H. E. Merwin and J. C. Hostetter, *Amer. Min.*, **4**. 126, 1919 ; G. Wunder, *Journ. prakt. Chem.*, (2), **4**. 347, 1870 ; P. Hautefeuille and A. Perrey, *Ann. Chim. Phys.*, (6), **21**. 419, 1890 ; *Compt. Rend.*, **110**. 1038, 1890 ; L. Bourgeois, *ib.*, **103**. 141, 1886 ; *Reproduction artificielle des minéraux*, Paris, 85, 1884 ; B. Doss, *Neues Jahrb. Min.*, ii, 147, 1894 ; i, 128, 1895 ; R. Brauns, *ib.*, ii, 237, 1892 ; i, 89, 1893 ; H. Traube, *Neues Jahrb. Min. B.B.*, **10**. 470, 1896 ; C. Winkler, *Ber.*, **23**. 2657, 1890 ; G. Cartaret and M. Devaux, *Brit. Pat. No.* 184132, 1921 ; F. A. Genth, *Proc. Amer. Phil. Soc.*, 400, 1882 ; K. Endell, *Sprech.*, **44**. 5, 1911 ; H. Geisow, *Beiträge zur Kenntnis der seltenen anorganischen Säuren*, München, 1902 ; C. Weizmann and J. Blumenfeld, *Brit. Pat. No.* 209441, 1922.

¹³ L. Wöhler and K. von Kraatz-Koschlau, *Tschermak's Mitt.*, (2), **18**. 460, 1899 ; H. Traube, *Neues Jahrb. Min. B.B.*, **10**. 472, 1895 ; J. W. Retgers, *Zeit. phys. Chem.*, **16**. 622, 1895 ; R. F. Wagner, *Ber.*, **21**. 960, 1888.

¹⁴ W. H. Miller, *Phil. Mag.*, (3), **17**. 268, 1840 ; (4), **19**. 326, 1860 ; *Introduction to Mineralogy*, London, 224, 227, 229, 1852 ; D. Brewster, *Trans. Roy. Soc. Edin.*, **20**. 547, 1853 ; *Phil. Mag.*, (4), **6**. 265, 1853 ; F. Hessenberg, *Mineralogische Notizen*, Frankfurt, **1**. 30, 1856 ; **2**. 11, 1858 ; **3**. 25, 1860 ; N. von Kokscharoff, *Materialen zur Mineralogie Russlands*, St. Petersburg, **1**. 50, 61, 1853 ; **2**. 273, 1857 ; **9**. 88, 90, 1884 ; *Proc. Russ. Min. Soc.*, 2, 1849 ; *Russ. Min. Journ.*, 273, 1849 ; *Pogg. Ann.*, **79**. 454, 1850 ; *Neues Jahrb. Min.*, 800, 1877 ; G. A. Kenngott, *Uebersichte der Resultate mineralogischer Forschungen*, Wien, 208, 1858 ; R. J. Haüy, *Traité de minéralogie*, Paris, **4**. 297, 1801 ; **4**. 333, 1822 ; W. J. Sollas, *Proc. Roy. Soc.*, **80**. A, 278, 1908 ; A. Breithaupt, *Vollständiges Handbuch der Mineralogie*, Dresden, **3**. 794, 1847 ; *Pogg. Ann.*, **77**. 302, 1849 ; E. Mallard, *Ann. Mines*, (7), **10**. 134, 1876 ; K. Romanowsky, *Russ. Min. Journ.*, **1**. 256, 1852 ; *Berg. Hütt. Ztg.*, **12**. 444, 1853 ; F. Wallerant, *Bull. Soc. Min.*, **24**. 206, 230, 1901 ; F. Pisani, *ib.*, **11**. 300, 1888 ; **12**. 44, 1889 ; E. Bertrand, *ib.*, **2**. 30, 1879 ; O. Hahn, *Zeit. Elektrochem.*, **29**. 189, 1923 ; L. Cahn, *Beitr. Kryst. Min.*, **2**. 7, 1919 ; G. Friedel, *Étude sur les groupe-*

ments cristallins, St. Etienne, 263, 307, 1904 ; A. des Cloizeaux, *Manuel de minéralogie*, Paris, 2. 200, 204, 1874 ; *Ann. Chim. Phys.*, (3), **10**. 417, 1844 ; F. S. Beudant, *Traité élémentaire de minéralogie*, Paris, **2**. 641, 1832 ; O. Mügge, *Centr. Min.*, 73, 1902 ; *Neues Jahrb. Min.*, i, 148, 1886 ; ii, 83, 1897 ; C. O. Trechmann, *ib.*, i, 204, 1884 ; F. Rinne, *ib.*, ii, 20, 1885 ; M. Bauer, *ib.*, i, 226, 1891 ; C. Klein, *ib.*. 900, 1872 ; 341, 1875 ; F. Wiser, *ib.*, 163, 1844 ; 181, 1855 ; 426, 1859 ; G. vom Rath, *Zeit. deut. geol. Ges.*, **14**. 398, 415, 1862 ; *Pogg. Ann.*, **113**. 431, 1861 ; **152**. 21, 1874 ; *Ber. Niederrh. Ges. Bonn*, 8, 1877 ; 158, 1886 ; *Zeit. Kryst.*, **1**. 15, 1877 ; R. L. Pa k∂r, *ib.*, **59**. 1, 1924 ; O. Luedecke, *ib.*, **4**. 544, 1880 ; **7**. 89, 1883 ; **10**. 200, 1885 ; C. Vrba, *ib.*, **5**. 417, 1861 ; **24**. 117, 1895 ; *Centr. Min.*, 504, 1901 ; H. Baumhauer, *Centr. Min.*, 672, 1903 ; *Sitzber. Akad. Berlin*, 322, 1906 ; *Zeit. Kryst.*, **33**. 653, 1900 ; **24**. 565, 1895 ; A. von Lasaulx, *ib.*, **8**. 69, 1884 ; W. C. Brögger, *ib.*, **16**. 133, 1890 ; R. L. Parker, *ib.*, **58**. 522, 1923 ; H. Tertsch, *ib.*, **58**. 293, 1923 ; R. W. Haare, *ib.*, **42**. 282, 1906 ; O. Lincio, *Atti Accad. Torino*, 39. 995, 1904 ; P. von Jeremejeff, *Proc. Russ. Min. Soc.*, **23**. 341, 1886 ; **26**. 427, 1890 ; 27. 407, 1890 ; *Russ. Min. Journ.*, 3. 263, 1887 ; G. Tschermak, *Tschermak's Mitt.*, (2), **1**. 363, 1878 ; A. Frenzel, *ib.*, (2), **9**. 399, 1888 ; O. Pohl, *ib.*, (2), **22**. 473, 1903 ; A. Brezina, *ib.*, (1), 3. 49, 1873 ; G. L∵ch∩er, *ib.*, (2), **22**. 79, 1902 ; A. Wichmann, *ib.*, (2), **8**. 338, 1887 ; G. Rose, *Pogg. Ann.*, **79**. 464, 1850 ; **115**. 643, 1862 ; H. S. Washington and W. E. Hidden, *Amer. Journ. Science*, (3), **33**. 501, 1887 ; A. E. Robinson, *ib.*, (4), **12**. 180, 1901 ; G F. Kunz and S. L. Penfield, *ib.*, (3), 43. 329, 1892 ; C. U. Shepard, *ib.*, (2), **2**. 250, 1846 ; (2), **4**. 279, 1847 ; S. L. Penfield, *ib.*, (3), **31**. 387, 1885 ; (3), **43**. 184, 1892 ; E. S. Dana, *ib.*, (3), **32**. 314, 1886 ; R. B. Riggs and J. S. Diller, *ib.*, (3), 35. 51, 1885 ; A. Stelzner, *Zeit. prakt. Geol.*, 3. 406, 1896 ; G. Boeris, *Atti Ist. Milano*, 40. 339, 1901 ; G. Seligmann, *Neues Jahrb. Min.*, ii, 269, 1881 ; ii, 281, 1882 ; *Zeit. Kryst.*, **9**. 420, 1884 ; **11**. 337, 1886 ; C. Busz, *ib.*, **20**. 557, 1892 ; *Neues Jahrb. Min.*, ii, 135, 1901 ; A. Johns∩r, *ib.*, i, 49, 1918 ; A. Grühn and A. Johnsen, *Centr. Min.*, 366, 1917 ; F. Millosevich, *Rend. Accad. Lincei*, (5), 14. 92, 1905 ; A. Sella, *ib.*, (4), **7**. 196, 1891 ; A. Streng, *Neues Jahrb. Min.*, i, 101, 1887 ; A. Lévy, *Ann. Phil.*, **9**. 140, 1825 ; *Description d'une collection de minéraux formée par M. Henri Heuland*, Londres, 3. 349, 1837 ; J. D. Dana, *A System of Mineralogy*, New York, 243, 1892 ; P. Groth, *Die Mineraliensammlung der Universität Strassburg*, Strassburg, 110, 1878 ; A. Schrauf, *Atlas der Krystallformen der Mineralreiches*, Wien, 1872 ; *Zeit. Kryst.*, 1. 306, 1877 ; *Sitzber. Akad. Wien*, **74**. 535, 1876 ; *Anz. Akad. Wien*, 66, 1873 ; *Neues Jahrb. Min.*, 163, 1871 ; 50, 1878 ; C. Palache, *Ze∂t. Kryst.*, **24**. 590, 1895 ; J. Beckenkamp, *ib.*, **58**. 1, 1923 ; A. Fornaro, *Arch. Sciences Genève*, (4), **10**. 435, 1900 ; L. Brugnatelli, *Riv. Min. Ital.*, **23**. 37, 1899 ; H. Buttgenbach, *Bull. Soc Géol. Belg.*, **40**. 378, 1913 ; G. Cesaro, *Bull. Acad. Belg.*, 313, 1907 ; W. Prinz, *ib.*, 706, 1907 ; H. P. Whitlock, *Bull. Amer. Museum Nat. Hist.*, **46**. 205, 1922 ; O. C. Farrington and E. W. Tillotson, *Bull. Field Col. Museum Geol.*, 3. 7, 1908 ; J. Schetelig, *Norsk. Geol. Tids.*, 2. 38, 1913 ; L. Colomba, *Riv. Min. Ital.*, **38**. 50, 1909.

¹⁵ O. Mügge, *Neues Jahrb. Min.*, i, 221, 1884 ; i, 147, 1886 ; i, 231, 1889 ; H. Traube, *Neues Jahrb. Min. B.B.*, **10**. 471, 1895 ; H. Baumhauer, *Zeit. Kryst.*, **24**. 576, 1895 ; A. Breithaupt, *Vollständiges Handbuch der Mineralogie*, Dresden, 3. 794, 1847 ; G. A. Kenngott, *Uebersicht der Resultate mineralogischer Forschungen*, Wien, 187. 1859 ; W. H. Miller, *Phil. Mag.*, (4), **19**. 326, 1860 ; A. Grühn and A. Johnsen, *Centr. Min.*, 366, 1917.

¹⁶ J. Grailich and V. von Lang, *Sitzber. Akad. Wien*, **27**. 68, 1857 ; J. Grailich, *Krystallographisch-optische Untersuchungen*, Wien, 210, 1858 ; A. Schrauf, *Zeit. Kryst.*, 1. 276, 1877 ; **9**. 473, 1884 ; V. von Zepharovich, *ib.*, **8**. 581, 1884 ; U. Panichi, *Mem. Accad. Lincei*, 4. 389, 1902 ; *Centr. Min.*, 322, 1902 ; A. des Cloizeaux, *Manuel de minéralogie*, Paris, 2. 407, 1864 ; *Compt. Rend.*, **55**. 654, 1862 ; *Nouvelles recherches sur les propriétés optiques des cristaux*, Paris, 555, 1867 ; *Ann. Mines*, (5), **61**. 334, 1857 ; (5), **14**. 361, 1858 ; (6), 2, 11, 1862 ; E. Mallard, *ib.*, (7), **10**. 134, 1876 ; A. Beer, *Pogg. Ann.*, **82**. 436, 1851 ; W. H. Miller, *Introduction to Mineralogy*, London, 228, 1852 ; W. P. Davey, *Phys. Rev.*, (2), **23**. 763, 1924.

¹⁷ L. Vegard, *Phil. Mag.*, (4), **31**. 83, 1916 ; (6), **32**. 505, 1916 ; G. Greenwood, *ib.*, (6), **48**. 655, 1924 ; A. Johnsen, *Centr. Min.*, 97, 1919 ; C. M. Williams, *Proc. Roy. Soc.*, **93**. A, 418, 1917 ; F. Rinne, *Das feinbauliche Wesen der Materie nach dem Vorbilde der Kristalle*, Berlin, 80, 1922 ; R. W. G. Wyckoff, *Journ. Franklin Inst.*, **195**. 349, 531, 1923 ; J. Beckenkamp, *Centr. Min.*, 353, 1917 ; *Zeit. Kryst.*, **58**. 1, 1923 ; H. Tertsch, *ib.*, **58**. 293, 1923 ; R. L. Parker, *ib.*, **58**. 522, 1923 ; M. L. Huggins, *Phys. Rev.*, (2), **21**. 719, 1923 ; H. Haga and F. M. Jäger, *Versl. Akad. Amsterdam*, **24**. 400, 443, 1012, 1135, 1403, 1410, 1916 ; M. Born and O. F. Bollnow, *Naturwiss*, **13**. 559, 1925 ; O. F. Bollnow, *Zeit. Physik*, **33**. 726, 1925 ; W. P. Davey, *Phys. Rev.*, (2), **23**. 763, 1924 ; R. A. Patterson, *ib.*, (2), **26**. 56, 1925.

¹⁸ S. Stevanovic, *Zeit. Kryst.*, **37**. 356, 1903 ; V. Goldschmidt, *Index der Krystallformen der Mineralien*, Berlin, **1**. 360, 1886 ; G. T. Prior, *Min. Mag.*, **13**. 220, 1903 ; H. Buttgenbach, *Ann. Soc. Geol. Belg.*, **23**. 75, 1896 ; M. Ladrey, *Compt. Rend.*, **34**. 56, 1852 ; J. D. Dana, *Amer. Journ. Science*, (2), **9**. 220, 1850 ; (2), **17**. 86, 1854 ; J. W. Retgers, *Zeit. phys. Chem.*, **16**. 621, 1895 ; **20**. 516, 1896 ; H. Traube, *Neues Jahrb. Min. B.B.*, **10**. 470, 1896 ; P. Groth, *Tabellarische Uebersicht der Mineralien*, Braunschweig, 34, 1882 ; 43, 1898 ; G. Rose, *Pogg. Ann.*, **107**. 602, 1859 ; *Neues Jahrb. Min.*, 735, 1859 ; G. Wunder, *Journ. prakt. Chem.*, (2), **2**. 206, 1870 ; A. Schrauf. *Zeit. Kryst.*, **9**. 433, 1884 ; O. Lehmann, *ib.*, **1**. 97, 1877 ; G. Linck, *ib.*, **26**. 287, 1896 ; R. Ruer, *Zeit. anorg. Chem.*, **43**. 282, 1905 ; W. T. Schaller, *Bull. U.S. Geol. Sur.*, 509, 1912.

¹⁹ H. Rose, *Pogg. Ann.*, **61**. 514, 1844 ; W. von Beck, **79**. 463, 1850 ; M. Frodmann, *ib.*, **79**. 463, 1850 ; R. Böttger, *Tabellarische Uebersicht der specifischen Gewichte der Körper*, Frankfurt, 1837 ; P. Hautefeuille, *Compt. Rend.*, **57**. 148, 1863 ; **90**. 868, 1880 ; *Ann. Chim. Phys.*, (4), **4**.

129, 140, 1865; H. Fizeau, *ib.*, (4), **8**. 335, 1866; A. Damour, *ib.*, (3), **10**. 414, 1844; *Bull. Soc. Géol.*, (2), **13**. 542, 1857; *Ann. Mines*, (4), **15**. 448, 1849; M. Weibull and A. Upmark, *Geol. För. Förh. Stockholm*, **18**. 523, 1896; C. J. B. Karsten, *Schweigger's Journ.*, **65**. 394, 1832; *Sitzber. Akad. Berlin*, 244, 1831; C. M. Kersten, *Journ. prakt. Chem.*, (1), **37**. 170, 1846; H. Müller, *ib.*, (1), **58**. 183, 1853; R. Hermann, *ib.*, (1), **46**. 404, 1849; (1), **50**. 200, 1850; M. H. Klaproth, *Beiträge zur chemischen Kenntniss der Mineralkörper*, Berlin, **2**. 223, 1797; T. Scheerer, *Pogg. Ann.*, **65**. 296, 1845; F. A. Henglein, *Zeit. anorg. Chem.*, **120**. 77, 1921; A. von Lasaulx, *Zeit. Kryst.*, **8**. 69, 1884; *Ber. Niederrh. Ges. Bonn*, 271, 1883; A. Virlet, *Bull. Soc. Géol.*, (2), **3**. 25, 1846; H. Kopp, *Liebig's Ann.*, **36**. 1, 1840; J. J. Ebelmen, *Compt. Rend.*, **32**. 230, 1851; *Ann. Chim. Phys.*, (3), **33**. 34, 1851; L. N. Vauquelin, *ib.*, (1), **42**. 72, 1802; C. F. Rammelsberg, *Handbuch der Mineralchemie*, Leipzig, 1008, 1860; H. Geisow, *Beiträge zur Kenntnis der seltenen anorganischen Säuren*, München, 1902; A. Breithaupt, *Vollständiges Handbuch der Mineralogie*, Dresden, **3**. 797, 1847; *Pogg. Ann.*, **77**. 302, 1849; W. B. Smith, *Proc. Colorado Scient.*, **2**. 175, 1887; W. P. Headden, *Amer. Journ. Science*, (3), **41**. 249, 1891; F. A. Genth, *ib.*, (3), **44**. 281, 1892; N. von Kokscharoff, *Materialen zur Mineralogie Russlands*, St. Petersburg, **1**. 47, 1853; *Proc. Russ. Min. Soc.*, **44**, 1853; E. Hussak, *Tschermak's Mitt.*, (2), **18**. 336, 1899; F. Mohs, *Charakteristik des naturhistorische Mineralsystems*, Dresden, **2**. 418, 1824; F. von Kobell, *Charakteristik der Mineralien*, Nürnberg, 329, 1830; A. des Cloizeaux, *Manuel de minéralogie*, Paris, **2**. 203, 1874; A. des Cloizeaux and A. Damour, *Ann. Mines*, (4), **15**. 447, 1849; C. Klein, *Neues Jahrb. Min.*, 346, 352, 1875; K. Romanowsky, *Berg. Hütt. Ztg.*, **12**. 444, 1853; *Russ. Min. Journ.*, **1**. 256, 1852; J D. Whitney, *Phil. Mag.*, (3), **35**. 192, 1849; *Amer. Journ. Science*, (2), **7**. 433, 1849; *Boston Journ. Nat. Hist.*, **6**. 42, 1848; A. Reis and F. Zimmermann, *Zeit. phys. Chem.*, **102**, 298, 1922; G. von Hevesy, *Zeit. anorg. Chem.*, **147**. 217, 1925.

²⁰ J. D. Dana, *Amer. Journ. Science*, (2), **9**. 220, 1850; G. T. Prior, *Min. Mag.*, **13**. 220, 1903; A. Schrauf, *Zeit. Kryst.*, **9**. 475, 1884; F. A. Henglein, *Zeit. anorg. Chem.*, **120**. 77, 1921; G. von Hevesy, *ib.*, **147**. 217, 1925; A. Reis and L. Zimmermann, *Zeit. Kryst.*, **57**. 449, 1923; P. W. Bridgman, *Amer. Journ. Science*, (5), **10**. 483, 1925; E. Madelung and R. Fuchs, *Ann. Phys.*, (4), **45**. 489, 1921; J. A. Deurs and P. E. Raaschou, *Zeit. angew. Chem.*, **38**. 382, 1925.

²¹ H. Kopp, *Liebig's Ann. Suppl.*, **3**. 289, 1865; *Liebig's Ann.*, **81**. 1, 1852; *Pogg. Ann.*, **86**. 156, 1852; H. Fizeau, *Compt. Rend.*, **62**. 1101, 1133, 1866; *Ann. Chim. Phys.*, (4), **8**. 335, 1866; H. de Sénarmont, *ib.*, (3), **21**. 457, 1847; (3), **22**. 179, 1848; *Compt. Rend.*, **25**. 459, 1847; E. Jannetaz, *ib.*, **114**. 1352, 1892; *Bull. Soc. Min.*, **15**. 138, 1892; A. Schrauf, *Zeit. Kryst.*, **9**. 464, 1884; F. E. Neumann, *Pogg. Ann.*, **23**. 1, 1831; L. F. Nilson and O. Petterson, *Zeit. phys. Chem.*, **1**. 34, 1887; W. G. Mixter, *Amer. Journ. Science*, (4), **27**. 229, 1908; (4), **33**. 45, 1912; H. V. Regnault, *Ann. Chim. Phys.*, (3), **1**. 129, 1841; A. Schuller and V. Wartha, *Ber.*, **8**. 1016, 1875; A. L. Fletcher, *Scient. Proc. Roy. Soc. Dublin*, (2), **13**. 443, 1913; R. Cusack, *Proc. Irish Acad.*, (3), **4**. 399, 1896; C. Doelter, *Handbuch der Mineralchemie*, Dresden, **3**. i, 22, 1918; R. Rieke, *Sprech.*, **41**. 405, 1908; W. R. Mott, *Trans. Amer. Electrochem. Soc.*, **34**. 255, 1918; O. Ruff, H. Sieferfeld, and J. Suda, *Zeit. anorg. Chem.*, **82**. 373, 1913; L. Weiss and H. Kaiser, *ib.*, **65**. 345, 1910; E. D. Clarke, *The Gas Blowpipe*, London, 1819; *Proc. Roy. Inst.*, **3**. 104, 1816; F. Born, *Zeit. Elektrochem.*, **31**. 309, 1925.

²² K. Bärwald, *Zeit. Kryst.*, **7**. 168, 1883; A. Madelung, *ib.*, **7**. 75, 1883; A. von Lasaulx, *ib.*, **8**. 74, 1884; E. Weinschenk, *ib.*, **26**. 405, 1896; L. Brugnatelli, *ib.*, **32**. 358, 1900; H. Thürach, *ib.*, **11**. 423, 1886; A. Ehringhaus and H. Rose, *ib.*, **58**. 460, 1923; G. Lincio, *Atti Accad. Torino*, **39**. 995, 1904; P. Ites, *Ueber die Abhängigkeit der Absorption des Lichtes von der Farbe in krystallisierten Körpern*, Göttingen, 1903; J. Königsberger, *Ueber die Absorption das Lichtes in festen Körpern*, Leipzig, 1900; *Ann. Physik*, (4), **28**. 889, 1909; A. Pfaff. *Pogg. Ann.*, **127**. 155, 1866; O. Mügge, *Neues Jahrb. Min.*, i, 234. 1889; C. Klein, *ib.*, 352, 1875; H. Traube. *Neues Jahrb. Min. B.B.*, **10**. 472, 1895; V. von Agafonoff, *Proc. Russ. Min.*, **39**. 497, 1902; O. Pohl, *Tschermak's Mitt.*, (2), **22**. 482, 1903; W. H. Miller, *Introduction to Mineralogy*, London, 229, 1852; *Phil. Mag.*, (3), **21**. 277, 1842; C. Doelter, *Neues Jahrb. Min.*, ii, 92, 1896; T. Liebisch and H. Rubens, *Sitzber. Akad. Berlin*, 211, 1921; A. Schrauf, *Sitzber. Akad. Wien*, **42**. 112, 1860; J. Grailich, *ib.*, **27**. 69, 1857; D. Brewster, *Trans. Edin. Roy. Soc.*, **20**. 547, 1853; F. Zirkel, *Lehrbuch der Petrologie*, Leipzig, **1**. 405, 1893; E. A. Wülfing in H. Rosenbusch, *Mikroskopische Physiographie der Mineralien und Gesteine*, Stuttgart, **1**. b, 54, 1905; E. Mallard, *Ann. Mines*, (7), **10**. 134, 1876; W. Crookes, *Proc. Roy. Soc.*, **32**. 206, 1881; *Chem. News*, **43**. 237, 1881; A. Michel-Lévy and A. Lacroix, *Les minéraux des roches*, Paris, 161, 1888; A. des Cloizeaux, *Nouvelles recherches sur les propriétés optiques des cristaux*, Paris, 521 1867; W. W. Coblentz, *Investigations of Infra-Red Spectra*, Washington, **3**. 67, 1906; **5**. 17, 34, 1909; **7**. 105, 1908; A. de Gramont, *Bull. Soc. Min.*, **18**. 229, 1895; N. von Kokscharoff, *Materialen zur Mineralogie Russlands*, St. Petersburg. **1**. 45, 1853; J. Joly, *Proc. Roy. Dublin Soc.*, **9**. 475, 1901; E. L. Nichols, *Phys. Rev.*, (2), **21**. 713, 1923; (2), **22**. 420, 1923; E. L. Nichols and H. L. Howes, *ib.*, (2), **19**. 300, 1922; E. L. Nichols and D. T. Wilber, (2), **17**. 707, 1923; H. J. Spanner, *Ann. Physik*, (4), **75**. 609, 1924; H. R. Robinson, *Phil. Mag.*, (6), **50**. 241, 1925; D. Coster, *ib.*, (6), **43**. 1070, 1923; Metal and Thermit Corporation, *Bril. Pat. No.* 232680, 1924; S. J. Lubowsky, *Canadian Pat. No.* 253964, 1925; J. J. Berzelius, *Lehrbuch der Chemie*, Dresden, **3**. 168, 1834; H. Rose, *Pogg. Ann.*, **61**. 509, 1844; **62**. 591, 1844; L. Wöhler, *Koll. Zeit.*, **11**. 241, 1912; J. Böhm. *Zeit. anorg. Chem.*, **149**. 217, 1925; A. des Cloizeaux, *Manuel de Minéralogie*, Paris. **2**. 203, 1874; C. Wagner, *Ber.*, **21**. 960, 1888; M. E. Chevreul, *Ann. Chim. Phys.*, (3), **13** 249, 1845.

²² F. Beijerinck, *Neues Jahrb. Min. B.B.*, **11**. 443, 1897 ; W. Schmidt, *Ann. Physik*, (4), **9**. 919, 1902 ; (4), **11**. 114, 1903 ; C. Doelter, *Sitzber. Akad. Wien*, **119**. 73, 1910 ; B. Bavink, *Beiträge zur Kenntnis der magnetischen Influenz in Krystallen*, Stuttgart, 1904 ; E. T. Wherry, *Amer. Min.*, **10**. 28, 1925 ; H. S. Roberts and L. H. Adams, *ib.*, **7**. 131, 1922. ²⁴ H. Rose, *Gilbert's Ann.*, **73**. 76, 1823 ; *Liebig's Ann.*, **53**. 267, 1845 ; *Pogg. Ann.*, **61**. 507, 1844 ; O. F. von der Pfordten, *Ber.*, **17**. 729, 1884 ; *Liebig's Ann.*, **237**. 201, 1887 ; A. Knop, *ib.*, **123**. 351, 1862 ; K. von der Grinten, *Compt. Rend.*, **178**. 2083, 1924 ; T. Graham, *Phil. Trans.*, **151**. 183, 1861 ; *Phil. Mag.*, (4), **23**. 204, 290, 368, 1862 ; (4), **28**. 314, 1864 ; *Proc. Roy. Soc.*, **11**. 243, 1862 ; **13**. 335, 1864 ; *Journ. Chem. Soc.*, **17**. 318, 1864 ; *Chem. News*, **4**. 86, 1861 ; E. A. Schneider, *Zeit. anorg. Chem.*, **8**. 96, 1895 ; H. Rose and R. Weber, *Pogg. Ann.*, **120**. 287, 1863 ; C. F. Rammelsberg, *Sitzber. Akad. Berlin*, 490, 1874 ; T. Carnelley and J. Walker, *Journ. Chem. Soc.*, **53**. 81, 1888 ; J. Tuttscheff, *Liebig's Ann.*, **141**, 111, 1867 ; *Bull. Soc. Chim.*, (2), **8**. 320, 1867 ; H. Geisow, *Beiträge zur Kenntnis der seltenen anorganischen Säuren*, Munchen, 16, 1902 ; S. Glixelli, *Anz. Akad. Krakau*, **102**, 1917 ; S. Klosky and C. Marzano, *Journ. Phys. Chem.*, **29**. 1125, 1925. ²⁵ A. Demoly, *Recherches sur le titane et ses combinaisons*, Paris, 1849 ; *Compt. Rend. Trav. Chim.*, **5**. 325, 1849 ; J. Tuttscheff, *Bull. Soc. Chim.*, (2), **8**. 320, 1867 ; *Liebig's Ann.*, **141**. 111, 1867 ; W. Delffs, *Neues Jahrb. Pharm.*, **7**. 291, 1857 ; E. Riley, *Journ. Chem. Soc.*, **15**. 311, 1862 ; V. Merz, *Untersuchungen über das Titan, Silicium, und Boron*, Zürich, 14, 1864 ; *Zürich Viertel-jahrschr.*, **9**. 77, 1864 ; *Journ. prakt. Chem.*, (1), **99**. 157, 1866 ; H. Rose, *Liebig's Ann.*, **53**. 267, 1845 ; *Pogg. Ann.*, **61**. 507, 1844 ; R. Weber, *ib.*, **120**. 287, 1863 ; *Sitzber. Akad. Berlin*, 358, 1863 ; T. Matsubara, *Bull. Osaka Ind. Lab.*, **4**. 13, 1923 ; O. F. von der Pfordten, *Liebig's Ann.*, **237**. 201, 1887 ; C. Dreher, *Färberei Ztg.*, **13**. 293, 1902 ; F. P. Dunnington, *Chem. News*, **64**. 302, 1891 ; L. Lévy, *Ann. Chim. Phys.*, (6), **25**. 433, 1892 ; *Journ. Pharm. Chim.*, (5), **16**. 56, 1887 ; A. Leclerc, *Compt. Rend.*, **137**. 50, 1904 ; H. Pellet and C. Fribourg, *Ann. Agron.*, (2), **2**. 20, 1905 ; P. Holland, *Chem. News*, **59**. 27, 1889 ; D. Forbes, *ib.*, **19**. 3, 1869 ; J. Brakes, *Journ. Soc. Chem. Ind.*, **18**. 1097, 1899 ; C. Baskerville, *ib.*, **19**. 419, 1900 ; *Journ. Amer. Chem. Soc.*, **16**. 427, 1894 ; H. Geisow, *Beiträge zur Kenntnis der seltenen anorganischen Säuren*, München, 1902 ; K. Bornemann and H. Schirmeister, *Met.*, **7**. 646, 1910 ; L. Weiss and M. Landecker, *Zeit. anorg. Chem.*, **64**. 67, 1909 ; H. Rheinboldt and E. Wedekind, *Koll. Beihefte*, **17**. 115, 1923 ; C. H. Milligan and E. E. Reid, *Science*, (2), **53**. 576, 1921 ; A. M. Morley and J. K. Wood, *Journ. Soc. Dyers. Col.*, **39**. 100, 1923 ; *Journ. Chem. Soc.*, **125**. 1626, 1924. ²⁶ J. J. Ebelmen, *Ann. Chim. Phys.*, (3), **20**. 385, 1847 ; E. Mallard, *ib.*, (4), **28**. 250, 1873 ; O. F. von der Pfordten, *Liebig's Ann.*, **237**. 212, 1887 ; T. König and O. F. von der Pfordten, *Ber.*, **22**. 2070, 1889 ; L. Meyer, *ib.*, **20**. 681, 1887 ; C. Winkler, *ib.*, **23**. 2657, 1890 ; L. Gatter-mann, *ib.*, **22**. 197, 1889 ; P. Sabatier and A. Mailhe, *Compt. Rend.*, **146**. 1376, 1908 ; **150**. 823, 1910 ; **152**. 669, 1212, 1911 : F. Wöhler, *Liebig's Ann.*, **73**. 34, 1850 ; *Ann. Chim. Phys.*, (3), **28**. 382, 1850 ; (3), **29**. 166, 1850 ; *Nachr. Gött.*, **137**. 169, 1849 ; F. Wöhler and H. St. C. Deville, *ib.*, 237, 1857 ; C. F. Rammelsberg, *Sitzber. Akad. Berlin*, 490, 1874 ; G. Rose, *ib.*, 129, 450, 1867 ; H. Rose, *ib.*, 200, 1848 ; *Pogg. Ann.*, **73**. 582, 1848 ; **74**. 562, 1848 ; *Journ. prakt. Chem.*, (1), **44**. 117, 1848 ; (1), **45**. 114, 1848 ; E. Schulze, *ib.*, (2), **21**. 402, 1880 ; E. J. Chapman, *ib.*, (1), **57**. 269, 1852 ; *Chem. Gaz.*, **10**. 297, 1852 ; F. Göbel, *Journ. prakt. Chem.*, (1), **6**. 387, 1835 ; E. Biewend, *ib.*, (1). **23**. 251, 1841 ; R. Brauns, *Neues Jahrb. Min.*, ii, 237, 1892 ; G. A. Kenngott, *ib.*, 438, 1867 ; R. Weber, *Pogg. Ann.*, **120**. 288, 1863 ; H. von Wartenberg, J. Broy, and R. Reinicke, *Zeit. Elektrochem.*, **29**. 214, 1923 ; L. Schönn, *Zeit. anal. Chem.*, **9**. 41, 330, 1870 ; E. Riley, *Journ. Chem. Soc.*, **12**. 13, 1859 ; M. E. Pennington, *Journ. Amer. Chem. Soc.*, **18**. 56, 1896 ; F. Bischoff and H. Adkins, *ib.*, **47**. 807, 1925 ; E. F. Smith, *ib.*, **20**. 289, 1898 ; D. P. Smith, *Zeit. anorg. Chem.*, **37**. 332, 1903 ; O. Hahn and H. Gille, *ib.*, **112**. 283, 1920 ; G. Tammann, *ib.*, **43**. 370, 1905 ; L. Weiss and M. Landecker, *ib.*, **64**. 71, 1909 ; C. Friedel and J. Guérin, *Bull. Soc. Chim.*, (2), **23**. 289, 1875 ; J. Tuttscheff, *ib.*, (2), **8**. 320, 1867 ; *Liebig's Ann.*, **141**. 111, 1867 ; T. Scheerer, *ib.*, **116**. 129, 1860 ; G. Rauter, *ib.*, **270**. 235, 1892 ; R. Bunsen, *ib.*, **138**. 257, 1866 ; I. L. Bell, *Chem. News*, **23**. 258, 267, 1871 ; E. A. Demarçay, *Compt. Rend.*, **104**. 111, 1887 ; P. Hautefeuille, *ib.*, **59**. 678, 732, 1864 ; L. Troost and P. Hautefeuille, *ib.*, **75**. 1819, 1872 ; L. Bourgeois, *ib.*, **104**. 231, 1887 ; *Bull. Soc. Chim.*, (2), **47**. 297, 1887 ; *Bull. Soc. Min.*, **15**. 194, 1893 ; A Burger, *Reduktion durch Calcium*, Basel, 27, 1907 ; W. Huppertz, *Versuche über die Herstellung von Titan und Titanlegierungen aus Rutil und Titanaten in elek-trischen Oefen*, Aachen, 1904 ; W. Borchers and W. Huppertz, *German Pat.*, *D.R.P.* 150557, 1904 ; C. Doelter, *Tschermak's Mitt.*, (2), **11**. 325, 1890 ; P. Müller, *Met.*, **7**. 537, 1910 ; K. Borne-mann and H. Schirmeister, *ib.*, **7**. 646, 1910 ; P. Camboulives, *Compt. Rend.*, **150**. 175, 221, 1910 ; A. Kling, *ib.*, **152**. 702, 1911 ; C. Darzens and F. Bourion, *ib.*, **153**. 270, 1911 ; *Ann. Chim. Phys.*, (8), **20**. 563, 1910 ; H. Moissan, *Le four électrique*, Paris, 1897 ; R. D. Hall and E. F. Smith, *Proc. Amer. Phil. Soc.*, **44**. 193, 1905 ; L. and O. Wöhler and W. Plüddemann, *Zeit. phys. Chem.*, **62**. 641, 1908 ; H. Traube, *Neues Jahrb. Min. B.B.*, **10**. 471, 1895 ; H. Baumhauer, *Zeit. Kryst.*, **24**. 576, 1895 ; H. Geisow, *Beiträge zur Kenntnis der seltenen anorganischen Säuren*, München, 1902 ; J. J. Berzelius, *The Use of the Blowpipe in Chemical Analysis*, London, 1822 ; M. Blondel, *Bull. Soc. Chim.*, (3), **21**. 262, 1899 ; A. Benrath, *Zeit. wiss. Photochem.*, **14**. 217, 1915 ; A. Benrath and A. Obladen, *ib.*, **22**. 65, 1922 ; C. Renz, *Helvetica Chim. Acta*, **4**. 961, 1921 ; C. N. Hinshelwood and B. Topley, *Journ. Chim. Soc.*, **123**. 1014, 1923 ; P. Sabatier and A. Mailhe, *Ann. Chim. Phys.*, (8), **20**. 289, 1910 ; H. Gall and W. Manchot, *Ber.*, **58**. B, 482, 1925.

§ 8. The Titanates

Titanium hydroxide, $Ti(OH)_4$, is amphoteric since it dissolves in the stronger acids to form salts, and in the stronger alkalies to form titanates. The *pertitanates* are described in connection with pertitanic acid—*vide infra*. H. Rose [1] showed that titanic acid is so feeble that it is unable to displace carbonic acid from aq. soln. of the carbonates at ordinary temp. E. J. Mills and D. Wilson studied the reaction between potassium carbonate and titanic oxide, at 880°, and stated that owing to the evolution of carbon dioxide, the reaction is incapable of simultaneous inversion. D. P. Smith, however, has shown that when titanic oxide is fused with alkali carbonate, the reaction is reversible in an atm. of carbon dioxide. At 900°–1100°, in an atm. of carbon dioxide at one atm. press., the conditions of equilibrium are $0.29Na_2CO_3 + 0.29TiO_2 \rightleftharpoons 0.71Na_2TiO_3 + xCO_2$; and $0.65K_2CO_3 + 0.65TiO_2 \rightleftharpoons 0.35K_2TiO_3 + xCO_2$. The power of displacing carbon dioxide from carbonates diminishes from silica, titania, zirconia, to thoria, and there is a corresponding increase in the basic power of the oxide. Expressing the solubilities in mgrms. per 100 c.c. of soln., V. Auger found the solubility of titanic oxide in a 10 per cent. soln. of *sodium hydroxide* to be 2.0–2.5; and in a 36 per cent. soln., 6–10; in a 10 per cent. soln. of *potassium hydroxide*, 30–45; and in a 40 per cent. soln., 70–90; in a sat. soln. of *potassium hydrocarbonate*, 700; a sat. soln. of *sodium carbonate* did not dissolve titanic oxide, but with a 10 per cent. soln. of *sodium hydrocarbonate*, the solubility was 25; a 30 per cent. soln. of *potassium carbonate*, 2; and a sat. soln., 30. All the titanic oxide present in the three last-named soln. was precipitated on diluting and boiling. When one part of titanic oxide is fused with 40 parts of sodium hydroxide, and the cooled melt extracted with water, the only crystalline material obtained is a hydrate of sodium hydroxide. A little titanic oxide remains in soln., the majority being precipitated even from conc. soln. Fusion of titanic oxide with potassium hydroxide, etc., affords a metastable soln. of a titanate (containing up to 1800 mg. of oxide per 100 c.c.), but this deposits most of its titanium (leaving about 100 mg. in soln.) in a few hours. Fusion of titanic oxide with sodium carbonate also gives metastable soln., containing 10–25 mg. of oxide per 100 c.c., all of this being precipitated on keeping.

The titanates are quite analogous to the silicates, and the two kinds of salt are isomorphous. P. Groth emphasized how titanium dioxide replaces silica isomorphously in many minerals—*e.g.* in biotite, augite, olivine, etc.; and the oxides, zirconia, thoria, and stannic oxide, may also replace silica isomorphously. None of these oxides, however, is known to form salts of such complexity as are formed by silica. A. Rosenheim and O. Sorge made some complex organic titanates.

The old text-books refer to a salt, *ammonium titanate*, obtained by H. Rose [2] as a coherent, flocculent precipitate easily washed on the filter. It is produced by adding aq. ammonia to the milky mixture of hydrated titanium dioxide and water; or by precipitating a soln. of titanium chloride or sulphate with ammonia. It is probably colloidal titanium hydroxide with adsorbed ammonia. J. J. Berzelius found that a clear glass is obtained by fusing the right proportions of alkali carbonate and titanium dioxide. The glass devitrifies on cooling, and in so doing becomes red hot. According to H. Rose, when a mol of titanium dioxide is fused with an excess of potassium carbonate, one mol of carbon dioxide is liberated. Two liquid strata are formed—the upper layer contains an excess of potassium carbonate with but a trace of titanium dioxide, and the lower layer is normal **potassium metatitanate,** K_2TiO_3. If the fusion is arrested before the action has ceased, the carbon dioxide still evolved from the interior of the mass, forces its way through the hardening surface and renders it uneven. L. N. Vauquelin made the same compound by fusing a mixture of titanium dioxide and potassium hydroxide. As indicated above, D. P. Smith, and E. J. Mills and D. Wilson studied the equilibrium relations between potassium carbonate and titanium dioxide. Potassium metatitanate forms a yellow fibrous mass which is more fusible than potassium carbonate. According to S. Motylewsky, the drop-weight of fused potassium metatitanate is 192 when that of water at 0° is 100 mgrms. The salt is decomposed by water into a soluble basic titanate, and an insoluble acid titanate. A. Demoly prepared **tetrahydrated potassium metatitanate,** $K_2TiO_3.4H_2O$, by boiling precipitated titanium dioxide with a soln. of potassium hydroxide; or by fusing the dioxide with an excess of potassium hydroxide, and extracting the mass with water. On evaporating the soln., colourless, prismatic crystals are produced. The salt is very hygroscopic, and readily soluble in water; the soln. has an alkaline reaction, and it gives a precipitate when treated with alcohol, or with a potassium, sodium, or ammonium salt.

According to L. N. Vauquelin, and H. Rose, hydrated titanium dioxide, and the potassium titanates are slightly soluble in an excess of potash-lye, and it is assumed that a basic titanate is formed. F. Wöhler also obtained a basic titanate by dropping a soln. of titanium tetrachloride into an excess of potash-lye; the precipitate first formed redissolves, but is reprecipitated on adding sulphuric acid. As indicated above, a soln. of a basic titanate is formed when a fused cake of titanium dioxide and potassium hydroxide is digested with water. C. F. Rammelsberg also noted that a precipitate is obtained by treatment with hydrochloric, sulphuric, nitric, or oxalic acid, and that the precipitate is soluble in excess. J. C. G. de Marignac made some observations on this subject. L. N. Vauquelin obtained a voluminous white mass of a hydrated potassium titanate by boiling titanium dioxide with potash-lye.

A. Demoly obtained an amorphous dihydrated **potassium paratrititanate,** $K_2O.3TiO_2.2H_2O$, or $K_2Ti_3O_7.2H_2O$, by adding potassium carbonate to a soln. of titanium tetrachloride. The product is insoluble in water. V. Auger could not verify the existence of this compound. H. Rose found the residue obtained by treating potassium metatitanate with cold water approximated *potassium hexatitanate,* $K_2O.6TiO_2.2(or 3)H_2O$; and A. Demoly obtained a similar substance by the action of conc. hydrochloric acid on the paratrititanate. The microcrystalline mass was found by H. Rose to be completely soluble in cold hydrochloric acid if it has been washed with only cold water; but after it has been dried at 100°, it is not completely soluble in that acid. The dried substance loses 14·48 per cent. of water at 100°. It is decomposed into titanium dioxide and potassium chloride when mixed with ammonium chloride and ignited. H. Rose found that if the metahexatitanate, be digested with conc. hydrochloric acid and the soln. saturated with ammonia and filtered, *potassium dodecatitanate,* $K_2O.12TiO_2$, is formed. H. Geisow prepared *enneahydrated potassium dodecatitanate,* $K_2O.12TiO_2.9H_2O$, as a white crystalline powder by melting titanium dioxide with 8–10 times its weight of potassium carbonate, washing the product with water until the runnings are free from alkali, and drying over conc. sulphuric acid. The product is not completely dehydrated at 105°. It is doubtful if these higher titanates are chemical individuals.

J. J. Berzelius, and R. Bunsen observed with sodium carbonate and titanium dioxide phenomena similar to those observed with potassium carbonate. As the cooling glass ceases to glow, the evolution of heat is so great that the mass again becomes red hot. E. Mallard reported the formation of **sodium orthotitanate,** Na_4TiO_4, by fusing sodium carbonate and titanium dioxide. H. Rose reported the formation of **sodium metatitanate,** Na_2TiO_3, by fusing a mixture of titanium dioxide with 5–12 times its weight of sodium carbonate. As with potassium carbonate, the upper layer consists mainly of sodium carbonate and the lower layer sodium metatitanate. E. Mallard made analogous observations. D. P. Smith studied the reversibility of the reaction. According to S. Motylewsky, the drop-weight of the fused salt is 216 when that of water at 0ᵛ is 100 mgrms. Sodium metatitanate is decomposed by water, sodium hydroxide passes into soln., and a hydrated acid titanate remains as a residue. A. Demoly prepared *tetrahydrated sodium metatitanate,* $Na_2TiO_3.4H_2O$, with properties like the corresponding potassium salt; but V. Auger could not confirm this. P. J. Holmquist prepared this salt, using sodium fluoride as a flux.

P. Cormimbœuf obtained what he regarded as a *sodium sesquititanate*, $2Na_2O.3TiO_3$, *i.e.* **sodium mesotrititanate,** $Na_4Ti_3O_8$, by heating for 12 hrs. five parts of sodium tungstate and a previously fused mixture of 2 parts of sodium carbonate and 1 of titanium dioxide at 800°. The milk-white, short, prismatic crystals are optically active, and belong to the monoclinic system. They are macled like the felspars. They are insoluble in water, but dissolve slowly in cold hydrochloric acid, more rapidly when heated. What P. Cormimbœuf called *sodium trititanate*, $Na_2O.3TiO_2$, *i.e.* **sodium paratrititanate,** $Na_2Ti_3O_7$, was obtained in long, highly birefringent needles by heating 10 parts of normal sodium tungstate and 5 parts of tungstic anhydride with a previously fused mixture of 2 parts of titanium dioxide and 4 parts of sodium carbonate. It is almost insoluble in boiling hydrochloric acid, and in sulphuric acid it dissolves about as readily as titanium dioxide. P. J. Holmquist obtained white, lustrous, acicular crystals of sodium paratrititanate by using sodium fluoride as a flux. The crystals belonged to the monoclinic system, and have the axial ratios $a : b : c = 1 : - : 1·2346$, and $\beta = 87° 48'$. The sp. gr. varied from 3·352 to 3·5077. The crystals have a strong double refraction like those of zircon. Boiling conc. sulphuric acid completely decomposed the salt. G. Wunder also obtained $Na_2O.3TiO_2$ by melting sodium phosphatotitanate with an excess of sodium carbonate. P. Cormimbœuf also made what he called *sodium dititanate*, $Na_2O.2TiO_2$, *i.e.* **sodium mesodititanate,** $Na_2Ti_2O_5$, in imperfect crystals of similar form by heating 20 parts of normal sodium tungstate and 5 parts of tungstic anhydride with a previously fused and finely powdered mixture of 4 parts of titanium dioxide and 8 parts of sodium carbonate. The crystals are insoluble in water and are very slowly attacked by cold hydrochloric acid, but dissolve rapidly when heated with this acid. When the composition of the fused tungstate approaches that of the normal tungstate, rutile separates instead of a titanate. The acid titanates seem unable to take up further quantity of base, even when fused with highly basic tungstates. When P. J. Holmquist tried to make this salt he always obtained the paratrititanate.

A number of other acid titanates have been reported without evidence as to their chemical individuality. Thus, H. Rose obtained a product approximating $2Na_2O.9TiO_2.5H_2O$ by the action of water on sodium metatitanate, and afterwards washing the residue until the runnings appear milky. H. Rose also obtained a product corresponding with $Na_2O.20TiO_2$ by treating sodium metatitanate with conc. hydrochloric acid, and then with an excess of ammonia.

In 1839, G. Rose [3] described a mineral from the Urals which contained calcium and titanium oxides. He called it *perofskite*, or **perowskite**, or *perovskite*, according to the transliteration adopted for the letters of the Russian's name after whom the mineral was called. Perowskite occurs in both eruptive and metamorphic rocks. It is one of the earliest minerals formed in the basic igneous rocks. A. Stelzner found it to be particularly in evidence in melilite-basaltic rocks. It occurs also in periodotites, leucitic and nephelitic rocks, crystalline schists, pyroxenic gneiss, chloritic slate of Achmatoosk, Ural; talcose schist of Zermatt, Switzerland; and the crystalline limestone of Schelingen, Kaiserstuhl. Reports on its occurrence have been made by E. Hussak, O. Mügge, G. H. Williams, J. S. Diller, W. C. Brögger, F. Hessenberg, G. vom Rath, H. Rosenbusch, C. Hintze, F. Zirkel, P. von Jeremejeff, N. von Kokscharoff, F. Seneca, C. V. Pantscherschinsky, etc. Analyses were reported by H. Rose, A. Damour, A. Brun, G. Strüver, A. Sauer, F. Millosevich, S. P. Popoff, P. Hautefeuille, and L. Bourgeois. The results show that the mineral is a **calcium metatitanate**, $CaTiO_3$, with a little of the calcium replaced by ferrous iron. The mineral *knopite* of Längörsholmen, Alnö, Sweden, reported by P. J. Holmquist, is considered to be a kind of perowskite contaminated with cerium sesquioxide —*vide* rare earths.

J. J. Ebelmen synthesized perowskite by fusing titanium dioxide, lime, and potassium carbonate ; and by the action of lime on an alkaline melt containing titanium dioxide and silica. P. Hautefeuille obtained crystals of the mineral by heating a mixture of calcium chloride, titanium dioxide, and silica to redness in a stream of moist carbon dioxide, or hydrogen chloride ; P. J. Holmquist obtained similar results by fusing mixtures of sodium and calcium carbonates, and titanium dioxide ; and L. Bourgeois, by fusing a mixture of calcium carbonate, titanium dioxide, and barium chloride. L. Bourgeois also obtained perowskite as a separation from various magmas with the same composition as natural magmas. G. Tammann gave 675° for the temp. of formation from its constituent oxides.

The colour of perowskite varies from pale yellow to orange-yellow, reddish-brown, and greyish-black by reflected light, and greyish-white, violet-grey, brown, red, or green in transmitted light. There is sometimes a zonal arrangement of the colours. The crystals may be transparent or opaque. The crystals are cubic or pseudo-cubic. Anhedral crystals are rare ; the euhedral crystals in rocks are generally octahedra modified by the dodecahedron and cube, but in crystalline schists the cubes are often highly modified. Although the geometric form of the crystals is fundamentally cubic, A. Ben-Saude, C. Klein, A. des Cloizeaux, N. von Kokscharoff, F. Fouqué and A. Michel-Lévy, R. Brauns, E. Mallard, G. Tschermak, P. Groth, etc., showed that the crystals are uniformly biaxial and usually positive. H. Baumhauer showed that the corrosion figures with hydrofluoric acid or potash-lye correspond with the rhombic system. G. R. Levi and G. Natta found the X-radiograms correspond with a central-faced cube of side 7·68 A., and containing eight molecules per unit cell. Sections of the cubic crystals from Ural and Zermatt, cut parallel to the (100)-face, show twin lamellæ parallel to both sets of cubic edges with diagonal extinction, and the bisectrix normal to a dodecahedral face ; sections of perowskite from Tyrol show fine twin lamellæ parallel to the diagonals while the bisectrix is perpendicular to the (100)-face. The general form and optical characters are partially explained by assuming that the crystals belong to the rhombic system and have a prismatic angle of 90° corresponding to the two pairs of cubic faces and twinned with (111), or sometimes (110), as the twinning plane. A. des Cloizeaux called the crystals *pseudocubique,* and G. Tschermak, *mimetisch-tesseral.* H. L. Bowman gave for the axial ratios of the crystals assumed to be rhombic, $a : b : c = 1 : 1 : 0·707$ approx. The fact that the structure differs in specimens from different localities led C. Klein to assume that the original form is cubic, and that the optical anomalies are due to secondary causes. Boracite is closely related to perowskite in structure and optical characteristics, and with it, an increase of temp. makes the crystals optically cubic. E. S. von Fedoroff refers to perowskite in the anomalous state at ordinary temp. as *metaperowskite.* The cubic faces of the crystals may be striated parallel to the edges, as if composed of penetration twins of pyritohedral individuals. The cleavage is cubic, parallel to (100), is well developed. The twinning in the octahedral face is in the form of interpenetrated cubes. The optic axial angle of the biaxial crystals $2V = 90°$ approximately. A. des Cloizeaux found the effect of raising the temp. to be :

	21·5°	47°	71·5°	95·5°	121°	146·5°	170·8°
2V .	87° 55′	88° 22′	89° 24′	90° 36′	91° 42′	92° 28′	93° 6′

H. Rose gave for the sp. gr. 4·107 ; A. Damour, 4·037–4·059 ; A. Brun, 3·974 ; P. J. Holmquist, 3·974 ; J. J. Ebelmen, 4·10 for the artificial crystals ; and P. Haute-feuille, 4·10. The hardness is 5–6. G. Spezia found that when heated in a blowpipe flame fed with oxygen, perowskite melted to a yellow glass. When heated in the oxidizing flame, a greenish bead is obtained which becomes colourless on cooling ; in the reducing flame, the bead is greyish-green when hot, and violet-blue when cold. The mineral is entirely decomposed by boiling sulphuric acid. Calcium metatitanate was found by P. J. Holmquist to dissolve readily in molten sodium paratrititanate at a red heat. On cooling, needle-like crystals are formed containing mixed crystals of the sodium paratrititanate and calcium metatitanate; and the sp. gr. of the mixed crystals with 16·6 per cent. of the calcium salt is 3·490; with 25·5 per cent., 3·504; and with 32·9 per cent., 3·512. The sp. gr. of the sodium salt alone is 3·352, and of the calcium salt, 3·974.

A. Piccini prepared **barium metatitanate,** $BaTiO_3$, as an amorphous mass by the ignition of barium oxyfluotitanate. J. A. Hedvall and N. von Zweigbergk showed that a mixture of molar proportions of barium dioxide and titanic oxide evolves oxygen below 300°, and above 300°, a titanate is formed; if the proportions are 2 : 1, a basic titanate, soluble in acetic acid, is formed. G. Tammann gave 300° for the temp. of formation from its constituent oxides. L. Bourgeois obtained **barium mesotrititanate,** $Ba_2Ti_3O_8$, by heating eq. quantities of barium carbonate and titanium dioxide using an excess of barium chloride as a flux. The cold mass was extracted with dil. hydrochloric acid, and there remained a pale yellow or yellowish-brown crystalline powder of sp. gr. 5·91. The crystals are strongly refracting. The corresponding **strontium mesotrititanate,** $Sr_2Ti_3O_8$, was obtained in an analogous manner. The crystalline powder has a feeble double refraction and a sp. gr. of 5·1. For the *barium silicotitanate—benitoite; sodium barium silicctitanate—leucosphenite;* and *calcium silicotitanate—sphene* or *titanite—vide* the titanium silicates.

P. Hautefeuille [4] fused a mixture of two parts of titanium dioxide, one of magnesia, and 10 of magnesium chloride for 4 hrs. at a red heat, and then extracted the cold mass with water. The crystals were washed with hot dil. acetic acid. The composition of the octahedral crystals corresponded with **magnesium orthotitanate,** Mg_2TiO_4. The sp. gr. was 3·52; and the hardness was greater than that of glass. The compounds are decomposed slowly by boiling nitric acid. L. Fletcher obtained rolled pebbles of a mineral from the gem-mines of Rakwana, Ceylon, and it was called **geikielite**—after A. Geikie. Analyses by A. Dick, F. Kaeppel, and T. Crook and B. M. Jones showed that geikielite is **magnesium metatitanate,** $MgTiO_3$, probably in solid soln. with a little ferrous metatitanate, and ferric oxide. P. Hautefeuille obtained crystals of magnesium metatitanate by heating white hot a mixture of one part titanium dioxide, 10 parts of magnesium chloride, and a little ammonium chloride, and extracting the cold melt with water and acetic acid. The crystals were also made by J. J. Ebelmen, C. Winkler, and L. Bourgeois. G. Tammann gave 725° for the temp. of formation from its constituent oxides. The crystals obtained by P. Hautefeuille were described as hexagonal or rhombic plates which scratch glass, and have a sp. gr. 3·91. The colour of the mineral is bluish- or brownish-black. P. Groth said that the crystals are rhombohedral, and are isomorphous with ferrous and manganous metatitanates; and with the wollastonite obtained in slags. P. Sustschinsky gave for the axial ratio $a : c$ of the rhombohedral crystals 1 : 1·370; and the sp. gr. 3·976; A. Dick found the sp. gr. 3·98–4·00, and the hardness 6. The birefringence is high, and the optical character negative. The powdered mineral is slowly decomposed by hot hydrochloric acid; and P. Hautefeuille said that fused ammonium hydrosulphate decomposes magnesium metatitanate. For *magnesium silicotitanate,* vide *titano-olivine.*

C. U. Shepard [5] described small, slender, prismatic crystals of a mineral which he found in the limestone of Edenville, New York, and called **warwickite;** T. S. Hunt called the mineral *enceladite.* Analyses by J. L. Smith correspond with **magnesium borotitanate,** $6MgO.FeO.2TiO_2.3B_2O_3$, or $Mg(BO_2)_2.Mg_2TiO_4$, with part of the magnesium replaced by ferrous iron. Analyses were also made by J. E. Whitfield, who gave the formula $4RO.TiO_2.B_2O_3$; and by W. M. Bradley, who gave the formula $(Mg,Fe)_3TiB_2O_6$, or

$$\begin{array}{c} Mg=O_2=B \\ Mg=O_2=B \end{array}\!\!>\!Ti\!<\!\begin{array}{c} O \\ O \end{array}\!\!>\!Mg$$

The crystals are dark brown or black in colour, with a copper-red tinge on the cleavage surface. The rhombic crystals, according to A. des Cloizeaux, have the axial ratios $a : b : c = 0.977 : 1 : -$. The (100) cleavage is perfect. A. Lacroix gave for the optic axial angle $2E = 125°$. The sp. gr. is 3·355, and the hardness 3–4. The double refraction is strong; and the optical character is negative.

When a mixture of titanium dioxide, zinc oxide, zinc sulphate, fluoride or chloride, and potassium sulphate is heated, L. Lévy [6] found that the nature of the product is determined by the temp. and by the composition of the mixture. At a dull red heat, the sesquititanate is always formed, but at higher temp. one of the other compounds is formed according to the composition of the mixture, the proportion of potassium sulphate being of great importance. It is probable that a potassium titanate is first formed, but is subsequently decomposed by the zinc salt. In fact, the zinc compounds can be obtained by the direct action of zinc sulphate on potassium titanate. He prepared **zinc orthotitanate,** Zn_2TiO_4, or, as he called it, bibasic zinc titanate, $2ZnO.TiO_2$, by heating to bright redness a mixture of 2 parts titanium dioxide, 15 parts each of zinc and potassium sulphates. It was also made by **heating** zinc orthodititanate with an excess of zinc sulphate or chloride. It forms black crystalline grains of sp. gr. 4·16 at 20°. It is decomposed by chlorine, but not by hydrogen; it is dissolved by hot dil. or by cold conc. acids and alkalies, and by a fused mixture of potassium nitrate and sodium carbonate. He made **zinc metatitanate,** $ZnTiO_3$, by heating to redness a mixture of titanic oxide, 2 parts; zinc sulphate, 8 parts; and potassium sulphate, 3 parts. G. Tammann gave 700° for the temperature of formation from its constituent oxides. L. Lévy found that zinc metatitanate is a pale violet substance with a conchoidal fracture and not infrequently forms silky needles; the sp. gr. at 20° is 3·17. It is decomposed by chlorine, but not by hydrogen. Boiling acids and conc. potash attack it with difficulty, but it is slightly attacked by a fused mixture of potassium nitrate and sodium carbonate, and is decomposed by fused potash. L. Lévy made **zinc orthodititanate,** $Zn_3Ti_2O_7$, or, as he called it, *zinc sesquititanate*, $3ZnO.2TiO_2$, by heating to redness a mixture of one part of titanic oxide. 5 parts of zinc sulphate, and 1·2 parts of potassium sulphate, and washing the product with dil. sulphuric acid. It forms a yellow, crystalline powder, which is not decomposed by heat. It is decomposed by chlorine or hydrogen, and slowly by warm sulphuric or nitric acid, or a mixture of sulphuric and hydrofluoric acids. It is completely dissolved by cold hydrochloric acid, and is decomposed by fused potash, but not by a mixture of potassium nitrate and sodium carbonate. L. Lévy prepared violet crystals of **zinc paratrititanate,** $ZnTi_3O_7$, contaminated with a little ferrous iron, by heating a mixture of 7 parts of titanium dioxide, 5 parts of zinc oxide, and a small quantity of zinc fluoride, or of 7 parts of titanium oxide and 30 parts of zinc fluoride, under a thin layer of potassium fluoride in a graphite crucible for an hour and a half, washing the product with water, and then treating it with conc. sulphuric acid to remove zinc oxide and titanium fluoride. With potassium chloride in place of the fluoride, the product is a greenish mass. With a mixture of potassium and sodium chlorides, the violet needles are obtained mixed with yellowish needles of potassium titanate. The crystals are insoluble in water, alcohol, and ether; they are not affected by hot dil. sulphuric, nitric, and hydrochloric acids, nor by boiling conc. soln. of alkaline hydroxides, but they are attacked with difficulty by boiling conc. sulphuric acid, and are decomposed by fusion with potassium hydroxide. They are infusible before the blowpipe, but change to a greenish mass without loss of weight; the sp. gr. at 15° is 4·92. The crystals are not attacked by hydrogen at a red heat, but they are partially volatilized in a mixture of chlorine and hydrogen chloride. When treated with acidified hydrogen dioxide, the latter acquires a characteristic yellow colour, but the decomposition is never complete. L. Lévy also reported that **zinc mesopentatitanate,** $Zn_4Ti_5O_{14}$, or, as he called it, *acid zinc titanate*, $4ZnO.5TiO_2$, is formed at a red heat from a mixture of titanium dioxide, 3 parts; zinc sulphate, 12 parts; and potassium sulphate, 1 part; the product being washed with dil. nitric acid. It forms small, pale brown, crystalline leaflets, and the sp. gr. at 19° is 3·68. It is insoluble in all ordinary solvents, and is decomposed by chlorine, but not by hydrogen. It is not attacked by conc. acids in the cold, but is dissolved by all except hydrochloric acid when heated, and is also dissolved by fused potassium hydrogen sulphate.

No *aluminium titanate* has been reported. R. Rieke [7] measured the fusibility of mixtures of titanic oxide and alumina, and found for the softening temp., or the m.p. :

TiO$_2$.	.	0	20	30	40	50	60	70	80	90	100%
M.p. .	.	2000°	1825°	1770°	1730°	1730°	1740°	1670°	1650°	1630°	1610°

H. St. C. Deville and H. Caron heated titanium dioxide with stannous oxide to a red heat, and obtained crystals resembling rutile with about 13·8 per cent. SnO$_2$, and 85·7 per cent. TiO$_2$. No definite *stannic titanate* was produced. E. Hussak and G. T. Prior described a mineral from the diamond-bearing sands of Minas Geraes, Brazil and named it **senaite**—after J. da Costa Sena. Analyses reported by E. Hussak and G. T. Prior, and E. Reitinger correspond with (Fe,Mn,Pb)O.TiO$_2$, *lead ferrous manganous metatitanate.*

The black crystals are trigonal, like those of ilmenite, and have the axial ratio $a : c = 1 : 0.997$. Twinning about the (11$\bar{2}$0)-plane is common. No cleavage is developed. The sp. gr. is 5·301, and the hardness 6. Altered crystals have a sp. gr. as low as 4·22. The crystals are optically uniaxial ; their birefringence is low ; and they are non-magnetic. T. H. Lee obtained a mineral from the Caldas region, Minas Geraes, Brazil, which he called *oliveiraite*—after F. de Paula Oliveira—and which had a composition corresponding with zirconium titanate, 3ZrO$_2$.2TiO$_2$.2H$_2$O. The colour is greenish-yellow, and there is no distinct crystalline structure.

According to P. Berthier,[8] titanic oxide requires eight times its weight of lead oxide for dissolution and the cold mass is pale coffee-brown, opaque, and with an even, shining fracture. G. Tammann found that the temp. of formation of **lead metatitanate,** PbTiO$_3$, from its constituent oxides is 470°. P. Hautefeuille made crystals of **manganese orthotitanate,** Mn$_2$TiO$_4$, by fusing a mixture of titanium dioxide, manganese fluoride or chloride, and sodium chloride. A. Hamberg found deep blood-red crystals of a mineral at the Harstig mine, Pajsberg, Sweden, and he called it **pyrophanite**—from πῦρ, fire; and φανός, shining —in allusion to its red colour and brilliant lustre. Analyses show that it is **manganese metatitanate,** MnTiO$_3$, with a little silicon replacing titanium. O. Derby found pyrophanite in Minas Geraes, Brazil. L. Bourgeois synthesized the mineral by fusing a mixture of titanium dioxide and manganese chloride at a red heat. The artificial crystals were yellowish-brown, uniaxial, optically negative, hexagonal plates. A. Hamberg found the thin, tabular, rhombohedral crystals of the mineral had the axial ratio $a : c = 1 : 1.3692$. The (0221)-cleavage is perfect, the (10$\bar{1}$2)-cleavage is less so. The basal plane has irregular striations. The corrosion figures are asymmetric. The crystals are not pleochroic.

The discovery of titanium in the black sands of Menaccan, Cornwall, by W. Gregor [9] has been described in connection with the history of titanium. The mineral was called *menaccanite.* Various spellings have been used. R. Kirwan, for example, used W. Gregor's term ; J. H. Collins wrote *manaccanite ;* R. P. Greg and W. G. Lettsom, *menacconite ;* M. H. Klaproth, *menakanite,* and also *eisenhaltige Titanerz, Titaneisen,* and *Titanosiderum ;* D. L. G. Karsten, *mänaken ;* and A. G. Werner, *Menakeisenstein.* R. J. Haüy called it *titane oxydé ferrifère.* A titaniferous iron sand from Iserwiese and Riesengebirge was called *iserin* by M. H. Klaproth, F. A. Reuss, A. Breithaupt, and A. G. Werner. J. F. L. Hausmann united menaccanite and iserin under the term *Titaneisstein.* A. G. Werner regarded iserin as *octahedral Titaneisen oxyde ;* and F. Mohs, *hexaderal Eisenerz.* The term **ilmenite** proposed by A. T. Kupffer to designate the crystals of titaniferous iron ore from Miask in the Ilmen Mts. is usually employed for the mineral ; but numerous varieties have been recognized ; they are mainly dependent on the proportions of iron and titanium. No satisfactory external characters have been recognized, and their true relations are in many cases doubtful.

F. Mohs referred to *axotome Titaneisen* from Hofgastein, and it was analyzed by F. von Kobell, and called *kibdelophane*—from κίβδηλος, false ; and φαίνεσθαι, to appear —in allusion to its resemblance to ilmenite and titaniferous iron ore. It contains about 50 per cent. of titanium dioxide. J. L. Bournon applied the term *crichtonite*—after J. Crichton—to a mineral from Dauphiné. Its composition was determined by J. J. Berzelius, F. S. Beudant, C. C. von Leonhard, A. Lacroix, J. C. G. de Marignac, G. Rose, H. Rose, P. Tschernik, and L. Colomba ; and it has 50-53 per cent. titanium dioxide. Normal *ilmenite* has 43-50 per cent. titanium dioxide, and menaccanite, about 42 per cent. A. Breithaupt called the titaniferous iron ore from Tvedestrand, Arendal, *hystatite*. It contained 25-33 per cent. titanium dioxide. A similar mineral was called *washingtonite* by C. U. Shepard. It was examined by J. C. G. de Marignac, and J. D. Dana. The *titanoferrite* of E. J. Chapman and the *mohsite* of A. Lévy are closely related to these minerals ; but their nature is unknown. J. D. Dana's *uddevallite* from Uddevalla, Sweden, and the titaniferous iron ore from Aschaffenberg have about 17 per cent. of titanium dioxide, and 70 per cent. of ferric oxide. The *Eisenrosen* of St. Gotthard was called *basanomelane* —from βάσανος, a touchstone ; and μέλας, black—by F. von Kobell ; it has 10-13 per cent. of titanium dioxide and is usually regarded as a titaniferous hæmatite. It was examined by G. B. Hogenraad. The hæmatite of Kragerö has about 5 per cent. of titanium dioxide. The so-called magnesium *menaccanite*, or the *picrotitanite*—from πικρος, bitter, in allusion to the contained magnesia—of J. D. Dana, or the *picro-ilmenite* of P. Groth, contains 10-15 per cent. of magnesia. Samples were analyzed by H. W. Foote, T. Crook and B. M. Jones, etc. A partially altered variety of ilmenite from Småland, Sweden, was named *hydro-ilmenite* by C. W. Blomstrand. The *paracolumbite* and *parailmenite* of C. U. Shepard, and the *haplotypite* of A. Breithaupt are varieties of ilmenite. A. Gavelin described black grains of a mineral he called högbomite in the Ruoutevare district of Swedish Lapland. It may occur in trigonal crystals with the axial ratio $a : c = 1 : 1.55$; the sp. gr. is 3·81 ; the hardness, $6\frac{1}{2}$; and the indices of refraction, $\omega = 1.853$, and $\epsilon = 1.803$. The analyses approximate $MgO.2(Al_2O_3.Fe_2O_3.TiO_2)$. T. L. Watson described a sample from Whittles, Pennsylvania, with $\omega = 1.848$ and $\epsilon = 1.817$.

Numerous analyses of the different varieties of ilmenite have been reported.[10] The earlier analyses have been previously indicated in connection with the discovery of the metal and of the mineral. A. Lévy,[11] and G. Rose showed that ilmenite is closely related with many of the different forms of titaniferous iron ore ; and the latter found that, although hæmatite and ilmenite have *die gleiche Krystallform*, they are not isomorphous because the constituents of ilmenite—FeO and TiO_2—are not isomorphous with ferric oxide. C. G. Mosander, however, regarded ilmenite as an isomorphous mixture of ferrous metatitanate and ferric oxide, and proved that the ferrous oxide of ilmenite can be replaced with magnesium, calcium, and manganese (ous) oxides. G. von Hevesy and V. T. Jentzen found no hafnia in the ilmenite examined by them. H. Rose said that " there can be no isomorphism between the two compounds since one is a salt derived from two oxides, and the other is a simple oxide." He assumed that ilmenite is really a mixture of Ti_2O_3 and Fe_2O_3 such that the composition $Fe_2O_3 + Ti_2O_3$ is eq. to $2FeTiO_3$. T. Scheerer, indeed, said that the blue colour developed when ilmenite is boiled with sulphuric acid favours the hypothesis that Ti_2O_3 is present in the mineral. According to E. Glatzel, the soln. contains some titanium, but T. König and O. F. von der Pfordten could find none. The last-named showed that ferric oxide and titanium sesquioxide can coexist in the same soln., so that probably no change of these oxides into titanium dioxide and ferrous oxide, as assumed by P. Groth, occurs when the mineral is treated with hot sulphuric acid. They found it to be impossible to prove in a chemical way that titanium sesquioxide exists in ilmenite. W. Manchot argued that because no hydrogen is developed when ilmenite is heated with alkali-lye or with hydrochloric or sulphuric acid, it is probable that no titanium sesquioxide is present. The mineral behaves chemically like ferrous oxide associated with titanium dioxide. J. J. Berzelius, and R. Hermann opposed H. Rose's assumptions because the magnetic properties of ilmenite indicate the presence of ferrous iron. C. F. Rammelsberg said that the constant presence of magnesium in ilmenite makes it probable that ferrous iron is also present; especially is this so in cases where the proportion of magnesium is high. He favoured C. G. Mosander's but not H. Rose's hypothesis. S. L. Penfield and H. W. Foote confirmed C. F. Rammelsberg's conclusions. C. Friedel and J. Guérin concluded that Fe_2O_3, $FeTiO_3$, and Ti_2O_3 are isomorphous, and that the titaniferous irons are mixtures of the first two, namely, $Fe.FeO_3$ and $Fe.TiO_3$. A. Hamberg also considered that the discovery of pyrophanite supported C. G. Mosander's hypothesis, and added that there is no need to assume that ferric oxide contains quadrivalent iron $Fe^{II}.Fe^{IV}O_3$, since the case of potassium nitrate and calcium carbonate as well as other cases indicated in connection with isomorphism—1. 11, 10—show that valency is not necessarily involved in the similarity of crystalline form. To summarize, the facts favour the assumption that normal ilmenite is **ferrous metatitanate,** $FeTiO_3$, and that in the ferruginous varieties the metatitanate is isomorphously associated with ferric oxide; and that the ferrous metatitanate may also be associated in a somewhat similar manner with magnesium, calcium, and manganous metatitanates. G. Tammann found the temp. of formation from its constituent oxides is 700°

Ilmenite is fairly widely diffused in nature; it is a common constituent of igneous rocks, and appears to have been one of the earliest minerals to separate from the molten magma. It occurs associated with hæmatite in granites, syenites, diorites, diabases, gabbros, basalts, and other eruptive rocks. It also occurs associated with magnetite. Ilmenite often forms inclusions in the felspar and pyroxene of gabbros and other basic rocks. It also occurs similarly in gneiss, mica-schist, and amphibolites. G. Rose [12] melted ilmenite with borax in the blowpipe flame and found hexagonal plates embedded in the cold glass. These were isolated by treatment with nitric acid, and were shown to be titaniferous iron oxide. L. Bourgeois synthesized the mineral by melting a mixture of ferrous chloride and titanium dioxide at a red heat. J. Morozewicz in his study of artificial magmas reported crystals of ilmenite in those of the basalt type. W. Bruhns obtained crystals of hexagonal plates of ilmenite, mixed with magnetite, by heating a mixture of finely divided iron, ferric oxide, titanium dioxide, and hydrofluoric acid in a platinum tube at 270°–300° for 24 hrs.

The colour of the opaque crystals of ilmenite is iron-black. The crystals are tetartohedral belonging to the trigonal system, and, according to N. von Kokscharoff,[13] have the axial ratio $a : c = 1 : 1.38458$; and, according to G. Boeris, $1 : 1.38235$. P. Sustschinsky found for specimens with different proportions of titanium dioxide:

Per cent. TiO_2	5.665	21.576	47.679	49.684	57.23
$a : c$	1 : 1.3680	1 : 1.3716	1 : 1.3772	1 : 3790	1 : 3844
Sp. gr.	5.041	4.910	4.852	4.614	—

The isomorphism of ilmenite with hæmatite is discussed above. Observations on the crystals were made by E. Artini, G. Doby and G. Melczer, M. Bauer, A Sadebeck, O. Mügge, A. Streng, F. Sandberger, M. Websky, G. Rose, H. Bücking, R. H. Solly, G. Boeris, F. Zambonini, A. Lacroix, A. des Cloizeaux, W. H. Miller, P. von Jeremejeff, H. Smith, etc. The habit of the euhedral crystals is usually tabular parallel to (0001), and with a six-sided outline, and, often like hæmatite, elongated to blade-like shapes, less frequently in steep rhombohedral forms. The anhedral crystals may be rounded or irregularly outlined; and sometimes in skeleton-like aggregates. Ilmenite also occurs massive and compact; and granular —embedded or sandy. The cleavage is not developed. The twinning is like that of hæmatite, being lamellar, parallel to (0001) or (10$\bar{1}$1). Parting parallel to the twinning planes is often shown in partly altered crystals. The X-radiograms of the hexagonal crystals were studied by P. F. Kerr.

The sp. gr. given by F. von Kobell was 4.78; by A. Breithaupt, 5.069–5.117; C. F. Rammelsberg, 5.060; and F. Pisani, 4.353. Most of the samples analyzed had their sp. gr. determined; and, as found by G. Doby and G. Melczer, the results show that the sp. gr. increases up to 5·3 with the proportion of ferric oxide. P. Sustschinsky's observations on this subject are indicated above. G. A. Kenngott found the sp. gr. of ilmenite to be 4·741–4·767, and after ignition, 4·833–4·857. The hardness is 5 to 6. E. Madelung and R. Fuchs found the coeff. of compressibility of ilmenite to be $3·25 \times 10^{-12}$ dynes per sq. cm.; and of titaniferous iron ore, $2·92 \times 10^{-12}$ dynes per sq. cm. The mineral is infusible before the blowpipe; but if the blowpipe be fed with warm air, G. Spezia found that it could be melted to a black mass. A. Brun also made observations on the action of the oxy-hydrogen flame. R. Lorenz and W. Herz studied the relation between the m.p. and the critical temp. F. Zirkel said the birefringence is strong, and that the mineral is distinctly pleochroic. A. de Gramont investigated the spark spectrum. F. Beijerinck said the mineral is a good conductor of electricity, and that the conductivity increases as the temp. rises. G. Cesaro made a similar observation, and J. Königsberger and K. Schilling found that the absolute resistance of α-ilmenite falls from 2,100,000 ohms at −188° to 218·7 at 18°, and to 9·0 ohms at 200°. There is a slow conversion into β-ilmenite at about 215° when the electrical resistance falls from 1·00 ohm at 215° to 0·085 ohm at 890° (Fig. 8). The electrical resistance parallel to the c-axis is rather greater than when measured vertical to that axis. E. T. Wherry found ilmenite to be a poor radio-detector. Ilmenite slightly influences the magnetic needle. B. Bavink studied the magnetic properties. E. Zalinsky found that finely powdered ilmenite dissolves slowly when boiled with conc. hydrochloric acid; and it was completely dissolved by hydrofluoric acid after 70 hrs.' action. The soln. deposited a white powder of ferric

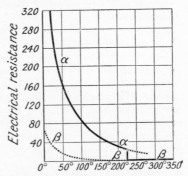

FIG. 8.—The Electrical Resistance of Ilmenite at Different Temperatures.

fluoride. Fused potassium hydrosulphate decomposes ilmenite and enables it to be dissolved in acid. For the action of sulphuric acid, vide supra. H. Lotz studied the action of air containing sulphur dioxide on titaniferous iron ore. For delorenzite—ferrous uranium yttrium metatitanate—and yttrocrasite—thorium yttrium metatitanate—vide rare earth minerals, 4. 38, 2. C. G. Mosander described a ferrosi-titanate, $(FeO)_3(Fe_2O_3)_4TiO_2$, or $Fe_{11}TiO_{17}$; and P. Groth, a titanomagnetite, $\{Fe(Fe,Ti)O_2\}_2$.

P. Hautefeuille [14] reported the formation of dark purple, rhombic, prismatic crystals of **ferrous orthotitanate,** Fe_2TiO_4, by the fusion of a mixture of titanium dioxide, a ferrous salt, and sodium chloride. A. Koch described a mineral from Aranyer Berg, Transylvania—which was regarded as a dimorphous modification of ilmenite, and called **pseudobrookite.** Analyses were reported by A. Koch, G. Lattermann, A. Cederström, H. Traube, and A. Frenzel. The analyses of A. Cederström, A. Frenzel, and H. Traube agree with $2Fe_2O_3.3TiO_2$, or, in agreement with P. Groth, **ferric orthotitanate,** $Fe_4(TiO_4)_3$; G. Lattermann gave $(FeO)_9Fe'''_5Mg(TiO_3)_{13}$. B. Doss' furnace product was called pseudobrookite, but its composition corresponded with Fe_2TiO_5. The mineral has been found in a few localities. T. König and O. F. von der Pfordten found that ferric orthotitanate, $Fe_4(TiO_4)_3$, is produced by heating a mixture of titanium dioxide, anhydrous ferrous fluoride, and a large proportion of sodium chloride. Contrary to P. Hautefeuille, they found that ferrous orthotitanate is not formed under these conditions. On ignition in hydrogen, ferric orthotitanate behaves like titanic iron ore, and is converted into iron and titanium dioxide. When warmed with conc. sulphuric acid, it turns green, and on diluting, the whole dissolves; the soln. contains titanium dioxide and ferric sulphate, but no ferrous salt. A. Koch said that the dark brown or black crystals of pseudobrookite are tabular parallel to (100), and ɔften prismatic. The (100)-faces may be striated horizontally. The crystals are rhombic with the axial ratios $a : b : c = 0.87776 : 1 : 0.88475$. The (001)-cleavage is distinct. A. Cederström gave 4·390, and A. Koch 4·98, for the sp. gr. The hardness is 6. The optic axial angle found by G. Lattermann is $2H = 84° 30'$. The optical character is positive. J. Königsberger and K. Schilling found a break in the electrical conductivity-temp. curve, and consequently inferred the existence of α-*pseudobrookite* and β-*pseudobrookite*. Pseudobrookite is attacked by acids with great difficulty. B. Doss found it is dissolved completely by dil. hydrofluoric acid, but the action is very slow. G. Lattermann said that boiling sulphuric acid leads to the separation of a greenish-white, crystalline powder soluble in hydrochloric acid. Pseudobrookite is completely dissolved by a mixture of sulphuric and hydrofluoric acids (2 : 1), by a mixture of sulphuric and hydrochloric acids, and by fused potassium hydrosulphate. B. Doss reported the formation of crystals of pseudobrookite in the firebricks of a soda-works at Schönebeck; and assumed that it was formed by the interaction of ferric and titanic chlorides; $TiCl_4 + 2FeCl_3 + 5H_2O = Fe'''_2TiO_5 + 10HCl$. The formula here assigned by B. Doss, is based on an analysis of the crystals, and corresponds with *ferryl metatitanate*, $(Fe''O)_2TiO_3$.

C. Palmer found a dark steel-grey mineral associated with gadolinite at Hackberry, Arizona, and he called it **arizonite**. Analyses correspond with **ferric metatitanate**, $Fe_2(TiO_3)_3$. C. Palmer suggested that the so-called iserin is really a mixture of ilmenite and arizonite; and that Brazilian titaniferous iron sand, analyzed by J. Mackintosh, is impure arizonite. The crystals are considered to be monoclinic with the axial ratios $a : b : c = 1.88 : 1 : 2.3$, and $\beta = 55°$. The sp. gr. is 4·25; the hardness is 5·5; and the index of refraction over 1·84. The mineral is feebly pleochroic; and it is completely decomposed by hot conc. sulphuric acid. E. Rinmann reported dark brown *kalkowskite*—named after L. Kalkowsky—to occur at Serra do Itacolumy, Minas Geraes, Brazil. The analysis agrees with $(Fe,Ce)_2O_3.4(Ti,Si)O_2$. Its sp. gr. is 4·01; hardness, 3 to 4; index of refraction, over 1·769; and it is non-pleochroic. The mineral is partially decomposed by hydrochloric acid, this is also the case with arizonite; and, added W. F. Foshag, if the silica found is foreign, the kalkowskite is not essentially different from arizonite. L. Bourgeois [15] melted cobalt chloride with titanium dioxide and obtained **cobalt metatitanate,** $CoTiO_3$; and **nickel metatitanate,** $NiTiO_3$, was obtained in a similar way.

REFERENCES.

[1] H. Rose, *Pogg. Ann.*, **61**. 507, 1844; **74**. 563, 1847; D. P. Smith, *Zeit. anorg. Chem.*, **37**. 332, 1903; P. Groth, *Tabellarische Uebersicht der Mineralien*, Braunschweig, 113, 1898; E. J. Mills and D. Wilson, *Journ. Chem. Soc.*, **33**. 360, 1878; *Chem. News*, **37**. 346, 1878; V. Auger, *Compt. Rend.*, **177**. 1302, 1923; A. Rosenheim and O. Sorge, *Ber.*, **53**. B, 932, 1920.

[2] H. Rose, *Gilbert's Ann.*, **73**. 78, 1823; *Pogg. Ann.*, **61**. 507, 1844; **74**. 563, 1847; F. Wöhler, *ib.*, **7**. 423, 1826; S. Motylewsky, *Zeit. anorg. Chem.*, **38**. 410, 1904; V. Auger, *Compt. Rend.*, **177**. 1302, 1923; E. J. Mills and D. Wilson, *Journ. Chem. Soc.*. **33**. 360. 1878; *Chem. News*, **37**. 246, 1878; A. Demoly, *Recherches sur la titane et ses combinaisons*, Paris, 1849; *Compt. Rend. Trav. Chim.*, **5**. 325, 1849; C. F. Rammelsberg, *Sitzber. Akad. Berlin*, 490, 1874; J. C. G. de Marignac, *Ann. Chim. Phys.*, (4), **13**. 9, 1867; L. N. Vauquelin, *Journ. Phys.*, **66**. 345, 1805; *Ann. Mus. Hist. Nat.*, **6**. 93, 1805; E. Mallard, *ib.*, (4), **28**. 86, 1873; *Compt. Rend.*, **75**. 472, 1872; P. Cormimbœuf, *ib.*, **115**. 823, 1892; D. P. Smith, *Zeit. anorg. Chem.*, **37**. 332, 1903; J. J. Berzelius, *Lehrbuch der Chemie*, Dresden, 2. i, 135, 1826; T. König and O. F. von der Pfordten, *Ber.*, **22**. 2074, 1889; G. Wunder, *Journ. prakt. Chem.*, (2), **4**. 347, 1871; R. Bunsen Liebig's *Ann.*, **138**. 257, 1866; P. J. Holmquist, *Bull. Geol. Inst. Upsala*, **3**. 211, 1897; H. Geisow, *Beiträge zur Kenntnis der seltenen anorganischen Säuren*, München, 15, 1902.

[3] G. Rose, *Reise nach dem Ural, dem Altai, und dem kaspischen Meere*, Berlin, 2. 128, 477. 1842; *Pogg. Ann.*, **48**. 558, 1839; G. vom Rath, *ib.*, **144**. 595, 1871; G. H. Williams, *Amer. Journ. Science*, (3), **34**. 137, 1887; J. S. Diller, *ib.*, (3), **37**. 219, 1889; A. Stelzner, *Neues Jahrb. Min. B.B.*, **2**. 390, 1883; O. Mügge, *ib.*, **4**. 581, 1886; E. Hussak, *Sitzber. Akad. Wien*, **77**. 330, 1878; *Neues Jahrb. Min.*, ii, 297, 1894; K. Schneider, *ib.*, i, 99, 1889; C. Klein, *ib.*, i, 245, 1884; P. J. Holmquist, *Bull. Geol. Inst. Upsala*, **8**. 36, 1896; *Geol. För. Förh. Stockholm*, **16**. 73, 1894; H. L. Bowman, *Min. Mag.*, **15**. 156, 1908; A. Ben-Saude, *Ueber den Perowskit*,

Göttingen, 1882; **G. A.** Kenngott, *Die Minerale den Schweiz nach ihren Eigenschaften und Fundorten*, Leipzig, 236, 1866; G. Tschermak, *Lehrbuch der Mineralogie*, Wien, 529, 1894; *Tschermak's Mitt.*, (2), **5.** 194, 1883; F. Hessenberg, *Mineralogische Notizen*, Frankfurt, **3.** 20, 1861; **4.** 20, 1861; **10.** 38, 1871; **11.** 1, 1873; N. von Kokscharoff, *Materialen zur Mineralogie Russlands*, St. Petersburg, **1.** 199, 1853; **6.** 398, 1874; **7.** 375, 1878; **8.** 39, 1881; *Proc. Russ. Min. Soc.*, **13.** 373, 1878; C. V. Pantscherschinsky, *ib.*, **25.** 387, 1888; P. von Jeremejeff, *ib.*, **29.** 248, 1892; F. Fouqué and A. Michel-Lévy, *Synthèse des minéraux et des roches*, Paris, 176, 1882; W. C. Brögger, *Zeit. Kryst.*, **16.** 508, 1890; A. Arzruni, *ib.*. **8.** 331, 1884; E. S. von Fedoroff, *ib.*, **20.** 74, 1892; H. Baumhauer, *ib.*, **4.** 187, 1880; **7.** 612, 1882; G. Spezia, *ib.*, **14.** 505 1888; *Atti Accad. Torino*, **22.** 419, 1887; A. Damour, *Ann. Mines*, (5), **6.** 512, 1854; A. des Cloizeaux, *Nouvelles recherches sur les propriétés optiques des cristaux*, Paris, 84. 1867; *Manuel de minéralogie*, Paris, **2.** 214, 1893; *Bull. Soc. Min.*, **16.** 218, 1893; *Ann. Chim. Phys.*, (3), **13.** 338, 1845; *Ann. Mines*, (5), **14.** 417, 1858; *Zeit. deut. geol. Ges.*, **26.** 932, 1874; *Neues Jahrb. Min.*, 279, 1875; 160, 1877; 372, 1878; E. Mallard, *Bull. Soc. Min.*, **5.** 233, 1882; A. Lacroix, *ib.*, **16.** 228, 1893; L. Bourgeois, *ib.*, **9.** 248, 1886; *Bull. Soc. Chim.*, (2), **46.** 262, 1886; *Compt. Rend.*, **103.** 141, 1886; *Ann. Chim. Phys.*. (5), **29.** 474, 1883; P. Hautefeuille, *ib.*, (4), **4.** 154, 1886; *Bull. Soc. Chim.*, (2), **3.** 64, 1864; *Compt. Rend.*, **59.** 732, 1864; J. J. Ebelmen, *ib.*, **32.** 710, 1851; **33.** 525, 1852; H. Moissan, *ib.*, **134.** 140, 1902; F. Seneca, *Liebig's Ann*, 104. 371, 1857; A. Piccini, *Gazz. Chim. Ital.*, **17.** 470, 1887; J. A. Hedvall and N. von Zweigbergk. *Zeit. anorg. Chem.*, **108.** 119, 1919; P. A. Dufrénoy, *Traité de minéralogie*, Paris, **2.** 408, 1856; R. Brauns, *Die optischen Anomalien der Krystalle*, Leipzig, 349, 1891; H. Rosenbusch, *Mikroskopische Petrographie der Mineralien und Gesteine*, Stuttgart, 336, 1892; G. R. Levi and G. Natta, *Atti Accad. Lincei*, (6), 2 ii, 39, 1925; F. Zirkel, *Lehrbuch der Petrographie*, Bonn, **1.** 414, 1893; C. Hintze, *Handbuch der Mineralogie*, Leipzig, **2.** 1645, 1897; *Zeit. Kryst.*, **2.** 310, 1878; A. Brun, *ib.*, **7.** 389, 1882; P. Groth, *Die mineralien-Sammlung der Universität Strassburg*, Strassburg, 252, 1878; *Tabellarische Uebersicht der Mineralien*, Braunschweig, 127, 1889; G. Strüver, *Atti Accad. Lincei*, (3), **4.** 210, 1880; F. Millosevich, *ib.*, (5), **10.** i, 209, 1901; A. Sauer, *Zeit. deut. Geol. Ges.*, **37.** 445, 1885; L. Liebener and J. Vorhauser, *Die Mineralien Tirols*. Innsbrücke, 33, 1866; E. Boricky, *Ber. Böhm. Ges. Wiss.*, 228, 1876; S. P. Popoff. *Russ. Min. Journ.*, **3.** 300, 1876; **G.** Tammann, *Zeit. anorg. Chem.*, 149 68, 1925; **H.** Rose. *Pogg. Ann.*, **62.** 596, 1844.

[4] P. Hautefeuille, *Ann. Chim. Phys.*, (4), **4.** 169, 1865; L. Bourgeois, *Bull. Soc. Min.*, **15.** 195, 1893; P. Groth, *Tabellarische Uebersicht der Mineralien*. Braunschweig, 46, 1898; P. Sustschinsky, *Zeit. Kryst.*, **37.** 59, 1902; F. Kaeppel, *ib.*, **37.** 60, 1902; C. Friedel, *Bull. Soc. Chim.*, (2), **5.** 202, 1863; J. J. Ebelmen, *Compt. Rend.*, **32.** 710, 1851; **33.** 525, 1852; C. Winkler, *ib.* **23.** 2657, 1890; A. Dick, *Min. Mag.*, **10.** 145, 1893; T. Crook and B. M. Jones. *ib..* **14.** 161, 1906; L. Fletcher, *Nature*, **46.** 620, 1892; **G.** Tammann, *Zeit. anorg. Chem.*, 149. 68, 1925.

[5] C. U. Shepard, *Amer. Journ. Science*. (1), **34.** 313, 1838; (1), **36.** 85, 1839; J. L. Smith, *ib.*, (2), **16.** 293, 1853; (3), **8.** 432, 1874; T. S. Hunt, *ib.*, (2), **2.** 30, 1846; (2), **11.** 352, 1851; W. M. Bradley, *ib.*, (4), **27.** 179, 1909; A. des Cloizeaux, *Manuel de minéralogie*, Paris. 2. 16, 1874; A. Lacroix, *Bull. Soc. Min.*, **9.** 74, 1886; J. E. Whitfield, *Bull. U.S. Geol. Sur.* 64, 1890.

[6] L. Lévy, *Compt. Rend.*, **105.** 378, 1887; **107.** 421, 1888; *Ann. Chim. Phys.*, (6), **25.** 433, 1892; G. Tammann, *Zeit. anorg. Chem.* 149. 68 1925.

[7] E. Hussak and G. T. Prior, *Min. Mag.*, **12.** 30, 1898; E. Reitinger, *Zeit. Kryst.*, **37.** 576, 1903; H. St. C. Deville and H. Caron, *Compt. Rend.*, **46.** 290, 274, 1858; **53.** 161, 1861; R. Ricke, *Sprech.*, **41.** 405, 1908; T. H. Lee, *Amer. Journ. Science*, (4), **47.** 126, 1919; *Rev. Soc. Brasil. Sciencias*, 31, 1917.

[8] A. Hamberg, *Geol. För. Förh. Stockholm*, **12.** 600, 1890; L. Bourgeois, *Bull. Soc. Min.*, **15.** 194, 1892; P. Berthier, *Traité des essais par la voie séche*, Paris, **1.** 513, 1834; O. Derby, *Amer. Journ. Science*, (4), **25.** 215, 1908; P. Hautefeuille, *Ann. Chim. Phys.*, (4), **4.** 129, 1865; G. Tammann, *Zeit. anorg. Chem.*. 149. 68. 1925.

[9] W. Gregor, *Crell's Ann.*. i, 40, 103, 1791; ii, 55, 1791; *Journ. Phys.*, **72.** 152, 1791; M. H. Klaproth, *Beiträge zur chemischen Kenntniss der Mineralkörper*, Berlin, **1.** 233, 245, 1795; **2.** 222, 226, 1797; **4.** 153, 1801; **5.** 208, 1810; A. Breithaupt, *Vollständiges Charakteristik der Mineralsystems*, Dresden, 103, 243, 1823; *Uebersicht des Mineralsystems*, Freiberg, 64, 1830; *Vollständiges Handbuch der Mineralogie*, Dresden, **3.** 780, 808, 1847; J. H. Collins, *A Handbook to the Mineralogy of Cornwall and Devon*, London, 57, 1876; J. D. Dana, *A System of Mineralogy*, New York, 527, 1844; 433, 1850; 115, 1855; 143, 1868; 217, 1892; R. P. Greg and W. G. Lettsom, *Manual of the Mineralogy of Great Britain and Ireland*, London, 262, 1858; D. L. G. Karsten, *Mineralogische Tabell n*, Berlin, 74, 1808; R. Kirwan, *Elements of Mineralogy*, London, 1796; J. F. L. Hausmann, *Handbuch der Mineralogie*, Göttingen. 1. 251, 1813; **2.** 1239, 1847; F. A. Reuss, *Lehrbuch der Mineralogie*. Leipzig 2. 598. 1803; A. Lévy, *Phil. Mag.*, (2), **1.** 221, 1827; A. T. Kupffer, *Karsten's Arch.*, **10.** 1, 1827; F. Mohs, *Grundriss der Mineralogie*, Dresden, **2.** 462, 1824; C. C. von Leonhard, *Handbuch der Oryktognosie*, Heidelberg, 354. 1821; J. J. Berzelius, *Nouveau système de minéralogie*, Paris, 268, 1819; F. S. Beudant, *Bull. Soc. Philom.*, 55, 1819; R. J. Haüy, *Traité de minéralogie*, Paris. 4. 98. 1822; J. L. Bournon, *Catalogue de la collection minéralogique*, Paris, 430, 1813; C. A. S. Hofmann, *Handbuch der Mineralogie*, Freiberg, **4. a**, 247, 257, 1817; **4. b**, 139, 1818; A. G. Werner, *Letztes Mineralsystem*, Freiberg, 20, 26, 52, 1817; A. Gavelin, *Bull. Geol. Inst. Upsala*, **15.** 289, 1916; T. L. Watson, *Amer. Min.*, **10.** 1, 1925; F. von Kobell, *Schweigger's Journ.*, **64.** 59, 1832; *Grundzuge der Mineralogie*, Nürnberg, 318, 1838; *Die Mineralnamen*, München, 61. 1853; G. B. Hogenraad, *Proc Acad.*

Amsterdam, **5**. 605, 1903 ; *Versl. Akad. Amsterdam*, **11**. 707, 1903 ; P. Groth, *Tabellarische Uebersicht der Mineralien*, Braunschweig, 143, 1898 ; C. U. Shepard, *Amer. Journ. Science*, (2), **43**. 364, 1842 ; (2), **12**. 209, 1851 ; (3), **20**. 56, 1880 ; J. C. G. de Marignac, *Ann. Chim. Phys.*, (3), **14**. 50, 1845 ; E. J. Chapman, *Practical Mineralogy*, London, 1843 ; A. Lacroix, *Minéralogie de la France et ses colonies*, Paris, **3**. 284, 1901 ; H. Rose, *Pogg. Ann.*, **3**. 167, 1825 ; **15**. 276, 1829 ; G. Rose, *ib.*, **9**. 289, 1827 ; L. Colomba, *Zeit. Kryst.*, **50**. 512, 1912 ; H. W. Foote, *ib.*, **28**. 597, 1897 ; P. Tschernik, *Journ. Russ. Phys. Chem. Soc.*, **36**. 457, 1904 ; T. Crook and B. M. Jones, *Min. Mag.*, **14**. 165, 1906 ; C. W. Blomstrand, *Minnesskrift. Fys. Sallisk. Lund*, **3**, 1878.

[10] F. M. Heddle, *The Mineralogy of Scotland*, Edinburgh, **1**. 92, 1901 ; *Trans. Roy. Soc. Edin.*, **30**. 438, 1882 ; *Min. Mag.*, **3**. 41, 1879 ; **5**. 152, 1883 ; T. Crook and B. M. Jones, *ib.*, **14**. 165, 1906 ; C. F. Rammelsberg, *Handbuch der Mineralchemie*, Leipzig, 156, 1875 ; *Pogg. Ann.*, **104**. 522, 1858 ; E. E. Schmid, *ib.*, **84**. 498, 1851 ; H. Rose, *ib.*, **3**. 167, 1825 ; **15**. 276, 1829 ; **62**. 121, 1844 ; G. Rose, *ib.*, **9**. 289, 1827 ; C. G. Mosander, *ib.*, **19**. 217, 1829 ; *Akad. Handl. Stockholm*, 220, 1829 ; G. Doby and C. Malczer, *Zeit. Kryst.*, **39**. 540, 1904 ; A. Cathrein, *ib.*, **6**. 249, 1881 ; **12**. 44, 1881 ; C. W. Blomstrand, *ib.*, **4**. 521, 1880 ; F. Kovar, *ib.*, **31**. 525, 1899 ; H. W. Foote, *ib.*, **28**. 597, 1897 ; P. Sustschinsky, *ib.*, **37**. 62, 1903 ; P. Tschernik, *Proc. Russ. Min. Soc.*, **41**. 315, 1903 ; *Journ. Russ. Phys. Chem. Soc.*, **36**. 457, 712, 1904 ; Anon., *Bull. Imp. Inst. London*, **2**. 73, 1904 ; E. B. Krerr and E. Brunner, *Journ. Amer. Chem. Soc.*, **6**. 413, 1884 ; G. M. Peek, *ib.*, **19**. 232, 1897 ; E. von Gerichten, *Sitzber. Phys. Med. Soc. Erlangen*, **5**, 1873 ; *Neues Jahrb. Min.*, 643, 1873 ; A. Hilger, *ib.*, ii, 38, 1892 ; E. Cohen, *ib.*, 696, 1877 ; J. Mackintosh, *Amer. Journ. Science*, (3), **29**. 342, 1885 ; J. S. Diller, *ib.*, (4), **32**. 604, 1899 ; F. Pisani, *ib.*, (2), **37**. 359, 1864 ; S. L. Penfield, *ib.*, (4), **4**. 108, 1897 ; R. Stören, *Zeit. prakt. Geol.*, **9**. 183, 1901 ; H. Tamm, *Geol. För. Förh. Stockholm*, **2**. 46, 1874 ; A. Liversidge, *Journ. Roy. Soc. New South Wales*, **29**. 316, 1895 ; T. Petersen, *Sitzber. Bayr. Akad.*, 146, 1873 ; F. A. Genth, *Bull. U.S. Geol. Sur.*, **14**, 1891 ; W. C. Brögger, *Die Mineralien der südnorwegischen Granitpegmatitgänge*, Kristiania, 39, 1906 ; R. Wedel, *Jahrb. Geol. Landesanst.*, **11**. 118, 1890 ; H. F. Keller, *Journ. Amer. Phil. Soc.*, **23**. 42, 1885 ; L. Azéma, *Bull. Soc. Min.*, **34**. 29, 1911 ; C. Klement, *Tschermak's Mitt.*, (2), **8**. 15, 1886 ; A. Delesse, *Sur l'emploi de l'analyse chimique dans les recherches de minéralogie*, Paris, 46, 1843 ; J. L. Smith, *Mines*, (4), **18**. 305, 1850 ; *Amer. Journ. Science*, (2), **10**. 354, 1850 ; A. Damour, *Ann. Chim. Phys.*, (3), **51**. 445, 1857 ; J. C. G. de Marignac, *ib.*, (3), **14**. 50, 1845 ; T. S. Hunt, *Rep. Canada Geol. Sur.*, 105, 1850 ; 501, 1863 ; *Journ. prakt. Chem.*, (1), **66**. 153, 1855 ; (1), **82**. 512, 1861 ; M. C. Whitaker, *Proc. Colorado Scient. Soc.*, **6**. 104, 1898 ; F. von Kobell, *Schweigger's Journ.*, **64**. 59, 245, 1832 ; *Journ. prakt. Chem.*, (1), **1**. 87, 1834 ; L. J. Igelström, *Œfvers. Akad. Stockholm*, 3, 1854 ; *Journ. prakt. Chem.*, (1), **64**. 62, 1855 ; P. Plantamour, *ib.*, (1), **24**. 302, 1841 ; *Bibl. Univ. Genève*, **32**. 335, 1841 ; A. Knop, *Progr. Gewerbsch. Chemnitz*, 1, 1856 ; *Liebig's Ann.*, **123**. 348, 1862 ; A. Vogel and C. Reishauer, *Bull. München Gelehrte Anz.*, **42**. 57, 1856 ; J. Müller, *Vierteljahr. prakt. Pharm.*, **8**. 331, 1859 ; J. A. Michaelson, *Svenska Akad. Förh.*, 505, 1862 ; C. von Hauer, *Sitzber. Akad. Wien*, **19**. 350, 1890.

[11] A. Lévy, *Phil. Mag.*, (2), **1**. 221, 1827 ; G. Rose, *Reise nach dem Ural dem Altai. und dem kaspischen Meere*, Berlin, **2**. 61, 1842 ; *Pogg. Ann.*, **9**. 286, 1827 ; H. Rose, *ib.*, **3**. 167, 1825 ; **15**. 276, 1829 ; **62**. 123, 1844 ; G. von Hevesy and V. T. Jentzen, *Journ. Chem. Soc.*, **123**. 3218, 1923 ; C. F. Rammelsberg, *Handbuch der Mineralchemie*, Leipzig, 148, 1875 ; *Pogg. Ann.*, **104**. 503, 1858 ; T. Scheerer, *ib.*, **64**. 489, 1845 ; C. G. Mosander, *ib.*, **19**. 219, 1830 ; *Akad. Handl. Stockholm*, 220, 1889 ; J. J. Berzelius, *Jahresb.*, **25**. 368, 1845 ; C. Friedel and J. Guérin, *Compt. Rend.*, **82**. 509, 1876 ; *Ann. Chim. Phys.*, (5), **8**. 38, 1876 ; P. Groth, *Tabellarische Uebersicht der Mineralien*. Braunschweig, 40, 1889 ; T. König and O. F. von der Pfordten, *Ber.*, **22**. 1494, 1889 ; E. Glatzel, *ib.*, **9**. 1829, 1839, 1876 ; A. Hamberg, *Geol. För. Förh. Stockholm*, **12**. 604, 1890 ; S. L. Penfield and H. W. Foote, *Amer. Journ. Science*, (4), **4**. 108, 1897 ; *Zeit. Kryst.*, **28**. 596, 1897 ; W. Manchot, *Zeit. anorg. Chem.*, **74**. 79, 1912 ; R. Hermann, *Journ. prakt. Chem.*, (1), **43**. 50, 1848 ; G. Tammann, *Zeit. anorg. Chem.*, **149**. 68, 1925.

[12] G. Rose, *Sitzber. Akad. Berlin*, 11, 1867 ; L. Bourgeois, *Bull. Soc. Min.*, **15**. 194, 1892 ; J. Morozewicz, *Tschermak's Mitt.*, (2), **18**. 113, 1898 ; W. Bruhns, *Zeit. Kryst.*, **8** 54, 1884.

[13] E. Artini, *Giorn. Min.*, **2**. 181, 1891 ; N. von Kokscharoff, *Materialen zur Mineralogie Russland*, St. Petersburg, **1**. 17, 1853 ; **6**. 355, 1870 ; G. Doby and G. Melczer, *Zeit. Kryst.*, **540**, 1904 ; P. Sustschinsky, *ib.*, **37**. 40, 1903 ; H. Bücking, *ib.*, **1**. 576, 1877 ; A. Brun, *ib.*. **39**. 203, 1904 ; **2**. 424, 1878 ; G. Spezia, *ib.*, **14**. 503, 1888 ; *Atti Accad. Torino*, **22**. 419, 1887 ; G. Boeris, *ib.*, **34**. 609, 1899 ; *Atti Accad. l.incei*, (5), **9**. 52, 1900 ; M. Bauer, *Zeit. deut. geol. Ges.*, **26**. 192, 1874 ; M. Websky, *ib.*, **16**. 536, 1864 ; **17**. 566, 1865 ; G. Rose, *ib.*, **19**. 286, 1867 ; *Reise nach dem Urals, dem Altai, und dem kaspischen Meere*, Berlin, **1**. 290, 1837 ; **2**. 145, 468, 584, 1842 ; O. Mügge, *Neues Jahrb. Min.*, ii, 46, 1886 ; A. Streng, *ib.*, ii, 196, 1888 ; K. Hofmann, *Die Basaltgesteine des südlichen, Bakong*, Budapest, 30, 1879 ; F. Sandberger, *Sitzber. Akad. München*, 146, 1873 ; A. Sadebeck, *Pogg. Ann.*, **156**. 558, 1875 ; *Neues Jahrb. Min.*, 287, 1878 ; G. Cesaro, *Bull. Acad. Belg.*, 115, 1904 ; R. H. Solly, *Min. Mag.*, **14**. 184, 1906 ; H. Smith, *ib.*, **14**. 258, 1907 ; F. Zambonini, *Rend. Accad. Napoli*, (3), **13**. 35, 1907 ; A. Lacroix, *Minéralogie de la France et de ses colonies*, Paris, **3**. 298, 1901 ; R. Lorenz and W. Herz, *Zeit. anorg. Chem.*, **135**. 374, 1924 ; A. des Cloizeaux, *Manuel de minéralogie*, Paris, **2**. 222, 1893 ; W. H. Miller, *Introduction to Mineralogy*, London, 241, 1852 ; P. von Jeremejeff, *Proc. Russ. Min. Soc.*, **24**.

457, 1887 ; **25**. 387, 1888 ; **A**. Breithaupt, *Vollständiges Handbuch der Mineralogie*, Dresden, **3**. 808, 1847 ; F. von Kobell, *Journ. prakt. Chem.*, (1), **1**. 87, 1834 ; C. F. Rammelsberg, *Pogg. Ann.*, **104**. 524, 1858 ; F. Pisani, *Amer. Journ. Science*, (2), **37**. 359, 1864 ; F. Zirkel, *Lehrbuch der Petrographie*, Bonn, **1**. 421, 1893 ; G. A. Kenngott, *Mineralogische Untersuchungen*, Breslau, 124, 1850 ; E. Madelung and R. Fuchs, *Ann. Physik*, (4), **65**. 289, 1921 ; E. Zalinsky, *Centr. Min.*, 648, 1902 ; F. Beijerinck, *Neues Jahrb. Min. B.B.*, **11**. 453, 1897 ; B. Bavink, *ib.*, **19**. 425, 1904 ; *Beiträge zur Kenntniss der magnetischen Influenz in Krystallen*, Stuttgart, 1904 ; J. Königsberger and K. Schilling, *Ann. Physik*, (4), **32**. 260, 1910 ; A. de Gramont, *Bull. Soc. Min.*, **18**. 230, 1895 ; P. F. Kerr, *Econ. Geol.*, **19**. 1, 1924 ; H. Lotz, *Die Verwitterung einiger gesteinsbildender Mineralien unter dem Einfluss von schwefliger Säure*, Giessen, 1912 ; E. T. Wherry, *Amer. Min.*, **10**. 28, 1925 ; C. G. Mosander, *Pogg. Ann.*, **19**. 217, 1839 ; P. Groth, *Tabellarische Uebersicht der Mineralien*, Braunschweig, 79, 1898.
  [14] C. Palmer, *Amer. Journ. Science*, (4), **28**. 353, 1909 ; J. Mackintosh, *ib.*, (3), **29**. 342, 1885 ; T. König and O. F. von der Pfordten, *ib.*, **22**. 1485, 1889 ; E. Rinmann, *Centr. Min.*, 18, 1925 ; W. F. Foshag, *Amer. Min.*, **10**. 135, 1925 ; P. Hautefeuille, *Compt. Rend.*, **59**. 733, 1864 ; *Ann. Chim. Phys.*, (4), **4**. 172, 1864 ; A. Koch, *Tschermak's Mitt.*, (2), **1**. 331, 1878 ; G. Lattermann, *ib.*, (2), **9**. 53, 1888 ; A. Frenzel, *ib.*, (2), **14**. 127, 1895 ; B. Doss, *Zeit. Kryst.*, **20**. 567, 1892 ; H Traube, *ib.*, **20**. 329, 1892 ; A. Cederström, *ib.*, **17**. 136, 1890 ; J. Königsberger and K. Schilling, *Ann. Physik*, (4), **32**. 179, 1910.
  [15] L. Bourgeois, *Bull. Soc. Min.*, **15**. 194, 1893.

§ 9. The Higher Oxides of Titanium—Pertitanates and Hypertitanates

H. Schönn,[1] and A. Weller showed that if hydrogen dioxide be added to a soln. of titanium sulphate, an orange-yellow colour is developed. The intensity of the colour depends on the proportion of titanium in soln. The phenomenon is employed for the colorimetric determination of titanium, a process discussed by C. Baskerville, J. Brakes, H. M. Ullmann and J. W. Boyer, A. Gautier, G. P. Pamfil, T. B. Osborne, W. F. Hillebrand, J. H. Walton, G. Steiger, J. Bruhat and H. Dubois, H. E. Merwin, E. Jackson, L. Lévy, C. Reichard, etc. The coloration is affected by the presence of fluorine, phosphoric acid, and potassium sulphate. According to A. Weller, if freshly precipitated titanium hydroxide be treated with neutral hydrogen dioxide, or if a soln. of titanium sulphate be treated with hydrogen dioxide and then with aq. ammonia, a yellow substance is obtained which, when dried over conc. sulphuric acid, furnishes a yellow horny mass. Analyses show the ratio $TiO_2 : O = 1 : 0.75$ to 0.81 ; and when heated it gives off oxygen and water, forming titanium dioxide. It is therefore assumed that the product is a more or less decomposed **hydrated titanium trioxide,** or **pertitanic acid,** $TiO_3.nH_2O$. It dissolves in acids, forming a reddish-yellow soln. ; the sulphuric acid soln. is fairly stable, but the hydrochloric acid soln. soon gives off chlorine. Ether is without action ; and reducing agents decolorize the liquid. **A.** Classen isolated the oxide as follows :

Titanium tetrachloride **was** added drop by drop to dil. alcohol, and the clear, very dil. **soln.** was treated with a large excess of hydrogen dioxide. Ammonia, ammonium carbonate, or aq. potassium hydroxide was added to the soln., and in the case of ammonia a yellow, and in the other cases, a reddish-yellow liquid was formed, which, after some time, gave a yellow precipitate. This **was** repeatedly washed by decantation, and dried on a porous plate.

A. Classen's analysis corresponded with $TiO_3.3H_2O$, or $Ti(OH)_6$. A. Piccini treated a soln. of titanium sulphate with barium hydroxide, and then with hydrogen dioxide. The yellow precipitate obtained on adding potassium hydroxide never contained more oxygen than corresponded with $TiO_2 : O = 2 : 1$; the soln., however, contained the eq. of $TiO_2.H_2O_2$ and free hydrogen dioxide, but it could not be demonstrated whether a true peroxide is formed or simply the addition product $TiO_2.H_2O_2$. L. Lévy attributed the discordant results of the analyses of the product of the action of hydrogen dioxide on titanium dioxide to the slowness of the reaction, and to the decomposition of the precipitate during desiccation. He mixed a soln. of hydrogen dioxide of known conc. with definite quantities of a soln. of titanium sulphate, and after standing a long time, he showed that any one of the three formulæ, TiO_3, $TiO_2.H_2O_2$, and $Ti_2O_5.H_2O_2$, agrees with the results. The composition of the higher chloride, and the existence of additive compounds of the oxyfluoride and alkali fluorides, afford additional evidence in favour of the formula TiO_3. P. Faber, and P. G. Melikoff and L. Pissarjewsky assume that during the action of hydrogen dioxide on soln. of salts of quadrivalent titanium, the titanium becomes sexivalent, but this is not in harmony with the position of titanium in the periodic table. If titanium be quadrivalent, hydrated titanium trioxide can be formulated :

$$(HO)_2=Ti<\begin{matrix}O\\ \overset{..}{O}\end{matrix} \qquad \textit{or} \qquad Ti\begin{matrix}O.OH\\ (OH)_3\end{matrix}$$

P. G. Melikoff and L. Pissarjewsky found that titanium trioxide has acidic properties, and unites with the alkali peroxides in the presence of hydrogen dioxide, forming hypertitanates, or salts of the unknown anhydride, *titanium heptoxide*, Ti_2O_7. O. and A. Dony-Hénault studied the conc. of hydrogen dioxide in soln. of titanium salts required before the hydrogen dioxide is able to affect photographic plates. On the assumption that the titanium oxide must be sat. with hydrogen dioxide, before the dioxide is free to affect the plate, they inferred that the compound $TiO_2.H_2O_2$ is stable in sulphuric acid soln.

P. Faber represents the phosphate with sexivalent titanium, thus, $(HO)_3Ti\equiv O_3\equiv P=O$. Pertitanic acid behaves like hydrogen dioxide, but is not quite so energetic. In the presence of organic reducing agents, such as formic or oxalic acid, hydrogen dioxide cannot be detected by the chromic acid—ether reaction—but is shown readily by the titanic acid test. The conversion of the quadrivalent titanium into the sexivalent state is due to a combination with the hydroxyl groups of the hydrogen peroxide. There exists an acetate of the sexavalent titanium which is stable at low temperatures. It has a yellow colour and is insoluble in acetic acid, but soluble in mineral acids and also in alkalies and ammonia. On heating, it shows decidedly explosive properties. M. Billy considers that the supposed salts of titanium trioxide are really complexes of hydrogen dioxide and pertitanic acid corresponding with *titanium pentoxide*, Ti_2O_5; and a hydrated compound, $Ti_2O_5.nH_2O$, was obtained by precipitation with alcohol from a soln. prepared by pouring equimolar proportions of potassium and titanyl sulphates into an excess of hydrogen dioxide. According to A. Classen, sulphuric acid soln. gives with potassium fluoride a white precipitate of potassium fluotitanate, and liberates hydrogen dioxide ; iodine separates from potassium iodide, and ferrous salts are oxidized. The strongly oxidizing properties of the soln. resemble those of soln. of hydrogen dioxide ; *e.g.* lead and manganese dioxides are reduced. A. Mazzucchelli and C. Barbero found that unlike hydrogen dioxide, the soln. gives a red precipitate with potassium ferrocyanide, a white precipitate with acetaldehyde, and a yellow precipitate with acetone. Chromic acid is not oxidized to perchromic acid by the soln. of titanium trioxide. L. Lévy found titanium trioxide, like hydrogen dioxide, decolorizes phenolphthalein, so that if an acid soln. of titanium dioxide be titrated after the addition of hydrogen dioxide, its acidity appears to be increased. L. Weiss and M. Landecker studied the reducing action of hydroxylamine, and of sulphur dioxide. A. Mazzucchelli and C. Barbero measured the electrolytic potential of titanium trioxide in the combination $Hg\,|\,HgSO_4$, N-H_2SO_4, $Ti(SO_4)_2$, $H_2O_2\,|\,Pt$, and found it to be the same as that of hydrogen dioxide. This corresponds with the existence of the compound $TiO_2.H_2O_2$ in soln. ; but it is possible that the reaction was completed before the potential was measured.

The aq. soln. of titanium trioxide may be considered to contain pertitanic acid, although it does not show an acid reaction towards indicators. The freshly precipitated trioxide is soluble in alkali-lye, and the soln. furnishes precipitates with alkaline soln. of copper, zinc, lead, and cobalt salts. No salts have been made which can be regarded as derivatives of pertitanic acid with hydrogen replaced by a metal. P. G. Melikoff and L. Pissarjewsky prepared a number of compounds which they considered to be complex salts of pertitanic acid, and a metal hydroperoxide. There are two series of salts : (i) *Yellow*.—The method of preparation of the yellow salts is to add well-cooled hydrogen dioxide to hydrated titanium trioxide, and then sufficient well-cooled alkali-lye to dissolve all the solid. The addition of alcohol gives a precipitate which is washed with alcohol and ether, and dried on a porous plate. Glistening yellow prisms of **ammonium peroxypertitanate,** $(NH_4)_2O_2.TiO_3.H_2O_2$, or $(NH_4O_2)_2.TiO_2.H_2O$, were so obtained. The dry salt is fairly stable, but it rapidly decomposes in soln. When heated over a free flame it gives a feeble explosion. The yellow oil first obtained with sodium compounds slowly crystallizes, forming a yellow powder of **sodium peroxypertitanate,** $Na_2O_2.TiO_3.3H_2O$. J. H. Walton made sodium peroxypertitanate from titanium dioxide and sodium dioxide. W. G. Mixter found the heat of formation of sodium peroxypertitanate to be 629 Cals. Assuming that the constitution of pertitanic acid is $(HO)_2Ti\langle {}^O_O$, since the soln. has all the characteristics of a peroxide, these two salts can be represented constitutionally :

$$\begin{array}{ll} {NaO.O \atop NaO}\rangle Ti\langle {O \atop O}, \ 3H_2O & {NH_4O.O \atop NH_4O.O}\rangle Ti\langle {O \atop O}, \ H_2O \\ \text{Sodium peroxypertitanate.} & \text{Ammonium peroxypertitanate.} \end{array}$$

The sodium salt can also be represented as a double compound of a pertitanate with hydrogen dioxide, namely, $(NaO)_2TiO_2.H_2O_2.2H_2O$; but this formulation is considered to be less probable than the other. By double decomposition with barium chloride, sparingly soluble **barium peroxypertitanate,** $BaO_2.TiO_3.5H_2O$, is obtained as a yellow, indefinitely crystalline powder. When these compounds are treated with dil. sulphuric acid, hydrogen dioxide is formed, which is not the case with pertitanic acid alone. With hydrochloric acid, some chlorine is evolved.

(ii) *Colourless*.—Another series of compounds is obtained by a process like that just described except that larger proportions of hydrogen dioxide and of alkali-lye are used ; the alkali-lye is added until the yellow soln. becomes colourless. The small, colourless prisms of **sodium peroxyhypertitanate,** $(Na_2O_2)_4.Ti_2O_7.10H_2O$, decompose with the evolution of oxygen when dissolved in water ; and the salt does not liberate iodine from potassium iodide. It undergoes no change during several hours' exposure to air. When confined over sulphuric acid, it loses water and oxygen. Minute crystals of **potassium hyperoxypertitanate,** $K_2O_4.K_2O_2.TiO_3.10H_2O$, were formed in a similar way. The salt is stable at 0°, but deliquesces at ordinary temp. at the same time losing oxygen, and acquiring a yellow colour. The constitution is represented graphically :

$$\begin{array}{ll} {KO.O \atop KO}\rangle Ti\langle {O \atop O}, \ K_2O_4.10H_2O & {(NaO.O)_3 \atop NaO}\rangle Ti.O.Ti\langle {(NaO.O)_3 \atop ONa}, \ 10H_2O \\ \text{Potassium hyperoxypertitanate.} & \text{Sodium peroxyhypertitanate.} \end{array}$$

but the evidence is not convincing. M. Billy made orange or yellow crystals of *potassium pertitanic sulphate* by mixing hydrated titanic acid, potassium carbonate and hydrogen dioxide. The salt readily decomposed giving off oxygen.

REFERENCES.

[1] A. Weller, *Ber.*, **15.** 2599, 1882 ; A. Classen, *ib.*, **21.** 370, 1519, 1888 ; C. Baskerville, *Journ. Soc. Chem. Ind.*, **19.** 419, 1900 ; J. Brakes, *ib.*, **20.** 23, 1901 ; H. M. Ullmann and J. W. Boyer, *Chem. Eng.*, **10.** 163, 1909 ; A. Gautier. *Chim.*, **1.** 177, 1910 ; *Rev. Gén. Chim.*, **14.** 14, 1910 : G. P. Pamfil, *Monit. Scient.*, (4), **24.** 643, 1911 ; H. E. Merwin, *Amer. Journ. Science*, (4), **28.** 119, 1909 ; W. G. Mixter, *ib.*, (4), **27.** 393, 1909 ; T. B. Osborne, *ib.*, (3), **30.** 329, 1885 ; *Chem. News*, **53.** 43, 1886 ; E. Jackson, *ib.*, **47.** 157, 1883 ; W. F. Hillebrand, *ib.*, **72.** 718, 1895 ; *Journ. Amer. Chem. Soc.*, **17.** 718, 1895 ; J. H. Walton, *ib.*, **29.** 481, 1907 ; G. Steiger, *ib.*, **30.** 219, 1908 ;

R. C. Wells, *ib.*, **33**. 504, 1911; C. Reichard, *Chem. Ztg.*, **28**. 16, 1904; P. Faber, *ib.*, **31**. 263, 1906; *Zeit. anal. Chem.*, **46**. 277, 1907; H. Schönn, *ib.*, **9**. 41, 330, 1870; *Dingler's Journ.*, **247**. 122, 1888; A. Mazzucchelli and C. Barbero, *Atti Accad. Lincei*, (5), **15**. ii, 35, 109, 1906; A. Piccini, *ib.*, (3), **6**. 180, 1882; *Gazz. Chim. Ital.*, **12**. 151, 1882; **13**. 57, 1883; **14**. 38, 1884; *Compt. Rend.*, **97**. 1064, 1883; J. Bruhat and H. Dubois, *ib.*, **140**. 506, 1905; M. Billy, *Ann. Chim. Phys.*, (9), **16**. 5, 1921; *Compt. Rend.*, **172**. 1411, 1921; L. Lévy, *ib.*, **108**. 294, 1889; *Ann. Chim. Phys.*, (6), **25**. 453, 1892; P. G. Melikoff and L. Pissarjewsky, *Ber.*, **31**. 678, 955, 1898; *Journ. Russ. Phys. Chem. Soc.*, **30**. 693, 1898; *Bull Soc. Chim.*, (3), **22**. 920, 1889; *Zeit. anorg. Chem.*, **18**. 95, 1898; L. Weiss and M. Landecker, *ib.*, **64**. 88, 1909; O. and A. Dony-Hénault, *Bull. Soc. Chim. Belg.*, **22**. 224, 1908.

§ 10. Titanium Fluorides

According to P. Hautefeuille,[1] when potassium fluotitanate, K_2TiF_6, is strongly heated in a stream of hydrogen mixed with a little hydrogen chloride, dark violet prismatic crystals are formed. At first, these crystals were considered to be *titanium difluoride*, TiF_2; but later P. Hautefeuille showed that **titanium trifluoride, TiF_3**, is formed. R. Weber also made the same salt by using a current of hydrogen only. P. Hautefeuille found that purple-red titanium fluoride crystallized from molten potassium chloride is readily soluble in water, while the violet product dissolves with difficulty. R. Weber found that the trifluoride could not be separated from the alkali fluoride, and that by the prolonged action of boiling water the trifluoride decomposes, forming with the alkali fluoride, potassium fluotitanate. V. Merz dissolved titanium in 27 per cent. hydrofluoric acid, and obtained a soln. which he supposed contained titanous fluoride. C. F. Rammelsberg obtained a soln. of titanium trifluoride by reducing a soln. of potassium fluotitanate with zinc and hydrochloric acid; and O. F. von der Pfordten used sodium amalgam as a reducing agent. C. Friedel and J. Guérin made some observations on this subject.

A number of complex fluorides, **fluotitanites,** have been obtained by the union of the metal fluorides with titanium trifluoride. These salts are derivatives of **fluotitanous acid, $HTiF_4$**, but the acid itself has not been isolated. A. Piccini obtained a violet precipitate of **ammonium pentafluotitanite,** $(NH_4)_2TiF_5$, by pouring a conc. soln. of ammonium fluoride into one of titanium trifluoride; if the sequence be reversed, and the latter soln. be poured into the former, **ammonium hexafluotitanate,** $(NH_4)_3TiF_6$, is formed. The better mode of preparing the latter salt is to reduce a soln. of a fluotitanate and ammonium fluoride by electrolysis. E. Petersen made it by reducing a soln. of potassium fluotitanate with cadmium and hydrochloric acid, and then adding the product to a soln. of ammonium fluoride. The crystalline violet precipitate is slightly soluble in water, but insoluble in a soln. of ammonium fluoride. If the precipitate be washed successively with water, a conc. soln. of ammonium fluoride, and conc. alcohol, and exposed to the air, its violet colour changes to dirty yellow, and when perfectly dry, it has a deep yellow colour, and ammonium fluoroxypertitanate is formed. According to E. Petersen, the salt $(NH_4)_3TiF_6$ is isomorphous with the corresponding salts of chromium, vanadium, and iron—$(NH_4)_3CrF_6$, $(NH_4)_3VF_6$, and $(NH_4)_3FeF_6$. A. Piccini made **potassium pentafluotitanite,** K_2TiF_5, as a deep violet precipitate by adding potassium hydrofluoride to the liquid obtained by treating titanium trifluoride with water. The salt is sparingly soluble in water, for, at 21°, 100 parts of water dissolve 1·27 parts of salt. The salt is readily dissolved by dil. acids, forming green soln. which give an azure-blue precipitate with aq. ammonia or potassium hydroxide, and gradually form titanic acid on exposure to air. Potassium permanganate is decolorized by a soln. of the salt.

O. Unverdorben[2] distilled titanium dioxide in a leaden retort with fluorspar and sulphuric acid; unlike the corresponding experiment with silicon dioxide, no gas is evolved, but after a time, yellow oily drops appear which were considered to be titanium fluoride. The product is decomposed by water with the separation of titanic acid, or titanium oxyfluoride. If a glass retort be used, it was said that a mixture of gaseous silicon tetrafluoride mixed with titanium tetrafluoride passes over. It is, however, very doubtful if the yellow oily liquid is really **titanium tetrafluoride,** TiF_4, because O. Ruff and R. Ipsen could not make the tetrafluoride by this process. H. Moissan obtained this compound by the direct union of the elements. O. Ruff and R. Ipsen said that, if gently warmed, titanium reacts with fluorine with incandescence, forming a white sublimate of titanium tetrafluoride contaminated with particles of the metal. E. Glatzel said that an aq. soln. of titanium tetrafluoride is obtained by dissolving titanium in hydrofluoric acid. O. Ruff and R. Ipsen could not make the tetrafluoride in this way ; nor could they obtain it by roasting hydrofluotitanic acid with sulphuric acid. They did obtain titanium tetrafluoride by the action of anhydrous hydrogen fluoride on red-hot titanium ; part of any carbon associated with the titanium remains, and part is converted into acetylene. The hydrogen fluoride should be obtained from potassium hydrofluoride, for, if obtained from calcium fluoride and sulphuric acid, the product is contaminated with titanium oxyfluoride. They recommended preparing this compound by passing thoroughly dried hydrogen fluoride over titanium tetrachloride : $TiCl_4 + 4HF = TiF_4 + 4HCl$. The yield is 90 per cent. The reaction takes place at ordinary temp. ; if the temp. be raised to $100°-120°$, the reaction is very fast. At ordinary temp., a layer of titanium tetrafluoride is formed over the surface of the tetrachloride, and this slackens the speed of the reaction. O. Ruff and co-workers recommended using pieces of coke soaked in the tetrachloride. The reaction between antimony tetrafluoride and titanium tetrachloride was found by O. Ruff and H. Graf to yield titanium tetrafluoride. According to J. J. Berzelius, when hydrofluotitanic acid is evaporated at a gentle heat, a syrupy liquid is obtained which furnishes crystals of titanium tetrafluoride. J. C. G. de Marignac obtained the impure tetrafluoride by igniting magnesium fluotitanate ; and F. Emich, by igniting barium fluotitanate.

Titanium tetrafluoride is a white solid at ordinary temp. O. Ruff and W. Plato gave 2·833 for the sp. gr. at 11°, and 2·798 at 20·5° ; the mol. vol. is 45·8 ; and the vap. density at 444° is 129·7–129·8 when the value calculated for TiF_4 is 124·1. The b.p. is 284° ; and, according to O. Ruff and R. Ipsen, the compound sublimes over 400°. The b.p. of the tetrafluoride is higher than that of the chloride, 136° ; this is in marked contrast with the corresponding salts of silicon, and the corresponding halides of other non-metals and metalloids. It thus relates titanium with the metals, and is possibly to be interpreted to mean that titanium tetrafluoride is polymerized near its b.p.

The saline nature of the tetrafluoride is emphasized by its hygroscopicity, and by its forming a clear soln. with water, which, on evaporation, deposits crystals of **dihydrated titanium tetrafluoride,** $TiF_4.2H_2O$. J. J. Berzelius said that the white powder deposited from aq. soln. of titanium tetrafluoride possibly contains *titanium oxyfluoride,* $TiOF_2$, because the fluorine is not all expelled even at a red heat. It can be driven off by ignition with ammonium carbonate. For the double salt $TiOF_2.BaF_2$, *vide infra.* Titanium tetrafluoride dissolves in conc. hydrofluoric acid, but no direct combination has been detected ; the hydrogen fluoride is given off at 25°. The vapour of iodine has a slight action. Indirectly a combination does occur, and hydrofluotitanic acid is formed which furnishes a series of salts—the fluotitanates. At ordinary temp., hydrogen sulphide has no appreciable action on the tetrafluoride, but at a red heat titanium disulphide and hydrogen fluoride are formed. No action was observed with sulphur chloride, SCl_2 ; thionyl chloride, $SOCl_2$; sulphuryl chloride, SO_2Cl_2 ; and sulphur trioxide. When the tetrafluoride is heated with conc. sulphuric acid, titanium dioxide is formed ; and, consequently, the tetrafluoride is not produced by heating a mixture of titanium dioxide, calcium fluoride, and sulphuric acid. Titanium tetrafluoride absorbs ammonia with the development of heat, forming in the cold **titanium tetrammino-tetrafluoride,** $TiF_4.4NH_3$; and at 120°, **titanium diamminotetrafluoride,** $TiF_4.2NH_3$, which sublimes without decomposition, and dissolves in water, forming a clear soln.

which slowly deposits titanic acid when boiled. With pyridine, it forms a white crystalline solid, $TiF_4.C_5H_5N$. No action was observed with the phosphorus chlorides ; but at 30°, phosphoryl chloride reacts, furnishing titanium tetrachloride : $3TiF_4+4POCl_3=3TiCl_4+4POF_3$. No reaction was observed with arsenic trichloride ; or with carbon disulphide, or carbon tetrachloride. It dissolves in dried alcohol with the evolution of heat, and the soln. when evaporated over phosphorus pentoxide, in vacuo, furnishes a crystalline mass of **titanium alcoholotetrafluoride,** $TiF_4.C_2H_5OH$. No reaction was observed with silicon tetrachloride, or silicon tetrabromide ; but O. Ruff and K. Albert found that when heated with trichlorosilane for a day at 100°, titanium tetrafluoride is converted into the tetrachloride and trifluorosilane, $SiHF_3$. O. Ruff and R. Ipsen found that at a red heat titanium tetrafluoride is reduced to titanium by sodium, calcium, magnesium, boron, aluminium, and iron ; but copper and silicon reduce it only to titanium trifluoride. No action was observed with chromic trioxide.

According to A. Piccini, pertitanic acid, $TiO_3.nH_2O$, forms a number of complex salts with various acids, for example, when a soln. of titanium fluoride is oxidized with hydrogen dioxide, and treated with an alkali or alkaline earth fluoride, crystalline **oxyfluopertitanates** are formed. These salts are derivatives of titanium trioxide with one oxygen atom replaced by two atoms of fluorine :

$$\overset{F}{\underset{\ddot{F}}{}}{>}Ti{<}\overset{O}{\underset{O}{}} \qquad\qquad \overset{H.F=F}{\underset{H.F=F}{}}{>}Ti{<}\overset{O}{\underset{O}{}}$$

Titanium peroxyfluoride.   Hydroxyfluopertitanic acid.

As A. Mazzucchelli pointed out, the introduction of an active oxygen atom into the mol. of titanium dioxide, is favourable to the formation of complex anions. They are decomposed by hydrofluoric acid, forming hydrogen dioxide and titanium tetrafluoride (or hydrofluotitanic acid) : $TiO_2F_2+2HF=TiF_4+H_2O_2$. This is taken as evidence that the two oxygen atoms form a bivalent radicle eq. to two fluorine atoms. A. Piccini prepared **hydro-oxyfluopertitanic acid,** $H_2TiO_2F_4$, or $TiO_2F_2.2HF$, in soln. by adding barium oxyfluopertitanate, in slight excess, to well-cooled dil. sulphuric acid (4–5 per cent.) contained in a platinum dish, filtering (using a silver funnel) from the barium sulphate and excess of oxyfluopertitanate, and cautiously precipitating the traces of barium in soln. with dil. sulphuric acid. When the acid is neutralized with ammonia, it is probable that normal **ammonium oxyfluopertitanate,** $(NH_4)_2,TiO_2F_4$, or $TiO_2F_2.2NH_4F$, is formed, but it was not obtained in definite crystals. Potassium carbonate under similar conditions furnishes the analogous potassium salt. If the acid be neutralized with ammonia and ammonium fluoride be added, octahedral **ammonium oxyfluopertitanate,** $3NH_4F.TiO_2F_2$, or $(NH_4)_2TiO_2F_4.NH_4F$, is formed. Similarly also when an excess of ammonia is added to hydro-oxyfluopertitanic acid. The same salt is formed when a soln. of ammonium fluotitanate, $3NH_4F.TiF_3$, is washed with a conc. soln. of ammonium fluoride, moistened with alcohol, and exposed to the air. The violet product gradually changes into an intense yellow mass, and when crystallized from its aq. soln., furnishes octahedral crystals. E. Petersen's idea that the oxidation does not occur is incorrect. The salt is also produced when ammonium oxyfluopertitanate is treated with hydrogen dioxide in the presence of an excess of ammonia and ammonium fluoride. The salt forms yellow octahedral crystals which are soluble in water. A. Mazzucchelli and C. Barbero compared the electrolytic potential of the soln. with that of hydrogen dioxide. The aq. soln. decolorizes potassium permanganate ; ammonium hydroxide precipitates a pale yellow flocculent mass which dissolves in sulphuric acid, forming an orange-red soln. The action of hydrofluoric acid is indicated above.

The octahedral crystals just mentioned are usually accompanied by yellow acicular crystals of ammonium oxyfluotitanate, $3NH_4F.2TiO_2F_2$, particularly if no excess of ammonium fluoride is present. The same salt is formed by oxidizing a 5 per cent. soln. of titanium dioxide in sulphuric acid, with barium dioxide ; adding ammonia to the filtrate until the precipitate no longer redissolves; and pouring the liquid into a conc. soln. of ammonium fluoride containing an excess of ammonia. The soln. is then crystallized in vacuo. A. Piccini also made $Ti_5O_4F_{12}.9NH_4F$, or $3(TiF_4.2NH_4F).2TiO_2.3NH_4F$. He found that if an excess of ammonia is added to a soln. of ammonium fluotitanate, $TiF.2NH_4F$, the whole of the titanic acid is precipitated. If, however, ammonia is added drop by drop to the warm soln. of the fluoride, the white precipitate which first forms redissolves later, until at a certain point the liquid has merely an opalescent appearance; if now allowed to remain, a white, crystalline precipitate of the composition just indicated, settles out. It is completely soluble in a soln. of ammonium fluotitanate, but is decomposed by water, titanic acid being precipitated.

A. Piccini prepared normal **potassium oxyfluopertitanate**, $K_2TiO_2F_4$, or $TiO_2F_2.2KF$, as a yellow crystalline powder by neutralizing a soln. of the acid with potassium hydroxide or carbonate; by the action of hydrogen dioxide on potassium fluotitanate; or by treating a soln. of the ammonium salt, $3NH_4F.TiO_2F_2$, with potassium chloride. The salt is probably isomorphous with potassium fluotitanate, K_2TiF_6. A. Piccini prepared **barium oxyfluopertitanate**, $BaTiO_2F_4$, or $TiO_2F_2.BaF_2$, as a flocculent precipitate by adding barium nitrate to a soln. of the octahedral ammonium fluoxypertitanate. Sometimes also, under conditions which are not accurately known, this was accompanied by a crystalline barium compound, probably $2TiO_2F_2.3BaF_2$, corresponding with the octahedral ammonium salt. When the amorphous barium salt is gently heated, oxygen is evolved and the yellow colour becomes white; but at a higher temp. it parts with its fluorine, and is converted into a white mass of barium metatitanate, $BaO.TiO_2$. The white intermediate product obtained at $150°-160°$ has the composition $BaF_2.TiO_2F_2$, or titanium barium oxyfluoride. It is easily soluble in dil. acids, and cannot therefore be a mixture containing titanium dioxide.

REFERENCES.

[1] P. Hautefeuille, *Compt. Rend.*, **57**. 151, 1863; **59**. 189, 1864; C. Friedel and J. Guérin, *ib.*, **81**. 889, 1875; A. Piccini, *ib.*, **97**. 1064, 1883; *Gazz. Chim. Ital.*, **14**. 38, 1884; **16**. 104, 1886; *Atti Accad. Lincei*, (4), **1**. 47, 1885; R. Weber, *Pogg. Ann.*, **120**. 291, 1863; *Journ. prakt. Chem.*, (1), **90**. 212, 1863; E. Petersen, *ib.*, (2), **40**. 44, 1889; *Vanadinet og dets naermeste analoger*, Copenhagen, 1888; C. F. Rammelsberg, *Sitzber. Akad. Berlin*, 490, 1874; O. F. von der Pfordten, *Liebig's Ann.*, **237**. 225, 1887; V. Merz, *Journ. prakt. Chem.*, (1), **99**. 157, 1866; *Zeit. Chem.*, (2), **3**. 122, 1867.

[2] O. Unverdorben, *Trommsdorff's Journ. Pharm.*, **9**. 1, 32, 1826; *Pogg. Ann.*, **7**. 320, 1826; J. J. Berzelius, *ib.*, **4**. 1, 1825; *Svenska Akad. Handl.*, **2**. 344, 1824; E. Glatzel, *Ber.*, **9**. 1829, 1876; O. Ruff and W. Plato, *ib.*, **37**. 673, 1904; O. Ruff and F. Eisner, *ib.*, **38**. 742, 1905; O. Ruff and K. Albert, *ib.*, **38**. 56, 1905; O. Ruff and H. Graf, *ib.*, **39**. 4317, 1906; O. Ruff and R. Ipsen, *ib.*, **36**. 1777, 1903; R. Ipsen, *Ueber das Titanfluorid*, Berlin, 1904; F. Emich, *Monatsh.*, **25**. 907, 1904; J. C. G. de Marignac, *Ann. Mines*, (5), **15**. 258, 1859; *Ann. Chim. Phys.*, (3), **60**. 257, 1860; A. Piccini, *ib.*, (7), **10**. 438, 1895; *Gazz. Chim. Ital.*, **14**. 38, 1884; **17**. 479, 1887; *Atti Accad. Lincei*, (4), **1**. 86, 1885; (4), **6**. i, 568, 1890; *Compt. Rend.*, **97**. 1064, 1884; H. Moissan, *ib.*, **120**. 293, 1895; E. Petersen, *Vanadinet og dets naermeste analoger*, Copenhagen, 1888; *Journ. prakt. Chem.*, (2), **40**. 44, 1889; A. Mazzucchelli, *Atti Accad. Lincei*, (5), **16**. ii, 349, 1907; A. Mazzucchelli and C. Barbero, *ib.*, (5), **15**. ii, 35, 109, 1906.

§ 11. Hydrofluotitanic Acid, and the Fluotitanates

As J. J. Berzelius [1] supposed, it is probable that a soln. of titanium dioxide in hydrofluoric acid contains **hydrofluotitanic acid**, H_2TiF_6, because heat is evolved during the reaction, and when the liquid is neutralized with bases, stable **fluotitanates**, R'_2TiF_6, are formed. J. J. Berzelius said that a soln. of the acid is obtained by decomposing crystalline titanium tetrafluoride with water; and by dissolving titanium in a warm mixture of hydrofluoric and nitric acids. W. von Kowalewsky found that the electrical conductivity of conc. hydrofluoric acid was 0·621, and that when 5 grms. of titanium dioxide were dissolved in 49·7 grms. of the acid, the conductivity rose to 0·690. This is taken to mean that the soln. contains a complex acid, H_2TiF_6, which is a better conductor than hydrofluoric acid.

F. Fischer and K. Thiele made hydrofluotitanic acid by adding lead carbonate to the acid so prepared, and treating the precipitated lead fluotitanate with hydrogen sulphide. Air was then bubbled through the filtered liquid for about an hour so as to remove the hydrogen sulphide. J. Thomsen gave for the heat of formation of hydrofluotitanic acid, $\{Ti(OH)_4, 6HF, aq.\}=30\cdot9$ Cals. Hydrofluotitanic acid is known only in soln. ; the free acid has not been isolated. The fluotitanates are usually sparingly soluble in water. According to J. J. Berzelius, J. C. G. de Marignac, and R. Weber, the fluotitanates are isomorphous with the corresponding fluosilicates, fluozirconates, and fluostannates. The complex nature of the fluotitanates was investigated by A. Mazzucchelli. O. Ruff and R. Ipsen showed that while sulphuric acid liberates volatile silicon tetrafluoride from the fluosilicates, titanium tetrafluoride is not vaporized when a fluotitanate is treated with sulphuric acid, but is converted quantitatively into titanium dioxide. F. Fischer and K. Thiele showed that an aq. soln. of the acid attacks glass, but does not react with neutral hydrogen dioxide, potassium ferrocyanide, or silver nitrate ; potassium salts give a white precipitate, and conc. sulphuric acid decomposes the soln. with the evolution of hydrogen.

J. J. Berzelius obtained normal **ammonium fluotitanate,** $(NH_4)_2TiF_6$, by adding ammonia to a soln. of titanium tetrafluoride, so long as the precipitate first formed redissolved, and evaporating the soln. to the point of crystallization. A. Piccini also made this salt. The brilliant scaly crystals were shown by J. C. G. de Marignac to belong to the trigonal system, and to be isomorphous with the corresponding fluostannate. The crystals do not lose weight at 100° ; but when the salt is distilled in a platinum vessel, at a temp. below redness, J. J. Berzelius said that it yielded a sublimate of ammonium fluoride, and there remained what he regarded as $NH_4F.TiF_4$, which fused at an incipient red heat, and sublimed unchanged in flakes which were soluble in water, and had a rough acid taste. After precipitating the titanium dioxide by adding an excess of potash-lye, the liquid smelled of ammonia. According to J. C. G. de Marignac, if an acidic or ammoniacal soln. of ammonium fluotitanate be mixed with an excess of ammonium fluoride, and allowed to crystallize, tetragonal crystals of **ammonium heptafluotitanate,** $3NH_4F.TiF_4$, are produced. The doubly-refracting crystals were said to be isomorphous with the corresponding fluosilicate. H. Baker obtained dendritic and rectangular crystals by the evaporation of a soln. of titanium dioxide in hydrofluoric acid, containing ammonium fluoride, and nearly neutralized with ammonia. E. Ebler and E. Schott prepared water-clear crystals of **hydrazine fluotitanate,** $(N_2H_5)_2TiF_6.2H_2O$, by dissolving titanium dioxide in cold fuming hydrofluoric acid in the proportions required to form hydrofluotitanic acid, adding 50 per cent. aq. hydrazine hydrate until the mixture was just alkaline, and evaporating the clear soln. in vacuo over sulphuric acid. E. Ebler and E. Schott prepared hydroxylamine fluotitanate, $(NH_3O)_2.H_2TiF_6$, by adding 2 per cent. hydroxylamine to a cooled soln. of hydrofluotitanic acid, and evaporating the soln. in vacuo ; the salt separates from methyl alcohol in white crystals. With quadrivalent titanium, hydroxylamine gives the same yellow coloration, caused by the formation of a higher oxide of titanium, as is produced by hydrogen dioxide.

P. Engelskirchen made dihydrated **lithium fluotitanate,** $Li_2TiF_6.2H_2O$, by dissolving lithium carbonate in hydrofluotitanic acid. The crystals effloresce on exposure to air, and they are readily soluble in water. Alcohol added to the aq. soln. precipitates a microcrystalline powder ; while the slow evaporation of the aq. soln. gives long, needle-like crystals. J. J. Berzelius obtained indistinct crystals of **sodium fluotitanate,** Na_2TiF_6, as a saline crust by evaporating the soln. obtained by adding sodium hydroxide to a soln. of the tetrafluoride until a permanent precipitate begins to form. M. A. Hunter employed a similar process. J. C. G. de Marignac obtained hexagonal prisms by the very slow evaporation of the soln., and they appeared to be isomorphous with the corresponding fluosilicate. J. J. Berzelius said that the sodium salt is more soluble in water than the potassium compound. **J. C. G.** de Marignac found that the mother-liquor containing an excess of sodium fluoride and hydrofluoric acid, deposited crystals of **sodium hydrofluotitanate,** $Na_2TiF_6.NaHF_2$, in rhombic prisms with the axial ratios $a : b : c = 0.5168 : 1 : 0.4663$. When heated on platinum foil, the salt decrepitates and gives off 7·65 per cent. of hydrogen fluoride, without melting. The salt is completely soluble in water, and the aq. soln. gives off carbon dioxide when treated with ammonium carbonate.

According to G. Marchetti, anhydrous **potassium fluotitanate,** K_2TiF_6, is prepared by adding the theoretical quantity of potassium hydrofluoride to a soln. of titanium dioxide in an excess of hydrofluoric acid. It crystallizes in small, very lustrous leaflets, which are denser than the crystals of the monohydrated fluotitanate, $K_2TiF_6.H_2O$. It can be crystallized without change from hot hydrofluoric acid, but when dissolved in water it is completely converted into the hydrated salt. Conversely, when the hydrated salt is dissolved in conc. hydrofluoric or hydrochloric acid, it is converted into the anhydrous salt. L. Weiss and H. Kaiser said that the anhydrous salt is most conveniently made by fusing rutile with potassium hydrofluoride and crystallizing the product from water containing a little hydrofluoric acid. Gebrüder Siemens made the alkali fluotitanates by adding hydrofluoric acid to a paste made of titanic acid and potassium fluoride. F. Stolba found that 100 parts of water at 21° dissolve 1·27 parts of the salt ; it is less soluble in soln. of alkali salts like potassium sulphate or nitrate ; and when treated with potassium hydroxide, it decomposes : $K_2TiF_6 + 4KOH = 6KF + Ti(OH)_4$, a reaction which can be employed for the volumetric determination of the hydrofluotitanic acid. According to O. Ruff and R. Ipsen, the salt is not decomposed when heated in a stream of hydrogen fluoride. **J. J.** Berzelius obtained **hydrated potassium fluotitanate,** $K_2TiF_6.H_2O$, by a process analogous to that employed for sodium fluotitanate. It is also obtained, as just indicated, from the anhydrous salt. J. J. Berzelius said the scaly crystals resemble those of boric acid, and when dried they become milk-white, and exhibit a silky lustre. J. C. G. de Marignac likened the crystals to those of the corresponding stannic salt, and found them isomorphous with potassium oxyfluo-columbate, and -tungstate. He said the crystals belong to the monoclinic system with the axial ratios $a : b : c = 0.9924 : 1 : 1.0520$, and $\beta = 98° 42'$. H. Töpsöe gave 2·992 for the sp. gr. The crystals lose all their water at 100°. According to J. J. Berzelius, when the salt is heated, water and titanium fluoride are given off, and at a white heat the salt melts without undergoing any further change. It dissolves readily in water without decomposition. J. C. G. de Marignac said that the salt is sparingly soluble in cold water, but readily soluble in boiling water, and that 100 parts of water dissolve S parts of K_2TiF_6, at

	0°	3°	6°	10°	14°	20°
S . . .	0·556	0·667	0·775	0·909	1·042	1·28

L. Weiss and H. Kaiser said that at 20°, 100 parts of water dissolve 1·28 parts of the salt, and at 100°, 10·64 parts ; much less is dissolved in the presence of hydrofluoric acid. G. Krüss and L. F. Nilson said that the salt is more soluble in a soln. of potassium oxyfluocolumbate. R. D. Hall and E. F. Smith said that the solubility in water is increased by hydrogen dioxide, and the soln. becomes deep yellow. Colourless crystals can be obtained from the soln. The addition of hydrofluoric acid bleaches the yellow soln. R. D. Hall found that the presence of potassium bromide or iodide lowers the solubility of the salts in water; and the crystals obtained from the soln. are associated with these halides. F. Wöhler found that while the titanic acid is immediately precipitated from the hot soln., this is not so with the cold soln. J. J. Berzelius said that when the salt is fused with potassium hydrosulphate, only a small proportion of titanium tetrafluoride is given off. The salt is decomposed with vivid incandescence when heated with potassium, and titanium and potassium fluoride are formed. L. Weiss and H. Kaiser observed a similar reaction with sodium ; and when aluminium is added to the fused salt, aluminium titanide, Ti_2Al_3, is formed. C. F. Rammelsberg reduced the soln. to titanium trifluoride by zinc and hydrochloric acid.

P. Engelskirchen prepared **rubidium fluotitanate,** Rb_2TiF_6, by adding rubidium acetate to a soln. of titanium tetrafluoride. M. E. Pennington made this salt by crystallization from a soln. of rubidium fluoride and titanium fluoride. The salt is purified by recrystallization from water. The small hexagonal plates are sparingly soluble in cold water, and more readily soluble in hot water ; the salt is precipitated by alcohol from the aq. soln. He also made **cæsium fluotitanate,** Cs_2TiF_6, in small columnar crystals by crystallization from a soln. of cæsium carbonate in hydrofluotitanic acid. The salt dissolves more readily in hot than in cold water ; and the solubility is greater than in the case of the rubidium salt. H. Behrens and P. D. C. Kley discussed the formation of these salts in microchemical analysis. M. E. Pennington found that when cæsium fluoride is added to a conc. soln. of titanium tetrafluoride, small lustrous crystals of **cæsium octofluotitanate,** Cs_4TiF_8, are produced. There is no loss of weight at 100° ; the salt is not decomposed by water ; and it is more soluble than the fluotantalate, $Cs_{15}TaF_{20}$.

J. J. Berzelius prepared tetrahydrated **copper fluotitanate,** $CuTiF_6.4H_2O$, by crystallization from a mixed soln. of the component salts. The pale, bluish-green, acicular or tabular crystals were found by J. C. G. de Marignac to belong to the monoclinic system, and to have the axial ratios $a:b:c=0.7471:1:0.5564$, and $\beta=104°\ 9'$. The crystals are isomorphous with the corresponding fluosilicate and fluostannate. They lose no water at 100° ; and, according to J. J. Berzelius, they dissolve in water with partial decomposition ; and readily and completely in acidulated water. If the aq. soln. of this be mixed with ammonium fluoride, and allowed to evaporate spontaneously, or at a gentle heat, J. C. G. de Marignac obtained ditetragonal bipyramidal crystals of **ammonium copper fluotitanate,** $CuF_2.NH_4F.TiF_4.4H_2O$, with the axial ratio $a:c=1:1.0729$. The crystals effloresce in air, and lose their water when warmed. They are soluble in cold water. Similar crystals of potassium copper fluotitanate, $CuF_2.KF.TiF_4.4H_2O$, were obtained by an analogous process. The yield is smaller than with the ammonium salt on account of the lower solubility of potassium fluotitanate. J. C. G. de Marignac obtained a crystalline, deliquescent **silver fluotitanate** by a process like that used for copper fluotitanate.

J. J. Berzelius evaporated a soln. of calcium carbonate in one of titanium tetrafluoride in hydrofluoric acid, and obtained prismatic crystals of **trihydrated calcium fluotitanate,** $CaTiF_6.3H_2O$. J. C. G. de Marignac prepared the same salt, and found the first crop of crystals to be isomorphous with strontium fluotitanate, and fluostannate, and they were assumed to be **dihydrated calcium fluotitanate,** $CaTiF_6.2H_2O$. According to J. J. Berzelius, the crystals dissolve in acidulated water without change, but they are decomposed by water alone. J. C. G. de Marignac made **dihydrated strontium fluotitanate,** $SrTiF_6.2H_2O$, in monoclinic crystals, with the axial ratios $a:b:c=1.2066:1:1.2295$, and $\beta=111°\ 6'$. At a temp. exceeding 100°, the crystals lose water and hydrogen fluoride ; they dissolve in cold water ; and the soln. becomes turbid when boiled. P. Engelskirchen obtained a fine-grained crystalline precipitate of **barium fluotitanate,** $BaTiF_6$, by adding barium chloride to a soln. of hydrofluotitanic acid. The salt is sparingly soluble in water, but readily soluble in dil. hydrochloric or nitric acid. F. Emich obtained **hemihydrated barium fluotitanate,** $BaTiF_6.\frac{1}{2}H_2O$, as a coarse, crystalline precipitate by adding barium chloride to a hot aq. soln. of potassium fluotitanate. The salt loses water of crystallization only on prolonged heating at a dull red-heat ; when heated to a higher temp., it decomposes with formation of titanium tetrafluoride.

J. J. Berzelius obtained **hexahydrated magnesium fluotitanate,** $MgTiF_6.6H_2O$, in long needle-like crystals by the spontaneous evaporation of a soln. of magnesium carbonate in hydrofluotitanic acid; and J. C. G. de Marignac obtained hexagonal crystals isomorphous with the corresponding fluostannate. The crystals lost

18·2 per cent. of water at 100°, and 40·33 per cent. at 300°; some titanium tetra-fluoride is lost at the higher temp. J. C. G. de Marignac similarly made **hexahydrated zinc fluotitanate**, $ZnTiF_6.6H_2O$, in hexagonal crystals with the axial ratio $a:c=1:0.513$; and isomorphous with the corresponding fluosilicate and stannate. B. Gossner found the sp. gr. to be 2·106. J. C. G. de Marignac's attempt to make a fluotitanate with more zinc fluoride was nugatory. P. Engelskirchen made **hexahydrated cadmium fluotitanate**, $CdTiF_6.6H_2O$, by evaporating a soln. of cadmium carbonate in hydrofluotitanic acid, or by treating the soln. with alcohol. The crystals appear in the form of needles, or hexagonal prisms. The salt effloresces slowly in air, and loses all its water over sulphuric acid. It is very soluble in water and in 50 per cent. alcohol. J. J. Berzelius obtained small colourless crystals of **lead fluotitanate.** They were sparingly soluble in water without decomposition. P. Engelskirchen obtained the *trihydrate*, $PbTiF_6.3H_2O$, by adding freshly precipitated lead carbonate to a filtered soln. of titanium dioxide in hot hydrofluoric acid; evaporating the soln. on a water-bath; and stirring the soln. while cooling. The crystals form in soln. containing a large excess of free hydrofluotitanic acid. They are pressed between filter-paper, washed with alcohol and ether, and dried for a day over calcium chloride. A boiling soln. of hydrofluotitanic acid and lead nitrate or acetate gives lead fluoride crystals on cooling to 50°. The colourless crystals dissolve in water with the separation of some lead fluoride. F. Fischer and K. Thiele found that on electrolysis of a soln. of lead fluotitanate a basic salt is precipitated on the lead anode. They obtained an acid salt in soln., but not in the solid state.

J. J. Berzelius, and J. C. G. de Marignac obtained hexagonal crystals of **hexahydrated manganese fluotitanate**, $MnTiF_6.6H_2O$, isomorphous with the corresponding fluosilicate. R. Weber prepared **ferrous fluotitanate**, $FeTiF_6.6H_2O$, in hexagonal yellowish green-crystals. J. J. Berzelius made **ferric fluotitanate** by the spontaneous evaporation of an aq. soln. of a mixture of the two salts. The pale yellow crystalline mass is decomposed by water. R. Weber obtained green crystals of **hexahydrated nickel fluotitanate**, $NiTiF_6.6H_2O$, from a soln. of nickel oxide and titanium dioxide in hydrofluoric acid. The salt is very soluble in water. P. Engelskirchen prepared **hexahydrated cobalt fluotitanate**, $CoTiF_6.6H_2O$, from a soln. of freshly precipitated cobalt carbonate in hydrofluotitanic acid, either by evaporation, or by the addition of alcohol. The red hexagonal prisms lose 3 mols of water at 100°–110°, and some hydrogen fluoride is then evolved. The salt is sparingly soluble in water, less so in 50 per cent. alcohol, and insoluble in absolute alcohol. A. Miolati and G. Rossi prepared **cobaltic hexamminofluotitanate**, or luteocobaltic fluotitanate, $2\{Co(NH_3)_6\}F_3.3TiF_4.2HF$, by adding a soln. of luteocobaltic carbonate or fluoride to a hydrofluoric acid soln. of titanic acid; the salt can be crystallized from water containing hydrogen fluoride, and it loses this gas at 110°. After long preservation in a desiccator over sulphuric acid, it assumes the composition $2Co(NH_3)_6.3TiF_4$.

REFERENCES.

[1] J. J. Berzelius, *Svenska Akad. Handl.*, 2. 344, 1824; *Pogg. Ann.*, 4. 1, 1825; R. Weber, *ib.*, 120. 287, 1863; J. Thomsen, *ib.*, 139. 212, 1870; J. C. G. de Marignac, *Ann. Mines*, (5), 15. 228, 1859; *Ann. Chim. Phys.*, (3), 60. 257, 1860; (4), 8. 65, 1866; *Compt. Rend.*, 60. 234, 1865; *Bull. Soc. Chim.*, (2), 3. 372, 1865; W. von Kowalewsky, *Zeit. anorg. Chem.*, 25. 193, 1900; F. Fischer and K. Thiele, *ib.*, 67. 302, 1910; G. Marchetti, *Ber.*, 29. 120, 1896; *Zeit. anorg. Chem.*, 10. 66, 1895; L. Weiss and H. Kaiser, *ib.*, 65. 345, 1910; B. Gossner, *Ber.*, 40. 2373, 1907; O. Ruff and R. Ipsen, *ib.*, 36. 1777, 1903; R. Ipsen, *Ueber das Titanfluorid*, Berlin, 1904; H. Baker, *Journ. Chem. Soc.*, 35. 763, 1879; Gebrüder Siemens, *German Pat., D.R.P.* 279011, 1915; A. Piccini, *Atti Accad. Lincei*, (4), 6. i, 568, 1890; A. Mazzucchelli, *ib.*, (5), 16. ii, 349, 1907; A. Miolati and G. Rossi, *ib.*, (5), 5. ii, 183, 223, 1896; E. Ebler and E. Schott, *Journ. prakt. Chem.*, (2), 81. 556, 1910; E. Schott, *Beiträge zur Kenntnis des Hydroxylamins und Hydrazins*, Heidelberg, 1908; F. Emich, *Monatsh.*, 25. 907, 1904; P. Engelskirchen, *Beiträge zur Kenntnis der Salze der Kiesel- und Titanfluowasserstoffsäure*, Berlin, 1903; M. A. Hunter, *Rensselaer Polyt. Inst.*, 1, 1911; C. F. Rammelsberg, *Sitzber. Akad. Berlin*, 490, 1874; F. Stolba,

Listy Chem., **7**. 86, 1882 ; F. Wöhler, *Ann. Chim. Phys.*, (3), **29**. 166, 1850 ; G. Krüss and
L. F. Nilson, *Œfvers. Akad. Förh.*, **5**, 1887 ; *Ber.*, **20**. 1684, 1887 ; R. D. Hall and E. F. Smith,
Proc. Amer. Phil. Soc., **44**. 207, 211, 1905 ; *Chem. News*, **92**. 220, 232, 242, 252, 262, 276, 1905 ;
R. D. Hall, *Observations on the Metallic Acids*, Easton, Pa., 1904 ; *Journ. Amer. Chem. Soc.*, **26**.
1246, 1904 ; M. E. Pennington, *ib.*, **18**. 58, 1896 ; *Derivatives of Columbium and Tantalum*,
Easton, Pa., 1895 ; *Chem. News*, **75**. 8, 18, 31, 38, 1897 ; H. Töpsöe, *Arch. Sciences Genève*, (2),
45. 223, 1872 ; H. Behrens and P. D. C. Kley, *Mikrochemische Analyse*, Leipzig, 110, 1921 ;
F. Fischer and K. Thiele, *Zeit. anorg. Chem.*, **67**. 308, 1910.

§ 12. Titanium Chlorides

Three titanium chlorides have been prepared—the di-, tri-, and tetra-chlorides.
The analysis of a titanium chloride by E. S. George [1] indicated half as much
chlorine as is present in the tetrachloride (*q.v.*), but this product seems to have
been very impure. According to F. Wöhler, **titanium dichloride**, $TiCl_2$, is probably
formed in colourless soln. when titanium is dissolved in hydrochloric acid. Much
hydrogen is, at the same time, evolved. O. F. von der Pfordten attributed the result
obtained by F. Wöhler to the use of titanium containing sodium which reduced
the salt to the dichloride. With metal free from sodium, O. F. von der Pfordten,
E. Glatzel, and H. Moissan obtained a violet soln. of the trichloride. A. Stähler
and H. Wirthwein favoured F. Wöhler's view. E. Knecht showed that the reduction of aq. soln. of titanium tetrachloride always furnishes the trichloride not the
dichloride. In preparing the trichloride by reducing the tetrachloride with hydrogen (*q.v.*), J. J. Ebelmen obtained golden-yellow scales which he considered to be
those of the dichloride, but C. Friedel and J. Guérin showed that it must have been
an oxychloride. A. Piccini and L. Marino's attempt to make compounds of the
type TiX_2 was not successful. C. Friedel and J. Guérin made the dichloride by
heating the trichloride to redness in a stream of hydrogen. In order to ensure
success, there must be an entire absence of air and moisture. They said that the
trichloride *se dédouble*, forming the tetrachloride which distilled, and the dichloride
which remained behind as a black powder. O. Ruff and F. Neumann used a
similar mode of preparation, by reducing the tetrachloride to trichloride (*q.v.*),
and transforming the latter in one operation. It is difficult to prepare a product
free from titanium, and the trichloride and oxychloride by this process. A. Stähler
and F. Bachran represented the reaction at 660°–700°, in an atm. of hydrogen, by
$2TiCl_3 \rightleftharpoons TiCl_2 + TiCl_4$. O. F. von der Pfordten reduced titanium tetrachloride at
ordinary temp. by sodium amalgam, and distilled off the unchanged tetrachloride
in a current of carbon dioxide. He also said that titanium tetrachloride is reduced
at ordinary temp. by hydrogen sulphide ; $TiCl_4 + H_2S = TiCl_2 + 2HCl + S$; but
A. Stähler and F. Bachran could not confirm this observation, though they did
obtain $TiSCl_2$ and TiS_2. Titanium tetrachloride was found by O. Ruff and F. Neumann to be reduced to the dichloride by sodium amalgam, and at the same time
some trichloride is formed by the interaction of the tetra- and di-chlorides. According to R. Schmidt, titanium dichloride, almost free from oxygen, is obtained by
the thermal decomposition of titanium trichloride in a carbon tube at temp. not
greatly exceeding 600° ; if glass or quartz tubes are used, oxygen is abstracted
from the silica with consequent production of oxygenated compounds. At 600°
(0·02 mm.), titanium dichloride slowly volatilizes and is decomposed into the tri-
and tetra-chlorides, which are deposited in the cooler portions of the tube. The
effect is due to decomposition of the dichloride into titanium and titanium tetrachloride and reduction of the latter by unchanged dichloride to give the trichloride.

According to C. Friedel and J. Guérin, titanium dichloride is a blackish powder,
which is occasionally in the form of flakes, very unstable in air, and in the presence
of moisture (with the latter it becomes lighter in colour). Thrown into water it
hisses like red-hot iron and dissolves, with a copious evolution of hydrogen.
On the addition of ammonia to this soln., a black precipitate is formed, hydrogen
being evolved at the same time. The black precipitate gradually changes to blue,

and eventually to white, and on throwing a few drops of water upon the dichloride (taking care not to moisten it completely), sufficient heat is generated to cause it to take fire in the air. On being heated in air, the di-chloride burns like tinder, fumes of the tetrachloride being evolved, and titanic acid remaining behind. It is insoluble in ether, carbon disulphide, and titanium tetrachloride, and on being heated gently with absolute alcohol, hydrogen is evolved, and a yellowish liquid formed, which on the addition of ammonia furnishes a blue-black precipitate. Dry ammonia gas passed over the dichloride at a red heat gives rise to the formation of the nitride, Ti_3N_4, hydrogen being set free according to the equation, $3TiCl_2+4NH_3=Ti_3N_4+6HCl+3H_2$. Bromine forms with the dichloride a fuming liquid, which boils at about 180°, and is probably $TiCl_2Br_2$. The various descriptions of the properties of titanium dichloride are not in agreement. Titanium dichloride is a black powder which dissolves in water and in alcohol with a brown coloration, but it is insoluble in ether. On exposure to the air, the aq. soln. deposits titanic acid ; the alcoholic soln. remains clear, but contains organic chlorine products. With potassium thiocyanate and ether, titanium dichloride exhibits a delicate and characteristic reaction ; the ether acquires a dark brown colour. O. Ruff and F. Neumann found that the dichloride does not vaporize appreciably at 600°. It is very reactive. H. Goerges and A. Stähler said that the black powder dissolved in fuming hydrochloric acid, forming a green soln. which contained bivalent titanium, and gave the following reactions. On boiling in the air, it became violet, with the formation of tervalent titanium. Nitric acid oxidized it first to the tervalent condition (violet), and then to the quadrivalent (colourless). Ammonium hydroxide, carbonate, or sulphide gave first a dark brown precipitate, which decomposed after a short time with the rapid evolution of hydrogen. Potassium thiocyanate gave a green soln., and sodium acetate, a green precipitate of the titanous acetate. On heating with mercuric chloride, calomel was precipitated. Indications were obtained that when the trichloride is reduced by hydrogen at a bright red heat, some metallic titanium is formed. When the soln. of the dichloride in hydrochloric acid is evaporated in vacuo, the crystals which are formed were supposed to be those of a hydrate, $TiCl_2.nH_2O$. When a hydrochloric acid soln. of titanium dichloride is mixed with one of titanium tetrachloride a violet coloration is produced owing to the formation of the trichloride. M. Coblens and J. K. Bernstein found that titanous chloride reduces nitric oxide and nitrous oxide to ammonia. Nitric oxide is evolved, and no ammonia is formed when a sodium nitrite soln. is added drop by drop to an acid titanous chloride soln. Titanous chloride has a specific decomposing effect on nitrous and hyponitrous acids. The gases escape before any appreciable reduction can take place.

Anhydrous **titanium trichloride,** $TiCl_3$, or *titanous chloride,* or as it was originally called *titanium sesquichloride,* was made by J. J. Ebelmen [2] by passing dried hydrogen through warm liquid titanium tetrachloride, and leading the mixture of hydrogen and tetrachloride vapour through a red-hot tube ; the trichloride collects as a mass of dark violet scales in the tube just beyond the heated zone. The current of hydrogen is continued till the tube is cold, and the salt is preserved out of contact with air. H. Goerges and A. Stähler made the trichloride by this reaction using a porcelain tube heated electrically by a wire spiral inside the tube, and surrounded by a glass tube cooled externally by a rapid current of cold water. The mixed gases traverse the space between the tubes. The reaction begins about 600°, and at 785°, the percentage decomposition was 21·7, and at 1200°, 94·3. The trichloride collects on the surface of the cold tube as a fine reddish-violet powder. According to F. Meyer and co-workers, titanium trichloride may be prepared by the reduction of the tetrachloride by means of hydrogen, provided that the products of the reaction are quickly cooled, and the hydrogen chloride is removed by means of metallic titanium. The trichloride so prepared consists of large violet crystals, which are fairly stable in the air. The reduction is not direct, but three reactions, $TiCl_4+H_2=TiCl_2+2HCl$; $TiCl_2+TiCl_4=2TiCl_3$; $2TiCl_3+2HCl=2TiCl_4+H_2$, may proceed simultaneously. F. Emich passed electric sparks through a mixture of hydrogen, and tetrachloride vapour, and obtained a deposit of violet crystals ; while F. Böck and L. Moser subjected a mixture of dry hydrogen and titanium tetrachloride vapour to the action of the silent electric discharge. At ordinary temp. a dark brown deposit was formed containing a mixture of the tri- and tetra-chlorides. When heated in vacuo at 100° the tetrachloride was removed, leaving the brown trichloride in which the tetrachloride had been occluded. Between 200° and 400°, the violet trichloride was formed free from occluded tetrachloride. The brown substance was considered to be a labile, allotropic, or monotropic form of the trichloride which changes to the violet form between 150° and 200° in vacuo. The change from brown to violet trichloride is not reversible ; for when the temp. was gradually raised above that at which transformation takes place, the heating curve of the brown modification did not differ appreciably from that of the cooling curve of the violet modification thereby formed. C. Friedel and J. Guérin made the trichloride by heating a mixture of the tetrachloride and reduced silver in a sealed tube at 180°–200° : $TiCl_4 + Ag \rightleftharpoons AgCl + TiCl_3$; and T. E. Thorpe, by shaking the tetrachloride with mercury in a sealed tube : $TiCl_4 + Hg \rightleftharpoons HgCl + TiCl_3$. The reaction is rapid and complete at 98°, but between 200° and 250° the reverse change is marked. K. Seubert and A. Schmidt reduced titanium tetrachloride vapour to the trichloride by passing it over magnesium at a red heat. L. Lévy obtained the trichloride by heating to 100° a mixture of titanium tetrachloride and mercury diethyl in an atm. of carbon dioxide : $2TiCl_4 + Hg(C_2H_5)_2 = HgCl_2 + C_4H_{10} + 2TiCl_3$. Titanium tetrachloride in benzene soln. is also partially reduced by mercury diphenyl. O. Ruff and F. Neumann found that at slightly elevated temp. titanium tetrachloride is reduced to the trichloride by aluminium, magnesium, zinc, mercury, silver, arsenic, and tin. Aluminium trichloride acts as a catalyst, and in its presence the reduction by aluminium is quantitative at 200°. The conditions for the reduction of the tetra- to the tri-chloride were studied by F. Meyer and co-workers. They found that the two requirements for the successful preparation of coarsely crystalline titanium trichloride by reduction of the tetrachloride are, first, a steep temperature gradient to ensure rapid cooling, and secondly, the depression of the hydrogen chloride concentration. The first condition is best secured by using a non-conducting (quartz) tube of narrow bore, with air cooling at the receiver end. The second is attained most easily by the addition of metallic titanium to the re-action mixture. This subject was discussed by R. Schmidt.

Anhydrous titanium trichloride forms dark violet, scaly crystals which, according to C. Friedel and J. Guérin, are isomorphous with those of ferric chloride. Titanium trichloride deliquesces on exposure to air, and decomposes rapidly. It oxidizes slowly in dry air, rapidly in moist air. The trichloride is non-volatile, but H. Goerges and A. Stähler found that when heated to 440°, it decomposes into the di- and tetra-chlorides : $2TiCl_3 \rightleftharpoons TiCl_2 + TiCl_4$; whereas to make it from the tetrachloride and hydrogen, a temp. of 600° is necessary ; even at ordinary temp. the trichloride decomposes and the vap. press. of the tetrachloride produced is appreciable. J. J. Ebelmen said that the trichloride decomposes at ordinary temp., and C. Friedel and J. Guérin observed that in closed vessels, the trichloride is decomposed, for the surface becomes white, and unlike the freshly prepared trichloride, it fumes in moist air. H. Goerges and A. Stähler found that the trichloride is best preserved in an atm. of dry carbon dioxide. O. Ruff and F. Neumann found that titanium tri-chloride is not decomposed at 425° under one mm. press., but at 450° the tetra-chloride and dichloride are formed. When the trichloride is heated in contact with air, J. J. Ebelmen observed that the tetrachloride is given off ; and some titanium dioxide remains. When dissolved in water it forms a violet-red soln. F. Böck and L. Moser gave for the heat of soln. (brown, $TiCl_3$, Aq.)$=48\cdot150–48\cdot837$ Cals. ; and (violet, $TiCl_3$, Aq.)$=44\cdot287–45\cdot800$ Cals. in agreement with the view that the brown and violet forms are monotropic modifications. G. S. Forbes and L. P. Hall calculated $-0\cdot349$ to $-0\cdot399$ volt for the normal potential of the reduction Ti···+H⇌Ti···+H· from the measurements of the e.m.f. of the cell ⁻Hg | TiCl₃,TiCl₂, 0·05N-HCl | 4N-KCl | 0·1N-HCl | Hg·. H. Goerges and A. Stähler observed that a mixture of the trichloride and liquid ammonia in a sealed tube furnishes a yellow emulsion ; a part of the trichloride seems to pass into soln.

According to R. Weber, a soln. of titanium trichloride is obtained by dissolving titanium in hydrochloric acid, and, according to C. F. Rammelsberg, no lower chloride is produced—vide the dichloride. E. Knecht reduced a soln. of the tetrachloride with tin and hydrochloric acid, and removed the tin with hydrogen sulphide ; he also obtained it by reducing a soln. of titanium dioxide in hydrochloric acid by zinc and hydrochloric acid ; and C. F. Rammelsberg similarly reduced a cold or boiling soln. of potassium chlorotitanate. J. N. von Fuchs, F. Pisani, and O. F. von der Pfordten also used zinc and hydrochloric acid for the reduction. E. Glatzel obtained a green mass of tetrahydrated titanium trichloride, TiCl₃.4H₂O, by evaporating a soln. of titanium in hydrochloric acid. The product dissolves in water, but the liquid is not clear ; it easily oxidizes on exposure to air E. Polidori had doubts about this hydrate ; and H. Goerges and A. Stähler could obtain only the hydrated dichloride by E. Glatzel's method. E. Polidori made violet hexahydrated titanium trichloride, TiCl₃.6H₂O, by reducing a soln. of the tetrachloride in 30 per cent. hydrochloric acid, by electrolysis with a carbon rod as positive electrode. The violet soln. was filtered through glass-wool, cooled with ice and salt ; and treated with a current of dry hydrogen chloride until the salt crystallized out. H. Spence also obtained the trichloride by the electrolytic reduction of a 20–25 per cent. soln. of the tetrachloride with dil. hydrochloric acid in the anode compartment ; using a lead cathode and a carbon or platinum-iridium anode, and 200 amp. per sq. metre, and 3 to 4 volts. The soln. was conc. under reduced press. until its sp. gr. at 65°–70°=1·5, when crystals of the hexahydrate were formed. Like chromium and vanadium trichlorides, titanium trichloride can exist in two forms—an unstable green hydrate, and a stable violet hydrate—for A. Stähler showed that if a conc. aq. soln. of the violet hydrate is covered with a layer of absolute ether and then sat. with hydrogen chloride and kept cool meanwhile, the green, unstable hydrate separates out in crystals ; when the hydrogen chloride is washed out with ether, the violet compound is again formed. Green vanadium trichloride does not change in colour when treated with ethereal hydrogen chloride. According to E. Polidori, the hexahydrated trichloride is deliquescent, and oxidizes very slowly in dry air, but rapidly in moist air.

According to J. J. Ebelmen, the violet-red soln. of titanium trichloride in water is decolorized on exposure to air owing to the formation of titanic acid ; the presence of a little hydrochloric acid prevents the precipitation of the titanic acid. When the aq. soln. is evaporated to dryness, it furnishes a blue oxy-chloride. When the aq. soln. is treated with potassium hydroxide, sodium hydroxide, or aq. ammonia, dark brown titanium trihydroxide is precipitated, and this quickly changes to black, blue, and finally white titanic acid, and hydrogen is at the same time evolved. Alkali carbonates behave similarly, but carbon dioxide and then hydrogen are evolved. The soln. is not appreciably changed by hydrogen sulphide ; ammonium sulphide acts like aq. ammonia. Nitric acid decolorizes the soln. with the evolution of nitric oxide ; and, according to E. Knecht, some ammonia is formed. The reduction of nitric acid by titanous salts has been studied by L. H. Milligan and G. R. Gillette. As indicated below, O. C. M. Davis prepared titanium nitrogen hexachlorotetrasulphide, N₄S₄.2TiCl₃, by the action of titanium tetrachloride on nitrogen sulphide—vide the addition compounds of titanium tetrachloride. A. Stähler prepared rubidium titanous pentachloride, or rubidium chlorotitanite, TiCl₃.2RbCl.H₂O, by passing hydrogen chloride into an aq. soln. of a mixture of rubidium and titanium chlorides, heated on a water-bath. The salt is green, and it forms a violet soln. with water. Green cæsium titanous pentachloride, or cæsium chlorotitanite, TiCl₃.2CsCl.H₂O, was obtained in a similar way.

A soln. of titanium trichloride, said J. J. Ebelmen, est un réductif des plus *énergiques ;* and E. Knecht and E. Hibbert found it is a more powerful reducing agent than stannous chloride. According to J. J. Ebelmen, potassium permanganate decolorizes the soln. and is itself decolorized. When sulphur dioxide is heated with the trichloride, sulphur is deposited, and E. Knecht found that hydrosulphurous acid is formed as an intermediate product. J. J. Ebelmen showed that mercury, silver, and gold are precipitated by the trichloride from soln of their salts. According to A. Stähler and F. Bachran, titanium trichloride reacts with a soln. of gold chloride producing colloidal gold analogous to purple of Cassius, and the reaction will detect one part of gold in 20 million parts of water. Chlorates and perchlorates are reduced to chlorides ; hydrogen dioxide to water ; and persulphates to sulphates. According to A. Monnier, platinum, iridium, and palladium chlorides give the respective metals. Selenates give red selenium ; and tellurates give tellurium when heated. Tungstates are reduced, giving a blue colour ; molybdates, a brown colour ; and vanadates are decolorized. Chromates and dichromates give green chromic salts. J. J. Ebelmen said that a trace of titanium trichloride brings violet chromic chloride into soln. Many organic substances are reduced by titanium trichloride. An excess of the trichloride was found by E. Knecht to reduce cupric sulphate to the metal. L. Moser described the application of the reaction for the determination of copper. J. J. Ebelmen showed that the trichloride reduces ferric to ferrous salts, and E. Knecht and E. Hibbert utilized the reaction for the volumetric determination of iron : $TiCl_3 + FeCl_3 = TiCl_4 + FeCl_2$. The end of the reaction is shown by alkali thiocyanate or methylene-blue as an external indicator. E. Knecht and co-workers, E. Zintl and A. Rauch, W. S. Hendrixson, etc., showed that the soln. of titanium trichloride (or sulphate) can also be used for the determination of copper, tin, chromium, hydrogen dioxide, chlorates, bromates, iodates, perchlorates, nitrates, hydroxylamine, hyposulphites, ferricyanides, and numerous organic compounds, and dye-stuffs. E. Zintl and A. Rauch, and W. S. Hendrixson discussed the application to ferricyanides, iodates, etc.; and I. M. Kolthoff and co-workers, and E. Zintl and A. Rauch, the titrometry of the trichloride.

E. S. George [3] discovered **titanium tetrachloride,** $TiCl_4$, in 1825 ; he obtained it by passing dried chlorine over titanium heated in a glass tube ; there is no reaction in the cold. The titanium available to E. S. George was shown by F. Wöhler to have been a carbonitride, and that in the reaction some cyanogen chloride is simultaneously produced and forms sulphur-yellow crystals. F. Wöhler also showed that while chlorine has but little action on titanium in the cold, the elements unite directly when warmed, forming the tetrachloride. E. Vigouroux and G. Arrivaut used ferrotitanium as a source of titanium ; if desired, most of the iron can be first removed by hydrochloric acid, and the residue heated in a stream of chlorine in a porcelain tube. The liquid was purified by fractional distillation. M. Billy purified titanium tetrachloride by treatment with sodium, amalgam followed by fractional distillation between 135°–137° ; ethane tetrachloride was removed by distillation in a current of dry air at 120°. The tetrachloride was finally kept at its b.p. for 2 hrs. in the presence of metallic titanium. H. R. Ellis ignited a mixture of rutile and powdered aluminium ; heated the product in a current of chlorine ; and purified the product from silicon tetrachloride by fractional distillation. M. A. Hunter, and H. Goerges and A. Stähler heated titanium carbide in a stream of chlorine, and purified the product by fractional distillation. C. Friedel and J. Guérin also found that at a high temp. chlorine reacts with titanium dioxide : $TiO_2 + 2Cl_2 \rightleftharpoons TiCl_4 + O_2$. J. B. A. Dumas made the tetrachloride by passing chlorine over a red-hot mixture of titanium dioxide and carbon—even the heat of a spirit lamp, said F. Wöhler, is sufficient for the purpose. If rutile is used instead of titanium dioxide, some ferrous or ferric chloride is formed. The liquid which is condensed has a reddish colour owing to the presence of ferric chloride ; most of this can be removed by fractional distillation. J. I. Pierre, A. Demoly, O. F. von der Pfordten, V. Merz, and R. F. Wagner used the chlorine-carbon process. O. Priesz found the temp. of the reaction can be reduced to 300° by adding a small proportion of chloride or oxide of cerium, zirconium, manganese, or a rare earth. F. de Carli used ferrotitanium in place of titanium. C. W. Watts and C. A. Bell passed carbon tetrachloride, chloroform, or a mixture of chlorine and carbon monoxide over red-hot titanium dioxide and obtained the tetrachloride : $TiO_2+2Cl_2+2CO=2CO_2+TiCl_4$. C. Renz used chloroform. O. Priesz found the yield is improved if a little carbon be mixed with the titanic oxide. The main reaction is represented : $TiO_2+2CHCl_3=TiCl_4$ $+2CO+2HCl$. The temp. determines the nature of the products of the secondary reaction, carbon dioxide, carbonyl chloride, hexachlorobenzene, etc. L. Meyer observed no change in the action of carbon tetrachloride on titanium dioxide at a high temp. ; but E. A. Demarçay found the action is fast at 440°, and he considered this to be one of the most convenient methods of preparation. H. E. Quantin studied the action of carbon tetrachloride on a number of metal oxides. F. Bourion made titanium tetrachloride by the action of the vapour of sulphur chloride, S_2Cl_2, and chlorine on red-hot titanium dioxide. The reaction is complicated by the formation of $2TiCl_4.SCl_4$.

J. B. A. Dumas freed the titanium tetrachloride from an excess of chlorine, which gives it a yellow colour, by agitation with small quantities of mercury, and distillation, two or three times, from mercury. F. Wöhler used copper ; and A. Bertrand employed reduced iron. H. Rose, and A. Demoly rectified the tetrachloride by distillation, four or five times, over mercury or potassium ; V. Merz distilled the liquid from sodium amalgam ; R. F. Wagner distilled the crude liquid over sodium to remove hydrogen chloride, chlorine, and ferric chloride ; and rectified the product by fractional distillation. O. F. von der Pfordten found that vanadium oxychloride imparts a yellow colour to the crude liquid, and is removed by the distillation over sodium. G. P. Baxter and G. J. Fertig described an elaborate method of purification for their at. wt. determination.

The physical properties of titanium tetrachloride.—Titanium tetrachloride at ordinary temp. is a transparent, colourless, mobile liquid. J. I. Pierre gave 1·76098 for the **specific gravity** at 0°/4° ; J. H. Gladstone gave 1·744 at 10·5° ; A. Stiefelhagen, 1·761 at 18° ; and T. E. Thorpe, 1·76041 at 0°/4° ; and 1·5222 at its b.p. O. Masson, and J. A. Groshans compared the mol. vol. and b.p. of the family of tetrachlorides. J. B. A. Dumas gave 6·836 (air, unity) or 197·4 (oxygen, 16) for the **vapour density** when the theoretical value is 190 (oxygen, 16). J. I. Pierre represented the **thermal expansion,** or the vols., v, occupied by unit vol. of liquid at $\theta°$, between 0° and 140°, when the vol. at 0° is unity, by the formula $v=1+0.03942569C04\theta+0.0_51345793937\theta^2+0.0_9888044\theta^3$; and T. E. Thorpe, $v=1+0.03982612\theta+0.0_65055280^2+0.0_8513052\theta^3$. J. J. Saslawsky studied the relation of the expansion coeff. with the structure. J. B. A. Dumas gave for the **boiling point,** 135° at 763 mm. ; J. I. Pierre, 136° at 762·3 ; T. E. Thorpe, 136·4° at 760 ; M. A. Hunter, 136·5° ; H. R. Ellis, E. Vigouroux and G. Arrivaut, and A. Stähler, 136° ; F. Emich, 134·8° at 735 mm. ; P. A. Bond and H. T. Beach, 136° at 750 mm. ; and B. F. Duppa, G. Gustavson, and C. Renz, 135°. J. I. Pierre said that the liquid remains clear at −25° ; the **melting point** given by F. Emich, and W. Biltz and E. Meinecke, is −23° ; W. H. Latimer, −30°; and by E. Haase, −25°. The **critical temperature** estimated by C. M. Guldberg is 358°. H. V. Regnault gave 0·18812 for the **specific heat** of the liquid between 13° and 99° ; and 0·12897 for the sp. ht. of the vapour at constant press. between 163° and 271°. W. H. Latimer gave for the mol. ht., C_p :

°K	86·7°	92·8°	99·3°	194·6°	231·8°	247·7°	251·6°	294·3°
C_p	4·26	4·40	4·54	6·19	6·31	6·21	7·26*	7·32*

where the numbers marked with an asterisk refer to the liquid, the others to the solid. The **heat of fusion** at 25° is 11·77 cals. per gram ; and the **entropy** at 25°, 59·51. F. Böch and L. Moser gave for the **heat of solution,** $(TiCl_4,Aq.)=59.03$

Cals.; and J. Thomsen, 57·866 Cals. The last-named gave for the **heat of neutralization**, ($TiCl_4$aq., 4NaOHaq.)=47·664 Cals.; and for the **heat of formation**, (TiO_2aq., 4HClaq.)=7·296 Cals. J. H. Gladstone gave for the **index of refraction** 1·5851 for the A-line; 1·6039 for the D-line; 1·6296 for the F-line; and 1·6814 for the H-line; for the **molecular refraction**, 65·20; and for the **molecular dispersion**, 10·74. H. Becquerel, and A. Stiefelhagen made some observations on this subject. A. Stiefelhagen gave for light of wave-length $\lambda=358$, 508, and 708$\mu\mu$, $\mu=1\cdot73447$, 1·62574, and 1·58859, and $\mu^2=1\cdot77849+0\cdot67263\lambda^2(\lambda^2-239\cdot69^2)^{-1}$. H. H. Marvin studied the optical dispersion. H. Becquerel gave values for the index of refraction, for the **magnetic rotation**, and **magnetization**. He also made observations on the **spectrum**.

J. H. Mathews found the **dielectric constant** at 24° to be 2·73. W. von Kowalewsky measured the **electrical conductivity** of some aq. soln.—*vide infra*. A. Stälher and F. Bachran could not obtain less chlorinated products by the electrolysis of soln. of titanium tetrachloride in anhydrous hydrogen cyanide. B. Diethelm and F. Förster studied the electro-reduction of titanium sulphate soln. and found the current efficiency to be greater with a copper or lead electrode than with one of bright platinum, and the velocity of the reduction is smaller with a bright platinum electrode than with a platinized platinum electrode. They found for the reduction $Ti^{\cdots\cdots}+H\rightleftharpoons Ti^{\cdots}+H^{\cdot}$, the normal potential —0·056 volt at 18°; and G. S. Forbes and L. P. Hall calculated for the reduction $Ti^{\cdots\cdots}+2H\rightleftharpoons Ti^{\cdots}+2H^{\cdot}$ —0·33 volt at 18°.

The chemical properties of titanium tetrachloride.—K. Fajans studied the electronic structure of the titanium halides. The tetrachloride emits dense white fumes in air, but, added J. I. Pierre, although this occurs at ordinary temp., the fuming does not appear below 0°. Titanium tetrachloride is reduced by **hydrogen** above 600°, forming the tri- and di-chlorides (*q.v.*); and at a red heat H. Goerges and A. Stähler found some titanium is produced. They also passed a mixture of the tetrachloride and hydrogen through a porcelain tube at different temp., and found that as the temp. rises from 785° to 1200° the percentage decomposition rises from 21·7 to 94·3—*vide supra*. A state of equilibrium was probably reached in the hot zone, but the trichloride remained as a deposit in the porcelain tube. Increasing the proportion of the hydrogen raised the percentage decomposition; and at a constant temp., it was found empirically that the ratio $[TiCl_3]^4/[TiCl_4]^3$ is approximately constant. When hydrogen chloride was added the percentage decomposition diminished. R. Schmidt found that at 600°, $H_2+TiCl_4=2HCl+TiCl_2$; and $TiCl_2+TiCl_4=2TiCl_3$. The trichloride is deposited in the cold part of the tube. E. A. Schneider's attempts to make *titano-chloroform*, $TiHCl_3$, or *titanium hydrotrichloride*, were unsuccessful. Dry hydrogen chloride reacts with titanium at 300°, forming a non-volatile substance. T. König and O. F. von der Pfordten found that with **water** it forms a series of oxychlorides, $TiCl_3.OH$; $TiCl_2(OH)_2$; $TiCl_2(OH)_3$; and with an excess of water, $Ti(OH)_4$ is formed—*vide infra*. R. F. Wagner found that when titanium tetrachloride is dropped into water a turbid liquid is produced, but a clear soln. of orthotitanic acid in titanium tetrachloride can be obtained by adding water drop by drop to the tetrachloride with constant agitation. The liquid fumes in air, and the possible use of the fumes for producing clouds in aeroplane warfare was discussed by G. A. Richter, and H. W. Walker. O. F. von der Pfordten's comparison of the properties of the three chlorides is given in Table VI. W. von Kowalewsky showed that titanium tetrachloride dissolves in water with the evolution of much heat, and the hydrochloric acid liberated during the hydrolysis suffices to re-dissolve the precipitated hydroxide first formed without any corresponding change in the electrical conductivity. The value of the electrical conductivity shows that equilibrium is established before the hydrolysis is complete; the hydrolysis is completed by boiling, or by heating in a sealed tube at 150°. The behaviour of titanium tetrachloride towards water is intermediate between silicon tetrachloride and tin tetrachloride. The same remark applies to the tendency to form complex salts. A. Demoly evaporated a strongly acid soln. of the tetrachloride and obtained very hygroscopic crystals of **pentahydrated titanium tetrachloride**, $TiCl_4.5H_2O$, and in vacuo, over sulphuric acid, **dihydrated titanium tetrachloride**, $TiCl_4.2H_2O$, was formed. O. Ruff

TABLE VI.—PROPERTIES OF THE TITANIUM CHLORIDES.

Soluble in	$TiCl_2$	$TiCl_3$	$TiCl_4$
Water or alcohol	Readily (brown)	Readily (violet, green)	Readily (colourless)
Ether	Insoluble	Insoluble	Readily (yellow)
Hydrochloric acid	Sparingly	Sparingly	Readily

and F. Eisner found that titanium tetrachloride reacts vigorously with **hydrogen fluoride ;** O. Ruff and R. Ipsen obtained a citron-yellow *titanium fluochloride,* approximately $TiClF_3$, by the action of titanium tetrachloride on hydrogen fluoride or silver fluoride. W. Biltz and E. Meinecke gave for the f.p. of mixtures of **chlorine** and titanium tetrachloride the results shown by Fig. 9. The titanium tetrachloride freezes at $-22.5°$. The eutectic is at $-108°$ and 87.5 at. per cent. chlorine. P. Haute-feuille found that boiling titanium tetrachloride reacts with hydrogen iodide, forming the tetraiodide. J. J. Ebelmen said that in the cold, **hydrogen sulphide** reduces titanium tetrachloride to the dichloride, and at a higher temp., titanium disulphide is formed. The reaction was studied by O. F. von der Pfordten, who showed that the disulphide is formed at a red heat, but at intermediate temp. *titanium sulphochloride*, TiSCl, is formed. A. Stähler and F. Bachran could not verify this observation, but observed that the thiochloride, $TiSCl_2$, is formed. At $800°–850°$,

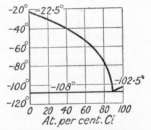

FIG. 9—Freezing-point Curves of $Cl_2 - TiCl_4$ Mixtures.

TiS_2 is produced. W. Biltz and E. Keunecke found that dry liquid hydrogen sulphide does not react with or dissolve titanium tetrachloride, but at a higher temp. there is formed a *monosulphohydrate*, $TiCl_4.H_2S$, and a *disulphohydrate*, $TiCl_4.2H_2S$, with the respective heats of formation 8.86 Cals. and 8.18 Cals. For the action of **sulphur chloride, chlorosulphonic acid, thionyl chloride, ammonia, nitrogen sulphide, hyponitrous acid, phosphine, phosphorus chlorides,** and **phosphoryl chloride,** *vide infra.* R. Wise found that selenium oxychloride dissolves 0.75 per cent. of titanium tetrachloride, and it forms the complex **titanium selenium dioxyoctochloride,** $TiCl_4.2SeOCl_2$. O. Ruff and H. Graf found that the reaction with **antimony pentafluoride** is quite violent, and titanium tetrafluoride is formed.

H. Rose showed that boiling titanium tetrachloride is not decomposed by **potassium ;** but the vapour passed over heated potassium or **sodium** is decomposed ; F. C. Robinson and C. C. Hutchins said that the reaction with sodium begins at 150°. O. F. von der Pfordten, on the contrary, said that sodium and sodium amalgam reduce titanium tetrachloride to the dichloride at ordinary temp. A. C. Vournasos found at the temp. of boiling toluene, titanium tetrachloride is reduced by potassium partly to the dichloride and partly to titanium. A. Stähler and F. Bachran showed that the tetrachloride is reduced to the trichloride by heating it with finely powdered **aluminium, antimony, arsenic,** or **tin** in a sealed tube at 400°. K. Seubert and A. Schmidt found that below redness **magnesium** reduces the tetrachloride to the trichloride and lower oxides, but the presence of titanium metal was not established with certainty. H. Goerges and A. Stähler obtained only a very slight reduction of the tetrachloride by **mercury** at ordinary temp. C. Friedel and

J. Guérin showed that when the vap. of titanium tetrachloride is passed over red-hot **ferric oxide,** rutile is formed, and ferric chloride volatilized.

P. Kohl found that the presence of many organic substances favours the electro-reduction of titanium tetrachloride. W. Dilthey made substitution products of titanium chloride ; thus, with acetylmethylacetone he obtained *triacetylmethyl-acetonyltitanium titanichloride,* $[Ti\{O.C(CH_3) : C(CH_3)(C_2H_3O)\}_3Cl]_2.TiCl_4$. Such compounds were called **titanonium salts** by analogy with the corresponding **siliconium salts,** and **boronium salts**—*e.g.* *triacetylmethylacetonylsiliconium ferrichloride,* $[Si\{O.C(CH_3) : C(CH_3)(C_2H_3O)\}_3Cl].FeCl_3$; and *diacetylacetonyl-boronium hydrochloride,* $[B\{O.C(CH_3) : CH(C_2H_3O)\}_2Cl].HCl$. F. Wöhler, and E. A. Schneider obtained the addition products, $TiCl_4.2HCy$, with **hydrogen cyanide ;** and $TiCl_4.CyCl$, with **cyanogen chloride.** A. Demoly, O. F. von der Pfordten, P. P. Bedson, H. R. Ellis, and A. Bertrand obtained $TiCl_4.(C_2H_5)_2O$, and $2TiCl_4.3(C_2H_5)_2O$, with **ether ;** E. A. Demarçay found that **alcohol** reacts with titanium tetrachloride, giving crystals of $Ti(OC_2H_5)_3Cl.HCl$, and that this reacts with sodium ethylate, forming **ethyl orthotitanate,** $Ti(OC_2H_5)_4$. G. Scagliarini also obtained complexes with other organic compounds. A. Benrath found that titanium tetrachloride in the presence of alcohol is slowly reduced by exposure to light ; and A. Benrath and A. Obladen found that the photochemical reaction is accompanied by autoxidation resulting in the formation of hydrogen dioxide. Numerous complexes with organic compounds have been prepared. A. Benrath showed that titanium tetrachloride, in the presence of **oxalic acid, mandelic acid,** or **lactic acid,** is slowly reduced in light. N. Parravano and C. Mazzetti found that, at 900°, titanium tetrachloride is reduced by **iron,** forming a titanide.

The oxychlorides of titanium.—As previously indicated, the titanium di-chloride prepared by J. J. Ebelmen was shown by C. Friedel and J. Guérin to have been **titanous oxychloride,** or **titanyl chloride,** TiOCl, or $Ti_2O_2Cl_2$. J. J. Ebelmen obtained it in golden spangles as a by-product in preparing titanium trichloride. C. Friedel and J. Guérin passed a mixture of hydrogen and the vap. of titanium tetrachloride over white-hot titanium dioxide. The titanous oxychloride is mixed with some trichloride. E. A. Demarçay regarded it as an intermediate product in the chlorination of heated titanium dioxide by the vapour of carbon tetrachloride. The rhombic brownish-red or yellow plates appear red in transmitted light. The crystals, said C. Friedel and J. Guérin, are not immediately attacked by water, or even by dil. nitric acid. When, however, they are exposed for some time to the air they become white and are transformed into titanic acid. They are attacked by ammonia, which first blackens them, and afterwards they become white, still retaining their shapes ; at the same time, there is an evolution of hydrogen. Heated in the air they are decomposed, giving off vapours of titanium tetrachloride, and leaving a residue of titanium dioxide.

L. Troost and P. Hautefeuille passed a mixture of oxygen and titanium tetra-chloride through a red-hot porcelain tube packed with porcelain shards. They obtained a white solid with a composition $Ti_2O_3Cl_2$, *i.e.* $TiO_2.TiOCl_2$. This product may be a chemical individual, titanium dioxide with adsorbed tetrachloride or chlorine ; or **titanic oxydichloride,** *i.e. titanyl dichloride*, $TiOCl_2$, contaminated with titanium dioxide. F. Bourion obtained a yellow liquid supposed to be an oxychloride by passing a stream of chlorine mixed with the vap. of sulphur chloride, over ignited titanium dioxide. R. Weber, and V. Merz examined the product of the action of water on titanium tetrachloride, and found it contained variable proportions of titanium hydroxide and tetrachloride, and water. V. Auger pre-pared **titanium trihydroxychloride,** $Ti(OH)_3Cl.2H_2O$, or $TiO_2.HCl.3H_2O$, by evaporating a cold soln. of titanic chloride in conc. hydrochloric acid, over sul-phuric acid. The colourless, rhombohedral plates are decomposed in moist air.

O. F. von der Pfordten [4] regulated the mixing of conc. hydrochloric acid with the titanium tetrachloride. In this way, T. König and O. F. von der Pfordten obtained the three intermediate stages in the hydrolysis of titanium tetrachloride.

The first stage of the hydrolysis is represented by **titanium hydroxytrichloride,** $Ti(OH)Cl_3$, which is obtained by mixing the theoretical quantities of titanium chloride and 36 per cent. hydrochloric acid, the reaction being extremely energetic. It is a yellow, spongy, very deliquescent mass which dissolves very readily in water and alcohol with a hissing noise ; it also dissolves in ether with a similar energetic reaction, but when more ether is added, a white deliquescent compound is precipitated. An aq. soln. is tolerably stable, but titanic acid is precipitated after continued boiling. When heated in the dry state, it is decomposed into titanic acid and titanic chloride ; the same decomposition takes place when it is heated in a current of hydrogen or hydrogen chloride. The second stage of the hydrolysis is represented by **titanium dihydroxydichloride,** $Ti(OH)_2Cl_2$, and this is prepared by adding titanium tetrachloride to a slight excess of hydrochloric acid ; by the action of titanium chloride on the calculated quantity of 36 per cent. hydrochloric acid ; or by adding titanium tetrachloride to the requisite quantity of well-cooled water. It is a very voluminous, yellow, exceedingly deliquescent mass or a vitreous solid, according to the method of preparation. It is soluble in alcohol and ether, but a white compound is precipitated when a soln. is strongly diluted with absolute ether. Titanic acid separates when an aq. soln. is boiled. When heated in the dry state, it is rapidly decomposed, yielding titanic acid and hydrogen chloride. The third or penultimate stage of the hydrolysis is represented by **titanium trihydroxychloride,** $Ti(OH)_3Cl$, which is formed when either of the preceding compounds is allowed to remain for some time exposed to the air at the ordinary temp. Both compounds deliquesce, with evolution of hydrogen chloride, but at the end of about a month's time, they solidify. The product contains, approximately, two mols of water after remaining for two months over sulphuric acid. When placed in a desiccator containing phosphoric anhydride, it loses a mol of water in 14 days, and after a long time the anhydrous compound is obtained sometimes in a crystalline form. It is a white compound which is stable in the air, and far less readily soluble in water than either of the other two hydroxychlorides. In order to obtain a clear aq. soln. of the anhydrous compound, a few drops of hydrogen chloride must be added ; titanic acid is precipitated from this soln. on boiling. It is insoluble in alcohol and ether. When heated, it yields titanic acid, hydrogen chloride, and water.

A. Mazzucchelli and E. Pantanelli prepared what they regarded as a salt of titanium trioxide, by treating a soln. containing hydrogen dioxide, titanium tetrachloride, and sodium chloride with alcohol. The composition corresponded with **sodium chloropertitanate,** $TiO_2Cl_2.2NaCl.9H_2O$. P. A. Bond and H. T. Beach found that with sulphur dioxide no compound is formed above the m.p. of sulphur dioxide, $-72°$; but the partially miscible liquids have a critical soln. temp. of $11·9°$.

The amminochlorides of titanium.—Three amminochlorides have been reported. H. Rose found that dry ammonia is rapidly absorbed by titanium tetrachloride, and there is a great evolution of heat. It is necessary to pass the gas for a long time with frequent agitation in order that the whole of the tetrachloride may be saturated with ammonia. The product can be preserved in well-stoppered bottles. If after standing some time the compound still smells of ammonia, it may be considered to have been saturated, but if it gives off white fumes, it should be again treated with ammonia. The analysis of the brownish-red product corresponded with **titanium tetramminotetrachloride,** $TiCl_4.4NH_3$. N. Whitehouse obtained the tetrammine as a canary-yellow powder in a similar manner. A. Rosenheim and O. Schütte obtained a white product with the same composition by keeping the hexammine over dry calcium chloride for some days ; on the other hand, A. Stähler and H. Wirthwein said that the hexammine remains unaltered over freshly-ignited calcium chloride in the absence of air, but changes to titanic acid, ammonium chloride, and ammonia ; $TiCl_4.6NH_3+4H_2O=Ti(OH)_4+4NH_4Cl+2NH_3$, when kept over ordinary calcium chloride or in the presence of air. According to H. Rose, when the ammino-chloride is heated, a little ammonia is first evolved, then some ammonium chloride is given off, then a quantity of hydrogen chloride, and finally a sublimate of ammonium chlorotitanate. He called the residue metallic titanium, but it is really a titanium nitride. The ammino-chloride greedily absorbs moisture, and becomes white ; it is decomposed by water, forming a turbid liquid from which ammonia does not precipitate all the titanic acid, and from which hydrochloroplatinic acid precipitates about half the "ammonia." This indicates, said H. Rose, that the amminochloride "dissolves in water without decomposition, and not as a mixture of ammonium chloride and titanium oxide." He also found that when the amminochloride is heated with potassium or sodium, it is decomposed with vivid incandescence.

J. Persoz obtained a pale yellow powder by H. Rose's process, and the analysis corresponded with **titanium hexamminotetrachloride,** $TiCl_4.6NH_3$. A. Stähler and H. Wirthwein also obtained this compound as a saffron-yellow powder by passing the vapour of titanium tetrachloride in a stream of dried hydrogen into ammonia. A. Rosenheim and O. Schütte obtained the hexammine as a dark yellow powder by passing dry ammonia into a dry ethereal soln. of titanium tetrachloride cooled with ice ; on the other hand, A. Stähler and H. Wirthwein said that the octammine is produced when dry ammonia gas is passed into titanium tetrachloride suspended in absolute ether. The hexammine is very hygroscopic ; and, losing ammonia when exposed to the air, becomes paler in colour. For the behaviour in a desiccator over calcium chloride, *vide supra*. According to A. Stähler and H. Wirthwein, **titanium octamminotetrachloride,** $TiCl_4.8NH_3$, is obtained as just indicated, and also as a pale yellow powder when titanium tetrachloride is shaken for 12 hrs. with liquid ammonia. This compound gives up ammonia very readily on exposure to air, and it becomes white. It is decomposed by water with the separation of titanic acid ; and when either the hexammine or the octammine is extracted with liquid ammonia, ammonium chloride is removed, and dark yellow *titanamide*, $Ti(NH_2)_4$, remains. When the ammonia is removed by careful heating in vacuo, at 270°, *titanium chloronitride*, $TiNCl$, is formed.

Addition-compounds of titanium tetrachloride.—R. Weber passed the dried vapours from aqua regia over titanium tetrachloride, and obtained a compound **titanium dinitrosyl hexachloride,** $TiCl_4.2NOCl$. W. Hampe obtained the same product by the action of hyponitrous acid on titanium tetrachloride. The yellow crystal aggregate does not fume in air ; it is decomposed by water giving off nitric oxide. O. C. M. Davis reported that **titanium nitrogen sulphotrichloride,** $2TiCl_3.N_4S_4$, is formed in orange crystals when titanium tetrachloride is added to a soln. of nitrogen sulphide in chloroform ; whereas H. Wölbling obtained **titanium nitrogen sulphotetrachloride,** $TiCl_4.N_4S_4$, by the interaction of the components dissolved in carbon tetrachloride. The amorphous, brownish-red precipitate is insoluble in most solvents. It decomposes in moist air, and reacts very vigorously with water, alkali-lye, or nitric acid—sometimes with incandescence. Hydrochloric acid or alcohol splits the compound into its components.

O. Ruff reported the formation of **titanium sulphooctochloride,** $TiCl_4.SCl_4$, by dropping acid sulphur chloride into a soln. of titanium tetrachloride in sulphuryl chloride. The yellow, acicular crystals are very hygroscopic ; they are stable in an atm. of chlorine, but give off chlorine at ordinary temp. in an atm. of carbon dioxide. In a sealed tube with chlorine, the crystals melt at 62°–64° ; and sublime at 100°. They are soluble in sulphuryl chloride, chloroform, carbon disulphide, and petroleum ether. H. Rose, and R. Weber, obtained what they regarded as $2TiCl_4.SCl_4$, but O. Ruff believed that this is really $TiCl_4.SCl_4$. H. Rose made the compound by the action of sulphur chloride on titanium trichloride at ordinary temp. ; and by the action of chlorine on titanium sulphide. R. Weber sat. a mixture of titanium tetrachloride and sulphur chloride with dry chlorine, and warmed the product in a stream of chlorine so as to remove the excess of titanium tetrachloride or sulphur chloride. F. Bourion obtained it by the action of a mixture of chlorine and sulphur chloride on titanium dioxide at a red heat; and G. Darzeus and F. Bourion obtained it by the action of thionyl chloride on heated titanium dioxide. F. Clausnizer obtained **titanium sulphatotetrachloride,** $TiCl_4.SO_3$, or $ClO_2.S.O.TiCl_3$, by dropping chlorosulphonic acid, $HO.SO_2Cl$, into titanium tetrachloride; some hydrogen chloride was evolved. The mixture was warmed on a water-bath. The resulting yellow powder is very hygroscopic and fumes in moist air. R. Weber obtained **titanium selenium dioxyoctochloride,** $TiCl_4.2SeOCl_2$, by dropping selenium oxydichloride into titanium tetrachloride. The yellow powder does not fume in air; it is decomposed by moisture, and by ammonia, and when heated, forms titanic oxide.

H. Rose showed that titanium tetrachloride absorbs phosphine, forming a brown solid—**titanium phosphinotetrachloride**—which fumes on exposure to air. No hydrogen chloride is evolved during the absorption, but when heated in a closed vessel, hydrogen chloride, phosphine, and a lemon-yellow sublimate of **phosphonium chlorotitanate,** $3TiCl_4.2PH_4Cl$, are given off, and a copper-red residue containing titanium remains. Titanium phosphinotetrachloride is decomposed by water, hydrochloric acid, and by a soln. of alkali hydroxides or carbonates, or ammonia—evolving phosphine with effervescence. A. Bertrand observed that phosphorus trichloride unites directly with titanium tetrachloride, forming yellow crystals of **titanium phosphorus heptachloride,** $TiCl_4.PCl_3$, which melts at 85·5°. J. Tuttscheff warmed a mixture of one mol of anhydrous titanium dioxide with three mols of phosphorus pentachloride, and after keeping the mixture warm for a long time to drive off the phosphoryl chloride, obtained **titanium phosphoric enneachloride,** $TiCl_4.PCl_5$; R. Weber obtained it by saturating a mixture of phosphorus trichloride and titanium tetrachloride with dry chlorine; and E. Wehrlin and E. Giraud, by heating equimolar proportions of the constituents in a sealed tube at 150°. J. Gewecke obtained this compound by burning titanium phosphide in an atm. of chlorine. The yellow product is very hygroscopic, and is decomposed by water and alcohol, but absolute alcohol, according to J. Tuttscheff, dissolves it without apparent decomposition; and phosphoryl chloride dissolves a small proportion. It is soluble in dil. acids, but the soln. gradually gelatinizes.

R. Weber prepared **titanium phosphoryl heptachloride,** $TiCl_4.POCl_3$, by dropping phosphoryl chloride into titanium chloride; and E. Wehrlin and E. Giraud, by heating a mol of titanium dioxide and two mols of phosphorus pentachloride in a sealed tube. The colourless crystals are hygroscopic, and are decomposed by water, alcohol, and ether; they melt at 110°, and boil at 140°. O. Ruff and R. Ipsen found that titanium tetrafluoride dissolves unchanged in cold phosphorus oxychloride, but at 30°, a vigorous action takes place, and the chloride and phosphorus oxyfluoride are produced; excess of phosphorus oxychloride gives a quantitative yield of the yellow **titanium diphosphoryl decachloride,** $TiCl_4.2POCl_3$, which melts at 107° and boils at 138°.

Hydrochlorotitanic acid and the chlorotitanates.—According to O. F. von der Pfordten, titanium tetrachloride dissolves in fuming hydrochloric acid with the evolution of much heat, forming a deep yellow liquid, which becomes colourless when diluted with water. W. von Kowalewsky measured the electrical conductivity of the soln. and showed it to be highly probable that the yellow liquid contains **hydrochlorotitanic acid,** H_2TiCl_6. A. Rosenheim and O. Schütte obtained a yellow liquid containing, presumably, the same acid by treating titanic acid with an alcoholic or ethereal soln. of hydrogen chloride. T. König and O. F. von der Pfordten could not isolate the acid by the action of hydrogen chloride on titanium tetrachloride alone or when dissolved in alcohol or ether.

A. Rosenheim and O. Schütte prepared dihydrated **ammonium chlorotitanate,** $(NH_4)_2TiCl_6.2H_2O$, in yellow crystals by shaking a mixture of eq. quantities of ammonium chloride and a hydrochloric acid soln. of titanium tetrachloride. The crystals were washed with ether, and dried in vacuo over sulphuric acid. They are very unstable in moist air, giving off hydrochloric acid, and becoming white.

V. Merz obtained the same salt. The compounds with pyridine, $(C_5H_5N)_2.H_2TiCl_6$; quinoline, $(C_9H_7N)_2.H_2TiCl_6$; and aniline, $(C_6H_5NH_2)_4.H_4TiCl_8$, were made by A. Rosenheim and O. Schütte.

P. Fireman obtained a double salt by heating titanium tetrachloride and ammonium chloride in a sealed tube : and O. Ruff and F. Eisner heated titanium hexamminotetra-chloride to the softening point of hard glass, and after the volatilization of most of the hexammino-salt, obtained a greenish-yellow sublimate consisting principally of titanium tetrachloride with one or two mols of ammonium chloride. The yellowish-white sublimate obtained by H. Rose by heating the tetrammino-salt—*vide supra*—contained $TiCl_4 + 3$ to $6NH_4Cl$.

REFERENCES.

[1] J. J. Ebelmen, *Journ. Pharm. Chim.*, (3), **12**. 437, 1846 ; *Ann. Chim. Phys.*, (2), **20**. 385, 1847 ; C. Friedel and J. Guérin, *ib.*, (5), **7**. 24, 1876 : *Compt. Rend.*, **81**. 889, 1875 ; H. Moissan, *ib.*, **120**. 290, 1895 ; *Ann. Chim. Phys.*, (7), **9**. 229, 1896 ; O. F. von der Pfordten, *Liebig's Ann.*, **234**. 257, 1886 ; **237**. 201, 1887 ; F. Wöhler, *ib.*, **73**. 34, 1849 ; **74**. 212, 1850 ; *Pogg. Ann.*, **11**. 148, 1827 ; A. Stähler and F. Bachran, *Ber.*, **44**. 2906, 1911 ; A. Stähler and H. Wirthwein, *ib.*, **38**. 2619, 1905 ; H. Goerges and A. Stähler, *ib.*, **42**. 3200, 1909 ; E. Glatzel, *ib.*, **9**. 1829, 1876 ; E. Knecht, *ib.*, **36**. 166, 1903 ; M. Coblens and J. K. Bernstein, *Journ. Phys. Chem.*, **29**. 750, 1925 ; A. Piccini and L. Marino, *Zeit. anorg. Chem.*, **32**. 55, 1902 ; O. Ruff and F. Neumann, *ib.*, **128**. 81, 1923 ; E. S. George, *Pogg. Ann.*, **3**. 171, 1825 ; *Ann. Phil.*, **9**. 18, 1825 ; R. Schmidt, *Ber.*, **58**. B. 400, 1925.

[2] J. J. Ebelmen, *Journ. Pharm. Chim.*, (3), **12**. 437, 1846 ; *Ann. Chim. Phys.*, (2), **20** 385, 1847 ; L. Lévy, *ib.*, (6), **25**. 477, 1892 : C. Friedel and J. Guérin, *ib.*, (5), **7**. 24, 1876 ; *Compt. Rend.*, **81**. 889, 1875 ; **82**. 509, 972, 1876 ; F. Pisani, *ib.*, **59**. 301, 1864 ; T. E. Thorpe, *Chem. News*, **51**. 260, 1885 ; F. Emich, *Ber.*, **28**. 1585, 1895 ; *Monatsh.*, **25**. 907, 1904 ; F. Böck and L. Moser, *ib.*, **33**. 1407, 1912 ; **34**. 1825, 1913 ; F. Meyer, A. Bauer, and R. Schmidt, *Ber.*, **56**. B, 1908 1923 : E. Glatzel, *ib.*, **9**. 1829, 1876 ; R. Schmidt, *ib.*, **58**. B, 400, 1925 ; A. Stähler, *ib.*, **37**. 4405, 1904 ; A. Stähler and F. Bachran, *ib.*, **44**. 2906, 1911 ; A. Stähler and H. Wirthwein, *ib.*, **38**. 2617, 1905 : H. Goerges and A. Stähler, *ib.*, **42**. 3200, 1909 ; E. Knecht, *German Pat.*, *D.R.P.* 138503, 1902 ; *Ber.*, **36**. 166 1549, 1903 ; **37**. 3482, 1904 ; **38**. 3318, 1905 ; **40**. 3819, 1907 ; E. Knecht and E. Hibbert, *ib.*, **36**. 1549, 1903 ; **43**. 3455, 1910 ; *New Reduction Methods in Volumetric Analysis*, London, 1910 ; *Journ. Soc. Dyers Color.*, **22**. 165, 330, 1906 ; **24**. 68, 1908 ; **25**. 135, 160, 1909 ; **34**. 94, 205, 241, 1918 ; **36**. 215, 1920 ; *Journ. Soc. Chem. Ind.*, **27**. 34, 1908 ; **28**. 189, 1909 ; **34**. 126, 1915 ; *Journ. Chem. Soc.*, **125**. 1537, 1924 ; E. Polidori, *Zeit. anorg. Chem.*, **19**. 306, 1899 ; O. Ruff and F. Neumann, *ib.*, **128**. 81, 1923 ; C. F. Rammelsberg, *Sitzber. Akad. Berlin*, 490, 1874 ; R. Weber, *ib.*, 358, 1863 : W. S. Hendrixson, *Journ. Amer. Chem. Soc.*, **45**. 2013, 1923 ; W. M. Thornton and J. E. Chapman, *ib.*, **43**. 91, 1923 ; L. H. Milligan and G. R. Gillette, *Journ. Phys. Chem.*, **28**. 744, 1924 ; O. C. M. Davis, *Journ. Chem. Soc.*, **89**. 1575, 1906 ; E. Zintl and A. Rauch, *Zeit. anorg. Chem.*, **146**. 281, 1925 ; H. Spence, *Brit. Pat. No.* 16238, 1902 ; *German Pat.*, *D.R.P.* 154542, 1902 ; *French Pat. No.* 324835, 1902 ; *U.S. Pat. No.* 723217, 1903 ; K. Seubert and A. Schmidt, *Liebig's Ann.*, **267**. 234, 1892 ; J. N. von Fuchs, *ib.*, **46**. 319, 1843 ; L. Moser, *Chem. Ztg.*, **36**. 1126, 1912 ; A. Monnier, *Ann. Chim. Anal.*, **20**. 1, 1915 ; G. S. Forbes and L. P. Hall, *ib.*, **46**. 385, 1924 ; E. Zintl and A. Rauch, *Zeit. Electrochem.*, **31**. 428, 1925 ; *Zeit. anorg. Chem.*, **146**. 281, 1925 ; I. M. Kolthoff, O. Tomicek, and C. Robinson, *ib.*, **150**. 157, 1926 ; I. M. Kolthoff and O. Tomicek, *Rec. Trav. Chim. Pays-Bas*, **43**. 775, 1924 ; O. F. von der Pfordten, *Liebig's Ann.*, **234**. 257, 1886 ; **237**. 201, 1887.

[3] E. S. George, *Ann. Phil.*. **9**. 18, 1825 ; *Schweigger's Journ.*, **44**. 48, 1825 ; *Pogg. Ann.*, **3**. 171, 1824 ; R. Weber, *ib.*, **118**. 476, 1863 ; **120**. 290, 1863 ; **125**. 327, 1865 ; **132**. 452, 1867 ; *Zeit. Chem.*, (2), **4**. 312, 1868 ; *Sitzber. Akad. Berlin*, 229, 1859 ; 156, 1865 ; *Journ. prakt. Chem.*, (1), **95**. 145, 1865 ; H. Rose, *Liebig's Ann.*, **40**. 240, 1841 ; *Pogg. Ann.*, **15**. 145, 1829 ; **16**. 57, 1829 ; **24**. 141, 1832 ; J. Thomsen, *ib.*, **139**. 212, 1870 ; F. Wöhler, *ib.*, **11**. 148, 1827 ; *Liebig's Ann.*, **73**. 36, 219, 1849 ; **74**. 212, 1850 ; K. Seubert and A. Schmidt, *ib.*, **267**. 235, 1892 ; W. Dilthey, *ib.*, **344**. 300, 1906 ; P. P. Bedson, *ib.*, **180**. 235, 1876 ; J. Tuttscheff, *ib.*, **141**. 111, 1867 ; O. F. von der Pfordten, *ib.*, **234**. 257, 1886 ; **237**. 202, 1887 ; T. König and O. F. von der Pfordten, *Ber.*, **22**. 1485, 1889 ; C. Friedel and J. Guérin, *Compt. Rend.*, **82**. 509, 972, 1876 ; *Bull. Soc. Chim.*, (2), **23**. 289, 1875 ; P. Hautefeuille, *ib.*, (2), **7**. 202, 1867 ; A. Bertrand, *ib.*, (2), **33**. 565, 1880 ; (2), **34**. 631, 1880 ; E. Vigouroux and G. Arrivaut, *ib.*, (4), **1**. 19, 1907 ; *Compt. Rend.*, **144**. 485, 1907 ; B. F. Duppa, *ib.*, **42**. 353, 1856 ; *Ann. Chim. Phys.*, (3), **47**. 164, 1856 ; J. B. A. Dumas, *Journ. Pharm. Chim.*, (1), **12**. 300, 1826 ; *Ann. Chim. Phys.*, (2), **33**. 337, 386, 1826 ; J. I. Pierre, *ib.*, (3), **20**. 21, 1847 ; (3), **23**. 21, 1847 ; J. Persoz, *ib.*, (2), **44**. 321, 1830 ; H. V. Regnault, *ib.*, (3), **1**. 129, 1841 ; M. Billy, *ib.*, (9), **16**. 5, 1921 ; V. Merz, *Journ. prakt. Chem.*, (1), **99**. 162, 1866 ; *Ueber das Titan, Silicium, und Boron*, Zürich, 1864 ; A. Demoly. *Recherches sur le titane et ses combinaisons*, Paris, 1849 ; *Compt. Rend. Trav. Chim.*, **5**. 325, 1849 ; R. F. Wagner, *Ber.*, **21**. 960, 1888 ; L. Meyer, *ib.*, **20**. 681, 1887 ; C. Renz, *ib.*, **39**. 249, 1906 ; R. Schmidt, *ib.*, **58**. B, 400, 1925 ; A. Stähler. *ib.*, **37**. 4405, 1904 ; A. Stähler and H. Wirthwein,

ib., **38**. 2619, 1905; H. Goerges and A. Stähler, *ib.*, **42**. 3200, 1909; A. Stähler and F. Bachran, *ib.*, **44**. 2906, 1911; O. Ruff, *ib.*, **37**. 4513, 1904; O. Ruff and F. Eisner, *ib.*, **41**. 2258, 1908; O. Ruff and H. Graf, *ib.*, **39**. 4317, 1906; O. Ruff and R. Ipsen, *ib.*, **36**. 1777, 1903; *Ueber das Titanfluorid*, Berlin, 1904; B. Diethelm and F. Förster, *Zeit. phys. Chem.*, **62**. 129, 1908; G. S. Forbes and L. P. Hall, *Journ. Amer. Chem. Soc.*, **46**. 385, 1924; G. A. Richter, *Trans. Amer. Electrochem. Soc.*, **35**. 323, 1919; J. J. Saslawsky, *Zeit. phys. Chem.*, **113**. 111, 1924; E. Haase, *Ber.*, **26**. 1053, 1893; H. E. Quantin, *Compt. Rend.*, **104**. 223, 1887; E. A. Demarçay, *ib.*, **80**. 51, 1875; **104**. 111, 1887; H. Moissan, *ib.*, **120**. 290, 1895; F. Bourion, *ib.*, **145**. 62, 1907; L. Troost and P. Hautefeuille, *ib.*, **73**. 563, 1871; H. Becquerel, *ib.*, **85**. 227, 1877; *Ann. Chim. Phys.*, (5), **12**. 35, 41, 82, 1877; G. Gustavson, *ib.*, (5), **2**. 200, 1874; C. W. Watts and C. A. Bell, *Journ. Chem. Soc.*, **33**. 442, 1878; J. H. Gladstone, *ib.*, **59**. 299, 1891; T. E. Thorpe, *ib.*, **37**. 141, 327, 1880; **47**. 119, 1885; *Proc. Roy. Soc.*, **24**. 283, 1876; H. H. Marvin, *Phys. Rev.*, (2), **17**. 421, 1921; H. R. Ellis, *Chem. News*, **95**. 122, 1907; J. H. Mathews, *Journ. Phys. Chem.*, **9**. 641, 1905; A. Rosenheim and O. Schütte, *Zeit. anorg. Chem.*, **26**. 239, 1901; W. von Kowalewsky, *ib.*, **25**. 189, 1900; A. C. Vournasos, *ib.*, **81**. 364, 1923; W. Biltz and E. Meinecke, *ib.*, **131**. 1, 1923; W. Biltz and E. Keunecke, *ib.*, **147**. 171, 1925; E. A. Schneider, *ib.*, **8**. 94, 1895; O. Priesz, *German Pat.*, *D.R.P.P.* 334248, 334249, 1917; F. de Carli, *Atti Cong. Chim. Pure Appl.*, 399, 1923; A. Stiefelhagen, *Dispersion flüssiger Trichloride und Tetrachloride für ultraviolette Strahlen*, Berlin, 1905; K.Fajans, *Naturwiss.*, **11**. 165, 1923; C. M. Guldberg, *Christiania Vet. Förh.*, 20, 1882; F. Emich, *Monatsh.*, **25**. 907, 1904; F. Böck and L. Moser, *ib.*, **34**. 1825, 1912; M. A. Hunter *Journ. Amer. Chem. Soc.*, **32**. 330, 1910; R. Wise, *ib.*, **45**. 1233, 1923; G. P. Baxter and G. J. Fertig, *ib.*, **45**. 1228, 1923; P. Kohl, *Ueber die elektrolytische Reduktion von Titansalzen*, München, 1910; N. Whitehouse, *Journ. Soc. Chem. Ind.*, **26**. 738, 1907; F. C. Robinson and C. C. Hutchins, *Amer. Chem. Journ.*, **6**. 74, 1884; W. H. Latimer, *Journ. Amer. Chem. Soc.*, **44**. 90, 1922; A. Benrath, *Zeit. wiss. Photochem.*, **14**. 217, 1915; A. Benrath amd A. Obladen, *ib.*, **22**. 65, 1922; N. Parravano and C. Mazzetti, *Rec. Trav. Chim. Pays-Bas*, **42**. 821, 1923; V. Auger, *Compt. Rend.*, **177**. 1302, 1923; J. J. Ebelmen, *Journ. Pharm. Chim.*, (3), **12**. 437, 1846; *Ann. Chim. Phys.*, (2), **20**. 385, 1847; G. Scagliarini, *Atti Accad. Lincei*, (6), **2**. ii, 269, 1925; H. W. Walker, *Journ. Eng. Ind. Chem.*, **17**. 1061, 1925; O. Masson, *Phil. Mag.*, (5), **30**. 412, 1890; J. A. Groshans, *ib.*, (5), **20**. 197, 1885; *Ber.*, **19**. 974, 1886.

⁴ O. F. von der Pfordten, *Liebig's Ann.*, **237**. 201, 1887; T. König and O. F. von der Pfordten, *Ber.*, **21**. 1711, 1888; **22**. 1485, 1889; F. Clausnizer, *ib.*, **11**. 2011, 1878; O. Ruff and R. Ipsen, *ib.*, **36**. 1777, 1903; *Ueber das Titanfluorid*, Berlin, 1904; A. Stähler and H. Wirthwein, *Ber.*, **38**. 2619, 1905; O. Ruff, *ib.*, **37**. 4513, 1904; O. Ruff and F. Eisner, *ib.*, **41**. 2252, 1908; E. Wehrlin and E. Giraud, *Compt. Rend.*, **85**. 288, 1877; J. Gewecke, *Liebig's Ann.*, **361**. 79, 1908; W. Hampe, *ib.*, **126**. 47, 1863; H. Rose, *ib.*, **40**. 240, 1841; *Pogg. Ann.*, **16**. 57, 1829; **24**. 141, 1832; R. Weber, *ib.*, **118**. 476, 1863; **120**. 290, 1863; **125**. 327, 1865; **132**. 452, 1867; *Zeit. Chem.*, (2), **4**. 312, 1868; *Sitzber. Akad. Berlin*, 229, 1859; 156, 1865; *Journ. prakt. Chem.*, (1), **95**. 145, 1865; V. Merz, *ib.*, (1), **99**. 162, 1866; *Ueber das Titan, Silicium, und Boron*, Zürich, 1864; A. Bertrand, *Bull. Soc. Chim.*, (2), **33**. 565, 1880; J. Tuttscheff, *Liebig's Ann.*, **141**. 111, 1867; A. Rosenheim and O. Schütte, *Zeit. anorg. Chem.*, **26**. 245, 1901; H. Wölbling, *ib.*, **57**. 282, 1908; W. A. von Kowalewsky, *ib.*, **25**. 189, 1900; J. Persoz, *Ann. Chim. Phys.*, (2), **44**. 321, 1830; J. J. Ebelmen, *ib.*, (3), **20**. 385, 1847; F. Bourion, *ib.*, (8), **20**. 563, 1910; G. Darzeus and F. Bourion, *Compt. Rend.*, **153**. 271, 1911; L. Troost and P. Hautefeuille, *ib.*, **73**. 563, 1871; E. A. Demarçay, *ib.*, **104**. 111, 1887; F. Bourion, *ib.*, **145**. 62, 1907; C. Friedel and J. Guérin, *ib.*, **82**. 509, 972, 1876; *Bull. Soc. Chim.*, (2), **22**. 481, 1874; N. Whitehouse, *Journ. Soc. Chem. Ind.*, **26**. 738, 1907; O. C. M. Davis, *Journ. Chem. Soc.*, **89**. 1576, 1906; P. Fireman, *Journ. Amer. Chem. Soc.*, **26**. 744, 1904; P. A. Bond and H. T. Beach, *ib.*, **48**. 348, 1926; A. Mazzucchelli and E. Pantanelli, *Atti Accad. Lincei*, (5), **18**. i, 608, 1909.

§ 13. Titanium Bromides

Titanium forms the tri- and tetra-bromides; but the dibromide corresponding with the dichloride has not been obtained. A. Stähler [1] prepared hexahydrated **titanium tribromide,** or **titanous bromide,** $TiBr_3.6H_2O$, by electrolyzing a soln. of titanium tetrabromide in 20 per cent. hydrobromic acid, contained in the cathode compartment, using a platinum anode and a carbon cathode. The anode compartment contained 30 per cent. hydrobromic acid. When the cathode liquor has acquired a dark violet colour, and a portion gives a bluish-black precipitate with ammonia, the liquid is filtered and conc. in vacuo. When strongly cooled, or when a current of hydrogen bromide is passed through the liquid, a mass of dark violet crystals separates. The crystals are drained on asbestos, and dried on a porous tile over soda-lime. This salt is intermediate in stability between the corresponding chloride and iodide. It deliquesces in air to a brown, strongly-fuming liquid.

F. B. Duppa first made **titanium tetrabromide**, or **titanic bromide**, $TiBr_4$, by passing bromine vap. over an intimate mixture of titanium dioxide and carbon at a red heat. O. Ruff and F. Eisner made it by passing bromine vap. in a current of carbon dioxide over heated titanium or titanium carbide contained in a hard glass tube ; the product was purified by two distillations.   T. E. Thorpe made it by the action of hydrogen bromide on titanium tetrachloride heated to a temp. below its b.p.   At ordinary temp., titanium tetrabromide forms amber-yellow crystals, which, according to F. B. Duppa, have a sp. gr. 2·6 ; m.p., 39° ; and b.p., 230° ; W. Biltz and E. Keunecke gave 39° for the m.p. ; and T. E. Thorpe, 40° for the m.p., and 229° for the b.p.   According to F. B. Duppa, the salt is very hygroscopic, and is hydrolyzed by water into hydrobromic and titanic acids ; and, added T. E. Thorpe, there is very little heat evolved when the compound dissolves in water, and the soln. is quite clear.   A. Rosenheim and O. Schütte obtained **titanium hydroxytribromide**, $Ti(OH)Br_3$, by the action of a freshly prepared ethereal soln. of hydrogen bromide on hydrated titanium dioxide.   The ethereal soln. furnishes yellow crystals which dissolve in water, but which are more readily decomposed than the corresponding chlorine compound.   The salt is considered to be either the hydroxytribromide, or an addition product of this compound with ether. It was too unstable for analysis.   They also made **titanium trihydroxybromide**, $Ti(OH)_3Br$, associated with $1\frac{1}{2}$ mols of water or alcohol.   The liquid obtained by the action of a soln. of hydrogen bromide in alcohol on hydrated titanium dioxide, when evaporated in vacuo, furnishes a white crystalline powder which, after washing with alcohol and ether, has the above composition.   The product is stable in air ; it dissolves in cold water, forming a clear liquid which deposits titanic acid when boiled.   W. Biltz and E. Keunecke found that the tetrabromide forms a *monosulphohydrate*, $TiBr_4.H_2S$, and a *disulphohydrate*, $TiBr_4.2H_2S$, with heats of formation 8·56 Cals. and 7·88 Cals. respectively.

A. Rosenheim and O. Schütte found that the tetrabromide dissolves in dry alcohol or dry ether, forming a yellow liquid.   When hydrogen bromide is passed to sat. in the alcoholic or ethereal soln., a blood-red liquid is formed which probably contains **hydrobromotitanic acid**, H_2TiBr_6, analogous to the corresponding hydrochlorotitanic acid.   The acid has not been isolated, but **ammonium bromotitanate**, $(NH_4)_2TiBr_6.2H_2O$, was made by mixing ammonium bromide with a soln. of titanium bromide in hydrobromic acid ; dark red crystals separate on cooling. This salt is less stable than the corresponding chlorotitanate.   The corresponding pyridine salt, $(C_6H_5N)_2.H_2TiBr_6$, was made in a similar manner.

O. Ruff and F. Eisner made **titanium octamminotetrabromide**, $TiBr_4.8NH_3$, by the action of ammonia gas on titanium tetrabromide at a low temp.   When the ammonia is removed by careful heating in vacuo, *titanium bromonitride*, $TiNBr$, is formed (m.p. 39°, b.p. 230°) ; and, according to O. Ruff and O. Treidel, when washed with liquid ammonia, it furnishes an orange-yellow, insoluble product having a composition between $2Ti(NH_2)_4.TiBr_4.8NH_3$ and $3Ti(NH)_2.TiBr_4.8NH_3$.

C. Friedel and J. Guérin reported two mixed bromochlorides.   One, obtained by the action of bromine on titanium dichloride, is considered to be **titanium dichlorodibromide**, $TiCl_2Br_2$, and it boils at 176° ; the other, obtained by the action of bromine on titanium trichloride, was represented as **titanium bromotrichloride**, $TiBrCl_3$, and it boiled at 154°.   There is no other evidence to show whether the products are chemical individuals or mixtures.

REFERENCES.

[1] A. Stähler, *Ber.*, **37**. 4409, 1904 ; O. Ruff and F. Eisner, *ib.*, **41**. 2260, 1908 ; O. Ruff and O. Treidel, **45**. 1364, 1912 ; F. B. Duppa, *Compt. Rend.*, **42**. 352, 1856 ; *Ann. Chim. Phys.*, (3), **47**. 164, 1856 ; *Proc. Roy. Soc.*, **8**. 42, 1857 ; T. E. Thorpe, *Journ. Chem. Soc.*, **47**. 126, 1885 ; A. Rosenheim and O. Schütte, *Zeit. anorg. Chem.*, **24**. 238, 1900 ; **26**. 247, 1901 ; W. Biltz and E. Keunecke, *ib.*, **147**. 171, 1925 ; C. Friedel and J. Guérin, *Compt. Rend.*, **81**. 889, 1875 ; *Ann. Chim. Phys.*, (5), **8**. 24, 1876.

§ 14. Titanium Iodides

The three titanium di-, tri-, and tetra-iodides have been prepared. E. Defacqz and H. Copaux [1] found that titanium tetraiodide is readily reduced to the di-iodide by silver or mercury by arranging two porcelain boats in a porcelain tube—the anterior boat containing mercury and the posterior one titanium tetraiodide. The temp. was gradually raised to dull redness while a current of hydrogen passed through the tube. A sublimate of mercuric iodide and unchanged tetraiodide was formed in the cooled receiver, and fine black lamellæ of **titanium di-iodide,** TiI_2, were formed near the exit of the tube. The sp. gr. is 4·3 at 20°. The crystals are very hygroscopic, and are not acted on by organic solvents. They are dissolved by conc. hydrofluoric acid and by boiling hydrochloric acid, forming a blue soln. ; they are violently attacked by nitric and sulphuric acids with loss of iodine ; and are decomposed by water and aq. soln. of the alkalies. Titanium di-iodide forms additive compounds with dry ammonia and with hydrogen chloride. It is reduced by hydrogen at a white heat, but not at a red heat, giving amorphous titanium, which is very readily oxidized.

A. Stähler prepared hexahydrated **titanium tri-iodide,** or titanous iodide, $TiI_3.6H_2O$, by the electrolysis of a soln. of hydrated titanium dioxide in hydriodic acid, as in the case of the corresponding bromide. The liquid, when concentrated in vacuo. gives a violet, crystalline mass when hydrogen iodide is passed through the liquid. When exposed to the air, the crystals rapidly deliquesce to a brown, fuming liquid; and the compound decomposes when kept in vacuo over soda-lime.

R. Weber made **titanium tetraiodide,** TiI_4, by passing the vapour of iodine over heated titanium, and removing the excess of iodine by heating the product in one leg of a sealed Λ-tube ; the iodine and some tetraiodide are condensed in the other leg. H. Moissan also made this compound by the action of iodine vapour on heated titanium. P. Hautefeuille prepared it by passing hydrogen iodide into warm titanium tetrachloride the temp. of which was gradually raised to the b.p. The product was repeatedly sublimed in a current of hydrogen in order to remove the excess of iodine. He also made the iodide by passing a mixture of hydrogen and the vapours of titanium tetrachloride and iodine through a tube heated to dull redness. Titanium tetraiodide collects in the cooler part of the tube, and is purified as in the previous process.

Titanium tetraiodide is a reddish-brown mass with a metallic appearance ; and, according to P. Hautefeuille, it melts at 150° to a yellowish-brown liquid which remains liquid even when cooled below 100°, but is eventually solidified, forming octahedral crystals which, after some days, form prismatic plates. W. Biltz and E. Keunecke gave 143·5° for the m.p. P. Hautefeuille found that the vap. press. of the solid is appreciable at ordinary temp., and it boils a little over 360°, forming an orange vapour. It can be distilled unchanged, the vap. density, 18·054 at 440°, corresponding with a mol. wt. of 520, when that of TiI_4 is 556. The solid fumes in air, and it is combustible, burning to iodine and titanium dioxide. It rapidly dissolves in water with the evolution of less heat than is the case with the tetrachloride. The aq. soln. becomes brown in air ; and it deposits titanic acid owing to hydrolysis. The dark red liquid obtained when the tetraiodide dissolves in fuming hydriodic acid was assumed by A. Rosenheim and O. Schütte to contain **hydriodotitanic acid,** H_2TiI_6, but the acid and its salts—the *iodotitanates*—were too unstable to be isolated. W. Biltz and E. Keunecke observed that titanium tetraiodide does not form a sulphohydrate with hydrogen sulphide.

REFERENCES.

[1] E. Defacqz and H. Copaux, *Compt. Rend.*, **147**. 65, 1908 ; H. Moissan, *ib.*, **120**. 290, 1895 ; P. Hautefeuille, *ib.*, **57**. 151, 1863 ; **59**. 189, 1864 ; **64**. 704, 1867 ; *Bull. Soc. Chim.*, (2), **7**. 202, 1867 ; A. Stähler, *Ber.*, **37**. 4405, 1904 ; R. Weber, *Pogg. Ann.*, **120**. 291, 1863 ; A. Rosenheim and O. Schütte, *Zeit. anorg. Chem.*, **26**. 239, 1900 ; W. Biltz and E. Keunecke, *ib.*, **147**. 171, 1925.

§ 15. The Titanium Sulphides

Titanium furnishes three sulphides—the mono-, sesqui-, and di-sulphides. A. Blair and P. W. Shimer [1] observed crystals of a titanium sulphide in commercial iron. H. Rose said that in preparing the disulphides by the process described below, some black sulphide—probably **titanium monosulphide,** TiS—is formed at the same time. O. F. von der Pfordten made the monosulphide by heating one of the higher sulphides in a platinum tube at a temp. above the softening temp. of glass ; A. E. van Arkel and J. H. de Boer, by passing the vapours of the tetrachloride over a heated tungsten filament; and T. E. Thorpe, by heating the sesquisulphide in a current of hydrogen.   Titanium monosulphide is a reddish solid with a metallic appearance recalling that of bismuth.   E. Wedekind obtained the value $5 \cdot 4 \times 10^{-6}$ for the magnetic susceptibility of the monosulphide.   It is stable in air at ordinary temp., but glows when heated, forming sulphur and titanium dioxides.   It is not appreciably affected by water, or by hydrochloric, hydrofluoric, and dil. sulphuric acids ; it is dissolved by conc. sulphuric acid ; it is not affected by alkali-lye ; and it is slowly oxidized by dil. nitric acid, and by aqua regia.   P. Pipereaut and A. Helbronner obtained pigments from mixtures of titanium sulphide, zinc sulphate, and barium sulphate.

H. Rose assumed that he made titanium disulphide by the action of carbon disulphide on red-hot titanium dioxide, but J. J. Ebelmen showed that the product has not a constant composition, and that its composition approaches more nearly to that of **titanium sesquisulphide,** Ti_2S_3, than it does to the disulphide, TiS_2. T. E. Thorpe made the sesquisulphide by strongly heating powdered titanium dioxide in a mixture of not quite dry hydrogen sulphide, and the vapour of carbon disulphide.   The green colour of Thorpe's product was attributed by O. F. von der Pfordten to the presence of vanadium ; and he prepared the sesquisulphide by heating the disulphide in a current of nitrogen or hydrogen, at a lower temp. than is needed to produce the monosulphide : $2TiS_2=Ti_2S_3+S$.   N. Whitehouse employed a similar process.   E. A. Schneider probably obtained it by passing a mixture of hydrogen and sulphur vapour over red-hot titanium nitride.   Titanium sesquisulphide is a greyish-black crystalline powder which is stable in air, and in contact with water, alkali-lye, dil. hydrochloric acid, or dil. sulphuric acid : it is soluble in conc. sulphuric acid, forming a green soln. ; it is not oxidized by dil. nitric acid, but furnishes a green soln. with conc. nitric acid.   Hydrofluoric acid does not react at the temp. of a water-bath.   It glows when heated in air, and is oxidized.

H. Rose prepared a dark green mass of what he supposed to be **titanium disulphide,** TiS_2, by pressing moistened titanium dioxide into lumps ; and, after drying, igniting them in a stream of the vapour of carbon disulphide in a porcelain tube.   N. Whitehouse also passed carbon disulphide over red-hot titanium dioxide to make the disulphide.   P. Berthier also obtained the disulphide in bronze-yellow scales by strongly heating a mixture of rutile, sodium carbonate, and sulphur, pressed into a crucible, and covered with a layer of charcoal.   The product was coarsely pulverized, lixiviated with water, treated with sulphuric acid, and again washed with water.   The product was necessarily crude and impure.   J. J. Ebelmen obtained the disulphide of a high degree of purity by passing a mixture of hydrogen sulphide and the vapour of titanium tetrachloride through a heated tube.   If the temp. be not too high, the interior of the tube will be lined with yellow scales.   O. Ruff and R. Ipsen used titanium tetrafluoride in place of the tetrachloride and obtained the brown disulphide.   O. F. von der Pfordten said that the reaction : $TiCl_4+2H_2S=TiS_2+4HCl$, occurs only at a very high temp. ; in the cold, the reaction is represented : $TiCl_4+H_2S=2HCl+S+TiCl_2$ (q.v.) ; and at intermediate temp., *titanium sulphochloride*, TiSCl, is formed.   To obtain a pure product by J. J. Ebelmen's process, it is necessary to free the hydrogen sulphide from oxygen by bubbling it through a soln. of a chromous salt, and from moisture by scrubbing the gas with phosphorus pentoxide.

The titanium disulphide obtained by J. J. Ebelmen was in the form of yellow, lustrous scales resembling mosaic gold. O. Ruff and R. Ipsen found that it sublimes rather less readily than the tetrafluoride. O. F. von der Pfordten showed that it is stable in air; J. J. Ebelmen said that in moist air it smells feebly of hydrogen sulphide, but O. F. von der Pfordten said that it is not decomposed by water. H. V. Regnault found that it easily decomposes when heated in a current of steam, forming hydrogen sulphide, hydrogen, sulphur, and titanium dioxide. O. F. von der Pfordten showed that the disulphide readily burns when heated in air, forming titanium and sulphur dioxides ; and a mixture with potassium nitrate detonates when heated. Dry chlorine converts it into sulphur chloride and titanium tetrachloride, and some admixed titanium dioxide may remain unattacked. H. Rose, and J. J. Ebelmen found that the disulphide dissolves in hydrochloric acid with the evolution of hydrogen sulphide. J. J. Ebelmen said that the disulphide dissolves in dil. sulphuric acid, and also in nitric acid, leaving very little residue. H. Rose, however, found that warm nitric acid dissolved very little of his product, since titanium dioxide and sulphuric acid were formed. O. F. von der Pfordten observed that when heated in a stream of carbon dioxide, the sulphur is separated, and the titanium forms the dioxide. H. Rose said that with an aq. soln. of potassium hydroxide, insoluble potassium titanate and soluble potassium sulphide are formed : $TiS_2+6KOH=K_2TiO_3+2K_2S+3H_2O$. The disulphide is insoluble in potassium hydrosulphide or sulphide, and therefore possesses no thioanhydridic properties.

O. F. von der Pfordten's titanium thiochloride, and the compounds of titanium tetrachloride with sulphur and sulphuryl chlorides, have been previously described. N. S. Maskelyne [2] found golden-yellow, octahedral crystals of what was considered to be a *calcium titanium oxysulphide* in the oldhamite and augite found in a meteorite which fell in Busti, India. It was named *osbornite*—after G. Osborne. A similar substance was prepared by J. W. Mallet by heating zircon with lime and alumina.

REFERENCES.

[1] H. Rose, *Akad. Handl. Stockholm*, 231, 1821 ; *Gilbert's Ann.*, 73. 61, 129, 1823 ; *Pogg. Ann.*, 15. 145, 1829 ; 16. 57, 1829; 42. 527, 1837 ; 99. 575, 1856; *Ann. Chim. Phys.*, (2), 70. 289, 1839 ; J. J. Ebelmen, *ib.*, (3), 20. 394, 1847 ; P. Berthier, *ib.*, (2), 50. 362, 1832 ; H. V. Regnault, *ib.*, (2), 62. 385, 1836 ; O. F. von der Pfordten, *Liebig's Ann.*, 234. 257, 1886 ; *Ber.*, 17. 727, 1885 ; T. König and O. F. von der Pfordten, *Wied. Ann.*, 22. 1485, 2070, 1889 ; *Bull. Soc. Chim.*, (2), 43, 558, 1885 ; (2), 47. 187, 1887 ; P. Pipereaut and A. Helbronner, *Brit. Pat. No.* 207555, 1923 ; T. E. Thorpe, *Journ. Chem. Soc.*, 47. 491, 1885 ; *Chem. News*, 51. 260, 1885 ; A. Blair and P. W. Shimer, *Trans. Amer. Inst. Min. Eng.*, 31. 748, 1902; N. Whitehouse, *Journ. Soc. Chem. Ind.*, 26. 738, 1907 ; E. A. Schneider, *Zeit. anorg. Chem.*, 8. 93, 1895 ; A. E. van Arkel and J. H. de Boer, *ib.*, 148. 345, 1925; O. Ruff and R. Ipsen, *Ber.*, 36. 1777, 1903 ; R. Ipsen, *Ueber das Titanfluorid*, Berlin, 1904 ; E. Wedekind, *Zeit. angew. Chem.*, 37. 87, 1924.

[2] N. S. Maskelyne, *Proc. Roy. Soc.*, 18. 149, 1870; *Phil. Trans.*, 160. 198, 1870 ; J. W. Mallet, *Amer. Journ. Science*, (2), 28. 347, 1859.

§ 16. The Titanium Sulphates

Titanium forms mono-, sesqui-, and di-sulphates, as well as a number of basic and double or complex sulphates. In this respect, titanium is in marked contrast with silicon, and germanium. According to A. Stähler and H. Wirthwein,[1] **titanium monosulphate,** $TiSO_4$, is formed by the evaporation of a soln. of titanium in sulphuric acid ; and not, as stated by E. Glatzel, the violet octohydrated **titanium sesquisulphate,** or **titanous sulphate,** $Ti_2(SO_4)_3.8H_2O$. J. J. Ebelmen reported that violet crystals of a titanium sulphate are produced by dissolving titanium trichloride in sulphuric acid, and evaporating the soln. in vacuo over caustic lime. Analysis showed rather more sulphuric acid than corresponded with $Ti_2(SO_4)_3$. The aq. soln. deposited titanic acid when boiled. F. Wöhler and H. St. C. Deville prepared a similar salt. A. Stähler and H. Wirthwein prepared the sesquisulphate by repeatedly evaporating a conc. soln. of the chloride with dil. sulphuric acid in vacuo at 60°. The crystalline mass after washing with acetic acid, and ether, has the composition $3Ti_2(SO_4)_3.H_2SO_4.25H_2O$, **titanous hydrosulphate.** The same salt may be obtained as a violet crystalline powder by heating titanium tetra-chloride with sulphuric acid until fuming ceases, dissolving the syrupy sulphate in 50 per cent. sulphuric acid, and electrolytically reducing the soln. for 5 to 6 hrs. The hydrosulphate dissolves slowly in water, forming a violet soln. When heated, the salt first gives off water, and then sulphuric acid, becoming at the same time green in colour. At a low red-heat, sulphur dioxide is evolved, and titanium dioxide remains. The anhydrous sesquisulphate, $Ti_2(SO_4)_3$, is deposited, after the protracted evaporation of the violet soln. of titanium sesquisulphate, with dil. sulphuric acid in absence of air. It is a green, crystalline powder insoluble in water, alcohol, ether, or conc. sulphuric acid, but soluble in dil. sulphuric or hydro-chloric acid giving a violet soln. for the reducing action—*vide supra*, the trichloride. W. H. Evans examined the effect of current density, concentration of soln. and temp. on the electrolytic reduction of titanic sulphate, and found that good yields of titanous sulphate could be obtained without the use of a diaphragm. If the current density at the anode is kept fairly high, oxygen is evolved without effecting any marked oxidation of the titanous salt. The yield diminishes rapidly with increase of current density. Rise of temp. increases the yield. The electrolytic reduction of a soln. of titanium disulphate in sulphuric acid was further studied by B. Diethelm and F. Förster.

The properties of titanium sesquisulphate are closely analogous with those of the corresponding vanadium salt. The hydrosulphate can also be called *titano-sulphuric acid* or *sulphatotitanic acid* because corresponding double or complex salts have been made. According to A. Stähler and H. Wirthwein, **ammonium titanous sulphate,** $3Ti_2(SO_4)_3.(NH_4)_2SO_4.18H_2O$, is obtained by boiling a mol of a soln. of the hydrosulphate with 2·5 mols of ammonium sulphate. The pale blue crystals are washed with water, alcohol, and ether. The crystals are stable in air. The salt is insoluble in water and sulphuric acid, but soluble in hydrochloric acid. Boiling sulphuric acid decomposes the salt into its components. By replacing the ammonium sulphate with rubidium sulphate, **rubidium titanous sulphate,** $3Ti_2(SO_4)_3.Rb_2SO_4.24H_2O$, is formed; and its properties are like those of the ammonium salt. A salt of a different type, a **sodium titanous sulphate,** $Na_2SO_4.Ti_2(SO_4)_3.5H_2O$, or $NaTi(SO_4)_2.2\frac{1}{2}H_2O$, has been prepared by P. and H. Spence, by the electrolytic reduction of titanium sulphate in the presence of sulphuric acid, with the addition of sodium sulphate, after which the solution thus formed is evaporated. The salt is lilac in colour, easily soluble in water, and forms a strong reducing agent. E. Knecht added that the salt is insoluble in alcohol, and it is a convenient source of a titanous salt as a reducing agent. H. Spence and co-workers found that a solid titanium salt of a mineral acid, such as titanous sodium sulphate, is obtained by adding a suitable organic acid (*e.g.* citric acid) or salt, and preferably also aluminium sulphate, to a soln. of the salt, and concen-trating the soln., if necessary, until the titanium sodium sulphate separates. Prepared in this way, the soln. of the double salt has little or no tendency to deposit titanium dioxide during use, *e.g.* in discharge dyes. T. Nakazono obtained a soln. of the salt by reduction with zinc amalgam in $4N$-H_2SO_4. A. S. Russell found that the soln. in $4N$-H_2SO_4 can be kept for 12 hrs. in a burette exposed to air, without losing its strength—*vide supra*, titanous chloride.

A. Piccini was unable to obtain *ammonium titanous alum*, $(NH_4)_2SO_4.Ti_2(SO_4)_3$. $24H_2O$, that is, **ammonium sulphatotitanite,** $(NH_4)Ti(SO_4)_2.12H_2O$, and *potassium* *titanous alum*, $K_2SO_4.Ti_2(SO_4)_3.24H_2O$, that is, **potassium sulphatotitanite**, $KTi(SO_4)_2.12H_2O$, in a crystalline form ; and he considered that cæsium sulphate is the best salt to employ for determining whether a sesquioxide is capable of forming alums. He obtained *cæsium titanous alum*, $Cs_2SO_4.Ti_2(SO_4)_3.24H_2O$, that is, **cæsium sulphatotitanite**, $CsTi(SO_4)_2.12H_2O$, by dissolving precipitated titanic acid in a slight excess of dil. sulphuric acid, adding the theoretical quantity of a cold soln. of cæsium sulphate, and then subjecting the mixture to electrolysis, using as a diaphragm an ordinary porous cylinder ; the soln. at the negative pole quickly becomes violet and deposits crystals of the alum. It is purified in an atm. of carbon dioxide by recrystallization from water acidified with sulphuric acid, when it forms pentagonal, hemihedral, bright violet crystals belonging to the cubic system ; it is very sparingly soluble in cold water, more so in hot water, and the soln. quickly becomes turbid on exposure to the air, with precipitation of titanic acid. When heated in the air, it is oxidized, giving off vapours of water and sulphuric acid. The corresponding *rubidium titanous alum*, $Rb_2SO_4.Ti_2(SO_4)_3.24H_2O$, that is, **rubidium sulphatotitanite**, $RbTi(SO_4)_2.12H_2O$, was obtained in a similar manner. It crystallizes in transparent, bright red crystals belonging to the cubic system ; and is very similar to the cæsium salt, but is more soluble in water.

Trihydrated titanium disulphate, $Ti(SO_4)_2.3H_2O$, was reported by E. Glatzel [2] to be a yellow amorphous mass obtained by evaporating a soln. of the sesquisulphate oxidized with nitric acid. There are grave doubts if this product is really the normal disulphate. In opposition to P. Faber, L. and P. Wöhler and W. Plüddemann were unable to get a product with a ratio higher than $SO_3 : TiO_2 = 1 : 1$ by heating titanium dioxide with sulphuric acid. A soln. of titanium dioxide in sulphuric acid is assumed to contain titanium disulphate, $Ti(SO_4)_2$. W. Ramsay and F. L. Usher claimed to have degraded titanium to carbon by the action of radium emanation on a soln. of titanium sulphate. A. Benrath found that titanium sulphate is photochemically reduced in the presence of alcohol, or oxalic acid. The reaction was also studied by A. Benrath, and A. Obladen. L. Wöhler and co-workers measured the vapour tension of the basic titanium sulphates at different temp. For the electro-reduction of titanium sulphate, *vide* titanic chloride. Quite a number of basic titanium sulphates have been reported. Probably some of them are mixtures and not chemical individuals, and represent different stages in the hydrolysis of titanium disulphate. Their composition seems to depend on the temp. and conc. of the mother-liquid. The question will be settled by an application of the phase rule. The existence of hydrated forms of the following seems likely :

$Ti{<}^{SO_4}_{SO_4}$	$O{<}^{Ti<^{SO_4}_{SO_4}}_{Ti<^{SO_4}_{SO_4}}$	$O{=}Ti{=}SO_4$
Titanium disulphate, $Ti(SO)_2$	Titanium oxytrisulphate, $Ti\,O(SO_4)_3$	Titanyl sulphate, $TiOSO_4$

According to M. Blondel, the first basic sulphate, trihydrated **titanium oxytrisulphate**, $Ti_2O(SO_4)_3.3H_2O$, is obtained by heating a soln. of titanium dioxide in conc. sulphuric acid in a sealed tube at 120°. The salt appears as a mass of silky crystals which are soluble in water acidified with hydrochloric acid. On raising the temp. to 225°, the mass changes into rhomboidal crystals of the second basic sulphate —anhydrous **titanyl sulphate,** $TiOSO_4$—which are slowly decomposed by water into a basic sulphate and sulphuric acid. By maintaining the soln. at 225°, the whole of the titanium present can be separated in this form. V. Merz made it as a white powder by evaporating a sulphuric acid soln. of titanic acid to dryness ; removing the excess of sulphuric acid by allowing the mass to stand on a porous tile ; and drying the residue at 350°–400°. The product is slowly decomposed by water. The hydrolysis of titanic sulphate has been studied by H. Rose, R. Weber, C. F. Rammelsberg, and R. Ruer ; and the results compared with those of stannic chloride by R. Lorenz, W. Mecklenberg, and L. Kayser. K. Someya studied the reduction of titanic sulphate by lead and zinc amalgams. L. and P. Wöhler and W. Plüddemann found the vap. press., P mm., of two products, $TiO_2.SO_3$, and $2TiO_2.SO_3$, at $0°$, to be

	TiO₂.SO₃, or TiOSO₄				2TiO₂.SO₂			
0° . . .	545°	560°	592°	595°	524°	574°	590°	610°
P° . . .	24	38	92	300	15	60	214	592

C. Weizmann and J. Blumenfeld made the salt from the titaniferous ore. The *monohydrate*, $TiOSO_4.H_2O$, appears to have been made by J. J. Berzelius, and H. Rose, by digesting finely powdered titanium dioxide in a mixture of sulphuric acid and water (2 : 1) until the whole of the water is expelled. The temp. is then raised, but not to redness, in order to drive off the excess of sulphuric acid. H. Rose also obtained this sulphate, from a soln. of hydrated titanium dioxide or acid potassium titanite in dil. sulphuric acid. H. Rose, and V. Merz precipitated it by adding sulphuric acid to a dil. soln. of titanium in hydrochloric acid. V. Merz, and A. Ditte obtained a similar product by thoroughly washing the first basic sulphate, $Ti_2O(SO_4)_3$. H. Rose said that the white product reddens moist litmus; and when dried, rapidly absorbs moisture. It dissolves in an excess of sulphuric acid, and in an excess of a hydrochloric acid soln. of titanium. When ignited, it furnishes titanium dioxide. A. Ditte, and M. Blondel made the *dihydrate*, $TiOSO_4.2H_2O$, by diluting a soln. of titanium dioxide in conc. sulphuric acid : the liquid at any temp. above 100°, deposits this salt in long needles which are readily soluble in water. A. Rosenheim and O. Schütte prepared the *pentahydrate*, $TiOSO_4.5H_2O$, as a white amorphous mass by boiling titanic acid with alcoholic sulphuric acid, evaporating off the alcohol, and precipitating with ether. The same hydrate was always obtained under wide variations in the experimental conditions.

M. Blondel also reported three basic sulphates with $TiO_2 : SO_3 : H_2O=2 : 1 : n$; $7 : 2 : n$; and $5 : 1 : 5$. He said that if one part of titanium dioxide be dissolved in 2 parts of conc. sulphuric acid, and water be added to the extent of $1\frac{1}{2}$ times the weight of the soln., the liquid deposits sulphates, the composition of which varies with the temp. of deposition; those formed at 100° correspond with the formula $2TiO_2.SO_3.nH_2O$, and those at 130°, with $7TiO_2.2SO_3.nH_2O$. Soln. of titanium dioxide in conc. sulphuric acid, when dil. with from 2 to 10 times their weight of water and heated, deposit various sulphates at temp. below 175°, but above this temp., the anhydrous dioxide crystalli es out; if, however, the soln. be strongly dil. (with 100 to 1000 parts of water) at ordinary temp., the compound $5TiO_2.SO_3+5H_2O$ is obtained, whilst at 100°, the deposit consists of the dioxide with traces of sulphuric acid which cannot be removed by washing. H. Geisow made a product corresponding with $4TiO_2.3SO_3$ by gradually heating a soln. of titanium dioxide in conc. sulphuric acid to 340°, and holding it at that temp. for 18 hrs., when the weight remained constant. When heated to 420°–430°, the composition was $2TiO_2.SO_3$.

F. Wöhler made anhydrous **potassium titanic sulphate**, $K_2SO_4.Ti(SO_4)_2$, by dissolving titanium dioxide in molten potassium hydrosulphate. The glassy mass became opaque in contact with water, and titanic acid separates as it dissolves. C. M. Warren digested the glass with conc. sulphuric acid, and evaporated most of the acid at a low temp. The crystalline mass was washed and the remaining crystals corresponded with $K_2SO_4.Ti(SO_4)_2$. The crystals are decomposed by much water. A. Rosenheim and O. Schütte investigated this subject. R. F. Weinland and H. Kühl made **calcium titanic sulphate**, $CaSO_4.Ti(SO_4)_2$, **strontium titanic sulphate**, $SrSO_4.Ti(SO_4)_2$; and **barium titanic sulphate**, $2BaSO_4.3Ti(SO_4)_2$, by mixing soln. of titanium dioxide in conc. sulphuric acid with soln. of the appropriate sulphates in the same solvent and concentrating. The calcium and strontium salts crystallize in small, well-formed, colourless, lustrous cubes ; the barium salt in slender needles. All the salts are decomposed by water with precipitation of titanic acid. They may be derived from complex titanic acids in which part of the oxygen is replaced by SO_4.

TITANIUM 95

M. Blondel reported the formation of cubic crystals of **ammonium titanium oxysulphate,** $(NH_4)_2SO_4.2TiO_2.SO_3.H_2O$, when a sulphuric acid soln. of titanium dioxide diluted with slightly ammoniacal water, is allowed to evaporate in vacuo. The crystals show tetrahedral hemihedrism ; they effloresce in air, and are slowly decomposed by water. A. Rosenheim and O. Schütte prepared white needles of **ammonium titanyl sulphate,** $(NH_4)_2SO_4.TiOSO_4.H_2O$, by adding a conc. soln. of ammonium sulphate to a soln. of titanium dioxide in conc. sulphuric acid. The salt is very soluble in water, but it cannot be crystallized from its aq. soln. without decomposition. F. M., D. D., and H. Spence made the ammonium salt by a process analogous to that used for **potassium titanyl sulphate,** $K_2SO_4.TiOSO_4$, namely, by fusing titanium dioxide with potassium hydrosulphate, extracting with 10 per cent. sulphuric acid, and evaporating the soln. until its sp. gr. is 1·4, when crystallization occurs. The titanium dioxide was digested with an excess of hot sulphuric acid ; and the soln. mixed with potassium sulphate ($TiO_2 : K_2SO_4 = 1 : 1$) and the soln. conc. for crystallization. These salts are soluble in cold water, but titanic acid gradually separates from their aq. soln. A. Rosenheim and O. Schütte found that **potassium trititanyl pentasulphate,** $2K_2SO_4.3TiOSO_4.10H_2O$, is deposited in colourless needles when a conc. aq. soln. of potassium sulphate is added to a sat. soln. of titanic acid in conc. sulphuric acid. F. M., D. D., and H. Spence made the **sodium titanyl sulphate,** $Na_2SO_4.Ti(SO_4)_2$, in a manner similar to that employed for the potassium salt. A. Mazzucchelli and E. Pantanelli prepared a series of salts by the addition of alcohol to a soln. containing titanium sulphate, hydrogen dioxide, and an alkali sulphate in rather less amount than corresponding with the ratio $TiO_2 : M_2SO_4$. The salts are readily dissolved by water. and are supposed to be derivatives of titanium trioxide. In this way, **ammonium sulphatopertitanate,** $TiO_2(NH_4SO_4)_2.nH_2O$; **lithium sulphatopertitanate,** $TiO_2(LiSO_4)_2.7H_2O$; **sodium sulphatopertitanate,** $TiO_2(NaSO_4)_2.10H_2O$; and **potassium sulphatopertitanate,** $TiO_2(KSO_4)_2.7H_2O$, were obtained.

REFERENCES.

[1] A. Stähler and H. Wirthwein, *Ber.,* **38.** 2619, 1905 ; E. Glatzel, *ib.,* **9.** 1829, 1876 ; E. Knecht, *ib.,* **36.** 166, 1903 ; W. H. Evans, *Mem. Proc. Manchester Lit. Phil. Soc.,* **49.** 1, 1904 ; *Chem. News,* **90.** 314, 1904 ; J. J. Ebelmen, *Ann. Chim. Phys.,* (2), **20.** 385, 1846 ; F. Wöhler and H. St. C. Deville, *ib.,* (3), **52.** 92, 1858 ; *Compt. Rend.,* **45.** 480, 1857 ; *Liebig's Ann.,* **103.** 230, 1857 ; P. and H. Spence, *Brit. Pat. No.* 18108, 1902 ; *French Pat. No.* 324205, 1902 ; *German Pat., D.R.P.* 149602, 1902 ; H. Spence, W. B. Llewellyn, and S. F. W. Crudall, *Brit. Pat. No.* 230877, 1923 ; W. Ramsay and F. L. Usher, *Ber.,* **42.** 2980, 1909 ; P. Faber, *Chem. Ztg.,* **31.** 263, 1907 ; A. Piccini, *Gazz. Chim. Ital.,* **25.** ii, 542, 1895 ; *Zeit. anorg. Chem.,* **17.** 355, 1898 ; B. Diethelm and F. Förster, *Zeit. phys. Chem.,* **62.** 129, 1908 ; L. and P. Wöhler and W. Plüddemann, *Ber.,* **41.** 703, 1908 ; T. Nakazono, *Journ. Japan Chem. Soc.,* **42.** 526, 1921 ; H. W. McCoy, *U.S. Pat. No.* 1559113, 1925 ; A. S. Russell, *Journ. Chem. Soc.,* **129.** 497, 1926.

[2] E. Glatzel, *Ber.,* **9.** 1829, 1876 ; L. and P. Wöhler and W. Plüddemann, *ib.,* **41.** 712, 1908 ; W. Ramsay and F. L. Usher, *ib.,* **95.** 624, 1909 ; W. Ramsay, *Journ. Chem. Soc.,* **95.** 624, 1909 ; M. Blondel, *Bull. Soc. Chem.,* (3), **21.** 262, 1899 ; A. Benrath, *Zeit. Wiss. Photochem.,* **74.** 217, 1915 ; **22.** 65, 1922 ; A. Rosenheim and O. Schütte, *Zeit. anorg. Chem.,* **26.** 239, 1901 ; L. Kayser, *ib.,* **138.** 43, 1924 ; R. F. Weinland and H. Kühl, *ib.,* **54.** 253, 1907 ; V. Merz, *Journ. prakt. Chem.,* (1), **99.** 157, 1866 ; *Ueber das Titan, Silicium, und Boron,* Zürich, 1864 ; H. Geisow, *Beiträge zur Kenntnis der seltenen anorganischen Säuren,* München, 12, 1902 ; R. Weber, *Pogg. Ann.,* **120.** 287, 1863 ; *Sitzber. Akad. Berlin,* 358, 1863 ; C. F. Rammelsberg, *ib.,* 490, 1874 ; R. Ruer, *Zeit. anorg. Chem.,* **43.** 282, 1903 ; W. Mecklenberg, *ib.,* **9.** 369, 1895 ; R. Lorenz, *ib.,* **64.** 368, 1909 ; **74.** 207, 1912 ; K. Someya, *ib.,* **145.** 168, 1925 ; A. Mazzucchelli and E. Pantanelli, *Atti Accad. Lincei,* (5), **18.** i, 518, 608, 1909 ; A. Ditte, *Compt. Rend.,* **104.** 172, 1887 ; C. M. Warren, *Pogg. Ann.,* **102.** 453, 1857 ; *Journ. prakt. Chem.,* (1), **75.** 361, 1858 ; F. M., D. D., and H. Spence, *Brit. Pat. No.* 4183, 1899 ; C. Weizmann and J. Blumenfeld, *ib.,* 209480, 1922 ; 210033, 1922 ; W. B. Llewellyn and H. and P. Spence, *ib.,* 200848, 1922 ; H. Rose, *Gilbert's Ann.,* **73.** 67, 129, 1823 ; *Pogg. Ann.,* **1.** 76, 1824 ; **3.** 163, 1825 ; **12.** 492, 1828 ; **15.** 145, 1829 ; **16.** 57, 1829 ; **24.** 141, 1832 ; **42.** 527, 1837 ; J. J. Berzelius, *ib.,* **4.** 1, 1825 ; F. Wöhler, *ib.,* **7.** 423, 1826 ; P. Faber, *Chem. Ztg.,* **31.** 263, 1907 ; A. Benrath and A. Obladen, *Zeit. wiss. Photochem.,* **22.** 65, 1922.

§ 17. Titanium Carbonates, Nitrates, and Phosphates

There is no evidence that *titanium carbonate* has yet been prepared. J. J. Berzelius [1] reported the formation of an **ammonium titanic carbonate** in soln., for, when an acid soln. of titanic acid is dropped into a large excess of an aq. soln. of ammonium carbonate, the precipitate which first forms is re-dissolved, and the soln. deposits titanic acid when boiled. Similarly, **potassium titanic carbonate,** but titanic acid is not precipitated by boiling the soln. ; this does occur, however, if ammonium chloride be present when the soln. is boiled. Many double salts with organic acids—formic, oxalic, and tartaric acids—have been prepared. V. Auger found that when titanic chloride is added to a mixture of potassium hydrocarbonate and its aq. soln., as much as 2000 mgrms. of titanium salt per 100 c.c. may remain in soln., but 1300 mgrms. are precipitated in a few hours. A double carbonate is considered to be present in the more conc. soln.

H. Rose prepared a soln. containing presumably **titanium nitrate** by dissolving hydrated titanium dioxide or potassium titanate in nitric acid. V. Merz evaporated the liquid over caustic lime, and obtained crystals of a basic salt, **titanium oxynitrate,** with the composition $5TiO_2.N_2O_5.6H_2O$. Complex or double salts have not yet been prepared.

H. Rose obtained what he regarded as a *titanium phosphite* by adding an aq. soln. of phosphorus trichloride to an aq. soln. of titanium chloride, and neutralizing with ammonia. When the white precipitate is heated in a retort, hydrogen and phosphorus vap. are evolved, and a black residue containing titanium dioxide remains. H. Rose also precipitated what he called *titanium phosphate* by adding phosphoric acid to a soln. of titanium dioxide in hydrochloric acid. The white, flaky precipitate is soluble in an excess of either phosphoric acid or titanium chloride ; and it dries to a gummy mass. L. Ouvrard obtained a product with the composition $TiO_2.P_2O_5$, which can be regarded as **titanyl metaphosphate,** $TiO(PO_3)_2$, by dissolving titanium dioxide in molten potassium or sodium metaphosphate, and slowly cooling the product. P. Hautefeuille and J. Margottet dissolved hydrated titanium dioxide in orthophosphoric acid, at a temp. when the dehydration begins. The octahedral crystals were assumed to have the composition $TiO_2.P_2O_5$. E. Wehrlin and E. Giraud obtained the same product from titanium chlorotriethoxyphosphate, $TiCl(OC_2H_5)_3.3H_3PO_4$. V. Merz obtained a titanium phosphate of the composition $2TiO_2.P_2O_5.3H_2O$, by precipitating a soln. of titanium chloride with a soluble phosphate, and thoroughly washing the product. *Vide* titanium chloride for a number of *chlorophosphates.*

According to L. Ouvrard, when titanium dioxide is fused with a large excess of potassium metaphosphate, octahedral crystals of $TiO_2.P_2O_5$ are formed ; with a higher proportion of titanic oxide, **potassium triphosphatotitanate,** $K_2O.4TiO_2.$ $3P_2O_5$, or $KTi_2(PO_4)_3$, is obtained in small, highly refractive, almost cubic crystals, isomorphous with the corresponding sodium salt. Potassium pyrophosphate or orthophosphate yields **potassium oxyphosphatotitanate,** $K_2O.2TiO_2.P_2O_5$, or $KTiOPO_4$, ir biaxial crystals, probably monoclinic, but closely resembling regular octahedra. With other proportions of titanic oxide, acicular crystals of rutile are obtained, and these are formed instead of the double phosphate if an excess of potassium chloride is present. J. J. Berzelius noted that titanium dioxide dissolves in molten microcosmic salt or sodium metaphosphate, forming a clear glass ; and G. Rose noted that the sat. soln. furnishes crystals of anatase. L. Ouvrard obtained crystals of **sodium titanium phosphate,** $Na_2O.4TiO_2.3P_2O_5$, or $Ti_3(PO_4)_4.TiNa_2(PO_4)_2$, from the soln. of titanium dioxide in molten sodium metaphosphate. A. Knop regarded the product as $3TiO_2.P_2O_5$, and G. Wunder and L. Ouvrard, as $Na_2O.4TiO_2.3P_2O_5$. R. Brauns supposed that some titanium sesquioxide was present. The rhombohedral crystals were supposed by G. Wunder to be isomorphous with the corresponding tin compound. G. Rose regarded the crystals as tetragonal; A. Knop, rhombic. According to G. Wunder, the salt is decomposed when fused with an excess of sodium carbonate, and when the product is extracted with water, sodium titanate remains undissolved. L. Ouvrard found that when titanium dioxide is dissolved in fused sodium pyrophosphate or ortho-phosphate, crystals of $6Na_2O.3TiO_2.4P_2O_5$, are formed in macled, striated prisms with longitudinal extinctions. G. Saring reported **potassium calcium phosphato-titanate,** $Ca_3(PO_4)_2(CaO)_2(K_2O)_2TiO_2$, analogous with the corresponding silicate.

P. Faber obtained a voluminous yellow precipitate of **titanium trihydroxy-orthophosphate,** $(HO)_3TiPO_4$, by adding sodium phosphate to a sulphuric acid soln. of pertitanic acid; and also by adding ammonium phosphate to an am-moniacal soln. of pertitanic acid. The product in each case was washed with acetic acid in which it is sparingly soluble. It is, however, soluble in hydrochloric, nitric, sulphuric, and phosphoric acids, in soln. of potassium hydroxide, ammonia, and ammonium carbonate or phosphate. It decomposes when heated to a high temp. P. Faber assumed that the product contained sexivalent titanium:

$$O=P{<}{\overset{O}{\underset{O}{}}}{-}O{-}Ti{<}{\overset{OH}{\underset{OH}{}}}OH$$

A. Mazzucchelli and E. Pantanelli could not verify P. Faber's observation, but they obtained instead **sodium phosphatopertitanates,** $Na_2O.TiO_3.P_2O_5.3H_2O$, and $O:TiO_2.P_2O_5.Na_2O_2.24H_2O$. M. Billy made an insoluble *pertitanic phosphate* by mixing soln. of acid titanium sulphate, sodium phosphate, and hydrogen dioxide, and precipitating with sodium acetate. The precipitate lost oxygen during the washing.

REFERENCES.

[1] J. J. Berzelius, *Pogg. Ann.*, **4.** 1, 1825; H. Rose, *ib.*, **9.** 47, 1827; **61.** 507, 1844; *Gilbert's Ann.*, **73.** 67, 129, 1823; V. Merz, *Ueber das Titan, Silicium, und Boron*, Zürich, 1864; *Journ. prakt. Chem.*, (1), **99.** 162, 1866; G. Wunder, *ib.*, (2), **4.** 339, 1871; A. Knop, *Liebig's Ann.*, **157.** 363, 1871; **159.** 36, 1871; *Zeit. Chem.*, (2), **1.** 216, 1871; *Bull. Soc. Chim.*, (2), **15.** 190, 1871; L. Ouvrard, *Compt. Rend.*, **111.** 177, 1890; P. Hautefeuille and J. Margottet, *ib.*, **102.** 1017, 1886; E. Wehrlin and E. Giraud, *ib.*, **85.** 228, 1877; M. Billy, *ib.*, **172.** 1411, 1921; V. Auger, *ib.*, **177.** 1302, 1923; R. Brauns, *Neues Jahrb. Min.*, ii, 237, 1892; P. Faber, *Zeit. anal. Chem.*, **46.** 277, 1907; A. Mazzucchelli and A. Pantanelli, *Atti Accad. Lincei*, (5), **18.** i, 608, 1909; G. Rose, *Sitzber. Akad. Berlin*, 130, 1867; G. Saring, *Versuch über den Aufschluss durch Kieselsäure bei hohen Temperaturen*, Dresden, 1906.

CHAPTER XLII

ZIRCONIUM

§ 1. History of Zirconium

THE bluish-violet mineral **hyacinth** (or jacinth)—from ὑάκινθος, a (lily) flower—has been known very many years as an inferior gem-stone. The minerals *sacondios, chrysolithos, melichrysos, crateritis,* and *hyacinthus,* mentioned in Pliny's *Historiæ naturalis* (**37**. 40–56), may possibly have been related to the hyacinth. The *lyncurium,* mentioned by Theophrastus, in his Περὶ Δίθων, about 300 B.C., was not known to Pliny (**36**. 13). The statements that the *lyncurium* was used for engraved signets, that it was electrified by friction, and that it was often amber-coloured, are the sole evidence for assuming that zircon was in question. Intagli of zircon are common among ancient gems. The different varieties of the genera range in tint from yellow, brown, to red, and they may also be colourless, green, rose-red, or violet. The name hyacinth is now usually confined to reddish varieties. Hyacinths were mentioned by many writers in the Middle Ages.[1] G. Agricola called it *jacinth ;* A. Cronstedt, *jargon ;* J. G. Wallerius, *clarus hyalinus ;* J. B. L. Romé de l'Isle, *diamant brut* or *jargon de Ceylon ;* F. de St. Fond said that *le nom d'hyacinte orientale* was applied to oriental rubies of an orange-red colour, and added, *il est usage d'appeler* **jargon** *toute pierre de peu de valeur, qui imite l'éclat de diamant sans avoir la dureté.* In the eighteenth century, colourless jargons were supposed to be inferior or imperfect diamonds, and, being common in the Matura district, Ceylon, were called *Matura diamonds.* J. B. L. Romé de l'Isle proved *jargon de Ceylon* to be a distinct mineral species which A. G. Werner designated **zircon,** or *silex circonius*—presumably from the Arabian *zerk,* a precious stone. According to J. Prinsep, and F. R. Mallet, the Singalese jewellers called the mineral *turmali.*

Near the end of the eighteenth century, M. H. Klaproth,[2] in the course of a *Chemische Untersuchung des Zircons,* fused specimens of yellowish-green and red zircon from Ceylon, with sodium hydroxide, and extracted the cold mass with hydrochloric acid. Potassium carbonate was added to the soln., and the precipitate filtered off and washed. The precipitate was again digested with sulphuric acid, and the soln. evaporated to dryness ; the residue was digested with sulphuric acid and the silica filtered off. The filtrate was tested for lime, magnesia, and alumina, but none was found. The liquid, however, did give a precipitate with potassium carbonate, which, unlike precipitated alumina, did not dissolve in alkali-lye, and, unlike precipitated magnesia, did not effervesce with acids. The precipitate, indeed, behaved like no other known substance, and accordingly, M. H. Klaproth stated :

I feel myself justified in concluding this precipitate to be a distinct and simple earth previously unknown. I propose to call it *Zirkonerde—terra circonia*—until it may be found in other minerals, or possessed of other properties which may suggest a more appropriate denomination.

The average of M. H. Klaproth's analyses of the zircon yielded : Silica, 31·5 ; iron oxide, 0·5 ; zircon earth, 68·0 per cent. M. H. Klaproth further found that a sample of hyacinth from Ceylon yielded on analysis : Silica, 25·0 ; iron oxide, 0·5 ; and zircon earth, 70·0 per cent. This result caused some surprise, because the standard analyses of this mineral by T. Bergman [3] indicated : Silica, 25 ; alumina,

40 ; lime, 20 ; iron oxide, 13 per cent. T. Bergman must have confused zirconia with alumina. In 1799, J. B. Trommsdorff tried unsuccessfully to obtain a metal from zirconia. The impure metal itself was isolated from Klaproth's *Zirconerde*, by J. J. Berzelius, in 1824, and he reported the results of numerous investigations on this element between 1824 and 1835.

M. H. Klaproth [4] also established the identity of hyacinth from Espailly (Haute-Loire), and of the mineral *zirconite*, reported by G. F. Schumacher from Fredriksvarn. with zircon or zirconium silicate, $ZrSiO_4$.

The composition of zircon and related minerals is very complex, for they may be associated with small quantities of many other elements—tin, lead, bismuth, aluminium, nickel, cobalt, iron, manganese, uranium, the rare earths, zinc, magnesium, calcium, hafnium, copper, lithium, sodium, potassium, and, maybe, traces of radium, $75-865 \times 10^{-12}$ grms. per gram, with occluded helium and neon.[5] Accordingly, B. Lindemann proposed to call this group of minerals *polycrasilites*—from πολύς, many ; κρᾶσις, a mixture.

Some of the impurities are retained very persistently by the zirconia precipitated during analysis, and mixtures have been reported as new elements or rather new earths—*e.g.* A. Breithaupt [6] reported the element *ostranium* from the mineral *ostranite*—a decomposition product of zircon ; L. F. Svanberg reported *Norerde* or *noria* to be a new earth from zircon and eudialyte ; the element was called *norium*—from Nore, the ancient name of Norway. In 1869, H. C. Sorby reported *jargonia* to be a new earth from zircon of Ceylon ; A. H. Church also considered that the spectroscope showed a new element as a companion of zirconia, and he named it *nigrum*. The spectrum of certain mixtures of zirconium and uranium oxides does not resemble the joint spectrum of the individual oxides. In 1901, K. A. Hofmann and W. Prandtl reported that about half of the so-called zirconia obtained from euxenite from Brevig really consisted of a similar earth—*Euxenerde* or *euxenia*—supposed to be an oxide of an element with a rather higher atomic weight than zirconium. None of these reports has been confirmed satisfactorily.

REFERENCES.

[1] G. Agricola, *De natura fossilium*, Basil, 295, 1546 ; *Interpretatio germanica vocum rei metallicæ*, Basil, 464, 1546 ; A. B. de Boodt, *Gemmarum et lapidum historia*, Lugduni Batavorum, 79, 1609 ; J. G. Wallerius, *Mineralogia*, Stockholm, 121, 1747 ; A. Cronstedt, *Mineralogie*, Stockholm, 42, 1758 ; J. B. L. Romé de l'Isle, *Cristallographie*, Paris, 2. 281, 1783 ; F. de St. Fond, *Sur les volcans eteints du Vivarais*, Paris, 302, 1778 ; A. G. Werner, *Letztes Mineralsystem*, Freyberg, 1817 ; J. Prinsep, *Journ. Asiatic Soc. Bengal*, 1. 357, 1832 ; F. R. Mallet, *A Manual of the Geology of India*, Calcutta, 4. 111, 1887.

[2] M. H. Klaproth, *Beobacht. Entdeck. Naturkunde*, 3. 2, 1789 ; *Beiträge zur chemischen Kenntniss der Mineralkörper*, Berlin, 1. 229, 1795.

[3] T. Bergman, *De terra gemmarum*, Upsala, 1777 ; *Opuscula physica et chimica*, Holmiæ, 2. 96, 1780 ; J. J. Berzelius, *Pogg. Ann.*, 4. 117, 1825 ; 8. 186, 1826 ; J. B. Trommsdorff, *Trommsdorff's Journ.*, 6. 116, 1799.

[4] G. F. Schumacher, *Verz. Min. Dän. Nord. Staaten Kopenhagen*, 105, 1801 ; M. H. Klaproth, *Beiträge zur chemischen Kenntniss der Mineralkörper*, Berlin, 3. 266, 1802 ; L. N. Vauquelin, *Ann. Chim. Phys.*, (1), 22. 179, 1797 ; L. B. G. de Morveau, *ib.*, (1), 21. 72, 1797.

[5] R. J. Strutt, *Proc. Roy. Soc.*, 78. A, 150, 1906 ; B. Lindemann, *Sitzber. Akad. Wien*, 91, 1009, 1885 ; 92. 427, 1885 ; *Chem. News*, 52. 220, 1885.

[6] A. Breithaupt, *Pogg. Ann.*, 5. 377, 1825 ; L. F. Svanberg, *ib.*, 65. 317. 1845 ; *Œfvers. Akad. Förh. Stockholm*, 34, 1845 ; H. Sjögren, *Pogg. Ann. Ergbd.*, 3. 465, 1853 ; N. J. Berlin, *Journ. prakt. Chem.*, (1), 58. 145, 1853 ; R. Hermann, *ib.*, (1), 31. 75, 1844 ; (1), 97. 321, 330, 1866 ; H. C. Sorby, *Proc. Roy. Soc.*, 17. 511, 1869 ; 18. 197, 1870 ; *Chem. News*, 19. 121, 1869 ; 20. 7, 1869 ; A. H. Church, *ib.*, 19. 121, 1869 ; J. D. Forbes, *ib.*, 19. 277, 1869 ; A. Knop, *Liebig's Ann.* 159. 45, 1871 ; K. A. Hofmann and W. Prandtl, *Ber.*, 34. 1064, 1901 ; J. C. G. de Marignac, *Ann. Chim. Phys.*, (3), 60. 257, 1860.

§ 2. The Occurrence of Zirconium

Zirconium does not occur free in nature. It is commonly found as silicate, oxide, etc. Zirconium was once considered to be a scarce element, but F. W. Clarke,[1] and F. W. Clarke and H. S. Washington have estimated that it is almost as abundant as carbon, and constitutes nearly 0·017 per cent. of the earth's lithosphere ; and

J. H. L. Vogt estimated 0·01 to 0·02 per cent. ; for comparison, F. W. Clarke, and J. Joly estimate that 27·7 per cent. of that crust is silicon, 0·46 per cent. titanium, and 0·002 per cent. thorium. This subject has been also discussed by J. F. Kemp, and W. Lindgren.

Although so widely distributed, large workable deposits are rare. Prior to the discovery of baddeleyite in 1892, zircon was the most important source of zirconium. Both these minerals are discussed elsewhere—baddeleyite with zirconium dioxide, zircon, with the silicates. In addition to the minerals [2] where zirconium occurs as an essential constituent, there are numerous others where it appears as a secondary constituent, and it is found as an occasional constituent of nearly all minerals. The oxide may be associated as an acidic radicle with the oxides of titanium, silicon, thorium, cerium, niobium, or tantalum.

The oxide $baddeleyite$ has 80 to 98 per cent. ZrO_2. Complex $zirconates$ are represented by $zirkelite$, $(Ca,Fe)O.2(Zr,Ti,Th)O_2$, which has 50 to 53 per cent. zirconia; $uhligite$, $Ca(Zr,Ti)_2O_5.Al_2TiO_5$, has up to 33 per cent. ZrO_2; $hiörtdahlite$, $4Ca(Si,Zr)O_3.Na_2ZrO_2F_2$, with 21 to 22 per cent. of ZrO_2; $guarinite$ is closely related to hiörtdahlite; $rosenbuschite$, $6CaSiO_3.2Na_2ZrO_2F_2.TiSiO_3.TiO_3$, with 18 to 20 per cent. ZrO_2; $wöhlerite$, $12R(Si,Zr)O_3.R(Cb_2O_5)$, with 15 to 23 per cent. ZrO_3; $polymigmite$, $5RTiO_3.5RZrO_3.R(Cb,Ta)_2O_6$, with 29 to 30 per cent. ZrO_2; and $eudialyte$, and $eucolite$, $Na_{13}(Ca,Fe)_6Cl(Si,Zr)_{20}O_{52}$, with 11 to 17 per cent. of ZrO_2. The silicate is represented by $zircon$, $ZrSiO_4$, with 61 to 67 per cent. ZrO_2, and its numerous varieties—e.g. $azorite$, $beccarite$, $calyptolite$, $hyacinth$, $jargon$, and $ostranite$—and altered forms—e.g. $adelpholite$, $alvite$, $anderberjite$, $auerbachite$, $cyrtolite$, $malacone$, $œrstedite$, $oliveiraite$, $orvillite$, and $tachyaphaltite$. A silicate $nœgite$, $ZrSiO_4$, is also associated with the rare earths. More complex silicates are represented by $lävenite$, $R(Si,Zr)O_3.Zr(SiO_3)_2.RTa_2O_6$, with 28 to 32 per cent. ZrO_2; $hainite$, $R(Si,Zr)O_3.Zr(SiO_3)_2.RTa_2O_6$, with 28 to 32 per cent. ZrO_2; $catapleiite$, $H_4(Na_2,Ca)ZrSi_3O_{11}$, with 30 to 40 per cent. ZrO_2; $elpidite$, $H_6Na_2ZrSi_6O_{18}$, with 20 to 21 per cent. ZrO_2.

The tantalum and columbium minerals—$annerödite$, with 1 to 2 per cent. ZrO_2; $chalcolamprite$, with 5 to 6 per cent. ZrO_2; $columbite$, with 1 to 11 per cent. ZrO_2; $fergusonite$, with up to about 2 per cent. ZrO_2; $loranskite$, with about 20 per cent. ZrO_2; $pyrochlore$, with 0 to 5 per cent. ZrO_2; $samarskite$, with 0 to 4 per cent. ZrO_2; $sipylite$, with 2 to 3 per cent. ZrO_2. The thorum minerals $auerlite$, and $thorianite$ have from 0 to 3 per cent. ZrO_2. The titanium mineral $leucosphenite$ has up to 5 per cent. ZrO_2; and $lorenzenite$ up to 12 per cent. ZrO_2. The scandium mineral $wiikite$; the uranium mineral, $uraninite$; the yttrium mineral $xenotime$; the cerium minerals $cerite$ and $monazite$, all may carry up to about 8 per cent. of zirconia. Similarly, also, with the complex rare earth minerals: $arrhenite$ has 3 to 4 per cent. ZrO_2; $tritomite$ has 1 to 3·6 per cent. ZrO_2; $erdmannite$ or $michaelsomite$ has 2·14 to 5·44 per cent. ZrO_2; $euxenite$ has up to 2 per cent. ZrO_2; $endeolite$ has up to 4 per cent. of ZrO_2; and $johnstrupite$ and $mosandrite$ have respectively 2·84 and 7·43 per cent. ZrO_2. Specimens of $arfvedsonite$ or $riebeckite$ correspond with a soda-hornblende, $FeSiO_3.2NaFe(SiO_3)_2$, and have up to 7 per cent. of zirconia ; H. S. Washington reported 2·67 per cent. of zirconia in $œgirite$.

Zirconium minerals—chiefly zircon—occur in many deposits—clays, sands, etc. —derived from the weathering of granitic and pegmatitic rocks. It occurs in the alluvial sands of Ceylon, and Travancore. According to J. P. Iddings,[3] it occurs in Norwegian syenites, and Canadian limestones. J. D. Dana reported it in various auriferous sands and gravels ; and H. Rösler, in many clays. M. Mazade[4] reported zirconium in the mineral waters of Nérac, and also in their ochreous deposits, but O. Henry questioned the accuracy of the analyses. N. G. Sefström reported zirconium in the furnace slags of Taberg, Sweden. According to H. A. Rowland,[5] F. W. Dyson, and J. N. Lockyer, zirconium occurs in the sun ; M. Merrill reported zirconium bands in the spectra of stars ; and H. Laspeyres, and E. Cohen, in meteorites.[6]

REFERENCES.

[1] F. W. Clarke, *The Data of Geochemistry*, Washington, 30, 1920 ; F. W. Clarke and H. S. Washington, *Proc. Nat. Acad. Science*, 8. 108, 1922 ; *The Composition of the Earth's Crust*, Washington, 1924 ; J. Joly, *Phil. Mag.*, (6), 17. 760, 1909 ; (6), 18. 140, 1909 ; (6), 20. 125, 1910 ; J. H. L. Vogt, *Zeit. prakt. Geol.*, 6. 225, 314. 377, 413, 1898 ; 7. 10, 274, 1899 ; J. F. Kemp, *Econ. Geol.*, 1. 207, 1905 ; W. Lindgren, *ib.*, 18. 419, 1923 ; L. Moser, *Œster. Chem. Ztg.*, 26. 67, 1923.

[2] C. Hintze, *Handbuch der Mineralogie*, Leipzig, 1. ii, 1628, 1915 ; H. Thurach, *Verh. Phys. Med. Ges. Würzburg*, 18. 10, 1884 ; J. Schilling, *Das Vorkommen der seltenen Erde im Mineralreiche*, München, 1, 1904 ; C. R. Böhm, *Chem. Ind.*, 29. 320, 350, 1906 ; E. Cahen and W. O. Wotton, *The Mineralogy of the Rarer Metals*, London, 1912 ; H. S. Washington, *Journ. Geol.*, 70. 300, 1914.

[3] J. P. Iddings, *Rock Minerals*, New York, 1906 ; J. D. Dana, *A System of Mineralogy*, New York, 1892 ; H. Rösler, *Beiträge zur Kenntniss einiger Kaolinlagerstätten*, Stuttgart, 1902.

[4] M. Mazade, *Compt. Rend.*, 34. 952, 1852 ; O. Henry, *Journ. Pharm. Chim.*, (3), 24. 305, 1853 ; *Phil. Mag.*, (4), 7. 149, 1853 ; N. G. Sefström, *Journ. tech. ökon. Chem.*, 10. 135, 1831.

[5] H. A. Rowland, *Preliminary Table of Solar Spectrum Wave-lengths*, Chicago, 1898 ; *Phil. Mag.*, (5), 36. 49, 1893 ; F. W. Dyson, *Phil. Trans.*, 206. A, 403, 1906 ; J. N. Lockyer, *Table of Wave-lengths of Enhanced Lines*, London, 1906 ; M. Merrill, *Pub. Astron. Soc. Pacific*, 35. 217, 1922.

[6] H. Laspeyres, *Zeit. Kryst.*, 24. 489, 1895 ; 27. 597, 1897 ; *Ber. Niederrh. Ges. Bonn.*, 114, 1894 ; E. Cohen, *Ann. Nat. Hist. Hofmuseum Wien*, 9. 112, 1894 ; *Sitzber. Akad. Berlin*, 1047, 1897 ; *Meteoritenkunde*, Stuttgart, 2. 262, 1903.

§ 3. The Extraction of Zirconia from the Minerals

The process employed for extraction of zirconium from the native and impure oxides, or the native silicates, depends on the degree of purity desired. In any case, it is necessary to pulverize the mineral to a fine state of subdivision, and this operation, said M. Weibull,[1] is facilitated by heating and suddenly cooling the mineral. Silica, and iron may not be objectionable, or it may be necessary to remove one or both these constituents. R. C. Gosreau concentrated the zircon of the crushed ore by means of pulsating tables. J. G. Thompson found that 90–95 per cent. of the silica can be removed from zirkite ore by heating a mixture of the ore and carbon in an electric furnace above 2220°. Hot sulphuric or hydrochloric acid, or aqua regia, will remove most of the iron from powdered red baddeleyite without undue loss by dissolution of the zirconia. E. Wedekind recommended sulphuric acid for baddeleyite. J. W. Bain and G. E. Gollop used conc. sulphuric acid for zirkite ore. A. J. Phillips mixed the zirconium with about 4 per cent. of petroleum coke, and heated the briquettes to 900° in a stream of moist chlorine. E. J. Pugh sublimed the zirconium as chloride by heating the ore in a stream of chlorine. G. Siebert and E. Korten, J. W. Bain and G. E. Gollop, A. L. D. d'Adrian, and H. von Siemens and H. Zander opened the raw material by heating it with halogens in the presence of carbon at a high temp. Hot conc. hydrofluoric acid will not remove the silica from zirconium silicate, $ZrSiO_4$. If silica is to be removed, or a high degree of purity is desired, it is necessary to open up the mineral by sintering or fusion, with suitable fluxes. According to K. Rördam, eudialyte can be opened by digestion with twice its weight of hydrochloric acid ; two-thirds of the zirconium passes into soln., and the remaining third is removed from the associated silica by digestion with sulphuric acid. E. Linnemann recommended a preliminary treatment of the powdered mineral with hydrochloric acid to remove the iron ; or else heating the zircon in the vap. of hydrogen chloride before the fusion with alkali, so as to obtain a porous, easily decomposed mass. In most cases, however, this operation is superfluous. The methods of extractions have been critically examined by E. Linnemann, W. R. Schoeller, R. Lehmann, and J. W. Marden and M. N. Rich.

1. *Fusion with alkali hydroxides or carbonates.*—M. H. Klaproth, and J. J. Berzelius fused the mineral with 4 to 5 parts of its weight of potassium hydroxide.

M. E. Chevreul, and F. Dubois and A. A. de Silveira used 2 parts of potassium hydroxide, and kept the mixture in a fused state for $2\frac{1}{2}$ hrs. in a silver crucible. J. J. Berzelius also used a mixture of potassium carbonate and sodium hydroxide; F. Wöhler, T. Scheerer, R. Hermann, E. C. Rossiter and P. H. Sanders, O. Ruff, L. M. Dennis and A. E. Spencer recommended sodium carbonate ; H. L. Wells and F. W. Foote used 4 parts of sodium carbonate to 1 of ore ; W. Henneberg, 0·5 part of potassium nitrate to 4 of sodium carbonate ; F. Stolba, a mixture of 3 parts of potassium carbonate and 2 of potassium fluoborate ; and F. G. Jackson and L. I. Shaw, a mixture of sodium carbonate and borax.   P. Berthier also used a mixture of sodium carbonate and sulphur ; and J. Gordon a mixture of the alkali hydroxide or carbonate with sodium or calcium chloride.   P. Berthier used either sodium hydroxide or carbonate, or a mixture of the two.   He said that the soda fluxes are preferable to the potash fluxes because the latter are more inclined to form sparingly soluble double salts.   J. W. Bain and G. E. Gollop examined the efficiency of the process.   P. Berthier, and D. E. Melliss recommended using 3 parts of sodium hydroxide to 1 of the powdered ore ; and E. Linnemann, G. H. Bailey, and F. P. Venable used 10 parts of sodium hydroxide and 1 of sodium fluoride to 1 of ore.   H. S. Cooper said that heating the ore to redness and quenching facilitates its decomposition by the fused alkali.   F. Stolba decomposed zircon by heating it with a soln. of sodium hydroxide in an autoclave. F. P. Venable thus applied this process :

The zircon is pulverized roughly in an iron mortar, and then ground in an agate mortar until the powder will pass through a 100-mesh sieve ; the powder is boiled repeatedly with strong hydrochloric acid and washed with water.   The fusion is conducted in a nickel crucible ; 400 grms. of sodium hydroxide are first fused, then 20 grms. of dry sodium fluoride are added, and when the mass is highly heated, the 100 grms. of zircon are dropped in ; any bubbling over of the mass is prevented by the temporary removal of the flame. When the action ceases, the molten mass is poured on to a sheet of nickel, and as soon as it has solidified it is plunged into water ; the sodium silicate and a negligible amount of the zirconate pass into soln., but the bulk of the latter remains behind, and is dissolved in hydrochloric acid.   The soln. is then subjected to repeated evaporation to dryness and treatment with hydrochloric acid, to remove silica and hydrofluoric acid ; the zirconium being ultimately precipitated as hydroxide by means of ammonia.   The hydroxide, after thoroughly washing by decantation, is dissolved in the smallest possible quantity of conc. hydrochloric acid, the soln. evaporated to dryness, and the zirconium oxychloride obtained washed in a funnel with a mixture of conc. hydrochloric acid with 4 parts of alcohol ; any zirconium oxychloride passing into soln. can be recovered.   The white mass in the funnel is then repeatedly crystallized from strong hydrochloric acid, the zirconium oxychloride being obtained in well-formed crystals of glistening whiteness.

During the fusion with alkali hydroxide or carbonate, the silica, zirconia, and titania are presumably changed respectively to the alkali silicate, zirconate, and titanate ; and the iron is converted to ferric oxide.   Some of the zirconia probably forms a double alkali zirconium silicate.   The fused mass is cooled, and leached with a little water—say 10 litres per kilogram.   Part of the sodium zirconate is hydrolyzed by the water, forming the hydroxide in a finely divided state difficult to filter. The insoluble matter consists of the hydroxides of iron, zirconium, and titanium, and some alkali zirconium silicate.   These substances, with the exception of silica, are soluble in acids.   The zirconium salts are isolated from the acid soln.   If hydrochloric acid is used for dissolving the cake, the oxychloride, $ZrOCl_2.8H_2O$, may be crystallized from conc. hydrochloric acid.   R. T. Glazebrook and co-workers gave $Zr_5O_8Cl_4.22H_2O$ for the composition of the product.   The oxychloride process was used by J. J. Berzelius, G. H. Bailey, R. Hermann, F. P. Venable and C. Baskerville, M. E. Chevreul, T. Scheerer, N. J. Berlin, E. Linnemann, F. P. Venable, H. Moissan and F. Lengfeld, J. M. Matthews, M. Hanriot, etc.   If sulphuric acid be employed for dissolving the cake, the basic sulphate can be crystallized out.   Zirconium sulphate has a maximum solubility in a soln. with 61 per cent. of SO_3 ; and, on standing, the acid sulphate, $Zr(SO_4)_2.H_2SO_4.3H_2O$, crystallizes out.   If a conc. soln. of the mixed sulphates of iron, titanium, and zirconium be kept boiling for some time, a basic sulphate is precipitated. Thus, K. Leuchs obtained $4ZrO_2.3SO_3.14H_2O$. R. T. Glazebrook and co-workers added alkali to the cold acid soln. until a permanent white precipitate began to form, and allowed the precipitation to continue without further addition of alkali. In illustration, E. C. Rossiter and P. H. Sanders' process may be cited :

Fifty grams of the powdered ore are fused in an iron crucible with 50 grms. of sodium hydroxide ; the mixture is stirred until frothing ceases, and a granular powder is obtained, the heating being then continued at dull redness for 2 hrs. The mass, while hot, is poured into 1·5 litres of water, the soln. filtered, the insoluble residue treated with hydrochloric acid, and evaporated to dryness. The dry residue is extracted with hot water and the soln. filtered. This soln. is diluted to 1·5 litres, boiled after the addition of a slight excess of sulphurous acid, and normal sulphuric acid is added gradually until the mixture becomes quite thick. After a short time, the whole of the zirconia is precipitated as a basic sulphate ; the precipitate is collected, washed, dried, and ignited to form the oxide, or the precipitate may be suspended in water, treated with alkali, and the hydroxide collected, dried, and ignited.

M. N. Rich allowed the soln. of sulphate to stand some days when the basic sulphate is precipitated. L. W. Ryan precipitated the basic sulphate in a granular form by adding sodium chloride and sodium carbonate or hydroxide to the soln. of the sulphate. The basic sulphate process was used by S. R. Paykull, C. M. Warren, R. Ruer, O. Hauser, etc. The basic sulphate can be converted into the oxide by ignition, or into the hydroxide by suspending it in water and agitating with ammonia. P. Askenasy, and B. Havas heated the acid soln., containing not more than 9 per cent. zirconium hydroxide, in an autoclave at, say, 200°. The zirconium hydroxide was precipitated in a form which is easily filtered. W. R. Loveman patented a process in which it was claimed that the treatment of the fused cold cake with water removed the silica from the cake obtained by melting the powdered ore with 8 times its weight of sodium carbonate. The residue, digested with hydrochloric acid (1 : 1), left a hydrated zirconium oxide which, after ignition, contained 99·55 per cent. of zirconium oxide ; 0·10 per cent. Fe_2O_3 ; 0·2 per cent. TiO_2 ; and 0·15 per cent. silica.

2. *Fusion with alkaline earths, or lead oxide.*—R. Bayer heated a mixture of the powdered mineral with $2\frac{1}{2}$ times its weight of barium carbonate at about 1400°, for $2\frac{1}{2}$ hrs. in a graphite crucible. The barium zirconate is extracted from the cold mass with hydrochloric acid, and the acid liquid is evaporated to dryness to make the silica insoluble. The residue is leached with hydrochloric acid, and, on conc., crystals of barium chloride first separate, and finally zirconium oxychloride, $ZrOCl_2.8H_2O$. This process is quite good for removing the silica, but not the iron. P. Berthier opened up the mineral by melting it with about $2\frac{1}{2}$ times its weight of lead oxide ; or by heating it with 0·3 times its weight of powdered quartz, and 1·1 times its weight of calcium carbonate, in a carbon crucible. In the latter case, the iron is reduced, and collects at the bottom of the crucible. J. Gordon used calcium oxide mixed with sodium or calcium chloride.

3. *Fusion with alkali pyrosulphate, or hydrosulphate.*—B. Franz, N. J. Berlin, A. Stromeyer, L. E. Barton and C. J. Kinzie, R. Hermann, R. Lehmann, and J. M. Matthews fused the mineral with potassium hydrosulphate. Alkali pyrosulphate, or nitre-cake can also be used. About 20 parts of the alkali sulphate to 1 of ore are used ; if the proportion is less than 10 : 1, the decomposition may be incomplete. A graphite, fused silica, or cast-iron crucible can be used. The cold cake can be heated with conc. sulphuric acid till all is dissolved ; and when cold, poured into cold water. The clear soln. is decanted or filtered from the silica which separates, and is then ready for the recovery of the zirconium. In the alternative process, the cold cake can be digested with hot water and the soln. filtered from the silica, etc. The filtrate contains the zirconium sulphate or oxysulphate, with some silica, iron, alumina, and sodium sulphate. This can be treated by the basic sulphate process—*vide supra*. J. H. de Boer fused the ore with potassium hydrosulphate, extracted the fused mass with water, precipitated the metals as hydroxides, and

redissolved the precipitate in conc. hydrochloric acid. From the strongly acid soln. zirconium is precipitated as the phosphate, $Zr(HPO_4)_2$, and is thereby separated from all other metals except hafnium. The phosphate is readily washed by decantation with hydrochloric acid and water, and may then be dissolved in hydrofluoric acid and the zirconium reprecipitated as hydroxide.

4. *Fusion with alkali hydrofluoride.*—J. C. G. de Marignac recommended fusing the mineral with 2 to 3 times its weight of potassium hydrofluoride : ZrO_2+4KHF_2 $=K_2ZrF_6+2H_2O+2KF$. The cold cake is boiled with water containing hydrofluoric acid, and the insoluble alkali fluosilicate filtered off. On cooling the hot soln., crystals of alkali fluozirconate are deposited, and this salt can be recrystallized from water. The fluozirconate can be treated with sulphuric acid and evaporated to dryness, and the potassium sulphate removed by lixiviation with water ; or, as recommended by R. Hornberger, the evaporation with sulphuric acid can be carried to a point where the hydrofluoric acid and most of the sulphuric acid are driven off, and the aq. soln. heated with ammonia as indicated below. This process, or a simple modification of it, was used by B. Franz, G. H. Bailey, H. Traube, H. Rose, J. W. Bain and G. E. Gollop, R. Lehmann, and J. Potyka. J. Körner fused the ore with sodium fluosilicate to get a product soluble in sulphuric acid.

5. *Heating the ore mixed with carbon, or calcium carbide, or oxide in a high-temperature electric furnace.*—L. Troost heated a mixture of calcium oxide, zircon, and carbon in an electric arc-furnace for a few minutes. The reaction is represented : ZrO_2 $+4C=ZrC_2+2CO$. All but about 1 to 1·5 per cent. of the silica was volatilized and also most of the iron oxide, and other impurities. The product was extracted with water and dil. hydrochloric acid ; and the residue was treated with chlorine at 300° so as to furnish zirconium chloride. There is a small loss of zirconia by volatilization at the high temp. employed. This process recalls F. Wöhler's process in which chlorine gas was passed over an intimate mixture of the ore and carbon heated in a porcelain or hard glass tube. He said, " The silicon chloride is volatilized and the zirconium chloride sublimed in such a state as to be completely soluble in hydrochloric acid." L. Troost, L. Burgess, and H. Moissan and F. Lengfeld prepared a crude zirconium carbide by heating a mixture of the mineral and carbon in the electric arc furnace. The carbide was heated in chlorine, and the resulting chloride dissolved in hydrochloric acid. E. Wedekind dissolved the zirconium in aqua regia and precipitated zirconium hydroxide with aq. ammonia. Crystalline zirconium oxychloride separates from the cooling soln. L. Renaux, and E. Wedekind said that in this process calcium carbide gives better results than carbon alone. The main reaction is represented : $ZrSiO_4+2CaC_2=ZrC+SiC+2CaO+2CO$. Modifications of the process have been patented by L. E. Barton, O. Hutchins, C. J. Kinzie, H. Herzfeld, T. R. Haglund, L. Burgess, and P. Jost and P. Plocker.

The zirconium hydroxide precipitated by ammonia from soln. of zirconium salts is contaminated with hydroxides of other elements which may be present, and which are likewise precipitated by this agent—e.g. iron, titanium, chromium, aluminium, vanadium, and the rare earths. The iron, titanium, and aluminium are the most difficult to separate from zirconium. Zirconium can be separated from iron by the use of the double fluorides; by the oxychloride process; basic and acid sulphate; hydrolytic dissociation; and the phosphate process. The last was recommended by J. H. de Boer. For the separation of hafnium, *vide infra*. In addition to the processes of separation just described, a number of others have been recommended mainly for purposes other than commercial.

(1) F. Dubois and A. A. de Silveira, and F. Wöhler boiled the precipitate obtained by adding ammonia, with a soln. of oxalic acid. and separated the soluble ferric oxalate from the insoluble zirconium oxalate by filtration and washing. The zirconium oxalate was converted to oxide by ignition, or dissolved in acid, and the hydroxide precipitated by aq. ammonia. N. J. Berlin found that if too much oxalic acid is used some zirconium oxalate is dissolved. (2) M. H. Klaproth, J. L. W. Gruner, J. J. Berzelius, T. Scheerer, G. Possetto, H. Geisow, and P. Horkheimer treated the mixed precipitate with alkali or ammonium hydroxide. (3) E. Linnemann, F. P. Venable, and J. M. Matthews separated ferric chloride

from zirconium chloride by extracting the mixed soln, with ether, the ferric chloride follows the ether. (4) F. S. Havens and A. F. Way, by exposing the mixed oxides at a temp. of 200° to a stream of hydrogen chloride and chlorine—the ferric chloride alone is volatilized. (5) E. T. Allen, by the addition of phenylhydrazine. when the zirconium and aluminium salts are precipitated. (6) H. Geisow, P. Horkheimer, E. Wedekind, F. Wöhler, L. M. Dennis and A. E. Spencer, R. Hermann, C. Baskerville, and P. Berthier, by treating the neutral soln. with sulphur dioxide, when basic zirconium sulphate is precipitated. (7) J. J. Berzelius, R. Hornberger, H. Geisow, P. Horkheimer, E. Wedekind, O. Hauser, C. F. Rammelsberg, C. F. Chandler, W. C. Brögger, and G. von Knorre, by adding ammonium sulphide to the alkaline soln. of the two chlorides in the presence of alkali tartrate, when ferric sulphide is alone precipitated. (8) M. F. Chancel, W. R. Loveman, R. Hermann, and A. Stromeyer, by boiling the slightly acid soln. with sodium thiosulphate, when zirconium is precipitated (9) G. H. Bailey, F. P. Venable, O. Hauser, R. Ruer, H. Geisow, and P. Horkheimer, by the action of conc. hydrogen dioxide on a feebly acid soln. of zirconium sulphate, when hydrated zirconium peroxide is precipitated—iron, aluminium, and titanium remain in soln. In alkaline soln., the iron is precipitated and the zirconium salt remains in soln. (10) G. von Knorre, and E. A. Atkinson and E. F. Smith separated the iron and zirconium by treatment of the liquid, acidified with tartaric acid, with a soln. of nitro-β-naphthol, iron is alone precipitated; and (11) L. E. Rivot, K. Daniel and co-workers, and A. Gutbier and co-workers, by heating the mixed oxides in a stream of hydrogen, when the iron is reduced to the metal, which is alone soluble in acids. (12) M. H. Klaproth used an alkali succinate as precipitant for the iron; and (13) C. R. Böhm, sodium nitrate as precipitant for the zirconium. (14) E. W. Washburn and E. E. Libman said that all but a trace of the iron can be removed by heating zirconium oxide at 300° in a stream of carbonyl chloride—*vide* carbonyl chloride. For separating titanium and zirconium, (15) G. Streit and B. Franz acidified the mixed soln. with dil. acetic and sulphuric acids, and, on boiling, the titanium oxide alone was precipitated; (16) F. Pisani reduced the titanium dioxide to the sesquioxide in acid soln. by means of zinc, and on the addition of potassium sulphate, zirconium potassium sulphate was precipitated; and (17) L. Fernandes used thallous sulphate as an auxiliary agent in separating zirconium and thorium from the rare earths. (18) According to W. F. Hillebrand, R. J. Carney, P. Hautefeuille and J. Margottet, and A. Knop, when hydrogen dioxide is added to a soln. containing sodium phosphate, a basic zirconium phosphate is precipitated; and, according to J. T. Davis, (19) by warming the faintly acid soln. with sodium iodate, zirconium iodate is precipitated—thorium iodate is insoluble in oxalic acid, but zirconium iodate is soluble.

REFERENCES.

[1] M. H. Klaproth, *Beiträge zur chemischen Kenntniss der Mineralkörper*, Berlin, 1. 203, 1795; J J. Berzelius, *Ann. Chim. Phys.*, (2), 29. 337, 1825; *Œfvers. Akad. Förm. Stockholm*, 295, 1824; *Schweigger's Journ.*, 21. 40, 1846; *Pogg. Ann.*, 4. 117, 1825; F. Wöhler, *ib.*, 48. 94, 1839; C. M. Warren, *ib.*, 102. 449, 1857; T. Scheerer, *ib.*, 59. 48, 1843; F. Dubois and A. A. de Silveira, *Ann. Chim. Phys.*, (2), 14. 110, 1820; M. E. Chevreul, *ib.*, (2), 13. 245, 1820; P. Berthier, *ib.*, (2), 50. 362, 1832; (2), 59. 192, 1843; (3), 7. 74, 1843; D. E. Melliss, *Bull. Soc. Chim.*, (2), 14. 204, 1870; C. F. Rammelsberg, *Ber.*, 4. 875, 1871; 20. 413, 1886; *Sitzber. Akad. Berlin*, 441, 18_6; C. F. Chandler, *Contributions to the Chemistry of Zirconium*, Göttingen, 1870; J. G. Thompson, *Journ. Phys. Chem.*, 26. 812, 1922; *Chem. News*, 126. 23, 1923; *Trans. Amer. Electrochem. Svc.*, 40. 445, 1921; L. Burgess, *ib.*, 47. 173, 1925; J. W. Mellor, *A Treatise on Quantitative Analysis*, London, 499, 1913; M. Weibull, *Lunds. Univ. Arsskrift*, 2. 18, 1882; E. Linnemann, *Monatsh.*, 6. 531, 899, 1885; *Sitzber. Akad. Wien*, 91. 1019, 1885; H. Rose, *Pogg. Ann.*, 48. 575, 1840; 108. 20, 1859; J. Potyka, *Untersuchungen über einige Mineralien*, Berlin, 1859; J. C. G. de Marignac, *Compt. Rend.*, 50. 952, 1860; *Ann. Chim. Phys.*, (3), 60. 257, 1860; B. Franz, *Ber.*, 3. 58, 1870; R. Hornberger, *Liebig's Ann.*, 181. 232, 1876; A. Stromeyer, *ib.*, 113. 127, 1862; A. Knop, *ib.*, 159. 36, 1871; J. M. Matthews, *Journ. Amer. Chem. Soc.*, 20. 815, 1898; L. M. Dennis and A. E. Spencer, *ib.*, 18. 673, 1896; C. Baskerville, *ib.*, 16. 745, 1894; F. P. Venable and C. Baskerville, *ib.*, 17. 448, 1895; E. T. Allen, *ib.*, 25. 426, 1903; J. T. Davis, *ib.*, 11. 26, 1889; E. A. Atkinson and E. F. Smith, *ib.*, 17. 688, 1895; H. L. Wells and H. W. Foote, *Amer. Journ. Science*, (4), 1. 18, 1896; *Zeit. anorg. Chem*, 10. 434, 1895; J. H. de Boer, *ib.*, 144. 190, 1925; W. Henneberg, *Journ. prakt. Chem.*, (1), 38. 508, 1847; G. Streit and B. Franz, *ib.*, (1), 108. 65, 1869; N. J. Berlin, *ib.*, (1), 58. 147, 1853; R. Hermann, *ib.*, (1), 95. 124, 1865; (1), 97. 340, 1866; F. Stolba, *Listy's Chem.*, 13. 119, 1889; *Chem. News*, 49. 174, 1884; G. H. Bailey, *Journ. Chem. Soc.*, 49. 149, 481, 1886; *Chem. News*, 60. 17, 32, 1889; F. P. Venable, *ib.*, 64. 315, 1891; *Journ. Anal. Chem.*, 5. 551, 1891; *Journ. Amer. Chem. Soc.*, 16. 469, 1894; F. G. Jackson and L. I. Shaw, *ib.*, 44. 2712, 1922; H. Traube, *Neues Jahrb. Min. B.B.*, 10. 470, 1896; K. Rördam, *Medd. Grönland*, 13. 7, 1888; O. Hauser, *Ber.*, 37. 2024, 1904; *Zeit. anorg. Chem.*, 45. 190, 1905; 54. 197, 1907; R. Ruer, *ib.*, 43. 282, 1905; 46. 485, 1905; A. Gutbier and G. Hüller, *ib.*, 32. 92, 1902; A. Gutbier, *ib.*, 36. 302, 1903; K. Daniel and H. Leberle, *ib.*, 34. 393, 1903; K. Daniel, *ib.*, 37. 475, 1903; H. Geisow and P. Horkheimer, *ib.*, 32. 372, 1902; E. Wedekind, *ib.*, 33. 81,

1903; *Zeit. angew. Chem.*, **19**. 1683, 1906; R. Bayer, *ib.*, **23**. 485, 1910; R. C. Gosreau, *Eng. Min. Press*, **119**. 405, 1925; J. W. Bain and G. E. Gollop, *Canadian Chem. Met.*, **7**. 35, 1923; L. Fernandes, *Gazz. Chim. Ital.*, **55**, i, 3, 1925; L. Renaux, *Contribution à l'étude de l'zircone*, Paris, 1900; R. Lehmann, *Untersuchungen über Zirkonoxyde und seine Verwendung*, München, 1908; H. Moissan, *Compt. Rend.*, **116**. 1222, 1893; H. Moissan and F. Lengfeld, *ib.*, **122**. 651, 1896; L. Troost, *ib.*, **61**. 109, 1865; **116**. 1227, 1428, 1893; F. Pisani, *ib.*, **57**. 298, 1863; **59**. 298, 1864; M. F. Chancel, *ib.*, **46**. 987, 1856; P. Hautefeuille and J. Margottet, *ib.*, **110**. 1038, 1890; J. W. Marden and M. N. Rich, *Investigations of Zirconium with especial reference to the Metal and the Oxide*, Washington, 1921; *Journ. Ind. Eng. Chem.*, **12**. 651, 1920; E. W. Washburn and E. E. Libman, *Journ. Amer. Cer. Soc.*, **3**. 634, 1920; F. S. Havens and A. F. Way, *Amer. Journ. Science*, (4), **8**. 217, 1899; W. F. Hillebrand, *Bull. U.S. Geol. Sur.*, **176**. 1900; *Some Principles and Methods of Rock Analysis*, Washington, 1900; G. von Knorre, *Zeit. anal. Chem.*, **28**. 234, 1889; L. E. Rivot, *Ann. Chim. Phys.*, (3), **30**. 188, 1852; P. Askenasy, *U.S. P t. No.* 1158769, 1915; *German Pat., D.R.P.* 262009, 1912; L. E. Barton, *ib.*, 1342084, 1351091, 1920; G. Siebert and E. Korten, *ib.*, 355485, 1920; J. Gordon, *ib.*, 1340888, 1920; W. R. Loveman, *ib.*, 1261948, 1918; 1297371, 1919; R. J. Carney, *ib.*, 1182880, 1916; B. Havas, *Brit. Pat. No.* 9153, 1913; *German Pat., D.R.P.* 262009, 1912; H. Herzfeld, *ib.*, 290878, 1914; P. Jost and P. Plocker, *ib.*, 285981, 1914; K. Leuchs, *ib.*, 285344, 1914; 295246, 1915; M. N. Rich, *U.S. Pat. No.* 1460766, 1923; O. Ruff, *ib.*, 1454564, 1923; J. Körner, *ib.*, 1467275. 1923; C. J. Kinzie, *ib.*, 1494426, 1924; H. S. Cooper, *ib.*, 1527470, 1925; L. W. Ryan, *ib.*, 1530139, 1540425, 1924; E. J. Pugh, *ib.*, 1376161, 1920; L. E. Barton and C. J. Kinzie, *ib.*, 1451004, 1923; A. L. D. d'Adrian, *ib.*, 1434485, 1434486, 1922; O. Hutchins, *ib.*, 1427816, 1922; R. T. Glazebrook, W. Rosenhain, and E. H. Rodd, *Brit. Pat. No.* 112973, 1918; Deutsche Gasglühlicht Auer Ges., *ib.*, 222486, 1924; Soc. d'Étude des Agglomérés, *ib.*, 223572, 1924; S. R. Paykull, *Œfvers. Akad. För. Stockholm*, **22**, 1873; **7**, 53, 1878; *Bull. Soc. Chim.*, (2), **20**. 65, 1873; M. Hanriot, *ib.*, (3), **7**. 161, 1892; M. H. Klaproth, *Beiträge zur chemischen Kenntniss der Mineralkörper*, Berlin, **1**. 203, 227, 1795; J. L. W. Gruner, *Gilbert's Ann.*, **13**. 495, 1903; G. Possetto, *Giorn. Farm. Chim.*, **48**. 49, 1898; W. C. Brögger, *Zeit. Kryst.*, **16**. 344, 362, 1890; C. R. Böhm, *Die Darstellung der seltenen Erden*, Leipzig, **2**. 27, 1905; A. J. Phillips, *Journ. Amer. Cer. Soc.*, **1**. 791, 1918; E. C. Rossiter and P. H. Sanders, *Journ. Soc. Chem. Ind.*, **40**. 70, T, 1921; W. R. Schoeller, *ib.*, **40**. 126, T, 1921; H. von Siemens and H. Zander, *Wiss. Veröffentl. Siemens. Konzern*, **2**. 484, 1922; J. H. de Boer, *Zeit. anorg. Chem.*, **144**. 190, 1925; T. R. Haglund, *Brit. Pat. No.* 232549, 1924; L. Burgess, *Zeit. Amer. Electrochem. Soc.*, **47**. 317, 1925.

§ 4. The Preparation of Zirconium

The isolation of zirconium of a high degree of purity is not easy. J. B. Trommsdorff's [1] and H. Davy's attempts were not successful. The chief difficulties are connected with the resistance offered by the oxide to reduction, the tendency of the metal to oxidation, the high m.p. of the metal, and the ease with which the reduced metal unites with other substances. According to G. H. Bailey, zirconia is not reduced by hydrogen; and, according to L. Weiss and E. Neumann, it is not reduced by the alkali metals. The metal can be obtained by reducing the halogen salts with the alkali metals, and by reducing the oxide with aluminium, magnesium, calcium, or carbon. The product, however, is usually impure because the metal so readily combines with the reducing agent, and with hydrogen, carbon, oxygen, and even nitrogen gas. In consequence, the early reports of the preparation and properties of this element refer not to the metal, but rather to the metal contaminated with from 5 to 10 per cent. of impurity—carbide, silicide, nitride, hydride, or oxide. The so-called crystalline zirconium of the nineteenth century was probably an alloy of the metal with aluminium. In illustration, six samples of zirconium, prepared by the early methods, were found by E. Wedekind and S. J. Lewis to contain from 24·98 to 92·64 per cent. of free zirconium; 2·55 to 53·68 per cent. of zirconium in the form of oxide; and 1·24 to 8·70 per cent. of zirconium in the form of nitride.

L. Troost claimed to have made *graphitic zirconium* by reducing sodium zirconate by iron at a red heat, but this has not been confirmed since iron does not reduce zirconia under these conditions. J. W. Marden and M. N. Rich tried zinc, lead, silver, and manganese as reducing agents for potassium fluozirconate or zirconia, but the results were inferior to those obtained with aluminium as a reducing agent. H. N. Warren reported that when a rod of magnesium is wrapped in coils of asbestos paper, and dipped into a soln. of a zirconium salt, zirconium metal is obtained. The report has not been confirmed.

E. Sander patented a method of making zirconium by heating the nitride or hydride under reduced press., pumping off the gases as they are formed. Other methods proposed for making zirconium are as follow:

(1) *The reduction of halides by the alkali metals.*—In J. J. Berzelius' process, a mixture of dry potassium fluozirconate and potassium was heated over a spirit-lamp in an iron tube—6 mm. diameter and 30 mm. long—closed at one end. The reduction proceeded quietly, and the mass was stirred frequently with an iron wire. The cold mass was washed successively with dil. hydrochloric acid; and a soln. of ammonium chloride; and finally with alcohol. L. M. Dennis and A. E. Spencer used a somewhat similar process. L. Weiss and E. Neumann found that the amorphous or colloidal product so obtained contained about 93·7 per cent. of zirconium. The chief impurity is zirconium oxide which is formed by the action of water or soda-lye during the washing. A 98 per cent. metal was obtained by treating the product first with absolute alcohol in place of water, and then washing with dil. acid, etc. E. Wedekind filled a copper tube under ether, with the mixture of potassium and potassium zirconium fluoride, and then pumped the air from the tube. The mixture was dried at 200° in vacuo, and then heated to 300°. The product contained 71 per cent. of free zirconium, and 16·6 per cent. of combined zirconium. The product was pyrophoric, and fired when exposed to the air 14 hrs. after cooling. Like J. J. Berzelius, subsequent workers have found that the best results are obtained when potassium fluozirconate is used as the source of zirconium. E. Wedekind, and L. Weiss and E. Naumann found sodium gave better results than potassium. L. Troost reduced zirconium tetrachloride by passing its vap. over hot sodium, or an alloy of zinc and sodium in a porcelain tube. D. Lely and L. Hamburger reduced the tetrachloride by sodium in a bomb. The metal was obtained in plates which could be pressed into rods. E. Podszus heated potassium fluozirconate and sodium in a steel bomb fitted with a molten lead seal. The closed bomb was revolved for about 40 hrs. at 200° to produce intimate admixture. A few minutes' heating started the reaction, and sodium vap. passed through the lead seal. The resulting finely crystalline metal contained 99·3 per cent. zirconium M. A. Hunter and A. Jones, and H. S. Cooper reduced zirconium chloride by a similar process and obtained the granular metal of 96 per cent. purity. J. W. Marden and M. N. Rich have reported on this process.

(2) *The reduction of the oxide by calcium.*—A. Burger obtained 98·7 per cent. zirconium and 0·18 calcium by heating a mixture of zirconia and an excess of calcium The reaction is $2ZrO_2+2Ca=CaZrO_3+Zr+CaO$; and at a higher temp., near 1050°, $CaZrO_3+2Ca=Zr+3CaO$. E. Wedekind, and H. Kuzel and E. Wedekind obtained very fair specimens of zirconium by heating an intimate mixture of zirconia with an excess of fine calcium shavings in an iron tube closed at one end, and under a reduced press., —0·1 to 0·5 mm. The heating was discontinued as soon as the reaction commenced. The cold product was powdered and washed successively with cold water; acetic acid; dil. hydrochloric acid; and then with water, until the washings showed the absence of calcium chloride. After a final washing with acetone, the product was dried—first at ordinary temp.; then in vacuo at from 250° to 300°; and finally in an evacuated porcelain tube between 800° to 1000°. The resulting metal contained 99·09 per cent. of zirconium; and the yield was 97·5 per cent. of the theoretical. An attempt to purify the product further by again heating it in a metal tube with calcium gave a less pure product. O. Ruf and H. Brintzinger obtained 97 per cent. zirconium by reducing the oxide with a sodium-calcium alloy.

(3) *The reduction of the oxide or halide by magnesium.*—According to T. L. Phipson and G. H. Bailey, zirconia is reduced by molten magnesium. C. Winkler passed hydrogen over a heated mixture of zirconia and magnesium, and obtained a mixture of zirconium hydride and unchanged zirconia. The unchanged zirconia is sup-

posed by some to be really a suboxide (*q.v.*). L. M. Dennis and A. E. Spencer obtained a product with 80·7 per cent. of zirconium, and 18·0 per cent. of oxygen. According to L. Troost, and W. R. Whitney, amorphous zirconium can be prepared by passing the vap. of zirconium tetrachloride over red-hot magnesium. E. Wedekind heated thin pencils of alkali fluozirconate with magnesium in an electric furnace, and obtained 96·55 per cent. zirconium and 4·14 per cent. oxygen. He also heated zirconia and 40 per cent. excess magnesium in a nickel crucible and obtained a colloidal form of zirconium. R. Escales patented a process for the preparation of zirconium involving the use of the rare-earth metals, or mixtures of their alloys with magnesium or aluminium.

(4) *The reduction of the halide or oxide by aluminium, etc.*—L. Troost passed the vapour of zirconium tetrachloride over heated aluminium and obtained a spongy mass. The surface layers had a crystalline structure. He also heated a mixture of sodium or potassium fluozirconate, R_2ZrF_6, with one and a half times its weight of aluminium in a crucible to the m.p. of iron, and treated the cold mass with hydrochloric acid (1 : 2) in order to isolate the metal. The product had a crystalline structure. B. Franz said that the fluozirconate, $3KF.ZrF_4$, gives better results than the normal fluozirconate. He used a graphite crucible, and obtained a metal with 1·03 per cent. aluminium, and 0·17 per cent. silicon. S. A. Tucker and H. R. Moody, and E. Wedekind found that the thermite process of H. Goldschmidt and C. Vautin gave a mixture of zirconium with unreduced zirconia and alumina which cannot be readily separated from the metal. L. Weiss and E. Neumann say that there is not enough difference between the heats of formation of zirconia and alumina to give good results by the thermite process involving the reaction : $3ZrO_2+4Al=2Al_2O_3+3Zr+253$ cals. K. A. Kühne patented a thermite process involving reaction : $ZrO_2+2Al+BaO_2=Al_2O_3+BaO+Zr$. J. W. Marden and M. N. Rich did not get good results by this process with zirconia, or potassium fluozirconate. J. W. Marden and M. N. Rich fused a mixture of a silicate ore of zirconium, sodium fluoride, and aluminium in the electric vacuum furnace, and obtained impure zirconium. E. Wedekind tried reducing potassium fluozirconate with aluminium in an electric furnace and obtained an alloy of zirconium with 34 per cent. of aluminium, which could not be removed by acids or alkalies. By melting the product in an electric furnace part, but not all, the aluminium was removed. L. Weiss and E. Neumann purified the zirconium obtained by J. J. Berzelius's process, or the aluminium reduction process, by squeezing the product into rods or pencils and following the method described in connection with titanium, **7**. 41, 4, Fig. 1. The process was investigated by J. W. Marden and M. N. Rich. When the experiment was made with the zirconium-aluminium alloy, in an atm. of nitrogen, at about 10 or 11 mm. press., the aluminium volatilized, and the globules had 99·76 to 99·89 per cent. zirconium. This was considered to be the purest zirconium ever made. H. Fischvoigt and F. Koref, and A. E. van Arkel and J. H. de Boer made zirconium by passing the vapour of the tetraiodide over a heated tungsten filament—*cide* titanium.

(5) *The reduction of zirconia by hydrogen, calcium carbide, carbon, boron, or silicon.*—L. Troost tried to eliminate silicon from zirconia by compressing intimate mixtures of zirconia and carbon into small cylinders and heating them in the electric arc furnaces in an atm. of carbon dioxide—the residual zirconium carbide contained up to 1·5 per cent. of silica. L. Renaux modified the process by using calcium carbide. The reaction, according to E. Wedekind, is : $ZrSiO_4+2CaC_2=ZrC+SiC+2CaO+2CO$, and it is possible by this process to volatilize the silicon carbide almost completely. In the attempt to reduce a similar mixture of zirconia and sugar-charcoal contained in a vessel lined with zirconia, heated in an arc-furnace, L. Troost, and H. Moissan obtained zirconium containing 4 to 5 per cent. of carbon which was present presumably as carbide. H. C. Greenwood, and J. N. Pring found that the reduction of zirconia by carbon begins about 1400°. H. Moissan stated that when zircon is heated in a carbon crucible in the electric arc-furnace, he obtained

a metal containing about 5 per cent. of carbon, and no nitrogen ; the silica passed off as white fumes. He obtained zirconium from this carbide by fusing it in the presence of an excess of fused zirconia, and said that the metal is free from carbon and nitrogen, but still contains some oxide. His description of zirconium shows that he was probably mistaken as to the purity of his preparation. He reduced zirconia with carbon, either together or admixed with lime, in an electric arc-furnace, and obtained zirconium carbide which he claimed is reduced to the metal when the zirconia is present in excess. L. Burgess modified the process a little. According to E. Wedekind, when a mixture of zirconia and boron is heated in the electric furnace, an impure metal containing boride and carbide is formed ; and with silicon as reducing agent, zirconium silicide is present. H. von Wartenburg and co-workers reduced zirconia by heating it in an atm. of hydrogen at 5 atm. press., and 2500°, provided a metal like tungsten is present to dissolve the zirconium.

(6) *The electrolytic reduction of zirconium salts.*—A. C. Becquerel electrolyzed a soln. of zirconium tetrachloride mixed with a small proportion of ferric chloride contained in the cathode compartment. The platinum wire cathode in 24 hrs. was covered with a steel-grey film of crystals of zirconium. The metal readily oxidized on exposure to air. According to L. Troost, the electrolysis of molten potassium fluozirconate, or sodium chlorozirconate, furnishes crystalline zirconium, but E. Wedekind vas able to obtain only an impure powder, greyish-black in colour, and easily oxidized. J. W. Marden and M. N. Rich could obtain only the impure amorphous metal by L. Troost's process.

J. J. Berzelius mentioned that in washing out the soluble matters from the product of the action of potassium on the alkali fluozirconate, a soln. of ammonium chloride in hydrochloric acid should be used because, with water alone, the whole of the zirconium is carried in a state of minute division, through the pores of the filter. The soln. of ammonium chloride or other saline substances thus flocculate the **colloidal zirconium** into large flakes. The suspended zirconium is also flocculated by heat. C. Winkler obtained similar results in the reduction of zirconium dioxide or tetrachloride with magnesium. E. Wedekind, H. Kuzel, and W. R. Whitney obtained analogous results.

REFERENCES.

[1] G. H. Bailey, *Chem. News*, 53. 55, 287, 1886 ; 60. 8, 1888 ; *Journ. Chem. Soc.*, 49. 149, 481, 1886 ; S. A. Tucker and H. R. Moody, *ib.*, 81. 14, 1902 ; H. C. Greenwood, *ib.*, 93. 1495, 1908 ; J. N. Pring, *ib.*, 93. 2101, 1908 ; H. Davy, *Phil. Mag.*, 32. 203, 1808 ; *Phil. Trans.*, 98. 333, 1808 ; L. Weiss, *German Pat.*, *D.R.P.* 314791, 1920 ; L. Weiss and E. Neumann, *Zeit. anorg. Chem.*, 65. 248, 1910 ; D. Lely and L. Hamburger, *ib.*, 87. 209, 1914 ; E. Podszus, *ib.*, 99. 123, 1917 ; O. Ruff and H. Brintzinger, *ib.*, 129. 267, 1923 ; E. Wedekind, *ib.*, 33. 81, 1902 ; 45. 385, 1905 ; *Ber.*, 35. 3929, 1902 ; *Zeit. Elektrochem.*, 10. 331, 1904 ; *Chem. Ztg.*, 31. 655, 1907 ; *Ber. Internat. Cong. App. Chem.*, 5. iv, 439. 1903 ; *Zeit. Koll.*, 2. 289, 1908 ; *Liebig's Ann.*, 395. 149, 1913 ; H. Kuzel and E. Wedekind, *Met. Chem. Engg.*, 12. 260, 1914 ; E. Wedekind and S. J. Lewis, *ib.*, 371. 266, 1910 ; 395. 149, 1912 ; *Journ. Chem. Soc.*, 95. 456, 1909 ; *Zeit. angew. Chem.*, 22. 725, 1909 ; S. J. Lewis, *Studien über das Elementare zirconium*, Stuttgart, 1912 ; H. Kuzel and E. Wedekind, *German Pat.*, *D.R.P.* 1088909, 1914 ; *Brit. Pat. No.* 23215, 1909 ; H. Kuzel, *ib.*, 186980, 197279, 1905 ; R. Escales, *ib.*, 145820, 1902 ; E. Sander, *ib.*, 147316, 154691, 1906 ; J. J. Berzelius, *Pogg. Ann.*, 4. 117, 1825 ; J. W. Marden and M. N. Rich, *Investigations of Zirconium with especial Reference to the Metal and the Oxide*, Washington, 1921 ; *Journ. Ind. Eng. Chem.*, 12. 651, 1920 ; J. W. Marden, *U.S. Pat. No.* 1437984, 1922 ; *Brit. Pat. No.* 173236, 1921 ; L. M. Dennis and A. E. Spencer, *Journ. Amer. Chem. Soc.*, 18. 673, 1896 ; H. von Wartenburg, J. Broy, and R. Reinicke, *Zeit. Elektrochem.*, 29. 214, 1923 ; L. Troost, *Compt. Rend.*, 61. 109, 1865 ; 116. 1227, 1428, 1893 ; T. L. Phipson, *ib.*, 61. 745, 1865 ; H. Moissan and F. Lengfeld, *ib.*, 122. 651, 1896 ; H. Moissan, *ib.*, 116. 1222, 1893 ; *Le four électrique*, Paris, 1897 ; London, 172, 1904 ; C. Winkler, *Ber.*, 23. 2642, 1890 ; 24. 888, 1891 ; B. Franz, *ib.*, 3. 58, 1870 ; W. R. Whitney, *Zeit. Elektrochem.*, 9. 633, 1903 ; K. A. Kühne, *U.S. Pat. No.* 910394, 1909 ; *German Pat.*, *D.R.P.* 179403, 1904 ; L. Renaux, *Contribution à l'étude de la zircone*, Paris, 1900 ; A. C. Becquerel, *Ann. Chim. Phys.*, (2), 48. 337, 1831 ; J. B. Tromms-dorff, *ib.*, (1), 29. 223, 1798 ; H. N. Warren, *Chem. News*, 61. 183, 1890 ; A. Burger, *Reduktionen durch Calcium*, Basel, 30, 1907 ; M. A. Hunter and A. Jones, *Trans. Amer. Electrochem. Soc.*, 44. 23, 1923 ; H. S. Cooper, *ib.*, 43. 209, 1923 ; L. Burgess, *U.S. Pat. No.* 1512271, 1924 ;

H. Goldschmidt and C. Vautin, *Journ. Soc. Chem. Ind.*, **17.** 543, 1898; A. E. van Arkel and J. H. de Boer, *Zeit. anorg. Chem.*, **148.** 345, 1925; A. E. van Arkel, *Physica*, **3.** 76, 1923; **4.** 286, 1924; *Chem. Weekbl.*, **22.** 248, 1925; H. Fischvoigt and F. Koref, *Zeit. tech. Phys.*, **6.** 296, 1925.

§ 5. The Physical Properties of Zirconium

Zirconium was formerly stated to exist in three forms : crystalline, graphitic, and amorphous. The variety formerly called **crystalline zirconium,** prepared by L. Troost,[1] was shown by E. Wedekind, and L. Weiss and E. Neumann to be really an alloy of aluminium and zirconium (*q.v.*), and it is necessary to distinguish between crystalline zirconium, an aluminium alloy ; crystalline zirconium in the ordinary sense of the term ; and the **graphitic zirconium** reported by L. Troost—*vide supra.* There are really only two forms now recognized, the crystalline metal and the amorphous. The 99 per cent. metal which has been heated in the electric furnace is crystalline, and the fractured surface is white, resembling cast iron. The brassy yellow of the metal is due to a surface film of nitride. The coherent metal, said J. W. Marden and M. N. Rich, has a white **colour,** a metallic lustre, and takes a fine polish like nickel. E. Wedekind obtained **amorphous zirconium** as a bluish-black powder when potassium fluozirconate or other halogen salt is reduced by magnesium or an alkali metal. The black powder resembles carbon, and is thought to be a colloid. When this powder is washed with a dil. acid, it forms a colloidal soln. which is dark blue by transmitted light. The soln. is coagulated by the addition of hydrogen dioxide, by salts with an alkaline reaction, and by warming. The gel retains water very pertinaciously so that it must be heated in vacuo to at least 200°, in order to eliminate the water. After heating to about 300° in vacuo, the amorphous zirconium is pyrophoric when exposed to the air. E. Wedekind said that it has not yet been clearly proved if the so-called colloidal zirconium is a zirconium hydride or nitride, or the amorphous form of the metal. The probability is in favour of the latter suggestion ; and that the so-called amorphous zirconium is the crystalline metal in a very finely divided state. A. W. Hull found that the **X-radiogram** of zirconium corresponds with the hexagonal system and the axial ratio $a : c = 1 : 1.59$. The space-lattice shows the atoms have a slightly distorted form of the close-packed hexagonal arrangement. The side of the unit triangular prism is 3.23 A., and the height, 5.14 A. The X-radiogram was also examined by A. E. van Arkel and J. H. de Boer. J. Königsberger said that the zirconium prepared by electrolysis crystallized in the cubic system.

The properties of zirconium reported by different workers are sometimes confused, and not always concordant. The reason will be obvious from what has been said on the purity of the metal. L. Troost gave 4.15 for the **specific gravity** of zirconium, probably contaminated with the aluminide ; S. Meyer, 4.08 ; and H. Moissan, 4.25, for a sample probably contaminated with carbide. E. Wedekind gave for the sp. gr. of the metal with 99.55 per cent. zirconium, and 4.14 per cent. of oxygen ; and L. Weiss and E. Neumann gave 6.4 for 99.8 per cent. zirconium. Accepting 6.4 as the best representative value, the **atomic volume** is 14.16. R. Gross, and E. Donath and J. Mayrhofer compared the properties of elements with respect to their at. vol. J. J. van Laar calculated b_c of J. D. van der Waals' equation as 0.00235 ; and for the valency attraction A, $\sqrt{A} = 37$. The **hardness** of the specimen prepared by H. Moissan was said to be 4.7, and he added that the metal will scratch glass and rubies. This, however, refers to a mixture of zirconium and its carbide. J. W. Marden and M. N. Rich add that pure samples of the coherent metal are softer than the impure metal. The sclerescopic hardness is 40 to 45. The metal is quite brittle, and can easily be broken by lightly pounding with a small hammer. The metal is still hard but less brittle at a red heat. L. Weiss and E. Neumann's 99 per cent. zirconium was hard enough to scratch quartz, but not topaz, so that its hardness was between 6 and 7. A. E. van Arkel and

J. H. de Boer found that the metal is soft and ductile like copper, and that it can be easily hammered out, drawn into wire, or rolled into sheet.

There are surprising differences in the reported values for the **melting point** of zirconium. E. Wedekind and H. Kuzel said that the amorphous metal prepared by the calcium reduction process sinters at 1000°; unless the metal softens below its m.p., this low number shows that the metal was impure. L. Troost said that the metal is less fusible than silicon. E. Wedekind reported that the metal of a high degree of purity has a m.p. between 1523° and 1533°—mean 1530°; W. von Bolton gave 2330° and 2380°—mean 2350°; W. R. Mott, 1500°; J. W. Marden and M. N. Rich, 1700°; H. S. Cooper, near 2800°; and W. Guertler and M. Pirani adopted 1700° as the best representative value for the m.p. J. W. Marden and M. N. Rich found that the metal could be sintered at 1600° when air is excluded. No signs of the volatilization of zirconium was observed at 3000°, but W. R. Mott calculated the **boiling point** to be 2900°. J. J. van Laar estimated the **critical temperature** to be 3920°, and the **critical pressure,** 760 atm. W. G. Mixter and E. S. Dana found the **specific heat** of zirconium between 0° and 99·7° to be 0·0660, but the specimen was contaminated with silicon; E. Wedekind and S. J. Lewis gave 0·06725; and E. Wedekind obtained a range from 0·0656 to 0·0735. L. Weiss and E. Neumann found for the highly purified sample, 0·0804, which makes the **atomic heat** unusually high, viz. 7·31. All these determinations were made between 0° and about 100°. J. Dewar gave 0·0262 for the sp. ht. and 2·38 for the at. ht. of zirconium between −253° and −196°. G. N. Lewis and co-workers gave 9·5 for the **entropy** of zirconium **at** 25°. According to **J. W.** Marden and M. N. Rich, the **thermal conductivity** of amorphous zirconium is very low, and that of crystalline zirconium high. The **heat of combustion** found by L. Weiss and E. Neumann is 1958·7 cals. per gram; 177·5 Cals. per gram-atom; or 44·7 Cals. per gram-eq.

J. H. Gladstone gave 0·242 for the **specific refraction** of zirconium, and 21·9 for the at. refraction. R. Thalén [2] first obtained the **spark spectrum** of zirconium. There are brilliant lines in the green, blue, violet, and in the ultra-violet. Further studies were made by L. Troost and P. Hautefeuille, R. Capron, E. Linnemann, H. A. Rowland, E. Demarçay, O. Lohse, A. de Gramont, F. Exner and E. Haschek, A. Hagenbach and H. Konen, A. G. G. Leonard, and J. M. Eder and E. Valenta. The results show that the most intense lines in the spark spectrum have the wavelengths 3392·20, 3438·39, 3496·40, 3556·89, 3698·41, 3751·85, 3836·98, 3958·39, 3991·31, 3999·18, 4149·43, 4209·21, 4380·12, 4443·31, 4494·78, 4497·27. The most persistent lines—A. de Gramont's *les raies ultimes*—with soln. of different normality N are :

N	0·01	0·001	0·00005	0·00001	0·000005
3698·16	+	?	.	.	.
3572·47	+	+	?	.	.
3505·66	+	+	+	.	.
3496·20	+	+	+	+	.
3438·23	+	+	+	?	.
3391·98	+	+	+	+	+
3273·04	+	+	.	.	.

Where the plus symbol indicates that the line is visible.

The **arc spectrum** was investigated by H. A. Rowland and C. N. Harrison, F. Exner and E. Haschek, W. Vahle, M. A. Catalan, J. M. Eder and E. Valenta, and A. Bachem. The most intense lines have the wave-lengths 3392·14, 3496·38, 3809·49, 3891·53, 3929·71, 3973·63, 4081·40, 4227·94, 4239·49, 4282·32, 4507·32, 4535·90, 4575·69, 4634·30, 4687·99, 4688·63, 4710·23, 4739·68, 4772·50, 4815·80, 6127·64. The effect of *pressure* on the spectral lines was studied by W. J. Humphreys; and the effect of a *magnetic field*—the **Zeeman effect**—by B. E. Moore, and E. F. du Bois. W. Huggins observed that in the oxy-hydrogen flame, zirconia gave a continuous spectrum. J. C. McLennan and A. C. Lewis examined the **ultra-violet spectrum.**

There is no **absorption spectrum** for the colourless zirconium salts. E. Linnemann showed that J. L. Soret's report of the absorption spectrum of zirconium salts was due to his using impure soln. If tincture of alkanna be added to a soln. of zirconium chloride, the violet soln. obtained has a red fluorescence, and it has an absorption spectrum with bands between 6030 and 6016 ; 5581 and 5570 ; and 5195 and 5186. With a soln. of the nitrate, the bands lie between 6058 and 6030 ; 5603 and 5581 ; and 5213 and 5195. In each case, however, the exact location of the bands depends on the conc. of the soln. For the solar spectrum, *vide* the occurrence of zirconium. The high frequency or **X-ray spectrum** was studied by H. G. J. Moseley, and E. Friman. B. Walter, B. B. Ray, A. Leide, F. C. Blake and W. Duane, and M. Siegbahn gave in Angström or 10^{-8} cm. units, for the K-series, $a_2a'=0.793$; $a_1a=0.788$; and $\beta_1\beta=0.705$. D. Coster, E. Hjalmar, and M. Siegbahn gave for the L-series, $a_1a=6.0559$; $a_3a''=6.0272$; and $\beta_1\beta=5.8228$. R. Berthold studied the relation between the photographic and ionizing effects of X-ray radiation from zirconium.

According to A. Gockel,[3] some samples of zirconium are **radioactive** owing, presumably, to the presence of thorium as impurity. A. von Antropoff's alleged production of argon from zirconium by the action of **radium rays** has not been confirmed ; nor has W. Ramsay's alleged degradation of zirconium into carbon by the action of radium emanation on zirconium nitrate.

The **electrical conductivity** of amorphous zirconium is low, but that of coherent crystalline zirconium is fairly good ; but J. W. Marden[4] said that its conductivity is less than that of iron. While compressed amorphous zirconium is a non-conductor at low voltages, it becomes a conductor after heating to 1000° in vacuo. The *Nernst lamp* is based upon the use of an electrolytic conductor as a luminous filament, that is to say, of a conductor of which the electric resistance diminishes when the temp. increases. The filaments of the lamp are formed of oxides of zirconium, thorium, and other rare earth-metals, which become conductors only at a temp. of 600°. The lamp, therefore, comprises, in the first place, an arrangement that permits of heating the filament to redness before passing a current through it and utilizing it as a luminous body. For this purpose, a heating coil of wire surrounds the filament. The coil is traversed first by the current, and after the filament has become incandescent, an interrupter operates automatically and cuts the current off from the heating apparatus. When the intensity of the current increases in the filament, the difference of potential at the terminals of the filament increases in the first place, remains constant for a short time, and afterward continues to diminish. The best conditions of operation are those in which the difference of potential is constant. Increases of a potential would have the great drawback of increasing the intensity of the current in the filament, and consequently of deteriorating it. In order to prevent this, a special resistance which offers an obstacle to variations in potential is mounted in series with the filament. The resistance is formed of a very fine iron wire placed in a bulb of hydrogen. Iron is the one metal whose resistance increases most with the temp. The result is that it is easily capable of compensating for the inverse variation of the electric conductivity of the Nernst filament. According to J. Königsberger and K. Schilling, the conductivity of an impure sample of zirconium is nearly the same as that of brass, and is greater than that of carbon, silicon, or titanium, and the resistance, R, shows a minimum value at about −100°, Fig. 1. P. Clausing found the ratio R/R_0 decreases uniformly with temp., when the sp. resistance, R_0, at 0° is 1.64×10^{-4} ohm to 1.81×10^{-4} ohm. C. R. Böhm measured the conductivity of zirconium filaments. P. W. Bridgman found the press. coeff. of the resistance is very small, being near -0.0_6398 at 0° and -0.0_6396 at 95°. Zirconium lies

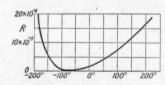

FIG. 1.—Electrical Resistance of Zirconium.

between palladium and silver in the **electrochemical series** : . . . Au, Pt, Pd, Ta, Zr, Ag, Hg, Cu, . . . when the metal is used as anode, with a platinum wire as **cathode**. In dil. hydrochloric acid, zirconium becomes coated with a film of ox de and it then appears to be passive for the current rapidly diminishes. For example, the current of a Zr : Pt-cell fell from 0·4 amp. to 0·2 amp. in 24 mins. Amorphous zirconium is paramagnetic ; L. Troost's aluminium-zirconium alloy was diamagnetic. S. Meyer gave for the **atomic magnetism** $-0·014 \times 10^{-6}$ at 17°. M. Owen examined the thermomagnetic properties of, presumably, the zirconium-aluminium alloy at different temp. K. Honda gave $-0·45 \times 10^{-6}$ for the **magnetic susceptibility** at 18°, and $-0·3 \times 10^{-6}$ at 1150°.

REFERENCES.

[1] J. J. Berzelius, *Pogg. Ann.*, **4.** 117, 1825 ; E. Wedekind, *Rev. Internat. Cong. App. Chem.*, **5.** iv, 439, 1903 ; *Ber.*, **35.** 3929, 1902 ; *Zeit. Elektrochem.*, **10.** 331, 1904 ; *Chem. Ztg.*, **31.** 655, 1907 ; *Zeit. Koll.*, **2,** 289, 1908 ; *Zeit. anorg. Chem.*, **33.** 81, 1902 ; **45.** 385, 1905 ; *Liebig's Ann.*, **395.** 149, 1913 ; E. Wedekind and S. J. Lewis, *ib.*, **371.** 266, 1910 ; *Chem. Ztg.*, **32.** 259, 735, 1908 ; *Journ. Chem. Soc.*, **95.** 456, 1909 ; *Zeit. angew. Chem.*, **22.** 725, 1909 ; S. J. Lewis, *Studien über das elementare Zirconium*, Stuttgart, 1912 ; E. Wedekind and H. Kuzel, *German Pat.*, *D.R.P.* 1088909, 1914 ; *Brit. Pat. No.* 23215, 1909 ; L. Troost, *Compt. Rend.*, **61.** 109, 1865 ; **116.** 1227, 1428, 1893 ; H. Moissan, *ib.*, **116.** 1222, 1893 ; *Le four électrique*, Paris, 1897 ; London, 174, 1904 ; L. Weiss and E. Neumann, *Zeit. angew. Chem.*, **65.** 248, 1910 ; G. N. Lewis, G. R. Gibson, and W. M. Latimer, *Journ. Amer. Chem. Soc.*, **44.** 1008, 1922 ; J. W. Marden and M. N. Rich, *Investigations of Zirconium with especial Reference to the Metal and the Oxide*, Washington, 1921 ; *Journ. Ind. Eng. Chem.*, **12.** 651, 1920 ; J. J. van Laar, *Die Zustandsgleichung von Gasen und Flussigkeiten*, Leipzig, 1924 ; *Proc. Acad. Amsterdam*, **18.** 1220, 1915 ; **19.** 2, 1916 ; **20.** 138, 492, 1918 ; A. W. Hull, *Phys. Rev.*, (2), **18.** 88, 1921 ; J. Königsberger, *Centr. Min.*, 565, 597, 1908 ; H. S. Cooper, *Trans. Amer. Electrochem. Soc.*, **43.** 219, 1923 ; W. G. Mixter and E. S. Dana, *Liebig's Ann.*, **169.** 390, 1873 ; *Amer. Journ. Science*, (3), **7.** 506, 1874 ; J. H. Gladstone, *Proc. Roy. Soc.*, **60.** 140, 1896 ; E. Donath and J. Mayrhofer, *Ber.*, **16.** 1588, 1883 ; W. Guertler and M. Pirani, *Zeit. Metallkunde*, **11.** 1, 1919 ; W. von Bolton, *Liebig's Ann.*, **371.** 387, 1909 ; W. R. Mott, *Trans. Amer. Electrochem. Soc.*, **34.** 255, 1918 ; S. Meyer, *Sitzber. Akad. Wien*, **108.** 171, 1899 ; J. Dewar, *Proc. Roy. Soc.*, **89.** A, 158, 1913 ; R. Gross, *Zeit. Elektrochem.*, **30.** 1, 1924 ; A. E. van Arkel and J. H. de Boer, *Zeit. anorg. Chem.*, **148.** 345, 1925.

[2] A. G. G. Leonard, *Proc. Roy. Soc. Dublin*, **11.** 270, 1908 ; A. Bachem, *Die Bogenspectrum des Zirkons*, Bonn, 1910 ; *Zeit. Wiss. Photochem.*, **8.** 316, 1910 ; W. Vahle, *ib.*, **18.** 84, 1918 ; R. Thalén, *Nova Acta Soc. Upsala*, (3), **6.** 1868 ; *Om spectralanalys*, Upsala, 1866 ; R. Capron, *Photographed Spectra*, London, 1877 ; W. Huggins, *Proc. Roy. Soc.*, **18.** 546, 1870 ; *Phil. Mag.*, (4), **40.** 302, 1870 ; H. A. Rowland, *ib.*, (5), **36.** 49, 1893 ; *Astron. Astrophys. Journ.*, **12.** 321, 1893 ; *Preliminary Table of Solar Spectrum Wave-lengths*, Chicago, 1898 ; E. Linnemann, *Sitzber. Akad. Wien*, **91.** 1019, 1885 ; J. M. Eder, *ib.*, **123.** 2289, 1914 ; J. M. Eder and E. Valenta, *ib.*, **119.** 9, 519, 1910 ; *Atlas typischer Spectren*, Wien, 1911 ; W. M. Watts, *B.A. Rep.*, 156, 1908 ; H. A. Rowland and C. N. Harrison, *Astrophys. Journ.*, **7.** 373, 1898 ; W. J. Humphreys, *ib.*, **6.** 169, 1897 ; O. Lohse, *ib.*, **6.** 95, 1897 ; *Sitzber. Akad. Berlin*, 179, 1897 ; *Pub. Astrophys. Obs. Potsdam*, **12.** 109, 1902 ; F. Exner and E. Haschek, *Die Spectren der Elemente bei normalen Druck*, Leipzig, 1912 ; *Wellenlängentabellen für spectralanalytische Untersuchungen auf Grund der ultravioletten Funkenspectren der Elemente*, Leipzig, 1902 ; *Wellenlagentabellen für spectralanalytische Untersuchungen auf Grund der ultravioletten Bogenspectren der Elemente*, Leipzig, 1904 ; *Sitzber. Akad. Wien*, **107.** 813, 1898 ; J. Formanek, *Die qualitative Spektralanalyse*, Berlin, 149, 1905 ; *Zeit. anal. Chem.*, **39.** 406, 673, 679, 1900 ; A. Hagenbach and H. Konen, *Atlas der Emissionsspectra*, Jena, 1905 ; H. Kayser, *Handbuch der Spectroscopie*, Leipzig, **6.** 864, 1912 ; E. Demarçay, *Spectres électriques*, Paris, 1895 ; J. L. Soret, *Arch. Sciences Genève*, (3), **4.** 261, 1880 ; A. de Gramont, *Analyse spectrale direct des minéraux*, Paris, 1895 ; *Bull. Soc. Min.*, **21.** 94, 1898 ; *Compt. Rend.*, **126.** 1513, 1898 ; **166.** 365, 1918 ; L. Troost and P. Hautefeuille, *ib.*, **73.** 620, 1871 ; F. W. Dyson, *Phil. Trans.*, **206.** A, 403, 1906 ; J. N. Lockyer, *ib.*, **172.** 173, 1881 ; *Tables of Wave-lengths of Enhanced Lines*, London, 1906 ; B. E. Moore, *Ann. Physik*, (4), **25.** 309, 1908 ; E. F. du Bois, *Phys. Zeit.*, **13.** 128, 1916 ; H. G. J. Moseley, *Phil. Mag.*, (6), **26.** 1024, 1913 ; (6), **27.** 703, 1914 ; E. Friman, *ib.*, (6), **32.** 497, 1917 ; F. C. Blake and W. Duane, *Phys. Rev.*, (2), **10.** 98, 697, 1917 ; M. Siegbahn, *Jahrb. Rad. Elektron.*, **13.** 296, 1916 ; D. Coster, *Compt. Rend.*, **174.** 378, 1922 ; A. Leide, *ib.*, **180.** 1203, 1925 ; E. Hjalmar, *Zeit. Physik*, **3.** 262, 1920 ; B. Walter, *ib.*, **30.** 363, 1924 ; J. C. McLennan and A. C. Lewis, *Proc. Roy. Soc.*, **98.** A, 109, 1920 ; M. A. Catalan, *Anal. Fis. Quim.*, **15.** 487, 1917 ; **16.** 513, 1918 ; B. B. Ray, *Phil. Mag.*, (6), **48.** 707, 1924 ; R. Berthold, *Ann. Physik*, (4), **76.** 409, 1925.

[3] A. Gockel, *Chem. Ztg.*, **33.** 1121, 1909 ; A. von Antropoff, *Zeit. Elektrochem.*, **14.** 585, 1908 ; W. Ramsay, *Journ. Chem. Soc.*, **95.** 624, 1909 ; W. Ramsay and F. L. Usher, *Ber.*, **42.** 2930, 1909.

[4] J. W. Marden and M. N. Rich, *Investigations of Zirconium with Especial Reference to the*

Metal and the Oxide, Washington, 1921; *Journ. Ind. Eng. Chem.*, **12**. 651, 1920; J. Königsberger and K. Schilling, *Ann. Physik*, (4), **32**. 195, 1910; *Phys. Zeit.*, **9**. 347, 1908; L. Troost, *Compt. Rend.*, **61**. 109, 1865; S. Meyer, *Sitzber. Akad. Wien*, **108**. 171, 1899; *Monatsh.*, **20**. 797, 1899; C. R. Böhm, *Chem. Ztg.*, **31**. 985, 1014, 1037, 1049, 1907; M. Owen, *Proc. Acad. Amsterdam*, **14**. 637, 1911; *Ann. Physik*, (4), **37**. 657, 1912; K. Honda, *ib.*, (4), **32**. 1027, 1910; P. W. Bridgman, *Proc. Amer. Acad.*, **56**. 61, 1921; P. Clausing, *Physica*, **4**. 372, 1924.

§ 6. The Chemical Properties of Zirconium

Le zirconium a plus d'analogie avec le silicum qu'avec aucun autre élément.—H. MOISSAN.

Zirconium adsorbs gases very tenaciously, and, according to E. Wedekind and H. Kuzel,[1] if it is to be completely deprived of these gases, it must be heated in vacuo to about 1000°. J. J. Berzelius found that amorphous zirconium can be heated to the softening temp. of glass, in vacuo or in an atm. of hydrogen, without change; but he added that if zirconium hydroxide be present, the metal became incandescent, and it oxidized by the water from the decomposing hydroxide. E. Wedekind and S. J. Lewis, however, found that when heated below about 700°, zirconium unites with hydrogen, forming the hydride. Carbon and silicon have a marked tendency to form hydrides, but the related elements titanium, zirconium, cerium, etc., do not exhibit the same tendency to unite with **hydrogen.** According to C. Winkler, when zirconia is reduced with magnesium in a stream of hydrogen, and the product treated with hydrochloric acid, a gas is evolved which gives a precipitate with silver nitrate, and is possibly a *gasförmigen Zirkoniumwasserstoff*. This, however, is doubtful. E. Wedekind used boron in place of magnesium as the reducing agent, and when the product was treated with acid, the hydrogen which was evolved burned with a non-luminous flame without smoke, and deposited nothing when passed through a hot tube, and gave no indications of a volatile zirconium hydride. R. Schwarz and H. Deisler obtained indications of C. Winkler's gaseous hydride, but R. Schwarz and E. Konrad could not find any signs of zirconium in the deposits obtained by passing the gas through heated glass tubes. The deposits consisted mainly of silicon from the silicon hydride; some phosphorus and sulphur hydrides are also evolved. J. W. Marden and M. N. Rich state that when zirconium is fused in an atm. of dry hydrogen, and rapidly cooled, it exhibits an effect like the *spitting* of silver in oxygen, and the metal may be left in a porous condition. Zirconium readily absorbs hydrogen, and L. Weiss and E. Neumann found that when a current of hydrogen is passed over powdered red-hot zirconium, a dark grey powder is formed with a composition approximating **zirconium dihydride,** ZrH_2, where the zirconium appears to be bi- not quadri-valent. It is contaminated with about 4 per cent. of zirconia. The product discolours the skin, and when heated in a test-tube, burns with incandescence, and some small detonations. The hydride is probably wholly decomposed at about 800°.

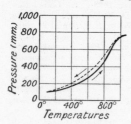

FIG. 2. — Dissociation Pressure of Zirconium Hydride.

The dissociation press. of the dihydride on a rising temp. were found to be rather smaller than on a falling temp., as shown in Fig. 2. A. Sieverts and E. Roell said that powdered zirconium, at different temp. and press., absorbs rather less hydrogen than is needed for the dihydride, and they assume that a solid soln., not a chemical compound, is formed.

	25°	50°	200°	600°	800°	837°
Heating	—	—	104	287	544	752 mm.
Cooling	99	100	107	308	752	— „

Amorphous or crystalline zirconium is stable in **air** at ordinary temp. If the powdered metal be heated in a test-tube and shaken into the air, the particles glow by oxidation, and similarly, if the powdered metal be dusted over a Bunsen's

flame, the particles glow brightly as they pass through the flame. According to
J. J. Berzelius, the amorphous metal burns to the oxide if heated below redness;
but, in agreement with the general observations that the compact crystalline metal
is less chemically active than the amorphous variety, the metal which has been
fused was found by L. Troost to be much more resistant, and, unless powdered,
does not begin to oxidize quickly until it is heated white hot, indeed, he said that
it required the oxy-hydrogen flame to start the combustion. These statements
refer to the zirconium contaminated with aluminium, but E. Wedekind found that
zirconium prepared with magnesium as the reducing agent is just as stable.
L. Troost also found that the metal obtained with carbon as the reducing agent
is quite stable in air at ordinary temp., and at a red heat, a little carbon may be
oxidized superficially. If the zirconium be strongly carburetted, it burns with
incandescence at a red heat. According to J. J. Berzelius, amorphous zirconium,
ignited in vacuo and exposed to the air as soon as it cools, is pyrophoric. H. Moissan
mentioned that an alloy contaminated with carbide and calcium carbide rapidly
disintegrates in air. J. W. Marden and M. N. Rich found that a piece of the compact
metal can be heated to bright redness in the blast-furnace with no more than a
very thin, bluish, superficial oxidation, but when finely divided burns in air when
heated to whiteness. According to E. Wedekind and S. J. Lewis, if the powdered
metal be heated to 100° or 200° in air, it gradually increases in weight by the
absorption of nitrogen, and oxygen. N. B. Pilling and R. E. Redworth studied
the oxidizibility of zirconium. Most zirconium preparations when strongly heated
give off ammonia. L. Troost found that crystalline zirconium resists the action
of **oxygen** at a red heat; *une couche mince irisée d'oxyde* is formed on the surface
protecting the rest of the metal from attack. He also found that the metal is
very stable towards **water;** there was no perceptible action after 12 hrs.' heating
at 70°.

J. J. Berzelius showed that amorphous zirconium, and L. Troost, that crystalline
zirconium. contaminated with aluminide, is rapidly dissolved by dil. or conc., hot
or cold **hydrofluoric acid;** and this acid is said to be *son véritable dissolvant*. A
mixture of nitric and hydrofluoric acids, said J. J. Berzelius, dissolves amorphous
zirconium with great rapidity. In general, said J. W. Marden and M. N. Rich, the
compact metal is insoluble in all acids except aqua regia and hydrofluoric acid.
According to H. Moissan, L. Troost, G. H. Bailey, A. Stähler and B. Denk, and
L. M. Dennis and A. E. Spencer, **chlorine** or **bromine** vap. attacks the heated metal,
forming the tetrahalide (*q.v.*). Liquid bromine acts but slowly; and **iodine** vap. is
active, only at a high temp. L. Troost found that **hydrogen chloride** is decomposed
when passed over the heated metal. and zirconium tetrachloride is formed. Cold
hydrochloric acid does not act on zirconium, but, according to L. Troost, the conc.
acid at 50°–100° acts very slowly on the crystalline metal contaminated with aluminide. Cold aqua regia acts very slowly; a gram of the metal required 5 hrs. to
dissolve in an excess of this menstruum; a mixture of hydrochloric acid and potassium chlorate also acts slowly on the crystalline metal. J. J. Berzelius, H. Moissan
and F. Lengfeld, and S. R. Paykull found that a mixture of powdered zirconium
and **sulphur** reacts when heated over the gas burner. The metal is not attacked
by cold **sulphuric acid,** but hot conc. sulphuric acid furnishes a little sulphur
dioxide. According to C. A. Matignon, and E. Wedekind, zirconium at a temp.
not exceeding 800°, reacts with **nitrogen,** forming the nitride; with **ammonia** gas,
under similar conditions, the nitride is formed; the product does not give off ammonia
in contact with cold water, but it does so with hot water. The metal is not attacked
by cold or hot **nitric acid.** According to J. Gewecke, when a mixture of red
phosphorus and zirconium is heated in an evacuated tube, the mass becomes
incandescent, and a black powder is formed which is not attacked by water or dil.
hydrochloric acid. M. Wunder and B. Jeanneret found that zirconium is dissolved
in a few minutes when heated with **phosphoric acid** of sp. gr. 1·75; any carbon
present remains undissolved. The addition of water or acid to the soln. produces

no precipitate. According to L. Troost, H. Moissan and F. Lengfeld, and
J. J. Berzelius, when zirconium is heated with **carbon,** the carbide is formed ;
according to E. Wedekind, L. Troost, and H. Moissan, **silicon** forms a silicide ; **silica**
at a red heat is reduced by zirconium to silicon. According to S. A. Tucker and
S. R. Moody, with **boron** a boride is formed ; L. Troost and E. Wedekind found that
boric oxide is not attacked when heated with zirconium. J. J. Berzelius said that
a mixture of hydrated borax and zirconium explodes when heated owing to the
action of zirconium on the oxygen of the water. J. W. Mallet found that when
zirconium is heated in **cyanogen** gas, a dark brown powder is formed—possibly
zirconium carbonitride. A. Korczynsky examined the catalytic action of zirconium
or its halides on the halogenation of aromatic compounds.

According to L. Troost, **alkali hydroxides** attack crystalline zirconium contaminated with aluminium, and hydrogen is evolved, but the action occurs only
when water is present. E. Wedekind found that purified zirconium is not attacked
by soln. of the alkali hydroxides ; there is a slight action with fused alkali hydroxides.
J. J. Berzelius said that when a mixture of an alkali hydroxide, or **zirconium
hydroxide** is heated, the reaction of zirconium with the oxygen of the water is
explosive. The amorphous zirconium is slowly oxidized and dissolved by the
fused alkali. He also said that when amorphous zirconium is heated with an **alkali
carbonate,** it combines with the oxygen of the carbon dioxide with a slight explosion.
Amorphous zirconium decomposes **potassium chlorate or nitrate** at a red heat, and
a mixture of amorphous zirconium and potassium chlorate takes fire when struck,
but not explosively. If a mixture of powdered zirconium and potassium nitrate
be heated in a test-tube, a reaction sets in with explosive violence soon after the salt
begins to melt. L. Troost said that his crystalline metal was not attacked by
either potassium nitrate or chlorate. J. W. Marden and M. N. Rich said that the
metal is not readily attacked by fused sodium hydroxide, **alkali hydrosulphates,**
etc. J. J. Berzelius said that amorphous zirconium is readily dissolved by fused
sodium hydrosulphate. A mixture of zirconium with the more easily reducible
oxides—*e.g.* **cupric oxide, lead oxide,** etc.—explodes more or less violently when
heated ; but with the oxides which are reduced only with difficulty—*e.g.* **chromic
oxide**—no reaction occurs at the temp. of the ordinary gas-flame.

Zirconium does not appear to alloy so readily with other metals as do silicon and
titanium. H. S. Cooper made alloys of zirconium with *copper,* and with *gold.*
J. W. Marden and M. N. Rich found that if silver be mixed with the other constituents in the preparation of zirconium by the thermite process, a *zirconium-
silver alloy* is obtained. When the alloy containing 10–20 per cent. of silver is
treated with acids, finely divided, cubic crystals are obtained. The alloy could not
be made by the direct fusion of the two elements. C. Winkler, and E. Wedekind
were unable to make a *zirconium-magnesium alloy.* Attempts to make a *zirconium-
mercury alloy,* or *zirconium amalgam,* were failures. H. Davy passed a current
through a slightly moistened zirconia anode arranged so that potassium amalgam
served as the cathode. After some time, the amalgam furnished a white powder
of zirconium when treated with water. Presumably a zirconium amalgam had been
formed. E. Becquerel, and W. Kettembeil attempted to make the amalgam by the
electrolysis of salt soln. with a mercury cathode, but the results were not successful.
As previously indicated, the metal formerly called crystalline zirconium, prepared
by L. Troost, was a *zirconium-aluminium alloy* containing 27 or more per cent. of
aluminium. L. Troost made the alloy by heating potassium fluozirconate, or sodium
chlorozirconate, in a carbon crucible to about 1500°. B. Franz, and S. Meyer
made an alloy in a somewhat similar way—*vide* the preparation of zirconium by
the aluminium process. These alloys were examined by E. Wedekind. They are
said to resemble the corresponding aluminium-titanium alloys, but to require a
higher temp. for their production ; and they are also said to have a lower tensile
strength. An alloy with 6 per cent. of zirconium exhibited the maximum tenacity
of 12·5 kgrms. per sq. mm. H. Schirmeister measured the tensile strength of these

alloys. E. Wedekind found that in the preparation of zirconium by reducing the oxide or halogen salt with an excess of aluminium and treating the resulting mass alternately with potash-lye and hydrochloric acid, an **aluminium hemizirconide,** $ZrAl_2$ (or perhaps $ZrAl_3$), remains. This compound forms a mass of crystalline plates resembling antimony in appearance and fracture; it is not appreciably attacked by the simple acids though hot hydrofluoric acid or aqua regia dissolves it slowly. If the alloy be melted in the electric furnace, the **aluminium tritetrita-zirconide,** Zr_3Al_4, is formed; this compound is very hard, and resists attack by chemical agents. It is not certain if these zirconides are really chemical individuals.

J. W. Marden and M. N. Rich were unable to make a *zirconium-tin alloy* or a *zirconium-lead alloy* directly or indirectly. H. S. Cooper made pyrophoric alloys of zirconium and 20–40 per cent. of tin. N. Petinot made a zirconium-lead alloy by charging a mixture of zirconium and calcium carbide into molten lead. E. Podszus made *tungsten-zirconium* and *tantalum-zirconium alloys* by reducing the mixed oxides in a current of ammonia gas at a temp. high enough to dissociate the nitrides; and cooling rapidly to prevent the formation of nitrides. J. B. Grenagle [2] obtained a *zirconium-tantalum* and a *columbium alloy*. E. Wedekind made an alloy carrying about one per cent. of zirconium by heating a mixture of iron and zirconium in vacuo, and J. L. Brown and H. S. Cooper, and J. B. Grenagle obtained *ferrozirconium alloy*, containing 65 per cent. of zirconium, by reducing a mixture of the finely-divided oxides with aluminium, or by heating the mixed oxides in a graphite crucible in an electric furnace. The use of zirconium as a scavenger for removing oxides and nitrogen from steel has been patented by L. Weiss. It is said that zirconium steel, *i.e.* steel with a small percentage of zirconium, is very hard and useful in making armour plates, armour-piercing projectiles, and bullet-shields. It is claimed that an armour plate 1 in. thick is equivalent to a plate of the best German steel, 3 in. thick. F. M. Becket has discussed these alloys. H. S. Cooper has patented a number of complex *nickel-zirconium* alloys; *cobalt-zirconium* alloys; and self-hardening nickel alloys with from 2 to 40 per cent. zirconium and less than 35 per cent. chromium. F. M. Becket, R. H. McKee, J. W. Marden and M. N. Rich, A. L. Feild, and G. K. Burgess and R. W. Woodward also prepared a number of iron-zirconium alloys. Ferrozirconium, said M. Wunder and B. Jeanneret, is dissolved by hot phosphoric acid of sp. gr. 1·75, giving a clear soln.—*vide* zirconium. H. S. Cooper made an alloy with *nickel*.

The valency of zirconium.—In 1824, J. J. Berzelius gave zirconia the formula ZrO_3; but later altered it to Zr_2O_3 by analogy with alumina, Al_2O_3, etc. The sesquioxide formula was employed by R. Hermann, but L. Gmelin preferred ZrO by analogy with magnesia, MgO; beryllia, BeO, etc. In 1857, H. St. C. Deville and L. Troost, after they had shown that the vap. density of zirconium chloride agreed with the formula $ZrCl_4$, naturally proposed the formula ZrO_2, for the oxide on the assumption that zirconium is quadrivalent. This conclusion has been confirmed by W. Biltz and J. A. Clinch from the determinations of the mol. wt. of zirconium acetylacetonate by the b.p. method: by W. G. Mixter and E. S. Dana from measurements of the sp. ht. of zirconium; by C. H. Pfaff, G. Rose, J. C. G. de Marignac, and J. W. Retgers from the isomorphism between rutile and zirconia, and between the fluozirconates, fluosilicates, fluotitanates, and fluostannates; by B. D. Steele, from the position of zirconium in the periodic system; by L. F. Nilson and O. Pettersson, by the approximate agreement of the mol. hts. of the dioxides of zirconium, thorium, cerium, titanium, tin, and manganese; by the analogies between the chloroplatinates of zirconium, thorium, and tin, indicated by L. F. Nilson, and between the metacarbonates, R_2CO_3, metasilicates, R_2SiO_3, metatitanates, R_2TiO_3, and metazirconates, R_2ZrO_3—where R represents a univalent radicle; and by H. G. J. Moseley, and E. Friman from measurements of the X-ray spectra. The hydride, ZrH_2 (*q.v.*), shows that zirconium may be bivalent; but the existence of the monoxide, ZrO, is doubtful.

The atomic weight of zirconium.—The at. wt. of zirconium was first deter-

mined by J. J. Berzelius,[4] and from the analysis of the neutral sulphate, he inferred
this to be 89·461 (O=16). R. Hermann obtained 89·354 from analyses of the
oxychloride and the tetrachloride ; J. C. G. de Marignac, 90·536 from analyses of
potassium zirconifluoride ; M. Weibull, 89·48 from analyses of the sulphate, and
90·13 from analyses of the selenate ; G. H. Bailey, 90·0 5 from analyses of the
sulphate ; F. P. Venable, 90·80 from analyses of the oxychloride. F. P. Venable
and J. M. Bell obtained the value 91·76 as an average of fourteen determinations
of the ratio of $ZrCl_4$: Ag (chlorine, 35·458 : silver, 107·88) ; the extreme variations
were 91·95 and 91·62. F. W. Clarke gave 90·621 as the average of the different
determinations available in 1910 ; and B. Brauner, 90·7. The International Table
of at. wts. gives 90·6 as the best representative value. The survey of the at. wt.
determinations by F. W. Clarke gave him the impression that "the at. wt. of
zirconium needs careful revision," but even then, with the variations in the proportions of hafnium in samples of zirconium from different sources, it is remarkable
that greater differences have not been observed. G. von Hevesy examined some
historical preparations of zirconium salts in chemical museums and estimated that
those used by J. J. Berzelius had 2 per cent. of hafnia ; those by R. Hermann,
1 per cent. ; those by J. C. G. de Marignac, 0·5 per cent. ; those by M. Weibull,
2·0 per cent. ; those by F. P. Venable and J. M. Bell, 0·7–1·0 per cent. ; and those
by O. Hönigschmid, none. The presence of 1 per cent. of hafnia raises the at. wt.
of zirconium by 0·6 unit. O. Hönigschmid and co-workers gave 91·22 for the
value corrected for hafnium, from the ratio $ZrBr_4$: 4AgBr, and $ZrBr_4$: 4Ag.
F. P. Venable and J. M. Bell corrected their results for hafnium and obtained
91·2 for the at. wt. of zirconium. This, said G. von Hevesy, agrees with the value
91·22 ± 0·1 of O. Hönigschmid, and this is the best representative value of the at.
wt. of zirconium. The **atomic number** of zirconium is 40. F. W. Aston reported the
three **isotopes** with at. masses 90, 92, and 94, with possibly another of at. mass 96.
For the alleged degradation of zirconium to carbon, *vide* zirconium nitrate. The
electronic structure of the atom was discussed by N. V. Sidgwick, C. P. Smyth,
and J. Beckenkamp—*vide* hafnium. H. Pettersson and G. Kirsch obtained a little
evidence of **atomic disintegration** when the atoms are bombarded by α-rays.

Reactions of analytical interest.—All aq. soln. of zirconium salts have an
acid reaction owing to hydrolysis ; hence, the neutralization of a soln. is only
temporary and approximate. According to G. J. Brush,[5] if turmeric paper be
moistened with a hydrochloric acid soln. of a zirconium salt, and dried, it has a
reddish-brown colour which is not produced by thorium salts. A. A. Noyes and
co-workers said the colour is pink. If zirconium hydroxide be dissolved in
hot hydrochloric acid, evaporated almost to dryness, digested with water, and
treated with conc. hydrochloric acid in the cold, a basic chloride, $ZrOCl_2.8H_2O$,
is precipitated. Otherwise hydrochloric acid, and hydrogen sulphide give no
precipitation with zirconium salt soln. In what follows, an aq. soln. of zirconium sulphate is supposed to be employed unless otherwise stated. According
to R Hermann, and J. J. Berzelius, aq. soln. of **ammonia,** or of **ammonium
sulphide,** furnish a white precipitate of the hydroxide, insoluble in excess.
These precipitations, said J. J. Berzelius, are not prevented by ammonium
chloride ; but, added E. A. Demarçay, if fluorides be present, the precipitation
by ammonia is only partial. Aq. soln. of the **alkali hydroxides** furnish a similar
precipitate, which, unlike the hydroxides of aluminium and beryllium, is insoluble
in an excess of the reagent. The freshly precipitated hydroxide produced in cold
soln. is readily soluble in dil. acids, but dissolves very slowly if produced in hot
soln. Conc. acids, however, dissolve both precipitates quickly. **Ammonium
carbonate** gives a white flocculent precipitate of basic carbonate, readily soluble
in excess, but **re**precipitated on boiling the soln. A similar precipitate, somewhat
soluble in excess, and reprecipitated by ammonia, is produced by **alkali carbonates**.
These properties were studied by J. J. Berzelius, A. Mandl, and R. Hermann.
According to J. N. von Fuchs, **calcium carbonate** precipitates a carbonate from

zirconium salt soln., and, according to H. Rose, there is but an incomplete precipitation when **barium carbonate** is added, even if the soln. be boiled. Both **oxalic acid** and **ammonium oxalate** give a crystalline precipitate of zirconium oxalate when added to a soln. of zirconium chloride, but no precipitate is given by aluminium and beryllium salt soln. The precipitate is soluble in an excess of oxalic acid, and ammonium oxalate, but sparingly soluble in hydrochloric acid. The soln. in ammonium oxalate, unlike the thorium salt, does not give a precipitate with hydrochloric acid. Ammonia precipitates all the zirconium as hydroxide from the soln. in ammonium oxalate. L. N. Vauquelin, N. J. Berlin, R. Ruer and co-workers, F. P. Venable and J. M. Bell, E. Glaser, and others have studied the action of oxalates on zirconium salts. Soln. of **sodium sulphate** or **ammonium sulphate** do not give precipitations, but, according to J. J. Berzelius, with a cold conc. soln. of **potassium sulphate, all** the zirconium is slowly precipitated as a complex salt which, unlike the aluminium or beryllium salt, is insoluble in an excess. The precipitate produced with cold soln. is readily soluble in dil. hydrochloric acid; but if produced in boiling soln., a basic sulphate is precipitated, which, unlike the thorium and cerium salt, is not soluble in dil. hydrochloric acid. According to J. F. Bahr, R. Hermann, M. Weibull, and A. Stromeyer, a soln. of **sodium thiosulphate** precipitates from the hot soln. all the zirconium as hydroxide mixed with sulphur. A feebly acid soln. of zirconium chloride, not the sulphate, gave a precipitate of the hydroxide when treated with **sulphur dioxide.** Unlike thorium and yttrium salt soln., zirconium salt soln. give no precipitation with **hydrofluoric acid.** A conc. soln. of **hydrogen dioxide** precipitates the zirconium as peroxide, $Zr(OH)_3.H_2O_2$, from slightly acid soln. I. T. Davis, and P. H. M. P. Brinton and C. James showed that a soln. of an **alkali iodate** gives a precipitate of zirconium oxyiodate preferably from hot soln. The precipitate is but sparingly soluble in water, in an excess of the precipitant, or in acids. F. P. Venable and I. W. Smithey used **iodic acid** in place of the iodate. According to L. Haber, **chromic acid** gives an orange-yellow flocculent precipitate, particularly in boiling soln. T. Curtius and A. Darapsky found that **sodium azide** completely precipitates zirconium as hydroxide from cold soln. **Phosphoric acid,** or **alkali phosphates,** give a white precipitate of zirconium phosphate. According to W. Biltz and W. Mecklenburg, if the soln. be strongly acidified with nitric or hydrochloric acid, and a few drops of a soln. of sodium phosphate added, and the liquid be warmed, a white gelatinous precipitate is produced even when as little as 0·0005 per cent. of zirconia is present. Iron, aluminium, rare-earth elements, beryllium, thorium, titanium, or silicon salt soln. do not give the precipitation in strongly acid soln.— *vide* hafnium, which also gives this reaction.

According to M. Dittrich and S. Freund, if a zirconium salt soln. be dropped into a boiling soln. of **sodium salicylate,** a precipitate of zirconium salicylate is formed—not so with titanium salts. According to H. Rose, A. Sjögren, R. Hornberger, J. J. Berzelius, and R. Hermann, a neutral soln. of zirconium chloride gives a white precipitate with **potassium ferrocyanide,** with acid soln. the precipitate is greenish-yellow. The precipitation is less complete in sulphate soln. In neutral sulphate soln. or acid chloride soln., H. Rose, and L. de Boisbaudran found that **potassium ferricyanide** gives a green precipitate; with **potassium cyanide,** H. Rose found that zirconium hydroxide is precipitated. **Tartaric acid** precipitates zirconium tartrate incompletely, and the precipitate is soluble in an excess, or in sodium acetate soln.; **alkali tartrates** give a white precipitate; with **citric acid** or **malic acid,** L. Haber obtained results similar to those with tartaric acid. **Sodium acetate** gives a white flocculent precipitate with boiling soln. A white precipitate is produced with **alkali succinates and benzoates.** Numerous other precipitations and colorations with organic compounds have been examined by L. Haber, C. Vincent, B. F. Hartwell, S. H. Harris, A. Mandl, E. Rimbach and P. Schneider, H. Kaserer, A. Mc. M. Jefferson, A. Müller, and A. Rosenheim and P. Frank. **Ammonium nitrosophenylhydroxylamine,** $C_6H_5N(NO)ONH_4$, conveniently called

cupferron, was shown by O. Bandisch and V. L. King to give a quantitative separation of zirconium and aluminium ; it precipitates quantitatively iron and zirconium from a soln. of the mixed salts. The method was used by E. Ferrari, J. Brown, C. E. F. Lundell and H. B. Knowles, W. M. Thornton and E. M. Hayden, J. W. Marden and M. N. Rich, etc. E. T. Allen recommended **phenylhydrazine** in faintly acid soln. which precipitates alumina and zirconia quantitatively. G. von Knorre used **nitroso-δ-naphthol** for separating zirconium and iron ; and I. Belluci and G. Savoia observed that coloured complex salts are produced by zirconium salts in acid soln. and α-nitroso-β-naphthol and β-nitroso-α-naphthol. F. Steidler found that various shades of brown are produced by zirconium and hafnium salts on linen or artificial silk dyed with **turmeric ;** and with **picric acid,** zirconium oxychloride gives a yellow precipitate of indefinite composition. J. H. de Boer found that salts of zirconium, titanium, aluminium, yttrium, cerium, erbium, thallium, columbium, tungsten, thorium, molybdenum, and uranium give a violet coloration with **alizarinsulphonic acid,** but the colour disappears on the addition of conc. hydrochloric acid with all except zirconium, and hafnium.

The uses of zirconium.—Zirconium and its compounds have some uses [6] in the arts and industries. The possible application of zirconium as a scavenger in steel, etc., has been previously discussed in connection with the zirconium alloys. The oxide has been used to replace the lime cylinders of the limelight—*vide* zirconia. Zirconia cylinders give a more intense illumination, and they are not affected by the moisture and carbon dioxide of the atm., which rapidly deteriorate lime cylinders. The early incandescent mantles made by A. von Welsbach [7] contained much zirconia, but a mixture of thoria and other rare earths is now used almost exclusively. The glower or filament of W. Nernst's lamp contain much zirconia, as well as thoria, etc. The mixture conducts the current electrolytically, and not like the metal and carbon filaments. The electrochemical decomposition at the electrodes is rendered harmless by the oxidizing action of air. Hence these lamps do not burn in vacuo. A single oxide is not so good a conductor nor so luminous as a mixture of oxides. Oxides are used because they are so stable, and the rare-earth oxides are used as they have a higher m.p. than other oxides. Since the luminous efficiency rises with the temp. the most infusible oxides possible are employed. Just as thoria alone has a much lower efficiency than a mixture of thoria with one per cent. of ceria, so zirconia alone is much less efficient than a zirconia rod containing a little thoria, ceria, or similar oxide. The rod or filament does not conduct at a low temp. but only when heated, hence Nernst's lamp has a supplementary coil to heat the filament externally whereby it becomes a good conductor. The luminous efficiency is stated to be 0·85 per cent. and the cost 0·004 pence per candle-power hour.

Zirconia is used in the manufacture of highly refractory [8] crucibles, muffles, resistance cores, etc. Ware made from zirconia not only resists high temps., but it also withstands many fluxes, slags, acids, and fused alkalies very well. If properly bonded with 3 to 10 per cent. of clay or magnesia, and fused in an electric furnace at about 2000°, ware made from zirconia is not easily broken, and is almost impervious to liquids ; it has a low coefficient of thermal expansion, and, like fused silica, does not therefore readily crack with sudden changes of temp., but, unlike fused silica, it does not readily devitrify. Firebricks made from zirconia with a bonding refractory clay, sodium silicate, magnesia, borates, phosphates, etc., require burning at a very high temp. in order that the bricks may not shrink unduly in use. Tests with such bricks on the hearth of a steel furnace are reported to have given excellent results. The use of zirconia for this purpose has not come up to expectations because in many furnaces the conditions are highly reducing, and zirconia disintegrates owing to the formation of carbide. As indicated above, the reaction begins about 1400°, but the actions may possibly be more difficult with the silicate. The use of purified zirconia and other compounds of zirconia in place of stannic oxide, antimony oxide, etc., as an opacifying agent [9] for glazes and

enamels or glazes for glazed bricks, tiles, sanitary ware, and enamelled iron has been the subject of many patents, and mixtures are sold under various names—
e.g. terrar, etc. The results are good with the right type of glaze or enamel. The use of zirconium in the manufacture of filaments for electric lamps [10] has been patented but has not been successful ; the carbide has also been recommended as an abrasive [11] since it is nearly as hard as topaz. The use of zirconium compounds —oxide, silicate, carbonate, basic sulphite, and phosphate—as pigments has been patented.[12] The paints are reputed to have a good covering power and to be non-poisonous. The basic acetate is sold as *Konstrastin* for weighting silk ; [13] and as a mordant in dyeing and in the preparation of lac-dyes,[14] and the oxide has been used in place of bismuth nitrate for defining the intestines for making X-ray photographs of the abdomen.[15] Zircon is used in making the knife-edges and planes for balances on account of its hardness. According to C. Willgerodt,[16] the chloride can be used as a catalytic agent for chlorinations in making aniline dyes, etc.

REFERENCES.

[1] H. Davy, *Phil. Trans.*, **98**. 333, 1908 ; *Phil. Mag.*, **32**. 203, 1808 ; S. Meyer, *Sitzber. Akad. Wien*, **109**. 767, 1870 ; E. Wedekind and H. Kuzel, *German Pat.*, *D.R.P.* 1088909, 1914 ; *Brit. Pat. No.* 23215, 1909 ; E. Becquerel, *Ann. Chim. Phys.*, (3), **48**. 200, 1856 ; E. Wedekind, *Liebig's Ann.*, **371**. 378, 1910 ; *Zeit. Elektrochem.*, **10**. 331, 1904 ; *Zeit. anorg. Chem.*, **45**. 385, 1905 ; *Chem. Ztg.*, **31**. 654, 1907 ; *Ber.*, **35**. 3929, 1902 ; C. Winkler, *ib.*, **23**. 2641, 1890 ; **24**. 888, 1891 ; E. Wedekind and S. J. Lewis, *ib.*, **371**. 366, 1910 ; **395**. 149, 1912 ; S. J. Lewis, *Studien über das elementare Zirconium*, Stuttgart, 1912 ; C. A. Matignon, *Compt. Rend.*, **131**. 837, 1900 ; L. Troost, *ib.*, **61**. 109, 1865 ; **116**. 1227, 1893 ; H. Moissan, *ib.*, **116**. 1222, 1893 ; H. Moissan and F. Lengfeld, *ib.*, **122**. 651, 1896 ; M. Wunder and B. Jeanneret, *ib.*, **152**. 1770, 1911 ; L. Weiss and E. Neumann, *Zeit. anorg. Chem.*, **65**. 264, 1910 ; E. Podszus, *ib.*, **99**. 123, 1917 ; W. Kettembeil, *ib.*, **38**. 213, 1904 ; J. J. Berzelius, *Pogg. Ann.*, **4**. 117, 1825 ; *Œfvers, Akad. Förh. Stockholm*, 295, 1824 ; S. R. Paykull, *ib.*, 22, 1873 ; 7, 53, 1878 ; *Bull. Soc. Chim.*, (2), **20**. 65, 1873 ; *Ber.*, **12**. 1719, 1879 ; J. W. Marden and M. N. Rich, *Investigations of Zirconium with especial Reference to the Metal and the Oxide*, Washington, 1921 ; *Journ. Ind. Eng. Chem.*, **12**. 651, 1920 ; A. Korczynsky, *Bull. Soc. Chim.*, (4), **29**. 283, 1921 ; G. H. Bailey, *Chem. News*, **60**. 8, 1889 ; *Journ. Chem. Soc.*, **58**. 705, 1889 ; *Proc. Roy. Soc.*, **46**. 74, 1889 ; S. A. Tucker and S. R. Moody, *Journ. Chem. Soc.*, **81**. 14, 1902 ; A. Stähler and B. Denk, *Ber.*, **37**. 1135, 1904 ; **38**. 2611, 1905 ; B. Franz, *ib.*, **3**. 58, 1870 ; R. Schwarz and H. Deisler, *ib.*, **52**. B, 1896, 1919 ; R. Schwarz and E. Konrad, *ib.*, **54**. B, 2122, 1921 ; L. M. Dennis and A. E. Spencer, *Journ. Amer. Chem. Soc.*, **18**. 673, 1896 ; J. B. Grenagle, *U.S. Pat. No.* 1334089, 1920 ; N. Petinot, *ib.*, 1335982, 1920 ; A. von Antropoff, *Zeit. Elektrochem.*, **14**. 585, 1908 ; J. Gewecke, *Liebig's Ann.*, **361**. 79, 1908 ; J. W. Mallet, *Amer. Journ. Science*, (2), **28**. 346, 1855 ; *Leibig's Ann.*, **113**. 362, 1860 ; H. S. Cooper, *Trans. Amer. Electrochem. Soc.*, **43**. 209, 1923 ; C. A. Matignon, *Chem. Ztg.*, **24**. 1062, 1900 ; N. B. Pilling and R. E. Bedworth, *Metal Ind.*, **22**. 560, 1923 ; *Journ. Inst. Metals*, **29**. 529, 1923 ; H. Schirmeister, *Beiträge zur Kenntnis der binären Aluminiumlegierungen hinsichtlich ihrer technischen Eigenschaften*, Düsseldorf, 1914 ; A. Sieverts and E. Roell, *Festschrift zur Jahrhundertfeier des physikalischen Vereins, Frankfurt a. M.*, 69, 1924.

[2] J. B. Grenagle, *U.S. Pat. Nos.* 1248648, 1917 ; 1334079, 1920 ; J. L. Brown and H. S. Cooper, *ib.*, 1151160, 1915 ; H. S. Cooper, *ib.*, 1221769, 1916 ; 1277046, 1917 ; 1278304, 1918 ; 1350359, 1920 ; 1762540, 1925 ; *Brit. Pat. No.* 112259, 1917 ; *Trans. Amer. Electrochem. Soc.*, **43**. 219, 1923 ; *Candian Pat. No.* 179121, 1917 ; 185436, 1918 ; J. W. Marden and M. N. Rich, *Investigations of Zirconium with especial Reference to the Metal and the Oxide*, Washington, 107, 1921 ; *Journ. Ind. Eng. Chem.*, **12**. 651, 1920 ; M. Wunder and B. Jeanneret, *Compt. Rend.*, **152**. 1770, 1911 ; G. K. Burgess and R. W. Woodward, *Tech. Paper Bur. Standards*, 207, 1922 ; F. M. Becket, *Trans. Amer. Electrochem. Soc.*, **43**. 261, 1923 ; *Journ. Ind. Eng. Chem.*, **16**. 197, 1924 ; A. L. Feild, *Trans. Inst. Min. Met. Eng.*, **70**. 201, 1924 ; L. Weiss, *U.S. Pat. No.* 982326, 1910 ; R. H. McKee, **156** 280, 1925.

[3] J. J. Berzelius, *Pogg. Ann.*, **4**. 126, 1825 ; *Lehrbuch der Chemie*, Dresden, **3**. 1242, 1843 ; L. Gmelin, *Handbuch der theoretischen Chemie*, Frankfurt a. M., 1817 ; R. Hermann, *Journ. prakt. Chem.*, (1), **31**. 75, 1844 ; H. St. C. Deville and L. Troost, *Ann. Chim. Phys.*, (3). **58**. 281, 1860 ; W. Blitz and J. A. Clinch, *Zeit. anorg. Chem.*, **40**. 221, 1904 ; C. H. Pfaff, *Schweigger's Journ.*. **28**. 102, 1820 ; **29**. 149, 1820 ; G. Rose, *Pogg. Ann.*, **107**. 602, 1859 ; J. C. G. de Marignac, *Ann. Chim. Phys.*, (3), **60**. 257, 1860 ; J. W. Retgers, *Zeit. phys. Chem.*, **16**. 620, 1895 ; B. D. Steele, *Chem. News*, **84**. 245, 1902 ; L. F. Nilson and O. Pettersson, *Ber.*, **13**. 1459, 1880 ; L. F. Nilson, *ib.*, **9**. 1142, 1876 ; H. G. J. Moseley, *Phil. Mag.*, (6), **26**. 1024, 1913 ; (6), **27**. 703, 1914 ; E. Friman, *ib.*, (6), **32**. 497, 1917 ; W. G. Mixter and E. S. Dana, *Liebig's Ann.*, **169**. 390, 1873 ; *Amer. Journ. Science*, (3), **7**. 506, 1874.

[4] F. W. Aston, *Phil. Mag.*, (6), **49**. 1191, 1925 ; *Nature*, **114**. 273, 1924 ; J. J. Berzelius, *Pogg. Ann.*, **4**. 126, 1825 ; R. Hermann, *Journ. prakt. Chem.*, (1), **31**. 77, 1844 ; J. C. G. de Marignac,

Œuvres complètes, Bruxelles, **1**. 687, 1860 ; **2**. 5, 1860 ; *Ann. Chim. Phys.*, (3), **60**. 270, 1860 ; W. G. Mixter and E. S. Dana, *Amer. Journ. Science*, (3), **7**. 506, 1874 ; M. Weibull, *Acta Univ. Lund.*, (2), **18**. 21, 1882 ; *Ber.*, **20**. 1394, 1887 ; J. Beckenkamp, *Zeit. anorg. Chem.*, **143**. 394, 1925 ; N. V. Sidgwick, *Journ. Soc. Chem. Ind.—Chem Ind.*, **42**. 1203, 1923 ; C. P. Smyth, *Phil. Mag.*, (6), **50**. 361, 1925 ; G. H. Bailey, *Proc. Roy. Soc.*, **46**. 74, 1890 ; *Chem. News*, **60**. 6, 1880 ; F. P. Venable, *Journ. Amer. Chem. Soc.*, **20**. 119, 1898 ; F. P. Venable and J. M. Bell, *ib.*, **39**. 1598, 1917 ; **46**. 1834, 1924 ; B. Brauner in R. Abegg, *Handbuch der anorganischen Chemie*, Leipzig, **3**. ii, 482, 1909 ; F. W. Clarke, *A Recalculation of the Atomic Weight*, Washington, 287, 1910 ; O. Hönigschmid, E. Zintl, and F. Gonzalez, *Zeit. anorg. Chem.*, **139**. 293, 1924 ; G. von Hevesy, *Nature*, **113**. 384, 1924 ; **115**. 335, 1925 ; H. Pettersson and G. Kirsch, *Atomzertrummerung*, 104, 1926.

⁵ L. Haber, *Monatsh.*, **18**. 687, 1897 ; W. Biltz and W. Mecklenburg, *Zeit. angew. Chem.*, **25**. 2110, 1912 ; G. von Knorre, *ib.*, **17**. 641, 1904 ; A. Mandl, *ib.*, **37**. 252, 1903 ; S. H. Harris, *Amer. Chem. Journ.*, **20**. 871, 1898 ; I. T. Davis, *ib.*, **11**. 26, 1889 ; E. Rimbach and P. Schneider, *Zeit. phys. Chem.*, **44**. 477, 1903 ; A. Müller. *Zeit. anorg. Chem.*, **52**. 316, 1907 ; M. Dittrich and S. Freund, *ib.*, **56**. 344, 1908 ; R. Ruer, *ib.*, **46**. 456, 1905 ; R. Ruer and M. Levin, *ib.*, **46**. 449, 1905 ; A. Rosenheim and P. Frank, *Ber.*, **40**. 809, 1907 ; C. Baskerville, *Journ. Amer. Chem. Soc.*, **16**. 475, 1894 ; E. T. Allen, *ib.*, **25**. 421, 1903 ; J. Brown, *ib.*, **39**. 2358, 1917 ; G. E. F. Lundell and H. B. Knowles, *ib.*, **41**. 1801, 1919 ; P. H. M. P. Brinton and C. James, *ib.*, **41**. 1080, 1919 ; F. P. Venable and J. M. Bell, *ib.*, **39**. 1598, 1917 ; F. P. Venable and I. W. Smithey, *ib.*, **41**. 1722, 1919 ; A. A. Noyes, W. C. Bray, and E. B. Spear, *ib.*, **30**. 481, 1908 ; A. Mc. M. Jefferson, *ib.*, **24**. 540, 1902 ; B. F. Hartwell, *ib.*, **25**. 1128, 1903 ; E. Glaser, *ib.*, **18**. 782, 1896 ; P. Nicolardot and A. Reglade, *Compt. Rend.*, **168**. 348, 1919 ; J. W. Marden and M. N. Rich, *Investigations of Zirconium with Especial Reference to the Metal and the Oxide*, Washington, 1921 ; *Journ. Ind. Eng. Chem.*, **12**. 651, 1920 ; O. Bandisch and V. L. King, *ib.*, **3**. 629, 1911 ; W. M. Thornton and E. M. Hayden, *Amer. Journ. Science*, (4), **38**. 137, 1914 ; G. J. Brush, *ib.*, (2), **18**. 415, 1854 ; E. Ferrari, *Atti 1st. Veneto*, **73**. 445. 1914 ; J. H. de Boer, *Chem. Weekbl.*, **21**. 404, 1924 ; *Rec. Trav. Chim. Pays-Bas*, **44**. 1071, 1925 ; H. Kaserer, *Chem. Ztg.*, **42**. 170, 1918 ; L. de Boisbaudran, *Compt. Rend.*, **94**. 1625, 1882 ; E. A. Demarçay, *ib.*, **100**. 740, 1885 ; M. Weibull, *Acta Univ. Lund.*, (2), **18**. 60, 1882 ; *Ber.*, **20**. 1394, 1887 ; J. J. Berzelius, *Schweigger's Journ.*, **21**. 40, 1817 ; *Œfvers. Akad. Förh. Stockholm*, 295, 1824 ; *Pogg. Ann.*, **4**. 117, 1825 ; T. Curtius and A. Darapsky, *Journ. prakt. Chem.*, (2), **61**. 412, 1900 ; N. J. Berlin, *ib.*, (1), **58**. 145, 1853 ; R. Hermann, *ib.*, (1), **31**. 75, 1844 ; (1), **97**. 321, 330, 1866 ; *Liebig's Ann.*, **52**. 440, 1844 ; C. Vincent, *Bull. Soc. Chim.*, (2), **27**. 194, 1877 ; (2), **33**. 156, 1880 ; H. Rose, *Pogg. Ann.*, **83**. 137, 1851 ; **107**. 602, 1859 ; A. Sjögren, *Pogg. Ann. Ergbd.*, **3**. 465, 1853 ; *Journ. prakt. Chem.*, (1), **55**. 298, 1852 ; R. Hornberger, *Liebig's Ann.*, **181**. 232, 1876 ; J. F. Bahr, *ib.*, **132**. 231, 1864 ; A. Stromeyer, *ib.*, **113**. 127, 1859 ; M. E. Chevreul, *Ann. Chim. Phys.*, (2), **13**. 245, 1820 ; L. N. Vauquelin, *ib.*, (1), **22**. 179, 1797 ; C. H. Pfaff, *Schweigger's Journ.*, **28**. 102, 1820 ; J. N. von Fuchs, *ib.*, **62**. 184, 1831 ; I. Bellucci and G. Savoia, *Atti Chim. Pure Appl.*, 483, 1823 ; F. Steidler, *Microchemie*, **2**. 131, 1924.

⁶ C. R. Bohm, *Chem. Ztg.*, **35**. 1261, 1911 ; *Die Verwendung der seltenen Erden*, Leipzig, 1913 ; R. J. Meyer, *Zeit. Elektrochem.*, **17**. 633, 1911 ; L. Moser, *Œster. Chem. Ztg.*, **26**. 67, 1923 ; L. Andrieux, *Ind. Chim.*, **8**. 478, 1922 ; F. Bertrand, *Rev. Univ. Mines*, **7**. 218, 1925

⁷ A. von Welsbach, *German Pat.*, *D.R.P.* 39162, 1885 ; E. Stern, *ib.*, 276423, 1914 ; *Zeit. angew. Chem.*, **27**. 500, 1914 ; R. E. Kirschner, *Chem. Ztg.*, **46**. 380, 1922.

⁸ J. A. Audley, *Trans. Cer. Soc.*, **16**. 119, 1917 ; **18**. 93, 1919 ; R. Hadfield, *Trans. Faraday Soc.*, **12**. 86, 1917 ; W. Rosenhain, *ib.*, **12**. 178, 1917 ; F. C. Nonamaker, *Chem. Met. Engg.*, **31**. 151, 1924 ; W. L. Shearer, *Ceramist*, **5**. 316, 1925 ; R. Rieke, *Eng. Min. Journ.*, **86**. 909, 1908 ; *Zeit. angew. Chem.*, **23**. 1010, 1910 ; R. Reike and K. Endell, *Silikat Zeit.*, **1**. 6, 1913 ; O. Ruff and O. Goecke, *Zeit. angew. Chem.*. **24**. 1459, 1911 ; E. Podszus, *ib.*, **30**. 17, 1917 ; O. Ruff and G. Lanschlse, *Zeit. anorg. Chem.*, **97**. 73, 1916 ; O. Ruff, H. Seiferheld, and O. Bruschke, *ib.*, **86**. 398, 1914 ; O. Ruff and J. Moczala, *ib.*, **133**. 193, 1924 ; O. Ruff and H. Seiferheld, *ib.*, **82**. 373, 1913 ; O. Ruff, *Forsch. Geb. Ing.*, 147, 1914 ; L. Bradford, *Metal. Ind.*, **12**. 241, 1918 ; C. R. Purdy, *Journ. Amer. Cer. Soc.*, **2**. 864, 1919 ; M. L. Hartmann and O. A. Hougen, *Brick and Clay Rec.*, **56**. 934, 1920 ; P. S. Devereux, *Chem. Trade Journ.*, **66**. 567, 1916 ; L. H. Walter, *Electrician*, **71**. 1057, 1913 ; C. Dantsizen, *U.S. Pat. No.* 1343040, 1920 ; F. Singer, *Dingler's Journ.*, **335**. 96, 1920.

⁹ J. Grünwald, *Sprech.*, **44**. 72, 1910 ; G. Gericke, *ib.*, **49**. 112, 1916 ; A. Hartmann, *Ker. Rund.*, **19**. 118, 1909 ; A. Hilbringhans and A. Heilemann, *German Pat.*, *D.R.P.* 189364, 1906 ; *Zeit anorg. Chem.*, **66**. 436, 1911 ; L. Weiss, *ib.*, **67**. 656, 1910 ; Landau, Kreidl, Heller, and Co., *Cer.*, **16**. 61, 1913 ; **17**. 52, 1914 ; *German Pat.*, *D.R.PP.* 283504, 1914 ; 294202, 1912 ; F. Rietz, *U.S. Pat. No.* 136101, 1920 ; H. F. Staley, *U.S. Bur. Standards Tech. Paper*, 142, 1919 ; A. Katz, *Zeit. angew. Chem.*, **26**. 135, 200, 432, 1913 : W. Borchers, *ib.*, **26**. 232, 1913 ; F. W. Burckherdt, *ib.*, **36**. 25, 1912 ; H. A. Seger and E. Cramer, *Chem. Ztg.*, **37**. 206, 1913 ; F. Thomas, *ib.*, **36**. 25, 1912 ; R. Moldenke, *Foundry*, **48**. 878, 1920 ; W. F. Wenning, *Bull. Amer. Cer. Soc.*, **2**. 102, 1923 ; R. R. Danielson and M. K. Frohafer, *Journ. Amer. Cer. Soc.*, **6**. 634, 1923 ; H. G. Wolfram, *ib.*, **7**. 1, 1924.

¹⁰ A. Korolkoff and A. Bartvszewiez, *Journ. Russ. Phys. Chem. Soc.*, **41**. 258, 1909 ; H. Kuzel, *German Pat.*, *D.R.P.* 204496, 1907 ; *U.S. Pat. No.* 871599, 1907 ; 899875, 914354, 1909 ; 969064, 969109, 1910 ; C. H. Weber, *Die elektrischen Metallfadengluhlampen insbesondere aus Osmium*,

Tantal, Zircon, Wolfram, Leipzig, 1914; H. Wedding, *Journ. Gasbeleucht.*, **48**. 203, 1905; *Elektrotech. Ztg.*, **26**. 85, 1905; C. R. Böhm, *Chem. Ztg.*, **30**. 694, 729, 753, 1906; **31**. 985, 1014, 1037, 1049, 1907.
[11] L. Weiss, *German Pat.*, *D.R.P.* 230757, 1910; *Zeit. anorg. Chem.*, **65**. 178, 1910.
[12] L. Weiss, *German Pat.*, *D.R.P.* 235495, 1910; D. Tyrer, *Brit. Pat. No.* 217323, 1923.
[13] E. Ristenpart, *Farber Ztg.*, **29**. 26, 1918; Landau, Kreidl, Heller, and Co., *German Pat.*, *D.R.P.* 258638, 1913; E. Rietz, *Brit. Pat. No.* 4457, 1915; E. Stern, *ib.*, 261142, 1913.
[14] J. Barnes, *Journ. Soc. Chem., Ind.*, **15**. 420, 1896; A. Scheurer and A. Bryliusky, *Bull. Soc. Mulhouse*, **68**. 124, 1898; P. Wengraf, *Farber-Ztg.*, **25**. 277, 1914.
[15] L. Weiss, *German Pat.*, *D.R.P.* 237624, 1911.
[16] C. Willgerodt, *Journ. prakt. Chem.*, (2), **35**. 393, 1887.

§ 7. The Zirconium Oxides

Five oxides of zirconium—ZrO; Zr_2O_3; ZrO_2; Zr_2O_5; and ZrO_3—have been reported, but evidence of the existence of the dioxide is alone satisfactorily definite. This oxide, ZrO_2, corresponds with other oxides of the members of the fourth group of the periodic classification, namely, CO_2, SiO_2, TiO_2, CeO_2, SnO_2, etc. A true bill seems to have been made out for the existence of a hydrated form of the trioxide, $ZrO_3.nH_2O$.

When zirconium is reduced with magnesium, and freed from magnesia and the excess of magnesium by washing with acids, an insoluble powder remains which has been reported by C. Winkler,[1] L. M. Dennis and A. E. Spencer, and E. Wedekind to consist largely of zirconium monoxide, ZrO; and in some cases a product containing oxygen almost eq. to ZrO has been obtained. It is said that the monoxide reacts less vigorously with chlorine than the metal, and if it were amorphous metal it would react more quickly being in a finer state of subdivision—unless, of course, the granules have protective surface films of dioxide; the sp. gr. is also said to be lower than that of an eq. mixture of finely divided metal and zirconia—the sp. gr. of zirconia, however, itself depends on the mode of preparation. The readiness with which the product obtained by reducing zirconia with magnesium is oxidized has been taken to show that a product more sensitive to oxygen than zirconium is present, but a pyrophoric condition is not unusual with metals in a finely divided state. W. H. Whitney and co-workers also cited the cataphoresis of the alleged zirconium monoxide as an argument in favour of the individuality of zirconium monoxide, but E. Wedekind's experiments do not agree with this, for the behaviour of colloidal zirconium seems to vary with the mode of preparation. The work of R. Schwarz and H. Deisler, and E. Wedekind has shown that it is highly probable that the supposed existence of zirconium monoxide—analogous with titanium monoxide, TiO—is a mal-inference from the analytical numbers obtained with what are really mixtures of zirconium metal and zirconia. The alleged monoxide gives volatile zirconium chloride, $ZrCl_4$, when treated with chlorine and in amounts corresponding with the presence of 31 per cent. of free zirconium, whereas non-volatile, $ZrOCl_2$, would have been anticipated had the monoxide been really present. The decrease in weight which occurs when the alleged monoxide is heated to 250° in chlorine, and the gain in weight when heated in oxygen are in harmony with this assumption. By the combustion of the hydride, ZrH_2, L. Weiss and E. Neumann obtained a greenish-white powder, analyses of which agree with zirconium sesquioxide, Zr_2O_3. This compound passes very slowly into the white dioxide, ZrO_2, when calcined in air. Here again evidence of chemical individuality is lacking. G. H. Bailey also reported zirconium hemipentoxide, $Zr_2O_5.nH_2O$, to be formed as a white precipitate when an acid soln. of zirconium disulphate is treated with 30 per cent. hydrogen dioxide. According to H. Geisow and P. Horkheimer, the alleged compound is probably partly decomposed zirconium trioxide, $ZrO_3.nH_2O$ (*q.v.*).

In 1892, L. Fletcher [2] reported the occurrence of monoclinic crystals of zirconia, ZrO_2, in the gem-bearing sands of Rakvana (Ceylon), and, almost simultaneously, E. Hussak reported the occurrence of a tantalo-columbate in the pyroxenitic sands from Jacupiranga (South Brazil); L. Fletcher named the Ceylonese mineral **baddeleyite**—after J. Baddeley—and E. Hussak called the Brazilian mineral *brazilite*. The latter term was subsequently abandoned in favour of baddeleyite. After E. Hussak had reported the analysis of brazilite and L. Fletcher that of baddeleyite, it became clear that the two minerals were chemically the same :

	ZrO_2	SiO_2	Al_2O_3	Fe_2O_3	CaO	MgO	$K_2O(Na_2O)$	Loss on ignition.
Brazilite . .	96·52	0·70	0·43	0·41	0·55	0·10	0·42	0·39
Baddeleyite . .	96·37	0·59	0·13	0·37	0·21	—	—	0·98

Baddeleyite is a constituent of the *jacupirangite* found by O. A. Derby in the magne-titic pyroxenites of Jacupiranga, Saõ Paulo, Brazil. The same mineral has also been reported by A. F. Rogers near Bozeman, Montana ; by E. Hussak at Alnö, Sweden ; by G. P. Tschernik, from Kuda Padi Oya, India; and by F. Zambonini at Mt. Somma, Vesuvius. Analyses have also been reported by G. S. Blake and G. F. H. Smith, L. Weiss, E. Wedekind, and R. Bayer. Large zirconia deposits occur on an undulating plateau in the Caldas region, partly in the States of Minas Geraes and Saõ Paulo, Brazil. Several large outcrops of the ore occur west of the plateau, where there are boulders weighing 30 tons. The massive ore, which occurs in fibrous, botryoidal, or columnar forms, is not baddeleyite, but rather a mixture of at least three minerals : baddeleyite, zircon, and an unnamed zirconium silicate which, on treatment with dil. hydrofluoric acid, passes into soln. along with the baddeleyite and leaves behind small crystals of zircon as a residue. The term *zirkite* has been registered as a trade name for zirconia ore. The massive ore occurs in various tints ranging from light grey, reddish-brown, to bluish-black ; the dark-coloured varieties show the largest proportion of zirconia ; some of the lighter-coloured material shows a minimum of about 70 per cent. zirconia. Alluvial pebbles, called *favas* —from the Portuguese *fava*, a bean—ranging up to 3 in. in diameter occur along small stream beds and the talus slopes of the lower ridges. The pebbles carry over 90 per cent. of zirconia oxide; their sp. gr. ranges from 4·8 to 5·2. L. Weiss and R. Lehmann's analyses of different samples are indicated in Table I. An

TABLE I.—ANALYSES OF ZIRCONIA ORE.

	Red and friable.	Pale red and hard.	Reddish-black, hard.	Grey and very dense.	Vitreous or glassy.
Zirconia, ZrO_2	80·54	87·99	88·97	93·12	95·46
Silica, SiO_2	6·21	5·89	5·87	3·06	1·35
Titanic oxide, TiO_2 . . .	0·12	0·74	0·96	0·69	0·76
Alumina, Al_2O_3 . . .	3·07	0·84	0·93	0·54	0·51
Ferric oxide, Fe_2O_3 . . .	9·03	3·78	3·54	3·03	2·84
Loss on ignition, H_2O . . .	2·01	0·54	0·51	0·07	—

approximately uniform grade with about 80 per cent. zirconia, ZrO_2, is obtained by sorting the crude ore. Amongst the elements of minor importance which have been reported in the ore are traces of the ceria earths, scandium, vanadium, and molybdenum. G. von Hevesy and V. T. Jantzen found 1 to 2 per cent. of hafnia to be present. According to A. von Antropoff, Brazilian zirconia earth is radio-active, and when heated in vacuo with sulphuric acid, furnishes argon and helium gases.

A pulverulent or granular form of **zirconia,** or **zirconium dioxide,** ZrO_2, is produced when the metal, the hydride, nitride, carbide, hydroxide, or the salt of a volatile acid, is heated in air, or oxygen. Zirconia, however, is usually extracted from zircon, baddeleyite, eudialyte, or other minerals rich in zirconia and as free as practicable from other impurities. The methods of extraction have been previously described. H. St. C. Deville and H. Caron [3] obtained small dendritic crystals, resembling those of ammonium chloride, by the action of boric oxide on zirconium fluoride heated in a carbon crucible. The reaction is symbolized : $3ZrF_4+2B_2O_3=3ZrO_2+4BF_3$; the boron fluoride is volatilized. A. E. Norden-skjöld obtained tetragonal crystals isomorphous with cassiterite, rutile, and thoria by melting zirconia with borax in a pottery oven. Analogous results were obtained by G. Wunder, W. Florence, A. Knop, and F. P. Venable and A. W. Belden. Similar results were reported by G. Wunder, and W. Florence by melting zirconia in fused microcosmic salt, but this does not agree with the observations of M. H. Klaproth, and F. P. Venable and A. W. Belden. L. Troost and L. Ouvrard obtained a phos-phate under very similar conditions; but they found that if the oxide, chloride, phosphate, or other compound of zirconium be dissolved in fused normal potassium phosphate mixed with a little potassium chloride, and heated to a very high temp., much of the potassium and phosphoric oxide is volatilized, and quadratic prisms of zirconia remain. These crystals were not isomorphous with those of thoria. L. Ouvrard obtained lamellar hexagonal crystals of zirconia by cooling a soln. of zirconia in fused potassium carbonate; and A. Michel-Lévy and L. Bourgeois, and J. Morozewicz obtained a similar result with fused sodium carbonate. K. A. Hofmann and K. Höschele obtained white tetragonal crystals from a soln. of zirconia in fused magnesium chloride; under other conditions, L. Bourgeois obtained magnesium metazirconate, $MgZrO_3$. H. Moissan fused zirconia in the electric arc-furnace and obtained a vitreous mass with dendritic crystals of zirconia. P. Hautefeuille and A. Perrey found that hydrogen chloride at atm. press. has no action on zirconia at a high temp., but under a press. of 3 atm. and at a temp. below dull redness, rhombic plates of zirconia are formed. At the same temp. and at atm. press., hydrogen chloride was found to have a mineralizing effect on zirconium carbonate, oxalate, and sulphate, but not on the oxide. The crystallization is attributed to successive formations and decompositions of a hydrochloride.

The **physical properties of zirconium dioxide.**—The **colour** of purified zirconium oxide is white; that of baddeleyite varies with the amount of ferric oxide which is present. In thin sections, baddeleyite is colourless, yellow, or brown; the colour may be zonally or irregularly variable, and it occasionally exhibits the hour-glass structure. O. Hahn studied the surface area of the particles of precipitated zirconia in terms of adsorbed radioactive matter. E. Hussak [4] found the **crystals** of baddeleyite to belong to the monoclinic system and to have the axial ratios $a : b : c = 0.9871 : 1 : 0.5441$, and $\beta = 81° 30'$; G. S. Blake and G. F. H. Smith gave $0.9905 : 1 : 0.5110$, and $\beta = 80° 32'$. So far as can be gathered from the meagre descriptions, probably the **crystals** obtained by P. Hautefeuille and A. Perrey, and W. Florence, also belonged to the monoclinic system; while those obtained from fused borax, etc., by A. E. Nordenskjöld, G. Wunder, A. Knop, F. P. Müller, and A. Michel-Lévy and L. Bourgeois, belonged to the tetragonal system. A. E. Nordenskjöld gave for the axial ratios $a : c = 1 : 1.0061$. The crystals of zirconium dioxide are therefore dimorphous, and possibly, according to J. W. Retgers, isodimorphous with those of silicon dioxide. H. Rose discussed the isomorphism of rutile, zirconia, silica, and stannic oxide. E. Hussak and J. Reitinger described favas occurring at Minas Geraes in reniform crusts, fibrous and concentric, which they regarded as an independent modification of zirconium dioxide, and not as a fibrous variety of baddeleyite. According to E. Hussak, the **habit** of the euhedral crystals of baddeleyite is tabular parallel to the (100)-face; the crystals usually show **twinning,** most commonly about the (100)-plane; there is also polysynthetic twinning; and both contact and penetration twins with lamellæ parallel to (110), but rarely parallel to (201). The **cleavage** of baddeleyite parallel to (001) is nearly perfect, and that parallel to (010), less so. There is a parting parallel to (110), in consequence of lamellar twinning. The **corrosion figures** with cold dil. hydrofluoric acid were examined by E. Hussak. L. Vegard, and W. P. Davey, J. Böhm and H. Niclassen, and J. Böhm studied the **X-radiogram** of zirconia, but the available data are not capable of establishing the structure —vide rutile; A. E. van Arkel said that the oxide has the same structure as fluorite with $d_{100} = 5.86A$ M. L. Huggins inferred that, in the tetragonal crystal, each zirconium atom is surrounded by four equidistant oxygen atoms, and each oxygen atom by two equidistant zirconium atoms, all at the tetrahedral corners. L. Fletcher found that the **optic axial angle** is large, varying from $2E = 70°-75°$.

For the **specific gravity** of baddeleyite, E. Hussak gave 5.006, and L. Fletcher, 6.025. For artificial crystals, A. E. Nordenskjöld gave 5.710–5.742; G. Wunder, 5.42–5.52; L. Ouvrard, 4.9; E. Podszus, 5.89; and A. Michel Lévy and L. Bourgeois, 5.726. For artificial zirconium dioxide, L. N. Vauquelin gave 4.35; and

N. J. Berlin, 4·90. These numbers are too low, probably on account of the inade
quate washing of the precipitate before calcination. R. Hermann gave for the
artificial dioxide, 5·45 ; A. Sjögren, 5·50 ; F. P. Venable and A. W. Belden, 5·49 ;
L. F. Nilson and O. Pettersson, 5·85 ; L. Bradford, 5·89 ; and R. Ruer, 5·65–5·66.
R. Lehmann gave 4·9695 at 17·5° for the sp. gr. of the raw dioxide, 5·482 at 18·5° for
that of the purified dioxide, and 5·75 at 15° for that of the fused oxide. G. von Hevesy
and V. Berglund found that the sp. gr. of zirconia and hafnia prepared by igniting
the respective sulphates at 1000°, are 5·73 for zirconia, 9·67 for hafnia at 20°. The
hafnia content of zirconia can be fairly accurately calculated from the sp. gr. G. von
Hevesy, and F. A. Henglein compared the mol. vol. of titanium, zirconium, hafnium,
thorium, and cerium oxides. H. Moissan said that the sublimed zirconia forms
small, white, rounded masses of sp. gr. 5·10 ; and that the transparent parts are
hard enough to scratch glass. L. Fletcher gave for the **hardness** of baddeleyite,
6·5, and E. Hussak, 5·54. P. Berthier, and L. N. Vauquelin found that when
hard lumps of the hydroxide are ignited the product scratches glass ; and, added
H. Davy, it will even scratch rock-crystal. V. Bodin found that briquettes made
from zirconia have a **crushing strength,** F kgrms. per sq. cm.

	20°	800°	1000°	1300°	1500°
F	395	275	345	90	10

thus showing a maximum at about 1100°, as is the case with clay briquettes.

M. Mayer and B. Havas measured the cubical coeff. of the **thermal expansion**
and obtained $3\alpha = 0.0_{4}2785$. R. Lehmann found between 20° and 210°, $3\alpha = 0.0_{5}9855$
for the crude oxide, and $0.0_{5}251$ for the purified fused oxide ; this makes the coeff.
of linear expansion of the purified dioxide $\alpha = 0.0_{6}84$ when that of fused quartz is
about $0.0_{6}7$. The **thermal conductivity** is low. J. W. Marden and M. N. Rich
say that it is about the same as that of fused quartz. L. F. Nilson and O. Pettersson
gave 0·1076 for the **specific heat** of amorphous zirconia, and 13·13 for the **molecular
heat.** L. Bradshaw and W. Emery found :

	0°–100°	25°–600°	25°–1000°	25°–1200°	25°–1400°
Sp. ht.	0·108	0·137	0·157	0·167	0·175

L. N. Vauquelin's zirconia fused at the heat of a smith's forge ; as pointed out
by J. J. Berzelius, it must have been contaminated with potash because he could not
fuse it at any temp. then accessible. H. Moissan fused it in the electric arc-furnace.
O. Ruff and co-workers gave 2585° for the **melting point ;** and a specimen of
98·75 per cent. ZrO_2 melted at 2565° ; A. Stansfield gave 2500°–2950° for the m.p. ;
W. R. Mott, 2500° ; E. Podszus, 2950°–3000° ; F. Henning, 2687° ; and E. W. Washburn and E. E. Libman gave 2700°—*vide* zirconium silicate. H. Moissan found that
zirconia readily sublimes in the electric arc-furnace and furnishes a sublimate with
a number of rounded white particles. O. Ruff and co-workers observed that the
vaporization of zirconia is small at the m.p., and that silica distils from zirconia
at 2000° under reduced press. W. R. Mott gave 4300° for the **boiling point** of
zirconia. F. Born estimated zirconia to be dissociated into metal and oxygen to
the extent of 10^{-11} at 2000°, and about 0·6 at 3000°. J. J. Berzelius found that the
zirconia becomes insoluble in acids and acquires a higher sp. gr. after being heated,
and H. Davy showed that the exothermal change produces a glowing—**calorescence**
—which is more marked than is the case with alumina (*q.v.*), so much so, that " even
at an incipient red heat, the zirconia becomes incandescent and appears as if it
had taken fire." J. Böhm showed by X-radiograms that the phenomenon is
connected with the passage from the amorphous to the crystalline state.

According to M. E. Chevreul, the calorescence is preceded by a blackening of
the mass, but R. Hermann showed that this arises from the presence of impurities.
According to R. Ruer, the incandescence appears at about 300°, and only when
the hydroxide has been dehydrated at a lower temp. than this and while it still
retains less than 1·9 per cent. of water. He also measured the heating curve shown

in Fig. 3, where the dotted line represents the course of the heating provided no singularity occurred. From the rise of temp. and the sp. ht. of zirconia, he calculated that the recalescence is attended by the evolution of over 9·2 Cals. per gram of zirconia. At higher temp., there are small explosions attended by the evolution of an extremely fine powder ; and this phenomenon is the cause of losses in the ignition of zirconia in analytical work. L. Weiss and E. Neumann gave 175·5 Cals. per gram-atom for the **heat of formation** of the oxide from the metal ; W. G. Mixter made some observations on this subject.

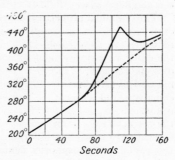

According to E. Hussak, the **index of refraction** and the **birefringence** of baddeleyite are high. C. P. Smyth discussed the relation between the refractivity and electronic structure of zirconium. The **optical character** is negative. The **pleochroism** is marked, being α, reddish-brown, β, oil-green, and γ, reddish-brown. In 1820,

FIG. 3.—Heating Curve of Zirconium Oxide.

R. Hare in an attempt to fuse zirconia in the oxy-hydrogen flame, noted the brilliancy of the light, and in 1826, T. Drummond found that when zirconia is heated in the oxy-hydrogen flame, it emits a very brilliant light. The relative intensities of lime, zirconia, and magnesia were stated to be respectively 37, 31, and 16 times the intensity of the light from an argand burner. The use of these agents for illuminating purposes was patented by G. H. Smith in 1862 ; H. Caron said that the light is about one-sixth as intense as that furnished by magnesia. A. W. Hofmann, however, pointed out that the zirconia is more durable than lime. According to E. Linnemann, the light is attended by the emission of very little heat, and the spectrum is continuous. The **light emissivity** of zirconia was studied by C. M. T. du Motay, W. E. Forsythe, A. Bettendorff, J. Philipp, E. Waller, J. W. Draper, W. Huggins, J. T. Taylor and W. H. Harrison, C. E. Mendenhall and L. R. Ingersoll, F. Schröter, H. Landolt, A. Payen, W. Kochs, G. P. Drossbach, and A. W. Hofmann. E. L. Nichols and co-workers investigated the blue glow which occurs when zirconia is heated in the oxy-hydrogen flame. According to W. W. Coblentz, purified zirconia is not an efficient radiator of white-light, and becomes so only when a small amount of cerium oxide or thorium oxide is added. With purified zirconia, there are two sharp emission bands with maxima respectively at $2\cdot78\mu$ and $4\cdot3\mu$. There are smaller maxima at 2μ, $2\cdot4\mu$, $3\cdot2\mu$, $4\cdot7\mu$, and $5\cdot4\mu$, Fig. 4. H. E. Ives and co-workers measured the emissivity and illuminating power of mantles made of zirconia and heated by the bunsen flame. The **reflecting power** of zirconium oxide used as a pigment for light of different wave-lengths is :

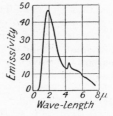

FIG. 4. — Ultra-red Emission Spectrum of Zirconia.

λmax.	0·54μ	0·60μ	0·95μ	0·95μ	4·4μ	8·8μ	24μ
Per cent.	82·2	85·8	84·1	83·0	23·2	5·1	5·4

E. L. Nichols and D. T. Wilbur, and J. Ewles studied the luminescence of zirconia exposed to the **cathode rays ;** E. L. Nichols and D. T. Wilbur, the **thermoluminescence** of zirconia. According to C. Kästle, zirconium dioxide and the zirconium salts are opaque to the **X-rays,** hence its possible use in place of bismuth nitrate for defining the intestines for X-ray photographs of the abdomen. J. Ewles found zirconia exhibits a faint blue cathodoluminescence ; and E. L. Nichols and H. L. Howes studied the **flame luminescence** of zirconia. H. J. Spanner studied the emission of electrically charged ions by zirconia.

The **electrical conductivity** of zirconia is low, and the **electrical resistance** is quoted by J. W. Marden and M. N. Rich to be $1 \cdot 2 \times 10^3$ ohms per cubic centimetre at 1200°. According to K. Angström, zirconia is diamagnetic, and S. Meyer gives $-0 \cdot 003 \times 10^{-6}$ for the **molecular magnetism;** and G. von Hevesy gave for the magnetic susceptibility $-0 \cdot 112 \times 10^{-6}$ units per gram.

The chemical properties of zirconium dioxide.—Early attempts by J. B. Trommsdorff,[5] and H. Davy to reduce zirconia were not successful. Many of the ordinary reducing agents are ineffective; **hydrogen** fails; but, according to L. E. Barton, the oxide is partially reduced when heated in a reducing flame; and it begins to dissociate about its m.p. E. Newbery and J. N. Pring found that zirconia is not reduced by hydrogen at 150 atm. press. at 2000°. F. Wöhler found that when zirconia is mixed with carbon and heated in **chlorine** or **bromine** vap., the tetrahalide is formed; and F. Bourion, and A. Rosenheim and J. Hertzmann showed that the tetrachloride is formed when zirconia is heated in a mixture of chlorine and the vapour of **sulphur chloride,** S_2Cl_2. E. F. Smith and H. B. Harris found that the vapour of **phosphorus pentachloride,** or of **carbon tetrachloride** or **carbonyl chloride** converts heated zirconium dioxide into the tetrachloride (*q.v.*). According to J. J. Berzelius, the affinity of zirconia for **acids** is very slight; the dioxide which has been heated to incandescence dissolves very slowly in hot **sulphuric acid,** for if zirconia be finely powdered, and digested in a hot mixture of 2 parts of sulphuric acid and one part of water, and then heated until the water and excess of acid are expelled, the residue contains soluble zirconium sulphate. F. P. Venable and A. W. Belden found that when dil. sulphuric acid, sp. gr. 1·56, is heated with powdered zirconia, only 0·672 per cent. of its weight of the oxide is dissolved. R. Ruer made some observations on the dissolution of zirconia in sulphuric acid. J. J. Berzelius said that the ignited oxide is slowly dissolved by **hydrofluoric acid;** and F. P. Venable and A. W. Belden found that strongly ignited zirconia is easily dissolved by hot hydrofluoric acid. According to F. P. Venable and T. Clarke, a little zirconia is dissolved during prolonged digestion with **hydrochloric acid.** E. Podszus said that zirconia dissolves in hydrochloric acid when the particles are less than 1μ; S. A. Tucker and H. R. Moody, and E. Wedekind found that zirconia is reduced when mixed with **boron** and heated in an electric furnace, zirconium boride is formed; and E. Wedekind and co-workers found that with **silicon,** zirconium silicide is formed. H. C. Greenwood, and J. N. Pring showed that with **carbon** the reduction of zirconia begins at about 1400°. C. Renz found that, unlike titania, zirconia is not photosensitive in the presence of organic liquids. F. P. Venable and T. Clarke said that zirconia is not attacked by molten **boric oxide.** H. Davy did not succeed in reducing zirconia satisfactorily with **potassium** G. H. Bailey, T. L. Phipson, and E. Wedekind reduced zirconia by heating it with **magnesium,** and an alloy was formed; E. Wedekind reduced zirconia by **calcium;** and S. A. Tucker and H. R. Moody found the reduction with **aluminium** is unsatisfactory, an alloy is formed. Zirconia is readily dissolved by fused **alkali hydroxides** producing a zirconate; and with molten **alkali carbonates** carbon dioxide is evolved and a zirconate is formed; molten **alkali and alkaline earth chlorides** form zirconates; and fused **alkali hydrosulphates** and fused **potassium hydrofluorides** furnish soluble zirconium salts; when zirconium dioxide is moistened with a soln. of a **cobalt salt** and calcined, it assumes a dirty violet colour. S. Medsforth examined the effect of zirconia on nickel as a catalyst in the reduction of carbon monoxide and dioxide by hydrogen; A. Mailhe and F. de Godon, as a catalyst in esterifications; and P. Sabatier and A. Mailhe, as a catalyst in dehydrating alcohol. For the uses of zirconia, *vide* zirconium.

The zirconium hydroxides.—A white, voluminous, gelatinous precipitate is obtained when a soln. of ammonia, alkali hydroxide, ammonium sulphide, or potassium cyanide is added to a soln. of a zirconium salt. The precipitate is usually regarded as a **zirconium hydroxide,** $Zr(OH)_4$, or **orthozirconic acid,** H_4ZrO_4. Unlike yttrium hydroxide, the precipitation of zirconium hydroxide is prevented if **tartaric acid** be present. R. Ruer said that the hydroxide appears to be more voluminous if precipitated from hot soln. than from cold soln. The composition varies with the conditions under which it is formed. As observed by L. N. Vau-quelin,[6] when the precipitate dries, it shrinks and forms a yellowish-white, shining, translucent, gum-like mass with a conchoidal fracture. The freshly precipitated hydroxide, washed with cold water, was found by J. M. van Bemmelen to contain 95 per cent. of water, corresponding with $ZrO_2.127H_2O$, and after drying in air, 47 per cent. of water, corresponding with $ZrO_2.6H_2O$. After drying in vacuo, H. Davy, and S. R. Paykull found numbers in agreement with $ZrO_2.1\frac{1}{3}H_2O$; and after drying over conc. sulphuric acid, R. Hermann, and A. Mandl obtained numbers corresponding with $ZrO_2.2H_2O$; after washing with petroleum ether, F. P. Venable and A. W. Belden found the composition nearly the same, $ZrO_2.2H_2O$; and after washing with alcohol and ether, J. M. van Bemmelen found the composition, $ZrO_2.0.7H_2O$ to $ZrO_2.0.8H_2O$. J. J. Berzelius, and S. R. Paykull found that the hydroxide dried at 100° has a composition corresponding with $ZrO_2.H_2O$, and, added R. Ruer, the same result is obtained whether the precipitated hydroxide be formed in hot or cold soln. A. Mandl obtained a similar result at 110°, and J. M. van Bemmelen at 140°–200°. The latter also found that at 300° the composition approximates $ZrO_2.0.6(to\ 0.7)H_2O$. For the recalescence which occurs when heated, *vide supra*, zirconium dioxide. The hydroxide dried over sulphuric acid at 65°, and having the composition $ZrO_2.2.7H_2O$, after heating to different temp. contained, according to J. M. van Bemmelen, $ZrO_2.nH_2O$:

	80°	100°–110°	140°	200°	260°–280°	7280°
n . . .	2.0	1.9–1.6	1.08	1.0	0.6–0.7	0.6–0.2

The hydroxide behaves as a gel up to about 140° because the proportion of water varies continuously with the temp., and the vap. press. of the water vap. Between 140° and 200°, the proportion of water is constant, and corresponds with $ZrO_2.H_2O$, or **metazirconic acid**, H_2ZrO_3, or **zirconyl hydroxide**, $ZrO(OH)_2$. This meta-zirconic acid is not the same as that obtained by R. Ruer—*vide infra*. The evidence is not decisive enough to affirm that a definite hydrate is formed, because the product still possesses an absorptive power. In the so-called *chemical hydrates*, the dehydration proceeds in stages and is reversible except when a simultaneous change in structure makes the change irreversible ; with the *colloidal hydrates*, the composition depends on the structure of the colloid, and varies continuously with changes of temp. or press. J. M. van Bemmelen found that the dehydration is only partially reversible because less water is taken up when the partly dehydrated product is rehydrated. Thus, in an atm. over sulphuric acid diluted to a conc. eq. to the vap. press. *p* mm. of steam, when the composition is represented by *n* mols of H_2O per mol of ZrO_2,

p . . .					9	8	6	4	2
n {Dehydration	.	.	.	.	6	5	5	4	3 }
{Rehydration	.	.	.	.	←	4	3	3	3

The power of rehydrating becomes less and less each time the hydrated dioxide is dehydrated. R. Ruer found that the gelatinous precipitate obtained by adding aq. ammonia to a soln. of metazirconium (*i.e.* zirconyl) chloride, is less voluminous than that obtained from the normal chloride, and its composition corresponds with metazirconic acid ; when dried at 100°, its composition is $ZrO_2.\frac{2}{3}H_2O$, and if boiled for some time its composition approximates $ZrO_2.\frac{1}{2}H_2O$. When heated, it forms ordinary zirconium dioxide without becoming incandescent. According to F. P. Venable and A. W. Belden, the sp. gr. of the hydroxide precipitated in the cold, and approximating $ZrO_2.2H_2O$, is 3.25. F. Haber observed no difference in the X-radiograms of zirconia soln. and precipitated zirconia ; both gave weak interference rings. H. T. S. Britton studied the electrometric precipitation of the hydroxide. A soln. of zirconium oxychloride slowly yields a precipitate when treated with sodium acetate; but not with the tetrachloride; zirconia is precipitated from the chloride or sulphate before the acidity has been reduced to $p_H = 10^{-2}$, which acetic acid can barely attain in conc. soln. No precipitation occurred during the titration of 100 c.c. of $0.01M\text{-}ZrCl_4$ with $0.1N$-sodium acetate, and the acidity of the soln. ranged from $p_H = 3.15$ to 4.81. With $0.1N$-sodium oxalate no precipitation occurred with zirconium sulphate, and with 100 c.c. of $0.01M\text{-}ZrCl_4$ a gelatinous precipitate occurred with 10 c.c. of the sodium oxalate. With $0.1N$-sodium tartrate and 100 c.c. of $0.01M\text{-}ZrCl_4$ a basic tartrate was precipitated when 10 c.c. of tartrate had been added, and $p_H = 1.66$, but it began to dissolve with 30 c.c. of tartrate, and the soln. was clear with 42·5 c.c. of tartrate.

F. P. Venable and A. W. Belden said that the hydrated dioxide is quite insoluble in water. The earlier workers, e.g. D. E. Melliss, said that it is slightly soluble in water, 100 parts of water dissolving 0·2 part of the dioxide. The aq. soln. was said to have an acid reaction; the alleged alkalinity towards turmeric has been attributed to the incomplete removal of alkali in the washing. In fact, if precipitated with an alkali, it is almost impossible to remove the adsorbed alkali by washing. According to J. J. Berzelius, J. B. Hannay, A. Sjögren, E. Linnemann, R. Ruer, A. Mandl, F. P. Venable and A. W. Belden, and O. Hauser, if the hydrated dioxide is precipitated and washed in the cold, it dissolves readily in hydrochloric, hydrobromic, nitric, sulphuric, or oxalic acid, and less readily in acetic, tartaric, or citric acid; but if the hydrated dioxide has been precipitated hot, or washed with boiling water, it dissolves only slowly in the conc. acids; but after a prolonged digestion the amount dissolved is the same with hydrated dioxide precipitated hot or cold. According to J. B. Hannay, the hydrated dioxide derived from zircons of high sp. gr. dissolves more slowly in oxalic acid than that derived from zircons of low sp. gr. S. R. Paykull said that it absorbs carbon dioxide from the air, and when heated in a current of this gas, 16·4 per cent. was absorbed, and most of this was given off again in a current of air. F. P. Venable and T. Clarke said that the hydrated dioxide is sparingly soluble in conc. alkali-lye, and almost insoluble in dil. alkali-lye. A litre of 50 per cent. potassium hydroxide dissolved 2·23 grms., and a litre of 33 per cent. sodium hydroxide dissolved 2·45 grms. F. P. Venable and A. W. Belden found that the hydrated dioxide is not perceptibly soluble in aq. ammonia of sp. gr. 0·90; and that 100 parts of aq. ammonia of sp. gr. 0·96, dissolve 0·01 part ZrO_2. J. J. Berzelius said that the hydrated dioxide is insoluble in boiling aq. soln. of ammonium salts. F. P. Venable and A. W. Belden showed that 100 parts of a sat. soln. of ammonium carbonate dissolve one part of the hydrated dioxide, while a soln. of ammonium tartrate dissolves rather less. R. Hermann stated that the hydrated dioxide is insoluble in soln. of alkali carbonates.

Zirconium hydroxide exhibits a tendency to polymerization, forming a series of hydroxides exhibiting different properties. In addition to the normal hydroxide obtained by treating a soln. of zirconyl chloride, or zirconium sulphate with ammonia, R. Ruer reported the formation of metazirconic acid when a soln. of zirconyl chloride is boiled—vide metazirconic chloride. There is also the hydroxide obtained by E. H. Rodd by adding ammonia to a soln. of zirconium octoxytetrachloride or octoxydisulphate. If this hydroxide be dissolved in hydrochloric acid, the soln. furnishes crystals of the octoxytetrachloride, a soln. of the ordinary hydroxide in the same acid furnishes zirconyl chloride. The hydroxide from the octoxytetrachloride is therefore regarded as having a constitution analogous to the basic chloride, namely, $Zr_5O_8(OH)_4$, or $Zr(O.ZrO.OH)_4$, or $ZrO_4(ZrO.OH)_4$, tetrahydroxyzirconyl zirconate. There is evidence of a partial decomposition of this compound by hydrochloric acid, because the last crop of crystals from the soln. is a mixture of $Zr_5O_8Cl_4$ and $ZrOCl_2$. Ordinary zirconium sulphate is produced by dissolving this hydroxide in sulphuric acid.

According to A. Lottermoser, the **hydrosol** of zirconium hydroxide is not formed **by** the dialysis of a soln. of the chloride, by the digestion of the hydroxide in water, **nor** of zirconia obtained from zirconium oxalate; but, according to W. Biltz, it can be obtained by the dialysis of zirconium nitrate, oxychloride, or acetate. W. Müller made it in the following manner :

Three grams of zirconium nitrate are dissolved in water, and precipitated in the cold with aq. ammonia ; and washed with cold water to remove the ammonia. The precipitate is then mixed with an aq. soln. of 10 grms. of zirconium nitrate for 15 mins. in the cold; heated for 15 mins. on a water-bath ; and then boiled. The filtered liquid is opalescent, and on evaporation furnishes a clear gum which swells up in water, forming a viscid soln. The liquid becomes turbid on dilution.

R. Ruer made the hydrosol by dialyzing a soln. of zirconium oxychloride, or zirconyl chloride ; and A. Rosenheim and J. Hertzmann, by the dialysis of a 1·5 per cent. soln. of zirconium acetate. The hydrosol obtained from zirconyl chloride soln. contains a chloride which is not directly precipitated by silver nitrate soln., and which is protected in some way by the colloid. On attempting to remove the last traces of chloride, a hydrogel is formed. The chloride is " accessible " to the silver nitrate after the soln. has been boiled with nitric acid—*vide infra*, metazirconic chloride. The zirconium hydroxides previously described are considered to be hydrogels.

W. Biltz found that the hydrosol is fairly stable when boiled, and when treated with electrolytes ; and it is positively charged against water. W. Biltz and co-workers gave 0·046 to 0·09 for the gold number (3. 23, 8) : P. Behre gave 0·05. The hydrosol prepared by dialyzing a soln. of zirconyl nitrate is clear in transmitted light, but cloudy in reflected light. When the hydrosol of orthozirconic acid is boiled, it forms the hydrosol of metazirconic acid ; and the opalescent liquid which is formed has been likened to the hydrosol of metastannic acid. According to W. Müller, the less ionized univalent salts have no effect on the hydrosol, but the strongly ionized salts cause coagulation ; salts of higher valency also cause flocculation ; the anions are active, the cations negligible. A. Rosenheim and J. Hertzmann obtained similar results with a clear hydrosol obtained by hydrolyzing zirconium acetate. B. Szilard obtained colloidal zirconium hydroxide almost free from electrolytes by decomposing a soln. of a zirconium salt with an excess of dil. aq. ammonia, and washing the residue for 3 to 6 days until it is quite free from ammonia. The product is a fine milky suspension in which the particles cannot be separated either by filtration or decantation ; it is precipitated by electrolytes and by the carbon dioxide of the air. B. Szilard also found that zirconium hydroxide can be peptized by uranyl nitrate, furnishing a yellow, turbid, opalescent, very stable soln. O. Ruff and J. Moczala studied the adsorption of zirconium nitrate, and of nitric, hydrochloric, phosphoric, and sulphuric acids by zirconia ; and the production of plastic masses of zirconia for making vessels of various kinds. W. Pauli considered the hydrogels are complexes : $Zr(OH)_4.Zr(OH)_2Cl_2$, etc. H. Freundlich and E. Schalek measured the viscosity and elasticity of colloidal soln. of zirconium hydroxide ; E. Schalek and A. Szegvari, the rate of coagulation of the sol of zirconium hydroxide ; and E. Wedekind and H. Wilke, adsorption and coagulation of the sol prior to chemical reaction with hydrogen dioxide, arsenious acid, arsenic acid, and phosphoric acid. The adsorption of dyes by zirconia gel was found by H. Rheinboldt and E. Wedekind to resemble the phenomenon with silica gel. They also examined the adsorption of phosphoric and boric acids, as well as of molybdenum-blue, and starch iodide soln. M. Adolf and W. Pauli found that sols of zirconia are coagulated by electrolytes only when the conc. exceeds 0·25N. The dried soln. was found by J. Böhm and H. Niclassen to furnish X-radiograms characteristic of amorphous substances, but, on ageing, the gel becomes crystalline.

According to P. T. Cleve,[7] when ammonia is added to a soln. of zirconium sulphate containing hydrogen dioxide a gelatinous **hydrated zirconium peroxide,** $Zr(OH)_3O.OH$, is precipitated : $Zr(OH)_4+HO.OH=H_2O+Zr(O.OH)(OH)_3$. G. H. Bailey obtained a higher oxide by adding a conc., feebly acid soln. of the sulphate. The object of the acid was to avoid the possible presence of zirconium hydroxide produced in the presence of an excess of ammonia. G. H. Bailey regarded his product as a pentoxide, $Zr_2O_5.nH_2O$, but H. Geisow and P. Horkheimer consider this to be a stage in the decomposition of the trioxide. A. Piccini did not obtain such precipitates, and H. Geisow and P. Horkheimer suggested that Piccini's soln. were too dil. ; they confirmed P. T. Cleve's results using a 30 per cent. hydrogen dioxide soln. and an alkaline soln. E. Wedekind obtained the peroxide by mixing an alkaline soln. of a zirconium salt, in the presence of alkali tartrate, with hydrogen dioxide. L. Pissarjewsky obtained a similar product by the action of an aq. soln. of sodium hypochlorite upon zirconium nitrate : $Zr(NO_3)_4 + NaOCl + 4H_2O = NaCl + Zr(OH)_3O.OH + 4HNO_3$, at a temp. not exceeding 10° ; and, by electrolyzing an aq. soln. of sodium chloride in which zirconium hydroxide is suspended ; the sodium chloride is converted into sodium hypochlorite, which acts as an oxidizing agent. The oxidation is an endothermal process : $Zr(OH)_4 + O = Zr(OH)_3(O.OH) - 21.78$ Cals. The gelatinous precipitate is rather unstable, and loses oxygen on standing. With dil. sulphuric acid, hydrogen dioxide is formed, and ozonized oxygen with the conc. acid. According to L. Pissarjewsky, the hydrated peroxide dissolves in potassium hydroxide soln. containing hydrogen dioxide, and the addition of alcohol to the soln. at about 3°, precipitates **potassium perzirconate**, $K_4Zr_2O_{11}.9H_2O$; and similarly with **sodium perzirconate**, $Na_4Zr_2O_{11}.9H_2O$. G. H. Bailey regarded the hydrated peroxide as a derivative of a zirconium pentoxide, $Zr_2O_5.4H_2O$; others have supposed it to be a derivative of a *zirconium trioxide*, $ZrO_3.nH_2O$; and others again have suggested that $Zr(OH)_3(O.OH)$ is an intermediate stage in the peroxidation of the tetrahydroxide, $Zr(OH)_4$, on the way to the tetraperzirconate $Zr(O.OH)_4$.

REFERENCES.

[1] W. H. Whitney, *Zeit. Elektrochem.*, **9**. 633, 1903 ; W. H. Whitney and J. E. Oder, *Zeit. anorg. Chem.*, **45**. 391, 1905 ; R. Schwarz and H. Deisler, *Ber.*, **52** B, 1896, 1919 ; **53**. B, 1, 1920 ; C. Winkler, *ib.*, **23**. 2642, 1890 ; L. M. Dennis and A. E. Spencer, *Journ. Amer. Chem. Soc.*, **18**. 673, 1896 ; E. Wedekind, *Zeit. anorg. Chem.*, **45**. 385, 1905 ; *Zeit. Koll.*, **2**. 289, 1908 ; E. Wedekind and J. Teletow, *Liebig's Ann.*, **395**. 149, 1913 ; G. H. Bailey, *Journ. Chem. Soc.*, **49**. 149, 481, 1886 ; *Chem. News*, **53**. 55, 287, 1886 ; L. Weiss and E. Neumann, *Zeit. anorg. Chem.*, **65**. 248, 1910 ; H. Geisow and P. Horkheimer, *ib.*, **32** 372, 1902.

[2] L. Fletcher, *Nature*, **46**. 20, 1892 ; *Min. Mag.*, **10**. 148, 1899 ; E. Hussak, *Neues Jahrb. Min.*, ii, 141, 1892 ; i, 89, 1893 ; ii, 228, 1898 ; *Tschermak's Mitt.*, (2), **14**. 395, 1894 ; (2), **18**. 339, 1899 ; *Zeit. Kryst.*, **24**. 164, 1895 ; **25**. 298, 1895 ; J Reitinger, *ib.*, **38**. 550. 1902 ; E. Hussak and J. Reitinger, *ib.*, **37**. 568, 1903 ; R. Bayer, *Zeit. angew. Chem.*, **23**. 485, 1909 ; E. Wedekind, *ib.*, **21**. 2270, 1908 ; *Ber.* **43**. 270, 1910 ; L. Weiss and R. Lehmann, *Zeit. anorg. Chem.*, **65**. 178, 248, 1909 ; L. Weiss, *ib.*, **65**. 178, 192, 1910 ; A. von Antropoff, *Zeit. Elektrochem.*, **14**. 585, 1908 ; G. von Hevesy and V. T. Jantzen, *Journ. Chem. Soc.*, **123**. 3218, 1923 ; G. P. Tschernik, *Bull. Acad. Russ.*, 267, 1920 ; O. A. Derby, *Journ. Geol. Soc.*, **43**. 457, 1887 ; **47**. 251, 1891 ; A. F. Rogers, *Amer. Journ. Science*, (4), **33**. 54, 1912 ; H. C. Meyer, *Met. Chem. Eng.*, **12**. 191, 1914 ; **13**. 362, 1915 ; G. S. Blake and G. F. H. Smith, *Min. Mag.*, **14**. 378, 1907 ; F. Zambonini, *Atti Accad. Lincei.*, (5), **20**. ii, 129, 1911 ; M. E. Wadsworth, *Amer. Journ. Science*, (4), 5 153, 1898 ; *Journ. Geol.*, **11**. 199, 1898.

[3] M. H. Klaproth, *Beiträge zur chemischen Kenntniss der Mineralkörper*, Berlin, **1**. 203, 227, 1795 ; K. A. Hofmann and K. Höschele, *Ber.*, **47**. 238, 1914 ; E. Hussak, *Tschermak's Mitt.*, (2), **18**. 339, 1899 ; *Neues Jahrb. Min.*, i, 89, 1893 ; E. Weinschenk, *Zeit. Kryst.*, **27**. 324, 1897 ; A. E. Nordenskjöld, *Œfvers. Akad. För. Stockholm*, 450, 1860 ; *Pogg. Ann.*, **114**. 625, 1861 ; A. Knop, *Liebig's Ann.*, **159**. 33, 1871 ; J. Morozewicz, *Anz. Akad. Cracow*, 207, 1909 ; W. Florence, *Neues Jahrb. Min.*, ii, 127, 1890 ; H. St. C. Deville and H. Caron, *Ann. Chim. Phys.*, (4), **5**. 109, 1865 ; P. Hautefeuille and A. Perrey, *ib.*, (6), **21**. 419, 1890 ; *Compt. Rend.*, **110**. 1038, 1890 ; L. Troost and L. Ouvrard, *ib.*, **102**. 1422, 1886 ; L. Ouvrard, *ib.*, **112**. 1444, 1891 ; H. Moissan, *ib.*, **116**. 1222, 1893 ; A. Michel-Lévy and L. Bourgeois, *ib.*, **94**. 812, 1882 ; *Bull. Soc. Min.*, **5**. 136, 1882 ; L. Bourgeois, *Réproduction artificielle des minéraux*, Paris, 137, 1884 ; G. Wunder, *Journ. prakt. Chem.*, (2), **1**. 475, 1870 ; (2), **2**. 211, 1870 ; F. P. Venable and A. W. Belden, *Journ. Amer. Chem. Soc.*, **20**. 273, 1898.

[4] E. Hussak, *Tschermak's Mitt.*, (2), **18**. 339, 1899 ; *Neues Jahrb. Min.*, i, 89, 1893 ; *Zeit. Kryst.*, **24**. 164, 1895 ; **27**. 324, 1897 ; E. Hussak and J. Reitirger, *ib.*, **37**. 506, 1903 ; C. M. T. du Motay, *Chem. News*, **18**. 276, 1868 ; **19**. 107, 213, 310, 1869 ; *French Pat. No.* 80810, 1868 ; *Mech. Mag.*, (2), **21**. 458, 1869 ; *Dingler's Journ.*, **191**. 252, 1869 ; W. Kochs, *ib.*, **278**. 235, 1890 ; F. P. Müller, *Beiträge Kryst. Min.*, **1**. 159, 1918 ; J. W. Retgers, *Zeit. phys. Chem.*, **16**. 620, 1895.

W. E. Forsythe, *Phys. Rev.*, (2), **20**. 101, 1922 ; L. Fletcher, *Nature*, **46**. 20, 1892 ; *Min. Mag.*, **10**. 148, 1899 ; A. W. Hofmann, *Bericht über die Entwickelung der chemischen Industrie*, Braunschweig, **1**. 1016, 1875 ; J. T. Taylor and W. H. Harrison, *Mech. Mag.*, **21**. 458, 1869 ; L. Vegard, *Phil. Mag.*, (6), **32**. 65, 1916 ; C. Kästle, *Münchever Mediz. Wochenschr.*, **57**. 1838, 1910 ; M. L. Huggins, *Phys. Rev.*, (2), **21**. 719, 1923 ; A. E. Nordenskjöld, *Œfvers. Akad. För. Stockholm*, **450**, 1860 ; Pogg. *Ann.*, **114**. 625, 1861 ; Messrs. Darker, *Wagner's Jahresb.*, **15**. 731, 1869 ; G. Wunder, *Journ. prakt. Chem.*, (2), **1**. 475, 1870 ; (2), **2**. 211, 1870 ; N. J. Berlin, *ib.*, (1), **58**. 145, 1853 ; R. Hermann, *ib.*, (1), **31**. 75, 1844 ; (1), **97**. 321, 330, 1866 ; A. Sjögren, *ib.*, (1), **55**. 298, 1852 ; Pogg. *Ann. Ergbd.*, **3**. 465, 1853 ; F. P. Venable and A. W. Belden, *Journ. Amer. Chem. Soc.*, **20**. 273, 1898 ; F. P. Venable and T. Clarke, *ib.*, **18**. 434, 1896 ; E. Waller, *Eng. Min. Journ.*, **51**. 520, 1891 ; G. P. Drossbach, *Chem. Ztg.*, **15**. 328, 1891 ; L. N. Vauquelin, *Ann. Chim. Phys.*, (1), **22**. 179, 1797 ; P. Berthier, *ib.*, (2), **50**. 362, 1832 ; (2), **59**. 192, 1843 ; (3), **7**. 74, 1843 ; M. E. Chevreul, *ib.*, (2), **13**. 245, 1820 ; J. Philipp, *Monit. Scient.*, (3), **8**. 481, 1878 ; L. F. Nilson and O. Pettersson, *Ber.*, **13**. 1459, 1880 ; *Compt. Rend.*, **91**. 232, 1880 ; O. Hahn, *Zeit. Elektrochem.*, **29**. 189, 1923 ; R. Ruer, *Zeit. anorg. Chem.*, **42**. 87, 1904 ; **43**. 85, 282, 1905 : **46**. 458, 1905 ; E. Tiede and E. Birnbrauer, *ib.*, **87**. 166, 1914 ; F. A. Henglein, *ib.*, **120**. 77, 1921 ; G. H. Smith, *Brit. Pat. No.* 2380, 1862 ; H. Moissan, *Compt. R nd.*, **116**. 1222, 1893 ; F Bourion, *ib.*, **145**. 62, 1907 ; H. Caron, *ib.*, **66**. 850, 1040, 1868 ; H. Landolt, *Zeit. anal. Chem.*, **35**. 714, 1896 ; S. Meyer, *Monatsh*, **20**. 797, 1899 ; C. E. Mendenhall and L. R. Ingersoll, *Phil. Mag.*, (6), **15**. 205, 1908 ; A. Bettendorff, *Liebig's Ann.*, **256**. 167, 1889 ; H. Davy, *Elements of Chemical Philosophy*, London, 1812 ; *Phil. Mag.*, **32**. 203, 1808 ; *Phil. Trans.*, **98**. 333, 1808 ; T. Drummond, *Edin. Journ. Science*, **5**. 319, 1826 ; *Phil. Trans.*, **120**. 383, 1830 ; E. Linnemann, *Sitzber. Akad. Wien*, **92**. 1248, 1886 ; *Monatsh.*, **6**. 531, 899, 1885 ; A. Payen, *Bull. Soc. Enc. Nat. Ind.*, (2), **16**. 602, 1869 ; *Précis de chimie industrielle*, Paris, **2**. 848, 1867 ; W. R. Mott, *Trans. Amer. Electrochem. Soc.*, **34**. 255, 1919 ; G. S. Blake and G. F. H. Smith, *Min. Mag.*, **14**. 378, 1907 ; A. Rosenheim and J. Hertzmann, *Ber.*, **40**. 810, 1907 ; K. Angström, *ib.*, **13**. 1465, 1880 ; L. Bradford, *Chem. Trade Journ.*, **62**. 284, 1918 ; *Metal. Ind.*, **12**. 241, 1918 ; O. Ruff, *Zeit. Elektrochem.*, **30**. 356, 1924 ; O. Ruff and G. Lauschke, *Zeit. anorg. Chem.*, **87**. 198, 1914 ; O. Ruff, H. Sieferheld, and J. Suda, *ib.*, **82**. 373, 1913 ; L. Weiss and E. Neumann, *ib.*, **65**. 248, 1910 ; H. E. Ives, E. F. Kingsbury, and E. Karrer, *Journ. Franklin Inst.*, **186**. 401, 1918 ; W. P. Davey, *Phys. Rev.*, (2), **23**. 763, 1924 ; O Ruff and O. Goecke, *Zeit. angew. Chem.*, **24**. 1459, 1911 ; E. Podszus, *ib.*, **30**. 17, 1917 ; E. L. Nichols and H. L. Howes, *Journ. Amer. Optical Soc.*, **6**. 42, 1922 ; *Phys. Rev.*, (2), **19**. 300, 1922 ; E. L. Nichols and D. T. Wilber, *ib.*, (2), **17**. 269, 707, 1921 ; M. Owen. *Ann. Physik*, (4), **37**. 657, 1912 ; J. Ewles, *Phil. Mag.*, (6), **45**. 957, 1923 ; W. W. Coblentz, *Journ. Franklin. Inst.*, **174**. 549, 1912 ; *Bull. Bur. Standards*, **4**. 533, 1908 ; *Investigations of Infra-red Spectra*, Washington, **7**. 108, 1908 ; E. W. Washburn and E. E. Libman, *Journ. Amer. Cer. Soc.*, **3**. 634, 1920 ; J. Ewles, *Phil. Mag.*, (6), **45**. 957, 1923 ; W. G. Mixter, *Amer. Journ. Science*, (4), **37**. 534, 1914 ; W. G. Mixter and E. S. Dana, *ib.*, (3), **7**. 506, 1874 ; J. W. Draper, *ib.*, (3). **14**. 208, 1877 ; R. Hare, *ib.*, (1), **2**. 292, 1820 ; G. von Hevesy and V. Berglund, *Journ. Chem. Soc.*, **125**. 2372, 1924 ; M. Mayer and B. Havas, *Sprech.*, **44**. 188, 207, 220, 1911 ; R. Lehmann, *Untersuchungen über Zirkonoxyd und seine Verwendung*, München, 1908 ; L. Bradshaw and W. Emery, *Trans. Cer. Soc.*, **19**. 84, 1920 ; V. Bodin, *ib.*, **21**. 44, 1922 ; H. Rose, Pogg. *Ann.*, *ib.*, **107**. 602, 1859 ; J. J. Berzelius, *ib.*, **4**. 117, 1825 ; *Schweigger's Journ.*, **16**. 405, 1816 ; **21**. 40, 1817 ; *Lehrbuch der Chemie*, Dresden, **1**. 841, 1825 ; A. Stansfield, *The Electric Furnace*, New York, 1914 ; J. W. Marden and M. N. Rich, *Journ. Ind. Eng. Chem.*, **12**. 651, 1920 ; *Investigations of Zirconium with Especial Reference to the Metal and the Oxide*, Washington, 20, 1921 ; W. Huggins, *Proc. Roy. Soc.*, **18**. 546, 1870 ; *Pnil. Mag.*, (4), **40**. 302, 1870 ; F. Schröter, *Zeit. tech. Phys.*, **4**. 2, 1923 ; H. J. Spanner, *Ann. Physik*, (4), **75**. 609, 1924 ; A. E. van Arkel, *Physica*, **4**. 286, 1924 ; F. Born, *Zeit. Elektrochem.*, **31**. 309, 1925 ; G. von Hevesy, *Danske Vid. Selv. Medd.*, **7**. 8, 1925 ; *Zeit. anorg. Chem.*, **147**. 217, 1925 ; C. P. Smyth, *Phil. Mag.*, (6), **50**. 361, 1925 ; J. Böhm, *Zeit. anorg. Chem.*, **149**. 217, 1925 ; J. Böhm and H. Niclassen, *ib.*, **132**. 1, 1923 ; P. Hautefeuille and A. Perrey, *Ann. Chim. Phys.*, (6), **21**. 419, 1890 ; *Compt. R nd.*, **107**. 1000, 1888 ; **110**. 1038, 1888 ; L. Ouvrard, *ib.*, **112**. 1444, 1891 ; **113**. 80, 1891 ; W. Florence, *Neues Jahrb. Min.*, ii., 102, 1898 ; A. Knop, *Liebig's Ann.*, **159**. 51, 1871 ; A. Michel-Lévy and L. Bourgeois, *Bull. Soc. Min.*, **5**. 136, 1882 ; *Compt. Rend.*, **94**. 812, 1882 ; F. Henning, *Naturwisse*, **13**. 661, 1925.

⁵ J. J. Berzelius, *Schweigger's Journ.*, **16**. 405, 1816 ; **21**. 40, 1817 ; Pogg. *Ann.*, **4**. 117, 1825 ; F. Wöhler, *ib.*, **48**. 94, 1839 ; H. C. Greenwood, *Journ. Chem. Soc.*, **93**. 1493, 1908 ; S. A. Tucker and H. R. Moody, *ib.*, **81**. 14, 1902 ; G. H. Bailey, *ib.*, **49**. 149, 481, 1886 ; J. N. Pring, *ib.*, **93**. 2101, 1908 ; F. Bourion, *Compt. Rend.*, **145**. 62, 1907 ; A. Rosenheim and J Hertzmann, *Ber.*, **40**. 810, 1907 ; E. Newbery and J. N. Pring, *Proc. Roy. Soc.*, **92**. A, 276, 1916 ; F. P. Venable and T. Clarke, *Journ. Amer. Chem. Soc.*, **18**. 434, 1896 ; F. P. Venable and A. W. Belden, *ib.*, **20**. 119, 1898 ; E. F. Smith and H. B. Harris, *ib.*, **17**. 654, 1895 ; R. Ruer, *Zeit. anorg. Chem.*, **43**. 282, 1905 ; E. Podszus, *Zeit. phys. Chem.*, **92**. 227, 1917 ; H. Davy, *Phil. Mag.*, **32**. 203, 1808 ; *Phil. Trans.*, **98**. 333, 1808 ; J. B. Trommsdorff, *Ann. Chim. Phys.*, (1), **29**. 223, 1798 ; L. E. Barton, *U.S. Pat. No.* 1351091, 1920 ; E. Wedekind and J. Pintsch, *German Pat.*, *D.R.P.* 294267, 1913 ; E. Wedekind, *Zeit. anorg. Chem.*, **45**. 385, 1905 ; *Liebig's Ann.*, **395**. 149, 1912 ; *Zeit. Elektrochem.*, **10**. 331, 1904 ; *Ber.*, **35**. 3929, 1902 ; E. Wedekind and S. J. Lewis, *Zeit. angew. Chem.*, **22**. 725, 1909 ; T. L. Phipson, *Compt. Rend.*, **61**. 745, 1865 ; C. Renz, *Helvetica*

Chim. Acta, **4**. 961, 1921 ; S. Medsforth, *Journ. Chem. Soc.*, **123**. 1452, 1923 ; L. Andrieux, *Ind. Chim.*, **8**. 478, 1922 ; A. Mailhe and F. de Godon, *Bull. Soc. Chim.*, (4), **29**. 101, 1921 ; P. Sabatier and A. Mailhe, *Ann. Chim. Phys.*, (8), **20**. 289, 1910.
    ⁶ J. J. Berzelius, *Schweigger's Journ.*, **21**. 40, 1817 ; Pogg. *Ann.*, **4**. 117, 1825 ; *Ann. Chim. Phys.*, (2), **26**. 43, 1824 ; L. N. Vauquelin, *ib.*, (1), **22**. 179, 1797 ; H. Rheinboldt and E. Wedekind, *Ber.*, **47**. 2142, 1914 ; *Koll. Chem. Beihefte*, **17**. 115, 1923 ; R. Ruer, *Zeit. anorg. Chem.*, **43**. 282, 1905 ; J. M. van Bemmelen, *ib.*, **49**. 125, 1906 ; A. Mandl, *ib.*, **37**. 290, 1903 ; O. Hauser, *ib.*, **45**. 185, 1905 ; W. Müller, *ib.*, **52**. 316, 1907 ; E. Wedekind, *Chem. Ztg.*, **48**. 185, 1924 ; E. Wedekind and H. Wilke, *Koll. Zeit.*, **34**. 83, 1924 ; **35**. 23, 1924 ; E. Schalek and A. Szegvari, *ib.*, **33**. 326, 1923 ; H. Freundlich and E. Schalek, *Zeit. Phys. Chem.*, **108**. 153, 1924 ; M. Adolf and W. Pauli, *Zeit. Koll.*, **29**. 173, 1921 ; W. Pauli, *ib.*, **28**. 49, 1921 ; *Trans. Faraday Soc.*, **16**. 15 (app.), 1921 ; F. P. Venable and A. W. Belden, *Journ. Amer. Chem. Soc.*, **20**. 273, 1898 ; F. P. Venable and T. Clarke, *ib.*, **18**. 434, 1896 ; E. H. Rodd, *Journ. Chem. Soc.*, **111**. 396, 1917 ; S. R. Paykull, *Œfvers. Vet. Akad. För.*, 22, 1873 ; 7, 53, 1878 ; *Bull. Soc. Chim.*, (2), **20**. 65, 1873 ; *Ber.*, **12**. 1719, 1879 ; A. Rosenheim and J. Hertzmann, *ib.*, **40**. 810, 1907 ; W. Biltz, *ib.*, **35**. 4431, 1902 ; **37**. 1095, 1904 ; W. Biltz and W. Geibel, *Gött. Nachr.*, 141, 1906 ; J. B. Hannay, *Journ. Chem. Soc.*, **26**. 703, 1873 ; A. Sjögren, *Pogg. Ann. Ergbd.*, **3**. 465, 1853 ; F. Haber, *Ber.*, **55**. B, 1717, 1922 ; E. Linnemann, *Mon.tsh.*, **6**. 335, 899, 1885 ; *Sitzber. Akad. Wien*, **91**. 1019, 1885 ; B. Szilard, *Journ. Chim. Phys.*, **5**. 488, 640, 1908 ; A. Lottermoser, *Ueber anorganischen Colloide*, Stuttgart, 9, 1901 ; D. E. Melliss, *Bull. Soc. Chim.*, (2), **14**. 204, 1870 ; *Contributions to the Chemistry of Zirconium*, Göttingen, 1870 ; H. Davy, *Phil. Mag.*, **32**. 203, 1808 ; *Phil. Trans.*, **98**. 333, 1808 ; R. Hermann, *Journ. prakt. Chem.*, (1), **31**. 75, 1844 ; (1), **97**. 321, 330, 1866 ; P. Behre, *Ueber einige Adsorptionserscheinungen*, Göttingen, 1908 ; H. Rose, *Pogg. Ann.*, **48**. 575, 1840 ; J. Böhm and H. Niclassen, *Zeit. anorg. Chem.*, **132**. 1, 1923 ; O. Ruff and J. Moczala, *ib.*, **133**. 193, 1924 ; H. T. S. Britton, *Journ. Chem. Soc.*, **125**. 1576, 1924 ; **127**. 2111, 1925 ; **129**. 125, 269, 192 .
    ⁷ P. T. Cleve, *Bull. Soc. Chim.*, (2), **43**. 453, 1885 ; G. H. Bailey, *Journ. Chem. Soc.*, **149**. 481, 1886 ; **58**. 705, 1889 ; *Chem. News*, **53**. 55, 287, 1886 ; **60**. 17, 1889 ; H. Geisow and P. Horkheimer, *Zeit. anorg. Chem.*, **32**. 372, 1902 ; E. Wedekind, *ib.*, **33**. 83, 1903 ; O. Hauser, *ib.*, **45**. 190, 1905 ; L. Pissarjewsky, *ib.*, **25**. 378, 1900 ; **31**. 359, 1903 ; A. Weller, *Ber.*, **15**. 2592, 1882 ; A. Piccini, *Gazz. Chim. Ital.*, **17**. 479, 1887.

§ 8. The Zirconates

Zirconium dioxide, or hydrated zirconium dioxide, is amphoteric in that it acts both as an acid and as a base. There are three main types of zirconium salts : (i) The *normal salts* in which the zirconium behaves as a quadrivalent radicle, in combination with the radicles of the stronger acids. (ii) A series of *basic salts* in which, in the simplest case, the bivalent radicle ZrO, **zirconyl**, acts as a base. These salts can often be regarded as but stages in the progressive hydrolysis of the normal salts. (iii) A series of zirconates or rather **metazirconates** in which zirconyl hydroxide, $ZrO(OH)_2$, acts as an acid, **metazirconic acid,** H_2ZrO_3. There is a tendency for the acid to form poly-zirconates analogous with the poly-silicates, and poly-titanates. The poly-zirconates can be named like the poly-silicates. The *perzirconates* are described in connection with perzirconic acid—*vide supra*.

The alkali zirconates are formed either by adding a soln. of a zirconium salt to alkali-lye, or by melting zirconium oxide with the alkali oxide, hydroxide, carbonate, or chloride, with boric oxide as a flux and *agent minéralisateur*. The products obtained in this manner have not a definite composition and are probably zirconates contaminated with more or less adsorbed base or acid. Both M. E. Chevreul,[1] and P. Berthier stated that when zircon and potassium hydroxide are fused together a *potassium silicozirconate* is produced (*q.v.*) ; L. Ouvrard, and D. E. Melliss also obtained the silicozirconates by fusing zircon with potassium carbonate ; but A. Knop found that when zircon is fused with potassium or sodium carbonate, the corresponding alkali zirconate remains when the cold mass is extracted with water to remove the soluble alkali silicate. L. Ouvrard obtained only crystalline zirconia by this procedure. F. P. Venable and T. Clarke showed that it is not practicable to prepare the potassium zirconates by the action of fused potassium carbonate on zirconia because only 0·5 per cent. dissolved after 10 hrs.' heating— but the amount dissolved must be largely determined by the temp. P. Hautefeuille and J. Margottet found that when potassium carbonate and zirconium phosphate are melted together, and then extracted with water, there remains insoluble potassium zirconate. According to J. J. Berzelius, by melting zirconia with potassium hydroxide, a **potassium zirconate,** insoluble in water and soluble in acids, is formed. F. P. Venable and T. Clarke showed that this zirconate is probably a poly-salt, $K_2O(ZrO_2)_{3\,to\,5}$, because if treated with acetic acid, the insoluble mass corresponds approximately with $K_2O(ZrO_2)_3$, or **potassium paratrizirconate,** $K_2Zr_3O_7$. According to R. Hermann, and F. P. Venable and T. Clarke, the addition of potassium hydroxide to a soln. of a zirconium salt gives a precipitate containing 3 to 4 per cent. of alkali ; F. P. Venable and T. Clarke found that zirconium hydroxide, $ZrO_2.H_2O$, dissolves in a soln. of potassium hydroxide :

KOH per cent.	12	25	33	50
ZrO_2 grms. per litre	0·09	0·75	0·90	2·30

and they accordingly inferred that the soln. contained potassium zirconate. They also found that a definite potassium zirconate is not obtained by fusing a mixture of potassium chloride and zirconia as in T. Hiortdahl's and L. Ouvrard s processes for the alkaline earth zirconates ; but J. J. Berzelius showed that when zirconia is dissolved in fused sodium hydroxide, it is not thereby rendered soluble in water, which merely washes away the excess of alkali ; and that, as in the corresponding case of potassium hydroxide, a **sodium zirconate** appears to be formed because the zirconia is thereby made soluble in acids. W. Gibbs, D. E. Melliss, and L. Bourgeois obtained *sodium silicozirconates* (*q.v.*) by the action of fused sodium carbonate on zircon ; but T. Scheerer could get only sodium zirconate. T. Hiortdahl heated zirconia with sodium carbonate, and measured the amount of carbon dioxide evolved. When equimolar proportions of the two were kept at a dull red heat for 9 hrs., all the available carbon dioxide was evolved, and there remained a crystalline hygroscopic mass which he assumed to be **sodium metazirconate,** Na_2ZrO_3 ; this was decomposed by water yielding sodium hydroxide and an insoluble white mass mainly zirconium oxide. If an excess of sodium carbonate be used, he found that the molar proportions of carbon dioxide evolved per mol. of zirconia were :

	Dull redness.	Bright redness.	Yellow heat.	White heat.
Hours	23	5½	5½	6
$ZrO_2.nCO_2$	1·20	1·41	1·45	1·92

Hence he concluded that **sodium orthozirconate** is formed, $2Na_2O.ZrO_2$, or Na_4ZrO_4. If this product be treated with water, sodium zirconate is obtained in hexagonal plates with a composition approximating $Na_2O.8ZrO_2.12H_2O$. Similar results were obtained when zircon was fused with an excess of sodium carbonate. R. Hermann, and T. Scheerer concluded that sodium zirconate is formed when a mixture of zircon and sodium carbonate is fused, and the cold mass extracted with water. By a similar process, A. Michel-Lévy and L. Bourgeois obtained rhombohedral plates of sodium zirconate accompanied by much crystallized zirconia. F. P. Venable and T. Clarke found that when zirconia is added to clear melted sodium carbonate, it sinks to the bottom and remains unattacked for hours. After leaching the cold fused mass with water, and treatment with dil. hydrochloric acid, the product contained soda and zirconia in the molar proportions $Na_2O : ZrO = 2 : 3$; and in another case, where the fusion occupied twice as long, the ratio was 3 : 2. When sodium hydroxide was fused in place of the carbonate, a much larger proportion of zirconia took part in the reaction.

According to L. Ouvrard, when a mixture of lithium chloride and zircon or zirconia is fused for some hours, and the mass extracted with water, prismatic crystals with a longitudinal extinction, and the composition of **lithium metazirconate,** Li_2ZrO_3, are formed. F. P. Venable and T. Clarke add that the mixture must be kept at a high temp., because with an ordinary fusion there is very little action. So also when lithium carbonate and zirconia are fused together, carbon dioxide is evolved, and zirconia crystallizes from the melt. F. P. Venable and C. Baskerville melted a mixture of zirconia and lithium hydroxide, and after extracting the mass with water and acetic acid obtained a residue corresponding with **lithium mesodizirconate,** $Li_2Zr_2O_5$. It is noteworthy that while the alkalies soda and potash have a great tendency to form polyzirconates, the alkaline earths gave the normal metazirconates ; and lithium oxide represents a kind of transition between the alkalies and alkaline earths.

According to P. Berthier, when a mixed soln. of cupric and zirconium salts is treated with ammonia, the precipitate of the zirconium hydroxide carries down with it cupric hydroxide which cannot be extracted by ammonia. The sky-blue precipitate becomes emerald-green on ignition. The precipitate gives up most of its cupric oxide to ammonium carbonate soln., but not to oxalic or acetic acid. There is nothing to show that a *copper zirconate* is formed.

L. B. G. de Morveau obtained a coherent mass by igniting a mixture of zirconia and calcium oxide. According to T. Hjortdahl, a crystalline powder of an acid calcium zirconate is formed when a mixture of calcium chloride in excess and zircon, or zirconia and silica, is heated for 5 or 6 hrs. at bright redness, and the cold product washed with dil. hydrochloric acid. L. Ouvrard obtained **calcium metazirconate,** $CaZrO_3$, by heating a mixture of zirconia and fused calcium chloride for 20 to 30 hrs. After leaching with water, a crystalline mass remained. G. Tammann gave 950° for the temp. of formation. F. P. Venable and T. Clarke found that the reaction during the fusion occurs only after calcium oxide has been formed ; and they obtained the same compound by heating a mixture of zirconia and calcium oxide for many hours, and washing the product with dil. acetic acid. The crystals found by L. Ouvrard have a marked action on polarized light and appeared to be isomorphous with calcium metastannate and perowskite or calcium metatitanate. L. Ouvrard prepared **strontium metazirconate,** $SrZrO_3$, by fusing zirconia and strontium chloride ; the reaction is not so easily inaugurated as in the case of calcium metazirconate. F. P. Venable and T. Clarke made it by heating a mixture of zirconia and strontium oxide, leaching the product with dil. acetic acid. The crystals resemble those of the calcium salt, and are quite soluble in dil. hydrochloric acid. L. Ouvrard, and F. P. Venable and T. Clarke made **barium metazirconate,** $BaZrO_3$, by processes analogous to those they employed for the strontium and calcium salts. The properties were similar. G. Tammann gave 300° for the temp. of formation. J. A. Hedvall and N. von Zweigbergk could not make barium zirconate by heating a mixture of zirconia and barium dioxide.

According to T. Hiortdahl, if a mixture of silica, zirconia, ammonium chloride, and an excess of magnesium chloride be fused at a white heat for an hour, a mass of hemihedral crystals of periclase, and prismatic crystals of **magnesium metazirconate,** $MgZrO_3$, are formed ; and they are isolated by leaching the cold cake with water. L. Bourgeois also described the preparation of this salt. F. P. Venable and T. Clarke obtained the prismatic crystals by heating a mixture of zirconia and four times its weight of magnesia, and leaching the mass with dil. acetic acid. G. Tammann gave 980° for the temp. of formation of **zinc zirconate,** $ZnZrO_3$; and 700°, for that of **lead zirconate,** $PbZrO_3$.

L. B. G. de Morveau fused together a mixture of alumina and zirconia. K. von Chroustchoff heated in a closed steel tube a mixture of gelatinous silica, gelatinous alumina, and gelatinous zirconium hydroxide. It was subjected to a gradually increasing heat for six days, and allowed to cool. The residue in the crucible was then found to consist of a white powder. in part distinctly crystalline. The crystals exhibited, under the microscope, hexagonal forms, and had a sp. gr. of 2 87. The analysis corresponds with $2Al_2O_3.ZrO_2.8SiO_2.4H_2O$; and K. von Chroustchoff likens it to a *zirconopyrophyllite.*

A black or dark brown mineral found associated with baddeleyite at Jacupiranga, Brazil, was named by E. Hussak and G. T. Prior [2] zirkelite—after F. Zirkel—although the same name had been previously applied to a rock by M. E. Wadsworth. The analysis

ZrO_2	TiO_2	ThO_2	Ce_2O_3	Y_2O_3	UO_2	FeO	CaO	MgO	Ignition
52·89	14·95	7·31	2·52	0·21	1·40	7·72	10·79	0·22	1·02

corresponds with $(Ca,Fe)O.2(Zr,Ti,Th)O_2$. In the idealized case the mineral is a calcium ferrous mesozirconate, $Ca,FeZr_2O_5$. The octahedral crystals belong to the cubic system, but G. S. Blake and G. F. H. Smith described the zirkelite crystals from Walaweduwa, Ceylon, as being probably hexagonal with $a : c = 1 : 1·1647$, and suggest that the Brazilian crystals are probably hexagonal or rhombohedral rather than cubic. P. Groth, and O. Hauser consider that like titanite a cubic modification is produced by melting the mineral. E. Hussak and G. T. Prior said that the crystals exhibit polysynthetic twinning ; spinel twinning ; and fourlings. The crystals are flattened and striated. There is no visible cleavage. The sp. gr. of Brazilian zirkelite is 4·706 to 4·741, and of the Singalese, 4·72 to 5·22. The hardness is 5·5 to 6·0.

O. Hauser found a black or dark brown mineral on the shore of Magad Lake, East Africa, and called it uhligite. This analysis corresponds with $3·3Ca(Zr,Ti)_2O_5,Al(Ti,Al)O_5$. It is related to zirkelite. The crystals belong to the cubic system ; the habit is octahedral ; and the cleavage cubic and imperfect.

REFERENCES.

[1] L. B. G. de Morveau, *Ann. Chim. Phys.*, (1), **21**. 72, 1797 ; M. E. Chevreul, *ib.*, (2), **13**. 245, 1820 ; P. Berthier, *ib.*, (2), **50**. 362, 1832 ; (2), **59**. 190, 1835 ; D. E. Melliss, *Bull. Soc. Chim.*, (2), **14**. 204, 1870 ; *Contributions to the Chemistry of Zirconium*, Göttingen, 1870 ; L. Bourgeois, *Bull. Soc. Philomath.*, (7), **8**. 50, 1884 ; *Reproduction artificielle des minéraux*, Paris, 137, 1884 ; W. Gibbs, *Pogg. Ann.*, **71**. 559, 1847 ; A. Knop, *Liebig's Ann.*, **159**. 44, 1871 ; L. Ouvrard, *Compt. Rend.*, **112**. 1444, 1891 ; **113**. 80, 1891 ; P. Hautefeuille and J. Margottet, *ib.*, **102**. 1017, 1886 ; A. Michel-Lévy and L. Bourgeois, *ib.*, **94**. 812, 1882 ; T. Hicrtdahl, *ib.*, **61**. 175, 213, 1865 ; F. P. Venable and T. Clarke, *Journ. Amer. Chem. Soc.*, **18**. 434, 1896 ; F. P. Venable and C. Baskerville, *ib.*, **17**. 448, 1895 ; **19**. 12, 1897 ; **20**. 321, 1898 ; J. J. Berzelius, *Pogg. Ann.*, **4**. 117, 1825 ; *Schweigger's Journ.*, **21**. 40, 1817 ; *Œfvers. Akad. Förh. Stockholm*, 295, 1824 ; R. Hermann, *Journ. prakt. Chem.*, (1), **31**, 75, 1844 ; T. Scheerer, *Pogg. Ann.*, **59**. 481, 1843 ; J. A. Hedvall and N. von Zweigbergk, *Zeit. anorg. Chem.*, **108**. 119, 1919 ; G. Tammann, *ib.*, **149**. 68, 1925 ; K. von Chroustchoff, *Bull. Acad. St. Petersburg*, (3), **35**. 343, 1892.

[2] E. Hussak, *Tschermak's Mitt.*, (2), **14**. 408, 1894 ; E. Hussak and G. T. Prior, *Min. Mag.*, **11**. 86, 1895 ; G. T. Prior, *ib.*, **11**. 180, 1897 ; G. S. Blake and G. F. H. Smith, *ib.*, **16**. 309, 1913 ; M. E. Wadsworth, *Amer. Journ. Science*, (4), **5**. 153, 1898 ; O. Hauser, *Zeit. anorg. Chem.*, **63**. 340, 1909 ; P. Groth, *Tableau systématique des minéraux*, Genève, 160, 1904.

§ 9. Zirconium Fluoride, and the Fluozirconates

According to J. J. Berzelius,[1] hydrofluoric acid dissolves zirconia until the liquid no longer has an acid taste. The soln. furnishes a crystalline salt when evaporated, and the product is resolved by water into a soluble acidic salt, and an insoluble basic salt. When the soln. is boiled, there is a further deposition of basic salt, and the liquid becomes still more acid. This description refers to **trihydrated zirconium fluoride,** $ZrF_4.3H_2O$; and it was made by J. C. G. de Marignac by heating ammonium fluozirconate to drive off the ammonium fluoride, dissolving the residue in hydrofluoric acid, and evaporating the soln. for crystallization. Anhydrous zirconium tetrafluoride, ZrF_4, was made by H. St. C. Deville by passing hydrogen chloride over a mixture of zircon and calcium fluoride contained in a carbon boat in a carbon tube heated to whiteness ; and H. St. C. Deville and H. Caron made it by passing hydrogen fluoride over zircon heated to whiteness as before. J. C. G. de Marignac, and J. Missenden made it by heating a mixture of zirconium dioxide with twice its weight of ammonium fluoride, or hydrofluoride. This method, said L. Wolter, has the disadvantage that this substance volatilizes more readily than it attacks the zirconium dioxide. This, however, can be overcome by using, instead of ammonium hydrofluoride, ammonium fluozirconate, $ZrF_4.2NH_4F$, which is readily prepared in a pure state by evaporating zirconium dioxide with excess of silica-free hydrogen fluoride and ammonia, and subliming the product in a platinum tube in a current of nitrogen. He found that theoretical yields of zirconium tetrafluoride of a high degree of purity are obtained by the action of anhydrous hydrogen fluoride on zirconium tetrachloride, the change readily taking place in accordance with the equation $ZrCl_4+4HF=ZrF_4+4HCl$.

L. Wolter's product was snow-white and crystalline ; and when sublimed, zirconium tetrafluoride forms small, strongly refracting, prismatic crystals with slightly curved facets. H. St. C. Deville said that the crystals probably belong to the hexagonal system. L. Wolter found the sp. gr. to be 4·4333 at 16°. The salt was found by H. St. C. Deville to be volatile. This agrees with E. Wedekind's observation that in analytical work, when a mixture of zirconia and silica is ignited with hydrofluoric acid to remove silica, some zirconium is lost by volatilization as fluoride. The loss is prevented by using a mixture of hydrofluoric acid and an excess of sulphuric acid. L. Wolter showed that the vap. density of zirconium tetrafluoride, 166·1, is in agreement with 166·7 calculated for the mol. wt. of ZrF_4. Zirconium tetrafluoride was stated by H. St. C. Deville to be insoluble in water, and acids ; but L. Wolter said that, unlike the other members of the carbon family, zirconium tetrafluoride is only sparingly soluble in water, 100 c.c. of water dissolve 1·388 grms. of the tetrafluoride, and he added that there is no sign of hydrolysis. When the aq. soln. is warmed to 50°, the trihydrate, $ZrF_4.3H_2O$, is precipitated, and no other hydrate or oxyfluoride was formed. With liquid ammonia, zirconium tetrafluoride forms a white powder of **zirconium hemipentitammino-tetrafluoride,** $5ZrF_4.2NH_3$, whilst with gaseous ammonia, pyridine, hydrogen sulphide, etc., practically no change takes place. It is suggested that the inactivity of the zirconium tetrafluoride compared with other members of the group is perhaps due to its small mol. vol.: TiF_4, 44·3 ; ZrF_4, 37·5 ; SnF_4, 40·7 It is assumed that with zirconium tetrafluoride the same number of atoms are condensed to a smaller vol., and hence the atoms have less freedom of motion. Zirconium tetrafluoride forms numerous complex salts with the metal fluorides, the so-called **fluozirconates,** R_2ZrF_6 ; but there are many fluozirconates more complex than this, the normal type.

The crystals of trihydrated zirconium tetrafluoride were found by J. C. G. de Marignac to be prismatic or tabular, and to belong to the triclinic pinacoidal system, having the axial ratios $a:b:c=0.7636:1:0.6390$, and $\alpha=104° 48'$; $\beta=110° 59'$; and $\gamma=103° 53'$. When heated, the crystals lose water and hydrogen fluoride, and even at a temp. below redness, furnish zirconia. According to E. A. Demarçay, ammonia precipitates only part of the zirconium as hydroxide in the presence of ammonium fluoride ; and when ammonia is added to the aq. soln., J. C. G. de Marignac said that part of the zirconium is precipitated as hydroxide, and part as a basic salt. J. J. Berzelius' observations on the hydrolysis of the aq. soln. of zirconium tetrafluoride are not in agreement with those of L. Wolter ; E. Chauvenet goes further, and argues the fact that the alleged trihydrate can be redissolved and recrystallized from water time and again is no proof that the hydrolysis does not occur ; he believed that the so-called trihydrate, $ZrF_4.3H_2O$, is really a hydrate of an acid zirconyl fluoride, namely, **dihydrated zirconyl dihydrofluoride,** $ZrOF_2.2HF.2H_2O$. He said that the salt is stable in air and in vacuo, but begins to lose water at 100° ; at 140°, in dry air, it loses two mols. of water, giving the anhydrous acid fluoride, which, when heated above 140° in air, loses two mols. of hydrogen fluoride, giving **zirconyl fluoride,** $ZrOF_2$; this, when cold, reabsorbs two mols. of hydrogen fluoride. The anhydrous normal zirconyl fluoride may also be obtained by crystallizing the hydrated acid fluoride from dil. aq. soln. and drying the **dihydrated zirconyl fluoride,** $ZrOF_2.2H_2O$, at 120°. If the anhydrous or hydrated acid fluoride is heated at 200° in an atm. of hydrogen fluoride, zirconium fluoride, ZrF_4, is obtained, which, in the cold, absorbs hydrogen fluoride, probably to form **hydrofluozirconic acid,** H_2ZrF_6. When dried and calcined, the salt furnishes zirconia.

According to H. L. Wells and H. W. Foote, the complex fluorides with fluorides of the alkali metals of small at. wt. give types with a relatively larger number of mols. of the alkali fluorides, while those of larger at. wt. give complex fluorides with a larger proportion of zirconium fluoride. This is illustrated by the following summary of the complex salts with the univalent radicles :

						4:1	3:1	5:2	2:1	5:3	1:1	2:3
Li	•	•	•	•	•	Li	—	—	Li	—	—	—
Na	•	•	•	•	•	—	—	Na	Na	—	—	—
K	•	•	•	•	•	—	K	—	K	—	K	—
Rb	•	•	•	•	•	—	Rb	—	Rb	—	—	—
Cs	•	•	•	•	•	—	—	—	Cs	—	Cs	Cs
NH_4	•	•	•	•	•	—	NH_4	—	NH_4	—	—	—
Tl	•	•	•	•	•	—	Tl	—	—	Tl	Tl	—

J. C. G. de Marignac found that when a mixed soln. of ammonium and zirconium tetrafluoride is evaporated, rhombic bipyramidal crystals of **ammonium fluozirconate,** $(NH_4)_2ZrF_6$, separate in the earlier stages of the evaporation; and in the later stages thin, tabular, hexagonal crystals appear. The salt is therefore dimorphous. The rhombic crystals have the axial ratios $a : b : c = 0.5739 : 1 : 0.6590$, and are isomorphous with those of the corresponding potassium salt. The hexagonal crystals were stated by B. Gossner to have a perfect cleavage parallel to the c-axis, and to have a feebly negative optical character. Ammonium fluozirconate is not changed when heated to 100°, but at a higher temp., ammonium fluoride is evolved, and zirconium tetrafluoride remains. G. von Hevesy and co-workers found the solubility of ammonium hexafluozirconate in water to be :

	0°	20°	45°	90°
Mols NH_3 per litre	1·226	2·115	3·680	5·93
Mols Zr per litre	0·611	1·050	1·842	2·96

The sp. gr. of the soln. at 20° is 1·154. This fluozirconate is decomposed when heated with sulphuric acid. J. C. G. de Marignac obtained another complex salt, **ammonium heptafluozirconate,** $3NH_4F.ZrF_4$, or $(NH_4)_3ZrF_7$, by evaporating a soln. of zirconium tetrafluoride containing a large excess of ammonium fluoride G. von Hevesy gave for the refractive index of the octahedral crystals of ammonium heptafluozirconate, 1·433. The regular octahedral crystals are not changed when heated to 100°. O. Hassel and H. Mark studied the X-radiogram of the salt, and found the unit cubic cell has a side of 9·35 A., and contains 4 mols. The salt is isomorphous with the corresponding hafnium compound. These two ammonium fluozirconates have compositions analogous with those of the two ammonium fluotitanates; but the salts are not isomorphous. G. von Hevesy and co-workers found the solubility of ammonium heptafluozirconate in water to be represented at 0°, by 1·230 and 0·425 mols respectively of NH_3 and Zr per litre; at 20°, by 1·756 and 1·588 mols.; and at 45°, by 2·357 and 0·788 mols. The sp. gr. of the soln. at 20° is 1·086. For a litre of soln. of the heptafluozirconate in ammonium fluoride at 20° :

Mols NH_4F	Mol NH_3	Mol Zr	Sp. gr.
0·002	1·655	0·551	1·086
0·462	1·125	0·375	—
0·966	0·726	0·242	—
1·941	0·292	0·0942	—
4·872	0·0678	0·0226	1·068
9·721	0·0515	0·01716	1·105

The results for mixed soln. of ammonium hexa- and hepta-fluozirconate in water at 20° are plotted in Fig. 5. The solid phases are indicated in the diagram. Comparisons of the solubilities of the two ammonium fluozirconates with the corresponding ammonium fluohafniates are shown in Figs. 1 and 3 in the next chapter on hafnium. M. M. Windsor prepared double fluorides with aniline, brucine, cinchonine, quinine, quinidine, and strychnine.

H. L. Wells and H. W. Foote made **lithium fluozirconate,** Li_2ZrF_6, by mixing soln. containing 0·7 to 2·0 grms. of lithium fluoride and 20 grms. of zirconium tetrafluoride. The hexagonal crystals show the prism and pyramid, and rarely the basal plane. These investigators also mixed soln. containing 5 to 7 grms. of lithium fluoride and 20 grms. of zirconium tetrafluoride, and obtained ill-defined crystals of **lithium octofluozirconate,** $4LiF.ZrF_4.\frac{2}{3}H_2O$. The lithium fluoride has a low solubility, and it was not possible sufficiently to concentrate soln. to obtain the double salt of a high degree of purity either with hot or cold soln. One crop of crystals contained both the 2 : 1 and the 4 : 1 salts, showing that there is probably no intermediate salt. The salt is decomposed by water, and the soln. furnishes lithium fluoride. Normal **sodium fluozirconate,** Na_2ZrF_6, was also obtained in very minute crystals of hexagonal outline by mixing 1 to 2 parts of sodium fluoride with 14 parts of zirconium tetrafluoride. The salt decomposes when the attempt is made to recrystallize it from water. The analysis indicated 0·50 to 1·96 per cent. of water "probably mechanically included" in the crystals. J. C. G. de Marignac prepared **sodium tridecafluodizirconate,** $5NaF.2ZrF_4$, by double decomposition of sodium chloride and ammonium fluozirconate, or by mixing soln. of the component salts under widely varying conditions. The salt can be recrystallized from water. The crystals were said to be monoclinic prisms with axial ratios $a:b:c$ $=2·108:1:1·516$, and $\beta=97°$ 13'. The crystals show twinning. H. L. Wells and H. W. Foote reported that the crystals resemble those of olivine, and the habit appears to be rhombic consisting usually of stout prisms made up of two prismatic planes terminated by a steep brachydome; less frequently the front pinacoid is broadly developed and the prisms are small. The optic axial angle is large, and the birefringence small. J. C. G. de Marignac found that the crystals suffer no loss in weight at a red heat; and that 100 parts of water at 18° dissolve 0·387 part of salt; and at 100°, 1·67 parts of salt.

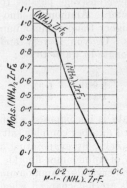

FIG. 5.—The Mutual Solubilities of Ammonium Hexa- and Hepta-fluozirconates.

J. J. Berzelius prepared **potassium pentafluozirconate,** $KF.ZrF_4.H_2O$, by adding a conc. soln. of potassium fluoride to an excess of one of zirconium tetrafluoride; and, as emphasized by J. C. G. de Marignac, it is decomposed in aq. soln. forming the normal salt. The pentafluozirconate furnishes monoclinic prisms. The aq. soln. does not effervesce when treated with ammonium carbonate. The water of crystallization is lost at 100°. The salt is considered by E. Chauvenet to be **potassium zirconyl dihydropentafluoride,** $KF.ZrOF_2.H_2F_2$. H. L. Wells and H. W. Foote obtained monoclinic crystals of **cæsium pentafluozirconate,** $CsF.ZrF_4.H_2O$, from mixtures containing approximately equimolar proportions of the component salts. The complex salt can be recrystallized from water without change. As just indicated, the salt obtained by the recrystallization of the product of the action of potassium fluoride on an excess of zirconium tetrafluoride is normal **potassium fluozirconate,** K_2ZrF_6. J. C. G. de Marignac obtained the same salt from eq. parts of a soln. of the component salts. J. Missenden made impure potassium fluozirconate by fusing together potassium hydrofluoride and hyacinth, $ZrSiO_4$. The rhombic bipyramidal crystals had the axial ratios $a:b:c=0·5717:1:0·6063$. D. E. Kerr-Lawson said that the crystals are monoclinic, not rhombic, and have the axial ratios $a:b:c=0·5731:1:0·6971$, and $\beta=89°$ 40'. G. von Hevesy gave 1·466 for the maximum, and 1·455 for the minimum refractive index of potassium hexafluozirconate. J. J. Berzelius said that the salt can be heated to redness without loss of weight, and J. C. G. de Marignac that at a red heat, in moist air, hydrogen fluoride is evolved. The salt is sparingly soluble in cold water, and abundantly soluble in hot water. J. Missenden gave for the solubility of potassium fluozirconate expressed in S parts of salt per 100 parts of water:

	10°	20°	30°	40°	50°	60°	70°	80°	90°	100°
S	1·22	1·55	1·92	2·37	2·94	3·81	5·06	6·90	11·11	23·53

G. von Hevesy and co-workers found the solubility of potassium hexafluozirconate in $0·125N$-HF, and $5·89N$-HF to be respectively 0·0655 and 0·1297 mol per litre at 20°—*vide* hafnium. On cooling a boiling conc. soln., a mass of acicular crystals is deposited, but less conc. soln. when cooled slowly furnish ill-defined crystals. According to J. J. Berzelius, when a fluozirconate heated with potassium, zirconium is formed. J. C. G. de Marignac found that 100 c.c. of water at 0° dissolve 0·781 grm. of the salt; 1·41 grms. at 15°; 1·69 grms. at 10°; and 25 grms.

at 100°. H. Behrens made rectangular prismatic crystals of normal **rubidium fluozirconate,** Rb_2ZrF_6, by adding rubidium chloride to a soln. of zirconium sulphate mixed with ammonium fluoride and hydrofluoric acid. H. L. Wells and H. W. Foote made normal **cæsium fluozirconate,** Cs_2ZrF_6, by mixing a soln. of zirconium tetrafluoride with an excess of one of cæsium fluoride. The salt can be recrystallized from water without change; and it furnishes hexagonal plates with a negative birefringence. According to J. J. Berzelius, if zirconium tetrafluoride be mixed with an excess of potassium fluoride, a salt corresponding with **potassium heptafluozirconate,** $3KF.ZrF_4$, is formed. This salt was also made by H. Behrens. According to J. C. G. de Marignac, the small octahedral crystals belong to the cubic system. G. von Hevesy gave 1·433 for the refractive index. There is no double refraction. The crystals decrepitate when heated; but if powdered and dried, there is no loss of weight at a red heat. H. Behrens made **rubidium heptafluozirconate,** $3RbF.ZrF_4$, in a similar manner, and obtained strongly refracting, octahedral crystals which were used for the micro-detection of rubidium or zirconium. According to H. L. Wells and H. W. Foote, when a large excess of a soln. of zirconium tetrafluoride is mixed with one of cæsium fluoride, small, sparingly soluble crystals were formed with the composition of **cæsium tetradecafluotrizirconate,** $2CsF.3ZrF_4.2H_2O$. The crystals acted on polarized light; and when the aq. soln. was crystallized, the pentafluozirconate was formed. E. Chauvenet represented the salt as $Cs_2ZrF_6.2(ZrOF_2.H_2F_2)$. J. C. G. de Marignac obtained prismatic crystals of **cupric tetradecafluodizirconate,** $3CuF_2.2ZrF_4.16H_2O$, by evaporating a mixed soln. of cupric and zirconium fluorides containing an excess of the latter. The monoclinic crystals have the axial ratios $a:b:c=1·0798:1:1·0337$, and $\beta=91°\ 46'$. The salt crystallizes unchanged from its aq. soln. During the evaporation of the soln., a pale blue crust is formed. This is very sparingly soluble in water, and is supposed to be zirconium fluoride impregnated with the copper salt. If a soln. of the salt be treated with cupric fluoride, monoclinic prisms of **cupric octofluozirconate,** $2CuF_2.ZrF_4.12H_2O$, are formed, having the axial ratios $a:b:c=1·255:1:1·661$, and $\beta=121°\ 17'$. The crystals are said to be isomorphous with the corresponding zinc and nickel salts. The salt dissolves in cold water, and when boiled it deposits a cupric fluoride, and the clear liquid then furnishes crystals of the preceding salt.

J. C. G. de Marignac did not succeed in preparing a well-defined **calcium fluozirconate.** When calcium carbonate was added to an acid soln. of zirconium fluoride, an insoluble precipitate was obtained; and this was assumed to be a mixture of the fluozirconate and zirconium fluoride. Analogous remarks apply to **strontium fluozirconate** and to **barium fluozirconate.** When barium chloride was added to a soln. of potassium fluozirconate, a precipitate with the composition $3BaF_4.2ZrF_4.2H_2O$, **barium tetradecafluozirconate,** was formed, but whether it is a chemical individual, or a mixture of the normal salt, $BaZrF_6$, with barium fluoride, has not been established.

J. C. G. de Marignac added magnesia to an acid soln. of zirconium fluoride, and obtained a precipitate which proved to be a mixture of magnesium fluoride and **magnesium fluozirconate,** $MgZrF_6.5H_2O$. A soln. of magnesium and zirconium fluorides, on evaporation, deposits small, six-sided, monoclinic plates with curved faces, and these crystals were said to be isomorphous with those of the corresponding salt of manganese. When calcined the salt is decomposed, furnishing a mixture of zirconia and magnesia. J. C. G. de Marignac prepared crystals of **zinc fluozirconate,** $ZnZrF_6.6H_2O$, from a soln. of the component fluorides. The long, hexagonal, prismatic crystals terminate in rhombodedra; they belong to the triclinic system; and have the axial ratio $a:c=1:0·5176$. The cleavage along the hexagonal faces is perfect. The crystals are isomorphous with those of the corresponding fluostannate, fluosilicate, chlorostannate, and chloroplatinate. B. Gossner gave 2·258 for the sp. gr. J. C. G. de Marignac added that when roasted, zirconia and zinc oxide are formed, and conc. hydrochloric acid extracts but imperfectly the zinc oxide from the residue. The corresponding salt of cadmium was not obtained. If a mixed soln. of zinc and zirconium fluorides contains an excess of the former component, crystals of zinc octofluozirconate, $2ZnF_2.ZrF_4.12H_2O$, were formed in monoclinic prisms usually twinned, and with the axial ratios $a:b:c=1.220:1:1.644$, and $\beta=119°\ 31'$. The crystals are isomorphous with those of the corresponding salt of nickel. The salt is readily soluble in cold water, but is decomposed by boiling water with the deposition of zinc fluoride. The corresponding **cadmium octofluozirconate**, $2CdF_2.ZrF_4.6H_2O$, was obtained in a similar manner in monoclinic prisms with axial ratios $a:b:c=1.1384:1:0.838$, and $\beta=119°\ 43'$. The crystals are isomorphous with the corresponding salt of manganese. The salt can be recrystallized from water without change. Soln. of cadmium and zirconium fluorides with an excess of the latter component furnish lamellated crystals of **cadmium decafluodizirconate**, $CdF_2.2ZrF_4.6H_2O$.

H. L. Wells and H. W. Foote found that anhydrous **thallous pentafluozirconate**, $TlF.ZrF_4$, is obtained in minute square plates from a mixed soln. of one part of thallous fluoride and 3–4 parts of zirconium tetrafluoride by evaporating until crystals begin to form and then cooling. If the soln. be cooled before precipitation occurs, the hydrated salt, $TlF.ZrF_4.H_2O$, is formed. The salt may be $TlF.ZrOF_2.H_2F_2$. The aq. soln. on crystallization furnishes needle-like crystals of **thallous heptadecafluotrizirconate**, $5TlF.3ZrF_4,H_2O$; and the same salt is produced from a mixture of 1–3.5 parts of thallous fluoride and one of zirconium tetrafluoride; if four parts of thallous fluoride are employed, the habit of the crystals changes to prisms with hexagonal outlines which are twinned like the hexagonal shaped crystals of aragonite. Both forms give acicular crystals from their aq. soln. This salt may be $TlF.2Tl_2ZrF_6.ZrOF_2.H_2F_2$. It was also found that aq. soln. containing 4–20 parts of thallous fluoride to one of zirconium fluoride furnish brilliant octahedral crystals of **thallous heptafluozirconate**, $3TlF.ZrF_4$. The salt recrystallizes from its aq. soln. without change.

J. C. G. de Marignac added manganese carbonate to a soln. of zirconium tetrafluoride in hydrofluoric acid, and obtained from the liquid monoclinic prisms of **manganese fluozirconate**, $MnZrF_6.5H_2O$, and the axial ratios $a:b:c=2.090:1:1.184$, and $\beta=123°\ 10'$. The cleavage is imperfect. The crystals sometimes have a tabular habit, and show twinning, and they are isomorphous with the corresponding magnesium salt. The salt is decomposed by sulphuric acid; and when heated, it furnishes a mixture of zirconia, and manganese oxide. J. C. G. de Marignac also made **manganese octofluozirconate**, $2MnF_2.ZrF_4.6H_2O$, from a soln. of the component salts containing an excess of manganese fluoride. The short thick prisms belong to the monoclinic system and have the axial ratios $a:b:c=1.3710:1:0.8362$, and $\beta=118°\ 41'$. The cleavage is perfect. The salt dissolves in cold water without decomposition, and the soln. can be boiled without becoming turbid, but if boiling water be poured directly on the crystals, they are decomposed with the separation of manganese fluoride, and the clear liquid, on evaporation, furnishes the normal fluozirconate. J. C. G. de Marignac prepared **nickel fluozirconate**, $NiZrF_6.6H_2O$, by evaporating a mixed soln. of the component salts. The green thick prisms belong to the trigonal system, and have the axial ratio $a:c=1:0.5176$, and are isomorphous with the corresponding fluosilicate and fluostannate, and with zinc fluozirconate. The cleavage is complete. When roasted, zirconia and nickel oxide are formed. If the mixed soln. of the component salts contains hydrofluoric acid and an excess of nickel fluoride, emerald-green prisms of **nickel octofluozirconate**, $2NiF_2.ZrF_4.12H_2O$, are formed. They belong to the monoclinic system, and have the axial ratios $a:b:c=1.2110:1:1.6265$, and $\beta=119°\ 10'$. The crystals generally show twinning or trilling. The salt dissolves in cold water without change, and if the aq. soln. is boiled, the soln. deposits some nickel fluoride. Mixed hot soln. of nickel and potassium fluozirconates at first deposit needle-like crystals of ordinary potassium fluozirconate; these are gradually redissolved and pale green prisms of the triple salt, **potassium nickel fluozirconate.**

$K_2Ni(ZrF_6)_2.8H_2O$, appear. The salt is sparingly soluble in water, and is deposited almost quantitatively from a mixture of eq. proportions of soln. of the component salts. The monoclinic crystals have the axial ratios $a:b:c$ =0·6589 : 1 : 1·1789, and β=95° 40'. The habit of the crystals is very variable. No water is lost at 100°, but at a higher temp., hydrogen fluoride is given off.

REFERENCES.

[1] J. J. Berzelius, *Œfvers. Akad. Förh. Stockholm*, 295, 1824; *Pogg. Ann.*, 4. 117, 1825; *Ann. Chim. Phys.*, (2), 26. 43, 1824; J. C. G. de Marignac, *ib.*, 60. 257, 1860; H. St. C. Deville, *ib.*, (3), 49. 84, 1857; H. St. C. Deville and H. Caron, *ib.*, (4), 5. 109, 1865; H. Behrens, *Microchemische Analyse*, Leipzig, 113, 1901; L. Wolter, *Chem. Ztg.*, 32. 606, 1908; O. Ruff and W. Plato, *Ber.*, 36. 1777, 1903; 37. 673, 1904; E. Wedekind, *ib.*, 44. 1753, 1911; E. A. Demarçay, *Compt. Rend.*, 100. 740, 1885; E. Chauvenet, *ib.*, 164. 727, 1916; *Ann. Chim. Phys.*, (9), 13. 59, 1920; B. Gossner, *Zeit. Kryst.*, 38. 147, 1904; P. Groth, *Chemische Krystallographie*, Leipzig, 1. 253, 1906; J. Missenden, *Chem. News*, 124. 327, 1922; H. L. Wells and H. W. Foote, *Amer. Journ. Science*, (4), 3. 461, 1897; *Zeit. anorg. Chem.*, 10. 434, 1895; G. von Hevesy, J. A. Christiensen, and V. Berglund, *ib.*, 144. 69, 1925; O. Hassel and H. Mark, *Zeit. Physik*, 27. 89, 1924; G. von Hevesy, *Danske Vid. Selsk. Medd.*, 7. 8, 1925; M. M. Windsor, *Journ. Amer. Chem. Soc.*, 48. 310, 1926; D. E. Kerr-Lawson, *Univ. Toronto Geol. Stud.*, 20. 63, 1925.

§ 10. Zirconium Chlorides and Chlorozirconates

O. Ruff and R. Wallstein [1] reduced zirconium tetrachloride by aluminium, magnesium, zinc, mercury, arsenic, and tin, and found that aluminium chloride acts as a stimulant. The product of the reduction at 250°–300° is **zirconium trichloride,** $ZrCl_3$, which is a brown solid at ordinary temp., and is converted into **zirconium dichloride,** $ZrCl_2$, and the tetrachloride: $2ZrCl_3=ZrCl_2+ZrCl_4$, above 330°; and when the dichloride is heated above 600°, zirconium and zirconium tetrachloride are formed: $2ZrCl_2=Zr+ZrCl_4$. J. J. Berzelius reported that when amorphous zirconium is gently heated in chlorine gas, it takes fire and burns, forming a white substance which does not volatilize. Subsequent investigations showed that the presence of moisture must be carefully excluded, and that **zirconium tetrachloride,** $ZrCl_4$, prepared in this way from thoroughly dried materials is volatile at about 300°; and in the presence of moisture hydrolysis readily occurs. G. H. Bailey used this mode of preparation; and L. Troost passed chlorine or hydrogen chloride over crystalline zirconium at a red heat. F. Wöhler made zirconium tetrachloride by passing a current of chlorine over a mixture of zirconia and carbon at a red heat. F. Wöhler also used zircon in place of zirconia. D. E. Melliss, C. M. T. du Motay, and R. Hornberger found that it is difficult to separate silicon tetrachloride from the product of this reaction when the raw material contains silica; although, as L. Troost and P. Hautefeuille have shown, when silicon tetrachloride is passed over heated zirconia, silica and zirconium tetrachloride are formed. H. S. Cooper passed chlorine over zirconium carbide at 500°–550°, and condensed the sublimed tetrachloride at 200°. L. Burgess obtained the chloride by the action of hydrogen chloride on the product obtained by heating a zirconium ore with carbon. L. Troost observed the formation of zirconium tetrachloride when boron trichloride is passed over heated zirconia; E. F. Smith and H. B. Harris, when phosphorus pentachloride and zirconia are heated in an evacuated glass tube between 150° and 190°; E. Wedekind, and H. Moissan and F. Lengfeld, when zirconium nitride is heated to dark redness in a stream of chlorine; and H. Moissan and F. Lengfeld, L. Renaux, E. Wedekind, and A. Stähler and B. Denk, by heating zirconium carbide to 300° in a current of chlorine. E. Chauvenet found that at 400°, carbonyl chloride reacted with zirconia, forming the tetrachloride. C. Baskerville used this reaction. F. P. Venable and D. H. Jackson said that better results are obtained by using a mixture of carbon monoxide and chlorine at 480° with the former in excess, and at 425°, with the latter in excess.   J. Barlot and E. Chauvenet treated zircon at 1250°–1300° with carbonyl chloride.   E. A. Demarçay obtained zirconium tetrachloride by the action of carbon tetrachloride on zirconia above 400° ;   V. Meyer and F. Wilkins said that they did not observe any reaction, but they probably used too small a proportion of carbon tetrachloride. D. Lely and L. Hamburger said that a mixture of carbon tetrachloride and chlorine reacts with zirconia at 800°, and F. P. Venable and J. M. Bell regard this as a most convenient method of making zirconium tetrachloride.   The reaction is quantitative, beginning at about 300°, and progressing rapidly at 550°–600°. F. Bourion made zirconium tetrachloride by the action of a mixture of the vap. of chlorine and sulphur chloride on zirconia at a dull red heat.   The contamination with sulphur chloride can be removed by reheating the product in a stream of chlorine.   The dissociation of dried zirconyl chloride, $ZrOCl_2$, at about 110° furnishes zirconium tetrachloride : $2ZrOCl_2=ZrO_2+ZrCl_4$.   The method was used by E. Chauvenet.   F. P. Venable and J. M. Bell said that the yield is less than 10 per cent., and that the reaction begins about 300°—D. Lely and L. Hamburger said 600°.   F. P. Venable said that the anhydrous tetrachloride cannot be obtained from aq. soln.

Zirconium tetrachloride forms white crystals which when exposed to moist air give off fumes of hydrogen chloride, produced by the hydrolysis of the salt. Zirconium tetrachloride can be recrystallized from conc. hydrochloric acid, but some hydrolysis occurs at the same time.   The salt sublimes when heated over 300°, forming clear crystals.   The salt hisses when placed in water, and the reaction is energetic, much heat is evolved, and zirconyl chloride passes into soln.   A. Voigt and W. Biltz measured the electrical conductivity of the fused salt.   S. R. Paykull, and R. Hornberger found that the aq. soln. does not form double salts of zirconium tetrachloride with alkali, barium, zinc, or auric chloride.   F. P. Venable and J. M. Bell gave 2·8 for the sp. gr. at room temp.   R. Hermann, and H. St. C. Deville and L. Troost found the vap. density of the tetrachloride at 440°–450° to be 8·15 when the theoretical value for $ZrCl_4$ is 7·73.   A. Voigt and W. Biltz showed that zirconium tetrachloride does not melt without decomposition.   L. Wolter found that dry hydrogen fluoride converts it into zirconium tetrafluoride.   According to W. Biltz and E. Meinecke, zirconium tetrachloride is insoluble in liquid chlorine.   F. P. Venable and R. O. Dietz found that zirconium tetrachloride reacts with hydrogen sulphide, forming a compound which when heated yields the sulphide.   W. Biltz and E. Keunecke observed that no sulphohydrate, $ZrCl_4.nH_2S$, could be prepared. F. P. Venable and R. O. Deitz also showed that zirconium tetrachloride reacts with carbon at a high temp., forming the carbide (q.v.) ; zirconium tetrachloride vap. reacts with methane at 400°, and with acetylene an exothermic reaction sets in at a gentle heat.   According to R. Hornberger, and O. Hinsberg, zirconium tetrachloride dissolves in absolute alcohol with a hissing noise, but A. Rosenheim and P. Frank could not prepare an alcoholate or hydrate from the alcoholic soln. R. Hornberger found that the alcoholic soln. gives off ethyl chloride when heated. If the alcoholic soln. be sat. with hydrogen chloride, complexes of the type $M_2H_2ZrCl_6$ are formed, where M represents pyridine, quinoline, etc.   J. M. Matthews found that zirconium tetrachloride is soluble in ether, and in the ethereal soln. it can form addition compounds when treated with ammonia or organic bases ; while, according to A. Rosenheim and J. Hertzmann, it forms an addition compound with ether, and with benzoic acid, salicylic acid, acetic acid, formic acid, propionic acid, ethyl benzoate, ethyl salicylate, aldehyde, ketone, etc.   W. Peters observed no reaction between zirconium tetrachloride and mercury ethide or phenylide at 200° in evacuated tubes.   G. T. Morgan and A. R. Bowen prepared derivatives by the interaction of β-diacetones with zirconium tetrachloride. E. Chauvenet studied the electrical conductivity of a 0·01N-soln. of zirconium chloride during progressive treatment with an 0·01N-soln. of sodium hydroxide, and also from measurements of the heat developed under similar conditions, and concluded that the results obtained point to the existence of the radicle (ZrO) in zirconium compounds.

J. Persoz found that zirconium tetrachloride rapidly absorbs ammonia at ordinary temp. S. R. Paykull obtained what he regarded as **zirconium tetrammino-tetrachloride**, $ZrCl_4.4NH_3$, in this way. According to J. M. Matthews, if the tetrachloride is cold, *zirconium diamminotetrachloride*, $ZrCl_4.2NH_3$, is formed, and if heated, the tetrammine. The diammine was probably not properly sat. with ammonia. On the other hand, A. Stähler and B. Denk obtained **zirconium octamminotetrachloride**, $ZrCl_4.8NH_3$, as a loose, white, hygroscopic powder by the action of ammonia on the anhydrous tetrachloride at 16°, until the weight was constant; and at 232°, he obtained **zirconium triamminotetrachloride**, $ZrCl_4.3NH_3$. J. M. Matthews prepared the octammine by the action of dry ammonia on a soln. of zirconium tetrachloride in ether. When the octammine is heated, ammonia is first evolved ; then ammonium chloride ; and finally zirconium nitride remains. The octammine is very hygroscopic in air, and loses ammonia ; it reacts with water, forming ammonium chloride, and precipitating zirconium hydroxide. F. P. Venable and R. O. Deitz found that the product of the action of ammonia on the tetrachloride furnishes the nitride when heated. J. M. Matthews obtained compounds of zirconium chloride with 4 mols. of methylamine, ethylamine, propylamine, aniline, toluidine, and β-naphthylamine. No combination occurred with nitrosyl chloride, nitrogen peroxide, sulphur monochloride, phosphorus chlorides, cyanogen, hydrogen cyanide, cyanogen chloride, acetonitrile, benzonitrile, diphenylamine, and acid amides. C. Vincent found that the organic amines produce with aq. soln. of zirconium chlorides precipitates similar to those obtained with ammonia. F. P. Venable and R. O. Deitz found that zirconium tetrachloride reacts with phosphine, forming a compound which, when heated, yields the phosphide. S. R. Paykull, and E. F. Smith and H. B. Harris observed a reaction between zirconium tetrachloride and phosphorus pentachloride, forming **zirconium phosphorus tridecachloride**, $2ZrCl_4.PCl_5$, as a white mass melting at 240°, and boiling at 325° ; J. H. de Boer and A. E. van Arkel gave 164·5° for the m.p., and 416° for the b.p. They also prepared **zirconium phosphorus oxyhena-chloride**, $2ZrCl_4.POCl_3$, boiling at 363°–364°. O. Ruff observed that zirconium tetrachloride united with sulphur chloride.

M. Weibull obtained what he regarded as **potassium chlorozirconate**—possibly K_2ZrCl_6—by passing the vap. of zirconium tetrachloride over fused potassium chloride ; and S. R. Paykull prepared **sodium chlorozirconate**, Na_2ZrCl_6, in an analogous manner. R. Ruer observed that in the electrolysis of a mixed soln. of zirconium and sodium chlorides, some zirconium passed to the anode compartment.

S. R. Paykull said that the tetrachloride cannot exist in aq. soln., and as emphasized by G. H. Bailey, when zirconium chloride is exposed to moist air or dissolved in water, it is hydrolyzed, and zirconyl chloride, $ZrOCl_2$, is formed. Aq. soln. of zirconium chloride thus have an acidic reaction. R. Ruer showed that the hydrolysis progresses slowly at ordinary temp., and it is influenced by both temp. and conc. Working with a $\frac{1}{4}N$-soln. of zirconyl chloride, $ZrOCl_2.8H_2O$, at 18°, R. Ruer found that, owing to the increasing conc. of the hydrochloric acid produced by the hydrolysis, the sp. conductivity increases at the rate of about 67×10^{-5} mho per min. during the first hour, and for the next 168 hrs. it is almost stationary :

Hours		0·083	0·169	1	5	24	48	72	168
Mho $\times 10^5$		1469	1556	1867	1980	2024	2071	2104	2107

After the lapse of 168 hrs., the soln. was boiled, and the sp. conductivity rose to 2777×10^{-5} mho, indicating the formation of a more basic chloride ; 72 hrs. later, the conductivity fell to 2722×10^{-5} mho, indicating a reversal of the reaction or the escape of some free acid. The hydrolysis of aq. soln. of zirconyl chloride of different conc., **at** 0° and 20°, was measured by F. P. Venable and D. H. Jackson by the sp. conductivity method, and by precipitation with iodic acid. The results were analogous. When ionized in soln., the zirconyl radicle acts as cation. In the presence of sodium chloride, R. Ruer found some of the zirconium passed to the anode compartment. There are four possible stages in the hydrolysis of zirconium tetrachloride, namely $ZrCl_4 \rightarrow Zr(OH)Cl_3 \rightarrow Zr(OH)_2Cl_2 \rightarrow Zr(OH)_3Cl \rightarrow Zr(OH)_4$. E. Chauvenet tried to obtain indications of the different stages by the progressive addition of $0.01N$-NaOH to a $0.01N$-soln. of zirconium chloride at 309°, and measuring the changes in the electrical conductivity. The results furnished a curve with two breaks corresponding with $ZrOCl_2$ and $Zr_2O_3Cl_2$.

J. J. Berzelius showed that when the aq. soln. of zirconium chloride, or the soln. of zirconium hydroxide in hydrochloric acid is conc. by evaporation, small, colourless, needle-like crystals with a bitter astringent taste are formed, and the mother-liquid has an excess of hydrochloric acid. The crystals represent normal basic salt, which E. Chauvenet showed to be **octohydrated zirconyl chloride,** $ZrOCl_2.8H_2O$, whether it be crystallized from water or from hydrochloric acid. This compound was also obtained by R. Hermann, and S. R. Paykull. According to F. P. Venable, if the soln. is made strongly acid, the crystallization is almost quantitative because the octohydrate is only slightly soluble in conc. hydrochloric acid. The addition of water precipitates this salt from an acid soln., and conc. hydrochloric acid precipitates it from an aq. soln. The precipitates are gradually redissolved on standing in their mother-liquids. The re-solution of the precipitate depends on the acidic conc. of the mother-liquid. J. M. Matthews obtained this chloride of a high degree of purity by adding water to an ethereal soln. of zirconium tetrachloride ; and O. Kulka, by evaporating a soln. of zirconium tetrachloride in alcoholic hydrochloric acid. The determination of the water is difficult because at 70° hydrochloric acid as well as water is given off, and O. Kulka, and R. Hermann represented the composition of the crystals $ZrOCl_2.9H_2O$, or $Zr(OH)_2Cl_2.8H_2O$. The crystals are soluble in hot conc. hydrochloric acid and are re-deposited on cooling. This furnishes a means of purifying the salt ; and R. Ruer recommended the formation of this salt as a means of detecting zirconium :

The precipitate obtained by adding aq. ammonia is separated from the filter-paper and dissolved in hydrochloric acid. The soln. is evaporated to dryness on the water-bath and then dissolved in a little water. Conc. hydrochloric acid is added drop by drop so as to obtain a precipitate of the oxychloride ; this precipitate goes into soln. on warming the liquid, and on cooling separates again in crystals which have a characteristic appearance (thin prisms) under the microscope.

According to M. Weibull, R. Ruer, and K. Haushofer, the crystals belong to the tetragonal system, and the axial ratio is $a : c = 1 : 0.3182$. G. von Hevesy gave $\omega = 1.563$ and $\epsilon = 1.552$ for the refractive indices of the needle-like crystals of the octohydrate. The crystals deliquesce in moist air, and they may be dried in air without loss of hydrochloric acid ; in dry air, the crystals effloresce, and, according to E. Chauvenet, the loss of water ceases when the composition becomes that of the *hexahydrate*, $ZrOCl_2.6H_2O$. R. Paykull said that the hydrate is $ZrOCl_2.6\frac{1}{2}H_2O$, and is produced by adding hydrochloric acid to a soln. of normal zirconyl chloride. F. P. Venable and C. Baskerville, however, showed that the composition is that of the hexahydrate. H. Lange gave $ZrOCl_2.5\frac{1}{2}H_2O$, and D. E. Melliss, $ZrOCl_2.4\frac{1}{2}H_2O$. H. Lange also claimed to have made the *tetrahydrate*, $ZrOCl_2.4H_2O$, by heating the normal hydrate. At 50°, J. J. Berzelius said that the crystals become opaque and lose half their acid together with their water of crystallization ; but E. Chauvenet said that in a stream of dry air at 50°, the limit of the desiccation is the *hemiheptahydrate*, $ZrOCl_2.3\frac{1}{2}H_2O$. J. Missenden found that the octohydrate loses 80 per cent. of its water below or at 36°, and all at 57°. F. P. Venable showed that if dried at 100°–125° in a stream of hydrogen chloride, the *trihydrate*, $ZrOCl_2.3H_2O$, is formed ; and if the temp. be raised to 150°, E. Chauvenet said that the *dihydrate*, $ZrOCl_2.2H_2O$, is formed ; and from his thermochemical data, he limited the hydrates of this compound to the octo-, hexa-, hemihepta-, and the di-hydrate. According to F. P. Venable, the last of the water of hydration is lost at 180°–210°. L. Troost and P. Hautefeuille made anhydrous zirconyl chloride, $ZrOCl_2.ZrCl_4$, or Zr_2OCl_6, by heating to redness zirconium tetrachloride in a stream of oxygen. E. Chauvenet said that this statement is based on an error. If the oxygen is not thoroughly dried, a small proportion of the zirconium tetrachloride is hydrolyzed, and the zirconyl chloride at 300° dissociates into zirconium tetrachloride and zirconia, and small amounts of zirconia may be entrained in the zirconium tetrachloride. Hence the alleged volatile zirconyl chloride is really a mixture of the tetrachloride and dioxide. F. P. Venable and D. H. Jackson found that when zirconium tetrachloride or any of the basic chlorides is heated to 1000° for a long time, a small portion of the chlorine is retained. According to J. J. Berzelius, zirconyl chloride is soluble in water and alcohol; and the dil. aq. soln. does not become turbid when boiled. J. J. Berzelius, R. Hermann, R. Ruer, and F. P. Venable and C. Baskerville showed that the salt is sparingly soluble in cold hydrochloric acid ; and that the solubility is less the more conc. the acid. A comparison of the solubility of the hafnium and zirconium oxychlorides in hydrochloric acid is shown in Fig. 4, in the chapter on hafnium.

E. Wedekind said that when heated to 100°–110°, zirconyl chloride becomes less soluble in water. E. Linnemann, R. Hermann, and, as just indicated, J. J. Berzelius observed the loss of acid which occurs when the soln. of zirconyl chloride is evaporated to dryness. The progressive hydrolysis of the aq. soln. of zirconyl chloride has just been discussed. R. Ruer showed that the behaviour of aq. soln. of zirconyl chloride towards oxalic acid and ammonium oxalate in the presence of acids and sulphates also indicated that a hydrolytic change had occurred. When an aq. soln. of zirconium oxychloride is boiled for a short time, the hydrolysis undergone and the alteration of the analytical behaviour of the soln. are marked. Such soln., for instance, form precipitates with sodium sulphate and ammonium sulphate respectively, which are redissolved by an excess of precipitant ; the precipitate, formed on the addition of dil. sulphuric acid, is slowly dissolved by an excess of the latter. C. W. G. Nylander also obtained products with a different composition when prepared in different ways. According to H. Endemann, if ether be added to a warm soln. of zirconyl chloride, a crystalline precipitate is formed with the composition $Zr_2O_3Cl_2.nH_2O$. It is soluble in water and separates as an amorphous powder on evaporation, and it passes into normal zirconyl chloride when warmed with hydrochloric acid. R. Ruer said that the precipitate from the ethereal soln. is amorphous. A. Rosenheim and P. Frank gave $Zr_2O_3Cl_2.5H_2O$ for the air-dried substance ; and E. Chauvenet represented it as *trihydrated zirconium trioxydichloride*, $Zr_2O_3Cl_2.3H_2O$, hydrated **zirconium trioxydichloride,** or $ZrOCl_2.ZrO_2.3H_2O$:

$$O=Zr{<}_{Cl}^{Cl} \atop O=Zr{<}_{Cl}^{O} \quad +3H_2O$$

It can also be regarded as $ZrO(OH)Cl.H_2O$. E. Chauvenet made the anhydrous salt by heating dihydrated zirconyl chloride to 230° in an atm. of hydrogen chloride. At 300°, the anhydrous salt dissociates into zirconia and zirconium tetrachloride.

More advanced stages in the hydrolysis were reported by H. Endemann, who said that when ether is added to a cold alcoholic soln. of zirconyl chloride, a gelatinous precipitate is formed which is soluble in water, and when dried has the composition $8ZrO_2.7HCl$. R. T. Glazebrook and co-workers dissolved zirconium hydroxide in hydrochloric acid, and after concentrating the soln., claimed that a crystalline precipitate of a mixture of octohydrated zirconyl chloride, $ZrOCl_2.8H_2O$, and another basic salt, *zirconium octoxytetrachloride*, $Zr_5O_8Cl_4.22H_2O$, is formed. On recrystallization from hydrochloric acid, sp. gr. 1·08, the latter is alone obtained. According to E. H. Rodd, this salt is a tetrachlorozirconyl zirconate :

$$\begin{matrix} Cl.ZrO.O \\ Cl.ZrO.O \end{matrix} > Zr < \begin{matrix} O.ZrO.Cl \\ O.ZrO.Cl \end{matrix} \quad \text{or} \quad \begin{matrix} Cl_2 = Zr.O.ZrO.O.ZrO.O.Zr = Cl_2 \\ O \underline{\quad\quad} O \underline{\quad\quad} O \end{matrix}$$

The aq. soln. of this chloride resembles freshly prepared soln. of zirconyl chloride in giving a precipitate with oxalic acid or ammonium oxalate which is soluble in an excess of the precipitant; it behaves similarly with ammonium carbonate; and gives a gelatinous precipitate with hydrogen dioxide. Unlike the soln. of zirconyl chloride, however, when treated with sulphates or sulphuric acid it furnishes the corresponding sulphato-salt by double decomposition. The soln. of zirconyl chloride which has been boiled resembles in many ways a soln. of tetrachlorozirconyl zirconate. Both soln. give a white precipitate with sulphuric acid ; an unboiled soln. of zirconyl chloride does not give such a precipitate ; the general properties of the hydroxides precipitated with ammonia are different in boiled and unboiled soln. of zirconyl chloride. The hydroxide from the unboiled soln. does not dissolve in a soln. of zirconyl chloride, while that from the boiled soln. is readily soluble on warming. A soln. of tetrachlorozirconyl zirconate in one of zirconyl chloride deposits crystals of both salts on evaporation. Attempts to obtain tetrachlorozirconyl zirconate from a boiled soln. of zirconyl chloride were not successful.

R. Ruer dialyzed a 3 per cent. aq. soln. of zirconyl chloride but could not get a ratio higher than $ZrO_2 : Cl = 50 : 1$. When silver nitrate is added to the soln. a faint opalescence appears and the soln. becomes gelatinous after a few minutes. When nitric acid is added along with silver nitrate, a slight turbidity appears, which becomes more marked when the soln. is boiled, until finally all the silver is deposited as chloride. From this and from the analogous behaviour of ferric hydroxide, the conclusion is drawn that the colloidal soln. in question contained chlorine in the form of hydrochloric acid or metallic chloride or oxychloride, dissociation having occurred partially. The behaviour of the soln. towards silver nitrate is attributed to a specific action of the colloidal hydroxide by which the silver chloride formed is retained in soln. in the colloidal form. R. Ruer evaporated a dil. soln. of zirconyl chloride to a small vol. and diluted and evaporated the product three or four times so as to drive off most of the hydrochloric acid liberated by hydrolysis. The finely divided precipitate which settled out was washed with water and hydrochloric acid by centrifugal action. The precipitate was dried over sulphuric acid and potassium hydroxide. It was only partly dehydrated at 130°, and it lost no hydrochloric acid at that temp. The analyses correspond with $(ZrO)_5(OH)Cl.nH_2O$. R. Ruer called it *metazirconic chloride*, but there is no satisfactory evidence of chemical individuality. This substance before drying is soluble in water, and when the soln. is hydrolyzed, the product has less than 1 per cent. of chlorine, and may be regarded as a zirconium hydroxide, although R. Ruer called it *metazirconic acid*. It is difficult to transform metazirconic chloride into zirconyl chloride by the action of hydrochloric acid ; for, after boiling 5 grms. with 500 c.c. of conc. acid for 3 hrs., only 20 per cent. was changed ; about 30 hrs. were needed for the complete conversion of metazirconic chloride into normal zirconyl chloride. M. Adolf and W. Pauli studied the ionization of aq. soln. of zirconium oxychloride soln.

REFERENCES.

[1] J. J. Berzelius, *Œfvers. Akad. Förh. Stockholm*, 295, 1824 ; *Pogg. Ann.*, **4**. 117, 1825 ; F. Wöhler, *ib.*, **48**. 94, 1839 ; O. Hinsberg, *Liebig's Ann.*, **239**. 253, 1887 ; D. E. Melliss, *ib.*, **153**. 328, 1870 ; *Zeit. Chem.*, (2), **6**. 296, 1870 ; *Bull. Soc. Chim.*, (2), **14**. 204, 1870 ; *Contributions to the Chemistry of Zirconium*, Göttingen, 1870 ; L. Troost, *Compt. Rend.*, **45**. 824, 1857 ; **61**. 109, 1865 ; H. St. C. Deville and L. Troost, *ib.*, **45**. 821, 1857 ; L. Troost and P. Hautefeuille, *ib.*, **73**. 563, 1871 ; **75**. 1819, 1872 ; E. Chauvenet, *Ann. Chim. Phys.*, (9), **13**. 59, 1920 ; *Compt. Rend.*, **154**. 821, 1234, 1912 ; **164**. 630, 1917 ; J. Barlot and E. Chauvenet, *ib.*, **157**.

1153, 1913; H. Moissan and F. Lengfeld, *ib.*, **122**. 551, 1896; E. A. Demarçay, *ib.*, **104**. 113, 1887; P. Camboulices, *ib.*, **150**. 175, 221, 1910; E. Wedekind, *Zeit. anorg. Chem.*, **33**. 81, 1902; D. Lely and L. Hamburger, *ib.*, **87**. 209, 1914; R. Ruer, *ib.*, **43**. 85, 282, 1904; **46**. 456, 1906; O. Ruff and R. Wallstein, *ib.*, **128**. 96, 1923; J. H. de Boer and A. E. van Arkel, *ib.*, **141**. 284, 289, 1924; A. Voigt and W. Biltz, *ib.*, **133**. 277, 1924; W. Biltz and E. Meinecke, *ib.*, **131**. 1, 1923; W. Biltz and E. Keunecke, *ib.*, **147**. 171, 1925; G. H. Bailey, *Chem. News*, **60**. 8, 1899; *Proc. Roy. Soc.*, **46**. 74, 1889; F. P. Venable, *ib.*, **64**. 315, 1891; *Zirconium and its Compounds*, New York, 1922; *Journ. Amer. Chem. Soc.*, **16**. 469, 1894; **20**. 118, 1898; F. P. Venable and C. Baskerville, *ib.*, **20**. 321, 1898; E. F. Smith and H. B. Harris, *ib.*, **17**. 654, 1895; J. M. Matthews, *ib.*, **20**. 815, 1898; F. P. Venable and J. M. Bell, *ib.*, **39**. 1598, 1917; F. P. Venable and D. H. Jackson, *ib.*, **42**. 2531, 1920; *Journ. Elisha Mitchell Scient. Soc.*, **35**. 87, 1920; F. P. Venable and R. O. Deitz, *ib.*, **38**. 74, 1921; R. Hornberger, *Liebig's Ann.*, **181**. 232, 1876; F. Bourion, *Ann. Chim. Phys.*, (8), **20**. 547, 1910; (8), **21**. 49, 1910; *Compt. Rend.*, **145**. 62, 1907; G. von Hevesy, *Danske Vid. Selsk. Medd.*, **7**. 8, 1925; R. T. Glazebrook, W. Rosenhain, and E. H. Rodd, *Brit. Pat. No.* 112973, 1917; W. Rosenhain and E. H. Rodd, *U.S. Pat. No.* 1307882, 1919; E. H. Rodd, *Journ. Chem. Soc.*, **111**. 396, 1917; A. Stähler and B. Denk, *Ber.*, **38**. 2611, 1905; W. Peters, *ib.*, **41**. 3175, 1908; V. Meyer and F. Wilkens, *ib.*, **20**. 681, 1887; O. Ruff, *ib.*, **37**. 4513, 1904; A. Rosenheim and J. Hertzmann, *ib.*, **40**. 810, 1907; A. Rosenheim and P. Frank, *ib.*, **38**. 812, 1905; M. Weibull, *Acta Univ. Lund*, (2), **18**. 21, 1882; *Ber.*, **20**. 1394, 1887; S. R. Paykull, *ib.*, **6**. 1467, 1873; **12**. 1719, 1879; *Œfvers. Akad. Förh. Stockholm*, 22, 1873; *Bull. Soc. Chim.*, (2), **20**. 65, 1879; C. Vincent, *ib.*, (2), **27**. 194, 1877; (2), **33**. 156, 1880; H. Endemann, *Journ. prakt. Chem.*, (2), **11**. 219, 1875; R. Hermann, (1), **31**. 75, 1844; L. Burgess, *U.S. Pat. No.* 1418528, 1921; L. Renaux, *Contribution à l'étude de la zircone*, Paris, 1900; M. Adolf and W. Pauli, *Zeit. Koll.*, **29**. 173, 1921; O. Kulka, *Beiträge zur Kenntnis einiger Zirkoniumverbindungen*, Bern, 1902; J. Missenden, *Chem. News*, **124**. 326, 1922; E. Linnemann, *Monatsh.*, **6**. 335, 899, 1885; C. M. T. du Motay, *Chem. News*, **18**. 276, 1868; L. Wolter, *Chem. Ztg.*, **32**. 606, 1908; J. Persoz, *Ann. Chim. Phys.*, (2), **44**. 315, 1830; C. W. G. Nylander, *Bidrag till Kännedom om Zirkonjord*, Lund, 21, 1864; *Acta Univ. Lund.*, **1**. 2, 1864; K. Haushofer, *Zeit. Kryst.*, **11**. 165, 1896; H. Lange, *Zeit. Naturwiss.*, **82**. 1, 1910; C. Baskerville, *Science*, (2), **50**. 443, 1919; H. S. Cooper, *Trans. Amer. Electrochem. Soc.*, **43**. 215, 1923; G. T. Morgan and A. R. Bowen, *Journ. Chem. Soc.*, **125**. 1252, 1924.

§ 11. Zirconium Bromides and Iodides

D. E. Melliss [1] prepared anhydrous **zirconium tetrabromide,** $ZrBr_4$, by passing carbon dioxide sat. with bromine vapour over an intimate mixture of zirconia and sugar charcoal. G. H. Bailey obtained the same salt by heating zirconium in the vap. of bromine. A. Stähler and B. Denk passed bromine vap. and carbon dioxide over zirconium carbide at a red heat; and E. Wedekind observed that bromine reacts with heated zirconium nitride *unter Feuererscheinung* producing the tetrabromide. According to D. E. Melliss, zirconium tetrabromide is a white microcrystalline powder which can be volatilized without decomposition at the heat of a Bunsen's burner. The salt is very hygroscopic. It is not reduced when heated in a current of hydrogen. When treated with water, it forms hydrogen bromide, bromine, and a soln. of zirconyl bromide. According to A. Rosenheim and P. Frank, it dissolves in alcohol with the formation of hydrogen bromide. It is soluble in ether. A. Stähler and B. Denk prepared **zirconium decammino-tetrabromide,** $ZrBr_4.10NH_3$, by saturating zirconium tetrabromide with dry ammonia at ordinary temp.; this occupies about 12 hrs. The white powder is very hygroscopic, and readily gives off ammonia; it changes very little, however, if dried air be passed over it for a short time. It is decomposed by water making a hissing noise. If dried ammonia be passed over warmed zirconium tetrabromide, J. M. Matthews found that white **zirconium tetramminotetrabromide,** $ZrBr_4.4NH_3$, is formed. When heated, either ammine furnishes the nitride, and if further heated in hydrogen, zirconium metal is produced. A. Rosenheim and P. Frank prepared addition compounds with ethylamine, aniline, and pyridine; and by adding pyridine and quinoline to a soln. of hydrogen bromide in alcohol sat. with zirconium hydroxide, they obtained the **bromozirconates,** $(C_5H_5NH)_2ZrBr_6$, and $(C_9H_7NH)_2ZrBr_6$, respectively.

J. B. Berthemot dissolved zirconium hydroxide in hydrobromic acid, allowed the soln. to crystallize, and obtained granular crystals of an astringent taste. It is difficult to dry the salt without decomposition, since D. E. Melliss showed that it loses water and hydrogen bromide at 100°, and F. P. Venable and C. Baskerville found these losses occurred in a current of dry air or over a desiccating agent. The composition of the salt, according to M. Weibull, and O. Kulka, approximates to **octohydrated zirconyl bromide,** $ZrOBr_2.8H_2O$; D. E. Melliss' analysis makes the salt approximate the heptahydrate ; and F. P. Venable and C. Baskerville obtained it with $13-14H_2O$. D. E. Melliss made it by evaporating an aq. soln. of the tetrabromide ; and O. Kulka by evaporating in vacuo a soln. of zirconium hydroxide in alcoholic hydrobromic acid. D. E. Melliss obtained acicular crystals which, according to M. Weibull, are optically uniaxial, tetragonal, and isomorphous with the corresponding chloride. F. P. Venable and C. Baskerville found the crystals to be more hygroscopic than those of zirconyl chloride, and to decompose on exposure to moist air. The salt is soluble in hot conc. hydrobromic acid, and is re-deposited on cooling. When the salt is dried at 100°–120° in a stream of hydrogen bromide, a hard crystalline mass is obtained with the composition of the *tetrahydrate,* $ZrOBr_2.4H_2O$, or $Zr(OH)_2Br_2.3H_2O$, and which is readily soluble in water. E. Chauvenet could find no evidence of the hydrates reported by A. Knop, and S. R. Paykull, for when the octohydrate is dried in a current of dry air or in vacuo, it furnishes a *hemiheptahydrate,* $ZrOBr_2.3\frac{1}{2}H_2O$, which is stable up to 60°–70°. Above this temp. it loses both water and hydrogen bromide, forming the basic salt $Zr_2O_3Br_2$, **zirconium trioxydibromide.** This basic bromide is slowly deposited from a $0.01N$-soln. of zirconyl bromide when allowed to stand for a long time ; and on adding ether to an alcoholic soln. of zirconyl bromide, **dodecahydrated zirconium trioxydibromide,** $Zr_2O_3Br_2.12H_2O$, is deposited. These basic salts are converted into zirconium tetrabromide when heated to redness in a current of hydrogen bromide.

F. P. Venable and C. Baskerville boiled for a long time a sat. soln. of zirconium hydroxide in conc. hydrobromic acid, and, when the soln. was evaporated on a water-bath, it deposited white, prismatic crystals of a basic salt, $ZrO(OH)_2.ZrOBr_2.4H_2O$, or **zirconyl hydroxybromide,** $ZrO(OH)Br.2H_2O$, or *zirconium trihydroxybromide,* $Zr(OH)_3Br.H_2O$. The soln. contained some gelatinous zirconium hydroxide, and, on further evaporation, furnished a crop of acicular crystals which on analysis had rather less water of hydration. The colloidal zirconia could be separated from the soln. by dialysis. M. Weibull reported a similar basic salt.

D. E. Melliss, and O. Hinsberg did not succeed in preparing **zirconium tetraiodide,** ZrI_4, by heating a mixture of zirconia and carbon in a current of iodine vap. carried along by carbon dioxide ; or by heating a mixture of zirconium tetrabromide and potassium iodide in a stream of carbon dioxide. G. H. Bailey, and L. M. Dennis and A. E. Spencer also achieved no success by heating zirconium to dull redness in a current of iodine vapour and hydrogen. The latter, however, obtained the tetraiodide by passing hydrogen iodide over zirconium. They said :

As the temp. of the tube containing the zirconium is gradually increased, an amorphous, white sublimate, probably of ferrous iodide obtained from traces of iron in the metal, is first formed, and finally, at a bright red-heat, a white, crystalline sublimate was deposited immediately beyond the red-hot portion of the tube. After cooling in a current of hydrogen, the zirconium was found to have changed from black to greyish-white, but contained very little iodine.

A. Stähler and B. Denk prepared the tetraiodide by heating zirconium or its carbide in a current of dried hydrogen iodide. A vigorous reaction sets in at 340° in the case of the metal, and at 490° in the case of the carbide. Unlike L. M. Dennis and A. E. Spencer, A. Stähler and B. Denk found that the sublimate is brown not white. The hydrogen iodide was driven from the apparatus by a current of hydrogen, and the sublimate digested with benzene at 160° in a sealed tube to remove the free iodine. The mixture was filtered in an atm. of hydrogen, washed with benzene and dried. L. M. Dennis and A. E. Spencer seem to have gone wrong in their description of zirconium tetraiodide, and the following observations were reported by A. Stähler and B. Denk. Zirconium tetraiodide is a yellow, microcrystalline powder which fumes in air, and dissolves in water and acids with a vigorous reaction. L. M. Dennis and A. E. Spencer said the iodide is unchanged by boiling it with water. The tetraiodide reacts energetically with alcohol, forming ethyl iodide and zirconium hydroxide; it is slightly soluble in benzene, and carbon disulphide; and it readily dissolves in dry ether, forming an addition product, $ZrI_4.4(C_2H_5)_2O$.

A. Stähler and B. Denk attempted to remove the iodine from the unpurified tetraiodide by heating in vacuo, or in a stream of carbon dioxide. The reddish-brown product so obtained when heated over 300° gave a dark brown vap. which condensed to a reddish-brown powder, with a constant composition, and in *vielleicht eine molekulare Verbindung*, **zirconium hexaiodide,** $ZrI_4.I_2$. The tetraiodide forms addition products with ammonia, ethylamine, and propylamine. When a stream of dry ammonia is passed over crystals of the tetraiodide, below 22°, until the salt is saturated, **zirconium octamminotetraiodide,** $ZrI_4.8NH_3$, is formed. This compound was also obtained by digesting the tetraiodide with liquid ammonia at 60°, and evaporating off the excess of liquid; and by passing dry ammonia into an ethereal soln. of the tetraiodide. A. Stähler and B. Denk raised the question if this product is really a mixture of ammonium iodide and zirconium tetramide, $ZrI_4.8NH_3=Zr(NH_2)_4+4NH_4I$, because, like boron hexamminotrichloride, and silicon hexamminotetrachloride, ammonium halide is removed by washing with liquid ammonia. On the other hand, when the octammine is heated, there is a gradual loss of ammonia on raising the temp. so that at 100°, the composition corresponds with **zirconium heptamminotetraiodide,** $ZrI_4.7NH_3$; at 150°, with **zirconium hexamminotetraiodide,** $ZrI_4.6NH_3$; and up to 200°, with **zirconium tetramminotetraiodide,** $ZrI_4.4NH_3$. Only at 200° is there any sign of ammonium iodide, corresponding with the decomposition of the salt to the nitride, etc., as in the analogous case of the ammines of zirconium tetrachloride and tetrabromide. It may be that those ammines are decomposed by liquid ammonia.

According to D. E. Melliss, an oxyiodide is not formed when zirconium hydroxide is dissolved in hydriodic acid; and F. P. Venable and co-workers found that zirconium hydroxide, precipitated from hot soln., is scarcely attacked by this acid, and even the hydroxide precipitated from cold soln. is only sparingly dissolved. The best results were obtained by passing hydrogen iodide into water in which the hydroxide was suspended. The evaporation of the soln. furnishes a hornlike mass coloured with iodine; if the evaporation be conducted in an atm. of carbon dioxide to limit the decomposition of the iodide, crystals of **octohydrated zirconyl iodide,** $ZrOI_2.8H_2O$, were obtained. The same salt was obtained in a similar manner by M. Weibull, and he removed the free iodine by washing with chloroform or carbon disulphide. A. Stähler and B. Denk prepared it by evaporating an aq. soln. of zirconium tetraiodide, and washing out the free iodine with ether. The salt so obtained appears in colourless needle-like crystals, which are very hygroscopic; soluble in water or alcohol; and decomposed by heat into zirconia and hydrogen iodide. O. Hinsberg prepared the basic salt $ZrO(OH)_2.ZrOI_2.5H_2O$, or **zirconyl hydroxyiodide,** $ZrO(OH)I.2\frac{1}{2}H_2O$, or *zirconium trihydroxyiodide,* $Zr(OH)_3I.1\frac{1}{2}H_2O$, by the double decomposition of soln. of barium iodide and zirconyl sulphate; evaporating the filtered soln. over conc. sulphuric acid; and washing out the free iodine with carbon disulphide. The amorphous, colourless powder decomposes in air and acquires a brown colour from the liberated iodine. It is soluble in water.

REFERENCES.

[1] D. E. Melliss, *Contributions to the Chemistry of Zirconium*, Göttingen, 1870; *Bull. Soc. Chim.*, (2), **14.** 204, 1870; *Zeit. Chem.*, (2), **6.** 296, 1870; *Liebig's Ann.*, **153.** 328, 1870; O. Hinsberg, *ib.*, **239.** 253, 1887; G. H. Bailey, *Chem. News*, **60.** 6, 17, 32, 1889; *Proc. Roy. Soc.*, **46.** 74, 1889; A. Rosenheim and P. Frank, *Ber.*, **38.** 814, 1915; A. Stähler and B. Denk,

ib., **37.** 1135, 1904 ; **38.** 2611, 1905 ; B. Denk, *Ueber das Zirkoniumjodid sowie über die zirkon-halogenammoniakverbindungen,* Berlin, 1905 ; E. Chauvenet, *Compt. Rend.,* **164.** 816. 1916 ; *Ann. Chim. Phys.,* (9), **13.** 59, 1920 ; E. Wedekind, *Zeit. anorg. Chem.,* **45.** 385, 1905 ; S. R. Paykull, *Bull. Soc. Chim.,* (2), **20.** 65, 1873 ; J. B. Berthemot, *Ann. Chim. Phys.,* (2), **44.** 393, 1830 ; A. Knop, *Liebig's Ann.,* **159.** 36, 1871 ; F. P. Venable and C. Baskerville, *Journ. Amer. Chem. Soc.,* **20.** 321, 1898 ; F. P. Venable and A. W. Belden, *ib.,* **20.** 273, 1898 ; J. M. Matthews, *ib.,* **20.** 839, 1898 ; L. M. Dennis and A. E. Spencer, *ib.,* **18.** 673, 1896 ; M. Weibull, *Ber.,* **20.** 1394, 1887 ; *Acta Univ. Lund,* (2), **18** 21, 1882 ; O. Kulka, *Beiträge zur Kenntnis einiger Zirkoniumverbindungen,* Bern, 1902.

§ 12. Zirconium Sulphides and Sulphates

Our knowledge of zirconium sulphide is not in a satisfactory state. J. J. Berzelius [1] heated zirconium with sulphur in an evacuated vessel and observed that combination occurred without the emission of light or heat ; when the two elements were heated in an atm. of hydrogen, there appeared a slight flame. The product must have been very impure because the zirconium then available was itself very crude. O. Hauser repeated J. J. Berzelius' experiment also with an impure zirconium. S. R. Paykull obtained an impure sulphide by subliming zirconium tetrachloride in an atm. of hydrogen sulphide. Oxygen was not entirely excluded, and the product was contaminated with oxide or oxysulphide. From analogy with other sulphides, it is inferred that **zirconium sulphide,** ZrS_2, was formed. H. Moissan and F. Lengfeld obtained a little sulphide by the action of sulphur vap. on zirconium carbide at a dull red heat. E. Frémy made an attempt to prepare the sulphide by heating zirconia in an atm. of carbon disulphide. He obtained steel-grey acicular crystals. F. P. Venable and R. O. Dietz obtained the sulphide by the action of hydrogen sulphide on zirconium tetrachloride ; and A. E. van Arkel and J. H. de Boer, by passing the vapours of the tetrachloride and sulphur over a heated tungsten filament. A. L. Feild found zirconium sulphide is present in zirconium steels containing 0·07 to 0·32 per cent. of sulphur, and it appears as grey inclusions when the polished surface is etched. It is soluble in hydrochloric acid (1 : 1).

J. J. Berzelius' sulphide was a cinnamon-brown powder which did not acquire a polish under the burnishing tool. A. E. van Arkel found that the crystals belong to the rhombohedral (hexagonal) system with axial ratio $a : c = 1 : 1·59$; and the edge of the hexagon 3·68 A. S. R. Paykull said that the sulphide is stable in air and water, and burns when heated, forming sulphur dioxide. E. Frémy, and S. R. Paykull said that the sulphide is not decomposed by ordinary acids excepting nitric acid, which oxidized it readily with the separation of sulphur. J. J. Berzelius found that the sulphide is decomposed by hydrofluoric acid with the evolution of hydrogen sulphide ; and that it is also attacked by aqua regia. S. R. Paykull heated the sulphide in chlorine and obtained zirconium tetrachloride and sulphur chloride. According to A. L. Feild, the normal sulphide, ZrS_2, is soluble in hydrochloric acid (1 : 1), but if more zirconium than corresponds with this ratio is present in the steel, the sulphur is not evolved as hydrogen sulphide upon treatment with the acid, and it is suggested that the excess zirconium is partitioned between the metal and the normal disulphide, the latter forming possibly an insoluble zirconium-zirconium sulphide solid soln., the proportion of sulphur rendered insoluble being 10 per cent. of the zirconium in excess of that required to form the normal disulphide. J. J. Berzelius showed that when zirconium sulphide is fused with potassium hydroxide, zirconia and potassium sulphide are formed. O. Hauser dried the sulphate at 380°–400°, and heated the product at a dull red heat in a current of hydrogen sulphide, and cooled it in the same gas. If removed from the tube before it is quite cold, the product ignites spontaneously in air. Analyses of the light-yellow powder correspond with **zirconyl sulphide,** $ZrOS$. The sp. gr. is 4·87.

Dried zirconia reacts with sulphuric acid very slowly, and ignited zirconia is scarcely attacked by that acid. J. J. Berzelius [2] prepared normal **zirconium**

sulphate, $Zr(SO_4)_2$, by dissolving zirconia or zirconium hydroxide in an excess of conc. sulphuric acid ; evaporating the soln. to dryness ; and heating the residue for 15 mins. just below a red heat. According to G. H. Bailey, O. Hauser, F. P. Venable, and M. Weibull, the temp. for driving off the excess of acid should not exceed $350°–400°$, or some of the combined acid will be expelled. O. Hauser said that only traces of acid are lost after heating the sulphate for 8 to 10 hrs. at $380°$. If a gas-flame is used for the heating, the product must be protected from the water formed in the combustion of the gas, or the sulphate will be partly hydrolyzed. According to J. J. Berzelius, the sulphates prepared by M. H. Klaproth, and L. N. Vauquelin were contaminated with the potassium salt. J. J. Berzelius obtained a gummy mass by the evaporation of an aq. soln. of zirconium sulphate, but if free sulphuric acid be present, crystals of the hydrated salt are formed. These can be washed free from adherent acid by means of alcohol. C. W. G. Nylander's analysis of the hydrate washed with alcohol, and dried by confining it for a short time over conc. sulphuric acid, gave $Zr(SO_4)_2.5H_2O$; but analyses by S. R. Paykull, M. Weibull, and O. Kulka showed that the salt is **tetrahydrated zirconium sulphate,** $Zr(SO_4)_2.4H_2O$. O. Kulka recommended the following process for making the tetrahydrate :

Dissolve zirconia in conc. sulphuric acid over the naked flame, and drive off only a part of the excess acid. Pour the cold, white mush into water. Much heat is developed and the sulphate is dissolved. The clear soln. is then evaporated on a water-bath until a crystalline crust appears on the surface of the liquid. On cooling, crystals of the salt are formed. These are separated from the mother-liquid by suction, and washed with alcohol so as to remove the tenaciously adsorbed acid. The crystals are then dried in air. The salt can be recrystallized from sulphuric acid, but not from water alone, because a basic sulphate would then be formed.

According to M. Weibull, the tetrahydrate furnishes hexagonal plates belonging to the rhombic system, and having the axial ratios $a : b : c = 0·6826 : 1 : 1·3350$. L. Fernandes found that the salt is completely miscible with cerous and uranium sulphates. According to S. R. Paykull, the tetrahydrate loses 3 mols of water at $100°$, E. Chauvenet said $120°$, and that **monohydrated zirconium sulphate,** $Zr(SO_4)_2.H_2O$, is formed. According to S. R. Paykull, the fourth mol is given off at about $380°$ below the temp. of decomposition. G. H. Bailey said the salt is stable at $400°$; O. Hauser, at $380°$. At a higher temp., sulphur trioxide is driven off ; but even after heating for some time at $900°–1000°$, the last traces of sulphur trioxide are not expelled, and G. H. Bailey said that re-igniting the product mixed with ammonium carbonate will remove the last traces of sulphur dioxide, but the process requires care since some zirconia may be lost by this procedure, being presumably carried away mechanically by the escaping vap. when the normal sulphate is heated in steam at $200°–300°$, O. Hauser showed that a basic sulphate, $2ZrO.SO_3$, is formed. According to L. Pissarjewsky, the heat of formation of normal zirconium sulphate from zirconium hydroxide and sulphuric acid is $11·67$ cals. ; and the heat of reaction with an excess of sulphuric acid is $-0·685$ cal. According to J. J. Berzelius, the anhydrous salt dissolves slowly but completely in cold water and rapidly in hot water. O. Hauser showed that 100 grms. of the aq. soln. at $39·5°$ contain $59·3$ grms. of the tetrahydrate ; and O. Kulka, that 100 grms. of soln. at $18°$ contain $52·5$ grms. of the tetrahydrate. As in the case of the normal chloride, the normal sulphate is readily hydrolyzed in aq. soln. imparting to the liquid a strong acid reaction. The extent of the hydrolysis depends upon the conc., the temp., and the age of the soln. Thus, R. Ruer and M. Levin found the sp. electrical conductivity of a $1·75$ per cent. aq. soln. at $18°$, after the lapse of one hour, to be $0·03105$ mho, and after 20 hrs., $0·03186$ mho ; when the soln. was boiled the conductivity rose to $0·03418$ mho ; and 24 and 72 hrs. later the conductivity was $0·03432$ mho. F. P. Venable and D. H. Jackson extended these observations working at $0°$ and $20°$ with soln. containing $2·026$, $20·26$, and $40·52$ grms. of $ZrOSO_4$ per litre. According to H. Rose, very dil. soln. of zirconium sulphate become turbid when boiled, owing to the separation of the hydroxide or a basic sulphate, and the soln. becomes clear again as the water is expelled by evaporation.

R. Ruer showed that a soln. of normal zirconium sulphate does not give the characteristic reactions exhibited by the chloride or nitrate when treated with oxalic acid or ammonium oxalate; nor do these reactions occur with soln. of zirconyl chloride to which ammonium or radium sulphate has been added. It is therefore inferred that in aq. soln. zirconium sulphate is constitutionally different from the chloride or nitrate. He suggested that in aq. soln. zirconium sulphate behaves as if it were **zirconyl hydrosulphate,** $ZrOSO_4.H_2SO_4$, or $ZrO(HSO_4)_2$, which, owing to the passage of the zirconium to the anode compartment during electrolysis, and to its forming characteristic potassium, sodium and ammonium salts, is considered to be *eine zweibasische Zirkonschwefelsäure,* **hydrodisulphato-zirconylic acid,** $H_2[ZrO(SO_4)_2]$, or $(HSO_4)_2Zr:O$. On this assumption, it is highly probable that normal zirconium sulphate can exist only in the absence of water, and that the so-called tetrahydrate is really **trihydrated zirconyl hydro-sulphate,** $H_2ZrO(SO_4)_2.3H_2O$. This is confirmed by the ease with which the sup-posed tetrahydrate loses 3 mols of water and the tenacity with which it retains the fourth mol—*vide supra*—which shows that the molecule is dissociated and water is reformed. E. Chauvenet and H. Gueylard found that the lowering of the f.p. of soln. of zirconium sulphate corresponded with a mol. wt. of 79·4 instead of 286·6. This is taken to mean that the salt is broken down into four mol. species, and this is considered to agree with a salt of the composition $ZrOSO_4.H_2SO_4$.

J. J. Berzelius did not observe the formation of an acid sulphate when zirconium sulphate is crystallized from its soln. in conc. sulphuric acid; and this also applies to the observations of R. Hermann, S. R. Paykull, and M. Weibull. H. Rose also said that the normal sulphate can be crystallized unchanged from sulphuric acid; but O. Hauser showed that a well-defined acid salt can be obtained from the sulphuric acid soln. of zir-conium sulphate, and it appears to have been overlooked because the crystals of the acid salt are formed so slowly. O. Hauser found that the solu-bility of zirconium sulphate in water of different conc. slowly decreases with increasing conc. of acid, as indicated in Fig. 6, and then begins to increase, rising to a maximum when 61 per cent. SO_3 is present; after that the solubility

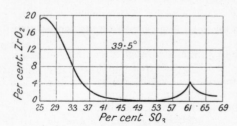

FIG. 6.—Solubility of Zirconium Oxide in Sulphuric Acid.

slowly diminishes again. Soln. containing 61 to 64 per cent. of sulphur trioxide deposit in 4 to 12 days crystals of an acid sulphate, **trihydrated zirconium dihydro-trisulphate,** $Zr(SO_4)_2.H_2SO_4.3H_2O$, or $ZrSO_4(HSO_4)_2.3H_2O$, which O. Hauser con-siders to be a *hydrosulphatozirconic acid,* $H_2[Zr(SO_3)_3]3H_2O$; for, on electrolysis, it furnishes a complex anion, $H_2[Zr(SO_4)_3]=2H+Zr(SO_4)''_3$. A temp. near 40° is favourable to the production of this acid sulphate, but it can be obtained at 22° in a similar way; the solubility curve at 22° is similar to that at 40°. The crystals of this salt furnish monoclinic prisms which are very hygroscopic, and which rapidly deliquesce in air to form the normal tetrahydrate, $Zr(SO_4)_2.4H_2O$. The sp. gr. is 2·02 at 19°. Soln. containing more than 70 per cent. SO_3 deposit crystals of **monohydrated zirconium dihydrotrisulphate,** $Zr(SO_4)_2.H_2SO_4.H_2O$. On melting the trihydrate with much conc. sulphuric acid in a glass tube, and allowing the whole to stand for some days, the monohydrate is deposited as a compact crystal-line powder of sp. gr. 2·05, which is even more hygroscopic than the trihydrate. E. Chauvenet reported acid zirconium sulphates with $ZrOSO_4:SO_3:H_2O$ $=1:1:0, 1:1:1$, and $1:1:4$.

According to J. J. Berzelius, a conc. soln. of normal alkali dissolves zirconium hydroxide, and when the soln. is evaporated, it furnishes a gum-like mass, which, when dried, is white and opaque. It swells up like alum when heated, and loses water. The gum-like mass dissolves in a little water, but the soln. precipitates a basic salt when treated with a large proportion of water. The product is also insoluble in acids. Analyses corresponded with $ZrO_2.SO_3$, or **zirconyl sulphate,** $ZrO.SO_4$. O. Kulka obtained a similar product by neutralizing with ammonia the soln. of zirconium hydroxide in zirconium sulphate. R. Ruer and O. Hauser consider that the soln. is really a suspension of colloidal hydroxide in the soln. of the sulphate. The fresh hydroxide precipitated in the cold is the most soluble form. Conc. soln. of the sulphate at $60°$ take up $ZrO_2 : SO_4 = 1.15 : 1$ in several days. O. Hauser could not prepare zirconyl sulphate by evaporating this soln. E. Löwenstein found the vap. press. of the hydrate to be a continuous function of the contained water; there is no break in the curve.

E. Chauvenet claimed to have made **tetrahydrated zirconyl sulphate,** $ZrOSO_4.4H_2O$, by evaporating a mixture of equimolar parts of zirconia and sulphuric acid; the same salt is precipitated when 2 mols of potassium hydroxide are added to one mol of the normal sulphate, assumed to be an acid zirconyl sulphate : $ZrOSO_4.H_2SO_{4aq.}+2KOH=ZrOSO_4+K_2SO_{4aq.}+2H_2O$; and when a mixture of soln. of acid zirconyl sulphate and ammonium sulphate is allowed to stand a few days, the tetrahydrate is again deposited. When exposed to dried air, it furnishes **dihydrated zirconyl sulphate,** $ZrOSO_4.2H_2O$; and when dried at $150°$, it becomes anhydrous, $ZrOSO_4$. He also obtained **monohydrated zirconyl sulphate,** $ZrOSO_4.H_2O$. The hemihydrate, $2ZrO.SO_4.H_2O$, which R. Ruer and M. Levin represented by $H_2(Zr_2O_3)(SO_4)_2$, or **hydrodisulphatodizirconylic acid,**

$$H-SO_4-Zr\lessgtr^O_O$$
$$H-SO_4-Zr\lessgtr^O_O$$

corresponds with the complex salts isolated by A. Rosenheim and P. Frank—*vide infra.* E. Chauvenet mixed varying proportions of zirconium oxide and sulphuric acid; dried the products at $200°$, and measured their sp. gr. in nitrobenzene at $12.4°$. He obtained with the molar ratio $H_2SO_4 : ZrO_2=1 : n$,

n	0.125	0.250	0.50	0.625	0.75	0.875	1	1.125	1.20
Sp. gr.	2.05	2.20	2.50	2.78	3.02	3.20	3.40	3.45	**3.47**

n	1.25	1.30	1.40	1.50	1.75	2.0	2.5	3.0
Sp. gr.	3.49	3.52	3.57	3.62	3.65	3.69	3.79	3.87

The breaks on the curve indicated the existence of normal sulphate, zirconyl sulphate, and basic sulphates with $Zr(SO_4)_2 : ZrO_2=5 : 7, 3 : 5, 1 : 2$, and $1 : 3$; but no signs of the $2 : 1, 7 : 5, 3 : 4$, or $1 : 5$ compounds or of the acid salt $H_2Zr(SO_4)_3$. By measuring the change in the electrical conductivity of a soln. of normal zirconium sulphate during the addition of $0.001N$-NaOH, the results furnished a curve with two breaks corresponding with the existence of zirconyl sulphate, and the $1 : 3$- and the $3 : 5$-salts. The $5 : 7$-salt can be regarded as $5ZrOSO_4.ZrO_2$, or **zirconium heptoxypentasulphate,**

$$SO_4.ZrO.SO_4.ZrO.SO_4.ZrO.SO_4.ZrO.SO_4$$
$$ZrO————————O————ZrO$$

The *dodecahydrate*, $(ZrO.SO_4)_5ZrO_2.12H_2O$, is precipitated when alcohol is added to a conc. soln. of ordinary zirconium sulphate. The salt becomes anhydrous at $100°$. The $3 : 5$-salt can be represented $3ZrOSO_4.ZrO_2$, *i.e.* **zirconium pentoxytrisulphate,** or

$$SO_4.ZrO.SO_4.ZrO.SO_4$$
$$ZrO——O———ZrO$$

and the *octohydrate* is a product of the hydrolysis of the precipitate obtained when potassium sulphate is added to a soln. of zirconyl chloride. The octohydrate becomes anhydrous at 100°. As a product of the further hydrolysis of this salt, E. Chauvenet obtained the 1 : 3-salt or $ZrOSO_4.ZrO_2$, *i.e.* **zirconium trioxysulphate,**

$$SO_4 < \begin{matrix} Zr \lessgtr \begin{matrix} O \\ O \end{matrix} \\ Zr \lessgtr O \end{matrix}$$

as an *octohydrate*, which becomes anhydrous at 100°.

According to J. J. Berzelius, when alcohol is added to an aq. soln. of normal zirconium sulphate, and the precipitate washed first with alcohol and then with water, a salt having the composition $3ZrO_2.2SO_3(nH_2O)$, possibly *zirconium tetroxydisulphate*, $Zr_3O_4(SO_4)_2(nH_2O)$, or $Zr_3(OH)_8(SO_4)_2(mH_2O)$,

$$\begin{matrix} O \\ O \end{matrix} < \begin{matrix} Zr \\ Zr \end{matrix} > SO_4 \qquad\qquad (HO)_3 \equiv Zr > SO_4$$
$$\begin{matrix} O \\ O \end{matrix} < \begin{matrix} Zr \\ Zr \end{matrix} > SO_4 \qquad\qquad (HO)_2 = Zr > SO_4$$
$$\qquad\qquad\qquad (HO)_3 \equiv Zr$$

is formed.

The same salt was said to be produced when the soln. of zirconyl chloride was largely diluted with water. The white flakes are insoluble in water, and soluble in hydrochloric acid. The composition of this salt agrees with E. Chauvenet's 1 : 2-salt, and the salt is said to be obtained when potassium sulphate is added to a soln. of zirconyl chloride, the *octohydrate*, $2ZrOSO_4.ZrO_2.8H_2O$, is precipitated. It loses all 8 mols. of water at 100°, and becomes anhydrous. S. R. Paykull, and H. Endemann likewise obtained a product of the same composition. O. Hauser found the b.p. of soln. of zirconium dihydrotrisulphate slowly decreased on prolonged heating, and he attributed this to the formation of the acid salt, **penta-hydrated dizirconium dihydroxytrisulphate,** $2ZrO_2.3SO_3.5H_2O$, or

$$HO-Zr \begin{matrix} SO_4 \\ SO_4 \\ SO_4 \end{matrix} \qquad\qquad O < \begin{matrix} Zr \\ Zr \end{matrix} \begin{matrix} SO_4 \\ SO_4 \\ SO_4 \end{matrix}$$
$$HO-Zr$$

Zirconium dihydroxytrisulphate.   **Zirconium oxytrisulphate.**

which separates in crystals from very conc. soln.—say 50 grms. of anhydrous zirconium sulphate and 60 grms. of water. The salt is washed with a little cold water and dried over conc. sulphuric acid. Dil. soln. do not give this precipitate, but a flocculent mass of indefinite composition. The sp. gr. of the salt is 2·834 at 19°; it is soluble in water; and readily soluble in acids. The aq. soln. has a feebly acid reaction. The zirconium is imperfectly precipitated as hydroxide from the aq. soln. by aq. ammonia and alkali-lye. The anhydride, **zirconium oxytrisulphate,** $2ZrO_2.3SO_3$, or $Zr_2O(SO_4)_3$, was prepared by O. Hauser by heating the hydrated salt to 300°. If the salt be allowed to stand in contact with water for a long time, it furnishes a salt more basic than zirconyl sulphate, which O. Hauser and H. Herzfeld represent as $4ZrO_2.3SO_3.15H_2O$ when dried over sulphuric acid of sp. gr. 1·256. The salt may be regarded as **decahydrated zirconium decahydroxytrisulphate,** $Zr_4(OH)_{10}(SO_4)_3.10H_2O$,

$$(HO)_2 = Zr < \begin{matrix} SO_4-Zr(OH)_3 \\ SO_4 \\ SO_4-Zr(OH)_3 \end{matrix} +10H_2O$$
$$(HO)_2 = Zr$$

or some **intermediate** stage, $HO.ZrO.SO_4.ZrO.SO_4.ZrO.SO_4.ZrO.OH+14H_2O$. O. Hauser found that the same salt is formed when soln. containing between $Zr(SO_4)_2 : H_2O=1 : 7$ and 1 : 120 are allowed to stand for about 10 hrs. at 39·5°. Soln. with less than the ratio 3 : 20 remain clear. The conc. of the soln. required for the deposition of this salt depends on the temp.; the lower the temp., the greater the conc. required for its formation. The speed of the reaction is small,

and is greater the higher the temp. The compound is not produced above 50°. The composition of the salt may be represented by $ZrO(OH)_2.3ZrOSO_4.13H_2O$ in agreement with the fact that very dil. soln. are opalescent, and yield colloidal zirconium hydroxide when dialyzed. This may mean that the salt is further hydrolyzed by dilution. If very dil. soln. of this basic sulphate be kept for a long time at 64°, (i) the crystalline salt is no longer deposited at a lower temp. ; (ii) the soln. gives a precipitate with hydrogen dioxide only after standing for some time ; and (iii) a small proportion of oxalic acid gives no precipitate. The time required to inaugurate the indifferent stage depends on the conc. of the soln. Conc. soln. which have been heated and then diluted behave differently from those which have been diluted and then heated. O. Hauser and H. Herzfeld found that the decahydroxytrisulphate is so well-defined a chemical individual that it can be used in at. wt. determinations. It furnishes microscopic, monoclinic, acicular crystals of sp. gr. 2·50, and it is very stable towards dil. acids. The solubility in water is less than 0·009 per cent. When dried over sulphuric acid of increasing conc., the loss of water is continuous until **dihydrated zirconium decahydroxy-trisulphate,** $Zr_4(OH)_{10}(SO_4)_3.2H_2O$, is formed. The process of dehydration is not reversible. If the salt be heated at 105°–115° for a long time, **zirconium decahydroxytrisulphate,** $Zr_4(OH)_{10}(SO_4)_3$, is formed. Attempts to replace the hydroxyl by chlorine gave indefinite results. O. Hauser and H. Herzfeld represent the composition of the salt $2ZrO_2.3SO_3.5H_2O$ by the formula $H_4[Zr_4(SO_4)_6(OH)_8].4H_2O$ in order to explain its acid properties and its ready conversion into either of the two salts described below. The 4 mols of water are lost at 225°. The salt $4ZrO_2.3SO_3.14H_2O$ is represented by the formula $Zr_4(SO_4)_3(OH)_{10}.9H_2O$, and it can be prepared in another form by dissolving zirconium sulphate tetrahydrate in cold water and keeping the 2 per cent. soln. for several days, when the salt is deposited in the form of needles differing only from the crystals of the first form in their optical properties. The first is not decomposed by boiling water, whilst the second loses part of its sulphuric acid. The more basic salt, $\{Zr_8(SO_4)_5(OH)_{22}\}8H_2O$, is prepared by dissolving anhydrous zirconium sulphate in five times its weight of water and precipitating with alcohol. The precipitate is then dissolved in a little warm water and dialyzed, and in the course of a few days the basic salt separates in the form of very characteristic spherical crystals which do not lose their shape when dehydrated. According to E. H. Rodd, when a soln. of the basic chloride $Zr_5O_8Cl_4.22H_2O$ is treated with sulphuric acid, or a soluble sulphate, a white, curdy basic sulphate is precipitated. If ammonium sulphate or magnesium sulphate is used, the precipitate first formed redissolves until about half the eq. quantity of sulphate has been added. With a quantity of sulphate eq. to the chlorine in the basic chloride, the zirconium appears to be completely precipitated. The basic sulphate again redissolves in excess of the precipitant. In the case of sulphuric acid the precipitate becomes permanent with a few drops of acid ; it redissolves, however, in a large excess. To make the basic sulphate, the oxychloride is dissolved in 30 times its weight of water and 2 molar proportions of sulphuric acid are added for each molar proportion of the basic sulphate. W. Rosenhain and E. H. Rodd made a basic sulphate by adding sodium hydroxide or ammonia to a soln. containing zirconium sulphate and hydrochloric acid until the acidity of the soln. had been so far neutralized that a permanent white precipitate began to form, and then allowing precipitation to continue without further addition of alkali. The air-dried precipitate had the composition $Zr_5O_8(SO_4)_2.14H_2O$,

$$SO_4 = \begin{matrix} ZrO.ZrO.O.ZrO.O.Zr = SO_4 \\ O\text{———}O\text{———}O \end{matrix} \quad \text{or} \quad SO_4 < \begin{matrix} ZrO.O \\ ZrO.O \end{matrix} > Zr < \begin{matrix} O.ZrO \\ O.ZrO \end{matrix} > SO_4$$

i.e. **zirconyl disulphatozirconate.** R. Ruer, and M. Levin boiled for a time a soln. of zirconyl chloride mixed with a molar proportion of sulphuric acid, and obtained a product with 48·65 per cent. ZrO_2 and 19·83 per cent. SO_3, which corresponds with no definite at. ratio ; but E. H. Rodd boiled a soln. of 6 grms. of octohydrated zirconyl chloride with 500 c.c. of water for 6 hrs., and an eq. of dil. sulphuric acid was added to the opalescent soln. About 60 per cent. of the zirconia in soln. was precipitated as a slimy mass which, when washed and dried in air, formed a hard glassy cake with a composition corresponding with disulphatozirconyl zirconate. This salt, however, when dried is insoluble in sulphuric acid, is not attacked by ammonia, and gives, on ignition, a hard, granular zirconia ; the basic sulphate prepared from the basic chloride, $Zr_5O_8Cl_4.22H_2O$, is soluble in sulphuric acid, decomposed by ammonia, and, on ignition, gives a loose, white powder.

H. Endemann added alcohol to a conc aq. soln. of the sulphate and obtained a basic sulphate with the composition $7ZrO_2.6SO_3.14H_2O$, or *zirconium octoxyhexasulphate*, $Zr_7O_8(SO_4)_6.14H_2O$, or $Zr_7(OH)_{16}(SO_4)_6.6H_2O$. The product dissolves in a small quantity of water, a large excess precipitates a more basic salt leaving a more acidic salt in soln. When the alcoholic precipitate is moistened with water, alcohol is given off, making it probable, said H. Endemann, that some alcohol takes the place of water of crystallization. It will be observed that both these salts have the same general formula : $Zr_nO_{n+1}(SO_4)_{n-1}$, or $Zr_n(OH)_{2n+}.(SO_4)_{n-1}$, and an indefinite number of these might be obtained by varying the conc. of the soln. : $nZr(SO_4)_2+2(n+1)H_2O=(n+1)H_2SO_4+Zr_n(OH)_{2n+2}(SO_4)_{n-1}$. They probably represent varying stages in the hydrolysis of normal zirconium sulphate ; and the establishment of their chemical individuality requires something more than analysis.

Complex products of **variable** composition have been obtained by dissolving zirconia in fused potassium hydrosulphate ; and by mixing soln. of potassium sulphate and zirconium sulphate. According to J. J. Berzelius,[3] molten potassium hydrosulphate dissolves zirconia, forming a clear liquid ; if a large excess of the hydrosulphate be present, the cold mass dissolves completely in water, but if otherwise, the product is decomposed by water into potassium hydrosulphate which dissolves, and a complex potassium sulphate which remains undissolved. B. Franz boiled the cold cake with dil. sulphuric acid and obtained an insoluble basic zirconium sulphate. C. M. Warren fused zirconia mixed with five times its weight of potassium hydrosulphate, dissolved the cold mass in an excess of sulphuric acid, evaporated the soln. to remove most of the sulphuric acid, and mixed the cold product with cold water. The undissolved portion had the composition $3K_2O.3ZrO_2.7SO_3.9H_2O$; the aq. soln. on evaporation furnished a crystalline powder with the composition $2K_2O.6ZrO_2.7SO_3.9H_2O$. There is nothing, however, to show that chemical individuals are involved.

According to J. J. Berzelius, when potassium sulphate in crystals or as a sat. soln. is added to neutral soln. of zirconium salts the whole of the zirconium in soln. is gradually precipitated as a crystalline basic double sulphate ; if the soln. be acidic, only part of the zirconium is precipitated, but all is deposited when the soln. is neutralized with potassium hydroxide. A similar precipitate is formed when a soln. of zirconium sulphate is mixed with any salt of potassium. J. J. Berzelius, and R. Hermann represented the composition of the product $3ZrO_2.SO_3.xH_2SO_4$. The product is sparingly soluble in water, and is redeposited when potassium sulphate is added ; if the precipitate be washed with only a small portion of water, it dissolves in acids, especially when aided by heat, but if it be thoroughly washed, or boiled in water, it becomes nearly insoluble in water or acids, and requires conc. acid to dissolve it. When ignited, it loses water and sulphuric acid, and is virtually insoluble in hot conc. sulphuric acid. Soln. of ammonia or potassium carbonate dissolve the salt imperfectly ; a soln. of ammonium carbonate dissolves it, but on boiling deposits it again in its insoluble condition. C. M. Warren, and S. R. Paykull made some observations on this subject.

A. Rosenheim and P. Frank reported the formation of **potassium zirconium trioxydisulphate,** $Zr_2O_3(KSO_4)_2.8H_2O$, in small crystalline plates, when a soln. of normal potassium sulphate is added to a cold aq. soln. of zirconium sulphate ; and **rubidium zirconium trioxydisulphate,** $Zr_2O_3(RbSO_4)_2.15H_2O$, and **cæsium zirconium trioxydisulphate,** $Zr_2O_3(CsSO_4)_2.11H_2O$, were made in a similar way.

O. Hauser and H. Herzfeld added that the composition of these basic salts is more complicated than this. In general, the basic double salts of zirconium sulphate, like the basic zirconium sulphates, form colloidal soln. From the hot aq. soln., gels are precipitated by electrolytes, and dil. acids. The gels are probably colloidal zirconium hydroxide which dissolves only slowly in acids. The composition of the basic double salts of zirconium sulphates is influenced to an unusual degree by the temp. and conc. of the soln. In general, the product which separates from a weakly acid soln. is more basic than that from a strongly acid soln. According to R. Ruer, soln. of both zirconium oxychloride, and nitrate when treated with oxalic acid give precipitates soluble in excess; the reaction does not occur with sulphates because the zirconium is masked, being a constituent of the anion, not the cation. When the soln. is aged, and hydrolysis has progressed until metazirconic acid is formed, the sulphates then give the reaction with oxalic acid. Aged soln. of the sulphate, if warm, give precipitates with sulphates which are soluble in an excess of the reagent; but freshly prepared soln. of the oxychloride, or nitrate give no precipitates with a sulphate. The different behaviour of aged and freshly prepared soln. is another complication which hinders the acquisition of clear definite knowledge about these salts. A. Rosenheim and P. Frank prepared hydrated **potassium zirconium tetrasulphate,** $Zr(KSO_4)_4.3H_2O$, but A. Rosenheim and J. Pinsker showed that the proportion of water of crystallization is variable. The salt is obtained in acicular crystals by adding an excess of freshly precipitated zirconium hydroxide to a hot conc. soln. of potassium hydrosulphate. The salt is hydrolyzed by water at 30°, with the formation of basic salts, but no product of definite composition was isolated. A. Rosenheim and P. Frank reported the formation of **sodium zirconium tetrasulphate,** $Zr(NaSO_4)_4.4H_2O$, in acicular crystals when a cold acid soln. of sodium hydrosulphate is sat. with freshly precipitated zirconium hydroxide. The aq. soln. is clear, but slowly hydrolyzes when boiled. A. Rosenheim and J. Pinsker obtained the corresponding hydrated **ammonium zirconium tetrasulphate,** $Zr(NH_4SO_4)_4.5H_2O$, from the mother-liquor in the preparation of ammonium zirconium octohydroxyhexasulphate (*q.v.*). The salt is deposited only when the acidity of the soln. has been increased sufficiently by the separation of the basic salt. A. Rosenheim and J. Pinsker obtained **tetrapotassium zirconium octohydroxypentasulphate,** $K_4Zr_4(OH)_8(SO_4)_5.8H_2O$, by mixing conc. soln. of zirconium sulphate and normal potassium sulphate. O. Hauser and H. Herzfeld prepared a potassium zirconyl sulphate of definite composition, $K_2Zr_4(OH)_8(SO_4)_5$, **dipotassium zirconium octohydroxypentasulphate,** by dropping a sat. soln. of potassium sulphate into a conc. soln. of tetrahydrated zirconium sulphate acidified with sulphuric acid. The corresponding zirconium sulphuric acid was not prepared. A. Rosenheim and J. Pinsker obtained a crystalline mass of **ammonium zirconium octohydroxyhexasulphate,** $(NH_4)_4Zr_4(OH)_8(SO_4)_6.4H_2O$, by evaporating over conc. sulphuric acid, mixed soln. of 10 grms. anhydrous zirconium sulphate in 10 c.c. of water, and 14 grms. of ammonium sulphate in 25 c.c. of water. The mother-liquid remaining after the crystalline crusts have separated, furnishes ammonium zirconium tetrasulphate. This basic salt is considered to be the ammonium salt of a zirconium sulphuric acid obtained by O. Hauser and H. Herzfeld. E. Chauvenet and H. Gueylard measured the f.p. and heats developed on mixing soln. of potassium or sodium hydroxide, or aq. ammonia with soln. of zirconium sulphate. The resulting curves indicated the existence of **sodium dizirconyl hexasulphate,** $2ZrOSO_4.SO_3.3Na_2SO_4.8H_2O$; **sodium trizirconyl hexasulphate,** $3ZrOSO_4.SO_3.2Na_2SO_4.7H_2O$; and **sodium trizirconyl tetrasulphate,** $3ZrOSO_4.Na_2SO_4$; **potassium trizirconyl tetrasulphate,** $3ZrOSO_4.K_2SO_4.8H_2O$; **ammonium trizirconyl tetrasulphate,** $3ZrOSO_4.(NH_4)_2SO_4$; **ammonium zirconyl trisulphate,** $ZrOSO_4.SO_3.(NH_4)_2SO_4.3H_2O$; and **ammonium zirconyl tetrasulphate,** $ZrOSO_4.SO_3.2(NH_4)_2SO_4.3H_2O$, A. Rosenheim and J. Pinsker did not succeed in isolating basic sodium zirconium sulphates on account of their great solubility. L. Fernandes prepared **thallous zirconium**

tetrasulphate, $2Tl_2SO_4.Zr(SO_4)_2.4H_2O$; **thallous zirconium pentasulphate,** $Tl_2SO_4.2Zr(SO_4)_2.8H_2O$; and **thallous zirconium enneasulphate,** $7Tl_2SO_4.2Zr(SO_4)_2$, by the crystallization of a mixed soln. of the component salts—the first by cooling hot soln., the last by evaporation at a low temp. The solubility of the enneasulphate expressed in grams of zirconia per 100 c.c. of water was found to be :

	0°	10°	20°	30°	40°	60°	80°	100°
ZrO_2	6·2	6·2	6·5	7·2	8·5	15·7	24·5	32·0

REFERENCES.

[1] S. R. Paykull, *Bull. Soc. Chim.*, (2), **20**. 65, 1873 ; *Ber.*, **12**. 1719, 1879 ; *Œfvers. Akad. Förh. Stockholm*, **22**, 1873 ; 7, 53, 1878 ; J. J. Berzelius, *ib.*, 295, 1824 ; *Pogg. Ann.*, **4**. 117, 1825 ; *Ann. Chim. Phys.*, (2), **29**. 337, 1825 ; E. Frémy, *ib.*, (3), **38**. 326, 1832 ; H. Moissan and F. Lengfeld, *Compt. Rend.*, **122**. 651, 1896 ; F. P. Venable and R. O. Dietz, *Journ. Elisha Mitchell Scient. Soc.*, **38**. 74, 1923 ; O. Hauser, *Zeit. anorg. Chem.*, **53**. 74, 1907 ; A. L. Feild, *Trans. Amer. Inst. Min. Met. Eng.*, **69**. 848, 1923 ; **70**. 201, 1924 ; *U.S. Pat. No.* 1544824, 1925 ; A. E. van Arkel, *Physica*, **4**. 286, 1924; A. E. van Arkell and J. H. de Boer, *Zeit. anorg. Chem.*, **148**. 345, 1925.

[2] J. J. Berzelius, *Œfvers. Akad. Förh. Stockholm*, 295, 1824 ; *Pogg. Ann.*, **4**. 117, 1825 ; *Ann. Chim. Phys.*, (2), **29**. 337, 1825 ; L. N. Vauquelin, *ib.*, (1), **22**. 179, 1797 ; O. Kulka, *Beiträge zur Kenntnis einiger Zirkoniumverbindungen*, Bern, 19, 1902 ; G. H. Bailey, *Chem. News*, **60**. 6, 17, 32, 1889 ; *Proc. Roy. Soc.*, **45**. 74, 1889 ; O. Hauser, *Ber.*, **37**. 2024, 1904 ; *Journ. prakt. Chem.*, (2), **76**. 363, 1907 ; *Zeit. anorg. Chem.*, **45**. 185, 1905 ; **53**. 74, 1907 ; **54**. 196, 1907 ; O. Hauser and H. Herzfeld, *ib.*, **67**. 369, 1910 ; **106**. 1, 1919 ; A. Rosenheim and J. Pinsker, *ib.*, **106**. 9, 1919 ; L. Pissarjewsky, *Journ. Russ. Phys. Chem. Soc.*, **32**. 609, 1900 ; *Zeit. anorg. Chem.*, **25**. 378, 1900 ; R. Ruer and M. Levin, *ib.*, **46**. 449, 1905 ; R. Ruer, *ib.*, **42**. 87, 1904 ; **43**. 282, 1905 ; J. M. van Bemmelen, *ib.*, **49**. 125, 1906 ; M. Weibull, *Acta Univ. Lund.*, (2), **18**. 34, 1881 ; *Ber.*, **20**. 1394, 1887 ; A. Rosenheim and P. Frank, *ib.*, **38**. 812, 1905 ; F. P. Venable, *Zirconium and its Compounds*, New York, 77, 1922 ; *Journ. Amer. Chem. Soc.*, **20**. 119, 1898 ; F. P. Venable and D. H. Jackson, *ib.*, **42**. 2531, 1920 ; M. N. Rich, *U.S. Pat. No.* 1460766, 1923 ; H. Rose, *Pogg. Ann.*, **83**. 143, 1851 ; C. W. G. Nylander, *Bidrag till Kännedom om Zirkonjord*, Lund, 21, 1864 ; M. H. Klaproth, *Beiträge zur chemischen Kenntniss der Mineralkörper*, Berlin, **1**. 203, 227, 1795 ; S. R. Paykull, *Œfvers. Akad. Förh. Stockholm*, **22**, 1873 ; 53, 1878 ; *Ber.*, **12**. 1719, 1879 ; R. Hermann, *Journ. prakt. Chem.*, (1), **31**. 75, 1844 ; (1), **97**. 321, 330, 1866 ; H. Endemann, *ib.*, (2), **11**. 219, 1875; E. Chauvenet and H. Gueylard, *Compt. Rend.*, **167**. 24, 126, 1918 ; E. Chauvenet, *ib.*, **164**. 630, 864, 946, 1916 ; **165**. 25, 1917 ; *Ann. Chim. Phys.*, (9), **13**. 59, 1920 ; E. Löwenstein, *Zeit. anorg. Chem.*, **63**. 69, 1909 ; *Ueber Hydrate, deren Dampfspannung sich kontinuierlich mit der Zusammensetzung ändert*, Göttingen, 1909 ; E. H. Rodd, *Journ. Chem. Soc.*, **111**. 396, 1917 ; W. Rosenhain and E. H. Rodd, *U.S. Pat. Nos.* 1307881, 1307883, 1919 ; R. T. Glazebrook, W. Rosenhain, and E. H. Rodd, *Brit. Pat. No.* 112973, 1917 ; L. Fernandes, *Gazz. Chim. Ital.*, **55**. ii, 290, 1925 ; *Atti Accad. Lincei*, (6), **2**. 182, 1925.

[3] J. J. Berzelius, *Œfvers. Akad. Förh. Stockholm*, 295, 1824 ; *Pogg. Ann.*, **4**. 117, 1825 ; C. M. Warren, *ib.*, **102**. 449, 1857 ; *Journ. prakt. Chem.*, (1), **75**. 361, 1858 ; R. Hermann, *ib.*, (2), **31**. 75, 1844 ; (2), **97**. 321, 330, 1866 ; O. Hauser and H. Herzfeld, *Zeit. anorg. Chem.*, **67**. 369, 1910 ; **106**. 1, 1919 ; R. Ruer, *ib.*, **35**. 4431, 1902 ; A. Rosenheim and J. Pinsker, *ib.*, **106**. 9, 1919 ; A. Rosenheim and P. Frank, *Ber.*, **38**. 812, 1905 ; **40**. 803, 1907 ; B. Franz, *ib.*, **3**. 58, 1870 ; S. R. Paykull, *Œfvers Akad. Förh. Stockholm*, **22**, 1873 ; 7. 53, 1878 ; *Ber.*, **12**. 1719, 1879 ; *Bull. Soc. Chim.*, (2), **20**. 65, 1873 ; E. Chauvenet and H. Gueylard, *Compt. Rend.*, **167**. 24, 126, 201, 1918 ; E. Chauvenet, *Ann. Chim. Phys.*, (9), **13**. 59, 1920 ; L. Fernandes, *Gazz. Chim. Ital.*, **55**. i, 3, 1925.

§ 13. Zirconium Carbonates

There is no evidence of the formation of normal *zirconium carbonate* or of normal *zirconyl carbonate*. N. J. Berlin,[1] and S. R. Paykull found that zirconium hydroxide, $ZrO_2.H_2O$, readily absorbs carbon dioxide from the atm. F. P. Venable and A. W. Belden found that basic carbonates of widely varying composition are formed when carbon dioxide is passed over the hydroxide at 100°–150°. Over 16 per cent. of the gas may be so absorbed, and a part is given off when the product is similarly heated in a current of air ; 7 per cent. of carbon dioxide may be absorbed when the gas is bubbled through water in which the hydroxide is suspended. M. H. Klaproth, and L. N. Vauquelin regarded the white powder which is obtained when a cold soln. of a zirconium salt is treated with potassium carbonate as a carbonate; and R. Hermann's analysis of the precipitate washed with cold water, and dried at 17·5° over sulphuric acid, corresponded with $3ZrO_2.CO_2.6H_2O$. A. Mandl also prepared a basic carbonate by passing carbon dioxide through an aq. soln. of zirconium nitrate and ammonium carbonate. The white flocculent basic carbonate precipitated by the alkali carbonate is soluble in an excess of the precipitant; and when boiling water is poured over the precipitate carbon dioxide is evolved.

According to J. J. Berzelius, zirconium hydroxide dissolves very slowly and imperfectly in a soln. of ammonium carbonate, but the basic carbonate dissolves more readily. When the soln. is boiled zirconium hydroxide, free from carbonate, is deposited—as a white powder from the soln. in ammonium hydrocarbonate, and in gelatinous masses from the soln. of the normal carbonate. It is assumed that the solute is a basic *ammonium zirconium carbonate*. Analogous results were obtained with the alkali carbonates, forming *sodium zirconium carbonate*, or *potassium zirconium carbonate*. No chemical individual has been definitely established.

REFERENCES.

[1] N. J. Berlin, *Journ. prakt. Chem.*, (1), **58**. 145, 1853; R. Hermann, *ib.*, (1), **31**. 75, 1844; S. R. Paykull, *Ber.*, **12**. 1719, 1879; *Œfvers. Akad. Förh. Stockholm*, **7**, 53, 1878; J. J. Berzelius, *ib.*, 295, 1824; *Pogg. Ann.*, **4**. 143, 1825; F. P. Venable and A. W. Belden, *Journ. Amer. Chem. Soc.*, **20**. 273, 1898; L. N. Vauquelin, *Ann. Chim. Phys.*, (1), **22**. 179, 1797; M. H. Klaproth, *Beiträge zur chemischen Kenntniss der Mineralkörper*, Berlin, **1**. 203, 227, 1795; A. Mandl, *Zeit. anorg. Chem.*, **37**. 252, 1903.

§ 14. Zirconium Nitrates

J. J. Berzelius [1] evaporated a soln. of zirconium hydroxide in nitric acid, and obtained a yellow, sticky mass with a sour taste, and which, when dried at a temp. below 100°, is completely soluble in water. The aq. soln. can dissolve a large additional quantity of zirconium hydroxide, forming a basic salt. Consequently, a comparatively large quantity of alkali-lye can be added to a soln. of the nitrate before a permanent precipitate occurs. L. N. Vauquelin said that water dissolves only a portion of the residue left on evaporating the nitric acid soln. to dryness. Basic nitrates, $3ZrO_2.2N_2O_5$, and $ZrO_2.N_2O_5$, were reported by R. Hermann, and S. R. Paykull, but these products represent indefinite stages in the hydrolysis of the nitrate. M. Weibull evaporated a soln. of zirconium hydroxide in nitric acid at 65°, and obtained a white powder with the composition $ZrO(NO_3)_2.2H_2O$, **dihydrated zirconyl nitrate**; A. Rosenheim and P. Frank obtained a crystalline mass of the same composition by evaporating the soln. over sulphuric acid. M. Weibull evaporated the soln. at 100°, and obtained a glassy mass with the composition of **zirconyl hydroxynitrate**, $ZrO(OH)NO_3$. When the powdered zirconyl nitrate is dissolved in boiling alcohol and the soln. treated with ether, a white powder with the composition $Zr_2O_3(NO_3)_2.5H_2O$, or **dihydrated zirconyl hydroxynitrate**, $ZrO(OH)NO_3.2H_2O$, is formed (*vide infra*). It is readily soluble in water. E. Chauvenet and L. Nicolle could not make the normal nitrate by evaporating a soln. of zirconium nitrate in nitric acid in a current of carbon dioxide sat. with nitric acid fumes. The dehydration is always accompanied by the loss of nitric acid. The product was always **hemiheptahydrated zirconyl nitrate**, $ZrO(NO_3)_2.3\frac{1}{2}H_2O$, when the evaporation was conducted below 10°, and $ZrO(NO_3)_2.2H_2O$, when above that temp. (*vide infra*). A. Mandl failed to make the normal nitrate by evaporating a nitric acid soln. of zirconium hydroxide at 100°; similar results were obtained when the soln. was mixed with potassium nitrate, and no double salt was formed. A. Müller was unable to make a nitrate of constant composition, and he said that during the evaporation of soln., the salt undergoes hydrolysis, nitric acid escapes, and the product obtained is always a mixture of the hydroxide and nitrate in varying proportions. The products

M

when treated with water furnish opalescent, partly colloidal soln. Reports of *pentahydrated zirconium nitrate*, $Zr(NO_3)_4.5H_2O$, by R. Hermann, M. Weibull, S. R. Paykull, and A. Rosenheim and P. Frank, formed in hygroscopic prisms by evaporating a nitric acid soln. of zirconium hydroxide over phosphorus pentoxide and sodium hydroxide, probably refer to an acidic zirconyl nitrate, $ZrO(NO_3)_2.2HNO_3.4H_2O$. Commercial zirconium nitrate is an indefinite basic salt. E. Löwenstein measured the vap. press. of the so-called pentahydrated zirconium nitrate, when confined over sulphuric acid of different conc., and found that the dihydrated and anhydrous salts were formed.

C. L. Wagner examined the gradual hydrolysis of soln. of zirconium nitrate by means of the ultramicroscope and obtained results like those with ferric chloride. W. Ramsay and F. L. Usher exposed soln. of zirconium nitrate to radium emanation and obtained carbon oxide gases which he attributed to the degradation of zirconium to carbon. The hypothesis has not been confirmed. E. Chauvenet and L. Nicolle found that dihydrated zirconyl nitrate remains unaltered in air, and does not fume if entirely freed from adsorbed nitric acid. A mol of the dihydrate was mixed with n mols of water and the heat of soln. of the mixture determined :

n .	.	.	. 0	1	1·5	2·17	2·76	4
Heat of soln. .		.	2·17	−0·50	−1·92	−2·77	−3·95	−5·90

The resulting curve gave one break corresponding with the hemiheptahydrate. This hydrate is readily formed at $0°$; it is unstable at $10°$; and it effloresces at ordinary temp. forming the dihydrate. When zirconyl nitrate is dissolved in water it is slowly hydrolyzed, forming a precipitate with the composition $ZrO(NO_3)_2.ZrO_2.nH_2O$, or $ZrO(HO)NO_3.mH_2O$. The rate of hydrolysis is represented by the conductivity of the $0·01N$-soln. at $29·5°$. A few minutes after the preparation the conductivity was $505·19$, which rose to 554 in a few hours, and to 600 in a few days. The conductivity thereafter remained constant for some months. The $0·01N$-soln. of zirconyl nitrate was treated with a $0·01N$-soln. of sodium hydroxide, and the conductivity determined after each addition. The resulting curve had two breaks corresponding respectively with the reactions $ZrO(NO_3)_2+NaOH=NaNO_3+ZrO(OH)NO_3$, and $ZrO(NO_3)_2+2NaOH=2NaNO_3+ZrO_2+H_2O$. Cryoscopic measurements gave the mol. wt. $92·9$ instead of $266·6$; this means that the original mol. breaks down into three parts. Hence, it was inferred that the dissociation of the soln. yields $Zr(OH)_3NO_3.HNO_3$. E. Chauvenet and L. Nicolle measured the effect of heating zirconyl nitrate at different temp., and found that at $120°$ in the presence of nitric acid vap., the dehydration is accompanied by a loss of nitric acid to form a basic nitrate $3ZrO(NO_3)_2.ZrO_2.7H_2O$; and when the dehydration occurs in air, there is formed at $110°$, the basic nitrate $2ZrO(NO_3)_2.ZrO_2.7H_2O$; at $150°$, $ZrO(NO_3)_2.2ZrO_2.4H_2O$; at $215°$, $ZrO(NO_3)_2.7ZrO_2.5H_2O$; at $250°$, $ZrO(NO_3)_2.10ZrO_2.4H_2O$; and above this temp., zirconia is formed. These products probably represent mixtures and not chemical individuals. W. Biltz dialyzed soln. of zirconyl nitrate and found that in about 5 days the outside water was free from nitric acid; and the resulting hydrosol was clear in transmitted light and turbid in reflected light. The sol. is flocculated by electrolytes; and the gold number is between $0·046$ and $0·09$. S. Meyer measured the magnetic susceptibility of zirconium nitrate. A. Kolb prepared **dihydrated zirconyl diamminonitrate**, $ZrO(NO_3)_2.2NH_3.2H_2O$, by the action of ammonia on zirconyl nitrate. The white crystalline mass is slightly hygroscopic, and is stable in air.

REFERENCES.

[1] S. R. Paykull, *Bull. Soc. Chim.*, (2), **20**. 65, 1873 ; *Ber.*, **12**. 1719, 1879 ; *Œfvers Akad. Förh. Stockholm*, 22, 1873 ; 7, 53, 1878 ; J. J. Berzelius, *ib.*, 295, 1824 ; *Pogg. Ann.*, **4**. 117, 1825 ; L. N. Vauquelin, *Ann. Chim. Phys.*, (1), **22**. 179, 1797 ; R. Hermann, *Journ. prakt. Chem.*, (1), **31**. 75, 1844 ; (1), **97**. 321, 330, 1866 ; A. Rosenheim and P. Frank, *Ber.*, **40**. 803, 1907 ; W. Biltz, *ib.*, **35**. 4431, 1902 ; S. Meyer, *Monatsh.*, **20**. 793, 1899 ; C. L. Wagner, *ib.*, **34**.

95, 931, 1913; A. Mandl, *Zeit. anorg. Chem.*, 37. 252, 1903; A. Müller, *ib.*, 52. 316, 1907; A. Kolb, *ib.*, 83. 143, 1913; E. Chauvenet and L. Nicolle, *Compt. Rend.*, 166. 781, 821, 1918; E. Chauvenet, *Ann. Chim. Phys.*, (9), 13. 59, 1920; W. Ramsay and F. L. Usher, *Ber.*, 42. 2930, 1909; W. Ramsay, *Journ. Chem. Soc.*, 95. 624, 1909; E. Löwenstein, *Zeit. anorg. Chem.*, 63. 69, 1909 · *Ueber Hydrate, deren Dampfspannung sich kontinuierlich mit der Zusammensetzung ändert*, Göttingen, 1909; M. Weibull, *Acta Univ. Lund*, (2), 18. 34, 1881 ; *Ber.*, 20. 1394, 1887.

§ 15. Zirconium Phosphates

The solubilities of zirconium in phosphoric acid, and of zirconia in fused sodium ammonium phosphate have been previously discussed; similarly also with the adsorption of phosphoric acid by colloidal zirconium dioxide. P. Hautefeuille and J. Margottet [1] heated zirconia with phosphoric acid to a temp. short of dehydration and found 100 parts of the acid dissolved 2 parts of the oxide. On cooling, two kinds of octahedral crystals separated out—one kind were doubly refracting, the other kind, singly refracting. The empirical formula was $2ZrO_2.P_2O_5$, or $(ZrO)_2P_2O_7$, **zirconyl pyrophosphate.** The crystals were not attacked by acids or potassium hydrosulphate, but were easily decomposed by fusion with alkali carbonates, giving insoluble alkali zirconates which could be freed from phosphoric acid by washing. A. Knop fused zirconia with sodium ammonium phosphate at a high temp. for some time, and lixiviated the cold mass with dil. hydrochloric acid. The rectangular parallelopipedal crystals resembled those of sodium zirconium phosphate. The analyses corresponded with $ZrO_2.P_2O_5$, corresponding either with **zirconium pyrophosphate,** ZrP_2O_7, or **zirconyl metaphosphate,** $ZrO(PO_3)_2$. R. Hermann obtained a product with the composition $ZrO_2.P_2O_5$, by dropping a soln. of zirconyl chloride into one of ammonium dihydrophosphate. M. Weibull added an aq. soln. of zirconyl chloride to an excess of a soln. of sodium hydrosulphate and obtained a white precipitate with the composition $ZrP_2O_7.2H_2O$; and a similar product, $ZrP_2O_7.1\frac{1}{2}H_2O$, was obtained by dropping a soln. of zirconium sulphate into one of sodium dihydropyrophosphate. These results show that when a soln. of a zirconyl salt is added to an excess of a soln. of a phosphate, either zirconium pyrophosphate, or zirconyl metaphosphate is formed—analysis does not distinguish between them. E. Wedekind and H. Rheinholdt supposed that **zirconium hydrophosphate,** $Zr(HPO_4)_2$, is formed. C. E F. Lundell and H. B. Knowles assumed that the secondary phosphate is precipitated by sodium hydrophosphate in acid soln., and when the product is ignited, it yields the normal pyrophosphate. J. H. de Boer and A. E. van Arkel said that zirconium is precipitated as the hydrophosphate from strongly acidic soln., which is insoluble in hydrochloric acid but soluble in hydrofluoric acid. Hence zirconium can be separated as the hydrophosphate from all metals except hafnium. The hydrophosphate is soluble in oxalic acid, and in conc. sulphuric and phosphoric acids only when freshly precipitated. The oxalic acid soln. is decomposed by heat or by the addition of alcohol or the mineral acids, and the soln. in sulphuric or phosphoric acid is decomposed by dilution. Alkali-lye converts the phosphate into hydroxide superficially, but complete decomposition is obtained in the presence of a substance capable of dissolving the hydroxide in alkaline soln., thus the aliphatic oxy-acids— *e.g.* tartaric, malic or lactic acid—alcohols with at least two hydroxyl groups on neighbouring carbon atoms—*e.g.* glycerol, dextrose, sucrose, pyrocatechol, and pyrogallol—and hydrogen dioxide. The hydrogen dioxide soln. precipitates the hydroxide when heated, and a perzirconate when alcohol is added ; the other soln. yield the hydroxide when they are partially neutralized with acid—preferably after precipitating the phosphoric acid with barium chloride. G. von Hevesy and K. Kimura found the **zirconyl dihydrophosphate,** $ZrO(H_2PO_4)_2$, is precipitated from $6N$-HCl soln. ; and its solubility is 0·00012 and 0·00023 mol per litre respectively in $6N$- and $10N$-HCl. On ignition, the phosphate loses 2 mols. of water forming zirconyl metaphosphate. The relation between the temp. and the progress of the reaction, $ZrO(H_2PO_4)_2 \rightarrow ZrO(PO_3)_2$, and similarly with the hafnium salt, are shown in Fig. 7.

R. Hermann, and S. R. Paykull mixed soln. of sodium hydrophosphate and zirconyl chloride, and obtained a product with the composition $5ZrO_2.4P_2O_5.8H_2O$; M. Weibull mixed soln. of zirconyl chloride and sodium phosphate and obtained a product with the composition $5ZrO_2.3P_2O_5.9H_2O$ when dried at 100°; and by adding a soln. of zirconyl chloride to one of sodium phosphate or of phosphoric acid, the product had the composition $3ZrO_2.2P_2O_5.5H_2O$. These results show that a *basic zirconium phosphate* may be formed, but until the products are more closely examined, the conditions better defined, and the previous history of the zirconium salt soln. indicated, the nature of these phosphates cannot be stated.

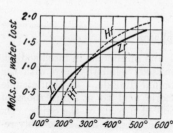

FIG. 7.—The Effect of Temperature on the Reaction: $RO(H_2PO_4)_2 \rightarrow RO(PO_3)_2$.

J. J. Berzelius found that zirconia dissolved slowly in molten sodium ammonium phosphate, and A. Knop kept the molten mixture at a white heat for two hours, and after washing the cold mass with dil. hydrochloric acid, and removing the amorphous portion, he obtained a mass consisting of small colourless crystals in the form of rectangular parallelopipeds which acted on polarized light. The composition corresponded with $Na_2O.4ZrO_2.3P_2O_5$, *i.e.* with $NaZr_2(PO_4)_3$, **sodium zirconium triorthophosphate,**

$$Na - PO_4 \begin{smallmatrix} Zr \equiv PO_4 \\ < \\ Zr \equiv PO_4 \end{smallmatrix}$$

L. Troost and L. Ouvrard obtained a similar salt by using sodium metaphosphate and sodium chloride as a flux. G. Wunder regarded the crystals as tetragonal combinations of prisms and basic pinacoids. A. Knop found the sp. gr. to be 3·12–3·14. When fused with potassium carbonate, crystalline zirconia was formed, but the phosphate is not decomposed by fused borax at a white-heat. L. Troost and L. Ouvrard found that when molten potassium metaphosphate is sat. with zirconia, zirconium chloride, or zirconium phosphate, and the cold mass extracted with acidulated water, the crystalline powder has an analogous composition, **potassium zirconium triorthophosphate,** $KPO_4(ZrPO_4)_2$. The trigonal crystals have a sp. gr. 3·18. Both salts are insoluble in simple acids and in aqua regia. L. Troost and L. Ouvrard also reported that a salt with the composition $6Na_2O.3ZrO_2.4P_2O_5$, corresponding with **sodium zirconium octa-orthophosphate,** $(Na_2PO_4)_2 = Zr\{PO_4 = Zr = (Na_2PO_4)_2\}_2$, is formed by dissolving zirconium chloride in a fused mixture of sodium chloride and molten sodium pyrophosphate and extracting the mass with water. The hexagonal plates are optically biaxial; and they act slightly on polarized light; the sp. gr. is 2·88; and the salt is soluble in acids. If a large proportion of sodium chloride be used in the preceding mixture, the product has a composition $4Na_2O.ZrO_2.2P_2O_5$, corresponding with **sodium zirconium tetra-orthophosphate,** $Zr(Na_2PO_4)_4$. The crystals act energetically on polarized light, and have longitudinal extinction. Their sp. gr. is 2·43; and they are soluble in acids. L. Troost and L. Ouvrard fused a zirconium salt with potassium pyrophosphate or potassium hydrophosphate and potassium chloride; and on extracting the cold mass with water, they obtained a crystalline powder of the composition $K_2O.ZrO_2.P_2O_5$, corresponding with **potassium zirconium diorthophosphate,** $Zr(KPO_4)_2$. The hexagonal plates have a sp. gr. 3·08; they were soluble in hot conc. nitric acid. If a large proportion of potassium chloride be employed, the same salt is obtained along with another consisting of tetragonal crystals the composition of which was not determined. If potassium orthophosphate be used in place of the pyrophosphate, the results were indefinite ; but if potassium chloride was also added, the same results were obtained as with the pyrophosphate. G. Saring reported **potassium calcium phosphato-zirconate,** $Ca_3(PO_4)_2(CaO)_2(K_2O)_2.ZrO_2$, analogous with the corresponding phosphatosilicate.

REFERENCES.

[1] P. Hautefeuille and J. Margottet, *Compt. Rend.*, **102**. 1017, 1886 ; L. Troost and L. Ouvrard. *ib.*, **102**. 1422, 1886 ; **105**. 30, 1887 ; M. Weibull, *Acta Univ. Lund*, (2), **18**. 21, 1882 ; *Ber.*, **20**. 1394, 1887 ; E. Wedekind and H. Rheinholdt, *ib.*, **47**. 2142, 1914 ; S. R. Paykull, *ib.*, **12**. 1719, 1879 ; *Œfvers. Akad. Förh. Stockholm*, **53**, 1878 ; J. J. Berzelius, *ib.*, 295, 1824 ; *Pogg. Ann.*, **4**. 117, 1825 ; A. Knop, *Liebig's Ann.*, **159**. 36, 1871 ; R. Hermann, *Journ. prakt. Chem.*, (1), **31**. 75, 1844 ; G. Wunder, *ib.*, (2), **109**. 475, 1870 ; G. Saring, *Versuche über den Aufschluss von Phosphaten durch Kieselsäure bei hohen Temperaturen*, Dresden, 1906 ; J. H. de Boer and A. E. van Arkel, *Zeit. anorg. Chem.*, **144**. 190, 1925 ; **148**. 84, 1925 ; G. von Hevesy and K. Kimura, *Journ. Amer. Chem. Soc.*, **47**. 2540, 1925 ; *Zeit. angew. Chem.*, **38**. 774, 1925 ; C. E. F. Lundell and H. B. Knowles, *Journ. Amer. Chem. Soc.*, **41**. 1801, 1919.

CHAPTER XLIII

HAFNIUM

§ 1. The History of Hafnium and Celtium

In 1911, G. Urbain [1] announced the discovery of a new element in some residues remaining after the separation of the lutecium-ytterbium fractions of the rare earths. He called it **celtium**. Subsequent observations showed that all the evidence in favour of this element was worthless. In May, 1922, A. Dauvillier found that the X-ray spectrum of these residues was in agreement with the presence of an element, atomic number 72, and G. Urbain applied the old term to the new element. The neo-celtium was not obtained in sufficient quantity, or sufficiently purified, to enable any other unequivocal statement to be made of its properties. Meanwhile, January, 1923, D. Coster and G. von Hevesy [2] reported a new element, discovered during their investigation of the zirconium minerals in quest of an element belonging to the zirconium family, and with an at. number 72, to fill the corresponding gap in the periodic table. The at. wt. is between 174 and 180. The new element was called **hafnium**, Hf—from *Hafnia*, an ancient name for Copenhagen. G. von Hevesy has summarized the known facts about hafnium in his *Recherches sur les propriétés du hafnium* (Köbenhavn, 1925); [3] and H. Rose in his *Das Hafnium* (Braunschweig, 1926).

After the discovery of hafnium, a controversy followed as to the priority of G. Urbain's [4] discovery—*vide* rare earths (5. 38, 25). G. Urbain claimed that he was the original discoverer of element 72, and that it should be called *celtium*. If the spirit of L. F. Svanberg were able to take part in the controversy, perhaps *norium* would be advocated ; if that of H. C. Sorby, *jargonium ;* if that of A. H. Church, *nigrum ;* and if those of K. A. Hoffmann and W. Prandtl, *euxenium.*

REFERENCES.

[1] G. Urbain, *Compt. Rend.*, **152**. 141, 1911 ; **174**. 1349, 1922 ; A. Dauvillier, *ib.*, **174**. 1347, 1922 ; *Nature*, **109**. 781, 1922.

[2] D. Coster and G. von Hevesy, *Journ. Soc. Chem. Ind.—Chem. Ind.*, **42**. 67, 258, 1923 ; *Naturwiss.*, **11**. 133, 1923 ; *Nature*, **111**. 79, 182, 252, 462, 1923.

[3] G. von Hevesy, *Chemical Reviews*, **2**. 1, 1925.

[4] L. F. Svanberg, *Pogg. Ann.*, **65**. 317, 1845 ; *Œfvers. Akad. Förh. Stockholm*, **34**, 1845 ; H. C. Sorby, *Proc. Roy. Soc.*, **17**. 511, 1869 ; **18**. 197, 1870 ; A. H. Church, *Chem. News*, **19**. 121, 1869 ; K. A. Hofmann and W. Prandtl, *Ber.*, **34**. 1064, 1901 ; T. L. Walker, *Nature*, **112**. 831, 1923 ; H. S. King, *ib.*, **112**. 9, 1923 ; G. Urbain, *Journ. Soc. Chem. Ind.—Chem. Ind.*, **42**. 764, 1923 ; Anon., *ib.*, **42**. 784, 1923 ; B. Brauner, *ib.*, **42**. 884, 1923.

§ 2. The Occurrence of Hafnium

D. Coster and G. von Hevesy [1] found up to 30 per cent. of hafnium in the different zirconium minerals investigated. These minerals were from Norway, Greenland, Italy, France, Russia, Ceylon, Brazil, and North Carolina. At least 1 per cent. of hafnium was found in commercial zirconium preparations, and G. von Hevesy and V. T. Jantzen found typical thorium minerals—thorite, thorianite, and orangite—to be free from hafnium. Minerals like baddeleyite and favas contain 1 to 2 per cent. of hafnium, while the most common silicates, and the zircons have between 1 and 7 per cent. The ratio $HfO_2 : ZrO_2$ was found to be appreciably greater in zirconium minerals than in less siliceous minerals. V. M. Goldschmidt and L. Thomassen found the richest hafnium content in the secondary minerals like *alvite*, regarded as *zirconium thorium hafnium orthosilicate*, $(Zr,Hf,Th)O_2.SiO_2$, and in *cyrtolite*, *nägeite*, and *malacone*. A specimen of the cyrtolite from Rockport, Mass., had 40 per cent. zirconium and 10 per cent. of hafnium. A. Piutti reported that Vesuvian zircon contains one per cent. of hafnium. E. and G. Urbain discussed the presence of both hafnium and the yttrium elements in some zirconium minerals, and found that the more hafnium is present the larger the proportion of rare earths. G. von Hevesy found that some historical preparations of zirconium from chemical museums contained 1 to 5 per cent. of hafnium. The relative amounts of the other members of the thorium family in the earth's crust, estimated by F. W. Clarke, and J. Joly, give silicon, Si, 27·7 per cent. ; titanium, Ti, 0·46 per cent. ; zirconium, Zr, 0·017 per cent. ; hafnium, Hf, over 0·002 per cent. ; and thorium, Th, 0·002 per cent.

REFERENCES.

[1] D. Coster and G. von Hevesy, *Journ. Soc. Chem. Ind.—Chem. Ind.*, 42. 67, 258, 1923 ; *Naturwiss.*, 11. 133, 1923 ; *Brit. Pat. No.* 219983, 1924 ; *Nature*, 111. 79, 182, 252, 462, 1923 ; T. E. Thorpe, *ib.*, 111. 252, 1923 ; H. M. Hassen and S. Werner, *ib.*, 111. 322, 1923 ; 112. 619, 1923 ; O. Hassel and H. Mark, *Zeit. Physik*, 27. 89, 1924 ; V. M. Goldschmidt and L. Thomassen, *Norsk Geol. Tids.*, 7. 61, 1923 ; G. von Hevesy, *Danske Vid. Selsk. Medd*, 7. 8, 1925 ; *Journ. Soc. Chem. Ind.—Chem. Ind.*, 42. 929, 1923 ; *Chem. News*, 127. 33, 186, 1923 ; *Ber.*, 56. B, 1503, 1923 ; A. Zacek, *Zeit. Physik*, 15. 31, 1923 ; D. Coster, *Physica*, 3. 133, 1923 ; *Phil. Mag.*, (6), 46. 956, 1923 ; *Chem. Weekbl.*, 20. 122, 1923 ; *Chem. News*, 127. 65, 1923 ; D. Coster, Y. Nishina, and S. Werner, *Zeit. Physik*, 18. 207, 1923 ; G. von Hevesy, *Chem. Ztg.*, 47. 345, 1923 ; *Zeit. anorg. Chem.*, 147. 217, 1925 ; *Nature*, 113. 384, 1924 ; 115. 335, 1925 ; G. von Hevesy, J. A. Christiansen, and V. Berglund, *Zeit. anorg. Chem.*, 144. 69, 1925 ; G. von Hevesy and E. Madsen, *Zeit. angew. Chem.*, 38. 228, 1925 ; G. von Hevesy and V. Berglund, *Journ. Chem. Soc.*, 125. 1372, 1924 ; G. von Hevesy and K. Kimura, *Journ. Amer. Chem. Soc.*, 47. 2540, 1925 ; *Zeit. angew. Chem.*, 38. 774, 1925 ; K. A. Gronvall, *Svenska Kem. Tids.*, 35. 68, 1923 ; G. Urbain, *Journ. Soc. Chem. Ind.—Chem. Ind.*, 42. 764, 1923 ; *Compt. Rend.*, 176. 459, 1923 ; E. and G. Urbain, *ib.*, 178. 265, 1924 ; F. W. Clarke, *The Data of Geochemistry*, Washington, 30, 1920 ; F. W. Clarke and H. S. Washington, *The Composition of the Earth's Crust*, Washington, 1924 ; J. Joly, *Phil. Mag.*, (6), 17. 760, 1909 ; (6), 18. 140, 1909 ; (6), 20. 125, 1910 ; G. Urbain and A. Dauvillier, *Compt. Rend.*, 176. 622, 1923 ; *Nature*, 111. 252, 1923 ; *Journ. Soc. Chem. Ind.—Chem. Ind.*, 42 1182, 1923 ; M. de Broglie and J. Cabrera, *Compt. Rend.*, 176. 433, 1923 ; J. Bardet, *ib.*, 176. 1711, 1923 ; J. Bardet and C. Toussaint, *ib.*, 180. 1936, 1925 ; Anon., *Journ. Soc. Chem. Ind.—Chem. Ind.*, 42. 784, 1923 ; G. von Hevesy and V. T. Jantzen, *Chem. News*, 127. 353, 1923 ; 130. 179, 1925 ; *Journ. Chem. Soc.*, 123. 3218, 1923 ; *Zeit. anorg. Chem.*, 133. 13, 1924 ; 136. 389, 1924 ; *Naturwiss.*, 12. 729, 1924 ; S. Meyer, *Phys. Zeit.*, 26. 51, 1925 ; O. Hönigschmid and E. Zintl, *Zeit. anorg. Chem.*, 140. 335, 1924 ; *Ber.*, 58. B, 453, 1925 ; J. H. de Boer and A. E. van Arkel, *Zeit. anorg. Chem.*, 141. 284, 289, 1924 ; 148. 345, 1925 ; J. H. de Boer, *ib.*, 150. 210, 1926 ; M. Marquis, P. and G. Urbain, *Compt. Rend.*, 180. 1377, 1925 ; B. B. Ray, *Phil. Mag.*, (6), 48. 707, 1924 ; Y. Nishina, *ib.*, (6), 49. 521, 1925 ; D. Coster and Y. Nishina, *Chem. News*, 130. 149, 1925 ; A. Piutti, *Rend. Accad. Napoli*, (3), 30. 122, 1924 ; Naamlooze Vennootschap Gloeilampenfabrieken, *Brit. Pat. Nos.* 219024, 219327, 226180, 1923 ; 219327, 1924 ; 220301, 1923 ; 238543, 1905 ; J. A. M. van Liempt, *Nature*, 115. 194, 1925 ; F. Steidler, *Microchemie*, 2. 98, 1924 ; N. Bohr, *Theory of Spectra and Atomic Constitution*, Cambridge, 1924 ; F. Henning, *Naturwiss*, 13. 661, 1925 ; W. Noethling and S. Tolksdorf, *Zeit. Kryst.*, 62. 255, 1925 ; D. H. Drophy and W. P. Davey, *Phys. Rev.*, (2), 25. 882, 1925.

§ 3. The Extraction of Hafnia

Hafnium is easily separated from the rare-earth elements ; and it was isolated by using methods employed for separating zirconium from thorium and titanium. According to G. von Hevesy and V. T. Jantzen, the mineral alvite was fused with ammonium hydrofluoride, and extracted repeatedly with boiling water, which dissolves very considerable amounts of ammonium fluosilicate, and zirconium.

hafnium, titanium, niobium, tantalum, vanadium, germanium, iron, and manganese, some of which are present only in very minute quantities, Thorium, the higher homologue of hafnium, and also the rare-earth elements present, remain insoluble, together with unattacked mineral and insoluble zirconium and hafnium fluoride compounds, such as sodium fluozirconate. Zirconium and hafnium can be separated by methods based on differences in the solubilities or vap. press. of corresponding compounds and partly on differences in their basicities. According to G. von Hevesy, the most practical method of separation is the crystallization of the double fluorides of potassium or ammonium. The mineral is melted with potassium hydrofluoride, and the hexafluozirconate extracted with boiling water, in which this compound is soluble to the extent of 25 per cent. On cooling, the greater part of the salt crystallizes out. G. von Hevesy and E. Madsen converted the product into the sulphate and then into the oxychloride, which is recrystallized, or treated with sulphur dioxide, which precipitates the hafnium and zirconium from the boiling soln., leaving most of the iron in soln. The double fluorides are best obtained by warming the dioxides with ammonium fluoride and hydrofluoric acid. The salt resulting from the fusion is unsuitable. The zirconium double fluoride being less soluble (2·6 per cent. at 20°) than the hafnium double fluoride (nearly 3 per cent. at 20°), the latter accumulates in the mother-liquor. Still more convenient is the crystallization of the highly soluble $(NH_4)_2ZrF_6$, soluble at 20° to the extent of 26 per cent. The ammonium double fluoride of hafnium crystallizes in prismatic (pseudo-hexagonal) crystals. The hafnium content is raised from 2 to 5 per cent. to 38 per cent. by fractionation of the ammonium compounds, and the subsequent fractionation of the potassium compounds furnishes a hafnium salt of 99·9 per cent. purity. The separation is controlled by X-ray spectroscopy and density determinations of the dioxides since the hafnia content x is obtained from the observed density D by $x = (D-5·73)/0·394$.   M. Marquis and P. and G. Urbain separated hafnium from malacone by the following process :

Small quantities of the mineral can be decomposed by fusion with potassium hydrosulphate; with large quantities of material it is better to decompose with sulphuric acid although some of the mineral remains unaffected. The excess of acid is expelled by heat and the soluble sulphates are extracted, leaving silica. Solid potassium sulphate is added in excess to the concentrated soln. of sulphates to precipitate zirconium and hafnium as insoluble sulphates. The precipitate is washed with cold saturated potassium sulphate soln. Although the solubilities of the two double sulphates differ appreciably they are unsuitable for fractionation because they are hydrolyzed to basic salts in water and are only stable in strongly acid soln. Saturated sodium carbonate forms double carbonates with zirconium and hafnium, but when a mixture of salts is treated with sodium carbonate, zirconium is extracted first. Alkali precipitates zirconium before hafnium from simple salt mixtures, and hafnium before zirconium from mixtures of complex salts. A series of fractions of the double carbonates in order of increasing hafnium content is treated with the same amount of sodium hydroxide. In each fraction the ratio Hf/Zr is greater in the precipitate than in the mother-liquor. The precipitate is filtered off, dissolved in sulphuric acid, and neutralized until a cloudy precipitate persists ; this soln. is then added to the mother-liquor from the precipitate in the succeeding stage of the fractionation. In this way hafnium preparations can be obtained in which the strong spectrum lines of zirconium are only faintly observed.

Another suitable method of separation is the crystallization of the ammonium-zirconium oxalate. A soluble zirconium salt, like the sulphate, is precipitated with ammonia, the hydroxide dissolved in an excess of oxalic acid and neutralized with ammonia. By crystallizing the oxalate formed, hafnium accumulates in the mother-liquor. Crystallizing the oxychlorides from about 12N-HCl gives better results than the oxalate method. If the acid be less than 9N-HCl, no separation occurs. The hafnium accumulates in the crystals.

Less satisfactory is the result of the crystallization of the complex sulphate, like the ammonium salt of zirconium and sulphuric acid. The hafnium concentrates in the mother-liquor. To purify zirconium from iron and other impurities it can be converted into the oxychloride. By repeatedly crystallizing this compound from hydrochloric acid pure zirconium is retained. Hafnium oxychloride is less soluble than zirconium oxychloride ; thus while purifying zirconium from iron, its hafnium content is raised at the same time. For example, starting from 100 g. $ZrOCl_2$ containing 1 per cent. hafnium, the 30 g. oxychloride residue obtained after ten successive crystallizations contained a little over 2 per cent. of hafnium. Hafnium is more basic than zirconium, and accordingly, when precipitating a soln. of a zirconium salt with ammonia the first precipitate contains less hafnium than the successive ones. For example, when precipitating one-half of an oxychloride soln. containing 1 per cent. hafnium with dil. ammonia, the precipitate contains only 0·8 per cent., whilst the hafnium content of the soln. is increased to 1·2 per cent. This difference can be somewhat increased by the presence of large amounts of ammonium chloride in the soln. By boiling a soln. of zirconium and hafnium with sodium thiosulphate, zirconium being more strongly hydrolyzed, the first precipitate contains a larger amount of zirconium than the successive ones. From a soln. of zirconium sulphate, diluted about 1 : 40, a basic zirconium compound precipitates on standing a few days at 39·5°. Also with this process, like many similar ones, the precipitate contains slightly more zirconium than the soln. G. von Hevesy and V. T. Jantzen found that in the fractional crystallization it is better to work with ammonium fluozirconate and fluohafniate than with the potassium salts. The ammonium fluohafniate collects in the mother-liquor and the ammonium fluosilicate and fluozirconate with the crystals. When a mixture of hafnium and columbium double fluorides is heated carefully, and afterwards treated with boiling water and acid ammonium fluoride, only the hafnium salt dissolves. This enables columbium and hafnium to be separated. The precipitation as basic chloride ; and with hydrogen dioxide ; and organic acids—benzoic, salicylic, or tartaric acid—did not give good results. D. Coster and G. von Hevesy recommended precipitating the oxychlorides to separate iron, aluminium, etc. The mixture of hafnium and zirconium oxychlorides is dissolved in 50 parts by weight of alcohol and 125 parts by weight of ether are added. The zirconium concentrates in the precipitate, hafnium in the mother-liquor. Acetone may also be used as precipitant. Amongst all the precipitation methods, said G. von Hevesy, preference is to be given to the fractional precipitation by adding sodium phosphate to the soln. in conc. nitric acid. The eighth fraction contained less than one-tenth the amount of hafnium present in the first precipitate. J. H. de Boer and A. E. van Arkel found that the compounds of hafnium tetrachloride with phosphorus pentachloride and oxychloride are more volatile than is the case with the corresponding zirconium compounds, and hence hafnium concentrates in the earlier fractions. D. H. Drophy and W. P. Davey found that zirconium citrate is relatively insoluble in pure water, while hafnium citrate is quite soluble. Zirconium citrate is also soluble in ammonium hydroxide or in an excess of citric acid. By adding a limited amount of an aq. soln. of citric acid to a soln. of crude zirconium nitrate, a precipitate of pure zirconium citrate is obtained which was identified by its X-ray absorption spectrum. X-ray absorption spectra of the water-soluble citrate showed the presence of hafnium. The conditions of the separation are such that although the precipitate is free from hafnium the soluble portion contains some zirconium. A number of methods of separating hafnium has been patented by the Naamlooze Vennootschap Gloeilampenfabrieken. This firm has also patented the use of hafnium nitrate admixed with tungstic oxide for making lamp filaments. The hafnium is supposed to prevent the recrystallization of the tungsten produced by reduction in hydrogen.

REFERENCES.

See § 2.

§ 4. Hafnium and its Properties

Metallic hafnium was prepared by reducing a hydrofluohafniate with sodium. A. E. van Arkel and J. H. de Boer made hafnium by passing the vapour of the tetraiodide over a heated tungsten filament—*vide* titanium; and J. H. de Boer reduced the tetrachloride with sodium. The metal has the same crystal structure as zirconium, for, according to W. Noethling and J. Tolksdorf, it crystallizes in the hexagonal system, and the X-radiogram shows that the side of the unit triangular prism is 3·32 A., and the height, 5·46 A., so that the axial ratio $a:c=1:1\cdot64$. The at. vol. is therefore 15·7. J. H. de Boer found the sp. gr. to be 12·1. A. E. van Arkel and J. H. de Boer found hafnium to be denser than zirconium, and also to possess a higher m.p.; and a higher electron emission. According to S. Meyer, hafnium is diamagnetic.

D. Coster and G. von Hevesy measured the X-ray spectra of a number of zirconium minerals, and found some characteristic lines in the L-series belonging to no known element. The wave-lengths interpolated from the two elements before and after the element with the atomic number 72, correspond closely with the observed lines, namely, $a=1565$; $a_2=1576$; $\beta=1371$; $\beta_2=1350$; $\gamma=1177$ X-units. A. Zacek found

	a_1	a_2	β_1	β_2	β_3
λ	1566·14	1576·70	1370·17	1349·1	1323·6
γ/R	24·122	24·041	25·789	25·990	26·239

where R denotes Rydberg's constant, and γ, the vibration frequency, the reciprocal of the wave-length. D. Coster examined the L-series of the X-ray spectrum. The X-ray method was employed for the quantitative determination of hafnium by using a known amount of the neighbouring element, 73—tantalum—and comparing the intensities of the lines of tantalum with those of the unknown element. H. M. Hansen and S. Werner measured 760 lines in the arc spectrum, and 683 in the spark spectrum of hafnium, and these all lie in the region 2253·95 A. and 7240·9 A. None of the lines ascribed to celtium was detected in the preparation of hafnium. Some of the weaker lines recorded by early investigation of zirconium really belong to hafnium, because the preparations all contained that element. J. Bardet also studied the arc spectrum. The X-ray spectra were examined by G. Urbain and A. Dauvillier, and B. B. Ray. D. Coster, and Y. Nishina measured the wave-lengths of the sixteen principal emission lines of the L-series, and two lines of the M-series. The K-absorption limit was also measured by D. Coster, and Y. Nishina, and the L-adsorption limit by M. de Broglie and J. Cabrera. The energy levels of the atoms of related elements have been computed.

REFERENCES.

See § 2.

§ 5. The Salts of Hafnium

The chemical properties of hafnium come between those of zirconium and thorium, but are much nearer those of zirconium. Any reaction characteristic of zirconium is also characteristic of hafnium. F. Steidler compared reactions with purified zirconium and purified hafnium—precipitation with potassium oxalate, rubidium chloride, ammonium fluoride, picric acid, and α-nitroso-β-naphthol—but not the slightest difference could be detected. The high m.p. and light emissivity of zirconia are shared by hafnia—**hafnium dioxide,** HfO_2; and the electronic emission of the heated metal exhibited by zirconium is also shown by

which, when corrected for the zirconium content by G. Hevesy, became 178·6. The presence of 1 per cent. zirconia lowers the at. wt. of hafnium 1·4 units.

According to N. Bohr's theory of the electronic structure corresponding with the number of electrons in the different groups of the neutralized atom of titanium, zirconium, hafnium, and thorium are :

Ti . . . (2) (4,4) (4,4,2) (2)
Zr . . . (2) (4,4) (6,6,6) (4,4,2) (2)
Hf . . . (2) (4,4) (6,6,6) (8,8,8,8) (4,4,2) (2)
Th . . . (2) (4,4) (6,6,6) (8,8,8,8) (6,6,6) (4,4,2) (2)

REFERENCES.

See § 2.

CHAPTER XLIV

THORIUM

§ 1. The History and Occurrence of Thorium

In 1815, J. J. Berzelius [1] obtained from a mineral from Finbo near Fahlun what he regarded as a new earth resembling zirconia. This earth was named *thorine* after the god Thor of Scandinavian mythology. In 1824, he showed that thorine was essentially yttrium phosphate. Four years later, J. J. Berzelius discovered another earth in a new mineral from Lövö near Brevig in Norway. He found this earth to be *sui generis*, distinct from all others, and he applied to the earth the old name *thoria* or *thorina*. The mineral in which the earth was discovered was named *thorite*.

C. Bergemann, [2] reported the discovery of a new earth in orangite, from Langesund fiord, Norway, and he named the element *donarium ;* but A. Damour, and N. J. Berlind identified donaria with thoria. J. F. Bahr [3] also reported a new earth in orthite ; and he named the element *wasmium.* J. Nicklès regarded wasmium as a didymiferous and terbiniferous yttria ; M. Delafontaine suggested that it is a mixture of cerite earth : O. Popp made a similar suggestion ; and J. F. Bahr himself later identified it with thoria —*vide* rare earths for *berzelium,* and *carolinium.*

Thorium is widely distributed in nature, but in very small proportions. J. Joly [4] estimates that the earth's lithosphere contains from 0.2×10^{-5} to 3×10^{-5} grm. per gram. F. W. Clarke's and J. Joly's estimates indicate that 27.7 per cent. of the earth's crust is silicon ; 0.46 per cent. titanium ; 0.017 per cent. zirconium ; and 0.002 per cent. thorium. J. H. L. Vogt estimated that the ten-mile crust, the hydrosphere, and lithosphere of the earth contained $n \times 10^{-9}$ per cent. of thorium ; and F. W. Clarke and H. S. Washington, $n \times 10^{-8}$ per cent. Frequently thorium and uranium occur in approximately the same proportions— *vide* radioactivity of thorium. Thorium occurs in Vesuvian lava ; T. L. Phipson found it in Norwegian granites ; A. L. Fletcher, in Leinster granites ; G. A. Blanc found in the syenites and granites of Vosges, 2×10^{-5} to 8×10^{-5} grm. of thorium per gram ; and 0.00145 per cent. of thorium in the soils near Rome ; J. Joly found 0.1×10^{-5} grm. of thorium per gram in limestones and dolomites ; 0.54×10^{-5} grm. per gram in sandstones from different localities ; and 1.14×10^{-5} in a number of argillaceous rocks. H. Lange found thoria is contained in fluorspar ; and, according to R. J. Strutt, a sample of Greenland fluorite contained 18.2×10^{-3} per cent. of thoria. J. Joly estimates that sea-water contains about 10^{-8} grm. of thorium per c.c. The occurrence of thorium in atm. air, spring waters, etc., is discussed in connection with thorium emanation (*q.v.*).

H. A. Rowland could not detect any thorium lines in the solar spectrum although G. Hofbauer gives a number of these lines. Thorium occurs associated in small quantities with the rare earths in most of the minerals discussed in connection with the rare earths ; and also with many tantalum, columbium, titanium, scandium, zirconium, and uranium minerals. The thorium minerals are largely conc. in about five districts : (i) Norway and Sweden—*e.g.* Arendal, Kragerö, Brevig, Hitterö Langesund, Bastnaes, Ytterby, etc. (ii) North America—*e.g.* North and South

174

Carolina at Burke, Cleveland, MacDowell, Spartanburg, etc.; in Llano County, Texas, Idaho at Idaho City, Placerville, Boisé City, etc.; in Virginia, and Colorado. (iii) Brazil—*e.g.* Bahia, Caravellas, Matto-Grosso, Goyaz, Minas Geraes, etc. (iv) Urals—*e.g.* Miask, etc. (v) Tasmania—*e.g.* Vegetable Creek, etc. Specimens have been reported from Scotland, Saxony, Ceylon, and Greenland. The dark brown or black mineral thorite was discovered on the island Lövö, in the fiord Langesund, Norway, in 1828 by H. M. T. Esmark,[5] and it was analyzed by J. J. Berzelius. In 1850, A. Krautz found the yellow mineral orangite which was analyzed by C. Bergemann, and named in allusion to its colour. For a time, these minerals were considered to be different species. In 1859, T. Scheerer argued that orangite and thorite are chemically and crystallographically similar, and that thorite is a transformation product of orangite. This view was supported by J. J. Chydenius, A. Breithaupt, A. E. Nordenskjöld, etc. Analyses have been made by J. J. Berzelius (1), C. Bergemann (2), A. Damour (3), N. J. Berlin, J. J. Chydenius, G. Lindström, W. E. Hidden and J. B. Mackintosh, L. Schilling (4, 10), P. G. Tschernik (5), W. R. Dunstan (6), P. Collier (7), A. E. Nordenskjöld (8), G. Lindström (9), etc.

TABLE I.—ANALYSES OF ORANGITE AND THORITE.

Source.	SiO_2	ThO_2	U_2O_3	PbO	Fe_2O_3	CaO	H_2O
1. Lövö, Norway . .	19·31	58·91	1·64	0·82	3·46	2·62	9·66
2. Brevig, Norway .	17·69	71·25	—	—	0·31	2·24	6·90
3. Brevig, Norway .	17·52	71·65	1·13	0·88	0·31	1·59	6·14
4. Arendal, Norway .	17·62	69·92	1·09	—	1·23	1·07	7·01
5. Batum, Asia Minor .	16·55	68·71	1·20	0·90	0·30	2·30	6·43
6. Kondrugala, Ceylon .	14·10	66·26	0·46	—	1·71	0·35	6·40
7. Champlain, N.Y. .	19·38	52·07	9·96	0·40	4·01	2·34	11·31
8. Arendal, Norway .	17·04	50·06	9·78	1·67	7·60	1·99	9·46
9. Arendal, Norway .	17·47	48·66	9·00	1·26	6·59	1·39	10·88
10. Brevig, Norway .	17·00	50·05	9·67	0·36	7·82	0·36	11·95

P. Truchot found 50–58 per cent. of thoria in thorite, and 71·65 per cent. in orangite; L. Schmelck, 50 per cent. in thorite, and 70 per cent. in orangite; G. P. Drossbach, 20–40 per cent. in thorite; W. R. Dunstan, 66·26 per cent.; B. Szilard, 42·5 per cent.; etc. J. Schilling found 69·92–74·20 per cent. in orangite; N. J. Berlin, 73·29 per cent.; A. Damour, 71–74 per cent.; J. J. Chydenius, 73·80 per cent.; etc. In addition to these constituents, the manganese oxide ranged up to 2·43; the alumina up to 0·84; the alkalies up to 0·82; magnesia up to 0·36; the stannic oxide up to 0·01; the phosphoric oxide up to 1·20; the ceria earths up to 1·54; the yttria earths up to 1·33; and the Cingalese sample had 2·23 per cent. of zirconia. G. von Hevesy and V. T. Jantzen reported no evidence of hafnium (or celtium) in thorite or orangite. The thoria in C. Bergemann's analysis was reported as donaria. E. Gleditsch found 0·0033 per cent. of lithium in thorite. Specimens (7–10) with the higher proportions of uranium oxide were called by P. Collier uranothorite. The results show that thorite is probably analogous with zircon, cassiterite, and rutile, and is an impure thorium orthosilicate, $ThSiO_4$, or $ThO_2.SiO_2$—*vide* zircon.

The specimens here analyzed contain water, showing that they are more or less weathered. A. Breithaupt, and A. E. Nordenskjöld consider thorite to be more impure than orangite. According to L. F. Nilson, the uranium is present as UO_2, and this agrees with C. W. Blomstrand's observations on the occurrence of the uranates. C. F. Rammelsberg wrote the formula (SiO_2, ThO_2), H_2O, or $3(SiO_2, ThO_2)$, $4H_2O$; F. Zambonini gave for thorite (SiO_2, ThO_2), nH_2O, where n ranges from 1·0–1·5; and for uranothorite, $(SiO_2.ThO_2.UO_2).nH_2O$, where n is greater than 1·5. The mineral occurs as pseudomorphs after orthoclase and zircon; and E. Zschau found the mineral to be tetragonal with the axial ratio $a : c = 1 : 0·642$.

and isomorphous with zircon, rutile, and cassiterite—and probably also with naegite, and xenotime; and, according to G. T. Prior, and W. T. Schaller, with ilmenorutile, strüverite, as well as with tapiolite or mossite. W. F. Hillebrand synthesized crystals resembling thorite by fusing uranium dioxide, UO_2, and thorium dioxide, ThO_2, with borax. L. Vegard obtained no evidence of crystalline structure in the X-radiogram of thorite; the sample used was presumably altered or weathered. M. L. Huggins found the structure to be like that of rutile and other tetragonal crystals. As a rule, with many exceptions, isomorphous compounds have mol. vols. of nearly equal value. Thorite (orangite), however, does not fit in with the series :

	Cassiterite $Sn(SnO_4)$	Rutile $Ti(TiO_4)$	Zircon $ZrSiO_4$	Thorite $ThSiO_4$	Xenotime YPO_4
Mol. vol.	44	38	39	60	41

Just as the proportion of water in thorite varies from specimen to specimen, so does the sp. gr. alter. J. J. Berzelius gave 4·8; J. J. Chydenius, 4·888–5·205 ; P. G. Tschernik, 3·36 ; W. R. Dunstan, 4·98 ; A. E. Nordenskjöld, 4·38 ; W. E. Hidden and J. B. Mackintosh, 4·322 ; A. Damour, 5·19 ; G. Lindström, 4·62–4·80 ; W. C. Brögger, 4·114 ; and P. Collier, 4·126. The values for orangite are usually greater than for thorite, being 4·4–4·8 for thorite, and 5·2–5·4 for orangite. The hardness ranges from 4·5–5·0 ; A. L. Fletcher gave 1255°–1270° for the m.p. of the mineral. F. Beijerinck said that thorite is a non-conductor of electricity. The radioactivity has been discussed by F. Pisani, F. Kolbeck and P. Uhlich, A. E. Nordenskjöld, R. J. Strutt, V. Goldschmidt, E. Gleditsch, G. F. Barker, B. B. Boltwood, H. M. Dadourian, H. N. McCoy and W. H. Ross, K. A. Hofmann and F. Zerban, etc. ; for the occurrence of helium in the mineral by W. Ramsay and co-workers, R. J. Strutt, etc.—vide the radioactivity of thorium. J. N. Lockyer reported some unknown lines in the spectrum of the mineral. O. Mann regards thorite as the decomposition product of a thorium phosphate analogous to mona-zite. R. J. Strutt estimated the age of thorite from the helium content—vide radioactivity of thorium. According to C. R. Böhm, the transformation or weathering of thorite furnishes auerlite, thorogummite, calciothorite, mackin-toshite, eucrasite, and freyalite.

The jet-black pseudocubic crystals occurring in the river-gravels or gem-gravels of Ceylon were once regarded as pitchblende, but the analyses of W. R. Dunstan [6] and co-workers showed that the crystals consist of 55–79 per cent. of thoria asso-ciated with 11–32 per cent. of uranium oxide, and 1–8 per cent. of oxides of the ceria earths, with smaller quantities of lead and iron oxides, zirconia, and silica. The mineral was named **thorianite.** Analyses have been reported by W. Ramsay, W. R. Dunstan and co-workers (3, 4), M. Ogawa (1, 2), P. Termier, R. J. Strutt, A. K. Coomaraswamy, T. L. Phipson, W. Jakob and J. S. Tolloczko, etc.

	SiO_2	TiO_2	ZrO_2	ThO_2	U_3O_8	$(Ce,La,Di)_2O_3$	PhO	Al_2O_3	Fe_2O_3.
1 . . .	0·20	–	0·09	78·00	14·54	1·41	2·66	0·15	1·54
2 . . .	0·20	0·88	0·15	58·27	33·27	1·05	3·80	0·03	1·83
3 . . .	—	—	—	72·24	11·19	6·90	2·25	—	1·92
4 . . .	—	—	—	78·86	15·10	1·02	2·59	—	0·40

Other constituents are present. G. von Hevesy and V. T. Jantzen found no hafnia in the mineral. M. Ogawa gave 0·02–0·03 of CuO ; 0·05, SnO_2 ; 0·11, Sb_2O_3 ; 0·10–0·27, CO_2 ; 0·60–3·20, H_2O ; and 0·13–1·13, CaO. A. Schoep has argued that the formula of thorianite is ThO_2 ; that that of uraninite is UO_2 ; and that these two minerals occur in isomorphous association. M. Kobayashi assumes that there are two varieties: α-thorianite with the ratio ThO_2 ; U_2O_3 =6 : 1 ; and β-thorianite with this ratio 2 : 1, and he explains the divergencies in the analytical results by assuming that mixtures of the two varieties have been analyzed. The helium content has been determined by W. Ramsay. R. J. Strutt, D. O. Wood, etc. ; the radioactivity by E. Gleditsch, H. Goldschmidt, F. Soddy

and R. Pirret, A. K. Coomaraswamy, etc. From the helium content, E. Rutherford estimated the age to be at least 4×10^8 yrs.—*vide* the radioactivity of
thorium.

E. H. Buchnen reported that thorianite contained a new element in the analytical
arsenic group, and two in the bismuth-cadmium group ; C. de B. Evans, that it contained
an element in the tin group ; and M. Ogawa, that thorianite and molybdenite contained
a new element closely allied to molybdenum, and which he called *nipponium*, Np. This
has not yet been confirmed. G. G. Boucher observed in certain specimens of iron and steel
a metal resembling molybdenum in some respects but different from it in others.
F. G. Ruddock, and C. H. Jones made some observations on this subject ; and A. Skrabal
and P. Artmann noted a similar metal in ferrovanadium.

W. R. Dunstan and co-workers assume that thorium and uranium dioxides are
isomorphous so that thorianite is a solid soln. of the two oxides ThO_2 and UO_2.
The constitution was discussed by G. Wyrouboff and A. Verneuil. G. Troost and
L. Ouvrard obtained octahedral crystals of thoria, and W. F. Hillebrand octahedral
crystals of uranous oxide belonging to the cubic system, whereas the crystals of
thorianite belong to the rhombohedral system. On the other hand, J. Nordenksjöld,
C. F. Rammelsberg, and W. F. Hillebrand obtained octahedral crystals of thorianite
by fusing the two oxides with borax. The sulphates of uranium and thorium were
shown by C. F. Rammelsberg, and W. F. Hillebrand and W. H. Melville, to be
isomorphous. It is therefore inferred that the two oxides are probably isomorphous. B. Szilard also assumes that uranium and thorium oxides form solid
soln. The twinning of the pseudocubic crystals of thorianite resembles that of
fluorspar ; but, like the zeolite chabazite, the optical properties correspond
with the symmetry of the rhombohedral system, and the angles are probably
very close to those of the cube. In view of the fact that both uranous oxide and
thoria form octahedral crystals, while a fused mixture of the two yields, on cooling,
cubic crystals, it is possible, but not proved, that the pseudocubic thorianite
becomes truly cubic at high temp. The values for the sp. gr. of thorianite reported
by W. R. Dunstan and co-workers range from 8·0–9·7 ; the hardness is 7 ; the
index of refraction, 1·8. C. Baskerville found that thorianite is decomposed when
heated in a stream of carbonyl chloride.

REFERENCES.

[1] J. J. Berzelius, *Afhand. Fysik, Kemi Min.*, **5**. 76, 1816 ; *Schweigger's Journ.*, **16**. 244,
302, 1816 ; **21**. 25, 1817 ; *Ann. Chim. Phys.*, (1), **3**. 140, 1816 ; *Svenska Akad. Handl.*, **4**. 315,
1824 ; **9**. 1, 1829 ; *Pogg. Ann.*, **16**. 385, 1829.

[2] C. Bergemann, *Sitzber. Akad. Berlin*, 221, 1851 ; *Pogg. Ann.*, **82**. 561, 1851 ; **85**. 558,
1852, *Liebig's Ann.*, **80**. 267, 1851 ; **84**. 239, 1852 ; A. Damour, *Compt. Rend.* **34**. 685, 1852 ;
Ann. Chim. Phys., (3), **35**. 241, 1852 ; N. J. Berlin, *Pogg. Ann.*, **85**. 556, 1852 ; **87**. 608, 1852.

[3] J. F. Bahr, *Œfvers. Akad. Förh.*, 415, 1862 ; *Pogg. Ann.*, **119**. 572, 1863 ; *Chem. News*,
8. 175, 185, 1864 ; *Liebig's Ann.*, **132**. 227, 281, 1864 ; J. Nicklès, *Compt. Rend.*, **57**. 740, 1863 ;
Journ. Pharm. Chim., (3), **45**. 25, 1864 ; M. Delafontaine, *Arch. Sciences Genève*, (2), **18**. 369,
1863 ; *Liebig's Ann.*, **131**. 368, 1864 ; O. Popp, *Liebig's Ann.*, **131**. 364, 1864 ; *Trennung des
Cers von Lanthan und Didym*, Göttingen, 1864.

[4] J. Joly, *Radioactivity and Geology*, London, 1909 ; *Phil. Mag.*, (6), **17**. 760, 1909 ; (6),
18. 140, 1909 ; (6), **20**. 125, 353, 1910 ; A. L. Fletcher, *ib.*, (6), **21**. 102, 1911 ; T. L. Phipson,
Chem. News, **43**. 145, 1896 ; G. A. Blanc, *Atti Accad. Lincei*, (5), **17**. i, 101, 1908 ; (5), **18**. i,
241, 1909 ; *Phys. Zeit.*, **9**. 294, 1908 ; H. Lange, *Naturwiss.*, **82**. 1, 1910 ; R. J. Strutt, *Proc.
Roy. Soc.*, **84**. A, 195, 1910 ; G. Hofbauer, *Sitzber. Akad. Wien*, **116**. 267, 1907 ; H. A. Rowland,
Amer. Journ. Science, (3), **41**. 243, 1891 ; *Chem. News*, **63**. 133, 1891 ; F. W. Clarke and
H. S. Washington, *The Composition of the Earth's Crust*, Washington, 1924 ; *Proc. Nat. Acad.
Sciences*, **8**. 108, 1922 ; J. H. L. Vogt, *Zeit. prakt. Geol.*, **6**. 225, 314, 377, 413, 1898 ; **7**. 10, 274,
1899 ; L. Moser, *Œster. Chem. Ztg.*, **26**. 67, 1923.

[5] J. J. Berzelius and H. M. T. Esmark, *Pogg. Ann.*, **15**. 633, 1828 ; H. M. T. Esmark, *Mag.
Naturwis. Christiana*, (2), **2**. 277, 1836 ; J. J. Berzelius, *Svenska Akad. Handl.*, 1, 1829 ; *Pogg.
Ann.*, **16**. 395, 1829 ; H. Rose, *ib.*, **48**. 555, 1839 ; C. Bergemann, *ib.*, **82**. 561, 1851 ; **85**. 558,
1852 ; N. J. Berlin, *ib.*, **85**. 555, 1852 ; H. Dauber, *ib.*, **92**. 250, 1854 ; A. Krautz, **82**. 586, 1851 ;
T. Scheerer, *ib.*, **65**. 298, 1845 ; *Neues Jahrb. Min.*, 642, 1843 ; 569, 1860 ; *Berg. Hütt. Ztg.*,
19. 124, 1859 ; A. Breithaupt, *ib.*, **25**. 82, 1866 ; A. Dufrénoy, *Traité de minéralogie*, Paris, **3**.
579, 1847 ; P. C. Weibye, *Karsten's Arch.*, **22**. 538, 1848 ; A. Damour, *Ann. Mines*, (4), **5**. 587,

1852 ; *Compt. Rend.*, **34**. 685, 1852 ; *Bull. Soc. Min.*, **1**. 32, 1878 ; F. Pisani, *ib.*, **59**. 65, 1904 ; W. R. Dunstan, *Nature*, **69**. 510, 1904 ; D. Forbes, *Edin. New Phil. Journ.*, (2), **3**. 60, 1856 ; P. G. Tschernik, *Proc. Russ. Min. Soc.*, **41**, 115, 1903 ; E. Zschau, *Amer. Journ. Science*, (2), **26**. 359, 1858 ; S. L. Penfield, *ib.*, (3), **24**. 252, 1883 ; W. E. Hidden and J. B. Mackintosh, *ib.*, (3), **41**. 438, 1891 ; G. F. Barker, *ib.*, (4), **16**. 161, 1903 ; B. B. Boltwood, (4), **21**. 415, 1906 ; H. N McCoy and W. H. Ross, *ib.*, (4), **21**, 433, 1906 ; H. M. Dadourian, *ib.*, (4), **21**. 427, 1906 ; K. A. Hofmann and F. Zerban, *Ber.*, **36**. 13093, 1903 ; J. J. Chydenius, *Kemisk Undersökning af Thorjord och Thorsalter*, Helsingfors, 1861 ; *Pogg. Ann.*, **119**. 43, 1861 ; F. Kolbeck and P. Uhlich, *Centr. Min.*, 208, 1904 ; A. des Cloizeaux, *Manuel de minéralogie*, Paris, 133, 1862 ; C. F. Rammelsberg, *Handbuch der Mineralchemie*, Leipzig, **1**. 173, 1875 ; A. E. Nordenskjöld, *Arkiv. Akad. Stockholm*, **2**. 1, 1905 ; *Geol. För. Förh. Stockholm*, **3**. 226, 1876 ; **4**. 28, 1879 ; **9**. 26, 434, 1887 ; S. R. Paykull, *ib.*, **3**. 350, 1877 ; G. Lindström, *ib.*, **5**. 270, 1882 ; A. Hamberg, *ib.*, **16**. 327, 1894 ; M. F. Heddle, *Trans. Roy. Soc. Edin.*, **28**. 197, 1877 ; *The Mineralogy of Scotland*, Edinburgh, **2**. 56, 1901 ; P. Collier, *Journ. Amer. Chem. Soc.*, **2**. 73, 1880 ; L. F. Nilson, *Œfvers. Akad. Förh.*, **7**, 1882 ; *Compt. Rend.*, **95**. 784, 1882 ; *Ann. Chim. Phys.*, (5), **30**. 429, 1883 ; G. Urbain, *ib.*, (7), **19**. 202, 1900 ; W. C. Brögger, *Neues Jahrb Min.*, i, 80, 1883 ; *Zeit. Kryst.*, **16**. 116, 1890 ; V. Goldschmidt, *ib.*, **45**. 490, 1908 ; G. Woitschach, *Abhand. Nat. Ges. Görlitz*, **17**. 147, 1883 ; G. Krüss and L. F. Nilson, *Ber.*, **20**. 2137, 1887 ; **21**. 558, 1888 ; G. Krüss and P. Kiesewetter, *ib.*, **21**. 2310, 1888 ; J. F. Kemp, *Trans. New York Acad.*, **13**. 76, 1893 ; J. N. Lockyer, *Proc. Roy. Soc.*, **59**. 133, 1895 ; R. J. Strutt, *ib.*, **76**. A, 88, 1905 ; **80**. A, 56, 1907 ; **82**. A, 166, 1909 ; **84**. A, 379, 1910 ; W. Ramsay, J. N. Collie, and M. W. Travers, *Journ. Chem. Soc.*, **67**. 684, 1895 ; L. Vegard, *Phil. Mag.*, (6), **32**. 65, 1916 ; M. L. Huggins, *Phys. Rev.*, (2), **21**. 719, 1923 ; G. von Hevesy and V. T. Jantzen, *Journ. Chem. Soc.*, **123**. 3218, 1923 ; J. Schilling, *Beiträge zur Chemie des Thoriums*, Heidelberg, 1901 ; *Zeit. angew. Chem.*, **15**. 921, 1902 ; *Das Vorkommen der Seltenen Erden im Mineralreiche*, München, 15, 1904 ; C. W. Blomstrand, *Journ. Prakt. Chem.*, (2), **29**. 200, 1884 ; W. F. Hillebrand, *Bull U.S. Geol. Sur.*, **113**. 41, 1891 ; *Zeit. anorg. Chem.*, **3**. 234, 1893 ; F. Zambonini, *Atti Accad. Napoli*, **14**. 67, 1908 ; G. T. Prior, *Min. Mag.*, **15**. 78, 1908 ; W. T. Schaller, *Bull. U.S. Geol. Sur.*, 509, 1912 ; F. Beigerinck, *Neues Jahrb. Min. B.B.*, **11**. 448, 1897 ; B. Szilard, *Le Radium*, **6**. 233, 1909 ; O. Mann, *Beiträge zur Kenntnis verschiediner Mineralien*, Leipzig, 1904 ; *Neues Jahrb. Min.*, ii, 189, 1905 ; E. Gleditsch, *Compt. Rend.*, **146**. 331, 1908 ; *Le Radium*, **5**. 33, 1908 ; G. P. Drossbach, *Journ. Gasbeleucht.*, **38**. 481, 1895 ; P. Truchot, *Chem. News*, **71**. 134, 1898 ; L. Schmelck, *Zeit. angew. Chem.*, **8**. 543, 1895 ; C. R. Böhm, *Chem. Ind.*, **29**. 321, 1906 ; G. G. Boucher, *Chem. News*, **76**. 99, 182, 1897 ; F. G. Ruddock, *ib.*, **76**. 118, 1897 ; C. H. Jones, *ib.*, **76**. 171, 1897 ; A. L. Fletcher, *Scient. Proc. Roy. Dublin Soc.*, (2), **13**. 433, 1913.
    ⁶ W. Ramsay, W. R. Dunstan, and G. S. Blake, *Proc. Roy. Soc.*, **76**. A, 253, 1905 ; W. R. Dunstan and B. M. Jones, *ib.*, **77**. A, 546, 1906 ; D. O. Wood, *ib.*, **84**. A, 70, 1910 ; O. Hahn, *ib.*, **78**. A, 385, 1906 ; R. J. Strutt, *ib.*, **76**. A, 98, 1905 ; **84**. A, 195, 379, 1910 ; W. Ramsay, *Nature*, **69**. 533, 559, 1904 ; W. R. Dunstan, *ib.*, **69**. 510, 1904 ; W. Jakob and J. S Tolloczko, *Bull. Acad. Cracow*, 558, 1911 ; W. F. Hillebrand, *Zeit. anorg. Chem.*, **3**. 243, 1893 ; *Bull. U.S. Geol. Sur.*, **113**. 41, 1893 ; W. Hillebrand and W. H. Melville, *ib.*, **90**. 30, 1892 ; G. von Hevesy and V. T. Jantzen, *Journ. Chem. Soc.*, **123**. 3218, 1923 ; H. Goldschmidt, *Zeit. Kryst.*, **45**. 490, 1908 ; J. Nordenskjöld, *Pogg. Ann.*, **110**. 643, 1860 ; G. Troost and L. Ouvrard, *Compt. Rend.*, **102**. 1422, 1886 ; B. Szilard, *ib.*, **143**. 1145, 1906 ; **145**. 463, 1907 ; E. Gleditsch, *ib.*, **149**. 267, 1909 ; E. Rutherford, *Phil. Mag.*, (6), **12**. 348, 1906 ; F. Soddy and R. Pirret, *ib.*, (6), **20**. 345, 1910 ; A. K. Coomaraswamy, *Spolia Zeylamica*, 2. iv, 57, 1904 ; P. Termier, *Bull. Soc. Min.*, **27**. 258, 1904 ; T. L. Phipson, *Journ. Gaslight.*, **87**. 380, 1904 ; **86**. 255, 503, 1904 ; E. H. Buchnen, *Chem. News*, **94**. 233, 1906 ; *Proc. Roy. Soc.*, **78**. A, 385, 1906 ; C. de B. Evans, *Journ. Chem. Soc.*, **93**. 666, 1908 ; G. Wyrouboff amd A. Verneuil, *Bull. Soc. Chim.*, (3), **21**. 118, 1899 ; *Compt. Rend.*, **128**. 1573, 1899 ; M. Ogawa, *Chem. News*, **98**. 249, 261, 1908 ; *Sakurai's Jubilee Papers*, 15, 16, 1908 ; M. Kobayashi, *Science Rep. Tohoku Univ.*, **1**. 201, 1912 ; C. F. Rammelsberg, *Pogg. Ann.*, **56**. 129, 1842 ; **150**. 219, 1873 ; *Handbuch der krystallograpisch-physikalischen Chemie*, Leipzig, **1**. 441, 1881 ; C. Baskerville, *Science*, (2), **50**. 443, 1917 ; A. Schoep, *Bull. Soc. Chim. Belg.*, **32**. 274, 1923 ; G. G. Boucher, *Chem. News*, **76**. 99, 182, 1897 ; F. O. Ruddock, *ib.*, **76**. 118, 1897.

§ 2. The Extraction of Thoria

J. J. Berzelius,[1] the discoverer of this earth, extracted it from thorite. The powdered mineral was warmed with hydrochloric acid ; some chlorine was evolved, and the mineral gelatinized. The whole was evaporated to dryness to make the silica insoluble. The residue was leached with dil. hydrochloric acid, and the lead, tin, etc., removed from the filtered soln. by hydrogen sulphide. The filtrate was treated with ammonia, and the washed precipitate dissolved in dil. sulphuric acid. The soln. was evaporated at a gentle heat, when thorium sulphate was deposited as a salt sparingly soluble in the hot liquid. The supernatant liquid was poured off, the crystals dried by press. and ignited for thoria. The mother-liquor was conc. by evap., neutralized with potassium carbonate, and mixed with a boiling sat. soln. of potassium sulphate. The double sulphate which separates on cooling was washed with a sat. soln. of potassium sulphate ; dissolved in water ; and thorium hydroxide precipitated by ammonia. The presence of manganese imparted a yellow colour to the ignited mass ; and J. J. Berzelius found it better to repeat the treatment with sulphuric acid rather than separate the thorium as oxalate. J. J. Chydenius used a similar process.

L. Troost heated a mixture of thorite with finely powdered coal in the electric arc furnace. All but about 1·5 per cent. of silica is volatilized, and this is said to facilitate greatly the subsequent treatment for thoria. O. N. Witt dissolved the washed precipitate in hydrochloric acid. Oxalic acid was then added so long as precipitation occurred. The washed precipitate was calcined. A little uranium, manganese, and rare earths were contained in the resulting thoria. J. J. Berzelius' process is based on the sparing solubility of thorium sulphate in comparison with the sulphates of the other earths. Modifications were suggested by M. Delafontaine, P. T. Cleve, L. F. Nilson and co-workers. J. J. Berzelius, and J. J. Chydenius also, purified the thoria by a process based on the sparing solubility of the double salt—potassium thorium sulphate—in a sat. soln. of potassium sulphate. The yttria earth sulphates are fairly soluble and are readily removed. Processes for the removal of the ceria earths based on the solubility of thorium oxalate in ammonium oxalate or ammonium carbonate, under conditions where the other oxalates are but sparingly soluble, have been given by A. Damour, R. Bunsen, H. Moissan and A. Étard, P. Jannasch and co-workers, J. Lesinsky, and G. Urbain. Vide the rare earths. V. I. Spitzin has measured the solubility of thorium oxalate in various soln.

J. J. Chydenius extracted thoria from euxenite by digesting the powdered mineral with conc. sulphuric acid ; the product was dissolved in cold water and the soln. boiled for some days. The greater part of the titanium and columbium was precipitated. The thoria was then extracted from the filtrate by J. J. Berzelius' process. J. L. Smith extracted the thoria from samarskite by digesting the powdered mineral with cold conc. hydrofluoric acid, finishing off the operation by warming the mass. The rare earth fluorides, thorium fluoride, and uranium fluoride remain undissolved ; the columbium, tantalum, iron, and manganese pass into soln. The insoluble mass is digested with sulphuric acid, and the soln. then treated for thoria by the oxalate process. G. Siebert and E. Korten treated the raw material with halogens in the presence of carbon at a high temp.

According to C. R. Böhm, most of the thorium compounds in commerce are extracted from monazite sand as described in connection with the rare earths. The deposits in the vicinity of Bahia, Espirito Santo, and Rio de Janeiro on the Brazilian coast, have been worked for many years. The deposits in North and South Carolina in the United States, and the deposits at Travancore, Southern India, are also worked. The monazite sands contain 2–60 per cent. of monazite. The monazite from Brazil contains 5–6 per cent. of thoria, while, according to E. White, Travancore monazite has 6–14 per cent. of thoria. The grains of monazite in the sand are associated with quartz, ilmenite, garnet, rutile, zircon, hornblende, etc. The sand is usually conc. until it contains at least 90 per cent. monazite.

The concentration of monazite sand has been discussed by H. B. C. Nitze, F. Freize, etc. In the wet process of extraction the sand is run with a stream of water on to one corner of a rectangular table. The table is so tilted that the material travels diagonally across it ; the passage of the particles across the table is assisted by the shaking or jigging motion mechanically imparted to the table. The particles roughly range themselves in the order of their sp. gr. The weakness of the process is the tendency for aggregates of small particles of high sp. gr. to behave like a smaller number of large particles of small sp. gr. Pneumatic processes can be used in which blasts of air take the place of currents of water. The initial concentration may be performed by a wet process, and the conc. then raised by electro-magnetic separation. Electro-magnetic separation is considered to be the most satisfactory method of obtaining a high-grade monazite. In this process, a belt, B_1, Fig. 1, carries the well-dried sand from a hopper, H, and pro-

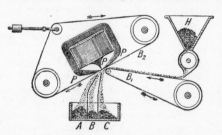

jects it against a second belt, B_2, which travels just beneath the poles, P, P, P, of a powerful electro-magnet. The constituent minerals of the sand are attracted towards the magnet in varying degrees and fall into collecting boxes, A, B, arranged in the order of their magnetic permeability. The non-magnetic discharge collects in the box C. Two repetitions of the process will usually give

Fig. 1.—Magnetic Concentration of Monazite Sand (Diagrammatic).

a concentrate with 90–95 per cent. of monazite. The subject is discussed in C. G. Gunther's *Electromagnetic Ore Separation* (New York, 1909), and D. Korda's *La séparation électromagnétique et électrostatique des minerais* (Paris, 1905).

C. R. Böhm thus outlines the process employed for extracting thorium from monazite concentrates. The conc. monazite may or may not require a preliminary grinding. It is then mixed with about twice its weight of conc. sulphuric acid (sp. gr. 1·84), and heated in cast-iron pans until the white pasty mass of sulphates, etc., is soluble in water, and no yellow grains of monazite remain undissolved. The product is then run into a leaden vat and the whole is well stirred. The mixture is allowed to stand in order to allow the insoluble or unattacked minerals to settle. The soln. containing the rare-earth phosphates is syphoned off. The ratio of thoria to the rare earths in the soln. is about 1 : 12. Thorium is more basic than the rare earths, so that when the acid soln. is gradually neutralized by adding ammonia, alkali hydroxide or carbonates, or, more usually, magnesite, thorium phosphate accumulates in the first precipitate. The thorium phosphate is filtered off, dissolved in the minimum quantity of acid, and the process repeated. This raises the proportion of thoria to the rare earths to about 4 : 1. The product is next to be freed from phosphoric acid and the remaining ceria earths.

Several processes have been suggested; but many of them are too expensive for commercial work. The actual procedure is kept a secret. In the oxalate process described by C. R. Böhm, the acid soln. of the phosphate is treated with a hot soln. of oxalic acid; the precipitated oxalates are washed, digested with a soln. of sodium carbonate, as recommended by O. N. Witt, and precipitated from the soln. with sodium hydroxide; or the mixed oxalates are treated with a warm soln. of ammonium oxalate, as recommended by R. Bunsen, when all the thorium oxalate dissolves and only small quantities of the other oxalates pass into soln., and these are nearly all precipitated when the soln. is diluted. O. N. Witt recommends applying the sodium thiosulphate precipitation—*vide infra*—before the oxalate treatment. The Société Minière et Industrie Franco-Brésilienne precipitated the thorium, cerium, etc., as anhydrous sulphates from the sulphuric acid soln. of monazite, and removed the phosphoric acid by centrifuging. M. Fronstein and J. Mai, J. W. Ling, G. Thesen, H. Moissan and A. Étard, G. Urbain, etc., used modifications of the oxalate process.

B. Kossmann treated the sulphuric acid soln. of monazite with ammonia; dissolved the precipitate in hydrochloric acid; sat. the feebly acid soln. with hydrogen sulphide; decanted the clear liquid from the precipitated aluminium and iron phosphates and tin sulphide, and treated the soln. with hydrogen dioxide, ammonia, and ammonium citrate. The precipitate contained aluminium phosphate mixed with thorium hydroxide—freed from didymium and cerium compounds. The precipitate was dissolved in nitric acid, and the thorium purified by the oxalate process, or by the acetate process. In F. Haber's form of the acetate process, the impure hydroxide is dissolved in acid, and the thorium precipitated from neutral soln. by sodium acetate. The treatment is repeated until the purification has been carried far enough. The results are said to be good, but too costly for large-scale work.

G. Wyrouboff and A. Verneuil recommend the following process :

The mineral is dissolved in the usual way, and the soln., which must contain sufficient acid to prevent precipitation of the phosphates, is precipitated with half the quantity of oxalic acid necessary for complete precipitation. The oxalates are washed until free from phosphoric acid, converted into carbonates by means of a hot soln. of sodium carbonate (1 : 10), and some sodium hydroxide added to ensure complete precipitation of the thorium. The carbonates are washed until free from oxalic acid, dissolved in just the necessary quantity of hydrochloric acid, and mixed with successive small quantities of barium peroxide suspended in water until the liquid gives no precipitate with hydrogen dioxide. The precipitated peroxide contains all the thorium, together with 20 30 per cent. of impurities ; it is washed and dissolved in cold conc. hydrochloric acid, barium eliminated by means of sulphuric acid, enough water added to yield a soln. containing 15 per cent. of acid, and the bases precipitated with oxalic acid. The oxalates are washed, and treated with a highly conc. soln. of ammonium carbonate mixed with sufficient ammonia to form the normal salt. By two or three successive treatments, all the thorium is dissolved, and the soln. is precipitated by means of sodium hydroxide, the precipitate well washed and dissolved in not more than the requisite quantity of nitric acid, and the liquid poured into sufficient water to yield a soln. containing not more than 2 per cent. of thorium. Excess of hydrogen dioxide is then added, and the precipitate is well washed. From this point, all the reagents must be pure. The precipitate is dissolved in nitric acid and re-precipitated with hydrogen dioxide in order to eliminate all the cerium. It is next dissolved in hydrochloric acid, precipitated with oxalic acid, and the oxalate decomposed by pure sodium hydroxide. After careful washing, the precipitate is again dissolved in hydrochloric acid and precipitated with ammonia. This final precipitate is well washed, dissolved in nitric acid, and the nitrate crystallized.

C. R. Böhm removed the phosphates by fusing the precipitate with sodium carbonate and leaching the mass with water. The phosphates and silicates pass into soln., while the thoria and rare earth oxides remain. W. Buddëus and L. Preussner used alkali hydroxides in place of the carbonate. L. Weiss heated a mixture of monazite with carbon in an electric furnace whereby carbides and phosphides are formed. The mass was treated with hydrochloric acid, and the phosphorus escaped as phosphine. C. Baskerville proposed to volatilize the phosphorus by heating a mixture of monazite, coke, calcium oxide, and fluorspar in an electric furnace until the fumes of phosphorus were no longer evolved. When the cold mass is treated with water, acetylene is evolved. The powder is well washed to remove the lime, and then dissolved in hydrochloric acid for the separation of thorium. etc.

The purification of thoria.—The thoria contains a little sulphate, phosphate, calcium oxide, alkalies, zirconia, and rare earths. The usual methods of purification are (i) the fractional crystallization of the sulphates ; (ii) the fractional soln. of the oxalates ; or (iii) the separation by double alkali carbonates. There are also a number of processes more or less adapted for special purposes, but which are usually too expensive for large-scale operations. These processes have been discussed in a special section dealing with the separation of the rare earths. The oxalate process is based on the property possessed by thorium oxalate of forming a soluble double salt with ammonium oxalate, while the cerium earth oxalates are but sparingly soluble in that medium. The relative solubilities of the various oxalates are :

Th	Yb	Y	Ce	Nd	Pr	La
2663·0	105·0	11·0	1·8	1·5	1·2	1·0

The method—vide supra—was employed by B. Brauner, C. Böttinger, P. Jannasch and co-workers, C. Winkler, J. Lesinsky, E. Rimbach and A. Schubert, etc.

The sulphate process is based upon the property which thorium possesses of forming a number of hydrated sulphates, some of which differ so much in solubility from the ceria earths that a separation can be readily obtained. The process was employed by L. F. Nilson, G. Krüss, P. T. Cleve, O. N. Witt, I. Koppel and H. Holtkamp, etc. G. Thesen fractionally crystallized the double sodium sulphates. C. Baskerville employed the following process :

The sulphate was taken up in cold water, treated with sodium sulphate and allowed to stand from twelve to twenty-four hours to insure separation of the remaining cerium salts, the percentage of which was quite small. The liquid was filtered and the hydroxide precipitated in tall cylinders by a large excess of purified sodium nitrate. This precipitate was washed by decantation from six to ten times, using each time 20 vols. of water to one of the precipitate. To remove the last of the sodium salts and other soluble impurities the precipitate was then dissolved in hydrochloric acid, reprecipitated by a slight excess of ammonium hydroxide and washed by decantation at least ten times, using 20 vols. of distilled water.

H. Erdmann used a modification of this process. The ammonium carbonate process of A. Damour is based on the solubility of thorium carbonate in a soln. of ammonium carbonate under conditions where only small proportions of the other carbonates are soluble.

L. M. Dennis and co-workers precipitated thorium hydroxide by boiling the chloride soln. for some minutes with potassium azide. G. Wyrouboff and A. Verneuil say that some cerium hydroxide is precipitated with the thorium hydroxide. W. B. Giles precipitated thorium by adding lead carbonate to a soln. of the nitrate in which the cerium had been reduced to the cerous state by hydrogen sulphide. The precipitate was dissolved in nitric acid, the lead precipitated by hydrogen sulphide, and the thorium by ammonia. W. Muthmann and E. Baur found that the thorium accumulates in the first precipitate obtained when a 6 per cent. soln. of potassium chromate is added to a soln. containing thorium nitrate. L. de Boisbaudran precipitated the thorium by cuprous oxide. A. Rosenheim, M. Koss, and F. Wirth precipitated thorium quantitatively by sodium hypophosphate; from soln. with 15 per cent. of free sulphuric acid the rare earths remain in soln. The thorium hypophosphate is then boiled with alkali hydroxide, converted into oxalate, etc. R. J. Carney and E. D. Campbell said that sodium pyrophosphate acts similarly. All these processes are detailed in connection with general processes for the separation of the rare earths.

M. Delafontaine separated zirconia from thoria by the following process :

The powdered mixture (ore or oxides) is fused in a platinum crucible with twice its weight of acid potassium fluoride, KHF_2. The zirconia is separated as potassium fluozirconate, K_2ZrF_6, from the solidified mass by means of boiling water containing a few drops of hydrofluoric acid. The insoluble fluorides are decomposed by sulphuric acid, and ignited below a dull red heat, which will leave thorium, cerium, and other earths as sulphates. Silica, if present, escapes as silicon fluoride. The sulphates are dissolved in water and precipitated by oxalic acid, the oxalates being treated by a sat. hot soln. of ammonium oxalate ; the thorium salt is dissolved and cerium left. The ignited oxalates leave the oxides in good condition for further work. Zirconia is thrown down from its fluo-salt by ammonium hydrate. Titanium, if present in the original mixture, is found as fluo-titanate soluble in hot water.

To separate the rare earths, R. Chavastelon treated a soln. of the chlorides with ammonia and hydrogen dioxide, and digested the precipitate with a soln. of an alkali hydrocarbonate. The cerium and thorium oxides pass into soln., and may be separated by either of the following processes : (1) reduction of the peroxides, and formation of the sulphites by the action of sulphurous acid, and the precipitation of thorium by hydrogen dioxide from a hydrochloric acid soln. of these salts ; (2) reduction of the brown soln. of ceric and thoric carbonates with sulphurous acid in the presence of sufficient sodium carbonate to keep the whole of the thorium dissolved as the double sodium sulphite. In the latter process, the soln. must be constantly agitated during the addition of the sulphurous acid in order to prevent the formation of acid sulphite, otherwise some of the cerium will be dissolved whilst traces of thorium will be precipitated. R. Chavastelon also recommended adding a neutral soln. of the salts of thorium and the rare earths to a sat. soln. of sodium sulphite; the thorium remains in soln. while the other elements are precipitated as sulphites. The precipitate is practically free from the rare earths, but the little which has escaped precipitation is recovered by converting the sulphites to chlorides, and treating the soln. by the hydrogen dioxide process. H. Grossmann said that this method is not of any technical value, but A. Batek said it can be used for separating the ceria earths from thoria. The Lindsay Light Co. used a modification of the fluoride process—*vide* rare earths.

J. J. Chydenius added sodium thiosulphate to a neutral or feebly acid soln. of the thorium salt, and on boiling the mixture or allowing it to stand, thorium thiosulphate and sulphur are precipitated, while cerium and zirconium are not precipitated. The precipitation, however, is not complete. R. Hermann, R. Bunsen, and O. N. Witt used modifications of the thiosulphate process. A. Rosenheim and co-workers devised a process based upon the fact that from a strongly acid soln. thorium is completely precipitated by the addition of hydrofluosilicic acid or a soluble silicofluoride, whereas the elements of the cerite and ytterbia earths remain almost entirely in soln. R. J. Meyer and M. Speter purified thoria from monazite by the iodate process :

Fifty grams of the sample are heated with 100 c.c. of conc. sulphuric acid for six hours at 250°, and, when cold, 500 c.c. of cold water are added. The soln. is filtered and, when cold, diluted to 1 litre, and 100 c.c. are then taken for analysis. After adding 50 c.c. of nitric acid, of sp. gr. 1·4, and cooling, a cold soln. of 15 grms. of potassium iodate in 50 c.c. of nitric acid and 30 c.c. of water is added, and, after half an hour, the thorium iodate is collected and washed with a soln. containing 2 grms. of potassium iodate in 50 c.c. of dil. nitric acid and 200 c.c. of water. The precipitate is returned to the beaker, and again stirred and washed. It is now again transferred to the beaker by means of a jet of hot water, heated to boiling, and dissolved in 30 c.c. of strong nitric acid ; addition of 4 grms. of potassium iodate dissolved in hot water causes it to reprecipitate. The precipitate is now collected on the same filter and washed as before, and is then quite free from cerium. It is dissolved in hydrochloric acid with the aid of sulphur dioxide, and precipitated with ammonia at the boiling heat. The hydroxide is washed with boiling water, redissolved in dil. hydrochloric acid, and precipitated with excess of oxalic acid. The precipitate is washed with water, acidified with hydrochloric acid, and then ignited to oxide.

L. Fernandes recommended separating thoria from the rare earths by the following process :

The mixture of hydroxides precipitated by means of ammonia is washed repeatedly with boiling water, and then dissolved in dil. sulphuric acid. The soln. is filtered and treated with excess of thallous sulphate ; the cerium metals are precipitated, and the precipitate is removed by filtration. The filtrate is heated on a water-bath until more than one-third of the solvent is expelled, and then filtered, to free it from the last traces of tervalent earth metals. When cooled, the clear liquid deposits the first fraction, which contains pure thorium. The soln. is again evaporated until almost conc. sulphuric acid is obtained, and the various thorium fractions which separate being removed. When the remaining strongly acid soln. is heated to boiling, the final traces of thorium separate as the normal sulphate, which is removed by filtration through asbestos or a porous crucible. The zirconium compounds separate when the filtrate is cooled.

Another set of processes, involving the use of organic compounds, has been also discussed in connection with the rare earths. Thus, I. Kreidl and G. Heller used the ethylsulphate process. C. R. Böhm converted the hydroxide into acetate, and found that thorium acetate is virtually insoluble in water. F. Garelli and G. A. Barbieri used the salicylic acid process ; A. C. Neish, and A. Kolb and H. Ahrle, the *m*-nitrobenzoic acid process ; F. G. Metzger, the fumaric acid process ; T. O. Smith and C. James, the sebacic acid process ; G. Urbain, and C. James, the acetylacetonate process ; and A. Kolb, the aniline process. J. W. Marden, and co-workers found thorium can be electrodeposited from a soln. obtained by dissolving the hydroxide in hydrofluoboric acid together with lead hydroxide or carbonate.

The separation of the radioactive constituents of thorium has been discussed by E. Rutherford and F. Soddy,[2] H. Schlundt and R. B. Moore, G. C. Ashman,

H. N. McCoy and W. H. Ross, B. Keetmann, etc.   The adsorption of thorium salt from a soln. containing uranium-X, has been discussed by A. Ritzel,[3] F. Soddy, and H. Freundlich and co-workers—*vide infra*.

REFERENCES.

[1] J. J. Berzelius, *Svenska Akad. Handl.*, 1, 1829 ; *Pogg. Ann.*, 16. 385, 1829 ; J. J. Chydenius, *ib.*, 119. 43, 1863 ; *Bull. Soc. Chim.*, (2), 6. 433, 1866 ; *Kemisk Undersökning af Thorjord och Thorsalter*, Helsingfors, 1861 ; J. Lesinsky, *Zur Kenntnis der Thoriumverbindungen*, Bonn, 1898 ; P. Jannasch, J. Locke, and J. Lesinsky, *Zeit. anorg. Chem.*, 5. 283, 1894 ; F. Wirth, *ib.*, 25. 1678, 1912 ; H. Grossmann, *ib.*, 44. 229, 1905 ; A. Batek, *ib.*, 45. 87, 1905 ; *Rozpravy. Roc.*, 11. 20, 1902, ; L. F. Nilson and G. Krüss, *Œfvers. Akad. Förh.*, 5, 1887 ; *Ber.*, 20. 1665, 1887 ; W. Remmler and P. Jannasch, *ib.*, 26. 1423, 1893 ; W. Muthmann and E. Baur, *ib.*, 33. 1756, 2028, 1900 ; E. Baur, *German Pat., D.R.P.* 120013, 1900 ; I. Kreidl and G. Heller, *ib.*, 233023, 1909 ; M. Fronstein and J. Mai, *ib.*, 93940, 1896 ; C. Winkler, *Ber.*, 24. 885, 1891 ; L. Troost, *Compt. Rend.*, 116. 1429, 1893 ; L. F. Nilson, *ib.*, 95. 729, 1882 ; L. de Boisbaudran, *ib.*, 99. 525, 1884 ; R. Chavastelon, *ib.*, 130. 781, 1900 ; H. Moissan and A. Étard, *ib.*, 122. 573, 1896 ; A. Damour, *ib.*, 34. 685, 1852 ; O. N. Witt, *Ueber den Cergehalt der Thorsalze*, Berlin, 1897 ; *Die chemische Industrie auf der columbischen Weltausstellung zu Chicago*, Berlin, 1894 ; *Chem. Ind.*, 17. 161, 1894 ; M. Delafontaine, *Arch. Sciences Genève*, (2), 18. 343, 1863 ; *Chem. News*, 75. 230, 1897 ; P. T. Cleve, *Bull. Soc. Chim.*, (2), 43. 53, 1885 ; G. Urbain, *ib.*, (3), 15. 339, 1896 ; *Ann. Chim. Phys.*, (7), 19. 184, 1900 ; A. Damour, *Ann. Mines*, (5), 1. 587, 1852 ; L. Fernandes, *Gazz. Chim. Ital.*, 55. i, 3, 1925 ; G. Siebert and E. Korten, *German Pat., D.R.P.* 355485, 1920 ; R. Bunsen, *Pogg. Ann.*, 155, 379, 1875 ; Lindsay Light Co., *Brit. Pat. No.* 179309, 1921 ; J. L. Smith, *Amer. Chem. Journ.*, 5. 44, 73, 1883 ; *Chem. News*, 48. 13, 29, 1883 ; 51. 289, 304, 1885 ; C. James, *ib.*, 97. 205, 1908 ; W. B. Giles, *ib.*, 92. 1, 1905 ; C. R. Böhm, *Chem. Ind.*, 29. 452, 1906 ; H. B. C. Nitze, *Journ. Franklin Inst.*, 144. 127, 1897 ; F. Freize, *Œster. Zeit. Berg. Hütt.*, 59. 272, 284, 1911 ; V. I. Spitzin, *Journ. Russ. Phys. Chem. Soc.*, 49. 357, 1917 ; J. W. Marden, J. E. Conley, and T. P. Thomas, *U.S. Pat. No.* 1487174, 1924 ; H. Erdmann, *Lehrbuch der anorganischen Chemie*, Braunschweig, 601, 1898 ; E. White, *Thorium and its Compounds*, London, 10, 1912 ; M. Koss, *Chem. Ztg.*, 36. 686, 1912 ; A. Rosenheim, *ib.*, 36. 812, 1912 ; G. Thesen, *ib.*, 19. 2254, 1895 ; J. W. Ling, *ib.*, 19. 1468, 1895 ; F. Garelli and G. A. Barbieri, *ib.*, 30. 433, 1906 ; R. J. Meyer and M. Speter, *ib.*, 34. 306, 1910 ; R. J. Meyer and I. Koppel, *German Pat., D.R.P.* 214886, 1909 ; I. Koppel and H. Holtkamp, *Zeit. anorg. Chem.*, 67. 287, 1910 ; C. Böttinger, *ib.*, 6. 1, 1894 ; E. Benz, *ib.*, 15. 297, 1902 ; C. Baskerville, *Internal Cong. App. Chem.*, 8. ii, 17, 1912 ; *Journ. Amer. Chem. Soc.*, 23. 762, 1901 ; L. M. Dennis and F. L. Kortright, *ib.*, 16. 79, 1894 ; R. J. Carney and E. D Campbell, *ib.*, 36. 1134, 1914 ; L. M. Dennis, *ib.*, 18. 947, 1896 ; F. G. Metzger, *ib.*, 24. 901, 1902 ; T. O. Smith and C. James, *ib.*, 34. 281, 1912 ; A. C. Neish, *ib.*, 26. 780, 1904 ; *Chem. News*, 90. 201, 1904 ; E. Rimbach and A. Schubert, *Zeit. phys. Chem.*, 67. 183, 1909 ; G. P. Drossbach, *Journ. Gasbeleucht.*, 38. 581, 1895 ; B. Kossmann, *Brit. Pat. No.* 18915, 1895 ; Société Minière et Industrielle Franco-Brésilienne, *ib.*, 189698, 1922 ; G. Wyrouboff and A. Verneuil, *Ann. Chim. Phys.*, (8), 6. 487, 1905 ; *Compt. Rend.*, 127. 412, 1898 ; *Bull. Soc. Chim.*, (3), 19. 219, 1898 ; R. Hermann, *ib.*, (2), 3. 187, 1864 ; *Journ. prakt. Chem.*, (1), 93. 108, 1864 ; A. Kolb, *ib.*, (2), 66. 59, 1902 ; A. Kolb and H. Ahrle, *Zeit. angew. Chem.*, 18. 92, 1905 ; L. Weiss, *German Pat., D.R.P.* 129416, 1901 ; W. Buddëus and L. Preussner, *ib.*, 95061, 1896 ; G. Siebert and E. Korten, *ib.*, 355485, 1920 ; B. Brauner, *Journ. Chem. Soc.*, 73. 951, 1899 ; *German Pat., D.R.P.* 97689, 1897 ; F. Haber, *Sitzber. Akad. Wien*, 106. 609, 1897 ; *Monatsh.*, 18. 687, 1897.

[2] E. Rutherford and F. Soddy, *Journ. Chem. Soc.*, 81. 321, 837, 1902 ; H. Schlundt and R. B. Moore, *Journ. Phys. Chem.*, 9. 682, 1905 ; *Chem. News*, 91. 259, 1905 ; B. Keetmann, *Jahrb. Rad. Elektron.*, 6. 265, 1909 ; H. N. McCoy and W. H. Ross, *Journ. Amer. Chem. Soc.*, 29. 1709, 1907 ; G. C. Ashmann, *Amer. Journ. Science*, (4), 27. 65, 1909.

[3] F. Soddy, *Journ. Chem. Soc.*, 99. 72, 1911 ; A. Ritzel, *Zeit. phys. Chem.*, 67. 724, 1909 ; H. Freundlich and M. Wreschner, *ib.*, 106. 366, 1923 ; H. Freundlich and H. Kämpfer, *ib.*, 90. 681, 1915 ; *Elster and Geitel's Festschrift*, 16, 1915 ; H. Freundlich, A. Neumann, and H. Kämpfer, *Phys. Zeit.*, 15. 537, 1914.

§ 3. The Radioactivity of Thorium

Soon after the discovery of radioactivity of uranium, G. C. Schmidt,[1] and independently M. S. Curie, found that thorium and its compounds, and thorium minerals are also radioactive.   The rays emitted can discharge a charged electroscope, and fog photographic plates.   Thorium products emit Becquerel's rays, that is, a mixture of α-, β-, and γ-rays ; the latter are more intense and penetrating than those of uranium.   Thorium products also emit a radioactive gas which retains its activity for about ten minutes. The radioactivity of thorium products is a complex effect due to the presence of a series of transformation products derived from thorium itself : Thorium→Mesothorium-1→mesothorium-2→Radiothorium →thorium-X→thorium emanation→active deposit of thorium. The radioactivity of freshly prepared thorium compounds is not constant, but decreases slowly for some years, reaches a minimum, and then slowly increases, and finally attains a maximum value. The variation is due to the growth in thorium of new radio-active substances which ultimately attain an equilibrium and constant value.

The ratio of uranium to thorium in the thorium minerals is far from constant, and this is taken to mean that it is improbable that there is any genetic relation between the two. This is illustrated by Table II, collected from results by

TABLE II.—RATIO OF URANIUM TO THORIUM IN SOME THORIUM MINERALS.

Mineral.	Per cent.		Mineral.	Per cent.	
	U	Th		U	Th
Auerlite	—	61–63	Sipilite	2·86	4·92
Freyalite	—	24	Gadolinite	2·94	8·60
Cyrtolite	—	13	Uranothorite	1·0–10·0	35–45
Orthite ; allanite	—	8·8	Crystolite	3·67	5·05
Monazite sand	—	1·0–2·5	Samarskite	3·0–15·0	4
Ancylite	—	0·17	Thorianite	9·0–13·0	65–77
Xenotime	0·5–3·0	0·5–3·0	Thorite	c. 9	c. 45
Orangite	1	65	Thorogummite	18	36
Fergusonite ; tyrite	1·5–6·0	1·0–3·0	Mackintoshite	20	42
Æschynite	2–9	1–8	Cleveïte	60	6
Euxenite	2·84	2·72	Bröggerite	c. 66	c. 14

R. J. Strutt, etc. S. Meyer has also studied the thorium uranium content of minerals. W. R. Dunstan found that Cingalese thorite contains very little uranium ; according to F. Soddy's analysis, the mineral contains 1·80 per cent. of residue insoluble in hydrochloric and hydrofluoric acids, and

ThO_2	SiO_2	Fe_2O_3	Ce_2O_3	ZrO_2	P_2O_5	Al_2O_3	U_3O_8	CaO	PbO	H_2O
61·95	11·91	5·18	4·99	3·92	0·66	0·80	0·85	0·40	0·39	7·06

In the early days of the discovery of the radioactivity of thorium, the question was raised whether thorium is primarily a radioactive element under all conditions independently of the source from which it is obtained. K. A. Hofmann and co-workers, and C. Baskerville maintained that thorium is inactive *per se*, and shows radioactivity only under certain conditions. Thus, K. A. Hofmann and E. Strauss maintained that the radioactivity of many thorium minerals is due to the contained uranium. K. A. Hofmann and F. Zerban claimed to have made inactive thorium from uranium-free monazite ; C. Baskerville and F. Zerban also claimed to have obtained inactive thorium from uranium-free minerals. These conclusions, said M. S. Curie, *demandent confirmation et ne sont pas en accord avec d'autres recherches sur l'activité du thorium dans ses minerais*, e.g. those of H. M. Dadourian, H. N. McCoy and W. H. Ross, A. S. Eve, and B. B. Boltwood. Further, F. Zerban, C. Winkler, and G. F. Barker also showed that all commercial preparations of thorium contain some uranium. K. A. Hofmann and F. Zerban showed that all the preparations of thorium became less active when kept for 1½ to 3 years. C. Basker-ville, and W. Crookes obtained indications of another constituent in thorium, but the result is now explained by the complex nature of the radioactive decay products contained in thorium. As M. S. Curie said : *Radioactivity is a specific property of thorium.*

There is no method known for separating radiothorium from thorium, and it is very difficult to prepare thorium free from all its decay products. In order to eliminate mesothorium, the soln. is treated with a barium salt, and barium sulphate precipitated. This carries down the mesothorium. The radiothorium still present in the soln. is allowed to decay ; at the same time, mesothorium gradually grows in the soln., and it furnishes more decay products. Hence, the mesothorium must be repeatedly removed to prevent the growth of more radiothorium. In about $6\frac{1}{2}$ years, the radiothorium can be reduced to one per cent., and in 20 years, to $0 \cdot 1$ per cent. The study of radioactively pure thorium is complicated by the disturbing effects due to the presence of the transformation products. M. de Broglie and J. Cabrera studied the γ-rays of the thorium family.

The at. wt. of thorium is taken to be 232. Thorium itself emits feeble α-rays which have a range of $2 \cdot 72$ cm. in air at $15°$, and an initial velocity of $1 \cdot 40 \times 10^9$ cm. per sec. H. Geiger and E. Rutherford found the number of α-particles emitted by a gram of thorium in equilibrium with its decay products to be $2 \cdot 7 \times 10^4$ per sec. ; and they estimate that without its decay products $4 \cdot 5 \times 10^3$ particles per sec. or $1 \cdot 42 \times 10^{11}$ per year would be emitted by thorium alone. Since a mol of gas contains $6 \cdot 07 \times 10^{23}$ molecules, a gram of thorium contains $2 \cdot 61 \times 10^{21}$ atoms ; and the decomposition constant in reciprocal years is $5 \cdot 44 \times 10^{11}$; this corresponds with a half-life period of $1 \cdot 28 \times 10^{10}$ years ; an average life period of $1 \cdot 84 \times 10^{10}$ years ; and a radioactive constant $\lambda = 1 \cdot 7 \times 10^{-18}$ sec. In view of the long life period of mesothorium it is probable that the thorium was not in equilibrium with its decay products. This would make the number of α-particles emitted too small. and the half-life period too long. H. N. McCoy estimated the half-life period of thorium to be $1 \cdot 86 \times 10^{10}$ years, the average life period, $2 \cdot 5 \times 10^{10}$ years ; and the radioactive constant $\lambda = 1 \cdot 2 \times 10^{-18}$ sec. G. C. Ashman found for the half-life period $1 \cdot 86 \times 10^{10}$ years ; L. Meitner, $2 \cdot 37 \times 10^{10}$ years ; B. Heimann, $1 \cdot 5 \times 10^{10}$ years ; H. Geiger and J. M. Nuttall, 10^8 years. A. Fleck discussed the isotopy of thorium, radioactinium, and uranium-X.

After the discovery of radiothorium, it was assumed that this radioactive element is formed directly from thorium itself. In 1906, as a result of the work of B. B. Boltwood, H. M. Dadourian, H. N. McCoy and W. H. Ross, and A. S. Eve, it was shown that the radioactivity of thorium minerals is directly proportional to the contained thorium, when due allowance is made for the contained uranium. The radioactivity of commercial thorium salts, however, was much smaller, in some cases not more than half of that normally shown by the minerals. It was naturally supposed by B. B. Boltwood that the deficiency was due to the separation of part of the radiothorium during the chemical purification of the thorium, and hence it was inferred that the half-life period of radiothorium must be six years but O. Hahn [2] found the half-life period to be about two years. O. Hahn, therefore, suggested that an unknown rayless product was formed between thorium and radiothorium. On testing this hypothesis, he found that the radioactivity of freshly prepared thorium salts was normal, but the activity gradually decreased with age attaining a minimum in about $4 \cdot 6$ years ; the radioactivity then rose towards the initial normal value. Taking the half-life period of radiothorium as two years, he inferred that the intermediate rayless product had a half-life period of about $5\frac{1}{2}$ years. This was confirmed by H. N. McCoy and W. H. Ross. The intermediary product was named **mesothorium,** and later **mesothorium-1,** $MsTh_1$ —from $\mu\acute{\epsilon}\sigma\sigma$, in the middle. E. Rutherford found the time curves of the decay of the activity of thorium preparations agreed well with these assumptions. H. N. McCoy and L. M. Henderson found the ratio of mesothorium to thorium in thorianite to be $0 \cdot 535 \times 10^{-7}$ to $0 \cdot 535 \times 10^{-7}$; in Indian monazite, $0 \cdot 507 \times 10^{-7}$; in Brazilian monazite, $0 \cdot 484 \times 10^{-7}$; and in thorium nitrate, $0 \cdot 508 \times 10^{-7}$ to $0 \cdot 559 \times 10^{-7}$. The average $0 \cdot 52 \times 10^{-7}$ is about one-sixth the value of the Ra : U-ratio, $3 \cdot 32 \times 10^{-7}$.

In preparing mesothorium-1, it is an advantage to use salts as old as possible so that the proportion of mesothorium-1 may approach the equilibrium value. According to B. B. Boltwood, mesothorium-1 can be separated from thorium by adding ammonia to a dil. soln. of the nitrate for 80–90 per cent. of the meso-thorium-1 then remains in the filtrate. He also noted that mesothorium-1 is entrained when barium is precipitated as sulphate or carbonate from a soln. of a thorium salt. F. Soddy showed that the mesothorium-1 is not absorbed by the barium sulphate, but that the co-precipitation depends on a chemical relationship between mesothorium-1 sulphate and barium sulphate. If radium be present, it too will be also precipitated. F. Soddy, and W. Marckwald could not separate radium from mesothorium-1 by the fractional crystallization of a mixture of the two; and mesothorium-1 and radium are considered to be isotopic. R. K. Strong, and J. L. Nierman studied the fractional crystallization of barium bromide mixed with radium and mesothorium bromides. Mesothorium-1 can be obtained from soln. of an aged preparation of thorium nitrate by adding ferric chloride, and treating the soln. at 70°–80° with sodium carbonate. The precipitated basic ferric carbonate entrains the mesothorium-1. According to S. Meyer and E. von Schweidler, radium-free mesothorium-1 is obtained by separating mesothorium and radium from a thorium preparation by the barium sulphate process; and after some years, precipitating the mesothorium-1 which has grown in the pre-paration. If the thorium was free from uranium, and ionium, no further radium would have been simultaneously formed.

Mesothorium preparations are used in medicine as a substitute for radium prepara-tions. Commercial mesothorium contains mesothorium-1, mesothorium-2, radiothorium, thorium-X, etc. Thorium minerals, monazite sand, or old gas mantles are used as raw material. This is digested with sulphuric acid. Part of the mesothorium is dissolved by the acid, but most remains undissolved. To prevent the dissolution of the meso-thorium, a little barium carbonate or chloride is added. The liquid must be stirred so that the barium sulphate is formed throughout the whole mass of liquid; and enough barium salt should be added to precipitate all the mesothorium and radium in the soln. The mixture is then treated with sodium carbonate to convert the sulphates to carbonates. or the sulphates are transformed into sulphides. The products are dissolved in hydro-chloric acid, and the chlorides purified as in the case of radium salts. F. Soddy, and C. Schwab have patented modifications of the process. F. Glaser precipitated mesothorium and thorium-X from a soln. of a thorium salt containing a little lead acetate, by the addition of dil. sulphuric acid. Other lead salts do not behave like lead sulphate. H. Schlundt has discussed the general methods of preparation from monazite.

The chemical properties of mesothorium resemble those of radium with which it is isotopic. M. S. Curie estimates the radium and mesothorium in mixtures by the measurement of the heat effect due to the emission of α-rays. The at. wt. of mesothorium-1 is 228. Mesothorium-1 is either rayless, or else it emits very soft β-rays. It decays into mesothorium-2. According to O. Hahn, and H. N. McCoy and W. H. Ross, the half-life period is 5·5 years; the average-life period, 7·9 years; and the radioactive constant. $\lambda = 4 \cdot 0 \times 10^{-9}$ sec., or 0·126 year. L. Meitner gave 6·7 years for the half-life period of mesothorium-1. If q_0 mgrm. of mesothorium are produced per annum by thorium, and N denotes the number of mgrm. of meso-thorium present at the time t, then λN-mgrm. of mesothorium change every year when λ is the radioactive constant of mesothorium. The rate of increase of meso-thorium, dN/dt, is equal to the rate of production q, less the rate of change, or $dN dt = q - N\lambda$. When t is very great the number of particles of mesothorium reaches a maximum, or $N = N_0$ when t is infinite; and $N = 0$ when $t = 0$. Then, by integration, the number of milligrams of mesothorium present at the time t is $N = N_0(1 - e^{\lambda t})$. For equilibrium, the amount, q_0 mgrm., of mesothorium produced per annum is equal to the number of milligrams, λN_0, which change per annum, or $q_0 = \lambda N_0$. Hence,

$$N = \frac{q_0}{\lambda}(1 - e^{\lambda t}) \quad \cdots \cdots \quad (1)$$

100,000 kgrm., or 10^{11} mgrm. of thorium are used approximately per annum in making gas mantles. Then, if the average-life period of thorium is $2 \cdot 6 \times 10^{10}$ years, and of mesothorium 7·9 years, and remembering that the radioactive constant is the reciprocal of the average-life period, $q_0=7\cdot9\times10^{11}\div2\cdot6\times10^{10}$, or $q=30$ mgrm., it follows from (1) that nearly 300 mgrm. of mesothorium will be produced per annum by 100,000 kgrm. of thorium.

Commercial mesothorium is a mixture of mesothorium, radiothorium, and other decay products. The β- and γ-ray activity rises to a maximum in about 2·3 years and the half-life period is 5·5 years. It is used as a convenient source of radioactive rays. Since the raw materials usually contain uranium and radium, commercial mesothorium also contains radium. About a quarter of the γ-ray activity of commercial mesothorium is due to radium. The activity of commercial samples is often expressed in terms of the γ-ray activity of radium in equilibrium with its decay products. Thus, " 5 mgrm. of mesothorium " indicates that one month after its separation the γ-ray activity of the meso-thorium plus that of the associated radium is eq. to 5 mgrm. of radium bromide. The activity of preparations of mesothorium is usually greater than that of an equal weight of radium bromide. After having been kept a year, much radiothorium is present. A soln. of an old preparation mixed with a little thorium nitrate and treated with ammonia gives a precipitate of radiothorium, while mesothorium and thorium-X remain in soln.

O. Hahn noticed that a few hours after rayless mesothorium-1 has been prepared, it emits β- and γ-rays. This was traced to the change of mesothorium-1 into another radioactive product of short life, which he called **mesothorium-2**, $MsTh_2$. He found that the two products can be separated by adding a trace of zirconium or thorium salt to the active soln., and precipitating with ammonia ; mesothorium-2 collects in the precipitate, while mesothorium-1 remains in the filtrate. H. N. McCoy used an aluminium salt, and W. Marckwald a ferric salt in place of O. Hahn's zirconium or thorium salt. In order to separate mesothorium-2 from thorium-B or thorium-C, a little lead, bismuth, or mercury salt is added, and the soln. treated with hydrogen sulphide, the mesothorium-2 remains in the filtrate. In order to remove radiothorium from mesothorium-2, a trace of a thorium or related salt is added, and precipitated with hydrogen dioxide. To prepare active films of mesothorium-2, H. N. McCoy and C. H. Viol recommend co-precipitation with barium sulphate from faintly acid soln. L. Meitner found that mesothorium-2 containing small proportions of the thorium active deposit is separated from a mesothorium soln. by precipitating iron in the soln. by ammonia. After the first few precipitations at daily intervals, the radiothorium and thorium-X are removed, and then the precipitates, obtained by a trace only of iron, consist of mesothorium-2 and a little thorium-B. By electrolysis of the hydrochloric acid soln. using a platinum cathode, the iron and the thorium-B are deposited. The soln. is nearly neutralized, boiled vigorously and electrolyzed with a silver cathode, when the mesothorium-2 is deposited. W. P. Widdowson and A. S. Russell separated mesothorium-2 from its parent substance by the addition of thorium, and precipitation with ammonia.

According to D. K. Yovanovitch, a conc. soln. of the chlorides of barium and radioactive elements was treated with hydrochloric acid in the cold. The precipitated barium chloride carried down with it mesothorium-I, thorium-X, and radium, leaving mesothorium-I radiothorium, and the active residue in soln. By this process, repeated at intervals, meso-thorium-I was obtained in the acid soln., nearly pure and practically free from barium. The final purification of mesothorium-I was carried out by repeated co-precipitation with salts of iron or aluminium, and further by reprecipitation as hydroxide. To eliminate radiothorium a trace of thorium was added and later removed by means of hydrogen dioxide. Thorium-C and thorium-B were removed by precipitation with lead and bismuth, which in turn were removed as sulphides. Mesothorium-I in soln. with elements of the cerium group was fractionally precipitated as oxalate, hydroxide, and as the double sulphate. Mesothorium-I in the presence of lanthanum and praseodymium appeared in greater quantity in the early fractions, but when mixed with neodymium and samarium was more conc. in the last fractions. In the fractionation of the double nitrates of the rare earths and ammonium, mesothorium-I tends to accumulate with lanthanum rather than with samarium.

The at. wt. of mesothorium-2 is 228. While the general properties of meso-thorium-1 resemble those of the alkaline-earth family, those of mesothorium-2 belong to the rare-earth group. Mesothorium-2 is isotopic with actinium, and the nearest member of its family in the periodic table is lanthanum. A. Fleck dis-cussed the isotopy of mesothorium-2 and actinium. Mesothorium-2 emits β- and γ-rays, but not α-rays. The β-rays are not homogeneous, but show, according to O. von Baeyer and co-workers, a magnetic spectrum involving rays of velocity 1·11, 1·17, 1·29, 1·50, 1·71, 1·80, and $1·98 \times 10^{10}$ cm. per sec. There is also a band with a velocity 2·1 and $2·85 \times 10^{10}$ cm. per sec. thought to belong to thorium-D. D. H. Black measured the β-ray spectrum of mesothorium-2; and J. Thibaud, and D. K. Yovanovitch the magnetic spectrum of the γ-rays from mesothorium-2. The absorption coeff. of the β-rays of velocity $1·17 \times 10^{10}$ cm. per sec. is 20·3 cm.$^{-1}$ of aluminium, and those of velocity $1·80 \times 10^{10}$ cm. per sec. 38·4 cm.$^{-1}$ of aluminium. F. Soddy and co-workers found the γ-rays from mesothorium-2 to be rather less penetrating than those from radium. They found the absorption coeff. of the γ-rays in cm. to be:

Pb	Sn	Zn	Cu	Fe	S	Al
0·620	0·305	0·300	0·373	0·316	0·083	0·116 and 26

E. Rutherford and H. Richardson also made observations on this subject. Mesothorium-1 is the parent of mesothorium-2, the latter decays into radiothorium. O. Hahn found the half-life period to be 6·20 hrs.; H. N. McCoy and C. H. Viol, 6·13 hrs.; and W. P. Widdowson and A. S. Russell, 5·95 hrs. O. Hahn's value for the average-life period is 8·9 hrs., and for the radioactive constant, $\lambda = 3·1 \times 10^{-5}$ per sec. or 0·112 per hr. W. P. Widdowson and A. S. Russell gave 0·116 per hour for the disintegration constant of mesothorium-2. P. Lemay and L. Jaloustre found mesothorium acted as a catalyst in oxidation processes in virtue of the α-radiations and not the formation of ozone.

O. Hahn [3] obtained a very active substance in the residues remaining after the separation of thorium from thorianite; he called it **radiothorium,** RaTh. G. A. Blanc found what proved to be radiothorium in the sediment deposited by the hot springs of Echaillon and of Salins Moutiers. The radiothorium is here assumed to have been derived from the mesothorium dissolved by the water, and carried to the surface. J. Elster and H. Geitel likewise observed what proved to be radiothorium in the sediment from the waters of Baden-Baden; and H. Mache, in the waters of the Gasteiner Reissacherit.

According to O. Hahn, H. N. McCoy and co-workers, radiothorium is chemically identical with thorium, and it is accordingly precipitated from a soln. of mesothorium by ammonia, the mesothorium remains in soln., and thorium-X, if present, likewise remains in the filtrate. Thorium-B, and thorium-C, if present, are precipitated with hydrogen sulphide, preferably by the addition of a little lead, mercury, or bismuth to the soln. before treatment. The radiothorium can then be precipitated with ammonia. Radiothorium is best co-precipitated with a little aluminium or ferric hydroxide; it can also be precipitated with basic ferric carbonate by adding sodium carbonate to the soln. About 50 per cent. is entrained with barium sulphate when the latter is precipitated from acid soln. of radiothorium. About 5 per cent. of the radiothorium is entrained with these sulphates. If the radiothorium be admixed with the isotopic uranium-X_1 and radioactinium, the soln. is allowed to stand for some months when these products will have decayed. Freshly prepared radiothorium may contain mesothorium-2 which will have decayed in 2–3 days; but thorium-X will have been formed. O. Knöfler found that radiothorium can be electrodeposited by the electrolysis of soln. containing a relatively large proportion of radiothorium and very little thorium.

The at. wt. of radiothorium is 228. According to G. von Hevesy, the diffusion constant of radiothorium is 0·33 sq. cm. per day, and this value is characteristic of a quadrivalent element. Radiothorium is isotopic with thorium, ionium, uranium-X_1, and radioactinium. Hence, if the starting material for the preparation of radiothorium be not free from uranium, the three last-named isotopes may be all present; and if the mesothorium contains thorium, then it too will be present. While the direct parent of radiothorium is mesothorium-2, the direct decay product is thorium-X. Radiothorium free from its decay products emits α-rays of range

3·87 cm. in air at 15°, and initial velocity $1·58 \times 10^9$ cm. per sec. at 0°. O. von Baeyer and co-workers found that radiothorium emits β-rays with velocities $1·41 \times 10^{10}$ and $1·53 \times 10^{10}$ cm. per sec.—the latter were formerly ascribed to thorium-X. J. Chadwick and A. S. Russell also observed the emission of very soft γ-rays by radiothorium. L. Meitner found that the β-ray change of thorium-X is free from γ-rays. O. Hahn gave 2 years for the half-life period, G. A. Blanc, 737 days=2·02 years, and M. S. Leslie, 710 days. Assuming the half-life period is 2 years, the average life period is 2·9 years, and the radioactive constant, $\lambda=1·09 \times 10^8$ sec. or 0·347 year. P. Lemay and L. Jaloustre found radiothorium acted as a catalyst in oxidation processes.

The time-variation in the activity of mesothorium, and of radiothorium, is obtained from the respective relations :

$$\text{Mesothorium, } M = M_0 e^{-\lambda_1 t} \text{ ; Radiothorium, } R = R_0 e^{-\lambda_2 t} \quad . \quad . \quad (2)$$

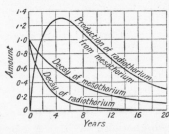

where M and R, respectively, denote the amounts of mesothorium and radiothorium at the time t ; M_0 and R_0, the respective amounts initially present ; and $\lambda=0·1265$ year and $\lambda_2=0·3466$ year, the corresponding radioactive constants. The corresponding curves for each element when $M_0=1$, and $R_0=1$ are shown in Fig. 2. Since mesothorium-1 and mesothorium-2 are in equilibrium two days after the preparation, the two may be assumed as one product with a half-life period of 5·5 years, and emitting β- and γ-rays ; the mesothorium is transformed into radiothorium and its decay products. If dQ be the amount of radiothorium formed in unit time, this is supplied by the amount, $\lambda_1 M$, of mesothorium less the amount, $\lambda_2 Q$, of radiothorium changed into thorium-X, or $dQ/dt = \lambda_1 M - \lambda_2 Q$; but, on substituting for M, from (2), and integrating for $Q=0$ when $t=0$, it follows that the amount, Q, of radiothorium present at the time t is :

FIG. 2.—Decay Curves of Mesothorium and Radiothorium.

$$Q = \frac{\lambda_1 M_0}{\lambda_2 - \lambda_1} (e^{-\lambda_1 t} - e^{-\lambda_2 t}) \quad \bullet \quad \bullet \quad \bullet \quad \bullet \quad \bullet \quad \bullet \quad (3)$$

The curve for $M_0=1$ is shown in Fig. 2. Since radiothorium alone emits α-rays, and the successive short-lived products together emit four α-ray products, the number of α-ray particles emitted at the time t is $5\lambda_2 Q$, so that the α-ray activity is proportional to the curve for the production of radiothorium. E. Rutherford showed that the β- or γ ray activity is proportional to $\lambda_1 M + k\lambda_2 Q$, where k is a constant dependent on the relative ionization due to the β- or γ-rays from mesothorium and the decay products thorium-C and thorium-D. The γ-ray activity when $k=1$ passes through a maximum in about 2·3 years, and then decays exponentially with the period of mesothorium. W. Bothe differentiated radium, mesothorium, and radiothorium by γ-ray measurement.

W. Crookes, and C. Baskerville obtained evidence of the presence of a radioactive substance in thorium compounds. E. Rutherford and F. Soddy showed that if ammonia be added to a soln. of a thorium salt, the thorium is precipitated as hydroxide, but a radioactive substance remains in the filtrate which is chemically free from thorium. The filtrate was evaporated, and the ammonium salts driven off by ignition. The residue was found to be, weight for weight, several thousand times more active than the thorium from which it was obtained. They named the active constituent **thorium-X,** ThX, by analogy with W. Crookes' uranium-X. The active constituent so obtained was largely contaminated with impurities from the thorium. It was also found that an active constituent could be separated from thorium oxide by shaking it with water for some time, and then filtering and evaporating the soln. W. Crookes found that by fractionally crystallizing thorium nitrate six times, the product at one end of the series was about three times as radioactive as that at the other end. Thorium sulphate gave negative results. H. Schlundt and R. B. Moore found that if pyridine, fumaric acid, or metanitrobenzoic acid be employed as precipitant in place of ammonia, the thorium-X is also accompanied by thorium-B. H. N. McCoy and C. H. Viol obtained thorium-X from aged radiothorium. A little aluminium salt is mixed with the soln., and ammonia added. The filtrate containing thorium-X and radiothorium is mixed with a trace of thorium salt and precipitated with ammonia. The acidified filtrate is mixed with a little lead, mercury, or bismuth salt, and treated with hydrogen sulphide. Thorium (-B, -C, and -D) sulphide collects with the precipitated sulphide. The filtrate is mixed with a little barium salt, and sulphuric acid. The thorium-X is precipitated with the barium sulphate. A mixed soln. of barium and thorium-X chlorides or nitrates was shown by D. Strömholm and T. Svedberg to furnish on crystallization an isomorphous mixture of the thorium-X and barium salts. According to F. von Lerch, the induced thorioactive matter, but not thorium-X, is precipitated from the hydrochloric acid soln. of thorium-X by magnesium, iron, zinc, amalgamated zinc, nickel, lead, copper, or aluminium. The induced thorioactive matter, sometimes along with traces of thorium-X, is also precipitated on electrolysis of acid thorium-X soln. ; but thorium-X is precipitated along with metals from alkaline soln. According to J. Lorenzen, when a colloidal soln. of thorium oxide is dialyzed, thorium-X passes through the membrane, yielding a pure soln. The thorium-X is regenerated continuously from the radiothorium present in ordinary thorium oxide, and further quantities can therefore be separated by renewing the distilled water in the dialyzer. The colloidal thorium oxide may be prepared by treating a conc. soln. of thorium nitrate with ammonia, washing the precipitated thorium hydroxide, and digesting it with a small quantity of water after addition of a trace of thorium nitrate. The Deutsche Gasglühlicht Aktien-Gesellschaft have patented a process for the preparation of thorium-X in commercial quantities. According to F. Glaser, the precipitation of thorium-X from a thorium soln. obtained from monazite sand is conditioned by the presence of lead which, as lead sulphate, absorbs thorium-X, and thorium-X may be separated from any thorium soln. containing sulphuric acid by the addition of a little lead acetate. Other lead salts do not behave like lead sulphate in this respect, so that by treating the radioactive lead sulphate with sodium carbonate soln., dissolving the washed residue in hydrochloric acid, and precipitating with hydrogen sulphide, the lead may be separated as sulphide, leaving thorium-X in soln.

The at. wt. of thorium-X is 224. According to G. von Hevesy, the diffusion constant is $0·66$ sq. cm. per day in agreement with that of a bivalent element. Thorium-X is isotopic with radium, mesothorium-1, and actinium-X. It follows all the reactions characteristic of radium, mesothorium-1, etc., and it belongs to the alkaline earth family. As indicated above, D. Strömholm and T. Svedberg found it crystallizes isomorphously with barium salts. Thorium-X emits α-rays. O. Hahn gave $5·7$ cm. for the range of the α-particles, while H. N. McCoy and C. H. Viol gave $4·08$ cm. at $15°$ in air, and H. Geiger and J. M. Nuttall gave $4·3$ cm. at 150 ; the initial velocity of the α-rays is $1·64 \times 10^9$ cm. per sec. The β-rays attributed by O. von Baeyer and co-workers to thorium-X may belong to radiothorium. E. Rutherford and F. Soddy's first estimate for the half-life period was about 4 days. F. von Lerch, and H. N. McCoy and C. H. Viol, gave $3·64$ days ; M. Levin, $3·65$; and J. Elster and H. Geitel, 56 days. Assuming the best representative value is $3·64$ days, the average-life period is $5·25$ days ; and the radioactive constant, $\lambda = 2·20 \times 10^6$ sec. or $0·190$ day. G. H. Briggs studied the electric change carried by thorium-X atoms. The parent of thorium-X is radiothorium, the first decay product is thorium emanation. E. Rutherford and F. Soddy found that when the thorium-X salt is separated from a thorium salt, the former completely loses its activity in a month's time, while the latter had completely gained its activity. The decay curve of the activity, I, of thorium-X was represented by

$I = I_0 e^{-\lambda t}$, where I represents the activity of the preparation at the time t, and I_0 the initial activity, λ is a constant; conversely the recovery of activity by the thorium is represented by $I = I_0(1 - e^{-\lambda t})$, where the constant λ is the same as before. P. Lemay and L. Jaloustre found thorium-X acted as a catalyst in oxidation processes.

Some thorium salts—particularly the oxide—behave very irregularly in the ionization of the ambient air. R. B. Owens[4] showed that the irregularities are produced by currents of air, and in 1900, E. Rutherford showed that thorium compounds continuously produce a radioactive emanation—**thorium emanation, or thoron,** ThEm—which has the properties of a gas, and which is the source of the disturbances observed by R. B. Owens. These observations were confirmed by E. Dorn, and the general properties of the emanation were studied by E. Rutherford and F. Soddy. Thorium emanation was discovered before the radioactive emanation from radium and actinium. A. Lepape discussed the detection of thorium emanation in thermal springs by the method of induced radioactivity.

Thorium emanation has a comparatively short life-period—approximately an hour. E. Rutherford found that a gram of thorium is in equilibrium with 1.2×10^{-13} mgrm. of the emanation; and, assuming the decay of the emanation is about 0.01 grm. per sec., the corresponding volume is 1.2×10^{-14} c.c. The gas is occluded by thorium and its compounds. It is obtained by the same methods as those employed for radium and actinium emanations. E. Rutherford and F. Soddy found that the occluded emanation is more readily driven off from some prepara-tions than from others. In general it is more readily obtained from moist than from dry compounds. It is not so easily obtained from dried thorium oxide as it is from the hydroxide; it is retained more tenaciously by thorium sulphate and nitrate than it is by the carbonate.

Observations by H. A. Bumstead, J. E. Burbank, A. Gockel, G. A. Blanc, and C. Runge have shown that part of the radioactivity of atm. air is due to the con-tained thorium emanation. H. M. Dadourian found that the ratio of radium emanation to thorium emanation is 30000 to 50000 : 1 at Newhaven (America), and 20000 to 30000 : 1 at Rome. W. E. Wilson obtained 9000 to 18000 : 1 for the former and 2600 to 4000 : 1 for the latter; and at Manchester he found 3700 : 1. D. Pacini found on the Apennines, 2300 to 15000 : 1, according to the strength of the wind; and he found that the amount of the emanation in air decreased with increasing barometric press. H. M. Dadourian found thorium emanation in under-ground air, and in the air of soils. J. C. Sanderson found an amount of thorium emanation in the soils corresponding with 1.35×10^{-6} grm. of thorium, this repre-sents 1.67×10^{-19} c.c. of thorium emanation; the corresponding value for radium emanation is 1.44×10^{-16} c.c., and the ratio of the latter to the former is nearly 8500 : 1. G. A. Blanc, G. von der Borne, C. Schäfer and C. Seebohm, O Angelucci, P. Artmann, G. Feliciani, and K. Aschoff have reported thorium emanation in gases, waters, and sediments from different mineral springs.

The mol. wt. of thorium emanation cannot be obtained from the density of the gas because so little of the gas can be made at one time. Attempts have been made to deduce values from the diffusion coeff. M. S. Leslie found the diffusion coeff. in air at 18° to be less than 0.85 sq. cm. per sec. E. Rutherford obtained the coeff. 0.097. W. Makower compared the diffusion coeff. of radium and thorium emana-tions and obtained the ratio 0.931, so that if the diffusion coeff. of radium emanation is 0.126, that of thorium emanation is 0.117. Assuming that the diffusion law is valid for the case of a minute proportion of the radioactive radiation, the mol. wt., x, is $1 : (0.931)^2 = 1 : x$, or $x = 0.867$ times less than that of niton. S. Russ measured the diffusion coeff. of thorium emanation in air and in argon at different press. He found for air :

p mm. .	.	.	.	.	82·5	175	375·2	761·2
Diffusion coeff.	.	.	.	.	9·66	4·36	2·11	1·03
Product	.	.	.	.	79·7	76·3	79·4	78·8

Hence, the coeff. in argon at 760 mm. is 0·103, and in air, 0·087.   M. S. Leslie noted that the value of the coeff. is modified by the form of the vessel, and she obtained in different vessels at 15° and 760 mm. press., 0·085, 0·115, and 0·111. It follows that there is not much difference in the coeff. of diffusion of thorium and radium emanations.   The results are too uncertain to furnish reliable values for the at. wt. M. S. Leslie compared the effusion of thorium emanation, with that of oxygen, and obtained a mol. wt. approximately 200.   On the assumption that the loss of an a-particle reduces the at. wt. of an element four units, the at. wt. of thorium emanation deduced from that of thorium is 232·4 less 3×4=220·4.

E. Rutherford and F. Soddy cooled the emanation admixed with a large proportion of gas, and found it liquefied at the temp. of liquid air.   The influence of the velocity of the stream and nature of the admixed gas is very much the same as with radium emanation ; A. Fleck, and S. Lorie noted small differences.   According to the latter, the first trace of vaporization occurs at −164° ; at −150°, about half the emanation is gaseous ; and at −125°, no liquid is perceptible ; but, on account of the small quantities available, it is very difficult to obtain accurate data. S. Kinoshita measured the properties of uncondensed gas at different temp. and press.   The condensation temp. of thorium emanation appears to be 2° or 3° higher than with actinium emanation.

Thorium emanation emits a-rays which, according to O. Hahn, have a range of 5·5 cm. in air at 760 mm. and 15° ; T. Barratt, and H. Geiger and J. M. Nuttall gave 5·00 cm. at 15°, and 4·74 cm. at 0°.   Some of the older observations were made on samples contaminated with thorium-A.   H. Geiger found the initial velocity calculated from $V^3=aR$ to be $1·85 \times 10^9$ cm. per sec. at 0°—where V denotes the velocity ; R, the range ; and a, a constant.   H. L. Bronson found that the emanation furnishes four a-particles for each a-particle furnished by the so-called active deposit from thorium emanation.   The phenomenon was further studied by H. Geiger and E. Marsden, and M. S. Leslie, and it is taken to show that the decay of the emanation gives a very short-lived product—the so-called thorium-A. J. Satterly found that an atom of thorium emanation in passing into thorium-A loses one a-particle.   According to J. M. W. Slater, thorium emanation emits soft β-rays—the so-called delta rays.   E. Rutherford and F. Soddy found the half-life period of thorium emanation to be about one minute.   C. le Rossignol and C. T. Gimingham gave 51 sec. ; H. L. Bronson, 54 sec. ; O. Hahn, 53·3 sec. ; M. S. Leslie, 54·3 sec. ; R. Schmid, 54·5 ± 0·03 sec. ; and P. B. Perkins, 54·53 ± 0·041 sec. The average life period is 78·7 sec., and the radioactive constant $\lambda = 1·27 \times 10^{-2}$ sec. The formulæ of H. Geiger and J. M. Nuttall, R. Swinne, and H. A. Wilson, discussed in connection with radium, apply very well for the relation between the range, R, of the a-particles and the radioactive constant.   G. H. Briggs studied the electric charge of the atoms of thorium emanation.

A. Klaus measured the absorption coeff. of thorium emanation in water and in petroleum, and found respectively $a = 1·052$ and 4·97.   R. W. Boyle arranged the following liquids in the order of increasing solubility : cupric sulphate soln., calcium chloride soln., water, sulphuric acid, alcohol, and petroleum.   The series is the same as for radium emanation, which, according to F. von Hevesy, indicates a close chemical relationship.   E. Rutherford, R. W. Boyle, and G. von Hevesy studied the occlusion of thorium emanation by different varieties of wood and tar charcoal.   Cocoa-nut charcoal was the strongest absorbent.   R. W. Boyle found the partition coeff. at 18° is greater than 50.   E. Rutherford and F. Soddy found that dil. or conc. acids and alkalies are without influence on thorium emanation ; it is not perceptibly attacked by white-hot platinum, lead chromate, zinc dust, magnesium dust, platinum sponge, or platinum black.   In these experiments, the emanation was always mixed with a large proportion of an inert gas, and in order to prove that the result is not due to a mere activation of the gas employed, carbon dioxide was passed over thorium oxide, air was then introduced, and the carbon dioxide removed by soda-lime.   The results were the same in different variations of the experiment. This shows the gaseous nature and the chemical inactivity of the emanation. S. G. Tracy, D. Minami, A. Bickel, and K. Kojo have studied the physiological action of thorium emanation.

When substances are exposed to thorium emanation they become radioactive, the so-called *induced radioactivity*. The induced radioactivity is due to the film of decay products of thorium emanation which is formed on the exposed surface. This product, for convenience, is called the *active deposit of thorium*. It is best obtained by exposing an insulated, negatively charged wire—110–220 volts—to the emanation, or in a vessel containing a preparation of thorium. After three days' exposure, the decay products are in equilibrium. The active deposit is a mixture of the successive decay products thorium (-A, -B, -C, and -D). The long-range particles—15·0 and 18·4 cm.—in addition to those of range 8·6 and 11·5 cm., were measured by L. F. Bates and J. S. Rogers. S. Rosenblum found the ratio of the speeds of the two groups of α-particles from the active deposit to be 1·209. Thorium-A is an ephemeral product with a very short half-life period—nearly one-eighth of a second. Thorium-B has a half-life period of about 10 hrs., thorium-C, about an hour. H. A. Erikson studied the mobility of the ions of the active deposits. The active deposit dissolves when boiled with acids.

L. Bronson found that twice as many α-particles were ejected by thorium emanation as were expelled from the active deposit of thorium ; and H. Geiger and E. Marsden noted that the particles from thorium emanation appeared almost as if they were double but with an average interval of $\frac{1}{5}$th sec. They hence inferred that the emanation must contain two α-ray products, one of which had an average life of $\frac{1}{5}$th sec. H. Geiger showed that the two α-particles have a different range. The ephemeral substance is non-gaseous, and is the first decay product of thorium emanation. It is called **thorium-A,** ThA. Prior to E. Rutherford and H. Geiger's observations, thorium-A represented the substance now known as thorium-B ; and the latter was thought to be the direct derivative of the emanation. The association of thorium-A with the emanation is due to the brevity of its life ; the greater part of it is transformed *in situ* before it has had time to diffuse to the surface of the containing vessel. When the emanation breaks down, an α-particle is ejected from the atom, and the residue forms an atom of thorium-A. E. Rutherford and H. Geiger showed that the atoms of thorium-A initially carry a positive charge, and are collected by concentration on a plate carrying an intense negative charge. Under ordinary conditions, thorium-A has all disappeared before the plate can be examined. Under ordinary conditions, therefore, thorium-A has to be very quickly examined along with the emanation. The product of the decay is thorium-B, and this quickly changes to thorium-C. In its decay, thorium-A emits α-radiations which H. Geiger and J. M. Nuttall found to have a range of 5·7 cm. at 15° in air—T. Barratt gave 5·4 cm.—the initial velocity is $1·80 \times 10^9$ cm. per sec. H. G. J. Moseley and K. Fajans found for the half-life period 0·145 sec., for the life period, 0·20 sec., and for the radioactive constant, $\lambda = 4·95$ secs. The at. wt. is taken to be 216. In its chemical nature thorium-A resembles tellurium ; and it appears to be isotopic with polonium. If an aq. soln. of thorium nitrate be treated with ammonia, thorium-A is precipitated along with the thorium ; and if the precipitate be treated with fumaric acid, thorium-A is dissolved. According to F. von Lerch, thorium-A is electrochemically a less rare element than its decay product thorium-B. If a nickel wire be dipped in a soln. of the active deposit of thorium, a radioactive deposit is obtained which contains no thorium-A ; if, however, the nickel wire be wrapped round with platinum wire, thorium-A is deposited on the platinum. G. H. Briggs studied the distribution of thorium-A in electrical fields.

E. Rutherford [5] found that a plate which has been exposed to constant supply of thorium emanation for several days acquires a radioactivity which decays slowly at first, but after a few hours, the rate of decay increases when the period is 10·6 hrs. whether the activity is measured by the α-, β-, or γ-rays. E. Rutherford and H. T. Brooks showed that with a plate which has had only a short exposure to the emanation, the activity starts from nearly zero, and passes through a maximum after about 220 min., and then decays with a period as before. A negatively charged wire which has been exposed for about a second to thorium emanation, has little more than thorium-B. E. Rutherford showed that the observations accord with the assumption that **thorium-B,** ThB. does not emit α-rays and is transformed into thorium-C which emits α-, β-, and γ-rays. The active deposit of thorium thus contains a mixture of thorium-B and thorium-C. Thorium-B was initially called thorium-A ; E. Rutherford and H. Geiger changed the name from thorium-A to thorium-B after the discovery of thorium-A. There are several methods of separating the two. J. M. W. Slater, and F. C. Gates showed that thorium-B is volatilized between 700° and 1000°, while thorium-C is not volatile under these conditions. The thorium-B can be sublimed on to a cold cylinder surrounding the electrically heated wire on which the active deposit has been collected. The actual temp. of volatilization was shown by F. von Lerch to depend to some extent upon the composition of the active deposit. According to S. Loria, the proportion of volatilization of thorium-B, formed from thorium emanation on platinum foil, at different temp. is given by

	650°	700°	750°	800°	850°	900°	950°	1000°	1100°
Per cent. ThB . .	0	8	40	73	82	90	94	97	100

T. Barratt and A. B. Wood also made some observations on this subject. S. Meyer found the volatilization of thorium-B from gold begins sooner than from platinum or palladium, and between 300° and 1000° is greater from gold than for the other two metals. F. von Lerch electrolyzed a soln. of the active deposit, and found that thorium-B is not so rare as thorium (-C and -D), so that the latter are deposited on the cathode while thorium-B remains in soln. According to F. Paneth and G. von Hevesy, like lead, thorium-B can be deposited electrolytically as a dioxide, $(ThB)O_2$, on the anode, and the element can be deposited on the cathode. G. von Hevesy and E. Rona showed that the anode deposit of thorium-B dioxide is less soluble in acids—nitric acid of various conc., and in nitric acid containing glycerol— than the cathode deposit. For a soln. of thorium-B, in presence of lead, deposition occurs with perceptible amounts of lead at −0·44 volt, but in absence of lead at −0·33 volt. The anodic deposition of thorium-B in absence of lead showed a sudden deposition between 1·0 and 1·1 vols., which is very near to that of lead dioxide. The thorium-B is deposited no longer as metal, but as dioxide. If a nickel plate be dipped in a soln. of the active deposit, thorium-B remains in soln., while thorium-C is precipitated. According to C. F. Hogley, thorium-B is more soluble in inorganic solvents, and less soluble in organic solvents than thorium-C. M. Levin also found that if lampblack be added to a mixed soln. of thorium-B and thorium-C, the latter is absorbed by the carbon, and thorium-B will be found in the soln. K. Horovitz and F. Paneth studied the adsorption of thorium-B by different salts and oxides. H. N. McCoy and C. H. Viol found that ferric iron precipitated by fumaric acid from a boiling soln. of thorium-B, carries down all the thorium-C, and only a small proportion of the thorium-B ; by redissolving the precipitate, and repeating the process, it is claimed that thorium-C can be obtained in which no thorium-B can be detected. J. A. Cranston and co-workers showed that the ferric hydroxide adsorbs the thorium-B and thorium-C in proportions varying regularly with the soln., and to get a separation the acidity must be above a certain limit. The absorption is said to be a true adsorption effect, and not due to the formation of a chemical compound. A. Fleck discussed the isotopy of thorium-B and lead, and of thorium-C, radium-C, and actinium-C with bismuth.

The at. wt. of thorium-B is 212. F. von Lerch found that thorium-B is not a rayless product as was at first supposed by E. Rutherford, but it emits soft β-rays. F. von Lerch said that 28 per cent. of the total β-ray activity of the active deposit is due to thorium-B ; while O. Hahn and L. Meitner estimated 43 per cent. According to O. von Baeyer and co-workers, the magnetic spectrum of the β-rays shows velocities of 1.89×10^{10} and 2.16×10^{10} cm. per sec., and for the latter an absorption coeff. in aluminium of 153 cm.$^{-1}$; O. Hahn gave 175 cm.$^{-1}$. D. R. Yovanovitch and J. d'Espine, and W. Pohlmeyer measured the magnetic spectrum of the rapid β-rays; D. H. Black, the magnetic spectrum of the β- and γ-rays. E. Rutherford and H. Richardson found 3 types of γ-rays with absorption coeff. in aluminium of 160 cm. $^{-1}$, 32 cm.$^{-1}$, and 0.36 cm.$^{-1}$. In its general properties, thorium-B resembles lead with which it is isotopic. G. von Hevesy found the diffusion coeff. to be 0·67 sq. cm. per day corresponding with a bivalent element. J. Groh and G. von Hevesy found the diffusion coeff. of thorium-B in lead to be 2·22 per sq. cm. per day at 343°. F. von Lerch, and H. N. McCoy and C. H. Viol found the half-life period to be 10·6 hrs.; J. E. Shrader gave 10·4 hrs. The corresponding average-life period is 15·3 hrs.; and the radioactive constant, $\gamma = 1.82 \times 10^{-5}$. The decay product of thorium-B is thorium-C. A. Piccard and G. Volkart found the rate of decay of thorium-B is not appreciably affected by a magnetic field of 83,000 gauss. K. Fajans and K. von Beckerath found that silver halides do not appreciably adsorb thorium-B, but in the presence of an excess of acid, adsorption proceeds proportionally with the conc. of the H·-ions. F. Paneth and co-workers found evidence of the formation of a **hydride** of thorium-B.

As indicated above, E. Rutherford inferred from the variation of the radio-activity of the active deposit of thorium with time, that an element with a half-life period is involved in the decay of the deposit. This element is called **thorium-C**, ThC; it is the direct decay product of thorium-B. The complex product here termed thorium-C was formerly regarded as a mixture of thorium-B and thorium-C. K. Fajans called thorium-C, thorium-C_1. M. Levin found that when a soln. of the active deposit is shaken for a short time with charcoal, thorium-C is absorbed, and most of the thorium-B remains in soln. S. Meyer studied the transformation of thorium-B to thorium-C. K. Horovitz and F. Paneth studied the adsorption of thorium-B and thorium-C by different oxides and salts. Oxides of copper, titanium, and tantalum adsorb thorium-C more readily than thorium-B. They found that, like bismuth compounds, salts of thorium-C are easily hydrolyzed in aq. soln. while salts of thorium-B resemble lead salts and are not readily hydrolyzed. F. von Lerch found that if nickel is dipped into a hot hydrochloric acid soln. of the active deposit, thorium-C is precipitated, and similarly when zinc is used in place of nickel. The electrolysis of the soln. also gives a deposit of thorium-C on the cathode, and the product is fairly pure. Thorium-X if present is not deposited. F. Paneth, and G. von Hevesy found that the amount of thorium-C deposited from a $0.01N$-nitric acid soln. on a platinum plate, kept at a constant voltage of 0·6 with reference to a normal calomel electrode, is greatly reduced if a few milligrams of bismuth be present. For thorium-C in the presence of bismuth, there is a sudden increase in the decomposition potential at −0·08 volt, an immersed bismuth plate shows a potential of 0·082 volt. They recommended generally that when the separation of one radio-element from another in a high state of purity is desired, the addition of an appreciable quantity of an element isotopic with the other element—for example, in the separation of pure thorium-C from thorium-B, lead should be added, the action being analogous to the prevention of adsorption of uranium-X, for example, by the presence of thorium. G. von Hevesy and E. Rona measured the rate of soln. of mixtures of thorium-B and thorium-C in water, nitric acid of various conc., and in nitric acid containing glycerol. They found that the rate of soln. of molecularly thin layers of the radioactive elements follows the same laws as for layers of finite thickness. H. N. McCoy and C. H. Viol found that when the soln. of the active deposit of thorium is treated with fumaric acid according to H. Schlundt and R. B. Moore's process, the thorium-B remains in soln. while thorium-C is precipitated with iron—*vide supra*, thorium-B. J. M. W. Slater, and F. C. Gates showed that thorium-B is more readily volatilized than thorium-C, between 700° and 1000°, and this furnishes a convenient means of separation. S. Loria showed that an electro-deposited mixture or a mixture obtained by the evaporation of mixed soln. is more readily separated than the active deposit derived from the emanation. The percentage of thorium-C volatilized from the active deposit and from the electro-deposit at different temp. was found to be :

	700°	750°	800°	900°	950°	1000°	1100°	1200°	1300°
Electro-dep.	0	0	0	5	20	32	70	93	98
Active dep.	0	15	21	33	40	70	95	100	—

S. Meyer found that the volatilization of thorium-C from gold is very similar to that from platinum ; and in both cases there is a discontinuity in the volatilization curve at 700° which is due to the formation of an oxide of thorium-C which is stable at this temp. The discontinuity is not shown with the volatilization of thorium-C from palladium. From T. Godlewsky's work it appears that recoil particlet are driven from the active deposit into the metal from the emanation, but nos from the electro-deposited or evaporation film. Thorium-C chloride is much more volatile than thorium-B chloride ; it begins to volatilize at 100°.

The at. wt. of thorium-C is 212. The element is isotopic with bismuth. W. Metzener found that the quantitative separation of thorium-C by means of nickel foil in a boiling hydrochloric acid soln. is hindered by the presence of bismuth, but the fraction of the radio-element precipitated on the foil is the same as the fraction of the bismuth also precipitated. Similarly, the volatilization is stopped if bismuth oxide is present. Precipitation of thorium-C by silver chloride or bromide is prevented by addition of bismuth. The proportion of thorium-C in the precipitate and filtrate is shown to be the same as that of the bismuth when the latter, in presence of thorium-C, is fractionally precipitated (i) as oxychloride, (ii) as bismuth magnesium nitrate, and (iii) as basic bismuth nitrate. G. von Hevesy found the diffusion constant to be 0·5 sq. cm. per day, corresponding with a ter-valent element. E. Rutherford found approximately 55 mins. for the half-life period ; G. B. Pegram, 60 mins. ; and F. von Lerch, 60·48 ± 0·035 mins. H. N. McCoy and C. H. Viol found 60·8 mins. for the half-life period, 87·7 mins. for the average-life period, and $1·90 \times 10^{-4}$ secs. for the radioactive constant λ. Thorium-C emits α- and β-rays. D. H. Black studied the magnetic spectrum of the γ-rays from thorium-C. L. Meitner found the α- and β-ray change of thorium-C to be free from γ-rays. W. Pohlmeyer, and D. H. Black studied the magnetic spectrum of the β-rays of thorium-C. W. Kolhörster showed that the average range of recoil atoms of thorium-C in hydrogen is 0·553 mm. at 15° and 760 mm., and for thorium-C_1, 0·963 mm. ; the corresponding values in air are respectively 0·129 mm. and 0·224 mm. L. Myssowsky studied the kinetic energy of the α-particles from thorium-C. O. Hahn's measurements of the range of the α-particles showed that two groups are present, one with a range of 8·6 cm., and the other with a range of 5 cm. E. Marsden similarly obtained 8·6 and 4·8 cm. It was at first concluded that two successive α-ray products were present, but O. Hahn and L. Meitner, and H. Geiger and E. Marsden observed no signs of any separation of the two by recoil. H. L. Bronson, and H. Geiger and E. Marsden showed that for three particles emitted by thorium emanation in equilibrium with the active deposit, only one was contributed by thorium-C, and since only three α-ray products are involved in the phenomenon—the emanation, thorium-A, and thorium-C, it follows that the α-particles from thorium-C correspond with but one product in equilibrium with the emanation. Besides α-particles with ranges 5·0 and 8·6 cm., about 1 in 10,000 has a range 11·3 cm. E. Rutherford showed that the last-named rays are emitted from the source, and are not a secondary product of bombardment. F. L. Bates and J. S. Rogers found in addition some particles of range 15·0 and 18·4 cm. are given off, and that the relative numbers of the particles 8·6 cm., 11·5 cm., 15·0 cm. and 18·4 cm. are 10^6, 220, 47, and 15 respectively. The energy differences for 8·6–11·5 cm. being $2·99 \times 10^{-6}$ ergs ; 11·5–15·0 cm., $3·29 \times 10^{-6}$ ergs ; and 15·0–18·4 cm., $2·99 \times 10^{-6}$ ergs. D. R. Yovanovitch and J. d'Espine measured the magnetic spectrum of the rapid β-rays.   E. Rutherford found that the mass of the α-particles from thorium-C is 4, not 3.   A. G. Shenstone and H. Schlundt found the ratio of the number of α-particles emitted by thorium-C and radium-C to be 0·75.   W. D. Harkins and R. W. Ryan studied photographically the tracks of the α-rays.   F. Paneth and co-workers obtained a **hydride** of thorium-C by the action of magnesium or zinc powder on soln. of the salts.

E. Marsden and T. Barratt found that the α-particles of range 5·0 and 8·6 cm. from thorium-C are not equal in number, since 65 per cent. had the longer range and 35 per cent. the shorter range.   Hence, thorium-C breaks up in two distinct ways. The component furnishing the α-rays of range 4·8 cm. is called thorium-C_1 or **thorium-D**, ThD, and that component with α-rays of range 8·6 cm. is called **thorium-C_2**, ThC$_2$.   These two components always appear together in constant ratio approximately thorium-C_2 : thorium-D$=2:1$.   The at. wt. of thorium-C_2 is about 212 ; it emits α-rays only.   A. B. Wood obtained 4·95 cm. for the range of the α-particles of thorium-C_2 and the velocity $1·714 \times 10^9$ cm. per sec. ; for thorium-C_2, the α-particles of range 8·6 cm. have a velocity $2·06 \times 10^9$ cm. per sec. E. Rutherford and A. B. Wood, also made observations on this subject.   E. Marsden and C. G. Darwin, and O. Hahn and L. Meitner could not separate by the recoil method the two components derived from thorium-C.   They found thorium-C emitted β-rays of greater penetrating power than those from thorium-D ; but thorium-C gave out little if any γ-rays in comparison with those from thorium-D. The α-ray transformation of thorium-C was assumed to give rise to thorium-D, which breaks up with the emission of β- and γ-rays ; the β-ray transformation of thorium-C was assumed to furnish thorium-C_2, which breaks up emitting the α-rays of range 8·6 cm.   G. H. Henderson obtained 8·167 cm.   The transformations are thus symbolized :

$$\text{ThA} \rightarrow \text{ThB} \rightarrow \text{ThC} \lessgtr \begin{array}{l} \text{ThD} \rightarrow \text{?} \\ \text{ThC}_2 \rightarrow \end{array}, \quad \text{or} \quad \text{ThC} \lessgtr \begin{array}{l} \text{ThC}_1 \rightarrow \text{ThD} \rightarrow \\ \text{ThC}_2 \rightarrow \end{array}$$

This view is in harmony with H. Geiger and J. M. Nuttall's relation between the period of the transformation and the range of the α-particles.   L. Meitner partially separated the two components of thorium-C.   E. Marsden and C. G. Darwin obtained the ratio Th-C : Th-C_2=0·35 ;   E. Albrecht also studied this subject.   Thorium-B was obtained by evaporating the slightly acid soln. of the active deposit to dryness after boiling it first with nickel foil, and the α- and γ-radiations from this preparation increased with time similarly, the curves running parallel.   If before treatment with nickel, stannous chloride be added to the soln., the α-rays from the evaporated soln. increase much less than the γ-rays, and attain their maximum somewhat earlier.   The range of the α-rays of thorium-C_2 shows that the period must be of the order of 10^{-12} sec. so that the non-parallelism of the α- and γ-curves shows that the two C-members cannot stand in direct genetic connection, and that thorium-D cannot be the product of both, for then the α- and γ-curves must necessarily be practically parallel.   When stannous chloride is added, at least part of that one of the two C-members which does not give thorium-D must remain in soln. instead of being precipitated by the nickel.   The β-rays of thorium-C have velocities $2·79 \times 10^{10}$ and $2·85 \times 10^{10}$ cm. per sec., and an absorption coeff. in aluminium of 14·4 per cm.   The at. wt. of thorium-C_2 is 212, the half-life period is about 10^{-11} sec., the average-life period about 10^{-11} sec., and the radioactive constant about 10^{11} secs.   For the mobilities of the gas ions, *vide* thorium-D.

The α- and β-rays from the active deposit of thorium were at first attributed to the thorium-C, but O. Hahn and L. Meitner showed that these rays were derived from a decay product of thorium-C which was named **thorium-D,** ThD.   This product is best separated from thorium-C by the recoil method on a negatively charged plate exposed a short distance above a film of the active deposit.   According to A. B. Wood, the recoil particles from thorium-C chloride are not thorium-D chloride, but thorium-D.   O. Hahn and L. Meitner also separated thorium-D by entraining it with precipitates formed with hydrogen sulphide, or by adding charcoal to a soln. of the active deposit. F. von Lerch and E. von Wartburg electrolyzed an acid soln. of the active deposit of thorium, using a feeble current (0·6 milliamp.) and platinum electrodes 1 cm. apart. Thorium-D was deposited on the cathode ; it was washed successively with water, alcohol, and ether. It is also precipitated by introducing a plate of nickel into the soln. Thorium-D is electrochemically less noble than thorium-C, and in conc. acids it is less soluble than thorium-B and thorium-C. Thorium-D is easily separated from thorium-A, -B, and -C by heating; and at a red-heat, it is more volatile than thorium-B. According to A. B. Wood, it volatilizes at 520°, and is completely evaporated at 700°. Thorium-D chloride volatilizes at 270°.

Thorium-D has an at. wt. about 208 ; and it is derived from thorium-C. It emits no α-rays but gives off β- and γ-rays. O. von Baeyer and co-workers found the magnetic spectrum of the β-rays to furnish rays with initial velocities 0·87, 1·08, 2·79, 2·85×10^{11} cm. per sec. J. Franck determined the mobility of the radioactive ions of thorium-D in air, nitrogen, and hydrogen. The ions of thorium-D were obtained by the use of plates on which thorium-A, -B, and -C had been deposited by exposing the negatively charged plates to the influence of the emanation of a radio-thorium preparation. The mobility of the positively charged thorium-D atoms is approximately equal to the mobility of the positive gaseous ions in air, nitrogen, and hydrogen. This leads to the conclusion that the gas ions are complex molecular aggregates. The absorption coeff. of the β-rays for aluminium is 21·6 cm.$^{-1}$, those from thorium-C have the absorption coeff. 14·4 cm.$^{-1}$. A. B. Wood found the relative intensities of the β-rays from thorium-C and thorium-D to be as 1·5 : 1. E. Rutherford and H. Richardson gave the absorption coeff. of the γ-rays as 0·096 cm.$^{-1}$ for aluminium; F. and W. M. Soddy and A. S. Russell found for lead, 0·462 cm.$^{-1}$, and they also measured the absorption coeff. for copper, brass, iron, tin, zinc, and aluminium. The half-life period is 3·1 mins. and the average-life period is 4·47 mins. ; the radioactive constant is 3·73×10^{-3} sec. E. Albrecht gives 3·20 mins. for the half-life period, and 3·61×10^{-3} sec. for the radioactive constant. According to W. Metzener, thorium-D forms mixed crystals with thallous nitrate, carbonate, and ammonio-sulphate. The proportion of thorium-D in the crystals and mother-liquor was the same, no separation or conc. being possible. Thorium-D is isotopic with radium-C_2, and actinium-D. C. D. Ellis measured the wave-length of the γ-rays from thorium-D ; and D. H. Black, their magnetic spectrum.

A summary of the radioactive properties of the members of the thorium series is given in Table III. The relation between the range and the radioactive constant

TABLE III.—PROPERTIES OF THE THORIUM FAMILY OF RADIOACTIVE ELEMENTS.

Element.	Symbol.	Atomic weight approx.	Half-life period.	Radioactive constan. sec.	Radiation.	Range of α-rays cm.	Velocity of α-rays cm. per sec.
Thorium . .	Th	232	$1 \cdot 3 \times 10^{10}$ yrs.	$1 \cdot 7 \times 10^{-18}$	α	2·72	$1 \cdot 41 \times 10^{6}$
Mesothorium-1 .	MTh$_1$	228	5·5 yrs.	$4 \cdot 0 \times 10^{-9}$	0	—	—
Mesothorium-2 .	MTh$_2$	228	6·2 hrs.	$3 \cdot 1 \times 10^{-5}$	β, γ	—	—
Radiothorium .	RaTh	228	2·0 yrs.	$1 \cdot 09 \times 10^{-8}$	α, β	3·87	$1 \cdot 58 \times 10^{9}$
Thorium-X .	ThX	224	3·64 days	$2 \cdot 20 \times 10^{-6}$	$\alpha, (\beta)$	4·30	$1 \cdot 64 \times 10^{9}$
Thorium emanation .	ThEm	220	54·53 secs.	$1 \cdot 27 \times 10^{-2}$	α	5·00	$1 \cdot 72 \times 10^{9}$
Thorium-A .	ThA	216	0·14 sec.	4·95	α	5·70	$1 \cdot 80 \times 10^{9}$
Thorium-B .	ThB	212	10·6 hrs.	$1 \cdot 82 \times 10^{-4}$	β, γ	—	—
Thorium-C .	ThC	212	60·8 mins.	$1 \cdot 90 \times 10^{-4}$	α, β	4·80	$1 \cdot 70 \times 10^{9}$
Thorium-C$_2$.	ThC$_2$	212	$c. 10^{-11}$ sec.	$c. 10^{11}$	α	8·60	$2 \cdot 06 \times 10^{9}$
Thorium-D .	ThD	208	3·1 mins.	$3 \cdot 73 \times 10^{-3}$	β, γ	—	—

GENEALOGICAL TREE OF THE THORIUM FAMILY.

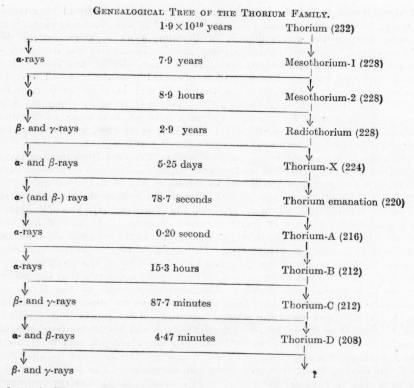

	$1\cdot9\times10^{10}$ years	Thorium (232)
α-rays	7·9 years	Mesothorium-1 (228)
0	8·9 hours	Mesothorium-2 (228)
β- and γ-rays	2·9 years	Radiothorium (228)
α- and β-rays	5·25 days	Thorium-X (224)
α- (and β-) rays	78·7 seconds	Thorium emanation (220)
α-rays	0·20 second	Thorium-A (216)
α-rays	15·3 hours	Thorium-B (212)
β- and γ-rays	87·7 minutes	Thorium-C (212)
α- and β-rays	4·47 minutes	Thorium-D (208)
β- and γ-rays		?

is shown in Fig. 3. This diagram should be compared with Fig. 11, **4.** 26, **7,** for radium, and with Fig. 16, **4.** 26, 13, for actinium. The genealogical tree of the thorium family is shown in Table III., indicating the average life of the radioactive

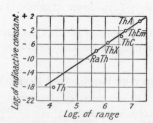

FIG. 3.—Relation between the Range of the α-particles and the Radioactive Constituent.

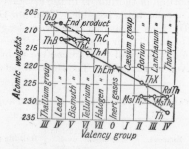

FIG. 4.—Arrangement of the Thorium Decay Products in the Periodic Table.

elements of the series on the assumption that the at. wt. of the members of the descendants of thorium follow the displacement rule, the positions of the members of the series in the periodic table are shown in Fig. 4. G. Kirsch assumes that the parent of thorium is a uranium isotope present in small amounts in terrestrial uranium at the time the oldest uranium minerals were formed, and which has since completely disappeared. W. Riss also discussed the genetic relations of thorium and uranium.

The nature of the end-product of the transformation of thorium is unknown. The next derivative of thorium-D has been called **thorium-E,** or **thorium-lead.** It is suggested by A. Holmes and R. W. Lawson that the end-product may be a stable isotope of lead—with a half-life period of 10^6 years ; and that the lead contents of a thorium-uranium mineral originally free from lead should owe its lead to the disintegration of both thorium and uranium. They conclude that thorium-E is an unstable isotope of lead, and that thorium-E must gradually disintegrate losing radiations which have so far eluded detection, and becoming transformed into a simpler element. If thorium-lead evolves β-rays, the result would be an isotope of bismuth. Starting from thorium with its at. wt. 232·12, there are six α-ray products. This would furnish an element with an at. wt. of 232·12 less 6×4, or 208·12. This suggests that bismuth, at. wt. 208·12, is the end-member of the series. The rate of transformation of thorium is about one-fifth of the rate of transformation of uranium, and, assuming that lead is the end-product of the uranium-radium series, then, since the ratio Pb/U is about 0·20, the ratio Bi/U should be about 0·04. Assuming that the methods of analysis are reliable enough to furnish the desired information, E. Rutherford has shown that the amount of bismuth actually observed in minerals is far too small to support this hypothesis. It has also been suggested that the further decay of thorium bismuth might furnish an isotope of thallium, but the evidence from analyses of the minerals is not sufficiently decisive.

REFERENCES.

[1] G. C. Schmidt, *Wied. Ann.*, **65**. 141, 1898 ; M. S. Curie, *Compt. Rend.*, **126**. 1101, 1898 ; **127**. 175, 1898 ; *Chem. News*, **78**. 49, 1898 ; *Traité de radioactivité*, Paris, **2**. 388, 1910 ; F. Soddy, *Journ. Chem. Soc.*, **105**. 1402, 1914 ; W. R. Dunstan, *Nature*, **69**. 510, 1904 ; K. A. Hofmann, *Die radioaktiven Stoffe*, Leipzig, 36, 1904 ; K. A. Hofmann and F. Zerban, *Ber.*, **35**. 531, 1902 ; **36**. 3094, 1903 ; K. A. Hofmann and E. Strauss, *ib.*, **33**. 3126, 1900 ; F. Zerban, *ib.*, **36**. 3911, 1903 ; **38**. 557, 1904 ; C. Winkler, *ib.*, **37**. 1655, 1904 ; C. Baskerville, *Chem. News*, **84**. 179, 187, 1901 ; *Journ. Amer. Chem. Soc.*, **23**. 761, 1901 ; C. Baskerville and F. Zerban, *ib.*, **26**. 1642, 1904 ; *Chem. News*, **91**. 74, 1905 ; W. Crookes, *Proc. Roy. Soc.*, **66**. 409, 1900 ; H. Geiger and J. M. Nuttall, *Phil. Mag.*, (6), **22**. 613, 1911 ; (6), **23**. 445, 1912 ; (6), **24**. 653, 1912 ; H. Geiger and E. Rutherford, *ib.*, (6), **20**. 691, 1910 ; A. Fleck, *Journ. Chem. Soc.*, **103**. 381, 1052, 1913 ; D. Yovanovitch, *Compt. Rend.*, **175**. 307, 1922 ; M. de Broglie and J. Cabrera, *ib.*, **176**. 295, 1923 ; *Anal. Fis. Quim.*, **20**. 467, 1922 ; H. N. McCoy and L. M. Henderson, *Journ. Amer. Chem. Soc.*, **40**. 1316, 1918 ; L. Meitner, *Phys. Zeit.*, **19**. 257, 1918 ; B. Heimann, *Sitzber. Akad. Wien*, **123**. 1369, 1914 ; H. N. McCoy, *Phys. Rev.*, (2), **1**. 403, 1913 ; G. C. Ashman, *Amer. Journ. Science*, (4), **27**. 65, 1909 ; H. M. Dadourian, *ib.*, (4), **21**. 427, 1906 ; A. S. Eve, *ib.*, (4), **22**. 477, 1900 ; B. B. Boltwood, *ib.*, (4), **21**. 415, 1906 ; (4), **24**. 93, 1907 ; *Phys. Zeit.*, **8**. 556, 1907 ; H. N. McCoy and W. H. Ross, *Journ. Amer. Chem. Soc.*, **29**. 1709, 1907 ; *Amer. Journ. Science*, (4), **21**. 433, 1906 ; G. F. Barker, *ib.*, (4), **16**. 161, 1903 ; R. J. Strutt, *Proc. Roy. Soc.*, **76**. 88, 312, 1905 ; *Nature*, **70**. 222, 1904 ; S. Meyer, *Sitzber. Akad. Wien*, **128**. 897, 1919.

[2] M. S. Curie, *Compt. Rend.*, **172**. 1022, 1921 ; P. Lemay and L. Jaloustre, *ib.*, **173**. 916, 1921 ; A. Fleck, *Journ. Chem. Soc.*, **103**. 381, 1052, 1913 ; D. K. Yovanovitch, *Compt. Rend.*, **175**. 307, 1922 ; *Journ. Chim. Phys.*, **23**. 1, 1926 ; H. Schlundt, *Mesothorium*, Washington, 1922 ; J. Thibaud, *Compt. Rend.*, **179**. 1052, 1322, 1924 ; D. H. Black, *Proc. Roy. Soc.*, **106**. A, 632, 1924 ; O. Hahn, *Ber.*, **40**. 1462, 1907 ; *Phys. Zeit.*, **8**. 277, 1907 ; **9**. 246, 392, 1908 ; **12**. 148, 1911 ; *Chem. Ztg.*, **35**. 845, 1911 ; L. Meitner, *ib.*, **12**. 1094, 1911 ; **19**. 257, 1918 ; O. von Baeyer, O. Hahn, and L. Meitner, *ib.*, **12**. 273, 378, 1099, 1911 ; **13**. 264, 1912 ; **15**. 649, 1914 ; **16**. 6, 1915 ; H. N. McCoy and W. H. Ross, *Journ. Amer. Chem. Soc.*, **29**. 1709, 1907 ; *Amer. Journ. Science*, (4), **21**. 433, 1906 ; B. B. Boltwood, *ib.*, (4), **28**. 93, 1907 ; W. Marckwald, *Ber.*, **43**. 3420, 1910 ; F. Soddy, *Journ. Chem. Soc.*, **99**. 72, 1911 ; *Brit. Pat. No.* 25504, 1911 ; C. Schwab, *German Pat.*, *D.R.P.* 269541, 1911 ; F. Glaser, *ib.*, 272429, 1913 ; *Chem. Ztg.*, **37**. 477, 1105, 1913 ; H. M. McCoy and L. M. Henderson, *Journ. Amer. Chem. Soc.*, **40**. 1316, 1918 ; H. N. McCoy and C. H. Viol, *Phil. Mag.*, (6), **25**. 333, 350, 1913 ; F. and W. M. Soddy and A. S. Russell, *ib.*, (6), **19**. 725, 1910 ; W. P. Widdowson and A. S. Russell, *ib.*, (6), **49**. 137, 1925 ; E. Rutherford and H. Richardson, *ib.*, (6), **25**. 722, 1913 ; (6), **26**. 324, 937, 1913 ; (6), **27**. 252, 1914 ; E. Rutherford, *Radioactive Substances and their Radiations*, Cambridge, 440, 1913 ; S. Meyer and E. von Schweidler, *Radioaktivität*, Leipzig, 398, 1916 ; J. L. Nierman, *Journ. Phys. Chem.*, **24**. 192, 1920 ; R. K. Strong, *Journ. Amer. Chem. Soc.*, **43**. 440, 1921.

[3] O. Hahn, *Proc. Roy. Soc.*, **76**. A, 115, 1905 ; *Jahrb. Rad. Elektron.*, **2**. 233, 1905 ; *Phil. Mag.*, (6), **12**. 82, 1906 ; H. N. McCoy and C. H. Viol, *ib.*, (6), **25**. 350, 1913 ; H N. McCoy and W. H. Ross, *Journ. Amer. Chem. Soc.*, **29**. 1709, 1907 ; *Amer. Journ. Science*, (4), **21**. 433, 1906 ; J. Elster and H. Geitel, *Phys. Zeit.*, **7**. 445, 1906 ; L. Meitner, *Zeit. Physik*, **26**. 169, 1924 ; *Phys. Zeit.*, **19**. 257, 1918 ; G. A. Blanc, *ib.*, **6**. 703, 1905 ; **7**. 620, 1906 ; **8**. 321, 1907 ; *Atti Accad. Lincei*, (5), **15**. i, 497, 1906 ; (5), **15**. ii, 90, 1906 ; H. Mache, *Sitzber. Akad. Wien*, **113**. 1329,

1904 ; F. von Lerch, *ib.*, **114**. 553, 1905 ; *Jahrb. Rad. Elektron.*, **2**. 471, 1905 ; *Monatsh.*, **26**. 899, 1905 ; O. von Baeyer, O. Hahn, and L. Meitner, *Phys. Zeit.*, **16**. 6, 1915 ; G. von Hevesy, *ib.*, **14**. 1202, 1913 ; J. Chadwick and A. S. Russell, *Proc. Roy. Soc.*, **88**. A, 217, 1913 ; *Nature*, **90** 690, 1913 ; *Chem. News*, **107**. 103, 1913 ; M. S. Leslie, *Le Radium*, **8**. 356, 1911 ; **9**. 276, 1912 ; J. A. Cranston, *Phil. Mag.*, (6), **25**. 712, 1913 ; H. Geiger and J. M. Nuttall, *ib.*, (6), **24**. 653, 1912 ; M. Levin, *ib.*, (6), **12**. 177, 1906 ; E. Rutherford, *ib.*, (5), **49**. 1, 1900 ; *Radioactive Substances and their Radiations*, Cambridge, 550, 1913 ; E. Rutherford and F. Soddy, *Phil. Mag.*, (6), **4**. 370, 569, 1902 ; (6), **5**. 561, 1902 ; *Journ. Chem. Soc.*, **81**. 321, 837, 1902 ; B. Brauner, *ib.*, **73**. 951, 1898 ; C. Baskerville, *Journ. Amer. Chem. Soc.*, **23**. 761, 1901 ; P. Lemay and L. Jaloustre, *Compt. Rend.*, **173**. 916, 1921 ; A. Lepape, *ib.*, **178**. 931, 1924 ; W. Crookes, *Proc. Roy. Soc.*, **66**. 409, 1900 ; H. Schlundt and R. B. Moore, *Journ. Phys. Chem.*, **9**. 682, 1905 ; D. Strömholm and T. Svedberg, *Zeit. anorg. Chem.*, **61**. 338, 1909 ; **63**. 197, 1909 ; *Deutsche Gasglühlicht Aktien-Gesellschaft, Brit. Pat. No.* 15919, 1912 ; *French Pat. No.* 444798, 1912 ; *German Pat., D.R.P.* 269692, 1912 ; J. Lorenzen, *ib.*, 278121, 1913 ; O. Knöfler, *ib.*, 269501, 1913 ; F. Glaser, *ib.*, 272429, 1913 ; *Chem. Ztg.*, **37**. 477, 1105, 1913 ; W. Bothe, *Zeit. Physik*, **24**. 10, 1924 ; G. H. Briggs, *Phil. Mag.*, (6), **50**. 600, 1925.

⁴ R. B. Owens, *Phil. Mag.*, (5), **48**. 377, 1899 ; E. Rutherford and H. Geiger, *ib.*, (6), **22**. 621, 1911 ; H. G. J. Moseley and K. Fajans, *ib.*, (6), **22**. 629, 1911 ; H. A. Wilson, *ib.*, (6), **23**. 981, 1912 ; E. Rutherford, *Phil. Trans.*, **204**. A, 169, 1904 ; *Radioactivity*, Cambridge, 233, 1904 ; *Nature*, **74**. 634, 1906 ; *Phil. Mag.*, (5), **49**. 1, 161, 1900 ; W. E. Wilson, *ib.*, (6), **17**. 321, 1909 ; W. Makower, *ib.*, (6), **9**. 56, 1905 ; S. Russ, *ib.*, (6), **17**. 412, 1909 ; A. Fleck, *ib.*, (6), **29**. 337, 1915 ; S. Kinoshita, *ib.*, (6), **16**. 121, 1908 ; J. M. W. Slater, *ib.*, (6), **10**. 460, 1905 ; H. Geiger and J. M. Nuttall, *ib.*, (6), **22**. 613, 1911 ; (6), **23**. 439, 1912 ; (6), **24**. 647, 1912 ; G. H. Briggs, *ib.*, (6), **41**. 357, 1921 ; H. L. Bronson. *Amer. Journ. Science*, (4), **19**. 185, 1905 ; *Phil. Mag.*, (6), **16**. 291, 1908 ; C. le Rossignol and E. T. Gimingham, *ib.*, (6), **8**. 107, 1904 ; P. B. Perkins, *ib.*, (6), **27**. 720, 1914 ; H. N. McCoy and C. H. Viol, *ib.*, (6), **25**. 350, 1913 ; E. Rutherford and F. Soddy, *ib.*, (6), **4**. 370, 569, 1902 ; (6), **5**. 445, 481, 561, 1903 ; *Journ. Chem. Soc.*, **81**. 321, 837, 1902 ; E Dorn, *Abh Nat. Ges. Halle*, **22**. 47, 1900 ; H. Geiger, *Phil. Mag.*, (6), **22**. 201. 1911 ; *Proc. Roy. Soc.*, **82**. A, 486, 1909 ; **83**. A, 505, 1910 ; L. F. Bates and J. S. Rogers, *ib.*, **105**. A, 97, 1924 ; H. Geiger and E. Marsden, *Phys. Zeit.*, **11**. 7, 1910 ; R. Swinne, *ib.*, **13**. 14, 1912 ; J. E. Burbank, *ib.*, **6**. 436, 1905 ; A. Gockel, *ib.*, **8**. 701, 1907 ; H. W. Schmidt and W. Kurz, *ib.*, **7**. 709, 1906 ; A. Klaus, *ib.*, **6**. 820, 1905 ; G. von Hevesy, *ib.*, **12**. 1214, 1911 ; *Journ. Phys. Chem.*, **16** 429, 1912 ; P. Artmann, *Zeit. Baln.*, **3**. 3, 1910 ; J. Satterly, *Proc. Cambridge Phil. Soc.*, **16**. 667, 1912 ; H. A. Bumstead, *Amer. Journ. Science*, (4), **18**. 1, 1904 ; H. M. Dadourian, *ib.*, (4), **19**. 16, 1905 ; J. C. Sanderson, *ib.*, (4), **32**. 169, 1911 ; T. Barratt, *Proc. Phys. Soc.*, **24**. 112, 1912 ; E. Marsden and T. Barratt, *ib.*, **23**. 50, 1911 ; C. Runge, *Gött. Nachr.*, 99, 1911 ; G. A. Blanc, *Phil. Mag.*, (6), **13**. 378, 1907 ; *Nuovo Cimento*, (6), **14**. 199, 1907 ; *Atti Accad. Lincei*, (5), **14**. 322, 1905 ; (5), **15**. 328, 1905 ; (5), **17**. i, 101, 1908 ; *Phys. Zeit.*, **6**. 703, 1905 ; **9**. 294, 1908 ; D. Pacini, *ib.*, **11**. 227, 1910 ; *Nuovo Cimento*, (5), **15**. 24, 1908 ; G. von der Borne, *Jahrb. Rad. Elektron.*, **2**. 142, 1905 ; O. Hahn, *ib.*, **2**. 233, 1905 ; *Phys. Zeit.*, **7**. 456, 557, 1906 ; *Phil. Mag.*, (6), **12**. 82, 1906 ; K. Aschoff, *Zeit. öffent. Chem.*, **15**. 93, 1905 ; **16**. 193, 1906 ; G. Feliciani, *Atti Accad. Lincei*, (5), **14**. 674, 1905 ; O. Angelucci, *ib.*, (5), **15**. 497, 1906 ; S. Rosenblum, *Compt. Rend.*, **180**. 1332, 1925 ; C. Schäfer and C. Seebohm. *Jahrb. Schles. Ges. vaterland. Cultur*, **86**. 4, 1908 ; M. S. Leslie, *Le Radium*, **8**. 356, 1911 ; *Compt. Rend.*, **153**. 328, 1911 ; *Phil. Mag.*, (6), **24**. 637, 1912 ; R. W. Boyle, *ib.*, (6), **17**. 389, 1909 ; *Macdonald Phys. Build. Bull.*, **1**. 52, 1910 ; *Le Radium*, **7**. 200, 1910 ; *Trans. Roy. Soc. Canada*, (3), **3**. 75, 1909 ; R. Schmid, *Sitzber. Akad. Wien*, **126**. 1065, 1917 ; S. Loria, *ib.*, **124**. 567, 829. 1077, 1915 ; *Phys. Zeit.*, **17**. 6, 1916 ; F. von Lerch, *Sitzber. Akad. Wien*, **114**. 553, 1905 ; *Ann. Physik*, (4), **49**. 781, 1912 ; **12**. 745, 1903 ; A. Bickel, *Klin. Wochenschr.*, **49**. 777, 1912 ; K. Kojo, *ib.*, **49**. 779, 1912 ; D. Minami, *ib.*, **49**. 781, 1912 ; S. G. Tracy, *Le Radium*, **1**. 23, 1904 ; H. A. Erickson, *Phys. Rev.*, (2), **26**. 629, 1925 ; A. Lepape, *Compt. Rend.*, **178**. 931, 1924 ; G. H. Briggs, *Phil. Mag.*, (6), **50**. 600, 1925.

⁵ E. Rutherford, *Phil. Trans.*, **204**. A, 169, 1904 ; *Radioactive Substances and their Emanations*, Cambridge, 599, 1913 ; *Phil. Mag.*, (6), **41**. 570, 1921 ; E. Rutherford and H. T. Brooks, *ib.*, (6), **4**. 1, 1902 ; E. Rutherford and H. Geiger, *ib.*, (6), **22**. 621, 1911 ; E. Rutherford and H. Richardson, *ib.*, (6), **26**. 937, 1913 ; C. F. Hogley, *ib.*, (6), **25**. 330, 1913 ; N. H. McCoy and C. H. Viol, *ib.*, (6), **25**. 351, 1913 ; O. Hahn, *ib.*, (6), **11**. 793, 1906 ; A. B. Wood, *ib.*, (6), **28**. 808, 1914 ; (6), **30**. 702, 1915 ; (6), **41**. 575, 1921 ; G. H. Henderson, *ib.*, (6), **42**. 538, 1921 ; E. Rutherford and A. B. Wood, *ib.*, (6), **31**. 379, 1916 ; H. Geiger and J. M. Nuttall, *ib.*, (6), **22**. 613, 1911 ; (6), **23**. 445, 1912 ; (6), **24**. 653, 1912 ; E. Marsden and R. H. Wilson, *ib.*, (6), **26**. 354, 1913 ; E. Rutherford and H. Richardson, *ib.*, (6), **26**. 937, 1913 ; F. and W. M. Soddy and A. S. Russell, *ib.*, (6), **21**. 130, 1911 ; H. L. Bronson, *ib.*, (6), **16**. 291, 1908 ; H. T. Brooks, *ib.*, (6), **8**. 373, 1904 ; J. M. W. Slater, *ib.*, (6), 628, 1905 ; J. A. Cranston and R. A. Burnett, *Journ. Chem. Soc.*, **119**. 2036, 1921 ; J. A. Cranston and R. Hutton, *ib.*, **123**. 1318, 1923 ; J. Groh and G. von Hevesy, *Ann. Physik*, (4), **63**. 85, 1920 ; D. H. Black, *Nature*, **115**. 226, 1925 ; *Proc. Roy. Soc.*, **109**. A, 166, 1925 ; F. C. Gates *Phys. Rev.* (1), **16**. 300, 1903 ; J. E. Shrader, *ib.*, (2), **6**. 292, 1915 ; G. B. Pegram, *ib.*, (1), **17**. 424, 1903 ; K. Fehrl, *Phys. Zeit.*, **3**. 130, 1902 ; F. von Lerch and E. von Wartburg, *Stizber. Akad. Wien*, **118**. 1575, 1909 ; F. von Lerch, *ib.*, **114**. 553, 1905 ; **116**. 1443, 1907 ; **123**. 699, 1914 ; *Ann. Physik*, (4), **12**. 745, 1903 ; W. D. Harkins and R. W. Ryan, *Nature*, **112**. 54, 1923 ; L. F. Bates and J. S. Rogers,

Proc. Roy. Soc., **105**. A, 97, 1924; S. Loria, *Sitzber. Akad. Wien*, **124**. 567, 829, 1077, 1915; *Phys. Zeit.*, **17**. 6, 1916; *Bull. Acad. Cracow*, 260, 1917; M. Levin, *ib.*, **8**. 129, 1907; *Phil. Mag.*, **12**. 177, 1906; T. Barratt and A. B. Wood, *Nature*, **93**. 367, 1914; *Proc. Phys. Soc.*, **26**. 248, 1914; A. Fleck, *Journ. Chem. Soc.*, **103**. 381, 1052, 1913; O. Hahn and L. Meitner, *Verh. deut. phys. Ges.*, **11**. 55, 1909; *Phys. Zeit.*, **13**. 390, 1912; **9**. 321, 1908; O. von Baeyer, O. Hahn, and L. Meitner, **11**. 488, 1910; **12**. 273, 378, 1099, 1911; **13**. 264, 390, 485, 1912; **14**. 321, 1913; G. von Hevesy, *ib.*, **14**. 1202, 1913; G. von Hevesy and E. Rona, *Zeit. phys. Chem.*, **89**. 294, 1915; K. Fajans and K. von Beckerath, *ib.*, **97**. 478, 1921; K. Horovitz and F. Paneth, *ib.* **89**. 513, 1915; *Monatsh.*, **34**. 1593, 1913; *Sitzber. Akad. Wien*, **122**. 1037, 1913; **123**. 1819, 1914; T. Godlewsky, *ib.*, **125**. 137, 1916; S. Meyer, *ib.*, **128**. 897, 1920; G. Kirsch, *ib.*, **131**. 551, 1922; W Riss, *ib.*, **133**. 91, 1924; L. Myssowsky, *Zeit. Physik*, **18**. 304, 1923; W. Kolhörster, *ib.*, **2**. 257, 1920; D. R. Yovanovitch and J. d'Espine, *Compt. Rend.*, **180**. 202, 1925; H. Schlundt and R. B. Moore, *Journ. Phys. Chem.*, **9**. 682, 1905; L. Meitner, *Phys. Zeit.*, **13**. 623, 1912; *Zeit. Physik*, **9**. 131, 1922; **11**. 35, 1922; **26**. 169, 1924; W. Pohlmeyer, *ib.*, **28**. 216, 1924; A. Piccard and G. Volkart, *Arch. Sciences Genève*, (5), **3**. 543, 1921; H. Geiger and E. Marsden, *Phys. Zeit.*, **11**. 7, 1910; K. Fajans, *ib.*, **16**. 474, 1915; E. Marsden and T. Barratt, *Proc. Phys. Soc.*, **24**. 50, 1911; E. Marsden and C. G. Darwin, *Proc. Roy. Soc.*, **87**. A, 17, 1912; J. Franck, *Verh. deut. phys. Ges.*, **11**. 397, 1909; W. Metzener, *Ber.*, **46**. 979, 1913; F. Soddy and H. Hyman, *Journ. Chem. Soc.*, **105**. 1402, 1914; A. Holmes and R. W. Lawson, *Sitzber. Akad. Wien*, **123**. 1373, 1914; *Nature*, **93**. 109, 479, 1914; *Phil. Mag.*, (6), **28**. 823, 1914; (6), **29**. 673, 1915; R. W. Lawson, *Sitzber. Akad. Wien*, **126**. 721, 1917; E. Albrecht, *ib.*, **128**. 853, 1919; S. Meyer, *Bull. Acad. Cracow*, 260, 1917; A. G. Shenstone and H. Schlundt, *Phil. Mag.*, (6), **43**. 1038, 1922; C. D. Ellis, *Proc. Roy. Soc.*, **101**. A, 1, 1922; F. Paneth, A. Johannsen, and M. Matthies, *Ber.*, **55**. 769, 1922.

§ 4. The Preparation and Properties of Thorium

The element thorium has not been obtained of a high degree of purity. This is partly due to the high m.p. of the metal, and to the ease with which it unites with hydrogen, oxygen, nitrogen, and carbon. J. J. Berzelius [1] obtained the impure metal by heating a mixture of potassium with potassium thorium fluoride or chloride, or thorium chloride in a glass tube; the act of decomposition was attended by a feeble explosion. The metal appeared as a grey powder. J. J. Chydenius used sodium in place of potassium. C. A. Matignon and M. Delépine said that with thorium chloride and sodium, the product contains 74 per cent. of thorium, and much thoria. L. F. Nilson heated to redness a mixture of sodium with a mol of thorium chloride and two mols of potassium chloride contained in alternate layers in an iron cylinder. The product was washed successively with water, alcohol, and ether. The product contained 20 per cent. of thoria as impurity. W. von Bolton heated in a crucible a mixture of thorium chloride with sodium and covered it with a layer of potassium chloride. The product was washed with alcohol to remove the sodium, then with cold and with boiling water, boiling dil. nitric acid, and finally with water. The powdered metal was hammered into a thick-walled copper tube 10 mm. in diameter; and this was rolled into 1 mm. wire. The copper was dissolved by dil. nitric acid, and a spongy wire of thorium was obtained. This was rolled into a coherent strip. W. von Bolton, P. Askenasy, and H. Karstens considered their product to be free from oxide; but R. J. Meyer claims that oxide must have been present. H. Moissan and O. Hönigschmid, and C. A. Matignon and M. Delépine prepared thorium chloride free from oxychloride, and reduced it with sodium both in air, and in vacuo, but they were unable to obtain a metal with less than 3 per cent. of oxide. E. Chauvenet heated to 600° a mixture of one mol of thorium chloride with four gram-atoms of lithium or sodium contained in an iron boat in a quartz tube, taking precautions to prevent the ingress of air. The product contained 3·2 per cent. of thoria. If a nickel boat be used, a nickel-thorium alloy is formed. D. Lely and L. Hamburger distilled sodium and thorium chloride into an exhausted steel cylinder, and heated the mixture to 700°. The product contained 1 per cent. of the oxide. The metal was compressed into a rod, and an alternating current passed through it in a vacuum furnace. The particles sintered together, and formed a compact metal.

Neither J. J. Berzelius, nor C. Bergemann was able to reduce thorium oxide by the alkali metals. O. Ruff and H. Brintzinger found that sodium at 900°–950° has very little action on thoria, but with calcium there is a 62 per cent. yield of the metal ; and with a sodium-calcium alloy, an 84 per cent. yield of thorium. C. Winkler tried to reduce the oxide by heating it with a 20 per cent. excess of magnesium in an evacuated tube, but the product was a mixture of magnesium and thorium with the oxides of the two metals. H. Kuzel and E. Wedekind reduced thoria by means of calcium. C. A. Matignon and M. Delépine also obtained an impure product by the action of magnesium or aluminium on the oxide. H. Goldschmidt and C. Vautin tried the thermite reaction with aluminium powder and thorium oxide, and found beads of thorium in the sintered mass. K. A. Kühne claimed to have obtained reguline thorium by adding some chlorate or perchlorate to the mixture in H. Goldschmidt's process. L. Troost fused a mixture of thorium carbide and oxide and obtained the impure metal. According to H. Moissan and A. Étard, when thoria is heated in the electric furnace with a sufficient quantity of sugar carbon, it yields a crystalline carbide ; when less carbon is employed, a fused mass is produced, consisting of an alloy of thorium and thorium carbide. H. C. Greenwood said that the reaction begins at about 1600°. O. Hönigschmid heated a mixture of thorium oxide and silicon in the electric arc furnace and obtained thorium silicide.

E. W. von Siemens and J. G. Halske proposed to remove the oxide by making the thorium form a fusible alloy with tin, lead, zinc, cadmium, copper, or aluminium ; they also heated the thorium with tantalum or another metal of the vanadium family which reduces the thoria to metal. When strongly heated, the tantalum pentoxide volatilizes before the thorium. E. Chauvenet prepared thorium by heating thorium hydride under 10 mm. press. ; E. W. von Siemens and J. G. Halske claimed to make thorium by heating, in the absence of air, thorium nitride or a compound of thorium with another element of the nitrogen family. If the nitride be shaped into a rod, and then heated with absence of air by an electric current, a coherent metal is formed. They also obtained thorium from the sulphide. E. W. von Siemens and J. G. Halske also obtained thorium by distilling sodium and thorium acetylacetonate through a red-hot tube.

H. Moissan and O. Hönigschmid did not succeed in preparing thorium of a high degree of purity by electrolytic processes. They electrolyzed potassium thorium chloride contained in a covered porcelain crucible at about 600°, using graphite electrodes, and an atm. free from oxygen. The porcelain vessels were always attacked, and the appearance of the metal, which is often obtained in definite crystals, indicates that the oxide contained in the bath becomes, in some way, mechanically interposed between the particles of metal at the moment of their deposition. H. von Wartenberg electrolyzed a mixture of thorium chloride and sodium or potassium chloride in a graphite crucible at 800° ; graphite electrodes were used. The yield was 40 per cent., and the product contained 88·2 per cent. of thorium ; 11·6 of thoria ; 0·04, sodium ; 0·03, silicon ; 0·06, iron ; and 0·15, carbon. A. Duboin said that the use of potassium fluoride gives no better results. E. Chauvenet proposed using rubidium thorium chloride. H. von Wartenberg reduced thoria in the electric furnace by hydrogen at 5 atm. press. in the presence of a metal like tungsten to dissolve the reduced thorium. G. Siebert and E. Korten prepared the metal by heating the halides to a high temp. in the presence of reducing agents—e.g. carbon ; and A. E. van Arkel and J. H. de Boer, by passing the vapour of the tetrahalide over a heated tungsten filament—vide titanium.

According to E. Wedekind, and H. Baumhauer, colloidal thorium is made by rubbing in a mortar finely divided thorium with cold dil. acetic acid. If a stronger acid be used, the metal is acted upon. The paste is brought on to a filter, and the acetic acid washed out with cold water. At a certain point, a colloidal soln. passes through. It shows grey opalescence by reflected light, and appears brown when light is transmitted through it. The hydrosol of thorium is fairly stable in the presence of certain electrolytes, but the alkalies readily bring about its precipitation, presumably because of decomposition of thorium acetate, which exerts a protective action on the colloid. It is stable against mineral acids. Freezing invariably brings about coagulation, the precipitate being readily observable on thawing. A freshly dialyzed colloidal thorium soln. was examined in an electrolytic cell. It was free from electrolytes. The space round the anode rapidly became clear when a difference of potential of 18 volts was set up between the electrodes, the particles moving to the cathode. Colloidal thorium, therefore, like colloidal zirconium, carries a positive charge. In a very dil. soln. particles can be resolved ultramicroscopically. They appear to be colourless, and smaller than those of zirconium; and to be in violent commotion. A comparison of the radioactivities of thorium as metal and as hydrosol showed that 0·0235 of the latter were eq. to 0·111 of the former. It is remarkable and not explained that although metallic thorium has a radioactivity of 15·4 uranium-potassium-sulphate units, and that of thorium oxide prepared from it is 8·6, yet that of the thorium hydrosol is smaller than that of thorium nitrate soln. The gel dried in a high vacuum, and at a high temp., was found to contain thorium 20·5 per cent., and thorium oxide 78 per cent.

The physical properties of thorium.—The thorium prepared by J. J. Berzelius was described as a dark, lead-grey powder, which when pressed in an agate mortar assumed an iron-grey **colour,** and a metallic lustre. L. F. Nilson said that thorium is a dark grey, shining powder which under the microscope appears to consist of small six-sided plates. The thorium obtained by W. von Bolton was described as microcrystalline before it was rolled; and the rolled metal was said to have the colour of platinum. H. von Wartenberg also described his product as crystalline. W. C. Brögger described the **crystals** as octahedrons, and C. F. Rammelsberg, and A. E. Nordenskjöld said that they are isomorphous with zirconium; and J. Herzfeld and O. Korn said that they are isomorphous with silicon and the diamond. P. T. Cleve said they are not isomorphous with any known element; and P. Groth added : *Ob eine Isomorphie mit dem Zirkonium besteht, ist, wie die Krystallform des letzteren, unbekannt.* A. W. Hull, and H. Bohlin found the **X-radiogram** of thorium corresponds with a face-centred cubic lattice with side 5·04 A., and the shortest distance between the atoms 3·54 A. The X-radiogram was also examined by J. Böhm and co-workers, J. E. van Arkel, and V. M. Goldschmidt and L. Thomassen.

L. F. Nilson gave 10·968 for the **specific gravity** of amorphous and matt thorium, and 11·230 for the crystals; W. von Bolton gave 11·32 for the powder and 12·16 for the rolled and heated metal; and K. Honda gave 11·3. Some low values for the sp gr.—*viz.* 7·35 by C. Bergemann; 7·657–7·795 by J. J. Chydenius; and 10·78 by L. F. Nilson—refer to mixtures of the metal with oxide. L. F. Nilson makes the at. vol. 20·94, and B. D. Steele has discussed the relation of the at. vol. to that of other metals. H. Moissan and A. Étard say that the metal is hard, and that it scratches glass but not quartz, and when struck with steel, it gives sparks. A. E. van Arkel and J. H. de Boer obtained ductile thorium by their mode of preparation. S. Dushman and I. Langmuir discussed the **diffusion** of thorium in tungsten. E. W. von Siemens and J. G. Halske say that thorium can be drawn into wire. L. F. Nilson gave 0·2757 for the **specific heat,** between 0° and 100°; and 6·41 for the at. ht. J. Dewar gave 0·0197 for the sp. ht. between the b.p. of hydrogen and nitrogen. L. F. Nilson said that the metal does not melt in the wind furnace, nor when burnt in oxygen. G. N. Lewis and co-workers, and E. D. Eastman gave, respectively, 13·6 and 12·4 Cals. per degree for the **entropy** of thorium at 25° and atm. press. W. von Bolton estimated the **melting point** to be near 1450°; and K. Honda gave 1450°. H. Moissan and O. Hönigschmid said that the metal does not melt at 1400°. H. von Wartenberg, however, said that the impure metal melts at 1690°, but if it were quite free from carbide, the m.p. would be over 1700°; and W. Guertler and M. Pirani estimate the m.p. to be over 1800°. W. R. Mott gave 1450° for the m.p., and estimated 2800° for the

boiling point ; and J. J. van Laar, 1840°. The latter also calculated for the **critical temperature,** 2940°, and for the **critical pressure,** 330 atm. F. Born estimated that the degree of dissociation of thorium oxide at 2000° is 10^{-27}, and at 3000°, about 6×10^{-6}.

R. Bunsen [2] said that purified thorium chloride gives no **flame spectrum,** nor does it show a spectrum with a feeble spark. W. Muthmann and C. Baur found that the purified thoria, and thorium sulphate give a pale blue light but no l.nes in the spectrum. H. Auerbach found only a continuous spectrum when thorium compounds are introduced into flames; while G. Meyer detected 0·01 mgrm. per c.c. by the spectral lines $\lambda=4391\cdot30$ and $4382\cdot10$. The **spark spectrum** of thorium has been studied by R. Thalén, J. M. Eder and E. Valenta, A. G. G. Leonard, F. Exner and E. Haschek, R. Bunsen, O. Lohse, A. Hagenbach and H. Konen, R. J. Lang, J. N. Lockyer, etc. R. Thalén observed the lines 4273, 4278, 4281, 4382, and 4393 in the violet ; 4864 in the blue ; 4919, 5375, 5446, 5537, 5640, and 5699 in the green. The **arc spectrum** has been studied by J. M. Eder and E. Valenta, F. L. Cooper, F. Exner and E. Haschek, A. Hagenbach and H. Konen, C. E. Gissing, etc. The more intense lines are 3188·20, 3511·76, 3741·36, 4019·29, 4382·02, 4391·29, 4752·62, 4863·38, 4919·99, 5017·39, 5049·93, 5989·20, and 6462·83. W. J. Humphreys studied the effect of press.; B. E. Moore, the effect of a magnetic field, the so-called **Zeeman effect ;** and R. J. Lang, the ultra-violet spectrum. Many of the lines are unsymmetrical in intensity and sharpness, the stronger component is a little displaced in the magnetic field, and some of the lines change their appearance without being separated. W. Ritz has discussed this subject. The line structure has been studied by P. G. Nutting. Thorium salts are colourless, and show no visible **absorption spectrum.** According to W. W. Coblentz, thoria gives no maiked emission bands. The emissivity above 7μ is nearly as great as that of a perfect radiator. The high frequency or **X-ray spectrum** has been examined by D. Coster, V. Dolejsek, H. Bohlin, and M. Siegbahn and E. Friman. W. Duane and co-workers, and M. Siegbahn and E. Jönsson measured the K-series. B. B. Ray, M. de Broglie, W. Duane and co-workers, D. Coster, and M. Siegbahn gave for the L-series in Angström units, $a_3a'=0\cdot96524$; $a_1a=0\cdot95342$; $\beta_1\beta=0\cdot76259$; $\beta_2\gamma=0\cdot7910$; $\gamma_1\delta=0\cdot65103$; $\epsilon=1\cdot11241$; $\beta_5\zeta=0\cdot76259$; $\beta_4\nu=0\cdot789$; $\beta_3\psi=0\cdot7521$; $\beta_6=0\cdot8262$, and $\gamma_6=0\cdot6301$. E. Hjalmar G. Wentzel, and P. A. Ross gave for the M-series, $a'=4\cdot413$; $a=4\cdot12915$; $\beta=9333$; $\gamma=3\cdot6565$; $\delta=3\cdot127$; and $\epsilon=3\cdot006$; D. Coster gave $M_1=3\cdot721$; $M_{II}=3\cdot552$; $M_{III}=3\cdot058$; $M_{IV}=2\cdot571$; and $M_V=2\cdot388$. P. A. Ross also measured the M-series of lines. For the N-series, V. Dolejsek gave $N_7P_1=9\cdot310$; $N_7P_2=9\cdot427$; $N_7O_3=11\cdot462$; N_6O_2 $11\cdot542$; $N_5O_1=13\cdot255$; $N_5O_2=13\cdot181$; and $N_5P_3=13\cdot111$. D. Coster also studied the N-series ; K. Teucke, the radiation produced when thoria is bombarded by **cathode rays ;** G. Fournier, the absorption of X-rays ; and S. Dushman and co-workers, and H. R. Robinson, the **emission of electrons** by thorium. The **radioactivity** of thorium is discussed in a special section. G. Bardel said that if no uranium be present thorium compounds do not affect a photographic plate. H. K. Onnes found that, like lead and mercury, thorium becomes a super-conductor at low temp. R. Hamer discussed the **photoelectric property.** W. von Bolton gave 0·401 for the sp. **electrical resistance** of thorium. R. Berthold studied the relation between the photographic and ionizing effects of X-rays from thorium. J. W. Marden and co-workers studied the electrodeposition of thorium from sol. of thorium hydroxide in fluoboric or hydrofluosilicic acid. K. H. Kingdom and I. Langmuir studied the spluttering of thorium from a filament by α-rays. A Heydweiller gave 23·5 for the **speed of migration,** $V°$, of the thorium cation, where $V=n\lambda$, when n denotes the transport number. and λ the eq. conductivity at 18°. B. Neumann and H. Richter found the **electrode potential** of thorium in thoric chloride 1·747 volts at 18°. Thorium is paramagnetic. K. Honda [3] gave $0\cdot177 \times 10^{-6}$ for the sp. **magnetic susceptibility** of powdered thorium, and he found the value increases rapidly up to 400°. S. Meyer gave 416×10^{-6} for the atomic magnetism.

The chemical properties of thorium.—W. Ramsay and J. N. Collie [4] found that neither **helium** nor **argon** is absorbed when thorium is obtained by heating thoria with magnesium in an atm. of these gases. C. A. Matignon observed no signs of combination of argon with thorium. C. Winkler noted that a thorium hydride is formed when thorium oxide is reduced by magnesium in an atm. of **hydrogen.** The analyses corresponded with ThH_2, but the product was very impure. C. A. Matignon heated thorium in a tube in a stream of hydrogen, and found the two elements unite vigorously with the evolution of light. E. Chauvenet also found that lithium hydride, LiH, at 600°, reacts with thorium chloride. In both cases, **thorium hydride,** ThH_4, is produced. C. A. Matignon and M. Delépine gave for the heat of formation $Th + 2H_2 = ThH_4 + 42 \cdot 8$ Cals. E. Chauvenet gave for the dissociation press. in mm. :

	282°	299°	328°	350°	367°	381°	384°	387°	390°
Press.	160	242·5	300	500	624	672	705	740	760

Externally, thorium hydride looks like thorium except that it is a little darker, and rather more matte. When heated in vacuo, it furnishes thorium and hydrogen. It explodes when heated in a small tube in the presence of air. It burns in oxygen ; chlorine does not immediately attack it at ordinary temp. ; it is not decomposed by water ; and hydrochloric acid attacks it—especially if heated. A. Klauber and J. M. von Mellenheim prepared what they regarded as a volatile thorium hydride by the action of water or dil. acids on magnesium thoride—best at 15°–20°. When passed through a heated glass tube, a ring of thorium was produced which is first brown and then grey, indicating two forms of thorium. It was said that the gas is unstable ; the composition was not determined ; the radioactivity is slight ; and it can be condensed by liquid air. R. Schwarz and E. Konrad denied the existence of the gaseous hydride, and said that the deposits in the heated tube are derived from the hydrides of sulphur, phosphorus, and silicon. E. Chauvenet [5] found that the thorium at ordinary press. is not oxidized in **air** or in **oxygen ;** but with higher press., the metal may be oxidized. N. B. Pilling and R. E. Bedworth studied the oxidation of thorium. L. F. Nilson said that the metal is stable in air at 120°, but H. Moissan and A. Étard found that the metal ignites when heated in air just below redness, and it burns brilliantly, forming the oxide and throwing out showers of incandescent sparks. The finely powdered metal ignites when rubbed or crushed. J. J. Berzelius, and J. J. Chydenius also noted that the powdered metal burns brilliantly in an alcohol flame ; L. F. Nilson, and W. von Bolton observed similar results with Bunsen's flame. When heated in oxygen, the metal burns with blinding brilliancy. H. Moissan and A. Étard found the metal ignites when thrown on molten potassium chlorate. L. F. Nilson said that **water** does not act on the metal ; but, according to H. Moissan and A. Étard, if 7 for 8 per cent. of carbide is present, the metal is slowly attacked, and a mixture of hydrogen, methane, acetylene, ethylene, and their homologues is slowly evolved.

L. F. Nilson showed that when thorium is heated in **chlorine,** the two elements unite vigorously with incandescence, and with the formation of thorium chloride ; H. Moissan and A. Étard said that the reaction begins below a dull red heat. L. F. Nilson, and H. Moissan and A. Étard also found that analogous results are obtained with **bromine** and **iodine.** According to J. J. Berzelius, thorium is not changed when treated with **hydrofluoric acid,** but with **hydrochloric acid** the reaction is slow in the cold and fast when hot—hydrogen is evolved. W. von Bolton found that about 15 per cent. of a grey residue remains unattacked when hydrochloric acid acts on thorium, and this residue is transformed by nitric acid into a lemon yellow product. R. J. Meyer said that the residue is **thoria ;** H. Karstens said that it is not thoria.

J. J. Berzelius, L. F. Nilson, and H. von Wartenberg noted that when thorium is heated with **sulphur** the two elements react vigorously and with incandescence, forming thorium sulphide. H. Moissan and A. Étard said that the reaction begins at a red heat ; with **hydrogen sulphide,** thorium sulphide is formed without incandescence. L. F. Nilson, and W. von Bolton found that **sulphuric acid** slowly attacks thorium ; and, according to the former, with the evolution of sulphur dioxide. J. J. Chydenius said that hot dil. sulphuric acid attacks thorium rapidly ; and J. J. Berzelius, that the action begins rapidly with the evolution of hydrogen, and then becomes very slow. C. A. Matignon and M. Delépine found that when thorium is heated with **nitrogen,** thorium nitride is formed. J. J. Berzelius said that **nitric acid** attacks thorium only during a prolonged heating ; J. J. Chydenius, that the action is rapid ; L. F. Nilson, that neither conc. nor dil. nitric acid attacks thorium ; and W. von Bolton that no perceptible action occurs with the boiling acid.

R. Escales found that thorium reduces many **metals** and metalloids from their compounds—e.g. phosphorus. J. J. Berzelius, and L. F. Nilson reported that soln. of the **alkali hydroxides** have no perceptible action on thorium, and W. von Bolton, that no action occurs with the boiling alkali. In its typical compounds thorium is quadrivalent, forming the oxide, ThO_2, and salts of the type ThX_4, where X is univalent. Unlike most members of the family group, thorium does not act as an acidic oxide. The colourless thorium salts are more stable in soln. than the corresponding ceric salts. The high basicity of thorium in comparison with the other members of the family corresponds with a much smaller tendency to form complex salts. A. Korczynsky studied the catalytic action of thorium and its salts on the hydrogenation of aromatic hydrocarbons ; and W. W. Russell and H. S. Taylor, the promotor action of thoria on nickel catalysts.

Very few alloys of thorium have been prepared. W. Kettembeil [6] could not prepare *thorium amalgam* by electrolyzing a soln. of a thorium salt using a mercury cathode. O. Hönigschmid obtained an alloy with aluminium as a by-product in making aluminium silicide. He reported the formation of a definite compound, **thorium trialuminide,** $ThAl_3$, from a mixture of the double fluoride of thorium and potassium, potassium silicofluoride, and aluminium at 1200°, and purified from free aluminium and silicon by treatment with potassium carbonate soln. It forms quadratic plates resembling graphite in colour, has a sp. gr. 7·96 at 16°, and when heated combines readily with the halogens, oxygen, sulphur, selenium, or hydrogen chloride, but is not attacked by hydrogen at a red heat. It is soluble in aq. soln. of the mineral acids, is not attacked by soln. of the alkali hydroxides, but is decomposed on fusion with sodium or potassium hydroxides. For analysis, the compound was dissolved in aqua regia or in a mixture of hydrofluoric and nitric acids, or decomposed by fusing with moist sodium hydroxide.

The uses of thorium.—In addition to the use of thoria in the preparation of incandescent mantles described in the next section, small pastilles of mixtures of thoria with a trace of ceria have been used for searchlights, headlights of motor cars, etc. The principal is that of the lime-light or zirconia light. Certain preparations of thorium have been recommended as constituents of magnesium flashlight powders—e.g. thorium chromate, tungstate, etc.[7]—the thoriferous flash-light powders are said to evolve less smoke than if magnesium is used alone. The use of thoria as a contact catalyst is indicated below. R. Escales [8] described the use of thorium alloys as reducing agents. E. W. von Siemens and J. G Halske recommended an alloy of tungsten and thorium in the manufacture of the filaments for incandescent lamps. W. Nernst used a mixture of zirconia, thoria, yttria, and sometimes a little ceria as a heating filament for his lamp. C. Kästle, and F. W. S. Valentiner and R. Schwarz used thoria as a screen for X-rays.

Reactions of analytical interest.—The reactions with a soln. of thorium sulphate may be taken to typify the characteristics of those of thorium salts in general. A soln. of **ammonia** or of an **alkali hydroxide** produces a white precipitate of thorium hydroxide, insoluble in excess, but readily soluble in dil. acids. A similar precipitate is produced by **ammonium sulphide.** When thorium hydroxide is ignited it forms thorium oxide which is soluble in conc. sulphuric acid, only after a prolonged digestion. White thorium carbonate is precipitated by **ammonium carbonate** or **alkali carbonate.** The precipitate is soluble in an excess of the reagent, and when the soln. is heated it becomes turbid owing to the separation of a basic carbonate ; the soln. clears again on cooling. Ammonia causes no precipitation in the soln. Thorium salts are completely precipitated by **barium carbonate** in the cold. With **potassium sulphate,** the double salt $K_4Th(SO_4)_4.2H_2O$ is precipitated ; the double salt is sparingly soluble in water, and virtually insoluble in a conc. soln. of potassium sulphate. The corresponding sodium salt is readily soluble in water. All the thorium is precipitated from a boiling soln. by the addition of sodium thiosulphate. A white gelatinous precipitate is produced by hydrofluoric acid or by an alkali fluoride. A white precipitate is produced in feebly acid and neutral soln. by **potassium ferrocyanide ;** and feebly acid soln. also give a white precipitate when treated with **potassium azide,** KN_3. Nitric acid soln. of thorium salts give a white crystalline precipitate with **iodic acid.** Boiling soln. of thorium salts in hydrochloric acid give a flocculent precipitate when treated with **sodium hypophosphate.** Neutral soln., or soln. feebly acidified with sulphuric acid, give a white precipitate with **hydrogen peroxide,** and in soln. of ammonium carbonate, all the thorium is precipitated as hydroperoxide.

If the soln. of the thorium salt be not too acid, **oxalic acid** precipitates white crystalline thorium oxalate very sparingly soluble in oxalic acid and dil. mineral acids. A similar precipitate is produced by **ammonium oxalate ;** this dissolves when boiled with a large excess of the reagent. The soln. remains clear on cooling provided too much free sulphuric acid is not present, and a sufficient excess of ammonium oxalate is employed. The addition of hydrochloric acid to the boiling soln. of ammonium oxalate precipitates nearly all the thorium as oxalate. If ammonium acetate be present, no precipitate is produced by ammonium oxalate, but if hydrochloric acid be added to the soln., nearly all the thorium is precipitated as oxalate. A neutral, aq. soln. of a thorium salt gives a white precipitate with *m*-**nitrobenzoic acid ;** and with aniline *m*-**nitrobenzoate,** the precipitation is complete. All the thorium is precipitated from a soln. of a thorium salt in 40 per cent. alcohol by a soln. of **fumaric acid** in the same menstruum. These reactions are discussed more in detail in connection with the rare earths (**4**. 38, 5). Processes for estimating thorium have been devised which are based on the radioactivity.[9]

The individuality of thorium.—C. A. von Welsbach,[10] and B. Brauner have raised doubts about the individuality of thorium, and C. Baskerville claimed to have separated thorium into three elements—*neo-thorium,* at. wt. 220·6 ; *carolinium,* at. wt. 255·7 ; and *berzelium,* at. wt. 220·3—by precipitation as basic sulphite, or as citrate, followed by fractional sublimation of the chlorides. R. J. Meyer and A. Gumperz tried the fractional precipitation of thorium as chromate, and fractional sublimation of the chlorides, but G. Eberhard could detect no spectral difference in the fractions. B. Brauner fractionally hydrolyzed ammonium thorium oxalate into two series of fractions, *viz.* α-thorium with an at. wt. 233·5, and β-thorium with an at. wt. 232·5 ; and later, he stated :

> The fact that α-thorium is inclined to form basic salts while β-thorium forms acid salts *beruht nur auf einem Zufall.* Apart from radioactive transformation products, thorium with an at. wt. 232·5 is an individual substance which is not admixed with any other quadrivalent element.

Hence, there is no sufficient reason for doubting the elementary nature of thorium. The evidence derived from the study of radioactivity, discussed in a later section, shows that thorium is slowly breaking down into radioactive degradation products and helium. F. Soddy estimated that 350 grms. of thorium nitrate furnished 2×10^{-10} grm. of helium in seven months.

The valency of thorium.—In 1828, J. J. Berzelius [11] ascribed the formula ThO to thoria, the argument was based on the analogies which thoria bears to ceria, lanthana, didymia, and magnesia. In 1845, he said :

Since in potassium thorium sulphate the component bases are each associated with the equal quantity of sulphuric acid, there is some reason to assume, although it is by no means certain, that thoria contains one atom of the radicle and one atom of oxygen.

With increasing knowledge, the rare earth elements were found to be tervalent, while magnesium remained, like oxygen, bivalent. M. Delafontaine argued in favour of the quadrivalency of thorium from the isomorphism of thoria with stannic oxide, and titanic oxide ; and from the analogy between potassium thorium fluoride, and potassium zirconium fluoride. D. I. Mendeléeff showed if thorium be quadrivalent, its properties fit better into the periodic table than if its valency has some other value. P. T. Cleve also argued that thorium is quadrivalent in such compounds as thorium ferrocyanide, $ThFeCy_6$, analogous with K_4FeCy_6 ; the double salts of mercuric cyanide with thorium trihydroxythiocyanate, $nHgCy_2.Th(OH)_3SCy$; thorium formate, $(H.CO.O)_4Th.3H_2O$; a series of hydrated sulphates, $Th(SO_4)_2.nH_2O$; thorium pyrophosphate, ThP_2O_7 ; and sodium thorium carbonate, $3Na_2CO_3.Th(CO_3)_2$. He added that the thorium compounds are closely related with those of zirconium, but thorium does not furnish a monoxide like ZrO. L. F. Nilson compared a number of corresponding compounds of zirconium, tin(ic), and thorium—e.g. the chloroplatinates ; and L. Troost and L. Ouvrard showed that thorium is probably quadrivalent in the silicate $ThO_2.SiO_2$.

L. F. Nilson's value for the sp. ht. of the metal fits the sp. ht. rule only if thorium be quadrivalent. P. S. Baker, and B. D. Steele also showed that the quadrivalency of thorium is in harmony with the relationship of thorium to the other elements. G. Wyrouboff and co-workers assume that thorium is bivalent like the rare earth elements. He rejects any consideration based on the physical properties of the elements, and the periodic law ; and he arbitrarily gives an overwhelming weight to evidence based on his own observations on the isomorphism of the silicotungstates of calcium and the rare earth elements. This mode of conducting an inquiry has not gained many converts. The vap. density of thorium chloride at the b.p. of zinc determined by L. Troost fits the assumption that thorium is bivalent ; but determinations by G. Krüss and L. F. Nilson showed that at $1400°$, thorium chloride dissociates, and if taken between $1050°$ and $1100°$, the observations fit the assumption that the element is quadrivalent. On the other hand, W. Biltz suggested that at $1400°$ the mol. wt. corresponds with $ThCl_3$, and at lower temp. Th_2Cl_3. Against this, W. Biltz found that the mol. wt. of thorium acetylacetonate by the b.p. method, agrees with the formula $Th(CH_3.CO.CHCO.CH_3)_4$. Hence, it is concluded that thorium is quadrivalent.

The atomic weight of thorium.—Quite a large number of determinations have been made of the at. wt. of thorium. In 1829, J. J. Berzelius [12] analyzed thorium sulphate, and from his value for the ratio $ThO_2 : 2BaSO_4$, the at. wt. of thorium is between $236·0$ and $240·1$; from the analysis of the double potassium sulphate, his value for the ratio $ThO_2 : 2BaSO_4$ gives $240·7$; and for the ratio $ThO_2 : 2K_2SO_4$, $236·9$. In 1861, J. J. Chydenius computed $237·3$ from the ratio $ThO_2 : 2SO_3$; $236·1$ from $K_4Th(SO_4)_4.2H_2O : ThO_2$; $237·3$ from $Th(CH_3.COO)_4 : ThO_2$; $241·2$ from $Th(H.COO)_4 : ThO_2$; and $231·4$ from $Th(C_2O_4)_2.2H_2O : ThO_2$. In 1863, M. Delafontaine gave $232·35$ from the ratio $Th(SO_4)_2.9H_2O : H_2O$; and $234·7$ from the ratio $Th(SO_4)_2.4\frac{1}{2}H_2O : ThO_2$. In the latter case, M. Delafontaine assumed the salt to be a tetrahydrate. In 1864, R. Hermann obtained $228·5$ from the ratio $Th(SO_4)_2.4H_2O : H_2O$; and $231·7$ from the ratio $ThO_2 : 2SO_3$. In 1874, P. T. Cleve obtained $234·03$ from the ratio $ThO_2 : 2SO_3$; and $233·97$ from the ratio $ThO_2 : 2CO_2$. In 1882, L. F. Nilson obtained $232·66$ from the ratio $Th(SO_4)_2.9H_2O : ThO_2$ weighed in air, and $232·51$ when the results are reduced for weighing in vacuo. He also obtained $232·16$ and $232·61$ from the ratio $ThO_2 : 2SO_3$, and $233·75$ from $Th(SO_4)_2 : 9H_2O$. In 1887, G. Krüss and L. F. Nilson obtained 232·61 from the ratio $ThO_2 : 2SO_3$ when weighed in air, and 232·49 when weighed in vacuo. In 1900, G. Urbain gave 233·79 from the ratio $ThO_2 : 2SO_3$; and 232·64 from the ratio $Th(SO_4)_2.8H_2O : ThO_2$. O. Hönigschmid and S. Horovitz obtained 232·15±0·016 from the ratio $ThBr_4 : 4Ag$; and 232·12±0·014 from the ratio $ThBr_4 : 4AgBr$. B. Brauner gave 232·21–232·39 from the ratio $ThO_2 : 2C_2O_3$; 232·34–232·52 from the ratio $ThO_2 : 2SO_3$; and 232·36 from the ratio $Th(SO_4)_2.9H_2O : ThO_2$. B. Brauner gave 232·49 for the best representative value, and F. W. Clarke, 232·6. The International Table for 1921 gives 232·4. The **atomic number** is 90. No **isotopes** have been reported by F. W. Aston. For the alleged **atomic degradation** of thorium to carbon, vide thorium nitrate. N. Yamada found that hydrogen is probably emitted by the bombardment of α-particles. F. Zambonini, and J. Beckenkamp investigated the atomic structure of thorium—vide hafnium.

REFERENCES.

[1] J. J. Berzelius, Svenska Akad. Handl., 1, 1829; Pogg. Ann., **16**. 385, 1829; J. J. Chydenius, ib., **119**. 43, 1863; Kemisk Undersökning af Thorjord och Thorsalter, Helsingfors, 1861; G. Meyer and M. Greulich, Phys. Zeit., **22**. 583, 1921; C. Bergemann, Sitzber. Akad. Berlin, 221, 1851; Pogg. Ann., **82**. 561, 1851; **85**. 558, 1852; Liebig's Ann., **80**. 267, 1851; **84**. 239, 1852; C. A. Matignon and M. Delépine, Compt. Rend., **131**. 838, 1900; 132. 37, 1901; Ann. Chim. Phys., (8), **10**. 136, 1907; H. Moissan and A. Étard, ib., (7), **12**. 429, 1897; A. Duboin, ib., (8), **17**. 355, 1909; H. Moissan and O. Hönigschmid, ib., (8), **8**. 182, 1906; Monatsh., 27. 685, 1906; O. Hönigschmid, ib., **27**. 205, 1906; Compt. Rend., **142**. 157, 1906; L. Troost, ib., **116**. 1230, 1893; E. Chauvenet, ib., **148**. 1519, 1909; Chem. Ztg., **34**. 940, 1910; W. von Bolton, Zeit. Elektrochem., **14**. 768, 1908; P. Askenasy, ib., **15**. 34, 1909; H. Karstens, ib., **15**. 33, 1909; R. J. Meyer, ib., **14**. 809, 1908; **15**. 105, 1909; H. von Wartenberg, ib., **15**. 867, 1909; L. F. Nilson and O. Pettersson, Ber., **11**. 383, 1878; L. F. Nilson, Œfvers. Akad. Förh., **39**. 7, 1882; Compt. Rend., **95**. 727, 1882; **96**. 346, 1883; Ber., **15**. 2544, 1882; **16**. 153, 1883; Chem. News, **47**. 122, 1883; C. Winkler, Ber., **24**. 885, 1891; H. Goldschmidt, Zeit. angew. Chem., **11**. 822, 1898; Liebig's Ann., **301**. 19, 1898; H. Goldschmidt and C. Vautin, Journ. Soc. Chem. Ind., **17**. 543, 1898; K. A. Kühne, U.S. Pat. No. 910394, 1909; German Pat., D.R.P. 179403, 1904; E. W. von Siemens and J. G. Halske, ib., 133958, 133959, 146503, 1900; 190233, 194349, 1906; H. Kuzel, ib., 186980, 1906; H. C. Greenwood, Journ. Chem. Soc., **93**. 1483, 1908; E. Wedekind and H. Baumhauer, Zeit. Koll., **5**. 190, 1909; W. Guertler and M. Pirani, Zeit. Metallkunde, **11**. 1, 1919; G. N. Lewis and G. E. Gilson, Journ. Amer. Chem. Soc., **39**. 2554, 1917; G. N. Lewis, G. E. Gilson, and W. M. Latimer, ib., **44**. 1008, 1922; E. D. Eastman, ib., **45**. 80, 1923; G. Siebert and E. Korten, German Pat., D.R.P. 355485, 1920; W. C. Brögger, Zeit. Kryst., **7**. 442, 1883; Compt. Rend., **96**. 346, 1883; Chem. News, **47**. 128. 1883; P. Groth, Chemische Krystallographie, Leipzig, **1**. 12, 1906; C. F. Rammelsberg, A. E. Nordenskjöld, and P. T. Cleve, Bull. Soc. Chim., (2), **21** 123, 1874; J. Herzfeld and O. Korn, Chemie der seltenen Erden, Berlin, 1901; J. Dewar, Proc. Roy. Soc., **89**. A, 158, 1913; K. Honda, Ann. Physik, (4), **32**. 1047, 1910; H. Bohlin, ib., (4), **61**. 421, 1920; B. D. Steele, Chem. News, **84**. 245, 1901; A. W. Hull, Phys. Rev., (2), **18**. 88, 1921; O. Ruff and H. Brintzinger, Zeit. anorg. Chem., **129**. 267, 1923; J. J. van Laar, Proc. Acad. Amsterdam, **18**. 1220, 1916; 20. 138, 492, 1918; W. R. Mott, Trans. Amer. Electrochem. Soc., **34**. 555, 1918; H. Wartenberg, J. Proy, and R. Reinicke, Zeit. Elektrochem., **29**. 214, 1923; F. Born, ib., **31**. 309, 1925; H. Kuzel and E. Wedekind, Met. Chem. Engg., **12**. 260, 1914; S. Dushman and I. Langmuir, Phys. Rev., (2), **20**. 113, 1922; A. E. van Arkel and J. H. de Boer, Zeit. anorg. Chem., **148**. 345, 1925; J. E. van Arkel, Physica, **4**. 286, 1924; V. M. Goldschmidt and L. Thomassen, Danske Vid. Skrift., 2, 1923; J. Böhm, Zeit. anorg. Chem., **149**. 217, 1925; J. Böhm and H. Niclassen, ib., **132**. 1, 1923; D. Leby and L. Hamburger, ib., **87**. 209, 1914.

[2] R. Thalén, Om spectralanalys, Upsala, 1886; Nova Acta Upsala, (3), **6**. 9, 1868; R. J. Lang, Phil. Trans., **224**. A, 571, 1924; E. Demarçay, Spectres électriques, Paris, 1895; W. J. Humphreys, Astrophys. Journ., **6**. 169, 1897; P. G. Nutting, ib., **23**. 64, 1906; F. L. Cooper, ib., **29**. 329, 1909; **30**. 400, 1909; B. E. Moore, ib., **30**. 144, 178, 1909; Phys. Zeit., **10**. 297, 1900; G. Eberhard, Ber., **38**. 826, 1905; A. G. G. Leonard, Proc. Roy. Soc. Dublin, (2), **11**. 270, 1903; H. Auerbach, Zeit. wiss. Photochem., **7**. 30, 41, 1909; W. von Bolton, Zeit. Elektrochem., **9**. 913, 1903; H. Bohlin, Ann. Physik, (4), **61**. 434, 1920; A. Hagenbach and H. Konen, Atlas der Emissionsspektra, Jena, 1905; J. N. Lockyer, Solar Physics Committee, London, 1906; O. Lohse, Sitzber. Akad. Berlin, 179, 1897; Pub. Astrophys. Obs. Potsdam, **12**. 109, 1902; F. Exner and E. Haschek, Tabellen der Funkenspectren, Leipzig, 1902; Tabellen der Bogenspectren, Leipzig, 1904; Die Spectren der Elemente bei normalen Druck, Leipzig, 1912; Sitzber. Akad. Wien, 108. 825, 1899; G. Hofbauer, ib., **116**. 267, 1907; J. M. Eder and E. Valenta, ib., **119**. 519, 1910; Atlas typischer Spectren, Wien, 1911; C. E. Gissing, Spark Spectra of the Metals, London, 1910; R. Bunsen, Pogg. Ann., **155**. 380, 1875; S. Dushman, Phys. Rev., (2), **20**. 109, 1922; S. Dushman, H. N. Rowe, and C. A. Kidner, ib., (2), **21**. 207, 1923; P. A. Ross,

ib., (2), **22**. 199, 221, 1923 ; M. Siegbahn and E. Friman, *Phil. Mag.*, (6), **32**. 39, 1916 ; *Phys. Zeit.*, **17**. 17, 61, 1916 ; *Ber. deut. phys. Ges.*, **18**. 278, 1916 ; G. Bardet, *Bull. Soc. Min.*, **27**. 63, 1904 ; W. Muthmann and C. Baur, *Ber.*, **33**. 1761, 1900 ; W. W. Coblentz, *Bull. Bur. Standards*, **5**. 173, 1908 ; W. Ritz, *Phys. Zeit.*, **10**. 307, 1909 ; D. Coster, *Phys. Rev.*, (2), **18**. 218, 1921 ; (2), **19**. 20, 1922 ; *Compt. Rend.*, **172**. 1176, 1921 : *Zeit. Physik*, **4**. 179, 1921 ; **6**. 185, 1921 ; E. Hjalmar, *ib.*, **7**. 341, 1921 ; **15**. 65, 1923 ; G. Meyer, *Phys. Zeit.*, **22**. 583, 1921 ; V. Dolejsek, *Nature*, **109**. 582, 1922 ; *Zeit. Physik*, **10**. 129, 1922 ; **21**. 111, 1924 ; K. Teucke, *Phys. Zeit.*, **25**. 115, 1924 ; W. Duane and R. A. Patterson, *Proc. Nat. Acad.*, **6**. 509, 1920 ; W. Duane, H. Fricke, and W. Stenström, *ib.*, **6**. 607, 1920 ; M. Siegbahn, *Jahrb. Rad. Elektron.*, **13**. 296, 1916 ; M. Siegbahn and E. Jönsson, *Phys. Zeit.*, **20**. 251, 1919 ; M. de Broglie, *Compt. Rend.*, **169**. 962, 1919 ; G. Wentzel, *Zeit. Naturwiss.*, **10**. 369, 1922 ; P. A. Ross, *Phys. Rev.*, (2), **22**. 221, 1923 ; K. H. Kingdom and I. Langmuir, *ib.*, (2), **22**. 148, 1923 ; R. J. Lang, *Phil. Trans.*, **224**. A, 371, 1924 ; R. Hamer, *Journ. Amer. Optical Soc.*, **9**. 251, 1924 ; J. W. Marden, J. E. Conley, and F. P. Thomas, *U.S. Pat. No.* 1487174, 1924 ; B. B. Ray, *Phil. Mag.*, (6), **48**. 707, 1924 ; R. Berthold, *Ann. Physik*, (4), **76**. 409, 1925 ; B. Neumann and H. Richter, *Zeit. Elektrochem.*, **31**. 296, 1925 ; H. K. Onnes, *Comm. Phys. Lab. Univ. Leyden*, Supp. 44, 1921 ; W. von Bolton, *Zeit. Elektrochem.*, **14** 768, 1908 ; A. Heydweiller, *Zeit. phys. Chem.*, **89**. 281, 1915 ; G. Fournier, *Compt. Rend.*, **180**. 1490, 1925 ; H. R. Robinson, *Phil. Mag.*, (6), **50**. 241, 1926.

³ K. Honda, *Ann. Physik*, (4), **32**. 1047, 1910 ; S. Meyer, *Wied. Ann.*, **68**. 324, 1899 ; *Monatsh.*, **20**. 369, 1899.

⁴ C. Winkler, *Ber.*, **24**. 886, 1891 ; R. Schwarz and E. Konrad, *ib.*, **54**. B, 2122, 1921 ; A. Klauber and J. M. von Mellenheim, *Zeit. anorg. Chem.*, **113**. 306, 1920 ; C. A. Matignon, *Compt. Rend.*, **131**. 891, 1900 ; C. A. Matignon and M. Delépine, *ib.*, **132**. 36, 1901 ; *Ann. Chim. Phys.*, (8), **10**. 137, 1907 ; E. Chauvenet, *Chem. Ztg.*, **34**. 940, 1910 ; W. Ramsay and J. N. Collie, *Proc. Roy. Soc.*, **60**. 53, 1896.

⁵ N. B. Pilling and R. E. Bedworth, *Metal Ind.*, **22**. 560, 1923 ; E. Chauvenet, *Chem. Ztg.*, **34**. 940, 1910 ; L. F. Nilson, *Œfvers. Akad. Förh.*, **39**. 7, 1882 ; *Compt. Rend.*, **95**. 727, 1882 ; **96**. 346, 1883 ; *Ber.*, **15**. 2544, 1882 ; **16**. 153, 1883 ; *Chem. News*, **47**. 122, 1883 ; J. J. Berzelius, *Svenska Akad. Handl.*, **1**, 1829 ; *Pogg. Ann.*, **16**. 385, 1829 ; J. J. Chydenius, *ib.*, **119**. 43, 1863 ; *Kemisk Undersökning af Thorjord och Thorsalter*, Helsingfors, 1861 ; W. von Bolton, *Zeit. Elektrochem.*, **14**. 768, 1908 ; H. Moissan and A. Etard, *Ann. Chim. Phys.*, (7), **12**. 429, 1897 ; R. J. Meyer, *Zeit. Elektrochem.*, **14**. 809, 1908 ; **15**. 105, 1909 ; H. Karstens, *ib.*, **15**. 33, 1909 ; H. von Wartenberg, *ib.*, **15** 867, 1909 ; C. A. Matignon and M. Delépine, *ib.*, **132**. 36, 1901 ; *Ann. Chim. Phys.*, (8), **10**. 137, 1907 ; R. Escales, *German Pat.*, *D.R.P.* 145820, 1902 ; A. Korczynsky, *Bull. Soc. Chim.*, (4), **29**. 283, 1921 ; W. W. Russell and H. S. Taylor, *Journ. Phys. Chem.*, **29**. 1325, 1925.

⁶ O. Hönigschmid, *Monatsh.*, **27**. 205, 1906 ; *Compt. Rend.*, **142**. 157, 280, 1906 ; W. Kettembeil, *Zeit. anorg. Chem.*, **38**. 217, 1903.

⁷ A. Lesmüller, *French Pat. No.* 403722, 1909 ; G. Krebs, *Brit. Pat. No.* 27267, 1904.

⁸ R. Escales, *German Pat.*, *D.R.P.* 145802, 1902 ; E. W. von Siemens and J. G. Halske, *ib.*, 154998, 1912 ; W. Nernst, *ib.*, 164802, 1903 ; F. W. S. Valentiner and R. Schwarz, *ib.*, 228375, 1909 ; C. Kästle, *Munchen. Med. Wochschr.*, **56**. 919, 1909 ; L. Moser, *Œsterr. Chem. Ztg.*, **26**. 67, 1923.

⁹ J Joly, *Phil. Mag.*, (6), **17**. 760, 1909 ; V. I. Spicin, *Journ. Russ. Phys. Chem. Soc.*, **49**. 357, 1917 ; G. H. Cartledge, *Journ. Amer. Chem. Soc.*, **41**. 42, 1919 ; H. H. Helmick, *ib.*, **43**. 2003, 1921.

¹⁰ C. A. von Welsbach, *Journ. Gasbeleucht.*, **44**. 661, 1901 ; *Chem. News*, **85**. 255, 1902 ; C. Baskerville, *ib.*, **90**. 151, 1904 ; *Journ. Amer. Chem. Soc.*, **23**. 764, 1901 ; **26**. 922, 1904 ; *Ber.*, **38**. 1444, 1905 ; R. J. Meyer and A. Gumperz, *ib.*, **38**. 817, 1905 ; G. Eberhard, *ib.*, **38**. 826, 1905 ; B. Brauner, *Journ. Chem. Soc.*, **81**. 1243, 1902 ; in R. Abegg, *Handbuch der anorganischen Chemie*, Leipzig, **3**. ii, 810, 1909 ; *Zeit. anorg. Chem.*, **34**. 207, 1903 ; F. Soddy, *Phil. Mag.*, (6), **16**. 513, 1908.

¹¹ M. Delafontaine, *Arch. Sciences Genève*, (2), **18**. 343, 1863 ; D. I. Mendeléeff, *Liebig's Ann. Suppl.*, **8**. 151, 1872 ; J. J. Berzelius, *Pogg. Ann.*, **16**. 385, 1829 ; *Lehrbuch der Chemie*, Dresden, **3**. 1224, 1845 ; P. T. Cleve, *Bihang. Svenska Akad. Handl.*, **2**. 6, 1874 ; *Bull. Soc. Chim.*, (2), **21**. 115, 1874 ; L. F. Nilson, *Ber.*, **9**. 1060, 1142, 1876 ; **16**. 162, 1882 ; **17**. 118, 1883 ; *Compt. Rend.*, **96**. 346, 1883 ; L. Troost, *ib.*, **101**. 360, 1885 ; G. Wyrouboff and A. Verneuil, *ib.*, **128**. 1573, 1899 ; *Bull. Soc. Chim.*, (3), **21**. 118, 1899 ; G. Wyrouboff, *Bull. Soc. Min.*, **19**. 285, 1896 ; L. Troost and L. Ouvrard, *ib.*, **105**. 257, 1887 ; G. Krüss and L. F. Nilson, *Zeit. phys. Chem.*, **1**. 301, 1887 ; *Ber.*, **20**. 1671, 1887 ; B. D. Steele, *Chem. News*, **84**. 245, 1902 ; W. Biltz, *Liebig's Ann.*, **331**. 338, 1904 ; *Ber.*, **37**. 1095, 1904 ; P. S. Baker, *Amer. Chem. Journ.*, **11**. 138, 1889 ; J. J. Berzelius, *Svenska Akad. Handl.*, **1**, 1829 ; *Pogg. Ann.*, **16**. 385, 1829.

¹² J. J. Berzelius, *Svenska Akad. Handl.*, **1**. 1829 ; *Pogg. Ann.*, **16**. 385, 1829 ; J. J. Chydenius, *ib.*, **119**. 43, 1863 ; *Kemisk Undersökning af Thorjord och Thorsalter*, Helsingfors, 1861 ; M. Delafontaine, *Arch. Sciences Genève*, (2), **18**. 343, 1863 ; O. Hönigschmid and S. Horovitz, *Sitzber. Akad. Wien*, **125**. 149, 1916 ; *Monatsh.*, **37**. 305, 1916 ; R. Hermann, *Journ. prakt. Chem.*, (1), **93**. 114, 1864 ; P. T. Cleve, *Bihang. Svenska Akad. Handl.*, **2**. 6, 1874 ; *Bull. Soc. Chim.*, (2), **21**. 115, 1874 ; L. F. Nilson, *Ber.*, **15**. 2519, 1882 ; G. Krüss and L. F. Nilson, *ib.*, **20**. 1665, 1887 ; B. Brauner, *Zeit. anorg. Chem.*, **34**. 207, 1903 ; *Journ. Chem. Soc.*, **73**. 951, 1898 ; *Chem. News*,

77. 160, 1898 ; *Proc. Chem. Soc.*, **17.** 67, 1901 ; in R. Abegg, *Handbuch der anorganischen Chemie*, **3.** ii, 800, 1909 ; **B.** Brauner and J. Picek, *Zeit. anorg. Chem.*, **38.** 338, 1904 ; G. Urbain, *Ann. Chim. Phys.*, (7), **19.** 223, 1900 ; G. Urbain and E. Budischowsky, *Compt. Rend.*, **124.** 618, 1897 ; C. Baskerville, *Journ. Amer. Chem. Soc.*, **23.** 761, 1901 ; **26.** 922, 1904 ; *Ber.*, **38.** 1444, 1905 ; R. Bunsen, *Pogg. Ann.*, **155.** 375, 1875 ; J. F. Bahr, *Liebig's Ann.*, **132.** 231, 1864 ; R. J. Meyer and A. Gumperz, *Ber.*, **38.** 817, 1905 ; G. Eberhard, *ib.*, **38.** 826, 1905 ; F. W. Clarke, *Amer. Chem. Journ.*, **3.** 263, 1881 ; *Phil. Mag.*, (5), **12.** 101, 1881 ; *A Recalculation of the Atomic Weights*, Washington, 295, 1910 ; A. S. Russell, *Nature*, **114.** 717, 1924 ; F. Zambonini, *Atti Accad. Lincei*, (5), **33.** ii, 16, 1924 ; J. Beckenkamp, *Zeit. anorg. Chem.*, **143.** 394, 1925 ; F. W. Aston, *Phil. Mag.*, (6), **49.** 1191, 1925 ; N. Yamada, *Compt. Rend.*, **180.** 1591, 1925.

§ 5. The Incandescent Mantle

In 1820, D. Brewster[1] suggested that the intense dazzling light which lime and other earths give in the blowpipe flame might be applied economically and usefully. He also showed that bits of wood, steeped in soln. of calcium or magnesium salts, after ignition, left the lime in a more attenuated state than ordinary lime, and gave a more intense light at a lower temp., and in 1835, W. H. F. Talbot showed that even the flame of a spirit-lamp sufficed to make lime incandescent provided the lime be in a very finely divided state such as obtained by incinerating blotting paper previously soaked in a soln. of a calcium salt. In 1826, T. Drummond showed that a cylinder of lime could be raised to incandescence by heating it in the flame of the oxy-hydrogen blowpipe, and he utilized the fact for producing an intense light, the so-called lime-light—*vide* hydrogen. The heat required to raise the cylinder of lime to the temp. of incandescence is considerable, because so much heat is dissipated by radiation and conduction. This is shown by heating coils of (i) thick, (ii) medium, and (iii) thin platinum wires in a Bunsen's flame ; the first becomes red hot, the second bright red, and the third may become incandescent and fuse. Buttons of zirconia and of magnesia heated by an oxy-coal gas flame were tried in Paris for street-lighting, but owing to the high cost, the project was soon abandoned. In 1848, J. P. Gillard tried heating a mantle of fine platinum gauze by the water-gas flame as a source of illumination. The results were good, but the surface of the metal was eroded by the flame gases, and the light-giving power deteriorated. In 1880, C. Clamond introduced lime and magnesia hoods, or mantles heated by coal gas flame fed with heated air. The hood was suspended in a net of fine platinum wire. Several modifications appeared—*e.g.* V. B. Lewis' incandescent burner, etc.

J. J. Berzelius in 1829, J. F. Bahr and R. Bunsen in 1866, and M. Delafontaine in 1874 showed that thoria, zirconia, yttria, erbia, and terbia emit *ein ausserordentlich blendendes Licht* at the temp. corresponding with that of a non-luminous gas flame. About 1880, C. A. von Welsbach[2] was attracted by the white or yellow incandescent light emitted by the rare earths when heated to a high temp. Erbia gave off a green light. In order to investigate the spectra of the incandescent earths, he soaked cotton with soln. of the earths, calcined the dried fabric, and obtained a coherent skeleton formed by the earth. The light emitted by lanthana was so bright that he tried a mantle of this earth as a source of illumination, but found that the mantle soon disintegrated to powder ; a mixture of lanthana and magnesia was more stable, but it became translucent and vitreous after 60–70 hrs.' use. He obtained better results with mixtures having zirconia as a base, but found that those containing thoria were best of all, but even here the results were not satisfactory. The thoria increased the emissive power of the associated earths, but it decreased very much after 50–60 hrs.' use. C. A. von Welsbach then found that the more he purified the thoria, the less the intensity of the emitted light. He thought that the process of purification resolved thorium into two substances, and that the luminous constituent accumulated in the mother-liquors. About 1890, he showed that the luminous constituent was cerium oxide. He found that a mixture of thoria with about 1 per cent. of cerium oxide has about three times

the emissive power of the older preparations. In 1892, this mixture—the so-called
Wel bach's mixture—was adopted for the manufacture of mantles, and, in spite
of numerous attempts, no improvement has been discovered. If, however, the
press. be greater than that of the atm., a rather larger proportion of cerium oxide
is needed.

The manufacture of incandescent mantles is described in monographs, etc., by
L. C. Andes, C. R. Böhm, L. Castellani, H. W. Fischer, W. Gentsch, E. Glinzer, G. Hartwig,
E Hintz, G. Kern, G. von Knorre, V. Loos, M. M. Merle, H. von Oeschelhäuser, M. Rubnur,
M. Söhren, etc. The flame is non-luminous like an ordinary Bunsen's burner ; and the
mantle is hung so that it is heated by the burning gas. The mantle becomes incandescent.
The mantles are made by saturating woven cotton, or artificial silk fabrics with a mixture
of, say. thorium nitrate (48–49 per cent. ThO_2), 1000 grms. ; cerium nitrate, 10 grms. ;
beryllium nitrate, 5 grms. ; magnesium nitrate, 1·5 grms. ; and water, 2000 grms. The
object of the beryllium and magnesium nitrates is to strengthen the ash skeleton. The
mantle is dipped in the soln. The fabric retains some of the salts in its pores. The
impregnated mantle is then allowed to dry, and burnt off in a stove ; at the same time. the
nitrates are transformed into oxides. The mantle is hardened and shaped in the blowpipe flame and the result is a kind of fragile pottery which retains the form and shape of
the original fabric. It would be too fragile for transit. It is therefore dipped in collodion
and dried. The collodion is burnt off the first time the mantle is placed in position when it
is no longer to be carried about. H. D. Griffith described the preparation of Nernst's
filaments for laboratory work.

The incandescent or light-emitting power of the mantle is somewhat sensitive
to variations in the composition of the mixture of earths. With the above-named
mixture, the light has ten times the illuminating power of a flat flame burner
using the same amount of gas. The photometry has been studied by H. Bunte,
H. Drehschmidt, W. Wedding, etc. W. MacKean, and E. Glinzer have discussed
the effect of various foreign matters on the light emissivity of the mantle. E. Baur
said that the presence of gadolinia in the thoria is deleterious. O. N. Witt found
that lanthana lessens the durability of the mantle ; didymia and yttria affect
the luminosity and the refractoriness of the mantle ; and erbia imparts a greenish
tinge to the light. H. E. Ives and co-workers tested the results obtained by
replacing the ceric oxide with uranium oxide, manganese oxide, nickel oxide,
lanthana, praseodymia, neodymia, and erbia.

The Welsbach mixture has a relatively high efficiency in translating heat into
light. V. B. Lewes gives the following relative values for the light-emitting power
of various oxides of commercial purity and of a high degree of purity :

	Pure.	Commercial.
Zirconia.	1·5	3·1
Thoria .	0·5	6·0
Cerium oxide	0·4	0·9
Lanthana	—	6·0
Yttria	—	3·2
Erbia .	0·6	1·7
Chromic oxide	0·4	0·4
Alumina	0·6	0·6
Baryta .	3·3	3·3
Strontia.	5·2	5·5
Magnesia	5·0	5·0

H. E. Ives and co-workers studied mantles made from the oxides indicated in
Table IV, under like conditions. The whole group has a low light emissivity.
The temp. of the flame was 2050°. Silica and beryllia have qualities almost comple-
mentary to those required for light production for their low temp. and the distribution of their emissive power with all the higher values in the infra-red, militate
against a high luminous efficiency ; zirconia even at a low temp. has a relatively higher emissive power. In addition to light-emitting power, the further
requirements are that the oxide employed must be (i) unaffected by atm. influences ;
(ii) sufficiently refractory to retain its porosity, and not to melt or even vitrefy
seriously at the temp. of the flame ; (iii) non-volatile ; and (iv) the shrinkage in

the burning and calcination of the nitrate-laden fabric must not be excessive. Hence, added E. St. John, the mantle is made from a fire-resisting material of small mass, small heat conductivity, large surface, and large light emissivity

TABLE IV.—LIGHT EMISSIVITY OF OXIDES.

Oxide.	Temp.	Rate of radiation.	Emissive power.	Radiant luminous efficiency.
Thoria . . .	1930°	1·10	0·044	0·000320
Zirconia . .	1670°	1·32	0·095	0·000143
Magnesia . .	1840°	1·10	0·053	—
Alumina . .	1725°	1·41	0·088	0·000390
Silica . . .	1650°	1·71	0·130	—
Beryllia . .	1690°	1·61	0·110	—

when heated in the hottest part of Bunsen's flame. When tested by these criteria, it is found that thoria occupies a unique position as a basis for the mantle. It is readily shaped at the temp. of the blowpipe flame; its thermal endurance in the oxy-coal gas flame is greater than that of any known oxide; and in the conversion of the fabric soaked with thorium nitrate into the thoria skeleton, the shrinkage is smaller than is the case with any of the other substances. In converting thorium nitrate into thoria there is a large expansion—almost tenfold. Hence, the product is very porous or spongy.

While thorium oxide alone has a relatively small light emissivity, this quality is awakened by the addition of a trace of cerium oxide, and, as the proportion of the last-named oxide is gradually increased, the light emissivity of the mantle grows greater and greater, until, when the ratio $CeO_2 : ThO_2$ by weight is nearly 1 : 99, the maximum luminosity is attained, and any further addition of cerium dioxide reduces the emissivity until, when about 10 per cent. of cerium dioxide is present, the light emissivity is very small. These observations are illustrated by the measurements of G. P. Drossbach, and J. Lux. The latter found :

Per cent. of CeO_2 . . .	0	1	2	3	4	5 ... 100
Illuminating power . .	3·3	143·3	120·5	105·6	91·0	82·9 4·0

A composite curve from the results of both observers is shown in Fig. 5. W. Muthmann and E. Baur believe that the thoria and cerium oxide form a solid soln. The powerful emissivity of the mixture could not have been foreseen from any known property of the constituent earths, and, added C. A. von Welsbach, "we can give no exact reason for the excitation of the emissive power of thoria by the cerium dioxide." Several hypotheses have been suggested to explain the increased luminosity : some consider the phenomenon to be a purely physical process due to temp. alone—e.g. W Nernst, and H. le Chatelier and O. Boudouard, vide infra. Others attribute the phenomenon to catalytic action. F. Westphal suggested that the peculiar glow is a manifestation of energy due to the slow combination of acidic and basic oxides. H. E. Armstrong and T. M. Lowry, C. Killing, and R. Moschelles assumed that the particles of the cerium oxide are alternately oxidized and reduced by the rapid transition from one state to the other producing mol. oscillations—oscillatory oxidation—which cause a rise of temp. In the words of C. A. von Welsbach, who once advocated this hypothesis :

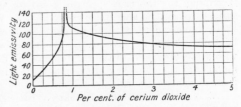

FIG. 5.—Effect of Cerium Dioxide on the Light Emissivity of Thoria.

The gas of the flame successively and very rapidly oxidizes and reduces the emissive substance at the points where it is situated in the mantle. If the constituents of the mixture could form a compound when one of them is in a state of higher or lower oxidation, the compound would be quickly destroyed at the moment when the body concerned passes from the usual to the other degree of oxidation. The earths are in a state of extremely fine division, and are surrounded by a mantle of flame both oxidizing and reducing. If reduction takes place there is also decomposition, and if oxidation, there is recombination of these elements ; these reactions may go on several million times a second, and mol. shocks are produced which give rise to luminous oscillations of the ether, and the body becomes incandescent.

This does not make it clear why the increased luminosity does not occur *pari passu* with an increase in the proportions of ceria. G. P. Drossbach, H. Bunte, R. J. Meyer and A. Anschütz, and V. B. Lewes ascribed the emissivity of Welsbach's mixture to some special action—catalytic action, or contact action—of the cerium dioxide in converting heat rays into light rays. Platinum foil continues to glow in a stream of coal gas after it has been heated to redness and the flame extinguished. It is assumed that a kind of surface combustion takes place. The metal is supposed to condense the coal gas and air on its surface, and render them so chemically active that they combine at a temp. below the ignition of the mixture, and the heat of the reaction suffices to keep the temp. of the foil at a red heat. H. Bunte showed that cerium oxide likewise lowers the temp. at which hydrogen and oxygen combine—from about 650° to 315·5°. This action is intensified by increasing the surface of the stimulant.

Spongy platinum, for example, without being previously heated may ignite the gas, and H. Bunte and H. Luggin have shown that the trace of finely divided cerium oxide, on the surface of the thoria, is so active that under suitable conditions the mantle can be kept luminous in a stream of coal gas and air :

A mica chimney is fixed over the mouth of a large Bunsen's burner so as to form a prolongation of the tube. The mixture of gas and air is ignited at the mouth of the chimney, and the air supply is regulated so as to give a non-luminous flame. An ordinary Welsbach's mantle is then hooked by its loop on to a platinum wire, and is held on the burning mixture of gas and air at the mouth of the chimney, until it glows and emits light in the usual way. On lowering the mantle through the flame into the mica chimney below, it continues to incandesce in the cold current of air and gas.

F. Haber and F. Richardt, however, state that the catalytic reactions on the mantle in Bunsen's flame have very little influence on its temp. The thoria, said A. Foix, serves as a carrier and dilution medium for the cerium oxide ; and, added C. Killing, the thoria is specially fitted for this purpose in virtue of its enormous surface (porosity) and its low sp. ht. F. Westphal, C. Killing, H. Bunte, and E. G. Love regarded the ceric oxide as a carrier of oxygen to the burning gas, but later, C. Killing gave up the hypothesis when he found that the mantle glowed with a greenish light in the chlorohydrogen flame ; H. E. Ives and co-workers also found that the efficiency of the mantle is but little if at all affected by the change from oxygen to chlorine.

A. A. C. Swinton found that Welsbach's mixture gave no more light than ordinary thoria when bombarded by the cathode rays ; and while purified thoria glowed brilliantly, purified ceric oxide gave scarcely any light. In the flame, on the contrary, the intensity of the glow with thoria and ceric oxide is nearly the same, although the colour is different. Observations on this subject were made by E. St. John, R. L. Swan, and R. J. Meyer and A. Anschütz. H. E. Ives and co-workers observed that the continued bombardment of the cathode rays imparted a bluish-grey colour to mixtures of thoria and ceric oxide, and the original colour was restored by heating the mantle in air. The cathode discharge thus acts as a reducing agent. The reducing condition increases the general emissive power of ceric oxide, and reduces the mantle temp. ; with thoria, as C. Fèry has shown, the reducing condition lowers the emissive power and augments the temp.

C. Fèry concluded that a mantle of cerium oxide gives no light because the radiation of heat is so great that the temp. cannot be raised sufficiently by the oxy-coal gas flame ; but when the cerium oxide is sufficiently attenuated by dilution with thoria, it can be raised to the required temp. E. St. C. Deville supported the view of C. Fèry. In further support of this view, V. B. Lewes showed that under similar conditions :

Per cent. CeO_2 in thoria	0·1	1·0	10·0	100
Temp. of mantle 6 mm. above burner	1610°	1570°	1355°	1125°
Temp. of flame in the same zone	1590°	1560°	1350°	1130°
Temp. of mantle 52 mm. above burner	1468°	1441°	1209°	1020°
Temp. of flame in the same zone	1430°	1439°	1234°	1032°
Illuminating power (candles per c. ft. of gas)	3·4	20·0	3·3	nil
Radiation value	140	152	218	234

Hence, added V. B. Lewes, thoria, owing to its low sp. ht., and low radiation power for heat, can be raised to the temp. of the flame while catalytic action on the still unburnt flame gases and air raises it a few degrees even above this point. Ceria when added in quantities up to 1·5 per cent. by weight, does not interfere with these conditions; but, by its still higher catalytic powers, it tends to focus the combustion of the extremely attenuated combustible constituents of the flame gases on the widely distributed ceria particles, and, by this localization, raise them to a far higher temp. than the mantle. This temp., however, cannot be detected by the thermocouple, which only gives the average temp. of the mass with which it is in contact, and fails to show the temp. of the 0·15 per cent. of ceria. The addition of more ceria to the mixture causes such a rapid cooling of both mantle and flame by radiation that the light at once begins to fall, and by the time 10 per cent. of ceria is in the mixture, the mantle gives us no more light than a thoria mantle, but a much increased heat radiation.

In 1898, H. le Chatelier and O. Boudouard claimed that the luminosity of mantles can be explained by the ordinary laws of selective radiation ; the subject was followed up by W. Nernst and E. Bose, who found that at equal temp. the radiation was nearly the same whether the mantle be heated by the gaseous products of combustion or electrically. Thus,

Wave-length	6880	5890	5160	4770	4470
Flame heating	0·770	1·000	1·36	2·39	4·21
Electric heating	0·790	0·987	1·37	2·34	4·09
Ratio	1·03	0·99	0·99	0·98	0·97

They conclude that since the substance of the mantle emits but little red light or ultra-red rays, and thus gives off but little energy in the form of heat, the mantle can, therefore, completely absorb the high temperature of the gas flame, and, in consequence, emit a relatively greater amount of light. H. Russell and A. F. Traver add that temp. alone cannot be the explanation because a slight change in the composition of the mantle should not cause so great a difference in the result— e.g. the luminosity of a mantle with 0·5 per cent. of cerium oxide is 13 times greater than a mantle of pure thoria even when the temp. is 100° less.

A. H. White and co-workers determined the temp. existing in mantles and in the flame. They found that with 0·342 sq. in. as unit area,

	Thoria mantle.	Welsbach's mantle.
Temp. inside mantle.	1600°	1600°
Temp. outside mantle	1510°	1410°
Heat conveyed to unit area of mantle (cals. per hr.)	15790	15790
Heat conveyed from unit area of mantle (cals. per hr.)	14380	13170
Heat transformed by unit area of mantle (cals. per hr.)	1410	2620
Illumination per unit area (candles)	0·2	4·0

Otherwise, expressed, the difference in the energy transformed by the two mantles is 64×10^1 ergs per sec. per sq. cm., and the difference in the light emitted is 1·7 candle power per sq. cm. Taking the mechanical eq. of the light of a Hefner lamp to be $1·5 \times 10^5$ ergs per sec., then, if all the 64×10^5 ergs per sec. were converted into visible light, the difference in the candle power would be 37·2 per sq. cm. The observed difference is therefore only 4·5 per cent. of the theoretical. According to H. E. Ives and co-workers, the total luminous efficiency of the mantle is 2·6 per cent. when heated by Bunsen's flame. In opposition to H. le Chatelier and O. Boudouard, and W. Nernst and E. Bose, A. H. White and co-workers found that the illumination is not solely a function of temp. because Welsbach's, at a temp. of 1410°, has a greater illuminating power than the thoria mantle at a temp. of 100° higher. They conclude that the exceptional efficiency of Welsbach's mixture is due to a solid soln. of cerium oxide in thoria, and that it has the power of transforming the heat of the flame into light more economically than other substances yet known.

G. C. Schmidt made spectro-photometric investigations on mixtures of thoria and cerium oxide, at various temp. He observed that the higher the temp., the bluer becomes the light yielded by the thoria. A similar result was obtained with mixtures of the two oxides all the time the ceria is below 0·5 per cent. of cerium oxide ; when 0·5–1·5 of cerium oxide is present, the red rays and illuminating power increase ; but beyond that percentage, the colour approaches that of cerium oxide, and the illuminating power decreases. Hence, added A. H. White and co-workers, the solid soln. of thoria and cerium oxide acts by so transforming the energy that more blue and green rays and less red rays are emitted by the glowing mantle than by the open flame. This means that more flame-energy is transformed into light and less into heat than is the case with the ordinary flame.

No reason is offered why 0·5–1·5 per cent. of cerium oxide and no other proportion has so marked an effect in exciting the light emissivity of the mantle. R. L. Swan found that the catalytic effect of mixtures of thoria and ceria on electrolytic gas is greatest when about 1 per cent. of ceria is present. It is suggested that the ceria acts by increasing the electron emission of the thoria, causing a greater ionization of the gases and a more efficient combination. W. Muthmann and E. Baur have suggested that thoria can form a solid soln. with up to about 1 per cent. of cerium dioxide, but if higher proportions be present, the excess acts as a foreign element diminishing the light emissivity of the mantle. R. J. Meyer and A. Anschütz, however, said that the thoria is sat. only when about 7 per cent. of ceric oxide is present, but they have not decided whether this is a solubility equilibrium, or whether a chemical compound, $9ThO_2.CeO_2$, is formed. Hence, it is not probable that the homogeneity of the solid soln. is an essential condition for the special light emissivity characteristic of the mantle ; but, if part of the solid soln. is dissociated, it is possible that the maximum emissivity occurs with that concentration for which the soln. is completely dissociated. This hypothesis corresponds with that suggested by E. Goldstein, and P. Wäntig for the luminescence of certain substances exposed to the cathode rays. E. St. John could detect scarcely any signs of phosphorescence or fluorescence by the mantle.

Various forms of the physical theory of the *auer*, or *Welsbach's mantle*, or the *incandescent mantle* have been discussed by W. Gentsch, E. St. John, W. Krebs, C. Hohmann, O. Lummer and E. Pringsheim, H. Thiele, E. Baur, F. Bössner, J. Swinburne, J. Hofmann, C. E. Guillaume, E. Podszus, etc. A physical theory has been developed by H. Rubens and co-workers. He showed that owing to the low emissive power of a thoria mantle, it attains a comparatively high temp., while a mantle of ceric oxide has a comparatively low temp. owing to its high emissivity. This is illustrated by H. E. Ives and co-workers' observations, Fig. 6, on the relation between the temp. for maximum luminosity and radiation on mantles with different proportions of thoria and ceric oxide. Ceric oxide has a sharp absorption (emission) band in the visible spectrum, and the radiation of energy is so great that the temp. of a cerium oxide mantle is kept comparatively low. Starting then

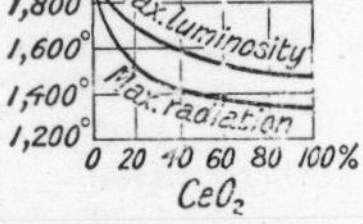

FIG. 6.—Relation between Composition and Temperature of Mantle.

with thoria, and introducing cerium oxide, the emission band broadens, and the total radiation increases, while the temp. is lowered. The maximum luminous efficiency is attained when the rise in the visible emission is balanced by the fall in temp. due to the increased radiation. R. L. Swan discussed this action. R. W. Wood, and H. E. Ives and co-workers gave a hydraulic analogy for the behaviour of the burner and mantle.

Imagine the mantle to be represented by a vertical cylindrical tank into which water is flowing at a constant rate from a tap (Fig. 7). Let the wall of the tank be perforated by holes of various sizes. The water which squirts out through these holes is the radiation, and the various sizes of holes represent various wave-lengths. If the smaller holes are more numerous at the top of the tank, then the higher the water rises the more will squirt out through the smaller holes, thus occupying the behaviour of a material radiator, water *height* being taken to represent *temperature*. If the tank contains many holes, the water will not rise very high, and, conversely. in one with only very few holes the water will rise higher, thus copying the behaviour of mantles of high and low emissive powers, in so far as their temp. characteristics are concerned. If the holes are all made small, only squirts of small size will be present, and the water will rise higher than if the holes of all sizes are present, thus copying the characteristics of a selective radiator like the mantle. In order for this tank to represent the behaviour of the mantle with respect to the amount of radiation, it is only necessary to imagine a vertical seam of the tank to have been left unsoldered, so that a bad leak is present, to represent the convection and conduction losses. The higher the water rises, as when the radiating holes are made in number, the more is lost through the leaky seam, and so the less is " radiated " through the holes. Obviously, with a constant rate of supply the advantage of increased " temperature " is being more and more offset by the leakage.

FIG. 7. — Hydraulic Analogy of Mantle and Burner.

REFERENCES.

[1] C. Clamond, *Brit. Pat. No.* 2110, 1880; 7990, 1887; 12091, 1889; 60, 1891; J. J. Berzelius, *Pogg. Ann.*, 16. 385, 1829; *Svenska Akad. Handl.*, 1, 1829; J. F. Bahr and R. Bunsen, *Liebig's Ann.*, 137. 11, 1866; M. Delafontaine, *Arch. Sciences Genève*, (2), 51. 45, 1874; G. Gurney, *A Course of Lectures on Chemical Science*, London, 1826; D. Brewster, *Edin Journ. Science*, 3. 343, 1820; T. Drummond, *ib.*, 5. 319, 1826; *Phil. Trans.*, 120. 383, 1830; W. H. F. Talbot, *Phil. Mag.*, (3), 7. 113, 1835; J. P. Gillard, *Brit. Pat. No.* 12858, 1849; V. B. Lewis, *Journ. Soc. Chem. Ind.*, 2. 235, 1883.

[2] C. A. von Welsbach, *Brit. Pat. Nos.* 15286, 1885; 3592, 9806, 1886; 6239,11195, 1887; *German Pat.*, *D.R.P.* 74745, 1891; *Chem. News*, 85. 255, 1902; E. St. John, *Wied. Ann.*, 56. 433, 1895; *Journ. Gasbeleucht.*, 49. 25, 1906; R. Moschelles, *Journ. Beleucht.*, 3. 102, 1897; J. Lux, *ib.*, 13. 246, 1907; A. H. White and H. Russell, *Amer. Journ. Gaslight.*, 74. 468, 1901; *Journ. Gaslight.*, 77. 878, 1901; A. H. White and A. F. Traver, *Journ. Soc. Chem. Ind.*, 21. 1012, 1902; *Journ. Gaslight.*, 79. 892, 1902; A. H. White, H. Russell, and A. F. Traver, *ib.*, 76 143, 1902; *Progressive Age*, 20. 106, 1902; O. N. Witt, *Ueber den Cergehalt der Thorsalze*, Berlin, 1897; *Chem. Ind.*, 17. 160, 1899; R. J. Meyer and A. Anschütz, *Ber.*, 40. 2639, 1907; W. Muthmann and E. Baur, *ib.*, 33. 2029, 1900; H. Thiele, *ib.*, 33. 186, 1900; E. Hintz, *Zeit. anal. Chem.*, 37. 504, 1898; *Ueber Gasglühlicht*, Wiesbaden, 1899; E. Baur, *Zeit. angew. Chem.*, 13. 1055, 1900; E. Glinzer, *ib.*, 8. 185, 1895; F. Bössner, *Zeit. Œster. Ing. Arch. Ver.*, 401, 1901; C. E. Guillaume, *Rev. Sciences*, 12. 358, 422, 1901; J. Swinburne, *Journ. Gaslight.*, 95. 523, 1906; V. B. Lewes, *ib.*, 89. 160, 1905; *Chem. News.*, 91. 62, 1905; E. Goldstein, *Sitzber. Akad. Berlin*, 818, 1900; L. C. Andes, *Das Gasglühlicht und die Herstellung der Glühstrümpfe*, Leipzig, 1902; C. R. Böhm, *Das Gasglühlicht seine Geschichte, Herstellung, und Anwendung*, Leipzig, 1905; *Das Gaslühlicht*, Leipzig, 1904; L. Castellani, *Das Gasglühlicht—Die Fabrikation der Glühretze*, Wien, 1901: H. W. Fischer, *Der Auerstrumpf*, Stuttgart, 1906; G. Hartwig, *Das Gasglühlicht*, Dresden, 1894; G. Kern, *Le bec auer*, Strassburg, 1899; P. Wäntig, *Zeit. phys. Chem.*, 51, 435, 1905; V. Loos, *Allgem. Ing. Ztg.*, 245, 1901; M. M. Merle, *Monit. Scient.*, (4), 11. 257, 1897; M. Rubner, *Arch. Hyg.*, 23. 193, 1895; *Hyg. Runds.*, 5. 193, 1895; H. E. Ives, E. F. Kingsbury, and E. Karrer, *Journ. Franklin Inst.*, 186. 401, 585, 1918; R. W. Wood, *Phys. Rev.*, (1), 24. 437, 1907; H. Bunte, *ib.*, 31. 5, 1898; *Zeit. angew. Chem.*, 11. 844, 1898; *Dingler's Journ.*, 306. 143, 1897; *Journ. Gasbeleucht.*, 38. 449, 451, 1895; H. Bunte and H. Luggin, *ib.*, 44. 411, 1901; C. Killing, *ib.*, 39. 697, 1896; 40. 339, 1897; 46. 450, 1903; 50. 90, 1907; E. Glinzer, *ib.*, 36. 310, 1893; E. St. C. Deville, *ib.*, 47. 21, 46, 75, 90, 95, 1904; F. Westphal, *ib.*, 88. 363, 1895; W. Krebs, *ib.*, 40. 552, 1897; C. Hohmann, *ib.*, 40. 456, 1897; W. Wedding, *ib.*, 38. 49, 466, 599, 705, 1895; F. Joly, *ib.*, 39. 602, 1896; H. Drehschmidt, *ib.*, 49. 765, 1903; M. Söhren, *ib.*, 39. 545, 561, 577, 1896; O Lummer, *ib.*, 40. 662, 1897; G. P. Drossbach, *ib.*, 40. 174, 1897; 41. 352, 1898; 44. 819, 1901; S. P. Langley, *Ann. Astrophys. Obs.*, 1. 240, 1900;

A. A. C. Swinton, *Proc. Roy. Soc.*, 65. 117, 1899 ; H. E. Armstrong, *ib.*, 70. 99, 1902 ; H. E. Armstrong and T. M. Lowry, *ib.*, 72. 258, 1903 ; R. L. Swan, *Journ. Chem. Soc.*, 125. 780, 1924; G. C. Schmidt, *Verh. deut. phys. Ges.*, 10. 14, 1898 ; W. MacKean, *Journ. Soc. Chem. Ind.*, 10. 196, 1891 ; A. Foix, *Compt. Rend.*, 144. 685, 1907 ; H. le Chatelier and O. Boudouard, *ib.*, 126. 1861, 1898 ; C. Féry, *Ann. Chim. Phys.*, (7), 27. 433, 1902 ; H. Rubens and E. Ladenburg, *Ber. deut. phys. Ges.*, 7. 171, 1905 ; H. Rubens, *Wied. Ann.*, 69. 576, 1899 ; *Ann. Physik*, (4), 18. 738, 1905 ; (4), 20. 600, 1906 ; O. Lummer and E. Pringsheim, *Phys. Zeit.*, 7. 89, 189, 1905 ; W. Nernst and E. Bose, *ib.*, 1. 289, 1900 ; F. Haber and F. Richardt, *Zeit. anorg. Chem.*, 38. 60, 1904 ; G. von Knorre, *Sitzber. Ver. Gewerbfl.*, 75. 156, 1896 ; H. von Oechelhäuser, *ib.*, 71. 276, 1892 ; W. Gentsch, *ib.*, 78. 57, 101, 141, 210, 225, 1899 ; *Gasglühlicht. Dessen Geschichte, Wesen, und Wirkung*, Stuttgart, 1895 ; H. D. Griffith, *Phil. Mag.*, (6), 50. 263, 1925 ; J. Hofmann, *Ueber das Emission von Oxyden*, Erlangen, 1904 ; E. Podszus, *Zeit. Physik*, 18. 212, 1923.

§ 6. Thorium Oxides and Hydroxides

According to J. R. Rydberg,[1] thorium furnishes only one oxide—*viz.* **thorium dioxide**, ThO_2, or **thoria**. J. Locke reported *thorium pentatritaoxide*, Th_3O_5, but H. P. Stevens regards this as one of the condensed or polymerized oxides classed as one of *meta-oxides* of G. Wyrouboff. According to G. Krüss, *thorium monoxide*, ThO, is not formed when thorium oxysulphide, $ThOS$, is heated to a red or white heat in a stream of hydrogen. G. P. Drossbach, and W. Bruno obtained what has been called *thorium peroxide*, Th_2O_7. There are also thorium hydroxide, $Th(OH)_4$, and a number of colloidal forms, as well as hydrated peroxides.

Thorium dioxide occurs associated with uranium dioxide as the mineral thorianite (*q.v.*). The amorphous oxide is obtained by heating the metal in air or in oxygen, or by oxidizing the metal with molten potassium chlorate. It is also produced when the hydroxide or various salts with the volatile oxyacids are calcined. J. F. Bahr,[2] and A. E. Nordenskjöld and J. J. Chydenius made crystals of the dioxide by heating the amorphous oxide with borax in a pottery oven ; L. Troost and L. Ouvrard, by heating the dioxide with molten potassium orthophosphate ; and A. Duboin, by melting thorium fluoride with sodium carbonate, or by melting a mixture of thorium dioxide, sodium fluoride, and sodium carbonate.

The amorphous oxide is a snow-white powder. O. Hahn studied the surface area of the particles of precipitated thoria in terms of adsorbed radioactive matter. The **crystals** obtained by the borax fusion were stated by A. E. Nordenskjöld to be tetragonal, and isomorphous with rutile and cassiterite ; while those obtained by the phosphate fusion were stated by L. Troost and L. Ouvrard to be octahedra belonging to the cubic system. A. Duboin said that the crystals he obtained were similar to those of thorium fluoride. G. Wyrouboff said that the crystals of thoria are isomorphous with those of cerium dioxide, and those of calcium or strontium monoxide. V. M. Goldschmidt and L. Thomassen, M. L. Huggins, A. E. van Arkel, and W. P. Davey studied the **X-radiogram** of thoria. The side of the elementary cube is $5·61 \times 10^{-8}$ cm., and there are 4 mols. per cube. G. R. Levi found that the precipitated hydroxide dried at temp. up to 340° is amorphous; but the oxide obtained by heating the hydroxide to 1050°, or the nitrate or oxalate to 750°, is crystalline with the same X-radiogram in all cases. J. J. Berzelius gave 9·402 for the **specific gravity** of the crystals ; A. Damour, 9·366 ; J. J. Chydenius, 9·228 ; J. F. Bahr, 9·77 ; A. E. Nordenskjöld, 9·21 ; C. Baskerville, 9·188–9·380 at 4° ; L. F. Nilson, 10·220 at 17° ; L. Troost and L. Ouvrard, 9·876 at 15° ; and B. Brauner, 9·690 at 20°/4°. According to L. F. Nilson and O. Pettersson, the deviations in the value of this constant are due to entrained air or moisture, and to the presence of impurities in the oxide. G. von Hevesy studied the mol. vol. of the oxides of this family of elements. L. F. Nilson and O. Pettersson gave 0·0548 for the **specific heat** of the oxide between 0° and 100°. The mol. ht. runs parallel with those of zirconium ; cerium ; titanium, tin, and manganese dioxides. G. B. Pegram and H. Webb found that owing to its radioactivity, a gram of thoria develops $9·60 \times 10^{-6}$ cal. per hour—*vide* the radioactivity of thorium.

E. Tiede and E. Birnbrauer said that the **melting point** approximates to 2000°, and the oxide at the same time volatilizes. O. Ruff and co-workers gave 2440° for the m.p. H. C. Greenwood observed no signs of the dissociation of thoria at high temp. F. Born estimated thoria to be dissociated into metal and oxygen to the extent of 10^{-27} at 2000°, and 6×10^{-6} at 3000°. W. R. Mott gave 4400° for the **boiling point** of thoria. H. von Wartenberg gave for the **heat of formation** from thorium, 326·0 Cals. with an error of ±0·5 per cent. C. A. Matignon said that the heat developed by the union is 42·8 Cals. per gram-atom of oxygen.

When purified thoria is strongly heated, it emits a pale blue light of feeble **illuminating power,** but if the thoria be mixed with one per cent. of cerium oxide, a brilliant light is emitted. Such a mixture is used in making the well-known incandescent mantles—*vide supra.* C. Féry found that in an oxidizing flame, the colour of the emitted light has a rose tint, and in the reducing flame, at the same temp., the light has a greenish tint. B. Monasch employed a thoria preparation as cathode in an arc-lamp. W. E. Forsythe measured the emissivity of thorium oxide for $\lambda = 0.665\mu$, and found 0·15 at 1800° K., and 0·4 at 1400° K. K. Teucke examined the radiation emitted when thoria is bombarded by cathode rays. W. W. Coblentz found the **ultra-red emission spectrum** has no marked emission bands, and the whole spectrum is suppressed up to 7μ; after which, as found by H. Rubens, the emissivity approaches that of a complete radiator. H. Schmidt-Reps studied the ultra-red emissivity of thoria. The **reflecting power** of thorium oxide, for light of wave-length 0.60μ, was found by W. W. Coblentz to be 86·1 per cent.; for light of wave-length $\lambda = 4.4\mu$, 46·9 per cent.; for $\lambda = 8.8\mu$, 7·11 per cent.; and for $\lambda = 24\mu$, 10 per cent. N. Ahmad measured the absorption of γ-rays by thoria. E. L. Nichols and D. T. Wilber, and W. Crookes found that when thoria is exposed to the **cathode rays,** it exhibits a feeble phosphorescence, so also in **ultra-violet light.** Thoriferous minerals, according to C. Baskerville, do not exhibit fluorescence or phosphorescence. A. Karl observed that thoria shows **triboluminescence.** E. L. Nichols and H. L. Howes found there is not a luminescent spectrum with the incandescent oxide. O. Hahn studied the emanating powers of thorium oxide and hydroxide prepared in different ways; and H. J. Spanner, the thermionic emission of electrically charged particles. L. F. Nilson and O. Pettersson, and K. A. Angström found that thorium dioxide is diamagnetic; and W. Gerlach studied the behaviour of thorium in a magnetic field.

According to W. Crookes,[3] thoria is hygroscopic and absorbs **gases** with some avidity; W. Biltz found that it is difficult to obtain a constant weight by calcination owing to the absorption of **moisture.** R. J. Meyer and A. Gumperz found that when calcined at a high temp. the oxide is less sensitive than when calcined at a lower temp. According to H. E. Ives and co-workers, when white thoria is calcined in a quartz tube heated by Bunsen's flame, no change in colour is perceptible. According to R. J. Meyer and A. Anschütz, if a mixed soln. of thorium and cerium nitrates be evaporated to dryness and ignited about 7 per cent. of the ceric oxide forms a solid soln. with the thoria. E. Newbery and J. N. Pring found that the dioxide is not reduced by **hydrogen** at 2000° and 150 atm. press. H. von Wartenberg and co-workers discussed the reduction of thoria by hydrogen under press., and found that it can be reduced by hydrogen in the presence of another metal —*e.g.* tungsten. At 1250°, tungsten dissolved 0·07 per cent. thorium, and at 2000°, 0·24 per cent. J. J. Berzelius and J. J. Chydenius found that strongly ignited thoria does not dissolve in **nitric or hydrochloric acid,** but N. J. Berlin, and G. Wyrouboff and A. Verneuil found that if the oxide, prepared by heating to redness the oxalate, nitrate, chloride, or hydroxide, be repeatedly evaporated with small quantities of these acids, a mass is formed which dissolves in water, forming an opalescent soln. resembling the so-called meta-oxides of zirconium and tin (ic). V. I. Spitzin found the solubility of thoria expressed in mgrm. ThO_2 per litre at 25° to be : N-H_2SO_4, 2·0; N-HNO_3, 0·6; N-HCl, 0·5; $0.8N$-$C_4H_6O_4$, 0·3; N-NaOH, less than 0·05; N-Na_2CO_3, less than 0·03; N-K_2CO_3, less than 0·02; and in water, less than 0·02. The solubility of thoria in salt soln. is small, but greater in sulphates than in chlorides. According to J. J. Berzelius, and J. J. Chydenius, when thoria is heated with **sulphuric acid,** it is slowly converted into the sulphate ; T. Sollmann and E. D. Brown made some observations on the solubility of thoria in this acid ; and they found that when thoria is fused with **sodium hydrosulphate,** the mass obtained is soluble in water. T. Hiortdahl found that no carbon dioxide is evolved when thoria is fused with **sodium carbonate ;** and J. J. Berzelius said that thoria does not become soluble in hydrochloric or nitric acid after it has been fused with **alkali hydroxides.** C. J. Smithells found that thoria is reduced to thorium by metallic **tungsten.**

J. J. Berzelius was not able to obtain the metal by the action of **carbon** or **potassium** on thoria, and H. C. Greenwood found that at 1600° in an evacuated atm., thorium carbide is formed. B. du Jassonneix obtained thorium boride by heating thoria with **boron** in an electric furnace ; and O. Hönigschmid, thorium silicide by heating thoria with **silicon.** When heated in **carbon tetrachloride,** a mixture of chlorine and **sulphur chloride,** a mixture of carbon monoxide and chlorine, **carbonyl chloride,** or **phosphorus pentachloride,** thorium chloride is formed—*vide* the chloride.

Ignited thoria has been used as a **catalytic agent** in many reactions. H. B. Baker found that it ionizes many gases, and accelerates the reaction between nitric oxide and moderately dried hydrogen ; but with thoroughly dried hydrogen there is no measurable change with 5 mins.' heating at 530°. L. and P. Wöhler and W. Plüddemann observed that it accelerates the oxidation of sulphur dioxide by oxygen. P. Sabatier and A. Mailhe observed that if an alcohol be passed over thoria at 300°–350°, the alcohol is decomposed in the same way that it would be by sulphuric acid to form olefines and water ; but if the temp. be kept low, an ether is formed ; A. Mailhe found that the vap. of esters are decomposed by heated thoria, forming ethers, olefines, primary alcohols, and carbon dioxide ; and he found that when a mixture of ammonia and alcohol vap. is passed over thoria at 380°, the main product is a primary amine, but some secondary and tertiary amines are also formed. J. B. Senderens, and R. H. Pickard and J. Kenyon obtained good yields of ketones by passing a mixture of the vap. of two organic acids over heated thoria. S. Medsforth examined the effect of thoria on nickel as a catalyst in the reduction of carbon monoxide and dioxide by hydrogen. J. Aloy and C. Rabaut found that the presence of thoria inhibits the saponification of benzoylated cyanhydrins by acetic acid. G. R. Levi, S. Komatsu and B. Masumoto, E. Sabatier and A. Mailhe, and J. N. Pearce and A. M. Alvarado studied the catalytic action of thoria on ethyl acetate, and on the dehydration of alcohol; and W. W. Russell and H. S. Taylor, on the hydrogenation of carbon dioxide.

According to J. J. Berzelius,[4] and P. T. Cleve, **thorium hydroxide,** $Th(OH)_4$, or $ThO_2.2H_2O$, is precipitated quantitatively from a soln. of thorium sulphate when alkali hydroxide or ammonia is added. The gelatinous precipitate is well washed, and when dried over sulphuric acid, it furnishes a white powder. When alkali hydroxide is employed, the precipitant is retained very tenaciously, and T. Sollmann and E. D. Brown found that nine times washing by a centrifuge are needed to furnish a liquid neutral to litmus. G. Krüss and W. Palmaer preferred to agitate solid thorium sulphate with warm aq. ammonia, and boil the resulting powder with dil. ammonia. The product was washed with water free from sulphates. Several other precipitating agents give the hydroxide—*e.g.* C. Baskerville, and H. Erdmann used sodium nitrite ; P. Jannasch and J. Schilling, hydroxylamine ; and L. M. Dennis and F. L. Kortright, potassium azide. F. J. Metzger boiled thorium thiosulphate or oxalate with potassium hydroxide. O. Angelucci noticed that thorium hydroxide is precipitated on the anode when a soln. of thorium nitrate is electrolyzed. H. T. S. Britton studied the electometric precipitation of the hydroxide. Sodium acetate yields a precipitate with thorium sulphate soln. when the acidity has attained the value $p_H=3.4$ obtained by adding 10 c.c. of sodium acetate soln., and with 25 c.c. the precipitation was a maximum, while with 30 c.c. of soln. the precipitate—chiefly basic sulphate—

dissolved. No precipitation occurred with thorium chloride soln., though F. Haler obtained one by boiling a soln. of the chloride with sodium acetate. With sodium tartrate, precipitation from soln. of thorium chloride began when the acidity had attained the value $p_H=1.75$. The precipitate consisted of basic tartrate.

P. T. Cleve's analysis of the product dried at 100° corresponds very nearly with $ThO_2.2H_2O$. As J. J. Berzelius, and G. Krüss and W. Palmaer have emphasized, the hydroxide readily absorbs carbon dioxide from the air; and accordingly in some cases, the analyzed hydroxides have been contaminated with some carbonate. G. Wyrouboff and A. Verneuil treated a soln. of thorium chloride with aq. ammonia; the washed product was dried over potassium hydroxide until the weight was constant. All the operations were conducted in the cold. The composition corresponded with $ThO_2.5H_2O$, or the *trihydrate*, $Th(OH)_4.3H_2O$; if dried at 130°, 8·8 per cent. of water was lost, and the product approximated $ThO_2.2·8H_2O$, say the *monohydrate* $Th(OH)_4.H_2O$. The hydroxide loses all its water when calcined at a white-heat. T. Sollmann and E. D. Brown said that the hydroxide is insoluble in water, but prolonged washing with water may peptize the hydroxide. H. A. McTaggart found that a small conc. of colloidal thorium hydroxide suspended in water imparts a positive electric charge to a sphere of immersed air (with water alone, the charge is always negative). There is a reversal in the sign of the charge as the size of the bubble of air decreases. According to P. T. Cleve, the hydroxide is not soluble in soln. of the alkali hydroxides, or in an aq. soln. of ammonia. The moist hydroxide, said J. J. Berzelius, dissolves quickly in acids, but the dried hydroxide dissolves rather slowly. According to T. Sollmann and E. D. Brown, the hydroxide dissolves quickly in conc. hydrochloric acid, and slowly in the dil. acid; the speed of dissolution is increased by raising the temp., but decreased if the washing of the hydroxide has been prolonged, or if the hydroxide has been allowed to stand for some time; but if the precipitated hydroxide be boiled in water or if it has stood for 15 hrs. at 100°, the solubility is not diminished. L. Pissarjewsky gave 29·893 Cals. for the heat of soln. of moist thorium hydroxide in nitric acid. P. T. Cleve found the moist hydroxide dissolves in bromine-water; and J. F. Bahr showed that if chlorine be passed through water in which the hydroxide is suspended, part of the latter is dissolved; and the undissolved portion dissolves in water. H. Grossmann noted that a little thorium hydroxide dissolves in sulphurous acid, and is re-precipitated on boiling the soln. Thorium hydroxide was found by T. Sollmann and E. D. Brown to be less soluble in citric acid and in tartaric acid than it is in hydrochloric acid; and to be soluble in a soln. of sodium chloride, sodium citrate, potassium sodium tartrate or ammonium oxalate. J. J. Chydenius said that it is insoluble in oxalic acid, molybdic acid, or hydrofluoric acid, but is transformed by these acids into the corresponding salts. According to K. C. Sen and N. R. Dhar, thorium hydroxide is not precipitated by alkali hydroxide from soln. of thorium salts in the presence of sugars, dextrin, starch, or glycerol, presumably owing to the peptization of the hydroxide. N. G. Chatterji and N. R. Dhar also investigated this subject. J. Böhm and H. Niclassen studied the crystallization of the amorphous hydroxide.

N. J. Berlin [5] reported that thorium dioxide, prepared by the gentle ignition of the oxalate or hydroxide, behaves in a peculiar way towards hydrochloric acid for, if repeatedly evaporated with a small quantity of hydrochloric or nitric acid, the syrupy liquid which is formed dissolves in water to form an opalescent soln. which may be coagulated by acids or salts. J. F. Bahr, and P. T. Cleve made thorium dioxide possessing these qualities by calcining the oxalate; H. P. Stevens, by calcining the nitrate; G. Wyrouboff and A. Verneuil, by calcining the hydroxide; and J. Locke, by heating thorium dioxide in a stream of hydrogen. J. Locke regarded the product as **thorium meta-oxide,** Th_3O_5, but H. P. Stevens, showed that the oxide has the same composition as ordinary thoria, $(ThO_2)_n$; and G. R. Levi, that the X-ray examination disproves the assumption that the meta-oxide is a distinct variety. G. Wyrouboff and A. Verneuil regarded the products as well-defined meta-oxides and not mixtures; and regarded them as *condensed oxides* of different degrees of polymerization; the condensation is necessarily accompanied by a change in the valency of the oxide. J. Locke's analysis showed the presence of water, but G. Wyrouboff and A. Verneuil, and H. P. Stevens showed that the water was derived from the incompletely dried gas, for the product is very hygroscopic. H. P. Stevens found that the weight of a gram of the oxide increased 2 per cent. when allowed to stand in the balance case for 5 mins. J. Locke gave 8·733 for the sp. gr. at 15°. G. Wyrouboff and A. Verneuil showed that the less condensed oxide, or rather the oxide which has been calcined at a relatively low temp., dissolves completely in hydrochloric acid or nitric acid when the mixture is heated to 120° in a sealed tube. The normal chloride or nitrate is formed ; and they added that if the calcination be carried too far, *i.e.* if the oxide be condensed too much, it loses the faculty of uniting with the acids. When the meta-oxide is heated with not too dil. sulphuric acid, the normal sulphate is formed. E. Chauvenet prepared soluble addition compounds with a number of acids. If one of these salts—*e.g.* thorium meta-oxychloride—be treated with aq. ammonia, **thorium metahydroxide** is produced. It resembles ordinary thorium hydroxide in appearance. Its composition $ThO_2 : H_2O$ is indefinite—presumably on account of its colloidal nature. H. P. Stevens compared it with metastannic acid, and called it *metathoric acid ;* and he also called ordinary thorium hydroxide, *thoric acid.* He said that unlike normal thorium hydroxide, thorium metahydroxide does not absorb carbon dioxide from the air, and is less basic. It is gradually converted into thorium hydroxide when allowed to remain in contact with water, and it dissolves in mineral acids if an excess of acid is carefully avoided. When prepared from a meta-oxychloride rich in chlorine, it requires more acid for dissolution than when prepared from a compound poor in chlorine, and a soln. of meta-oxychloride requires more acid to precipitate it as the percentage of chlorine increases.

The least polymerized form of the meta-hydroxide was stated by G. Wyrouboff and A. Verneuil to be somewhat impure ; it is not stable, and begins to polymerize at 110° with the elimination of water, and approximates closer and closer to $6ThO_2.H_2O$. It is insoluble in hydrochloric or nitric acid, but forms compounds with these acids with the evolution of much heat. The products are then said to be soluble in water. If these compounds are dried, and treated with ammonia, they lose the acid radicle, and form a horn-like mass. According to G. Wyrouboff and A. Verneuil, the hydroxide, $6ThO_2.H_2O$, is precipitated by treating the more condensed form of the meta-oxychloride or meta-oxynitrate with ammonia. They gave the formula $12ThO.H_2O$ in accord with their view that thorium is bivalent. P. T. Cleve obtained $4ThO_2.H_2O$ by treating a colloidal soln. of thorium hydroxide with ammonia. J. Locke obtained $3ThO_2.2H_2O$, which he represented as $Th_3O_5.2H_2O$, by evaporating the meta-oxide to dryness with hydrochloric acid, dissolving the residue in hot water, and treating it with ammonia. When dried at 100°, it loses a mol. of water and furnishes $3ThO_2.H_2O$, which is also obtained by treating the meta-oxide with hydrochloric acid. G. Wyrouboff and A. Verneuil also reported $2ThO_2.H_2O$; and $8ThO_2.9H_2O$. The latter was produced by treating $Th_{16}O_7(OH)_{16}Cl_2.2HCl$, solid or soln., with ammonia and drying to constant weight over potassium hydroxide.

Opalescent liquids were obtained by J. F. Bahr, P. T. Cleve, G. Wyrouboff and A. Verneuil, etc., by evaporating to dryness a mixture of hydrochloric or nitric acid and thorium meta-oxide and taking up the mass with water. The sol. is **colloidal thorium oxide or hydroxide.** It is not flocculated by heat, but is coagulated by acids and many other salts ; and the colloid is peptized when the salts are removed by water. W. Biltz and co-workers [6] dialyzed dil. aq. soln. of thorium nitrate, which on evaporation yielded a gum-like mass insoluble in water. The hydrosol has a positive charge, and when the suspension in water is electrolyzed, it migrates to the cathode. O. Hauser and F. Wirth obtained a flocculent hydrogel by boiling a very dil. aq. soln. of thorium sulphate. A. Müller prepared a conc. hydrosol of thorium hydroxide by thoroughly washing the hydrogel from 20 grms. of thorium nitrate, and boiling it with water containing 10 grms. of the nitrate per 50 c.c. Colloidal forms were also described by E. Stiasny, I. Kreidl and G. Heller, and J. Duclaux. B. Szilard prepared colloidal thorium hydroxide, free from electrolytes.

by decomposing thorium nitrate with excess of dil. ammonia and washing the residue until free from ammonia, which takes three to six days. The product is a fine, milky suspension, in which the particles cannot be separated either by filtration or decantation; it is precipitated by electrolytes and by the carbon dioxide of the air. He also made colloidal thorium hydroxide, containing a little electrolyte, by adding precipitated thorium hydroxide to thorium tetrachloride so long as the former is dissolved. This soln. is much more stable than that free from electrolytes, is not affected by light or by boiling, and is not precipitated by small quantities of electrolytes or by weak acids. K. C. Sen and N. R. Dhar studied the peptization of colloidal thorium hydroxide by soln. of sugars, starch, glycerol, and dextrin. According to F. Haber, the hydrogel shows a feeble X-radiogram which is regarded as evidence of crystallinity. J. Böhm and H. Niclassen found that X-radiograms of the dried soln. were characteristic of amorphous substances, and that on ageing becomes crystalline. H. Rheinboldt and E. Wedekind studied the adsorption of dyes by the colloid.

L. de Boisbaudran,[7] P. T. Cleve, L. Pissarjewsky, and G. Wyrouboff and A. Verneuil obtained what was called **thorium peroxide** by treating a cold soln. of a thorium salt with ammonia and hydrogen dioxide. L. Pissarjewsky also obtained a similar product by treating thorium hydroxide with hydrogen peroxide; and W. Bruno, by treating a conc. soln. of a thorium salt at 60° with 30 per cent. hydrogen dioxide. According to L. Pissarjewsky, the white gelatinous precipitate is a hydrated thorium peroxide derived from the hypothetical **thorium hemiheptoxide**, Th_2O_7. It is assumed that hydrogen dioxide is a monobasic acid which reacts with thorium hydroxide, forming **thorium tetrahydroperoxide**, $Th(O_2H)_4$; and that this compound hydrolyzes in stages furnishing **thorium dihydroperoxide**, $Th(O_2H)_2(OH)_2$, and **thorium monohydroperoxide**, $Th(O_2H)(OH)_3$. The last-named product is considered to be a hydrated form of *thorium trioxide*, namely, $ThO_3.2H_2O$. G. Wyrouboff and A. Verneuil do not agree with L. Pissarjewsky's interpretation of these reactions, and believe that a complex mol. is formed containing peroxidized oxygen, hydroxyl radicles, and an acid residue. Thorium tetrahydroperoxide is very unstable, and slowly loses oxygen, passing into the hydrated trioxide, which is much more stable. When heated, it loses oxygen. When the hydrated hemiheptoxide is kept under water free from carbon dioxide, or on a porous tile over sulphuric acid, and soda-lime, it gradually reverts to thorium dioxide. The heat of neutralization $Th(OH)_4 + H_2O_2$ is 8·810 Cals.; the heat of soln. of $\frac{1}{2}Th_2O_7$ in dil. nitric acid is 17·184 Cals. When treated with dil. sulphuric acid, hydrogen dioxide is formed, and with conc. sulphuric acid, ozonized oxygen is evolved. The precipitate obtained by the action of hydrogen dioxide and ammonia is a mixture of the different products of the hydrolysis of the hemiheptoxide. L. Pissarjewsky also made the monohydroperoxide by the action of soln. of sodium hypochlorite on thorium hydroxide; by the action of chlorine on a suspension of thorium hydroxide in $2N$-sodium hydroxide; and by the anodic oxidation of a suspension of thorium hydroxide in an alkaline soln. of sodium chloride. L. Pissarjewsky found that the monohydroperoxide behaves towards dil. and conc. sulphuric acid like the tetrahydroperoxide, and he gives for the heat of formation of $ThO_2.nH_2O + O = ThO_3.nH_2O$ $-14·290$ Cals. The monohydroperoxide showed no signs of decomposition after keeping 24 hrs. According to G. P. Drossbach, when a thorium salt soln. is treated with anodic oxygen; or with hydrogen dioxide; or shaken with air, and the soln. evaporated, the product contains more oxygen than corresponds with thorium dioxide. If heated, or treated with strong acids, the excess oxygen is given off by the peroxidized salt.

REFERENCES.

[1] J. R. Rydberg, *Œfvers. Akad. Förh.*, 69, 1885; G. Krüss, *Zeit. anorg. Chem.*, 6. 55, 1894; H. P. Stevens, *ib.*, 27. 47, 1901; G. Wyrouboff, *ib.*, 28. 90, 1901; J. Locke, *ib.*, 7. 347, 1894; G. P. Drossbach, *Zeit. angew. Chem.*, 19. 1427, 1906; W. Bruno, *ib.*, 10. 1389, 1906.

[2] J. F. Bahr. *Œfvers. Svenska Akad. Förh.*, 415, 1862 ; *Chem. News*, 8. 175, 185, 1864; *Pogg. Ann.*, 119. 572, 1863 ; A. E. Nordenskjöld and J. J. Chydenius, *ib.*, 110. 642, 1860 ; *Œfvers. Svenska Akad. Förh.*, 3, 1860 ; L. Troost and L. Ouvrard, *Ann. Chim. Phys.*, (6), 17. 237, 1889 ; A. Duboin, *ib.*, (8), 17. 356, 1909 ; *Compt. Rend.*, 146. 490, 1908 ; A. Karl, *ib.*, 146. 1104, 1908 ; W. Crookes, *ib.*, 92. 1281, 1881 ; *Proc. Roy. Soc.*, 32. 209, 1881 ; *Chem. News*, 43. 237, 1881 ; *Ann. Chim. Phys.*, (5), 23. 555, 1881 ; C. Féry, *ib.*, (7), 27. 433, 1902 ; C. A. Matignon, *Monit. Scient.*, (4), 14. 353, 1900 ; A. E. Nordenskjöld, *Pogg. Ann.*, 110. 642, 1860 ; 114. 625, 1861 ; 150. 219, 1873 ; C. B. Pegram and H. Webb, *Le Radium*, 5. 271, 1908 ; B. Monasch, *Journ. Gasbeleucht.*, 1122, 1910 ; G. Wyrouboff, *Bull. Soc. Min.*, 28. 233, 1905 ; A. Damour, *ib.*, 1. 32, 1878 ; *Compt. Rend.*, 34. 685, 1852 ; *Ann. Mines*, (4), 5. 587, 1852 ; J. J. Berzelius, *Svenska Akad. Handl.*, 1, 1829 ; *Pogg. Ann.*, 16. 385, 1829 ; J. J. Chydenius, *ib.*, 119. 43, 1863 ; *Kemisk Undersökning af Thorjord och Thorsalter*, Helsingfors, 1861 ; H. von Wartenberg, *Zeit. Elektrochem.*, 15. 869, 1909 ; B. Brauner, *Journ. Chem. Soc.*, 73. 951, 1898 ; W. W. Coblentz, *Investigations of Infra-red Spectra*, Washington, 7. 112, 1908 ; *Journ. Franklin Inst.*, 174. 549, 1912 ; H. Rubens, *Phys. Zeit.*, 6. 790, 1905 ; K. Teucke, *ib.*, 25. 115, 1924 ; E. L. Nichols and D. T. Wilber, *Phys. Rev.*, (2), 17. 707, 1921 ; M. L. Huggins, *ib.*, (2), 21. 719, 1923 ; W. E. Forsythe, *ib.*, (2), 25. 252, 1925 ; N. Ahmad, *Proc. Roy. Soc.*, 105. A, 507, 1924 ; E. L. Nichols and H. L. Howes, *Phys. Rev.*, (2), 19. 300, 1922 ; W. R. Mott, *Trans. Amer. Electrochem. Soc.*, 34. 255, 1918 ; C. Baskerville, *Journ. Amer. Chem. Soc.*, 23. 761, 1901 ; 26. 922, 1904 ; *Chem. News*, 88. 263, 1904 ; V. M. Goldsıhmidt and L. Thomassen, *Die Krystallatruktur natürlicher und synthetischer Oxyde von Uran, Thorium und Cerium*, Kristianiä, 1923 ; L. F. Nilson, *Œfvers. Akad. Förh.*, 39. 7, 1882 ; *Ber.*, 15. 2536, 1882 ; L. F. Nilson and O. Pettersson, *ib.*, 13. 1459, 1880 ; *Compt. Rend.*, 91. 232, 1880 ; *Œfvers. Akad. Förh.*, 37. 1, 1880 ; E. Tiede and E. Birnbrauer, *Zeit. anorg. Chem.*, 87. 129, 1914 ; O. Ruff, H. Seiferheld, and J. Suda, *ib.*, 82. 373, 1913 ; O. Ruff and G. Lauschke, *ib.*, 97. 73, 1916 ; O. Hahn, *Zeit. Elektrochem.*, 29. 189, 1923 ; O. Ruff, *ib.*, 30. 356, 1924 ; F. Born, *ib.*, 31. 309, 1925 ; S. Medsforth, *Journ. Chem. Soc.*, 123. 1452, 1923 ; W. P. Davey, *Phys. Rev.*, (2), 23. 763, 1924 ; K. A. Angström, *Ber.*, 13. 1465, 1880 ; H. C. Greenwood, *Journ. Chem. Soc.*, 93. 1483, 1908 ; A. E. van Arkel, *Physica*, 4. 286, 1924 ; 5. 162, 1925 ; H. J. Spanner, *Ann. Physik*, (4), 75. 609, 1924 ; W. Gerlach, *ib.*, (4), 76. 163, 1925 ; *Phys. Zeit.*, 25. 618, 1924 ; G. von Hevesy, *Zeit. anorg. Chem.*, 147. 217, 1925 ; G. R. Levi, *Atti Accad. Lincei*, (6), 2. ii, 419, 1925 ; H. Schmidt-Reps, *Zeit. tech. Physik.*, 6. 322, 1925.

[3] W. Crookes, *Proc. Roy. Soc.*, 32. 209, 1881 ; *Compt. Rend.*, 92. 1281, 1881 ; *Ann. Chim. Phys.*, (5), 23. 555, 1881 ; *Chem. News*, 43. 237, 1881 ; H. B. Baker, *ib.*, 99. 126, 1909 ; H. E. Ives, E. F. Kingsbury, and E. Karrer, *Journ. Franklin. Inst.*, 186. 401, 585, 1918 ; C. J. Smithells, *Journ. Chem. Soc.*, 121. 2236, 1922 ; R. J. Meyer and A. Gumperz, *Ber.*, 38. 820, 1905 ; R. J. Meyer and A. Anschütz, *ib.*, 40. 2639, 1907 ; H. C. Greenwood, *Journ. Chem. Soc.*, 93. 1483, 1908 ; R. H. Pickard and J. Kenyon, *ib.*, 103. 1923, 1913 ; B. du Jassonneix, *Bull. Soc. Chim.*, (3), 35. 278, 1906 ; *Compt. Rend.*, 141. 191, 1905 ; O. Hönigschmid, *ib.*, 142. 157 1906 ; G. Wyrouboff and A. Verneuil, *ib.*, 127. 865, 1898 ; T. Hiortdahl, *ib.*, 61. 176, 1865 ; J. B. Senderens, *Ann. Chim. Phys.*, (8), 28. 148, 1913 ; *Compt. Rend.*, 148. 927, 1909 ; P. Sabatier and A. Mailhe, *ib.*, 148. 1734, 1909 ; 150. 823, 1910 ; *Ann. Chem. Phys.*, (8), 20. 289, 1910 ; J. N. Pearce and A. M. Alvarado, *Journ. Phys. Chem.*, 29. 256, 1925 ; A. Mailhe, *Chem. Ztg.*, 33. 29, 1909 ; 34. 1173, 1182, 1201, 1911 ; L. and P. Wöhler and W. Plüddemann, *Zeit. phys. Chem.*, 62 641, 1908 ; T. Sollmann and E. D. Brown, *Amer. Journ. Physiol.*, 18. 427, 1907 ; H. von Wartenberg, J. Broy, and R. Reinicke, *Zeit. Elektrochem.*, 29. 214, 1923 ; J. J. Berzelius, *Svenska Akad. Handl.*, 1, 1829 ; *Pogg. Ann.*, 16. 385, 1829 ; N. J. Berlin, *ib.*, 85. 558, 1852 ; J. J. Chydenius, *ib.*, 119. 43, 1863 ; *Kemisk Undersökning af Thorjord och Thorsalter*, Helsingfors, 1861 ; W. Biltz, *Liebig's Ann.*, 331. 352, 1904 ; V. I. Spitzin, *Journ. Russ. Phys. Chem. Soc.*, 49. 357, 1917 ; J. Aloy and C. Rabaut, *Bull. Soc. Chim.*, (4), 19. 44, 1916 ; S. Komatsu and B. Masumoto, *Mem. Coll. Science Kyoto*, 9. 15, 1925 ; W. W. Russell and H. S. Taylor, *Journ. Phys. Chem.*, 29. 1325, 1925 ; G. R. Levi, *Atti Accad. Lincei*, (6), 2. ii, 419, 1925 ; S. Medsforth, *Journ. Chem. Soc.* 123. 1452, 1923 ; E. Newbery and J. N. Pring, *Proc. Roy. Soc.* 92, A. 276, 1916.

[4] C. Baskerville, *Journ. Amer. Chem. Soc.*, 23. 762, 1901 ; F. J. Metzger, *ib.*, 24. 917, 1920 ; H. Erdmann, *Lehrbuch der anorganischen Chemie*, Braunschweig, 601, 1898 ; P. T. Cleve, *Bihang. Svenska Handl.*, 2. 6, 1874 ; *Bull. Soc. Chim.*, (2), 21. 115, 1874 ; K. C. Sen and N. R. Dhar, *Koll. Zeit.*, 33. 193, 1923 ; N. G. Chatterji and N. R. Dhar, *Chem. News*, 121. 253, 1920 ; J. Böhm and H. Niclassen, *Zeit. anorg. Chem.*, 132. 1, 1924 ; J. J. Berzelius, *Svenska Akad. Handl.*, 1, 1829 ; *Pogg. Ann.*, 16. 385, 1829 ; J. F. Bahr, *ib.*, 119. 572, 1863 ; *Œfvers. Svenska Akad. Förh.*, 415, 1862 ; J. J. Chydenius, *Pogg. Ann.*, 119. 43, 1863 ; *Kemisk Undersökning af Thorjord och Thorsalter*, Helsingfors, 1861 ; P. Jannasch and J. Schilling, *Journ. prakt. Chem.*, (2), 72. 28, 1905 ; L. M. Dennis and F. L. Kortright, *Amer. Chem. Journ.*, 16. 79, 1894 ; *Zeit. anorg. Chem.*, *ib.*, 6. 36, 1894 ; G. Krüss and W. Palmaer, *ib.*, 14. 361, 1897 ; L. Pissarjewsky, *ib.*, 25. 394, 1900 ; H. Grossmann, *ib.*, 44. 233, 1905 ; O. Angelucci, *Atti Accad. Lincei*, (5), 16. ii, 196, 1907 ; T. Sollmann and E. D Brown, *Amer. Journ. Physiol.*, 18. 427, 1907 ; G. Wyrouboff and A. Verneuil, *Amer. Chim. Phys.*, (8), 6. 503, 1905 ; H. A. McTaggart, *Phil. Mag.*, (6), 44. 386, 1922 ; H. T. S. Britton, *Journ. Chem. Soc.*, 127, 1899, 2110, 1925 ; 129, 125, 269, 1926 ; F. Haber, *Monatsh.*, 18. 687, 1897.

[5] N. J. Berlin, *Pogg. Ann.*, 85. 558, 1852 ; P. T. Cleve, *Bull. Soc. Chim.*, (2), 21. 116, 1874 ; H. P. Stevens, *Zeit. anorg. Chem.*, 27. 47, 1901 ; J. Locke, *ib.*, 7. 347, 1894 ; G. Wyrouboff, *ib.*, 28. 90, 1901 ; G. Wyrouboff and A. Verneuil, *Bull. Soc. Chim.*, (3), 21. 125, 1899 ; *Ann.*

Chim. Phys., (8), **6**. 497, 1905 ; E. Chauvenet, *ib.*, (8), **23**. 425, 1911 ; J. F. Bahr, *Liebig's Ann.*, **132**. 227, 1864; G. R. Levi, *Atti Accad. Lincei*, (6), **2**. ii, 419. 1925.
    [6] W. Biltz, *Ber.*, **35**. 4436, 1902 ; **37**. 1095, 1904 ; W. Biltz and F. Zimmermann, *ib.*, **40**. 4983, 1907 ; A. Müller, *ib.*, **39**. 2857, 1906 ; *Zeit. anorg. Chem.*, **57**. 314, 1908 ; O. Hauser and F. Wirth, *ib.*, **60**. 243, 1908 ; J. Böhm and H. Niclassen, *ib.*, **132**. 1, 1923 ; K. C. Sen and N. R. Dhar, *Koll. Zeit.*, **33**. 193, 1923 ; *Journ. Phys. Chem.*, **29**. 435, 1925; N. G. Chatterji and N. R. Dhar, *Trans. Faraday Soc.*, **16**. 122, 1921 ; F. Haber, *Ber.*, **55**. B, 1717, 1922 ; E. Stiasny, *Der Gerber*, **33**. 109, 1907 ; I. Kreidl and G. Heller, *German Pat.*, *D.R.P.* 228203, 1919 ; B. Szilard, *Journ. Chim. Phys.*, **5**. 488, 636, 1907 ; J. Duclaux, *Compt. Rend.*, **148**. 714, 1909 ; H. Rheinboldt and E. Wedekind, *Koll. Beihefte*, **17**. 115, 1923.
    [7] L. de Boisbaudran, *Chem. News.*, **51**. 148, 1885 ; *Compt. Rend.*, **100**. 605, 1885 ; G. Wyrouboff and A. Verneuil, *ib.*, **126**. 340, 342, 1898 ; **127**. 412, 1898 ; *Ann. Chim. Phys.*, (8), **6**. 441, 1905 ; *Bull. Soc. Chim.*, (3), **19**. 219, 1898 ; P. T. Cleve, *ib.*, (2), **43**. 57, 1885 ; *Œfvers. Svenska Akad. Förh.*, 1, 1885 ; L. Pissarjewsky, *Zeit. anorg. Chem.*, **25**. 378, 1900 ; **31**. 359, 1902 ; *Journ Russ. Phys. Chem. Soc.*, **32**. 609, 1900 ; W. Bruno, *Zeit. angew. Chem.*, **19**. 1388, 1906 ; G. P. Drossbach, *ib.*, **19**. 1427, 1906 ; *German Pat.*, *D.R.P.* 117755, 1899.

§ 7. Thorium Fluorides

According to J. J. Berzelius,[1] when thorium hydroxide is treated with an excess of hydrofluoric acid, a heavy, insoluble, white powder is formed, **tetrahydrated thorium fluoride,** $ThF_4.4H_2O$. J. J. Chydenius obtained the same product as a gelatinous precipitate by adding hydrofluoric acid to a soln. of thorium chloride ; when dried in air, the composition corresponds with $ThF_4.8H_2O$, but four mols. of water are lost when dried in vacuo. E. Chauvenet made the same compound by decomposing thorium nitrate with silver fluoride, and drying the product in vacuo over sulphuric acid until the weight was constant. According to J. J. Chydenius, the hydrate loses up to 6·94 per cent. of water at 100° ; 8·26 per cent. at 140°. The loss of two mols. of water from a mol. of the salt represents 9·42 per cent. loss. The salt is partially hydrolyzed during the calcination, but J. J. Berzelius said that the fluoride is not completely decomposed by ignition, or by heating it with potassium. A litre of water at 25° was found by V. I. Spitzin to dissolve 0·17 mgrm. of tetrahydrated thorium tetrafluoride.

H. Moissan and H. Martinsen found that fluorine displaces chlorine from the anhydrous chloride, or bromine from the anhydrous bromide, forming anhydrous **thorium fluoride,** ThF_4 ; E. Chauvenet obtained the same product by passing dried hydrogen fluoride over the heated chloride, or, better, the bromide. A. Duboin made anhydrous thorium fluoride by melting potassium thorium fluoride, $KThF_5$, with an excess of potassium chloride or bromide ; and also by melting in a crucible lined with potassium chloride or a mixture of sodium and potassium chloride, a mixture of a mol of anhydrous thorium sulphate and 4 mols of potassium or sodium fluoride. The crystals belong to the cubic system, elongated in the direction of one of the axes as in certain specimens of cuprite, they melt at a red heat, are not attacked by conc. sulphuric acid, are slowly decomposed by the dil. acid or by hydrochloric acid, and on fusion with sodium carbonate yield transparent crystals of thoria which closely resemble the crystals of the original fluoride.

When tetrahydrated thorium fluoride, or thorium fluosilicate, is heated to 800° in a platinum boat in a stream of dry hydrogen fluoride, E. Chauvenet found that it is converted into **thorium oxyfluoride,** $ThOF_2$, a white, insoluble, amorphous powder, which is decomposed by sulphuric acid. A. Duboin melted potassium thorium fluoride with a small excess of potassium chloride and gradually added thorium sulphate. The cold mass was digested with water, and cubic crystals of an oxyfluoride of indefinite composition remained.

According to M. Delafontaine, thorium fluoride forms double fluorides analogous with those of zirconium. Neither J. J. Chydenius, nor A. Rosenheim and co-workers succeeded in preparing *ammonium thorium fluoride* or *sodium thorium fluoride* by processes analogous to those employed for preparing the double potassium salt. According to A. Rosenheim, **potassium dithorium enneafluoride,** $KTh_2F_9.6H_2O$, is formed by precipitation with potassium hydrofluoride from a soln. of a thorium salt as a gelatinous precipitate which soon becomes pulverulent when allowed to stand in contact with the mother-liquor. If potassium fluoride be the precipitant, monohydrated **potassium thorium pentafluoride,** $KThF_5.H_2O$, is formed. J. J. Chydenius regarded it as a tetratahydrate, $KThF_5.\frac{1}{4}H_2O$. A. Rosenheim and co-workers obtained the anhydrous salt by melting thorium fluoride with an excess of potassium fluoride, and washing the cold mass with water until no more alkali fluoride dissolves. A. Duboin made it by heating to redness a soln. of thorium oxide in molten potassium hydrogen fluoride, and extracting the mass with water. H. L. Wells and J. M. Willis heated a soln. of thorium chloride with an aq. soln. of potassium hydrofluoride. J. J. Chydenius found that the weight of the salt is not changed at 150°; and A. Duboin, that it melts at a dull red heat. J. J. Chydenius, and A. Rosenheim and co-workers obtained tetrahydrated **potassium thorium hexafluoride,** $K_2ThF_6.4H_2O$, by boiling thorium hydroxide with a soln. of potassium fluoride in the presence of hydrofluoric acid; or by boiling thorium fluoride with a soln. of potassium hydrofluoride. A litre of water at 25° was found by V. I. Spitzin to dissolve 0·4 mgrm. of thorium from $K_2ThF_6.4H_2O$. A. Kauffmann mentioned a complex $K_8Th_7F_{36}.6H_2O$. H. L. Wells and J. M. Willis add that " on account of the insolubility of thorium fluoride, and of these double salts, it is probable that there may be some doubt about the correctness of these formulæ." A. Rosenheim made trihydrated **rubidium thorium pentafluoride,** $RbThF_5.3H_2O$, by precipitation from a thorium salt soln. by one of rubidium hydrofluoride. On attempting to prepare *cæsium thorium fluoride,* H. L. Wells and J. M. Willis found that " thorium fluoride is practically insoluble even in conc. soln. of cæsium fluoride containing hydrofluoric acid. There is no doubt that the two fluorides combine under the circumstances, but since only finely divided precipitates were obtained there was no certainty as to their purity."

REFERENCES.

[1] J. J. Berzelius, *Svenska Akad. Handl.,* 1, 1829 ; *Pogg. Ann.,* 16. 385, 1829 ; J. J. Chydenius, *ib.,* 119. 43, 1863 ; *Kemisk Undersökning af Thorjord och Thorsalter,* Helsingfors, 1861 ; H. Moissan and H. Martinsen, *Compt. Rend.,* 140. 1510, 1905 ; E. Chauvenet, *ib.,* 146. 974, 1908 ; A. Duboin, *ib.,* 146. 489, 1908 ; *Ann. Chim. Phys.,* (8), 17. 355, 1909 ; A. Rosenheim, V. Samter, and J. Davidsohn, *Zeit. anorg. Chem.,* 35. 432, 1903 ; M. Delafontaine, *Chem. News,* 75 229, 1897 ; H. L. Wells and J. M. Willis, *Amer. Journ. Science,* (4), 12. 191, 1901 ; O. Kauffmann, *Zur Kenntnis einiger neuer Thoriumsalz,* Rostock, 1911 ; V. I. Spitzin, *Journ. Russ. Phys. Chem. Soc.,* 49. 357, 1917.

§ 8. Thorium Chlorides

As previously indicated, thorium when warmed unites vigorously with chlorine ; and H. Moissan and A. Étard,[1] and H. Moissan and O. Hönigschmid made the chloride by heating thorium carbide or thorium containing carbide in a stream of chlorine. G. Krüss and L. F. Nilson prepared the chloride by heating the metal to low redness in a stream of dried hydrogen chloride, and subsequently resubliming the salt. H. Moissan and H. Martinsen found that thorium chloride is produced by the action of chlorine on thorium bromide.

J. J. Berzelius prepared anhydrous thorium chloride, $ThCl_4$, by the process used by H. C. Oersted for aluminium chloride. An intimate mixture of thoria and sugar was carbonized in a covered crucible, and the carbonaceous mass was heated in a porcelain tube through which passed a stream of chlorine. The reaction proceeds slowly. Most of the thorium chloride which is formed is deposited as a white, semi-fused mass just where the tube ceases to glow ; when this mass is sublimed, brilliant, colourless crystals are produced. J. J. Chydenius, J. M. Matthews, and C. Baskerville employed modifications of this process. W. von Bolton, and C. A. Matignon and M. Delépine heated thoria in the vap. of carbon tetrachloride, and obtained an almost quantitative yield of thorium chloride; $ThO_2+2CCl_4=ThCl_4+2COCl_2$, or $ThO_2+CCl_4=ThCl_4+CO_2$. C. A. Matignon, and A. Duboin mixed the vapour of carbon tetrachloride with some chlorine. C. A. Matignon and M. Delépine also prepared thorium chloride by passing a mixture of carbon monoxide and chlorine over heated thoria, but found the reduction slow. E. Chauvenet, and C. Baskerville passed the vap. of carbonyl chloride over thoria at 650°: $ThO_2+2COCl_2=ThCl_4+2CO_2$. C. A. Matignon and F. Bourion, F. Bourion, H. von Wartenberg, and R. J. Meyer and A. Gumperz passed a mixture of chlorine and sulphur chloride vap. over thoria heated to 800°. The thorium chloride sublimes and condenses in the cooler part of the tube.

E. F. Smith and H. B. Harris heated eq. proportions of phosphorus pentachloride and thoria in an evacuated and sealed glass tube at about 240°. When the tube is opened, the phosphoryl chloride and phosphorus pentachloride can be distilled off. According to C. A. Matignon, the process is not a good one. E. Chauvenet found that thorium oxychloride is decomposed at a red heat, forming the dioxide and tetrachloride : $2ThOCl_2=ThO_2+ThCl_4$. The chloride can be separated from the oxide by sublimation. E. Chauvenet obtained the anhydrous chloride by treating hydrated thorium chloride with ammonium chloride and heating the product to 500°.

Anhydrous thorium chloride, purified by sublimation, furnishes colourless, prismatic **crystals** ; which, according to P. Groth, probably belong to the rhombic system. The crystals were examined by A. E. Nordenskjöld. H. Moissan and H. Martinsen found the **specific gravity** of the crystals to be 4·59. W. Biltz and E. Birk studied the mol. vol. I. I. Saslawsky gave 0·95 for the ratio of the mol. vol. to the sum of the at. vols. of the constituent elements. According to F. E. Bartell and O. E. Madison, in the **osmosis** of soln. of thorium chloride the membrane becomes electropositive to the soln. ; the soln. side of the membrane is electropositive ; and the osmosis is positive. E. Chauvenet gave 0·407 for the **specific heat** between −23° and 17° ; and 149·8 for the mol. ht. K. Jauch found the sp. ht. of soln. with N eq. of thorium chloride per litre to be :

N	0·5	1·0	2·0	3·0	4·0
Sp. ht.	0·9443	0·8954	0·8118	0·7435	0·6860

J. J. Chydenius said that the salt melts in the gas blowpipe flame ; and H. Moissan and H. Martinsen gave 820° for the **melting point** of the salt. A. Voigt and W. Biltz gave 567° for the f.p., and 618° for the **boiling point.** J. J. Chydenius found no perceptible **volatilization** at 440°, but A. Duboin observed that volatilization occurs at a red heat ; and F. Bourion noted that in a stream of chlorine and sulphur chloride, volatilization is complete between 700° and 780°. G. Krüss and L. F. Nilson measured the **vapour density** of thorium chloride, and found (air unity) :

	1057°	1102°	1140°	1270°	1400°
Vapour density	12·424	12·418	11·556	11·232	9·835

The theoretical density for $ThCl_4$ is 12·93. The vapour also dissociates at a temp. of about 400°. L. Troost made some observations which are vitiated by impurities in the samples used—*vide* the valency of thorium. According to E. Chauvenet, the heat of formation is 339·43 Cals., and, according to H. von Wartenberg, 300·2 ± 2·02 Cals. E. Chauvenet gave 56·75 Cals. for the heat of soln. at 12·5° ; and C. A. Matignon gave 53·80 Cals. per mol in 2700 mols of water at 18°—*vide infra* for the different hydrates. H. Moissan and H. Martinsen showed that the salt has a feeble **radioactivity.** A. E. Lindh studied the **X-ray absorption spectrum** of thorium chloride. A. Heydweiller measured the sp. gr. and **electrical conductivity** of soln. of thorium chloride ; and A. Voigt and W. Biltz, that of the molten chloride, which, at 814°, has a sp. conductivity of 0·61 mho ; at 866°, 0·71 mho ; and at 922°, 0·78 mho. B. Neumann and H. Richter gave 1·70 volts for the **decomposition voltage** of the chloride at 765°; the temp. coeff. is $1·875 \times 10^{-3}$.

H. Moissan and H. Martinsen said that the crystals are stable in light; and J. J. Berzelius, J. J. Chydenius, C. Baskerville, and H. Moissan and H. Martinsen remarked on the great **hygroscopicity** of the salt—E. Chauvenet said that 0·0183 grm. of water are absorbed from the atm. per gram per hour—but G. Krüss and L. F. Nilson, and C. A. Matignon and F. Bourion said that if the salt is well purified it is not markedly hygroscopic. The salt readily dissolves in **water** with the development of heat, forming a colourless soln. which, according to C. Baskerville, reacts acid. At a red heat, **oxygen** converts thorium tetrachloride into the dioxide. H. Moissan and H. Martinsen found that **fluorine** displaces the chlorine at ordinary temp., and if warmed, the mass becomes incandescent. W. Biltz and E. Meinecke found thorium chloride to be insoluble in liquid **chlorine.** A. Rosenheim and J. Schilling could not prepare **hydrochlorothoric acid,** H_2ThCl_6, but they obtained the pyridine chlorohydrate, $(C_5H_5N)_2H_2ThCl_6$, in well-defined crystals. This is considered to establish the existence of this acid. When heated in **sulphur** vap. and hydrogen, at a dark red heat, hydrogen chloride is formed, and thorium sulphide is produced; **selenium** vap. acts similarly. A. Duboin found that **hydrogen sulphide** reacts with the chloride at a dull red heat, forming thorium sulphide. For the action of ammonia, *vide infra.* H. Moissan and H. Martinsen found that at a red heat **phosphorus** forms a phosphide; neither **boron** nor **silicon** react with the chloride at 600°. Thorium chloride is reduced by **calcium ;** and, according to J. J. Berzelius, thorium chloride is decomposed by **potassium** " with a slight detonation and combustion." H. Moissan and H. Martinsen observed that molten **potassium nitrate** rapidly decomposes the chloride without incandescence, and that molten **potassium chlorate** behaves similarly. E. Chauvenet noted that a homogeneous liquid is obtained when thorium chloride is fused with **lithium chloride,** and complexes with the other **alkali chlorides** have been formed by fusion—*vide infra.* H. Moissan and H. Martinsen said that thorium chloride is insoluble in **carbon disulphide, chloroform, turpentine, toluene,** and **benzene ;** it is soluble in absolute **alcohol** and in 95 per cent. alcohol; it is soluble in water sat. with **ether.** C. Baskerville said that one part of the salt is soluble in 1000 parts of dried ether.

J. M. Matthews found that in addition to the octammine and the hexammine, thorium chloride forms addition compounds with **methyl-, ethyl-, propyl-,** and **β-naphthyl-amines,** and with **aniline, toluidine, pyridine,** and **quinoline ;** but not with **diphenylamine,** the **acid amides, nitrosyl chloride, nitrogen peroxide, sulphur monochloride,** the **phosphorus chlorides, cyanogen, dicyanogen, hydrogen cyanide, cyanogen chloride, acetonitrile, formonitrile,** or **benzonitrile.** Analogous results were obtained with the tetrachlorides of zirconium and lead, but not with titanium, and tin. A. Rosenheim and co-workers, and J. M. Matthews have obtained many compounds of thorium tetrachloride with organic bases, alcohol, etc., but not with ether.

Thorium tetrachloride forms a number of hydrates with water, but these have not yet been examined in the light of the phase rule. J. J. Berzelius noted that when a soln. of thorium hydroxide in hydrochloric acid is evaporated to a small bulk, it solidifies on cooling to a mass of radiating needle-like crystals, especially is this so if an excess of acid be present, for then the salt is less soluble. P. T. Cleve showed that the product is **octohydrated thorium tetrachloride,** $ThCl_4.8H_2O$. They are produced by allowing the aq. soln. to stand over sulphuric acid. According to P. T. Cleve, the product, dried over sulphuric acid, is either the hena- or the **dodecahydrated thorium tetrachloride,** $ThCl_4.12(or\ 11)H_2O$. G. Krüss and W. Palmaer obtained this hydrate by the crystallization of the heptahydrate from alcohol. A. Rosenheim and co-workers, and H. Moissan and H. Martinsen also obtained crystals of the octohydrate by evaporating an aq. soln. of the chloride at ordinary temp. E. Chauvenet gave for the heat of formation from the anhydrous salt, 45·25 Cals., and from the heptahydrate, 3·25 Cals. ; the heat of soln. of the octohydrate in water is 11·45 Cals. **P. T.** Cleve found the crystals deliquesce in moist air. According to E. Chauvenet, the prismatic crystals lose no more than a mol of water in a desiccator at ordinary temp. and press., but in vacuo over sulphuric acid, four mols of water are given off, and on a water-bath, six mols. If the temp. exceeds 100°, an oxychloride, $Th(OH)Cl_3.H_2O$, is first formed, then $ThOCl_2$, and finally thorium dioxide. J. J. Berzelius noted that the aq. soln. becomes turbid when boiled, owing to hydrolysis; he also noted that the salt is very soluble in water and in alcohol. J. J. Chydenius stated that the soln. gives no precipitate with potassium dichromate. E. Chauvenet found that when the octohydrate is heated on a water-bath, it furnishes **dihydrated thorium tetrachloride,** $ThCl_4.2H_2O$, and that the heat of formation from the anhydrous salt is 15·62 Cals., and the heat of soln., 41·08 Cals. If the octohydrate be slowly heated in a current of hydrogen or dry hydrogen chloride, or if it is allowed to stand several days in vacuo, **tetrahydrated thorium tetrachloride,** $ThCl_4.4H_2O$, is formed. The heat of formation from the anhydrous chloride is 30·47 Cals., and from the dihydrate, 14·85 Cals., the heat of soln. is 26·23 Cals. According to E. Chauvenet, if the octohydrate be dried to a constant weight in a dry atm., **heptahydrated thorium tetrachloride,** $ThCl_4.7H_2O$, is formed. He also said that this hydrate is produced by A. Rosenheim and J. Schilling's method for $Th(OH)Cl_3.11H_2O$—*vide infra*. G. Krüss and W. Palmaer prepared the heptahydrate by treating thorium hydroxide suspended in absolute alcohol with hydrogen chloride, and allowing the soln. thus obtained to crystallize in a vacuum over sodium hydroxide and sulphuric acid. It crystallizes in rhombic pyramids, deliquesces in the air, and effloresces when allowed to remain in a desiccator, water and hydrogen chloride being given off. The anhydrous chloride cannot be prepared by heating the crystals in a current of hydrogen chloride or chlorine, as under these conditions a mixture containing oxychloride is obtained. When heated, it decomposes with formation of thorium oxide and evolution of water and hydrogen chloride. It is very easily soluble in water and alcohol, yielding an acid soln., and the addition of ether to the alcoholic soln. causes a precipitate of the unaltered salt. E. Chauvenet added that when heated in a stream of dry hydrogen chloride the oxychloride $Th(OH)Cl_3.H_2O$ is formed. The heat of formation from the anhydrous chloride is 42·00 Cals., and from the tetrachloride 11·53 Cals.; the heat of soln. is 14·75 Cals. at 13·5°. According to A. Rosenheim and co-workers, G. Krüss and W. Palmaer's process just described furnishes **enneahydrated thorium tetrachloride,** $ThCl_4.9H_2O$; but E. Chauvenet could not prepare this hydrate; nor could W. Biltz and E. Keunecke prepare a sulphohydrate, $ThCl_4.nH_2S$.

According to J. J. Berzelius,[2] in the preparation of the anhydrous chloride by the action of chlorine on a mixture of thoria and carbon, a white cloud passes along with the chlorine gas, and condenses in the receiver as a white amorphous sublimate, assumed to be a thorium oxychloride because water resolves it into soluble thorium chloride, and thoria. J. J. Chydenius, however, regarded the cloud as thorium chloride. C. A. Matignon and M. Delépine found that **thorium oxychloride,** or *thoryl chloride,* $ThOCl_2$, is an intermediate compound in the preparation of the tetrachloride by the action of carbon tetrachloride, or a mixture of chlorine and carbon monoxide on heated thoria; and they isolated it by stopping the reaction when the product contains $ThO_2 : ThCl_4 = 1 : 8$ or 9, and extracting the cold mass with absolute alcohol. The oxychloride is then obtained as a residue of small colourless needles. E. Chauvenet obtained it by heating heptahydrated thorium tetrachloride to 250° in a stream of hydrogen chloride, but G. Krüss and W. Palmaer could not make it at temp. between 150° and bright red heat. They said that the preparation of a pure compound of the composition $ThOCl_2$ has not been accomplished; nothing but impure products were obtained by heating the chloride in a current of hydrogen chloride or chlorine, or by heating the hydroxide in a current of hydrogen chloride. The product obtained by heating the crystalline chloride alone always contains more thorium oxide than is required by the above formula. According to C. A. Matignon, and W. Palmaer, the white needle-like crystals are very hygroscopic; readily soluble in water, insoluble in absolute alcohol ; R. J. Meyer also said the salt is soluble in water, while H. Karstens said it is insoluble in this menstruum. E. Chauvenet said that the heat of soln. in water is 28·15 Cals. at 13°.

A. Rosenheim, V. Samter, and J. Davidsohn obtained white acicular crystals of **pentahydrated thorium dihydroxydichloride,** $Th(OH)_2Cl_2.5H_2O$, by treating freshly precipitated thorium hydroxide with alcohol sat. with hydrogen chloride, and evaporating off the alcohol first on a water-bath, and then in vacuo over sulphuric acid. The crystals are fairly stable in air, readily soluble without decomposition in water and in alcohol. According to C. A. Matignon and M. Delépine, if the evaporation be allowed to proceed further, the *tetrahydrate*, $Th(OH)_2Cl_2.4H_2O$, is formed. They also found that if thorium oxychloride be allowed to stand at 10° to 15° in an atm. sat. with water vap., water corresponding with $ThOCl_2.6H_2O$, *i.e.* the pentahydrate $Th(OH)_2Cl_2.5H_2O$ is absorbed ; and if this product be allowed to stand in a dry place, $ThOCl_2.5H_2O$, *i.e. the tetrahydrate,* $Th(OH)_2Cl_2.4H_2O$, is formed. If the cold soln. of thorium hydroxide in the alcoholic soln. of hydrogen chloride be evaporated in the cold under reduced press., 50 mm., over sulphuric acid and potassium hydroxide, A. Rosenheim and J. Schilling found that the *octohydrate*, $Th(OH)_2Cl_2.8H_2O$, is formed.

According to A. Rosenheim, V. Samter, and J. Davidsohn, if freshly precipitated thorium hydroxide be dissolved in an alcoholic soln. of hydrogen chloride, but not sat., white leaflets of **heptahydrated thorium hydroxytrichloride,** $Th(OH)Cl_3.7H_2O$, separate on evaporation. By distilling the alcohol almost completely from the alcoholic soln. of octohydrated thorium dihydroxydichloride, digesting the syrupy residue with hydrochloric acid of sp. gr. 1·12, and evaporating the soln. over conc. sulphuric acid, A. Rosenheim and J. Schilling obtained the *henahydrate*, $Tl(OH)Cl_3.11H_2O$; but E. Chauvenet said that heptahydrated thorium tetrachloride is formed under these conditions. According to the last-named, when the latter salt is heated between 120° and 160° to constant weight in a stream of hydrogen chloride, *the monohydrate*, $Tl(OH)Cl_3.H_2O$, is produced. If the temp. be 100°, a hydrated product intermediate between $Tl(OH)_2Cl_2$ and $Tl(OH)Cl_3$ is formed. The monohydrate is very deliquescent, and has a heat of dissolution 47·63 Cals. at 13·5°. E. Chauvenet prepared **lithium thorium oxychloride,** $LiThOCl_3$ by heating $LiThCl_5.8H_2O$ to 400° in a stream of dry hydrogen chloride. Towards 800°, the salts decompose and thorium and lithium chlorides volatilize, leaving thoria behind. E. Chauvenet also found that if the double chloride of thorium and lithium be heated to 200°, it forms **lithium thorium hydroxytrichloride,** $LiCl.Th(OH)Cl_3$; similarly the potassium salt furnishes **potassium thorium hydroxytrichloride,** $KCl.Th(OH)Cl_3$; and the sodium salt, **sodium thorium hydroxytrichloride,** $NaCl.Th(OH)Cl_3$. If the temp. exceeds 200°, a mixture of thoria, thorium tetrachloride, and the alkali chloride is formed. G. Wyrouboff and A. Verneuil assume that a hydrated *thorium peroxychloride*, $Th_2O_7Cl_2.nH_2O$, is formed by the action of hydrogen peroxide on the normal chloride.

According to H. P. Stevens, when thorium meta-oxide, prepared from the oxalate, is treated with dry hydrogen chloride, it is converted into an oxychloride which contains chlorine varying from 0·61 to 10 per cent., dependent on the amount of water contained in the thorium meta-oxide. Thorium meta-oxide, like silicic acid, retains water persistently, but when it is dried by heating in a current of dry air it is no longer acted on by hydrogen chloride. The reaction which takes place between the oxide containing water and chlorine corresponds with the formula $ThO_2,xThCl_4$ for the oxychloride. **Thorium meta-oxychloride** is a white, hygroscopic powder which dissolves in water to a clear soln. when it contains 9 to 10 per cent. of chlorine ; the preparations with less chlorine yield a more or less opalescent soln. It has an acid reaction, is insoluble in absolute alcohol, dissolves in alcohol containing a small quantity of water, behaves towards reagents in a similar manner to metastannic chloride, and is precipitated by many normal salts and by excess of acid, this precipitation taking place more easily the less chlorine it contains. When treated with silver nitrate, it does not give a precipitate of silver chloride.

G. Wyrouboff and A. Verneuil prepared a series of **hydrochlorides of thorium meta-oxide.** Partially dehydrated thorium hydroxide was digested in water, and hydrochloric acid added drop by drop until no further precipitate was formed. The less the hydroxide is heated the more hydrochloric acid is required for this purpose. The liquid was decanted from the precipitate, and the latter again treated with water and acid. The product was washed with water until the filtrate gave no precipitate with ammonia. The product gives an opalescent liquid when digested with water, the soln. has an acid reaction; silver nitrate gives no precipitate. The soln. is flocculated by dil. sulphuric acid, or neutral sulphates. The precipitate is insoluble in water. The product thus behaves like a typical colloid. The ratios $ThO_2 : Cl : H_2O$ in the product are very variable; the more strongly the calcination of the original hydroxide, the smaller the proportion of chlorine. G. Wyrouboff and A. Verneuil claimed to have made a series of hydrated **thorium hydroxyhydrochlorides,** $24ThO_2.4HCl.6H_2O$, which is dehydrated without decomposition at $250°$; $10ThO_2.4HCl.11H_2O$, which loses nine mols of water at $130°$; and $Th_8O_7(OH)_{16}Cl_2.2HCl$. W. von Bolton also reported $10ThO_2.4HCl$ to be formed when powdered thorium is shaken with cold, 5 per cent. hydrochloric acid, the first portion which dissolves (about 10 per cent. of the whole metal) forms a complex acid, $(ThO_2)_{10}(HCl)_4$, the soln. of which contains neither thorium nor chlorine ions; its principal reactions are: with oxalic acid or sulphuric acid, a small precipitate, soluble in excess, is produced; ammonium oxalate gives a gelatinous precipitate, insoluble on boiling; ammonium carbonate and citric acid give gelatinous precipitates, insoluble in excess. R. J. Meyer, and H. Karstens have discussed W. von Bolton's observations and consider that the thorium was contaminated with some meta-oxide. W. Biltz and E. Keunecke found that dry, liquid hydrogen sulphide does not react with or dissolve thorium tetrachloride at $-78.5°$.

H. Moissan and H. Martinsen[3] found that when the thorium chloride is treated with liquid ammonia, a complex is formed which is sparingly soluble in that menstruum. Addition compounds of thorium chloride have been obtained with ammonia, methylamine, ethylamine, propylamine, aniline, toluidine, pyridine, quinoline, and β-naphthylamine. It also forms crystalline addition compounds with alcohol, $ThCl_4.4C_2H_5OH$; acetaldehyde, $ThCl_4.2CH_3CHO$; acetone, $ThCl_4.2CH_3COCH_3$; cinnamic aldehyde; benzaldehyde; salicyl aldehyde; etc. These compounds have been studied by J. M. Matthews, and A. Rosenheim and co-workers. E. Chauvenet divides the **thorium amminochlorides** into three groups: (i) Those formed by the action of dry liquefied ammonia on thorium chloride and the subsequent evaporation of the excess of ammonia at different temp. and under different conditions. The members of this group are represented by the formula $Th(NH_3)_nCl_4$; (ii) The compounds formed by leaving the chloride in contact with gaseous ammonia at ordinary temp. (or warmed) are regarded as $Th(NH_3Cl)_4$ or $Th(NH_3Cl)\{NH_2(NH_4)Cl\}_3$; and (iii) the compounds formed by the action of liquid ammonia on the members of the second group. Their composition is represented by $Th(NH_3Cl)_4.nNH_3$. The approximate temp. of formation and dissociation at ordinary press.; the heat of formation (Cals.) from thorium tetrachloride; and the heat of dissolution (Cals.) in hydrochloric acid are shown in Table V. The hexa- and the hepta-ammines in the last two series are identical; hence there remain ten compounds or five pairs of isomeric compounds. The higher members of the first series rapidly lose ammonia, forming the tetrammine. They are all decomposed by water. The members of the second series are not decomposed in vacuo or when treated with water; and in the third series, the dodeca- and the octodeca-ammines are decomposed in vacuo or by water. The temp. of dissociation at 100 mm. press. are by G. L. Clark.

TABLE V.—THE AMMONIA COMPOUNDS OF THORIUM CHLORIDE.

General formula.	Compound.	Temp. of formation and dissociation.	Temp. of dissociation at 100 mm. press.	Heat of formation from $ThCl_4$.	Heat of dissolution in HCl.
$ThCl_4.nNH_3$	$ThCl_4.4NH_3$	15° in vacuo	305°	80	61·7
	$ThCl_4.6NH_3$	45°	168°	111·06	73·14
	$ThCl_4.7NH_3$	15°	84°	122·7	82·75
	$ThCl_4.12NH_3$	−5°	17°	172	139·7
	$ThCl_3.18NH_3$	−23°	1°	225	214·2
$Th(NH_3Cl)_4$	$ThCl_4.4NH_3$	120° (5 days)	406°	104·4	37·3
	$ThCl_4.6NH_3$	90°−100° (month)	—	148·7	35·5
	$ThCl_4.7NH_3$	20° (25 days)	—	169·43	36·02
$Th(NH_3Cl)_4nNH_3$	$ThCl_4.6NH_5$	55°	362°	148·9	35·3
	$ThCl_4.7NH_3$	20°	323°	171·3	34·15
	$ThCl_4.12NH_3$	−5°	31°	218	93·7
	$ThCl_4.18NH_3$	−23°	−20°	267·3	171·9

According to E. Chauvenet, **thorium tetramminochloride**, $ThCl_4.4NH_3$, and $Th(NH_3Cl)_4$—*vide supra*—give *thorium tetramide*, $Th(NH_2)_4$ and hydrogen chloride at 250°-300°; at a red heat, *thorium diimide*, $Th(NH)_2$, and ammonia; and at a still higher temp., the nitride is probably formed. J. M. Matthews prepared **thorium hexamminochloride**, $ThCl_4.6NH_3$—according to E. Chauvenet: $Th(NH_3Cl)_4.2NH_3$—by passing ammonia over thorium tetrachloride. Much heat is developed, and the white product fumes in air. E. Chauvenet's work on the two isomers is summarized in Table I; similarly also with the isomeric forms of **thorium heptamminochloride**, $ThCl_4.7NH_3$, and $Th(NH_3Cl)_4.3NH_3$. J. M. Matthews prepared **thorium octamminochloride**, $ThCl_4.8NH_3$, as a white flocculent mass, by passing dry ammonia into a soln. of thorium chloride in desiccated ether. The dried product is stable. The properties of E. Chauvenet's isomeric forms of **thorium dodecamminochloride**, $ThCl_4.12NH_3$, and $Th(NH_3Cl)_4.8NH_3$, are indicated in Table I. E. Chauvenet made the two isomers of **thorium octodecamminochloride**, $ThCl_4.18NH_3$, and $Th(NH_3Cl)_4.14NH_3$, as indicated above. The former was also made by passing ammonia gas through a tube reaching to the bottom of a small distillation flask with a constricted neck containing anhydrous thorium chloride, a long manometer tube containing a mercury index being sealed to the side-tube. The air being displaced, the flask was immersed in acetone and snow until a quantity of liquid ammonia had accumulated. The excess was then evaporated by placing the flask in liquid methyl chloride. The neck was then sealed off, at the same time the necessary mercury being poured into the gauge. The dissociation press., p, of the **octo**decammine is:

		−22·5°	−10°	0°	8°
Dissociation pressure		246	560	1031	1630 mm.

The heat of formation of the octodecammine from the dodecammine is $8·83 \times 6$ Cals. The sp. ht. is 0·524 per gram. The value of the heat of formation, Q, computed from Clapeyron's equation and the calculated values of p agree closely with the observed values.

A number of complex salts have been prepared. J. J. Chydenius [4] mixed ammonium chloride with a soln. of thorium oxide in hydrochloric acid, and after evaporation to dryness, he heated the dry mass in hydrogen chloride and obtained a crystalline mass which he regarded as *ammonium thorium dodecachloride*, $(NH_4)_8ThCl_{12}.8H_2O$, but G. Krüss and W. Palmaer could not confirm the existence of such a compound. E. Chauvenet obtained crystals of **ammonium thorium hexachloride**, $(NH_4)_2ThCl_6.10H_2O$, from a soln. containing 3 mols of ammonium chloride to one mol of thorium chloride. The heat of soln. is −3·9 Cals. When this compound is heated to 150°, **ammonium thorium pentachloride,** NH_4ThCl_5, is produced. It furnishes thorium tetrachloride at 500°. The heat of formation is 13·12 Cals., and the heat of soln., 39·82 Cals.

E. Chauvenet prepared **lithium thorium hexachloride,** $ThCl_4.2LiCl$, by melting two mols of lithium chloride with one mol of thorium chloride. The heat of formation is 4·67 Cals., and the heat of soln., 68·83 Cals. E. Chauvenet inferred that combination occurred because of the difference in the heats of soln. of the product and of the sum of the component chlorides ; with this test, no combination occurred with equi-molar proportions of the two chlorides to form $LiThCl_5$. By evaporating mixed soln. of the component salts, he obtained octohydrated **lithium thorium pentachloride,** $LiThCl_5.8H_2O$. The heat of formation is 37·65 Cals. The heat of soln. is 25·2 Cals. The salt cannot be dehydrated by heat because in a stream of dry hydrogen chloride at 200°, the oxychloride $LiTh(OH)Cl_4$ is formed. As in the case of lithium, E. Chauvenet could prepare only **sodium thorium hexachloride,** Na_2ThCl_6, by the fusion process. The heat of formation is 4·3 Cals., and the heat of soln. 50·04 Cals. He also made decahydrated **sodium thorium pentachloride,** $NaThCl_5.10H_2O$, as in the case of the octohydrated lithium salt. The heat of formation is 37·65 Cals., and the heat of soln., —5·74 Cals. It yields the oxychloride $NaTh(OH)Cl_4$ at 200° in a stream of hydrogen chloride.

J. J. Berzelius described the preparation of a double salt by heating a dried mixture of the component salts in a stream of hydrogen chloride, and by crystallization from aq. soln. P. T. Cleve evaporated the mixed soln. of equi-molar proportions of the component salts and obtained a crop of crystals of potassium chloride, followed by one of colourless crystals of **potassium thorium enneachloride,** $KTh_2Cl_9.18H_2O$. The crystals lose 7·1 per cent. of water when dried over sulphuric acid. The salt is very soluble in water. J. J. Berzelius thought that the salt can be dehydrated in a stream of hydrogen chloride, but in view of E. Chauvenet's work this is doubtful. L. F. Nilson, and H. Moissan and O. Hönigschmid obtained a double salt by evaporating a soln. of two mols of potassium chloride to one mol of thorium chloride. The product does not appear to have been analyzed. E. Chauvenet prepared **potassium thorium hexachloride,** K_2ThCl_6, by the same process as that employed for the lithium salt. The heat of formation is 9·14 Cals., and the heat of soln., 39·12 Cals. He also made enneahydrated **potassium thorium pentachloride,** $KThCl_5.9H_2O$, by crystallization from a soln. containing three mols of potassium chloride to one mol of thorium chloride. The heat of formation is 37·65 Cals., and the heat of soln., 3·5 Cals. While the five alkali chlorides when fused in the right proportions furnish double salts of the type $2MCl.ThCl_4$, cæsium and rubidium chlorides in addition furnish salts of the type $4MCl.ThCl_4$. E. Chauvenet prepared **rubidium thorium octochloride** Rb_4ThCl_8, with a heat of formation 26·3 Cals., and a heat of soln., 10·65 Cals., and **rubidium thorium hexachloride,** Rb_2ThCl_6, with a heat of formation 19·3 Cals., and a heat of soln., 27·5 Cals. A mixed soln. of two mols of rubidium chloride and one mol of thorium chloride yields crystals of the *enneahydrate,* $Rb_2ThCl_6.9H_2O$, with a heat of formation 26·9 Cals., and a heat of soln., 0·6 Cal. It loses water in a stream of dried hydrogen chloride at 150°. E. Chauvenet's **cæsium thorium octochloride,** Cs_4ThCl_8, has a heat of formation from the component salts of 18·11 Cals., and a heat of soln., 19·79 Cals. ; and **cæsium thorium hexachloride,** Cs_2ThCl_6, prepared like the lithium salt, has a heat of formation 14·9 Cals., and a heat of soln. 32·46 Cals. An aq. soln. of two mols of cæsium chloride and one mol of thorium chloride gives crystals of the *octohydrate,* $Cs_2ThCl_6.8H_2O$, with a heat of formation 29·86 Cals., and a heat of soln. 2·6 Cals. The water of crystallization is lost in a stream of dry hydrogen chloride at 150°. According to H. L. Wells and J. M. Willis, a mixed soln. of 65 grms. of thorium chloride and 30 to 100 grms. of cæsium chloride in hydrochloric acid gives small, colourless, hygroscopic crystals of the *henahydrate,* $Cs_2ThCl_6.11H_2O$, which gradually lose their water of crystallization in a desiccator over sulphuric acid. They also reported colourless hygroscopic crystals of the *dodecahydrate*, $Cs_2ThCl_6.12H_2O$, derived from a soln. containing 12 grms of thorium chloride, and 30–110 grms. of cæsium chloride.

REFERENCES.

[1] J. J. Berzelius, *Svenska Akad. Handl.*, 1, 1829 ; *Pogg. Ann.*, 16. 385, 1829 ; J. J. Chydenius, *ib.*, 119. 43, 1863 ; *Kemisk Undersökning af Thorjord och Thorsalter*, Helsingfors, 1861 ; H. C. Oersted, *Œfvers. Danska Vid. Selsk. Förh.*, 15, 1825 ; J. M. Matthews, *Journ. Amer. Chem. Soc.*, 20. 817, 1898 ; C. Baskerville, *ib.*, 23. 769, 1901 ; E. F. Smith and H. B. Harris, *ib.*, 17. 656, 1895 ; G. Krüss and L. F. Nilson, *Zeit. phys. Chem.*, 1. 303, 1887 ; *Ber.*, 20. 1673, 1887 ; W. von Bolton, *Zeit. Elektrochem.*, 14. 770, 1908 ; H. von Wartenberg, *ib.*, 15. 866, 1909 ; E. Chauvenet, *Chem. Ztg.*, 34. 940, 1910 ; *Ann. Chim. Phys.*, (8), 23. 278, 1911 ; *Compt. Rend.*, 147. 1046, 1908 ; 148. 1268, 1908 ; 149. 290, 1909 ; 152. 87, 1911 ; C. A. Matignon and F. Bourion, *ib.*, 138. 631, 1904 ; C. A. Matignon and M. Delépine, *ib.*, 132. 37, 1901 ; *Ann. Chim. Phys.*, (8), 10. 130, 1907 ; H. Moissan and A. Étard, *ib.*, (7), 12. 430, 1897 ; H. Moissan and O. Hönigschmid, *ib.*, (8), 8. 184, 1906 ; A. Duboin, *ib.*, (8), 17. 357, 1909 ; *Compt. Rend.*, 146. 815, 1908 ; L. Troost, *ib.*, 101. 360, 1885 ; C. A. Matignon, *ib.*, 147. 1292, 1908 ; *Bull. Soc. Chim.*, (4), 5. 92, 1909 ; F. Bourion, *Ann. Chim. Phys.*, (8), 21. 55, 1910 ; *Compt. Rend.*, 148. 171, 1909 ; H. Moissan and H. Martinsen, *ib.*, 140. 1510, 1905 ; R. J. Meyer and A. Gumperz, *Ber.*, 38. 822, 1905 ; A. Rosenheim and J. Schilling, *ib.*, 33. 977, 1900 ; A. Rosenheim and W. Lévy, *ib.*, 37. 3667, 1904 ; A. Rosenheim, V. Samter, and J. Davidsohn, *Zeit. anorg. Chem.*, 35. 449, 1903 ; G. Krüss and W. Palmaer, *ib.*, 14. 362, 1897 ; A. E. Nordenskjöld, *Pogg. Ann.*, 119. 48, 1863 ; B. Neumann and H. Richter, *Zeit. Elektrochem.*, 31. 296, 1925 ; A. Voigt and W. Biltz, *Zeit. anorg. Chem.*, 133. 277, 1924 ; W. Biltz, *ib.*, 133. 306, 1924 ; W. Biltz and E. Meinecke, *ib.*, 131. 1, 1923 ; W. Biltz and E. Birk, *ib.*, 134. 125, 1924 ; W. Biltz and E. Keunecke, *ib.*, 147. 171, 1925 ; I. I. Saslawsky, *ib.*, 146. 315, 1925 ; P. Groth, *Chemische Krystallographie*, Leipzig, 1. 230, 1906 ; P. T. Cleve, *Bihang. Svenska Akad. Handl.*, 2. 6, 10, 1874 ; *Bull. Soc. Chim.*, (2), 21. 116, 1874 ; A. E. Lindh, *Zeit. Physik*, 6. 303, 1921 ; F. E. Bartell and O. E. Madison, *Journ. Phys. Chem.*, 24. 593, 1920 ; A. Heydweiller, *Zeit. anorg. Chem.*, 116. 42, 1921 ; K. Jauch, *Zeit. Physik*, 4. 441, 1920 ; C. Baskerville, *Science*, (2), 50. 443, 1919.

[2] J. J. Berzelius, *Svenska Akad. Handl.*, 1, 1829 ; *Pogg. Ann.*, 16. 385, 1829 ; J. J. Chydenius, *ib.*, 119. 43, 1863 ; *Kemisk Undersökning af Thorjord och Thorsalter*, Helsingfors, 1861 ; C. A. Matignon and M. Delépine, *Ann. Chim. Phys.*, (8), 10. 133, 1907 ; E. Chauvenet, *Compt. Rend.*, 147. 1048, 1908 ; 148. 1519, 1909 ; G. Krüss and W. Palmaer, *Zeit. anorg. Chem.*, 14. 365, 1897 ; H. P. Stevens, *ib.*, 27. 44, 1907 ; A. Rosenheim, V. Samter, and J. Davidsohn, *ib.*, 35. 425, 1903 ; H. Karstens, *Zeit. Elektrochem.*, 15. 33, 1909 ; R. J. Meyer, *ib.*, 15. 105, 1908 ; W. von Bolton, *ib.*, 14. 769, 1908 ; A. Rosenheim and J. Schilling, *Ber.*, 33. 978, 1900 ; A. Rosenheim and W. Lévy, *ib.*, 37. 3667, 1904 ; G. Wyrouboff and A. Verneuil, *Ann. Chim. Phys.*, (8), 6. 494, 1905 ; *Bull. Soc. Chim.*, (3), 21. 118, 1899 ; J. M. Matthews, *Journ. Amer. Chem. Soc.*, 20. 815, 1898 ; H. Moissan and H. Martinsen, *Compt. Rend.*, 140. 1510, 1905 ; W. Biltz and E. Keunecke, *Zeit. anorg. Chem.*, 147. 171, 1925.

[3] E. Chauvenet, *Ann. Chim. Phys.*, (8), 23. 275, 1911 ; *Compt. Rend.*, 151. 387, 1910 ; H. Moissan and H. Martinsen, *ib.*, 140. 1512, 1905 ; J. M. Matthews, *Journ. Amer. Chem. Soc.*, 20. 824, 1898 ; G. L. Clark, *Amer. Journ. Science*, (1), 7. 1, 1924.

[4] J. J. Berzelius, *Svenska Akad. Handl.*, 1, 1829 ; *Pogg. Ann.*, 16. 385, 1829 ; J. J. Chydenius, *ib.*, 119. 43, 1863 ; *Kemisk Undersökning af Thorjord och Thorsalter*, Helsingfors, 1861 ; G. Krüss and W. Palmaer, *Zeit. anorg. Chem.*, 14. 361, 1897 ; E. Chauvenet, *Compt. Rend.*, 148. 1268, 1519, 1909 ; L. F. Nilson, *ib.*, 95. 727, 1882 ; *Ber.*, 15. 2539, 1882 ; H. Moissan and O. Hönigschmid, *Ann. Chim. Phys.*, (8), 8. 182, 1906 ; P. T. Cleve, *Bihang. Svenska Akad. Handl.*, 2. 10, 1874 ; *Bull. Soc. Chim.*, (2), 21, 116, 1874 ; H. L. Wells and J. M. Willis, *Amer. Journ. Science*, (4), 12. 191, 1901.

§ 9. Thorium Bromides

As previously indicated, thorium unites directly with bromine to form **thorium bromide**, $ThBr_4$. H. Moissan and H. Martinsen [1] prepared the anhydrous bromide by passing dried bromine vap. over thorium carbide as in the analogous preparation of thorium chloride. The sublimate was re-sublimed in a stream of hydrogen, and then in vacuo. L. Troost and L. Ouvrard prepared the bromide by H. C. Oersted's reaction indicated in connection with the chloride, *i.e.* by passing bromine vap. over a red-hot mixture of thoria and carbon. F. Bourion made the anhydrous bromide by passing a mixture of sulphur monochloride vap. and hydrogen bromide over thoria heated not above a red heat, and subliming in hydrogen bromide. According to L. Troost and L. Ouvrard, the white acicular crystals are very hygroscopic. H. Moissan and H. Martinsen found the sp. gr. of the crystals to be 5·62, and that of the white vitreous solid, 5·67. W. Biltz and E. Birk studied the mol. vol. I. I. Saslawsky gave 0·99 for the ratio of the mol. vol. to the sum of the at. vols. of the constituent elements. The crystals melt and volatilize more readily than do those of the chloride. Sublimation begins between 600° and 620° ; volatilization is complete at 700° ; the b.p. is 725°. The salt is feebly radioactive.

Thorium bromide in a sealed tube slowly decomposes when exposed to light, and it acquires a grey colour owing to the separation of bromine. The salt is attacked by fluorine at ordinary temp., and the warm bromide is attacked by chlorine. A. Rosenheim and J. Schilling could not isolate hydrobromothoric acid, H_2ThBr_6, but they obtained a crystalline compound of this acid with pyridine hydrochloride. H. Moissan and H. Martinsen found that when heated in oxygen, thorium bromide gives off bromine and forms thorium dioxide; at a dull red heat, hydrogen sulphide forms thorium sulphide, and hydrogen selenide, thorium selenide. The bromide at a dull red-heat is reduced by calcium.

Thorium bromide is very soluble in water, and, according to L. Troost and L. Ouvrard, there is a partial hydrolysis with the formation of an acidic soln., and an insoluble precipitate. H. Moissan and H. Martinsen noted that when the aq. soln. is boiled in air, thorium oxybromide, $ThOBr_2$, is formed. E. Chauvenet gave 70·19 Cals. for the heat of soln. A number of hydrates has been reported, but they have not been tested by the phase rule. J. J. Berzelius obtained a gummy mass by evaporating at ordinary temp. a soln. of thorium hydroxide in hydrobromic acid. E. Chauvenet considers the product to have been an oxybromide. A. Rosenheim and J. Schilling reported heptahydrated thorium tetrabromide, $ThBr_4.7H_2O$, to be formed, in acicular crystals, by the evaporation of the mother-liquor remaining after the preparation of henahydrated thorium dihydroxydibromide. E. Chauvenet gave 47·64 Cals. for the heat of formation from the anhydrous bromide, and 22·55 Cals. for the heat of soln. H. Moissan and H. Martinsen prepared octohydrated thorium tetrabromide, $ThBr_4.8H_2O$, by allowing the aq. soln. to stand over sulphuric acid. J. Lesinsky and C. Gundlich prepared the same salt by dissolving thorium hydroxide in hydrobromic acid and allowing the soln. to stand in darkness over sulphuric acid in vacuo. The product was washed with ligroïn and chloroform, and recrystallized from alcohol. E. Chauvenet claimed that these processes give the heptahydrate not the octohydrate. The crystals absorb carbon dioxide from atm. air ; they melt at 100°, and give off all their water at a higher temp. The salt is very soluble in water and alcohol. E. Chauvenet obtained needle-like crystals of dodecahydrated thorium tetrabromide, $ThCl_4.12H_2O$, by evaporating on a water-bath a soln. of thorium hydroxide in alcoholic hydrogen bromide, and drying the product on a porous tile. The heat of formation is 67·89 Cals., and the heat of soln., 2·30 Cals. In dry air, decahydrated thorium tetrabromide, $ThBr_4.10H_2O$, is formed. A. Rosenheim and co-workers made the decahydrate by crystallization from a soln. of thorium hydroxide in alcoholic hydrogen bromide ; and P. Jannasch and co-workers, by concentrating over sulphuric acid, in vacuo, a soln. of thorium hydroxide in hydrobromic acid. The needle-like or prismatic crystals are very hygroscopic and decompose if left in contact with moist air. E. Chauvenet gave 60·35 Cals. for the heat of formation from the anhydrous bromide, and 9·84 Cals. for the heat of soln. The salt loses some hydrogen at 100°. The crystals are very soluble in water and in alcohol.

As indicated above, aq. soln. of thorium bromide are readily hydrolyzed. and oxybromides are formed. Thus, said E. Chauvenet, when a soln. of thorium bromide is evaporated, as in J. J. Berzelius' mode of preparation, vide supra, the product approximates in composition $ThBr_4.Th(OH)Br_3.16H_2O$. A. Rosenheim and co-workers obtained crystals of decahydrated thorium hydroxytribromide, $Th(OH)Br_3$, from an alcoholic soln. of hydrogen bromide not completely sat. with thorium hydroxide. H. Moissan and H. Martinsen obtained thorium oxydibromide, $ThOBr_2$, by boiling an aq. soln. of thorium bromide exposed to air, and drying the product at 160°; F. Bourion obtained it by passing a slow current of sulphur mono-chloride mixed with hydrogen bromide over thoria at 125°. The white amorphous powder so obtained is soluble in water. A. Rosenheim and co-workers made the *tetrahydrate* of **thorium dihydroxydibromide,** $Th(OH)_2Br_2.4H_2O$, by evaporating in vacuo over conc. sulphuric acid, alcoholic hydrogen bromide completely sat. with thorium hydroxide. The white microscopic needles are fairly stable in air, but slowly lose hydrogen bromide. The salt is easily soluble in water and in alcohol. A. Rosenheim and J. Schilling obtained small quadratic crystals of the *henahydrate,* $Th(OH)_2Br_2.11H_2O$, from a soln. of thorium hydroxide in alcoholic hydrogen bromide, sat. in the cold, and evaporated slowly over sulphuric acid and potassium hydroxide.

J. M. Matthews, and A. Rosenheim and co-workers prepared a number of complexes of thorium bromide with ammonia and the substituted ammonias, pyridine, aniline, etc. According to H. Moissan and H. Martinsen, thorium tetra-bromide dissolves in liquid ammonia at −40°, and forms an ammino-compound. J. M. Matthews reported **thorium triamminobromide,** $ThBr_4.3NH_3$, to be formed by passing dry ammonia over warmed thorium bromide. J. J. Berzelius reported *potassium thorium bromide* to be formed from mixed soln. of the component salts.

REFERENCES.

[1] J. J. Berzelius, *Svenska Akad. Handl.*, 1, 1829; *Pogg. Ann.*, **16**. 385, 1829; H. Moissan and H. Martinsen, *Compt. Rend.*, **140**. 1513, 1905; F. Bourion, *ib.*, **145**. 243, 1907; E. Chauvenet, *ib.*, **149**. 291, 1909; L. Troost and L. Ouvrard, *Ann. Chim. Phys.*, (6), **17**. 229, 1889; J. Lesinsky. *Zur Kenntnis der Thoriumverbindungen*, Bern, 1898; J. Lesinsky and C. Gundlich, *Zeit. anorg, Chem.*, **15**. 81, 1897; W. Biltz and E. Birk, *ib.*, **134**. 125, 1924; I. I. Saslawsky, *ib.*, **146**. 315, 1925; P. Jannasch, J. Locke, and J. Lesinsky, *ib.*, **5**. 286, 1894; A. Rosenheim, V. Samter, and J. Davidsohn, *ib.*, **35**. 429, 1903; A. Rosenheim and J. Schilling, *Ber.*, **33**. 977, 1900; J. M. Matthews, *Journ. Amer. Chem. Soc.*, **20**. 817, 1898; H. C. Oersted, *Œfvers. Danska Vid. Selsk. Förh.*, 15, 1825.

§ 10. Thorium Iodides

L. F. Nilson,[1] and H. Moissan and A. Étard obtained anhydrous **thorium tetraiodide,** ThI_4, by burning thorium in iodine vap. J. J. Chydenius evaporated thorium hydroxide in a soln. of hydriodic acid, and obtained a gummy mass which turned brown on exposure to air. P. Jannasch and co-workers, and J. Lesinsky and co-workers obtained similar results, and they also obtained prismatic crystals so unstable that no analyses were made. The salt is decomposed on heating, or on exposure to light with the evolution of iodine. W. Biltz and E. Birk studied the mol. vol. A. Rosenheim and co-workers prepared acicular or prismatic crystals of **decahydrated thorium tetraiodide,** $ThI_4.10H_2O$, from the mother-liquor remaining after the preparation of **decahydrated thorium hydroxytriiodide,** $Th(OH)I_3.10H_2O$, which is formed by saturating an alcoholic soln. of hydrogen iodide with thorium hydroxide, and allowing the soln. to crystallize in the dark in vacuo over sulphuric acid. This compound slowly decomposes into hemihepta-hydrated thorium oxydiiodide, $ThOI_2.3\frac{1}{2}H_2O$, which then changes to white anhydrous thorium oxydiiodide, $ThOI_2$, and this, in turn, becomes yellow on exposure to light.

According to A. Duboin, when thorium iodide, prepared by the action of hydriodic acid on thorium carbonate, and mercuric iodide are alternately dissolved in water at a gentle heat to saturation, the liquid on cooling deposits, first, mercuric iodide and then a mass of extremely deliquescent crystals of **mercuric thorium tetradecaiodide,** $Hg_5ThI_{14}.18H_2O$ or $ThI_4.5HgI_2.18H_2O$, easily decomposed by water, and quickly changed by exposure to air, becoming red. The mother-liquor is dark brown in colour, owing to the presence of free iodine, and the latter is removed by shaking with mercurous iodide, giving a yellow liquid of sp. gr. 3·512 at $18 \cdot 90°$; its composition corresponds with $Hg_5Th_2I_{18}.21H_2O$. When this liquid is evaporated, filtered from the mercuric iodide which separates, and again evaporated, it furnishes crystals of **mercuric thorium octoiodide**, $Hg_2ThI_8.12H_2O$.

REFERENCES.

[1] L. F. Nilson, *Œfvers. Akad Förh.*, **39**. 7, 1882 : *Ber.*, **15**. 2541, 1882 ; H. Moissan and A. Étard, *Ann. Chim. Phys.*, (7), **12**. 429, 1897 ; A. Duboin, *ib.*, (8), **16**. 283, 1909 ; *Compt. Rend.*, **146**. 1027, 1908 ; E. Chauvenet, *Ann. Chim. Phys.*, (8), **23**. 425, 1911 ; J. Lesinsky, *Zur Kenntnis der Thoriumverbindungen*, Bern, 1898 ; P. Jannasch, J. Locke, and J. Lesinsky, *Zeit. anorg. Chem.*, **5**. 287, 1894 ; J. Lesinsky and C. Gundlich, *ib.*, **15**. 83, 1897 ; A. Rosenheim, V. Samter, and J. Davidsohn, *ib.*, **35**. 430, 1903 ; W. Biltz and E. Birk, *ib.*, **134**. 125, 1924 ; J. J. Chydenius, *Pogg. Ann.*, **119**. 43, 1863 ; *Kemisk Undersökning af Thorjord och Thorsalter*, Helsingfors, 1861.

§ 11. Thorium Sulphides

J. J. Berzelius,[1] L. F. Nilson, H. von Wartenberg, etc., made **thorium sulphide**, ThS_2, by the action of sulphur or hydrogen sulphide on heated thorium. H. Moissan and A. Étard also prepared this sulphide by passing the vap. of sulphur over heated thorium carbide; and G. Krüss and C. Volck, by heating a mixture of thorium chloride and potassium chloride in a stream of dry hydrogen sulphide. A. Duboin thus describes the preparation :

When a mixture of thorium chloride with an excess of sodium or potassium chloride, contained in a porcelain boat, is heated in a current of dry hydrogen sulphide, the product, after washing out the alkali chloride, consists chiefly of brown, micaceous lamellæ, together with small quantities of yellow crystals and of an amorphous substance. The brown lamellæ of thorium sulphide can be isolated by means of a sieve.

E. Kunheim used a similar process, but added diatomaceous earth or asbestos to the mixture to be heated in the hydrogen sulphide. J. J. Chydenius passed a mixture of hydrogen and the vap. of carbon disulphide over thorium meta-oxide at a white heat and claimed to have made thorium sulphide, but G. Krüss said that thorium oxysulphide, $ThOS$, not thorium sulphide, is formed, and E. W. von Siemens and J. G. Halske said that the product contains carbon. To eliminate this, they recommended using a mixture of hydrogen sulphide and carbon disulphide in place of the last-named vap. and hydrogen. A. E. van Arkel and J. H. de Boer made the sulphide by passing the vapour of the chloride mixed with hydrogen sulphide over a heated tungsten filament.

Pulverulent thorium sulphide, prepared by the different processes, has a yellow colour ; L. F. Nilson, and H. Moissan and A. Étard's preparations were black ; and A. Duboin's dark brown, lamellar crystals. J. J. Chydenius gave $8 \cdot 29$ for the sp. gr., but this number is probably too high, because H. von Wartenberg obtained $6 \cdot 8$, and A. Duboin $6 \cdot 7$ at $0°$ for this constant. The last-named also said that the crystals act feebly on polarized light. The crystals burn with a blue flame when heated in air ; and J. J. Berzelius said that when heated in a tube, the sulphur may be distilled off, and thorium oxide remains. H. von Wartenberg said that the compound is stable in water and soln. of the alkali hydroxides, even when boiled ; and with hot dil. acids, sulphur separates out. J. J. Chydenius found that the compound is not changed when heated in hydrogen ; when fused with potassium hydroxide it forms thorium oxide and potassium sulphide ; and with hydrochloric acid, it forms thorium chloride. J. J. Berzelius added that with dil. sulphuric acid, some hydrogen sulphide is at first evolved, without dissolution ; hydrochloric acid and nitric acid attack it a little ; and hot aqua regia oxidizes the sulphide to sulphate. A. Duboin said that the brown crystals are violently attacked by nitric acid.

As indicated above, A. Duboin obtained a mixture of brown plates and small quantities of a yellow substance, when thorium and sodium chlorides are heated in hydrogen sulphide. When the mixed product is treated with nitric acid, at 40°, the brown plates are vigorously attacked, while the yellow crystals are attacked slowly. He found that the yellow crystals are **thorium oxysulphide**, or *thoryl sulphide*, ThOS. G. Krüss obtained thorium oxysulphide by a similar process; and by the action of carbon disulphide on heated thoria. O. Hauser also made it by heating anhydrous thorium sulphate at 380°–400°, in a stream of dry air to remove the last trace of moisture, and then to redness in a current of hydrogen sulphide; after two hours the product is cooled in a stream of the same gas. The oxysulphide obtained by these processes is a brown or black powder; but that prepared by A. Duboin is in the form of orange-yellow crystals which resemble pyrites. O. Hauser gave 6·44 for the sp. gr., and A. Duboin, 8·42 at 0°. The latter said that the crystals are uniaxial and optically negative. According to O. Hauser, the oxysulphide inflames spontaneously when exposed to air. When heated in air or oxygen, thoria is formed. G. Krüss found that the compound is soluble in aqua regia, but, according to A. Duboin,conc. nitric acid attacks the oxysulphide very slowly. J. J. Chydenius also described a compound *thorium tetroxydisulphide*, $2ThO_2.ThS_2$, which he obtained by the action of a mixture of hydrogen and carbon disulphide on thoria obtained by igniting the hydroxide at a low temp. G. Krüss and C. Volck, however, denied the existence of the compound which they regarded as a mixture of thorium sulphide, carbonyl sulphide, and unchanged thoria.

REFERENCES.

[1] J. J. Berzelius, *Svenska Akad. Handl.*, 1, 1829; *Pogg. Ann.*, **16**. 385, 1829; J. J. Chydenius, *ib.*, **119**. 43, 1863; *Kemisk Undersökning af Thorjord och Thorsalter*, Helsingfors, 1861; L. F. Nilson, *Œfvers. Akad. Förh.*, **39**. 7, 1882; *Ber.*, **15**. 2537, 1882; H. Moissan and A. Étard, *Compt. Rend.*, **122**. 573, 1896; A. Duboin, *ib.*, **146**. 815, 1908; *Ann. Chim. Phys.*, (8), **17**. 357, 1909; H. von Wartenberg, *Zeit. Elektrochem*, **15**. 871, 1909; C. A. Matignon, *Monit. Scient.*, (4), **14**. 353, 1900; G. Krüss and C. Volck, *Zeit. anorg. Chem.*, **5**. 75, 1894; G. Krüss, *ib.*, **6**. 52, 1894; O. Hauser, *ib.*, **53**. 74, 1907; E. W. von Siemens and J. G. Halske, *German Pat.*, *D.R.P.* 187546, 1906; E. Kunheim, *ib.*, 201894, 1907; A. E. van Arkel and J. H. de Boer, *Zeit. anorg. Chem.*, **148**. 345, 1925.

§ 12. Thorium Sulphates

J. J. Berzelius [1] made anhydrous **thorium sulphate**, $Th(SO_4)_2$, by digesting finely divided thoria with a mixture of sulphuric acid (2 : 1) for several hours, and removing the excess of acid by evaporation. G. Krüss and L. F. Nilson, and R. J. Meyer and A. Gumperz showed that there is a condition of equilibrium between the temp. and the proportion of normal, basic, or acid sulphate. L. F. Nilson obtained the anhydrous sulphate by dehydrating one of the hydrates—according to P. T. Cleve, the temp. of calcination should be below redness; and, according to G. Krüss and L. F. Nilson, G. Wyrouboff, and R. J. Meyer and A. Gumperz, about 400°. The white, earthy product is, according to G. Wyrouboff, microcrystalline. G. Krüss and L. F. Nilson gave 4·2252 (17°) for the sp. gr.; and L. F. Nilson and O. Pettersson, 0·0972 for the sp. ht., and 41·21 for the mol. ht. L. and P. Wöhler and W. Plüddemann found the vap. press. of the sulphur trioxide in equilibrium with oxygen and sulphur dioxide to be :

	575°	610°	660°	698°	720°	755°	785°
Vap. press. . .	.16	32	44	80	144	198	344 mm.

Both mols of sulphur trioxide have the same vap. press., so that there is no evidence of the formation of a basic salt. The heat of dissociation is 21 cals. According to P. T. Cleve, at a red heat, the sulphate loses all its sulphur trioxide. J. J. Berzelius said that the salt detonates a little when heated with potassium and is reduced to potassium sulphide and thoria.

Anhydrous thorium sulphate, said J. J. Chydenius, dissolves in cold water with a hissing noise ; and, added J. J. Berzelius, if a large proportion of water is present, the rate of soln. is slow, but if only a small proportion of water is present, the speed is faster and the temp. rises. It seems as if the thorium sulphate dissolves in, say, ten times its weight of water by first forming a hydrate which then passes into soln. P. T. Cleve said that the heat of soln. is positive. P. T. Cleve, L. F. Nilson, G. Wyrouboff, E. Demarçay, and H. W. B. Roozeboom made observations on the solubility, and from the results of the last-named it follows that about 25 parts of the salt can dissolve in 100 parts of water, forming soln. which are metastable between 0° and 100°, and which when kept, spontaneously deposit crystals of the hydrates. According to E. Löwenstein, thorium sulphate forms five hydrates respectively with 9, 8, 6, 4, and 2 mols of water. A trihydrate and a hemienneahydrate have also been reported.

According to J. J. Berzelius, aq. soln. at 10°–15° deposit crystals of **enneahydrated thorium sulphate,** $Th(SO_4)_2.9H_2O$; H. W. B. Roozeboom gave 0°–43° for the range of stability, and H. M. Dawson and P. Williams, 0°–47°. H. W. B. Roozeboom's solubility curves of the different hydrates are shown in Fig. 8. The enneahydrate was obtained by J. J. Berzelius, J. J. Chydenius, and E. H. Kraus, by the spontaneous evap. of acidified soln. of the sulphate—P. T. Cleve used feebly acid soln. J. J. Berzelius found alcohol precipitates the enneahydrate from cold aq. soln., and C. Manuelli and B. Gasparinetti from a strongly acid soln. L. F. Nilson allowed an aq. soln. of thorium sulphate in 50 parts of water to stand in air at 15° until crystals began to separate, and when heated to a rather higher temp., only crystals of the enneahydrate were deposited. G. Wyrouboff said

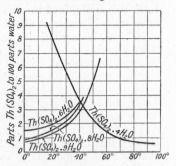

FIG. 8.—Solubility Curves of Thorium Sulphate.

that the easiest and quickest way of making the enneahydrate is to stir the tetrahydrate with water at 5°–10°—*vide infra,* the solubility of thorium sulphate in acids.

The monoclinic, prismatic crystals of the enneahydrate have been described by J. J. Chydenius, H. Töpsöe, P. T. Cleve, G. Wyrouboff, C. Manuelli and B. Gasparinetti, A. Fock, F. Zambonini, etc. According to E. H. Kraus, the axial ratios are $a : b : c = 0.5972 : 1 : 0.6667$, and $\beta = 98°\ 17'$. The corrosion figures with water were studied by E. H. Kraus. C. F. Rammelsberg, W. F. Hillebrand and W. H. Melville, and E. H. Kraus discussed the isomorphism of the salt with uranyl sulphate, $(UO_2)SO_4.9H_2O$. H. Töpsöe gave 2·767 for the sp. gr., and E. H. Kraus, 2·766 at 16°. According to P. T. Cleve, and J. J. Chydenius, the crystals effloresce on exposure to air ; J. J. Berzelius said that at 15° and less, the crystals are stable in air, but at a higher temp. they lose 60 per cent. of their water, and at 60°, all is lost. M. Delafontaine said that at 100°, 17·01 per cent. of water is given off ; while P. T. Cleve said that nearly 7 mols or 21·33 per cent. of water is lost. P. T. Cleve found 7 mols of water evolved over conc. sulphuric acid, and E. Löwenstein noted the amounts of water lost when the enneahydrate is confined in atm. of different humidities corresponding with sulphuric acid of different conc.

Per cent. H_2SO_4	30	40	50	60	70	80	90	100
Loss of water	0	2·88	3·14	9·31	15·32	15·3	21·57	21·68

J. J. Chydenius said that if not powdered this hydrate dissolves with difficulty in water ; and P. T. Cleve said that the unbroken crystals can stay a long time in water without their corners rounding. Observations on the solubility have been made by E. H. Kraus, P. T. Cleve, L. F. Nilson, etc. The following results are due to H. W. B. Roozeboom, and are expressed in grams of the anhydrous salt per 100 grms. of water :

	0°	10°	20°	30°	40°	51°	55°
Grms. Th(SO$_4$)$_2$ . .	0·74	0·98	1·38	1·995	2·998	5·22	6·76

The results are plotted in Fig. 27. Some observations by E. Demarçay, and G. Wyrouboff are in agreement with these data. H. W. B. Roozeboom observed that crystals of the tetrahydrate appear if the soln. be kept some time at 60°. H. W. B. Roozeboom said that the enneahydrate is stable over the range 0°–43° ; and H. M. Dawson and P. Williams found that densimetric observations gave 47·5° for the transition temp. ; dilatometric measurements gave 46·5° ; and electrical conductivity data, 48°. P. T. Cleve said that the enneahydrate is not soluble in alcohol.

According to P. T. Cleve, the evaporation of a neutral soln. of thorium sulphate, at about 24°, furnishes crystals of **octohydrated thorium sulphate**, Th(SO$_4$)$_2$.8H$_2$O. L. F. Nilson obtained the salt by crystallization from a soln. of the anhydrous salt in 50 parts of water at about 25°—but J. J. Chydenius obtained the tetrahydrate at 25°. G. Wyrouboff also prepared this hydrate. H. W. B. Roozeboom obtained it by allowing a soln. of anhydrous thorium sulphate in 15 parts of water at 0° to stand for some time ; and I. Koppel and H. Holtkamp treated a conc. soln. of thorium nitrate with the calculated quantity of sulphuric acid below 42°—*vide infra*, the solubility of thorium sulphate in acids. The crystals were washed with water and dried in air. P. T. Cleve, and L. F. Nilson have described the crystals. According to G. Wyrouboff the monoclinic, prismatic crystals have the axial ratios $a : b : c = 0·7535 : 1 : 0·5570$, and $\beta = 93°$; and they are feebly doubly refracting. He said that the crystals can be kept for a month in a badly closed vessel without changing the proportion of water ; the loss of water observed by L. F. Nilson is attributed to the presence of some free sulphuric acid. I. Koppel and co-workers gave 22·1–25·13 mm. for the vap. press. of the octohydrate at 30°. P. T. Cleve found that the water is all expelled below a red heat. G. Wyrouboff, and H. W. B. Roozeboom have measured the solubility in water. The latter found for the solubility in grams of the anhydrous salt in 100 grms. of water :

	0°	15°	25°	44°
Grms. of Th(SO$_4$)$_2$ . .	1·0	1·38	1·85	3·71

The results are plotted in Fig. 5. I. Koppel gave 14·944 Cals. for the molar heat of soln. According to H. W. B. Roozeboom, the crystals are relatively stable, and at 42° they pass into the tetrahydrate, and this the more rapidly the higher the temp. Much time is required for the completion of the transformation, even at 60°.

According to H. W. B. Roozeboom, crystals of **hexahydrated thorium sulphate**, Th(SO$_4$)$_2$.6H$_2$O, were produced in a soln. of the octohydrate, acidified with sulphuric acid, after it had stood two years. Although this hydrate is metastable, it hydrates in water very slowly. The solubility expressed in grams of the anhydrous sulphate in 100 grms. of water is approximately (Fig. 5) :

	0°	15°	30°	45°	60°
Grms. Th(SO$_4$)$_2$ . .	1·50	1·63	2·45	3·85	6·64

M. Delafontaine heated a neutral aq. soln. of thorium sulphate on a water-bath, and dried the crystals at 100°. The analysis corresponded with **hemienneahydrated thorium sulphate**, Th(SO$_4$)$_2$.4½H$_2$O. E. Kunheim treated a 60 per cent. soln. of thorium nitrate with sulphuric acid of sp. gr. 1·53, the precipitated crystals were washed with a little water, and dried in air. The analysis also corresponded with the hemienneahydrate. According to M. Delafontaine, the microscopic, needle-like crystals are not hygroscopic. Between 185° and 265°, after nearly 6 hrs., over 6 per cent. of water was lost ; and between 400° and 450°, the crystals lose about 15·68 per cent. of water. E. Kunheim found that the hydrate must be heated to dull redness before all the water is driven off, and some sulphur trioxide is slowly given off. G. Wyrouboff inferred that in water at 30°–40°, the salt hydrates before it dissolves. At a higher temp., there is evidence of hydrolysis in the acidity of the soln. and the formation of a basic sulphate. The evidence that the hemi-enneahydrate is a chemical individual is not above suspicion.

J. J. Berzelius, and J. J. Chydenius obtained **tetrahydrated thorium sulphate**, $Th(SO_4)_2.4H_2O$, by evaporating a neutral or acid soln. of thorium sulphate provided the temp. does not exceed 25°; H. W. B. Roozeboom said the evaporation temp. should be over 43°; and H. M. Dawson and P. Williams, over 47°. The crystals are washed with water, and dried over conc. sulphuric acid. J. J. Berzelius found that alcohol precipitates the tetrahydrate from hot aq. soln. *Vide infra*—the solubility of thorium sulphate in acids. N. J. Berlin also described the preparation of this hydrate. The product consists of microscopic needles, which, according to W. F. Hillebrand and W. H. Melville, are isomorphous with those of uranium sulphate, $(U(SO_4)_2.4H_2O$. J. J. Chydenius found that the salt loses 6·39 per cent. of water at 100°. J. J. Berzelius, E. Demarçay, and H. W. B. Roozeboom made observations on the solubility of the salt. Expressing the results in grams of anhydrous salt per 100 grms. of water, the last-named found (Fig. 5) :

	17°	40°	50°	60°	70°	95°
Grms. $Th(SO_4)_2$	9·41	4·04	2·54	1·63	1·09	(0·71)

The bracketed result is by E. Demarçay. The solubility curve of the tetrahydrate cuts that of the enneahydrate at 43°. The two hydrates therefore cannot exist at this temp. The transformation of the tetrahydrate into the enneahydrate, however, proceeds very slowly below 43°. H. W. B. Roozeboom said that at 42°, the tetrahydrate passes into the octohydrate. I. Koppel gave 13·523 Cals. for the heat of transformation of the tetrahydrate into the octohydrate ; and 28·467 Cals. for the molar heat of soln. of the tetrahydrate. E. Demarçay showed that when the tetrahydrate is boiled with water, the dihydrate, $Th(SO)_2.2H_2O$, and basic sulphate, $ThOSO_4.2H_2O$, are formed. According to I. Koppel and H. Holtkamp, if the octohydrate is boiled with dil. sulphuric acid, the tetrahydrate is formed, and, according to the acidity, the soln. will contain :

Per cent. H_2SO_4	5	10	15
Per cent. $Th(SO_4)_2$	0·7407	0·4808	0·3882

According to J. J. Chydenius, *trihydrated thorium sulphate*, $Th(SO_4)_2.3H_2O$, is obtained by boiling a feebly acid soln. of thorium sulphate ; P. T. Cleve obtained it once. As H. W. B. Roozeboom pointed out, it is very doubtful if this hydrate really exists as a chemical individual.

J. J. Chydenius prepared **dihydrated thorium sulphate**, $Th(SO_4)_2.2H_2O$, by boiling a dil. aq. soln. of thorium sulphate ; G. Wyrouboff obtained it by heating one of the other hydrates to 100°, or, according to H. W. B. Roozeboom, at 110°. The last-named found the hydrate dissolves slowly in water at low temp., and the soln. then contains a mixture of the tetra- and ennea-hydrates.

According to E. Demarçay, aq. soln. of thorium sulphate are easily super-saturated. M. Barre found that the lowering of the f.p. of a soln. of 1·5 grms. of the enneahydrate in 100 grms. of water is 0·06°, and the mol. lowering is 23—calculated 22. He also gave for the sp. electrical resistance of aq. soln. with 0·1, 0·01, and 0·001 eq. of the salt per litre, 8·33, 3·16, and 1·26 respectively. J. L. Soret noted that the soln. is fluorescent when exposed in a quartz vessel to the light of the cadmium arc. E. Kunheim studied the action of carbon on thorium sulphate in the electric arc furnace.

O. Hauser and F. Wirth kept an aq. soln. of thorium sulphate for many months in the cold without its becoming turbid, and E. Demarçay said that a cold soln. suffers no perceptible dissociation, but both dil. and conc. soln. are much dissociated when heated. J. J. Berzelius, E. Demarçay, O. Hauser and F. Wirth, and

H. W. B. Roozeboom noted that basic sulphates are obtained from hot aq. soln. M. Barre said that the aq. soln. begins to decompose at about 55°. H. G. Denham showed that aq. soln. are considerably hydrolyzed ; the **hydrolysis** of a $\frac{1}{64}N$-soln. amounts to 46 per cent. As indicated above, L. and P. Wöhler and W. Plüddemann obtained no evidence of the formation of basic sulphates during the thermal decomposition of anhydrous thorium sulphate. G. Wyrouboff reported monohydrated **thorium oxysulphate,** $ThOSO_4.H_2O$, to be formed when the hemienneahydrate is heated over 50° in the presence of water ; and O. Hauser and F. Wirth obtained the same product by heating a soln. of one part of thorium sulphate in 140 parts of water in a sealed tube for four or five hours at 160°–180°. The product was washed with cold water, and dried over calcium chloride. The needle-like crystals are feebly doubly refracting, and are quite insoluble in water and dil. acids. G. Wyrouboff obtained the *dihydrate*, $ThOSO_4.2H_2O$, by heating hemienneahydrated thorium sulphate with water at 100°. The salt was also made by M. Barre, and O. Hauser and F. Wurth. The percentage solubility is 0·023 at 100°. M. Barre also reported an unstable trihydrate, $ThOSO_4.3H_2O$, to be formed from a soln. of the normal sulphate at 55°. F. Halla made the pentahydrate, $ThOSO_4.5H_2O$, by the action of magnesium carbonate on a mixture of anhydrous thorium sulphate with a little water. The same salt is obtained as a flocculent precipitate on adding magnesium sulphate to a boiling soln. of thorium sulphate or nitrate. The titration with potassium hydroxide soln. using phenolphthalein as indicator proceeds to $ThOSO_4 : KOH=1 : 1·75$. It is not possible to wash thorium hydroxide free from sulphates by aq. ammonia. Magnesium hydroxide and thorium sulphate, or magnesium sulphate and thorium hydroxide, yield a transparent jelly. O. Hauser and F. Wirth made octohydrated **thorium oxyheptasulphate,** $ThOSO_4.2H_2O.3\{Th(SO_4)_2.2H_2O\}$, or $4ThO_2.7SO_3.8H_2O$, by heating in a sealed tube for 2–3 hrs. between 105°–115°, a mixture of a gram of anhydrous thorium sulphate with 120–150 c.c. of water, filtering and washing with cold water. The product is partly soluble in cold water ; and it may be a mixture. There is a clerical error in the analysis. E. Demarçay also made a similar product.

G. Wyrouboff and A. Verneuil reported a number of condensed products which they regarded as **thorium meta-oxysulphates.** They were made by adding dil. sulphuric acid, or a soln. of a normal sulphate—*e.g.* ammonium sulphate—to a soln. of a condensed chloride or nitrate. The salt $24ThO_2.SO_3.12H_2O$ is obtained from the corresponding chloride ; the chloride $Th_8O_7(OH)_{16}Cl_2.2HCl$ furnishes the salt $Th_8O_7(OH)_{16}.H_2SO_4$; which, when washed free from soluble sulphates, gives $Th_8(OH)_{16}SO_4$. The compounds are not stable in water.

If a soln. of thorium sulphate be treated with hydrogen dioxide, P. T. Cleve found that a **thorium peroxysulphate,** $Th_2O_7.SO_3$, is formed. The solubility of thorium sulphate in aq. soln. of hydrochloric acid at 30° has been measured by I. Koppel and H. Holtkamp. Expressing the conc. of the soln. in grams of the anhydrous sulphate per 100 grms. of sat. soln., they found :

Per cent. HCl.	0	4·55	12·14	15·71	18·33	20	23·9
Grms. Th(SO₄)₂	2·15	3·541	2·811	2·360	2·199	2·110	1·277
			$Th(SO_4)_2.8H_2O$			$Th(SO_4)_2.4H_2O$	

likewise for nitric acid, at 30° :

Per cent. HNO₃	0	5·17	16·68	21·99	28·51	33·17	38·82
Grms. Th(SO₄)₂	2·15	3·68	4·84	4·47	3·88	3·34	2·51

and for sulphuric acid, at 30° :

Per cent. H₂SO₄	0	0·466	4·97	15·03	32·68	37·80	45·69	74·0	80·5
Grms. Th(SO₄)₂	2·152	2·055	2·323	1·484	0·3364	0·077	0·0213	0·1208	0
			$Th(SO_4)_2.8H_2O$				$Th(SO_4)_2.4H_2O$		

They also made observations at 20°, and at the b.p. of the soln.   F. Wirth reported some results at 25° :

| N-H_2SO_4 | • | • | 0 | 1·1 | 2·16 | 4·32 | 6·68 | 9·68 | 10·89 | 15·15 |
| $Th(SO_4)_2$ | • | • | 1·593 | 1·831 | 1·488 | 0·8751 | 0·4312 | 0·1045 | 0·0636 | 0·0308 |

$$Th(SO_4)_2.9H_2O \qquad\qquad Th(SO_4)_2.8H_2O \quad Th(SO_4)_2.4H_2O$$

J. J. Berzelius reported an acid sulphate.   I. Koppel and H. Holtkamp say that acid sulphates appear as solid phases with soln. of the octohydrated sulphate in 74–80 per cent. sulphuric acid.   B. Brauner and J. Picek found that if conc. sulphuric acid be added to a cold sat. soln. of thorium nitrate, and the product heated in vacuo at 130° to remove the excess of sulphuric acid, fine, needle-like crystals are obtained and are very hygroscopic.   Analyses correspond with **thorium dihydrotrisulphate,** $Th(HSO_4)_2(SO_4)$.   C. Manuelli and B. Gasparinetti obtained white crystals of **thorium dihydropentasulphate,** $Th_2H_2(SO_4)_5.2H_2O$, by fusing 50 grms. of the ash of gas-mantles with 150 grms. of sodium hydrosulphate. and allowing the product to stand in contact with dil. hydrochloric acid.   The salt is very soluble in water, and when crystallized from aq. soln., the enneahydrate is formed.

Thorium sulphate forms a series of complex salts with the sulphates of the alkali metals and ammonium.   P. T. Cleve [2] mentioned **thorium ammonium tetrasulphate,** $2(NH_4)_2SO_4.Th(SO_4)_2$, as being formed in masses of needle-like crystals by the spontaneous evaporation of a mixed soln. of the component salts. The double salt was said to be very soluble in water, and in a sat. aq. soln. of ammonium sulphate.   This salt may be analogous with the dihydrate prepared by A. Rosenheim and co-workers by shaking tetrahydrated thorium sulphate with a conc. soln. of ammonium sulphate, and allowing the filtrate to evaporate over sulphuric acid.   M. Barre's solubility curve, Fig. 9, shows the limits of stability

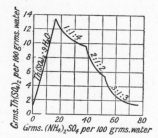

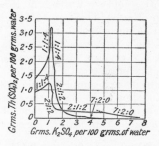

FIG. 9.—The Solubility of Thorium Sulphate in Solutions of Ammonium Sulphate.

FIG. 10.—The Solubility of Thorium Sulphate in Aqueous Solutions of Potassium Sulphate.

of this complex salt.   M. Barre measured the solubility of thorium sulphate in aq. soln. of ammonium sulphate at 60°, expressing the conc. in grams of salt in 100 grms. of water, and the composition of the solid phase as $(NH_4)_2SO_4 : Th(SO_4)_2 : H_2O$,

$(NH_4)_2SO_4$	•	•	•	2·13	10·02	16·56	35·20	49·05	52·88	69·74
$Th(SO_4)_2$	•	•	•	3·361	8·947	13·330	9·821	5·750	4·583	1·653
Solid phase	•	•		0:1:9		1:1:4	2:1:2		3:1:3	

The results are plotted in Fig. 10.   Consequently with soln. with up to 16·5 per cent. of ammonium sulphate, the solid phase is enneahydrated thorium sulphate ; and with 35·2–51·0 per cent. of ammonium sulphate, the solid phase is $(NH_4)_4Th(SO_4)_4.2H_2O$.   A. Rosenheim and co-workers obtained tetrahydrated **ammonium thorium trisulphate,** $(NH_4)_2SO_4.Th(SO_4)_2.4H_2O$; and M. Barre showed that the salt is stable in soln. containing 16·5–35·2 per cent.

of ammonium sulphate, Fig. 10. M. Barre also found that with soln. containing over 51·0 per cent. of ammonium sulphate, as indicated in Fig. 10, the solid phase is trihydrated **ammonium thorium pentasulphate,** $3(NH_4)_2SO_4.Th(SO_4)_2.3H_2O$, which is found in prismatic crystals. A. Rosenheim and co-workers also reported plates of dihydrated **ammonium thorium hexasulphate,** $4(NH_4)_2SO_4.Th(SO_4)_2.2H_2O$, by allowing a soln. of thorium sulphate with an excess of ammonium sulphate to stand over sulphuric acid. The salt is very soluble in water. This salt does not appear on M. Barre's diagram.

P. T. Cleve could not make **lithium thorium sulphate,** but M. Barre showed that the solubility of thorium sulphate steadily increases as the proportion of lithium sulphate in soln. increases ; thus, expressing conc. in grams of salt per 100 grms. of water at 25°,

Li_2SO_4 . .	0	2·57	6·98	11·13	13·18	20·49	25·18
$Th(SO_4)_2$ . .	1·722	4·13	7·95	11·05	12·54	16·92	18·87

Although the solid phase in all cases is thorium sulphate, and the evaporation of the soln. gives crystals of each constituent, he added ; *il semble cependant presque certain qu'il existe en solution un sel complexe provoqnant cet énorme accroissement de solubilité de* 1·722 *à* 18·87. M. Barre found the solubility curve of thorium sulphate with increasing proportions of sodium sulphate has a well-defined maximum ; thus, expressing conc. in grams of salt per 100 grms. of water at 16° :

Na_2SO_4 .	1·094	1·960	2·98	4·11	6·79	9·35	12·24	15·36
$Th(SO_4)_2$.	1·743	2·387	3·962	3·375	2·136	1·379	1·169	1·048

The solid phase in all cases was hexahydrated **sodium thorium trisulphate,** $Na_2SO_4.Th(SO_4)_2.6H_2O$. P. T. Cleve also prepared this salt by the spontaneous evaporation of a mixed soln. of the component salts. The needle-like crystals are very soluble in water. A. Rosenheim and co-workers also prepared a *dodeca-hydrate,* $Na_2SO_4.Th(SO_4)_2.12H_2O$, by shaking a conc. soln. of ammonium sulphate with thorium sulphate for a few hours. Needle-like crystals separate from the filtered soln. after standing some days ; and they are dried in air. They also made needle-like crystals of the *tetrahydrate,* $Na_2SO_4.Th(SO_4)_2.4H_2O$, by a somewhat analogous process with dil. soln. The crystals lose their water at 125°. They failed to make a complex richer in the alkali component.

According to M. Barre, the solubility of thorium sulphate in soln. of potassium sulphate rises rapidly as the conc. of the alkali sulphate increases, and then gradually falls to zero. Thus, expressing conc. in grams of salt per 100 grms. of water, at 16° :

K_2SO_4 .	0	0·424	1·348	1·378	3·092	4·050	4·825
$Th(SO_4)_2$	1·390	1·667	1·706	1·637	0·070	0·027	0·003
	0:1:9		1:1:4	2:1:2		7:2:0	

and at 75° :

K_2SO_4 .	0	0·865	1·270	1·852	4·659	5·932	9·706
$Th(SO_4)_2$	0·9248	1·137	0·907	0·297	0·256	0·123	0·022

The results are plotted in Fig. 10. The break in the solubility curve corresponds with the formation of definite complex salts. The lowering of the f.p. ; and the electrical conductivities of the soln. with one per cent. of potassium sulphate correspond with the formation of complex salts. In 1825, J. J. Berzelius found that if crystals of potassium sulphate be added to a soln. of thorium sulphate, the liquid gradually becomes turbid, and deposits a white, crystalline powder of dihydrated **potassium thorium tetrasulphate,** $2K_2SO_4.Th(SO_4)_2.2H_2O$. If the soln. of alkali sulphate is neutral and conc., the thorium sulphate is not all pre-cipitated because a film of the double salt protects the alkali sulphate from the soln., but if a boiling sat. soln. of potassium sulphate be added to the soln. of thorium sulphate, as long as a turbidity is produced, all the thorium can be precipitated even though the soln. contains an excess of acid ; the double salt, however, is then contaminated with potassium sulphate. M. Barre's observations show the limits of stability of this salt in aq. soln. J. J. Berzelius made the salt by fusing a mixture of thorium and potassium sulphates at a red heat. He purified the salt and obtained it in " transparent, colourless, rectangular prisms " by recrystallization either by the spontaneous evaporation of the aq. soln., or by cooling the hot aq. soln. According to G. Wyrouboff, the crystals are triclinic pinacoids with axial ratios $a : b : c = 0.6029 : 1 : 0.5926$; and $a=85° 0'$; $\beta=95° 12'$; and $\gamma=85° 45'$. M. Barre obtained confirmatory results. J. J. Berzelius found that the clear crystals are permanent in air at ordinary temp., but when gently heated, they become turbid and lose their water of crystallization ; M. Barre added that the salt is dehydrated below 100°. J. J. Berzelius further noted that the salt dissolves slowly in cold water and abundantly and with ease in hot water ; and, unlike the yttrium salt, it is quite insoluble in a sat. soln. of potassium sulphate. The boiling aq. soln. slowly deposits a basic salt, while potassium hydrosulphate remains in soln., but the decomposition reaches a limiting value. The basic salt, unlike the corresponding zirconium salt, is soluble in dil. acids, and it does not dissolve in alcohol. T. Sollmann and E. D. Brown add that it is soluble in tartaric acid soln. J. J. Berzelius observed no signs of combination with fused potassium hydrosulphate. Prismatic crystals of the anhydrous salt $K_4Th(SO_4)_4$ were made by A. Rosenheim and co-workers by shaking a cold soln. of potassium sulphate for many hours with an excess of tetrahydrated thorium sulphate, and allowing the filtered liquid to stand for some hours. M. Barre made acicular crystals of tetrahydrated **potassium thorium trisulphate**, $K_2Th(SO_4)_3.4H_2O$, from soln. of the component salts of the conc. indicated in Fig. 10 ; he also reported small, probably triclinic, crystals of **potassium thorium henasulphate**, $K_{14}Th_2(SO_4)_{11}$, from soln. of the component salts of the conc. indicated in Fig. 10. They are quite insoluble in soln. of potassium sulphate over 5 per cent. conc. J. J. Chydenius made crystals of dihydrated **potassium thorium hexasulphate**, $K_2Th(SO_4)_6.2H_2O$, by the method for potassium thorium tetrasulphate, but working at 60°–70°.

C. Manuelli and B. Gasparinetti always obtained dihydrated **rubidium thorium trisulphate**, $Rb_2Th(SO_4)_3.2H_2O$, by crystallization from soln. of the component salts no matter what the conc. It is best to work with eq. quantities and the smallest possible amount of water ; the soln. should not be boiled ; and conc. partly on the water-bath and partly over sulphuric acid. The crystals are sparingly soluble in water, and the aq. soln. crystallizes with difficulty ; they prepared dihydrated **cæsium thorium trisulphate**, $Cs_2Th(SO_4)_3.2H_2O$, in a similar manner. V. Cuttica and L. Bonamici found that *thorium and ceric sulphates* have a limited miscibility. L. Fernandes found that when a conc. soln. of thorium sulphate is poured into an excess of a soln. of thallium sulphate, *bellissimi* crystals of **thallous thorium enneasulphate**, $7Tl_2SO_4.2Th(SO_4)_2$, are deposited. If a small proportion of the thallous salt is used, and the soln. evaporated, at a low temp., crystals of tetrahydrated **thallous thorium trisulphate**, $Tl_2SO_4.Th(SO_4)_2.4H_2O$, are formed. The solubility of the former salt expressed in decigrams of thoria, ThO_2, of salt per 100 c.c. of water is :

	0°	20°	40°	60°	70°	80°	90°	100°
ThO_2	2·8	4·15	5·84	6·96	7·14	7·12	6·9	6·3

The maximum in the curve corresponds with the *trihydrate*, $7Tl_2SO_4.2Th(SO_4)_2.3H_2O$. R. F. Weinland and H. Kühl obtained **stannic thorium tetrasulphate**, $ThSn(SO_4)_4.2H_2O$, in fine needle-like crystals, from a mixed soln. of thorium and stannic sulphates. They consider the water to be constitutional:

$$Sn\begin{bmatrix}(SO_4)_2 \\ (HSO_4)_2 \\ (OH)_2\end{bmatrix}Th$$

REFERENCES.

¹ J. J. Berzelius, *Svenska Akad. Handl.*, 1, 1829 ; *Pogg. Ann.*, 16. 385. 1829 ; J. J. Chydenius, *ib.*, 119 43, 1863 ; *Kemisk Undersökning af Thorjord och Thorsalter*, Helsingfors, 1861 ; G. Krüss and L. F. Nilson, *Œfvers. Akad. Förh.*, 44. 5, 1887 ; *Ber.*, 20. 1665, 1887 : R. J. Meyer and A. Gumperz, *ib.*, 38. 817, 1905 ; L. and P. Wöhler and W. Plüddemann, *ib.*, 41. 703, 1908 ; L. F. Nilson, *ib.*, 15. 2521, 1882 ; *Compt. Rend.*, 95. 729, 1882 ; L. F. Nilson and O. Pettersson, *ib.*, 91. 232, 1880 ; *Ber.*, 13. 1459, 1880 ; *Œfvers. Akad. Förh.*, 37. 1, 1880 ; H. W. B. Roozeboom, *Arch. Néerl.*, 24. 233, 1891 ; *Zeit. phys. Chem.*, 5. 205, 1890 ; H. M. Dawson and P. Williams, *Proc. Chem. Soc.*, 15. 211, 1899 ; *Zeit. Elektrochem.*, 6. 141, 1899 ; H. G. Denham, *Journ. Chem. Soc.*, 93. 62, 1908 ; E. Löwenstein, *Zeit. anorg. Chem.*, 63. 112, 1909 ; I. Koppel and H. Holtkamp, *ib.*, 128. 1573, 1898 ; I. Koppel, *ib.*, 67. 299, 1910 ; O. Hauser and F. Wirth, *ib.*, 60. 243, 1908 ; F Wirth, *ib.*, 76. 174, 1912 ; 79. 357, 1913 ; B. Brauner and J. Picek, *ib.*, 38. 332, 1904 ; F Halla, *ib.*, 79. 260, 1912 ; M. Barre, *Compt. Rend.*, 150. 1599, 1910 ; 151. 231, 1910 ; E. Demarçay, *ib.*, 96. 1861, 1883 ; J. L. Soret, *ib.*, 88. 1077, 1879 ; G. Wyrouboff and A. Verneuil, *ib.*, 128. 1573, 1898 ; *Bull. Soc. Chim.*, (3), 21. 126, 1899 ; *Ann. Chim. Phys.*, (8), 6. 494, 1905 ; G. Wyrouboff, *Bull. Soc. Min.*, 24. 114, 1901 ; *Bull. Soc. Chim.*, (3), 25. 124, 1901 ; G. Urbain, *ib.*, (3), 15. 347, 1896 ; N. J. Berlin, *Pogg. Ann.*, 85. 577, 1852 : V. Cuttica and L. Bonamici, *Gazz. Chim. Ital.*, 53. ii, 761, 1923 ; V. Cuttica and A. Tocchi, *ib.*, 54, i, 628, 1924 ; W. F. Hillebrand and W. H. Melville, *Amer. Chem. Journ.*, 14. 1, 1892 ; H. Töpsöe, *Bihang. Svenska Akad. Handl.*, 2. 5, 1874 ; P. T. Cleve, *ib.*, 2. 6, 1874 ; *Bull. Soc. Chim.*, (2), 21. 115, 1874 ; (2), 43. 57, 1885 ; C. Manuelli and B. Gasparinetti, *Gazz. Chim. Ital.*, 32. ii, 524, 1902 ; F. Zambonini, *ib.*, 32. ii, 525, 1902 ; E. H. Kraus, *Zeit. Kryst.*, 34. 423, 1901 ; A. Fock, *ib.*, 32. 252, 1900 ; C. F. Rammelsberg, *Sitzber. Akad. Berlin*, 603, 1886 ; J. C. G. de Marignac, *Arch. Sciences Genève*, (2), 18. 345, 1863 ; M. Delafontaine, *ib.*, (2), 18. 343, 1863 ; E. Kunheim, *Ueber Einwirkung des Lichtbogens auf Gemische von Sulfaten mit Kohle*, Berlin, 1900.

² P. T. Cleve, *Bull. Soc. Chim.*, (2), 21. 115, 1874 ; M. Barre, *ib.*, (4), 11. 646, 1912 ; *Ann Chim. Phys.*, (8), 24. 145, 1911 ; *Compt. Rend.*, 150. 1321, 1599, 1910 ; 151. 871, 1910 ; A. Rosenheim, V. Samter, and J. Davidsohn, *Zeit. anorg. Chem.*, 35. 435, 1902 ; T. Sollmann and E. D. Brown, *Amer. Journ. Physiol.*, 18. 427, 1907 ; L. Fernandes, *Gazz. Chim. Ital.*, 55. i, 3, 1925 ; G. Wyrouboff, *Bull. Soc. Min.*, 24. 115, 1901 ; J. J. Berzelius, *Svenska Akad. Handl.*, 1, 1829 ; *Pogg. Ann.*, 16. 385, 1829 ; J. J. Chydenius, *ib.*, 119. 43, 1863 ; *Kemisk Undersökning af Thorjord och Thorsalter*, Helsingfors, 1861 ; R. F. Weinland and H. Kühl, *Zeit. anorg. Chem.*, 54. 244, 1907 ; C. Manuelli and B. Gasparinetti, *Gazz. Chem. Ital.*, 32. ii, 524, 1902 ; V. Cuttica and L. Ponamici, *ib.*, 53. ii, 761, 1923.

§ 13. Thorium Carbonates

Normal thorium orthocarbonate, $Th(CO_3)_2$, has not been prepared. J. J. Berzelius [1] showed that thorium hydroxide absorbs carbon dioxide from the air, and that alkali carbonates precipitate a basic carbonate from soln. of a thorium salt. According to J. J. Chydenius, the product obtained by passing carbon dioxide through water in which thorium hydroxide is suspended contains 81·48 per cent. of thoria ; and the precipitate obtained by treating a thorium salt soln. with sodium carbonate, not in excess, contains 81·83 per cent. of thoria, and 7·33 per cent. carbon dioxide ; P. T. Cleve obtained respectively 82·8 and 8·68 per cent. According to E. Chauvenet, when thorium dioxide is treated with carbon dioxide at atm. press., the product has the composition $2Th(OH)_4.CO_2$; but if the reaction occurs under a press. of 30–40 atm., dihydrated thorium oxycarbonate or **thorium metacarbonate**, $ThO.CO_3.2H_2O$, is formed. Under similar conditions, thoria, which has been ignited at a temp. not exceeding 430°, furnishes $Th_7O_{13}CO_3$, or $ThOCO_3.6ThO_2$, or **thorium tridecaoxycarbonate.** Octohydrated **thorium oxycarbonate**, $ThOCO_3.8H_2O$, is formed by the action of sodium carbonate on an aq. soln. of a thorium salt ; in vacuo it loses water and forms the dihydrate ; and at 120°, it forms **thorium trioxycarbonate**, $ThO_2CO_3.ThO_2.1\frac{1}{2}H_2O$, or $ThO_3CO_3.1\frac{1}{2}H_2O$.

The precipitates are soluble in an excess of the alkali carbonate owing to the formation of complex salts. This is the basis of a process of separating thoria from the rare earths. When the soln. in alkali carbonate is boiled, it deposits the basic carbonate. T. Sollmann and E. D. Brown observed that the soln. at room temp. gives a precipitate with sodium hydroxide, but not with sodium hydrophosphate, sodium fluoride, or proteids ; they also reported that the basic thorium carbonate precipitated from soln. of thorium salts is soluble in hot soln. of ammonium oxalate :

insoluble in sodium citrate or tartrate ; soluble in dil. acids, and in tartaric acid. When the soln. of thorium salt is treated with sodium hydrocarbonate, the precipitate may be a *thorium hydrocarbonate;* it is but sparingly soluble in a hot soln. of ammonium oxalate.

The solubility of thorium hydroxide or basic carbonate in soln. of ammonium carbonate is attributed to the formation of complex salts. A. Rosenheim and co-workers prepared hexahydrated **ammonium thorium carbonate,** $(NH)_2Th(CO_3)_3.6H_2O$, as a microcrystalline powder by saturating with carbon dioxide a soln. of thorium hydroxide and ammonium carbonate, and adding alcohol. According to J. J. Berzelius, thoria does not dissolve in sodium carbonate fused before the blowpipe, and, according to T. Hiortdahl, no carbon dioxide is evolved. P. T. Cleve prepared dodecahydrated **sodium thorium pentacarbonate,** $Na_6Th(CO_3)_5.12H_2O$, by dropping a soln. of thorium chloride or nitrate in an excess of boiling sodium carbonate soln., carbon dioxide is evolved, white flecks appear, and they dissolved on stirring the soln. Alcohol is added and the complex salt precipitated. A. Rosenheim and co-workers prepared prismatic crystals of this salt by warming on a water-bath a soln. of sodium hydrocarbonate in which thorium hydroxide is suspended, and at the same time passing in a current of carbon dioxide. An equal vol. of alcohol was then added to the filtered soln. When kept over sulphuric acid, the *tetrahydrate* is formed, and at 100°, the *dihydrate.* The salt is soluble in cold water but hydrolyzes, so that when warmed thorium hydroxide is precipitated. J. J. Berzelius noted that thorium oxide or carbonate dissolves in a conc. aq. soln. of potassium carbonate. A. Rosenheim and co-workers prepared prismatic crystals of decahydrated **potassium thorium pentacarbonate,** $\overline{K}_6Th(CO_3)_5.10H_2O$, by the method used for the sodium salt. They also made **thallium thorium carbonate,** $Tl_6Th(CO_3)_5$, as a crystalline precipitate by adding a soln. of thallium salt to a soln. of thorium hydroxide in ammonium carbonate.

REFERENCES.

[1] J. J. Berzelius, *Svenska Akad. Handl.*, 1, 1829; *Pogg. Ann.*, **16**. 385, 1829 ; J. J. Chydenius, *ib.*, **119**. 43, 1863 ; *Kemisk Undersökning af Thorjord och Thorsalter,* Helsingfors, 1861 ; P. T. Cleve, *Bull. Soc. Chim.*, (2), **21**. 115, 1874 ; A. Rosenheim, V. Samter, and J. Davidsohn, *Zeit. anorg. Chem.*, **35**. 435, 1902 ; T. Sollmann and E. D. Brown, *Amer. Journ. Physiol.*, **18**. 427, 1907 ; E. Chauvenet, *Compt. Rend.*, **153**. 66, 1911 ; T. Hiortdahl, *ib.*, **61**. 175, 1865.

§ 14. Thorium Nitrates

As J. J. Berzelius [1] showed, a soln. of thorium nitrate is obtained by dissolving thorium hydroxide in nitric acid, and on evaporating over sulphuric acid, it furnishes six-sided, lamellar crystals of **dodecahydrated thorium nitrate,** $Th(NO_3)_4.12H_2O$. If evaporated under ordinary conditions a thick syrupy liquid is obtained, and finally a clear glass. The salt is very deliquescent, and the aq. soln. does not become turbid when boiled. J. F. Bahr said that when the glassy mass is treated with water, it furnishes clear, tabular and lamellar crystals, and then dissolves completely. I. Koppel and H. Holtkamp made this hydrate by treating a soln. of the commercial salt with ammonia, boiling the liquid for a short time, filtering and washing the precipitate until no sulphates could be detected in the runnings, dissolving the residue in conc. nitric acid, etc. C. R. Böhm, and A. C. Neish also described the purification of thorium nitrate. The commercial nitrate is not a definite hydrate, or even a single compound. It generally contains water eq. to the tetrahydrate, and a little thorium sulphate. The last-named salt imparts to the nitrate qualities which fit the calcined product for incandescent mantles. The detection of impurities in the commercial salt has been described by R. J. Meyer and A. Gumperz, W. Biltz and F. Zimmermann, C. R. Böhm, G. P. Drossbach, etc. When the dodecahydrate is allowed to stand over conc. sulphuric acid, it loses eight mols of water, and forms the *tetra-hydrate*, $Th(NO_3)_4.4H_2O$. R. Jacoby, and O. Fuhse found that the *hexa-hydrate*, $Th(NO_3)_4.6H_2O$, is obtained by crystallization from hot soln. The tetragonal bipyramidal crystals lose no water when dried over sulphuric acid, and when well dried, the salt is only slightly hygroscopic. B. Brauner obtained the *pentahydrate*, $Th(NO_3)_4.5H_2O$, by heating a mixture of thorium oxalate with nitric acid until a clear soln. is obtained, the greater part of the nitric acid is evaporated off at 80° until crystals begin to form. The acid liquor is then cooled to ordinary temp. H. R. Robinson studied the X-ray spectrum of thorium nitrate.

· Thorium nitrate is soluble in water and in alcohol. When heated, it passes into the oxide. R. J. Meyer and A. Anschütz said the decomposition is complete at 500°. I. Koppel and H. Holtkamp gave for the sp. gr. and index of refraction of soln. at 15° containing per 100 c.c.

Grms. ThO_2	.	0·4	1	2	4	6	8	10	12
Sp. gr. 15°/15°		1·0061	1·0140	1·0327	1·0639	1·0962	1·1297	1·1609	1·1926
Index of refraction		1·33478	1·33582	1·33804	1·34283	1·34724	1·35235	1·35732	1·36188

A. C. Neish and J. W. Burns measured the hydrogen ion conc. of soln. of thorium nitrate. Observations on the radioactive disintegration products have been made by W. Crookes, A. T. Cameron and W. Ramsay, etc. F. Soddy estimated that 350 grms. of thorium nitrate in seven months developed 2×10^{-10} grms. of helium—*vide infra*, radioactivity of thorium. O. Angelucci found that during the electrolysis of a soln. of thorium nitrate, a layer of thorium-A is deposited on the cathode, and thorium hydroxide containing some thorium-X appears on the anode. W. Ramsay and F. L. Usher claimed to have degraded thorium to carbon by the action of radium emanation on a soln. of thorium nitrate. J. O. Perrine observed no sign of the excitation of fluorescence by the X-rays.

R. Jacoby could not prepare an acid salt, *thorium hydronitrate*. B. Szilard studied the peptization of various oxides by soln. of thorium nitrate. H. A. McTaggart found that thorium nitrate in aq. soln., and in conc. as well as in dil. 8×10^{-9} normal soln., gives a positive electric charge to the surface of a sphere of air immersed in it. (In distilled water the charge is always negative.) For conc. in the neighbourhood of 6×10^{-6} normal a sphere initially negative becomes gradually positive as the sphere diminishes in size. G. Wyrouboff and A. Verneuil obtained thorium peroxynitrate by adding a soln. of hydrogen dioxide to a soln. of a thorium salt—*vide* thorium peroxide. According to F. Halla, the titration of thorium nitrate with potassium hydroxide and phenolphthalein is complete when 3·5 mols. KOH are present for 1 atom Th. The addition of ammonium carbonate to a mixed soln. of magnesium chloride and thorium nitrate yields a transparent emulsion, the globules of which change to a hard glass on drying. A. C. Brown studied the adsorption of thorium and uranium-X nitrate soln. by basic ferric acetate ; and H. Freundlich and co-workers, by charcoal.

T. Sollmann and E. D. Brown noted that the aq. soln. of thorium nitrate reacts acidic towards blue litmus ; and P. T. Cleve, that gelatinous thorium hydroxide is precipitated by an aq. soln. of the nitrate. In aq. soln., therefore, the salt is hydrolyzed : $Th(NO_3)_4 + 4H_2O \rightleftharpoons 4HNO_3 + Th(OH)_4$. G. Krüss and W. Palmaer obtained **thorium oxynitrate** with $Th : NO_3 = 1 : 2$ by dissolving thorium hydroxide in a soln. of thorium nitrate, or by heating a mol of the hydroxide with two mols of nitric acid. R. Jacoby also obtained a similar microcrystalline product by boiling a soln. of thorium nitrate with fuming nitric acid, and cooling the soln. G. Wyrouboff and A. Verneuil made **thorium metanitrate,** $6ThO_2.HNO_3$, and $5ThO_2.2HNO_3$ by the action of nitric acid on the corresponding chloride ; and by the action of nitric acid on his polymerized or condensed oxides—*q.v.*

A. Kolb and co-workers prepared a number of complex salts of thorium nitrate with antipyrine, pyridine, quinoline, diethylamine, etc. R. Jacoby prepared plates of pentahydrated **ammonium thorium pentanitrate,** $NH_4Th(NO_3)_5.5H_2O$, by crystallization from a soln. containing one to two mols of ammonium nitrate per mol of thorium nitrate. It loses three mols of water in a desiccator and forms a white powder of the *dihydrate*. A soln. of one to two mols of ammonium nitrate to one mol of thorium nitrate in nitric acid of sp. gr. 1·25 furnishes crystals of anhydrous **ammonium thorium hexanitrate,** $(NH_4)_2Th(NO_3)_6$, when dried on a porous tile. The crystals do not change in a desiccator. If the soln. contains a large excess of ammonium nitrate, an acid salt, *ammonium thorium hydronitrate*, is formed. R. Jacoby could not make a *lithium thorium nitrate* since the component salts crystallize separately from the aq. soln. of ordinary temp. He could make only one sodium salt, namely, enneahydrated **sodium thorium pentanitrate,** $NaTh(NO_3)_5.9H_2O$, from a soln. of equi-molar parts of sodium and thorium nitrates in dil. nitric acid. The solubility in cold water is less than that of the corresponding potassium salt. When this **salt is** kept in a desiccator for 14 days, what appears to be the trihydrate is formed. It is not clear if this product is a mixture or a compound.

J. J. Berzelius prepared what now appears to have been enneahydrated **potassium thorium pentanitrate,** $KTh(NO_3)_5.9H_2O$; and R. Jacoby obtained it by evaporating over sulphuric acid and potassium hydroxide, a soln. of equimolar parts of potassium and thorium nitrates in water or dil. nitric acid (1 : 33). The tabular crystals are hygroscopic. By slowly evaporating in an air-bath at 80° a soln. of two mols of potassium nitrate and one mol of thorium nitrate in dil. nitric acid, R. Jacoby obtained prismatic crystals of **potassium thorium hexanitrate,** $K_2Th(NO_3)_6$, which do not change in a desiccator or at 100°, but attract moisture from the air. R. Jacoby prepared isomorphous mixtures of ammonium thorium nitrate and potassium thorium nitrate. If a soln. of three mols of potassium nitrate and one mol of thorium nitrate in nitric acid of sp. gr. 1·25, be evaporated over sulphuric acid and potassium hydroxide, R. Jacoby found that crystals of tetrahydrated **potassium thorium trihydrodecanitrate,** $K_3ThH_3(NO_3)_{10}.4H_2O$, are formed which slowly effloresce in the desiccator. When heated, the salt loses 3 mols of nitric acid and the water. The crystals are deliquescent in air, and are decomposed by water. The salt can be recrystallized from nitric acid of sp. gr. 1·25, and the solubility of the complex is greater than that of the individual salts. R. Jacoby prepared crystals of **rubidium thorium hexanitrate,** $Rb_2Th(NO_3)_6$, from a soln. of a mol of thorium nitrate in one to three mols of rubidium nitrate in nitric acid of sp. gr. 1·25. The solubility in nitric acid is rather greater than that of the ammonium, sodium, or potassium salt. He made **cæsium thorium hexanitrate,** $Cs_2Th(NO_3)_6$, in an analogous manner. V. Cuttica and co-workers found that *ceric and thorium nitrates* are partially miscible. R. Jacoby could not make *thallous thorium nitrate*, since the unchanged salts crystallize separately at ordinary temp., and when the soln. is heated, oxidation to thallic nitrate occurs. He also found that *silver thorium nitrate* could not be obtained because the component salts separate when the soln. is evaporated.

A series of double salts with the general formula $M(NO_3)_2.Th(NO_3)_4.8H_2O$, with M represented by an atom of magnesium, zinc, nickel, cobalt, and manganese, was made by R. J. Meyer and R. Jacoby. By evaporating a soln. of equimolar parts of magnesium and thorium nitrates in a mixture of equal vol. of water and nitric acid of sp. gr. 1·4, over sulphuric acid and potassium hydroxide, the prismatic crystals of octohydrated **magnesium thorium hexanitrate,** $MgTh(NO_3)_6.8H_2O$, which are formed belong to the monoclinic system, and, according to A. Sachs, have the axial ratios $a : b : c = 1.0251 : 1 : 1.5228$, and $\beta = 97° 3.5'$. The double refraction is negative and feeble. R. Jacoby said that the hygroscopic crystals slowly effloresce in a desiccator. They cannot be dehydrated by heat without losing some nitric acid. The corresponding monoclinic crystals of octohydrated **zinc thorium hexanitrate,** $ZnTh(NO_3)_6.8H_2O$, were found by A. Sachs to have the axial ratios $a : b : c = 1.0437 : 1 : -$. They have a feebly negative double refraction.

REFERENCES.

[1] J. J. Berzelius, *Svenska Akad. Handl* , 1, 1829 ; *Pogg. Ann.*, 16. 385, 1829 ; J. J. Chydenius, *ib.*, 119. 43, 1863 ; *Kemisk Undersökning af Thorjord och Thorsalter*, Helsingfors, 1861 ; T. Sollmann and E. D. Brown, *Amer. Journ. Physiol.*, 18. 427, 1907 ; P. T. Cleve, *Bull. Soc. Chim.*, (2), 21. 115, 1874 ; C. R. Böhm, *Chem. Ind.*, 29. 460, 1906 ; A. C. Neish and J. W. Burns, *Journ. Canadian Inst. Chem.*, 5. 69, 1921 ; J. O. Perrine, *Phys. Rev.*, (2), 22. 48, 1923 ; H. Freundlich and M. Wreschner, *Zeit. phys. Chem.*, 106. 366, 1923 ; V. Cuttica and L. Bonamici, *Gazz. Chim. Ital.*, 53. ii, 761, 1923 ; V. Cuttica and A. Tocchi, *ib.*, 54. i, 628, 1924 ; A. C. Neish, *Journ. Amer. Chem. Soc.*, 26. 781, 1904 ; *Chem. News*, 90. 196, 1904 ; B. Brauner, *Journ. Chem. Soc.*, 73. 984, 1898 ; A. T. Cameron and W. Ramsay, *ib.*, 91. 1606, 1907 ; O. Fuhse, *Zeit. angew. Chem.*, 10. 116, 1897 ; J. F. Bahr, *Pogg. Ann.*, 119. 578, 1863 ; I. Koppel and H. Holtkamp, *Zeit. anorg. Chem.*, 67. 290, 1910 ; A. Kolb, *ib.*, 60. 124, 1908 ; G. Krüss and W. Palmaer, *ib.*, 14. 366, 1897 ; R. J. Meyer and R. Jacoby, *ib.*, 27. 359, 1901 ; *Ber.*, 33. 2135, 1900 ; A. C. Brown, *Journ. Chem. Soc.*, 121. 1736, 1922 ; R. Jacoby, *Die Doppelnitrate des vierwertigen Ceriums und des Thoriums*, Berlin, 1901 ; R. J. Meyer and A. Anschütz, *Ber.*, 40. 2639, 1907 ; R. J. Meyer and A. Gumperz, *ib.*, 38. 818, 1905 ; W. Biltz and F. Zimmermann, *ib.*, 40. 4983, 1907 ; A. Sachs, *Zeit. Kryst.*, 34. 163, 1901 ; A. Kolb, G. Melzer, A. Merckle, and C. Teufel, *Zeit. anorg. Chem.*, 60. 123, 1908 ; A. Kolb, *ib.*, 83. 143, 1913 ; F. Halla, *ib.*, 79. 260, 1912 ; W. Crookes, *Proc. Roy. Soc.*, 66. 409, 1900 ; F. Soddy, *Phil. Mag.*, (6), 16. 513, 1908 ; G. P. Drossbach, *Journ. Gasbeleucht.*, 38. 482, 1895 ; O. Angelucci, *Atti Accad. Lincei*, (5), 16. ii, 196, 1907 ; B. Szilard, *Journ. Chim. Phys.*, 5. 636, 1907 ; G. Wyrouboff and A. Verneuil, *Ann. Chim. Phys.*, (8), 6. 492, 1905 ; *Compt. Rend.*, 127. 865, 1898 ; H. A. McTaggart, *Phil. Mag.*, (6), 44. 386, 1922 ; H. R. Robinson, *ib.*, (6), 50. 241, 1925 ; W. Ramsay and F. L. Usher, *Ber.*, 42. 2930, 1909 ; W. Ramsay, *Journ. Chem. Soc.*, 95. 624, 1909.

§ 15. Thorium Phosphates

J. J. Berzelius,[1] P. T. Cleve, and T. Sollmann and E. D. Brown prepared tetrahydrated **thorium orthophosphate**, $Th_3(PO_4)_4.4H_2O$, as a white gelatinous mass by adding a soln. of sodium hydrophosphate to one of a thorium salt. The product, said J. J. Berzelius, is insoluble in water and in aq. phosphoric acid ; and, according to P. T. Cleve, in acetic and mineral acids. T. Sollmann and E. D. Brown added that it is insoluble in dil. hydrochloric, acetic, citric, and tartaric acids and in soln. of sodium citrate and tartrate. Carbonates, citrates, and oxalates, but not the tartrates, hinder the precipitation of the phosphate. The citrate mixture is again precipitated by boiling, long standing, or adding hydrochloric acid, but not by citric, or tartaric acid, or sodium hydroxide. The salt dissolves in 30 per cent. hydrochloric acid, and the soln. is not precipitated by dilution. The salt is also soluble in a soln. of ammonium citrate. According to A. Colani, if 2–3 grms. of anhydrous thorium metaphosphate, or an alkali phosphate, be heated with 40 grms. of anhydrous thorium chloride, in a tube through which dry carbon dioxide is passed, some of the thorium chloride is volatilized ; and the white crystalline powder which remains after washing with water, is a **thorium chlorophosphate**, $ThCl_4.Th_3(PO_4)_4$, or $ThCl(PO_4)$. It is insoluble in water, and, with the exception of boiling sulphuric acid, it is scarcely attacked by dil. or conc. acids; but it is easily broken down by fused alkali carbonates. The corresponding **thorium bromophosphate**, $Th(PO_4)Br$, is obtained in a similar manner. Where the thorium metaphosphate was similarly treated with anhydrous calcium chloride, small, optically inactive crystals of calcium thorium orthophosphate, $CaTh(PO_4)_2$. were formed. With strontium chloride, optically active crystals of **strontium thorium orthophosphate**, $SrTh(PO_4)_2$, were obtained. The corresponding **barium thorium orthophosphate** was an amorphous powder.

K. A. Wallroth made **sodium thorium orthophosphate**, $NaTh_2(PO_4)_3$, by saturating fused microcosmic salt with thoria, and treating the cold mass with hydrochloric acid. L. Troost and L. Ouvrard have stated that normal sodium phosphate does not form a double salt with thorium phosphate. The prismatic crystals are insoluble in all acids. L. Troost and L. Ouvrard made **potassium thorium orthophosphate**, $KTh_2(PO_4)_3$, by melting potassium metaphosphate, KPO_3, and saturating it with thorium oxide, phosphate, or anhydrous chloride. The slowly cooled mass was washed with acidulated water. The microcrystalline prisms act on polarized light; their sp. gr. is 5·75 at 12°; they are insoluble in hydrochloric or nitric acid, and in aqua regia. If the potassium pyrophosphate be used in place of the metaphosphate in the preceding process, **dipotassium thorium orthophosphate,** $K_2Th(PO_4)_2$, is formed in microcrystalline octahedra. The sp. gr. is 4·688 at 7°; and the salt is insoluble in water but soluble in nitric acid. The corresponding **disodium thorium orthophosphate,** $Na_2Th(PO_4)_2$, was made in a similar manner; the crystals probably belong to the triclinic system. L. Troost and L. Ouvrard reported hexagonal plates of the **potassium thorium phosphate,** $K_{12}Th_3(PO_4)_8$, $6K_2O.3ThO_2.4P_2O_5$, of sp. gr. 3·98 at 12°; and a white powder of $Na_5Th(PO_4)_3$, or $5Na_2O.2ThO_2.3P_2O_5$, of sp. gr. 3·843 at 7°. G. Saring prepared **potassium calcium phosphatothorate,** $Ca_3(PO_4)_2(CaO)_2(K_2O)_2ThO_2$, analogous with the corresponding phosphatosilicate.

P. T. Cleve, and C. Volck made monohydrated **thorium hydrophosphate,** $Th(HPO_4)_2.H_2O$, as a white gelatinous mass, by mixing soln. of orthophosphoric acid, and thorium chloride. The washed precipitate was dried to constant weight at 60°–100°. P. T. Cleve said that the salt loses water when calcined; and C. Volck found it to be soluble in boiling water. P. T. Cleve made **thorium pyrophosphate,** $ThP_2O_7.2H_2O$, by adding a soln. of pyrophosphoric acid to one of thorium chloride; or a soln. of normal sodium pyrophosphate to one of thorium nitrate. The washed precipitate was dried at 100°. It is soluble in soln. of pyrophosphoric acid or sodium pyrophosphate. The last-named soln. is precipitated neither by ammonia nor by oxalic acid. It will be observed that the salt is isomeric with monohydrated thorium hydrophosphate. P. T. Cleve made **sodium thorium pyrophosphate,** $Na_4Th(P_2O_7)_2$, as a white crystalline powder by dissolving thorium pyrophosphate in a boiling sat. soln. of sodium pyrophosphate, and allowing the mixture to stand some days. The soln. is precipitated neither by ammonia nor by oxalic acid.

K. R. Johnsson made **thorium metaphosphate,** $Th(PO_3)_4$, by R. Maddrell's process in which phosphoric acid at a red-heat is treated with thorium sulphate, and heated until the sulphur trioxide is expelled. The excess of phosphoric acid is removed by decantation with water. L. Troost and L. Ouvrard also made it by the action of an excess of metaphosphoric acid on anhydrous thorium chloride or bromide; and they gave 4·08 for the sp. gr. of the rhombic plates at 16·4°; K. R. Johnsson gave 3·922 for the sp. gr. of the microscopic plates. A. Colani found the salt to be isomorphous with uranium metaphosphate, $U(PO_3)_4$, with which it forms mixed crystals. L. Troost and L. Ouvrard said that the salt is insoluble in water; they also made **sodium thorium metaphosphate** in triclinic prisms of sp. gr. 5·62 at 16°; the crystals act on polarized light; and are soluble in nitric and hydrochloric acid.

The Lindsay Light Co. prepared **thorium sulphatometaphosphate,** $Th(PO_3)_2SO_4$, in the form of white, acicular crystals, by dissolving 120 grms. of octohydrated thorium sulphate, in 50 c.c. of 80 per cent. phosphoric acid, and heating for 10 hrs. at 280°. Water and sulphuric acid fumes are evolved and the product forms a nearly solid, crystalline mass, insoluble in water or dil. acids. The same substance is also obtained by heating thorium phosphate with an equal weight of sulphuric acid, preferably in presence of 20–40 per cent. of phosphoric acid, for 10 hrs. at a temp. above 260°.

REFERENCES.

[1] J. J. Berzelius, *Svenska Akad. Handl.*, 1, 1829; *Pogg. Ann.*, 16. 385, 1829; P. T. Cleve, *Bull. Soc. Chim.*, (2), 21. 115, 1874; T. Sollmann and E. D. Brown, *Amer. Journ. Physiol.*, 18. 427, 1907; C. Volck, *Zeit. anorg. Chem.*, 6. 163, 1894; Lindsay Light Co., *U.S. Pat. No.* 1323735, 1920; *Brit. Pat. No.* 156892, 1920; A. Colani, *Compt. Rend.*, 149. 207, 1909; *Ann. Chim. Phys.*, (8), 12. 59, 1907; L. Troost and L. Ouvrard, *ib.*, (6), 17. 229, 1889; *Compt. Rend.*, 101. 211, 1885; 102. 1423, 1886; 105. 30, 1887; K. R. Johnsson, *Ber.*, 22. 979, 1889; K. A. Wallroth, *Œfvers. Akad. Förh.*, 40. 3, 1883; *Bull. Soc. Chim.*, (2), 39. 321, 1883; R. Maddrell, *Mem. Chem. Soc.*, 3. 273, 1848; *Phil. Mag.*, (3), 30. 322, 1847; G. Saring, *Versuche über den Aufschluss von Phosphaten durch Kieselsäure bei hohen Temperaturen*, Dresden, 1906.

CHAPTER XLV

GERMANIUM

§ 1. The Discovery and Occurrence of Germanium

K. G. A. von Weissenbach,[1] and A. Breithaupt described a mineral, obtained from St. Michaelis, near Freiberg (Saxony), which was called *Plusinglanz*—from πλούσιος, rich—in allusion to the lustre. An earth from Himmelsfürst in the same district was described by E. W. Neubert, and A. Weisbach, and named **argyrodite**—from ἀργυρώδης, argentiferous—in allusion to its composition. A. Weisbach reported an analysis indicating the presence of a small proportion of mercury. C. Winkler obtained 74·72 per cent. Ag; 17·13, S; 0·66, FeO; 0·22, ZnO; and 0·31, Hg. The result was about 7 per cent. too low. He attributed the deficiency to the presence of an unknown element, precipitated as sulphide in the hydrogen sulphide group, and *dem Antimon in mancher Beziehung ähnlichen*, but yet quite different. The new element was called **germanium** from the Latin name *Germania*.

On account of the likeness of argyrodite to antimony glance (stibnite), C. Winkler at first assumed the new element must be D. I. Mendeléeff's unknown eka-antimony, occupying a place between antimony and bismuth in the periodic table. When C. Winkler had worked over the properties of germanium it was found that it did not fit well into the places assigned in the periodic table to eka-antimony and eka-cadmium, but it did fit well into the place reserved for eka-silicon. This is illustrated by Table IV, **1**. 6, 4. G. A. Quesneville proposed to use D. I. Mendeléeff's term eka-silicon in place of germanium, but this was not adopted.

The analyses of C. Winkler, S. L. Penfield, V. M. Goldschmidt, F. Kolbeck, A. Frenzel, and G. T. Prior and L. J. Spencer show that different samples of argyrodite contain from 4·99 to 7·05 per cent. of germanium ; and that the mineral is best regarded as $4Ag_2S.GeS_2$—C. Winkler first gave $3Ag_2S.GeS_2$—*i.e. silver sulphogermanate*, Ag_8GeS_6. T. Kolbeck, and A. Frenzel showed that the mineral *Plusinglanz* is a variety of argyrodite. A. Weisbach first described argyrodite as belonging to the monoclinic system. S. L. Penfield obtained a similar mineral from Potosi, Bolivia, but furnishing cubic crystals, thence he inferred that argyrodite is dimorphous, and he assigned the name canfieldite—after F. A. Canfield—to the cubic form. A. Weisbach subsequently showed that the mineral from Freiberg is cubic, and tetrahedral. S. L. Penfield described a mineral from La Paz, Bolivia, which was previously thought to be argyrodite, but which was shown to be a kind of stanniferous argyrodite with Ge : Sn=5 : 12, and he transferred the name canfieldite from the Bolivian argyrodite to the isomorphous stanniferous form. As emphasized by A. W. Stelzner, tin and germanium belong to the same chemical group, and are isomorphous with one another, and that silver sulphostannate isomorphous with argyrodite is to be anticipated. Canfieldite, said S. L. Penfield, may therefore be regarded as *silver sulphostannate*, Ag_8SnS_6, which occurs in Bolivia admixed with the isomorphous sulphogermanate, furnishing $Ag_8(Ge,Sn)S_6$. The Bolivian mineral has about 1·83 per cent. Ge, and 6–10 per cent. Sn. The deposits of argyrodite have been described by A. W. Stelzner, A. Frenzel, R. Peele, and

254

H. Reck. V. M. Goldschmidt emphasized the analogy between the formula of fahlerz, $3R_2S.R^i_2R^vS$, of sp. gr. 4·921, and mol vol. 165, and argyrodite $3R_2S.R^i_2R^{iv}S$, of sp. gr. 6·266 and mol. vol. 180. The sp. gr. is 6·1–6·3 ; and the hardness 2–3. J. L. C. Schröder van der Kalk discussed the colour of argyrodite ; and A. de Gramont, the spark spectrum. G. T. Prior and L. J. Spencer showed that A. Damour's *brongniardite* is nothing but a variety of argentiferous argyrodite. The dark reddish-grey mineral *germanite* obtained by O. Pufahl from Tsumeb, S.W. Africa, has a composition approximating $Cu_5(Cu,Fe)_6AsGeS_{12}$. Analyses were reported by H. Schneiderhöhn, F. W. Kriesel, W. Keil, and E. Thomson. The latter represented it by the formula $10Cu_2S.4GeS_2.As_2S_3$. J. Lunt made a spectroscopic analysis of germanite. The black mineral, *ultrabasite* reported by V. Rosicky and J. Sterba-Böhm from the Himmelsfürst mine, Freiberg, has the composition of a *silver germanium lead sulphantimonite,* $11Ag_2S.28PbS.3GeS_2.2Sb_2S_3$, and P. Groth and K. Mieleitner suggest that it is a mixture of lead germanium sulphide, $3GePb_2S_4$, with $2Pb_3(SbS_3)_2$, $16PbS$, and $11Ag_2S$. The axial ratios of the rhombic or pseudo-tetragonal crystals are $a : b : c = 0.988 : 1 : 0.462$, when those of teatlite are $a : b : c = 0.93 : 1 : 1.31$. The hardness of ultrabasite is 5, and sp. gr. 6·026. It decrepitates and decomposes when heated ; and is slowly attacked by hydrochloric and nitric acids.

Germanium is a scarce element. J. H. L. Vogt [2] estimated that the igneous rocks in the earth's crust contain $n \times 10^{-12}$ per cent. of this element ; and F. W. Clarke and H. S. Washington made a similar estimate. According to H. A. Rowland, lines in the solar spectrum correspond with those of germanium, and indicate the presence of that element in the sun. C. Winkler [3] said that germanium although sparse may be really more widely distributed than it is at present assumed to be because, owing to the want of a delicate and sharp distinguishing test, its presence may easily be overlooked. G. Urbain examined the ultra-violet spectrum of 64 samples of *zinc blende*, and he found germanium to be present in 38 samples, and appreciable quantities were found in five samples from Webb City, Missouri ; Stolberg, Aix-la-Chapelle ; Turkey in Europe ; Raible, Corinth ; and Mexico. A. del Campo y Cerdan also examined 68 zinc blendes and found germanium to be present in 50 of the samples—*vide* indium, 5. 35, 1. G. H. Buchanan also found germanium present in many zinc blendes, and J. H. Müller, in the smithsonite ore of Kentucky, and in the mine-water and ore washings. W. F. Hillebrand and J. A. Scheerer found it in zinc blendes and carbonate ores from Missouri, Idaho, Colorado, Nevada, and Utah.

The mineral *franckeite*, $5PbS.Sb_2S_5.2SnS_2$, described by A. Stelzner was found to contain about 0·10 per cent. of germanium. G. Krüss found up to about 0·1 per cent. of germanium in euxenite ; K. von Chrustschoff, in harmony with D. I. Mendeléeff's suggestion, found this element to be present in many tantalum and columbium minerals ; up to 1·5 per cent. in *samarskite ;* 0·01 per cent. in *tantalite ;* 0·03 per cent. in *columbite* and *fergusonite ;* and traces in *gadolinite.* G. Krüss and L. F. Nilson reported germanium in fergusonite from Arendal. G. Lincio failed to find any trace of germanium in samarskite ; and L. M. Dennis and J. Papish found none in American samarskite, and they suggested that K. von Chrustschoff's methods were unsatisfactory. A. Hadding found germanium in *cassiterite* from Finbo, and Mamacka, but none in cassiterite from Finland, and Bohemia. G. Neumann also reported germanium to be present in tin compounds. G. H. Buchanan found up to about 0·25 per cent. of germanium in *zinc oxide,* and *spelter* prepared from Missouri and Wisconsin zinc blendes. C. Winkler found no germanium in the flue-dust from the roasting chambers of the ores from the Freiberg mine where argyrodite occurs. J. Bardet reported germanium to be present in the mineral waters of Vichy to the extent of one part in 40,000,000 parts of water. E. Cornec detected traces of germanium in the ashes of the marine plant *Laminaria.*

REFERENCES.

¹ A. Breithaupt, *Vollständiges Charakteristik der Mineralsystems*, Dresden, 277, 1832;
K. G. A. von Weissenbach, *Journ. tech. ökon. Chem.*, 10. 205, 1831 ; *Jahrb. Berg. Hütt. Sachsen*,
226, 1831 ; E. W. Neubert, *ib.*, 84, 1886 ; A. Weisbach, *ib.*, 89, 163, 1886 ; *Chem. News*, 53.
257, 1886 ; *Neues Jahrb. Min.*, ii, 67, 1886 ; i, 98, 1894 ; C. Winkler, *Journ. prakt. Chem.*, (2),
34. 188, 1886 ; (2), 36 177, 1887 ; *Ber.*, 19. 210, 1886 ; 30. 15, 1897 ; 32. 307, 1899 ; 39. 4528,
1906 ; *Chem. News*, 53. 127, 1886 ; 54. 136, 1886 ; V. M. Goldschmidt, *Zeit. Kryst.*, 45. 552,
1908 ; A. Frenzel, *Jahrb. Berg. Hütt. Sachsen*, 27, 61, 1900 ; *Tschermak's Mitt.*, (2), 19. 244,
1909 ; *Neues Jahrb. Min.*, ii, 125, 1893 ; S. L. Penfield, *Amer. Journ. Science*, (3), 46. 107,
1893 ; (3), 47. 451, 1894 ; F. Kolbeck, *Centr. Min.*, 331, 1908 ; J. L. C. Schröder van der Kalk,
ib., 79, 1901 ; A. de Gramont, *Bull. Soc. Min.*, 18. 241, 1895 ; L. Moser, *Chem. Ztg.*, 26.
67, 1923 ; F. W. Kriesel, *Chem. Ztg.*, 48. 961, 1924 ; *Metall. Erz*, 20. 257, 1923 ; H. Schneiderhöhn, *ib.*, 17. 364, 1920 ; O. Pufahl, *ib.*, 19. 324, 1922 ; E. Thomson, *Univ. Toronto Geol. Studies*,
17, 1924 ; *Amer. Min.*, 9. 66, 1924 ; J. Lunt, *South African Journ. Science*, 20. 157, 1923 ;
D. I. Mendeléeff, *Liebig's Ann. Suppl.*, 8. 133, 1871 ; A. W. Stelzner, *Neues Jahrb. Min.*, ii, 114,
1893 ; *Bol. Soc. Min. Santiago*, 10. 62, 1893 ; *Zeit. deut. geol. Ges.*, 49. 140, 1910 ; G. T. Prior
and L. J. Spencer, *Min. Mag.*, 12. 5, 1898 ; H. Reck, *Petermann's Geogr. Mitt.*, 247, 1867 ;
R. Peele, *Eng. Min. Journ.*, 57. 78, 1894 ; G. A. Quesneville, *Chem. News*, 54. 49, 1886 ;
A. Damour, *Ann. Mines*, (4), 16. 227, 1849 ; W. F. Hillebrand and J. A. Scheerer, *Journ. Ind.
Eng. Chem.*, 8. 225, 1916 ; V. Rosicky and J. Sterba-Böhm, *Zeit. Kryst.*, 55. 430, 1916 ; P. Groth
and K. Mieleitner, *Mineralogische Tabellen*, München, 29, 1921 ; W. Keil, *Zeit. anorg. Chem.*, 152.
101, 1926.
² J. H. L. Vogt, *Zeit. prakt. Geol.*, 6. 225, 314, 337, 413, 1898 ; 7. 10, 274, 1899 ; F. W. Clarke
and H. S. Washington, *Proc. Nat. Acad. Sciences*, 8. 108, 1922 ; *The Composition of the Earth's
Crust*, Washington, 1924 ; W. Lindgren, *Econ. Geol.*, 18. 419, 1923 ; H. A. Rowland, *Johns
Hopkins Univ. Cir.*, 85, 1891 ; *Amer. Journ. Science*, (3), 41. 243, 1891 ; *Chem. News*, 63. 133,
1891.
³ G. Urbain, *Compt. Rend.*, 149. 602, 1909 ; G. Urbain, M. Blondel, and M. Obiedoff, *ib.*,
150. 1758, 1910 ; J. Bardet, *ib.*, 157. 224, 1913 ; 158. 1278, 1914 ; E. Cornec, *ib.*, 168. 513,
1919 ; A. del Campo y Cerdan, *Anal. Fis. Quim.*, 12. 80, 1914 ; K. von Chrustschoff, *Journ.
Russ. Phys. Chem. Soc.*, 24. 130, 1892 ; *Neues Jahrb. Min.*, ii, 229, 1894 ; *Proc. Russ. Min. Soc.*,
31. 412, 1894 ; G. Krüss, *Ber.*, 21. 132, 2312, 1888 ; G. Krüss and L. F. Nilson, *ib.*, 20. 1696,
1887 ; G. Lincio, *Centr. Min.*, 142, 1904 ; A. Hadding, *Zeit. anorg. Chem.*, 123. 171, 1922 ;
L. M. Dennis and J. Papish, *ib.*, 120. 1, 1921 ; *Chem. News*, 123. 190, 1921 ; *Journ. Amer. Chem.
Soc.*, 43. 2142, 1921 ; G Neumann, *Monatsh.*, 12. 515, 1891 ; A. Stelzner, *Neues Jahrb. Min.*,
ii, 114, 1893 ; D. I. Mendeléeff, *Liebig's Ann. Suppl.*, 8. 200, 1871 ; G. H. Buchanan, *Journ. Ind.
Eng. Chem.*, 8. 585, 1916 ; 9. 661, 1917 ; J. H. Müller, *ib.*, 16. 604, 1924 ; C. Winkler, *Journ.
prakt. Chem.*, (2), 34. 177, 1886 ; (2), 36. 177, 1887; W. F. Hillebrand and J. A. Scheerer, *Journ.
Ind. Eng. Chem.*, 8. 225, 1916.

§ 2. The Extraction and Preparation of Germanium

The chief associates of germanium are silver, copper, zinc, cadmium, gallium,
indium, titanium, tin, lead, arsenic, antimony, tantalum, and columbium. Germanium sulphide is precipitated by hydrogen sulphide from highly acidified soln.,
and the sulphide is readily soluble in ammonium sulphide ; consequently, germanium is easily separated from the majority of its associates. The main difficulty
is the removal of arsenic and tin—which occur in the same analytical group—
vide infra, reactions of analytical interest.

C. Winkler [1] extracted germanium from argyrodite by heating a mixture of the
finely powdered mineral with sodium carbonate and sulphur at a moderate red heat.
The product was extracted with water, and the soln. treated with the exact amount
of sulphuric acid necessary to decompose the whole of the sodium sulphide present.
After being left for a day, the soln. was separated from the precipitate consisting
of sulphur, and arsenic and antimony sulphides, and treated with hydrochloric
acid so long as a precipitate was formed. The whole was then sat. with hydrogen
sulphide, filtered, and the white voluminous precipitate of germanium sulphide
washed with 90 per cent. alcohol sat. with hydrogen sulphide. The sulphide was
roasted at a low temp. warmed with conc. nitric acid, and the oxide so obtained
ignited.

G. Krüss fused euxenite with potassium hydrosulphate and heated the product
with hydrogen chloride to remove the iron. The washed product was treated with

ammonium sulphide at 100° for 8 days. The germanium was separated from the soln. by C. Winkler's process just described. G. Urbain and co-workers treated the acid soln. of Mexican zinc blende with hydrogen sulphide. The mixed precipitate of the sulphides of arsenic, molybdenum, and germanium was dissolved in the minimum amount of ammonia and the soln. fractionally precipitated by diminishing concentration. In this way, the germanium was left alone in soln. 550 grms. of the blende yielded 5 grms. of purified germanium.

G. H. Buchanan based a process for separating the element from germaniferous zinc oxide on the volatility of germanium tetrachloride. A mixture of the crude oxide and conc. hydrochloric acid was heated in a distilling flask and the distillate treated with hydrogen sulphide. The germanium sulphide so obtained would be contaminated with arsenic. L. M. Dennis and co-workers prevented the arsenic volatilizing as trichloride along with the germanium tetrachloride by passing a current of chlorine through the apparatus during the distillation. This maintained the arsenic in the quinquevalent form which does not volatilize with the germanium tetrachloride. J. H. Müller was unable to obtain germanium tetrachloride free from arsenic by the distillation of the hydrochloric acid soln. in a current of chlorine; but L. M. Dennis and co-workers found that if the distilling flask be fitted with a fractionating column, the arsenic trichloride, boiling at 129°, and germanium tetrachloride, boiling at 86°, can be adequately separated, and a distillate free from arsenic obtained. H. C. Fogg and C. James described the extraction of germanium from zinc oxide. J. S. Thomas and W. Pugh extracted germanium from germanite, reducing the dioxide by fusion with potassium cyanide and carbon. W. Keil digested the powdered mineral with a hot mixture of nitric and sulphuric acids, until white fumes of sulphuric acid were given off, and cooled the mass. The product was suspended in hydrochloric acid, and distilled in a current of chlorine. Germanium tetrachloride collected below the hydrochloric acid in the receiver. The two liquids were separated, and the free chlorine removed by shaking with mercury. The tetrachloride was then distilled and converted into sulphide or oxide as required.

C. Winkler found that small quantities of germanium oxide or sulphide can be reduced by heating in a current of hydrogen. The operation is *lästig*. The metal is also precipitated as a brown or grey powder from soln. of its salts. Powdered germanium is also obtained by heating a mixture of potassium fluogermanate and sodium, but it is difficult to separate the powdered metal from the sodium fluoride. C. Winkler found the most convenient method of preparation is to mould little balls from a mixture of the powdered oxide with 15–20 per cent. of starch and a little boiling water. These were dried and carbonized at a dull red heat; and introduced into a crucible between layers of charcoal. A porous regulus of germanium was obtained by heating the crucible and contents at bright redness for an hour. The regulus was then fused under borax glass, and germanium was obtained as a metallic bead. A little germanium oxide dissolves in the borax. L. M. Dennis and co-workers obtained a poor yield by reducing the dioxide with aluminium; and they used C. Winkler's method fusing the powdered metal below molten sodium chloride in place of borax.

The lode of argyrodite at Freiburg is virtually exhausted; germanite has not been worked. Another possible source of germanium is in the mineral water of Vichy. The evaporation of a quarter million litres furnishes a residue containing about 0·06 grm. of germanium oxide per 100 kgrms. of residue. Hence, the water has the equivalent of about 0·00024 mgrm. per litre.

REFERENCES.

[1] C. Winkler, *Journ. prakt. Chem.*, (2), **34**. 177, 1886; (2), **36**. 177, 1887; G. H. Buchanan, *Journ. Soc. Chem., Ind.*, **8**. 585, 1916; **9**. 661, 1917; J. S. Thomas and W. Pugh, *Journ. Chem. Soc.*, **125**. 816, 1924; J. H. Müller, *Journ. Amer. Chem. Soc.*, **43**. 2131, 2549, 1921; L. M. Dennis and J. Papish, *ib.*, **43**. 2131, 1921; L. M. Dennis and E. B. Johnson, *ib.*, **45**. 1380, 1923:

L. M. Dennis, K. M. Tressler, and F. E. Hance, *ib.*, **45**. 2033, 1923 ; H. C. Fogg and **C. James,** *ib.*, **41**. 947, 1919 ; P. W. Bridgman, *Proc. Amer. Acad.*, **58**. 165, 1923 ; G. Krüss, *Ber.*, **21**. 131, 1888 ; G. Urbain, M. Blondel. and M. Obiedoff, *Compt. Rend.*, **150**. 1758, 1910 ; L. Moser, *OEsterr. Chem. Ztg.*, **26**. 67, 1923 ; W. Keil, *Zeit. anorg. Chem.*, **152**. 101, 1926.

§ 3. The Properties of Germanium

According to C. Winkler,[1] germanium is a greyish-white metal which has a conchoidal fracture and a crystalline structure. The **crystals** are octahedral. According to L. M. Dennis and co-workers, the slow cooling of the metal fused under sodium chloride gave a button whose upper surface had a fine crystalline structure. The metal is an aggregate of elongated crystals bounded in some cases by octahedral faces. Some of the crystals are nitched, or covered with dendritic branches. **X-radiograms** by A. W. Hull, R. N. Pease, and N. H. Kolkmeijer and co-workers show that the crystals are cubic, and the space-lattice has the same arrangement as the diamond with the edge of unit cube 5·61 to 5·63 A. M. L. Huggins deduced an **electronic structure** of the metal. C. Winkler gave 5·469 for the **specific gravity,** at 20·4°. L. M. Dennis and co-workers found the sp. gr. 5·35 at 20°/20°, and A. W. Hull and co-workers calculated 5·36. M. L. Huggins calculated the **atomic radius** to be 1·22 A. J. J. van Laar calculated the value of b of J. D. van der Waals' equation, $b=0·00210$; and for a, $\sqrt{a}=0·07$; and for the valency attraction A, $\sqrt{A}=36$. L. M. Dennis and co-workers found that germanium is so brittle, that it cannot be drilled, and that Brinell's hardness test could not be applied owing to the shattering of the blocks. The metal scratches adularia, but not epidote so that its **hardness** on Moh's scale is 6·25. Cast germanium was found by P. W. Bridgman to have a **compressibility** of $\kappa=1·378\times10^{-6}$ at 30° ; and the proportional change of compressibility with press. $d\kappa/dp=0·98\times10^{-5}$, where $d\kappa/dp=2b$, and $\kappa=a$ of the formula $\delta v=v(-ap+bp^2)$ for the change of volume when the press., p, is expressed in kgrms. per sq. cm. The **melting point** is near 900°. The beads of metal unite into one globule only when fused under borax ; potassium cyanide or sodium carbonate give too great a loss by scorification. W. Biltz found that the metal melts at 958°±5° in an atm. of hydrogen ; and if sat. with oxide, at 916°±5°. W. R. Mott gave 958° for the m.p. ; and L. M. Dennis and co-workers made observations on the sprouting of the metal which has been melted and quickly cooled. The phenomenon is ascribed to the great increase in vol. which occurs when the molten metal solidifies. L. M. Dennis and co-workers showed that the effect is not due to the absorption of gas by the liquid and its expulsion on solidification as in the spitting of silver. The metal does not volatilize appreciably at its m.p., and at 1350°, V. Meyer found it to be slightly volatile, but even at 1500°, L. F. Nilson and O. Pettersson found that the **volatility** is too low for measuring its vap. press., or determining its vap. density. C. Winkler attributed the white cloud rising from a crucible in which germanium was melted under borax to " the vaporization temp. being only slightly above its m.p." W. Biltz showed that the cloud is due to the volatilization of germanous oxide, not the metal; and L. M. Dennis and co-workers showed that the metal alone is not volatile at a temp. 300° above its m.p. W. Biltz said that the metal is not appreciably volatile in nitrogen at 1250°, but in the presence of some oxide, vapour is observed from 750° upwards.

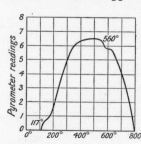

FIG. 1.—Heating and Cooling Curves of Germanium.

When germanium is heated below its m.p., there is evidence of inversion points at 117° and 560°, Fig. 1, which L. M. Dennis and co-workers take to show that the solid passes through at least two modifications—

vide infra, electrical properties. According to the calculations of W. R. Mott, the b.p. of germanium is 1900° at atm. press. ; J. J. van Laar gave 2610° ; and for the **critical temperature**, 4170°, and the **critical pressure**, 910 atm. L. F. Nilson and O. Pettersson found the **specific heat** between 0° and 100° to be 0·0737 ; between 0° and 300°, 0·0768 ; between 0° and 400°, 0·0757, thus making the **atomic heat** 5·34, 5·57, and 5·49 respectively.

Germanium compounds do not colour the bunsen flame, but the **spark spectrum** of germanium has a number of bright lines particularly in the blue and violet. This was investigated by C. Winkler, A. de Gramont, J. Lunt, and F. Exner and E. Haschek. The most intense lines are 2592·65, 2651·29, 2651·69, 2709·69, 2754·68, 3039·20, 4179·20, and 4226·76. The **arc spectrum** was examined by H. A. Rowland and R. Tatnall, J. Papish, and F. Exner and E. Haschek. The most intense lines are 2592·64, 2651·28, 2651·69, 2691·45, 2709·70, 2754·69, 3039·22, and 3269·62. J. Papish considers the blue line of wave-length 468·1 in the spark spectrum is most suitable for the identification of germanium. W. J. Humphreys measured the effect of press. ; L. de Boisbaudran calculated the at. wt. from the spectral lines ; W. N. Hartley and H. Ramage examined the banded flame spectrum. E. Paulson found three triplets in the line spectrum of germanium. Germanium salts give no absorption spectrum, and J. Formánek found the salts do not react with alkanna tincture. H. J. C. Ireton measured the ultra-violet spectrum from 213·8 A to 319·7 A. In the **X-ray spectrum**, W. Duane and co-workers, B. Walter, A. Leide, and M. Siegbahn gave for the K-series in Angström units, or 10^{-8} cm. units, $a_2a=1·261$; $a_1a=1·257$; $\beta_1\beta=1·131$; and $\beta_2\gamma=1·121$; and E. Hjalmar gave for the L-series, $a_1a=10·4136$.

C. Benedicks found the **electrical resistance** of germanium is between that of silicon and that of tin. C. C. Bidwell measured the electrical resistance of germanium at different temp., and the results are shown by the continuous curve, Fig. 2. There are well defined minima at —116° and 645°. From —188° to 100°, the resistance follows the exponential law, $R=A(1+a\theta+\beta\theta^2)e^{Q/kT}$, where A, a, β, Q, and k are constants. This equation requires a minimum at —116°, and a change in the temp. coeff. from positive to negative. Above 600°, the law applies but with different constants. In the intermediate region, the law is obscured by an allotropic transformation. Carbon seems to have a minimum at some high temp. According to J. Königsberger, and K. Schilling, silicon, titanium, and zirconium seem to

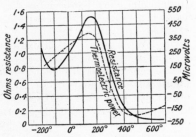

FIG. 2.—The Resistance and Thermoelectric power (Pt Ge) of Germanium at Different Temperatures.

follow a similar law ; silicon has a negative temp. coeff. and a minimum obscured by transformation at a lower temp. than carbon ; titanium has a minimum at about 100° ; zirconium has an inflexion at a lower temp. ; and H. K. Onnes and G. Holst found that tin approaches a minimum at a still lower temp. The **thermoelectric power** of the Ge-Pt couple is shown by the dotted line, Fig. 2. The curve is straight from about —183° to 125°, and again straight from 450° to 700° ; between these temp. there is a slow reversible transformation beginning at about 125° and reaching completion at about 450°. Up to 300° the thermoelectric current is positive with reference to platinum ; it becomes zero at 300°, and is negative beyond that temp. The positive sign means that the current flows across the hot junction from platinum to germanium ; or in the external circuit the direction of flow is from the germanium to the platinum. C. Benedicks found the thermoelectric force of the Cu-Ge couple to be extraordinarily high being —380 microvolts per degree. This is surpassed by only one other element, silicon. E. Merritt showed that the contact rectification of germanium is less than that of silicon. The relation of the **diamagnetic** properties of germanium to the electronic structure of the atom has been studied by B. Cabrera, and A. Dauvillier.

The gas developed by the action of germanium on molten potassium hydroxide is not germanium hydride, but, as C. Winkler showed, it is nothing but hydrogen. Germanium and **hydrogen** are not known to unite directly. J. H. Müller said that there is a loss by heating the metal over 700° in hydrogen owing to the formation of a volatile hydride, but L. M. Dennis showed that there is no loss below 800°, and the molten metal does lose in weight when heated in hydrogen. J. H. Müller and N. H. Smith's observation was attributed to the contamination of the metal by chloride which is reduced by hydrogen to volatile germanous chloride—*vide infra*. D. I. Mendeléeff's eka-silicon should have properties between those of silicon and tin, and germanium has these qualifications. According to C. Winkler, fused and crystallized germanium does not oxidize at ordinary temp. either in dry or in moist **air**; and it does not lose its lustre. Pieces of germanium may be heated nearly to redness without change, but at an incipient red heat, the metal becomes covered with a thin film of oxide. The pulverulent metal which has not been melted is much more readily oxidized. The metal burns with incandescence when heated in **oxygen.** L. M. Dennis and co-workers found that oxidation does not begin appreciably at 600° during 30 hrs., but at 605°, oxidation occurs and proceeds rapidly at 615° but is not completed at 900°. It is not possible to oxidize germanium below 730°, and at higher temp. there is a loss by the volatilization of germanous oxide, which is then further oxidized. No appreciable effect occurs when germanium is kept at room temp., or at 90° in contact with **water**; but at room temp., a 3 per cent. soln. of **hydrogen dioxide** forms some dioxide which dissolves in the liquid; the action is fast at 90°, and faster still at 100°. When a drop of the fused metal is allowed to fall on paper, it divides itself into several globules which move continually over the surface of the paper, forming black tracks. Germanium which has been fused preserves its lustre at ordinary temp in **chlorine,** but when heated, it burns with a bluish-white flame, forming germanium tetrachloride; pulverulent germanium inflames spontaneously in chlorine at ordinary temp. When heated in **bromine** vap., the metal burns with a yellowish flame, forming germanium tetrabromide. When germanium is heated in **iodine** vap. to incipient redness, an iodide is formed. Germanium is not attacked by **hydrofluoric acid** at ordinary temp.; L. M. Dennis and co-workers observed only a loss of 0·1 per cent. in 19N-HF at room temp., and at 90°, a loss of 0·7 per cent. C. Winkler showed that **hydrochloric acid** has very little action; and L. M. Dennis observed no appreciable change in hydrochloric acid conc. or diluted (1 : 1) at room temp. or at 90°. According to C. Winkler, when germanium is heated in a stream of **hydrogen chloride,** hydrogen is liberated and germanium chloroform, $GeHCl_3$, is produced : $Ge+3HCl=H_2+GeHCl_3$. C. Willgerodt did not observe any signs of its accelerating the chlorination of organic products, catalytically. According to C. Winkler, when germanium is heated with **sulphur** to incipient redness, germanous sulphide is formed. L. M. Dennis and co-workers observed no attack by **hydrogen sulphide** below 200°, and the attack is comparatively slight until the dissociation of the gas begins (400°–440°), when a reaction occurs between the germanium and the sulphur. They also found that **sulphur dioxide** acts on crystalline germanium somewhat below 500°, and the reaction is rapid between 510° and 530°—germanium disulphide and dioxide are formed. According to C. Winkler, when germanium is heated with conc. **sulphuric acid,** sulphur dioxide is given off, and a white sulphate is formed which is soluble in water. L. M. Dennis and co-workers observed no change in the metal kept at room temp., or at 90° in 1 : 1 sulphuric acid ; with conc. sulphuric acid at room temp. there was no appreciable action, but at 90° there was a loss of 1 per cent. in about a week. According to C. Winkler, the action of powdered germanium on **nitric acid** is very violent at first, nitric oxide and germanium dioxide are formed. According to L. M. Dennis and co-workers, 1 : 1 nitric acid acted on the metal superficially at room temp. with a loss of 7 per cent., and at 90° with a loss of 1 per cent. Conc. nitric acid at room temp. darkened the surface of the metal, but there was no appreciable loss in weight. According to C. Winkler, the metal readily dissolves in **aqua regia**. When melted under borax, germanous oxide, GeO, is formed. A conc. soln. of **potassium hydroxide** has no action ; but when powdered germanium is projected on the fused alkali, there is a violent reaction, hydrogen is set free, and potassium germanate is formed. L. M. Dennis and co-workers found that a 50 per cent. soln. of sodium hydroxide had no appreciable action during a week's exposure at room temp. and at 90° ; but with a 10 per cent. soln., there was a slight action, and a loss of about 0·5 per cent. The metal dissolves quickly in fused sodium and potassium hydroxides, and the cold mass dissolves in water giving a clear, colourless soln. The metal is attacked and dissolved by fused **sodium carbonate ;** and it is slowly attacked by fused **potassium hydrosulphate.** The reaction with fused **sodium dioxide** is vigorous, and the metal is dissolved. Fused **sodium chloride** has no action, but there is a slight reduction of fused **sodium sulphate.** Molten **potassium cyanide** had no appreciable action. According to C. Winkler, fused borax dissolves a little germanium. Mixtures of germanium with **potassium nitrate** or **potassium chlorate** detonate when heated ; L. M. Dennis found that fused potassium chlorate slowly attacks and dissolves germanium ; and that fused potassium nitrate is immediately reduced, gas is evolved, and some of the metal is oxidized and dissolved. C. Winkler found that when heated with **mercuric chloride** or **bromide,** germanium chloride or bromide is formed. Molten germanium does not attack **porcelain,** but it alloys with **platinum,** forming a brittle, fusible alloy.

Reactions of analytical interest.—Germanium salt soln. give no precipitate with **hydrochloric acid ;** but when the acid soln. is treated with **hydrogen sulphide,** white germanium sulphide, GeS_2, is precipitated ; the precipitation is complete only in the presence of a large excess of conc. acid. Germanium sulphide is either soluble in or peptized by water and by aq. soln. of hydrogen sulphide ; it must therefore be washed with dil. hydrochloric or sulphuric acid sat. with hydrogen sulphide, then with alcohol sat. with the same gas, and finally with ether. The precipitate is readily soluble in a soln. of ammonium sulphide, forming a stable sulphosalt. The addition of an excess of acid precipitates the sulphide unchanged. If the germanium sulphide is mixed with antimony and tin sulphides, the germanium sulphide alone dissolves when the mixture is treated with a soln. of ammonium carbonate. Arsenic sulphide, if present, can be separated by fractional distillation from a hydrochloric acid soln. in a stream of chlorine. The germanium tetra-chloride is the most volatile. The chlorine keeps the arsenic in the quinquevalent state ; potassium chlorate, permanganate, or chromate act similarly. This subject has been discussed by G. H. Buchanan,[2] L. M. Dennis and co-workers, and P. E. Browning and S. E. Scott. K. Haushofer tested minerals for germanium by heating the powder in hydrogen sulphide and examining the sublimate of germanium sulphide, which, when warmed with nitric acid, forms white germanium dioxide soluble in water and dil. nitric acid. Soln. of germanium tetrachloride give no precipitate with **alkali hydroxide** because the hydrated germanium dioxide becomes colloidal, and an excess of alkali forms a soluble germanate. Soln. of **ammonia,** or **ammonium or sodium carbonate,** partially precipitate the hydrated dioxide. O. Brunck found **sodium hyposulphite** gives no precipitate with neutral or acid soln. of germanium salts. Brown, pulverulent germanium is slowly deposited when **zinc** is placed in a soln. of a germanium salt. The analysis of germanium ores was described by S. L. Penfield, G. T. Prior and L. J. Spencer, and V. M. Gold-schmidt. In quantitative work, L. M. Dennis and E. B. Johnson recommended precipitating the germanium as the disulphide, oxidizing the sulphide with 3 per cent. hydrogen dioxide, and finally weighing it as germanium dioxide.

The atomic weight of germanium.—Germanium forms two series of compounds in which the element is respectively bivalent and quadrivalent. The latter com-pounds are the more stable. The quadrivalency of the element with a hydrogen eq. of 18 is in agreement with Avogadro's hypothesis applied to the vap. densities of the volatile tetrachloride and bromide ; it is also in agreement with the sp. ht. rule ; with the law of isomorphism applied to the fluosilicates and fluogermanates ; and with the periodic law as indicated.   C. Winkler [3] decomposed the tetrachloride by sodium carbonate ; added a known excess of standard silver soln., and titrated back with ammonium thiocyanate.   He thus obtained for the ratio $Ag : GeCl_4$, 0·201512 : 1.   This agrees with the at. wt. 72·3.   G. P. Baxter and W. C. Cooper analyzed the tetrachloride and obtained 72·6 for the at. wt. of germanium ; and with the tetrabromide, 72·599–72·609.   J. H. Müller computed 72·41–72·45 from the ratio $K_2GeF_6 : 2KCl$.   Using different standards, F. W. Clarke calculated 72·504 ; and B. Brauner, 72·41.   The International Table gives 72·5 for the best representative value.   The **atomic number** of germanium is 32.   F. W. Aston found indications of three **isotopes** of germanium with at. wts. 70, 72, and 74 respectively, and in agreement with the average at. wt. 72·5.   The Ge_{70} isotope is isobaric with the weakest and heaviest component of zinc, and Ge_{74} is isobaric with the weakest and lightest isotope of selenium.   The **electronic structure** of the atom was discussed by N. V. Sidgwick, and H. G. Grimm and A. Sommerfeld.

REFERENCES.

- C. Winkler, *Journ. prakt. Chem.*, (2), **34**. 177, 1886 ; (2), **36**. 177, 1887 ; C. Willgerodt, *ib.*, (2), **35**. 391, 1887 ; A. W. Hull, *Phys. Rev.*, (2), **20**. 113, 1922 ; C. C. Bidwell, *ib.*, (2), **19**. 389, 447, 1922 ; P. W. Bridgman, *Proc. Amer. Acad.*, **58**. 195, 1923 ; A. J. Bijl and N. H. Kolkmeijer, *Chem. Weekbl.*, **15**. 1264, 1918 ; *Proc. Acad. Amsterdam*, **21**. 405, 494, 501, 1919 ; N. H. Kolkmeijer, *ib.*, **25**. 125, 1922 ; *Versl. Akad. Amsterdam*, **31**. 155, 1922 ; D. I. Mendeléeff, *Liebig's Ann. Suppl.*, **8**. 133, 1871 ; V. Meyer, *Ber.*, **20**. 498, 1887 ; H. K. Onnes and G. Holst, *Comm. Phys. Lab. Univ. Leiden*, 142, 1914 ; L. F. Nilson and O. Pettersson, *Zeit. phys. Chem.*, **1**. 27, 1887 ; J. Königsberger and K. Schilling, *Ann. Physik*, (4), **32**. 179, 1910 ; J. J. van Laar, *Die Zustandsgleichung von Gasen und Flussigkeiten*, Leipzig, 1924 ; *Proc. Acad. Amsterdam*, **18**. 1220, 1915 ; **19**. 2, 1916 ; **20**. 138, 492, 1918 ; G. Kobb, *Wied. Ann.*, **29**. 670, 1886 ; *Journ. prakt. Chem.*, (2), **34**. 206, 1886 ; R. N. Pease, *Journ. Amer. Chem. Soc.*, **44**. 1497, 1922 ; L. de Boisbaudran, *Compt. Rend.*, **102**. 1291, 1886 ; A. de Gramont, *ib.*, **134**. 1205, 1902 ; **144**. 1101, 1907 ; *Analyse spectrale directe des minéraux*, Paris, 1895 ; *Bull. Soc. Min.*, **18**. 171, 1895 ; H. A. Rowland and R. Tatnall, *Astrophys. Journ.*, **1**. 149, 1895 ; W. J. Humphreys, *ib.*, **6**. 169, 1897 ; L. M. Dennis, K. M. Tressler, and F. E. Hance, *Journ. Amer. Chem. Soc.*, **45**. 2033, 1923 ; J. H. Müller and N. H. Smith, *ib.*, **44**. 1909, 1922 ; M. L. Huggins, *ib.*, **44**. 1841, 1922 ; *Phys. Rev.*, (2), **21**. 205, 1923 ; F. Exner and E. Haschek, *Sitzber. Akad. Wien*, **108**. 1071, 1899 ; *Tabelle der Bogenspectra*, Wien, 1902 ; *Tabellen der Funkenspectra*, Wien, 1904 ; *Die Spektren der Elemente bei normalem Druck*, Leipzig, 1912 ; W. N. Hartley and H. Ramage, *Trans. Roy. Dublin Soc.*, (2), **7**. 339, 1901 ; C. Benedicks, *Internat. Zeit. Metallog.*, **7**. 225, 1915 ; W. Biltz, *Zeit. anorg. Chem.*, **72**. 313, 1911 ; W. R. Mott, *Trans. Amer. Electrochem. Soc.*, **34**. 255, 1918 ; E. Hjalmar, *Zeit. Physik*, **3**. 262, 1920 ; G. F. Clark and W. Duane, *Proc. Nat. Acad.*, **10**. 92, 1924 ; W. Duane and K. F. Hu, *Phys. Rev.*, (2), **14**. 516, 1919 ; G. L. Clark and W. Duane, *Proc. Nat. Acad. Science*, **10**. 92, 1924 ; M. Siegbahn, *Jahrb. Rad. Elektron.*, **13**. 296, 1916 ; B. Walter, *Zeit. Physik*, **30**. 357, 1924 ; H. J. C. Ireton, *Trans. Roy. Soc. Canada*, (3), **18**. 103, 1924 ; A. Leide, *Compt. Rend.*, **180**. 1203, 1925 ; J. Lunt, *Monthly Notices Roy. Astron. Soc.*, **85**. 38, 148, 1924 ; J. Papish, *Zeit. anorg. Chem.*, **122**. 262, 1922 ; *Chem. News*, **124**. 3, 1922 ; E. Voegelen, *ib.*, **30**. 325, 1902 ; W. Biltz, *ib.*, **72**. 313, 1914 ; A. Fowler, *Series in Line Spectra*, London, 163, 1922 ; E. Paulson, *Beiträge zur Kenntnis der Linienspectren*, Lund, 1914 ; *Astrophys. Journ.*, **40**. 298, 1914 ; **41**. 72, 1915 ; J. Formánek, *Die qualitative Spektralanalyse*, Berlin, 153, 1905 ; A. Dauvillier, *Compt. Rend.*, **176**. 1802, 1923 ; B. Cabrera, *Anal. Fis. Quim.*, **20**. 92, 1923 ; E. Merritt, *Proc. Nat. Acad.*, **11**. 743, 1925.

[2] G. H. Buchanan, *Journ. Ind. Eng. Chem.*, **8**. 585, 1916 ; **9**. 661, 1917 ; P. E. Browning and S. E. Scott, *Amer. Journ. Science*, (4), **46**. 663, 1918 ; L. M. Dennis and J. Parish, *Journ. Amer. Chem. Soc.*, **43**. 2131, 1921 ; L. M. Dennis and E. B. Johnson, *ib.*, **45**. 1380, 1923 ; **47**. 790, 1925 ; O. Brunck, *Liebig's Ann.*, **336**. 281, 1904 ; K. Haushofer, *Sitzber. München. Akad.*, 133, 1887 ; S. L. Penfield, *Amer. Journ. Science*, (3), **46**. 107, 1893 ; (3), **47**. 451, 1894 ; G. T. Prior and L. J. Spencer, *Min. Mag.*, **12**. 5, 1898 ; V. M. Goldschmidt, *Zeit. Kryst.*, **45**. 552, 1908 ; G. P. Baxter and W. C. Cooper, *Journ. Phys. Chem.*, **28**. 1049, 1924 ; *Proc. Amer. Acad.*, **59**. 235, 1924.

[3] C. Winkler, *Journ. prakt. Chem.*, (2), **34**. 177, 1886 ; B. Brauner in R. Abegg, *Handbuch der anorganischen Chemie*, Leipzig, **3**. ii, 461, 1909 ; F. W. Clarke, *A Recalculation of the Atomic Weights*, Washington, 286, 1910 ; F. W. Aston, *Nature*, **111**. 771, 1923 ; **112**. 449, 1923 ; *Journ. Soc. Chem. Ind.—Chem. Ind.*, **42**. 935, 1923 ; *Phil. Mag.*, (6), **47**. 385, 1924 ; (6), **49**. 1191, 1925 :

N. V. Sidgwick, *ib.*, **42**. 1203, 1923 ; J. H. Müller, *Journ. Amer. Chem. Soc.*, **43**. 1085, 1921 ; G. P. Baxter and W. C. Cooper, *Journ. Phys. Chem.*, **29**. 1364, 1925 ; *Proc. Amer. Acad.*, **59** 235, 1924 ; H. G. Grimm and A. Sommerfeld, *Zeit. Physik*, **36**. 36, 1926.

§ 4. Germanium Hydrides

As indicated above, hydrogen and germanium do **not** unite directly. E. Voegelen [1] obtained **germanium tetrahydride, or monogermane or germanomethane**, GeH_4, by an indirect process. If germanium chloride is reduced with sodium amalgam, the hydrogen evolved, even when bubbled through sodium hydroxide soln., burns with a bluish-red flame, and deposits a mirror on a cold porcelain surface. Germanium hydride, to which this phenomenon is attributed, may be prepared like antimony and arsenic hydrides, in testing for these substances ; the mirror obtained by heating the tube through which the issuing gas passes is red in transmitted, green in reflected, light ; it is soluble in sodium hypochlorite, difficultly so in hot hydrochloric acid ; heating in air or with conc. nitric acid changes the mirror into white germanic oxide, which, when acted on with hydrogen sulphide in hydrochloric acid soln., gives a white precipitate of germanium sulphide soluble in ammonium sulphide. When germanium hydride is passed through silver nitrate soln., a black compound of germanium and silver is precipitated ; this, when treated with conc. nitric acid, leaves a white residue of germanic oxide. Analyses of the germanium silver compound, and the results obtained by passing the gas over finely divided sulphur show that the formula is more likely to be GeH_4 than GeH_2 or Ge_2H_4. This is in agreement with the composition of *germanium tetraethide*, $Ge(C_2H_5)_4$, prepared by C. Winkler, and described by L. M. Dennis and F. E. Hance. Analyses by R. Schenck and A. Imker, and F. Paneth and co-workers agree with the formula GeH_4. R. Schenck and A. Imker's value for the vap. density was 76·93 in agreement with the theoretical value 76·50. L. M. Dennis and co-workers also obtained confirmatory results, since a litre of the gas at 0° and 760 mm. weighed 3·420 grms. ; and the sp. gr. of the liquid at —142° was 1·523 ; F. Paneth and co-workers prepared germane by the action of sulphuric acid on an alloy of germanium and zinc or magnesium ; and R. Schenck and A. Imker prepared it by the action of hydrochloric acid on an alloy of magnesium and germanium in a stream of hydrogen, and cooling the product in liquid air ; some *germanium-chloroform* or *trichlorogermane*, $GeHCl_3$, was produced by cooling the gas with a freezing mixture before it is cooled by liquid air. The hydride has a nauseating odour, and the purified product has a m.p. —165°. R. Schenck and A. Imker found the b.p. to be —90° to —91°, in agreement with the value —88·5° obtained by F. Paneth and co-workers ; and the —90° of L. M. Dennis and co-workers. A lower value, —126°, was obtained with a sample which had been in contact with mercury over-night, and consequently was partially decomposed. F. Paneth and co-workers obtained —164·5° for the m.p ; and 3·65 Cals. for the mol. heat of evaporation. The vap. press., p, was found by R. Schenck and A. Imker to be :

	—155°	—140°	—120°	109°	—101°	—96°	—92°	—91°	90°
p . . .	2	15	83	190	336	485	648	714	782 mm.

The general reactions of the gas show that it is endothermic, and analogous in properties to the hydrides of arsenic, antimony, tin, and bismuth. E. Paneth and co-workers said that the hydride is unusually stable, being unaffected by 50 per cent. potassium hydroxide soln., or phosphoric oxide, and requires a relatively high temp. for its decomposition. J. H. Müller and N. H. Smith prepared the hydride by the action of electrolytic hydrogen, sodium amalgam, or aluminium and dil. alkali-lye, on a soln. of a germanium salt. The germanium mirror obtained like the arsenic mirror in testing for arsenic, enables 0·00006 grm. of germanium to be detected.

L. M. Dennis, R. B. Corey and R. W. Moore prepared some germanium hydride by the action of aluminium on a soln. of germanium dioxide in potash-lye; and by the electrolysis of a 50 per cent. soln. of orthophosphoric acid using a germanium rod as cathode, and condensing the gas from the cathode by liquid air. The yields in both cases are small. They obtained a mixture of germanium hydrides by the method employed by A. Stock and C. Somiesky for the silicon hydrides (*q.v.*). The fractional distillation of the condensate in the vessel cooled by liquid air furnished a mixture of mono-, di-, and tri-germanes. 67·5 grms. of a magnesium-germanium alloy, containing 40·5 grms. of germanium, yielded 7·15 grms. of monogermane, 2·12 grms. of digermane, and 0·43 grm. of trigermane. This corresponds with the conversion of only 22·7 per cent. of the germanium into the hydrides, and of this 73·6 per cent. appeared as monogermane, 22 per cent. as digermane, and 1 per cent. as trigermane. Part of the 77·3 per cent. of the unconverted germanium may form compounds analogous with the so-called silico-oxalic acid.

The fractionation product of the mixed liquid, collected between −77° and −72°, consisted of **digermane,** or **germanoethane,** Ge_2H_6, in agreement with the analyses, and with the vap. density 6·7405—theory for digermane gave 6·743. The sp. gr. of the colourless liquid is 1·98 at −109°; the m.p. is −109°, and the b.p. 29° at 760 mm. The vap. press., *p* mm., is :

	−98·2°	−72·0°	−53·5°	−44·0°	−34·0°	−22·0°	−18·0°	−6·0°	0°
p	3·0	6·0	15·9	31·4	48·4	87·6	105·4	189·0	243·1

When exposed to air, digermane became first yellow, then light brown, and finally a dark brown solid. It is not usually spontaneously inflammable in air, but by admitting air suddenly to the gas under reduced press., a flash of light occurred, and the walls of the vessel acquired a dark brown film. The vap. ignites with almost explosive violence, and the liquid burns with great rapidity, forming a reddish-brown solid with black and white streaks. When oxygen is admitted into a vessel containing digermane, no reaction occurs at first, but in about 10 mins. a white solid is formed, which, in about an hour, becomes yellow. No reaction occurs at first with water, and the two liquids do not mix; after a time, however, a white gelatinous substance forms in the water layer, and this then becomes yellow and light brown; with 33 per cent. soda-lye, a colourless combustible gas is given off; monogermane does not react with lye of this conc. even when heated. Digermane mixes with carbon tetrachloride, heat is evolved and a clear colourless soln. is formed. When this has stood in contact with air a white solid is deposited, this slowly turns yellow and then disappears.

The fractionation of the residue left after the removal of digermane furnished a colourless liquid the analysis of which agreed with **trigermane** or **germanoproptane,** Ge_3H_8. The vap. density 10·005 corresponds with Ge_3H_8 which has a theoretical value 10·07. The sp. gr. of the liquid is 2·20; the m.p., −105·6°; and the b.p., 110·5°. The vap. press., *p* mm., is :

	2·4°	10·0°	30·0°	45·0°	55·0°	70·3°	90·3°	104·0°	111·5°
p	15·5	21·3	50·9	90·9	138·5	238·5	429·2	620·4	773·4

When exposed to air, trigermane quickly turned to a white solid; and when a few drops of trigermane are ignited on a watch-glass, the liquid burns with a yellow flame, forming a voluminous, pulverulent residue with black, brown, and white streaks. The reactions with oxygen, water, and carbon tetrachloride resemble those with digermane, but with 33 per cent. soda-lye no reaction was observed between the two liquids.

REFERENCES.

[1] E. Voegelen, *Zeit. anorg. Chem.*, **30**. 325, 1902 ; J. H. Müller and N. H. Smith, *Journ. Amer. Chem. Soc.*, **44**. 1909, 1922 ; L. M. Dennis, K. M. Tressler, and F. E. Hance, *ib.*, **45**. 2033, 1923; L. M. Dennis, R. B. Corey, and R. W. Moore, *ib.*, **46**. 657, 1924 ; R. B. Corey, A. W. Lauben-

gayer, and L. M. Dennis, *ib.*, **47**. 112. 1925; L. M. Dennis and F. E. Hance, *ib.*, **47**. 370, 1925; F. Paneth and E. Schmidt-Hebbel, *Ber.*, **55**. B, 2615, 1922; F. Paneth, M. Matthics, and E. Schmidt-Hebbel, *ib.*, **55**. B, 785, 1922; F. Paneth, W. Haken, and E. Rabinovitsch, *ib.*, **57**. B, 1891, 1924; **58**. B, 1138, 1925; A. Stock and C. Somiesky, *ib.*, **49**. 111, 1916; R. Schenck and A. Imker, *Ber.*, **58**. B, 271, 1925; *Rec. Trav. Chim. Pays-Bas*, **41**. 569, 1922; C. Winkler, *Journ. prakt. Chem.*, (2), **34**. 177, 1886; (2), **36**. 177, 1887.

§ 5. The Germanium Oxides and Hydroxides

Germanium forms two oxides, GeO and GeO_2. The former, **germanium monoxide** or **germanous oxide,** GeO, was prepared by C. Winkler [1] by fusing powdered germanium with borax, and washing the cold mass with water. It formed a reddish-yellow **germanous hydroxide,** $Ge(OH)_2$, which was converted into the oxide by heating it in a current of carbon dioxide. It was also made by heating germanic oxide with magnesium; but W. Biltz could not make it by heating germanic oxide with germanium: $Ge+GeO_2=2GeO$. C. Winkler made it by the action of alkali hydroxide on germanium chloroform:

The germanium chloroform was treated with water to form an oxychloride; the product was treated with sodium carbonate until it had an alkaline reaction, and evaporated almost to dryness on a water-bath. The product was washed with water three times—a part passed into soln. The soln. filtered badly because it choked up the pores of the paper. The precipitate was washed with alcohol, and finally with ether. When dried in vacuo, the hydroxide was obtained which passed into the oxide when heated in a stream of carbon dioxide.

Germanium monoxide is a dark grey powder, which, according to W. Biltz, is not volatile. The oxide readily dissolves in hydrochloric acid, forming germanous chloride. The soln. gives a yellow hydroxide when treated with alkali hydroxide; a white ferrocyanide, with potassium ferrocyanide; and a brown sulphide, with hydrogen sulphide. It reduces soln. of chromates and permanganates; precipitates gold from auric chloride soln.; and reduces soln. of mercuric chloride to mercurous chloride and to mercury. Litmus is at once bleached by the soln. The yellow hydroxide, prepared as indicated above, is either soluble in or is peptized by water, forming a yellow liquid which remains turbid after passing through filter-paper. An excess of alkali gives a similar result. The hydroxide is often superficially white owing to oxidation. If the hydroxide be heated with the liquid from which it has been precipitated, it becomes red. A. Hantzsch attributes this to the tautomeric change: $Ge(OH)_2 \rightleftharpoons O+Ge(OH)H$, the latter formula representing the germanium analogue of formic acid—**germano-formic acid,** $H.GeO.OH$. The hypothesis is strengthened by the fact that germanous hydroxide is produced by the action of water on germanium chloroform: $HGeCl_3+2H_2O=3HCl+HGeO.OH$, followed by $H.GeO.OH \rightleftharpoons Ge(OH)_2$. The hydroxides of zinc, beryllium, lead, tin(ous), and germanium were shown by A. Hantzsch to behave like feeble acids whose strengths increase in the order given. Germanous hydroxide thus appears to be rather weaker than acetic acid. The acidity of the hydroxides of germanium, tin, and lead increases with decreasing at. wt.; and seems to be connected with their ability to form quadrivalent compounds. The solubility of germanous hydroxide in alkali hydroxides is attributed to the formation of soluble **germanites**; and the germanites are considered to be salts of germanoformic acid, $H.GeO.OH$.

C. Winkler prepared **germanic oxide** or **germanium dioxide,** GeO_2, by heating the metal in oxygen; by roasting the sulphide in air; by heating the metal with nitric acid; by treating the sulphide with sulphuric acid, and calcining the product at a red heat. The decomposition of the germanium tetrachloride by water gives an oxide of a high degree of purity: $GeCl_4+2H_2O=4HCl+GeO_2$. The addition of ammonia lessens the amount of oxide dissolved by the hydrochloric acid produced by the hydrolysis. The colloidal product is difficult to wash, and the last traces of chlorine are retained very tenaciously. C. Winkler purified the oxide extracted from the mineral, by dissolving it in hydrofluoric acid, and adding the calculated quantity of potassium fluoride required to form potassium fluogermanate, K_2GeF_6. This salt is purified by crystallization. The oxide cannot be obtained satisfactorily by heating the fluogermanate with sulphuric acid because of the volatility of germanium fluoride ; it is therefore fused with sodium carbonate and sulphur as indicated in connection with the extraction of germanium. J. H. Müller and H. R. Blank purified the dioxide in the following manner :

Germanium dioxide can be freed from arsenic and other metals by repeated distillation in chlorine from hydrochloric acid soln., and precipitation from the distillates by hydrogen sulphide. The final distillation of the tetrachloride gives a product from which oxide can be prepared by simple hydrolysis. Germanium dioxide made by the hydrolysis of the tetrachloride contains detectable amounts of chloride, and the oxide prepared by the oxidation of the sulphide by nitric acid retains appreciable amounts of sulphur. It is usually assumed that these impurities will be removed by continued ignition, but larger quantities of the oxide are not readily freed from either of them by this method. Germanic oxide may therefore readily be prepared free from either chlorides or sulphates, but it is rather difficult to eliminate both of these impurities from the same portion of material. Sulphates can be removed by ignition alone, provided it be continued for a very long time at a very high temp. Prolonged ignition over a Meker burner was found insufficient when 10 grms. or more of the oxide were involved. Immediate fusion at about 1100° also failed to produce a pure oxide, as sulphates could be detected in the aq. soln. of the resulting glass. Ignition above 950° for about 36 hrs. in an electric furnace, completely removed the sulphates from 10 or 15 grms. of the oxide. The ignition described above was found insufficient for the removal of the last traces of chlorine from 10–15 grms. of material. Heating the oxide in a current of superheated steam slowly carries out much hydrogen chloride, as may be seen by treating the condensed steam with silver nitrate. Repeated moistening of the oxide with water, followed by evaporation and ignition at 950°, is an effective method. It seems probable that the small quantity of water tenaciously held by germanium dioxide up to 900° plays an important part in completing the hydrolysis of the chloride, for unless this water was repeatedly renewed and expelled, the oxide did not lose all of its retained chlorine even at 950°.

Germanium dioxide is a dense, white, gritty powder which can be crystallized by very slowly evaporating the aq. soln. The microscopic vermiculites so obtained belong, according to K. Haushofer, to the rhombic system. A. E. van Arkel, and V. M. Goldschmidt studied the X-radiogram. C. Winkler found the sp. gr. to be 4·703 at 18° ; and L. F. Nilson and O. Pettersson, the sp. ht. between 0° and 100°, 0·1291. C. Winkler said that the oxide can be heated to bright redness without change ; and W. Biltz, that the oxide can be melted to a clear liquid without volatilization, at 1025°. E. L. Nichols gave 1400° for the m.p., but J. H. Müller and H. R. Blank found the oxide melts between 1090° and 1100°. J. O. Perrine observed no sign of the excitation of fluorescence by the X-rays. E. L. Nichols studied the emissivity of the oxide between 837° and 1370°. J. H. Müller and H. R. Blank found that on ignition between 226° and 1100°, part of the oxide becomes insoluble in water and inert towards acids and alkalies, and it becomes soluble again after fusion. The speed of conversion of the soluble to the insoluble form increases to a maximum at 380°, and then decreases to the m.p. It is suggested that there are at least two allotropic forms of germanium dioxide, and that the conversion from the soluble to the insoluble form never reaches 100 per cent. ; they found that like other oxides, GeO_2 when heated shows in its radiation deviations from black-body intensity. At temp. near 900°, the blue part of the spectrum is radiated at black-body intensity, the red at only 4 per cent. of black-body intensity ; at about 1225°, the radiation is of black-body composition but about 10 per cent. of black-body intensity ; at 1370°, the red is of black-body intensity, but the blue much weaker. A hydrogen flame impinging on GeO_2 excites luminescence—pale blue-green at low temp., red at higher.

According to C. Winkler, the calcined oxide is somewhat soluble in water, for

100 parts of water at 20° dissolve 0·405 part of the oxide, and at 100°, 1·05 parts. J. H. Müller and M. S. Iszard gave 10·9 grms. per litre at 100°. The ignited oxide, said J. M. van Bemmelen, forms an emulsion with water, and this becomes clear when heated owing to the formation of a colloidal soln. The evaporation of the aq. soln. furnishes the anhydrous oxide. The aq. soln. has an acid reaction. Neither *germanium hydroxide*, Ge(OH)$_4$, nor *germanyl hydroxide*, GeO(OH)$_2$, has been definitely prepared. C. Winkler found that the product obtained by the hydrolysis of the tetrachloride when dried over sulphuric acid contained 3·63 per cent. of water; when dried at 100°, 3·19 per cent.; at 200°, 2·32 per cent.; and at 250°, 1·74 per cent. By oxidizing germanium sulphide in ammoniacal soln. with hydrogen dioxide, the product dried at 100° contained 1·22 per cent. of water. The precipitates obtained by adding ammonia or alkali carbonates to a soln. of a salt of germanium contained alkali and carbon dioxide; germanates appear to be formed. J. M. van Bemmelen passed carbon dioxide into a soln. of germanium dioxide in soda-lye and obtained a colourless, amorphous precipitate which, when dried in air, had a composition $\frac{1}{2}$Na$_2$O.GeO$_2$.1·8H$_2$O; when dried over sulphuric acid, it retained a mol. of water; and when dried at 100°, 0·4 mol. Very little water was lost between 100° and 150°; but at 160°, all the water was expelled. No carbon dioxide was present. It was very difficult to remove the alkali by washing. L. M. Dennis and co-workers found that dehydration is complete in 3 hrs. at 950°, and no volatilization occurs below 1250°.

According to C. Winkler, when germanium dioxide is heated in a stream of hydrogen it is slowly reduced to the metal—*vide supra*. The oxide readily dissolves in hydrofluoric acid—*vide infra*. When hydrochloric acid is poured over the dioxide, and the mixture evaporated to dryness, a large proportion of the germanium is volatilized as chloride. The dioxide is but sparingly soluble in acids. The oxide is amphoteric, and the acidic character preponderates. J. M. van Bemmelen found that the crystalline dioxide dissolves neither in conc. sulphuric acid nor in the acid diluted to H$_2$SO$_4$.4H$_2$O; a little is taken up when the mixture is warmed. Hydrated germanium dioxide retains sulphuric acid very tenaciously. According to C. Winkler, when germanium dioxide or germanium is heated with potassium iodide or sulphur no chemical change occurs. Germanium dioxide is reduced by charcoal in the reducing flame and at the same time, a white deposit of germanium dioxide is formed on the charcoal; the dioxide readily dissolves in the borax bead, and the cold glass is colourless whether produced in the oxidizing or reducing flame; the dioxide also dissolves readily in molten microcosmic salt. When the dioxide is moistened with a soln. of a cobalt salt and heated, no coloration is developed. L. M. Dennis and co-workers found that germanium dioxide is readily reduced when heated with aluminium. According to C. Winkler, molten alkali hydroxides or carbonates readily dissolve germanium dioxide. The cold products are readily soluble in water. When the conc. aq. soln. is treated with an acid, germanium dioxide is precipitated, but not from dil. soln. The feebly acidified soln. is not precipitated by potassium hydroxide, but a partial precipitation of germanium dioxide occurs by the addition of sodium carbonate or hydrocarbonate, ammonia, or ammonium carbonate. The precipitates dissolve when warmed with an excess of the precipitant, and are re-deposited on cooling.

F. S. Hammett and co-workers [2] compared the toxicity of arsenic trioxide and germanium dioxide when applied subcutaneously to albino rats. Arsenic trioxide usually produced fatal results in a dose of 8 mgrms. per kilogram of body weight; and sublethal doses produce sloughing at the point of injection. Germanium dioxide in doses as great as 180 mgrms. per kilogram of body weight produced neither death nor any apparent evidences of harmful effects; sloughing did not occur at the point of injection. Hence, with respect to toxicity, germanium resembles the members of the tin group of elements rather than those of the arsenic group. G H. Bailey and co-workers found 4 mgrms. to be a toxic dose for rabbits.

REFERENCES.

¹ C. Winkler, *Journ. prakt. Chem.*, (2), **34.** 177, 1886 ; (2), **36.** 177, 1887 ; *Ber.*, **24.** 891, 1891 ;
L. M. Dennis, K. M. Tressler, and F. E. Hance, *Journ. Amer. Chem. Soc.*, **45.** 2033, 1923 ; W. Biltz,
Zeit. anorg. Chem., **72.** 313, 1911 ; A. Hantzsch, *ib.*, **30.** 316, 1902 ; K. Haushofer, *Sitzber.
München. Akad.*, **133.** 1887 ; L. F. Nilson and O. Pettersson, *Zeit. phys. Chem.*, **1.** 27, 1887 ;
J. M. van Bemmelen, *Rec. Trav. Chim. Pays-Bas*, **6.** 205, 1887 ; J. O. Perrine, *Phys. Rev.*, (2),
22. 48, 1923 ; E. L. Nichols, *Proc. Nat. Acad. Science*, **9.** 248, 1923 ; J. H. Müller and M. S. Iszard,
Journ. Amer. Med. Science, **163.** 364, 1922 ; H. R. Blank, *Journ. Franklin Inst.*, **198.** 402, 1924 ;
Allotropy of Germanium Dioxide, Philadelphia, 1924 ; J. H. Müller and H. R. Blank, *Journ.
Amer. Chem. Soc.*, **46.** 2358, 1924 ; G. P. Baxter and W. C. Cooper, *Journ. Phys. Chem.*, **28.**
1049, 1924 ; *Proc. Amer. Acad.*, **59.** 235, 1924 ; A. E. van Arkel, *Physica*, **5.** 162, 1925 ;
V. M. Goldschmidt, *Naturwiss.*, **14.** 295, 1926.
² F. S. Hammett, J. H. Müller, and J. E. Mowrey, *Journ. Pharm. Exp. Therapeutics*, **19.**
337, 1922 ; G. H. Bailey, P. B. Davidson, and C. H. Bunting, *Journ. Amer. Med. Assoc.*, **84.**
1722, 1925.

§ 6. The Germanium Fluorides

C. Winkler [1] could not prepare **germanous fluoride** or **germanium difluoride,**
GeF_2, but when potassium fluogermanate is warmed in a stream of hydrogen, there
is evidence of the formation of some germanous fluoride because when the dark
brown mass is treated with water some germanium is deposited, and the soln.
furnishes germanous sulphide, GeS, when treated with hydrogen sulphide.

Anhydrous **germanic fluoride** or **germanium tetrafluoride,** GeF_4, has not been
obtained of a high degree of purity. Germanium dioxide dissolves in 20 per cent.
hydrofluoric acid with hissing and the evolution of much heat ; with 40 per cent.
acid the reaction is so violent that some oxide may be projected from the containing
dish. If a soln. be evaporated over sulphuric acid, a syrupy liquid is formed which
gradually solidifies, forming a white, imperfectly crystalline mass of *trihydrated*
germanium tetrafluoride, $GeF_4.3H_2O$. It readily melts in its water of crystallization on the water-bath, and it becomes covered with a pellicle of oxide while some
hydrogen fluoride escapes ; at a higher temp., about half the germanium present
is volatilized as fluoride, and the other half remains as oxide. The trihydrate is
very hygroscopic ; it dissolves in water, and the soln. is probably hydrolyzed
because it attacks glass. When the soln. is heated some germanium fluoride is
volatilized along with the hydrogen fluoride. When the trihydrate is heated in a
stream of carbon dioxide, the anhydrous fluoride appears to be formed. The
hydrated fluoride is formed when a mixture of germanium dioxide, calcium fluoride,
and sulphuric acid is distilled. C. Winkler also said that germanium tetrafluoride
is volatilized when a mixture of potassium fluogermanate and sulphuric acid is
heated until the acid begins to evaporate. G. Krüss and L. F. Nilson said that
germanium dioxide is formed—*vide infra.* C. Winkler said that the proportion of
fluoride formed in this reaction depends on the proportion of the acid which determines the speed of the decomposition.

When the vap. of germanium tetrafluoride is passed into water, a soln. of
germanic oxide or acid is formed and of **hydrofluogermanic acid,** H_2GeF_6. This
colourless liquid has an acidic reaction, and when evaporated over sulphuric acid,
it furnishes a syrupy liquid, evolving germanium tetrafluoride, and at the same time
deposits needle-like crystals of germanic oxide. Hydrofluogermanic acid appears
to be volatile at ordinary temp., and it can be distilled in vacuo over a water-bath ;
but its b.p. lies above that of water. The acid has not been isolated. The soln.
attacks glass. The addition of a small proportion of ammonia produces no change,
but with a large proportion white germanium dioxide is precipitated ; the precipitate
dissolves when the soln. is warmed, and is re-deposited on cooling. When the
acid soln. is treated with potassium hydroxide, or a potassium salt, **potassium
fluogermanate,** K_2GeF_6, is formed as a white precipitate. C. Winkler obtained the
same salt by adding potassium chloride to a soln. of the oxide in hydrofluoric acid ;
G. Krüss and L. F. Nilson prepared potassium fluoride, and they added that the
salt can be recrystallized from its aq. soln. J. H. Müller described the preparation

of the salt of a high degree of purity. According to G. Paykull and W. C. Brögger, the white, crystalline powder consists of hexagonal crystals isomorphous with ammonium fluosilicate. The axial ratio is $a : c = 1 : 1\cdot6078$. The double refraction is negative. C. Winkler said that the salt melts to a white glass at a dull red heat; and at a full red heat, white vap. are evolved, and the product obtained after heating for one hour gives, with water, white germanium dioxide and an alkaline liquid. G. Krüss and L. F. Nilson said that it does not melt at a red heat; and is not decomposed. According to C. Winkler, 100 parts of water at 180° dissolve 0·575 part of salt, and at 100°, 2·93 parts; G. Krüss and L. F. Nilson said that 100 parts of water at 18° dissolve 0·542 part of salt, and at 100°, 2·58 parts. C. Winkler noted the formation of germanous fluoride (q.v.) when potassium fluogermanate is heated to redness in a stream of hydrogen. If the aq. soln. be mixed with an excess of sulphuric acid and evaporated on a water-bath, G. Krüss and L. F. Nilson said that long acicular crystals are formed, probably those of a double salt, *potassium germanium sulphate*. This decomposes when further heated, and particularly if mixed with ammonium carbonate, forming a mixture of germanium dioxide and potassium sulphate. C. Winkler said that when potassium fluogermanate is heated with sulphuric acid germanium tetrafluoride is volatilized. A. Skrabal and J. Gruber prepared **rubidium fluogermanate,** Rb_2GeF_6, by dissolving germanium dioxide in hydrofluoric acid and adding a soln. of rubidium fluoride; **cæsium fluogermanate,** Cs_2GeF_6, was made in a similar way.

REFERENCES.

[1] C. Winkler, *Journ. prakt. Chem.*, (2), **34**. 177, 1886; (2), **36**. 177, 1887; G. Krüss and L. F. Nilson, *Ber.*, **20**. 1696, 1887; G. Paykull and W. C. Brögger, *Œfvers. Akad. Förh. Stockholm*, 302, 1887; J. H. Müller, *Journ. Amer. Chem Soc.*, **43**. 1085, 1921; A. Skrabal and J. Gruber, *Monatsh.*, **39**. 19, 1917.

§ 7. The Germanium Chlorides

Two chlorides have been prepared, $GeCl_2$ and $GeCl_4$; a hydrotrichloride, $GeHCl_3$, analogous in composition with chloroform, $CHCl_3$; and an oxychloride—possibly $GeOCl_2$. C. Winkler [1] obtained impure germanous chloride, or germanium dichloride, $GeCl_2$, by the action of hydrogen chloride on germanous sulphide, GeS; and a soln. of germanous chloride is probably formed when germanous oxide or sulphide is dissolved in hydrochloric acid. C. Winkler said that when germanium is heated in a stream of hydrogen chloride either germanous chloride or germanium chloroform is produced—both hypotheses proved to be correct. The product is a mixture.

As indicated above, C. Winkler found that if hydrochloric acid be added to an aq. soln. of germanium dioxide and the soln. evaporated, all the germanium is volatilized as **germanium tetrachloride,** $GeCl_4$. The chloride is obtained by heating germanium in a stream of chlorine, and the product purified by shaking it with mercury to remove free chlorine. J. H. Müller could not remove the last traces of arsenic by distillation in a stream of chlorine and hydrogen chloride. L. M. Dennis and F. E. Hance said that the reaction between germanium and chlorine begins at about 80°; there is a rapid combination at 180°; and at 360°, the metal glows brilliantly in chlorine gas. The fused germanium freed from adherent flux, and pulverized, was placed in an alundum boat, and heated in a glass tube. The exit was connected with a U-tube having a bulb at the bend to collect the liquid germanium tetrachloride which was condensed in the tube surrounded by a freezing mixture of ice and salt. The product was freed from chlorine by passing air through the liquid contained in a flask with a long neck packed with glass wool and the side-arm of the flask connected with a U-tube cooled by ice and salt. This prevented an undue loss of tetrachloride. In about 7 hrs. the free chlorine was removed. The liquid was then fractionally distilled and the fraction boiling at 85·6° collected. C. Winkler also made the tetrachloride by heating a mixture of powdered germanium or germanium sulphide and mercuric chloride.

According to C. Winkler, germanium tetrachloride is a colourless, mobile liquid which fumes strongly in contact with air. The vap. coats glass with a white pellicle. Its sp. gr. is 1·887 at 18°; L. M. Dennis and F. E. Hance gave 1·874 at 25°/25°; and A. W. Laubengayer and D. L. Tabern, 1·879 at 20°/20°. I. I. Saskowsky found the ratio of the mol. vol. to the sum of the at. vols. of the constituent elements to be 1·45. C. Winkler gave 86° for the b.p.; L. M. Dennis and F. E. Hance, 86·5° at 760 mm.; and A. W. Laubengayer and D. L. Tabern, 83°; C. Winkler said that the liquid is perceptibly volatile even at ordinary temp., and L. F. Nilson and O. Pettersson found the vap. press,, p atm., to be:

	10·7°	30·0°	50·0°	70·7°	185·0°	215·0°	255·0°	276·9°
p	0·073	0·151	0·33	0·67	7·0	15·0	28	38

R. Lorenz and W. Herz discussed these data. The vap. density at 301·5° was 7·45, and at 739°, 7·44; the value calculated for $GeCl_4$ is 7·43. The critical temp. is 276·9°. C. Winkler said that the liquid can be cooled to −100° without freezing; L. M. Dennis and F. E. Hance gave −49·5° ± 0·2° for the m.p. The index of refraction was 1·3606 at 27°; A. W. Laubengayer and D. L. Tabern gave 1·4683 at 12·5°, and 1·4602 at 27°. W. Hampe found that the liquid is a non-conductor of electricity at ordinary temp. and at its b.p. M. E. Lear gave 2·6 at 30° for the dielectric constant.

If the liquid be kept in an imperfectly closed vessel, small crystals are formed near the surface of the liquid; C. Winkler thought that they might be those of a hydrate. When a mixture of the vap. and hydrogen is passed through a red-hot tube, a small proportion is reduced to germanium, and a little germanous chloride, while the greater proportion is not altered. Germanium tetrachloride is decomposed by water, much heat is developed, and germanium dioxide is formed. If the tetrachloride be dropped into cold water, each drop in falling becomes covered with a white film which becomes thicker and partially protects the interior; and there is a crackling sound emitted which persists several hours if the liquid be not shaken. L. M. Dennis and F. E. Hance found that when dropped into conc. sulphuric acid at room temp., the germanium chloride sinks to the bottom of the vessel and is not attacked; H. Friedrich said that germanium tetrachloride can be distilled from the conc. acid without decomposition. L. M. Dennis and F. E. Hance found that when the tetrachloride sinks to the bottom of conc. nitric acid, there is a slow reaction at the surface of contact, and the tetrachloride becomes yellow. Agitation hastens the reaction. With dil. nitric acid (2 : 1), the decomposition is slow and uniform. Much heat is developed when ammonia gas is passed into the tetrachloride, and a white precipitate is developed. A 1 : 4 soln. of potassium hydroxide develops so much heat that some tetrachloride is distilled off before the reaction is complete. The germanium dioxide which is formed dissolves in an excess of the reagent, and is re-precipitated by carbon dioxide. The tetrachloride is soluble in absolute alcohol, carbon disulphide, carbon tetrachloride, benzene, chloroform, and ether without decomposition; but the soln. in acetone forms an orange-coloured liquid.

C. Winkler found that when germanium is gently heated in a current of hydrogen chloride, the metal becomes red-hot, hydrogen is evolved, and two liquids of almost the same sp. gr. are produced. They are separated by fractional distillation. The lighter one is the oxychloride—*vide infra*. The analysis of the heavier. colourless liquid corresponds with **germanochloroform** or **germanium hydrotrichloride**, $GeHCl_3$. L. M. Dennis and co-workers obtained it by the action of hydrogen chloride on germanous chloride. V. Meyer found its vap. density at 178° is 5·55, when the value calculated for $GeHCl_3$ is 6·23. C. Winkler found the b.p. to be 72°; L. M. Dennis and co-workers gave 75·2°; −71° for the m.p.; 1·93 for the sp. gr. of the liquid; and a litre of the gas weighs 7·980 grms. The compound fumes strongly in air, possibly owing to the formation of an oxychloride. The vapour of the hydrotrichloride coats glass with a white pellicle, and colours cork an intense red, while it decomposes when strongly heated—probably $2GeHCl_3=Ge+GeCl_4+2HCl$. If 3 vols. of water be added to the liquid, a white substance, possibly an oxychloride, is formed ; if another 3 vols. of water be added, a yellow precipitate is formed ; and on the addition of still more water and boiling the mixture, the orange precipitate becomes reddish-brown and germanous hydroxide (*q.v.*) is formed : $2GeHCl_3+4H_2O=6HCl+2Ge(OH)_2$. The white precipitate also passes into germanous chloride in contact with much water. Germanium hydrotrichloride dissolves in hydrochloric acid with the development of heat, and when the soln. is diluted with water germanous hydroxide is precipitated. With sodium carbonate it forms germanous hydroxide : $2GeHCl_3+3Na_2CO_3+H_2O=6NaCl+3CO_2$ $+2Ge(OH)_2$. Germanium hydrotrichloride acts as a reducing agent. G. T. Morgan and H. D. K. Drew found that it reacted with acetylacetone, forming germanium *bis*acetylacetone dichloride.

Germanium hydrotrichloride reacts with oxygen when exposed to air. forming a white substance which C. Winkler regarded as **germanium oxychloride,** or **germanyl chloride,** $GeOCl_2$; the reaction is symbolized : $2GeHCl_3+O_2=2GeOCl_2+2HCl$. If a current of air or oxygen be passed through germanium hydrotrichloride, heat is developed, hydrogen chloride is given off, and the soln. becomes turbid. On standing, the emulsion separates into a liquid which collects at the bottom of the vessel. Its formation by the action of hydrogen chloride on germanium is indicated above, and is presumably the result of the presence of air in the gases. The colourless, non-fuming liquid boils above 100° ; it is not miscible with germanium hydrotrichloride, and is not decomposed by distillation. It has not been obtained in a state of purity.

REFERENCES.

[1] I. I. Saskowsky. *Zeit. anorg. Chem.*, **146**. 315, 1925; C. Winkler, *Journ. prakt. Chem.*, (2), **34**. 177, 1886 ; (2), **36**. 177, 1887 ; L. F. Nilson and O. Pettersson, *Zeit. phys. Chem.*, **1** 27, 1887 ; V. Meyer, *Ber.*, **20**. 498, 1887 ; R. Lorenz and W. Herz, *Zeit. anorg. Chem.*, **143**. 336, 1925 ; M. E. Lear, *Journ. Phys. Chem.*, **28**. 889, 1924 ; A. Skrabal and J. Gruber, *Monatsh.*, **39**. 19, 1917 ; W. Hampe, *Chem. Ztg.*, **12**. 173, 1888 ; L. M. Dennis and F. E. Hance, *Journ. Amer. Chem. Soc.*, **44**. 299, 2855, 1922 ; J. H. Müller, *ib.*, **43**. 1085, 1921 ; H. Friedrich, *Monatsh.*, **14**. 505, 1893 ; G. T. Morgan and H. D. K. Drew, *Journ Chem. Soc.*, **125**. 1261, 1924 ; L. M. Dennis, W. R. Orndorff and D. L. Tabern, *Journ. Phys. Chem.*, **30**. 1049, 1926 ; A. W. Laubengayer and D. L. Tabern, *ib.*, **30**. 1047, 1926.

§ 8. Germanium Bromide and Iodides

C. Winkler [1] prepared **germanium tetrabromide,** $GeBr_4$, from its elements. L. M. Dennis and F. E. Hance found that when the bromine vap. is passed into a glass tube containing an alundum boat with pulverulent germanium, the action begins at 25° but soon ceases ; when the temp. is gradually raised, slow union occurs at 180° ; and at 220°, germanium tetrabromide is rapidly produced, and collects in the condensing tubes. The liquid distillate forms a yellowish-white solid below 26°. Agitation with mercury to remove the free bromine gave a product which retained a little mercury. The product was therefore purified by fractional distillation, and the fraction boiling at 183°–186° was collected. C. Winkler obtained tetrabromide by heating germanium tetrachloride and potassium bromide in a sealed tube—the reaction was incomplete—and by heating a mixture of germanium and mercuric bromide.

C. Winkler said that germanium tetrabromide is a colourless, mobile, strongly fuming liquid which freezes to a crystalline mass at about 0°. L. M. Dennis and F. E. Hance found that it shows to a marked degree the phenomenon of undercooling, for the undisturbed liquid could be cooled to —18° without solidification. The m.p. is 26·1° and the corrected b.p. 185·9° at 760 mm. The observed b.p., $\theta°$, is corrected for the barometric press., p, at $0°$, by adding on $0.0001235(760-p)(273+\theta)$. The crystals are flattened octahedra, and isotropic, thus belonging to the cubic system. The sp. gr. is 3.1315 at $25°/25°$; the index of refraction, 1.6296 at $20.70°$; 1.6283 at $22.20°$; and 1.6269 at $25°$. I. I. Saskowsky found the ratio of the mol. vol. to the sum of the at. vols. of the constituent elements to be 1.21. L. M. Dennis and F. E. Hance found the sp. electrical conductivity to be less than 0.000078 mho at $30°$.

C. Winkler said that the tetrabromide is decomposed by water, forming germanium dioxide. L. M. Dennis and F. E. Hance also studied the hydrolysis and noted a slight crackling sound when the tetrabromide is dropped into water. No action was observed when the tetrabromide was allowed to stand in contact with sulphuric acid for several days, at room temp. With nitric acid, the tetrabromide becomes yellow and turbid, and a layer of white germanium dioxide is formed between the two liquids; in about 15 mins. the tetrabromide has changed to a black colour and there is a copious evolution of nitric oxide. Dry ammonia forms a white solid in contact with germanium tetrabromide. An aq. soln. of potassium hydroxide $(1:4)$ reacts at once with the tetrabromide, and heat is evolved; germanium oxide separates out, but immediately passes into soln. Carbon dioxide precipitates the oxide from the soln. of potassium germanate. Germanium tetrabromide is soluble in absolute alcohol, carbon tetrachloride, benzene, and ether without decomposition; but the soln. in acetone slowly liberates bromine. G. T. Morgan and H. D. K. Drew found that it reacted sluggishly with acetylacetone, forming germanium *bis*acetylacetone dibromide.

L. M. Dennis and F. E. Hance found that in the preparation of germanium tetraiodide by the action of the vap. of iodine on germanium at $360°$, yellow crystals of **germanous iodide,** or **germanium diiodide,** GeI_2, collected between the red tetraiodide and the germanium. C. Winkler made some **germanic iodide** or **germanium tetraiodide,** GeI_4, by heating a mixture of germanium tetrachloride and potassium iodide in a sealed tube—the reaction was incomplete, and he could not separate the germanic chloride and iodide by fractional distillation. He also prepared the iodide by heating pulverulent germanium in the vap. of iodine carried along by a slow current of carbon dioxide. It was necessary to sublime the product repeatedly in an atm. of carbon dioxide to eliminate the iodine. L. M. Dennis and F. E. Hance observed that the reaction begins at $212°$, and at $360°$, the combination is rapid. During the resublimation of the product, they noticed that the colour gradually changed from a bright red to a chocolate-brown, showing that the compound is partially decomposed when sublimed.

C. Winkler said that germanium tetraiodide has an orange colour; L. M. Dennis and F. E. Hance said that while the powder is orange, the fused iodide in lump form is coral-red at ordinary temp. At $-185°$, the colour is canary-yellow; at $-50°$, buff; at $-10°$, orange; at $35°$, salmon; at $50°$, brick-red; at $90°$, red; and at $144°$, ruby-red. The crystals are octahedra with the plane angles $60°$; and being isotropic without birefringence, they must belong to the cubic system. The sp. gr. is 4.3215 at $26°/26°$. C. Winkler, and L. M. Dennis and F. E. Hance found the m.p. to be $144°$; and the first-named said that on cooling it forms a crystalline mass with a marked decrease in volume. It boils at $350°-400°$, forming a yellow vap., and as the iodide condenses some violet iodine vap. remains, indicating that the iodide has suffered some dissociation. L. F. Nilson and O. Pettersson said that the compound is not decomposed at $440°$, but dissociates at a higher temp. They measured the vap. density, and found 20.46 at $440°$, when the calculated value for GeI_4 is 20.09; at $658°$, the vap. density is 17.19, indicating that dissociation has taken place. L. M. Dennis and F. E. Hance obtained an analogous result, and showed that the agreement between the observed and calculated values does not indicate that there is no dissociation. The vap. was shown to be a mixture of germanium diiodide and iodine: $GeI_4 \rightleftharpoons GeI_2 + I_2$.

C. Winkler said that the vap. of germanium tetraiodide is inflammable in air;

and that a mixture of the vap. with air explodes feebly with a reddish flame, forming germanium dioxide and iodine. He added that the tetraiodide is *sehr hygroskopisch*, and deliquesces in air, forming a brown liquid coloured by free iodine and which gradually forms white germanium dioxide owing to the volatilization of the iodine. He found a 50 per cent. gain in weight the first day, and a steady loss during the next 18 days, so that the residue weighed about a fourth as much as the original sample. *Au contraire*, L. M. Dennis and F. E. Hance observed no signs of a gain or loss of weight when exposed in air for 2 days; and only a slight decrease in weight after 5 months' exposure owing to the formation of a slight white incrustation. Presumably the hygroscopic sample was contaminated with something other than the tetraiodide. C. Winkler found that the tetraiodide is decomposed by a small proportion of water, forming germanium dioxide, which dissolves when more water is added, forming a clear, colourless soln. having an acid reaction. The soln. acquires a coloration on standing owing to the separation of iodine from the hydriodic acid. L. M. Dennis and F. E. Hance obtained analogous results, and found that the tetraiodide is not affected by conc. sulphuric acid at room temp. during 24 hrs.; but at 85°, iodine was slowly liberated. At room temp., conc. hydrochloric acid slowly dissolves the tetraiodide, dissolution being complete after some weeks. The tetraiodide is decomposed under conc. nitric acid, with the evolution of nitric oxide. The acid acquires a black coloration. When dropped into conc. aq. ammonia, the compound is at once decomposed and decolorized, forming a white solid; with dry ammonia gas, a white powder is slowly formed which is soluble in water. When placed in a soln. of potassium hydroxide (1 : 4), germanium tetraiodide is slowly dissolved. The tetraiodide dissolves in benzene, in monochlorobenzene, and in carbon disulphide, forming an orange-red soln.; in methyl alcohol, forming a deep orange soln.; in ethylene chloride, and in carbon tetrachloride, forming light orange soln.; and in ethylene glycol, and in ethylene chlorohydrin, forming light yellow soln. These soln. underwent no visible change on standing 4 months; but there was a distinct change of colour with soln. of the tetraiodide in hexane (orange-red), chloroform (pale orange), nitrobenzene (orange-red), petroleum (pink), butanol (orange), and glacial acetic acid (pale yellow), owing to the liberation of iodine. Soln. in acetone, ether, turpentine, oil of lavender, absolute alcohol, isopropyl alcohol, pyridine, and amyl alcohol decomposed at once.

REFERENCES.

[1] C. Winkler, *Journ. prakt. Chem.*, (2), **34**. 177, 1886; (2), **36**. 177, 1887; L. F. Nilson and O Pettersson, *Zeit. phys. Chem.*, **1**. 27, 1887; L. M. Dennis and F. E. Hance, *Journ. Amer. Chem. Soc.*, **44**. 299, 1922; G. T. Morgan and H. D. K. Drew, *Journ. Chem. Soc.*, **125**. 1261, 1924; I. I. Saskowsky, *Zeit. anorg. Chem.*, **146**. 315, 1925.

§ 9. The Germanium Sulphides

Germanium forms two sulphides, **germanous sulphide,** or **germanium monosulphide,** GeS; and germanic sulphide or germanium disulphide, GeS_2. C. Winkler[1] made the former by heating to redness a mixture of germanium disulphide with an excess of germanium in a current of carbon dioxide. The product appeared partly as dark grey crystals, and partly as a reddish-brown powder. He obtained a crystalline mass of the monosulphide by heating the disulphide in a stream of hydrogen—hydrogen sulphide was evolved. If argyrodite be similarly heated in a stream of hydrogen, germanium monosulphide appears as a brown dust the microscopic appearance of which has been described by K. Haushofer. C. Winkler observed that when hydrogen sulphide is passed into a soln. of germanous oxide in hydrochloric acid, reddish-brown, amorphous germanous sulphide is precipitated. The amorphous powder readily forms with water an orange-red or brown, opalescent, **colloidal germanium monosulphide.** It can be kept without change in a closed vessel, but in air it is oxidized and loses its colour. Acids flocculate the suspended colloid.

Germanium monosulphide appears as a brown powder and in crystals of different habits ; those prepared by heating the disulphide in hydrogen appear in thin plates with a lustre and colour recalling the appearance of iodine, or iron glance. According to A. Weisbach, the plates are doubly refracting and either monoclinic or rhombic. L. F. Nilson and O. Pettersson found that germanous sulphide melts to a dark liquid which, in turn, freezes to a crystalline mass. The vap. density is 3·54 at 1100°, and 3·09 at 1500°. The monosulphide dissociates at a white heat. According to C. Winkler, when germanium monosulphide is heated in air, sulphur dioxide is evolved and germanium dioxide is formed. When heated in a stream of hydrogen, most of the monosulphide is volatilized undecomposed, but in the hottest part, a part of the monosulphide is reduced forming octahedral crystals of germanium. The amorphous sulphide readily dissolves in hot conc. hydrochloric acid with the evolution of hydrogen sulphide and the formation of germanous chloride ; crystalline germanous sulphide dissolves in hydrochloric acid with difficulty. Germanous sulphide dissolves vigorously in molten potassium hydroxide, and it is readily soluble in an aq. soln. of potassium hydroxide, especially when warmed, any germanium present remains undissolved. When the soln. is acidified, amorphous, reddish-brown germanous sulphide is precipitated. Amorphous germanous sulphide dissolves in a soln. of ammonium sulphide, $(NH_4)_2S$, forming a thiogermanate, and the soln. deposits white germanic sulphide when treated with an acid. Crystalline germanous sulphide is said to be insoluble in a soln. of ammonium sulphide. When the sulphide is mixed with potassium nitrate and heated, it detonates.

According to C. Winkler, when acid soln. of germanium dioxide are treated with hydrogen sulphide, a white precipitate of **germanic sulphide** or **germanium disulphide,** GeS_2, is formed. An aq. soln. of germanium dioxide gives no precipitate with hydrogen sulphide, but when the soln. is acidified with sulphuric or hydrochloric acid, a white turbidity appears which settles to a voluminous white precipitate. With a feebly acidified soln., the germanium is only partially precipitated as sulphide ; for complete precipitation a strongly acidified soln. is necessary. Acetic acid and other organic acids will not do. Germanium disulphide is precipitated when an alkali sulphogermanate is treated with an acid, and for complete precipitation a large excess of sulphuric or hydrochloric acid is necessary, and the soln. should be sat. with hydrogen sulphide. The sulphide precipitated from acid soln. is peptized when washed, forming **colloidal germanium disulphide,** which is opalescent after long standing and repeated filtration—one such soln. had one part of germanium sulphide in 221·9 parts of water. The sol is flocculated by acids, and with metal salt soln. it gives colorations characteristic of the metal sulphides. It also decomposes, giving off hydrogen sulphide.

Germanium disulphide shows but little tendency to crystallize or volatilize. When the white amorphous disulphide is heated in a stream of carbon dioxide, it shrinks very much and acquires a yellow or yellowish-grey colour ; if the temp. is raised to bright redness, a part is volatilized, forming a white coating which is partly crystalline. When germanium disulphide is heated in air, it forms sulphur and germanium dioxides, and possibly also an *oxysulphide* since the complete elimination of sulphur is not possible by mere roasting. When heated with hydrogen, the monosulphide is formed (*q.v.*). The dried and calcined sulphide decomposes in moist air ; and when the moist disulphide is dried on a water-bath some hydrogen sulphide is given off. Acids favour the reaction. When the disulphide is evaporated with hydrochloric acid, the germanium is volatilized as tetrachloride ; when evaporated with sulphuric acid, until a large proportion has been driven off, germanium dioxide is formed and it retains some adsorbed acid very tenaciously ; and when treated with nitric acid, there is a vigorous reaction and the resulting germanium dioxide retains some sulphuric acid. Aqua regia dissolves germanium disulphide with the separation of sulphur. The disulphide dissolves readily in aq. ammonia, and in soln. of the alkali hydroxides, or alkali sulphides. Presumably **sulphogermanates** are formed, but none has been isolated. The soln. of germanium disulphide in potassium sulphide gives precipitates—possibly sulphogermanates—when treated with salts of the heavy metals. If the soln. of germanium disulphide in potassium hydroxide be treated with chlorine or bromine, sulphur is separated. The soln. of germanium disulphide in aq. ammonia is oxidized by hydrogen dioxide without the separation of sulphur. *Argyrodite* and *canfieldite* can be regarded as a basic **silver sulphogermanate,** a derivative of the acid $Ge(SH)_4.2H_2S$. S. L. Penfield [2] represented its composition by Ag_8GeS_6, and that of canfieldite, by $Ag_8(Sn,Ge)S_6$—*vide supra.* A. Weisbach described a steel-grey mineral as monoclinic, but S. L. Penfield showed that the crystals belong to the cubic system. The sp. gr. is 6·085–6·111 ; and the hardness 2·5. E. T. Wherry found argyrodite to have poor qualities as a radio-detector. O. Pufahl's mineral *germanite* previously indicated has a composition $Cu_5(Cu,Fe)_6AsGeS_{12}$, and sp. gr. 4·46.

C. Winkler [3] reported the formation of a white *germanous phosphate* when a soluble phosphate is added to a germanous salt soln. ; but otherwise *germanium phosphates, nitrates, carbonates, and sulphates* have not been described.

REFERENCES.

[1] C. Winkler, *Journ. prakt. Chem.*, (2), 34. 177, 1886 ; (2), 36. 177, 1887 ; K. Haushofer, *Sitzber. München. Akad.*, 133, 1887 ; L. F. Nilson and O. Pettersson, *Zeit. phys. Chem.*, 1. 27, 1887 ; A. Weisbach, *Jahrb. Berg. Hütt. Sachsen*, 89, 1886 ; *Neues Jahrb. Min.*, ii, 67, 1886.

[2] S. L. Penfield, *Amer. Journ. Science*, (3), 46. 107, 1893 ; (3), 47. 451, 1894 ; A. de Gramont, *Bull. Soc. Min.*, 18. 241, 1895 ; G. T. Prior and L. J. Spencer, *Min. Mag.*, 12. 5, 1898 ; O. Pufahl, *Metall Er:*, 19. 324, 1922 ; E. T. Wherry, *Amer. Min.*, 10. 28, 1925 ; A. Weisbach, *Jahrb. Berg. Hütt. Sachsen*, 89. 163, 1886 ; *Chem. News*, 53. 257, 1886 ; *Neues Jahrb. Min.*, ii, 67, 1886; i, 98, 1894.

[3] C. Winkler, *Journ. prakt. Chem.*, (2), 34. 177, 1886 ; (2), 36. 177, 1887.

CHAPTER XLVI

TIN

§ 1. The History of Tin

IT is generally believed that tin is one of the metals which has been known since very ancient times, and that this metal was employed in the arts at the time of Herodotus, Homer, and Moses. The proof of the great antiquity of tin, however, is not so convincing as in the case of copper, silver, gold, mercury, lead, and iron. The metal tin was not found native by the ancients, and they could have obtained it only by extraction from its ore. It is true, however, that the ore is found near the surface of the earth, and that it gives up its metal more readily than some of the ores of the other metals. Thus, according to J. F. Reitemeyer,[1] the early Britons smelted the ore by a very simple process :

They placed the ore in a hole dug in the ground, and laid wood between and around it. They then set fire to the wood. The fire smelted the ore. The slag was run from the molten metal through a pipe or furrow into a second hole. Many of these slag-hearths are still found in Cornwall. The whole smelting process was as effective as it was simple ; proof of this is found in the fact that the slag residues do not contain sufficient ore to warrant a second separation by more modern methods.

Tin ores occur in only a few countries which were not readily accessible to the Romans or Greeks, and accordingly, as J. Beckmann has pointed out, it appears probable that the metal would be scarce and costly among these people. Assuming that the metal believed to be tin was really such, it does not appear to have been accounted of much value. The few references to tin do not allude to objects made of this metal as being valued possessions. Again, although more durable than lead or copper, vessels of tin are very rarely found among Greek or Roman antiquities under conditions where vessels of lead and copper are comparatively common.

There are good grounds for doubting whether the scholars have been always correct in translating the ancient terms by what is now connoted by the word " tin." Moses, in the book of *Numbers* (31. 22), gives a list of the metals then known, and his term *bedil* was translated κασσίτερος in the old Greek versions of the Hebrew books ; and *cassiteros* in turn was translated *stannum* in the Latin versions. Stannum was rendered by *tin* in Low German and English ; by *tenn* in Swedish ; by *Zinn* in High German ; by *estain* in French ; by *estano* in Spanish ; and by *stagno* in Italian. Pliny, in his *Historia naturalis* (34. 47), regarded tin as a variety of lead. He said :

There are two kinds of *plumbum—nigrum*, and *candidum* or *album, i.e.* black lead, and shining or white lead. The *plumbum candidum* is the most valuable, and it was called *cassiteros* by the Greeks. There is a fabulous story told of their going in quest of it to the islands in the Atlantic Ocean, and of its being brought in boats made of osiers covered with hides. The *plumbum candidum* occurs as a black sand found on the surface of the earth, and is to be detected only by its weight ; it is mingled with small pebbles, particularly in the dried beds of rivers. The miners wash the sand, which is then melted in the furnace and becomes converted into *plumbum album*.

Pliny's *plumbum candidum* was no doubt tin just as his *plumbum nigrum* was lead. Pliny then described the production of lead from ores containing both lead and silver. He said that the metal which first becomes liquid in the furnace is called *stannum*, the next is *argentum*, and part which remains in the furnace is called *galena*. These three substances were regarded by Pliny as the component parts of the ore. When the galena was once more fused it furnished *plumbum nigrum* or lead. The scholars tell us that the Phœnician word *stan* is the source of the Latin word *stannum*. Several conjectures have been made as to the meaning of *stannum*. It is evidently not *tin* nor a peculiar metal, but rather, as emphasized by J. Beckmann, a mixed or compounded metal or alloy analogous to the German *Werkblei*, or the English *base-bullion*. This view was taken by G. Agricola, C. Encelius, G. Fallopius, L. Savot, M. A. Bernia, and J. Jung. Pliny described Roman vessels made of copper and coated with *stannum ;* and mentioned the use of an imitation *stannum* made from a mixture of two parts of *plumbum candidum* with one part of *aes candidum*. J. Beckmann believed that the *cassiteron* of the Greeks was equivalent to the Roman *stannum*, being a mixture of lead, silver, and other accidental metals. The term *cassiteron* is used by Homer, *Iliad* (**11**. 25 ; **18**. 565, 574, 612 ; **22**. 561); and Pliny said : " *Plumbum candidum* was esteemed in the days even of the Trojan war, a fact, attested by Homer, who called it *cassiteros*." The fourth and sixth century translators of Dionysius' Περιήγησις, written about the fourth century, rendered the Greek *cassiteros* by *stannum ;* and, according to J. Beckmann, the cumberous term *plumbum candidum* began to be exchanged for *stannum ;* and as tin was becoming common, the older meaning of *stannum* was soon forgotten.

J. P. Rossignol said that the history of tin among the ancient peoples can be divided into two periods. The first corresponds with the exploitation of tin in Asia ; and the second with the importation of the metal from Great Britain by the Phœnicians. According to M. Berthelot, the analyses of articles of copper alloys found in Mesopotamia, belonging to a period 1000 B.C., show that tin was not used in their manufacture ; but the analysis of an Egyptian bronze mirror belonging to a period 1600 B.C., shows that tin was present. Bronze seems to be an Oriental discovery—*vide* copper (**3**. 21, 1)—and, according to O. Olshausen, objects made of tin are very rarely found associated with vessels of the Bronze Age. A. H. Church said that the use of tin by the Egyptians, 700–600 B.C., has been proved by the finding of a strip of tin free from lead and silver, in the wrappings of an Egyptian mummy of an age not later than 600 B.C. M. Winer also refers to the use of tin by the ancient Egyptians. F. von Richthofen said that the Chinese bronze industry flourished 1800–1500 B.C., so that tin must have been known in China in that period. This subject has been discussed by K. Faulmann, and F. Lenormant.

According to H. Dufrené, the Egyptian word for tin is *khespet ;* and, according to E. Reyer, the old Indian name for tin is *naga ;* the Persian name, *aonia ;* the Chaldean and Hebrew, *anak ;* and the Æthiopian, *naak.* P. Diergart has discussed the etymology of the term *tin* W. C. Borlase considered that κασσίτερος is a word of Phœnician or Chaldean origin. From the assumption that *kastira* is a Sanscrit word, it has been inferred that κασσίτερος was derived from *kastira*, and that the earliest tin must have come from India ; but F. C. Movers, and F. Lenormant, hold that the term *kastira* was derived from κασσίτερος when the metal was carried from the West to India through the ordinary trade channels.

There are only scanty references to the tin trade of the Phœnicians, the Greeks, the Gauls, and the Romans. Herodotus (**3**. 115) said : " I am not acquainted with the Cassiterides Islands from whence comes our tin." There are also references by Hesiod (258) ; by Aristotle, *De mirabilibus auscultationibus* (81) ; by Strabo, *Geographica* (**3**. 2, 9) ; and by Cæsar, *De bello gallico* (**5**. 12). The fabulous story narrated by Pliny—*vide supra*—could very well refer to the transport of tin or tin ore from the Scilly Islands and Cornwall by vessels resembling the coracles of the ancient Britons. About 1000 B.C., the Phœnicians appear to have worked tin mines in Cornwall, and they seem to have conveyed there a body of colonists who established an emporium. The metal was also obtained from the inhabitants by barter, and imported into Greece and Asia. They called the Scilly Islands and shores of Cornwall, the Cassiterides or Tin Islands—Dionysius, in his Περιήγησις, written near the beginning of the fourth century, called them Hesperides.

Ezekiel (27. 12) refers to the tin (bedil) of the Phœnicians, and to the commerce with this metal at Tyre. The Phœnicians' trade with Britain has been discussed by W. C. Borlase, R. Edmonds, S. Greathead, C. Hawkins, J. Henry, A. H. L. Heeren, J. Kendrick, G. C. Lewis, G. Rawlinson, E. Reyer, C. R. G. Napier, J. Rhys, C. D. Saunders, L. Simonin, G. Smith, J. Taylor, A. Tylor, R. N. Worth, etc. W. D. Cooley said:

Tin in all ages has been a principal export of India. It is enumerated as such by Arrian, who found it abundantly in the ports of Arabia, at a time when the supplies of Rome flowed chiefly through that channel. The tin mines of Banca are, probably, the richest in the world. But tin was unquestionably brought from the West at a later period.

The work of Periplus of Arrian, on which this opinion is based, is supposed by W. Vincent to have been written about A.D. 64, that is, about the time of Pliny's Historia naturalis. G. Smith's examination of the available evidence has shown that W. D. Cooley's opinion is highly improbable; that tin was invariably exported from Egypt to the East; that the Phœnicians, finding tin in Britain 1500-1200 B.C., carried the metal into the Eastern markets. Diodorus Siculus, in his Bibliotheca historica (5. 347, 361), written about 30 B.C., said that the Britons carried tin from Cornwall to the island called Ictis, when it was conveyed abroad by Gallic merchants to different parts of Italy. W. C. Borlase argued that this Ictis must have been nearer to Cornwall than the Isle of Wight, and he assumed that the Ictis is a generic term for a peninsula, bay, or a depôt for merchandise.

The assumption that the Cassiterides was really Britain is supported by T. R. Holmes, E. O. von Lippmann, S. Reinach, etc. Some hold that the locality was off the north-west coast of Spain. This view is supported by quotations from writers prior to A.D. 150. Many of these, however, might have been able to say with Herodotus (3. 115), "Nor am I better acquainted with the Islands called Cassiterides from which we are said to get our tin."

Strabo alone, in his Geographica (15. 10), has said that tin is found in Drangiana; but if this country be a part of Persia, all travellers—e.g. J. Chardin, and J. B. Tavernier—say that tin is not found anywhere in the Persian Empire; and if Drangiana be part of India, then Pliny, in his Historia naturalis (34. 17), asserted that no tin had then been found in that country. The production of tin in Spain is mentioned by Strabo and Pliny; in Lusitania by Pliny, and Strabo; in Iberia by Diodorus Siculus; and in Artabra by Strabo. The exploitation of tin in ancient France was discussed by L. Davy, L. Simonin, E. Mallard, S. R. Pattison, and A. G. Werner. The history of tin in general has also been treated by G. Bapst, M. Gsell, J. P. Rossignol, F. X. M. Zippe, A. Rössing, E. Beyer, E. Reyer, A. Frantz, B. Neumann, H. Dufrené, E. O. von Lippmann, A. Mongez, etc.

The Spanish tin mines appear to have been abandoned under the government of the Moors. Much of the world's supply of tin about the thirteenth century came from Cornwall, but about that time, tin mines were discovered in Saxony and Bohemia, and not at the end of the eighth century, as stated by W. Hagec. According to M. Paris, a Cornishman fled to Germany because of a murder, and there discovered tin in 1241. The story has not been authenticated, and is not mentioned by J. F. Gmelin; while P. von Lichtenfels said that the German tin mines were discovered in 1146 near Grauppen. The subject has been discussed by E. Reyer, and A. Schmidt. It is not known when tin was first obtained from the Malay States and the East Indies, but, according to E. O. von Lippmann, the source of the metal is mentioned by Arabian writers of the eighth and ninth centuries. J. Beckmann indicates a number of sixteenth-century writers who mentioned East Indian tin, and Malacca tin. He added that the mines at Banca were discovered in 1711, and said that there are ten pits being there worked by the Chinese in 1776. J. A. Schuurman wrote on the history of the Banca tin mines. According to W. Gowland, tin was not used much by the early Japanese. A general idea of the early smelting furnaces is described in connection with lead. J. J. Becher claimed to have been the first to use coal in Cornwall for smelting tin ore ; but, added J. Percy, the claim is not substantiated.

The early Greek alchemists called tin *Hermes ;* but about A.D. 500, the alchemists called it *Zeus* or *Jupiter*, and represented it by the symbol ♃, which is said to represent the thunderbolts of Jupiter. This idea is perhaps a good illustration how easily the mind can believe there is a connection between things which have no relation to each other. According to J. Beckmann,[2] the origin of the symbol for tin is not, as A. Y. Goguet supposed, the remains of an Egyptian hieroglyph used by the Arabians ; rather is it a corruption of the first and last letters of ζεύς, for in the fourth century *Mathesis* of J. Firmicus Maternus, the capital Z is used, and in order to render the abbreviation more distinct, the last letter ς was sometimes added at the bottom. Owing to the property possessed by tin of forming brittle alloys with other metals it was also called *diabolus metallorum*—the devil of the metals. The alchemists of the Middle Ages observed many other properties of tin—*vide* the oxide, chloride, and sulphide. The Latin Geber, in his *Summa perfectionis magisterii*, probably written about the twelfth century, said :

I intimate to the sons of learning that tin is a metallic substance which is white, but not pure white ; it has a little ring, and emits a creaking sound ; it partakes of a little earthiness ; and possesses in its root both hardness and softness ; it melts rapidly without catching fire ; it does not take cupellation—*cineritium et cementum non exspectans ;* and it is extensible when hammered. Its vice is that, when alloyed, it makes every metallic body brittle excepting Saturn and pure Sol.

REFERENCES.

[1] J. Beckmann, *Beyträge zur Geschichte der Erfindungen*, Leipzig, 4. 321, 1797 ; London, 2. 206, 1846 ; G. Agricola, *Bermannus sive de re metallica*, Basileæ, 450, 485, 1546 ; C. Encelius (Entzel), *De re metallica*, Franckfurti, 1. 62, 1551 ; G. Fallopius, *De metallis*, Franckfurti, 1. 322, 1606 ; L. Savot, *Discours sur les médailles antiques*, Paris, 2. 48, 1627 ; M. A. Bernia in U. Aldrovandi, *Museum metallicum*, Bononiæ, 181, 1648 ; J. Jung, *Doxoscopia*, Hamburg, 5, 1662 ; W. C. Borlase, *Observations on the Ancient and Present State of the Island of Scilly, and their Importance to the Trade of Great Britain*, Oxford, 72, 1756 ; *Antiquities, historical and monumental, of the County of Cornwall*, London, 29, 1769 ; *Historical Sketch of the Tin Trade in Cornwall, from the Earliest Period to the Present Day*, Plymouth, 7, 1774 ; R. Edmonds, *Trans. Plymouth Inst.*, 3. 17, 1868 ; S. Greathead, *Trans. Roy. Soc. Cornwall*, 2. 359, 1822 ; J. Hawkins, *ib.*, 4. 70, 1838 ; C. Hawkins, *Observations on the Tin Trade of the Ancients in Cornwall, and on the Ictis of Diodorus Siculus*, London, 1811 ; S. R. Pattison, *Journ. Roy. Inst. Cornwall*, 2. 343, 1867 ; J. Henry, *Ann. Rep. Roy. Inst. Cornwall*, 45. 29, 1863 ; *Min. Journ. Railw. Comm. Gaz.*, 34. 65, 1864 ; A. Tylor, *ib.*, 53. 1395, 1883 ; E. Reyer, *ib.*, 49. 1299, 1879 ; *Oest. Zeit. Berg. Hütt.*, 28. 499, 514, 1880 ; *Iron Age*, 24. 5, 1879 ; *Trans. Min. Assoc. Cornwall*, 4. 138, 1893 ; L. Simonin, *Compt. Rend.*, 62. 346, 1866 ; M. Berthelot, *ib.*, 104. 265, 1887 ; *Le chimie au moyen age*, Paris, 359, 1893 ; J. Taylor, *Phil. Mag.*, 5. 357, 1800 ; C. R. G. Napier, *B.A. Rep.*, ii, 177, 1876 ; M. Winer, *Berg. Hütt. Ztg.*, 40. 467, 1881 ; A. Frantz, *ib.*, 39. 437, 1880 ; L. Davy, *Compt. Rend.*, 125. 337, 1897 ; A. G. Werner, *Neu Theorie von der Entstehung der Gänge, mit Anwendung auf den Bergbau besonders den freibergischen*, Freiburg, 149, 1791 ; *Journ. Mines*, 3. 90, 1796 ; J. A. Schuurman, *Jaarb. Mijnw. Ned. Oost-Indië*, 2. 1, 1898 ; E. Mallard, *Mem. Soc. Creuse*, 3. 161, 1862 ; *Ann. Mines*, (6), 10. 321, 1866 ; J. J. Becher, *Alphabetum minerale*, Truro, 1682 ; J. Percy, *The Metallurgy of Lead*, London, 218, 1870 ; J. Kendrick, *Phœnicia*, London, 212, 1855 ; G. Rawlinson, *Phœnicia*, London, 66, 1898 ; A. Mongez, *Mém. Acad. Inscript.*, 8. 363, 1827 ; *Mem. L'Inst. France*, 3. 441, 1818 ; G. C. Lewis, *An Historical Survey of the Astronomy of the Ancients*, London, 450, 1862 ; J. Rhys, *Early Britain*, London, 44, 204, 287, 1904 ; C. D. Saunders, *Ann. Rep. Cornwall Polyt. Soc.*, 33. 42, 1865 ; R. N. Worth, *ib.*, 40. 63, 1872 ; *Trans. Plymouth Inst.*, 42. 120, 1874 ; *Trans. Devon. Assoc. Science*, 8. 311, 1876 ; G. Bapst, *Études sur l'étain dans l'antiquité et au moyen age*, Paris, 1884 ; H. Dufrené, *Étude sur l'histoire de la production et du commerce de l'étain*, Paris, 1881 ; *Ann. Gén. Civ.*, 9. 649, 793, 1880 ; M. Gsell, *Eisen, Kupfer and Bronze bei den alten Aegyptern*, Karlsruhe, 1910 ; O. Olshausen, *Verh. Berlin Ges. Anthrop.*, 18. 475, 1886 ; A. H. Church, *Chem. News*, 36. 168, 1877 ; A. H. L. Heeren, *De la politique et du commerce des peuples des l'antiquité*, Paris, 1830 ; J. P. Rossignol, *Les métaux dans l'antiquité*, Paris, 1863 :

F. von Richthofen, *China : Ergebnisse eigener Reisen und darauf gegründenen Studien*, Berlin, **1**. 369, 1877 ; H. Blümmer, *Terminologie und Technologie der Gewerbe und Künste bei Griechen und Römern*, Leipzig, **4**. 83, 1886 ; J. Chardin, *Voyages de M. le Chevalier Chardin en Perse, et autres lieux de l'Orient*, Amsterdam, 1711 ; *Journal du voyages*, Rouen, **4**. 65, 1723 ; J. B. Tavernier, *Les six voyages de Jean Baptiste Tavernier*, Paris, **1**. 162, 1676 ; London, 1678 ; E. Beyer, *Zinn. Eine geologische, montanistische, historische Monographie*, Berlin, 1881 ; F. X. M. Zippe, *Geschichte der Metalle*, Wien, 1857 ; B. Neumann, *Die Metalle, Geschichte, Vorkommen, und Gewinnung*, Halle a. S., 1904 ; A. Rössing, *Geschichte der Metalle*, Berlin, 1901 ; G. Smith, *The Cassiterides : An Inquiry into the Commercial operations of the Phœnicians in Western Europe, with particular reference to the British Tin Trade*, London, 154, 1863 ; E. O. von Lippmann, *Entstehung und Ausbreitung der Alchemie*, Berlin, 577, 1919 ; F. Lenormant, *Die Anfänge der Kultur*, Jena, 1875 ; *Die Magie und Wahrsagekunst der Chaldäer*, Jena, 1878 ; London, 1878 ; W. D. Cooley, *The History of Maritime and Inland Discovery*, London, **1**. 131, 1830 ; W. Vincent, *Commerce and Navigation of the Ancients in the Indian Ocean*, London, **1**. 308, 1807 ; **2**. 3, 1807 ; S. Reinach, *L'Anthropologie*, **3**. 275, 1892 ; T. R. Holmes, *Ancient Britain*, Oxford, 483, 1907 ; J. R. Partington, *Journ. Soc. Chem. Ind.*, **42**. 696, 1923 ; R. H. Atkinson, *ib.*, **42**. 696, 1923 ; Anon., *ib.*, **42**. 671, 696, 1923 ; J. L. Ideler, *Physici et Medici græci minores*, Berlin, 1841 ; K. Faulmann, *Illustrirte Culturgeschichte, für Laser aller Stände*, Wien, 1881 ; E. Meyer, *Geschichte der Alterthums*, Stuttgart, 1884 ; F. C. Movers, *Die Phönizier*, Berlin, 1856 ; L. Friedländer, *Darstellungen aus der Sittengeschichte Roms, in der Zeit von August Biszum Ausgang der Antonine*, Leipzig, 1910 ; W. Hagec, *Böhmische Chronik*, Nürnberg, 53, 1697 ; M. Paris, *English History*, London, **1**. 373, 1852 ; *Monachi Albanensis Angli, Historia Major*, Londoni, 765, 1571 ; J. F. Gmelin, *Beyträge zur Geschichte des deutschen Bergbaues*, Halle, 121, 1783 ; P. von Lichtenfels, *Versuch über die Geschichte der böhmischen und mährischen Bergwerke*, Wien, 85, 1780 ; A. Schmidt, *Montan. Ztg. Oest. Ungarn*, **7**. 479, 1900 ; P. Diergart, *Journ. prakt. Chem.*, (2), **61**. 525, 1900 ; J. F. Reitemeyer, *Geschichte des Bergbaues und Hüttenwesens bei den alten Völkern*, Göttingen, 1785 ; W. Gowland, *Trans. Japan. Soc.*, London, **13**. 20, 1915.
    [2] A. Y. Goguet, *De l'origine des loix, des arts, et des sciences et de leurs progrès chez les anciens peuples*, Paris, **2**. 370, 1758 ; Edinburgh, 1761 ; J. Beckmann, *Beyträge zur Geschichte der Erfindungen*, Leipzig, **3**. 373, 1792 ; London, **2**. 23, 1846.

§ 2. The Occurrence of Tin

Tin, though one of the common metals, is the most sparsely distributed metal in common use. The known workable deposits of gold cover one and a half million square miles, while the known workable deposits of tin cover but one-twelfth of this area. There is scarcely a country where gold has not been or might be profitably obtained ; tin is confined to about a dozen districts in the world. The tin deposits of Cornwall so long famed in history are nearing exhaustion ; the same might be said of the deposits in Bohemia, Tuscany, South Spain, and the Pyrenees. There are, indeed, comparatively few known workable deposits of tin in the World.—ANON.

Although so common and well known a metal tin is really a scarcer element than many less familiar elements usually ranked with the scarce and rare elements— *e.g.* cerium and yttrium, lithium, beryllium, titanium, zirconium, vanadium, etc. According to the estimates of J. H. L. Vogt,[1] the igneous rocks on the earth's crust contain $n \times 10^{-5}$ per cent. of tin ; F. W. Clarke and H. S. Washington estimated $n \times 10^{-6}$ per cent. For the amount in the **earth's** crust, the estimate is $0.0000x$ per cent. The most abundant source of tin is the oxide, cassiterite, found in association with granitic rocks. The greater portion of the world's supply is derived from alluvial deposits in which the cassiterite originally occurred in veins and lodes in highly acid igneous rocks. The tinstone of the detrital deposit is associated with other durable constituents of the rock—quartz, ilmenite, tourmaline, and topaz. The formation of tin deposits was discussed by W. R. Jones, R. H. Rastall, etc.

A general idea of the distribution of the tin deposits will be obtained from Fig. 1. Tin deposits are thus widely distributed, but 85 per cent. of the world's supply comes (i) from the area embracing the deposits at Malay, Siam, and China ; and (ii) from the deposits at Bolivia.[2]

Only a small proportion of the world's supply comes from Europe. Cornwall [3] is practically the only source of tin in *Great Britain*, although a small proportion comes from the adjoining parts of Devon. In 1919, Cornwall produced 5156 tons of ore with 66·4 per cent., and Devon, 28 tons. The tin bearing lodes on the *Bohemian* and *Saxony* sides of the Erzgebirge were an important source of tin in mediæval times, but they are now mainly of historical interest being practically exhausted.   There is a tin-smelting industry in *France*, but the production is small and erratic.   Ore occurs at Montebras, Vaulry, Cieux, Chanteloube, Meymac, Puy les Vignes, and Charrier.   *Holland* is not a producer, but is rather a distributing centre for the tin produced in Dutch East Indies.   Iron and tin were mined in early times at Campiglia Marittima, Tuscany, in *Italy*, and the deposits were rediscovered in 1871.   The production is very small.   Tin has been produced in *Portugal* from the time of the Phœnicians.   The output from deposits at Mirandella, Montesinhos, Parada, Coelhoso, Marao Angueria, and Valle Seixo ;   and near Ramalhoso, Vizeu, and Belmonte, is small.   The deposits in *Spain* are also historically famous, having been worked by the Phœnicians and the Romans.   The output is now small.   The deposits occur mainly at Penuta, Romilo, Verin, Monertey, Almaraz, Lumbrales, Viana del Bollo, Pontevedra, Terrubias, and Santo Tomé de Rozadas near Salamanca, San Isodoro and Marinera near Cartagena, and near Almeria.   Very little tin is produced in *Russia*, but a number of deposits are known on the rivers Onon, and Ignoda, and their tributaries.[4] There are mines at Olovianaia, north-west of Nerchinsk, and in Onon-Borzia, in the Transbalkans province of Siberia.   There is an occurrence at Pitkaranta, Finland ;   and deposits at Sossnowics and Dombroff, *Poland*.

In Asia, *China* furnishes about seven per cent. of the world's supply of tin.   Cassiterite

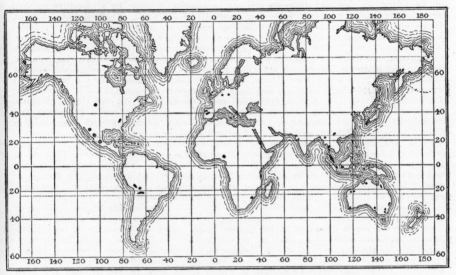

FIG. 1.—The Geographical Distribution of the Chief Deposits of Tin Ore.

occurs in the provinces of Hunan, Yunnan, Kwangsi, Kwangtung, and Tukien.   Ninety per cent. of the 8000 tons of crude tin produced per annum in China comes from the Kochiu district of Yunnan in Southern China.   There are deposits in Kowloon, Hong Kong.   Tin has been worked from ancient times by the Chinese in the French colony, *Indo-China*.   There is a little tin ore in the neighbourhood of Kaobang, north of Tonkin, and there are deposits at Ban ta coua, Laos, and in the neighbourhood of Pia-Ouac.   *Japan* has a very small output.   Deposits occur in Taniyama, Satsuma ;   Kyushu and Nagao in Osumi ;   Iwato and Mitate in Hyuga ;   and Kiura in Bungo ;   Nayegi in Mino ;   and Sudzukoya in Hitachi. There is a great stanniferous belt stretching from Banca through the Malay peninsula into Burma.   The chief production of *Siam* is from the detrital deposits on the west side of the main range, in Monthon Puket, and smaller amounts come from Chumporn Nakorn, Stamarat, and Patani.   Some is obtained by dredging at Tongkah Harbour, and Renong. The ore occurs in the valley of the Nam Sak river.   In the *Dutch East Indies*, the principal centres of the tin industry are the islands Banca, Billiton, and Singkep.   Some tin is also produced at Siak, on the River Indrigiri, Sumatra, and on the Karimon Islands.   At Singapore and Penang, in the *Straits Settlements*, are large smelteries which treat the ores from the surrounding countries.   Malacca is the only producer of ore ;   there is a deposit at Chin-Chin.   The *Federated Malay States* are the largest producers of tin ore, and that of an exceptionally good quality.   The mines in Perak produce more than those in Selangor, Negri Sembilan, and Pahang combined.   In the Kinta district of Perak, there are mines at Kampar, Malim Nawar, Sungei Siput, Gopeng, Pulai, Ulu Piah, Tambun, Tanjong, Rambutan, Menglembu, Penkalan, Lahat, Rotan Dahan, Redhills, Pusing Lama, Pusing

Baharu, Siputeh, Tronoh, and Tanjong Toh Allang.   There are also pipes at Ayer Dangsang, and Changkat Pari.   In the Larut district, Perak, there are mines at Selama and Blanda Mabok.   There is a lode on Gunong Paku, Intan ; and veins of ore at Bruseh.   In Selangor there are stanniferous deposits near Tanjong Malim, Kalumpang, Serendah, Kuala Lumpur, Salak, Sungei Besi, Rawang, Kepong. Setapek, Ampang, and Serdang.   In Negri Sembilan, there are lodes at Titi, on the Triang and Kenaboi rivers, at Kuala Pilah Pantai, Rasa, Chukong, Gebok, and Lukut.   In the Pehang district there are deposits at Bentong, Tras, Machi, and Belat, and on the Kuantan river and its tributaries Blat, and Sungei Lembing.   The *Unfederated Malay States* have tin deposits at Muar. Batu Pahat, and Kota Tinggi in Johore ; at Kuala Muda. Kulim, Krian, and Kubang Pasu in Kedah ; at Bukeit Yong, Palua Chondong, and Uli Kelatan and on the Nenggiri in Kelantan ; at Setul in Perlis ; at Bundi, Sungei Ayam, Sungei Sendok, Sungei Paka, Sungei Kajang, and Bukit Tawang, and on the Dungan river in Trengganu.   There are no deposits of commercial importance in *Ceylon*, though cassiterite occurs in the gem-gravels of Balangoda.   The production of tin ore in *India* is small ; Burma and the Southern Shan States are responsible for most of the tin.   Stanniferous deposits occur at Maliwun, Karanthuri, Yaungwa, Bokpyin, Yengan, Manoron. Mergui, Thabalik, and the Great Tenasserim Valley, King's Island, Kissering, Davies Island, Amherst, Tavoy, Chota Nagpur, Narunga, Chappatand, and the Palanpur State.

In Africa, tin ore was formerly smelted in Bauchi, *Nigeria*, by a primitive method regarded as a family secret.   It is now produced at Naraguta, Ngell, Bukuru, Forum, Ropp, etc., on the Bauchi Plateau.   Tinstone also occurs in the Ningi and Burra hills ; in the Vere hills, and the Shebshi hills ; and near Gadama, Fagam, Jemaa, Amari, Gantam, Aribi Eri, and Akwa Ibami.   In the *Gold Coast*, stream tin occurs in the Winnebah district, in Mankofa, and the Mankwadi.   In *Rhodesia*, there are deposits in the Enterprise, Ndanga, Mazoe, and Shamva districts, in the Odzi Reserve, and along the Tsungiwesi and the Umniati rivers.   In *South-West Africa*, formerly a German colony, the tin-bearing belt extends from Otjimboyo to Uis ; and there are deposits at Ameib, Dawib, Aubinhonis, Tsomsaub, Neineis, Uis, Kawab Otjumue, and Kohero East.   In the Union of South Africa the chief tin-mining districts are in the Eaterberg area, Western Transvaal, and Swaziland.   There are deposits at Annex Langverwacht, Vredehoek, and Tygerrberg in *Cape Province ;* in Umfuli in Natal , in Zaaiplaats, Roodepoort, Groenfontein, Solomon's Temple, Doornhoek Kromkloof, Welgevonden, Zwartkloof, Elandsfontein, Witfortein, Newbery, Rhenosterpoort, Quaggafontein, Weynek, Leeuwpoort, Enkeldorn, Vlaklaagte, Roodepoortje, Mutue Fides, and Stavoren in the *Transvaal*.   The districts of Mbubane and Forbes Reef are the two important tin-bearing districts in *Swaziland*.   In *Portuguese East Africa* there are deposits at Chimoio, and Moçambique ; and in *Belgian Congo* there are deposits at Busanga, Muika, Kiambi, Muanga, and Mulongo.

In America, there is no production of tin in *Canada*, but deposits of cassiterite occur at New Ross, Nova Scotia ; in New Brunswick, British Columbia, and the Yukon district. Very little tin ore is produced in the *United States*.   Deposits of economic importance have been found at Alaska ; and ore occurs in the Hot Springs district, at Gaffney, Carolina ; in the Black Hills, South Dakota and Wyoming ; Mount Franklin, Texas ; in Lander County, Nevada ; Shenandoah Valley, Virginia ; San Diego County, and Temescal, California ; etc.   Cassiterite is widely distributed in *Mexico*, and has been worked by natives in Durango, Jalisco, Guanajciato, San Luis Potosi, Aguas Calientes, and Coalhuila.   Tin mining in Mexico has been carried on since the Aztec period.   The annual output is small.   The output of tin from *Bolivia* is second only to that of the Federated Malay States.   The Bolivian mines are situated on the Eastern Cordillera, and the high plateau between Eastern and Western Cordillera.   Most ore comes from Potosi, and other centres are Araca, Cruro, Machacamarca, Huanuni, Llallogua, Uncia, Sala Sala, Chocaya, and Chorolque.   At the time of the Spanish domination, the Bolivian mines were worked only for gold, silver, and copper.   The rejected tin ores accumulated on dumps and in old stopes, and they have been proved valuable acquisitions.   Most Bolivian ore now comes from simple tin lodes.   In the *Argentina*, cassiterite occurs at Catmarca and La Rioja.   Bohemian ore is exported from *Chile* and *Peru*, but there is no noteworthy production in these countries.

Tin mining began in Australasia in 1872.   In *New South Wales*, the chief centres are Emmaville and Tingha, ore occurs at Elsmore, Ardlethan, Newstedd, Stannifer, Stanborough, Cope's Creek, Catarrh Creek, Rose Valley, Ruby, Maryland, Herding Yard, Cemetry, Wilson's Downfall, Wylie, Two Mile Creek, Bookookoorara Creek, Mount Tallabong, Lachlan Valley, Burra Burra, Mandanah, Albury, Jingellie, Germanton, Tumbarumba, Wagga Wagga, Bungonia, Jindabyne, Euriourie, Poolamacca, near Byron Bay, near Port Macquarrie, near Seal Rocks, at Shell-harbour, Termeil, Oban, etc.   Very little tin ore is produced in the *Northern Territory*.   There are deposits at Mount Wells, Burrundei, Horseshoe Creek, Maranboy, Hayes' Creek, Rum Jungle, etc.   The tin fields of *Queensland* are in the north with the exception of those at Stanthorpe and Nanango. There are the tin fields in Herberton, Chillagoe, Annan River, Stannhills, Lode Hill, Kangaroo Hills, Charters Towers. etc.   In *South Australia*, cassiterite occurs near Earea Dam, Tarcoola.   In *Tasmania* there are mines near Middlesex, in the Ben Lomond and

Avoca districts. The Mount Bischoff mine has been the most important mine in Tasmania. There are mines in the North Dundas tin field, and in the X-River district ; in the Zeehan Field ; in the Heemskirk district and in the Stanley River and Mount Balfour districts. The output of tin from *Victoria* is comparatively small. There are deposits at Glen Wills, Beechworth, Eldorado, Chiltern, Stanley, Rutherglen, Koetong, Cudgewa, Toora, Tin Creek, Agnes River, Bruthen, Gembrook, Neerim, Darnum, Bunyip River, Tarago River, Upper Yarra, Mount Cudgewa, Mount Wills, Pilot Range, Mitta Mitta, Eskdale, Tallandoon, and Mount Singapore. In *Western Australia* there are tin fields in Greenbushes, and Pilbara. A deposit occurs in West Kimberley. *New Zealand* does not produce tin ore, but deposits have been reported in various localities on the West Coast—Mokihinui, Canoe Creek, Clark River. It has been reported at Slaty Creek, near Lake Brunner, Hauraki, and Port Pegasus, Stewart's Island.

Between 1742 and 1759, Cornwall alone produced 39,600 tons of metal at an average price of £80 2s. per ton ; between 1840 and 1847, 51,768 tons at an average price of £99 per ton ; in 1860, 6656 tons at £136 3s. per ton ; in 1872, 9560 tons at £152 15s. per ton ; in 1878, 10,106 tons at £65 12s. 3d. per ton. The world's output in tons of 2240 lbs. was :

	1880	1890	1900	1910	1918	1920
Output .	38,321	55,098	80,824	104,073	122,513	119,211
Average price	£91 5s. 0d.	£97 13s. 3d.	£133 11s. 6d.	£155 6s. 2d.	£329 11s. 2d.	£296 1s. 7d.

The total world's production of 142,000 tons (of 2240 lbs.) of tin ore, in 1924, was distributed as follows :

Malay States	.	.	.	.	46,913	Bolivia .	. . . .	31,610
Australia .	.	.	.	.	3,069	Dutch East Indies	. .	31,558
Nigeria	.	.	.	.	6,162	China . .	. . .	7,000
Cornwall .	.	.	.	.	1,986	Siam . .	. . .	7,950
Union of South Africa		.	.	1,162	Belgian Congo, etc.	. .	645
India	.	.	.	.	1,375	Portugal, Spain .	. .	400

Native stannum is of no commercial significance. Reports of the occurrence of native tin were made by J. Matthesius,[5] and J. C. Richter. In 1750, J. G. Wallerius said that *stannum nativum* is very rarely seen ; and T. Bergman added, in 1780 : " Many testimonies concur in asserting that tin is found native in England ; but I have never seen any specimens of it." C. Linnæus, and R. J. Haüy had doubts about its occurrence. Neither A. G. Werner, nor A. Estner mentioned native tin. J. B. L. Romé de l'Isle had a specimen alleged to be native tin ; but, added L. A. Emmerling, the specimens of native tin supposed to have been found in Cornwall and in Bohemia are probably derived from the remains of old tin smelteries. Now, however, there is no reason for doubting that tin sometimes occurs naturally in the metallic state. Native tin occurring with gold in Russia has been described by C. von Tscheffkin,[6] R. Hermann, and P. von Jeremejeff ; from Bolivia, by D. Forbes, F. Nies, H. Reck, and A. W. Stelzner ; from French Guiana, by A. Damour ; from Guanajuanto, Mexico, by A. Frenzel ; and from Pennsylvania, by C. M. Wetherill. J. D. Dana considered that these reports are not unimpeachable ; but there is no doubt about the occurrence of tin in rounded grains, 0·1–1·0 mm. in diameter, along with platinum, iridosmine, gold, copper, cassiterite, and corundum in the washings from the tributaries of the Clarence river, near Oban, New South Wales. Besides cassiterite a little *stannite, tin pyrites,* or *bell-metal ore,* $SnS_2.Cu_2S.FeS$, has been worked in Bolivia, New South Wales, and Tasmania. Other tin minerals of no economic importance are : *cuprocassiterite,* $4SnO_2.Cu_2Sn(OH)_6$; *frankeite,* $Pb_5Sn_3Sb_2S_{12}$; *cylindrite,* $Pb_6SnSb_2S_{12}$; *teallite,* $PbSnS_2$; *plumbostannite,* $Sn_2Sb_2Pb_2(Fe,Sn)_2S_{11}$; *canfieldite,* $Ag_8(Sn,Ge)S_6$; *nordenskjöldine,* $CaSnO_4(BO)_2$; and *stokesite,* $CaO.SnO_2.3SiO_2.2H_2O$.

Tin occurs in small quantities as an accessory constituent of a number of other minerals. Thus, J. J. Berzelius,[7] G. Jenzsch, H. Rose and R. Weber, A. E. Nordenskjöld, R. Hermann, E. S. Dana and O. D. Allen, C. A. Schaeffer, T. S. Hunt, H. Müller, J. L. Smith, F. A. Genth, and E. S. Hall and A. Smith reported up to 2 per cent. of stannic oxide in specimens of

columbite from different localities.   O. Hauser and L. Finckh found it in *plumbocolumbite.*
G. Jenzsch, C. F. Chandler, L. Weiss and M. Landecker, H. Rose and R. Weber,
J. C. G. de Marignac, C. F. Rammelsberg, A. Arzruni, and A. G. Maitland up to 6 per cent.
of stannic oxide in various samples of *tantalite*.   J. J. Chydenius reported tin in *yttro-
tantalite ;* A. E. Nordenskjöld, in *iriolite ;* A. Damour, in tin oxide in *titaniferous iron ore ;*
R. Hermann, in *ferroilmenite ;* G. Friedel and F. Grandjean, in *rutile ;* R. Hermann, in
ilmenorutile ; J. W. Mallet, and A. Damour, in *euclase ;* H. Rose and R. Weber,
C. F. Rammelsberg, W. E. Hidden and J. W. Mallet, and R. Hermann, in *fergusonite ;*
R. Hermann, J. T. Donald, G. C. Hoffman, E. S. Dana and E. H. Swallow, in *samarskite ;*
A. Thorpe, and C. W. Blomstrand, in *monazite ;* F. Zambonini, in *delorenzite ;* O. Hauser,
in *risörite ;* J. C. G. de Marignac, in *œschinite ;* W. J. Knowlton, in *cyrtolite ;* H. Sjögren,
in *fredricite ;* C. W. Blomstrand, in *polycrase ;* S. R. Paykull, in *eucrasite ;* J. W. Mallet,
in *sipylite ;* C. F. Rammelsberg, in *ferberite ;* A. E. Nordenskjöld, in *tapiolite ;* F. P. Möller,
in *tritomite ;* A. E. Nordenskjöld, and C. F. Rammelsberg, in *hjelmite ;* C. F. Rammelsberg,
in *tyrite ;* A. E. Nordenskjöld, in *malacone ;* E. Linnemann, and G. Woitschach, in *zircon ;*
F. A. Genth, and H. Traube, in *scheelite ;* J. L. Smith, O. D. Allen, and F. A. Genth, in
hatschettolite ; K. F. Föhr, and H. Trenkler, in *phonolite ;* A. E. Nordenskjöld, and
F. P. Dunnington, in *microlite ;* F. Farsky, in *olivine ;* G. J. Brush, in *pyrophillite ;*
C. A. de Gouvenain, and S. Meunier, in *kaolin ;* G. vom Rath, in *cryolite ;* H. Schröder,
in *mica ;* F. Sandberger, in *lepidolite ;* G. Sobrero, in *mangano-epidote,* and *pyrolusite ;*
A. Piutti and E. Stoppani, in *pyrite ;* J. M. Saitao, in *fahlerz ;* A. des Cloizeaux, in
sperrylite ; J. H. Collins, in *zinc blende ;* H. J. Sjögren, in *thalenite ;* and L. Hundeshagen,
in *tourmaline.*

A. Bergeat [8] observed tin in the exhalations from Stromboli.   The presence of
stannic oxide has been reported in numerous meteorites.[9]   Spectral observations
by J. N. Lockyer,[10] C. Hutchins and E. L. Holden, and H. A. Rowland have shown
that tin occurs in the atm. of the sun ; and similar observations by J. Lunt showed
that it is present in the atm. of some stars.   Traces of tin have been reported in
a number of natural waters by J. J. Berzelius,[11] C. F. Rammelsberg, etc.   Water
distilled through a still-head and worm of tin was shown by H. Fleck [12] to contain
traces of that metal ; J. and H. S. Pattinson found tin in commercial antimony,
and H. Hager, in commercially pure hydrochloric acid.   According to O. Hehner,
every article of food preserved in a tin canister dissolves some of the tin coating
of the metal and becomes contaminated with tin in quantities depending upon
the acidity of the material, the time of contact, and the quality of the tinplate.
Condensed milk takes up a mere trace, acid fruits quite tangible amounts.   From
every sample of tinned food, without exception, weighable traces of tin can be
separated.   A. P. Smith, A. R. Leeds, R. Kayser, F. Wirthle, L. Medicus, H. Serger,
E. F. Kohman and N. H. Sanborn, K. B. Lehmann, A. J. J. Vandevelde, E. Ungar
and G. Bodländer, F. A. Norton, and J. Attfield found it in preserved fruits ;
A. Sam, in preserved beans ; E. Ungar, in asparagus ; J. B. M. Coebergh, in canned
spinach ; R. Kayser, in eels ; T. Günther, A. Rössing, and G. Salomone, in preserved
fish ; T. L. Phipson, and J. Mayrhofer and A. Hilger, in sugar ; G. Gimel, in
yeast ; and A. Eckardt, in animal and vegetable substances.   H. Serger discussed
the occurrence of tin in canned foods ; A. Beythein, in cosmetics.

REFERENCES.

[1] J. H. L. Vogt, *Zeit. prakt. Geol.,* **6**. 225, 314, 377, 413, 1898 ; **7**. 10, 274, 1899 ; F. W. Clarke
and H. S. Washington, *Proc. Nat. Acad. Sciences,* **8**. 108, 1922 ; *The Composition of the Earth's
Crust,* Washington, 1924 ; H. S. Washington, *Journ. Franklin Inst.,* **190**. 757, 1920 ; W. R. Jones,
Trans. Amer. Inst. Min. Met., **29**. 320, 1920 ; R. H. Rastall, *ib.,* **29**. 352, 1920 ; C. C. Cullis,
ib., **29**. 348, 1920.
[2] G. M. Davies, *Tin Ores,* London, 1919 ; Imperial Mineral Resources Bureau, *Tin,* London,
1922 ; *Bull. Imp. Inst.,* **17**. 411, 1919 ; F. Peters, *Glückauf,* **57**. 607, 662, 1921 ; S. Fauers,
Tin Deposits of the World, London, 1907 ; G. R. Lewis, *The Stannaries, A Study of the English
Tin Mines,* London, 1908 ; F. L. and E. Hess, *Bibliography of the Geology and Mineralogy of Tin,*
Washington, 1912 ; G. R. Oswald, *Metal Ind.,* **24**. 25, 1924 ; W. R. Jones, *The Tin Fields of the
World,* London, 1925 ; J. Czochralsky, *Zeit. Metallkunde,* **18**. 43, 1926.
[3] H. B. Cronshaw, *Trans. Inst. Min. Met.,* **30**. 408, 1921 ; E. H. Davison, *Mining Mag.,* **29**.
22, 1923 ; **31**. 15, 1924 ; T. C. F. Hall, *ib.,* **27**. 201, 1922 ; H. Louis, *ib.,* **16**. 15, 1917.
[4] M. M. Petyaev, *Comité Geol. Mat.,* **32**, 1918 ; P. P. Sushchinsky, *ib.,* **5**, 1916.

⁵ T. Bergman, *De minerarum docimasia humida*, Upsala, 1780 ; J. G. Wallerius, *Mineralogia,* Stockholm, 386, 1750 ; J. B. L. Romé de l'Isle, *Cristallographie*, Paris, 3. 407, 1783 ; R. J. Haüy, *Traité de minéralogie*, Paris, 4. 132, 1801 ; 4. 148, 1822 ; A. Estner, *Versuch einer Mineralogie*, Wien, 1804 ; L. A. Emmerling, *Lehrbuch der Mineralogie*, Giessen, 2. 430, 1796 ; A. G. Werner, *Letztes Mineralsystem*, Freiberg, 1817 ; J. Matthesius, *Berg Postilla oder Sarepta*, Nürnberg, 1562 ; C. Linnæus, *Systema naturæ*, Lugduni Batavorum, 236, 1768 ; J. C. Richter, *Museum Richterianum*, Lipsiæ, 75, 1743.

⁶ P. von Jeremejeff, *Gornyi Journ.*, 3. 263, 1887 ; C. von Tscheffkin, *Isis*, 434, 1837 ; *Neues Jahrb. Min.*, 59, 1838 ; A. Frenzel, *ib.*, 802, 1873 ; R. Hermann, *Bull. Soc. Nat. Moscow*, 4. 876, 1844 ; *Journ. prakt. Chem.*, (1), 33. 300, 1844 ; C. M. Wetherill, *ib.*, (1), 58. 447, 1853 ; J. D. Dana, *A System of Mineralogy*, New York, 25, 1892 ; A. Damour, *Compt. Rend.*, 52. 688, 1861 ; A. W. Stelzner, *Zeit. deut. geol. Ges.*, 49. 81, 88, 1897 ; H. Rock, *Peterman's Mitt.*, 320, 1867 ; F. Nies, *Verh. Naturk. Württemberg*, 45. 292, 1889 ; F. A. Genth, *Proc. Amer. Phil. Soc.*, 23. 30, 1885 ; D. Forbes, *Phil. Mag.*, (4), 29. 129, 1865 ; (4), 30. 142, 1866.

⁷ A. Piutti and E. Stoppani, *Gazz. Chim. Ital.*, 35. ii, 29, 1905 ; H. Rose and R. Weber, *Pogg. Ann.*, 104. 85, 1858 ; 107. 590, 1859 ; G. Jenzsch, *ib.*, 97. 104, 1856 ; J. J. Berzelius, *ib.*, 4. 6, 1825 ; G. vom Rath, *ib.*, 144. 596, 1871 ; J. J. Chydenius, *ib.*, 111. 284, 1860 ; A. E. Nordenskjöld, *ib.*, 111. 278, 1860 ; 122. 604, 1864 ; *Zeit. Kryst.*, 1. 158, 1877 ; 34. 692, 1901 ; *Acta Soc. Fenn.*, 5. 163, 1857 ; G. Woitschach, *Zeit. Kryst.*, 7. 86, 1882 ; C. W. Blomstrand, *ib.*, 4. 524, 1880 ; 20. 368, 1892 ; S. R. Paykull, *ib.*, 2. 308, 1878 ; F. Zambonini, *ib.*, 45. 76, 1908 ; R. Hermann, *Journ. prakt. Chem.*, (2), 2. 113, 1870 ; H. Müller, *ib.*, (1), 58. 138, 1852 ; E. S. Dana and O. D. Allen, *Amer. Journ. Science*, (3), 32. 386, 1888 ; C. A. Schaeffer, *ib.*, (3), 28. 430, 1884 ; O. D. Allen, *ib.*, (3), 14. 128, 1377 ; W. J. Knowlton, *ib.*, (2), 44. 224, 1867 ; H. Sjögren, *ib.*, (3), 20. 72, 1880 ; *Geol. För. Förh.*, 28. 93, 1908 ; T. S. Hunt, *Amer. Journ. Science*, (2), 14. 340, 1852 ; J. L. Smith, *ib.*, (3), 13. 359, 1877 ; J. W. Mallet, *Phil. Mag.*, (4), 5. 127, 1853 ; *Amer. Journ. Science*, (3), 14. 397, 1877 ; G. J. Brush, *ib.*, (2), 26. 68, 1858 ; W. E. Hidden and J. W. Mallet, *ib.*, (3), 24. 372, 1882 ; E. S. Dana and E. H. Swallow, *ib.*, (3), 11. 201, 1876 ; F. A. Genth, *ib.*, (2), 28. 252, 1860 ; *Proc. Acad. Philadelphia*, 10, 1889 ; *Bull. U.S. Geol. Sur.*, 70, 1892 ; C. F. Chandler, *Miscellaneous Chemical Researches*, Göttingen, 1856 ; C. Sobrero, *Mem. Accad. Torino*, 38. 75, 1835 ; *Ann. Chim. Phys.*, (2), 61. 171, 1836 ; J. C. G. de Marignac, *Arch. Sciences Genève*, (2), 25. 24, 1865 ; C. F. Rammelsberg, *Sitzber. Akad. Berlin*, 175, 1864 ; *Ber.*, 3. 926, 1870 ; *Pogg. Ann.*, 144. 65, 1871 ; A. Arzruni, *Proc. Russ. Min. Soc.*, 22. 12, 1888 ; E. S. Hall and A. Smith, *Proc. Amer. Phil. Soc.*, 44. 177, 1905 ; A. Damour, *Bull. Géol. Soc.*, (2), 13. 542, 1856 ; *Compt. Rend.*, 40. 942, 1855 ; A. Meunier, *ib.*, 68. 1136, 1869 ; C. A. de Gouvenain, *ib.*, 78. 1032, 1874 ; A. des Cloizeaux, *ib.*, 108. 77, 1889 ; G. C. Hoffmann, *Amer. Journ. Science*, (3), 24. 475, 1882 ; J. T. Donald, *Chem. News*, 49. 259, 1884 ; A. Thorpe, *ib.*, 72. 32, 1895 ; E. Linnemann, *ib.*, 52. 233, 1885 ; F. Sandberger, *Berg Hütt. Ztg.*, 37. 202, 1878 ; H. Schröder, *Sitzber. Naturforsch. Leipzig*, 70, 1883 ; H. Traube, *Neues Jahrb. Min.*, i, 237, 1890 ; K. F. Föhr, *ib.*, i, 233, 1884 ; F. P. Möller, *Liebig's Ann.*, 120. 241, 1861 ; H. Trenkler, *Tschermak's Mitt.*, (2), 20. 129, 1901 ; F. P. Dunnington, *Amer. Chem. Journ.*, 3. 130, 1881 ; F. Farsky, *Verh. Geol. Reichsanst. Wien*, 205, 1876 ; J. M. Saitao, *Ann. Mines*, (5), 1. 122, 1852 ; J. H. Collins, *Min. Mag.*, 2. 92, 1879 ; A. G. Maitland, *Bull. Geol. Sur. West. Australia*, 23. 65, 1908 ; A. Lacroin, *Bull. Soc. Min.*, 31. 312, 1908 ; G. Friedel and F. Grandjean, *ib.*, 32. 52, 1909 ; L. Hundeshagen, *Eng. Min. Journ.*, 87. 1003, 1909 ; O. Hauser and L. Finckh, *Ber.*, 42. 2270, 1909 ; O. Hauser, *Zeit. anorg. Chem.*, 60. 230, 1908 ; L. Weiss and M. Landecker, *ib.*, 64. 65, 1909.

⁸ A. Bergeat, *Zeit. prakt. Geol.*, 7. 43, 1899.

⁹ E. Goldschmidt, *Journ. Franklin. Inst.*, 164. 369, 1907 ; C. A. Joy, *Liebig's Ann.*, 86. 35, 1853 ; E. Uricoechea, *ib.*, 91. 249, 1854 ; E. P. Harris, *ib.*, 110. 181, 1859 ; H. S. Ditten, *Journ. prakt. Chem.*, (1), 64. 121, 1854 ; F. Leydolt, *Sitzber. Akad. Wien*, 20. 289, 1856 ; W. Haidinger, *ib.*, 44. 29, 1861 ; 49. 497, 1864 ; J. E. Willet, *Amer. Journ. Science*, (2), 17. 331, 1854 ; J. W. Mallet, *ib.*, (3), 2. 10, 1871 ; (4), 21. 347, 1906 ; O. A. Derby and G. Florence, *ib.*, (3), 49. 101, 1895 ; C. U. Shepard, *ib.*, (3), 21. 117, 1881 ; E. Pugh, *Miscellaneous Chemical Analyses*, Göttingen, 1856 ; H. Abich, *Bull. Acad. St. Petersburg*, (3), 2. 404, 1860 ; M. Tichnravoff and M. Petroff, *Journ. Russ. Phys. Chem. Soc.*, 20. 513, 1888 ; *Bull. Acad. St. Petersburg*, (3), 32. 513, 1888 ; J. A. Antipoff, *ib.*, (4), 9. 91, 1898 ; F. Pisani, *Compt. Rend.*, 58. 169, 1864 ; C. Grewingk and C. Schmidt, *Neues Jahrb. Min.*, 99, 1865 ; F. Kodera, *ib.*, i, 367, 1907 ; *Journ. Geogr.*, Tokyo, 13. 3, 1902 ; A. E. Nordenskjöld, *Pogg. Ann.*, 141. 205, 1870 ; E. Divers and T. Shimidzu, *Chem. News*, 45. 216, 1882.

¹⁰ J. N. Lockyer, *Proc. Roy. Soc.*, 27. 279, 1878 ; C. C. Hutchins and E. L. Holden, *Phil. Mag.*, (5), 24. 325, 1887 ; H. A. Rowland, *Amer. Journ. Science*, (3), 41. 243, 1891 ; *Chem. News*, 63. 133, 1891 ; *Johns Hopkins Univ. Circ.*, 85, 1891 ; J. Lunt, *Month. Notices Roy. Astron. Soc.*, 67. 487, 1907.

¹¹ J. J. Berzelius, *Compt. Rend.*, 9. 165, 1839 ; P. Garrigou, *ib.*, 84. 963, 1877 ; M. Mazade, *ib.*, 32. 685, 1851 ; H. Will, *Liebig's Ann.*, 61. 192, 1847 ; E. F. von Gorup-Besanez, *ib.*, 79. 54, 1851 ; F. Keller, *Journ. prakt. Chem.*, (1), 40. 442, 1847 ; P. J. van Kerckhoff, *ib.*, (1), 43. 350, 1848 ; R. Fresenius, *ib.*, (1), 98. 321, 1866 ; C. F. Rammelsberg, *Pogg. Ann.*, 72. 571, 1847 ; H. Göttl. *Œsterr. Zeit. Pharm.*, 253, 1853 ; W. Stein and C. Bley, *Arch. Pharm.*, (2), 129. 1, 1864 ; H. von Fehling, *Württemberg. Naturwiss. Jahresh.*, 16. 129, 1860 ; R. Bunsen, *Zeit. anal. Chem.*, 10. 391, 1871 ; *Anleitung zur Analyse der Aschen und Mineralwasser*, Heidelberg,

1874; L. A. Buchner, *Anz. Gel. München,* **24** 601, 1847; **25.** 1025, 1847; **26.** 756, 1848; *Journ. prakt. Chem.,* (1), **40** 447, 1847.
¹² H. Fleck, *Répert. Chim. Appl.,* **1.** 424, 1858; J. and H. S. Pattinson, *Journ. Soc. Chem. Ind.,* **17.** 211, 1898; H. Hager, *Pharm. Centrh.,* **27.** 338, 1886; E. Ungar, *ib.,* **24.** 560, 1883; E. Ungar and G. Bodländer, *Répert. anal. Chem.,* **3.** 383, 1883; O. Hehner, *Analyst,* **5.** 218, 1880; A. P. Smith, *Chem. News,* **42.** 34, 1880; T. L. Phipson, *ib.,* **59.** 255, 1889; F. A. Norton, *Journ. Amer. Chem. Soc.,* **28.** 1503, 1906; A. R. Leeds, *ib.,* **3.** 1302, 1881; E. F. Kohman and N. H. Sanborn, *Journ. Ind. Eng. Chem.,* **16.** 290, 1924; L. Medicus, *Zeit. Elektrochem.,* **8.** 690, 1902; F. Wirthle, *Chem. Ztg.,* **24.** 263, 1900; K. B. Lehmann, *Arch. Hyg.,* **45.** 88, 1902; A. J. J. Vandevelde, *Hand. Vlaamsch Natuur-Geneeskundig Congress,* **4,** 1902; A. Eckardt, *Zeit. Unters. Nahr. Genuss.,* **18.** 193, 1909; G. Gimel, *Compt. Rend.,* **147.** 1324, 1908; J. B. M. Coebergh, *Pharm. Weekbl.,* **49.** 429, 489, 1912; H. Serger, *Zeit. Öffent. Chem.,* **27.** 133, 1921; J. Attfield, *Pharm. Journ.,* (3), **14.** 719, 1884; J. Mayrhofer, *Pharm. Ztg.,* **34.** 246, 1889; J. Mayrhofer and A. Hilger, *Chem. Ztg.,* **12.** 1264, 1888; A. Sam, *Rev. Internal. Falsif.,* 151, 1898; T. Günther, *Zeit. Unters. Nahr. Genuss.,* **2.** 915, 1899; A. Beythein, *ib.,* **43.** 47, 1922; R. Kayser, *ib.,* **4.** 29, 1890; *Forschungsber. Lebensmitt.,* **1.** 63, 1894; A. Rössing, *Zeit. anal. Chem.,* **39.** 147, 1900; G. Salomone, *Giorn. Pharm. Chim.,* **55.** 241, 1906; H. Serger, *Zeit. öffent. Chem.,* **27.** 133, 1921.

§ 3. The Extraction and Purification of Tin

Tin ore is usually treated by a series of operations to concentrate the cassiterite and remove a large proportion of gangue, and associated impurities. The resulting *black tin* is smelted by dry methods, and then refined. Wet processes and electrolytic methods are confined to the extraction of the metal from tin-scrap. Manufacturing details belong to metallurgical works such as:

H. Lewis, *Metallurgy of Tin,* New York, 1911; H. Mennicke, *Die Metallurgie des Zinns,* Halle a. S., 1910; P. J. Thibault, *Metallurgy of Tin,* Sydney, 1908; A. G. Charleton, *Tin Mining, Dressing, and Smelting,* London, 1884; P. van Diest, *Banca and its Tin Stream Works,* Truro, 1867; S. Fawns, *Tin Deposits of the World with a Chapter on Tin Smelting,* London, 1907; A. H. Sexton and J. S. G. Primrose, *The Common Non-ferrous Metals,* Manchester, 169, 1910; W. Gowland, *The Metallurgy of the Non-ferrous Metals,* London, 401, 1914; C. Schnabel, *Handbuch der Metallhuttenkunde,* Berlin, 2. 404, 1896; London, 2. 473, 1907; A. Ditte, *L'étain et composés,* Paris, 1884; F. L. and E. Hess, *Bibliography of the Geology and Mineralogy of Tin,* Washington, 1912; W. Borchers, *Zinn, Wismuth, Antimon,* Halle (Saale), 1924.

*Preliminary concentration of tin ore.*¹—Alluvial deposits of tinstone occur associated with gravel which may be more or less bonded by argillaceous matters, and covered with more or less overburden consisting of soil, clay, etc. These are worked by washing with running water, so as to break up the gravel, and carry away the lighter pebbles while the heavier tinstone is retained and recovered. The mode of washing is adapted to suit local conditions, thus, it may be done in sluices as in gold-washing. Dredging is largely used where the conditions are suitable. The *concentrates* are hand-picked to remove non-stanniferous materials; and may be re-washed in small sluice boxes, and conc. by hand jigging. Tin ore found in lodes, beds, etc.—*lode-tin, reef-tin*—in the older rocks—granite, gneiss, mica-schist, grisen, clay-slate, etc.—is associated with a comparatively large proportion, may be 95–99 per cent., of gangue consisting of earthy impurities like silica and siliceous minerals, metallic minerals like iron, copper, lead, and zinc sulphides, magnetic oxide of iron, arsenical pyrites, etc., and wolfram, a tungstate of iron and manganese of high sp. gr. closely resembling tinstone. The ore is first crushed to pass approximately a 20's screen (20 holes per linear inch), and concentrated by washing. The finely washed ore in the slimes is treated in settling tanks, or on slime tables. The tailings discharged into rivers are in some cases separated by the stream and the tinstone deposited lower down. This is recovered from time to time.

The roasting of tin ore.—The concentrates containing sulphides and arsenides and about 25–30 per cent. of tin are then roasted to remove sulphur and arsenic, and the latter is often collected as arsenic trioxide in condensing chambers attached to the furnaces. There are three main types of roasting furnaces, namely, (i) those like a reverberatory furnace with a fixed chamber ; (ii) those with a partly movable chamber in which the charge is rabbled by the rotation of the bed below two or three fixed racks—*Brunton's calciner*—Fig. 2, or the bed may be fixed and the racks movable ; and (iii) those with a movable roasting chamber usually in the form of an inclined revolving cylinder—*Oxland's calciners*, Fig. 3. In Fig. 2, the ore is fed to the conical rotating bed A viâ the hopper B ; the ore gradually works to the edge and finally lands at the discharge shoot C. The heat is supplied. D is the fire mouth. In Fig. 3, the ore is fed into the inclined revolving cylinder, A, viâ the hopper B ; the ore gradually passes by gravity to the discharge C_1C_2. The burning gases travel from the fire mouth D and are accompanied by an excess of air from openings E. The hot gases pass from the upper part of the revolving cylinder into the condensing chambers $F_1F_2F_3F_4F_5$, where arsenic trioxide is deposited, and thence to the chimney.

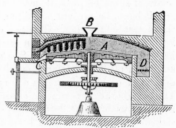

FIG. 2.—Roasting Furnace with Revolving Bed.

The second concentration of tin ore, and the removal of tungsten.—The cassiterite and wolfram are not changed by the roasting, and the metal sulphides and arsenides

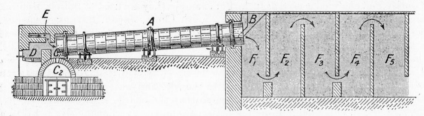

FIG. 3.—Roasting Furnace with Revolving Cylinder.

will have been converted into oxides which can be readily removed by a second washing. Prior to washing, the roasted ore is sometimes treated in magnetic separators in which the roasted ore is carried on a series of endless belts through a strong magnetic field, when iron oxide and wolfram are deflected from the main stream of non-magnetic tinstone, etc., and delivered in separate receivers. The tinstone is then ready for the smelter. Details have been described by E. Walker,[2] and they are modified to suit local conditions. The iron ore and wolfram may retain sufficient tinstone to pay for its being recrushed and returned to the magnetic separator. If copper be present, the oxide can be removed by heating the concentrate with sulphuric acid, etc. Iron and bismuth oxides are also removed by this treatment.

In R. Oxland's process for removing tungsten, the ore is mixed with sodium carbonate or salt-cake and heated in a reverberatory furnace ; the hot mass is extracted with water to remove the soluble sodium tungstate which is recovered by evaporation. The residual black tin is ready for the smelter. In L. J. Michel's process, the concentrate is mixed with sodium chloride and roasted—the wolfram forms sodium tungstate ; the copper, cupric chloride ; the arsenic, antimony, and bismuth form volatile chlorides. The copper is precipitated from the wash-liquor by iron ; and the tungsten is precipitated as calcium tungstate by adding calcium chloride. These processes are expensive.

The smelting of the black-tin.—The smelting [3] of the black-tin concentrate containing say 65–70 per cent. of tin depends on the reduction of stannic oxide by carbon monoxide ; the reduction of the tin ore commences at about 1000°–1100°

while the metal itself melts at about 232°. Any reducible oxides also present furnish metals which alloy with the tin. Owing to the amphoteric character of the oxide, if silica be present, a tin silicate will be formed, which is not readily fusible, and if bases be present, say lime, calcium stannate will be formed. In either case, tin is lost in the slag. The use of fluorspar, lime, etc., as fluxes should be kept as low as possible to keep down the proportion of slag. As a rule, smelting works in England, Australia, France, Spain, Germany, Mexico, California, Malay Peninsula, and the Pulo Brani Island, employ a reverberatory furnace to reduce the tinstone, and shaft or blast furnaces are employed for the treatment of slags and residues. The reverberatory furnace is charged with a mixture of two to three tons of ore which is mixed with about 20 per cent. of its weight of finely divided anthracite, a little slaked lime, and maybe a little fluorspar, along with any stanniferous slag which it is desired to treat. The charge is damped with water and spread over the floor of the furnace. In about 3 hrs., the molten charge is rabbled to mix the charge and separate the metal from the slag. The temp. is then raised, the mixture is again rabbled, allowed to settle, and the slag raked off. The slag first pulled is usually clean enough to be thrown away, while that pulled next contains prills of tin, and is reserved for further treatment. The tin is then tapped, and cast into ingots ready for refining, or it may be partly refined before casting. A glassy liquid slag runs out after the tin. The slag left in the furnace is raked out, the furnace bottom repaired if necessary, and a new charge introduced.

Blast furnaces, however, are employed where the ore is rich and of a high degree of purity, and charcoal is used as fuel. For example, they are used at Bolivia, Billiton, Banca, Malay Peninsula, Siam, Burma, South China, Japan, Saxony, Bohemia, and Finland. Small blast furnaces of a primitive type are used by the Chinese in the Malay Peninsula. The blast furnace is first filled with charcoal, or coke, which is ignited and the blast introduced ; charges of about $\frac{1}{2}$ cwt. of ore and $\frac{1}{4}$ cwt. of slag are introduced about 3 times per hour. Charcoal is introduced between each charge. The furnace is kept filled to the top, and water sprinkled on top of each charge. The tap-hole is kept open so that the charge runs out as it melts. The fore hearth is kept full of molten material, and the overflowing slag is led to a tank of water. The metal is tapped about twice in 24 hrs. Details of course vary with the local conditions, and the particular design of furnace employed.

Some advantages of the reverberatory furnace are that it enables ore of extreme fineness to be used ; such an ore is obtained when the tin ore has been highly conc. Ordinary coal, producer gas, or petroleum can be used as fuel. On the average, the tin is purer than the blast furnace because a lower temp. is attained and less foreign oxides are reduced ; there is also less loss by volatilization. In some cases the loss in the blast furnace is said to reach 9 per cent. The main disadvantages of the reverberatory furnace are due to the retention of tin by the refractories in the bed of the furnace ; and this is recoverable only when the furnace is down for repairs. The slags are richer in tin than the blast furnace slags ; and the process is intermittent. According to W. Pryce, *Mineralogia cornubiensis* (London, 282, 1778), apart from the early methods of smelting in hearths built in the ground, blast furnaces were used in Cornwall up to 1705, when reverberatory furnaces were introduced. J. Harden discussed the electro-smelting of tin ores.

The tin in slag may be present in the form of fine pills, which may be largely recovered by washing the powdered material. The tin may also be in combination. If over 5 per cent. is present, the slag may be smelted either in reverberatory or in a blast furnace. The tin so obtained is a lower grade than that first obtained. The recovery is never complete, and on an average about 6 per cent. is lost. Tin drosses consisting of tin oxide and metallic tin may be smelted with the slag or with the ore. It may be advisable first to remove the metallic tin by liquation. D. M. Levy and D. Ewan [4] have described a method of bessemerizing *hardhead* obtained in the refining of tin ; and M. Guggenheim. recovered tin by volatilization in the vapour of sulphur, hydrogen sulphide, or carbon disulphide at 800°–900°.

The refining of crude tin.[5]—The purity of the metal largely depends on the purity of the ore. The ore at Banca and Billiton may yield a metal with 99·9 to 99·97 per cent. of tin and does not need refining, being, indeed, of a higher degree of purity than much of the metal obtained elsewhere by refining. When only a small proportion of impurity is present, the metal can be kept in a molten state for some time and the upper portions ladled into moulds for the market, usually, however, the metal has to be refined since the metal obtained by the ordinary operations of smelting is contaminated with iron as the chief impurity, and smaller proportions of copper, tungsten, lead, arsenic, antimony, bismuth, etc. The process of refining involves two operations—liquation and poling, tossing, or boiling. *Liquation* is based on the fact that alloys of tin with iron, etc., are less fusible than tin. Consequently, if the impure tin be kept at a temp. just above the m.p. of tin, the tin melts and drains away while the impure metal containing ore, copper, tungsten, etc., remains in a pasty or unfused condition. The fusible compounds with lead and bismuth liquate with the tin. The phenomenon was studied by W. Kroll. In applying the process to the refining of tin, the residue in the furnace is then melted, and tapped into a float. It separates into two layers—the upper layer is impure tin, and the lower layer, consisting chiefly of tin and iron sulpharsenides, is called *hardhead*. It is used for the manufacture of tin-lead and tin-antimony alloys. The tin remaining after liquation still contains small amounts of iron, tungsten, copper, bismuth, and lead ; and it is then violently agitated so as to bring every portion into contact with air, which, in consequence of the large surface exposed, oxidizes the impurities with some tin so as to form a scoria which floats on the surface of the metal. The agitation may be effected by pouring the molten tin from a considerable height ; by *tossing* it to a series of pots ; by *poling* or boiling in which a stick of green wood is plunged beneath the surface of the molten metal, and the steam and gases which are given off bring every portion of the metal in contact with air. After the scoria has been removed, the metal is allowed to stand just above its m.p. so as to allow the less pure portions to settle. The purer upper portion is ladled into moulds as *refined tin*, and the remainder is cast as *block tin*. The bottoms, if less pure, are returned to the liquation furnace. If the molten refined tin is allowed to fall from a height, it breaks up into irregular columnar crystals, forming the so-called *grain tin ;* the same name is applied to the fragments obtained by breaking up the ingots with a mallet. T. Goldschmidt and W. Lüty removed arsenic, antimony, and copper as a scum by adding an element like sodium, calcium, zinc, or aluminium and bringing its product in contact with air or water.

The electrical smelting of tin.—According to H. Krebs,[6] tin ores become conductors of electricity at moderate temp., so that by using large pieces of ore as a resistance, sufficient heat can be developed to melt it and reduce it to metal on the addition of coal. It is not generally necessary to add any slagging material, as the ore is usually self-fluxing, nor is it necessary to protect the tin oxide from going into the slag. R. S. Wile recommended the use of a siliceous slag with a high electrical resistance. It is preferable to carry out the process in a trough furnace with a low charging shaft and two or more electrodes dipping into the bath. Ore and coal are charged in as required, and the metal is tapped from the bottom until the hearth is nearly full of slag, which should be rich in tin. The ore chute is arranged to preheat the charge, and to serve as a condenser for metal vapour rising from the smelting trough. The slag is cleaned by adding a charge of coal so as to separate its tin as metal. Although electric smelting gives satisfactory results, most tin ore is smelted as indicated above. Electric smelting is said to give a metal of a high degree of purity, and to furnish a slag with the tin content reduced as low as 0·3 per cent., while the losses by volatilization are said to be much less than by the reverberatory or shaft-furnace process. H. Herrenschmidt, and F. Mattonett discussed the smelting of tin in the electric furnace.

Electrolytic methods of refining tin.—A. Brand [7] made experiments on the refining of tin in a bath with the tin to be refined as anodes, and a soln. of stannous chloride containing 71·84 grms. per litre, and 2·5 per cent. of conc. hydrochloric acid by vol. The tension was 0·058 volt, and 14·8 amp.; and with 7·5 per cent. hydrochloric acid, the tension was 0·031 volt. For the deposition of a kgrm. of tin per hour, 455·6 amps. are needed, i.e. 26·424 watts, are consumed per kgrm. of tin ; assuming the conversion of mechanical to electrical energy involves a 12 per cent. loss, and with 25 per cent. other losses, the actual consumption of energy is given as 0·054 H.P. per kgrm. of tin. The process has not been successfully applied on a large scale. T. Rocksch precipitated crystals of tin free from spongy metal by the electrolysis of a soln. of 200 grms. stannous chloride and 2·30 grms. of 30 per cent. hydrochloric acid per litre. I. Barlot investigated the rate of deposition of tin. C. F. Claus and H. S. Sutton used sodium thiostannate as electrolyte, and the tin to be refined as anodes. The electrolyte is made by melting impure tin with an eq. amount of sulphur and soda, or sodium sulphate and carbon, and extracting the melt with water. All the impurities except antimony and arsenic are precipitated as sulphides or else collect in the anode slimes ; antimony and arsenic are precipitated with the tin on the cathode, and are then used as anodes in a bath of sodium thiosulphate and hydrochloric acid ; this removes antimony and arsenic as insoluble sulphides. In some cases an electrolyte of sodium sulphide or of alkali hydroxide is recommended. The process was recommended by S. Coles-Cowper, B. Neumann, and A. J. M. Thirot. O. Steiner electrolyzed a soln. of tin alkali sulphides ; P. Watanabe, a soln. in alkali hydroxides ; and H. Mennicke, and E. F. Kern, a soln. of tin in hydrofluoric or hydrofluosilicic acid. F. C. Mathers and B. W. Cockrum did not obtain good deposits of tin from baths containing tin salts of the mineral acids ; the best results were obtained from soln. of stannous fluoborate containing clove oil, or 0·1 per cent. of digitalin ; and from soln. of stannous perchlorate with 0·1 per cent. of phloridzin. F. Halla used soln. of the fluosilicates. E. A. C. Smith treated the ore with a gaseous reducing agent, extracted the tin with acid, and recovered the metal by electrodeposition; J. R. Stack reduced with producer gas and obtained the tin by liquation ; and E. B. Thornhill, with carbonaceous matters. R. Saxon obtained good deposits from soln. of cassiterite in soln. of alkali nitrates, sulphates, or chlorides.

The extraction of tin by wet processes.—These processes are so very costly that they offer no prospect of success commercially, although in exceptional cases —say in the preparation of tin compounds, or in preparing tin or its compounds for chemical investigations—wet processes may be used. O. J. Stannard [8] described various chemical processes of extracting tin from its ore. W. Muir dissolved the tin from the cuttings by *hydrochloric acid* and precipitated it from the soln. by means of zinc. Steam was led into the soln. during the precipitation ; milk of lime precipitated first the zinc hydroxide and then the iron hydroxide from the residual liquor. C. Künzel described an analogous process. M. Moulin and M. Dolé allowed gaseous hydrogen chloride to act on the cuttings until the iron was attacked. The products were washed out with water and precipitated from the soln. by zinc. J. J. Collins converted tin oxide in the concentrated ore into chloride. G. Lunge described the preparation of tin chloride by treating tinned plate with chlorine gas. The stannic chloride collected as a fuming liquid. A. Lambotte used a mixture of chlorine and air at 100°. T. Rondelli treated a mixture of the ore and carbonaceous matter with chlorine at 600°–800°. C. B. Schultze treated the cuttings with an acid soln. of *ferric chloride;* and the soln. was filtered through a mixture of stannous and ferric oxides until sat. If the neutralized soln. contains stannous salts, the tin can be precipitated by iron. M. G. Bachimont heated the tin ore with a *metal chloride—e.g.* ferric chloride, and the resulting tin chloride was extracted with water and precipitated by iron or electrolytically. F. von Kügelgen and H. Daneel electrolyzed a soln. of the ore in molten *sodium chloride ;* the stannic oxide was reduced to metal at the cathode. C. A. Burghardt fused the ore with *sodium hydroxide*, extracted the sodium stannate with water, and electrolyzed the soln. at 60° using sheet-iron anodes, and tin or iron cathodes. If arsenic, antimony, or sulphur are present they should be removed by roasting before the fusion. J. Shears suggested a modification of the process. W. Borchers said that the deposition of tin oxide on the anode soon stops the current. G. Vortmann and A. Spitzer fused the ore, etc., with sodium carbonate and sulphur so as to form a soluble *sulphostannate;* the aq. soln. was mixed with an ammonium compound and electrolyzed, using lead anodes and tinned sheet copper cathodes. W. Borchers said the losses of tin and the cost of refractories in the production of the sulphostannate are fatal to the success of the process. E. Bohne extracted tin from slags by treating the granulated slag with hot dil. *sulphuric acid* in lead-lined wooden boxes; the tin was precipitated electrolytically from the filtered liquid by using anodes of hardhead. H. Brandenberg and A. Weyland heated the powdered slag with a soln. of *alkali hydrosulphate*, the filtered liquor was then electrolyzed. W. O. Snelling reduced cassiterite in the presence of hydrochloric acid by using zinc as anode, and cassiterite as cathode.

The recovery of tin from scraps of tinned plate.—This subject has been discussed by L. Hackspill,[9] G. Vié, C. E. Williams and fellow-workers, A. C. Hopper, etc. A. Gutensohn proposed scouring off the tin by a sand blast. The separation of tin from tinned plate by fusion is unsatisfactory because of the formation of an alloy of tin and iron, the adhesion of the tin to the iron, and the proneness of the tin to oxidation in consequence of the large surface exposed. L. and A. Larocque melted the tin plate admixed with finely powdered wood-charcoal and a half per cent. of sodium chloride; R. C. Thompson melted the tin in an atm. of water-gas; and W. L. Brockway, by the exclusion of air. J. F. Duke and F. Redman extracted the tin by melting tin-plate with lead; and A. Harpf, and J. S. Morgan used a modification of the process. F. Wüst melted the alloy with silicon to form ferro-silicon and tin in layers. Wet methods of extracting tin have been proposed, and also for preparing tin salts from the cuttings of tin-plated sheet and from the waste waters of dye-works.

M. Moulin and M. Dolé[10] converted the tin into volatile chloride by the action of gaseous hydrogen chloride or chlorine; the Verein chemischer Fabriken, Mannheim, used a modification of the process; A. Lambotte, R. Lucion, G. Lunge, T. Goldschmidt, H. Mennicke, T. Rondelli, H. Davies and M. A. Adam, and F. Winteler used chlorine; F. W. Preto,[11] S. Davis, L. Wirtz, J. W. Worsey, and C. Formenti used hydrochloric acid; C. B. Schultze, dil. sulphuric acid; E. Donath and F. Müllner, a dil. mixture of hydro-chloric and nitric acids; M. Mennons, a dil. mixture of sulphuric and nitric acids; A. Nodon, a mixture of sulphuric acid and ammonium chloride. C. J. Jakobsen[12] used alkali-lye, and others proposed to accelerate the action by the use of oxidizing agents—e.g. P. H. Voughan, J. M. G. Bonnet and co-workers, and J. Bang and A. Ruffin used a blast of air; W. D. Walbridge added sodium chloride or nitrate; F. A. Reinecken, and J. Bang and A. Ruffin, alkali nitrate; T. Roberts and J. Dale, alkali nitrite; E. Schunck, lead oxide or potassium chromate; F. A. Reinecken and L. Poensgen, lead oxide; and E. Donath, manganese dioxide. T. Twynam[13] used finely powdered coke mixed with a soln. of sodium chloride; C. B. Schultze, and H. Davies and M. A. Adam, a soln. of ferric or stannic salts; R. S. Wile, a 20 per cent. soln. of stannic chloride; R. Garcia, a hot soln. of ferric chloride; T. G. Hunter, a soln. of cupric sulphate; A. Kissock, and E. Schunck, a boiling soln. of sodium sulphide; and G. Vortmann and A. Spitzer heated the tin-plate with a mixture of sodium carbonate and sulphur, and precipitated the tin from aq. soln. by electrolysis.

In a number of processes, the dissolution of the tin is hastened by the aid of an electric current. J. H. Smith[14] used dil. sulphuric acid; and A. Gutensohn, and O. Meyer dil. hydrochloric acid. J. Pusch, and P. Nauhardt recommended acid soln. in preference to an alkaline soln. Alkali-lye was recommended by J. Apitz, W. Beatson, O. Kersten, P. Keppich, E. Kotzar, A. P. Price, and L. Keith. Soln. of stannic chloride were used by C. V. Schon,[15] J. J. Collins, and P. Bergsöe; tin salts and tartaric acid, by F. Veasey; stannic chloride, ammonium chloride, and organic acids, by H. Mennicke; alkali nitrate, by E. D. Kendall; and tin sulphate and an ammonium salt, by E. Quintaine; ferric sulphate or a sulphuric acid soln. of sodium nitrate, by H. W. Hemingway; ferric chloride, by J. M. Neil; soln. of fluorine compounds, by C. Luckow. Modifications were described by P. Nauhardt, C. G. Luis, J. Pusch, H. R. S. Coleman, A. S. John, G. Cruickshank, J. Matthews and W. Davies, etc. When an alloy of tin and iron is melted with aluminium, silicon or ferrosilicon, F. Wüst found that these metals combine with the iron and liberate the tin.

Tin occurs in commerce in various grades of different degrees of purity. The block-tin from Banca and Billiton is usually of the highest degree of purity as is illustrated by the analyses from trade catalogues [16] indicated in Table I. Analyses have been reported by T. Thomson, P. Berthier, G. J. Mulder, A. Löwe, M. von Lill,

TABLE I.—ANALYSES OF SOME COMMERCIAL SAMPLES OF TIN.

—	Sn	Sb	As	Pb	Bi	Cu	Fe	Ag	S	Co
Banca • •	99·950	0·007	nil	trace	nil	0·018	0·045	nil	trace	—
Billiton • •	99·960	0·006	nil	nil	nil	0·023	nil	nil	nil	—
Penang • •	99·939	trace	0·013	trace	nil	0·016	0·028	nil	0 004	—
Singapore •	99·870	0·008	0·045	0 034	0·003	0·052	0·003	0·006	0 005	—
Mt. Bischoff •	99·795	0·015	0·063	0 037	0·005	0·035	0·042	trace	0·008	—
Pyrmont .	99·938	0·017	0·019	trace	nil	0·022	trace	nil	0·004	—
Redruth .	99·160	0·176	0·053	0·177	0·017	0·445	0·041	0·006	0·008	0·012
Wing Hong, No. 1	99·343	0·031	0·040	0·434	0·007	0·052	0·010	trace	0 011	0·072
Wing Hong, No. 2	98·662	0·039	0·035	1·035	0·012	0·134	0·014	trace	0·011	0·058
Wing Hong, No. 3	95·280	0·381	0·050	3·995	0·020	0·106	0·026	0·018	0·008	0·116

P. G. J. Gueterbock and G. N. Nicklin, L. Addicks and W. A. Cowan, C. Himly, C. Stölzel, J. H. Baldock, C. Kopp and G. Engel, J. McKillop and T. F. Ellis, A. Stürenberg, A. Chevallier, C. L. Vlaanderen, C. M. Kersten, and numerous others. B. Kayser found mercury in a sample of commercial tin. According to F. Mylius, the purest obtainable commercial samples of tin contain 0·0013 per cent. lead, 0·0009 per cent. of iron, 0·0012 per cent. of copper, 0·0024 per cent. stannic oxide, and a trace of sulphur. Tin can be registered as *standard tin*, Class A, on the London Metal Exchange only when it assays 99·75 per cent. of tin, and is of good merchantable quality as judged by the character of a wedge-shaped piece cut from the ingot, nicked in the middle, and bent double. Table II, by

TABLE II.—ANALYSES OF VARIOUS BRANDS OF COMMERCIAL TIN.

Impurity.	Standard tins.						Ordinary tins.		
	A	B	C	D	E	F	X	Y	Z
Pb • •	0·0025	0·0371	0·038	0·0601	0·0110	0·0582	0·714	0·1570	0·1540
Sb • •	0·0031	0·0210	0·040	0·0233	0·0067	0·0200	0·020	0·0740	0·1100
Cu • •	0·0004	0·0014	0·012	0·0360	0·0016	0·0743	0·016	0·2740	0·4730
Bi • •	0·0004	0·0048	0·003	0·0026	0·0019	0·1600	0·056	0·3300	0 0700
As • •	nil	0·0113	0·050	0·0500	0·0020	0·0150	nil	0·0100	0·0300
S • •	0·0002	0·0015	0·0003	0·0060	0·0039	0 0034	0·0012	0·0038	0·0039
Fe • •	0·0016	0·0170	0·002	0·0110	0·2055	0·0065	0·0048	0·0053	0·0380
Zn • •	nil	nil	trace	nil	nil	0·004	nil	nil	0 0028
Ag and Au	nil	nil	0·0003	0·0005	nil	0·0024	0·0135	0·0036	0·0100
Total •	0·0082	0·0941	0·1456	0·1895	0·2326	0·3402	0·8255	0·8577	0·8917
Tin diff. .	99·9918	99·9059	99·8544	99·8105	99·7674	99·6598	99·1745	99·1423	99 108

P. G. J. Gueterbock and G. N. Nicklin, gives the analyses of nine commercial brands of tin. A to F are registered as standard tin ; X to Z do not conform to this standard. G. F. Taylor [17] described the preparation of *filaments* of tin.

G. Bredig and F. Haber [18] made **colloidal tin** by passing a current at 24–72 volts through a cathode of a bright plate or wire of tin dipping in alkali-lye (1 : 2), and in conjunction with an anode of platinum. The tin is momentarily pulverized and a fine metal powder falls through the liquid. The effect does not occur with an electrolyte of dil. sulphuric or nitric acid. T. Svedberg obtained colloidal soln. of tin in organic solvents by suspending tin-foil in the solvent, and using electrodes of iron or aluminium with a potential difference of 110 volts, and a current density so small that it can scarcely be measured by an ordinary ammeter. A second method consists in connecting a glass condenser of 225 sq. cm. surface with the induction coil and attaching the secondary poles to the electrodes, which are immersed in the liquid contained in a porcelain dish. The metal is used in a granular form or as wire chippings. When the current is passed, sparks play between the metal particles, and in the course of a few minutes dark-coloured soln. are obtained. These contain no large particles and hence need not be filtered. In the third method, T. Svedberg obtained tin in colloidal soln. by placing a piece of the metal, with its surface freed from oxide, in a flat dish; covering it with the dispersion medium; and submitting it to the action of intense ultra-violet rays. L. Gurvich obtained tin in a highly dispersed state by shaking small pieces of the metal with a liquid for a few hours.

The preparation of a highly purified tin.—In preparing tin of a high degree of purity for research purposes where cost of production is not of prime importance, it is usually convenient to start with Banca tin. C. T. Barfoed [19] digested the granulated metal with nitric acid; washed the hydrated oxide with dil. hydrochloric acid, and water; and reduced the dried oxide by heating it with sugar-charcoal: or the hydrated oxide can be dissolved in conc. hydrochloric acid; the soln. diluted with water; and treated with dil. sulphuric acid. The washed product is dried, mixed with sugar-charcoal and ammonium carbonate, and heated in a porcelain crucible to redness. E. Cohen and E. Goldschmidt removed any oxide dissolved in the metal, by heating the tin in a stream of hydrogen. F. W. Schmidt dissolved the metal in conc. hydrochloric acid, and in order to remove arsenic, passed hydrogen chloride through the boiling soln. for an hour and a half. The boiling soln. was treated with sodium carbonate, and the precipitate digested with nitric acid to wash out the zinc oxide. The washed and dried precipitate was reduced with sugar-charcoal as before. E. Quintaine electrolyzed an acidified soln. of tin sulphate mixed with an ammonium salt. J. Bongartz and A. Classen recommended heating Banca tin in a current of dry chlorine to form stannic chloride; the fraction boiling at 120° was dissolved in four times its weight of water, and treated with a conc. soln. of sodium sulphide, and sodium hydroxide eq. to about half the amount of sodium sulphide employed. The clear soln. of sodium thiostannate was electrolyzed in a platinum dish, the tin washed with water, and alcohol; and dried at 100°.

REFERENCES.

[1] S. H. Ball and M. K. Shaler, *Bull. Amer. Inst. Min. Eng.*, **41**. 189, 1910; F. G. Glaziot *Bull. Soc. l'Ind. Min.*, **13**. 22, 1910; W. E. Koch, *Eng. Min. Journ.*, **91**. 168, 1910; E. Edwards, *Mines Minerals*, **31**. 309, 1910; M. Carcanaques, *Ann. Mines*, (7), **14**. 209, 1878; J. H. Collins, *Min. Mag.*, 521, 1906; *Bull. Inst. Min. Met.*, **15**. 524, 1906; R. A. Thomas, *ib.*, **7**. 175, 1899; C. Brackenbury, *ib.*, **17**. 52, 1909; C. Thomas, *Ann. Rep. Polyt. Soc. Cornwall*, **50**. 182, 1882; A. A. Lockwood, *Brit. Pat. No.* 205122, 1922; A. L. and R. O. Simon, *Bull. Inst. Min. Met.*, 245, 1925; C. F. Thomas, *Journ. Chem. Met. Min. Soc. South Africa*, **11**. 164, 1910; R. E. Commans, *Proc. Inst. Civ. Eng.*, **116**. 3, 1894; W. Doormann, *Glückauf*, **45**. 844, 1909; H. T. Ferguson, *Proc. Inst. Mech. Eng.*, 119, 1873; J. J. Collins, *Min. Mag.*, **23**. 285, 1920; R. J. Trecheirille, *Trans. Min. Inst. Cornwall*, **1**. 93, 1887; J. Hicks, *ib.*, **4**. 111, 1895; W. J. Henwood, *Trans. Roy. Geol. Soc. Cornwall*, **4**. 145, 1838; R. Pearce, *Mech. Mag.*, **6**. 339, 1861; W. B. Kunhardt, *School Mines Quart.*, 103, 1884; R. Pearce, *Mech. Mag.*, **6**. 339, 1861; *Ann. Rep. Polyt. Soc. Cornwall*, **36**. 23, 1868; *Min. Journ.*, **77**. 116, 1904; J. Phillips, *ib.*, **15**. 184, 1845; S. L. Terrell, *ib.*, **83**. 714, 1903; W. Tregay, *ib.*, **50**. 49, 76, 105, 190, 221, 1880; R. H. Williams, *ib.*, **47**. 487, 684, 796, 1877; E. Skewes, *Eng. Min. Journ.*, **76**. 424, 1903; J. Taylor, *Journ. Geol. Soc.*, **2**. 309, 1814; A. G. Charleton, *Tin*, London, 1884; W. Branton, *Brit. Pat. No.* 5621, 1828; R. and C. Oxland, *ib.*, 2950, 1868; 7285, 1885.

[2] L. J. Michel, *Recherches sur quelques tungstates, molybdates, seleniates et tellurates cristallisés*, Paris, 1889; R. Oxland, *Chem. News*, **18**. 205, 1868; E. Walker, *Eng. Min. Journ.*, **83**. 941, 1907; A. Treloar and G. Johnson, *Elektrochem. Zeit.*, **16**. 10, 1909; H. Mennicke, *ib.*, **15**. 78, 101, 123, 148, 173, 198, 224, 251, 274, 1908.

[3] W. de L. Benedict, *Eng. Min. Journ.*, **54**. 3, 1892; J. N. Millen, *ib.*, **82**. 1135, 1907; E. Bahlsen, *Met.*, **1**. 3, 1904; H. Louis, *Min. Ind.*, **5**. 533, 1897; **6**. 648, 1898; **7**. 716, 1899; **8**. 629.

1900 ; *Metallurgy of Tin*, New York, 1911 ; J. McKillop and T. F. Ellis, *Proc. Inst. Civ. Eng.,* 125. 145, 1896 ; R. W. E. McIvon and M. Pradd, *Brit. Pat. No.* 10943, 1905 ; P. H. van Diest, *Jaar. Mijnw. Nederl. Oost-Indië,* 1. 217, 1872 ; *Berg. Hütt. Ztg.,* 32. 423, 1873 ; E. Reyer, *ib.,* 47. 181, 1888 ; *Zinn*, Berlin, 1881 ; E. Bohne, *Zeit. Elektrochem.,* 6. 245, 1899 ; J. Rowe, *Ann. Rep. Polyt. Soc. Cornwall,* 66. 102, 1898 ; *Trans. Min. Assoc. Inst. Cornwall,* 1. 153, 1887 ; W. Pryce, *Mineralogia cornubiensis*, London, 272, 1778 ; C. Cramer, *Œsterr. Zeit. Berg. Hütt.,* 42. 543, 1894 ; W. F. Collins, *Trans. Inst. Min. Met.,* 12. 425, 1903 ; F. Dietzsch, *ib.,* 15. 2, 1906 ; H. W. Hutchin, *ib.,* 18. 69, 1909 ; F. Browne, *Chem. Ztg.,* 95. 3, 1907 ; J. H. Croockewit, *Over de wijze van uitsmelting van den tinerts door de Chineezen op Banka*, Batavia, 1852 ; T. J. Flower-Ellis, *Proc. Chem. Met. Soc. South Africa,* 2. 5, 1897 ; L. F. Glaser, *Chim. Ind.,* 10. 1155, 1923 ; T. W. H. Hughes, *Rec. Geol. Sur. India,* 22. iv, 235, 1889 ; J. Taylor, *Journ. Geol. Soc.,* 5. 358, 1821 ; A. Thiollier, *Bull. Soc. Ind. Min.,* (2), 14. 575, 1885 ; H. Schüphaus, *Met.,* 7. 539, 1910 ; J. Harden, *Chem. Met. Engg.,* 9. 453, 1911 ; C. W. Gudgeon, *Chem. Eng. Min. Rev.,* 16. 7, 1923.
    [4] D. M. Levy and D. Ewan, *Trans. Inst. Min. Met.,* 18. 466, 1909 ; L. McKillop and T. F. Ellis, *Proc. Inst. Civ. Eng.,* 125. 145, 1896 ; C. A. L. W. Witter, *U.S. Pat. No.* 801290, 1905 ; R. Hoffmann, *Chem. Ztg.,* 31. 666, 1907 ; E. Bohne, *German Pat., D.R.P.* 96198, 1897 ; M. Robertson and M. Bense, *ib.,* 188021, 1906 ; H. Brandeberg and A. Weyland, *ib.,* 123764, 1901 ; Elektrochemische Fabrik Kempen, *ib.,* 146965, 1903 ; H. Daneel, *Zeit. Elektrochem.,* 8. 140, 1902 ; W. Borchers, *Elektrometallugie*, Leipzig, 2. 458, 1903 ; J. Shears, *Brit. Pat. No.* 9821, 1899 ; M. Guggenheim, *ib.,* 235157, 1924.
    [5] I. von Curter, *Strummer's Ing.,* 3. 58, 1875 ; *Dingler's Journ.,* 215. 469, 1875 ; A. Kuhnt and R. Deissler, *ib.,* 264. 328, 1887 ; J. A. Phillips, *ib.,* 156. 155, 1860 ; *Rev. Univ. Mines,* 7. 84, 1860 ; L. Peetz, *Met.,* 1. 280, 1904 ; T. Goldschmidt and W. Lüty, *Brit. Pat. No.* 196938, 1923 ; T. Goldschmidt, *German Pat., D.R.P.* 417741, 1923 ; W. Kroll, *Metall Erz,* 19. 317, 1922.
    [6] H. Krebs, *Metall Erz,* 18. 77, 1921 ; R. S. Wile, *Trans. Amer. Electrochem. Soc.,* 18. 203, 1910 ; 26. 252, 1914 ; J. Harden, *Met. Chem. Engg.,* 9. 453, 1911 ; H. Herrenschmidt, *German Pat., D.R.P.* 204004, 1906 ; F. Mattonett, *Eng. Min. Journ.,* 5. 186, 1908.
    [7] A. Brand in O. Dammer, *Handbuch der chemischen Technologie*, Stuttgart, 2. 35, 1895 ; C. F. Claus and H. S. Sutton, *Brit. Pat. No.* 297, 1895 ; W. P. Thompson, *ib.,* 185808, 1921 ; W E. Hughes, *Beama,* 10. 138, 1923 ; L. D. Simpkins, *U.S. Pat. No.* 1452573, 1923 ; J. R. Stack, *Trans. Amer Electrochem. Soc.,* 45. 279, 1924 ; E. F. Kern and E. A. Capillon, *ib.,* 45. 353, 1924 ; C. L. Manteil, *Trans. Amer. Electrochem. Soc.,* 45. 269, 1924 ; E. F. Kern, *ib.,* 38. 187, 1920 ; C. P. Linville, *U.S. Pat. No.* 1487111, 1924 ; J. R. Stack, *ib.,* 1487124, 1924 ; H. H. Alexander, *ib.,* 1487136, 1924 ; J. Barlot, *Compt. Rend. Assoc. France,* 45. 399, 1921 ; M. Altmayer, *Journ. Four. Élect.,* 32. 66, 1923 ; H. Mennicke, *Elektrochem. Zeit.,* 12. 1, 27, 180, 1905 ; P. Watanabe, *Met.,* 2. 145, 1905 ; B. Neumann, *Zeit. Elektrochem.,* 27. 256, 1921 ; *German Pat., D.R.P.* 198289, 1905 ; A. J. M. Thirot, *ib.,* 203519, 1906 ; O. Steiner, *ib.,* 193523, 1907 ; *Chem. Ztg.,* 31. 1222, 1907 ; *Elektrochem. Zeit.,* 15. 33, 1908 ; S. Coles-Cowper, *Amer. Elect. Eng.,* 22. 81, 1898 ; *Proc. Inst. Civ. Eng.,* 136. ii, 442, 1899 ; A. Lottermoser, *Zeit. Elektrochem.,* 27. 573, 1921 ; A. Lottermoser and H. Brehm, *ib.,* 27. 573, 1921 ; K. Fischbeck, *Zeit. anorg. Chem.,* 148. 97, 1925 ; R. Saxon, *Chem. News,* 131. 324, 1925 ; T. Rocksch, *German Pat., D.R.PP.* 370194, 376775, 1922 ; F. C. Mathers and B. W. Cockrum, *Trans. Amer. Electrochem. Soc.,* 26. 133, 1914, 29. 405, 411, 1916 ; F. C. Mathers and W. H. Bell, *ib.,* 38. 135, 1920 ; E. F. Kern, *ib.,* 33. 155, 1919 ; F. Halla, *Zeit. Elektrochem.,* 30. 124, 1924 ; E. A. C. Smith, *U.S. Pat. No.* 1526571, 1925 ; E. B. Thornhill, *ib.,* 1544198, 1924 ; J. R. Stack, *ib.,* 1566352. 1925 ; *Trans. Amer. Electrochem. Soc.,* 45. 441, 1924.
    [8] C. B. Schultze, *Dingler's Journ.,* 276. 279, 1890 ; *Proc. Inst. Civ. Eng.,* 102. 400, 1890 ; *Berg. Hütt. Ztg.,* 53. 208, 1894 ; C. Künzel, *ib.,* 33. 57, 1874 ; G. Lunge, *Berichte über die chemische Industrie auf der Schwitzer Landes-Aufstellung in Zürich*, Zürich, 29, 1884 ; S. O. Cowper-Coles, *Amer. Elect. Eng.,* 22. 81, 1898 ; *Proc. Inst. Civ. Eng.,* 136. 442, 1899 ; W. Muir, *Brit. Pat. No.* 1907, 1892 ; C. A. Burghardt, *ib.,* 659, 1889 ; J. Shears, *ib.,* 9821, 1889 ; H. Brandenberg, H. Weyland, and A. R. Kempen, *ib.,* 16377, 1903 ; T. Rondelli, *ib.,* 229359, 1923 ; A. Lambotte, *German Pat., D.R.P.* 32517, 1884 ; G. Vortmann and A. Spitzer, *ib.,* 73826, 1893 ; H. Branden berg and A. Weyland, *ib.,* 123764, 1901 ; E. Bohne, *ib.,* 96198, 1897 ; M. G. Bachimont, *ib.,* 80225, 1895 ; Deutschen Solvay Werke, *ib.,* 82980, 1894 ; H. Mennicke, *ib.,* 152989, 1902 ; *Elektrochem. Zeit.,* 12. 1, 27, 180, 245, 1805 ; M. Moulin and M. Dolé, *Dingler's Journ.,* 210. 318, 1873 ; *French Pat. No.* 94460 872 ; J. J. Collins, *Min. Mag.,* 23. 285, 1920 ; W. Borchers, *Elektrometallurgie*, Leipzig, 2. 455, 1903 ; F. von Kügelgen and H. Daneel, *U.S. Pat. No.* 771646, 1904 ; O. J. Stannard, *Min. Mag.,* 15. 15, 1916 ; W. O. Snelling, *Met. Chem. Engg.,* 8. 347, 1910.
    [9] L. and A. Larocque, *Bull. Soc. Chim.,* (2), 25. 188, 1876 ; J. S. Morgan, *U.S. Pat. No.* 147973. 1924 ; R. C. Thompson, *Brit. Pat. No.* 12937, 1888 ; W. L. Brockway, *ib.,* 8111, 1891 ; A. Gutensohn, *ib.,* 3772, 1881 ; J. F. Duke and F. Redman, *ib.,* 7151, 1892 ; A. Harpf, *Œsterr. Zeit. Berg. Hütt.,* 45. 453, 1897 ; L. Hackspill, *Chim. Ind.,* 2. 1161, 1919 ; G. Vié, *L'Age de Fer,* 36. 763, 1920 ; C. E. Williams, C. E. Sims, and C. A. Newhall, *Trans. Amer. Electrochem. Soc.,* 43. 191, 1923 ; F. Wüst. *Brit. Pat. No.* 228103, 1924 ; A. C. Hopper, *Chem. Trade Journ.,* 77. 503, 1925.
    [10] M. Moulin and M. Dolé, *French Pat. No.* 94460, 1872 ; A. Lambotte, *German Pat., D.R.P.* 32517, 1884 ; Verein chemischer Fabriken Mannheim, *ib.,* 36205, 1885 ; T. Goldschmidt, *ib.,* 176456, 176457, 188018, 1905 ; T. Rondelli, *Atti Congr. Naz. Chim. Ind.,* 343, 1924 ; *Gen. Civ.,* 25. 51, 1924 ; G. Lunge, *Berichte über die chemische Industrie auf der Schurtzer Landes-Austellung*

in Zürich, Zürich, 29, 1884 ; R. Lucion, *Ind. Moderne,* 113, 1888 ; H. Mennicke, *Zeit. Elektrochem.,* **12.** 245, 1906 ; F. Winteler, *Electrochem. Ind.,* **2.** 339, 1904 ; H. Davies and M. A. Adam, *U.S. Pat. No.* 1565425, 1925 ; C. L. Mantell, *Metal Ind.,* **28.** 481, 1926 ; *Trans. Amer. Electrochem. Soc.,* **49.** 87, 1926.

¹¹ F. W. Preto, *Brit. Pat. No.* 17594, 1900 ; S. Davis, *ib.,* 952, 1902 ; L. Wirtz, *ib.,* 20496, 1902 ; J. W. Worsey, *Min. Scient. Press,* 83. 121, 1901 ; C. Formenti, *Boll. Chim. Farm.,* 45. 145, 1906 ; W. Mennons, *Bull. Soc. Chim.,* (2), **25.** 190, 1876 ; *French Pat. No.* 105467, 1876 ; E. Donath and F. Müllner, *Dingler's Journ.,* 267. 179, 1888 ; C. B. Schultze, *German Pat., D.R.P.* 50718, 1888 ; A. Nodon, *ib.,* 199729, 1906 ; J. Perino, *ib.,* 212757, 1907.

¹² H. W. von der Linde, *German Pat., D.R.P.* 94741, 1897 ; W. D. Walbridge, *ib.,* 2739, 1877 ; F. A. Reinecken and L. Poensgen, *ib.,* 21628, 21633, 1882 ; F. A. Reinecken, *ib.,* 30245, 1884 ; J. Bang and A. Ruffin, *ib.,* 54136, 1889 ; *Journ. Soc. Chem. Ind.,* **9.** 950, 1890 ; C. J. Jakobsen, *Dingler's Journ.,* 144. 116, 1857 ; T. Roberts and J. Dale, *ib.,* 153. 205, 1859 ; E. Schunk, *ib.,* 113. 372, 1849 ; E. Donath, *ib.,* 253. 206, 1883 ; P. H. Voughan, *Brit. Pat. No.* 2269, 1871 ; J. M. G. Bonnet, F. M. Sallinger, and J. Bernheim, *U.S. Pat. No.* 459034, 1891 ; E. Kardos, *ib.,* 1471469, 1925 ; W. J. Buttfield, *ib.,* 1511590, 1924.

¹³ C. B. Schultze, *Proc. Inst. Civ. Eng.,* **102.** 400, 1890 ; *Dingler's Journ.,* 276. 279, 1890 ; *German Pat., D.R.P.* 50718, 1888 ; G. Vortmann and A. Spitzer, *ib.,* 73826, 1893 ; R. Garcia, *Brit. Pat. No.* 18726, 1890 ; H. Davies and M. A. Adam, *ib.,* 209124, 1922 ; T. G. Hunter, *ib.,* 132, 1894 ; E. Schunck, *Chem. Gaz.,* **7.** 327, 1849 ; *Brit. Pat. No.* 12345, 1848 ; *Amer. Journ. Science,* (2), **9.** 279, 1850 ; *Dingler's Journ.,* 113. 372, 1849 ; R. S. Wile, *U.S. Pat. No.* 859792, 1906 ; T. Twynam, *ib.,* 703165, 1902 ; R. A. Holland, *Canada Pat. No.* 233677, 1923 ; A. Kissock, *U.S. Pat. No.* 1501413, 1924

¹⁴ J. H. Smith, *Journ. Soc. Chem. Ind.,* **4.** 312, 1885 ; A. Gutensohn, *German Pat., D.R.P.* 12883, 1880 ; J. Apitz, *ib.,* 94506, 1896 ; E. Kotzar, *ib.,* 84776, 1895 ; O. Meyer, *U.S. Pat. No.* 660116, 1900 ; H. Mennicke, *Zeit. Elektrochem.,* 8. 315, 358, 381, 1902 ; J. Pusch, *Electrochem. Zeit.,* **12.** 244, 1906 ; P. Nauhardt, *Chem. Ztg.,* **26.** 50, 1902 ; J. B. C. Kershaw, *Electrochem. Rev.,* **44.** 939, 1905 ; L. Keith, *Deut. Ind. Ztg.,* 455, 1877 ; P. Keppich, *Œsterr. Chem. Ztg.,* 5. 73, 1902 ; O. Kersten, *German Pat., D.R.P.* 3889, 1885 ; A. P. Price, *Brit. Pat. No.* 2119, 1884 ; A. S. John, *ib.,* 204387, 1922 ; W. Beatson, *ib.,* 12200, 1892 ; J. Neurath, *ib.,* 240147, 1905 ; E. Kardos, *U.S. Pat. No.* 1471469, 1923 ; R. A. Holland, *ib.,* 1511967, 1924.

¹⁵ F. Veasey, *Monit. Scient.,* (4), **1.** 304, 1887 ; *French Pat. No.* 1002, 1886 ; C. Luckow, *German Pat., D.R.P.* 184023, 1904 ; E. Quintaine, *ib.,* 118358, 1900 ; H. Mennicke, *ib.,* 152989, 1902 ; C. G. Luis, *ib.,* 142423, 1900 ; H. R. S. Coleman and G. Cruickshank, *Brit. Pat. No.* 15402, 1899 ; 3524, 1900 ; J. Matthews and W. Davies, *ib.,* 21533, 1900 ; P. Bergsöe, *ib.,* 7026, 1900 ; J. J. Collins, *ib.,* 166695, 1920 ; W. Beatson, *ib.,* 12200, 1892 ; A. S. John, *ib.,* 204387, 1923 ; J. M. Neil, *Journ. Soc. Chem. Ind.,* **24.** 121, 1905 ; J. Pusch, *Électrochem* Zeit., **12.** 244, 1906 ; H. W. Hemingway, *Électricien,* **28.** 48, 1904 ; C. V. Schon, *Elect. Rev.,* **45.** 589, 1904 ; P. Nauhardt, *Chem. Ztg.,* **27.** 50, 1903 ; E. D. Kendall, *U.S. Pat. No.* 656982, 1902 ; L. Addicks and W. A. Cowan, *Amer. Soc. Testing Materials,* **16.** 59, 1916 ; F. Wüst, *German Pat., D.R.P.* 417459, 1924.

¹⁶ L. Addicks and W. A. Cowan, *Amer. Soc. Testing Materials,* 59, 1916 ; L. H. Quin, *Metal Handbook and Statistics,* London, 136, 1921 ; J. McKillop and T. F. Ellis, *Proc. Inst. Civ. Eng.,* **125.** 145, 1896 ; P. Berthier, *Ann. Mines,* (1), **13.** 463, 1826 ; A. Löwe, *Berg. Hütt. Jahrb.,* **13.** 63, 1864 ; G. J. Mulder, *Journ. prakt. Chem.,* (1), **48.** 41, 1849 ; *Chem. Gaz.,* **7.** 344, 1849 ; *Schiekundige Onderzoek Lab. Utrecht,* 5. 259, 1849 ; F. Mylius, *Zeit. anorg. Chem.,* **74.** 407, 1912 ; P. G. J. Gueterbock and G. N. Nicklin, *Journ. Soc. Chem. Ind.,* **44.** 370, T, 1925 ; *Metal Ind.,* **27.** 118, 1925 ; M. von Lill, *Berg. Hütt. Ztg.,* **23.** 323, 1864 ; C. L. Vlaanderen, *ib.,* **34.** 454, 1875 ; *Jaarb. Mijnwezen Nederland. Oost-Indië,* **4.** 233, 1875 ; B. Kayser, *Chem. Ztg.,* **12.** 152, 755, 1888 ; C. Himly, *Unters. Chem. Lab. Kiel,* **1.** 6, 1878 ; A. Chevallier, *Journ. Chim. Med.,* **16.** 250, 1882 ; A. Stürenberg, *Liebig's Ann.,* **29.** 216, 1839 ; C. Kopp and G. Engel, *Dingler's Journ.,* **229.** 195, 1878 ; C. Stölzel, *ib.,* **155.** 124, 1860 ; C. M. Kersten, *ib.,* **108.** 25, 1847 ; *Arch. Min. Geog. Berg. Mitt.,* **22.** 662, 1848 ; J. H. Baldock, *Chem. News,* 5. 59, 1862 ; *Journ. Pharm. Chim.,* (2), **3.** 378, 1862 ; T. Thomson, *Ann. Phil.,* **10.** 166, 1817.

¹⁷ G. F. Taylor, *Phys. Rev.,* (2), **23.** 655, 1924.

¹⁸ G. Bredig and F. Haber, *Ber.,* **31.** 2745, 1898 ; T. Svedberg, *ib.,* **38.** 3619, 1905 ; **42.** 4376, 1909 ; L. Gurvich, *Koll. Zeit.,* **33.** 321, 1923.

¹⁹ C. T. Barfoed, *Danske Vid. Selsk. Skr.,* (5), **7.** 236, 1866 ; *Journ. prakt. Chem.,* (1), **101.** 368, 1867 ; F. W. Schmidt, *Zeit. Koll.,* **1.** 131, 1907 ; E. Cohen and E. Goldschmidt, *Chem. Weekb.,* **1.** 437, 1904 ; J. Bongartz and A. Classen, *Ber.,* **21.** 2900, 1888 ; E. Quintaine, *German Pat., D.R.P.* 118358, 1900.

§ 4. The Physical Properties of Tin

The **colour** of tin is white with a slight bluish tinge. According to M. Faraday,[1] a thin film of tin in transmitted light appears to have various shades of brown ; pressing the film with an agate diminished the transmission. A. W. Wright found a thin film of tin to be brownish-grey ; and W. L. Dudley **said** the vapour is blue or bluish-green. Tin has a brilliant lustre. In its lustre and whiteness tin approaches silver. The lustre depends to a large extent on the temp. at which the molten metal is poured. If the temp. is too high, the surface of the metal may show iridescent colours produced by a film of oxide ; and if poured at too low a temp., the surface is dull. The presence of small quantities of foreign metals —lead, arsenic, antimony, bismuth, iron—decreases the lustre of tin, and imparts to the metal a yellowish tinge. The structure of tin is distinctly crystalline, for the cast metal is a mass of anhedral crystals. M. Volmer studied the growth of the crystals during electrodeposition. If the surface of tinned-plate or tin-foil be etched with hydrochloric acid containing a little free chlorine, or with a soln. of stannous chloride, the surface has patterns—*moiré metallique*—resembling the frost flowers on windows in frosty weather. H. Behrens found that nitric acid is not suitable for the etching ; fuming hydrochloric acid is poor, and the ordinary acid acts too slowly ; the best results were obtained with a mixture of fuming hydrochloric acid and potassium chlorate. The crystalline structure of tin is further evidenced by the fact noted by Geber in his *Summa perfectionis magisterii*, that when a bar of tin is bent it emits a characteristic creaking sound, called the *cry of tin ;* this is supposed to be produced by the grinding of the crystals against one another during the bending of the metal.

S. Kalischer inferred that the crystalline structure is the natural form of the metal. The metal may lose this structure by mechanical working, but regains it

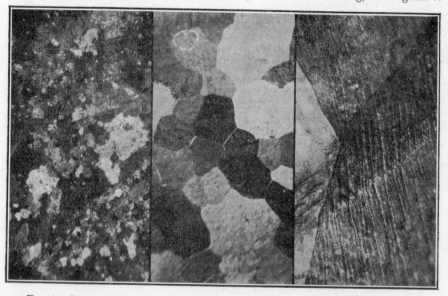

FIG. 4.—Structure of   FIG. 5.—Structure of   FIG. 6.—Slip-bands in
Hammered Tin.   Annealed Tin.   Crystals of Tin.

under the influence of heat. According to H. Behrens, crystalline tin which has been cast at a low temp., becomes amorphous by mechanical work ; but recrystallization occurs if the metal be heated below its m.p.—say at 110° for half an hour, or a few minutes at 150°. W. Campbell obtained fine, dendritic, surface crystals by casting the metal on a surface of polished steel. G. Tammann and Q. A. Mansuri studied the temp. of recrystallization of metals. J. A. Ewing and W Rosenhain observed that with commercial tin plate, the intercrystalline boundaries are shown by fine grooves or channels. The presence of these channels is readily accounted for by the method of manufacture, during which the plates are drawn from a bath of molten tin and allowed to drain. The crystals of tin force any more fusible impurity to the intercrystalline junctions, and the still fluid impurities drain off, leaving a minute channel. They also found that the fine-grained structure obtained by quenching molten tin in water is not changed by exposing the metal for long periods to temp. short of the m.p. ; but a block of tin reduced to a minutely crystalline structure by severe compression recrystallizes at 150°. Fig. 4 (×33), by W. Campbell, shows the structure of hammered tin, etched with hydrochloric acid, and Fig. 5 (×16) shows the appearance of the same metal when annealed for 7 days on a hot plate at about 180°. The crystals sometimes show lines which are due to stresses set up during the rapid growth ; and Fig. 6 shows **slip-bands** normal to the direction of the stress. When a metal is strained beyond its elastic limit, dark lines—slip-bands—appear more or less perpendicular to the direction of the stress ; this is not due to fissuring, but is rather a result of the slipping of the components of the crystal past one another as shown by J. A. Ewing and W. Rosenhain, and by W. Campbell. The subject was investigated by O. Haase and E. Schmid. The crystallization of tin has been studied by J. Czochralsky, and W. Fraenkel, who represented his results by Fig. 7, which shows the influence of the annealing temp. and of the mechanical work on the average grain-size of the crystals. No growth of crystal grains, even after annealing, was observed during a month at 210°. A surface strained in polishing always gives a minutely crystalline structure which becomes coarser with deep etching. The deformed grains produced by tension or bending readily crystallize

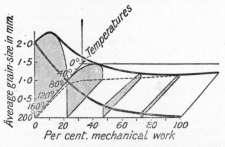

FIG. 7.—The Effect of Temperature and Mechanical Work on the Grain-size of Tin.

even in boiling water. The greater the amount of cold work applied, the lower the temp. at which recrystallization sets in. The size of grain on annealing increases with the temp., and is greater the less the amount of cold work. The size of the crystals is independent of the thickness of the sheet—*vide infra*, hardness. W. Deutsch found the growth of crystal grains in a stressed annealed metal—tension or compression—is great, but practically zero where no stress occurs. The subject was investigated by G. Masing, and P. Ludwik. The former showed that cold-rolled tin commences to recrystallize at ordinary temp. immediately after rolling, and the grain size, after standing for 18 hrs., is approximately the same as that obtained by annealing at temp. up to 150°, and depends on the amount of rolling the tin has undergone. If the annealing is carried out at 170°–180°, secondary recrystallization, in which the smaller crystals grow at the expense of their neighbours, sets in, and the resulting metal has a very coarse crystalline structure. If it is rolled again and once more allowed to stand, then the primary crystals that form are larger than before, but of about the same size as those produced by annealing up to 150°. In this case no secondary recrystallization takes place at temp. below 150°, similar to that produced by a change in the method of working, *e.g.*, hammering instead of rolling. The secondary crystallization following a secondary deformation is characteristic of that deformation, and does not take place if the metal, after casting, is subjected to a similar deformation without being subjected to a primary deformation. I. V. Obreimoff and L. V. Shubnikoff obtained single crystals of tin. H. Mark and co-workers found that a tin crystal elongated to a wire and heated at 150° for 3 min. is disrupted by recrystallization which begins at the ends of the wires, and grows at the rate of approximately 1 mm. per sec. The new crystal is so oriented with respect to the original that the width of the wire is not changed on elongation. If an extensible tin crystal is fractured in liquid air, in which only a low percentage elongation occurs, non-extensible fragments are produced. M. Polanyi and E. Schmid examined the extensibility of single crystals of tin. G. Tammann and Q. A. Mansuri found that there is evidence of the coalescence of the grains of powdered tin by recrystallization at 142°. The subject was studied by M. Cook and U. R. Evans, and H. C. Burger. The **velocity of crystallization** was found by J. Czochralsky to be about 90 mm. per minute at 232°. J. A. M. van Liempt measured the heat of recrystallization, finding for 50 per cent. deformation 6·5 Cals., and for 100 per cent. deformation, 13·0 Cals.

R. J. Haüy said that the crystals of tin are en *parallélépipédes rectangulaires*, and *en aiguilles croisées ;* and J. B. L. Romé de l'Isle, en *dendrites ou en feuilles de fougère, composées d'octaèdres implantés les uns sur les autres.* In 1786, J. C. Ilsemann found that when zinc is brought in contact with a soln. of stannous chloride, the tin separates as a mass of dendritic crystals known as the *tin-tree,* or *arbor jovis.* R. Lüpke described the production of the tin-tree. J. H. Bowman found that if conc. soln. of a salt of tin is mixed with a conc. soln. of zinc chloride, glycerol, or other viscous substance, spread in a thin layer on a glass slip, and sprinkled with zinc filings, straight branched crystallites of tin are produced. The slides may be dried and the dendrites mounted in Canada balsam. P. H. Dowling found that distinct clicks occur during the cooling of tin, and these are accompanied by sudden violent deflections of an electrometer connected to the tin.

M. L. Frankenheim concluded erroneously that the crystals belong to the cubic system. W. W. Mather obtained right-angled, four-sided crystals on a piece of metal immersed in a soln. of tin chloride. Modifications of the process were used by C. F. Bucholz, A. Ditte and R. Metzner, F. Wöhler, and W. Holz. A very finely powdered tin—technically called *argentine*—is obtained by immersing a zinc or aluminium plate in a conc. soln. of stannous chloride. The argentine is used as a powder for imitating silver bronze. L. Vignon, G. Buchner, C. Goldschmidt, E. Kopp, E. Puscher, H. Harpf, and R. Jakobson have described processes for producing finely powdered tin. A. Ditte obtained crystals of tin by warming a soln. of stannous hydroxide in one of potassium hydroxide where the stannite is converted into stannate, and tin is precipitated. H. J. Brooke obtained eight-sided needles by slowly cooling molten tin until it has partially solidified, and pouring off the still liquid portion ; and L. Pajot said that he obtained rhombic plates by a similar process. A. Breithaupt reported that he had obtained short, regular, six-sided prisms from a Cornish tin furnace, but W. H. Miller said that the crystals must have been tin hemicupride, Sn_2Cu. According to W. H. Miller, when a feeble current is passed through an aq. soln. of stannous chloride, using an anode of tin, square, prismatic crystals of tin are deposited on the cathode in the course of a few days. These crystals were shown by W. H. Miller to belong to the tetragonal system, and to have the axial ratio $a : c = 1 : 0·3857$. The tetragonal crystals were obtained similarly by C. F. Rammelsberg. Modifications of the process were used by F. Stolba, A. Ssaposchnikoff, R. Zsigmondy, W. Pfannhauser, F. Schidlowsky, and F. Gelstharp. According to H. von Foullon, the tetragonal form of tin is always obtained in the reduction of tin from soln. of the chloride as indicated above. W. G. Mixter obtained the same kind of tin by placing a sodium-tin alloy, approximating Na_2Sn, in absolute alcohol, and gradually adding water ; and afterwards boiling the residue with water.

C. O. Trechmann described rhombic crystals of tin obtained from a Cornish tin furnace ; H. von Foullon obtained similar crystals from a Bohemian tin furnace ; and W. P. Headden described monoclinic crystals of stannous sulphide which were afterwards found by S. Stevanovic to be rhombic. L. J. Spencer showed that in all probability the analysis of C. O. Trechmann's product was made on a sample different from that on which the crystal constants were determined, and that the so-called crystals of rhombic tin are really crystals of stannous sulphide.

The **twinning** of the tetragonal crystals was described by W. H. Miller ; P. Gaubert showed that when tin is melted in a thin layer between two plates of polished glass, crystals are formed which have an area of several sq. cm. when the cooling is slow enough. If the plate be punctured with a needle, a cross appears in relief on the reverse side, and several systems of parallel twins 0·5 mm. wide. Certain bands intersect at 87°, and these form a close network like that of microcline. There are also two systems intersecting at 71°, and sometimes three systems intersecting at 45°, 71°, and 64°. Bending or twisting also produces twins. The cry of tin is said to be due to this formation. H. C. H. Carpenter and C. A. Edwards, and J. Czochralsky have discussed the formation of twinned crystals during the straining of metals. O. Mügge found the twinning lamellæ above 161° indicate the crystallographic similarity of tin above and below this temp. The **corrosion figures** of tin were described by J. A. Ewing and W. Rosenhain, and H. S. Rawdon and co-workers, The corrosion figures obtained by P. Gaubert with cold hydrochloric acid are either rectangular or triangular on the original surface, but always triangular on the twinned crystals. The **X-radiogram** of tetragonal tin was examined by A. J. Bijl and N. H. Kolkmeijer, E. C. Bain, P. Niggli, M. Born and O. F. Bollnoff, G. L. Clark and co-workers, and H. Mark and co-workers. The unit prism contains three atoms in the co-ordinate positions (000), $(\frac{1}{2}0\frac{1}{2})$, and $(0\frac{1}{2}\frac{1}{2})$, and has $a=5·84$ A., and $c=3·16$ A., corresponding with the axial ratio $a:c=1:0·406$. W. C. Phebus and F. C. Blake gave for the diamond tetragonal of white tin $a=8·235$ A., and $c=1·850$ A. H. Mark and M. Polanyi represented the arrangement of the atoms in the elementary ditetragonal-bipyramidal lattice by Fig. 8, where there are 4 atoms per unit. A. E. van Arkel found the lattice about half the size of that obtained by H. Mark and M. Polanyi. The effect of cold work on the X-radiogram of tin was examined by R. J. Anderson and J. T. Norton. S. Nishikawa and G. Asahara studied the X-radiograms of tin before and after heat-treatment; and M. Polanyi, after the metal had been cold-worked. The so-called rhombic tin was thought to be identical with C. O. Trechmann's rhombic tin (*vide supra*) until L. J. Spencer showed that the latter was really stannous sulphide. O. Mügge failed to detect any crystallographic change at this temp. K. Weissenberg studied the structure of the crystals; and M. L. Huggins, the **electronic structure** of tin atoms.

FIG. 8.—
Arrangement of Atoms in the Space Lattice of White Tin.

C. F. Rammelsberg noted the different sp. gr. of different forms of tin—grey tin of sp. gr. 5·77–5·957, electrolytic tin of sp. gr. 6·969; and ordinary tin which has been melted of sp. gr. 7·2795; and H. von Foullon concluded from his examination of the crystalline form that tin is trimorphous—grey tin of sp. gr. **5·781–5·809**; rhombic tin of sp. gr. 6·52–6·57; and tetragonal tin of sp. gr. 7·196. He regarded C. F. Rammelsberg's pre-melted tin as of doubtful significance. F. Stolba had previously shown that at about 200° tin becomes brittle enough to be pulverized in a mortar. This is usually attributed to a transformation of the tetragonal crystals into γ-tin assumed without proof to be rhombic tin; the γ-form also appears when tin cools slowly from the molten state, and it is thought that grain tin owes its peculiar structure to this modification, which, according to A. Smits and J. Spuyman, has a transition point at 200·3°. E. Janecke observed the change at 190° and 7000 atm. press. M. Werner found the heat of transformation of tetragonal to γ-tin to be 0·02 cal. per gram, and the increase in vol., 0·00017 c.c. per gram. E. Cohen and E. Goldschmidt gave for the transition temp. 195°, and later, on the strength of the observations of N. Werigin and co-workers, 175°; and later still, from the observations of P. N. Degens, 161°; M. Werner gave 161°; and A. Smits and H. L. de Leeuw, 202·8°.

Many observers have noted that ordinary tin changes into a grey powder when exposed to great cold, and medallions and coins in museums acquire a surface crust of pulverulent grey tin which gradually grows *jusqu'à la décomposition et la destruction complète*. This is the so-called *tin pest* of the museums, alluded to by E. Babelon,[2] A. Blanchet, E. Cohen, R. Brauns, etc.   According to E. Krause,[3] there is a reference to the change, which tin undergoes when exposed to great cold, in *De mirabilibus auscultationibus* attributed to Aristotle, but more probably the work of a later writer.   In 1851, O. L. Erdmann [4] noted a structural change in the tin organ-pipes of a church at Zeitz which was thought to be an effect of vibration Ö. J. Fritzsche observed that some blocks of Banca tin, after exposure to the Russian winter of 1867–8, when the temp. on January 26, 1868, was —38°, had disintegrated to granular crystalline pieces, and coarse powder.   E. Cohen cited observations to the same effect by P. Lewald, C. F. Rammelsberg, A. C. Oudemans, I. Walz, F. Petri, A. Schertel, W. Markownikoff, E. E. Emeljanoff, H. R. Richards, G. H. Engleheart, P. Hamberger, E. Hjelt, H. Hoeveler, H. Stockmeier, and K. Schaum.   W. Gowland thus referred to the change in an old vessel consisting of 94·35 per cent. Sn; 5·06 per cent. lead; 0·59 per cent. oxygen, and carbon dioxide; and traces of iron and copper :

The extraordinary mol. change which the metal of this vessel has undergone is of more interest to the physicist and metallurgist than to the antiquary.   The metal is not much oxidized, yet it is so exceedingly brittle that it can be easily broken with the fingers.   The effect of time upon it has resulted in a complete alteration of its mol. structure, the mass of the alloy being converted into an agglomeration of crystals, and to this its brittleness is due.   On smelting and casting a small fragment I found that the crystalline structure disappeared and the metal regained its original toughness.

In the tin afflicted with the disease, there are spots of a grey colour, the metal becomes brittle, and the product occupies a greater vol. than the unaffected tin. The expansion produces pustule-like excrescences at the affected centres.   This is

Fig. 9.—Surface of Tin afflicted with the Tin-pest.

illustrated by E. Cohen's photograph, Fig. 9, of a piece of infected Banca tin. The transformation travels outwards from the spots until the whole mass is infected, and the metal readily disintegrates to a brittle powder.   The disease is infectious and can be propagated by inoculation, so that if a grain of the powder be placed on a piece of sound metal, the transformation begins ; once a piece is infected, the whole mass is in danger ; the metal is " sick."   The analysis of the pulverulent grey tin is the same as that of the ordinary white metal.   In other words, grey tin, white tetragonal tin, and white rhombic tin are allotropic modifications of this element.   E. Cohen and C. van Eijk showed that the cause of the tin-pest is due to the enantiomorphic change of ordinary white tetragonal tin into the so-called *grey tin*.   If white tin be powdered, mixed with some grey tin, and kept at a low temp., say —50°, for a few days, the entire mass changes to grey tin ; and conversely, grey tin changes to white tin by warming the mass on a water-bath. Measurements of the potential difference of the two forms of tin in a cell with stannous chloride as electrolyte, give a zero value at 18° ; at higher temp., the grey form is the positive pole, and at lower temp., the white. The transition temp. is 18°. Consequently,, when the ordinary metal is kept below 18°, it is metastable, and before equilibrium can occur, it must change into the grey form. As E. Cohen and K. Inouye expressed it, white tin under ordinary conditions is in a metastable state ; but under ordinary atm. conditions, the change is exceedingly slow. The rate of change is accelerated by lowering the temp., reaching a maximum at about —50°, and thereafter diminishes as illustrated by Fig. 10. E. Jänecke observed the change through an extended interval of temp. about 20° and 600 atm. press. N. I. Stepanoff studied the rate of transformation of grey and white tin.

According to R. von Hasslinger, a tinned iron vessel, which had been kept for two years at 16°–45°, showed a crystalline, brittle surface. Other masses of tin, inoculated with small portions of the crystalline tin, underwent the same change, the area affected increasing in diameter 3–5 mm. daily. No difference between experiments at 7°, 19°, and 37° could be noted. When tin-foil was inoculated, the

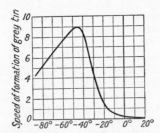

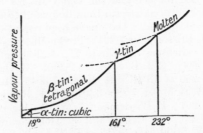

FIG. 10.—Relative Speeds of Transformation of Ordinary Tin to Grey Tin at Different Temperatures.

FIG. 11.—Equilibrium of the Allotropic Forms of Tin (Diagrammatic).

change extended through the thickness of the foil. The crystalline tin preserves its appearance up to near the m.p., but becomes normal after melting and again solidifying. E. Cohen showed that the structural change of the worked metal consists in a recrystallization process, the result of which is the formation of larger tin crystals from smaller ones ; and that the various forms of mechanically worked tin are in a metastable condition with reference to unstrained tetragonal tin above 18°, and also with reference to grey tin below 18°. The so-called *moiré metallique*, which results when tin-plate is etched by means of hydrochloric acid and potassium chlorate, corresponds with the recrystallized tin ; and this can be used to start the change in other samples of tin-plate.

The X-radiograms of grey tin by A. J. Bijl and N. H. Kolkmeijer show that grey tin crystallizes in the cubic system, and has a space-lattice of the diamond type with the edge of unit cube $a=6.46$ A. The three allotropes of tin are (i) grey tin, cubic tin, or α-tin ; (ii) ordinary tin, white tin, tetragonal tin, or β-tin ; and (iii) the so-called rhombic or brittle tin, or γ-tin. According to the X-radiograms of C. von Simson, γ-tin is hexagonal. The allotropic forms of tin with their transition points are indicated in Fig. 11, where the dotted lines represent the metastable states. This is summarized in the scheme :

$$18° \quad\quad 161° \quad\quad 232°$$
$$Sn_\alpha \leftrightarrows Sn_\beta \leftrightarrows Sn_\gamma \leftrightarrows Sn_{liquid}$$

O. Mügge found tin above 161° to be crystallographically the same as at ordinary temp., and S. Nishikawa and G. Asahara found no change in the X-radiogram. R. von Hasslinger, E. Cohen, and H. M. Howe examined cases where tin dulled in a certain way when pressed against bright cold-worked tin, *e.g.* tin-foil, inoculates it with a similar dullness and the infected spots thus carry the infection to others

—slowly at ordinary temp., rapidly at higher temp. This is not a case of allotropic change. The bright tin is a case of crystalline distortion produced by work ; the dulled state is a state of readjustment. The phenomena is thus a case of crystalline distortion and readjustment. Cold-worked metals are in a metastable condition owing to the production of a superficial deformed layer discussed by G. T. Beilby. E. B. Wolff has also discussed the *strain disease* of tin. A. Thiel applied the term *disglomeration* to the crumbling of a reguline metal into a powder composed of small crystallites when the metal is attacked by a suitable reagent—*e.g.* tin rods which are allowed to stand in a soln. of stannous chloride which has been partially oxidized to stannic acid.

In the tenth century *The Book of the Best Things for the Knowledge of Mineral Substances* by Ahu-r-Raihan,[5] the **specific gravity** of tin is stated to be 7·31, which is near the value accepted to-day. Another Arabian writer, Al-Khazini, in his *Book on the Balance of Wisdom*, written in the twelfth century, gave 7·32 for the sp. gr. An early determination by R. Boyle gave 7·320 ; and D. G. Fahrenheit, 7·364 for Malacca tin, and 7·313 for English tin. D. Forbes gave 7·052 for the sp. gr. of native tin from Bolivia ; it contained about 79 per cent. of tin and 20 per cent. of lead. Data have been recorded by many observers.[6] For the cast metal, J. Brisson gave 7·291 ; P. van Muschenbrock, 7·295 ; L. B. G. de Morveau, 7·2914 ; J. Crichton, 7·278 at 15·5° ; A. T. Kupffer, 7·2911 at 17° ; T. J. Herapath, 7·5565– 7·600 ; C. J. B. Karsten, 7·2905 ; G. Quincke, 7·267 at 0° ; O. Brill and co-workers, 7·290 at 18°/4° ; H. Kopp, 7·3043 ; L. Playfair and J. P. Joule, 7·306 at 3·9° ; W. H. Miller, 7·285–7·3043 ; C. F. Rammelsberg, 7·2759 ; J. Pohl, 7·196 ; R. Mallet, 7·291 ; E. Wiedemann, 7·25 ; W. Jäger and H. Diesselhorst, 7·28 at 18° ; W. Gede, 7·284 ; E. Cohen and E. Goldschmidt, 7·287 at 15°, etc. R. Hoffmann and W. Stahl gave 7·312 at 0°/4° for 99·8 per cent. tin, and 7·311 at 20°/4° in vacuo. The best representative value for ordinary tin may be taken at 7·28 at 18°. The sp. gr. of tin obtained by metallic precipitation or by electrolysis the numbers are usually lower; thus, W. H. Miller gave 7·18 ; and C. F. Rammelsberg, 6·969–7·155 ; E. Cohen and E. Goldschmidt say that the low numbers are due to inclusions of mother-liquor with the crystals of tin. C. F. Rammelsberg gave 7·143 –7·166 for the metal reduced by hydrogen from stannous chloride, and after melting 7·310. C. J. St. C. Deville gave 7·373 for the metal slowly cooled from the liquid state, and 7·239 for the metal rapidly cooled. The sp. gr. of tin which has been hammered or rolled is usually higher. J. Brisson gave 7·299 ; A. Matthiessen, 7·294 at 12·8° ; W. Spring found that, at 10°, unpressed tin had a sp. gr. of 7·286 ; after being once pressed for 3 weeks at 20,000 atm., 7·292 ; and twice pressed, 7·296. E. Jänecke found tin which had been repeatedly compressed had a sp. gr. 7·32. F. C. A. H. Lantsberry gave 7·231 for the sp. gr. of the annealed metal, and 7·2827 for the cold-worked metal. T. M. Lowry and R. G. Parker found the sp. gr. of tin *en masse* to be 7·2877, and for filings of the same metal 7·2784. They also found an increase in the vol. during partial annealing at 100°. G. W. A. Kahlbaum and E. Sturm found the sp. gr. of a tin rod to be 7·2932 ; when drawn to wire one mm. diameter, 7·2840 ; and when the wire was annealed for 10 mins. at 200°, 7·2840. P. G. J. Gueterbock and G. N. Nicklin measured the effect of impurities on the sp. gr. of tin. F. Paur, and F. Nies and A. Winkelmann assumed that the sp. gr. of molten tin is greater than that of solid tin because the latter floated on the former. E. Wiedemann, and W. C. Roberts-Austen and T. Wrightson, however, showed that the converse is true, the sp. gr. of the solid is less than that of liquid, and the floating is a result of convection currents in the molten metal. M. Töpler showed that tin expands 2·8 per cent. on melting, and A. Hess found a 2·5 per cent. expansion. G. Quincke gave 7·144 for the sp. gr. of the molten metal at 230° ; L. Playfair and J. P. Joule gave 6·934 ; and W. C. Roberts-Austen and T. Wrightson, 6·974–7·025. G. Vicentini and D. Omedei gave for the sp. gr. of solid tin at 232°, 7·1835 ; and of molten tin at 232°, 6·988. H. Endo found a change in vol. of 2·80 per cent. during the melting of tin. C. Benedicks measured the sp. gr. of molten tin.   A. L. Day and co-workers found the sp. gr. oɪ the molten metal to be :

	250°	300°	500°	700°	900°	1000°	1200°	1400°	1600°
Sp. gr. .	6·982	6·943	6·814	6·695	6·578	6·518	6·399	6·280	6·162

R. Arpi obtained 6·94 at 255°, 6·87 at 360°, 6·82 at 454°, and 6·76 at 536° ; and C. E. Fawsitt, 7·00 at 234°, and 6·98 at 267°.   T. R. Hogness gave for the sp. gr. of tin at 302°, 6·99 ; at 319°, 6·95 ; and at 396°, 6·89 ; and he represented the sp. gr. of the molten metal at $\theta°$ by $7·01-0·00074$ $(\theta-232°)$.   P. Pascal and J. Jouniaux gave 6·98 for the sp. gr. of the liquid at the m.p., 6·86 at 400° ; 6·77 at 600° ; 6·69 at 800° ; and 6·56 at 1000° ; M. Plüss, 6·967 at 280° ; and the last-named said that the sp. gr. curve has a point of inflexion at 620° in one atm. press. of an inert gas.   Observations on allotropic tin were made by A. Schertel, R. H. Richards, etc.   For the sp. gr. of grey tin, H. Stockmeier gave 5·8466 at 18° ; A. Wigand, 5·85 ; and E. Cohen and J. Olie, 5·751 at 18° ; and 5·768 at −163·3°. For white tetragonal tin, E. Cohen and J. Olie found 7·282 at 25°/4° ; and 7·350 at −163·3°, and calculated 7·647 at −273°.   For rhombic tin, C. O. Trechmann gave 6·52-6·56 at 15·8°.   The **specific volume** of ordinary tin at 20° was given as 0·1395 by A. Hess.   K. Bornemann and P. Siebe found that the sp. vol. up to 900° is proportional to the temp. :

	409°	474°	523°	574°	602°	648°	675°	704°
Sp. vol. . .	0·1462	0·1473	0·1479	0·1486	0·1490	0·1499	0·1501	0·1506

The sp. vol. of tin computed from the observed data by A. L. Day and co-workers is indicated in Fig. 12.   There is an abrupt increase of about 5·5 per cent. of the vol. of the solid at the m.p. 231·9°.   J. J. van Laar calculated for b of J. D. van der Waals' equation, $b=0·00265$; for a, $\sqrt{a}=0·09$, and for the valency attraction A, $\sqrt{A}=38$. R. N. Pease, M. L. Huggins, and W. H. Bragg calculated the **atomic radius** of tin to be 1·40 A.

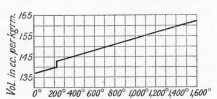

FIG. 12.—Specific Volume of Tin.

Tin is soft enough to be cut with a knife, but it files very badly because it chokes up the teeth of the file.   Tin is softer than gold, and **harder** than lead.   J. R. Rydberg [7] gave for the **hardness** of tin on Mohs' scale 1·8, when that of lead is 1·5, and that of gold is 2·5.   S. Bottone gave for the relative hardness of tin 0·0651 when that of gold was 0·0979, and that of lead 0·0570 ; T. Turner gave 2·5 for the relative hardness of tin when that of lead was 1·0, and that of copper 8·0 ; and C. A. Edwards, 9·0 when that of copper is 53.   F. Auerbach gave 11 for the absolute hardness of tin.   A. Kürth, F. Sauerwald, C. A. Edwards, K. Ito, and Z. Jeffries measured the hardness of tin.   F. Sauerwald and K. Knehaus gave for Brinell's hardness of tin, 40·2 at 17° ; 33·5 at 67° ; 27·5 at 117° ; 21·4 at 166° ; 16·6 at 216° ; 15·2 at 226° ; and 14·3 at 231°.   K. Honda and R. Yamada measured the abrasive hardness of tin.   H. J. Coe gave for Brinell's hardness of cast tin 5·2, and 5·0 for the metal annealed at 100°.   Tests were also made by J. Okubo. P. Ludwik, and P. G. J. Gueterbock and G. N. Nicklin measured the hardness of tin alloyed with various proportions of various metals.   P. Ludwik also measured the hardness by the indentation method, and found that it varied with temp., exhibiting a point of inflexion between 150° and 200°, as shown in Fig. 13.   P. Nicolardot showed that tin is hardened by hammering.   T. K. Rose found the hardness of cast tin to be 4·0-4·2 ; tin rolled at −25° (ratio of thickness 8 : 1), 13·0 ; the same after being 30 mins. at −20°, 14·0 ; after 30 mins. at 0°, 13·0 ; after 1½ hrs. at 14°, 10·0-10·5 ; after 20 hrs. at 13°, 6·5-6·6 ; and 24 hrs. at

15°, 4·5 ; tin rolled at 15°, 9·5–10·0 ; the same after being 97 days at ordinary temp., 4·5 ; and after 217 days at ordinary temp., 4·2 ; after being heated to 50° and quenched, 8·6 ; and after being heated to 100° and quenched, 5·2. These

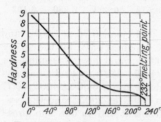

data show that the spontaneous annealing of tin occurs at ordinary atm. temp. The lower limit of annealing appears to be near 0°, for there is virtually no change after being half an hour at that temp. C. A. Edwards and M. A. Herbert gave 3·5 for the **plasticity** number when that of copper is 49·3.

FIG. 13.—Hardness of Tin at Different Temperatures.

G. Quincke [8] gave 598–681·2 mgrms. per mm. for the **surface tension** of tin ; H. Siedentopf gave 624 mgrms. per mm. in an atm. of carbon dioxide at 226° ; L. L. Grunmach, 352–359 dynes per cm. ; S. W. Smith, 480 dynes per cm. ; and W. Hagemann for the surface tension in vacuo at 247°, 539·8 dynes per cm. ; at 271°, 538·0 dynes per cm. ; at 346°, 534·8 dynes per cm. ; and at 398°, 533·9 dynes per cm. T. R. Hogness gave for the surface tension, σ, of the molten tin :

	300°	350°	400°	450°	500°
σ	526	522	518	514	510 dynes per cm.

or at $\theta°$, $\sigma=531-0\cdot080\ (\theta-232)$. For the **capillary constant**, a^2, H. Siedentopf gave 17·87 sq. mm. at 226° ; G. Quincke, 19·43 sq. mm. ; L. L. Grunmach, 10·87 sq. mm. ; S. W. Smith, 14·55–14·97 sq. mm. ; and W. Hagemann, 15·74 sq. mm. at 247°, and at 271° ; 15·77 sq. mm. at 346° ; and 15·83 sq. mm. at 398°. For the **internal pressure** of the solid, I. Traube gave 68,700 megabars, or 10^6 dynes per sq. cm. J. H. Hildebrand and co-workers calculated relative values for the internal press. by different methods. D. Saito and K. Hayashi measured the **fluidity** of the metal for casting ; and G. Subrahmanian, the **viscosity** of tin. M. von Wogau [9] gave for the coeff. of **diffusion**, k, per sq. cm. per day of tin into mercury, $k=1\cdot53$ at 10·7° ; and R. Kremann and A. Hrasovec made observations on this subject. W. C. Roberts-Austen found $k=4\cdot65$ at 500° for the diffusion of tin into gold ; and $k=3\cdot18$ at 500° for the diffusion of lead in tin. O. Bauer and E. Piwowarsky studied the diffusion of molten tin in solid copper.

Tin emits a peculiar smell when rubbed. This smell is not due to the metal, but to the organic substances—the fingers, for example—which come in contact with it. According to A. I. F. Levol,[10] tin is sonorous when a bar of the metal is struck. According to E. F. F. Chladni, the **velocity of sound** in tin is 2490 metres per sec. ; A. Masson gave 2640·4, and G. G. Gerosa, 2490 at 13°. J. Kleiber developed a relation between the velocity of sound, the sp. ht., and the coeff. of linear expansion of solid metals, which was applicable to tin—*vide* copper. M. Plüss found the **viscosity** of molten tin to be $\eta=0\cdot01678$ at 280° ; 0·01664 at 296° ; 0·01421 at 357° ; and 0·0311 at 389°. C. E. Fawsitt gave 0·0275 at 234° and 0·0235 at 267°, and these numbers are probably too high. R. Arpi gave :

	255°	308°	360°	396°	454°	507°	536°
η . . .	0·0116	0·0108	0·0103	0·0100	0·0094	0·0092	0·0090

D. Saito and K. Hayashi measured the fluidity of molten tin. N. Werigin and co-workers found the relation between the temp. and the velocity at which tin could be squeezed through a small opening.

E. Jänecke found that the press. required to produce the **plastic flow** of tin through an aperture increases regularly with temp., and no discontinuity corresponding with the transformation of tetragonal into rhombic tin was observed, even after heating for a long time at 200°, and cooling slowly. The plastic flow of tin depends on its previous history, slowly cooled tin flows under a press. one-third as great as that required to cause rapidly cooled cast tin to flow. The subject was studied by O. Haase and E. Schmid, and M. Polanyi and E. Schmid. J. Smithson found that tin could be forced through cast iron much as water can be forced by press. through gold. C. J. Burton and W. Marshall [11] found that when the press. on tin is suddenly increased to 300 atm. the temp. rises $0 \cdot 277°$, and when the press. is released the temp. falls $0 \cdot 264°$. W. Spring reported that by great press. clean and dry tin filings can be welded to a block (cf. **1**. 13, 18).

T. W. Richards gave for the average **compressibility** of tin at 20°, $\beta = 1 \cdot 9 \times 10^{-6}$ per megabar at 300 megabars press. L. H. Adams and co-workers gave $1 \cdot 89 \times 10^{-6}$ at atm. press., and $1 \cdot 64 \times 10^{-6}$ at 10,000 megabars press. corresponding with a 13 per cent. decrease when the press. changes from 0 to 10,000 megabars ; and they represented the change in vol. which occurs between a press. p_0 and p by $-1 \cdot 1 \times 10^{-4} + 1 \cdot 843 \times 10^{-6}(p - p_0) + 1 \cdot 27 \times 10^{-11}(p - p_0)^2$. E. Grüneisen found the compressibility of tin at $-190°$ to be $2 \cdot 1 \times 10^{-6}$; and at 15·2°, $3 \cdot 1 \times 10^{-6}$. P. W. Bridgman observed the compressibility $\kappa = 1 \cdot 953 \times 10^{-6}$ for extruded tin, and $1 \cdot 701 \times 10^{-6}$ for cast tin at 30° ; and at 75°, $2 \cdot 011 \times 10^{-6}$ and $1 \cdot 737 \times 10^{-6}$. He gave for the proportional change of compressibility with press., $d\kappa/\kappa dp$, respectively $0 \cdot 98 \times 10^{-5}$ and $0 \cdot 60 \times 10^{-5}$ here $d\kappa/dp = 2b$, and $\kappa = a$ in the formula for the volume change $\delta v = v(-ap + bp^2)$, where p is expressed in kgrms. per sq. cm. H. J. Coe found the press. giving critical plasticity to be 1·08 tons per sq. in. for cast tin, and 1·24–1·39 tons per sq. in. for tin annealed at 100°. P. G. J. Gueterbock and G. N. Nicklin measured the effect of impurities on the compressibility of tin.

Tin can be rolled into very thin plates and the metal is then called *tin-foil*, or *silver-leaf*. R. Granja said that a pound of tin can be rolled 11,000 to 14,000 sq. in. The ductility of tin comes between that of copper and that of platinum. P. Nicolardot [12] showed that tin can be hardened by hammering. Tin is most ductile at a temp. in the vicinity of 100° ; and at about 200°, it becomes so brittle that it breaks to pieces when hammered, and at that temp. it can be pulverized in a mortar. W. Rosenhain and D. Ewen found the temp. of brittle intercrystalline fracture to be 223° when the m.p. is 232°.

The **tensile strength** of tin is low being about a ton per sq. in. H. J. Coe found 1·31 tons to be the maximum load of annealed tin in tension ; the elastic limit was 0·1 ton per sq. in. ; the elongation, 86 per cent. ; and the metal was reduced to a narrow wedge. G. W. A. Kahlbaum and E. Sturm said that tin cannot be drawn into wire, but it can be rolled into that form. L. B. G. de Morveau found that tin at 100° can be drawn into wire, but at that temp. the metal readily breaks ; a wire of 1 sq. mm. sectional area ruptured with a load of 3·5 kgrms. J. Dewar gave for the breaking stress of a rod of cast tin 0·2 in. in diameter, 200 lbs. at 15°, and 390 lbs. at $-182°$. The elongation before breaking is about the same at 15° as at $-182°$. J. Dewar found that the elastic rebound of a tin sphere at $-182°$ is much greater than at 15°. P. Ludwik, and D. H. Ingall studied the effect of temp. on the tensile strength of tin. Although flexible, the metal is elastic only within certain narrow limits. A distinct elevation of temp. occurs during repeated bending, and the metal may become so hot that it cannot well be borne by the hand ; both the cry of tin—*vide supra*—and the rise of temp. are attributed to the friction of the crystals on one another. B. MacNutt and A. Concilio found that a sensitive microphone attached to a test-piece of tin in a testing machine, showed that a noise occurred in the neighbourhood of the yield-point.

G. Wertheim found the **elastic modulus** or **Young's modulus** of tin to be 4148 kgrms. per sq. mm. ; W. Voigt, 5410 kgrms. per sq. mm. ; H. Hess, 1700 kgrms. per sq. mm. for the cast metal, and 4100 kgrms. per sq. mm. for the rolled metal ; J. Kiewiet gave 4768 kgrms. per sq. mm. for the rolled metal. The best representative value may be taken as 4500 kgrms. per sq. mm. For Young's modulus at 15°, W. Sutherland gave 420 grms. per sq. cm. with the extremes 277–513 grms. per sq. cm. A. Mallock found the ratio of Young's modulus at 0° to that at $-273°$ to be 2·22. O. Faust and G. Tammann gave 3400 kgrms. per sq. mm. for the elastic limit of tin, *i.e.* the load at which the first markings appear on a polished surface examined microscopically ; and the highest elastic limit at which the metal begins to flow freely is 5480 kgrms. per sq. mm. A. H. Stuart showed that the elastic modulus, $E=0.225Q$, where Q denotes the number of calories of heat per gram which would be absorbed by a rod in doubling the length under the action of heat alone. He also estimated that $Q=Dc/a$, where D denotes the sp. gr., 7·3 ; c, the sp. ht., 0·0559 ; and a, the coeff. of linear expansion, $2·234\times10^5$. Hence, $Q=1·83\times10^4$ cals. ; the calculated value $E=4·13\times10^3$ agrees with the observed $4·17\times10^3$ kgrms. per sq. mm. The elastic after-effect with tin was investigated by H. Shoji. W. Sutherland gave for the **rigidity** or **torsion modulus** between 0° and 20° in grms. per sq. cm. $109\times10^6-157\times10^6$ with the mean value 135×10^{-6} at 15°, and for the ratio of the value at 100° to that at absolute zero, 0·638. F. Horton gave 1530 ; W. Voigt, 1730 ; and J. Kiewiet, 1543 kgrms. per sq. mm. H. Shoji found that the relation between the time t occupied in applying the stress and the torsion angle x can be represented by $x=c/t^a$, or $x=a-b\log t$, where a, a, b, and c are constants. **Poissan's ratio,** or the ratio of the lateral contraction to the longitudinal extension under the influence of a longitudinal stress, is 0·33. O. Faust and G. Tammann measured the elastic

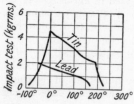

FIG. 14.—Impact Tests on Tin and Lead.

limit as evidenced by the appearance of slip-bands in the crystals; W. E. Dalby, the elastic properties and plastic extension of tin ; elongation is not proportional to load, and contraction proceeds spontaneously after the load is removed. R. H. Greaves and J. A. Jones found the results indicated in Fig. 14 for the notched bar **impact test** for tin. The curve falls uniformly and rapidly from 0° to −100°; and it also falls as the temp. rises from 0° to 190°; after that the fall is more rapid. There is an inflection in the curve at about 16°, and one between 160° and 200°.

P. W. Bridgman, and E. von Gomperz measured the elastic properties of single crystals of tin ; and P. G. J. Gueterbock and G. N. Nicklin, the effect of impurities on the elastic properties of tin.

The coeff. of the linear **thermal expansion** of tin was found by P. S. Laplace and A. L. Lavoisier [13] to be $0·0_4194-0·0_4217$; by L. B. G. de Morveau, $0·0_4216$; by J. K. Horner, $0·0_4209$; by J. F. Daniell, $0·0_4177$; by H. Kopp, $0·0_4226$ between 12° and 40°, and $0·0_4233$ between 16° and 99° ; by A. Matthiessen, $0·0_42296$ between 0° and 100° ; by F. C. Calvert and R. Johnson, $0·0_42717$ between 0° and 100° ; and by H. Fizeau, $0·0_42234$ at 40°, and $0·0_42269$ at 50° ; E. Grüneisen found the coeff. of linear expansion of tin $0·0_42257$ between −183° and 16°, and $0·0_42703$ between 18° and 100° ; P. W. Bridgman gave the proportional change of the thermal expansion, a, with press., p, to be $-da/adp=1·92\times10^{-5}$ for extruded tin, and $1·19\times10^{-5}$ for cast tin. For the coeff. of the cubic expansion of tin, H. Kopp gave $0·0_470$ between 9° and 72°. G. Vincentini and D. Omodei found that the coeff. of cubical expansion of the solid metal near the m.p. is $0·0_3114$, and that of the liquid near the m.p. $0·0_4689$. A. Matthiessen found for the vol., v, of tin at θ° between 0° and 100°, $v=v_0(1+0·00006610\theta+0·00000007890\theta^2)$. P. Glatzel found that a decimetre rod expanded 0·002212 mm. per degree. R. Hoffmann and W. Stahl gave $0·0_4957$ for the coeff. of cubical expansion of tin between 0° and 480°.

If the **thermal conductivity** of silver be 100, C. M. Despretz [14] found that of tin to be 31·2 ; F. C. Calvert and R. Johnson, 42·2 , and E. Wiedemann and R. Franz, 14·5. In absolute units, G. Kirchhoff and G. Hausemann gave 0·1528 at 15° ; H. F. Weber, 0·1446 at 0° ; G. Wiedemann, 0·153 at 18° ; A. Berget, 0·151 at 15° ; M. O'Day, 0·1575 at 25° ; L. Lorenz, 0·1528 at 0°, and 0·1423 at 100° ; and C. H. Lees, 0·157 at 18°, and 0·195 at −170° ; G. Glage found 0·149 at 35° ; and he gave 0·378 for what he called the temperature conductivity at 35°. M. Jakob

gave 0·19 at −190° ; 0·155 at 0° ; 0·15 at 100° ; and 0·145 at 200°.   According to
S. Konno, the effect of temp. is shown by the following data :

	18°	108°	125°	209°	292°	417°	498°
Heat conductivity	0·157	0·151	0·149	0·143	0·081	0·079	0·078
		Solid.				Liquid.	

This shows that the thermal conductivity of solid tin decreases with rise of temp.
up to the m.p. ; there is then an abrupt fall, and the conductivity of the liquid tin
decreases but slightly with rise of temp. W. B. Brown made analogous measurements and obtained 0·1428 at 50° ; 0·1404 at 102° ; and 0·1297 at 209°. E. H. Hall
deduced the thermal conductivity from the electronic hypothesis. S. Laussana
showed that at 1300 atm. press., the thermal conductivity of tin is 0·99 per cent.
larger than its value at one atm. press. ; and at 2600 atm., 1·93 per cent. larger.
The average coeff. of thermal conductivity up to 2600 atm. press. was 0·0$_5$719 with
the press. expressed in kgrms. per sq. cm. P. W. Bridgman gave 0·0$_4$122 up to
12,000 kgrms. per sq. cm. press; he also examined the thermal conductivity of
single crystals.

P. L. Dulong and A. T. Petit [15] found the specific heat of tin to be 0·0514 ;
H. V. Regnault found 0·055 between 0° and 100° ; C. C. Person, 0·05623 between
0° and 100° ; W. Jäger and H. Diesselhorst, 0·0523 at 18°, and 0·0564 at 100° ;
W. Voigt, 0·0551 between 19° and 99° ; P. Schübel, 0·0556 between 18° and 100°,
and 0·0582 between 18° and 200° ; R. Ewald, 0·0541 at 18°, and 0·0467 at −135° ;
W. A. Tilden, 0·0577 between 15° and 180°, and 0·0499 between 15° and −182° ;
H. Schimpff, 0·0542 between 17° and 100°, and 0·0488 between 17° and −190° ;
U. Behn, 0·0518 between 18° and −79°, and 0·0486 between −79° and −186° ;
T. W. Richards and F. G. Jackson, 0·0502 between 20° and −188° ; J. Dewar,
0·0286 between −196° and −253° ; L. Schütz, 0·0541 between 20° and −79°,
and 0·0556 between 20° and 100° ; F. A. Waterman, 0·05453 between 24° and
100° ; W. Louguinine, 0·05374 at 100° ; A. Bartoli and E. Stracciati, 0·05555
between 100° and 115° referred to water at 15° ; F. Glasser, 0·055176 at 102°,
0·0562863 at 168·9°, and 0·114950 at 260° ; E. H. and E. Griffiths, 0·0536 at 0°
and 0·0569 at 98° ; and C. Forch and P. Nordmeyer, 0·0530 between 14° and
−190°. W. Spring gave 0·05506 between 21° and 109°, 0·05876 between 16° and
197°, and 0·05·16 between 24° and 169°. He also gave for molten tin, 0·0637.
J. Pionchon represented the sp. ht. of tin at θ° by $c=0·061293−0·0_42094820$
$+0·0_7163998\theta^2$; and for the sp. ht. of molten tin between 237·7°, the m.p., and
1100°, $14·375+0·61·90−0·0_41047\theta^2+0·0_71034\theta^3$; and E. Béde gave $c=0·0500$
$+0·0000440\theta$ for solid tin. I. Iitaka found for solid tin, 0·0662 at the m.p., and
0·0615 for liquid tin at the same temp. ; J. Pionchon gave 0·0580 for molten tin
at 250°, and 0·0758 at 1100° ; C. C. Person, 0·0637 between 250° and 350°.
A. Eucken gave for liquid tin at the m.p., $C_p=6·90$, and for the solid, $C_p=7·0$,
so that the sp. ht. of solid and liquid tin at the m.p. are nearly the same.
J. N. Brönsted gave at −193° for white tin 0·0390, and for grey tin 0·0319 ; and
between 0° and 20°, 0·0538 for white tin and 0·0496 for grey tin. W. H. Rodebush
found J. N. Brönsted's values rather low. A. Wigand gave for white tin between
0° and 15°, 0·052, and 0·050 for grey tin. H. E. Schmitz gave 5·91 for the atomic
heat at −85°, and 6·57 at 60° ; J. Dewar's value is 3·41 between −196° and
−253°. F. Lange gave for the at. ht. of grey and white tin :

	Grey.				White.			
Abs. temp.	15·5°	31·5°	92·5°	283·7°	22·4°	56·7°	101·1°	286·3°
At. heat	0·599	1·675	4·42	6·13	1·27	4·06	5·40	6·27

E. D. Eastman made estimates of the thermal energy of the electrons in tin.
The melting point of tin was stated by G. A. Erman [16] to be 222·5° ; J. Crichton
gave 238° ; A. T. Kupffer, 230° ; L. B. G. de Morveau, 267° ; J. F. Daniell, 228° ;

F. Rudberg, 228·5° ; C. C. Person, 232·7° with an air thermometer, and 235° with a mercury thermometer ; A. van Riemsdijk, 228·5° ; F. Nies and A. Winkelmann, and G. Vincentini and D. Omodei, 226·5° ; C. T. Heycock and F. H. Neville, 231·91° ; E. Cohen and E. Goldschmidt, 231° ; K. Scheel, 231·85° ; H. L. Callendar, 231·9 ° ; G. Hindrichs, 231·5° ; W. R. Mott, 231·8° ; E. H. Griffiths, 232·03° ; L. Holborn and F. Henning, 231·83°–231·88° ; L. I. Dana and P. D. Foote, 231·9° ; and L. H. Adams and J. Johnston, 231·84°. C. W. Waidner and G. K. Burgess gave 231·85°–231·99° for the commercially pure metal. Numbers between 231° and 233° were found by G. J. Petrenko, A. G. C. Gwyer, R. Lorenz and D. Plumbridge, R. Vogel, N. Parravano and P. de Cesaris, W. von Lepkowsky, A. Bucher, A. Stoffel, L. Donsky. D. Mazzotto, A. P. Schleicher, K. Lewkonja, S. F. Schemtschuschny and S. W. Belynsky, F. Giolitti and G. Tavanti, E. S. Shepherd and E. Blough, E. Isaac and G. Tammann, W. J. van Heteren, D. P. Smith, P. Bogaderoff, G. Grube, N. S. Kurnakoff and N. I. Stephanoff, R. S. Williams, G. Voss, C. H. Mathewson, P. N. Degens, W. Geurtler, and W. Biltz and W. Macklenburg. A circular of the Bureau of Standards for 1919 gave 231·9° as the best representative value ; and W. Guertler and M. Pirani, 232°. L. Losana represented the relative changes in the vol. of tin during melting by the curve, Fig. 15. H. Endo said that there is a 2·80 per cent. change in vol. during solidification. An increased press. raises the m.p. of tin as it does with sulphur. The rise of temp. per atm. is about +0·003275°.

FIG. 15.—The Volume Change of Tin during Melting.

G. Tammann gave for the effect of press. on the m.p., 0·00216 (p−1) when the press. is expressed in kgrms. per sq. cm., or, if θ_m denotes the m.p., $d\theta_m/dp=0·0022°$ per kgrm. per sq. cm. ; and expressing the press. in atm., L. H. Adams and J. Johnston found the m.p. of tin at different press. to be :

Pressure	1	500	750	1000	1490	2000 atm.
M.p .	230·61°	232·26°	233·09°	233·89°	235·47°	237·18°

This is in agreement with the linear rule $\delta\theta=0·003275p$. Introducing C. C. Person's datum for the latent heat (14·25 cals. per gram) and G. Vincentini and D. Omodei's for the change in vol. on melting (0·003894 c.c. per gram)., the observed value $d\theta_m/dp=0·00328$ per atm. agrees closely with the value 0·00334 calculated from Clapeyron's equation (1. 9, 4). The result means that the m.p. of tin is raised 3·28° per 1000 atm. increased press. If the liquid phase is free to escape, so that the press. acts only on the solid phase, the m.p. is greatly lowered by the press. whether the substance expands or contracts on melting. J. Johnston showed that if Q denotes the latent heat of fusion per gramme ; D, the sp. gr. at the m.p. ; and T_m, the absolute m.p. ; then the press, ϕ, necessary to melt a substance at the absolute temp. T is $\phi=95·1QD\log(T_m/T)$, and for tin, $T_m=505°$; $Q=14·1$; and $\phi=2200$ atm. at 27° or 300° K. E. Jänecke verified this result. P. R. Heyl found the m.p. was raised not more than 2° when a strong electric current was passing through the metal. R. Lorenz and W. Herz studied the relation between the m.p. and the critical temp. ; G. von Hevesy, the break-down of the space-lattice during melting ; and W. R. Fielding, the polymerization of liquid and solid tin. P. H. Dowling observed that audible clicks occur when tin cools in a glass vessel ; the phenomenon is accompanied by electrical effects and is considered to be a triboelectrical phenomenon. P. G. J. Gueterbock and G. N. Nicklin measured the effect of impurities on the m.p. of tin.

According to E. Demarçay,[17] a considerable **volatilization** of tin takes place in vacuo at 360°. A. Schuller, however, said that E. Demarçay's metal must have been impure because no perceptible volatilization was observed at a red heat in vacuo. According to F. Krafft, tin is very difficult to volatilize and in this respect approaches carbon and silicon ; no appreciable volatilization occurs at 110C in a quartz bulb in vacuo. A. Schuller, indeed, said that tin is more difficult to volatilize than gold, but H. Moissan distilled tin at a lower temp. than gold ; and H. Moissan and A. J. P. O'Farrelley found that when an alloy of lead, tin, and copper is heated in an electric furnace, the lead and copper can be distilled off leaving the tin as a residue. For the separation of tin and lead by distillation in vacuo, *vide* lead. H. Moissan and P. Watanabe place these metals in the order of their volatility : lead, silver, copper, tin—the last being the least volatile. According to E. Tiede and F. Fischer, tin can be readily distilled when heated in the cathode-light vacuum. They found that with the purest samples of commercial tin, a deposit of tin sulphide formed on the cold walls of the glass tube, which was at first brass-yellow in colour, finally becoming dark brown to black. Pure tin, prepared from stannic chloride, did not give this deposit ; but a short exposure to the atm. of the laboratory is sufficient for some tin sulphide to be formed. W. G. Duffield measured the velocity of evaporation of molten tin. C. Zengelis considered he proved that tin can volatilize at ordinary temp. G. W. A. Kahlbaum could distil only traces of tin in vacuo at 1430° ; E. Tiede and E. Birnbräuer said that tin volatilizes at 880° in vacuo, and H. von Wartenberg that, at 2130°, tin does not volatilize rapidly enough to enable its vap. density to be measured. T. Carnelley and W. C. Williams said that the **boiling point** of tin is between 1450° and 1600° ; this is much too low. H. F. Wiebe's formula gives an equally poor result. J. J. van Laar estimated the b.p. of tin at atm. press. to be 2440°. H. C. Greenwood gave 2270° for the b.p. of tin ; J. A. M. van Liempt, 2218° ; O. Ruff and B. Bergdahl, 2270 ; and W. R. Mott, 2270°. J. J. van Laar estimated the **critical temperature** of tin to be 3730°, and the **critical pressure,** 650 atm. O. Ruff and co-workers found the **vapour pressure** of tin to be :

	2005°	2045°	2160°	2190°	2195°	2270°
Vap. press. . .	126	178	372	485	502	755 mm.

H. C. Greenwood gave 101 mm. at 1970° ; 262 mm. at 2100° ; and 760 mm. at 2270°. The vap. press. curve given by J. A. M. van Liempt is $\log_{10} p = -18680T^{-1} + 7\cdot5$; and for the sublimation curve, $\log_{10} p = -19050T^{-1} + 8\cdot22$. J. H. Hildebrand [18] gave for the vap. press. curve of tin, $\log p = -14444T^{-1} + 7\cdot85 + \log 4\cdot6$ mm. ; and J. Johnston, $\log p = -15100T^{-1} + 8\cdot83$, calculating the b.p. to be :

	10^{-3}	10^{-2}	10^{-1}	1	10	50	100	760 mm.
Boiling point .	1010	1130	1270	1440	1660	1850	1940	2260

W. Herz studied some regularities in the vap. press. of tin and other elements. C. C. Person found for the latent **heat of fusion,** 14·252 Cals. ; F. Rudberg, 13·314 Cals. ; W. Spring, 14·651 ; D. Mazzotto, 13 617 ; J. Guinchant, 14·3 Cals. ; J. Pionchon, 14·6 ; and F. W. Robertson, 14·05 ; J. W. Richards calculated 1712 Cals. for the atomic heat of fusion. J. A. M. van Liempt gave 85·55 Cals. for the **heat of vaporization ;** and for **Trouton's constant,** 34·34. A. Henglein computed 0·132 Cal. for the mol. heat of evaporation. The atomic **entropy** of tin was calculated by G. N. Lewis and co-workers to be 11·17 Cals. per degree at 25° ; and E D. Eastman estimated 11·5–14·1 Cals. per degree. The former obtained for grey tin 9·23 Cals. per degree.

The **refractive index,** and the **absorption index** of tin by P. Drude,[19] and G. Quincke are :

	Solid.					Molten.
γ	431	486	527	589	630	589
Refractive index . .	0·96	0·97	1·04	1·48	1·66	2·10
Absorption index . .	2·05	2·77	2·92	5·25	5·48	4·50
Reflecting power . .	52·3	66·5	67·8	82·5	82·2	71·9 per cent.

A. K. Aster found a refractive index 0·398 and absorption coeff. 1·46, for the molten metal. The percentage **reflecting power,** R, **of** tin is indicated **above.** W. W. Coblentz found :

λ			1·0	2·0	4·0	7·0	10·0	12·0μ
R			54	61	72	81	84	85 per cent.

Observations were made by E. Conroy, and F. H. de la Provostaye and E. F. Desains. H. von Wartenberg gave 7·48 for the index of refraction for light of wave-length 0·589μ; 5·25 for the absorption coeff.; and 8·2 for the reflecting power. A. K. Aster found the optical properties of tin from its m.p. to 500° are independent of the temp. A. Ghira calculated the **atomic refraction** of tin in stannous chloride to be 29·98 from the μ-formula, and 15·70 from the μ^2-formula; and for tin in tin methide, 35·73; and in tin ethide, 26·36 from the μ-formula. J. H. Glad-stone calculated the at. refraction of tin to be 18·6–27·0. A. Haagen found the **refraction equivalent** $(\mu-1)/D=0·1686$; and the sp. refractory power 19·89. E. van Aubel gave 1·66 for the index of refraction of tin in its salts. M. Faraday found thin films of tin depolarized and rotated a ray of polarized light, as was also the case with thin films of gold.

N. R. Campbell[20] found ordinary tin to be feebly radioactive ; but not so with the purified metal. W. H. Bragg gave 3·37 for the stopping power of tin for the α-**rays ;** J. Crowther gave for the absorption coeff., μ, for the β-**rays,** $\mu/D=9·46$; and A. S. Russell and F. Soddy for the γ-**rays** from radium, $\mu/D=0·281$; from uranium, 0·341; from thorium-D, 0·236; and from mesothorium, 0·305. N. Ahmad studied the absorption of the hard γ-rays by tin. The mean absorption coeff., μ/D, of tin for the **X-rays** with tin as absorber :

Radiator .			Cr	Fe	Co	Ni	Cu	Zn	As	Se	Ag
μ/D			714	472	392	328	272	225	132	112	16

A. H. Compton studied the absorption of X-rays by tin. D. Hurmuzesca found the sp. absorption of the X-rays by tin is greater than with aluminium, and smaller than with lead, iron, or silver. C. G. Barkla and A. E. M. M. Dallas measured the energy of the corpuscular radiation from tin bombarded by X-rays. W. J. Russell, and R. L. Vanzetti studied the action of tin on photographic plates. W. Ramsay and J. F. Spencer made tests on the **photoelectric action** of a number of metals in air at atm. press., and arranged them in the order Al, Mg, Zn, Sn, Cd, Pb. . . . ; and K. Herrmann, in the order Al, Zn, Mg, Sn, Bi, Cd, Pb, . . . G. Reboul, M. de Broglie, G. A. Dima, T. C. Sutton, and A. E. Hennings and W. H. Kadesch examined the selective photoelectric action of tin. T. C. Sutton developed a relation between the photoelectric effect and the at. ht. R. Hamer found the limiting frequency of the photoelectric effect to be $\lambda=3185\pm55$. N. Iiltschikoff said that tin emits positive Noser rays.

Tin salts do not furnish a **flame spectrum** in the ordinary sense of the term. W. F. Barrett[21] observed scarlet and green parts at the place where the hydrogen flame comes in contact with tin. G. Salet found that soln. of tin salts communicate to the hydrogen flame a blue colour which was ascribed to the oxide. Near the centre of the flame there are two concentric rings ; the inner one with a blue colour is attributed to chlorine, with bromine the colour is green, and with iodine, yellow. The spectrum is continuous. The outer ring is carmine-red. O. Schmatolla obtained a bluish-white flame by holding a porcelain or glass rod moistened with a conc. hydrochloric acid soln. of tin—antimony does not interfere, but arsenic does. A. Gouy, W. N. Hartley, O. Vogel, W. von der Seipen, C. de Watteville, and J. M. Eder and E. Valenta studied the spectrum in the oxyhydrogen and other flames. The **spark spectrum** of tin was examined by D. Alter, A. J. Angström, R. Arnolds, L. de Boisbaudran, W. von Bolton, J. C. McLennan and co-workers, M. Kimura, R. Capron, E. Demarçay, A. Ditte, J. M. Eder and E. Valenta, F. Exner and E. Haschek, H. Finger, A. de Gramont, C. E. Gissing, A. Hagenbach and H. Konen, F. Handke, W. N. Hartley and co-workers, W. Huggins, C. C. Hutchins

and E. L. Holden, A. Kalähne, C. Keller, H. Konen and H. Finger, G. Kirchhoff,
J. N. Lockyer, A. Masson, W. A. Miller, S. R. Milner, H. W. Morse, J. Parry and
E. Tucker, J. Plücker, F. R. Robinson, B. de la Roche, G. Salet, V. Schumann,
R. Thalén, C. de Watteville, C. Wheatstone, J. A. Carroll, G. A. Hemsalech and
A. de Gramont, etc. The most marked lines in the spark spectrum are shown in
Fig. 16—the orange-yellow line 6453 ; the yellow line 5799 ; the yellowish-green line

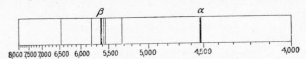

FIG. 16.—The Spark Spectrum of Tin.

5632β ; the green lines 5589, 5563, and 5331 ; and an indigo-blue line 4525α. The α-
and β-lines are characteristic. If the spark be intensified with a Leyden jar, the lines
5589 and 5563 appear stronger than 5632 and 4525. There are a number of lines
in the ultra-violet. F. Exner and E. Haschek give for the most intense lines in the
spark spectrum 6452·00, 4585·80, 4524·90, 3801·32, 3262·42, 3175·15, 2863·33, and
2840·10. The arc spectrum of tin has been studied by H. Kayser and C. Runge,
T. Royds, F. M. Walters, S. K. Mitra, J. C. McLennan and co-workers, H. Crew and
R. Tatnall, R. Arnolds, L. Arons, O. H. Besquin, G. A. Hemsalech and
A. de Gramont, R. A. Porter, F. Exner and E. Haschek, W. Gallenkamp, B. Huber,
and J. M. Eder and E. Valenta. According to F. Exner and E. Haschek, the
most intense lines in the arc spectrum are : 4524·90, 3801·19, 3330·80, 3262·50,
3175·16, 3034·25, 3009·33, 2863·53, and 2840·17. The *sensitiveness* of the spectral
lines were studied by F. Brasack, and A. de Gramont ; the *enhanced lines*, by
M. Kimura and G. Nakamura, and J. Steinhausen ; the influence of *self-induction*,
by G. A. Hemsalech, G. Berndt, E. Néculcéa, and B. Huber ; the influence of
pressure, by W. J. Humphreys ; the influence of the *intensity of the electric
current*, by P. Joye ; and the influence of a *magnetic field*, the **Zeeman effect,** by
P. Zeeman, A. A. Michelson, P. Zonta, P. A. van der Harst, and J. E. Purvis ;
and the **Stark effect,** by H. Nagaoka and Y. Sugiura. The **band spectrum** was
examined by A. Mitscherlich, G. Salet, G. D. Liveing and J. Dewar, W. Jevons,
W. von der Seipen, R. J. Strutt, etc. ; and the **absorption spectrum** of the vapour
of tin was studied by J. N. Lockyer and W. C. Roberts-Austen, E. O. Hulburt,
J. C. McLennan and co-workers, R. V. Zumstein, J. G. Frayne and A. W. Smith,
A. L. Narayan and K. R. Rao, and W. Grotrian. The vapour exhibits a strong
absorption in the blue, and a feeble one in the red. W. Grotrian found
absorption lines for $\lambda=3009·2$, 2963·4, and 2706·6 for the vapour of tin at 1050°.
R. V. Zumstein studied the regularities in the spectral lines of tin. J. Formanek
showed that tin salts in soln. give no absorption spectrum, and they do not react
with alkanna tincture ; but they do give a characteristic absorption with brasiline.
J. K. Robertson studied the spectrum of tin vapour in the electrodeless discharge
tube. The **ultra-violet spectrum** was studied by G. D. Liveing and J. Dewar,
R. J. Lang, W. A. Miller, J. M. Eder, L. and E. Bloch, and H. Deslandres ; and
the **ultra-red spectrum,** by H. Becquerel, V. P. Lubovich and E. M. Pearen,
and H. M. Randall. The **series spectrum** was investigated by P. G. Nutting,
H. Sponer, P. Klein, A. Fowler, N. K. Sur and R. K. Sharma, R. Arnolds,
L. Janicki, J. C. McLennan and co-workers, F. Hund, A. E. Ruark and
R. L. Chenault, J. A. Carroll, and T. van Lohuizen. The last-named found six
series with the variable terms given by $N/(m+1·651630-657·42\lambda^{-1})^2$, and three
series with the variable terms given by $N/(m+1·384406+446·70\lambda^{-1})^2$. S. Smith
studied the spectrum of electrically exploded tin wire.

P. Lewis found that the vapour of tin is not luminescent under the influence
of **cathode rays.** M. Kimura and G. Nakamura [22] studied the cathodic spectrum of
tin in a vacuum tube with an aluminium anode. G. Shearer studied the electronic

emission of tin under the influence of the **X-rays** ; and A. C. Foley, the spectrum after exposure to ultra-violet light, and to X-rays. The high frequency spectrum or the **X-ray spectrum** of tin has been investigated by H. Kulenkampff, H. Robinson, E. C. Stoner, B. B. Ray, K. Lang, S. K. Mitra, A. Leide, B. Walter, N. Bohr and D. Coster, A. H. Compton, E. Friman, M. de Broglie, H. G. J. Moseley, etc. In the K-series, W. Duane and co-workers, A. Leide, M. Siegbahn and co-workers, K. Chamberlain, F. K. Richtmyer, S. M. J. Alleh, J. M. Cork and B. R. Stevenson found, in Angström or 10^{-8} cm. units, $a_2a'=0.49385$, $a_1a=0.48947$; and $\beta_1\beta=0.42$. D. Coster, E. Hjalmar, and M. Siegbahn gave for the L-series, $a_2a'=3.60108$; $a_1a=3.59218$; $\beta_1\beta=3.37792$; $\beta_2\gamma=3.16284$; $\gamma_1\delta=2.99493$; $\beta_4v=3.337$; and $\beta_3\phi=3.29768$. C. G. Barkla and A. E. M. M. Dallas studied the energy of the K-radiations ; Y. Nishina, the L-radiations. A. H. Compton, S. J. M. Allen, F. W. Warburton and F. K. Richtmyer, studied the absorption coeff. of tin for the X-rays ; E. A. Owen and co-workers, the **X-rays ;** and R. Berthold, the relation between the photographic and ionizing effects of the X-ray radiation from tin. H. R. von Traubenberg found the range of the a-rays in tin is 29.4×10^{-4} cm. J. E. P. Wagstaff gave $v=2.24\times10^{12}$ for the **vibration frequency** of tin.

A. Coehn and A. Curs [23] studied the contact electricity of tin for quartz, and glass. The **electrical conductivity** of tin is about one-seventh that of silver, for A. C. Becquerel found that if the conductivity of silver is 100, that of tin is 14.01, and A. Matthiessen, 11.05. Measurements were also made by L. Weiller, F. A. Schulze, N. J. Stepanoff, H. F. Weber, H. Ihle, G. Kirchhoff and G. Hausemann, etc. J. R. Benoit gave 87,400 mhos at 0° ; L. Lorenz, 93,500 mhos ; A. Oberbeck and J. Bergmann gave 87,260 mhos at 0°, and 60,910 mhos at 100° ; and W. Jäger and H. Diesselhorst gave 88,200 mhos at 18°, and 65,300 at 100° ; J. Dewar and J. A. Fleming's results, calculated by H. Dickson, gave :

Mhos .	−183°	−78°	0°	91·45°	176°
	294,000	114,000	76,600	54,800	42,300

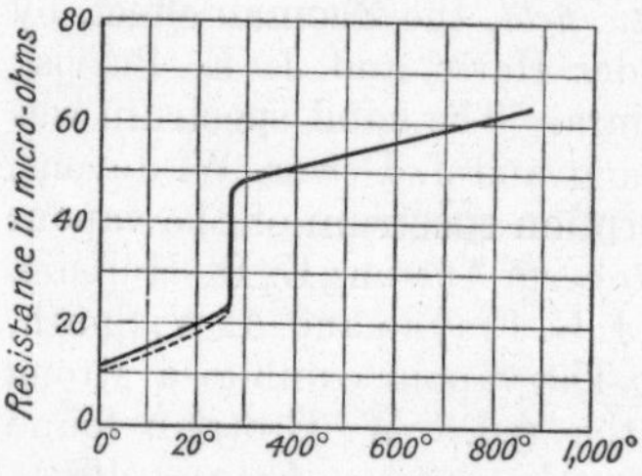

FIG. 17.—Electrical Resistance of Tin.

G. Vassura found a conductivity of 44,900 mhos of the solid at the m.p. 226·5°, and 21,100 mhos for the liquid metal at the same temp. P. Müller found 19,800 mhos at 358°, and 15,400 mhos at 860°. O. Jaamaa and Y. E. G. Leinberg measured the conductivity of powdered tin mixed with various non-conducting powders. W. von Siemens noted an abrupt decrease in the conductivity of tin during melting. E. F. Northrup and V. A. Suydam's observations on the variation of the **electrical resistance**—micro-ohms per c.c.—with *temperature* are plotted in Fig. 17. They found :

R .	225°	300°	400°	500°	600°	700°	750°
	22·00	49·44	52·00	54·62	57·22	59·88	61·22

Just before fusion, the resistance is 22 microhms, and just after fusion, 47·4 microhms. F. A. Schulze gave $0.0_4 13048$ for the sp. electrical resistance of tin. J. Dewar and J. A. Fleming represented their measurements of the electrical resistance at a temp., $\theta°$, between $-100°$ and $0°$ by $R=R_0(1+0.00509\theta)$; L. Cailletet and E. Bouty, between $-85°$ and $0°$, by $R=R_0(1+0.00424\theta)$; W. Jäger and H. Diesselhorst, between 18° and 100°, $R=R_0(1+0.00465\theta)$; and G. Vicentini and D. Omodei, between 0° and 226·5°, $R=R_0(1+0.0049510\theta+0.0_58544\theta^2+0.0_835\theta^3)$. F. A. Schulze gave for the sp. resistance of the solid at the m.p., 21.7×10^{-6}, and of the liquid 47.8×10^{-6}, and he noted no discontinuity in the curve for allotropic tin at 161°. H. K. Onnes and co-workers, and C. A. Crommelin found that the resistance of tin decreases normally with falling temp. down to $-269.2°$ or $3.8°$ K, and when the resistance suddenly becomes immeasurably small, the metal becomes a super-conductor. S. Smith measured the electrical resistance of tin vapour ; G. J. Sizoo and H. K. Onnes, stretching or pressure lowers the temp. at which the resistance disappears. P. W. Bridgman found the following relative values for the resistance at different temp. ; and also the *pressure* coeff. of the resistance :

		0°	25°	50°	75°	100°
Resistance	. . .	1·0000	1·1080	1·2179	1·3306	1·4473
Press. coeff.	0 kgrm. .	$-0·0_41044$	$-0·0_41055$	$-0·0_41062$	$-0·0_41064$	$-0·0_41062$
	12,000 kgrms.	$-0·0_5833$	$-0·0_5836$	$-0·0_5839$	$-0·0_5841$	$-0·0_5844$
	Average .	$-0·0_59204$	$-0·0_59280$	$-0·0_59357$	$-0·0_59434$	$-0·0_59510$

B. Beckman gave $-0·0_592$ for the average press. coeff. at 0°, and P. W. Bridgman $-0·0_41044$. E. D. Williamson studied this subject. L. Grunmach and F. Weidert measured the effect of a *magnetic field* on the resistance of tin. L. Guillet and M. Ballay found the electrical resistance of tin was not increased by *cold work.* W. H. Preece found $12·8d^{1·5}$ for the current strength necessary to melt a tin wire d mm. diameter. P. G. J. Gueterbock and G. N. Nicklin measured the effect of *impurities* on the electrical conductivity of tin ; and Y. E. G. Leinberg, the electrical resistance of finely powdered tin mixed with marble, sulphur, pumice, etc. O. Jaamaa and Y. E. G. Leinberg measured the electrical conductivity of finely powdered tin. A. Stein discussed a relation between the m.p. and the electrical resistance of tin and other metals ; Z. A. Epstein, the relation of the electrical conductivity and the periodic law ; and A. T. Waterman, the theory of electrical conduction.

According to R. D. Kleeman and W. Fredrickson, tin acquires a magnetic charge when immersed in distilled water. N. A. Hesehus, showed that in a closed circuit with hot and cold tin, a current flows from the hot to the cold part. The **Seebeck effect** or **thermoelectric force** of the *iron-tin couple* was found by C. G. Knott to be $-0·001$ volt per degree difference of temp. ; and for the *lead-tin couple*, K. Noll found $-0·067$ microvolt at 50° ; and J. Dewar and J. A. Fleming, with the one junction at 0°, and the other junction at $\theta°$:

$\theta°$	. .	100·1°	50·5°	12·4°	$-2°$	$-11·7°$	$-64°$	$-100·9°$	$-208·8°$
E.m.f.	. .	570	340	50	0	-80	-240	-260	-440

W. Haken, and P. G. Tait measured the Seebeck effect of the tin-lead couple. For the *tin-platinum couple*, W. Jäger and E. Diesselhorst, and E. Rudolfi, gave 0·42 millivolt ; J. Dewar and J. A. Fleming, 0·45 millivolt ; K. Noll, 0·40 millivolt ; W. H. Steele, 0·41 millivolt ; H. Pélabon, 5·17 microvolts ; and E. Wagner, 0·44 millivolt. A. Smits and J. Spuyman found that with an *iron-tin couple*, the transition point of tin was indicated by a sharp break in the curve at 200·2° ; and with the *copper-tin couple*, at 200·5°. With the *tin-silver couple*, R. Räthjen found an e.m.f. of $-2·57$ microvolts. C. Benedicks found the thermoelectric force of ordinary white tin against copper to be -3 microvolts, while the value for grey tin is positive. P. W. Bridgman examined the thermoelectric force of single crystals. T. R. Harrison found for the *solid-liquid tin* couple at the m.p., 0·6 millivolt. P. H. Dowling measured the contact e.m.f. of nickel with solid and molten tin. H. K. Onnes and co-workers studied the effect of low temp. on the **Hall effect ;** and L. J. Neuman, the effect of the crystalline texture. P. Cermak found that the thermoelectric force and the **Peltier effect** with the *tin-constantin couple* does not change with the melting of the tin. E. Edlund measured the Peltier effect between copper and tin. P. Räthjen gave for the Hall coefficient, $-0·4 \times 10^{-4}$. P. W. Bridgman measured the effect of press. in kgrms. per sq. cm. on the Seebeck effect, the Peltier effect, and the **Thomson effect** with couples made with the compressed and uncompressed metals, and a selection from the results is given in Table III. M. O'Day measured the Thomson effect. Observations on the effect of temperature from $-183°$ to 93° were made by G. Borelius and F. Gunneson, who found that at $-173°$ the effect is 0·86 ; at $-143°$, 0·85 ; at $-73°$, 0·42 ; at 27°, $-0·07$; and at 137°, $-0·45$. P. W. Bridgman observed that the Seebeck effect is small and rises to about 0.4×10^{-6} volts and reverses sign with temp. At 12,000 kgrms. per sq. cm. press., the e.m.f. passes through a negative maximum at about 25°. E. Wagner made an observation with tin, and found -0.95×10^{-6} volt at 100° and 300 kgrms. per sq. cm. press. P. W. Bridgman found that the Peltier and Thomson effects

TABLE III.—THE EFFECT OF PRESSURE ON THE SEEBECK, PELTIER, AND THOMSON EFFECT.

—	Seebeck effect. Volts $\times 10^6$.			Peltier effect. Joules per coulomb $\times 10^6$.			Thomson effect. Joules per coulomb $\times 10^6$.		
Temp.	Press. kgrms. per sq. cm.			Press. kgrms. per sq. cm.			Press. kgrms. per sq. cm.		
	2000	6000	12000	2000	6000	12000	2000	6000	12000
0°	40·001	−0·014	−0·136	0	−0·66	−4·92	−0·3	+5·9	+28·9
40°	0·024	+0·042	−0·081	+0·41	+1·06	+2·63	+0·6	+3·0	+6·6
60°	0·052	0·111	+0·103	0·43	1·13	3·03	−0·5	−0·7	−2·0
100°	0·087	0·165	0·390	0·11	0·90	1·75	−1·1	−2·0	−5·0

change sign. At low temp., the Peltier effect is negative, *i.e.* heat is absorbed by the positive current in flowing from the compressed to the uncompressed metal across the junction, but at higher temp. the effect of all press. is to make the effect positive. It then passes through a maximum and decreases again. The Thomson effect is initially positive for low temp., and becomes negative at higher temp.

The **Volta difference of potential** of two metals in contact in air varies with the condition of the metal surface, and the nature of the surrounding atm. W. E. Ayrton and J. Perry [24] gave for ordinary commercial metals at 18°, in volts :

	C	Pt	Cu	Brass	Fe	Pb	Zn	Zn-Hg
Sn . .	−0·795	−0·690	−0·456	−0·372	−0·313	0·099	0·281	0·463

W. Hankel, F. Exner and J. Tuma, and H. Pellat made observations on this subject. A. Volta, J. W. Ritter, J. C. Poggendorff, T. Seebeck, J. C. E. Péclet, P. S. Munk, J. M. Gaugain, and C. H. Pfaff placed tin near the middle of the **electrochemical series** :

K, Ba, Mg, Al, Mn, Zn, Cd, Fe, Co, Ni, **Sn**, Pb, H, Cu, Bi, Sb, Hg, Ag, Pd, Pt, Au.

A. Coehn and A. Lotz found tin to be electronegative towards glass. G. T. Fechner measured the series obtained using water, and a soln. of sodium chloride as electrolytes ; H. Davy, M. Faraday, and J. C. Poggendorff, dil. sulphuric acid ; A. de la Rive, M. Faraday, and S. Avogadro and V. Michelotti, dil. and conc. nitric acid ; M. Faraday, hydrochloric acid ; P. Marianini, sea-water ; J. C. Poggendorff, soln. of ammonium chloride, potassium cyanide, and potassium ferrocyanide ; and H. Davy, and M. Faraday, soln. of potassium hydroxide and sulphide. F. W. Bergstrom found the electrochemical series in liquid ammonia : Pb, Bi, Sn, Sb, As, P, Te, Se, S, I.

A. Naccari and M. Bellati found for carbon and tin in an aq. soln. of chromic acid, 67·0 when the e.m.f. of a normal Daniell's cell is taken as 100 ; C. Hocken and H. A. Taylor observed 0·571–0·626 volt with the zinc-tin couple in dil. sulphuric acid ; and 0·509–0·531 volt in a conc. soln. of zinc sulphate. A. Oberbeck and J. Edler observed the effect with the mercury-tin couple in soln. of the hydroxides, carbonates, nitrates, chlorides, bromides, iodides, and sulphates of potassium, sodium, zinc, and cadmium, and with sulphuric, nitric, and hydrochloric acids, and with aq. ammonia.

According to C. M. van Deventer, owing to the formation of a layer of a badly conducting salt, tin may become cathodic to lead in a mixture of alcohol and water. P. H. Dowling found that there is no contact e.m.f. between liquid and solid tin.

E. Newbery found that in acid electrolyte, tin shows no signs of **passivity,** but readily becomes passive in alkali-lye. At the same time, a black coating is formed similar to that obtained with zinc. The nature of these black substances is under investigation. The electrical resistance of the coating is considerable, since an applied electromotive force of 8 volts only produced a current of 0·4 ampere per c.c. The over-voltage rises to a very high value, and is very erratic. The apparent over-voltage is probably raised artificially to some extent by the action of the badly conducting coating forming a small capacity condenser which is charged by the primary exciting current and then discharged through the potentiometer. The passivity and the **polarization** of tin were investigated by C. F. Bucholz, J. W. Ritter, G. T. Fechner, C. F. Schönbein, C. Wetzlar, M. Eckardt and H. Goldschmidt, F. Förster and M. Dolch, G. C. Schmidt, M. Dresbach and H. R. Hosmer, and R. Steinherz. According to V. Rothmund, tin becomes passive in soln. of sulphuric, hydrofluosilicic, and the halogen acids, but not in nitric, iodic, perchloric, or acetic acid. The metal goes into soln. to form stannous salts from both the active and passive states. The **over-voltage** of tin was examined by F. Meunier, and W. D. Harkins and H. S. Adams. C. Hambuechen gave 0·55 volt for the over-voltage of hydrogen on tin ; and A. Thiel and W. Hammerschmidt, 0·401 for 0·01N-H_2SO_3. H. von Steinwehr calculated $1·3 \times 10^{-5}$ atm. for the **electrolytic solution pressure** of tin Sn$\rightarrow$Sn''.

N. T. M. Wilsmore measured the **electrode potential** of tin referred to the hydrogen electrode and found less than 0·192 volt; A. A. Noyes and K. Toabe gave 0·146 volt. B. Neumann found the potential of tin against a soln. of stannous chloride to be —0·985 volt ; A. Fischer found the potential against a $2N$-$(NH_4)_2S$ to be —0·244 volt ; ($\frac{1}{13}N$-Sn) soln. of $(NH_4)_2SnS_3$, —0·237 volt ; sat. soln. $(NH_4)_2SnS_2$, —0·263 volt ; N-NaSH, —0·545 volt ; ($\frac{1}{15}N$-Sn) soln. of Na_2SnS_3, —0·598 volt; N-Na_2S, —0·610 volt ; $3N$-Na_2S, —0·620 volt ; and N-NaOH, —0·654 volt. E. Müller found the potential difference required to produce the smallest visible quantity of hydrogen from normal sulphuric acid to be 0·43 volt. G. Tammann measured the potential of tin against fused cuprous and silver chlorides. N. R. Dhar studied some anomalies in the electrochemical behaviour of tin ; and M. Schlötter, the electrodeposition of tin.

G. Magnanini measured the potential difference in centi-volts between zinc in a normal soln. of sulphuric acid, and tin placed in the given soln. of the molar conc. —M mols per litre—named :

0·5M-H_2SO_4, 51·3 ; M-NaOH, 0·2 ; M-KOH, —1·2 ; 0·5M-Na_2SO_4, 51·4 ; M-$Na_2S_2O_3$, 45·7 ; M-KNO_3, 31·1 ; M-$NaNO_3$, 40·9 ; 0·5M-K_2CrO_4, 40·9 : 0·5M-$K_2Cr_2O_7$, 68·1 ; 0·5M-K_2SO_4, 40·9 ; 0·5M-$(NH_4)_2SO_4$, 57·6 ; 0·25M-K_4FeCy_6, 41·2 ; 0·334M-K_3FeCy_6, 130·9 ; M-KCyS, 52·7 ; 0·5M-$Sr(NO_3)_2$, 48·7 ; 0·125M-$Ba(NO_3)_2$, 52·8 ; 0·2M-$KClO_3$, 57·7 ; 0·167M-$KBrO_3$, 50·9 ; M-NH_4Cl, 50·9 ; M-KF, 50·8 ; M-NaCl, 50·3 ; M-KBr, 52·5 ; M-KCl, 52·6 ; 0·5M-Na_2SO_3, 31·0 ; M-NaOBr, 70·6 ; M-$C_4H_6O_6$, 54·4 ; 0·5M-$C_4H_6O_6$, 57·6 ; 0·5M-$C_4H_4KNaO_6$, 42 to 47. Measurements for a number of salts were also made by E. F. Herroun, and by C. R. A. Wright and C. Thompson.

O. Sackur gave —0·440 volt for the **electromotive force** of a cell with Sn $|0·05N$-$Sn(CO_3)_2|0·5KNO_3|N$-KCl against a calomel electrode at 25° ; N. R. Dhar, Sn $|$ NaCl$_{soln.}|$ KCl $|$ 0·1N-calomel electrode, etc.

F. Förster and J. Yamasaki found with a normal calomel electrode against Sn $|0·897N$-$SnCl_2|$ sat. KCl $| N$-KCl, —0·471 volt at 18·5°–19° ; against Sn $| 0·092N$-$SnCl_2|$ sat. KCl $| N$-KCl, —0·480 volt at 18·5°–19° ; Sn $0·492N$-$SnSO_4$ sat. KCl $| N$-KCl, —0·473 volt at 18° ; against Sn $| 0·010N$-$SnSO_4$ sat. KCl $| N$-KCl, —0·494 volt at 18° ; against Pt $| 0·45SnCl_2$, 0·05N-$SnCl_4$, N-NH_4Cl sat. KCl $| N$-KCl, 0·181 volt at 18° ; against Pt $|0·05N$-$SnCl_2$, 0·45N-$SnCl_4$, N-NH_4Cl $|$ sat. KCl $| N$-KCl, —0·122 volt at 18° ; and for the cell Pt $| 0·45SnCl_2$, 0·05N-$SnCl_4$, 0·5N-HCl $|$ sat. NH$_4$NO$_3$ $|$ 0·5N-H_2SO_4, solid Hg$_2$SO$_4$ $|$ Hg, 0·552 volt at 18° ; and Pt $| 0·05N$-$SnCl_2$, 0·45SnCl$_4$, 0·5N-HCl $|$ sat. NH$_4$NO$_3$ $|$ 0·5N-H_2SO_4, Hg$_2$SO$_4$ solid $|$ Hg, —0·506 volt at 18°.

W. Ostwald gave 20 Cals. for the **heat of ionization** of Sn''-ions from the element tin ; A. Günther-Schulze [25] observed no **electrolytic valve action** with

tin; but **W. Winter** observed a strong anodic valve action with potash-lye.
G. von Hevesy and R. Lorenz found the **electrocapillary phenomenon** with
the system Sn : LiCl, KCl resembled that with the ordinary mercury-sulphuric
acid electrometer. According to J. Smrz, tin is deposited reversibly on the
dropping cathode from freshly prepared acidic soln. of stannous chloride, the
normal deposition potential being -0.285 volt relative to the calomel electrode.
From freshly-prepared alkali stannite soln., tin is deposited reversibly; a $4 \times 10^{-4}M$
stannite soln. deposits tin at -1.10 and -1.05 volts from N- and $0.1N$-sodium
hydroxide soln., respectively. These soln. are unstable owing to the gradual
formation of colloidal stannous hydroxide and to partial auto-oxidation of stannite to stannate. In normal sodium hydroxide soln., the solubility product
$[Sn^{..}][OH']^2$=about 10^{-28} ; the acidic solubility product of stannous hydroxide,
$[SnO_2H'][H\cdot]$=6×10^{-13} ; the constant for the formation of the complex anion
K_A=$[Sn(OH)'_3]/[Sn^{..}][OH']^3$=$4 \times 10^{24}$. Of the hydroxides of lead, zinc, and tin,
lead hydroxide is the strongest and stannous hydroxide the weakest, the acidic
order being the reverse. The **electric discharge** between tin electrodes has been
studied by F. Fischer and co-workers, V. L. Christler, V. Kohlschütter and
co-workers, and F. Müller ; and the spluttering of the tin cathode, by W. Crookes.
F. Fischer and G. Iliovici examined the spluttering of tin in liquid argon. For
spluttering under water, etc., *vide* colloidal tin. According to R. D. Kleeman and
W. Fredrickson, if an electric current be passed through water in which a rod of
tin and one of carbon are immersed, the metal acquires a negative charge.

Tin is paramagnetic. For the **magnetic susceptibility** A. P. Wills [26] gave
$+0.35 \times 10^{-6}$ vol. units ; M. Owen, $+0.02 \times 10^{-6}$ mass units ; and O. C. Clifford,
$+0.31 \times 10^{-6}$ mass units. K. Honda gave $+0.03 \times 10^{-6}$ mass units at $18°-240°$,
for white tin, and -0.4×10^{-6} mass units at $18°$ for grey tin. M. Owen also gave
-0.255×10^{-6} mass units for grey tin. For liquid tin, K. Honda gave -0.04×10^{-6}
mass units over $240°$. The magnetic susceptibility of a number of tin salts has
been determined by P. Pascal, A. Dauvillier, S. Meyer, G. Quincke, and
C. Chéneveau ; the magnetic moment of tin by W. Gerlach and A. C. Alliers.

REFERENCES.

[1] M. Faraday, *Phil. Trans.*, **147**. 145, 1857; *Phil. Mag.*, (4), **14**. 512, 1857; A. W. Wright, *Amer. Journ. Science*, (3), **13**. 49, 1877 ; (3), **14**. 169, 1877 ; W. L. Dudley, *Amer. Chem. Journ.*, **14**. 185, 1892 ; *Chem. News*, **66**. 163, 1892 ; I. V. Obreimoff and L. V. Shubnikoff, *Zeit. Physik*, **25**. 31, 1924 ; *Trans. Phys. Lab. Leningrad*, **100**. 21, 1925 ; A. E. van Arkel, *Proc. Acad. Amsterdam*, **27**. 97, 1924 ; H. C. Burger, *Physica*, **2**. 56, 1922 ; S. Kalischer, *Ber.*, **14**. 2747, 1881 ; **15**. 701, 1882 ; R. Lüpke, *Grundzüge der Elektrochemie auf experimenteller Basis*, Berlin, 1907 ; London, 11, 1903 ; W. Campbell, *Met.*, **4**. 832, 1907 ; J. A. Ewing, *Journ. Inst. Metals*, **8**. 4, 1912 ; J. A. Ewing and W. Rosenhain, *Proc. Roy. Soc.*, **67**. 115, 1900 ; *Phil. Trans.*, **193**. A, 353, 1899 ; **195**. A, 279, 1900 ; F. Schidlowsky, *Journ. Russ. Phys. Chem. Soc.*, **9**. 50. 1877 ; F. Stolba, *Journ. prakt. Chem.*, (1), **96**. 178, 1865 ; *Ber. Böhm. Ges. Wiss.*, 333, 1873 ; *Bull. Soc. Chim.*, (2), **21**. 560, 1874 ; H. Behrens, *Das mikroskopische Gefüge der Metalle und Legierungen*, Hamburg, 49, 1894 ; R. J. Haüy, *Traité de minéralogie*, Paris, **4**. 147, 1822 ; J. B. L. Romé de l'Isle, *Cristallographie*, Paris, **3**. 408, 1783 ; L. Pajot, *Journ. Phys.*, **38**. 52, 1791 ; A. Breithaupt, *Schweigger's Journ.*, **52**. 171, 1828 ; H. von Foullon, *Verh. Geol. Reichsanst. Wien*, 237, 1881 ; *Jahrb. Geol. Reichsanst. Wien*, **34**. 382, 1884 ; C. F. Bucholz, *Gehlen's Journ.*, **3**. 234, 423, 1804 ; W. W. Mather, *Amer. Journ. Science*, (1), **27**. 254, 1834 ; W. G. Mixter, *ib.*, (4), **27**. 229, 1909 ; M. L. Frankenheim, *Verh. Leop. Carol. Akad.*, **19**. 528, 1837 ; *Pogg. Ann.*, **40**. 456, 1837 ; O. Haase and E. Schmid, *Zeit. Physik*, **33**. 413, 1925 ; M. Polanyi and E. Schmid, *ib.*, **32**. 684, 1925 ; E. C. Bain, *Trans. Amer. Inst. Min. Met.*, **68**. 625, 1922 ; *Chem. Met. Engg.*, **25**. 657, 1921 ; P. H. Dowling, *Phys. Rev.*, (2), **25**. 812, 1925 ; C. F. Rammelsberg, *Sitzber. Akad. Berlin*, 225, 1880 ; *Handbuch der krystallographische-physikalischen Chemie*, Leipzig, **1**. 144, 1881 ; W. H. Miller, *Phil. Mag.*, (3), **22**. 263, 1843 ; *Introduction to Mineralogy*, London, 128, 1852 ; F. Wöhler, *Liebig's Ann.*, **85**. 253, 1853 ; J. C. Ilsemann, *Crell's Ann.*, i, 400, 1786 ; A. J. Bijl and N. H. Kolkmeijer, *Chem. Weekbl.*, **18**. 1077, 1264, 1918 ; *Proc. Acad. Amsterdam*, **21**, 405, 494, 501, 1919 ; C. O. Trechmann, *Min. Mag.*, **3**. 186, 1880 ; L. J. Spencer, *ib.*, **19**. 113, 1921 ; M. Volmer, *Zeit. phys. Chem.*, **102**. 267, 1922 ; E. Cohen and C. van Eijk, *Versl. Akad. Amsterdam*, **8**. 36, 102, 1899 ; *Zeit. phys. Chem.*, **30**. 601, 1899 ; E. Cohen, *ib.*, **33**. 57, 1900 ; **35**. 508, 1900 ; **36**. 513, 1901 ; **68**. 223, 1909 ; E. Cohen and E. Goldschmidt, *ib.*, **50**. 215, 1904 ; *Chem. Weekbl.*, **1**. 437, 1904 ; K. Schaum, *Liebig's Ann.*, **308**. 18, 1899 ;

W. Campbell, *Met.*, **4**. 329, 1907 (I am greatly indebted to Prof. W. Campbell for permission to publish Figs. 4 to 6) ; *Journ. Franklin Inst.*, **154**. 1, 131, 201, 1902 ; L. A. Mathews, *ib.*, **153**. 1, 119, 211, 1902 ; G. Masing, *Naturwiss.*, **11**. 413, 1923 ; *Zeit. Metallkunde*, **12**. 457, 1920 ; *Wiss. Veröff. Siemens-Konzern*, **1**. 96, 1921 ; M. L. Huggins, *Journ. Amer. Chem. Soc.*, **44**. 1842, 1922 ; J. H. van't Hoff, *Zinn. Gips. und Stahl vom physikalischen-chemischen Standpunkt*, München, 1901 ; J. Czochralsky, *Zeit. phys. Chem.*, **92**. 219, 1917 ; *Internat. Zeit. Metallog.*, **8**. 1, 1916 ; W. Fraenkel, *ib.*, **13**. 142, 1921 ; G. Masing, *ib.*, **12**. 457, 1920 ; *Wiss. Veröffent. Siemens-Konzern*, **1**. 31, 96, 1922 ; W. Deutsch, *Zeit. phys. Chem.*, **90**. 557, 1915 ; H. J. Brooke, *Edin. Phil. Journ.*, **12**. 1, 1825 ; A. Ditte and R. Metzner, *Compt. Rend.*, **117**. 691, 1893 ; A. Ditte, *ib.*, **94**. 792, 1882 ; L. Vignon, *ib.*, **107**. 734, 1888 ; W. Holz, *Phys. Zeit.*, **7**. 660, 1906 ; A. Ssaposchnikoff, *Zeit. angew. Chem.*, **17**. 624, 1904 ; G. Buchner, *Chem. Ztg.*, **18**. 1904, 1894 ; C. Goldschmidt, *ib.*, **28**. 1229, 1904 ; Tin Electro-smelting Co., *German Pat.*, *D.R.P.* 146610, 1901 ; E. Kopp, *Monit. Scient.*, (3), **1**. 402, 1871 ; R. Jakobson, *Chem. Tech. Repert.*, ii, 69, 1872 ; *Deut. Ind. Ztg.*, 209, 1873 ; H. Harpf, *Papier Ztg.*, 2584, 1891 ; E. Puscher, *Kunst. Gewerbe*, 156, 1882 ; R. Zsigmondy, *Elektrochem. Zeit.*, **2**. 57, 1895 ; W. Pffannhauser, *Zeit. Elektrochem.*, **8**. 41, 1902 ; F. Gelstharp, *Chem. News*, **90**. 324, 1904 ; P. N. Degens, *Legierungen von tin en lood*, Dordrecht, 1909 ; *Zeit. anorg. Chem.*, **63**. 207, 1909 ; A. A. M. van Liempt, *ib.*, **129**. 263, 1923 ; M. Werner, *ib.*, **83**. 275, 1913 ; G. Tammann and Q. A. Mansuri, *ib.*, **126**. 119, 1923 ; N. Werigni, J. Lewkojeff, and G. Tammann, *Ann. Physik*, (4), **10**. 647, 1903 ; G. Tammann, *Gött. Nachr.*, **1**, 1918 ; A. Smits and H. L. de Leeuw, *Versl. Akad. Amsterdam*, **21**. 661, 1912 ; A. Smits and J. Spuyman, *ib.*, **29**. 327, 1921 ; *Proc. Acad. Amsterdam*, **23**. 687, 1921 ; P. Niggli, *Naturwiss.*, **10**. 391, 1922 ; H. Mark, M. Polanyi, and E. Schmid, *ib.*, **11**. 256, 1923 ; *Zeit. Physik*, **32**. 684, 1925 ; H. Mark and M. Polanyi, *Zeit. Physik*, **18**. 75, 1923 ; M. Polanyi, *ib.*, **17**. 42, 1923 ; E. von Gomperz, *ib.*, **8**. 184, 1922 ; C. Burger, *Physica*, **1**. 241, 1921 ; P. Gaubert, *Compt. Rend.*, **159**. 680, 1914 ; C. A. Edwards, *Journ. Inst. Metals*, **14**. 116, 1915 ; H. C. H. Carpenter and C. A. Edwards, *Journ. Iron Steel Inst.*, **89**. i, 138, 1914 ; J. H. Bowman, *Journ. Amer. Chem. Soc.*, **37**. 1468, 1915 ; R. N. Pease, *ib.*, **44**. 769, 1922 ; P. Ludwik, *Internat. Zeit. Metallog.*, **8**. 53, 1916 ; W. C. Phebus and F. C. Blake, *Phys. Rev.*, (2), **25**. 107, 1925 ; R. J. Anderson and J. T. Norton, *Trans. Amer. Inst. Min. Met. Eng.*, **71**. 720, 1925 ; M. Cook and U. R. Evans, *ib.*, **71**. 627, 1924 ; K. Weissenberg, *Zeit. Kryst.*, **61**. 58, 1925 ; H. S. Rawdon, A. I. Krynitzky, and J. F. T. Berliner, *Chem. Met. Engg.*, **26**. 212, 1922 ; S. Nishikawa and G. Asahara, *Phys. Rev.*, (2), **15**. 38, 1920 ; W. P. Headden, *Proc. Colorado Scient. Soc.*, **6**. 74 1901 ; *Amer. Journ. Science*, (4), **5**. 93, 1898 ; O. Mügge, *Centr. Min.*, 233, 1917 ; M. Born and O. F. Bollnoff, *Naturwiss.*, 1 j. 559, 1925 ; G. L. Clark, E. W. Brugmann, and S. D. Heath, *Journ. Ind. Eng. Chem.*, **17**. 1142, 1925.

² E. Babelon, *Traité des monnaies grecques et romaines*, Paris, **1**. 373, 1901 ; A. Blanchet, *Guide pratique de l'antiquaire*, Paris, 1899 ; E. Cohen. *Zeit. phys. Chem.*, **63**. 625, 1908 ; R. Brauns, *Natur*, **1**. 738, 1906.

³ E. Krause, *Prometheus*, **11**. 701, 1900 ; E. Cohen, *Zeit. phys. Chem.*, **36**. 513, 1901 ; **48**. 243, 1904.

⁴ O. L. Erdmann, *Journ. prakt. Chem.*, (1), **52**. 428, 1851 ; A. Schertel, *ib.*, (2), **19**. 322, 1879 ; C. J. Fritzsche, *Mém. Acad. St. Petersburg*, (1), **7**. 15, 1870 ; *Compt. Rend.*, **47**. 106, 1868 ; *Phil. Mag.*, (4), **38**. 207, 1869 ; *Ber.*, **2**. 112, 540, 1869 ; C. F. Rammelsberg, *ib.*, **3**. 724, 1870 ; *Zeit. Chem.*, (2), **6**. 733, 1870 ; *Sitzber. Akad. Berlin*, 225, 1880 ; P. Lewald, *Das Ausland*, **43**. 71, 1870 ; *Dingler's Journ.*, **196**. 369, 1870 ; A. C. Oudemans, *Rev. Chim. Scient. Ind.*, **3**. 557, 1872 ; H. R. Richards, *Berg. Hütt. Z g.*, **44**. 563, 1885 ; G. H. Engleheart, *Archaeologia*, **56**. 1, 1899 ; W Gowland, *ib.*, **56**. 13, 1899 ; I. Walz, *Amer. Artizan*, (3), **1**. 129, 1872 ; F. Petri, *Wied. Ann.*, **2**. 304, 1877 ; W. Markownikoff, *Journ. Russ. Phys. Chem. Soc.*, **13**. 358, 1881 ; *Bull. Soc. Chim.*, (2), **37**. 347, 1882 ; E. E. Emeljanoff, *Congress Russ. Nat. Soc. St. Petersburg*, (8), **8**. 1, 1890 ; *Chem. Ztg.*, **14**. 145, 1890 ; H. Hoeveler, *ib.*, **16**. 1339, 1892 ; E. Hjelt, *ib.*, **16**. 1197, 1892 ; *Œfvers. Finska Förh.*, 32, 1890 ; H. Stockmeier, *Verh. Ges. Nat. Aerzte Nürnberg*, 97, 1893 ; P. Hamberger, *ib.*, 190, 1904 ; K. Schaum, *Liebig's Ann.*, **308**. 18, 1899 ; *Die Arten der Isomerie*, Marburg, 1899 ; O. Lehmann, *Molekularphysik*, Leipzig, **1**. 182, 1888 ; E. B. Wolff, *Zeit. Elektrochem.*, **19**. 19, 1913 ; A. Smits and J. Spuyman, *Proc. Acad. Amsterdam*, **23**. 687, 1921 ; *Versl. Akad. Amsterdam*, **29**. 327, 1921 ; E. Cohen and C. van Eijk, *ib.*, **8**. 36, 102, 1899 ; *Zeit. phys. Chem.*, **30**. 601, 1899 ; E. Cohen and E. Goldschmidt, *ib.*, **50**. 225, 1905 ; *Chem. Weekbl.*, **1**. 437, 1904 ; E. Cohen and K. Inouye, *ib.*, **6**. 881, 1909 ; E. Cohen, *ib.*, **2**. 450, 1905 ; **6**. 625, 1909 ; *Trans. Faraday Soc.*, **7**. 122, 1911 ; *Zeit. Elektrochem.*, **18**. 616, 1912 ; **19**. 23, 1913 ; *Zeit. phys. Chem.*, **33** 57, 1900 ; **35**. 588, 1900 ; **36**. 513, 1901 ; **48**. 243, 1904 ; **63**. 625, 1908 ; **68**. 214, 1909 ; E. Cohen and A. L. T. Moesveld, *Proc. Acad. Amsterdam*, **28**. 347, 1925 ; *Zeit. phys Chem.*, **115**. 151, 1 25 ; E. Jänecke, *ib.*, **90**. 257, 313, 1915 ; A. Wigand, *Ann. Physik*, (4), **22**. 64, 1906 ; R. von Hasslinger, *Sitzber. Akad. Wien*, **117**. 501, 1908 ; *Monatsh.*, **29**. 787, 1908 ; A. Thiel, *Ber.*, **54**. B, 2755, 1921 ; N. I. Stepanoff, *Ann. Inst. Phys. Chem. Leningrad*, **2**. 500, 1924 ; A. J. Bijl and N. H. Kolkmeijer, *Chem. Weekbl.*, **15**. 1264, 1918 ; *Proc. Acad. Amsterdam*, **21** 405, 494, 501, 1919 ; H. M. Howe, *Met. Chem. Engg.*, **9**. 79, 1911 ; S. Nishikawa and G. Asahara, *Phys. Rev.*, (2), **15**. 38, 1920 ; G. T. Beilby, *Journ. Inst. Metals*, **6**. 5, 1911 ; *Aggregation and Flow of Solids*, London, 1921 ; *Proc. Roy. Soc.*, **89**. A, 593, 1914 ; M. Werner, *Zeit. anorg. Chem.*, **83**. 275, 1913 ; C. O. Trechmann, *Min. Mag.*, **3**. 186, 1879 ; L. J. Spencer, *ib.*, **19**. 113, 1921 ; O. Mügge, *Centr. Min.*, 233, 1917 ; C. von Simson, *Zeit. phys. Chem.*, **109**. 183, 1924.

⁵ J. J. C. Mullet, *Journ. Asiatique*, (5), **11**. 379, 1876 ; N. Khanikoff, *Journ. Amer. Oriental Soc.*, **6**. 1, 1859 ; H. C. Bolton, *Quart. Journ. Science*, **13**. 494, 1876 ; R. Boyle, *Hydrostatic Balance*, London, 1690 ; D. G. Fahrenheit, *Phil. Trans.*, **33**. 114, 1726.

⁶ J. Brisson, *Pésanteur spécifique des corps*, Paris, 1787 ; P. van Muschenbrock, *Phil. Trans.*, **33**. 370, 1726 ; L. B. G. de Morveau, *Nicholson's Journ.*, (1), **1**. 110, 1798 ; *Ann. Chim. Phys.*, (1), **24**. 127, 1797 ; (1), **71**. 189, 1809 ; *Nicholson's Journ.*, **26**. 102, 1810 ; J. Crichton, *Phil. Mag.*, **15**. 147, 1803 ; **16**. 48, 1803 ; T. J. Herapath, *ib.*, (1), **64**. 321, 1824 ; W. H. Miller, *ib.*, (3), **22**. 263, 1843 ; C. J. St. C. Deville, *ib.*, (4), **11**. 144, 1867 ; *Compt. Rend.*, **20**. 1453, 1845 ; **40**. 769, 1855 ; C. Benedicks, *ib.*, 179, 389, 1924 ; P. Pascal and J. Jouniaux, *ib.*, **158**. 414, 1914 ; G. Quincke, *Pogg. Ann.*, **134**. 356, 1868 ; **135**. 642, 1868 ; A. Matthiessen, *ib.*, **110**. 317, 1860 ; P. G. J. Gueterbock and G. N. Nicklin, *Journ. Soc. Chem. Ind.*, **44**. 370, T, 1925 ; C. F. Rammelsberg, *Sitzber. Akad. Berlin*, 225, 1880 ; *Ber.*, **3**. 725, 1870 ; W. Spring, *Bull. Acad. Belg.*, (3), **6**. 507, 1883 ; 1066, 1903 ; *Ber.*, **16**. 2724, 1883 ; C. E. Fawsitt, *Journ. Chem. Soc.*, **93**. 1299, 1908 ; E. Cohen and E. Goldschmidt, *Chem. Weekbl.*, **1**. 437, 1904 ; *Zeit. phys. Chem.*, **50**. 225, 1904 ; E. Cohen and J. Olie, *ib.*, **71**. 385, 1910 ; R. Hoffmann and W. Stahl, *Metall Erz*, **20**. 5, 41, 1923 ; F. C. A. H. Lantsberry, *Proc. Birmingham Met. Soc.*, **5**. 101, 1913 ; G. Vicentini and D. Omodei, *Atti Accad. Torino*, **23**. 38, 1887 ; A. Wigand, *Ann. Physik*, (4), **22**. 64, 1906 ; W. Jäger and H. Diesselhorst, *Wiss. Abhand. Phys. Tech. Reichsanst.*, **3**. 269, 1900 ; F. Paur, *Monit. Scient.*, (3), **9**. 800, 1879 ; F. Nies and A. Winkelmann, *Wied. Ann.*, **13**. 43, 1881 ; E. Wiedemann, *ib.*, **20**. 228, 1883 ; M. Töpler, *ib.*, **53**. 343, 1894 ; T. R. Hogness, *Journ. Amer. Chem. Soc.*, **43**. 1621, 1921 ; A. Hess, *Ber. deut. phys. Ges.*, **3**. 403, 1905 ; O. Brill and C. de Brereton-Evans, *Proc. Chem. Soc.*, **24**. 185, 1908 ; *Journ. Chem. Soc.*, **93**. 1442, 1908 ; T. M. Lowry and R. G. Parker, *ib.*, **107**. 1005, 1160, 1915 ; C. O. Trechmann, *Min. Mag.*, **3**. 186, 1880 ; A. L. Day, R. B. Sosman, and J. C. Hostetter, *Amer. Journ. Science*, (4), **37**. 1, 1914 ; J. Johnston, *Journ. Franklin Inst.*, **183**. 1, 1917 ; J. J. van Laar, *Die Zustandsgleichung von Gasen und Flussigkeiten*, Leipzig, 1924 ; *Proc. Akad. Amsterdam*, **18**. 1220, 1915 ; **19**. 2, 1916 ; R. H. Richards, *Trans. Amer. Inst. Min. Eng.*, **11**. 235, 1883 ; A. Schertel, *Journ. prakt. Chem.*, (2), **19**. 322, 1879 ; A. Baudrimont, *ib.*, (1), **7**. 278, 1836 ; *Ann. Chim. Phys.*, (3), **30**. 304, 1850 ; A. T. Kupffer, *ib.*, (2), **25**. 356, 1824 ; C. J. B. Karsten, *Schweigger's Journ.*, **65**. 394, 1832 ; L. Playfair and J. P. Joule, *Mem. Chem. Soc.*, **3**. 68, 1848 ; H. Kopp, *Liebig's Ann.*, **93**. 129, 1855 ; R. Mallet, *Phil. Mag.*, (4), **49**. 231, 1875 ; *Proc. Roy. Soc.*, **22**. 366, 1873 ; **23**. 29, 1875 ; W. C. Roberts-Austen and T. Wrightson, *Nature*, **24**. 470, 1881 ; *Phil. Mag.*, (5), **11**. 295, 1881 ; (5), **13**. 360, 1882 ; D. Forbes, *ib.*, (4), **29**. 129, 1865 ; (4), **30**. 142, 1865 ; J. Pohl, *Jahr. Geol. Reichsanst. Wien*, **34**. 369, 1884 ; W. Gede, *Phys. Zeit.*, **4**. 104, 1902 ; H. Stockmeier, *Verh. Ges. Nat. Aerzte Nurnberg*, 97, 1893 ; G. W. A. Kahlbaum and E. Sturm, *Zeit. anorg. Chem.*, **46**. 256, 1905 ; M. Plüss, *Zur Kenntnis der Viskosität und Dichte geschmolzener Metalle und Legierungen*, Basel, 1915 ; *Zeit. anorg. Chem.*, **93**. 1, 1915 ; E. Jänecke, *Met.*, **8**. 68, 1911 ; R. Arpi, *Internat. Zeit. Metallog.*, **5**. 142, 1914 ; W. H. Bragg, *Phil. Mag.*, (6), **40**. 169, 1920 ; K. Bornemann and P. Siebe, *Zeit. Metallkunde*, **14**. 329, 1922 ; H. Endo, *Science Rep. Tohoku Univ.*, **13**. 193, 1924 ; *Journ. Inst. Metals*, **30**. 121, 1923 ; R. N. Pease, *Journ. Amer. Chem. Soc.*, **44**. 769, 1922 ; M. L. Huggins, *Phys. Rev.*, (2), **21**. 205, 1923.

⁷ J. R. Rydberg, *Zeit. phys. Chem.*, **33**. 353, 1900 ; T. K. Rose, *Trans. Faraday Soc.*, **10**. 282, 1915 ; Z. Jeffries, *Journ. Amer. Inst. Metals*, **11**. 300, 1918 ; C. A. Edwards, *Journ. Inst. Metals*, **20**. 61, 1918 ; C. A. Edwards and M. A. Herbert, *ib.*, **25**. 175, 1921 ; F. Sauerwald, *Zeit. Metallkunde*, **16**. 315, 1924 ; F. Sauerwald and K. Knehaus, *Zeit. anorg. Chem.*, **140**. 227, 1924 ; K. Ito, *Science Rep. Tohoku Univ.*, **12**. 137, 1923 ; K. Honda and R. Yamada, *ib.*, **14**. 63, 1925 ; J. Okubo, *ib.*, **11**. 455, 1922 ; A. Kürth, *Phys. Zeit.*, **8**. 417, 1907 ; *Zeit. Ver. deut. Ing.* **53**. 85, 209, 1909 ; F. Auerbach, *Wied. Ann.*, **43**. 61, 1891 ; **45**. 262, 1892 ; **53**. 1000, 1894 ; **58**. 357, 1896 ; *Ann. Physik*, (4), **3**. 108, 116, 1900 ; S. Bottone, *Chem. News*, **27**. 215, 1873 ; T. Turner, *Journ. Iron Steel Inst.*, **75**. i, 434, 1909 ; P. Ludwik, *Die Kugeldruckprobe*, Berlin, 1908 ; *Zeit. Ver. deut. Ing.*, **59**. 657, 1915 ; *Zeit. anorg. Chem.*, **94**. 161 1915 ; *Zeit. phys. Chem.*, **91**. 232, 1916 ; H. J. Coe, *Metal Ind.*, **23**. 245, 1923 ; *Journ. Inst. Metals*, **30**. 309, 1923 ; P. Nicolardot, *Compt. Rend.*, **168**. 558, 1919 ; P. G. J. Gueterbock and G. N. Nicklin. *Journ. Soc. Chem. Ind.*, **44**. 370, T, 1925.

⁸ G. Quincke, *Pogg. Ann.*, **134**. 356, 1868 ; *Phil. Mag.*, (4), **36**. 267, 1868 ; (4), **38**. 78, 1869 ; *Wied. Ann.*, **52**. 1, 1894 ; **61**. 267, 1897 ; T. R. Hogness, *Journ. Amer. Chem. Soc.*, **43**. 1621, 1921 ; J. H. Hildebrand, T. R. Hogness, and N. W. Taylor, *ib.*, **45**. 2828, 1923 ; H Siedentopf, *Wied. Ann.*, **61**. 235, 1897 ; L. L. Grunmach, *Ann. Physik*, (4), **3**. 660, 1900 ; J. Kleiber, *ib.*, (4), **46**. 1054, 1915 ; S. W. Smith, *Journ. Inst. Metals*, **12**. 168, 1914 ; **17**. 65, 1917 ; W. Hagemann, *Ueber die Oberflächenspannung geschmolzener Metalle*, Freiburg, 1914 ; I. Traube, *Ber. deut. phys. Ges.*, 231, 1909 ; *Ber.*, **42**. 86, 1909 ; D. Saito and K. Hayashi, *Mem. Coll. Eng. Kyoto Univ.*, **2**. 83, 1919 ; G. Subrahmanian, *Phil. Mag.*, (7), **1**. 1074, 1926.

⁹ M. von Wogau, *Ann. Physik*, (4), **23**. 345, 1907 ; W. C. Roberts-Austen, *Proc. Roy. Soc.*, **59**. 281, 1896 ; **67**. 101, 1900 ; *Phil. Trans.*, **187**. 383, 1896 ; *Chem. News*, **74**. 289, 1896 ; O. Bauer and E. Piwowarsky, *Metall Erz*, **20**. 416, 1923 ; R. Kremann and A. Hrasovec, *Monash.*, **46**. 409, 1925.

¹⁰ A. I. F. Levol, *Ann. Chim. Phys.*, (3), **56**. 110, 1859 ; E. F. F. Chladni, *Akustik*, Leipzig, 266, 1802 ; J. Smithson, *Ann. Phil.*, **1**. 271, 1821 ; A. Masson, *Pogg. Ann.*, **103**. 272, 1858 ; E. Jänecke, *Met.*, **8**. 68, 1911 ; R. Arpi, *Internat. Zeit. Metallog.*, **5**. 142, 1914 ; D. Saito and K. Hayashi, *Mem. Coll. Eng. Kyoto Univ.*, **2**. 83, 1919 ; G. G. Gerosa, *Rend. Accad. Lincei*,

(4), **4**. i, 127, 1888 ; **M**. Plüss, *Zur Kenntnis der Viskosität und Dichte geschmolzener Metalle und Legierungen*, Basel, 20, 1915 ; *Zeit. anorg. Chem.*, **93**. 1, 1915 ; C. E. Fawsitt, *Proc. Chem. Soc.*, **24**. 146, 1908 ; *Journ. Chem. Soc.*, **93**. 1299, 1908 ; *Proc. Roy. Soc.*, **80**. A, 290, 1908 ; N. Werigin, J. Lewkojeff, and G. Tammann, *Ann. Physik*, (4), **10**. 651, 1903 ; J. Kleber, *ib.*, (4), **46**, 1054, 1915 ; O. Haase and E. Schmid, *Zeit. Physik*, **33**. 413, 1925.

¹¹ C. J. Burton and W. Marshall, *Proc. Roy. Soc.*, **50**. 130, 1891 ; W. Spring, *Zeit. phys. Chem.*, **2**. 532, 1888 ; T. W. Richards, *Zeit. Elektrochem.*, **13**. 519, 1907 ; *Journ. Amer. Chem. Soc.*, **37**. 1643, 1915 ; T. W. Richards and W. N. Stull, *Zeit. phys. Chem.*, **51**. 196, 1908 ; T. W. Richards and E. P. Bartlett, *Journ. Amer. Chem. Soc.*, **37**. 470, 1915 ; L. H. Adams, E. D. Williamson, and J. Johnston, *ib.*, **41**. 12, 1919 ; E. Grüneisen, *Ann. Physik*, (4), **33**. 1239, 1910 ; F. Streintz, *ib.*, (4), **8**. 847, 1902 ; (4), **33**. 436, 1910 ; R. Granja, *Journ. Soc. Chem. Ind.*, **20**. 1191, 1901 ; P. W. Bridgman, *Proc. Amer. Acad.*, **58**. 165, 1923 ; *Proc. Nat. Acad. Sciences*, **10**. 411, 1925 ; H. J. Coe, *Metal Ind.*, **23**. 245, 1923 ; *Journ. Inst. Metals*, **30**. 309, 1923 ; P. G. J. Gueterbock and G. N. Nicklin, *Journ. Soc. Chem. Ind.*, **44**. 370, T, 1925 ; M. Polanyi and E. Schmid, *Zeit. Physik*, **32**. 684, 1925.

¹² G. W. A. Kahlbaum and E. Sturm, *Zeit. anorg. Chem.*, **46**. 217, 1905 ; P. G. J. Gueterbock and G. N. Nicklin, *Metal Ind.*, **27**. 118, 143, 1925 ; *Journ. Soc. Chem. Ind.*, **44**. 370, T, 1925 ; L. B. G. de Morveau, *Ann. Chim. Phys.*, (1), **71**. 189, 1809 ; *Nicholson's Journ.*, **26**. 102, 1810 ; G. Wertheim, *ib.*, (3), **12**. 385, 1844 ; (1), **23**. 52, 1849 ; F. Horton, *Proc. Roy. Soc.*, **73**. 334, 1904 ; **74**. 401, 1905 ; *Phil. Trans.*, **204**. A, 1, 1905 ; P. W. Bridgman, *Proc. Nat. Acad. Sciences*, **10**. 411, 1925 ; H. Shoji, *Bull. Inst. Phys. Chem. Japan*, **2**. 334, 1923 ; J. Dewar, *Chem. News*, **71**. 200, 1895 ; W. Voigt, *Wied. Ann.*, **48**. 674, 1893 ; J. Kiewiet, *ib.*, **29**. 650, 1866 ; *Untersuchungen über die Biegungselasticität von reinem Zink, Kupfer, Zinn und ihren Legierungen*, Leipzig, 1886 ; H. J. Coe, *Metal Ind.*, **23**. 245, 1923 ; *Journ. Inst. Metals*, **30**. 309, 1923 ; H. Hess, *Ann. Physik*, (4), **8**. 405, 1902 ; W. E. Dalby, *Phil. Trans.*, **221**. A, 117, 1920 ; E. von Gomperz, *Zeit. Physik*, **7**. 184, 1921 ; A. MacNutt and A. Concilio, *Phys. Rev.*, (2), **20**. 95, 1922 ; D. H. Ingall, *Metal Ind.*, **25**. 371, 1924 ; P. Ludwik, *Zeit. Ver. deut. Ing.*, **59**. 657, 1915 ; W. Sutherland, *Phil. Mag.*, (5), **32**. 31, 215, 524, 1891 ; O. Faust and G. Tammann, *Zeit. phys. Chem.*, **75**. 108, 1910 ; W. Rosenhain and D. Ewen, *Journ. Inst. Metals*, **8**. 149, 1912 ; **10**. 119, 1913 ; A. H. Stuart, *Proc. Inst. Mech. Eng.*, 1155, 1912 ; *Journ. Inst. Metals*, **14**. 168, 1915 ; P. Nicolardot, *Compt. Rend.*, **168**. 558, 1919 ; A. Mallock, *Proc. Roy. Soc.*, **95**. A, 429, 1919 ; H. Shoji, *Bull. Japan Inst. Phys. Chem. Research*, **2**. 334, 1923 ; O. Faust and G. Tammann, *Zeit. phys. Chem.*, **75**. 108, 1910 ; R. H. Greaves and J. A. Jones, *Journ. Inst. Metals*, **35**. 34, 1925.

¹³ P. S. Laplace and A. L. Lavoisier, *Mém. Acad.*, 355, 1780 ; *Recueil des mémoires de chimie de Lavoisier*, Paris, **1**. 121, 1805 ; L. B. G. de Morveau, *Ann. Chim. Phys.*, (1), **71**. 189, 1809 ; J. F. Daniell, *Phil. Trans.*, **82**. 257, 1830 ; **83**. 443, 1831 ; R. Hoffmann and W. Stahl, *Metall Erz*, **20**. 41, 1923 ; H. Kopp, *Liebig's Ann.*, **81**. 29, 1851 ; **93**. 129, 1855 ; *Phil. Mag.*, (4), **3**. 268, 1852 ; A. Matthiessen, *ib.*, (4), **31**. 149, 1866 ; (4), **32**. 472, 1866 ; *Phil. Trans.*, **156**. 231, 1866 ; *Proc. Roy. Soc.*, **15**. 220, 1866 ; *Pogg. Ann.*, **130**. 50, 1867 ; P. Glatzel, *ib.*, **160**. 497, 1877 ; H. Fizeau, *Compt. Rend.*, **68**. 1125, 1869 ; F. C. Calvert and R. Johnson, *Mem. Manchester Lit. Phil. Soc.*, (2), **15**. 113, 1858 ; *Phil. Mag.*, (4), **17**. 114, 1859 ; *Chem. News*, **3**. 315, 1859 ; A. Hess, *Ber. deut. phys. Ges.*, **3**. 403, 1905 ; G. Vincentini and D. Omodei, *Atti Accad. Torino*, **23**. 38, 1887 ; E. Grüneisen, *Ann. Physik*, (4), **33**. 65, 1910 ; P. W. Bridgman, *Proc. Amer. Acad.*, **58**. 165, 1923 ; J. K. Horner, *Ueber Maase und Gewichte*, Zürich, 1813 ; *Gilbert's Ann.*, **39**. 468, 1811.

¹⁴ C. M. Despretz, *Ann. Chim. Phys.*, (2), **19**. 97, 1822 ; F. C. Calvert and R. Johnson, *Compt. Rend.*, **47**. 1071, 1858 ; *Phil. Trans.*, **148**. 349, 1858 ; H. F. Weber, *Sitzber. Akad. Berlin*, 457, 1880 ; *Zürich Vierteljahr.*, **25**. 184, 1880 ; E. H. Hall, *Proc. Nat. Acad.*, **6**. 613, 1920 ; M. Jakob, *Zeit. Metallkunde*, **16**. 353, 1924 ; G. Kirchhoff and G. Hausemann, *Wied. Ann.*, **13**. 406, 1881 ; L. Lorenz, *ib.*, **13**. 422, 1881 ; *Danske Vid. Selsk. Skr.*, (6), **2**. 37, 1886 ; G. Wiedmann, *Pogg. Ann.*, **108**. 393, 1859 ; G. Wiedemann and R. Franz, *ib.*, **89**. 497, 1853 ; *Phil. Mag.*, (4), **32**. 472, 1866 ; G. Glage, *Ann. Physik*, (4), **18**. 904, 1905 ; A. Berget, *Compt. Rend.*, **110**. 76, 1890 ; W. B. Brown, *Phys. Rev.*, (2), **22**. 171, 1923 ; M. O'Day, *ib.*, (2), **23**. 245, 1924 ; S. Konno, *Phil. Mag.*, (6), **40**. 542, 1920 ; *Science Rep. Tohoku Univ.*, **8**. 169, 1919 ; C. H. Lees, *Phil. Trans.*, **208**. A, 381, 1908 ; S. Lussana, *Nuovo Cimento*, (6), **15**. 130, 1918 ; P. W. Bridgman, *Proc. Amer. Acad.*, **57**. 77, 1922 ; *Phys. Rev.*, (2), **18**. 115, 1921 ; *Proc. Nat. Acad.*, **11**. 608, 1925.

¹⁵ H. V. Regnault, *Ann. Chim. Phys.*, (2), **73**. 42, 1840 ; C. C. Person, *ib.*, (3), **21**. 295, 1847 ; (3), **24**. 136, 1848 ; W. Louguinine, *ib.*, (5), **27**. 398, 1882 ; P. L. Dulong and A. T. Petit, *ib.*, (2), **10**. 395, 1819 ; P. Schübel, *Zeit. anorg. Chem.*, **87**. 81, 1914 ; W. Spring, *Bull. Acad. Belg.*, (3), **11**. 355, 1886 ; R. Bunsen, *Pogg. Ann.*, **141**. 1, 1870 ; J. Pionchon, *Compt. Rend.*, **102**. 675, 1454, 1886 ; *Ann. Chim. Phys.*, (6), **11**. 33, 1887 ; L. Schütz, *Wied. Ann.*, **46**. 177, 1892 ; W. Voigt, *ib.*, **49**. 709, 1893 ; F. A. Waterman, *Phys. Rev.*, (1), **4**. 161, 1896 ; *Phil. Mag.*, (5), **40**. 419, 1895 ; U. Behn, *Ann. Physik*, (4), **1**. 257, 1900 ; C. Forch and P. Nordmeyer, *ib.*, (4), **20**. 423, 1906 ; R. Ewald, *ib.*, (4), **44**. 1213, 1914 ; A. Wigand, *ib.*, (4), **22**. 64, 1907 ; *Zeit. Elektrochem.*, **20**. 38, 1914 ; F. Glasser, *Met.*, **1**. 127, 1904 ; A. Naccari, *Rend. Accad. Torino*, **23**. 107, 1887 ; A. Bartoli and E. Stracciati, *Gazz. Chim. Ital.*, **25**. i, 389, 1895 ; *Rend. Ist. Lombardo*, **2**. 28, 1895 ; A. Eucken, *Ber. deut. phys. Ges.*, **18**. 18, 1916 ; H. E. Schmitz, *Proc. Roy. Soc.*, **72**. 177, 1903 ; J. Dewar, *Proc. Roy. Soc.*, **89**. A, 158, 1913 ; W. H. Rodebush, *Journ. Amer. Chem. Soc.*, **45**. 1413, 1923 ; E. D. Eastman, A. M. Williams, and T. F. Young, *ib.*,

46. 1184, 1924 ; T. W. Richards and F. G. Jackson, *Zeit. phys. Chem.*, **70**. 414, 1910 ; H. Schimpff, *ib.*, **71**. 257, 1910 ; F. Lange, *ib.*, **110**. 343, 1924 ; J. N. Brönsted, *ib.*, **88**. 479, 1914 ; *Zeit. Elektrochem.*, **18**. 714, 1912 ; W. A. Tilden, *Phil. Trans.*, **203**. A, 139, 1904 ; E. H. and E. Griffiths, *ib.*, **213**. 119, 1913 ; *Proc. Roy. Soc.*, **88**. A, 549, 1913 ; W. Jäger and H. Diesselhorst, *Wiss. Abhand. Phys. Tech. Reichsanst.*, **3**. 269, 1900 ; E. Bède, *Mém. Acad. Belg.*, **27**. 1, 1855 ; P. Schübel, *Zeit. anorg. Chem.*, **87**. 81, 1914 ; I. Iitaka, *Science Rep. Tohoku Univ.*, **8**. 99, 1919.

[16] G. A. Erman, *Rationis quæ inter volumina corporis ejusdem : solidi, liquescenti, liquidi, intercedit*, Berolensis, 1826 ; *Pogg. Ann.*, **9**. 557, 1827 ; *Quart. Journ. Science*, **1**. 404, 1829 ; J. Crichton, *Phil. Mag.*, **15**. 147, 1803 ; **16**. 48, 1803 ; L. B. G. de Morveau, *Ann. Chim. Phys.*, (1), **71**. 189, 1809 ; *Mém. l'Inst.*, **12**. ii, 89, 1811 ; C. C. Person, *ib.*, (3), **24**. 122, 1848 ; A. T. Kupffer, *ib.*, (2), **25**. 356, 1824 ; F. Rudberg, *Liebig's Ann.*, **64**. 183, 1848 ; L. I. Dana and P. D. Foote, *Trans. Faraday Soc.*, **15**. 186, 1920 ; J. F. Daniell, *Phil. Trans.*, **120**. 257, 1830 ; **121**. 443, 1831 ; *Phil. Mag.*, (3), **11**. 191, 268, 350, 1830 ; A. van Riemsdijk, *Chem. News*, **20**. 32, 1869 ; *Arch. Néerl*, **3**. 357, 1868 ; F. Nies and A. Winkelmann, *Wied. Ann.*, **13**. 43, 1881 ; J. Pionchon, *Compt. Rend.*, **103**. 1122, 1886 ; *Ann. Chim. Phys.*, (6), **11**. 106, 1887 ; W. R. Fielding, *Chem. News*, **122**. 289, 1921 ; **123**. 1, 1921 ; C. T. Heycock and F. H. Neville, *Journ. Chem. Soc.*, **67**. 190, 1895 ; *Phil. Trans.*, **202**. A, 1, 1903 ; E. Cohen and E. Goldschmidt, *Chem. Weekbl.*, **1**. 437, 1904 ; *Zeit. phys. Chem.*, **50**. 225, 1904 ; E. Jänecke, *ib.*, **90**. 257, 313, 1915 ; W. R. Mott, *Trans. Amer. Electrochem. Soc.*, **34**. 255, 1918 ; G. Tammann, *Zeit. anorg. Chem.*, **40**. 45, 1904 ; G. Hindrichs, *ib.*, **59**. 416, 1908 ; G. J. Petrenko, *ib.*, **53**. 210, 1907 ; R. Vogel, *ib.*, **46**. 64, 1905 ; A. G. C. Gwyer, *ib.*, **49**. 315, 1906 ; A. Bucher, *ib.*, **98**. 117, 1916 ; R. Lorenz and D. Plumbridge, *ib.*, **83**. 243, 1913 ; A. Stoffel, *ib.*, **53**. 148, 1907 ; E. Tiede and E. Birnbräuer, *ib.*, **87**. 129, 1914 ; R. Lorenz and W. Herz, *ib.*, **135**. 374, 1924 ; W. von Lepkowsky, *ib.*, **59**. 287, 1908 ; L. Donsky, *ib.*, **57**. 213, 1908 ; K. Lewkonja, *ib.*, **59**. 298, 1908 ; S. F. Schemtschuschny and S. W. Belynsky, *ib.*, **59**. 368, 1908 ; E. Isaac and G. Tammann, *ib.*, **53**. 285, 1907 ; W. J. van Heteren, *ib.*, **42**. 129, 1904 ; D. P. Smith, *ib.*, **56**. 131, 1908 ; G. Grube, *ib.*, **46**. 79, 1905 ; N. S. Kurnakoff and N. I. Stephanoff, *ib.*, **46**. 184, 1905 ; R. S. Williams, *ib.*, **55**. 26, 1907 ; C. H. Mathewson, *ib.*, **46**. 101, 1905 ; G. Voss, *ib.*, **57**. 38, 1908 ; P. N. Degens, *ib.*, **63**. 212, 1909 ; W. Biltz and W. Mecklenburg, *ib.*, **64**. 231, 1909 ; S. Tamaru, *ib.*, **61**. 42, 1909 ; P. Bogaderoff, *Proc. Russ. Phys. Chem. Soc.*, **25**. 7, 1893 ; H. Endo, *Journ. Inst. Metals*, **30**. 121, 1923 ; G. von Hevesy, *Zeit. phys. Chem.*, **101**. 337, 1922 ; N. Parravano and P. de Cesaris, *Internat. Zeit. Metallog.*, **2**. 1, 1912 ; D. Mazzotto, *ib.*, **4**. 13, 1913 ; A. P. Schleicher, *ib.*, **2**. 76, 1912 ; W. Guertler and M. Pirani, *ib.*, **11**. 1, 1919 ; W. Guertler, *Zeit. Elektrochem.*, **15**. 129, 1909 ; K. Scheel, *Zeit. angew. Chem.*, **32**. 347, 1919 ; E. S. Shepherd and E. Blough, *Journ. Phys. Chem.*, **10**. 630, 1906 ; F. Giolitti and G. Tavanti, *Gazz. Chim. Ital.*, **38**. ii, 209, 1908 ; P. H. Dowling, *Phys. Rev.*, (2), **25**. 812, 1925 ; L. Losana, *Gazz. Chim. Ital.*, **53**. ii, 393, 1923 ; G. Vicentini and D. Omodei, *Atti Accad. Torino*, **23**. 38, 1888 ; P. G. J. Gueterbock and G. N. Nicklin, *Journ. Chem. Soc. Ind.*, **44**. 370, T, 1925 ; H. L. Callendar, *Phil. Mag.*, (5), **48**. 519, 1899 ; E. H. Griffiths, *Proc. Roy. Soc.*, **48**. 220, 1890 ; C. W. Waidner and G. K. Burgess, *Bull. Bur. Standards*, **6**. 162, 1909 ; P. R. Heyl, *Phys. Rev.*, (1), **19**. 281, 1904 ; L. Holborn and F. Henning, *Ann. Physik*, (4), **35**. 761, 1911 ; L. H. Adams and J. Johnston, *Amer. Journ. Science*, (4), **31**. 501, 1911 ; (4), **33**. 534, 1912 ; J. Johnston, *Journ. Amer. Chem. Soc.*, **34**. 788, 1912.

[17] T. Carnelley and W. C. Williams, *Journ. Chem. Soc.*, **35**. 563, 1879 ; E. Demarçay, *Compt. Rend.*, **95**. 183, 1882 ; H. Moissan, *ib.*, **116**. 1429, 1893 ; **141**. 980, 1905 ; H. Moissan and A. J. P. O'Farrelley, *ib.*, **138**. 1659, 1904 ; H. Moissan and P. Watanabe, *ib.*, **144**. 18, 1907 ; A. Schuller, *Wied. Ann.*, **18**. 317, 1883 ; *Zeit. anorg. Chem.*, **37**. 69, 1903 ; H. von Wartenberg, *ib.*, **56**. 330, 1907 ; O. Ruff and B. Bergdahl, *ib.*, **106**. 76, 1919 ; O. Ruff and S. Mugdan, *ib.*, **117**. 147, 1921 ; J. A. M. van Liempt, *ib.*, **114**. 105, 1920 ; E. Tiede and E. Birnbräuer, *ib.*, **87**. 129, 1914 ; C. Zengelis, *Zeit. phys. Chem.*, **50**. 219, 1904 ; A. Henglein, *Zeit. Elektrochem.*, **26**. 431, 1920 ; P. G. J. Gueterbock and G. N. Nicklin, *Journ. Chem. Soc. Ind.*, **44**. 350, T, 1925 ; F. Krafft, *Ber.*, **36**. 1704, 1903 ; H. C. Greenwood, *Proc. Roy. Soc.*, **82**. A, 396, 1909 ; G. W. A. Kahlbaum, *Phys. Zeit.*, **1**. 63, 1899 ; *Zeit. anorg. Chem.*, **29**. 182, 1902 ; M. R. Mott, *Trans. Amer. Electrochem. Soc.*, **34**. 255, 1918 ; J. J. van Laar, *Proc. Acad. Amsterdam*, **18**. 1220, 1916 ; **20**. 138, 492, 1918 ; E. Wertheimer, *Ber. deut. phys. Ges.*, **21**. 692, 1919 ; H. F. Wiebe, *Ber.*, **12**. 788, 1879 ; E. Tiede and F. Fischer, *Ber.*, **144**. 1711, 1911 ; J. Johnston, *Journ. Ind. Eng. Chem.*, **9**. 873, 1917 ; W. G. Duffield, *Phil. Mag.*, (6), **45**. 1104, 1923.

[18] C. C. Person, *Ann. Chim. Phys.*, (3), **24**. 36, 156, 1848 ; F. Rudberg, *Pogg. Ann.*, **19**. 125, 1830 ; D. Mazzotto, *Mem. 1st. Lombardo*, **16**. 29, 1886 ; F. W. Robertson, *Journ. Chem. Soc.*, **81**. 1241, 1902 ; J. Pionchon, *Ann. Chim. Phys.*, (6), **11**. 106, 1887 ; J. W. Richards, *Journ. Franklin Inst.*, **143**. 379, 1897 ; *Chem. News*, **68**. 58, 69, 82, 93, 105, 1893 ; J. Guinchant, *Compt. Rend.*, **145**. 320, 1907 ; W. Spring, *Bull. Acad. Belg.*, (3), **11**. 355, 1886 ; J. A. M. van Liempt, *Zeit. anorg. Chem.*, **114**. 105, 1920 ; E. D. Eastman, *Journ. Amer. Chem. Soc.*, **45**. 80, 1923 ; G. N. Lewis, G. E. Gibson, and G. M. Latimer, *ib.*, **44**. 1008, 1922 ; J. H. Hildebrand, *ib.*, **40**. 84, 1918 ; A. Henglein, *Zeit. Elektrochem.*, **26**. 431, 1920 ; W. Herz, *ib.*, **25**. 45, 1919.

[19] P. Drude, *Wied. Ann.*, **39**. 481, 1890 ; G. Quincke, *Pogg. Ann. Jubelbd.*, 336, 1874 ; W. W. Coblentz, *Bull. Bur. Standards*, **2**. 457, 1906 ; **7**. 197, 1911 ; A. Haagen, *Pogg. Ann.*, **131**. 117, 1867 ; A. Ghira, *Atti Accad. Lincei*, (3), **3**. i, 332, 1894 ; E. van Aubel, *Zeit. Phys. Chem.*, **30**. 565, 1899 ; E. Conroy, *Proc. Roy. Soc.*, **35**. 26, 1883 ; **37**. 36, 1884 ; J. H. Gladstone, *ib.*, **18**. 49, 1869 ; *Phil. Trans.*, **159**. 13, 1869 ; M. Faraday, *ib.*, **147**. 145, 1857 ; F. H. de la Provostaye

and E. F. Desains, *Ann. Chim. Phys.*, (3), **30**. 431, 1850 ; **A**. K. Aster, *Phys. Rev.*, (2), **20**. 349, 1922 ; H. von Wartenberg, *Verh. deut. phys. Ges.*, **102**. 105, 1910.
20 N. R. Campbell, *Phil. Mag.*, (6), **9**. 531. 1905 ; (6), **11**. 206, 1906 ; C. G. Barkla, *ib.*, (6), **11**. 812, 1906 ; T. C. Sutton, *ib.*, (6), **29**. 734, 1915 ; C. G. Barkla and A. E. M. M. Dallas, *ib.*, (6), **47**. 1, 1924 ; W. H. Bragg, *Proc. Phys. Soc.*, **34**. 51, 1922 ; *Phil. Mag.*, (6), **11**. 617, 1906 ; J. Crowther, *ib.*, (6), **12**. 379, 1906 ; A. H. Compton, *ib.*, (6), **46**. 897, 1923 ; A. S. Russell and F. Soddy, *ib.*, (6), **21**. 130, 1911 ; C. G. Barkla and C. A. Sadler, *ib.*, (6), **17**. 739, 1909 ; W. Ramsay and J. F. Spencer, *ib.*, (6), **12**. 397, 1906 ; T. C. Sutton, *ib.*, (6), **29**. 734, 1915 ; J. Borgmann, *Journ. Russ. Phys. Chem. Soc.*, **37**. 77, 1905 ; D. Hurmuzesca, *Ann. Sciene Jassy*, **3**. 258, 1906 ; R. L. Vanzetti, *Atti Accad. Lincei*, (5), **17**. ii, 285, 1908 ; W. J. Russell, *Chem. News*, **75**. 302, 1897 ; K. Herrmann, *Beiträge zum Hallwachseffekt*, Berlin, 1908 ; G. Reboul, *Compt. Rend.*, **158**. 477, 1914 ; A. E. Hennings and W. H. Kadesch, *Phys. Rev.*, (2), **8**. 209, 1916 ; N. Admad, *Proc. Roy. Soc.*, **105**. A, 508, 1924 ; G. A. Dima, *Bull Soc. Stiinte Clui*, **1**. 321, 1922 ; R. Hamer, *Journ. Amer. Opt. Soc.*, **9**. 251, 1924 ; M. de Broglie, *Nature*, **115**. 461, 1925 ; N. Piltschikoff, *Phys. Zeit.*, **7**. 69, 1906.
21 H. Ramage, *Chem. News*, **89**. 253, 1904 ; C. Wheatstone, *ib.*, **3**. 198, 1861 ; *Phil. Mag.*, (3), **7**. 299, 1835 ; C. C. Hutchins and E. L. Holden, *ib.*, (5), **24**. 325, 1887 ; W. F. Barrett, *ib.*, (4), **30**. 327, 1865 ; H. Crew and R. Tátnall, *ib.*, (5), **38**. 379, 1894 ; *Astron. Astrophys.*, **13**. 741, 1894 ; P. Zeeman, *Metingen over Strahlings verschijnselen in het magnetisch veld*, Amsterdam, 1897 ; *Phil. Mag.*, (5), **45**. 197, 1898 ; *Versl. Akad. Amsterdam*, **6**. 408, 1897 ; A. Masson, *Ann. Chim. Phys.*, (3), **31**. 295, 1851 ; G. Salet, *ib.*, (4), **28**. 5, 1873 ; *Compt. Rend.*, **71**. ; A. Ditte, *ib.*, **73**. 738, 1871 ; L. de Boisbaudran, *ib.*, **77**. 937, 1873 ; *Spectres lumineux*, Paris, 1874 ; R. Capron, *Photographed Spectra*, London, 1877 ; J. Parry and E. Tucker, *Engg.*, **27**. 127, 429, 1879 ; **28**. 141, 1879 ; A. J. Angström, *Svenska Akad. Handl.*, **229**, 1853 ; *Pogg. Ann.*, **94**. 141, 1855 ; J. Plücker, *ib.*, **107**. 497, 738, 1859 ; A. Mitscherlich, *ib.*, **121**. 459, 1864 ; C. E. Gissing, *Spark Spectra of the Metals*, London, 1910 ; R. J. Strutt, *Proc. Roy. Soc.*, **85**. A, 219, 1911 ; G. Kirchhoff, *Sitzber. Akad. Berlin*, **63**, 1861 ; 227, 1863 ; H. Kayser and C. Runge, *ib.*, **7**, 1893 ; *Wied. Ann.*, **52**. 93, 1894 ; L. Arons, *ib.*, **58**. 73, 1896 ; A. Kalähne, *ib.*, **65**. 815, 1898 ; D. Alter, *Amer. Journ. Science*, (2), **18**. 55, 1854 ; F. R. Robinson, *Phil. Trans.*, **152**. 939, 1862 ; R. J. Lang, *ib.*, **224**. A, 371, 1924 ; W. A. Miller, *ib.*, **152**. 861, 1862 ; W. Huggins, *ib.*, **154**. 139, 1864 ; J. N. Lockyer, *ib.*, **163**. 253, 1873 ; *Compt. Rend.*, **86**. 317, 1878 ; *Proc. Roy. Soc.*, **27**. 279, 1878 ; J. N. Lockyer and W. C. Roberts-Austen, *ib.*, **23**. 344, 1875 ; W. N. Hartley, *ib.*, **54**. 5, 1893 ; *Trans. Roy. Soc., Dublin*, (2), **1**. 231, 1883 ; (2), **9**. 88, 1906 ; *Journ. Chem. Soc.*, **41**. 84, 1882 ; *Phil. Trans.*, **175**. 325, 1884 ; **185**. A, 151, 1894 ; W. N. Hartley and W. E. Ardeney, *ib.*, **175**. 63, 1884 ; F. Brasack, *Abhand. Nat. Ges. Halle*, **9**. 1, 1864 ; R. Thalén, *Om Spectralanalyse*, Upsala, 1866 ; *Ann. Chim. Phys.*, (4), **18**. 237, 1866 ; *Nova Acta Soc. Upsaia*, (3), **6**. 9, 1868 ; A. Gouy, *Compt. Rend.*, **85**. 439, 1877 ; H. Becquerel, *ib.*, **97**. 71, 1883 ; **99**. 374, 1884 ; *Ann. Chim. Phys.*, (5), **30**. 5, 1883 ; H. Deslandres, *ib.*, (6), **15**. 5, 1888 ; P. Joye, *ib.*, (8), **21**. 148, 1910 ; *Influence de l'intensité maximum du courant sur le spectre de la décharge oscillante*, Freiburg, 1910 ; G. D. Liveing and J. Dewar, *Proc. Roy. Soc.*, **34**. 119, 1882 ; *Phil. Trans.*, **174**. 187, 1883 ; V. Schumann, *Phot. Rund.*, **41**. 71, 1890 ; J. M. Eder, *Denks. Akad. Wien*, **60**. 1, 1893 ; **68**. 531, 1899 ; J. M. Eder and E. Valenta, *Atlas typisches Spectren*, Wien, 1911 ; *Sitzber. Akad. Wien*, **118**. 511, 1077, 1909 ; **119**. 519, 1910 ; E. Haschek, *ib.*, **111**. 232, 1902 ; F. Exner and E. Haschek, *ib.*, **106**. 54, 1897 ; *Wellenlängentabellen zu spectralanalytischen Untersuchungen auf Grund der ultravioletten Funkenspectren der Elemente*, Leipzig, 1904 ; *Wellenlängentabellen zu spectranalytischen Untersuchungen auf Grund der ultravioletten Bogenspectren der Elemente*, Leipzig, 1904 ; *Die Spectren der Elemente bei normalen Druck*, Leipzig, 1912 ; O. Vogel, *Zeit. anorg. Chem.*, **5**. 42, 1894 ; W. von Bolton, *Zeit. Elektrochem.*, **9**. 913, 1903 ; A. A. Michelson, *Nature*, **59**. 440, 1899 ; N. K. Sur and R. K. Sharma, *Journ. Science Assoc. Vizianagaram*, **1**. 121, 1924 ; E. Demarçay, *Spectres électriques*, Paris, 1895 ; A. de Gramont, *Analyse directe spectrale des minéraux*, Paris, 1895 ; *Bull. Soc. Min.*, **18**. 216, 1895 ; *Compt. Rend.*, **144**. 1101, 1907 ; **170**. 31, 1920 ; E. Néculcéa, *Recherches théoretiques et expérimentales zur la constitution des spectres ultraviolettes d'étincelles oscillantes*, Paris, 1906 ; *Compt. Rend.*, **135**. 25, 1902 ; C. de Watteville, *ib.*, **135**. 1329, 1902 ; *Spectres de flammes*, Paris, 1904 ; *Phil. Trans.*, **204**. A, 139, 1904 ; S. R. Milner, *ib.*, **209**. A, 71, 1908 ; *Proc. Roy. Soc.*, **81**. A, 299, 1908 ; T. Royds, *ib.*, **107**. A, 360, 1925 ; W. J. Humphreys, *Astrophys. Journ.*, **6**. 169, 1897 ; O. H. Besquin, *ib.*, **14**. 1, 1901 ; P. Lewis, *ib.*, **16**. 31, 1902 ; R. A. Porter, *ib.*, **15**. 274, 1902 ; H. W. Morse, *ib.*, **19**. 162, 1904 ; **21**. 223, 1905 ; P. G. Nutting, *ib.*, **33**. 64, 220, 1906 ; H. M. Randall, *ib.*, **34**. 1, 1911 ; H. Kayser and C. Runge, *Sitzber. Akad. Berlin*, **3**, 1893 ; *Wied. Ann.*, **52**. 93, 1894 ; G. A. Hemsalech and A. de Gramont, *Phil. Mag.*, (6), **43**. 287, 1922 ; G. A. Hemsalech, *Recherches expérimentales sur les spectres d'étincelles*, Paris, 1901 ; W. von der Seipen, *Ueber das Flammenspectrum des Zinns*, Bonn, 1906 ; *Zeit. wiss. Photochem.*, **5**. 69, 1907 ; J. Steinhausen, *ib.*, **3**. 45, 1905 ; *Ueber "enhanced lines*," Bonn, 1904 ; G. Berndt, *Ueber den Einfluss von Selbstinduction auf die durch den Inductionsfunken erzengten Metallspectra im Ultraviolett*, Halle, 1901 ; H. Nagaoka and Y. Sugiura, *Science Papers Inst. Phys.*, **2**. 139, 1924 ; M. Kimura, *Japan. Journ. Phys.*, **3**. 217, 1924 ; P. Zonta, *Nuovo Cimento*, (5), **7**. 321, 1904 ; A. Hagenbach and H. Konen, *Atlas der Emissionsspectra*, Jena, 1905 ; C. Keller, *Zeit. wiss. Photochem.*, **4**. 209, 1906 ; W. Gallenkamp, *ib.*, **5**. 299, 1907 ; R. Arnolds, *ib.*, **13**. 313, 1914 ; P. Klein, *ib.*, **12**. 16, 1913 ; H. Finger, *ib.*, **7**. 329, 369, 1909 ; *Verh. deut. phys. Ges.*, **11**. 369, 1909 ; H. Konen and H. Finger, *Zeit. Elektrochem.*, **15**. 165, 1909 ; J. E. Purvis, *Proc. Phil. Soc. Cambridge*, **13**. 82,

1905 ; **14**. 216, 1907 ; S. K. Mitra, *Ann. Physique*, (9), **19**. 315, 1923 ; F. M. Walters, *Scient. Papers Bur. Standards*, **17**. 161, 1921 : L. and E. Bloch, *Compt. Rend.*, **174**. 1456, 1922 ; **177**. 1025, 1923 ; *Journ. Phys. Rad.*, (6), **2**. 229, 1921 ; O. Schmatolla, *Chem. Ztg.*, **25**. 468, 1901 ; L. Janicki, *Ann. Physik*, (4), **29**. 833, 1909 ; B. Huber, *Einfluss der Selbstinduction auf die Spectren von Metallen und besonders von Legirungen*, Freiburg, 1909 ; F. Handke, *Untersuchungen im Gebiete der Schumannstrahlen*, Berlin, 1909 ; A. Fowler, *Series in Line Spectra*, London, 163, 1922 ; H. Kayser, *Handbuch der Spectroscopie*, Leipzig, **6**. 509, 1912 ; J. Formanek, *Die Qualitative Spektralanalyse anorganischer und organischer Körper*, Berlin, 152, 1905 ; T. von Lohuizen, *Proc. Acad. Amsterdam*, **15**. 31, 1912 ; W. Grotrian, *Zeit. Physik*, **18**. 169, 1923 ; V. P. Lubovich and E. M. Pearen, *Trans. Roy. Soc. Canada*, (3), **16**. 195, 1922 ; J. C. McLennan and R. V. Zumstein, *ib.*, (3), **15**. 3941, 1920 ; J. C. McLennan, J. F. T. Young, and A. F. T. McLay, *ib.*, (3), **18**. 57, 1924 ; J. C. McLennan, J. F. T. Young, and H. J. C. Ireton, *ib.*, (3), **13**. 7, 1919 ; R. V. Zumstein, *ib.*, (3), **12**. 59, 1918 ; P. A. van der Harst, *Proc. Akad. Amsterdam*, **22**. 300, 1920 ; B. de la Roche, *Bull. Soc. Chim.*, (4), **25**. 305, 1919 ; E. O. Hulburt, *Phys. Rev.*, (2), **24**. 129, 1924 ; R. V. Zumstein, *ib.*, (2), **27**. 50, 1926 ; H. Sponer, *Zeit. Physik*, **32**. 19, 1925 ; F. Hund, *ib.*, **33**, 345, 345, 1925 ; J. A. Carroll, *Phil. Trans.*, **225**. A, 357, 1926 ; S. Smith, *Astrophys. Journ.*, **61**. 186, 1925 ; W. Jevons, *Proc. Roy. Soc.*, **110**. A, 365, 1926 ; J. C. Frayne and A. W. Smith, *Phil. Mag.*, (7), **1**. 732, 1926 ; J. K. Robertson, *ib.*, (7), **1**. 752, 1926 ; A. L. Narayan and K. R. Rao, *ib.*, (6), **50**. 645, 1925 ; A. E. Ruark and R. L. Chenault, *ib.*, (6), **50**, 943, 1925 ; K. Kimura and G. Nakamura, *Science Papers Japan. Inst. Phys. Chem. Research*, **3**. 51, 1925.

²² H. Robinson, *Proc. Roy. Soc.*, **104**. A, 455, 1923 ; N. Bohr and D. Coster, *Zeit. Physik*, **12**. 342, 1923 ; E. Hjalmar, *ib.*, **1**. 439, 1920 ; **7**. 341, 1921 ; K. A. Wingardti, **8**. 363, 1922 ; A. H. Compton, *Phil. Mag.*, (6), **46**. 897, 1923 ; G. Shearer, *ib.*, (6), **44**. 793, 1922 ; H. G. J. Moseley, *ib.*, (6), **26**. 1024, 1913 ; (6), **27**. 703, 1914 ; E. Friman, *Die Hochfrequenzspektra der Elemente*, Lund, 1916 ; *Ann. Physik*, (4), **49**. 616, 1916 ; *Phil. Mag.*, (6), **32**. 497, 1916 ; J. E. P. Wagstaff, *ib.*, (6), **47**. 84, 1924 ; C. G. Barkla and A. E. M. M. Dallas, *ib.*, (6), **47**. 1, 1924 ; D. Coster, *Compt. Rend.*, **174**. 378, 1922 ; *Zeit. Physik*, **25**. 83, 1924 ; M. de Broglie, *ib.*, **174**. 939, 1922 ; A. Leide, *ib.*, **180**. 1203, 1925 ; M. Siegbahn, *Jahrb. Rad. Elektron.*, **13**. 296, 1916 ; **18**. 240, 1921 ; M. Siegbahn and E. Jönsson, *Phys. Zeit.*, **20**. 251, 1919 ; F. C. Blake and W. Duane, *Phys. Rev.*, (2), **10**. 98, 697, 1917 ; S. J. M. Allen, *ib.*, (2), **23**. 291, 1924 ; F. W. Warburton and F. K. Richtmyer, *ib.*, (2), **23**. 291, 1924 ; F. K. Richtmyer, *ib.*, (2), **27**. 1, 1926 ; H. Kulenkampff, *Ann. Physik*, (4), **69**. 548, 1922 ; S. K. Mitra, *Ann Chim. Phys.*, (9), **19**. 315, 1923 ; E. C. Stoner and L. H. Martin, *Proc. Roy. Soc.*, **107**. A, 312, 1925 ; E. C. Stoner, *Phil. Mag.*, (6), **48**. 719, 1924 ; B. B. Ray, *ib.*, (6), **48**. 707, 1924 ; Y. Nishina, *ib.*, (6), **49**. 521, 1925 ; K. Lang, *Ann. Physik*, (4), **75**. 489, 1924 ; E. A. Owen, N. Fleming, and W. E. Fage, *Proc. Phys. Soc.*, **36**. 355, 1924 ; M. Kimura and G. Nakamura, *Japan. Journ. Phys.*, **3**. 29, 43, 1924 ; R. Berthold, *Ann. Physik*, (4), **76**. 409, 1925 ; H. R. von Traubenberg, *Zeit. Physik*, **2**. 268, 1920 ; B. Walter, *ib.*, **30**. 357, 1924 ; K. Chamberlain, *Phys. Rev.*, (2), **26**. 525, 1925 ; J. M. Cork and B. R. Stevenson, *ib.*, (2), **27**. 106, 530, 1926 ; S. J. M. Allen, *ib.*, (2), **27**. 266, 1926 ; A. L. Foley, *Proc. Indiana Acad.*, **34**. 185, 1925.

²³ A. C. Becquerel, *Ann. Chim. Phys.*, (3), **17**. 262, 1846 ; A. Coehn and A. Curs, *Zeit. Physik*, **29**. 186, 1924 ; A. Matthiessen, *Phil. Mag.*, (4), **16**. 219, 1858 ; *Pogg. Ann.*, **103**. 428, 1858 ; W. von Siemens, *ib.*, **113**. 91, 1861 ; E. F. Northrup and V. A. Suydam, *Journ. Franklin Inst.*, **175**. 152, 1913 : L. Weiller. *Dingler's Journ.*, **253**. 134, 1884 ; *Elektrotech. Zeit.*, **3**. 83, 157, 1882 ; P. Müller, *ib.*, **13**. 72, 1892 ; *Met.*, **7**. 730, 1910 ; J. R. Benoit, *Arch. Sciences Genève*, (2), **51**. 284, 1874 ; *Etudes expérimentales sur la résistance électrique des métaux et sa variation sous l'influence de la temperature*, Paris, 1873 ; *Compt. Rend.*, **76**. 342, 1873 ; L. Cailletet and E. Bouty, *ib.*, **100**. 1188, 1885 ; L. Guillet and M. Ballay, *ib.*, **176**. 1800, 1923 ; *Rev. Mét.*, **20**. 398, 1923 : H. F. Weber, *Sitzber. Akad. Berlin*, 457, 1880 ; G. Kirchhoff and G. Hausemann, *Wied. Ann.*, **13**. 406, 1881 ; A. Oberbeck and J. Bergmann, *ib.*, **31**. 792, 1887 ; L. Lorenz, *ib.*, **13**. 582, 1881 ; K. Noll, *ib.*, **53**. 874, 1894 ; P. G. J. Gueterbock and G. N. Nicklin, *Journ. Soc. Chem. Ind.*, **44**. 350, T, 1925 ; P. W. Bridgman, *Proc. Amer. Acad.*, **52**. 573, 1917 ; **53**. 269, 1918 ; **61**. 101, 1926 ; *Proc. Nat. Acad.*, **10**. 411, 1925 ; **11**. 608, 1925 ; *Journ. Washington Acad.*, **11**. 455, 1921 ; A. T. Waterman, *Phys. Rev.*, (2), **22**. 259, 1923 ; E. D. Williamson, *Journ. Franklin Inst.*, **193**. 491, 1923 ; G. Vassura, *Nuovo Cimento*, (3), **31**. 25, 1892 ; G. Vicentini and D. Omodei, *Atti Accad. Torino*, **25**. 30, 1890 ; P. Cermak, *Ann. Physik*, (4), **26**. 521, 1908 ; G. Borelius and F. Gunneson, *ib.*, (4), **65**. 520, 1921 ; F. A. Schulze, *ib.*, (4), **9**. 555, 1902 ; *Zeit. Metallkunde*, **15**. 33, 155, 1923 ; **16**. 48, 1924 ; *Ueber das Verhalten einiger Legierungen zum Gesetz von Wiedmann und Franz*, Marburg, 1902 ; H. Ihle, *Jahresb. Gymn. Dresden-Neustadt*, **3**. 1896 ; W. H. Preece, *Proc. Roy. Soc.*, **44**. 109, 1888 ; Z. A. Epstein, *Zeit. Physik*, **32**. 620, 1925 ; J. Dewar and J. A. Fleming, *Phil. Mag.*, (5), **36**. 271, 1893 ; (5), **40**. 111, 1895 ; W. H. Steele, *ib.*, (5), **37**. 218, 1894 ; H. Dickson, *ib.*, (5), **45**. 525, 1898 ; W. Jäger and H. Diesselhorst, *Abhand. Phys. Tech. Reichsanst.*, **3**. 269, 1900 ; O. Jaamaa and Y. E. G. Leinberg, *Comment. Phys. Math. Soc. Fenn.*, **1**. 21, 1922 ; T. R. Harrison, *Phys. Rev.*, (2), **21**. 106, 1923 ; P. H. Dowling, *ib.*, (2), **25**. 812, 1925 ; L. Grunmach and F. Weidert, *Ber. deut. phys. Ges.*, **4**. 359, 1907 ; N. A. Heschus, *Journ. Russ. Phys. Chem. Soc.*, **39**. 1, 1907 ; B. L. Rosing, *ib.*, **30**. 100, 1898 ; C. G. Knott, *Trans. Roy. Soc. Edin.*, **30**. 271, 1879 ; P. Cermak, *Ann. Physik*, (4), **26**. 521, 1908 ; E. Wagner, *ib.*, (4), **27**. 955, 1908 ; B. Beckman, *ib.*, (4), **46**. 481, 931, 1915 ; *Ark. Mat. Astron. Fysik*, **7**. 42, 1912 ; *Phys. Zeit.*, **16**. 59, 1915 ; P. Räthjen, *ib.*, **25**. 84, 1924 ; N. J. Stepanoff, *Zeit. anorg. Chem.*, **60**. 209, 1908 ; **78**. 1, 1912 ; E. Rudolfi, *ib.*, **67**. 65, 1910 ; A. Stein, *Phys. Zeit.*, **13**. 287, 1912 ; W. Haken, *Ann. Physik*,

(4), **32.** 291, 1910 ; E. Wagner, *ib.*, **(4), 27.** 955, 1908 ; P. G. Tait, *Trans. Roy. Soc. Edin.*, **27.** 125, 1873 ; E. Edlund, *Pogg. Ann.*, **140.** 435, 1870 ; **143.** 404, 534, 1871 ; Y. E. G. Leinberg, *Soc. Sci. Fenn. Comment.*, **1.** 21, 1922 ; C. A. Crommelin, *Jahrb. Rad. Elektron.*, **19.** 38, 1922 ; H. K. Onnes, *Comm. Phys. Lab. Leiden Univ.*, **10.** 119, 120 b, 1911 ; **11.** 122 b, 124 c, 1911 ; **12.** 133, a, b, c, d, 1913 ; **13.** 13 f, 140 b, c, 141 b, 1914 ; *Suppl.*, **13.** 29, 1911 ; **13.** 34 b, 35, 1913 ; H. K. Onnes and G. Holst, *Comm. Phys. Lab. Leiden Univ.*, 142, 1914 ; W. Tuyn and H. K. Onnes, *Journ. Franklin Inst.*, **201.** 379, 1926 ; *Proc. Acad. Amsterdam*, **26.** 504, 1923 ; G. J. Sizoo and H. K. Onnes, *ib.*, **28.** 656, 1925 ; A. Schulze, *Zeit. Metallkunde*, **16.** 48, 1924 ; C. Benedicks, *Internat. Zeit. Metallog.*, **7.** 225, 1915 ; H. Pélabon, *Compt. Rend.*, **176.** 1305, 1923 ; *Ann. Physique*, (9), **13.** 169, 1920 ; A. Smits and J. Spuyman, *Proc. Acad. Amsterdam*, **23.** 687, 1921 ; R. D. Kleeman and W. Fredrickson, *Phys. Rev.*, (2), **22.** 134, 1923 ; M. O'Day, *ib.*, (2), **23.** 245, 1924 ; S. Smith, *Astrophys. Journ.*, **61.** 186, 1925 ; L. J. Neuman, *Phys. Rev.*, (2), **27.** 643, 1926.
²⁴ N. T. M. Wilsmore, *Zeit. phys. Chem.*, **35.** 291, 1900 ; B. Neumann, *ib.*, **14.** 218, 1894 ; A. Günther-Schulze, *Ann. Physik*, (4), **24.** 43, 1907 ; E. F. Herroun, *Phil. Mag.*, (5), **21.** 15, 1886 ; C. R. A. Wright and C. Thompson, *ib.*, (5), **17.** 209, 1884 ; (5), **19.** 1, 1885 ; H. von Steinwehr, *Zeit. Instrk.*, **33.** 321, 1915 ; E. Müller, *Zeit. anorg. Chem.*, **26.** 28, 1901 ; N. R. Dhar, *ib.*, **118.** 75, 1921 ; G. Tammann, *ib.*, **133.** 267, 1924 ; A. Fischer, *ib.*, **42.** 400, 1904 ; A. A. Noyes and K. Toabe, *Journ. Amer. Chem. Soc.*, **39.** 1537, 1917 ; A. Oberbeck and J. Edler, *Wied. Ann.*, **42.** 209, 1891 ; W. Ostwald, *Grundriss der allgemeinen Chemie*, Leipzig, 281, 1899 ; *Zeit. phys. Chem.*, **11.** 501, 1893 ; G. Magnanini, *Rend. Accad. Lincei*, (4), **6.** 182, 1890 ; *Gazz. Chim. Ital.*, **20.** 308, 1890 ; F. Förster and J. Yamasaki, *Zeit. Elektrochem.*, **17.** 361, 1911 ; O. Sackur, *Arb. Gesundh*, **20.** 539, 1903 ; A. Coehn and A. Lotz, *Zeit. Physik*, **5.** 242, 1921 ; A. Volta, *Gilbert's Ann.*, **10.** 421, 1802 ; F. W. Bergstrom, *Journ. Amer. Chem. Soc.*, **47.** 1503, 1925 ; T. Seebeck, *Sitzber. Akad. Berlin*, 295, 1822 ; J. C. E. Péclet, *Ann. Chim. Phys.*, (3), **2.** 243, 1841 ; S. Avogadro and V. Michelotti, *ib.*, (2), **22.** 364, 1823 ; A. de la Rive, *ib.*, (2), **37.** 225, 1828 ; P. S. Munk, *Pogg. Ann.*, **35.** 55, 1835 ; C. H. Pfaff, *ib.*, **51.** 209, 1840 ; *Journ. Phys.*, **8.** 196, 1794 ; *De electricitate sic dicta animali*, Stuttgart, 1793 ; W. D. Harkins and H. S. Adams, *Journ. Phys. Chem.*, **29.** 205, 1925 ; J. M. Gaugain, *Compt. Rend.*, **59.** 493, 1864 ; J. W. Ritter, *Beiträge zur Kenntniss des Galvanismus*, Jena, **1.** 47, 1800 ; P. Marianini, *ib.*, **49.** 52, 1827 ; A. Naccari and M. Bellati, *Nuovo Cimento*, (2), **11.** 120, 1872 ; C. Hocken and H. A. Taylor, *Journ. Soc. Tel. Eng.*, **8.** 282, 1879 ; E. Newbery, *Journ. Chem. Soc.*, **109.** 1051, 1916 ; P. H. Dowling, *Phys. Rev.*, (2), **25.** 812, 1925 ; G. C. Schmidt, *Zeit. phys. Chem.*, **106.** 105, 1923 ; V. Rothmund, *ib.*, **110.** 384, 1924 ; C. F. Bucholz, *Allgem. Journ. Chem.*, **3.** 324, 1804 ; J. W. Ritter, *ib.*, **4.** 253, 1805 ; G. T. Fechner, *Schweigger's Journ.*, **53.** 61, 141, 1828 ; **57.** 9, 1829 ; *Pogg. Ann.*, **41.** 224, 1837 ; **42.** 481, 1837 ; C. F. Schönbein, *Phil. Mag.*, (3), **9.** 53, 1836 ; *ib.*, **37.** 390, 1836 ; G. Wetzlar, *Schweigger's Journ.*, **49.** 470, 1827 ; **50.** 88, 129, 1827 ; M. Eckardt and H. Goldschmidt, *Zeit. phys. Chem.*, **56.** 385, 1906 ; F. Förster and M. Dolch, *Zeit. Elektrochem.*, **16.** 599, 1910 ; R. Steinherz, *ib.*, **30.** 279, 1924 ; H. Davy, *Phil. Trans.*, **116.** 408, 1826 ; M. Faraday, *ib.*, **123.** 675, 1833 ; W. E. Ayrton and J. Perry, *ib.*, **171.** 1, 1880 ; *Proc. Roy. Soc.*, **27.** 196, 1878 ; W. Hankel, *Ber. Säch. Ges.*, **6.** 1, 1861 ; **7.** 385, 1865 ; *Pogg. Ann.*, **115.** 57, 1862 ; **126.** 286, 1865 ; J. C. Poggendorff, *ib.*, **50.** 263, 1840 ; **66.** 597, 1845 ; **73.** 619, 1848 ; C. F. Schönbein, *ib.*, **43.** 96, 1838 ; F. Exner and J. Tuma, *Sitzber. Akad. Wien*, **97.** 917, 1888 ; C. M. van Deventer, *Zeit. phys. Chem.*, **91.** 687, 1916 ; *Chem. Weekbl.*, **13.** 173, 1916 ; H. Pellat, *Compt. Rend.*, **80.** 990, 1880 ; *Difference de potentiel des couches électriques qui recouvert deux métaux au contact*, Paris, 1881 ; *Journ. Phys.*, (1), **10.** 68, 1881 ; N. R. Dhar, *Zeit. anorg. Chem.*, **118.** 75, 1921 ; A. Thiel and W. Hammerschmidt, *ib.*, **132.** 15, 1923 ; C. Hambuechen, *Chem. Met. Engg.*, **8.** 634, 1910 ; M. Dresbach and H. R. Hosmer, *Amer. Journ. Physiol.*, **68.** 122, 1924 ; M. Schlötter, *Metal Ind.*, **28.** 53, 1925 ; F. M unier, *Journ. Chim. Phys.*, **22.** 395, 1925.
²⁵ G. von Hevesy and R. Lorenz, *Zeit. phys. Chem.*, **74.** 443, 1910 ; F. Müller, *Journ. Russ. Phys. Chem. Soc.*, **39.** 267, 1907 ; F. Fischer and G. Iliovici, *ib.*, **41.** 4449, 1908 ; **42.** 342, 527, 1909 ; F. Fischer and O. Hähnel, *Zeit. Elektrochem.*, **14.** 366, 433, 1908 ; V. Kohlschütter, *ib.*, **12.** 869, 1906 ; **14.** 417, 437, 1908 ; V. Kohlschütter and T. Goldschmidt, *ib.*, **14.** 221, 1908 ; V. Kohlschütter and R. Müller, *ib.*, **12.** 365, 1906 ; V. L. Christler, *Astrophys. Journ.*, **54.** 273, 1921 ; R. D. Kleeman and W. Fredrickson, *Phys. Rev.*, (2), **22.** 134, 1923 ; W. Crookes, *Proc. Roy. Soc.*, **50.** 88, 1891 ; A. Günther-Schulze, *Ann. Physik*, (4), **24.** 43, 1907 ; (4), **65.** 233, 1921 ; J. Smrz, *Rec. Trav. Chim. Pays-Bas*, **44.** 580, 1925 ; W. Winter, *Phys. Zeit.*, **14.** 823, 1913.
²⁶ A. P. Wills, *Phil. Mag.*, (5), **45.** 432, 1898 ; *Phys. Rev.*, (1), **20.** 188, 1905 ; O. C. Clifford, *ib.*, (1), **26.** 424, 1908 ; S. Meyer, *Monatsh.*, **20.** 369, 797, 1899 ; *Wied. Ann.*, **68.** 325, 1899 ; **69.** 236, 1899 ; *Ann. Physik*, (4), **1.** 664, 1900 ; M. Owen, *ib.*, (4), **37.** 657, 1912 ; K. Honda, *ib.*, (4), **32.** 1027, 1910 ; *Science Rep. Tohoku Univ.*, **1.** 1, 1912 ; **2.** 25, 1913 ; **3.** 139, 223, 1914 ; **4.** 215, 1915 ; G. Quincke, *Wied. Ann.*, **24.** 347, 1885 ; **34.** 401, 1888 ; P. Pascal, *Compt. Rend.*, **158.** 1895, 1914 ; **159.** 129, 1914 ; A. Dauvillier, *ib.*, **176.** 1802, 1923 ; C. Chéneveau, *Journ. Phys.*, **9.** 163, 1910 ; W. Gerlach and A. C. Alliers, *Zeit. Physik*, **26.** 106, 1924 ; W. Gerlach, *Phys. Zeit.*, **25.** 618, 1924 ; *Ann. Physik*, (4), **76.** 163, 1925.

§ 5. The Chemical Properties of Tin

Tin is chemically related to silicon, titanium, zirconium, germanium, and cerium. The metal is not affected, chemically, by **hydrogen** ; and L. L. Bircumshaw [1] found that absorption of hydrogen by tin at about 800° can be represented by $w = 3 \cdot 8 - 2 \cdot 86e^{-0 \cdot 0074} - 0 \cdot 52e^{-0 \cdot 0666t}$, where w represents the amount of gas dissolved at the time t. F. H. Newman found that with tin electrodes in an electric discharge tube nitrogen, but not hydrogen, is absorbed. C. W. G. Kastner said that a **tin hydride** can be prepared, but E. Voegelen's attempts to make such a compound were nugatory. On the other hand, there are numerous alkyl derivatives of tin tetrahydride, or tin-methane. D. P. Smith, and F. Paneth have shown that the position of tin in the periodic table is not incompatible with the formation of a hydride. F. Paneth and K. Fürth found that when the gas, obtained by the action of $4N$-hydrochloric or sulphuric acid, is passed through cotton-wool, dried by calcium chloride and phosphoric anhydride, and led through a heated hard-glass tube, a mirror of metallic tin is formed in close proximity to the hot part of the tube, which, when well developed, consists of three zones, a whitish-grey, blackish-grey to black, and finally brown in colour. The reactions of the mirror are characteristic of tin, the most distinctive of them being the insolubility in cold, conc. nitric acid; and the formation of purple of Cassius and calomel by gold and mercuric chlorides, respectively, after a preliminary treatment of the ring with dry, gaseous hydrogen chloride. The gas can be condensed by liquid air and re-evaporated without decomposition. The yields, however, by these processes are poor—only a few thousandths per cent. of the tin of the alloy are converted into the hydride. W. Vaubel said that the compound Ag_4Sn is produced by the action of tin hydride on soln. of silver nitrate. He also found that a 5 per cent. soln. of acetic acid, or a 1 per cent. soln. of oxalic acid, acts on tin-plate containing rusty spots, or with iron in contact with tin, producing tin hydride; and added that the formation of tin hydride in soln. may account for cases of poisoning by eating food from tins showing rusty spots. E. J. Weeks obtained this hydride by the action of hydrogen on tin dihydride. F. Paneth and E. Rabinovitsch prepared tin hydride by the electrolysis of a soln. of tin sulphate between tin or lead electrodes. The presence of a small proportion of colloids—e.g. 0·5 per cent. of dextrin, gelatin, gum arabic, or agar-agar—or of certain crystalloids—e.g. sugar—greatly increases the yield, and also stabilizes it.

Electrolysis is effected conveniently in a crystallizing dish or beaker, in which the anode, made of lead rod, is placed in a small, porous cell. The cathode is formed by melting lead in a curved glass tube, through one end of which a copper wire is inserted into the metal while hot; the metal at the other end of the tube is affixed to a lead disc. The junction between metal and glass is rendered liquid-tight by gypsum or paraffin. The cathode is placed under a small bell. This form of cathode has the advantage that it may be removed without disturbing the remainder of the apparatus. The cathode requires a preliminary treatment so as to cover it with a loose, black deposit of the spongy metal. Zinc, mercury, or amalgamated zinc or lead are not suited for cathodes, but lead, tin, cadmium, or platinum can be used. The current density employed is 0·5–7·5 amps. per sq. cm. The tin hydride is washed by water and alkaline lead acetate soln., dried by passage through tubes at $-80°$ to $-100°$ and condensed by liquid air. It can be further purified by fractional distillation and condensation.

The analysis agrees with SnH_4, and no indications of other tin hydrides were observed. Tin hydride has a m.p. of $-150°$; its vap. press. is log $p = -1000T^{-1} + 7 \cdot 4$; the latent heat of evaporation is 4·55 Cals. Tin hydride is fairly stable. It decomposes spontaneously in a few days when kept in glass vessels, but the change is not accelerated by light. The gas decomposes immediately at $145°$–$150°$. The mirror obtained from the purified gas is generally pale grey or silvery; and it is formed in front of or in the heated part of the tube. The brown mirrors obtained with the impure gas are those of tin sulphide. Tin hydride is very sensitive to the nature of the surface with which it is in contact. The instability of the gas in contact with solid desiccating agents (calcium chloride, phosphoric oxide) is probably a manifestation of this phenomenon. It is unaffected by dil. alkali hydroxide soln. (up to 15 per cent.), dil. sulphuric acid, dil. and conc. nitric acid, and most metallic salts (sodium carbonate, copper sulphate, lead acetate, ferric chloride) ; it is absorbed to some extent by conc. alkali hydroxide soln. or by conc. sulphuric acid, completely by solid alkali hydroxide and soda-lime. It is quantitatively absorbed by silver nitrate (or sulphate) soln., giving a black precipitate which contains silver and tin in varying proportions, whilst tin is also present in the soln. It appears to reduce mercuric chloride to mercurous chloride. E. J. Weeks prepared **tin dihydride,** Sn_2H_2, by adding aluminium foil to an alkaline soln. of potassium stannite : $2KHSnO_2 + 2Al = 2KAlO_2 + Sn_2H_2$. The dihydride quickly oxidizes in air, and when heated, forms tin and water; with fused potassium nitrate, it forms nitrogen peroxide : $Sn_2H_2 + 5KNO_3 = KNO_2 + H_2O + 2K_2SnO_2 + 4NO_2$.

B. Delachanal found that tin occludes some gases, for, by heating 1000 grms. of tin in an evacuated porcelain tube, he obtained a mixture containing 3·25 c.c. of hydrogen, 2·80 c.c. of methane, 2·05 c.c. of carbon monoxide, 1·94 c.c. of carbon dioxide, and 1·56 c.c. of nitrogen. It was assumed that the methane was produced by a reaction between the hydrogen and carbon monoxide. A. Sieverts and co-workers observed no evidence of the dissolution of hydrogen by molten tin. F. Fischer and G. Iliovici obtained no sign of a combination of tin with argon when an electric arc between tin electrodes was formed beneath liquid **argon.** F. H. Newman studied the adsorption of gases by tin in the electric discharge tube. Tin is but a little affected by **air** at ordinary temp. even in the presence of moisture. Consequently, tin is much used in the form of tinned iron—tin-plate— for culinary utensils, etc. The metal seems to acquire a superficial pellicle of oxide which protects it from further action. G. Tammann [2] estimated that the metal in dry air would take 36×10^8 years to form the first visible layer of oxide. L. Vignon found that the metal precipitated by zinc from stannous chloride, when washed and dried in air appears to be infusible. It is really a mixture of 22·5–33·4 per cent. of stannous oxide and tin. The latter can be separated by liquation. The precipitated tin is partly converted to stannous oxide during the drying, and the oxidation takes place the more readily, the less the proportion of free acid present in the liquid from which the tin was precipitated ; if much free acid is present, the tin does not oxidize during the drying. G. Buchner said that tin which has been precipitated by zinc or aluminium from alkaline soln. is more stable than tin derived from acidic soln. These differences are probably due to variations in the grain-size of the pulverulent metal. L. Vignon said that if tin be cleaned by dipping in molten zinc chloride ; exposed to moist air for a month ; and again treated with zinc chloride, it loses weight, probably owing to oxidation. C. O. Bannister found that the corrosion product of a specimen of old tin—99·98 per cent. Sn— contained : hydrated stannous oxide, 43·35 per cent. ; SnO_2, 54·68 ; CuO, 0·81 ; SO_3, 0·85 ; Fe_2O_3, etc., 0·12 ; and CaO, 0·10. S. Kappel found that when tin is warmed in contact with ammonia or **alkalies,** and in a stream of purified air, some hydrogen dioxide is formed.

The production of stannic oxide by heating tin in air or **oxygen** was discussed in connection with stannic oxide. A. P. Bolley said that when the metal is heated to near its b.p., it burns in air with a pale white flame. According to L. Vignon, finely-divided tin precipitated by zinc from a dil. soln. of stannous chloride, washed, and dried, in air, burns like tinder when heated in air at a temp. below the m.p. of the metal. Powdered tin, obtained by agitating the melted metal in a wooden box, contains stannous oxide, and when heated with resin, borax, or any other substance which is commonly used as a flux for soldering, the metal becomes readily fusible. Zinc chloride soln. has no effect, but the fused salt simply dissolves the stannous oxide ; ammonium chloride forms stannous chloride with liberation of ammonia ; resin reduces the stannous oxide to metal. E. Jordis and W. Rosenhaupt said that tin darkens in colour when heated to 145° in dry oxygen for a long time, but the amount oxidized in very small—38·727 grms. consumed a c.c. of oxygen in 264 hrs. Moist oxygen acts more quickly. G. C. Schmidt found very little change in the potential of tin when oxygen or hydrogen is passed over the metal. According to F. Emich, when pure block tin is heated in a stream of air or in an open porcelain crucible, drops of molten metal ooze after some hours from beneath the superficial crust of stannic oxide, and, becoming superficially oxidized, gradually assume curious globular and vermiculitic forms, recalling Pharaoh's serpents. If tin containing 0·5 per cent. of iron be treated similarly, most of the iron is eliminated with the first portions of stannic oxide, a mere trace (0·001 per cent.) being left in the tin. The stannic oxide assumes a colour varying from brown to yellow with the amount of iron, thus serving as a good qualitative test for that impurity. The oxide formed after the iron has been eliminated is snow-white. W. Manchot found that air containing one per cent. of **ozone** acts on molten tin at 500°. M. Traube, and R. Wolfenstein showed that tin is not oxidized by a soln. of **hydrogen dioxide,** nor is the latter decomposed catalytically by the tin.

H. Fleck [3] reported the presence of traces of tin in **water** which had been distilled through a still-head and condensing worm of that metal ; he added that the action of cold water is very slight, but hot water acts a little faster. The action of water on tin and lead was discussed by M. E. Chevreul. M. Traube-Mengarini and A. Scala said that in contact with distilled water, tin furnishes a colloidal sol, and that the minute particles can be detected by the ultramicroscope. J. L. Gay Lussac, and H. V. Regnault found that steam is decomposed by red-hot tin, forming stannic oxide. W. G. Whitman and R. P. Russell examined the effect of oxygen dissolved in acids on the corrosion of tin. **Salt solutions** act on tin more quickly than does water alone. A. Claudius, and A. W. Lindes showed that warm aq. soln. of *ammonium chloride, sodium chloride, potassium hydrosulphate,* and *potassium aluminium sulphate* dissolve tin, but soln. of *sodium nitrate, potassium nitrate, sodium tetraborate,* and *sodium hydrosulphate* have very little action. Soln. of *potassium carbonate, sodium sulphate, calcium chloride, barium chloride,* and *magnesium sulphate* act in the presence of air, forming stannic oxide. K. K. Järvinen studied the attack of tin by sodium chloride soln. E. J. Hallock said that conc. soln. of sodium or calcium chloride and *ammonium nitrate* readily attack tin, while soln. of ammonium chloride have very little action. A. Wagner said that in the presence of air freed from carbon dioxide, sodium carbonate has but little action on tin ; and alkali chlorides, ammonium chloride, magnesium chloride, and *potassium sulphate* have still less action ; while distilled water, and lime-water have no action at all. E. Cohen found tin to be attacked by sea-water and atm. air. A. J. Hale and H. S. Foster found that $\frac{1}{5}N$-soln. of magnesium chloride, calcium chloride, and sodium chloride at 17°–20° dissolved per sq. dcm. of metal respectively 0·16, 0·13, and 0·00 grm. per day during 7 days ; and 0·10, 0·08, and 0·08 grm. per day during 28 days. A $\frac{1}{5}N$-sodium carbonate soln. had no appreciable action during 28 days. C. Reichelt said that water containing sodium chloride oxidizes tin more readily than water alone, but no tin is dissolved. S. P. Sharples found a block-tin tank was " riddled by corrosion " and coated with oxide by water free from nitrates but containing a little calcium sulphate and sodium chloride. A. M. Knight also gave a similar example. Soln. of *alkali hydroxides* dissolve tin very slowly, forming alkali stannates, and, as indicated in connection with the wet process for stripping tin from tin-plate, the action is accelerated in the presence of air, or of oxidizing agents. O. P. Watts and N. D. Whipple found that with 190 c.c. of N-sodium hydroxide at 37·5° for 45 hrs., 0·0005 grm. per sq. cm. was dissolved from tin ; and when 0·25 grm. sodium arsenate, 10 grms. potassium permanganate, or 10 grms. potassium nitrate, were added per 190 c.c. of the alkali-lye, then 0·0005, 0·00113, or 0·0005 grm. of tin per sq. cm. was respectively dissolved ; with a soln. of 200 grms. of sodium hydroxide per litre, and 5 grms. of picric acid per 180 c.c., 0·0622 grm. of tin per sq. cm. was dissolved in 45 hrs. at 46° ; and with tin amalgam, SnHg, and the same alkali soln. with and without the picric acid, 0·00512 and 0·00001 grm. per sq. cm. was respectively dissolved. A. J. Hale and H. S. Foster found that $\frac{1}{5}N$-NaOH at 17°–20° dissolved tin at the rate of 0·30 grm. per sq. dcm. per day during 7 days, and 0·50 grm. per sq. dcm. per day during 28 days. According to K. Elbs and H. Thümmel, a tin anode dissolves in soln. of sodium chloride or sulphate, or in hydrochloric or sulphuric acid, almost entirely in the stannous condition. For the action of soln. of *alkali sulphides*, and the anodic dissolution of tin in soln. of alkali hydroxides or alkali sulphides, *vide* wet processes for stripping tin-plate, similarly also for the action of soln. of ferric salts, stannic salts, and of copper salts. Objects made of tin have been reported from old pile-dwellings in a good state of preservation ; but they are also found encrusted with white or brown layers of hydrated stannic oxide ; and sometimes the oxidation has advanced so far that no trace of metallic tin remains. The corrosion of tin by various reagents was discussed by H. F. Whittaker ; by acidic mine-waters, by R. E. Hall and W. H. Teaque ; and by photographic soln., by J. I. Crabtree and co-workers.

The halogens unite directly with tin, forming stannic salts. H. Moissan [4] said that **fluorine** does not react with tin at low temp., but at 100° it forms stannic fluoride. Dried **chlorine** and **bromine** were found by R. Cowper, and R. Lorenz to act on tin at ordinary temp. E. Beckmann and P. Geib also found that liquid chlorine attacks tin. J. L. Gay Lussac found that **iodine** at 50° unites directly with tin. In agreement with the thermal values of the reaction, said M. Berthelot, tin is easily attacked by **hydrogen iodide** and **hydrogen bromide**, and less readily by **hydrogen chloride**. Tin is feebly attacked by **hydrofluoric acid**, and is slowly dissolved by dil. **hydrochloric acid ;** with hot, conc. hydrochloric acid, hydrogen is evolved and stannous chloride is formed. The dissolution of tin in this acid is accelerated by the presence of a little platinic chloride, or if the tin is in contact with copper, silver, lead, or platinum. C. Nöllner said that the action of hydrochloric acid ceases when the soln. contains a mol of stannous chloride for every 2 mols of hydrogen chloride. O. P. Watts and N. D. Whipple found that with N-HCl, 0·0016 and 0·0015 grm. per sq. cm. was dissolved from hammered and cast tin, respectively, at 38° in 20 hrs., and if 10 grms. of potassium permanganate were present per 180 c.c. of soln., 0·057 grm. per sq. cm. was dissolved from cast tin. A. J. Hale and H. S. Foster found that $\frac{1}{5}N$-HCl dissolved tin at the rate of 0·42 grm. per sq. dcm. per day during 7 days at 17°–20°, and 0·90 grm. during 28 days. W. G. Whitman and R. P. Russell found that the corrosion of tin by hydrochloric acid is increased in the presence of oxygen. K. K. Järvinen studied the attack of tin by one per cent. hydrochloric acid. According to E. Salkowsky, if hydrogen dioxide be present, free chlorine is developed, and the tin is attacked more vigorously. H. J. Prins found that the presence of easily reducible substances, like benzaldehyde or nitrobenzene, accelerates the attack on tin by acids. C. F. Rammelsberg found that electrolytic tin dissolves about ten times as quickly as tin which has been melted. In the former case, presumably a greater surface area per gram of metal is exposed to the acid. L. P. Cailletet found that under press., acids have very little action on tin. According to W. Vaubel, during the dissolution of polished tin in hydrochloric acid, a black powder is deposited which dissolves only very slowly even in the conc. acid ; it is suggested that this is a peculiar modification of the metal which is produced by the reduction of stannous chloride by nascent hydrogen. He also found that the dissolution of tin in hydrochloric acid produces a gas that has a peculiar metallic odour sometimes resembling the odour of stewed meat. The gas burns with a luminous flame, gives a mirror of metallic tin, and reacts with silver nitrate soln., indicating that it contains a volatile tin compound such as stannous chloride or hydride or a mixture of these. Hot **hydrobromic acid** or **hydriodic acid** also readily dissolves tin. J. L. Gay Lussac showed that with mixtures of hydrochloric and nitric acids, stannous chloride, stannic chloride, or stannic acid may be obtained according to the proportion of nitric acid present. E. Divers and T. Haga also observed the formation of ammonia and hydroxylamine when mixtures of hydrochloric and nitric acids act on tin. A. J. Balard said that dil. **hypochlorous acid** acts on tin only in the presence of other acids; and that conc.

hypochlorous acid acts only when chloric acid is formed.   According to A. D. White, **calcium hypochlorite** in contact with tin furnishes oxygen; and hypochlorous acid slowly oxidizes tin to stannic oxide with the evolution of chlorine. E. Soubeiran found that soln. of **alkali hypochlorites** act on tin, forming an oxychloride and evolving oxygen—A. J. Balard said the oxygen is mixed with chlorine. S. S. Sadtler found that the presence of hypochlorous acid accelerates the action of sodium hydroxide on tin.   W. S. Hendrixson found that **chloric acid** dissolves in tin, forming stannic chloride no hydrogen is evolved, and very little stannic acid is produced.

Tin unites directly with **sulphur** when a mixture of the two elements is heated —*vide* the tin sulphides.   The reaction is vigorous and is usually accompanied by incandescence.   K. Jellinek and J. Zabowsky[5] made estimates of the affinity of tin for sulphur.   P. G. J. Gueterbock and G. N. Nicklin studied the effect of sulphur as an impurity on the physical properties of tin.   A. Ditte found that **hydrogen sulphide** does not act on tin at ordinary temp., but at 100°–400°, it forms stannous sulphide.   E. Priwoznik showed that **ammonium sulphide** attacks tin, and O. B. Kühn, that when tin is fused with **sodium sulphide,** stannous sulphide is formed.   For the action of aq. soln. of these salts, *vide supra.*   K. Heumann and P. Köchlin found that **sulphuryl chloride** acts slowly on tin, forming stannic chloride.   P. Nicolardot showed that **sulphur monochloride,** S_2Cl_2, attacks tin. A. F. de Fourcroy and L. N. Vauquelin, and C. Geitner found that an aq. soln. of **sulphur dioxide** attacks tin, forming stannous sulphide; and, according to J. J. Berzelius, and M. J. Fordos and A. Gélis, some stannous thiosulphate, and sulphite are formed.   According to K. Heumann and P. Köchlin, **chlorosulphonic acid** acts on tin in the cold, heat is evolved, and the reaction is symbolized : $Sn+4HSO_3Cl=SnCl_4+2SO_2+2H_2SO_4$.   Dil. **sulphuric acid** was found by F. C. Calvert and R. Johnson not to react on tin in the cold, but by increasing the conc. of the acid to $H_2SO_4.6H_2O$, action begins.   According to A. Ditte, with cold dil. sulphuric acid, hydrogen is given off, and with the hot conc. acid, sulphur dioxide, hydrogen sulphide, and sulphur are formed.   M. M. P. Muir and C. E. Robbs showed that with the molar proportions $H_2SO_4 : H_2O$, 7 : 2, at 20°–25°, there is but little action, no hydrogen sulphide is produced, but a little sulphur and a trace of sulphur dioxide are formed, and at 110°–120°, a trace of hydrogen sulphide and much sulphur and sulphur dioxide are produced; with the 1 : 1 acid at 20°–25°, a trace of hydrogen sulphide and a little sulphur are formed, and at 110°–120°, a little hydrogen and sulphur, some hydrogen sulphide, and much sulphur dioxide are formed; with the 1 : 3 acid at 20°–25° there is no action, but at 110°–120°, much hydrogen sulphide and a trace of sulphur dioxide are formed; and with the 1 : 5 acid at 20°–25°, there is no action, and at 110°–120° hydrogen, with a trace of hydrogen sulphide, is given off.   O. P. Watts and N. D. Whipple found that with N-H_2SO_4, 0·0006 grm. per sq. cm. of tin was dissolved in 20 hrs. at 38°, and if 10 grms. of potassium dichromate or chlorate per 180 c.c. of acid were present, respectively 0·0003 and 0·1306 grm. per sq. cm. was dissolved.   A. J. Hale and H. S. Foster found that with a sq. dcm. of tin and $\frac{1}{5}N$-H_2SO_4 at 17°–20°, 0·022 grm. per day was lost during 7 days and 0·25 grm. per day during 28 days.   H. Bassett found that a mixture of 1 vol. of sulphuric acid, 2 vols. of nitric acid, and 3 vols. of water, dissolves tin in the cold, with the evolution of nearly pure nitrous oxide, producing at the same time a clear soln. of stannic sulphate.   If, however, the temp. has been allowed to rise, the soln. becomes opalescent, and on heating in a water-oven for an hour, it becomes nearly solid and opaque.   When the soln., containing nitric acid, is poured into boiling water, the whole of the tin is precipitated as metastannic acid. W. G. Whitman and R. P. Russell found that the presence of oxygen favours the attack of tin by sulphuric acid.   E. Salkowsky found that the presence of hydrogen dioxide does not affect the rate of dissolution of tin by dil. sulphuric acid.   H. Nissenson and E. Crotogino said that if the soln of tin in conc. sulphuric acid is diluted with water the tin is quantitatively precipitated as stannic acid. E. Divers and T. Shimidzu showed that **pyrosulphuric acid** dissolves tin with the evolution of heat, forming stannous sulphate and sulphur sesquioxide. M. G. Levi and co-workers showed that tin is rapidly attacked by a soln. of **potassium persulphate** or of **ammonium persulphate,** without the evolution of gas, forming stannic oxide, or a metastannic acid. H. Ditz said that when tin is heated with a soln. of ammonium persulphate in dil. sulphuric acid, there is a smell of ozone, and the soln. gradually becomes turbid, and finally stannic hydroxide is precipitated ; the initial darkening of the soln. is supposed to be due to the formation of stannous oxide. Tin reacts vigorously with **selenium** or **tellurium** when a mixture of the two is heated—*vide* selenides and tellurides. E. B. Hutchins found that tin is attacked by hot **telluric acid.**

Tin does not form a compound by direct union with **nitrogen.** F. Fischer and G. Iliovici [6] passed arc and spark discharges beneath liquid nitrogen, and obtained a mixture of metal, tin nitride, and some oxide. T. Curtius and co-workers found that tin is attacked by a 17 per cent. soln. of **hydrazoic acid,** a gas is developed containing a large proportion of ammonia, and a non-explosive product is formed. C. Matignon and G. Desplantes showed that tin is not changed by aq. **ammonia** even in the presence of oxygen. A. J. Hale and H. S. Foster found that $\frac{1}{5}N$-NH_4OH did not dissolve anything from tin during 28 days at $17°$–$20°$. G. G. Henderson and J. C. Galletly found that ammonia at $170°$ is decomposed by tin, but no nitride is formed. F. W. Bergstrom represented the reaction with a soln. of **alkali amide** in liquid ammonia : $10Sn + 6KNH_2 = 2SnNK(NH_3)_2 + K_4Sn_8$. E. Divers and T. Haga reported that **hydroxylamine hydrochloride** is not perceptibly changed by tin and hot hydrochloric acid. According to E. Ludwig and T. Hein, and E. Divers and T. Haga, when **nitric oxide**—in the absence of air—is passed into a mixture of tin and hydrochloric acid, hydroxylamine, but no ammonia, is formed. E. Müller and H. Barck found that nitric oxide does not act on tin at temp. below $400°$; at $450°$, a tin nitride is formed ; less nitride is produced at $500°$, and none at $600°$. R. Weber said that tin is inert towards nitrogen pentoxide. R. Boyle remarked on the action of aqua fortis in "eating up or destroying" more tin than it dissolves ; and J. J. Berzelius showed that hot **nitric acid** oxidizes tin completely to hydrated stannic oxide. S. L. Mitchill said that conc. nitric acid does not act on tin, but if water be added the metal dissolves. R. Weber said that dil. or conc. nitric acid dissolves the metal without the evolution of gas provided the temp. is kept low ; and G. Hay, that dil. nitric acid dissolves tin, forming a straw-yellow liquid which is decomposed on boiling. E. J. Maumené showed that the products of the action of nitric acid on tin vary with the temp. and conc. of the acid ; but the dil. acid—$HNO_3.4H_2O$—can produce stannous oxide which for the most part remains undissolved. A. J. Hale and H. S. Foster found that with $\frac{1}{5}N$-HNO_3 the loss of metal per sq. dcm. at $17°$–$20°$ was 4.0 grms. per day in 7 days and 7.20 grms. per day in 28 days. It is generally supposed that the soln. of tin in dil. nitric acid contains stannous nitrate ; R. Engel, indeed, said that with nitric acid of sp. gr. 1.42 diluted with two vols. of water, at $0°$, stannous nitrate gel is formed, but if diluted with one vol. of water, stannic nitrate is produced. J. J. Acworth and H. E. Armstrong obtained at $11°$–$14°$ the following results :

TABLE IV.—ACTION OF NITRIC ACID ON TIN.

Conc. of acid.	Gram tin.	C.c. of gas.	Percentage composition of gas.		
			NO.	N_2O.	N_2.
1 : 0	0·4135	21·54	1·08	85·14	13·78
1 : 1	0·4140	31·02	16·38	73·82	9·80
1 : 2	0·4145	33·09	14·47	75·55	9·98
1 : 8	0·4150	4·66	3·27	85·02	11·80

According to C. Montemartini, nitric acid, up to a conc. of 12 per cent., always attacks tin with formation of stannous salt, which partially decomposes, forming a turbid soln. ; gas is always evolved, although slowly. Nitric acid, of a conc. from 12 to 45 per cent., completely dissolves the metal to a yellow soln., with abundant evolution of gas ; the soln., when left, slowly becomes turbid, but the precipitation may be retarded by adding hydrochloric acid. The tin is present in these soln., as stannous nitrate, and the turbidity is due partly to the oxidation of this salt and partly to its conversion into insoluble stannous compounds, which, in turn, yield hydrated stannic oxide. Nitric acid of more than 45 per cent. conc. does not dissolve tin, but converts it into a white substance. If 70 per cent. acid is used, this white oxidation product is soluble in water, but the soln., after a few seconds, becomes turbid, and hydrated stannic oxide is deposited ; the addition of hydrochloric acid to the clear soln. greatly retards the precipitation. The soluble, white substance is stannic nitrate, $Sn(NO_3)_4$; it is stable in presence of conc. nitric acid at 90°, but is immediately decomposed at 100°. The soln. of a gram of tin in excess of 27·5 per cent. acid yields 0·0180 grm. of ammonia, 0·1060 grm. of nitrous oxide, and 0·0051 grm. of nitrogen. The maximum quantity of ammonia is obtained when one per cent. nitric acid is used, but the rate of diminution in the amount of this gas produced, as stronger acid is used, is small ; even 70 per cent. acid causes the formation of much ammonia. The hypothesis that the nitric acid is reduced by nascent hydrogen is insufficient for the explanation of the phenomena observed during the action of nitric acid on tin. E. Divers and co-workers said that the action of nitric acid on tin resembles in some respects its action on zinc (q.v.). C. H. H. Walker concluded from his observations that metallic tin dissolves in nitric acid, forming both a stannous and a stannic salt, according to the conditions of temp. and the conc. of the acid. The proportion of stannous salt formed is but little affected by the mass of tin present. In the case of very dil. acids, increase of temp. causes a slight decrease in the proportion of stannous salt, but in the case of more conc. acid, the effect is more marked, so that an alteration of 10° reduces the amount of stannous salt to nil. An increase in the conc. of the acid, other conditions remaining the same, decreases the amount of stannous salt. The white or yellowish-white substance deposited from fairly conc. soln. is a hydrated stannic nitrate of rather indefinite composition. F. H. van Leent said that in the presence of iron, chromium, or aluminium, tin is wholly converted by conc. nitric acid into insoluble stannic acid, while the other products pass into soln. A. Quartaroli also studied this reaction, and found that in the presence of 4 per cent. of urea, tin is dissolved as stannous nitrate without the appearance of insoluble stannic nitrate. W. G. Whitman and R. P. Russell found that the presence of oxygen favoured the attack of tin by nitric acid. For H. Bassett's work on the action of a mixture of sulphuric and nitric acids on tin, vide supra. R. Weber found that moist **potassium nitrate** does not act on tin, but with **copper nitrate,** an explosive basic nitrate is formed—vide basic stannous nitrates ; and L. Loviton showed that fused **ammonium nitrate** does not affect tin at 150°.

From the observations of B. Pelletier,[7] O. Emmerling, C. Künzel, S. Natanson and G. Vortmann, and A. Schrötter, molten tin unites with **phosphorus,** forming a phosphide. A. C. Vivian found that when mixtures of tin and yellow phosphorus are heated in sealed glass tubes, alloying commences as soon as the tin is molten, for an appreciable amount of the alloy is formed at 400° ; with red phosphorus, no evidence of alloying occurs below the temp. at which the red changes to yellow phosphorus. At 400°, only very little alloying had occurred. Phosphorus also appears to be quite insoluble in solid tin. R. Lüpke melted tin covered with ammonium carbonate in a crucible and added the calculated quantity of red phosphorus ; A. Schrötter, and P. Vigier passed phosphorus vap. mixed with carbon dioxide into molten tin ; G. Landgrebe melted equal parts of tin and fused microcosmic salt ; P. Berthier heated in a carbon crucible a mixture of tin filings or stannic oxide, carbon, quartz, boric acid, and bone-ash, and P. Mellmann, and J. L. Seyboth used an analogous process. S. Natanson and G. Vortmann heated a mixture of metaphosphoric acid, carbon, and tin ; and A. Granger, a mixture of tin and phosphorus chloride at 500°. H. Rose treated stannic phosphine chloride with water, and found that tin phosphide was precipitated ; when dried out of contact with air, the composition approximated SnP_4. The phosphor-tin used in making phosphor bronze was discussed by F. von Friese, R. F. Nursey, and W. G. Otto—*vide* the tin phosphides. J. Heimann found tin to be soluble in a soln. of **metaphosphoric acid.** E. Baudrimont [8] found that **phosphorus pentachloride** reacts on finely granulated tin at 170°, forming a complex $SnCl_4.PCl_5$; but, according to H. Goldschmidt, the reaction is $Sn+2PCl_5=SnCl_4+2PCl_3$. B. Reinitzer and H. Goldschmidt found that **phosphorus oxychloride** reacts with tin at 100° without forming phosphoric oxide.

According to T. Bergman,[9] molten tin can take up half its own weight of arsenic, and the product is lustrous and white. A. F. Gehlen, and A. Vogel found that when pulverized **arsenic** is stirred about in melted tin, the union of the elements is attended by the evolution of heat and light. The former also obtained an alloy by heating tin with arsenic trioxide. C. Bülles obtained the alloy in a similar way. A. Descamps heated the two elements under a layer of boric acid fused at the lowest possible temp. and obtained a brittle mass which he regarded as *tin hemitriarsenide*, Sn_2As_3. W. Spring exposed a mixture of the two elements to a great press. and obtained what he regarded as *tin tetratritarsenide*, Sn_3As_4 ; P. Jolibois and E. L. Dupay obtained *tin tritetritarsenide*, Sn_4As_3, by the action

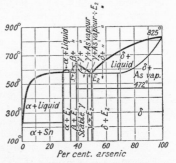

FIG. 18.—Fusion Curves of Binary Mixtures : As–Sn.

of a soln. of ferrous chloride, on an alloy with 7 per cent. of arsenic used as the anode of a cell ; and W. P. Headden obtained six-sided plates of what he regarded as *tin hexitarsenide*, Sn_6As, from the hearth of an old dismantled tin furnace of the Trethellan Tin Works, Truro, Cornwall. There is no other evidence of the individuality of these products. J. E. Stead isolated **tin ditritarsenide,** Sn_3As_2, from alloys of the two elements ; N. A. Puschin obtained evidence of the same compound from his measurements of the e.m.f. of the cells $Sn \mid N\text{-}H_2SO_4 \mid SnAs_n$; and $Sn \mid N\text{-}KOH \mid SnAs_n$. The crystals of the tritadiarsenide obtained by J. E. Stead in an alloy of tin with 5 per cent. arsenic are shown in Fig. 19. According to N. Parravano and P. de Cesaris, the fusion curves of mixtures of the two elements, show the existence of both tin tritadiarsenide and **tin monoarsenide,** SnAs. P. Jolibois and E. L. Dupay prepared the latter compound.

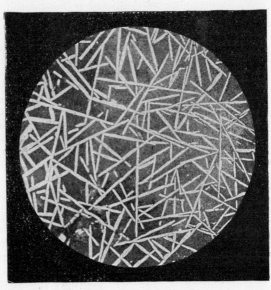

FIG. 19.—Crystals of Tin Tritadiarsenide, Sn_3As_2. ×2.

Q. A. Mansuri's equilibrium curve is shown in Fig. 18, where the two eutectics are denoted by E_1 and E_2, and the solid soln. by the Greek letters. N. A. Puschin commented on the great hardness imparted to tin when alloyed with arsenic, and he noted the great tendency of the alloys to crystallize. According to E. Soubeiran, the alloy is white, sonorous, and brittle if the arsenic be not in too great an excess. The texture is lamellar. W. Campbell examined the microstructure; and M. Padoa, the electrical conductivity. When fused in an open vessel, arsenic is evolved; and with hydrochloric acid, arsenic hydride is evolved; an alloy with an excess of arsenic is not attacked by this acid. P. G. J. Gueterbock and G. N. Nicklin studied the effect of arsenic as an impurity on the physical properties of tin.

Molten tin dissolves **antimony,** and the two elements unite without the evolution of heat or light. The alloy can also be made by fusing antimony sulphide with an excess of tin. C. W. G. Kastner [10] noted that an alloy with 12·5 per cent. of antimony has a fine musical tone ; and L. J. Chaudet noted that a 10 : 1 alloy is quite ductile, while the 3 : 1 alloy is less ductile than tin, and the 1 : 1 alloy is extremely brittle and readily pulverized. The brittle alloys are more ductile if a small amount of lead be present. He added that alloys with more than 90 per cent. of tin give up the whole of the tin to boiling hydrochloric, leaving the antimony as a black powder—some stibine is evolved. The various physical properties were studied by A. W. Smith, and P. G. J. Gueterbock and G. N. Nicklin. R. Kremann and P. G. von Rehenburg found that on electrolysis, the tin accumulates at the anode, the antimony at the cathode. A. Wagner said that the alloy with 10 per cent. of antimony, in the presence of air free from carbon dioxide, is attacked quickly by soln. of sodium chloride , and slightly by soln. of sodium carbonate or nitrate; and not at all by water or lime-water. If the carbon dioxide of the air has also access, soln. of ammonium chloride and potassium sulphate have no action, and soln. of alkali chlorides, magnesium chloride, and sodium nitrate have very little action. L. J. Chaudet examined the action of hydrochloric acid. According to A. Czerwek, the tin-antimony alloys are dissolved by a mixture of nitric and tartaric acids. J. R. Johnson, C. Karmarsch, H. Gautier, L. J. Thénard, A. M. Fairlie, R. H. Thurston, F. G. Thompson and F. Orme, and W. Campbell made observations on the properties of these alloys with or without the addition of other metals. The last-named examined the ternary alloys with copper, silver, zinc, cadmium, aluminium, lead, arsenic, and bismuth. The tin-antimony alloys form the base of the so-called *britannia metal*, which is mainly tin hardened with antimony, and contains 6·0 to 9·2 per cent. of antimony; *algiers metal* has 10 to 25 per cent. of antimony; 33 per cent. marks the extreme limit of these alloys, when the latter is very hard. Numerous modifications of the alloy employed in commerce are associated with zinc, bismuth, lead, and copper. H. Gautier, and A. Matthiessen showed that the sp. gr. of the tin-antimony alloys is rather less than that calculated from the sp. gr. of the components ; consequently, an expansion takes place when the metals are alloyed. M. Chikashige studied the colour of the alloys; E. von Maey, the sp. vol.; E. Elsässer, the electrical conductivity of these alloys; and N. S. Konstantinoff and W. A. Smirnoff, working at 25°, obtained the results plotted in Fig. 20. C. T. Heycock and F. H. Neville noted that the m.p. of a dil. soln. of antimony in tin is higher than that of tin alone ; A. van Bijlert tried to find if solid soln. of the two elements are formed. F. W. Küster, and F. E. Gallagher observed no evidence of chemical combination although they considered that crystals of four different solid soln. were produced. G. Charpy said that although solid soln. are produced, alloys with 10–40 per cent.

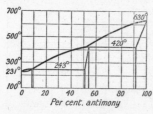

FIG. 20.—Fusion Curves of Binary Mixtures : Sn–Sb.

of antimony contain well-formed cubic crystals of **tin monantimonide,** SnSb ;
H. Behrens made a similar observation ; and J. E. Stead added that alloys with

7·5 per cent. of antimony contain
some of these crystals. They are
particularly well-formed in alloys
with 25 per cent. of antimony ;
and alloys with over 40 per cent.
antimony contain tabular crystals. The crystals of tin antimonide obtained by J. E. Stead
in an alloy of tin with 20 per
cent. of antimony are illustrated
in Fig. 21. G. Tammann and
K. Dahl measured the plastic
deformation. H. Gautier, T.
Thompson, C. R. A. Wright,
W. Reinders, R. S. Williams,
N. S. Konstantinoff and W. A.
Smirnoff studied the f.p. of the
thermal diagram. R. S. Williams'
curves are shown in Fig. 20.
There are breaks at 243° and
420°, but none corresponding
with the break at 310°–319° observed by F. E. Gallagher, and
W. Reinders. By keeping the

Fig. 21.—Crystals of Tin Antimonide, SnSb. ×50.

alloys at a high temp. for some hours, three series of mixed crystals were formed
containing 0–8, 49·8–52·8, and 90–100 at. per cent. of antimony. The end-

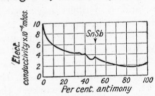

Fig. 22.—Electrical Conductivities of the
Sn–Sb Alloys.

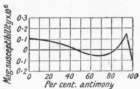

Fig. 23.—Magnetic Susceptibilities of the
Sn–Sb Alloys.

member of the middle series may be regarded as tin monantimonide. G. Charpy,
W. Campbell, and H. Behrens and H. Baucke examined the microstructure
of these alloys. N. S. Konstaninoff and W. A. Smirnoff obtained evidence of the
formation of **tin ditritaantimonide,** Sn_3Sb_2, on the
f.p. curve ; and N. A. Puschin measured the e.m.f. of
the cells Sn | SnCl$_2$ | SnSb$_n$; Sn | N-H$_2$SO$_4$ | SnSb$_n$;
Sn | N-KOH | SnSb$_n$, and obtained breaks corre-
sponding with tin monantimonide and tin trita-
diantimonide, Sn_4Sb_2. G. Wertheim studied the
elastic properties ; and A. W. Smith, the thermal
conductivity. The magnetic susceptibilities of these
alloys were measured by H. Endo, and P. Leroux,
and the results are plotted in Fig. 23. W. Rollmann,
A. Naccari and M. Bellate, and A. Battelli investigated the thermoelectric properties ; and C. C.
Hutchins' measurements are graphed in Fig. 24.

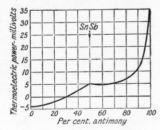

Fig. 24.—Thermoelectric
Powers of the Sn–Sb Alloys.

A. P. Laurie, and H. le Chatelier measured the e.m.f. of cells with an electrode
of these alloys. W. Campbell, and J. E. Stead studied the ternary system :

Sn–Sb–As. A. Mazzucchelli and A. Vercillo found that antimony trichloride and tin form tin diantimonide, $SnSb_2$.

According to F. Rudberg,[11] when a molten alloy of tin with 54·6 per cent. of bismuth is cooled, there is a fairly sharp f.p. at 143°; but alloys with other proportions of these elements have two f.p. The higher *point of separation* is accompanied by the separation of the excess of one or other metal, or of a definite alloy with an excess of one of the metals, until the composition of the remaining fluid has 54·6 per cent. of bismuth, when all solidifies at 143°. F. Rudberg found the point of separation to be variable, for with the proportions Sn : Bi=8 : 1 it was 190°; 2 : 1, 150°; 4 : 3, 170°; and 1 : 1, 190°. He regarded the lowest melting alloy as a definite compound, Sn_3Bi. P. G. J. Gueterbock and G. N. Nicklin studied the effect of bismuth as an impurity on the physical properties of tin. Observations on the m.p. of specific mixtures were made by L. J. Chaudet, C. M. Marx, W. Lewis, H. V. Regnault, J. W. Döbereiner, H. von Jüptner, A. Matthiessen, A. Riche, J. Würschmidt, D. H. Andrews and J. Johnston, K. Honda and T. Ishigaki, etc. F. Guthrie gave 133° for the eutectic temp.,

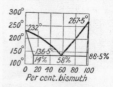

FIG. 25.—
Fusion Curves of Binary Mixtures Sn–Bi.

for an alloy with 46·1 per cent. of bismuth. E. S. Shepherd said that no *tin bismuthide* is formed. Thermal analyses have been made by A. Bucher, A. Stoffel, A. W. Kapp, and W. von Lepkowsky, and the results are indicated in Fig. 25. The phenomena were also studied by C. T. Heycock and F. H. Neville, C. R. A. Wright, H. Gautier, F. Guthrie, T Thomson, C. L. Weber, A. W. Smith, and G. Charpy. D. H. Andrews and J. Johnston studied the solubility of bismuth in tin. H. Behrens and K. Bux investigated the microstructure; and C. H. Green, and A. M. Portevin, the structure of the eutectic. The sp. gr. of the alloys were determined by T. Thomson, H. V. Regnault, A. Matthiessen, and A. Riche, and the sp. vol. by E. von Maey, and K. Gilbert; K. Bornemann and P. Siebe, and K. Gilbert measured the sp. vols. of the alloys up to 900° and found them to be proportional to the temp. C. di Capua measured the hardness; M. Plüss, the viscosity and sp. gr. of the liquid; G. Wertheim, the elastic constants; A. Matthiessen, the coeff. of thermal expansion; and G. Vicentini and D. Omodei, D. Mazzoto, and C. C. Person, the latent heat of fusion; H. Kopp, and A. Schulze, the sp. ht.; A. Levi, the mol.

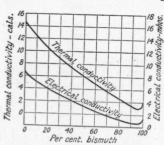

FIG. 26.—Thermal and Electrical Conductivities of the Tin-Bismuth Alloys.

heat; and L. H. Adams and co-workers, the coeff. of compressibility of the alloys. C. R. Darling and R. H. Rinaldi studied the thermoelectric properties of the alloy against copper. F. A. Schultze's results for the thermal and electrical conductivities are plotted in Fig. 26. The electrical conductivity and resistance of the alloys were measured by A. Righi, G. Wiedemann, C. L. Weber, A. Sundell, A. Bucher, E. van Aubel, A. Matthiessen and C. Vogt, F. A. Schultze, and G. Vicentini and C. Cattaneo. R. Kremann and P. G. von Rehenburg found that on electrolysis, the tin accumulates at the cathode, the bismuth at the anode. H. Pélabon measured the thermoelectric power. G. Faè studied the effect of a magnetic field on

the electrical resistance. A. P. Laurie, H. le Chatelier, E. S. Shepherd, and A. Sundell studied the e.m.f. of cells with these alloys as electrodes; the thermoelectric power was measured by A. Matthiessen, G. Spadavecchia, A. Sundell, G. Vicentini and D. Omodei, H. Pélabon, C. C. Hutchins, A. Battelli, E. Becquerel, W. Rollmann, and A. E. Caswell and C. A. McKay. The results are plotted in Fig. 27. The curve for the Thomson effect by S. C. Laws, and A. E. Caswell and C. A. McKay is shown in Fig. 27. A. von Ettinghausen and W. Nernst, and

E. van Aubel studied the thermoelectric phenomena. A. Righi, S. C. Laws, and E. van Aubel studied the magnetic susceptibility of the alloys, and the results of T. Gnesotto and M. Binghinotto are shown in Fig. 28. C. R. A. Wright investigated the ternary system Sn–Bi–Al; C. di Capua, the hardness of the Zn–Bi–Cd alloys; and W. Campbell, the system Sn–Bi–Sb. F. E. Brown and J. E. Snyder [12] observed that **vanadium oxytrichloride** has no action on tin.

H. Moissan [13] said that tin does not unite directly with **carbon** to form a carbide (*q.v.*). O. Ruff and B. Bergdahl said that molten tin dissolves only a trace of carbon. E. Gudeman found that water sat. with **carbon dioxide** attacks tin. F. H. Rhodes

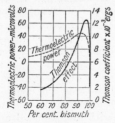

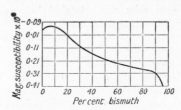

FIG. 27.—Thermoelectric Properties of the Tin-Bismuth Alloys.

FIG. 28.—Magnetic Susceptibilities of the Tin-Bismuth Alloys.

and J. T. Carty found tin is resistant to the moist vapour of carbon tetrachloride; there is a slight pitting of the surface. W. R. Hodgkinson showed that tin is unaffected by **acetylene** at temp. up to its m.p. F. Malméjac said that tin is appreciably attacked by **alcohol** in the course of six months; but G. Heinzelmann denied this. W. Ipatieff found that if alcohol vapour be passed through a glass tube containing tin at 660° no decomposition occurs, but finely divided tin obtained by the reduction of the oxide forms acetaldehyde and ethylene. J. Trummer discussed the action of tin on **wine ;** and F. Schönfeld, J. Dehnicke, L. Nathan and A. Schmidt, K. Dinklage, and C. Sellenscheidt, on **beer.** H. Fleck, and F. P. Hall observed that tin is but slightly attacked by **organic acids,** but if air be present, the metal may be dissolved ; thus, **acetic, tartaric, and citric acids** act on the metal in the presence of air ; and W. G. Whitman and R. P. Russell found that the presence of oxygen favoured the attack by acetic acid. E. Salkowsky said that the presence of hydrogen dioxide does not affect the dissolution of tin by glacial acetic acid. A. Hébert found that **stearic acid** is decomposed by distillation over finely divided tin ; and J. H. Matthews showed that **trichloroacetic acid,** in nitrobenzene soln., is blackened by tin, but no aniline is formed. F. H. Jeffery studied the effect of tin anodes on **potassium oxalate** soln. F. A. Norton found that **organic substances** in the presence of sodium sulphite form stannic sulphide. C. F. Böhringer studied the electrolytic reduction of **nitro- and azo-compounds** by a cathode of spongy tin. O. W. Brown and C. O. Henke found tin an excellent catalytic agent in reducing nitrobenzene by hydrogen ; and A. Korczynsky, in the bromination of benzene. For the action of tin on **food-stuffs,** *vide supra,* the occurrence of tin. E. Gudeman emphasized the solubility of tin in the liquids used with canned food products, and in the peculiar liquids produced in the decomposition of foods. D. Klein and A. Berg said that hot soln. of **sugar** do not attack tin ; but K. K. Järvinen found that the metal is attacked by 30 per cent. soln. of sugar. J. Merrick found that tin is but slightly affected by **turpentine ;** and F. Pfaff observed a similar result with **fatty oils.** I. J. Redwood said that at ordinary temp. tin is not attacked by **rape oil,** and **whale oil ;** and the percentage loss with **olive oil** was 0·01637 ; **tallow oil,** 0·03400 ; **lard oil,** 0·01976 ; **cotton-seed oil,** 0·46075 ; **sperm oil,** 0·22847 ; with **seal oil,** 0·08503 ; and with a mineral lubricant, 0·02587. A. Gawalowsky observed no action between tin and **petroleum or mineral oils ;** and U. Ehrhardt and G. Pfleiderer found 0·22 mgrm. of tin per sq. cm. was dissolved in 4 weeks by crude **tar oils** containing phenol.

J. J. Berzelius, and C. Winkler found that molten tin dissolves some **silicon**—but E. Vigouroux said that no tin silicide is formed (q.v.). H. Moissan said that tin alloys with **titanium.** G. Tammann and P. Schafmeister [14] measured the partition of tin between lead and zinc, lead and aluminium, and zinc and bismuth.

The physiological action of tin.—According to J. D. Mann,[15] no fatal case of poisoning by tin salts had been recorded up to 1908; and cases of poisoning by this agent are extremely rare and have resulted only from accident—generally the use of tinned meat and fruit. Cases have been recorded by A. P. Luff and G. H. Metcalfe, T. L. Phipson, B. Dyer, R. Kayser, T. Günther, E. Ungar and G. Bodländer, A. Eckardt, F. P. Wightwick, and W. A. Campbell. W. Vaubel found that stannous salts are only slightly poisonous, but they are readily oxidized to the more poisonous stannic salts. G. Pouchet and co-workers emphasized the harmful nature of the one-time practice in Belgium and France of putting stannous chloride—up to 2·5 per cent.—into ginger-bread in order to obtain with inferior materials an appearance like that due to fine flour. Experiments by O. Hehner, and T. P. White, on animals show that tin compounds are toxic; and F. Jolyet and A. Cahours found the tin alkyl compounds to be very poisonous. The rarity of tin poisoning contrasted with the extended use of that metal for cooking vessels show that the risks are very small; and, according to K. B. Lehmann, no case is known of chronic tin-poisoning from the consumption of canned foods. If the tin is alloyed with lead, R. Weber, and G. Ambühl showed that lead poisoning may occur. There are no special pharmaceutical preparations of tin or of its compounds, although powdered tin has been recommended for tape-worms. F. Marcet also found tin to be poisonous to plants. H. Micheels and P. de Heen found that colloidal tin exercises a stimulating action on germinating wheat; and G. Gimel found that a trace of stannous chloride (1 : 10000) stimulates the alcoholic fermentation of yeast.

Some reactions of analytical interest.—No precipitation occurs when stannous salts are treated with **hydrochloric acid,** but conc. soln. of stannous salts become turbid in aq. soln. owing to oxidation : $3SnCl_2+O+H_2O=2Sn(OH)Cl+SnCl_4$; the formation of the basic salt is prevented by hydrochloric acid, and oxidation is pre-vented by keeping the acidic soln. in contact with granulated tin. The soln. of stannic chloride are hydrolyzed by water : $SnCl_4+4H_2O \rightleftharpoons 4HCl+Sn(OH)_4$. Moderately conc. soln. of stannic chloride give no precipitate with hydrochloric acid or **sulphuric acid** even on long standing, but with soln. of β-stannyl chloride, sulphuric acid precipitates white stannyl sulphate. A very dil. sulphuric acid soln. of ordinary stannic chloride, sometimes gives a precipitate of basic sulphate ; and a dil. hydro-chloric acid soln. may become turbid on boiling, owing to hydrolysis. When **hydrogen sulphide** is passed into soln. of a stannous salt, not acidified too strongly, brown stannous sulphide, SnS, is precipitated (q.v.). This precipitate is soluble in conc. hydrochloric acid, so that no precipitation occurs if a large proportion of acid be present. The precipitation is complete in soln. weakly acidified. For L. Dede and P. Bonin's [16] observations on the effect of the conc. of the acid and the presence of chloride, vide the analytical reactions of lead, which are said to be similar in the case of tin. According to F. Jackson, a visible coloration is produced if the soln. has 1 part of tin in 64,000 ; C. H. Pfaff said 1 in 120,000. According to F. W. Clarke, oxalic acid hinders the precipitation. H. N. Warren also found ferrocyanides hinder the precipitation. Unlike arsenic and antimony sulphides, stannous sulphide is insoluble in aq. ammonia, ammonium carbonate, or colourless ammonium sulphide ; stannous sulphide dissolves in yellow ammonium sulphide, forming ammonium sulphostannate, $(NH_4)_2SnS_3$, and if the soln. be acidified yellow stannic sulphide is precipitated : $(NH_4)_2SnS_3+2HCl=2NH_4Cl+H_2S+SnS_2$. Stannous sulphide is soluble in soln. of potassium or sodium hydroxide, so that the sulphide is not precipitated by hydrogen sulphide from strongly alkaline soln. If heated in a stream of chlorine, or of bromine vap. and carbon dioxide ; or if heated with a mixture of ammonium chloride and nitrate, stannous sulphide is completely decomposed and volatilized. Hydrogen sulphide precipitates stannic sulphide from both α- and β-stannic salt soln. if they are not acidified too strongly. If strongly acidified, no precipitation occurs because the sulphide is soluble in the acid. With β-salts, the precipitate is formed slowly and in the hydrosol form unless flocculating salts are present. According to F. Jackson, a coloration can be detected with one part of tin in 32,000 parts of liquid. The precipitation is hindered by oxalic acid (F. W. Clarke)—*vide infra*, stannic sulphide. F. Fischer and K. Thiele found that hydrofluoric acid hinders the precipitation with stannic but not stannous or antimony salts ; and G. Vortmann and A. Metzl, the presence of phosphoric acid hinders the precipitation of stannic sulphide, but not antimony sulphide. Yellow stannic sulphide is soluble in alkali sulphide soln. from which acids re-precipitate the yellow sulphide. The sulphide is almost insoluble in aq. ammonia, ammonium carbonate, or potassium hydrosulphite ; but it readily dissolves in soln. of potassium or sodium hydroxide, sodium dioxide, alkali polysulphide, conc. boiling hydrochloric acid, aqua regia, or a soln. of oxalic acid. It dissolves incompletely in a soln. of ammonium monosulphide. It is converted into stannic acid by nitric acid, and into stannic oxide by roasting in air. A soln. of **ammonium sulphide** precipitates hydrated stannous sulphide from stannous salt soln., and hydrated stannic sulphide from stannic salt soln. The precipitate is soluble in excess as indicated above. The corresponding sulphide is precipitated from stannous or stannic salt soln. by **ammonium thioacetate,** and if the soln. is warm the precipitation is complete. G. Vortmann found that **sodium thiosulphate** gives a white precipitate with stannous and stannic salt soln., the white precipitate in both cases being a mixture of stannic hydroxide and sulphide. According to E. Donath, stannous salts reduce **sulphur dioxide,** forming stannic chloride : $3SnCl_2+6HCl+SO_2=H_2S+2H_2O+3SnCl_4$. The hydrogen sulphide acts on both the stannic and stannous salt. O. Brunck said that **sodium hydrosulphite** precipitates stannous hydrosulphite from stannous salt soln., and A. Röhrig said that the precipitate is a basic sulphite. An excess of **alkali sulphate** may precipitate β-stannic acid from soln. of salts of β-stannic acid, but not of α-stannic acid.

Stannous salt soln. give a voluminous, white, gelatinous precipitate of stannous hydroxide when treated with **alkali hydroxide ;** the precipitate is soluble in excess, forming alkali stannite, say, K_2SnO_2 ; it is also soluble in hydrochloric acid, forming stannous chloride. The precipitate often blackens, particularly if the soln. be heated or a conc. soln. of alkali-lye be used. The blackening is due either to the formation of stannous oxide : $Sn(OK)_2+H_2O=2KOH+SnO$; or the separation of finely divided tin : $2Sn(OK)_2+H_2O=2KOH+Sn+SnO(OK)_2$. The precipitation is hindered by tartaric acid. A similar precipitate is obtained with aq. **ammonia** or **alkali carbonate,** but the precipitate is very sparingly soluble in an excess. With a soln. of α-stannic salts, the precipitate produced with alkali hydroxide is likewise soluble in excess ; the precipitated hydroxide also dissolves in aq. ammonia in the absence of ammonium salts. With soln. of β-stannic salts, alkali hydroxides give a precipitate of β-stannic acid not soluble in an excess unless the precipitant is dil., for the resulting alkali β-stannate is soluble in water and dil. alkali hydroxide. The precipitation of β-stannic salts with aq. ammonia gives β-stannic acid and, unlike the result with α-stannic salts, the precipitation occurs in the presence of tartaric acid. The precipitate of α-stannic acid is obtained by adding **alkali carbonate** to a soln. of a stannic salt. α-stannic acid is soluble in excess ; this is not the case with the precipitate obtained from β-stannic salt soln. According to F. Jackson, the precipitation by ammonia with stannous salts is sensitive to 1 : 8000, and with stannic salts to 1 : 4000 ; and with sodium hydroxide in both cases to 1 : 2000. H. Demarçay, and E. Frémy found that barium, strontium, calcium, and magnesium carbonates precipitate the hydroxide from stannic salts even in the cold.

A white precipitate of mercurous chloride is produced by **mercuric chloride** with soln. of stannous salts, and if stannous salt be in excess, the precipitate will become grey owing to the separation of mercury.   Stannic salts give no precipitate with mercuric chloride.   A trace of a stannous salt added to a soln. of **auric chloride** gives a separation which is brown by transmitted light and bluish-green by reflected light—*vide* gold, and purple of Cassius (**3**. 23, 6 and 11); no precipitate occurs with stannic salts alone.   According to L. Vanino and F. Treubert, a soln. of alkali stannite when treated with **bismuth nitrate** gives a white precipitate: $Bi_2O_3+K_2SnO_2$ $=K_2SnO_3+2BiO$, which rapidly blackens : $BiO+K_2SnO_2=K_2SnO_3+Bi$.   Stannous salt soln. give a white precipitate with **potassium ferrocyanide** soluble in hydrochloric acid ; the white precipitate with **potassium ferricyanide** behaves similarly. With stannic salt soln., potassium ferrocyanide slowly forms a white turbidity, and finally a yellow, gelatinous precipitate insoluble in hydrochloric acid; potassium ferricyanide gives no precipitate with stannic salts.   A mixture of ferric chloride and potassium ferricyanide was found by J. Löwenthal to give a precipitate of Berlin blue in contact with stannous chloride ; the reaction is very sensitive.   L. Blum added **ferric chloride** to stannous chloride, and tested the resulting ferrous chloride by the brown colour produced with sulphuric acid and potassium nitrate.   According to J. Fages, **sodium nitroprusside** in alkaline soln. gives with stannous salts a greyish-red colour which turns blue when hydrochloric acid is added.   J. P. Longstaff found that **ammonium molybdate** gives a blue coloration with stannous salts, enabling one part of the latter to be detected in 1,500,000 parts of soln. G. Denigès said other reducing agents must be absent.   Stannous chloride gives a yellowish-white precipitate with **potassium iodide,** and with an excess of the reagent, orange, needle-like crystals of a double salt are formed, and with conc. soln. stannic chloride gives a yellow precipitate.   Stannous salts give a white precipitate with **oxalic acid,** but not stannic salts.   Stannous salts give a yellow precipitate with **tannin.**   J. Löwenthal found that stannous chloride gives a yellow coloration with β-stannic acid.   White precipitates are formed when **sodium phosphate** is added to a soln. of stannous or a stannic salt.   According to C. H. Pfaff, **succinic acid** and the **alkali benzoates** give white precipitates with stannous salts visible when the dilution is 1 : 10000 ;   and J. J. Berzelius found stannic salts are precipitated completely by **ammonium succinate.**   J. von Liebig found that when a stannic chloride soln. is boiled with **sodium acetate** or **potassium formate,** a precipitate is formed which re-dissolves on cooling.   C. Reichard observed a darkening occurs when uric acid is moistened with a drop of soln. of stannic chloride, not stannous chloride, and warmed with conc. soda-lye.

The metallic precipitation of tin.—According to N. W. Fischer,[17] when **zinc** or **cadmium** is immersed in an aq. soln. of a stannous or stannic salt, tin is deposited in an arborescent or dendritic form called *tin-tree*, or *arbor jovis*.   Stannous acetate, however, is not reduced under these conditions.   Tin is reduced by **iron** from the chloride or acetate provided the iron is made to dip into water in which is likewise immersed a bladder containing the tin-soln. so that the latter may mix very slowly with the water by endosmosis.   Iron does not precipitate tin from a boiling soln. of stannous chloride.   B. Schulze said that iron precipitates tin only from neutral soln., and when ferrous salts alone are present.   J. Thiele said that electrolytic iron readily precipitates tin from its salt soln., but not if the iron has been heated to redness.   N. Bouman found *ferrum reductum* will precipitate tin from soln. of stannous chloride with $2N$-HCl ; but I. M. Kolthoff found that in hydrochloric acid soln., tin is not precipitated by iron.   N. Bouman measured the potentials of the tin and iron in the soln. of stannous chloride.   At the beginning, the potential of the iron was —505, and that of tin, —533·5 ; after an hour, the potentials of both were —603, and nearly all the tin had been precipitated.   H. Reinsch said that **copper** precipitates tin from strongly acid soln. of the chloride and particularly if the soln. be boiling.   Tin is readily precipitated from its salt soln. by **magnesium or aluminium.**   With magnesium powder, said H. Mouraour, much hydrogen is evolved.   When **lead** is first immersed in a soln. of a salt tin, some tin is precipitated in small needles, but the action ceases as soon as the lead becomes covered with a coating of metallic tin. On the other hand, A. Pleischl said that tin is quantitatively precipitated by lead from soln. of the nitrate or chloride. According to M. Lazowsky, soln. of tin salts are reduced by **charcoal,** and the metal is deposited on the carbon.

The uses of tin.—On account of its silvery-white colour, its resistance to atmospheric influences and chemical agents, its low fusing temp., and its malleability, tin is used excessively in making vessels for domestic and industrial purposes. When rolled very thin, it forms tin-foil used in wrapping tobacco, etc. ; but on account of the cost of the metal, tin-foil is replaced by lead-foil whenever possible. Tin readily forms alloys with other metals, furnishing brass, bronze, britannia metal, pewter, solder, white bearing metal, etc. " Tin" articles are now made largely from sheet iron or rather mild steel coated with a layer of tin. The layer of tin protects the iron from oxidation, although once the layer of tin is broken through, oxidation goes on rapidly. Tin-amalgam is used in making mirrors. Tin condensers are used for laboratory stills. L. T. Sherwood and G. Alleman [18] employed a tin cathode in place of platinum for the electrodeposition of zinc, copper, silver, cadmium, and nickel. Tin in conjunction with an acid is used as a reducing agent. C. Willgerodt, and A. G. Page discussed its use as a catalytic agent in chlorinations— the former obtained favourable, the latter unfavourable, results. Stannic oxide is used as a polishing powder, and as an opacifying agent in glasses, glazes, and enamels ; tin sulphide or mosaic gold is used as a bronzing powder, and the two chlorides are used as a mordant, in weighting silk, and in dyeing.

The atomic weight of tin.—There was some doubt about the eq. of tin at the beginning of the nineteenth century. J. Dalton [19] represented the at. wt. by 50 when $O=7$, *i.e.* 57 when $O=8$. In 1812 J. J. Berzelius regarded the eq. as 118 when that of oxygen is 8, and he represented the formulæ of the two oxides SnO_2 and SnO_4, and titanic oxide was represented TiO_4. J. L. G. Meinecke used 36 (oxygen, 8) ; C. G. Bischoff, 117·6 (O, 8) ; and T. Thomson, 60 (O, 8). This must have been somewhat disquieting. In 1826, J. J. Berzelius halved the eq. he employed in 1812, and obtained 59 (O, 8). He therefore represented the formulæ of stannous oxide, SnO, and stannic oxide, SnO_2, the same as is done to-day. The same year, J. B. A. Dumas measured the vap. density of *spiritus fumans Libavii*, and although he obtained a value in agreement with the formula $SnCl_4$, he unfortunately assumed that the at. wt. of tin is represented by that quantity of tin which unites with two vols. of chlorine to form tin perchloride. This made the eq. of tin 29·5 when that of oxygen is 8, and the formulæ of stannic oxide and chloride were respectively SnO and $SnCl_2$, and those of stannous oxide and chloride respectively Sn_2O and SnCl. In the same year, 1826, L. Gmelin employed 59 (O, 8). P. T. Meissner, 1834, O. B. Kühn, 1837, and P. F. Cauchy, 1838, represented the eq. of tin by 58·8 or 58·9 (O, 8). Accordingly, if the at. wt. of oxygen be 16, the at. wt. of tin will approximate 118 ; and tin will be quadrivalent in the stannic compounds and bivalent in the stannous compounds. This is in harmony with Avogadro's law applied to the volatile compounds of tin, and with the extension of that law to soln. It also fits in very well with the sp. ht. rule ; and with the law of isomorphism applied to the oxides and the complex fluorides of tin, titanium, and zirconium. With this value for tin, the element fits very well in the periodic table as a member of the silicon family of elements.

The at. wt. of tin has been calculated from the ratio $Sn : SnO_2$ obtained by treating tin with nitric acid and igniting the product ; or else by roasting the metal ; thus, with $O=16$, J. L. Gay Lussac obtained 117·65 ; J. J. Berzelius, 117·65–118·08 ; G. J. Mulder, 116·30–117·00 ; C. L. Vlandeeren and G. J. Mulder, 118·16 ; J. B. A. Dumas, 118·06 ; J. D. van der Plaats, 118·09 ; J. Bongartz and A. Classen, 119·34 ; and F. W. Schmidt, 118·5. B. Brauner and H. Krepelka said that the oxidation of tin by nitric acid is useless because of the adsorbed products in the metastannic acid. It yields by simple calcination $Sn : SnO_2$, 118·02 ; and this is raised to 118·66 when the stannic oxide is fused with potassium hydrosulphate. J. D. van der Plaats also reduced stannic oxide with hydrogen, and from the ratio

$SnO_2 : O$ obtained 118·07. **J. B. A. Dumas** obtained 117·98 from the ratio $SnCl_4 : 4Ag$. **B. Brauner** and **H. Krepelka** obtained 118·7 from the ratio $SnBr_4 : 4Ag$; and H. Krepelka, 118·699. **J. Bongartz** and **A. Classen** electrolyzed a soln. of ammonium chlorostannate in one of ammonium oxalate, and from the ratio $(NH_4)_2SnCl_6 : Sn$ obtained 119·09 (O, 16); and by similarly treating potassium chlorostannate, they obtained 119·07 from the ratio $K_2SnCl_6 : Sn$. **B. Brauner** and **H. Krepelka** said that the electrolysis of ammonium chlorostannate is useless because of the difficulties involved in completely reducing the cathode deposit. This makes the result too high. **J. Bongartz** and **A. Classen** also electrolyzed a soln. of stannic bromide in one of ammonium oxalate, and from the ratio $SnBr_4 : Sn$, they calculated 118·97. **G. P. Baxter** and **H. W. Starkweather** electrolyzed a soln. of stannic chloride in 0·3N-HCl, and from the ratio $SnCl_4 : Sn$ computed 118·703. **J. Bongartz** and **A. Classen** also converted tin into stannic sulphide, separated the sulphur and weighed it as barium sulphate. From the ratios $Sn : SnS_2 : 2BaSO_4$, they obtained 119·08. **A. L. Bernoulli** computed 119·46 from physical data. Calculations of the best representative values from the observed data were made by **L. Meyer** and **K. Seubert**, and **W. Ostwald**. **F. W. Clarke** gave 119·057; and **B. Brauner**, 119·05. The International Table gave 118·70 for the best representative value in 1925.

A. Jouniaux inferred from the latent heat, and from the effect of tin on the f.p. of other metals, that above 630°, the mol. of tin is monatomic; and that about 115°, the mol. is triatomic. He also inferred that the mol. is probably complex when associated with lead, and simple when associated with cadmium and zinc.

The **atomic number** of tin is 50. **F. W. Aston** [20] found that the positive-ray analysis of tin tetramethyl gave eight **isotopes** for tin, with the respective at. wts. 116, 117, 118, 119, 120, 121, 122, and 124. The differences between these values are integral to the degree of accuracy attainable, which is 1 in 1000. **A. S. Russell, H. Collins**, and **F. H. Loring** discussed this subject. **A. L. Narayan** found the results did not agree with **J. C. McLennan's** view that the spectral displacement of the isotopes is given by the at. number multiplied by the displacement calculated from the assumed structure of the atom. **E. Rutherford** and **J. Chadwick** found no sign of **atomic disintegration** as evidenced by the emission of long-range particles when tin was bombarded by α-rays; but **H. Pettersson** and **G. Kirsch** were able to disrupt the atoms. **J. Beckenkamp**, and **H. G. Grimm** and **A. Sommerfeld** studied the electronic structure of tin.

REFERENCES.

[1] C. W. G. Kastner, *Kastner's Arch.*, **19**. 423, 1830; E. Voegelen, *Zeit. anorg. Chem.*, **30**. 330, 1902; B. Delachanal, *Compt. Rend.*, **148**. 561, 1909; G. Guillemin and B. Delachanal, *ib.*, **151**. 881, 1910; A. Sieverts, *Zeit. phys. Chem.*, **77**. 591, 1911; F. Paneth and K. Fürth, *Ber.*, **52**. B, 2020, 1919; F. Paneth, *ib.*, **53**. 1710, 1920; *Zeit. phys. Chem.*, **100**. 367, 1922; *Zeit. Elektrochem.*, **29**. 97, 1923; F. H. Newman, *Proc. Phys. Soc.*, **33**. 73, 1921; D. P. Smith, *Journ. Phys. Chem.*, **23**. 186, 1919; *Vide* 1. 7, 8; W. Vaubel, *Chem. Ztg.*, **48**. 351, 1924; *Ber.*, **57**. B, 515, 1924; A. Sieverts and W. Krumbhaar, *ib.*, **43**. 893, 1910; F. Fischer and G. Iliovici, *ib.*, **42**. 527, 1909; F. Paneth, A. Johannsen, and M. Matthies, *Ber.*, **55**. B, 769, 1922; F. Paneth and E. Rabinovitsch, *ib.*, **57**. B, 1877, 1924; F. Paneth, M. Matthies, and E. Schmidt-Hebbel, *ib.*, **55**. B, 775, 1922; F. Paneth, W. Haken, and E. Rabinovitsch, *ib.*, **57**. B, 1891, 1924; C. O. Bannister, *Journ. Inst. Metals*, **35**. 71, 1926; L. L. Bircumshaw, *Phil. Mag.*, (7), **1**. 510, 1926; E. J. Weeks, *Rec. Trav. Chim. Pays-Bas*, **45**. 201, 1926.

[2] F. Emich, *Monatsh.*, **14**. 345, 1893; A. P. Bolley, *Bull. Soc. Chim.*, (2), **7**. 399, 1867; L. Vignon, *Compt. Rend.*, **107**. 734, 1888; **108**. 96, 1889; G. Tammann, *Rec. Trav. Chim. Pays-Bas*, **42**. 547, 1923; G. Tammann and W. Köster, *Zeit. anorg. Chem.*, **123**. 196, 1922; G. Buchner, *Chem. Ztg.*, **18**. 1004, 1894; E. Jordis and W. Rosenhaupt, *ib.*, **32**. 19, 1908; *Zeit. angew. Chem.*, **21**. 60, 1908; S. Kappel, *Arch. Pharm.*, (3), **21**. 897, 1886; W. Manchot, *Ber.*, **42**. 3946, 1909; G. C. Schmidt, *Zeit. phys. Chem.*, **106**. 105, 1923; M. Traube, *Ber.*, **18**. 1885, 1885; R. Wolfenstein, *German Pat.*, *D.R.P.* 206566, 1907.

[3] H. Fleck, *Répert. Chim. Anal.*, **1**. 424, 1858; *Jahresb. Chem. Centralstelle Dresden*, **51**, 1888; J. L. Gay Lussac, *Ann. Chim. Phys.*, (2), **1**. 40, 1816; H. V. Regnault, *ib.*, (2), **62**. 337, 1836; H. F. Whittaker, *Chem. Met. Engg.*, **31**. 77, 1924; J. I. Crabtree, H. A. Hartt, and G. E. Matthews.

Journ. Ind. Eng. Chem., **16**. 13, 1924 ; W. G. Whitman and R. P. Russell, *Journ. Ind. Eng. Chem.*, **17**. 348, 1925 : M. Traube, *Ber.*, **18**. 1885, 1885 ; M. Traube-Mengarini and A. Scala, *Zeit. Koll*. **10**. 113, 1912 ; S. P. Sharples, *Chem. News*, **30**. 6, 1874 ; A. M. Knight, *ib.*, **30**. 46, 1874 ; R. Wolfenstein, *German Pat., D.R.P.* 206566, 1907 ; S. S. Sadtler, *Trans. Amer. Electrochem. Soc.*, **1**. 142, 1902 ; K. Elbs and H. Thümmel, *Zeit. Elektrochem.*, **10**. 365, 1904 ; R. Weber, *Journ. prakt. Chem.*, (2), **26**. 121, 1882 ; A. Claudius, *ib.*, (1), **9**. 161, 1836 ; A. W. Lindes, *Berl. Jahrb. Pharm.*, **32**. 99, 1831 ; C. Reichelt, *Kunst. Gewerbebl. Bayern*, **41**. 663, 1864 ; M. E. Chevreul, *Compt. Rend.*, **77**. 1137, 1873 ; E. J. Hallock, *Amer. Chem.*, **6**. 52, 1875 ; A. Wagner, *Dingler's Journ.*, **221**. 259, 1876 ; G. J. Jakobsen, *ib.*, **144**. 116, 1857 ; O. P. Watts and N. D. Whipple, *Trans. Amer. Electrochem. Soc.*, **32**. 257, 1917 ; A. J. Hale and H. S. Foster, *Journ. Soc. Chim. Ind.*, **34**. 464, 1915 ; E. Cohen, *Journ. Inst. Naval Architects*, **44**. 215, 1902 ; P. Olshausen, *Zeit. Ethnologia*, **29**. 348, 1897 ; R. E. Hall and W. H. Teaque, *Tech. Bull. Carnegie Inst.*, 15, 1924 ; K. K. Järvinen, *Zeit. Unters. Nahr. Genuss.*, **50**. 221, 1925.

[4] J. L. Gay Lussac, *Ann. Chim. Phys.*, (2), **1**. 40, 1816 ; (3), **23**. 228, 1848 ; H. Moissan, *ib.*, (6), **24**. 247, 1891 ; E. Soubeiran, *ib.*, (2), **48**. 126, 1831 ; A. J. Balard, *ib.*, (2), **57**. 252, 1834 ; *Taylor's Scientific Memoirs*, **1**. 269, 1837 ; L. P. Cailletet, *Compt. Rend.*, **68**. 393, 1869 ; M. Berthelot, *ib.*, **87**. 619, 1878 ; C. F. Rammelsberg, *Sitzber. Akad. Berlin*, 225, 1880 ; R. Lorenz, *Zeit. anorg. Chem.*, **10**. 44, 1895 ; G. Tammann and W. Köster, *ib.*, **123**. 196, 1922 ; E. Beckmann and P. Geib, *ib.*, **51**. 96, 1906 ; W. S. Hendrixson, *Journ. Amer. Chem. Soc.*, **26**. 747, 1904 ; R. Cowper, *Journ. Chem. Soc.*, **43. 76**, 1883 ; E. Divers and T. Haga, *ib.*, **47**. 623, 1885 ; E. Divers, *ib.*, **43**. 443, 1883 ; A. D. White, *Journ. Soc. Chem. Ind.*, **22**. 132, 1903 ; S. S. Sadtler, *Trans. Amer. Electrochem. Soc.*, **1**. 142, 1902 ; C. Nöllner, *Liebig's Ann.*, **115**. 233, 1860 ; O. P. Watts and N. D. Whipple, *Trans. Amer. Electrochem. Soc.*, **32**. 257, 1917 ; A. J. Hale and H. S. Foster, *Journ. Soc. Chem. Ind.*, **34**. 464, 1915 ; E. Salkowsky, *Chem. Ztg.*, **40**. 448, 1916 ; H. J. Prins, *Proc. Acad. Amsterdam*, **23**. 1449, 1922 ; W. Vaubel, *Ber.*, **57**. B, 515, 1924 ; K. K. Järvinen, *Zeit. Unters. Nahr. Genuss.*, **50**. 221, 1925 ; W. G. Whitman and R. P. Russell, *Journ. Ind. Eng. Chem.*, **17**. 348, 1925 ; *München. Med. Wochenschr*, **72**. 1161, 1925.

[5] A. F. de Fourcroy and L. N. Vauquelin, *Ann. Chim. Phys.*, (1), **24**. 229, 1797 ; A. Ditte, *ib.*, (6), **19**. 68, 1891 ; *Compt. Rend.*, **96**. 1790, 1883 ; P. Nicolardot, *ib.*, **147**. 1305, 1908 ; M. J. Fordos and A. Gélis, *ib.*, **16**. 1070, 1843 ; F. C. Calvert and R. Johnson, *Journ. Chem. Soc.*, **19**. 435, 1866 ; E. Divers and T. Shimidzu, *ib.*, **47**. 636, 1885 ; E. Divers, *ib.*, **43**. 443, 1883 ; P. G. J. Gueterbock and G, N. Nicklin, *Journ. Soc. Chem. Ind.*, **44**. 370, T, 1925 ; E. B. Hutchins, *Journ. Amer. Chem. Soc.*, **27**. 1180, 1905 ; E. Priwoznik, *Liebig's Ann.*, **164** 51, 1872 : O. B. Kühn, *ib.*, **84**. 110, 1852 ; E. Salkowsky, *Chem. Ztg.*, **40**. 448, 1916 ; M. M. P. Muir and C. E. Robbs, *Chem. News*, **45**. 69, 1882 ; H. Bassett, *ib.*, **53**. 172, 1886 ; S. L. Mitchill, *Phil. Mag.*, **7**. 83, 1800 ; O. P. Watts and N. D. Whipple, *Trans. Amer. Electrochem. Soc.*, **32**. 257, 1917 ; K. Jellinek and J. Zabowsky, *Zeit. anorg. Chem.*, **142**. 1, 1925 ; W. G. Whitman and R. P. Russell, *Journ. Ind. Eng. Chem.*, **17**. 348, 1925 ; M. G. Levi, E. Migliorini, and G. Ercolini, *Gazz. Chim. Ital.*, **38**. i, 583, 1908 ; A. J. Hale and H. S. Foster, *Journ. Soc. Chem. Ind.*, **34**. 464, 1915 ; H. Ditz, *Journ. prakt. Chem.*, (2), **78**. 354, 1908 ; J. J. Berzelius, *Ann. Chim. Phys.*, (1), **87**. 50, 1813 ; (2), **5**. 149, 1817 ; *Schweigger's Journ.*, **6**. 290, 1812 ; K. Heumann and P. Köchlin, *Ber.*, **15**. 416, 1736, 1882 ; H. Nissenson and E. Crotogino, *Chem. Ztg.*, **26**. 984, 1902 ; C. Geitner, *Ueber das Verhalten des Schwefels und der schwefligen Säure zu Wasser bei hohen druck und hohen Temperatur*, Göttingen, 1863 ; *Liebig's Ann.*, **129** 359, 1864.

[6] R. Boyle, *Reflections on the Hypothesis of Alkali and Acidum*, London, 1670 ; *Experiments and Observations on Colours*, London, 1670 ; J. J. Berzelius, *Ann. Chim. Phys.*, (1), **87**. 50, 1813 ; (2), **5**. 149, 1817 ; *Schweigger's Journ.*, **6**. 290, 1812 ; W. G. Whitman and R. P. Russell, *Journ. Ind. Eng. Chem.*, **16**. 348, 1925 ; T. Curtius and J. Rissom, *Journ. prakt. Chem.*, (2), **58**. 299, 1898 ; T. Curtius and A. Darapsky, *ib.*, (2), **61**. 420, 1900 ; R. Weber, *ib.*, (2), **6**. 351, 1872 : (2), **26**. 121, 1882 ; C. Matignon and G. Desplantes, *Compt. Rend.*, **140**. 854, 1905 ; R. Engel, *ib.*, **125**. 709, 1897 ; E. J. Maumené, *Bull. Soc. Chim.*, (2), **35**. 598, 1881 ; *Chem. News*, **44**. 59, 1881 ; H. Bassett, *ib.*, **53**. 172, 1886 ; G. Hay, *ib.*, **32**. 298, 1875 ; F. H. van Leent, *Monit. Scient.*, (4), **12**. 866, 1899 ; G. G. Henderson and J. C. Galletly, *Journ. Soc. Chem. Ind.*, **27**. 389, 1908 ; L. Loviton, *Ann. Chim. Anal. Appl.*, **14**. 325, 1909 ; E. Divers and T. Haga, *Journ. Chem. Soc.*, **47**. 623, 1885 ; E. Divers, *ib.*, **43**. 443, 1883 ; J. J. Acworth and H. E. Armstrong, *ib.*, **32**. 54, 1877 ; C. H. H. Walker, *ib.*, **63**. 845, 1893 ; C. Montemartini, *Gazz. Chim. Ital.*, **22**. i, 384, 1892 ; A. Quartaroli, *ib.*, **53**. i, 345, 1923 ; E. Ludwig and T. Hein, *Ber.*, **2**. 672, 1869 ; E. Müller, and H. Barck, *Zeit. anorg. Chem.*, **129**. 309, 1923 ; A. J. Hale and H. S. Foster, *Journ. Soc. Chem. Ind.*, **34**. 464, 1915 ; F. Fischer and G. Iliovici, *Ber.*, **42**. 527, 1909 ; F. W. Bergstrom, *Journ. Phys. Chem.*, **30**. 15, 1926.

[7] W. G. Otto, *Metallarbeiter*, 395, 1882 ; O. Emmerling, *Ber.*, **12**. 155, 1879 ; S. Natanson and G. Vortmann, *ib.*, **10**. 1459, 1877 ; *Bull. Soc. Chim.*, (2), **30**. 245, 1878 ; G. Landgrebe, *Schweigger's Journ.*, **53**. 460, 1828 ; **56**. 104, 1820 ; **60**. 184, 1830 ; P. Jolibois, *Compt. Rend.* **148**. 636, 1909 ; B. Pelletier, *Ann. Chim. Phys.*, (1), **1**. 105, 1789 ; (1), **13**. 120, 1792 ; (1), **14**, 113, 1792 ; A. Granger, *ib.*, (7), **17**. 78, 1898 ; P. Vigier, *Bull. Soc. Chim.*, (1), **2**. 5, 1861 ; *Ann. Chim. Phys.*, (4), **11**. 409, 1867 ; P. Berthier, *ib.*, (2), **33**. 180, 1826 ; H. Rose, *ib.*, (2), **51**. 5, 1832 ; *Pogg. Ann.*, **24**. 159, 1832 ; A. Schrötter, *Sitzber. Akad. Wien*, **2**. 301, 1849 ; J. E. Stead, *Journ. Soc. Chem. Ind.*, **16**. 206, 1897 ; W. Gemmel and S. L. Archbutt, *ib.*, **27**. 427, 1908 ; M. Ragg, *Œster. Chem. Ztg.*, **1**. 94, 1898 ; R. Mahn, *Jena Zeit.*, **5**. 158, 1870 ; A. C. Vivian, *Journ. Inst. Metals*, **23**. 325, 1920 ; *Metal Jud.*, **16**. 287, 1920 ; C. Künzel, *Dingler's Journ.*,

270. 166, 1888 ; F. von Friese, *ib.*, 225. 314, 1877 ; R. Lüpke, *Zeit. phys. chem. Unterr.*, 3. 280, 1890 ; P. Mellmann, *German Pat.*, *D R.P.* 45175, 1887 ; J. L. Seyboth, *ib.*, 106966, 1899 ; P. F. Nursey, *Chem. Ztg.*, 9. 641, 1885.

⁸ E. Baudrimont, *Ann. Chim. Phys.*, (4), 2. 43, 1864 ; B. Reinitzer and H. Goldschmidt, *ib.*, 81. 820, 1880 ; H. Goldschmidt, *Chem. Centrb.*, (3), 12. 489, 1881.

⁹ A. F. Gehlen, *Schweigger's Journ.*, 15. 501, 1815 ; E. Soubeiran, *Ann. Chim. Phys.*, (2), 43 407, 1830 ; Q. A. Mansuri, *Journ. Chem. Soc.*, 123. 214, 1923 ; A. Vogel, *Journ. prakt. Chem.*, (1), 6. 345, 1835 ; A. Descamps, *Compt. Rend.*, 86. 1065, 1878 ; W. Spring, *Bull. Acad. Belg.*, (4), 5. 229, 1883 ; *Ber.*, 16. 324, 1883 ; J. E. Stead, *Journ. Soc. Chem. Ind.*, 16. 200, 1897 ; *Journ. Inst. Metals*, 22. 127, 1919 (I am much indebted to the Secretary of the Institute of Metals for permission to publish Fig. 19) ; W. Campbell, *Journ. Franklin Inst.*, 154. 1, 131, 201, 1902 ; P. G. J. Gueterbock and G. N. Nicklin, *Journ. Soc. Chem. Ind.*, 44. 370, T, 1925 ; W. P. Headden, *Amer. Journ. Science,* (4), 5. 95, 1898 ; N. A. Puschin, *Journ. Russ. Phys. Chem. Soc.*, 39. 528, 1906 ; C. Bülles, *German Pat.*, *D.R.P.* 46214, 1889 ; S. Stevanovic, *Zeit. Kryst.*, 40. 326, 1905 ; P. Groth, *Chemische Krystallographie*, Leipzig, 1. 66, 1906 ; N. Parravano and P. de Cesaris, *Internat. Zeit. Metallog.*, 2. 1, 1912 ; P. Jolibois and E. L. Dupay, *Compt. Rend.*, 152. 1312, 1911 ; T. Bergman, *De arsenico*, Stockholm, 1777 ; M. Padoa, *Gazz. Chim. Ital.*, 55. ii., 975, 1925.

¹⁰ C. T. Heycock and F. H. Neville, *Journ. Chem. Soc.*, 55. 666, 1889 ; 57. 376, 1890 ; 61. 895, 1892 ; *Chem. News*, 59. 175, 1889 ; N. A. Puschin, *Journ. Russ. Phys. Chem. Soc.*, 39. 528, 1906 ; A. Matthiessen, *Pogg. Ann.*, 103. 412, 428, 1858 ; 110. 21, 190, 1860 ; 130. 50, 1867 ; *Journ. Chem. Soc.*, 20. 201, 1867 ; *B.A. Rep.*, 37, 1863 ; A. Battelli, *Mem. Accad. Torino*, (2), 36. 487, 1885 ; *Phil. Trans.*, 148. 369, 383, 1858 ; 150. 171, 161, 177, 1860 ; 156. 861, 1866 ; A. Matthiessen and C. Vogt, *ib.*, 154. 167, 1864 ; *Pogg. Ann.*, 116. 369, 1862 ; 122. 19, 1864 ; *Phil. Mag.*, (4), 23. 171, 1862 ; A. Naccari and M. Bellate, *Ellectricista*, 1. 329, 362, 1877 ; E. Elsässer, *Wied. Ann.*, 8. 455, 1879 ; C. C. Hutchins, *Amer. Journ. Science*, (3), 48. 226, 1894 ; P. Leroux, *Compt. Rend.*, 156. 1764, 1913 ; W. Campbell, *Journ. Amer. Chem. Soc.*, 26. 1306, 1904 ; C. Karmarsch, *Dingler's Journ.*, 129. 438, 1858 ; A. Guettier, *ib.*, 114. 199, 1849 ; J. R. Johnson, *Chem. Gaz.*, 13. 180, 1855 ; *Brit. Pat. No.* 817, 1854 ; L. J. Chaudet, *Ann. Chim. Phys.*, (2), 3. 376, 1816 ; G. Wertheim, *ib.*, (3), 12. 581, 1848 ; A. W. Smith, *Journ. Franklin Inst.*, 192. 69, 157, 1921 ; R. S. Williams, *Zeit. anorg. Chem.*, 55. 1, 1907 ; W. Reinders, *ib.*, 25. 113, 1900 ; J. E. Stead, *Journ. Soc. Chem. Ind.*, 16. 204, 506, 1897 ; 16. 1111, 1898 ; *Journ. Inst. Metals*, 22. 127, 1919 (I am much indebted to the Secretary of the Institute of Metals for permission to publish Fig. 18) ; C. W. G. Kastner, *Kastner's Arch.*, 19. 424, 1830 ; F. E. Gallagher, *Journ. Phys. Chem.*, 10. 93, 1906 ; A. van Bijlert, *Zeit. phys. Chem.*, 8. 343, 1891 ; E. von Maey, *ib.*, 38. 292, 1901 ; F. W. Küster, *ib.*, 12. 508, 1893 ; W. Campbell, *Journ. Franklin Inst.*, 154. 1, 131, 201, 1902 ; *Journ. Amer. Chem. Soc.*, 26. 1311, 1904 ; H. Gautier, *Bull. Soc. Enc. Nat. Ind.*, (5), 1. 1316, 1896 ; G. Charpy, *ib.*, (5), 2. 384, 1897 ; (5), 3. 670, 1898 ; *Contribution à l'étude des alliages*, Paris, 119, 1901 ; *Compt. Rend.*, 126. 1646, 1898 ; L. J. Thénard. *Ann. Chim. Phys.*, (1), 55. 276, 1805 ; N. S. Konstantinoff and W. A. Smirnoff, *Internat. Zeit. Metallog.*, 2. 154, 1912 ; *Journ. Russ. Phys. Chem. Soc.*, 43. 1201, 1911 ; A. F. Gehlen, *Schweigger's Journ.*, 20. 353, 1817 ; A. Wagner, *Bayer. Ind. Gewerbebl.*, 1, 1876 ; *Dingler's Journ.*, 221. 262, 1876 ; A. Czerwek, *Zeit. anal. Chem.*, 45. 505, 1906 ; A. M. Fairlie, *Metal Ind.*, 4. 217, 1906 ; *Engg. Rev.*, 15. 390, 1906 ; A. P. Laurie, *Journ. Chem. Soc.*, 65. 1031, 1894 ; H. le Chatelier, *Bull. Soc. Enc. Nat. Ind.*, (4). 10. 192, 1895 ; W. Reinders, *Zeit. anorg. Chem.*, 25. 113, 1900 ; G. Tammann and K. Dahl, *ib.*, 126. 104, 1923 ; W. Rollmann, *Pogg. Ann.*, 83. 77, 1851 ; 84. 275, 1851 ; 89. 90, 1853 ; T. J. Seebeck, *ib.*, 6. 148, 1826 ; T. Thomson, *Proc. Phil. Soc. Glasgow*, 1. 77, 1844 ; R. H. Thurston, *Non-ferrous Metals and Alloys*, New York, 1884 ; C R. A. Wright, *Journ. Soc. Chem. Ind.*, 13. 1014, 1894 ; A. W. Smith, *Phys. Rev.*, (7), 23. 307, 1923 ; R. Kremann and P. G. von Rehenburg, *Zeit. anorg. Chem.*, 140. 1, 1924 ; H. Behrens, *Das mikroskopische Gefüge der Metalle und Legierungen*, Hamburg, 52, 1894 ; H. Behrens and H. Baucke, *Versl. Akad. Amsterdam*, 7. 58, 1899 ; P. G. J. Gueterbock and G. N. Nicklin, *Journ. Soc. Chem. Ind.*, 44. 370, T, 1925 ; F. G. Thompson and F. Orme, *Journ. Inst. Metals*, 22. 203, 1919 ; H Endo. *Science Rep. Tohoku Univ.*, 1 ₅. 479, 1925 ; K. Honda and T. Ishigaki, *ib.*, 14. 219, 1925 ; A. Mazzucchelli and A. Vercillo, *Atti Acad. Lincei*, (6), 1. 233, 1925 ; M. Chikashige, *Zeit. anorg. Chem.*, 15 ½, 333, 1926.

¹¹ F. Rudberg, *Pogg. Ann.*, 18. 240, 1830 ; 71. 460, 1847 ; G. Wiedemann, *ib.*, 108. 393, 1859 ; W. Rollmann, *ib.*, 83. 77, 1851 ; 84. 275, 1851 ; 89. 90, 1853 ; A. Sundell, *ib.*, 149. 144, 1873 ; A. Matthiessen, *ib.*, 103. 412, 428, 1858 ; 110. 21, 190, 1860 ; 130. 50, 1883 ; *Journ. Chem. Soc.*, 20. 201, 1867 ; *B.A. Rep.*, 37, 1863 ; *Phil. Trans.*, 148. 369, 383, 1858 ; 150. 111, 161, 177, 1860 ; 156. 861, 1866 ; A. Matthiessen and C. Vogt, *ib.*, 154. 167, 1864 ; *Pogg. Ann.* 116. 369, 1862 ; 122. 19, 1864 ; *Phil. Mag.*, (4), 23. 171, 1862 ; J. W. Döbereiner, *Kastner's Arch.*, 3. 90, 1824 ; L. J. Chaudet, *Ann. Chim. Phys.*, (2), 5. 142, 1817 ; E. Becquerel, *ib.*, (4), 8. 389, 1866 ; C. C. Person, *ib.*, (3), 24. 129, 1848 ; G. Wertheim, *ib.*, (3), 12. 581, 1848 ; H. V. Regnault, *ib.*, (1), 76. 136, 1810 ; A. Riche, *Compt. Rend.*, 55. 143, 1862 ; D. Mazzotto, *Mem. 1st. Lombardo*, 16. 29, 1883 ; *Rend. 1st. Lombardo*, (2), 18. 165, 1885 ; (2), 19. 458, 1886 ; E. van Aubel, *Bull. Acad. Belg.*, (3), 15. 198, 1888 ; *Arch. Sciences Genève*, (3). 19. 105, 1888 ; *Phil. Mag.*, (5), 25. 191, 1888 ; (5), 28. 332, 1889 ; A. von Ettinghausen and W. Nernst, *Wied. Ann.*, 33. 474, 1888 ; C. L. Weber, *ib.*, 34. 580, 1888 ; N. A. Puschin, *Journ. Russ. Phys. Chem. Soc.*, 39. 353, 1906 ; W. von Lepkowsky, *ib.*, 40. 626, 1907 ; *Zeit. anorg. Chem.*, 59. 283, 1908 ;

A. Bucher, *ib.*, **98**. 97, 1916; M. Plüss, *ib.*, **93**. 1, 1915; *Zur Kenntnis der Viskosität und Dichte Geschmolzener Metalle und Legierungen*, Leipzig, 1915; J. Würschmidt, *Zeit. Physik*, **5**. 39, 1921; K. Bux, *ib.*, **14**. 316, 1923; R. Kremann and P. G. von Rehenburg, *Zeit. anorg. Chem.*, **140**. 1, 1924; K. Gilbert, *Zeit. Metallkunde*, **14**. 245, 1922; E. S. Shepherd, *Journ. Phys. Chem.*, **6**. 519, 1902; **7**. 15, 1903; S. C. Laws, *Phil. Mag.*, (6), **8**. 49, 1904; F. Guthrie, *ib.*, (5), **17**. 462, 1884; T. Thomson, *Proc. Glasgow Phil. Soc.*, **1**. 77, 1844; C. M. Marx, *Schweigger's Journ.*, **58**. 454, 1830; **60**. 1, 1830; W. Lewis, *Commercium philosophico-technicum*, London, 1766; C. T. Heycock and F. H. Neville, *Journ. Chem. Soc.*, **55**. 666, 1889; **57**. 384, 1890; **61**. 896, 1892; *Chem. News*, **62**. 280, 1890; C. R. A. Wright, *Journ. Soc. Chem. Ind.*, **13**. 1016, 1894; E. von Maey, *Zeit. phys. Chem.*, **38**. 292, 1901; G. Faè, *Atti 1st. Veneto*, (6), **5**. 201, 1886; *Lumière élect.*, **23**. 169, 1887; *Phil. Mag.*, (5), **23**. 540, 1887; H. von Jüptner, *Stahl Eisen*, **19**. 23, 1899; A. Righi, *Journ. Phys.*, (2), **3**. 355, 1884; G. Vicentini and C. Cattaneo, *Atti Accad. Lincei*, (5), **1**. 420, 1892; G. Vicentini and D. Omodei, *ib.*, (4), **4**. i, 718, 805, 1888; (4), **4**. ii, 19, 39, 75, 1888; (5), **1**. i, 419, 1892; A. Schulze, *Phys. Zeit.*, **13**. 425, 1912; F. A. Schultze, *Ann. Physik*, (4), **9**. 555, 1902; *Ueber das Verhalten einiger Legierungen zum Gesetz von Wiedemann und Franz*, Marburg, 1902; A. Stoffel, *Zeit. anorg. Chem.*, **53**. 147, 1907; G. Grube, *ib.*, **44**. 118, 1905; H. Behrens, *Das mikroskopische Gefäge der Metalle und Legierungen*, Hamburg, 63, 1894; H. Gautier, *Contribution à l'étude des alliages*, Paris, 93, 1901; *Bull. Soc. Enc. Nat. Ind.*, (5), **1**. 1293, 1896; G. Charpy, *ib.*, (5), **2**. 391, 1897; *Contribution à l'étude des alliages*, Paris, 119, 1901; *Journ. Phys.*, (3), **7**. 145, **1898**; H. Pélabon, *Compt. Rend.*, **176**. 1305, 1923; A. W. Kapp, *Ann. Physik*, (4), **6**. 771, 1901; *Ueber vollständige Gefrierpunktskurven binärer Metallegierungen*, Königsberg, 1901; W. Campbell, *Journ. Amer. Chem. Soc.*, **26**. 1309, 1904; *Journ. Franklin Inst.*, **154**. 1, 131, 201, 1902; L. H. Adams, E. D. Williamson, and J. Johnston, *ib.*, **41**. 12, 1919; A. M. Portevin, *Journ. Inst. Metals*, **29**. 257, 1923; A. E. Caswell and C. A. McKay, *Phys. Rev.*, (2), **12**. 226, 1916; T. Gnesotto and M. Binghinotto, *Atti 1st. Veneto*, (8), **12**. 1382, 1910; A. Battelli, *ib.*, (6), **5**. 1137, 1887; A. Levi, *ib.*, (8), **18**. 627, 19 6; C. R. Darling and R. H. Rinaldi, *Proc. Phys. Soc.*, **36**. 281, 1924; A. W. Smith, *Journ. Franklin Inst.*, **192**. 69, 157, 1921; H. Kopp, *Liebig's Ann. Suppl.*. **3**. 289, 1864; A. P. Laurie, *Journ. Chem. Soc.*, **65**. 1031, 1894; H. le Chatelier, *Bull. Soc. Enc. Nat. Ind.*, (4), **10**. 192, 1895; *Rev. Gén. Sciences, Pure Appl.*, **6**. 529, 1895; *Contribution à l'étude des alliages*, Paris, 441, 1901; G. Spadavecchia, *Nuovo Cimento*, (4), **9**. 432, 1899; E. S. Shepherd, *Journ. Phys. Chem.*, **7**. 15, 1903; C. di Capua, *Atti Accad. Lincei*, (5), **31**. i, 162, 1922; (5), **33**. i, 141, 1924; *Gazz. Chim. Ital.*, **55**. ii., 582, 1925; D. H. Andrews and J. Johnston, *Journ. Inst. Metals*, **32**. 385, 1924; K. Honda and T. Ishigaki, *Science Rep. Tohoku Univ.*, **14**. 219, 1925; C. H. Green, *Trans. Amer. Inst. Min. Met. Eng.*, **71**. 651, 1925; P. G. J. Gueterbock and G. N. Nicklin, *Journ. Soc. Chem. Ind.*, **44**. 370, T, 1925; C. C. Hutchins, *Amer. Journ. Science*, (3), **48**. 226, 1894; K. Bornemann and P. Siebe, *Zeit. Metallkunde*, **14**. 329, 1922; K. Gilbert, *ib.*, **14**. 245, 1922.

¹² F. E. Brown and J. E. Snyder, *Journ. Amer. Chem. Soc.*, **47**. 2671, 1925.

¹³ H. Moissan, *Bull. Soc. Chim.*, (3), **13**. 959, 1859; *Compt. Rend.*, **125**. 841, 1898; E. Vigouroux, *ib.*, **123**. 115, 1896; J. J. Berzelius, *Pogg. Ann.*, **1**. 220, 1824; E. Gudeman, *Met. Chem. Engg.*, **8**. 680, 1910; C. Winkler, *Journ. prakt. Chem.*, (1), **91**. 193, 1864; F. Malméjac, *Journ. Pharm. Chim.*, (6), **13**. 169, 1901; J. C. Bull, *Brit. Pat. No.* 19148, 1889; K. B. Lehmann, *Arch. Hyg.*, **63**. 67, 1907; *München. Med. Wochschr.*, **49**. 340, 1902; O. Ruff and B. Bergdahl, *Zeit. anorg. Chem.*, **106**. 76, 1919; F. Pfaff, *Industrie Blatt.*, 102, 1878; W. G. Whitman and R. P. Russell, *Journ. Ind. Eng. Chem.*, **17**. 348, 1925; F. P. Hall, *Journ. Amer. Chem. Soc.*, **4**. 440, 1883; F. A. Norton, *ib.*, **28**. 1503, 1906; J. Trummer, *Veränderung der Weine beim Aufbewahren in Metallgefässen*, Klosterheuberg, 1907; D. Klein and A. Berg, *Compt. Rend.*, **102**. 1170, 1886; I. J. Redwood, *Journ. Soc. Chem. Ind.*, **5**. 362, 1886; W. Ipatieff, *Ber.*, **35**. 1053, 1902; J. Merrick, *Amer. Chem.*, **4**. 289, 1874; G. Heinzelmann, *Zeit. Spiritusind.*, **27**. 399, 1904; H. Fleck, *Répert. Chim. Anal.*, **1**. 424, 1858; *Jahresb. Chem. Centralstelle Dresden*, 51, 1888; A. Gawalowsky, *Zeit. anal. Chem.*, **38**. 769, 1899; C. F. Böhringer, *German Pat.*, *D.R.P.* 121835, 1900; F. H. Jeffery, *Trans. Faraday Soc.*, **20**. 392, 1925; C. O. Henke and O. W. Brown, *Journ. Phys. Chem.*, **28**. 71, 1924; L. Nathan and A. Schmidt, *Centrb. Bakteriol.*, (2), **16**. 482, 1906; F. Schönfeld, *Wochschr. Brauw.*, **21**. 133, 1904; J. Dehnicke, *ib.*, **25**. 224, 1908; C. Sellenscheidt, *ib.*, **21**. 144, 1904; J. H. Matthews, *Journ. Phys. Chem.*, **9**. 659, 1905; A. Hébert, *Bull. Soc. Chim.*, (3), **29**. 316, 1903; *Compt. Rend.*, **136**. 682, 1903; K. Dinklage, *Zeit. Ges. Brauw.*, **27**. 209, 1904; E. Gudeman, *Met. Chem. Engg.*, **8**. 680, 1910; E. Salkowsky, *Chem. Ztg.*, **40**. 448, 1916; O. W. Brown and C. O. Henke, *Journ. Phys. Chem.*, **27**. 739, 1923; W. R. Hodgkinson, *Journ. Soc. Chem. Ind.*, **37**. 86, 1918; A. Korczynsky, *Bull. Soc. Chim.*, (4), **29**. 283, 1921; U. Ehrhardt and G. Pfleiderer, *Gesammelte Abh. Kennt. Kohle*, **5**. 576, 1920; F. H. Rhodes and J. T. Carty, *Journ. Ind. Eng. Chem.*, **17**. 909, 1925; K. K. Järvinen, *Zeit. Unters. Nahr. Genuss.*, **50**. 221, 1925.

¹⁴ G. Tammann and P. Schafmeister, *Zeit. anorg. Chem.*, **138**. 219, 1924.

¹⁵ J. D. Mann, *Forensic Medicine and Toxicology*, London, 507, 1908; O. Hehner, *Analyst*, **5**. 1343, 1880; B. Dyer, *ib.*, **5**. 222, 1880; F. P. Wightwick, *Lancet*, 1121, 1888; W. A. Campbell, *Therap. Gaz.*, (3), **9**. 152, 1893; T. P. White, *Pharm. Journ.*, (3), **17**. 166, 1886; A. P. Luff and G. H. Metcalfe, *Brit. Med. Journ.*. i, 833, 1890; T. L. Phipson, *Chem. News*, **59**. 255, 1889; F. Marcet, *Ann. Chim. Phys.*, (2), **29**. 200, 1829; H. Micheels and P. de Heen, *Bull. Acad. Belg.*, **119**, 1907; R. Weber, *Lingler's Journ.*, **232**. 153, 264, 1879; G. Ambühl, *Chem. Ztg.*, **4**. 7, 1880; E. Ungar and G. Bodländer, *ib.*, **8**. 1454, 1884; **9**. 873, 1885; **11**. 593, 1887; K. B. Lehmann,

Arch. Hyg., **45**. 88, 1902 ; T. Günther, *Zeit. Unters. Nahr. Genuss.*, **2**. 915, 1899 ; A. Eckardt, *ib.*, **18**. 193, 1909 ; R. Kayser, *ib.*, **4**. 29, 1890 ; *Forschungsber. Lebensmitt.*, **1**. 63, 1894 ; G. Gimel, *Compt. Rend.*, **147**. 1324, 1908 ; C. Girard, A. Riche, and G. Pouchet, *Ann. d'Hyg.*, (3), **27**. 44, 1892 ; F. Jolyet and A. Cahours, *Ber.*, **2**. 312, 1869 ; W. Vaubel, *München. Med. Wochenschr.*, **72**. 1161, 1725.
    [16] H. N. Warren, *Chem. News*, **61**. 63, 1890 ; J. P. Longstaff, *ib.*, **80**. 282, 1899 ; F. W. Clarke, *ib.*, **21**. 124, 1870 ; G. Vortmann and A. Metzl, *Zeit. anal. Chem.*, **44**. 525, 1905 ; G. Vortmann, *Ber.*, **12**. 2307, 1889 ; L. Vanino and F. Treubert, *ib.*, **31**. 1113, 1898 ; C. H. Pfaff, *Handbuch der analytischen Chemie*, Altona, **2**. 337, 1822 ; F. Jackson, *Journ. Amer. Chem. Soc.*, **25**. 992, 1903 ; F. Fischer and K. Thiele, *Zeit. anorg. Chem.*, **67**. 302, 1910 ; O. Brunck, *Liebig's Ann.*, **336**. 283, 1904 ; A. Röhrig, *Journ. prakt. Chem.*, (2), **37**. 217, 1888 ; J. Löwenthal, *ib.*, (1), **60**. 267, 1853 ; (1), **77**. 321, 1859 ; E. Donath, *Zeit. anal. Chem.*, **36**. 663, 1897 ; L. Blum, *ib.*, **44**. 10, 11, 1905, J. I. Crabtree, H. A. Hartt and G. E. Matthews, *Journ. Ind. Eng. Chem.*, **16**. 13, 1924 ; L. Dede and P. Bonin, *Ber.*, **55**. B, 2327, 1922 ; J. Fages, *Ann. Chim. Anal. App.*, **7**. 442, 1902 ; G. Denigès, *Journ. Pharm. Chim.*, (5), **30**. 207, 1894 ; J. J. Berzelius, *Ann. Chim. Phys.*, (1), **94**. 187, 1815 ; J. von Liebig, *Liebig's Ann.*, **17**. 69, 1836 ; E. Frémy, *Ann. Chim. Phys.*, (2), **23**. 393, 1823 ; H. Demarçay, *ib.*, (2), **55**. 398, 1833 ; C. Reichard, *Pharm. Centrh.*, **47** 391, 1906.
    [17] N. W. Fischer, *Pogg. Ann.*, **9**. 263, 1827 ; 10. 603, 1827 ; *Das Verhältniss der chemischen Verwandtschaft zur galvanischen Electricität in Versuchen dargestellt*, Berlin, 1830 ; M. Lazowsky, *Journ. Chim. Méd.*, (3), **3**. 629, 1847 ; *Chem. Gaz.*, **6**. 43, 1848 ; A. Pleischl, *Sitzber. Akad. Wien*, **43**. 555, 1861 ; H. Reinsch, *Journ. prakt. Chem.*, (1), **24**. 248, 1841 ; B. Schulze, *Ber.*, **23**. 974, 1890 ; I. M. Kolthoff, *Rec. Trav. Chim. Pays-Bas*, **39**. 606, 1920 ; N. Bouman, *ib.*, **39**. 537, 711, 1920 ; J. Thiele, *Liebig's Ann.*, **263**. 361, 1891 ; H. Mouraour, *Compt. Rend.*, **130**. 141, 1900.
    [18] L. T. Sherwood and G. Alleman, *Journ. Amer. Chem. Soc.*, **29**. 1065, 1907 ; C. Willgerodt, *Journ. prakt. Chem.*, (2), **34**. 284, 1886 ; A. G. Page, *Liebig's Ann.*, **225**. 199, 1884 ; Anon., *Metal Ind.*, **25**. 418, 1924.
    [19] J. L. Gay Lussac, *Ann. Chim. Phys.*, (1), **80**. 160, 1811 ; J. B. A. Dumas, *ib.*, (2), **33**. 386, 1826 ; (3), **55**. 154, 1859 ; *Compt. Rend.*, **45**. 409, 1857 ; J. D. van der Plaats, *ib.*, **100**. 52, 1885 ; J. J. Berzelius, *Gilbert's Ann.*, **40**. 235, 1812 ; *Pogg. Ann.*, **8**. 184, 1826 ; *Afhand. Fysik. Kemi*, **5**. 144, 1812 ; G. J. Mulder, *Journ. prakt. Chem.*, (1), **48**. 259, 1849 ; *Liebig's Ann.*, **72**. 212, 1849 ; *Scheik. Onderz. Utrecht*, (1), **5**. 253, 1851 ; C. L. Vlandeeren and G. J. Mulder, *ib.*, (2), **2**. 150, 1859 ; *Répert. Chim. Appl.*, **1**. 237, 1859 ; J. Bongartz and A. Classen, *Ber.*, **21**. 2900, 1888 ; F. W. Schmidt, *ib.*, **27**. 2743, 1894 ; F. W. Clarke, *Phil. Mag.*, (5), **12**. 101, 1881 ; *Chem. News*, **63**. 76, 1891 ; *A Recalculation of the Atomic Weights*, Washington, 290, 1910 ; L. Meyer and K. Seubert, *Die Atomgewichte der Elemente*, Leipzig, 26, 1883 ; W. Ostwald, *Lehrbuch der allgemeinen Chemie*, Leipzig, **1**. i, 124, 1903 ; B. Brauner in R. Abegg, *Handbuch der anorganischen Chemie*, Leipzig, **3**. ii, 523, 1909 ; G. P. Baxter and H. W. Starkweather, *Journ. Amer. Chem. Soc.*, **42**. 905, 1920 ; B. Brauner and H. Krepelka, *ib.*, **42**. 917, 1920 ; H. Krepelka, *ib.*, **42**. 925, 1920 ; A. L. Bernoulli, *Zeit. Elektrochem.*, **13**. 554, 1907 ; *Phys. Zeit.*, **9**. 745, 1908 ; *Ber. deut. phys. Ges.*, **6**. 636, 1908 ; J. Dalton, *A New System of Chemical Philosophy*, Manchester, **2**. 352, 1810 ; J. L. G. Meinecke, *Die chemische Messkunst*, Halle, 1817 ; C. G. Bischoff, *Lehrbuch der Stöchiometrie*, Erlangen, 1819 ; T. Thomson, *Ann. Phil.*, (2), **2**. 120, 1821 ; L. Gmelin, *Leonhard's Taschenbuch Min.*, **19**. 429, 1825 ; A. Jouniaux, *Bull. Soc. Chim.*, (4), **37**. 67, 1925 ; P. T. Meissner, *Chemische Æquivalenten-oder Atomenlehre*, Wein, 1834 ; O. B. Kühn, *Lehrbuch der Stöchiometrie*, Leipzig, 1837 ; P. F. Cauchy, *Principes généraux de chimie inorganique*, Bruxelles, 1838.
    [20] F. W. Aston, *Phil. Mag.*, (6), **42**. 140, 1921 ; (6), **45**. 934, 1923 ; (6), **49**. 1191, 1925 ; *Nature*, **109**. 813, 1922 ; E. Rutherford and J Chadwick, *ib.*, **107**. 41, 1921 ; **113**. 457, 1924 ; *Phil. Mag.*, (6), **42**. 809, 1921 ; (6), **44**. 417, 1922 ; A. S. Russell, *ib.*, (6), **48**. 365, 1924 ; A. L. Narayan, *Nature*, **112**. 651, 1923 ; J. C. McLennan and D. S. Ainslie, *Proc. Roy. Soc.*, **101**. A, 342, 1922 ; J. C. McLennan, D. S. Ainslie, and F. M. Cale, *ib.*, **102**. A, 33, 1922 ; F. H. Loring, *Chem. News*, **125**. 5, 1922 ; H. Collins, *ib.*, **131**. 403, 1925 ; J. Beckenkamp, *Zeit. anorg. Chem.*, **143**. 394, 1925 ; H. G. Grimm and A. Sommerfeld, *Zeit. Physik*, **36**. 36, 1926 ; H. Pettersson and A. Kirsch, *Atomzertrümmerung*, Leipzig, 104, 1926.

§ 6. The Alloys of Tin with the Alkali Metals

W. Guertler [1] studied the affinity of tin for the metals generally. P. Lebeau made a tin-lithium alloy by the electrolysis of a mixture of potassium and lithium chlorides, using a tin cathode. J. L. Gay Lussac and L. J. Thénard found that a mixture of 7 vols. of tin-filings to 2 vols. of potassium united with slight incandescence, forming a fusible, brittle alloy which exhibited a fine-grained fracture ; oxidized quickly in air ; and effervesced when treated with water. If a larger proportion of potassium be employed, the alloy takes fire when pulverized in air. According to G. S. Sérullas, when granulated tin is heated with potassium tartrate, or if stannic oxide be heated with charred potassium tartrate, and carbon, a pyrophoric alloy is formed which evolves hydrogen slowly when in contact with water. G. Bredig and F. Haber obtained the alloy by the disintegration of the metal electrode in electrolysis, by an alternating current; P. Lebeau, by the method used for the lithium alloys. C. T. J. Vautin described the preparation of alloys of tin with the alkali metals by electrolysis. According to D. P. Smith, the two elements are miscible in all proportions in the fused state; and most of the alloys melt at a temp. higher than the m.p. of the components. The alloys rapidly attack glass and even steel, so that the results of the thermal analysis, indicated in Fig. 29, were not very conclusive. Evidence was obtained of the existence of **potassium monostannide**, KSn; **potassium hemistannide**, K_2Sn; **potassium distannide**, KSn_2, with a transition point at 413°; and of **potassium tetrastannide**, KSn_4. F. W. Bergstrom observed a break in the solubility curve of tin in a soln. of potassium amide in liquid ammonia, corresponding with K_4Sn_8 or KSn_2. G. Tammann studied the electrode potential and chemical properties of these alloys;

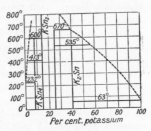

FIG. 29.—Equilibrium Curves of the Potassium-Tin Alloys.

and R. Kremann and E. Pressfreund found evidence of K_2Sn, KSn_2, KSn_4, and possibly KSn, in their measurements of the electromotive behaviour of these alloys.

J. L. Gay Lussac and L. J. Thénard prepared an alloy of tin with sodium by a process analogous to that which they employed for the potassium alloy; G. S. Sérullas obtained the alloy by heating a mixture of tin with charred soap; and C. Löwig, and H. Caron, emphasized the need for the exclusion of air. C. T. Heycock and F. H. Neville found that the f.p. of tin was raised 11·61° by adding 4·57 at. per cent. of sodium. A. Weiller made an alloy of the two metals on a large scale; C. T. J. Vautin made it electrolytically; and C. Bredig and F. Haber, by the process indicated above. H. Bailey melted tin with an excess of sodium, and heated the product in a closed crucible and obtained a tin-sodium alloy approximating **sodium hemistannide**, Na_2Sn. W. Hume-Rothery said that the crystals show octahedral cleavage. W. Biltz and W. Holverscheit gave 12 Cals. for the heat of formation; 45 Cals. for the heat of oxidation: 3·111 for the sp. gr. at 25°, and 52·9 for the mol. vol. when the additive rule gave 63·7. P. Lebeau separated **sodium tetritastannide**, Na_4Sn, by treating a sodium-tin alloy with liquid ammonia. C. A. Kraus and H. F. Kurtz observed the formation of the tetritastannide as an unstable compound in the reduction of tin salts by sodium amalgam. W. Biltz and W. Holverscheit gave 21 Cals. for the heat of formation; 47 Cals. for the heat of oxidation; 2·315 for the sp. gr. at 25°, and 91·0 for the mol. vol. when the additive rule gave 111·1. C. H. Mathewson made a thermal analysis of the tin-sodium alloys. The m.p. curve consists of six branches, Fig. 30. There are two well-marked maxima at 477° and 27·92 per cent. of sodium, and 576° and 16·23 per cent. of sodium respectively. Five distinct compounds of tin and sodium exist, namely: (1) sodium tetritastannide, Na_4Sn, which at 405° undergoes transformation according to the equation $Na_4Sn \rightleftharpoons 0.091Na_2Sn+$ fused alloy (3·82 mols $Na+0.91$ mol Sn).

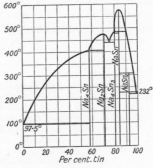

FIG. 30.—Equilibrium Curves of the Sodium-Tin Alloys.

F. Paneth and co-workers found that this alloy gave no iron hydride when treated with acids. (2) Sodium hemistannide, Na_2Sn, which, according to C. H. Mathewson, has a m.p. of 477°, and, according to W. Hume-Rothery, 470°. (3) **Sodium tritetritastannide**, Na_4Sn_3, is the hardest and most brittle of the five compounds. At 478°, it melts with transformation according to the equation $Na_4Sn_3 \rightleftharpoons 0.375NaSn + $fused alloy (3·62 mols Na + 2·62 mols Sn). It occurs in two crystalline modifications, α and β; the transformation of the β-into α-crystals is attended by a considerable increase of vol. W. Biltz and W. Holverscheit gave 36 Cals. for the heat of formation; 43 Cals. for the heat of oxidation; 3·570 for the sp. gr. at 25°; and 125·6 for the mol. vol. when the additive rule gave 143·7. (4) According to C. H. Mathewson, **sodium mono-stannide**, NaSn, with a m.p. of 576° undergoes, at 483°, a polymorphic transformation. W. Biltz and W. Holverscheit gave 11 Cals. for the heat of formation of the monostannide; 42 Cals. for the heat of oxidation; 3·990 for the sp. gr. at 25°, and 35·5 for the mol. vol. when the additive rule gives 40·0 Cals. (5) **Sodium distannide**, $NaSn_2$, is the softest and toughest of the five compounds, and, like NaSn, has the appearance of tin. F. W. Bergstrom found a break in the solubility curve of tin in a soln. of sodium amide in liquid ammonia, corresponding with Na_4Sn_8 or $NaSn_2$. W. Biltz and W. Holverscheit found that at 305°, it undergoes transformation in accordance with the equation $NaSn_2 \rightleftharpoons 0.667NaSn$ + fused alloy (0·333 mol Na + 1·333 mols Sn); they gave 15 Cals. for the heat of formation of distannide; 39 Cals. for the heat of oxidation; 4·725 for the sp. gr.; and 55·1 for the mol. vol. when the additive rule gives 56·3. According to C. H. Mathewson, a freshly cut surface of the tetrita- or hemi-stannide soon becomes covered in the air with a bronze film, but under vaseline, the surface of the former resembles that of tin, whilst the latter is steel-blue; the tritetri-tastannide shows a pale blue colour on a fresh surface; no film colour appears on oxidation. R. Kremann and J. Gmachl-Pammer found that the electrical conductivity curve showed singular points corresponding with Na_4Sn, Na_2Sn, NaSn, and $NaSn_2$. G. Tammann studied the electrode potential and chemical properties of these alloys; A. Battelli, the thermoelectric properties; and C. Vickers, the deoxidizing qualities for copper and bronze,

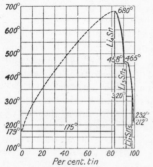

FIG. 31.—Equilibrium Curves of Lithium-Tin Alloys.

G. Masing and G. Tammann[2] showed that lithium and tin form three compounds. The f.p. curves are indicated in Fig. 31. There is a maximum on the curve at 680°, representing **lithium tetritastannide**, Li_4Sn; a flat maximum at 465°, representing **lithium ditritastannide**, Li_3Sn_2; and an unstable compound, **lithium hemipentastannide**, Li_2Sn_5, reacting with the melt at 320°.

REFERENCES.

[1] G. Tammann, *Zeit. anorg. Chem.*, **118**. 92, 1921; C. Löwig, *Liebig's Ann.*, **84**. 308, 1852; H. Bailey, *Chem. News*, **65**. 18, 1892; P. Lebeau, *Compt. Rend.*, **130**. 502, 1900; *Bull. Soc. Chim.*, (3), **33**. 250, 1900; C. H. Mathewson, *Zeit. anorg. Chem.*, **46**. 94, 1905; D. P. Smith, *ib.*, **56**. 109, 1907; A. Weiller, *Berg. Hütt. Ztg.*, **56**. 4, 1897; C. T. J. Vautin, *German Pat.*, *D.R.P.* 81710, 1894; C. T. Heycock and F. H. Neville, *Journ. Chem. Soc.*, **55**. 666, 1889; **57**. 380, 1890; H. Caron, *Compt. Rend.*, **48**. 440, 1859; A. Battelli, *Atti 1st. Veneto*, (6), **5**. 1137, 1886; G. Bredig and F. Haber, *Ber.*, **31**. 2741, 1898; F. Haber, *Zeit. Elektrochem.*, **4**. 410, 1898; *Trans. Amer. Electrochem. Soc.*, **2**. 189, 1902; F. Haber and M. Sack, *ib.*, **8**. 245, 1902; M. Sack, *Ueber die Entstehung und Bedeutung von Natriumlegierungen bei der kathodischen Polarisation*, Karlsruhe, 1903; *Zeit. anorg. Chem.*, **34**. 286, 1903; C. Vickers, *Trans. Amer. Electrochem. Soc.*, **40**. 15, 1921; G. S. Sérullas, *Ann. Chim. Phys.*, (2), **21**. 200, 1822; *Journ. Phys.*, **93**. 115, 1821; W. Guertler, *Metall Erz*, **22**. 199, 1925; J. L. Gay Lussac and L. J. Thénard, *ib.*, (2), **1**. 40, 1816; R. Kremann and J. Gmachl-Pammer, *Zeit. Metallkunde*, **12**. 257, 1920; R. Kremann and E. Pressfreund, *ib.*, **13**. 19, 1921; F. Paneth, A. Johannson, and M. Matthies, *Ber.*, **55**. B, 769, 1922; W. Biltz and W. Holverscheit, *Zeit. anorg. Chem.*, **140**. 261, 1924; C. A. Kraus and H. F. Kurtz, *Journ. Amer. Chem. Soc.*, **47**. 43, 1925; F. W. Bergstrom, *Journ. Phys. Chem.*, **30**. 12, 1926; W. Hume-Rothery, *Journ. Inst. Metals*, **35**. 295, 1926.
[2] G. Masing and G. Tammann, *Zeit. anorg. Chem.*, **67**. 183, 1910.

§ 7. The Alloys of Tin and Copper

The term **bronze** is applied to the alloys of copper and tin, although alloys with proportions of these two elements within more or less ill-defined ranges may receive specific names, *vide infra*. The Alloy Committee [1] recommended that the term bronze be reserved for copper-tin alloys containing over 50 per cent. of copper ; and that the presence of one or more metals, intentionally added, be denoted by a prefix—*e.g.* an alloy with 1 per cent. of zinc, 29 per cent. of tin, and 70 per cent. of copper would be a *zinc-bronze*. If additional metals be present they can be indicated in a similar way, or the term *complex bronze* may be used when it is not necessary to mention the other elements specifically. The history of bronze has been discussed in connection with copper, **3**. 21, 1 ; and brass, **4**. 30, 21. A large number of analyses of ancient bronzes from different countries, and of Chinese and Japanese art-bronzes, have been reported.[2] The bronzes made by the ancients varied considerably in the proportion of tin and copper employed. Other ingredients were added purposely, or occurred as accidental impurities from the use of complex ores. The ancients made instruments of various kinds from these alloys, and weapons of war and of chase of great strength, with a keen cutting edge, and harder than iron—rivalling steel.

The presence of tin hardens the copper, and the resulting alloy can take a high polish, its m.p. is comparatively low, and when melted, it can be cast very well. The addition of a small proportion of tin to copper, however, prevents the product rolling well when hot, and if more tin is used, the alloy is not malleable when cold. Bronze is tempered by heating it to the required temp., and rapidly cooling in water : this is the reverse of the process employed in tempering steel. Modern bronzes are rarely simple binary alloys ; and are usually ternary or quaternary. Sometimes even more constituents are added. Among the commercial varieties of bronze are the so-called **gun-metals,** which were formerly much employed in the construction of ordnance. Each country seems to have preferred a mixture of its own which usually varied from 8–11 parts of copper to one of tin. The typical alloy is 90 : 10. The thermal history of the alloy is almost as important as a knowledge of its chemical composition. The modern gun-metals are frequently ternary alloys containing zinc, as well as copper and tin, and are sometimes grouped with the so-called *machine-brasses*. These alloys are employed for different parts of machinery, *e.g.* the bearings and parts subjected to great friction. They are also employed for parts of pumps, propeller blades and boxes, mechanical instruments, etc.

J. A. Phillips emphasized as special characteristics of **phosphor-bronze :**

Its freedom from corrosion by salt water, which is apparently largely due to its freedom from zinc ; its high qualities as a mechanical constructive material as compared with an ordinary zinc-free bronze ; the small effect which a rise of temp. has upon its mechanical properties, which remain practically unimpaired at temp. at which zinc copper alloys exhibit serious drops in strength ; and the fact that a spark cannot be readily obtained from it by a blow. Phosphor-bronzes of high phosphorus content possess low friction coefficients for most metals, and are hard enough to resist abrasion well.

The properties of these alloys were described by H. Behrens,[3] X. Müller, E. Priwoznik, J. B. Grief, W. Hampe, E. S. Sperry, W. C. Roberts-Austen, H. Morin, S. Kalischer, E. J. Maumené, etc. The subject is discussed in A. H. Hiorns, *Mixed Metals or Metallic Alloys* (London, 1901) ; W. T. Brannt, *The Metallic Alloys* (Philadelphia, 1908). Alloys of copper and tin with a small quantity of phosphorus and maybe other elements are called **phosphor-bronzes.** They are used for making tubes, wire-ropes, springs, screws, pinions, valves, steam and boiler fittings, pumps, axle-bearings, bushes, cog-wheels, parts of machinery exposed to great friction, ornamental castings, etc. In 1848, A. and H. Parkes patented the use of phosphorus in conjunction with copper, and brass; but they did not mention bronze. F. A. Abel described some results obtained with phosphorized copper; and H. de Ruolz and A. de Fontenay observed the great increase in tenacity and resistance to abrasion obtained by adding phosphorus to bronze, and C. Künzel and co-workers demonstrated the improvement in the mechanical properties of bronze to which a little phosphorus had been added. The proportion of phosphorus rarely exceeds 1 per cent., and if upwards of 4 per cent. be present, the alloy is considered to be useless. E. S. Sperry said that if the phosphor-bronze is to be rolled it should have no more than 0·5 per cent. of phosphorus and no zinc. A. Phillips reported nearly 100 analyses of commercial phosphor-bronzes, and in these the copper ranged from 82·3–97·1 per cent.; tin from 2·2–14·5 per cent.; lead in seven samples up to 6·23 per cent; zinc, in six samples up to 2·74 per cent.; and phosphorus up to 1·56 per cent. Analyses have been reported by J. Bayschinger and K. Stölzel, E. Priwoznik, A. Ledebur, C. Künzel, etc. Phosphor-bronze resists the corrosive action of sea-water better than copper; and mine-water, better than iron or steel. A. Weiller devised an alloy of copper, tin, and silicon, called silicon bronze, said to be specially adapted for telegraphic and telephonic purposes, since its electrical conductivity is much higher than that of phosphor-bronze. The alloys used in the manufacture of bells—bell-metals—usually contain copper, 74–85 per cent.; tin, 15–26 per cent. Other proportions are used to produce different sounds, and other metals—zinc, iron, lead, bismuth, silver, antimony, or manganese—may be added either for cheapness or to produce a special tone. The typical alloy is 80 : 20. The sound from brass bells is of inferior quality. In some of the white table bells, tin is the dominant component. Some white alloys, usually approximating Cu_4Sn, admit of a brilliant polish, and were formerly much used for mirrors, and hence were called speculum metals. They are now sometimes used in the construction of mirrors for optical instruments. Their composition ranges from 30–34 per cent. tin, and 62–69 per cent. copper. In some cases lead, zinc, arsenic, silver, nickel, or antimony has been added. The typical alloy is 70 : 30. The term art-bronzes is applied to alloys which are employed for statuary, vases, and ornaments of various kinds. In a number of statues, the proportion of copper ranges from 72–91 per cent.; tin, 0·14–10·2 per cent.; zinc, 0·1–26 per cent.; lead, up to 3 per cent.—small proportions of iron, nickel, and antimony may also be present.

According to A. F. Gehlen,[4] if the two elements, tin and copper, are simply fused together, bronze is produced; if the mixture be not stirred, two liquid layers containing very different proportions of the two elements are formed. The combination is attended without the production of light or heat. A similar result was obtained by C. J. B. Karsten, C. Bischoff, A. Guettier, and W. Campbell with molten tin. Segregation phenomena were studied by O. Bauer and H. Arnd, and G. Masing. Bronze is usually manufactured by melting a charge of say 90 lbs. in fireclay or plumbago crucibles; and for large castings, a reverberatory furnace or a large number of crucibles is employed. The copper is well melted and kept in fusion some time before the tin is added. The oxidation which occurs during the melting removes 3 or 4 parts of copper to one of tin, and due allowance must be made for this loss. H. S. Primrose has discussed the preparation of gun-metal; and F. W. Rowe, the effect of the casting temp. on the metal. In preparing small samples, and to avoid oxidation losses, E. S. Shepherd and G. B. Upton added tin to molten copper in an atm. of coal-gas. Other methods were used by A. P. Laurie, A. Saxer, H. Behrens, and A. Sentex and co-workers. E. Lenssen showed that if a little cupric salt be added to a not too conc. soln. of stannous oxide in alkali-lye, a black flocculent precipitate is formed which acquires a yellow metallic lustre under the burnishing-tool, and consists of a tin-copper alloy mixed with some cuprous and stannous oxides. W. Spring said that the alloy is formed when a mixture of powdered tin and copper is subjected to a high press.—vide 1. 13, 18. H. Wiess studied the mutual diffusion of copper and tin. B. E. Curry obtained the alloy electrolytically from a soln. of salts of copper and tin, oxalic acid, and ammonium oxalate. A current density of 0·2–0·3 amps. was used and a rotating anode. Tartrates were not satisfactory. C. H. Proctor used a bath of a soln. containing the two metal sulphides, an alkali sulphide, and potassium cyanide ; C. Langbein used a soln. of cupric phosphate, stannous chloride, and sodium pyrophosphate ; C. de la Salzede, a soln. of cupric and stannous chlorides, potassium carbonate and cyanide, but C. Langbein said only tin is deposited from this soln. G. Ongaro, S. Ledermann, F. Förster, F. C. Mathers and S. Sowder, R. Kremann and co-workers, W. D. Treadwell and E. Beckh, studied the conditions for the simultaneous electrodeposition of tin and copper.

The equilibrium diagram for the bronzes, the copper-tin alloys, represents one of the most complicated binary systems known. All parts are not yet known with certainty. H. le Chatelier,[5] W. C. Roberts-Austen and E. Stansfield, and C. T. Heycock and F. H. Neville studied the f.p. curves of the alloys, and in 1903, the last-named investigators gave an exploration covering the whole field. The plan so prepared has served as a guide for subsequent workers. As a result of the work of E. S. Shepherd and co-workers, S. L. Hoyt, J. E. Outerbridge, E. Heyn,

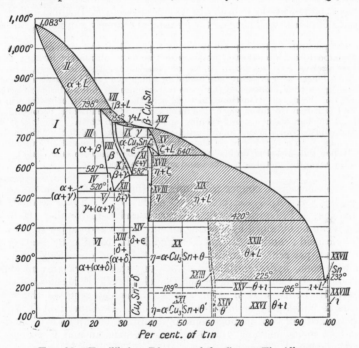

FIG. 32.—Equilibrium Diagram of the Copper-Tin Alloys.

F. Giolitti and G. Tavanti, W. Guertler, H. Endo, D. Stockdale, K. Honda and T. Ishigaki, and J. L. Haughton, modifications of specific portions of the plan have been made. The observations of O. Bauer and O. Vollenbruck are summarized in Fig. 32.

The area I represents a solid soln. of tin in copper, i.e. α-bronze. W. Guertler proposed to call it kuprite. The conc. of the tin varies with temp. and according to W. Guertler, E. S. Shepherd and E. Blough, and O. Bauer and O. Vollenbruck, may reach a maximum of about 13 per cent. ; W. Broniewsky said 10 per cent. Area II represents the region where the α-crystals are stable in contact with the molten alloy ; III, mixed crystals of α- and β-bronze ; IV, mixed crystals of α+(α+γ) bronze, and V, mixed crystals of γ+(α+γ) bronze ; VI, mixed crystals of α+(α+δ) bronze ; and XIII, mixed crystals of δ+(α+δ);

bronze. On account of the analogy of the $a+\delta$ area—VI and XIII—with the pearlite of steel, W. Guertler proposed to call it *bronzite*. Area VII represents β-crystals stable in contact with the molten alloy; VIII, homogeneous crystals of yellow β-bronze; IX, homogeneous crystals of white γ-bronze; X, mixed crystals of β- and γ-bronzes; XI, mixed crystals of β- and γ-bronzes; XII, mixed crystals of δ- and γ-bronzes; XIII, *vide supra*; XIV, mixed crystals of δ- and ϵ-bronzes; XV, ζ-bronze stable in contact with the molten alloy; XVI, homogeneous ζ-bronze; XVII, mixed crystals of η- and ζ-bronzes; XVIII, homogeneous η-bronzes; XIX, η-bronze stable in contact with the molten alloy; XX, mixed crystals of η- and θ-bronzes; XXI, mixed crystals of η- and θ'-bronzes; XXII, θ-bronze stable in contact with the molten alloy; XXIII, homogeneous θ-bronze; XXIV, homogeneous θ'-bronze; XXV, mixed crystals of θ- and ι-bronzes; XXVI, mixed crystals of θ'- and ι-bronzes; XXVII, ι-bronze stable in contact with the molten alloy; and XXVIII, ι-bronze, *i.e.* a solid soln. of copper in tin.

The eutectic at 228° has about 98 per cent. of tin. Evidence for the existence of the polymorphic transformation of tin in the copper-tin alloys at 161° is wanting. It probably occurs rather lower than with pure tin owing to the presence of a small proportion of dissolved copper. The regions corresponding with the allotropic changes of tin are represented by dotted lines to show that they have not yet been observed.

The part played by the phosphorus was discussed by M. Beuling, and H. Behrens, etc. J. T. Milton thus described the freezing of ordinary gun-metal, Cu : Sn=9 : 1.

The first portions to solidify are richer in copper than the average. These separate out in skeleton form, the skeleton portions in the space ultimately forming one crystal, arrange themselves with a certain degree of parallelism; that is to say, with the same orientation. These skeleton forms are nuclei on which more solid separates out, containing rather less copper than before, and therefore rather more tin, but still richer in copper than the average of the metal. On these, in turn, a further deposition of metal still poorer in copper and richer in tin takes place, the skeleton forms meanwhile becoming gradually thicker and thicker, with less intervening spaces between them. The metal remaining liquid gradually becomes richer in tin, until at last, if there is sufficient tin in the crystal, a kind of eutectic, much richer in tin than the average of the metal, fills up all the interspaces. When gun-metal is broken at a red heat this structure is revealed, but it can also be seen when the metal is polished and suitably etched.

Only one compound, **copper tritastannide,** Cu_3Sn, is shown on the equilibrium diagram, Fig. 32. Analyses, etc., were made by F. Mylius and O. Fromm; H. le Chatelier, A. P. Laurie, and C. T. Heycock and F. H. Neville, H. le Chatelier said that it can be obtained by treating an alloy of tin and copper (2 : 1) with conc. hydrochloric acid; and C. T. Heycock and F. H. Neville, by heating an alloy with 38–70 at. per cent. of tin for 72 hrs. at 454°, and quenching. The product treated with conc. hydrochloric acid at 30° furnishes a dark grey residue of this compound. A. P. Laurie, O. Bauer and O. Vollenbruck, F. Mylius and O. Fromm, F. Förster, H. Behrens, E. J. Ball, and A. Riche also reported this compound. It appears as bluish-grey or bluish-white lamellæ. O. Bauer and O. Vollenbruck say that it exists in two modifications, an a-form stable up to 676°, and a stable β-form which melts unchanged at 720°. K. Bornemann and F. Sauerwald, and H. Alterthum found 23 per cent. dissociation at 900° and 16 per cent. at 1200°. The tritastannide is but slowly attacked by hydrochloric acid, and is fairly stable towards acids generally. Hot conc. hydrochloric acid was found by F. Mylius and O. Fromm to decompose it more rapidly. O. Sackur and H. Pick gave 0·45 volt for the potential against zinc; and N. A. Puschin, 0·50 volt. A. W. Smith has shown that the different physical properties agree with the existence of copper tritastannide. K. Bornemann and F. Sauerwald found only one break in the sp. gr. curve of molten copper-tin alloys; and this is taken to show that this is the only compound of these elements stable in the liquid. G. Tammann and M. Hansen found the binary alloys of Cu_3Zn_3 and Cu_3Sn have the typical V-curve with the eutectic at about 700° and 18 per cent. Cu_3Sn.

Observations on many of the physical properties of the various copper-tin alloys give curves with singular points sometimes attributed to the presence of definite compounds, but such evidence is not adequate and sufficient. Thus, C. T. Heycock and F. H. Neville, W. C. Roberts-Austen, E. J. Ball, A. Riche, R. Ledoux, H. Behrens, and W. Guertler, suggested the possibility of the existence of **copper tetritastannide**, Cu_4Sn, and O. Bauer and O. Vollenbruck consider that they were able definitely to prove its existence. G. Tammann and M. Hansen found that the binary alloys of Cu_4Sn and Cu_2Zn_3 have the V-shaped f.p. curve with the eutectic at 725° and 63 per cent. of Cu_4Sn. P. Braesco also obtained evidence of the existence of the tetritastannide. A. Riche, N. A. Puschin, and O. Sackur and H. Pick reported *copper hemistannide*, Cu_2Sn ; A. Riche, and F. Förster, *tin cupride*, or *copper monostannide*, CuSn ; W. H. Miller, and R. Roth, *copper di-tannide*, Sn_5Cu ; C. F. Rammelsberg, *copper tritaheptastannide*, Sn_7Cu_3 ; A. Riche, *copper tristannide*, Sn_3Cu, and *copper pentastannide*, Sn_5Cu. H. Moissan and J. P. O'Farrelly found that the alloy with a constant composition when boiled in the electric furnace corresponds with CuSn. J. E Stead held that the crystallites which separated from alloys rich in tin were composed of SnCu, and not $SnCu_3$, and that the crystallites obtained by dissolving away the excess of tin in dil. acid from alloys with between 3 and 34 per cent. copper consist of two definite constituents—one covering the other. The one crystallizing out first contains most copper, and the second constituent, probably SnCu, crystallizes on the surface of this. H. le Chatelier said that neither Cu_4Sn nor Cu_2Sn exists as a chemical individual. R. Ledoux found no evidence of CuSn. O. Bauer and O. Vollenbruck reported *copper pentahexitastannide*, Cu_6Sn_5, which they isolated from alloys with over 60 per cent. of tin. It is stable below the eutectic at 225° in all alloys with over 61 per cent. of tin.

According to R. Mallet,[6] the **colour** of the copper-tin alloys containing 82·81–84·29 per cent. of copper is reddish-yellow ; with 78·97–81·10 per cent., yellowish-red ; with 72·80–76·29 per cent., pale red ; with 68·21 per cent., ash-grey ; 61·69 per cent., dark grey ; with 51·75 per cent., greyish-white ; 34·92 per cent. white, becoming still whiter with increasing proportions of tin. Observations were made by H. Behrens, C. Bischoff, E. S. Shepherd, and F. J. Otto. M. Chikashige examined the effect of a beam of light reflected four times from the surface of bronze. Starting with copper, the exposure to the multi-reflected red ray required to produce equal blackness on a panchromatic plate, increased with the proportion of tin until 35 per cent. of tin was present, when the alloy contained ε-bronze and tin tricupride, which is nearly white. The exposure then diminished to the tin end of the series. The intensity of reflection is greatest with the hardest alloys which take the best polish. C. F. Rammelsberg, and W. Miller discussed the form of the **crystals** of copper-tin alloys. E. C. Bain studied the X-radiograms. According to E. Heyn and O. Bauer, the **fracture** of alloys which have been cooled rapidly have a uniform colour, but if slowly cooled, there may be grey and yellow flecks. R. Mallet, and J. Rieffel found that the fracture of alloys with 84·29–81·10 per cent. of copper is fine-grained ; with 78·97 per cent., vitreous and conchoidal ; with 76·29 per cent., vitreous ; with 72·80–68·21 per cent., conchoidal ; with 61·69 per cent., lamellar and granular ; with 51·75 per cent., vitreous and conchoidal ; with 34·92 per cent., lamellar and granular ; with 21·15–15·17 per cent., vitreous and granular ; with 11·82 per cent., vitreous and lamellar ; and with 9·68 per cent., earthy. H. Behrens said that the alloy with 15–25 per cent. of tin is fine-grained ; and with 25–40 per cent. of tin, conchoidal. The effect of annealing on the physical properties of bronze has been discussed by C. H. Mathewson,[7] H. S. Rawdon, W. Wyss, J. S. G. Primrose, L. Grenet, C. F. Smart, O. Smalley, R. J. Anderson and C. H. Eldridge, etc. ; and P. G. J. Gueterbock and G. N. Nicklin, the effect of copper as an impurity on the physical properties of tin. G. H. Gulliver calculated the difference in the relative proportions of solid and liquid between the liquidus and solidus curves for very slow and rapid cooling. A. M. Portevin found **Widmanstätten figures** developed on some copper-tin alloys ; and he studied the structure of the eutectic. A. Westgren and G. Phragmen studied the **X-radiograms** of these alloys.

Observations on the **specific gravity** of the tin-copper alloys have been made by J. H. Croockewit,[8] C. Bischoff, R. H. Thurston, G. Kamensky, A. L. Norbury, R. Mallet, A. Riche, S. L. Kneass, E. von Maey, T. Turner and J. L. Haughton, K. Bornemann and F. Sauerwald, J. Rieffel, E. S. Shepherd and E. Blough, and F. C. Calvert and R. Johnson. The subject has been examined in some detail by H. Heape, and the results with chill casting and sand casting are plotted in Fig. 33. The following is a selection from the observed data :

Cu	.	5·45	22·30	30·10	48·72	59·90	79·66	90·06	97·73° per cent.
Chill	.	7·389	775·4	8·008	8·498	8·839	8·802	8·752	8·833
Sand	.	7·408	7·734	7·989	8·382	8·669	8·716	8·704	8·712

There is a difficulty in obtaining sound castings for these determinations. C. Bischoff noted that quenching decreased the sp. gr. of the alloys. The differences in the two types of cast bronze illustrate the effect of casting on the result. H. Heape found that except for a small portion of the sand-cast curve, both curves lie above the admixture rule in which it is assumed that the alloying occurs without change of vol. This means that there is a contraction due to the alloying, and this with the subsequent contraction which occurs during solidification, produces a decrease in vol. as the resultant effect with all alloys. The chill-cast alloy has invariably a higher sp. gr. than those for the sand-cast specimens except in the case of those with about 5 per cent. of copper. The zero point with alloys containing 8 per cent. of copper corresponds

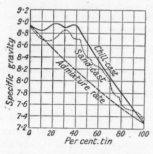

FIG. 33.—The Specific Gravity of Cu–Sn Alloys.

with the points of zero expansion observed by T. Turner and J. L. Haughton. R. Mallet's curve had a maximum with 76 per cent. copper, and a minimum with 20 per cent. copper ; A. Riche's curve had a maximum with 61 per cent. copper, and a small dip with 10 per cent. of copper. T. Turner and J. L. Haughton's curve had a maximum with about 70 per cent. of copper ; E. von Maey's curve, K. Börnemann and F. Sauerwald's curve had a maximum near 60 per cent. of copper. H. Heape did not get the maximum with 60 per cent. of copper, but expansions occur with 99, 55, and 20 per cent. of copper. There is no confirmation of an expansion with 70 per cent. of copper, though there is one with 35 per cent. of copper. E. von Maey gave for the **specific volumes :**

Sn	.	.	0	5·6	9·0	25	28	39·2	56	70·3	100 per cent.
Sp. vol.	.	.	0·1121	0·1139	0·1142	0·1132	0·1123	0·1113	0·1197	0·1254	0·1374

C. Schmidt attempted to calculate the composition from the sp. gr. of the alloy. K. Bornemann and F. Sauerwald found the sp. gr. of molten copper-tin alloys, and there is only one break in the curve corresponding with the tricupride, which thus appears to be the only compound stable in the liquid state. A. L. Norbury estimated the sp. vol. of the solute atoms of tin in copper. J. H. Chamberlain found that when some alloys of copper and tin are heated, there is a small contraction ; thus, between 700° and 760°, a bar with 89·6 per cent. copper contracted 0·012 cm.; one with 91 per cent. copper, 0·0045 cm.; and one with 89·7 per cent. copper, 0·00015 cm. It is assumed that an expansion is produced in casting the bars owing to the chilling of the liquid soln. between the dendrites of the α-solid soln.; and on heating, there is a more complete soln. of the α-crystals which produces a greater homogeneity and causes a contraction in vol. P. Braesco studied the change in volume accompanying various transformations. E. A. Smith said that segregation nearly always takes place during the solidification of a plumbiferous bronze, but if nickel is present, the lead is not so liable to separate. G. Masing studied the changes in vol. during liquation.

The **hardness** of the copper-tin alloys was measured by H. Heape, A. Martens, F. C. Calvert and R. Johnson, J. Rieffel, P. Ludwik, H. le Chatelier, N. S. Kurnakoff and S. F. Schemtschuschny, H. S. and J. S. G. Primrose, O. Bauer and O. Vollenbruck, W. L. Kent, T. Matsuda, T. Matsuda and J. Shiba, A. Mallock, and T. Isihara. J. P. J. d'Arcet noted the decrease in the hardness of the copper-tin alloys brought about by quenching. H. Behrens added that the presence of zinc or lead softened these alloys. The increased hardness conferred by a minute proportion of phosphorus was indicated by C. Montefiori-Levi and C. Künzel, M. Beuling, H. Behrens, F. von Friese, H. de Ruolz and H. de Fontenay, and A. Polain. The following values for the scleroscope hardness of sand-cast specimens were selected from data by T. Turner and J. L. Haughton. The curve, Fig. 34, represents :

Cu .	. 4·0	29·4	41·0	60·7	62·6	72·7	80·4	95·5 per cent.
Hardness	5	29	60	72	59	100	53	7

Brinell's hardness numbers for chill-cast and for sand-cast bronzes were measured by H. Heape, and the following is a selection from the observed data :

Cu	.	. 5·45	25·34	33·86	58·21	72·75	89·56	97·73 per cent.
Chill	.	. 8·9	26·8	39·0	95·4	182·6	41·0	29·7
Sand	.	. 7·6	13·9	21·5	50·3	166·2	31·2	27·9

D. Saito and K. Hayashi [9] tested the **fluidity** of molten bronzes for casting, and F. von Friese of phosphor-bronzes. G. Subrahmanian studied the viscosity, G. Tammann and K. Dahl, the plastic deformation, and O. Bauer and O. Vollenbruck, the **malleability** of bronzes at different temp. R. Mallet, R. Baumann, R. H. Thurston, A. Riche, L. Guillet, M. Beuling, H. Behrens, G. Wertheim, A. Guettier, B. E. Curry, W. D. Bancroft, O. Bauer and O. Vollenbruck, and C. T. Heycock and F. H. Neville measured the **tensile strength** of copper with different proportions of tin ; and R. H. Greaves and J. A. Jones, the notched bar **impact test**. J. P. J. d'Arcet found the tenacity and **ductility** is increased by quenching. L. Guillet quenched the bronze from 600°–800° and found the mechanical properties were improved ; and F. Giolitti and E. Pannain emphasized the importance of considering the rate of cooling on the mechanical properties. According to E. S. Shepherd and G. B. Upton, curve A, Figs. 35 and 36, refer to a bronze which has been held one week at 540° and water-quenched ; curve B, to a bronze tested as cast ; and curve C, to a bronze held one week at 400°, and furnace-cooled. They found that the tensile strength of bronzes consisting

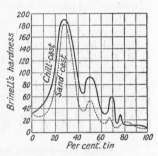

FIG. 34.—The Hardness of the Cu–Sn Alloys.

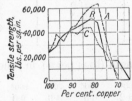

FIG. 35.—Tensile Strength of Bronzes.

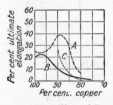

FIG. 36.—Ductility of Bronzes.

of pure α is affected but slightly by heat treatment. Bronzes containing 74–87 per cent. of copper are much stronger if annealed above the inversion temp. (510°) than if annealed below. Prolonged annealing tends to coarsen the crystalline structure, to decrease the tensile strength, and to increase the ductility. The tin-rich crystals are stronger than those low in tin. The strongest bronzes, containing 78–81 per cent. copper, annealed below 510°, consist of mixtures of α and δ crystals. Bronzes containing no α crystals have very low tensile strengths. When tested as cast, the ductility of bronzes decreases with decreasing copper content. The ductility of cast bronzes can be increased about 5 per cent. by bringing to a

red-heat, and then quenching in water. With bronzes containing less than 8
per cent. of copper, this treatment increases the strength markedly. Annealing
at 540° for one week, causes an enormous increase in the ductility, especially
of bronzes containing 88–90 per cent. of copper. Annealing the 85–90 per cent
copper bronzes at 400° for one week causes an effect on ductility similar to, bu
less than that due to, annealing for the same time at 540°. It is possible t
make a cast bronze with an ultimate tensile strength of over 60,000 lbs. per sq
in. and an ultimate elongation of about 1·5 per cent., or a bronze with an ulti
mate tensile strength of 45,000 lbs. per sq. in. and an ultimate elongation o
39 per cent. By suitable heat treatment, it is possible to vary the ultimate
elongation of a bronze containing 90 per cent. copper from 10 per cent. to 3
per cent. without affecting the tensile strength materially. The bronzes have no
maximum load in the sense that iron and steel have. The ultimate **resilience** o
bronzes containing more than 95 per cent. of copper is low because the breaking
strengths are low. With bronzes containing less than 85 per cent. of copper, the
resilience is low because the elongation is small. The maximum resilience occurs
between 90 per cent. and 87 per cent. of copper ; it is some 15 per cent. higher than
that of the wrought-iron curve. A. Philip reported on about a hundred samples
of commercial phosphor-bronze and found the tensile strength to range from 7·76 to
46·04 tons per sq. in.; and the percentage elongation on 2 ins., to range from 1 to 59 ins.
The improved mechanical properties of phosphor-bronze over ordinary bronzes was
indicated by C. Montefiori-Levi and C. Künzel, J. Arnott, J. Kiewit, R. T. Rolfe,
C. B. Dudley, R. Jenny and co-workers, J. Bauschinger and K. Stölzel, A. Philip,
M. Beuling, etc. A. K. Huntington, F. C. Lea, C. P. Karr, H. S. Gulick, and
J. C. Longbottom and A. Campion measured the effect of temp. on the mechanical
properties of gun-metal. The first-named used an alloy with 97·673 per cent.
copper ; 2·408 per cent. tin ; and 0·024 per cent. lead ; and found the results
indicated in Table V. H. S. and J. S. G. Primrose measured the influence of the

TABLE V.—TENSILE STRENGTH OF BRONZE AT DIFFERENT TEMPERATURES.

Temp.	Yield in tons per sq. in.	Breaking load in tons per sq. in.	Elongation per cent. in 2 ins.	Reduction area per cent.
15·5	4·83	19·13	56·0	75·0
204·0	2·84	16·77	53·0	68·6
260·0	2·84	16·25	45·0	56·4
316·0	2·84	14·54	23·5	26·0
371·0	2·55	11·36	21·0	22·5
427·0	3·12	12·97	36·5	29·4
465·0	2·84	12·31	38·5	42·2

quenching temp. of gun-metal on the tensile strength (tons per sq. in.) and found :

	—	500°	600°	700°	800°
Tensile strength	15·6	8·2	6·5	4·9	9·0
Elongation per cent.	28·0	12·0	7·5	3·0	5·5

With chilled castings the effects of annealing for 30 mins. at different temp. were :

	—	500°	600°	650°	700°	750°	800°
Tensile strength	18·6	16·7	15·0	19·5	22·5	21·0	18·6
Elongation per cent.	20·0	9·0	7·0	27·0	45·0	40·0	34·0

and for specimens annealed at 700° for different periods of time :

Time (mins.).	—	5	10	20	30	60	100
Tensile strength	16·5	19·6	20·4	21·4	23·1	21·2	20·5
Elongation per cent.	15·0	23·0	35·0	40·0	48·5	39·5	37·0

J. Arnott, J. Czochralsky, F. Johnson, and R. T. Rolfe discussed the effect of impurities; J. S. Brown, the effect of the time factor; and W. E. Alkins and W. Cartwright, the effect of cold-drawing on the mechanical properties of gun-metal. H. Pealing found no bifilar effect for small oscillations with phosphor-bronze strips, but when first used varying values were obtained for the **rigidity** according to the load. The restoring couple per unit angle increased for some days. After annealing, the rigidity becomes constant for varying loads. The anomaly is due to overstrain. A. Weiller, and X. Müller studied the effect of deoxidizers on the alloys. The effect of small proportions of lead, iron, and zinc was examined by F. W. Dick, J. Dewrance, J. Arnott, R. H. Thurston, etc. The **elastic modulus** of an alloy with 88 per cent. of copper was given by W. Voigt as 10,000, and W. Pscheidl as 9194 kgrms. per sq. mm. H. E. Tresca, G. F. Comstock, and F. C. Lea examined the elastic constants of some bronzes. W. Voigt gave 4060 kgrms. per sq. mm. for the rigidity of a 12 per cent. tin bronze; and T. Matsuba studied the **impact test** of bronzes.

H. le Chatelier found the coeff. of **thermal expansion** of an alloy with 10 per cent. of tin to be 0·0000220 at 900°; of one with 20 per cent. of tin, 0·0000270 at 800°; and of one with 30 per cent. of tin at 700°, 0·0000295. P. Braesco gave 0·0$_4$60 for bronzes with 14–29 per cent. of tin between 100° and 300°. P. Hidnert found the coeff. of expansion of cold-rolled alloys to be less than that of cast alloys. F. C. Calvert and co-workers also measured the thermal expansion of these alloys. The curve for the **thermal conductivity** of the bronzes, Fig. 37, was shown by R. Ledoux to be very similar to that for the electrical conductivity. Observations were also made by F. C. Calvert and R. Johnson. C. Künzel found the heat conductivity of an alloy with 4 per cent. of tin was 960 when that of copper was 1000.

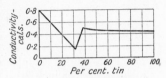

FIG. 37.—The Thermal Conductivity of Bronzes.

The **melting point** was shown by R. Mallet, and A. Riche to fall with increasing proportions of tin. The observations of C. T. Heycock and F. H. Neville have been previously indicated. M. Beuling found that lead, and phosphorus made the alloys more fusible, but not so with manganese. According to H. W. Gillet and A. B. Norton, the m.p. of some commercial bronzes, with Cu : Zn : Sn : Pb in the following percentage proportions, are gun-metal (88 : 2 : 10 : 0), 995°; leaded gun-metal (85·4 : 1·9 : 9·7 : 3·0), 980°; red-brass (85 : 5 : 5 : 5), 970°; low-grade red brass (81·5 : 10·4 : 3·1 : 5·0), 980°; bronze with lead (80 : 0 : 10 : 10), 945°; bronze with zinc (84·6 : 5 : 10·4 : 0), 980°; half yellow, half red (75 : 20 : 2 : 3), 920°; naval brass (61·7 : 36·5 : 1·4 : 0), 855°: and manganese bronze, 870°. They also gave for the m.p. of the alloy Cu : Sn in parts by weight, 95 : 5, 1050°; 90 : 10, 1005°; 85 : 15, 960°; and 80 : 20, 890°. C. Künzel found that copper with 10 per cent. of tin and 1 per cent. of phosphorus melted at 1250°; with 9·97 per cent. of tin and 1·17 per cent. of phosphorus, 1242°; and with 10 per cent. of tin and 1·08 per cent. of phosphorus, 1233°. H. Moissan and J. P. O'Farrelly said that an alloy corresponding with CuSn does not change in composition if boiled in the electric furnace, and it is produced when alloys richer in either component are boiled. M. Kühnel, and O. Bauer and H. Arndt investigated the liquation of these alloys; and P. Weise, the electrolytic separation of the copper and tin. W. Biltz found that copper tritastannide has a **heat of formation,** 8 Cals.; a heat of oxidation, 23 Cals.; and that it suffers a 20 per cent. **dissociation** at 1000°.

W. Guertler[10] found that the **electrical conductivity** of copper-tin alloys with the proportion of copper gradually increasing up to that required for CuSn fell from 8·6×10⁻⁴ to 7·3×10⁻⁴ mho; the conductivity then remained nearly constant to Cu₃Sn when there was a sudden rise to 9·2×10⁻⁴ mho followed by an abrupt fall to 2×10⁻⁴ mho; there was then a slow rise to 6·6×10⁻⁴ with alloys containing 9·7 per cent. of copper, and subsequently a rise up to that of pure copper.

R. Ledoux's results are shown in Fig. 38.   R. Ledoux found singular points on the conductivity curve corresponding with Cu_4Sn, and Cu_3Sn, but not with $CuSn$. E. Bornemann and K. Wagenmann found evidence of Cu_3Sn in their observations

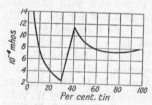

on the electrical conductivity of liquid alloys. Measurements were also made by W. C. Roberts-Austen, G. Kamensky, A. Matthiessen and co-workers, R. Edler, W. Harris, O. J. Lodge, E. J. Ball, and R. Ihle. A. Matthiessen and C. Vogt found the conductivity of hard-drawn wires with 1·41 per cent. of tin to be $62·463 - 0·16713\theta + 0·0003163\theta^2$; with 6·02 per cent. of tin, $19·71 - 0·019626\theta + 0·01390\theta^2$;

FIG 38.—The Electrical Conductivity of Bronzes.

with 11·61 per cent. of tin, $12·102 - 0·0083587\theta + 0·05367 4\theta^2$; with 12·35 per cent. of tin, $10·154 - 0·0067656\theta + 0·041203\theta^2$; with 14·91 per cent. of tin, $8·8223 - 0·0048266\theta + 0·052593\theta^2$; and with 83·60 per cent., $12·764 - 0·04257\theta + 0·04873 4\theta^2$. H. le Chatelier found the **electrical resistance** of an alloy with 10 per cent. of tin to be $0·150 + 0·031 90\theta$ ohms. J. Obata studied the effect of a magnetic field on the resistivity of phosphor-bronze. J. Dewar and J. A. Fleming gave for the sp. resistance of commercial phosphor-bronze:

	100°	18·75°	0·8°	−80°	−100°	−182°
Sp. resistance	9071	8581	8483	8054	7883	7371

in electromagnetic units. L. Guillet and M. Ballay examined the influence of cold-work on the electrical resistance. The so-called *bronze silicieux* used for high conductivity wires was shown by F. Gautier to have no silicon; but silicon was probably used in its manufacture as a deoxidizing agent. A. Weiller, and E. Debié measured the conductivity of phosphor-bronze. M. Herschkowitsch, C. Hocken and H. A. Taylor, G. Kamensky, A. P. Laurie, H. le Chatelier, and G. Tammann measured the electrode potential of the Cu–Sn alloys. A. G. Warren and F. Murphy found the **thermoelectric force** of phosphor-bronze against bronze to be −0·5–

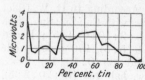

0·16 microvolt per degree. R. Ledoux found on the curve for the thermoelectric power, singular points corresponding with Cu_3Sn and Cu_4Sn, Fig. 39. Observations were made by A. Battelli, S. H. J. Wilson, T. J. Seebeck, and E. Steinmann. N. A. Puschin[11] found that the **electrolytic potentials** in $N\text{-}H_2SO_4$ of copper-tin alloys with up to 65 at. per cent. of copper are nearly the same as that of tin alone; but with 65–68 at. per cent. of copper, there is an abrupt fall,

FIG. 39.—The Thermoelectric Power of Bronzes.

and with up to 74 at. per cent. of copper, it remains nearly the same as that of Cu_2Sn; with 74–77 at. per cent. of copper, there is a sharp rise very nearly to that required for pure copper. Expressing the proportion of the one element as at. percentages, and the potential, E, in millivolts:

Cu	10	30	40	50	57	60	65	68	73	77	100
E	−4	−2	−4	+4	−3	+4	−3	46	39	480	495

According to M. Herschkowitsch, the potentials of tin towards the copper-tin alloys in a sat. soln. of stannous chloride are:

Sn	11·8	18·6	20·7	25·43	28·19	30·3	34·5	49·7	68·1	80·9
E	188	184	190	195	125	18	5·5	0·6	0·4	0·3

Observations were made by H. E. Armstrong, F. Haber, O. Sackur and H. Pick, P. Lebeau, and A. P. Laurie. G. Tammann and W. Wiederholt studied the cathodic polarization of copper-tin alloys; and R. Kremann and R. G. Rehenburg their electrolysis. O. C. Clifford measured the **magnetic susceptibility** of copper mixed with different proportions of tin, and found :

Sn   .   0   1·0   7·0   13·8   24·2   33·2   66·4   97·9   100 per cent.
$k \times 10^{-6}$.   −1·22   −1·13   −1·40   −1·88   −2·07   −2·06   −1·43   +0·28   +0·31

The results are plotted in Fig. 40. The absence of singularities on the curve may be due to the points near the compound Cu_3Sn being too far apart.

G. Tammann [12] studied the chemical activity of the copper-tin alloys. E. S. Shepherd and G. B. Upton found that molten bronze absorbs gases which produce blebs as they are evolved on cooling; bronzes with over 84 per cent. of copper show the effect more than bronzes with a lower proportion of copper. G. Guillemin and B. Delachanal found that phosphor-bronze retains very little occluded gas, and this consists chiefly of carbon dioxide and hydrogen. The presence of phosphorus seems to diminish the solubility of hydrogen in bronzes as it also does in the case of iron and steel. J. Pintsch found bronze does not resist very well corrosion by the gases from gas-engines. J. B. A. Dumas stated that the tin in

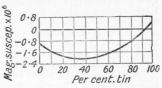

FIG. 40.—Magnetic Susceptibility of Bronzes.

the molten alloy is oxidized by **air** faster than the copper; E. S. Shepherd and G. B. Upton showed that alloys with over 84 per cent. of copper oxidize most readily, and C. T. Heycock and F. H. Neville found that the higher the proportion of copper in the alloy the faster is it oxidized by air at ordinary temp. or when heated. E. Heyn and O. Bauer said that cuprous oxide is first formed during the oxidation of the alloy, and that this is immediately reduced by the tin so that the oxygen is always present as stannic oxide which appears as an impurity between the crystals. The stannic oxide remains as anode-mud when the alloy is made the anode in sulphuric acid. Phosphorus is a deoxidizing agent; and A. Philip, and F. von Friese noticed that phosphor-bronzes resist the action of air better than ordinary bronzes. C. and A. Tissier said that the presence of 1 per cent. of aluminium prevents the oxidation. This subject was examined by O. Bauer, C. Ratner, B. Setlik, and H. Goldschmidt. E. Jordis and W. Rosenhaupt said that at 145°, an alloy with 30 per cent. of tin is attacked by dry **oxygen** more rapidly than by the moist gas; and at 280°, the reverse is true. S. L. Kneass said that **water-vapour** acts mechanically on the surface of bronze, and that the resistance to attack is conditioned by homogeneity, and sp. gr.

H. von Fellenberg classed ancient bronze objects according to the material in which they have been found : (i) Bronzes from peat-mud are covered by a black earthy mass easily removed ; and the bronze has been preserved owing to the exclusion of the oxygen of the air by the mud of organic origin. (ii) Bronzes found in water in the beds of lakes and rivers are usually fairly well preserved and are covered with a thin calcareous deposit. (iii) Bronzes found in the earth—e.g. in graves—have a fine green crust of dark or light verdigris which sometimes has a vitreous lustre. This crust is known as *patina*—also called *patina antiqua, ærugo nobilis*, and *verde antico*. Patina varies from a thin film to one several mm. thick. B. G. Sage, and H. Davy noted that below the green crust is a reddish layer of cuprous oxide which comes between the external crust and the bronze itself. This encrustation is characteristic of bronze which has been slowly changed in moist earth. According to F. Wibel, there are several kinds of patina : Malachite, $CuCO_3.Cu(OH)_2$; copper oxychloride or atacamite, $CuCl_2.3Cu(OH)_2$; and azurite, $2CuCO_3.Cu(OH)_2$, admixed with silver, stannic oxide, iron oxide, and cupric and lead chlorides. F. A. Reuss found patinized bronzes with the malachite in direct contact with the bronze, or separated from that metal by a black or bluish layer of cupric oxide. F. Wibel does not believe that the layer of crystallized cuprous oxide—not always present—represents the first stage in the oxidation of the copper, while the carbonates represent the later completed stage, as supposed by R. Weber, etc. L. A. Bucholz showed that a strip of copper partly immersed in water and partly in a conc. neutral soln. of copper nitrate, becomes coated with copper and cuprous oxide ; hence, argued F. Wibel, the layer of crystalline cuprous oxide is a reduction product of copper carbonate by the copper of the bronze. He thus described the formation of the patina :

Bronze objects are attacked by waters which contain oxygen, carbon dioxide, and a greater or less percentage of salts. Such soluble salts as are formed are removed by soln., while the bronzes become covered, according to circumstances, with an insoluble layer either of carbonate or of oxide, whereby the form of the objects is preserved. The water then penetrates by capillary action through the porous coating into the interior, and attacks further portions of the metal, forming a layer of soluble cupric salt ; a portion of which is able to pass by diffusion through the external layer. For the same reasons the liquid, bounded as it is on one side by the metal and on the other by the almost insoluble crust, shows varying degrees of conc. : thus, all the conditions necessary for reduction are fulfilled. If the water is rich in salts, a conc. copper soln. is formed and even metallic copper may be deposited from it furnishing the copper crystals of some bronzes ; but if, as is usually the case, the water contains only small quantities of salt, cuprous oxide crystals only are formed. The fact that the process takes place chiefly in the pores made by the water itself is readily understood, because of the comparative quiescence of the liquid ; and that it causes a marked progressive change in the object arises from the continual exchange of a portion of the copper soln. already formed with fresh solvent from outside. Where the absence of carbon dioxide, or other circumstances, hinders the formation of an almost insoluble crust, the reactions detailed above may, under favourable conditions, take place directly upon the surface of the bronze ; if, on the other hand, there is a too rapid change of liquid (as, for example, in very wet localities), the process may altogether fail to set in, since the necessary conditions of rest are wanting. Since the absence of the necessary conditions may arise from a number of purely accidental causes, it will be easily understood that bronzes from one and the same grave may show the same percentage of carbonates, but very dissimilar percentages of cuprous oxide. In short, all actually observed conditions in which bronzes are found are accounted for by the explanations given above.

E. von Bibra has emphasized the variability of the conditions which determine the formation of patina on bronzes. For example, the effect is dependent on (i) the composition of the alloy ; (ii) the physical character of the alloy—good or bad mixing, fine or coarse grain, etc. ; (iii) the locality in which the alloy has lain ; and (iv) the length of time during which the alloy has been exposed to particular conditions. The effects of organic matter, and of bacteria were emphasized by L. Mond and G. Cuboni. Analyses of bronzes and of the accompanying patinas have been made by A. Terreil, T. Matsuno, J. Schuler, K. Natterer, H. Bassett, A. Arche and C. Hassack, O. Olshausen, and others cited below. The Sn : Cu ratio is often higher in the patina than in the underlying bronze. One of the causes, said J. Schuler, lies in the fact that basic copper carbonate is soluble in water holding carbon dioxide in soln., while stannic hydroxide is insoluble ; and another cause may be found in the action of water containing in soln. ammonia or ammonium carbonate derived from the decomposition of organic matter. In confirmation, several analyses indicate the presence of small quantities of ammonia in patina. E. Friedel noted a peculiar smell associated with a malignant patina. In the extreme case, O. Olshausen, A. H. Layard, H. von Fellenberg, C. Bischoff, A. Philip, and O. Kröhnke found an object originally bronze is represented only by insoluble stannic oxide, all the copper compounds have been leached away. According to F. Rathgen, the blue or green patinas containing oxides and carbonates are more or less stable, and such patinas have been called Edelpatina, or noble patinas ; they are not necessarily prejudicial to the preservation of bronzes. They show a crystalline structure. Carbonate patinas were analyzed by A. Arche and C. Hassack, C. Mitzopulos, J. Schuler, F. Stolba, etc. In addition, some patinas contain chlorides—vide 3. 21, 6—and these, as a rule, are malignant, being the source of one of the métaux malades—the rogna or caries of bronze—which gradually destroys the bronzes—statues, coins, vases, etc.—in museums, the rapidity with which the destruction proceeds being dependent on a number of unknown conditions. Not all malignant patinas are chloriferous. The presence of chlorides in patina was recognized by W. Haidinger, M. E. Chevreul, A. Terreil, J. Elster, H. Schliemann, and E. Krause. M. Berthelot's observations on this subject will be found 3.21,6: J. Elster regarded the presence of chlorides in the patina of ancient bronzes as a proof that the patina was manufactured intentionally, but F. de Villenoisy showed that it is produced by natural causes and not by the art and methods of the ancient workers in metal. Another series of patinas contains sulphides and sulphates, which were reported by E. Priwoznik, E. Chuard, V. A. Skinder, C. A. de Gouvenain, R. Weber, A. Daubrée, etc. According to F. Rathgen, the presence of sulphides and sulphates does not make a patina malignant. The brown and black colours of patinas described by F. de Villenoisy, F. Rathgen, and J. J. Rein are probably produced by plumbiferous bronzes and sulphides. The production of artificial patina on bronze is described by L. Vanino and E. Seitter, J. Elster, etc., and the cleaning of patina, etc., from bronzes, by F. Rathgen, J. W. Brühl, E. Buchner, etc.

According to L. Révillon and P. Beauverie,[13] **hydrogen dioxide** in alkaline soln. rapidly colours the α-constituent of phosphor-bronze red, blue, and violet ; and the phosphide constituent is coloured brown. The bronzes are much less readily attacked by **sea-water** and other corrosive agents than are the brasses or copper. If the bronze contains a large proportion of tin, the alloy behaves very much like brass. M. Ledy [14] showed that bronze containing only traces of lead, iron, and zinc is scarcely affected by sea-water because a vessel which had lain at the bottom of the sea for 300 years was only superficially changed. C. Diegel, W. P. Jorissen, and W. A. Tilden confirmed the slowness of the attack by sea-water. A. Philip, and F. von Friese noted that phosphor-bronzes resist the action of sea-water and acids better than ordinary bronzes. The erosion of bronze propeller blades in high-speed steamships varies under apparently identical conditions. The primary cause is usually attributed to the filing action of the water when the propeller is travelling at high velocities, but the fact that the maximum erosive action seldom occurs at the tip of the blades where the helical velocity is greatest, shows that other causes enter largely into the action. O. Silberrad showed that dirt in the casting has little to do with the action ; and since there is no increase in the conc. of the copper in the eroded areas, there is not likely to be galvanic action. R. J. Anderson and G. M. Enos, and W. A. Selvig and G. M. Enos studied the corrosion of the bronzes and brasses by acid mine-waters ; and the former showed that the grain-size of the metal, between 0·01 and 0·10 mm., does not affect the corrodibility of the metal, although the coarser-grained metal corrodes more readily than when the grain is finer. Some Swedish guns with the inscriptions 1535 and 1622 were recently salvaged from the sea, and the bronze had suffered very little action although it had been submerged nearly 300 years.

M. Herschkowitsch [15] found that **bromine** water readily attacks bronze. D. Mushet found that a small proportion of tin diminishes the attack of copper by **hydrochloric acid ;** and, said L. J. Chaudet, the boiling acid acts preferentially on the contained tin. F. C. Calvert and R. Johnson showed that hydrochloric acid of sp. gr. 1·1, attacks bronze with a small proportion of copper more strongly than tin. H. Behrens made some observations on the action of this acid ; and C. T. Heycock and F. H. Neville found that alloys with at least 50 at. per cent. of tin resist best the action of hydrochloric acid mixed with ferric choride ; and an alloy corresponding with 80 at. per cent. of copper best resists hydrochloric acid alone. W. A. Tilden found that 7 per cent. hydrochloric acid at 13°–15° dissolved 0·172 grm. per sq. cm. in 14 days, and 0·229 grm. per sq. cm. in 21 days from bronze with 93·31 per cent. copper. The ratio of copper to zinc and tin in the original metal was 100 : 7, and in the dissolved portion 100 : 35. J. G. A. Rhodin measured the rates of evolution of hydrogen when the metals indicated are acted on by 10N-HCl. He assumed that the rate of dissolution is directly proportional to the heats of formation of the ultimate compounds, and to the electrical conductivity of the dissolving metal. He also stated that the barometric press. considerably affects the rate of dissolution. H. E. Armstrong studied the action of acids on the tin-copper alloys. A. Ledebur found that bronzes usually contain some **sulphur** as well as oxygen, and when heated with hydrogen give off hydrogen sulphide. F. C. Calvert and R. Johnson said that **sulphuric acid** attacks bronze much less vigorously than either of its components. E. Harbeck said that sulphuric acid of sp. gr. 1·53 has virtually no action on bronze even if that alloy be made the anode of a cell. W. A. Tilden found that with sulphuric acid, $H_2SO_4.2H_2O$, no action was observed at 150°, but at 185°–190° in $1\frac{1}{2}$ hrs., 0·115 grm. per sq. cm. was lost by the bronze indicated in connection with hydrochloric acid.

According to H. Behrens, a conc. soln. of **ammonia** dissolves copper from bronze containing 1–12 per cent. of tin, and it is almost without action on bronze with 25 per cent. of tin, and C. T. Heycock and F. H. Neville obtained a similar result with an alloy with 20 at. per cent. of tin. F. C. Calvert and R. Johnson showed that **nitric acid** of sp. gr. 1·25 acts on bronze less vigorously than on copper ; and H. Behrens found that the conc. acid attacks alloys with 1–12 per cent. of tin ; and alloys with 15–25 per cent. of tin, less rapidly. Electro-deposited bronzes were found by B. E. Curry, and F. Förster, to be attacked with difficulty by this acid. A. Matthiessen also made observations on the action of this acid. W. A. Tilden found that with the bronze previously employed, nitric acid of sp. gr. 1·42 mixed with 15 vols. of water dissolved 0·034 grm. per sq. cm. in 23 days, and the ratio of copper to tin and zinc in the dissolved portion was 10 : 12. B. Feuer studied the corrosion of bronze by aq. soln. of **potassium nitrate.**

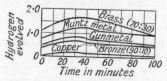

FIG. 41.—Rates of Dissolution of Metals and Alloys in Hot Hydrochloric Acid.

H. Behrens found that alloys with 40–90 per cent. of tin are readily attacked by soln. of **potassium hydroxide.** B. Neumann found that during the electrolysis of a soln. of **alkali sulphide** at 70°, with a cupriferous tin anode, the tin was separated from the copper. B. E. Curry determined the rates of corrosion of bronzes of different composition in aq. soln. of different salts, when the bronze was made the anode and a platinum wire the cathode ; the proportion of copper in the bronzes varied from 95 per cent. to 5 per cent., with 5 per cent. intervals. Usually a 7 per cent. soln. of the salt was employed, the following soln. being used : sodium sulphate, sodium nitrate, sodium acetate, sodium carbonate, alkaline sodium tartrate, ammonium oxalate containing oxalic acid, sodium chloride, sodium persulphate, ammonium sulphate, and copper sulphate. The results with sodium chloride and sulphate are illustrated by Fig. 42. The α-bronzes corrode more rapidly than any others, almost pure copper dissolving ; from the α+δ- and α+β alloys, copper dissolves more rapidly than tin. The β, δ, β+γ, δ+η, η+ε, and ε-bronzes undergo very little change and tend to become passive. The ε+ζ-bronzes become rich in copper on the surface, and tend to

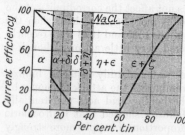

FIG. 42.—Electrolytic Corrosion of Bronzes by Aqueous Solutions of Sodium Sulphate and Chloride.

disintegrate as the tin dissolves. The cause of certain of the bronzes becoming passive appears to be the formation of a film of stannic oxide. The ε-bronze is most resistant to corrosion. No bronze becomes passive in soln. of chlorides, a high current efficiency being observed whatever be the composition of the bronze. In all other salts the curve of current efficiency shows well-marked fields, an abrupt change in the rate of corrosion occurring at the appearance or disappearance of a phase in the equilibrium diagram. The effects of chemical corrosion were in most cases found to be similar in nature to those of electrolytic corrosion.

F. Giolitti and O. Ceccarelli also emphasized the effect of the structure of the bronze on its corrodibility. Under similar conditions, the simultaneous presence in a bronze of the α- and β-solid soln., and especially of the product of segregation of these, accelerates the corrosive action. With bronzes containing not much more than 7 per cent. of tin, the velocity of corrosion increases with the proportion of the β-soln. present, no matter whether such increased proportion is due to a different composition of the alloy or to different thermal treatment, such as altered velocities of solidification and of subsequent cooling. When the proportions of α- and β-solns., and of their segregation products, remain constant, the velocity of corrosion is greater when the differences of conc. of the nuclei and margins of the separate mixed crystals of the two series are greater. As such differences of conc. are observable under the microscope, the degree of resistance of a bronze to corrosion may be determined beforehand by the same means. According to O. Sackur and H. Pick, copper-tin alloys containing 0–56 per cent. of copper precipitate lead from a soln. of lead chloride up to the same equilibrium point as does tin itself, so that they contain free tin. Alloys containing 57–60 per cent. of copper do not precipitate lead from lead chloride soln., or copper from cuprous iodide soln., but cause the separation of copper from soln. of cuprous chloride and bromide. Alloys containing more than 60 per cent. of copper do not precipitate copper from the two soln. last mentioned, but do so from soln. of the chloride and sulphate.

L. Guillet [16] found that an ammoniacal soln. of cuprous chloride is a good etching fluid for these alloys. A. Gawalowsky observed that brewers' mash does not attack bronze, and he examined the action of raw petroleum, mineral lubricating oil, rape oil, and ice-cream on the metal.

A. Weiller [17] examined the effect of *sodium* on copper-tin alloys; and A. Detlik [18] and co-workers, C. Bürgel, and M. Reiche, the effect of *calcium*. The effect of *zinc* in forming zinc-bronzes, and tin-brasses has been discussed by H. Behrens,[19] J. B. A. Dumas, etc. The ternary alloys with over 60 per cent. of copper were examined by G. Tammann and M. Hansen. The m.p. curve is given in Fig. 43. It was found that the constituents of alloys containing less than 35 per cent. Zn resemble those of the binary copper-tin alloys, α-, β-, and-γ series of ternary mixed crystals being formed. The solubility of tin in α mixed crystals decreases with increasing zinc content. Copper-rich alloys, on cooling from the melt, deposit first α ternary mixed crystals. If sufficient tin and zinc are present, these undergo a peritectic reaction corresponding to the change α+liquid→β; this change occurs at about 800° in the binary copper-tin alloys, and the temp. is little affected by small quantities of zinc, but is raised by larger quantities. Alloys containing less copper, on cooling from the melt, deposit first β crystals which may undergo a peritectic reaction corresponding to the change β+liquid→γ. The β and γ ternary mixed crystals both undergo eutectoid transformations in the solid state, corresponding to the changes β→α+γ, and γ→α+δ.

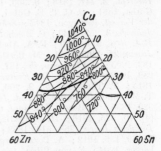

Fig. 43.—Melting-point Curves of Cu–Zn–Sn Alloys with over 60 per cent. of Copper.

The former change occurs at about 580°, and its temp. is little affected by increasing zinc content. The latter is little affected by increasing zinc content. The latter change occurs at about 520° in the binary copper-tin alloys, and its temp. is raised by the addition of zinc until, if sufficient zinc is present, the two reactions proceed simultaneously, β+γ→α+δ. The δ-phase consists of the compound Cu₄Sn and does not form mixed crystals. Alloys containing more than 35 per cent. Zn, and only small amounts of tin, give rise to ternary β and β' constituents resembling those of the copper-zinc binary alloys, but the range of the ternary alloys having constituents which resemble those of the copper-tin system is much the larger. The structure of the technically important alloys depends greatly on the conditions of cooling and heat treatment. The effect of *cadmium* was examined by G. Chandoir, and M. Gruber.

E. S. Sperry,[20] C. and A. Tissier, H. Grossmann and F. Krupp, T. Matsuda, M. H. Lançon, and Chemische Fabrik vorm. E. Schering examined the effect of *aluminium*; T. Slater,[21] the effect of *chromium*; M. Beuling,[22] E. W. L. Biermann, A. H. and E. H. Cowles, C. Künzel, H. Behrens, M. Lévitzky, A. Ledebur, E. S. Sperry, and P. M. Parsons, the effect of *manganese.* H. S. Primrose, L. C. Glaser and H. J. Seemann, and M. Levi-Malvano and F. S. Orofino [23] studied alloys of tin, copper, and *phosphorus.* They found the f.p. of the binary system Cu_3P–Cu_3Sn to be:

| Cu_3P | . | . | 68·65 | 60·00 | 40·00 | 20·00 | 10·00 | 5·00 | 1·00 per cent. |
| F.p. | . | . | 870° | 830° | 740° | 650° | 690° | 700° | 710° |

with the eutectic at 650°, and 22 per cent. Cu_3P. They also studied the ternary system Cu–Cu_3P–Cu_3Sn. The alloys of tin and copper with *antimony* have been investigated by C. Karmarsch, [24] G. Charpy, W. Schulte, etc. ; they are used as *anti-friction or bearing metals*, because they do not heat so rapidly by the revolving metal it supports. The bearing metals are represented by *babbit metal*—88·88 per cent. Sn ; 7·4 per cent. Sb ; and 3·7 per cent. copper. Antimony is used in *die-casting alloys* to lessen the shrinkage. These alloys are of three types according as zinc, lead, or tin are the basal metals. Those with a zinc base vary from 73 to 92 per cent. of zinc, up to 31 per cent. of tin, 1 to 20 per cent. of copper; up to 10 per cent. of antimony; up to 6 per cent. of aluminium; and up to 10 per cent. of lead. T. J. Johnston gives the following list of alloys of antimony. Taking the percentage amounts of lead, antimony, and tin in order, *electrotype*, 94, 4, 3 ; antimonial lead, 80 to 87, 13 to 20, — ; *jacoby metal*, 85, 10, 5 ; *linotype*, 83, 12, 5 ; *magnolia*, 80, 15, 5 ; standard *sohite-metal*, 71, 24, 5 ; *graphite metal*, 68, 17, 15 ; and standard *type-metal*, 58, 26, 15 with ore per cent. of copper. The alloys of tin and copper with *bismuth* were studied by C. Bischoff, [25] J. Novel, etc. ; and those with *vanadium*, by N. A. Helouis. [26] The tin-copper alloys with *lead* have been examined by A. Erdmann, [27] A. Salvétat, M. Donovan, etc. ; with *iron*, by O. Skinder, [28] C. Bischoff, R. Hunt, E. Edmonds, and E. J. Maumené ; with *nickel*, by C. Bischoff, [29] L. Elsner, etc. ; and with *cobalt*, R. Wagner [30] made a violet bronze. **Bronze coins of the Sung Dynasty in China contained 20–25 per cent. of lead.** [31]

REFERENCES.

[1] *Journ. Inst. Metals,* **11.** 45, 1914 ; A. Rosenheim, *ib.,* **7.** 191, 1912 ; C. P. Karr, *Metal Ind.,* **6.** 15, 1914 ; H. Wachenfeld, *Giesserei Ztg.,* **18.** 425, 1921 ; W. Guertler, *Internat. Zeit. Metallog.,* **6.** 23, 1914 ; W. M. Corse and V. Skillman, *Met. Chem. Engg.,* **12.** 113, 1914 ; F. Doerinckel, E. Philipi, E. Bauer, M. Wunder, and E. H. Schulz, *Metall Erz,* **16.** 591, 1919.

[2] E. von Fellenberg, *Mitt. Naturf. Ges. Bern,* 69, 1860 ; 12, 1865 ; G. Mongez, *Mém. Acad. Inscript.,* **3.** 441, 1818 ; **8.** 363, 1827 ; H. O. Lenz, *Mineralogie der alten Griechen und Römer,* Gotha, 1861 ; C. C. T. E. Göbel, *Ueber den Einfluss der Chemie auf die Ermittelung der Völker der Verzeit,* Erlangen, 1842 ; *Schweigger's Journ.,* **60.** 407, 1830 ; H. von Fehling, *Würtemburg Jahresb.,* **3.** 253, 1847 ; C. Bischoff, *Das Kupfer und seine Legierungen,* Berlin, 1865 ; G. Coffey, *B.A. Rep.,* 873, 1899 ; F. A. Abel, *Chem. News,* **18.** 111, 1848 ; J. Matsuno, *Journ. Chem. Ind. Japan,* **24.** 1369, 1921 ; M. Berthelot, *Ann. Chim. Phys.,* (7), **23.** 5, 1901 ; *Compt. Rend.,* **140.** 183, 1905 ; G. Chesneau, *ib.,* **137.** 653, 1903 ; B. Roux, *ib.,* **52.** 1046, 1861 ; A. Colson, *ib.,* **134.** 989, 1902 ; F. Wibel, *Die Kultur der Bronzezeit,* Kiel, 1865 ; E. D. Clarke, *Ann. Phil.,* **7.** 73, 1815 ; T. Thomson, *ib.,* **2.** 209, 1810 ; M. Chikashige, *Journ. Chem. Soc.,* **117.** 917, 1920 ; T. Matsuno, *Journ. Chem. Ind. Japan,* **24.** 1369, 1921 ; W. Huppertz, *Zeit. Ver. deut. Ing.,* **29.** 329, 1885 ; E. Busse, *Zeit. anal. Chem.,* **17.** 53, 1878 ; C. H. Mathewson, *Amer. Journ. Science,* (4), **40.** 525, 1916 ; H. Spirgatis, *Liebig's Ann.,* **181.** 394, 1876 ; A. Arche and C. Hassack, *Dingler's Journ.,* **253.** 514, 1883 ; L. Marquardt, *ib.,* **254.** 138, 1884 ; H. Kühl, *Giesserei Ztg.,* **9.** 169, 155, 1912 ; A. Bezzenberger, *Analysen vorgeschichtlicher Bronzen Ost-preussens,* Königsberger, 1904 ; E. von Bibra, *Die Bronzen und Kupferlegierungen der alten und ältesten Völker,* Erlangen, 1869 ; O. Vogel, *Stahl Eisen,* **29.** 60, 1909 ; X. Müller, *Arch. Anthrop.,* **15.** 323, 1884 ; O. Skinder, *Mitt. Kaukas. Mus.,* **3.** 1, 1907 ; *Bull. Acad. St. Pe ersburg,* (6), **2.** 209, 1908 ; O. von Struve, (2), **9.** 282, 1866 ; W. Gowland, *Journ. Inst. Metals,* **7.** 23, 1912 ; H. Garland, *ib.,* **10.** 329, 1913 ; F. Henrich and P. Roters, *Zeit. angew. Chem.,* **20.** 1322, 1907 ; M. Busch, *ib.,* **27.** 512, 1914 ; A. Commaille, *Journ. Pharm. Chim.,* (3), **44.** 5, 1863 ; J. Girardin, *ib.,* (3), **23.** 252, 1853 ; F. Stolba, *Ber. Böhm. Ges. Wiss.,* 38, 1860 ; M. Hawranek, *Sitzber. Akad. Wien,* **9.** 273, 1854 ; J. A. Phillips, *Journ. Chem. Soc.,* **4.** 252, 1851 ; W. Flight, *ib.,* **41.** 134, 1882 ; E. Reichardt, *Repert. Pharm.,* **22.** 680, 1873 ; *Arch. Pharm.,* (3), **2.** 513, 1873 ; A. Erdmann, *Journ. prakt. Chem.,* (1), **69.** 213, 1857 ; E. Reyer, *ib.,* (2), **25.** 258, 1882 ; M. Blanckenhorn, *Mitt. Ges. Med. Naturw.,* **6.** 375, 1907 ; C. Reichelt, *Kunst-Gewerbebl. Bayern,* 647, 1852 ; P. Rhoussopoulos, *Chem. Ztg.,* **29.** 1198, 1905 ; C. Zenghelis, *ib.,* **31.** 1116, 1907 ; G. Bergeron, *Monit. Scient.,* (2), **6.** 1125, 1869 ; P. Burckhard, *Jena. Zeit.,* **5.** 393, 1870 ; *Zeit. Chem.,* (2), **6.** 212, 1870.

[3] W. C. Roberts-Austen, *Journ. Soc. Arts.,* **36.** 1111, 1125, 1137, 1888 ; H. Morin, *Compt. Rend.,* **78.** 811, 1874 ; E. J. Maumené, *ib.,* **80.** 1009, 1875 ; S. Kalischer, *Dingler's Journ.,* **215.** 93, 1875 ; *Ber.,* **15.** 702, 1882 ; M. Beuling, *Zeit. Ver. deut. Ing.,* **31.** 117, 1887 ; *Dingler's Journ.,* **270.** 170, 1888 ; W. Hampe, *Chem. Ztg.,* **12.** 893, 1888 ; *Berg. Hütt. Ztg.,* **47.** 304, 1888 ; E. Priwoznik, *Zeit. angew. Chem.,* **1.** 181, 1893 ; X. Müller, *Dingler's Journ.,* **254.** 492, 1884 ; J. B. Grief, *ib.,* **254.** 492, 1884 ; **256.** 422, 1885 ; *Anleitung zur Errichtung und Instandhaltung obserirdischer Telegraphen und Telephon-Linen aus Lazare Weiller's Patent Silicum-Bronze Draht,* Wien, 1885 ;

H. Behrens, *Das mikroskopische Gefüge der Metalle und Legierungen*, Hamburg, **122**, 1894 ; H. Weiss, *Ann. Chim. Phys.*, (9), **20**. 131, 1923 ; E. S. Sperry, *Brass World*, **1**. 399, 1905 ; **3**. 399, 1907 ; *Metallurgist*, **2**. 519, 1905 ; A. Philip, *Journ. Inst. Metals*, **1**. 165, 1909 ; A. Ledebur, *Chem. Ztg.*, **19**. 303, 1885 ; A. and H. Parkes, *Brit. Pat. No.* 12325, 1848 ; A. Parkes, *ib.*, 12537, 1849 ; C. Montefiore-Levi and C. Künzel, *Essais sur l'emploi de divers alliages*, Bruxelles, 1871 ; *Compt. Rend.*, **74**. 314, 1872 ; C. Montefiore-Levi, *Journ. Iron Steel Inst.*, **6**. 408, 1873 ; *Amer. Chem.*, **5**. 178, 1874 ; *Dingler's Journ.*, **200**. 379, 1871 ; C. Künzel, *Die Bronzelegierungen*, Dresden, 44, 1875 ; H. de Ruolz and A. de Fontenay, *Compt. Rend.*, **73**. 1468, 1871 ; W. Koort, *Dingler's Journ.*, **270**. 166, 211, 1888 ; A. Riche, *Compt. Rend.*, **55**. 143, 1862 ; **67**. 1138, 1868 ; **69**. 343, 985, 1869 ; *Ann. Chim. Phys.*, (4), **30**. 351, 1873 ; C. F. Gaywood, *Journ. Inst. Metals*, **1**. 185, 1909 ; F. A. Abel, *Chem. News*, **12**. 172, 1865 ; *B.A. Rep.*, **27**, 1865 ; J. Baschinger and K. Stölzel, *Bayer. Ind. Gewerbebl.*, **7**. 247, 1875 ; E. Priwoznik, *Berg. Hütt. Ztg.*, **45**. 352, 1886 ; F. A. Abel, *Chem. News*, **18**. 111, 1848.

⁴ H. S. Primrose, *Metal Ind.*, **7**. 293, 323, 368, 1915 ; **10**. 105, 1917 ; W. Campbell, *Journ. Franklin Inst.*, **154**. 1, 1902 ; W. J. Lambert, *Engg. Production*, **2**. 227, 1921 ; W. Spring, *Zeit. phys. Chem.*, **15**. 65, 1894 ; *Bull. Acad. Belg.*, (3), **28**. 23, 1894 ; (3), **37**. 790, 1899 ; C. J. B. Karsten, *Schweigger's Journ.*, **65**. 587, 1832 ; A. Guettier, *Dingler's Journ.*, **114**. 128, 196, 279, 1849 ; *Guide pratique des alliages métalliques*, Paris, 1865 ; W. Hampe, *Zeit. Berg. Hütt. Sal.*, **21**. 218, 1873 ; **22**. 93, 1874 ; **24**. 6, 1876 ; A. Weiller, *Centrb. Opt. Mech.*, **6**. 28, 1885 ; *Bull. Soc. Internat. Electriciens*, **1**. 203, 1884 ; C. Bischoff, *Das Kupfer und seine Legierungen*, Berlin, 1865 ; H. Weiss, *Ann. Chim. Phys.*, (9), **20**. 131, 1923 ; E. S. Shepherd and G. B. Upton, *Journ. Phys. Chem.*, **9**. 441, 1905 ; B. E. Curry, *ib.*, **10**, 515, 1906 ; *Trans. Amer. Electrochem. Soc.*, **9**. 249, 1906 ; A. P. Laurie, *Journ. Chem. Soc.*, **53**. 110, 1888 ; A. Saxer, *Met.*, **4**. 517, 1907 ; S. G. Homfray and F. Adam, *Metal Ind.*, **23**. 558, 1923 ; H. Behrens, *Das mikroskopische Gefüge der Metalle und Legierungen*, Hamburg, 71, 1894 ; A. Sentex, C. Maréchal, and A. Saunier, *Brit. Pat. No.* 1886, 1888 ; F. C. Mathers and F. Sowder, *Trans. Amer. Electrochem. Soc.*, **37**. 525, 1920 ; E. Lenssen, *Journ. prakt. Chem.*, (1), **79**. 90, 1860 ; C. H. Proctor, *Met. Ind.*, **5**. 105, 1907 ; *Rev. Electrochim.*, **1**. 294, 1907 ; *Proc. Inst. Mech. Eng.*, 254, 1895 ; *Engg.*, **59**. 778, 1895 ; F. W. Rowe, *Journ. Inst. Metals*, **31**. 217, 1924 ; G. Ongaro, *Met. Ital.*, **15**. 63, 1923 ; S. Ledermann, *Zeit. Metallkunde*, **15**. 74, 98, 1923 ; G. Masing, *ib.*, **17**. 251, 1925 ; O. Bauer and H. Arndt, *Stahl Eisen*, **42**. 1346, 1922 ; C. Langbein, *Handbuch der galvanischen Metallniederschläge*, Leipzig, 337, 1903 ; C. de la Salzede, *Brit. Pat. No.* 11878, 1847 ; F. Förster, *Zeit. anorg. Chem.*, **10**. 318, 1895 ; A. F. Gehlen, *Schweigger's Journ.*, **20**. 353, 1817 ; R. Kremann, C. T. Suchy, J. Lorber, and R. Mass, *Monatsh.*, **35**. 219, 1914 ; W. D. Treadwell and E. Beckh, *Zeit. Elektrochem.*, **21**. 75, 1915 ; O. E. Selby, *Trans. Amer. Inst. Metals*, **11**. 359, 1917.

⁵ W. Broniewsky, *Rev. Mét.*, **12**. 961, 1915 ; L. Révillon and T. Beauverie, *ib.*, **5**. 885, 1908 ; M. Slavinsky, *Journ. Russ. Met. Soc.*, 548, 1913 ; S. Kalischer, *Ber.*, **15**. 702, 1882 ; A. Matthiessen, *B.A. Rep.*, 37, 1863 ; *Journ. Chem. Soc.*, **20**. 201, 1867 ; T. Matsuda, *Science Rep. Tohoku Univ.*, **11**. 223, 1922 ; L. J. Guervich and J. S. Hromalko, *Trans. Amer. Inst. Min. Met Eng.*, **61**. 1351, 1919 ; A. W. Smith, *Journ. Franklin. Inst.*, **192**. 69, 157, 1921 ; J. L. Haughton, *Journ. Inst. Metals*, **13**. 222, 1915 ; **25**. 309, 1921 ; S. L. Hoyt, *ib.*, **10**. 235, 1913 ; *Trans. Amer. Inst. Min. Met. Eng.*, **60**. 198, 1919 ; W. Campbell, *Journ. Inst. Metals*, **20**. 104, 1920 ; Anon., *Metal. Ind.*, **23**. 505, 1923 ; A. Riche, *Ann. Chim. Phys.*, (4), **30**. 351, 1873 ; F. W. Rowe, *Metal Ind.*, **23**. 483, 1923 ; W. Guertler, *Metallographie*, Berlin, **1**. i, 660, 1912 ; *Zeit. anorg. Chem.*, **51**. 417, 1906 ; N. A. Puschin, *ib.*, **56**. 17, 1908 ; F. Förster, *ib.*, **10**. 318, 1895 ; O. Sackur and H. Pick, *ib.*, **58**. 46, 1908 ; A. Smits and J. Skuyman, *Proc. Acad. Amsterdam*, **23**. 689, 1921 ; P. Braesco, *Ann. Physique*, (9), **14**. 5, 1920 ; K. L. Meissner, *Zeit. Metallkunde*, **16**. 439, 1924 ; E. S. Shepherd and G. B. Upton, *Journ. Phys. Chem.*, **9**. 441, 1905 ; E. S. Shepherd and E. Blough, *ib.*, **10**. 630, 1906 ; B. E. Curry, *ib.*, **10**. 515, 1906 ; *Trans. Amer. Electrochem. Soc.*, **9**. 249, 1906 ; C. T. Heycock and F. H. Neville, *Phil. Trans.*, **189**. A, 63, 1897 ; **202**. A, 1. 1903 ; *Proc. Roy. Soc.*, **71**. 409, 1903 ; W. C. Roberts-Austen and E. Stansfield, *ib.*, **56**. 238, 1895 ; W. C. Roberts-Austen, *ib.*, **50**. 367, 1902 ; *Phil. Mag.*, (5), **8**. 58, 551, 1879 ; *Report Alloys Research Committee*, 269, 1895 ; 67, 1897 ; M. Herschkowitsch, *Zeit. phys. Chem.*, **27**. 147, 1898 ; E. von Maey, *ib.*, **38**. 302, 1901 ; H. Gautier, *Contribution à l'étude des alliages*, Paris, 93, 1901 ; *Bull. Soc. Enc. Nat. Ind.*, (5), **1**. 1300, 1896 ; G. Charpy, *ib.*, (5), **2**. 402, 1897 ; (5), **4**. 191, 1899 ; *Contribution à l'étude des alliages*, Paris, 119, 241, 1901 ; *Compt. Rend.*, **124**. 957, 1897 ; H. le Chatelier, *ib.*, **120**. 835, 1895 ; R. Ledoux, *ib.*, **155**. 35, 1912 ; H. Moissan and J. P. O'Farrelly, *ib.*, **138**. 1659, 1904 ; *Bull. Soc. Chim.*, (3), **31**. 1023, 1904 ; W. Campbell, *Proc. Inst. Mech. Eng.*, 1211, 1901 ; *Journ. Franklin Inst.*, **154**. 1, 131, 201, 1902 ; **158**. 166, 1904 ; *Proc. Phys. Soc.*, **17**. 337, 1900 ; E. J. Ball, *Journ. Chem. Soc.*, **53**. 170, 1888 ; A. P. Laurie, *ib.*, **27**. 147, 165, 1898 ; P. Lebeau, *Ber. Internat. Congress. App. Chem.*, **5**. iv, 477, 1904 ; J. Jacobsen, *Bull. Soc. Chim. Belg.*, **20**. 214, 1906 ; F. Giolitti and G. Tavanti, *Gazz. Chim. Ital.*, **38**. ii, 352, 1908 ; F. Mylius and O. Fromm, *Ber.*, **27**. 637, 1894 ; C. F. Rammelsberg, *Pogg. Ann.*, **120**. 54, 1863 ; R. Roth, *ib.*, **36**. 478, 1835 ; W. H. Miller, *Phil. Mag.*, (3), **6**. 3, 107, 1835 ; J. E. Stead, *Journ. Soc. Chem. Ind.*, **16**. 506, 1897 ; **17**. 1115, 1898 ; C. R. A. Wright, *ib.*, **13**. 1014, 1894 ; A. E. Outerbridge, *Journ. Franklin Inst.*, **147**. 18, 1899 ; E. Heyn, *ib.*, **147**. 447, 1899 ; J. T. Milton, *Journ. Inst. Metals*, **1**. 57, 1909 ; G. H. Mundey, C. C. Bissett, and J. Cartland, *ib.*, **28**. 141, 1922 ; A. Philip, *ib.*, **1**. 165, 1909 ; D. Stockdale, *ib.*, **34**. 111, 1915 ; E. Heyn, *Zeit. Ver. deut. Ing.*, **44**. 137, 175, 1900 ; M. Beuling, *ib.*, **31**. 117, 1887 ; *Dingler's Journ.*, **270**. 170, 1888 ; F. Sauerwald, *Zeit. Elektrochem.*, **29**. 85, 1923 ; K. Bornemann and F. Sauerwald, *Zeit. Metall-*

kunde, **14**. 145, 254, 1922; H. Alterthum, *ib.*, **15**. 199, 1923; O. Bauer and O. Vollenbruck, *ib.*, **15**. 119, 191, 1923; T. Isihara, *Metal Ind.*, **24**. 253, 1924; *Journ. Inst. Metals*, **31**. 315, 1924; *Science Rep. Tohoku Univ.*, **13**. 75, 1924; H. Endo, *ib.*, **14**. 479, 1925; G. Tammann and M. Hansen, *Zeit. anorg. Chem.*, **138**. 137, 1924; H. Behrens, *Das mikroskopische Gefüge der Metalle und Legierungen*, Hamburg, 1894; P. Braesco, *Ann. Physique*, (9), **14**. 5, 1920; K. Honda and T. Ishigaki, *Science Rep. Tohoku Univ.*, **14**. 219, 1925.

⁶ R. Mallet, *Proc. Roy. Irish Acad.*, **2**. 95, 1842; *Phil. Mag.*, (3), **21**. 66, 1842; M. Chikashige, *Zeit. anorg. Chem.*, **124**. 335, 1922; J. Rieffel, *Compt. Rend.*, **37**. 450, 1853; E. Heyn and O. Bauer, *Mitt. Material pr. Amt*, **22**. 137, 1904; *Zeit. anorg. Chem.*, **45**. 68, 1905; H. Behrens, *Das mikroskopische Gefüge der Metalle und Legierungen*, Hamburg, 1894; *Versl. Akad. Amsterdam*, **2**. 79, 1894; E. C. Bain, *Chem. Met. Engg.*, **28**. 21, 1923; F. J. Otto, *Liebig's Ann.*, **102**. 66, 1857; E. S. Shepherd, *Journ. Phys. Chem.*, **8**. 421, 1904; C. Bischoff, *Das Kupfer und seine Legierungen*, Berlin, 1865; W. Miller, *Phil. Mag.*, (3), **6**. 105, 1835; C. F. Rammelsberg, *Sitzber. Akad. Berlin*, 188, 1863; *Pogg. Ann.*, **120**. 54, 1863; **128**. 441, 1866.

⁷ A. Westgren and G. Phragmen, *Koll. Zeit.*, **36**. 86, 1925; C. H. Mathewson, *Amer. Journ. Science*, (4), **40**. 525, 1916; C. H. Mathewson and P. Davidson, *Internat. Zeit. Metallog.*, **8**. 181, 1916; C. F. Smart, *Trans. Amer. Inst. Min. Met. Eng.*, 1875, 1919; O. Smalley, *Journ. Soc. Chem. Ind.*, **37**. 191, 1918; R. J. Anderson and C. H. Eldridge, *Trans. Amer. Inst. Min. Met. Eng.*, 1259, 1923; H. S. Rawdon, *Journ. Washington Acad.*, **5**. 589, 1915; W. Wyss, *Ferrum*, **10**. 167, 1913; H. S. and J. S. G. Primrose, *Journ. Inst. Metals*, **9**. 158, 1913; A. Portevin, *Compt. Rend.*, **171**. 350, 1920; *Journ. Inst. Metals*, **29**. 239, 1923; *Rev. Mét.*, **16**. 141, 1919; G. H. Gulliver, *ib.*, **9**. 120, 1913; **11**. 252, 1914; **13**. 263, 1915; L. Grenet, *Compt. Rend. Soc. Ind. Min.*, **14**. 138, 1911; F. C. Thompson, *Journ. Birmingham Met. Soc.*, **7**. 597, 1920; *Metal Ind.*, **18**. 404, 1921; P. G. J. Gueterbock and G. N. Nicklin, *Journ. Soc. Chem. Ind.*, **44**. 370, T, 1925.

⁸ J. H. Croockewit, *Specimen chemicum de conjunctionibus chemicia metallorum*, Amsterdam, 1848; *Journ. prakt. Chem.*, (1), **45**. 87, 1848; E. von Maey, *Zeit. phys. Chem.*, **38**. 291, 1901; R. H. Thurston, *Copper-Tin Alloys*, Washington, 377, 1879; *A Treatise on Brasses, Bronzes, and Other Alloys*, New York, 1893; M. Beuling, *Zeit. Ver. deut. Ing.*, **31**. 117, 1887; A. L. Norbury, *Trans. Faraday Soc.*, **19**. 586, 1924; *Dingler's Journ.*, **270**. 170, 1888; H. Behrens, *Das mikroskopische Gefüge der Metalle und Legierungen*, Hamburg, 71, 1894; F. C. Calvert and R. Johnson, *Phil. Mag.*, (4), **17**. 114, 1859; *Mem. Manchester Lit. Phil. Soc.*, **15**. 113, 1860; R. Mallet, *Proc. Roy. Irish Acad.*, **2**. 95, 1842; *Phil. Mag.*, (3), **21**. 66, 1842; O. J. Lodge, *ib.*, (5), **8**. 554, 1879; G. Kamensky, *Proc. Phys. Soc.*, **6**. 53, 1883; *Chem. News*, **47**. 304, 1883; J. Rieffel, *Compt. Rend.*, **37**. 450, 1853; F. Osmond and G. Gartaud, *ib.*, **139**. 404, 1904; H. le Chatelier, *Bull. Soc. Enc. Nat. Ind.*, (4), **10**. 388, 1353, 1895; *Compt. Rend.*, **120**. 835, 1895; H. de Ruolz and H. de Fontenay, *ib.*, **83**. 783, 1876; H. Moissan and J. P. O'Farrelly, *ib.*, **138**. 1659, 1904; *Bull. Soc. Chim.*, (3), **31**. 1023, 1904; A. Polain, *Rev. Univ. Mines*, (2), **35**. 595, 1874; T. Isihara, *Science Rep. Tohoku Univ.*, **11**. 207, 1922; O. Bauer and O. Vollenbruck, *Zeit. Metallkunde*, **16**. 426, 1924; G. Masing, *ib.*, **17**. 251, 1925; C. Montefiori-Levi and C. Künzel, *Compt. Rend.*, **74**. 314, 1872; *Essais sur l'emploi de divers alliages*, Bruxelles, 1871; F. von Friese, *Dingler's Journ.*, **225**. 314, 1887; E. A. Smith, *Metal. Ind.*, **18**. 65, 1912; C. Schmidt, *Chem. Ztg.*, **45**. 825, 1921; A. Riche, *ib.*, **69**. 343, 985, 1869; *Ann. Chim. Phys.*, (4), **30**. 351, 1873; J. P. J. d'Arcet, *ib.*, (2), **54**. 331, 1833; A. L. Norbury, *Trans. Faraday Soc.*, **19**. 140, 1923; P. Ludwik, *Metal Ind.*, **16**. 125, 1920; A. Martens, *Mitt. Tech. Versuchsanst.*, **8**. 236, 1890; N. S. Kurnakoff and S. F. Schemtschuschny, *Journ. Russ. Phys. Chem. Soc.*, **39**. 1148, 1907; *Zeit. anorg. Chem.*, **60**. 7, 1908; E. Heyn and O. Bauer, *ib.*, **45**. 68, 1905; *Mitt. Material Pruf. Amt*, **22**. 137, 1904; F. Wüst, *Met.*, **6**. 769, 1909; H. Heape, *Journ. Inst. Metals*, **29**. 467, 1923; T. Turner and J. L. Haughton, *ib.*, **6**. 192, 1911; J. H. Chamberlain, *ib.*, **10**. 193, 1913; H. S. and J. S. G. Primrose, *ib.*, **9**. 158, 1913; S. L. Kneass, *Journ. Franklin Inst.*, **159**. 65, 1905; K. Bornemann and F. Sauerwald, *Zeit. Metallkunde*, **14**. 145, 1922; F. Sauerwald, *ib.*, **18**. 137, 1926; T. Isihara, *Science Rep. Tohoku Univ.*, **11**. 207, 1922; E. S. Shepherd and E. Blough, *Journ. Phys. Chem.*, **10**. 630, 1906; C. Bischoff, *Das Kupfer und seine Legierungen*, Berlin, 232, 1865; F. C. Calvert and R. Johnson, *Phil. Mag.*, (4), **17**. 114, 1859; (4), **18**. 354, 1859; P. Braesco, *Ann. Physique*, **14**. 5, 1920; A. Mallock, *Nature*, **117**. 787, 1926, W. L. Kent, *Journ. Inst. Metals*, **35**. 45, 1926; T. Matsuba, *Science Rep. Tohoku Univ.*, **13**. 401, 1925; T. Matsuba and J. Shiba, *ib.*, **13**. 413, 1925.

⁹ R. Mallet, *Proc. Roy. Irish Acad.*, **2**. 95, 1842; *Phil. Mag.*, (3), **21**. 66, 1842; R. H. Thurston, *Copper-Tin Alloys*, Washington, 377, 1879; *A Treatise on Brasses, Bronzes, and Other Alloys*, New York, 1893; J. Arnott, *Trans. Faraday Soc.*, **17**. 209, 1921; F. C. Calvert and R. Johnson, *Phil. Trans.*, **148**. 349, 1858; F. C. Calvert, R. Johnson, and G. C. Lowe, *Phil. Mag.*, (4), **20**. 230, 1860; *Chem. News*, **3**. 315, 357, 371, 1861; J. Kiewit, *Wied. Ann.*, **29**. 617, 1886; A. le Chatelier, *Génie Civil*, **19**. 59, 73, 107, 1891; W. D. Bancroft, *Proc. Amer. Chem. Soc.*, 20, 1905; *Met.*, **2**. 194, 1905; E. S. Shepherd and G. B. Upton, *Journ. Phys. Chem.*, **9**. 441, 1905; B. E. Curry, *ib.*, **10**. 515, 1906; *Trans. Amer. Electrochem. Soc.*, **9**. 249, 1906; A. Riche, *Compt. Rend.*, **60**. 343, 1869; *Ann. Chim. Phys.*, (4), **30**. 351, 1873; J. P. J. d'Arcet, *ib.*, (2), **54**. 331, 1833; G. Wertheim, *ib.*, (3), **12**. 581, 1848; R. Baumann, *Die Festigkeitseigenschaften der Metalle in Wärme und Kälte*, Stuttgart, 1907; L. Guillet, *Rev. Mét.*, **2**. 116, 1905; **4**. 627, 1907; *Compt. Rend.*, **144**. 1008, 1273, 1907; H. E. Tresca, *ib.*, **76**. 1232, 1873; H. le Chatelier, *ib.*, **108**. 1097; 1889; H. Moissan and J. P. O'Farrelly, *ib.*, **138**. 1659, 1904; *Bull. Soc. Chim.*, (3), **31**. 1023;

1904; H. W. Gillet and A. B. Norton, *Metal Ind.*, **6**. 12, 1914; D. Saito and K. Hayashi, *Mem. Coll. Eng. Kyoto Univ.*, **2**. 83, 1919; F. C. Lea, *Proc. Inst. Civ. Eng.*, **209**. 394, 1921; G. F. Comstock, *Chem. Met. Engg.*, **22**. 1113, 1920; J. Bauschinger and K. Stölzel, *Bayer. Ind. Gewerbebl.*, 247, 1875; R Jenny, J. Uchatius, and D. Kirkaldy, *Deut. Ind. Ztg.*, 313, 1873; *Dingler's Journ.*, **209** 186, 1908; C. Montefiori-Levi and C. Künzel, *Compt. Rend.*, **74**. 314, 1872; *Essais sur l'emploi de divers alliages*, Bruxelles, 1871; C. Künzel, *Die Bronzelegierungen*, Dresden, 44, 1875; J. Arnott, *Trans. Faraday Soc.*, **17**. 209, 1921; *Foundry Trade Journ.*, **23**. 2, 1921; J. Czochralsky, *Zeit. Metallkunde*, **13**. 171, 276, 380, 1921; **14**. 70, 1922; P. Hidnert, *Scient. Paper Bur. Standards*, 410, 1921; F. C. Lea, *B.A. Rep.*, 363, 1920; P. Braesco, *Ann. Physique*, (9), **14**. 5, 1920; W. Biltz and W. Holverscheit, *Zeit. anorg. Chem.*, **140**. 261, 1924; W. Biltz, *ib.*, **134**. 45, 1924; J. B. A. Dumas, *Compt. Rend.*, **73**. 530, 1871; C. B. Dudley, *Journ. Franklin Inst.*, **133**. 82, 1892; J. C. Longbottom and A. Campion, *Trans. Inst. Eng. and Shipbuilders, Scotland*, **57**. 574, 1914; F. von Friese, *Dingler's Journ.*, **225**. 314, 1877; A. K. Huntington, *Journ. Inst. Metals*, **8**. 126, 1912; **13**. 23, 1915; H. S. and J. S. G. Primrose, *ib.*, **9**. 158, 1913; H. S. Primrose, *ib.*, **12**. 254, 1914; *Metal Ind.*, **7**. 293, 323, 368, 1915; H. Pealing, *Phil. Mag.*, (6), **30**. 203, 1915; M. Kühnel, *Zeit. Metallkunde*, **14**. 462, 1922; P. Weise, *Zeit. Elektrochem.*, **28**. 327, 1922; G. Tammann and K. Dahl, *Zeit. anorg. Chem.*, **126**. 104, 1923; W. Biltz, *ib.*, **134**. 25, 1924; O. Bauer and O. Vollenbruck, *Zeit. Metallkunde*, **17**. 60, 1925; *Mitt. Materialprüf. Amt.*, **44**. 9, 1926; H. S. Gulick, *Foundry*, **45**. 68, 1917; C. P. Karr, *Trans. Amer. Inst. Min. Met.*, 2485, 1919; F. Johnson, *Journ. Inst. Metal*, **20**. 167, 1918; R. T. Rolfe, *ib.*, **20**. 263, 1918; **24**. 233, 1920; **26**. 85, 1921; *Foundry Trade Journ.*, **23**. 455, 1921; *Metal Ind.*, **18**. 265, 1921; **20**. 413, 437, 1922; R. R. Clarke, *ib.*, **20**. 56, 1922; R. Ledoux, *ib.*, **155**. 35, 1912; W. Pscheidl, *Sitzber. Akad. Wien*, **79**. 114, 1879; H. Behrens, *Das mikroskopische Gefüge der Metalle und Legierungen*, Hamburg, 1894; J. Dewrance, *Journ. Inst. Metals*, **11**. 214, 1914; A. Philip, *ib.*, **1**. 164, 1909; W. E. Alkins and W. Cartwright, *ib.*, **26**. 203, 1921; W. Hampe, *Dingler's Journ.*, **221**. 188, 1876; A. Guettier, *ib.*, **114**. 199, 1849; F. W. Dick, *ib.*, **250**. 30, 1883; X. Müller, *ib.*, **254**. 492, 1884; C. T. Heycock and F. H. Neville, *Phil. Trans.*, **189**. A, 25, 1897; **202**. A, 19, 1903; *Chem. News*, **59**. 175, 1889; *Journ. Chem. Soc.*, **55**. 666, 1889; **57**. 379, 1890; **61**. 911, 1892; **71**. 383, 1897; *Proc. Roy. Soc.*, **68**. 171, 1901; **69**. 320, 1902; W. Voigt, *Wied. Ann.*, **48**. 674, 1893; A. Weiller, *German Pat.*, *D.R.P.* 27590, 1883; F. Giolitti and E. Pannain, *Atti Accad. Lincei*, (5), **17**. ii, 668, 1908; M. Beuling, *Zeit. Ver. deut. Ing.*, **31**. 117, 1887; *Dingler's Journ.*, **270**. 170, 1888; O. Bauer and H. Arndt, *Mitt. Material prüf. Amt.*, **39**. 79, 1921; R. H. Greaves and J. A. Jones, *Journ. Inst. Metals*, **35**. 34, 1925; T. Matsuba, *Science Rep. Tohoku Univ.*, **13**. 419, 1925; J. S. Brown, *Metal Ind.*, **27**. 285, 1925; G. Subrahmanian, *Phil. Mag.*, (7), **1**. 1074, 1926.

[10] W. Guertler, *Zeit. anorg. Chem.*, **51**. 417, 1906; E. J. Ball, *Journ. Chem. Soc.*, **53**. 170, 1888; A. P. Laurie, *ib.*, **53**. 104, 1888; **65**. 1031, 1894; G. Kamensky, *Proc. Phys. Soc.*, **6**. 53, 1884; *Chem. News*, **47**. 304, 1883; A. Matthiessen, *B.A. Rep.*, 37, 1863; 128, 1864; A. Matthiessen and M. Holzmann, *Phil. Trans.*, **150**. 85, 1860; *Pogg. Ann.*, **110**. 190, 1860; A. Matthiessen and C. Vogt, *ib.*, **122**. 19, 1864; *Phil. Mag.*, (4), **24**. 30, 1862; W. C. Roberts-Austen, *ib.*, (5), **8**. 58, 551, 1879; J. L. Haughton, *Trans. Faraday Soc.*, **16**. 392, 1921; R. Schenck, *Zeit. Elektrochem.*, **15**. 650, 1909; R. Ihle, *Jahrb. Gymn. Dresden-Neustadt*, **22**. 3, 1896; F. Gautier, *Journ. Iron Steel Inst.*, **39**. ii, 243, 1889; A. Weiller, *Centrb. Opt. Mech.*, **6**. 28, 1885; H. le Chatelier, *Bull. Soc. Enc. Nat. Ind.*, (4), **10**. 192, 388, 1895; *Rev. Gén. Sciences Pure App.*, **6**. 529, 1895; *Contribution à l'étude des alliages*, Paris, 63, 1901; *Compt. Rend.*, **111**. 455, 1890; **120**. 835, 1895; R. Ledoux, *ib.*, **155**. 35, 1912; O. J. Lodge, *Phil. Mag.*, (5), **8**. 554, 1879; J. Dewar and J. A. Fleming, *ib.*, (5), **34**. 333, 1892; J. Obata, *Researches Electrotech. Lab. Tokyo*, 101, 1921; A. G. Warren and F. Murphy, *Electricien*, **70**. 602, 1908; E. Debié, *Dingler's Journ.*, **270**. 170, 1888; E. Bornemann and K. Wagenmann, *Ferrum*, **11**. 276, 1914; T. J. Seebeck, *Pogg. Ann.*, **6**. 148, 1826; E. Steinmann, *Compt. Rend.*, **130**. 1300, 1900; S. H. J. Wilson, *Journ. Inst. Metals*, **31**. 165, 1924; G. Tammann and W. Wiederholt, *Zeit. anorg. Chem.*, **125**. 67, 1922; G. Tammann, *Zeit. anorg. Chem.*, **118**. 93, 1921; R. Edler, *Elektrotech. Maschinenbau*, **41**. 305, 1923; A. Battelli, *Atti Ist. Veneto*, (6), **5**. 1137, 1887; W. Harris, *Phil. Trans.*, **117**. 18, 1827; M. Herschkowitsch, *Zeit. phys. Chem.*, **27**. 123, 1898; C. Hocken and H. A. Taylor, *Journ. Soc. Tel. Eng.*, **8**. 282, 1879; L. Guillet and M. Ballay, *Compt. Rend.*, **176**. 1800, 1923; R. Kremann and R. G. Rehenberg, *Monatsh.*, **45**. 311, 1924.

[11] M. Herschkowitsch, *Zeit. phys. Chem.*, **27**. 147, 1898; A. P. Laurie, *Journ. Chem. Soc.*, **53**. 111, 1888; F. Haber, *Zeit. Elektrochem.*, **8**. 543, 1902; H. E. Armstrong, *Chem. News*, **52**. 212, 1886; N. A. Puschin, *Zeit. anorg. Chem.*, **56**. 17, 1908; O. Sackur and H. Pick, *ib.*, **58**. 46, 1908; G. Tammann and W. Wiederholt, *ib.*, **125**. 67, 1922; P. Lebeau, *Ber. Internat. Congress App. Chem.*, **5**. iv, 477, 1904; O. C. Clifford, *Phys. Rev.*, (1), **26**. 424, 1908.

[12] H. Behrens, *Das mikroskopische Gefüge der Metalle und Legierungen*, Hamburg, 1894; E. S. Shepherd and G. B. Upton, *Journ. Phys. Chem.*, **9**. 441, 1905; B. E. Curry, *ib.*, **10**. 474, 1906; *Trans. Amer. Electrochem. Soc.*, **9**. 173, 1906; C. T. Heycock and F. H. Neville, *Phil. Trans.*, **202**. A, 1, 1903; W. Haidinger, *Jahrb. Geol. Wien*, 145, 1850; J. B. A. Dumas, *Traité de chimie appliquée aux arts*, Paris, **3**. 512, 1831; E. Chuard, *Compt. Rend.*, **113**. 194, 1891; A. Daubrée, *ib.*, **80**. 462, 1875; **93**. 527, 1881; C. A. de Gouvenain, *ib.*, **80**. 1297, 1875; M. E. Chevreul, *ib.*, **43**. 735, 1856; G. Tammann, *Zeit. anorg. Chem.*, **118**. 93, 1921; E. Jordis and W. Rosenhaupt, *Zeit. angew. Chem.*, **21**. 64, 1908; O. Bauer, *ib.*, **18**. 245, 1905; E. Heyn and O. Bauer, *Mitt. Materialpruf. Amt.*, **22**. 137, 1904; H. von Fellenberg, *Mitt. Naturf. Ges. Bern,*

69. 1860; 12, 1865; C. Ratner, *Chem. Ztg.*, **27**. 703, 1903; B. Setlik, *ib.*, **27**. 454, 1903; F. A. Reuss, *Neues Jahrb. Min.*, 813, 1860; F. Wibel, *ib.*, 400, 1865; *Die Kultur der Bronzezeit*, Kiel, 1865; R. Weber, *Dingler's Journ.*, **244**. 214, 1882; **245**. 86, 1882; J. W. Brühl, *ib.*, **243**. 251, 1882; H. Kämmerer, *ib.*, **257**. 196, 1885; J. Elster, *ib.*, **244**. 214, 1882; *Verh. Beförd. Gewerbf.*, 182, 1869; E. Priwcznik, *Dingler's Journ.*, **204**. 483, 1878; J. Schuler, *ib.*, **232**. 333, 1879; A. Arche and C. Hassack, *ib.*, **253**. 514, 1884; F. Rathgen, *ib.*, **301**. 45, 1896; *The Preservation of Antiquities*, Cambridge, 15, 1905; C. Mitzopulos, *Berg. Hütt. Ztg.*, **37**. 329, 1878; K. Natterer, *Monatsh.*, **21**. 256, 1900; H. Bassett, *Proc. Chem. Soc.*, **19**. 95, 1903; L. Mond and G. Cuboni, *Atti Accad. Lincei*, (5), £. 498, 1893; F. de Villenoisy, *Rev. Archéologique*, **28**. 67, 202, 1896; V. A. Skinder, *Mitt. Kaukas. Mus.*, **3**. 1, 1907; *Bull. Acad. St. Petersburg*, (6), **2**. 209, 1908; F. Stolba, *Ber. Böhm. Ges. Wiss.*, 38, 1860; L. Vanino and E. Seitter, *Die Patina*, Wien, 1903; F. von Friese, *Dingler's Journ.*, **225**. 314, 1877; A. Philip, *Journ. Inst. Metals*, **1**. 164, 1909; G. Guillemin and B. Delachanal, *Compt. Rend.*, **151**. 881, 1910; T. Matsuno, *Journ. Chem. Ind. Japan*, **24**. 1369, 1921; Anon., *Brass World*, **19**. 297, 1923; E. Buchner, *Bayr. Ind. Gewerbebl.*, **22**. 239, 1890; M. Berthelot, *ib.*, (7), **22**. 457, 1901; *Bull. Soc. Chim.*, (3), **11**. 861, 1894; *Compt. Rend.*, **118**. 764, 768, 1894: E. Friedel, *Eintheilsplan des märkischen Provinzial Museums der Stadt Berlin*, Berlin, 20, 1882; S. L. Kneass, *Journ. Franklin Inst.*, **159**. 65, 1905; L. A. Bucholz, *Liebig's Ann.*, **85**. 253, 1853; A. H. Layard, *Discoveries in the Ruins of Nineveh and Babylon*, London, 191, 1853; H. Goldschmidt, *Electrochem. Ind.*, **6**. 244, 1908; C. and A. Tissier, *Compt. Rend.*, **43**. 885, 1856; J. Pintsch, *Automobile*, **15**. 917, 1906; C. Bischof, *Das Kupfer und seine Legierungen*, Berlin, 43, 1865; E. von Bibra, *Die Bronzen und Kupferlegierungen der alten und ältesten Völker*, Erlangen, 206, 1869; J. J. Rein, *Japan*, Leipzig, **2**. 528, 1886; H. Schliemann, *Ilios*, Leipzig, 527, 571, 1881; O. Kröhnke, *Chemische Untersuchungen an vorgeschichtlichen Bronzen Schleswig-Holsteins*, Kiel, 41, 1897; A. Terreil, *Bull. Soc. Chim.*, (2), **3**. 40, 1865; E. Krause, *Verh. anthropol. Ges. Berlin*, 537, 1882; O. Olshausen, *Zeit. Ethnologie*, **16**. 532, 1884; **29**. 346, 1897; B. G. Sage, *Mém. Acad.*, 210, 1779; H. Davy, *Phil. Trans.*, **114**. 151, 242, 1824; **115**. 328, 1825.

[13] L. Révillon and P. Beauverie, *Rev. Met.*, **5**. 886, 1908.

[14] Anon., *Engg.*, **89**. 54, 1910; *Brass World*, **19**. 199, 1923; R. J. Anderson and C. H. Eldridge, *Trans. Amer. Inst. Min. Met. Eng.*, **69**. 990, 1923; R. J. Anderson and G. M. Enos, *ib.*, **70**. 391, 1924; *Carnegie Inst. Tech.*, **5**, 1923; W. A. Selvig and G. M. Enos, *ib.*, **4**, 1922; O. Silberrad, *Journ. Soc. Chem. Ind.*, **40**. 38, T, 1921; W. Ramsay, *ib.*, **40**. 65, T, 1921; *Engg.*, **93**. 687, 1912; **96**. 690, 761, 1913; E. W. Sargeant, *ib.*, **96**. 726, 1913; J. T. Corner, *Journ. Inst. Metals*, **5**. 115, 1911; G. D. Bengough, *ib.*, **5**. 28, 1911; **27**. 51, 1922; G. D. Bengough and R. M. Jones, *ib.*, **10**. 13, 1913; W. E. Gibbs, R. H. Smith, and G. D. Bengough, *ib.*, **15**. 37, 1916; G. D. Bengough and O. F. Hudson, *ib.*, **21**. 37, 1919; G. D. Bengough, R. M. Jones, and R. Pirret, *ib.*, **23**. 65, 1920; G. D. Bengough and J. M. Stuart, *ib.*, **28**. 37, 1922; A. Philip, *ib.*, **7**. 50, 1912; **9**. 61, 1913; **12**. 133, 1914; C. H. Desch, *ib.*, **14**. 189, 1915; C. H. Desch and S. Whyte, *ib.*, **10**. 304, 1913; **12**. 235, 1914; S. Whyte, *ib.*, **13**. 80, 1915; W. R. Webster, *Trans. Amer. Soc. Testing Material*, **17**. 204, 1917; P. T. Bruhl, *Met. Chem. Engg.*, **20**. 239, 1919; P. D. Merica and R. W. Woodward, *Proc. Amer. Soc. Testing Materials*, **19**. 278, 1919; J. H. Reedy and B. Feuer, *Journ. Ind. Eng. Chem.*, **12**. 541, 1920; B. Feuer, *Chem. Met. Engg.*, **22**. 1197, 1920; E. H. Schulz, *Zeit. Metallkunde*, **12**. 49, 1920; G. Stauch, *Electrotech. Zeit.*, **41**. 202, 1920; B. E. Curry, *Journ. Phys. Chem.*, **10**. 474, 1906; E. Bate, *Engg. World*, **23**. 16, 1921; C. G. Gillespie, *Tech. Rev.*, **7**. 44, 1920; H. E. Yerbury, *ib.*, **8**. 82, 1921; *Journ. Inst. Elect. Eng.*, **57**. 118, 1920; W. D. Richardson, *Chem. Met. Engg.*, **23**. 23, 1920; *Brass World*, **17**. 275, 1921; *Trans. Amer. Electrochem. Soc.*, **38**. 245, 1920; J. F. Thomson, *ib.*, **39**. 213, 1922; H. S. Rawdon, *ib.*, **39**. 227, 1922; R. J. MacKay, *ib.*, **39**. 177, 1922; G. B. Jones, *Chem. Trade Journ.*, **70**. 274, 1922; *Chem. Age*, **6**. 200, 1922; W. D. Bancroft, *Raw Materials*, **5**. 267, 1922; L. Belladen, *Met. Ital.*, **14**. 73, 119, 1922; A. A. Bado and R. A. Trelles, *Anal. Asoc. Quim. Argentina*, **10**. 16, 1922; E. E. Thum, *Chem. Met. Engg.*, **26**. 301, 1922; G. K. Burgess, *ib.*, **26**. 772, 1922; A. S. Cushman, *ib.*, **26**. 773, 1922; P. Davidson, *ib.*, **26**. 773, 1922; C. G. Fink, *Journ. Ind. Eng. Chem.*, **14**. 338, 1922; B. D. Saklatwalla, *ib.*, **15**. 39, 1923; P. West, *ib.*, **14**. 601, 1922; F. von Warstemburger, *Rev. Mét.*, **18**. 687, 1921; *Zeit. Metallkunde*, **14**. 23, 59, 1922; L. A. Day, *Journ. Amer. Water Works Assoc.*, **9**. 696, 1922; M. Ledy, *Echo Mines*, **26**. 2719, 1889; *Berg. Hütt. Ztg.*, **59**. 105, 1900; W. A. Tilden, *Journ. Soc. Chem. Ind.*, **5**. 84, 1886; W. P. Jorissen, *Zeit. angew. Chem.*, **23**. 2305, 1910; C. Diegel, *Verh. Ver. Gewerbfl.*, 313, 1899; A. Philip, *Journ. Inst. Metals*, **1**. 165, 1909; F. von Friese, *Dingler's Journ.*, **225**. 314, 1877.

[15] D. Mushet, *Phil. Mag.*, (3), **6**. 444, 1835; L. J. Chaudet, *Ann. Chim. Phys.*, (2), **7**. 275, 1818; F. C. Calvert and R. Johnson, *Journ. Chem. Soc.*, **19**. 435, 1866; A. Matthiessen, *ib.*, **19**. 502, 1866; H. E. Armstrong, *Chem. News*, **53**. 211, 1886; H. Behrens, *Das mikroskopische Gefüge der Metalle und Legierungen*, Hamburg, 1904; B. E. Curry, *Trans. Amer. Electrochem. Soc.*, **9**. 173, 1906; *Journ. Phys. Chem.*, **10**. 474, 1906; E. Harbeck, *German Pat.*, *D.R.P.* 189876, 1906; B. Neumann, *ib.*, 198289, 1905; C. T. Heycock and F. H. Neville, *Phil. Trans.*, **202**. A, 1, 1903; M. Ledy, *Echo Mines*, **26**. 57, 1900; *Berg. Hütt. Ztg.*, **59**. 105, 1900; C. Diegel, *Verh. Ver. Gewerbfl.*, 313, 1899; *Stahl. Eisen*, **24**. 573, 1904; O. Sackur and H. Pick, *Zeit. anorg. Chem.*, **58**. 46, 1908; F. Förster, *ib.*, **10**. 309, 1895; L. Guillet, *Rev. Mét.*, **4**. 1036, 1907; A. Gawalowsky, *Zeit. anal. Chem.*, **38**. 769, 1899; A. Ledebur, *Chem. Ztg.*, **9**. 303, 1885; M. Herschkowitsch, *Zeit. phys. Chem.*, **27**. 147, 1898; W. A. Tilden, *Journ. Soc. Chem. Ind.*, **5**. 84, 1886; F. Giolitti and O. Ceccarelli, *Gazz. Chim. Ital.*, **39**. ii, 557, 1909; F. Giolitti and G. Tavanti, *ib.*, **38**. ii, 209,

1908 ; J. G. A. Khodin, *Trans. Faraday Soc.*, **1.** 119, 1905 ; *Eng.*, **104.** 53, 1905 ; B. Feuer, *Chem. Met. Engg.*, **22.** 1197, 1920.
  [16] L. Guillet, *Rev. Mét.*, **4.** 1036, 1907 ; A. Gawalowsky, *Zeit. anal. Chem.*, **38.** 769, 1899.
  [17] A. Weiller, *Berg. Hütt. Ztg.*, **56.** 4, 1897.
  [18] A. Detlik, M. Stanek, and M. Milbauer, *Riga Ind. Ztg.*, **9.** 111, 1905 ; C. Bürgel, *Electrochem. Zeit.*, **13.** 209, 1907 ; M. Reiche, *German Pat., D.R.P.* 205083, 1907.
  [19] H. Behrens, *Das mikroskopische Gefüge der Metalle und Legierungen*, Hamburg, 70, 92, 1894 ; J. B. A. Dumas, *Traité de chimie appliquée aux arts*, Paris, **3.** 512, 1831 ; H. Fizeau, *Compt. Rend.*, **68.** 1125, 1869 ; P. Berthier, *Ann. Chim. Phys.*, (2), **44.** 121, 1830 ; C. Bischoff, *Das Kupfer und seine Legierungen*, Berlin, 217, 1865 ; R. H. Thurston, *Copper-Tin Alloys*, Washington, 1879 ; *A Treatise on Brasses, Bronzes, and Other Alloys*, New York, 1893 ; *Dingler's Journ.*, **254.** 377, 1884 ; A. Guettier, *ib.*, **114.** 199, 1849 ; O. Smalley, *Metal Ind.*, **21.** 56, 75, 101, 124, 149, 1922 ; S. L. Hoyt, *Journ. Inst. Metals*, **10.** 235, 1913 ; S. L. Hoyt and P. H. M. P. Brinton, *ib.*,· **14.** 178, 1915 ; O. F. Hudson and R. M. Jones, *ib.*, **14.** 98, 1915 ; W. E. H. Jobbins, *Journ. Franklin Inst.*, **117.** 88, 184, 260, 1884 ; *Monit. Scient.*, (3), **15.** 481, 1885 ; C. B. Dudley, *Journ. Franklin Inst.*, **133.** 82, 1892 ; F. Henning, *Zeit. Instr.*, **27.** 115, 1907 ; G Tammann and M. Hansen, *Zeit. anorg. Chem.*, **138.** 137, 1924 ; W. Jäger and H. Diesselhorst, *Abhand. Phys. Tech. Reichsanst.*, **3.** 425, 1900 ; R. Clarke, *Metal Ind.*, **20.** 56, 1922 ; A. P. Laurie, *Journ. Chem. Soc.*, **65.** 1031, 1894 ; F. C. Calvert and R. Johnson, *ib.*, **19.** 435, 1866 ; G. H. Bailey, *Journ. Soc. Chem. Ind.*, **21.** 531, 1902 ; L. Guillet, *Rev. Mét.*, **2.** 104, 1905 ; J. Jones, *Metal Ind.*, **3.** 171, 1906 ; *Metallurgist*, **3.** 167, 1906 ; W. E. Newton, *Brit. Pat. No.* 1777, 1853 ; A. F. Cothias, *ib.*, 14479, 1896 ; T. J. and R. Wibrin, *U.S. Pat. No.* 900810 1908 ; F. Auerbach, *Ann. Physik*, (4), **3.** 108, 1900 ; A. Hupertz, *Zeit. Ver. deut. Ing.*, **29.** 329, 1885 ; A T. Lincoln, D. Klein, and P. E. Howe, *Journ. Phys. Chem.*, **11.** 526, 1907 ; W. Hamp, *Chem. Ztg.*, **12.** 893, 1888 ; J. S. Périssé, *Génie Civ.*, **6.** 380, 1885 ; R. van Langhenhove, *Rev. Univ. Mines*, (3), **8.** 53, 1889 ; R. R. Clarke, *Metal Ind.*, **20.** 56, 1922 ; F. W. Rowe, *ib.*, **24.** 251, 1924 ; *Journ. Inst. Metals*, **31.** 217, 1924 ; S. H. J. Wilson, *ib.*, **31.** 165, 1924 ; *Metal Ind.*, **24.** 254, 1924 ; F. P. Venable, *Chem. News*, **40.** 1897, 1879 ; R. B. Wheatley, *French Pat. No.* 379403, 1907 ; F. W. Fletcher, and L. W. J. Digby, *German Pat., D.R.P.* 203557, 1906 ; *U.S. Pat. No.* 867194, 1906 ; G. Chandoir, *ib.*, 820954, 1906 ; M. Gruber, *German Pat., D.R.P.* 197510, 1906.
  [20] E. S. Sperry, *Brass World*, **2.** 219, 1906 ; *Metallurgist*, **3.** 804, 1906 ; E. Schering, *Chem. Ztg. Rep.*, **11.** 64, 1887 ; T. Matsuda, *Science Rep. Tohoku Univ.*, **11.** 223, 1922 ; M. Wählert, *Zeit. Metallkunde*, **18.** 299, 1921 ; H. Grossmann and F. Krupp, *Electrochem. Ind.*, **6.** 254, 1908 ; C. and A. Tissier, *Compt. Rend.*, **43.** 885, 1856 ; M. H. Lançon, *French Pat. No.* 217892, 1891 ; *German Pat., D.R.P.* 66389, 1891 ; A. A. Read and R. H. Greaves, *Journ. Inst. Metals*, **15.** 264, 1916 ; Chemische Fabrik vorm. E. Schering, *Chem. Ztg.*, **11.** 64, 1887.
  [21] T. Slater, *Brit. Pat. No.* 9460, 1884.
  [22] M. Beuling, *Zeit. Ver. deut. Ing.*, **31.** 117, 1887 ; *Dingler's Journ.*, **270.** 170, 1888 ; E. S. Sperry, *Brass World*, **1.** 399, 1905 ; A. H. and E. H. Cowles, *U.S. Pat. No* 415832, 1889 ; *Metallurgist*, **5.** 303, 1908 ; H. Behrens, *Das mikroskopische Gefüge der Metalle und Legierungen*, Hamburg, 125, 1894 ; E. W. L. Biermann, *Berg. Hütt. Ztg.*, **37.** 184, 1878 ; M. Lévitzky, *ib.*, **39.** 64, 1880 ; *Rev. Univ. Mines*, (2), **6.** 24, 1879 ; P. M Parsons, *Brit. Pat. Nos.* 482, 1876 ; 11512, 1888 ; A. Ledebur, *Chem. Ztg.*, **19.** 303, 1885 ; C. Künzel, *Die Bronzelegierungen*, Dresden, 43, 1875.
  [23] M. Levi-Malvano and F. S. Orofino, *Gazz. Chim. Ital.*, **41.** ii, 297, 1911 ; L. C. Glaser and H. J. Seeman, *Zeit. tech. Phys.*, **7.** 42, 1926 ; J. S. Primrose, *Metal Ind.*, **28.** 569, 19.6.
  [24] G. Charpy, *Compt. Rend.*, **127.** 1646, 1898 ; W. Schulte, *Ueber die Abscheidung des Antimons aus seiner Sulfantimonatlösung*, Berlin, 72, 1908 ; L. Sempell, *Metallurgist*, **4.** 669, 1907 ; W. Richter, *German Pat., D.R.P.* 195792, 1905 ; R. I. Roman, *ib.*, 82819, 1894 ; A. Manhardt, *ib.*, 152784, 1902 ; F. W. Fletcher and L. W. J. Digby, *German Pat., D R P.* 203557, 1906 ; *U.S. Pat. No.* 867194, 1906 ; T. J. and R. Wirbin, *ib.*, 900810, 1908 ; M. Lafond, *Génie Ind.*, **8.** 302, 1854 ; H. Kirchweger, *ib.*, 201, 1854 ; E. S. Sperry, *Brass World*, **2.** 75, 1906 ; A. H. Mundey, C. C. Bisset, and J. Cartland, *Journ. Inst. Metals*, **28.** 141, 1922 ; O. F. Hudson and J. H. Darley, *ib.*, **24.** 361, 1920 ; *Metal Ind.*, **17.** 519, 1920 ; A. Baumgärtl, *Kunst Gewerbeblatt*, **28.** 558, 1850 ; H. Bechmann, *ib.*, **39.** 12, 1861 ; C. Karmarsch, *Dingler's Journ.*, **130.** 41, 1853 ; F. Volk, *Pract. Masch. Const.*, **2.** 292, 1869 ; *Dingler's Journ.*, **197.** 378, 1870 ; A. Faist, *ib.*, **127.** 398, 1853 ; A. Pauli, *ib.*, **130.** 171, 1853 ; F. Köller, *ib.*, **114.** 236, 1849 ; *Verh. Niederost. Gewerb. Ver.*, **15.** 96, 1849 ; H. Behrens, *Das mikroskopische Gefüge der Metalle und Legierungen*, Hamburg, 60, 1894 ; O. F. Hudson, *Journ. Inst. Metals*, **24.** 361, 1920 ; H. E. Fry and W. Rosenhain, *ib.*, **22.** 217, 1919 ; T. J. Johnston, *Mech. World*, **54.** 129, 1914.
  [25] C. Bischoff, *Das Kupfer und seine Legierungen*, Berlin, 312, 1865 ; J. Novel, *Compt. Rend.*, **116.** 256, 1893 ; M. H. Lançon, *French Pat. No.* 217892, 1891 ; *German Pat., D.R.P.* 66398, 1891 ; A. Bauer and X. Schmidlechner, *ib.*, 72684, 1892.
  [26] N. A. Helouis, *Metal Ind.*, **5.** 291, 1907 ; *Rev. Electrochim.*, **1.** 419, 1907.
  [27] A. Erdmann, *Journ. prakt. Chem.*, (1), **40.** 374, 1847 ; A. Souchay, *ib.*, (1), **82.** 275, 1861 ; J. Boeck, *ib.*, (2), **40.** 158, 1889 ; H. F. Staley and C. P. Karr, *Trans. Amer. Inst. Min. Met. Eng.*, 2511, 1919 ; H. Behrens, *Das mikroskopische Gefüge der Metalle und Legierungen*, Hamburg, 92, 1894 ; C. B. Dudley, *Journ. Franklin Inst.*, **133.** 82, 1892 ; D. Mazzotto, *Atti Accad. Torino*, **17.** 111, 1881 ; G. H. Bailey, *Journ. Soc. Chem. Ind.*, **21.** 531, 1902 ; A. French, *ib.*, **8.** 36, 1889 ; F. Heinrich and P. Roters, *Zeit. angew. Chem.*, **20.** 1322, 1907 ; W. Sonne, *ib.*, **1.** 508, 1888 ;

B. Neumann, *ib.*, **20.** 2026, 1907 ; G. H. Clamer and J. G. Hendrickson, *U.S. Pat. No.* 12880,
1908 ; W. Gowland, *Journ. Roy. Soc. Arts*, **43.** 423, 1895 ; M. Donovan, *Chem. Gaz.*, **8.** 176, 1850 ;
C. H. B. Hambly, *ib.*, **14.** 216, 1856 ; J. Percy, *ib.*, **8.** 1, 1850 ; J. A. Phillips, *Journ. Chem. Soc.*,
4. 252, 1851 ; E. J. Ball, *ib.*, **53.** 167, 1888 ; W. Flight, *ib.*, **41.** 134, 1882 ; A. H. Church, *ib.*,
18. 215, 1865 ; H. F. Staley and C. P. Karr, *Trans. Amer. Inst. Min. Met. Eng.*, **64.** 420, 1921 ;
A. Salvétat, *Ann. Chim. Phys.*, (3), **30.** 361, 1850 ; H. Morin, *ib.*, (5), **3.** 141, 1874 ; *Compt. Rend.*,
78. 811, 1874 ; E. J. Maumené, *ib.*, **80.** 1009, 1875 ; P. Christofle and H. Bouilhet, *ib.*, **78.** 1019,
1874 ; L. Guillet, *ib.*, **172.** 1038, 1921 ; S. de Luca, *ib.*, **84.** 271, 1877 ; B. Roux, *ib.*, **52.** 1046,
1861 ; J. Girardin, *Journ. Pharm. Chim.*, (3), **23** 252, 1853 ; A. Commaille, *ib.*, (3), **44.** 5, 1863 ;
E. Reichardt, *Arch. Pharm.*, (2), **101.** 142, 1860 ; A. Arche and C. Hassack, *Dingler's Journ.*, **253.**
514, 1884 ; G. Marquard, *ib.*, **254.** 138, 1884 ; A. Vogel, *ib.*, **136.** 458, 1855 ; F. Ginsky, *ib.*, **236.**
347, 1880 ; *Mitt. Gebiete Seewesens*, **8.** 172, 1880 ; V. A. Skinder, *Bull. Acad. St. Petersburg*, (6),
2. 209, 1908 ; *Mitt. Kankas. Mus.*, **3.** 1, 1907 ; R. Pumpelly, *Amer. Journ. Science*, (2), **42.** 43,
1866 ; F. A. Genth, *Journ. Franklin Inst.*, **36.** 261, 1858 ; *Phil. Mag.*, (4), **16.** 420,
1859 ; S. K. Patterson, *Electrochem. Ind.*, **7.** 21, 1909 ; J. Jones, *Metal Ind.*, **3.** 171, 1906 ;
Metallurgist, **3** 167, 1906 ; H. Mennicke, *Elektrochem. Zeit.*, **15.** 150, 1908 ; J. P. Reitz, *Chem. Ind.*
8. 350, 1885 ; *German Pat., D.R.P.* 33104, 1885 ; G. Stöckel, *ib.*, 56241, 1890 ; W. Richter, *ib.*,
195792, 1905 ; H. Kämmerer, *ib.*, **257.** 196, 1885 ; S. Kern, *Chem. News*, **93.** 47, 1906 ; F. Varrentrapp, *Mitt. Gewerbever. Braunschweig*, 12, 1864 ; C. Reichelt, *Bayer. Kunst. Gewerbebl.*, 647,
1852 ; A. Terreil, *Bull. Soc. Chim.*, (2), **3.** 110, 1865 ; G. Arnaudon, *ib.*, (1), **1.** 245, 1860 ; S. Kali-
schen, *Ber.*, **7.** 1113, 1874 ; H. Hyman, *Metal Ind.*, **22.** 581, 1923 ; M. Moussier, *Le Technologiste*
11. 196, 1850 ; M. Wilkins, *Ann. Phil.*, **2.** 471, 1813 ; T. Thomsen, *ib.*, **2.** 209, 1813 ;
E. W. L. Biermann, *Berg. Hütt. Ztg.*, **37.** 184, 1878 ; H. F. Höveler, *Journ. Ztg.*, **16.** 1339, 1892 ;
M. Uhlenhuth, *Zeit. Ver. deut. Ing.*, **19.** 376, 1875 ; M. Grinand, *Le Technologiste*, (3), **2.** 737,
1879 ; C. Bischoff, *Das Kupfer und seine Legierungen*, Berlin, 1865 ; W. C. Roberts-Austen,
Phil. Trans., **187.** A, 383, 1896 ; *Proc. Inst. Mech. Eng.*, 31, 1897.

²⁸ O. Skinder, *Mitt. Kaukas Mus.*, **3.** 1, 1907 ; *Bull. Acad. St. Petersburg*, (6), **2.** 209, 1908 ;
W. J. May, *Mechanical World*, **69.** 389, 1921 ; E. J. Maumené, *Compt. Rend.*, **80.** 1009, 1875 ;
C. Bischoff, *Das Kupfer und seine Legierungen*, Berlin, 1865 ; R. Hunt, *Edin. Phil. Journ.*, **50.**
59, 1851 ; E. Edmonds, *Trans. Nat. Hist. Antiq. Soc. Penzance*, **1.** 347, 1849.

²⁹ C. Bischoff, *Das Kupfer und seine Legierungen*, Berlin, 273, 1865 ; L. Elsner, *Chem.
Tech. Mitt.*, **11.** 86, 1862 ; V. Schmidt, *German Pat., D.R.P.* 44536, 1888 ; R. B. Wheatley,
Brit. Pat. No. 8097, 1901 ; J. Webster, *ib.*, 12344, 1885 ; 8320, 1886 ; *Dingler's Journ.*, **253.**
426, 1884 ; **254.** 387, 1884 ; R. H. Sauvage, *ib.*, **215.** 377, 1875 ; C. Diegel, *Verh. Ver. Gewerbefl.*,
313. 1899 ; *Stahl Eisen*, **24.** 571, 1904 ; E. Grüneisen, *Ann. Physik*, (4), **22.** 817, 1907 ;
P. H. Ashberry, *Brit. Pat. No.* 740, 1866.

³⁰ R. Wagner, *Dingler's Journ.*, **190.** 252, **1868.**

³¹ Anon., *Science China*, **7.** 839, 1922

§ 8. Alloys of Tin with Silver and Gold

A. F. Gehlen[1] observed that silver and tin readily combine without
incandescence, and the sp. gr. of the product exceeds the mean between the sp. gr.
of the constituents. An alloy with silver and tin in the proportion 2 : 1 is hard, and
one with the proportion 1 : 2 is malleable. The molten elements, said
C. R. A. Wright, are mutually soluble in all proportions. H. Weiss studied the
neutral diffusion of silver and tin. F. Mylius and O. Fromm obtained an alloy with
a variable composition, by adding tin to a dil. soln. of silver sulphate. The thermal
diagram was studied by C. T. Heycock and F. H. Neville, H. Gautier, and G. Charpy.
R. A. Joyner, like G. I. Petrenko, found that if well annealed, the silver-tin alloys
show the presence of one compound, Ag_3Sn ; and with alloys containing over 50
per cent. of tin, a solid soln. of silver in silver tritastannide ; the latter compound
becomes stable below 490°. If the cooling be rapid, the solid soln. may be retained
in the solid castings. The fusion curves obtained by G. I. Petrenko are shown in
Fig. 44. The eutectic is at 220° with a mixture containing 3·5 per cent. of silver.
The sat. solid soln. with 25 per cent. of tin decomposes on cooling, forming **silver
tritastannide,** Ag_3Sn, and a solid soln. with 19 per cent. of tin. The tritastan-
nide is dimorphous $\alpha\text{-}Ag_3Sn \rightleftharpoons \beta\text{-}Ag_3Sn$ with a transition temp. 232°, nearly.
A. J. Murphy could not confirm this transition point ; but by electrical measure-
ments he found a transformation occurs at 60°. He also found that the solid soln.
of tin in silver contains a maximum of 13·3 per cent. tin at 724°, and this slowly
falls to just below 11 per cent. at 100°. This α-soln. reacts with liquid at 724° to

form a second solid soln., β, which is the sole constituent of alloys containing 12·5–19 per cent. tin at 20°, and of alloys containing 13–24 per cent. tin at 480°; at 724°, it contains 14·5 per cent. tin. The α+β field is a narrow belt extending over the range 13·3–14·5 per cent. tin at 724° and 11–13 per cent. tin at 20°. The γ-constituent is the compound Ag₃Sn, which exists in a narrow range of less than one per cent. in the vicinity of 26 per cent. Sn., the β+γ field occupying the space between the β and γ ranges mentioned above. Alloys containing more than 27 per cent. Sn. are all composed of γ and tin containing less than 0·1 per cent. silver in solid soln. The α-solid soln. is characterized by prolific twinning accompanied by the development of finer marking following the course of cleavage planes in the crystals. The β-solid soln. consists entirely of polygonal crystals without any surface markings, and the compound Ag₃Sn, after prolonged annealing, of polygonal crystals with fine cross-hatch markings.

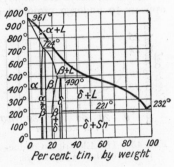

FIG. 44.—The Fusion Curves of the Sn–Ag Alloys.

The addition of even very small quantities of silver to tin suppresses both the allotropic transformations, 0·1 per cent. silver preventing the tin from changing to the grey variety even after three weeks at −78°. The sp. gr. of the aged filings of the tritastannide is 9·83; the X-radiogram correspond with a close-packed hexagonal lattice of side $2·98 \times 10^{-8}$ cm., and axial ratio $a : c = 1 : 1·61$; and the mean coeff. of linear expansion is 0·0000222 between 16° and 236°. Measurements of the electrical resistance were also made. D. H. Andrews and J. Johnston studied the solubility of silver in tin.

W. Vaubel said that *silver tetritastannide* is produced by the action of tin hydride on soln. of silver nitrate. The microstructure of the alloys was examined by G. I. Petrenko, A. J. Murphy, C. T. Heycock and F. H. Neville, G. Charpy, R. A. Joyner, W. Campbell, and K. Endell and H. Hanemann. A. Westgren and G. Phragmen studied the X-radiograms of these alloys; and F. Schmidt, the surface-tension of tin-amalgams. A. Matthiessen gave for the sp. gr.:

	14·8°	12·9°	13·9°	16·3°	19·3°	18·4°	18·8°	18·6°
Ag : Sn .	4 : 1	2 : 1	1 : 1	1 : 2	1 : 3	1 : 6	1 : 9	1 : 18
Sp. gr. .	9·953	9·507	8·823	8·223	7·963	7·666	7·551	7·421

E. von Maey found the sp. vol. curve had a singular point corresponding with the tritastannide. H. Behrens said that there are maxima in the hardness curve corresponding with Ag₄Sn and Ag₂Sn. H. Gautier, and G. Charpy also made observations on the hardness of these alloys. W. C. Roberts-Austen measured the diffusion of silver in tin; and F. Saeftel and G. Sachs, and G. Wertheim, the elastic properties. J. J. van Laar, W. C. Roberts-Austen, and A. W. Smith discussed the m.p. curves. J. Marttinen and J. R. Tiihonen studied the sp. ht. and the latent heat of tin amalgams; A. W. Smith, the thermal conductivity; and A. L. Bernoulli, the optical properties. The relation between the thermal and electrical conductivities was studied by A. L. Bernoulli, C. Hardenbeck, and R. Schenck. Some of A. Matthiessen and co-workers' observations on the electrical conductivity are indicated in Fig. 45. The thermoelectric force of an alloy with 4 per cent. of tin against copper was 7·6 microvolts at 18°, and 5·5 at 80°. M. Herschkowitsch found that the curve showing the electrolytic potentials of these alloys has a singular point corresponding with Ag₄Sn. N. A. Puschin showed that the e.m.f. of the cell Sn | N-H₂SO₄ | SnAg_n corresponded with the existence of Ag₅Sn or Ag₆Sn. M. Herschkowitsch measured the electrode potentials of these alloys. T. J. Seeback, and A. Batelli studied their thermoelectric properties. The alloy oxidizes readily; and, added J. J. Berzelius, the tin is best separated by distilling the alloy in the form of filings with mercuric chloride. According to H. Moissan and T. Watanabe, if an alloy with 36·98 per cent. of silver is heated for 10 mins. in a high temp. electric furnace, the residue retains only 2·93 per cent. silver.

Silver-tin alloys are employed in making *dental-amalgams*, and the binary alloy appears to undergo profound changes through the lapse of time. G. V. Black

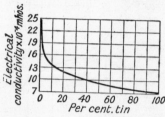

FIG. 45.—The Electrical Conductivities of the Sn-Ag Alloys.

showed that the fresh filings require for amalgamation half as much mercury again as similar filings which have been kept for some months, or heated for half an hour to 100°. The ageing does not occur in a bar of alloy during several weeks' heating under conditions where the filings are aged in half an hour. Exclusion of air does not affect the results. Amalgams obtained from freshly prepared filings exhibit volume changes different from those made from aged filings. The effect of *the ageing of silver-tin alloys* low in silver is as pronounced as with alloys containing much

of that metal. R. A. Joyner found no difference in the solid amalgams from aged and unaged filings. W. A. Knight and J. A. Joyner showed that the ageing is not due to the formation of a film of oxide, to the adsorption of oxygen, or to the acceleration of a polymorphic change due to the introduction of iron during the filing. W. A. Knight also showed that the filings are not aged by ozone, and there is no evidence of the formation of any film of oxide during ageing. He found that in the ageing of silver-tin alloys—during which the filings lose part of their power of combining with mercury—there is no perceptible change in weight, but the vol. diminishes, and with the alloy Ag_3Sn, the change is about 0·4 per cent. In solid soln. containing silver, the ageing is roughly proportional to the amount of silver tritastannide present, vanishing completely for pure tin—*vide infra*, mercury alloys. For H. Péchaux's hypothesis, *vide infra*, aluminium-silver alloys. Alloys of aluminium with tin, bismuth, or magnesium appear to exhibit the phenomenon of ageing, but not those of aluminium with lead or zinc. Observations were also made on this subject by J. W. McBain and co-workers, A. Fenchel, and A. W. Gray. The last-named regarded the ageing as a process analogous to the annealing of brasses, bronzes, etc., for it consists in the recrystallization of amorphous material produced by the severe deformation of silver tritastannide crystals during the comminution of the alloy—3. 21, 5. G. T. Beilby has shown that the result of mechanical work on metals may change them from the crystalline to the amorphous state. G. Tammann studied the electrode potential and chemical properties of these alloys.

According to C. Hatchett,[2] small quantities of tin make gold less ductile but do

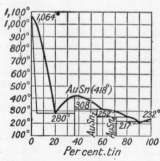

FIG. 46.—The Fusion Curves of the Sn–Au Alloys.

not make it brittle ; gold and tin in the proportion 11 : 1 make a pale yellow, slightly malleable alloy with a fine-grained fracture, and a sp. gr. 17·307, indicating that the vol. is less than the sum of the vols. of the constituents. F. Mylius and O. Fromm prepared an alloy of variable composition by the action of tin on a soln. of auric chloride. C. F. Rammelsberg discussed the crystalline character of the alloy ; and F. M. Raoult, the substitutions of the constituents by other metals in soln. of their salts. R. Vogel found that the curve of fusion, Fig. 46, falls sharply from the m.p. of gold to a eutectic point at 280° and 20 per cent. of tin. It then rises to a well-defined maximum at 418°, corresponding with 37·63 per cent. of tin and

representing **gold monostannide,** AuSn, which forms a silver-grey mass more brittle and hard than either gold or tin, and with an electrical conductivity greater than all the gold-tin alloys excepting those with over 95 per cent. of gold. It is as resistant as gold to the action of sulphuric, nitric, or hydrochloric acid, and is only slowly attacked by aqua regia. The fusion curve, after passing through the maximum at 418°, falls to a second eutectic at 217° and 90 per cent. of tin, finally rising to the m.p. of tin. The curve between the first maximum and the second eutectic has two breaks, one at 308°, and 60 per cent. of tin corresponds with **gold distannide,** $AuSn_2$, which appears as large crystals in the slowly cooled alloy, and it is as resistant towards acids as the monostannide. At 308°, it is transformed $AuSn \rightleftharpoons 0.59AuSn$ $+$ fused alloy $(0.403Au+1.403Sn)$. The second break at 252° and 80 per cent. of tin, corresponds with **gold tetrastannide,** $AuSn_4$. This compound is coloured brown by nitric acid while the distannide is not changed. At 252°, it is transformed $Sn+AuSn \rightleftharpoons 0.85AuSn_2+$ fused alloy $(0.15Au+0.15Sn)$. C. T. Heycock and F. H. Neville, R. Vogel, H. le Chatelier, W. C. Roberts-Austen, and C. H. Desch made observations on the eutectic mixture, and microstructure. A. Matthiessen found the sp. gr. of a number of gold-tin alloys :

	15·4°	14·2°	14·6°	23·70°	23·7°	23·7°	24·6°	23·1°	22·9°
Au : Sn	4 : 1	2 : 1	1 : 1	2 : 3	1 : 2	1 : 3	1 : 4	1 : 6	1 : 50
Sp. gr.	16·37	14·243	11·833	10·794	10·168	9·405	8·931	8·470	7·441

E. von Maey measured the sp. vol. of these alloys ; W. C. Roberts-Austen, the tensile strength, and also the diffusion of gold into tin ; C. T. Heycock and F. H. Neville, and J. A. Mathews, the lowering of the f.p. ; A. Matthiessen, the coeff. of cubical expansion, and the electrical conductivity. There were two minima on the conductivity curve corresponding with Au_4Sn and Au_2Sn_5. N. A. Puschin found no evidence of the tetrastannide in his measurements of the electrolytic potential of these alloys, but he did find singularities in the curve corresponding with SnAu, and Sn_2Au. A. P. Laurie, and H. le Chatelier discussed the e.m.f. of a cell with a gold-tin alloy in a soln. of stannic chloride and gold in a soln. of auric chloride. G. Tammann studied the electrode potential and chemical properties of the gold-tin alloys ; and G. Tammann and W. Wiederholt, the cathodic polarization.

REFERENCES.

¹ A. Matthiessen, *Phil. Trans.*, 150. 161, 177, 1860 ; *B.A. Rep.*, 37, 1863 ; *Pogg. Ann.*, 110. 21, 190, 1860 ; A. Matthiessen and M. Holzmann, *ib.*, 110. 21, 1860 ; *Phil. Trans.*, 150. 85, 1860 ; *Pogg. Ann.*, 110. 222, 1860 ; A. Matthiessen and C. Vogt, *ib.*, 116. 369, 1862 ; T. J. Seebeck, *ib.*, 10. 203, 1827 ; G. Wertheim, *Ann. Chim. Phys.*, (3). 12. 581, 1848 ; H. Weiss, *ib.*, (9), 20. 131, 1923 ; N. A. Puschin, *Journ. Russ. Phys. Chem.*, 39. 520, 1907 ; J. J. Berzelius, *Lehrbuch der Chemie*, Dresden, 2. i, 212, 1826 ; W. Campbell, *Journ. Franklin Inst.*, 154. 1, 131, 201, 1902 ; E. von Maey, *Zeit. phys. Chem.*, 50. 206, 1905 ; M. Herschkowitsch, *ib.*, 27. 148, 1898 ; F. Schmidt, *Ann. Physik*, (4), 39. 1108, 1912 ; H. Moissan and T. Watanabe, *Compt. Rend.*, 144. 16, 1907 ; H. Péchaux, *ib.*, 138. 1170, 1904 ; 140. 1535, 1905 ; J. J. van Laar, *Proc. Acad. Amsterdam*, 5. 424, 1903 ; 6. 21, 1903 ; *Arch. Néerl*, (2), 8. 264, 1903 ; A. W. Smith, *Phys. Rev.*, (2), 23. 307, 1924 ; A. Batelli, *Atti Ist. Veneto*, (6), 5. 19, 1137, 1887 ; R. A. Joyner, *Journ. Chem. Soc.*, 99. 198, 1911 ; W. A. Knight, *ib.*, 105. 639, 1914 ; W. A. Knight and R. A. Joyner, *ib.*, 103. 2247, 1913 ; J. W. McBain and R. A. Joyner, *Dental Cosmos*, 54. 641, 1912 ; 57. 630, 1915 ; G. V. Black, *A Work on Operative Dentistry*, Chicago, 2. 309, 1914 ; *Dental Cosmos*, 37. 353, 469, 553, 571, 637, 737, 1895 ; 38. 43, 965. 982. 1896 ; A. Fenchel, *ib.*, 50. 553, 1908 ; 52. 30, 1910 ; *Oester.- Unger. Viertelj. Zahnheilkunde*, 26. 394, 1910 ; W. Vaubel, *Ber.*, 57. B, 515, 1924 ; A. Westgren and G. Phragmen, *Koll. Zeit.*, 36. 86, 1925 ; A. W. Gray, *Trans. Amer. Inst. Min. Met. Eng.*, 60. 684, 693, 1919 ; 64. 507, 1920 ; *Journ. Nat. Dental Assoc.*, 6. 913, 918, 1919 ; 8. 491, 1921 ; 9. 324, 1922 ; *Oral Topics*, London, 2. 24, 33, 1922 ; *Phys. Rev.*, (2), 18. 108, 1921 ; (2), 19. 405, 1922 ; *Journ. Inst. Metals*, 29. 139, 1923 ; G. T. Beilby, *Aggregation and Flow of Solids*, London, 1921 ; C. T. Heycock and F. H. Neville, *ib.*, 55. 667, 1889 ; 57. 376, 656, 1890 ; *Phil. Trans.*, 189. A, 40, 1897 ; *Chem. News*, 59. 175, 1889 ; G. I. Petrenko, *Zeit. anorg. Chem.*, 50. 138, 1906 ; 53. 200, 1907 ; K. Endell and H. Hanemann, *ib.*, 83. 267, 1913 ; G. Tammann, *ib.*, 118. 93, 1921 ; F. Mylius and O. Fromm, *Ber.*, 27. 630, 1894 ; J. Marttinen and J. R. Tiihonen, *Soc. Scient. Fenn. Comment.*, 1. 11, 1922 ; H. Behrens, *Das mikroskopische Gefüge der Metalle und Legierungen*, Hamburg, 39, 1894 ; *Versl. Akad. Amsterdam*, 2. 79, 1894 ; A. F. Gehlen, *Schweigger's Journ.*, 20. 353, 1817 ; C. R. A. Wright, *Journ. Soc. Chem. Ind.*, 13. 1016, 1894 ; H. Gautier, *Compt. Rend.*, 123. 172, 1896 ; *Contribution à l'étude des alliages*, Paris, 93, 1901 ; *Bull. Soc. Enc. Nat. Ind.*, (5), 1. 1316, 1896 ; G. Charpy, *ib.*, (5), 2. 415, 1897 ; R. Schenck, *Zeit. Elektrochem.*, 15. 650, 1909 ; A. L. Bernoulli.

ib., **15**. 647, 1909 ; *Ann. Physik*, (4), **33**. 702, 1910 ; C. Hardenbeck, *ib.*, (4), **32**. 261, 1910 ; *Ueber das Verhalten einiger Legierungen zum Gesetze von Wiedemann und Franz*, Aachen, 1909 ; A. W. Smith, *Journ. Franklin Inst.*, **192**. 69, 157, 1921 ; F. Saeftel and G. Sachs, *Zeit. Metallkunde*, **17**. 155, 258. 294, 1925 ; *Naturwiss.*, **13**. 744, 1925 ; A. J. Murphy, *Journ. Inst. Metals*, **35**. 107, 1926 ; D. H. Andrews and J. Johnston, *ib.*, **32**. 385, 1924 ; W. C. Roberts-Austen, *Proc. Roy. Soc.*, **59**. 281, 1896 ; **67**. 101, 1900 ; *Phil. Trans.*, **187**. 383, 1896 ; *Chem. News*, **74**, 289, 1896.

² C Hatchett, *Phil. Trans.*, **93**. 43, 1803 ; A. Matthiessen, *Pogg. Ann.*, **110**. 21, 190, 1860 ; **130**. 50, 1867 ; *Phil. Mag.*, (4), **32**. 472, 1866 ; *Phil. Trans.*, **150**. 161, 177, 1860 ; *B.A. Rep.*, **37**, 1863 ; *Proc. Roy. Soc.*, **10**. 220, 1860 ; A. Matthiessen and M. von Bose, *ib.*, **11**. 433, 1861 ; *Phil. Trans.*, **152**. 1, 1862 ; *Pogg. Ann.*, **115**. 353, 1862 ; A. Matthiessen and M. Holzmann, *Pogg. Ann.*, **110**. 21, 1860 ; *Phil. Trans.*, **150**. 85, 1860 ; A. Matthiessen and C. Vogt, *Pogg. Ann.*, **122**. 19, 1864 ; *Phil. Trans.*, **154**. 167, 1864 ; H. le Chatelier, *Bull. Soc. Enc. Nat. Ind.*, (4), **10**. 192, 1895 ; *Rev. Gén. Sciences Pure Appl.*, **6**. 529, 1895 ; *Contribution à l'étude des alliages*, Paris, 441, 1901 ; C. F. Rammelsberg, *Sitzber. Akad. Berlin*, **188**, 1863 ; F. M. Raoult, *Compt. Rend.*, **76**. 156, 1873 ; E. von Maey, *Zeit. phys. Chem.*, **38**. 294, 1901 ; N. A. Puschin, *Journ. Russ. Phys. Chem. Soc.*, **39**. 353, 1907 ; R. Vogel, *Zeit. anorg. Chem.*, **43**. 165, 1905 ; **46**. 60, 1905 ; G. Tammann and W. Wiederholt, *ib.*, **125**. 67, 1922 ; G. Tammann, *ib.*, **118**. 93, 1921 ; F. Mylius and O. Fromm, *Ber.*, **27**. 630, 1894 ; C. T. Heycock and F. H. Neville, *Journ. Chem. Soc.*, **55**. 666, 1889 ; **57**. 378, 1890 ; A. P. Laurie, *ib.*, **53**. 104, 1888 ; *Phil. Mag.*, (5), **33**. 97, 1892 ; J. A. Mathews, *Eng. Min. Journ.*, **72**. 852, 1901 ; C. H. Desch, *Trans. Faraday Soc.*, **9**. 165, 1911 ; W. C. Roberts-Austen, *Phil. Trans.*, **179**. A, 344, 1888 ; **187**. A, 383, 1896 ; *Proc. Roy. Soc.*, **50**. 367, 1892 ; *Proc. Inst. Mech. Eng.*, 31. 1897 ; W. C. Roberts-Austen and F. Osmond, *Bull. Soc. Enc. Nat. Ind.*, (5), **1**. 1137, 1896 ; *Contribution à l'étude des alliages*, Paris, 71, 1901.

§ 9. Alloys of Tin with the Metals of the Alkaline Earths, and of the Zinc Family

J. L. Gay Lussac and L. J. Thénard [1] failed to make a *tin-barium alloy* by heating a mixture of baryta and charcoal with tin to a white heat ; but H. Caron claimed to have obtained such an alloy by heating a mixture of sodium carbonate, barium chloride, carbon, and finely divided tin until sodium vap. was no longer evolved. J. L. Gay Lussac and L. J. Thénard failed to make a *strontium-tin alloy* by heating tin with a mixture of strontia and carbon to whiteness ; nor was a *calcium-tin alloy* obtained from a mixture of lime and carbon. H. Moissan said that tin heated to a temp. above its b.p., unites with calcium to form a crystalline alloy which has a sp. gr. 6·70 when 3·82 per cent. of calcium is present. This alloy decomposed cold water very slowly. B. Setlik made a brittle, crystalline alloy by melting the two metals under borax, when much calcium was lost in the operation. C. T. Heycock and F. H. Neville measured the lowering of the f.p. of tin by calcium.

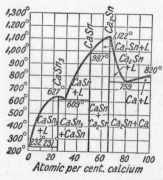

Fig. 47.—The Fusion Curves of the Ca–Sn Alloys.

E. Kordes studied the eutectic mixtures ; and M. Chikashige, the colour of the alloys. L. Donsky found that calcium dissolved in tin at about 650°, and he examined alloys with up to 18 per cent. of calcium. The f.p. curve, Fig. 47, rises steeply from the m.p. of tin to a mximum at 623° and 10·1 per cent. of calcium, corresponding with calcium tristannide, $CaSn_3$, and then falls to a eutectic point at 603° and 14·9 per cent. of calcium. According to W. Hume-Rothery, the addition of calcium to tin produces a sharp rise in the f.p., and the liquidus rises to a maximum at 627°, Fig. 47, corresponding with the pure compound $CaSn_3$. From here the liquidus falls slightly to a eutectic point of composition 31·2 at. per cent. calcium and temp. 609°, the eutectic constituents being the compounds $CaSn_3$ and $CaSn$. From this point the liquidus rises to 987°, the m.p. of the compound $CaSn$, which corresponds to a slight break in the liquidus but not to a maximum. The liquidus continues rising to a maximum at 1122° C., corresponding to the compound Ca_2Sn, and falls abruptly to a eutectic of Ca_2Sn and calcium at 759° C., the eutectic composition being 81·41 at. per cent. calcium, from which point the liquidus rises to the m.p. of calcium. No evidence of the existence of solid soln. has been found. The system Ca-Sn is similar to the system Ca–Pb, except that the three compounds all have slightly higher m.p. than the corresponding lead compounds. The white crystals of **calcium hemistannide**, Ca_2Sn, have a sp. gr. 3·47 at 0°, and melt at 1124°. As with the preceding compound, the hemistannide is immediately attacked by air, water, and dil. hydrochloric acid. The crystals of **calcium stannide**, CaSn, cleave into thin plates a little paler in colour than mercury. The sp. gr. is 4·17 at 0°. As in the case of the preceding compound, it is immediately attacked by air, water, and dil. acid—the reaction with water is more violent than with dil. acid. The silver-white **calcium tri tannide**, $CaSn_3$, has a sp. gr. 6·01 at 0°, and it melts at 627°; it probably crystallizes in the cubic system. It quickly tarnishes in air, and the calcium, not the tin, is oxidized. The natural faces of the crystals are less rapidly attacked than ground or polished surfaces. The compound is at once attacked by water, forming tin and calcium hydroxide; it gives off hydrogen with hydrochloric acid. W. Biltz and W. Holverscheit gave 43 Cals. for the heat of formation of the tristannide; 45 Cals. for the heat of oxidation; 5·989 for the sp. gr. at 25°; and 66·15 for the mol. vol. when the additive rule gives 74·8. According to L. Donsky, alloys containing up to 4 per cent. of calcium are harder than tin and fairly tough; with a further increase of calcium they become brittle. Those containing 2 per cent. of calcium are acted on by cold water. O. Ruff and H. Hartman studied the absorption of nitrogen by these alloys. C. G. Carroll and W. H. Adams patented an alloy of tin and calcium as a solder for aluminium. They claimed that the calcium reduced the oxide on the surface of the metal to be soldered. R. Kremann and co-workers measured the e.m.f. of calcium against the calcium-tin alloys. K. Jellinek and J. Wolff studied the equilibrium relations in the electrolysis with tin electrodes of fused mixtures: $Ba+2KCl \rightleftharpoons BaCl_2+2K$, and with sodium in place of potassium. C. A. Kraus and H. F. Kurtz observed the formation of *calcium pentitastannide*, Ca_5Sn, in the reduction of tin salts by calcium amalgams.

J. Parkinson [2] melted a mixture of *tin and magnesium* in an atm. of hydrogen, and obtained brittle alloys; he also melted the two metals under a layer of fused sodium chloride and calcium fluoride. E. Beck found that the preparation of the alloys from the oxides under a flux of fluorides was not satisfactory. T. L. Phipson also made alloys of these elements by the fusion paocess. G. Masing said that if a mixture of the finely divided elements be compressed a small proportion of an alloy is formed. W. Borchers and E. Beck made the alloys electrolytically. G. Grube studied the m.p. curve, Fig. 48. W. Hume-Rothery also studied the f.p. curve; E Kordes, the eutectic. Magnesium does not seem to be soluble in tin, but it dissolves about 6 per cent. of tin. G. Grube found that the curve falls from the m.p. of magnesium to a eutectic point corresponding with the temp. 564·8° and 39 per cent. of tin; it then rises to a maximum point at 783·4° and 70·95 per cent. of tin. From the maximum point, which indicates the existence of **magnesium hemistannide**,

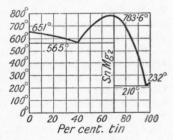

FIG. 48.—The Fusion Curves of the Sn–Mg Alloys.

$SnMg_2$, it falls to a second eutectic point at 209·4° and 97·5 per cent. of tin, and finally rises to the m.p. of tin. $SnMg_2$ is formed with considerable development of heat on melting together its constituents in hydrogen at 700°–800°; it crystallizes well, is brittle, and easily tarnishes in the air. Analogous observations were made by N. S. Kurnakoff and N. J. Stepanoff; they placed the eutectics at 580° and 203·5°; and gave 795° for the m.p. of the hemistannide.

The compound has a well-marked octahedral cleavage which makes the alloys brittle. According to L. Pauling, the X-radiograms of the hemistannide correspond with the calcium fluoride structure, there being eight magnesium atoms round each tin atom at the corners of a cube, and four tin atoms round each magnesium at the corners of a tetrahedron. The constants are $d_{100}=6\cdot78$ A., and the closest approach of the tin and magnesium atoms in the lattice, $2\cdot94\pm0\cdot01$ A. The sp. gr. of the compound is $3\cdot591$ at $20°/4°$, and its hardness $3\cdot5$. W. Biltz and W. Holverscheit gave $3\cdot625$ for the sp. gr. at $25°$, and $46\cdot2$ for the mol. vol. when the additive rule gives $44\cdot3$. According to N. S. Kurnakoff and N. J. Stepanoff, the atomic lowering of the f.p. of tin by magnesium agrees with the calculated value —1. 10, 13. C. T. Heycock and F. H. Neville also measured the lowering of the f.p. of tin by magnesium: and W. Hume-Rothery found the lowering of the f.p. agrees with the formula Mg_4Sn_2. A. von Vegesack gave $565°$ and $209°$ for the two eutectics, and $783°$ for the m.p. of the hemistannide. W. Biltz and W. Holverscheit found the heat of formation of the hemistannide to be 49 Cals., and the heat of oxidation 57 Cals. T. L. Phipson's alloy with 85 per cent. of tin was lavender-blue, and decomposed water at ordinary temp. E. Beck said that the molten alloy containing 50·1 per cent. of tin absorbs 40 per cent. of nitrogen ; and W. Borchers and E. Beck recommended it for a process for extracting nitrogen from the air.

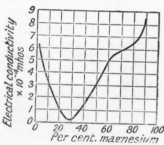

FIG. 49.—The Electrical Conductivities of the Sn–Mg Alloys.

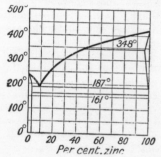

FIG. 50.—Fusion Curves of the Binary System: Sn–Zn.

The curve, Fig. 49, by N. J. Stepanoff represents the electrical conductivities of these alloys; he also measured the temp. coeff. of the resistance. C. H. Green studied the eutectic structure of the alloys. The subject was discussed by A. W. Smith, and C. A. Kraus. G. Tammann studied the electrode potential and chemical properties of these alloys. R. Kremann and H. Ruderer found evidence of the formation of $MgSn_2$ in their study of the e.m.f. of these alloys.

F. Rudberg[3] found that the *zinc-tin alloys* are readily formed and that the combination Sn_6Zn has one f.p., *viz.* $204°$, while other alloys have a higher f.p., which varies with the nature of the alloy, and which separates first on cooling. When the excess has crystallized out, the Sn_6Zn combination separates last at, in modern language, the eutectic temp. G. Charpy, R. H. Thurston, and C. T. Heycock and F. H. Neville found that the two metals are mutually soluble in all proportions in the fluid state. B. E. Curry found that, at $180°$, a solid soln. with up to 7 per cent. of zinc is formed. C. R. A. Wright assumed that a compound, *zinc tetritastannide*, Zn_4Sn, is formed, but this has not been confirmed. C. T. Heycock and F. H. Neville, W. Guertler, E. Crepaz, R. Lorenz and D. V. Plumbridge; M. Levi-Malvano and O. Ceccarelli, P. T. Arnemann, and L. Losana and E. Carozzi investigated the fusion curve of the tin-zinc alloys. The results are summarized in Fig. 50. The eutectic is at $197°$, and 9·7 per cent. of tin. The transformation with 53 per cent. of tin at $348°$ represents a modification of zinc indicated by L. Losana ; another transformation occurs at $161°$. F. Rudberg gave $204°$ for the eutectic temp. ; W. Campbell, and D. Mazzotto, between $190°$ and $195°$; G. H. Wiedemann,

197°; and C. T. Heycock and F. H. Neville, 198°. P. G. J. Gueterbock and G. N. Nicklin studied the effect of zinc as an impurity on the physical properties of tin; D. H. Andrews and J. Johnston, the solubility of zinc in tin; and A. M. Portevin, and E. Kordes, the eutectic mixture. G. Vicentini said that the microstructure is difficult to interpret owing to the tendency of the alloy to liquate or segregate. The microstructure was studied by B. E. Curry, C. H. Green, H. Gautier, P. Rosbaud and E. Schmid, and H. Behrens; J. H. Croockewit, G. C. Lowe and co-workers, A. Matthiessen, and T. Thomson measured the sp. gr. of some alloys; and F. C. Calvert and R. Johnson found that with the at. ratio:

Zn : Sn	1:2	1:1	2:1	3:1	4:1	5:1	10:1
Sp.gr	7·274	7·262	7·188	7·180	7·155	7·140	7·135

E. von Maey studied the sp. vol. of these alloys; E. Wiedemann, and C. M. Marx, the change in vol. during freezing; L. Guillet, G. Sachs, and C. di Capua, the hardness of these alloys; G. Wertheim, the elastic properties. A. Matthiessen measured the cubical coeff. of thermal expansion of the $Sn_4 : Zn$ alloy and found that at $\theta°$, $v=v_0(1-0·0_4236\theta+0·0_7822\theta^2)$. F. A. Schultze found the thermal conductivity of the alloy. Fig. 51, was in accord with G. Wiedemann and R. Franz's rule. W. B. Brown, and A. W. Smith measured the thermal con-

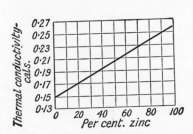

FIG. 51.—The Thermal Conductivities of the Sn–Zn Alloys.

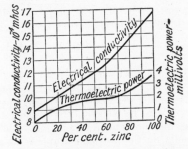

FIG. 52.—The Electrical Conductivity and Thermoelectric Power of the Sn–Zn Alloys.

ductivity. A. Magnus and M. Mannheimer observed a rise of temp. when molten tin and zinc are mixed. M. Herschkowitsch found for the heats of formation, per gram-atom of zinc, for alloys with 32·73, 62·60, 83·60, and 90·82 per cent. of zinc the respective values 106·9, 106·3, 97·63, and 97·59 Cals. J. Tayler also measured the heats of formation of these alloys. D. Mazzotto found the latent heat of fusion of the $Sn_{20} : Zn$-alloy, 15·091; $Sn_{12} : Zn$, 16·252; $Sn_2 : Zn$, 23·484; and $Sn_7 : Zn$, 16·20 cals. The electrical conductivity was measured by A. Matthiessen and C. Vogt, W. Guertler, W. S Harris, H. le Chatelier, and G. Vicentini and C. Cattaneo. The results of F. A. Schultze, plotted in Fig. 52, for the vol. percentage of zinc, are :

Zn	100	70·19	53·83	36·95	23·34	12·78	8·93	0
Cond. ×10⁻⁶	16·20	13·28	12·35	11·10	10·09	9·59	9·28	8·57

M. Herschkowitsch measured the electrolytic potential of the alloys against zinc in N-$ZnSO_4$; and A. P. Laurie, P. Fuchs, and N. W. Taylor made observations on this subject. R. Kremann and O. Baukovac studied the electrolysis of these alloys. The thermoelectric force was measured by W. Rollmann, A. Battelli, and E. Rudolfi. The results of the last-named are plotted in Fig. 52. H. E. Armstrong reported some tests on the action of acids on this alloy. C. Montemartini and E. Colonna investigated the action of nitric acid on these alloys, and the formation of ammonia during the reaction. C. Karmarsch, and A. Guettier studied the technical uses of different zinc-tin alloys; J. W. Richards suggested the $Sn_4 : Zn_3$

alloy as a solder for aluminium ; and J. Habermann recommended the alloy with 83 per cent. of zinc for the production of hydrogen from acids. S. D. Muzaffar studied the ternary system Sn–Zn–Bi ; and S. L. Hoyt, H. L. Reason, L. Guillet, O F. Hudson and R. M. Jones, and G. Tammann and M. Hansen, Cu–Zn–Sn—*vide* Cu–Sn alloys. H. B. Lambert used a tin, zinc, antimony alloy as a solder for aluminium. W. Campbell studied the ternary system Zn–Sn–Sb, and C. R. A. Wright, and W. Campbell, Zn–Sn–Bi.

F. Rudberg,[4] and B. Wood prepared *cadmium-tin alloys.* The equilibrium

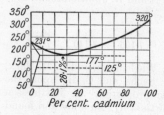

FIG. 53.—The Fusion Curves of the Sn–Cd Alloys.

diagram, and the m.p. of the alloys have been examined by A. Stoffel, C. T. Heycock and F. H. Neville, A. W. Kapp, A. P. Schleicher, H. Behrens, D. Mazzotto, R. Lorenz and D. V. Plumbridge, H. le Chatelier, K. Honda and T. Ishigaki, and A. Bucher. According to A. Bucher, tin and cadmium are mutually soluble to the extent of 3 per cent. in the solid state. A. Stoffel's results are indicated in Fig. 53. No definite compound appears to be formed, but the solid alloy has a transition point at 125° which is thought to indicate the possible formation of *cadmium tetrastannide*, $CdSn_4$. H. Behrens, C. H. Green, E. Schrader, and A. Stoffel examined the microstructure of these alloys. A. Matthiessen measured the sp. gr. of the alloys with different atomic proportions :

Sn : Cd			6 : 1	4 : 1	3 : 1	1 : 1	1 : 1	1 : 4	1 : 6
Sp. gr.			7·434	7·489	7·690	7·904	8·139	8·336	8·432

M. Herschkowitsch gave 103·7, 94·82, and 84·29 Cals. for the heat of formation of alloys with respectively 26·35, 56·05, and 92·21 at. per cent. of cadmium. E. Schrader examined the heating curves. L. Schüz found the sp. ht. of an alloy Sn_2 : Cd to be 0·0560 at 100°, and 0·0554 at −77°. The electrical conductivity was measured by A. Stoffel, A. Bucher, A. Schulze, and A. Matthiessen. The results by the last-named appear as a straight line in Fig. 54. The electrolytic

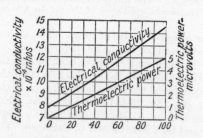

FIG. 54.—The Electrical Conductivity, and Thermoelectric Power of the Sn–Cd Alloys.

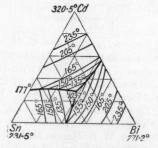

FIG. 55.—Freezing-point Curves of the Ternary System : Sn–Cd–Bi.

potential was measured by A. P. Laurie, H. le Chatelier, P. Fuchs, N. W. Taylor, and M. Herschkowitsch, and the thermoelectric power, by E. Rudolfi, A. Battelli, and A. Bucher. The results by the first-named are indicated in Fig. 54. A. Gawalowsky used the alloy with 60 per cent. of cadmium for colour making. A. Magnus and M. Mannheimer observed that a rise of temp. occurs when molten tin and cadmium are mixed. W. Campbell studied the ternary system Sn–Cd–Sb ; A. Räder, Sn–Cd–Zn ; and W. Spring, and D. H. Andrews and J. Johnston, Sn–Cd–Bi ; A. Stoffel investigated the f.p. of the ternary system Sn–Cd–Bi, and the results are indicated in Fig. 55. The eutectic at 103·7° corresponds with 33·2 per cent. of tin, 27·5 per cent. of cadmium, and 39·3 per cent. of lead.

No compounds are formed. R. Kremann and K. Thomis measured the e.m.f. of those ternary alloys.

Tin and mercury unite quickly even at ordinary temp., and still more rapidly if mercury be poured into molten tin. J. F. Daniell [5] said that

A piece of tin, the lower end of which is immersed for four weeks in mercury, is penetrated through and through by the mercury, and exhibits cracks ; its lower end becomes attenuated by soln. of the metal, and the immersed part is found to be covered with six-sided tables, some of which float about in the mercury. If a square bar of tin, whether cast in a square form, or hammered or filed square from a round bar, be kept for a few days under mercury, it splits in directions proceeding from the lateral edge to the opposite diagonals, thereby dividing itself into four triangular prisms, easily separated by a knife ; at the same time, a four-sided pyramid is formed at each end of the square bar. If the piece of tin has any other form, cracks are produced in other directions.

R. H. Weber made amalgams rich in tin by bringing the metals together under a layer of mercury. J. Schumann poured molten tin into mercury. A. C. Becquerel made them by his electrocapillary process. E. N. Horsford, R. Böttger, and L. Arons also made the amalgams from the constituent elements. J. Nicklès said that tin is attacked by mercury less rapidly than zinc, but more rapidly than lead. A. Gouy measured the solubility of tin in mercury ; and R. A. Joyner gave :

	14°	25·4°	63·2°	90°	163°
Sn	1·05	1·24	4·04	18·0	66·7 at. per cent.

J. Regnauld said that heat is absorbed during the reaction ; and D. Mazzotto found that the heat of soln. of a 0·25 grm. of tin in a gram of mercury is —1·50 Cals. ; with 4 grms. of tin, —3·62 Cals. ; with 0·25 grm. of mercury and a gram of tin, —0·89 Cal. ; and 10 grms. of mercury and a gram of tin, —7·70 Cals. H. W. B. Roozeboom and W. J. van Heteren gave 1000 cals. for the heat of soln. of a gram-atom of tin in mercury at 25°. R. Böttger made tin amalgam by immersing sodium amalgam in a conc. soln. of stannous chloride ; J. Schumann treated sodium amalgam with a soln. of stannic chloride ; and A. C. Becquerel used the process they employed for copper amalgam. J. P. Joule made the amalgam electrolytically with a mercury cathode. He also found that the proportion of tin in tin amalgam can be augmented by strong compression ; an amalgam richer in mercury oozes out. According to E. N. Horsford, the liquid amalgam which drops from a rod of tin sat. with mercury contains 1·55 per cent. of tin.

According to H. W. B. Roozeboom and W. J. van Heteren, liquid tin and mercury are miscible in all proportions, and the temp. at which such mixtures solidify rise from tin to mercury forming two curves ; the first extends from 231·6° to —34·5° for conc. ranging from 100 to —0·3 at. per cent. of tin ; and the second from —34·5° to —38·6° for conc. with 0·3 to 0 at. per cent. of tin—Fig. 56. The first curve is almost a straight line until 120°, when it gradually bends until 40° is attained, at which point it falls almost vertically with the temp. axis. Consequently, at low temp., the amount of tin in the sat. liquid amalgams is very small. Liquid amalgams represented by this curve deposit either pure tin or tin associated with very little mercury. The solid phase at 25° contained 94 per cent. of tin. On cooling the amalgams containing 0·3–85 per cent. of tin to —34·5°, a change takes place which is accompanied by a development of heat and a diminution of vol. The maximum change occurs when the amalgam contains about 50 per cent. of tin. All amalgams containing up to 60 per cent. of tin solidify finally at —38·6°. Between —34·5° and —38·5°, mixed crystals separate and expansion takes place. It has not been found possible to determine what modification of tin is then

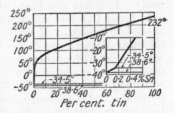

Fig. 56.—Fusion Curves of Alloys of Mercury and Tin.

deposited, but its sp. vol. must be smaller than that of grey tin and larger than that of the ordinary variety. Observations on the f.p. of tin amalgams were also made by E. Wiedemann, N. A. Puschin, R. A. Joyner, G. Tammann, D. Mazzotto, G. McP. Smith, A. Battelli, F. Guthrie, H. V. Regnault, H. Behrens, C. T. Heycock and F. H. Neville, K. Bornemann, and L. Schüz. A compound $HgSn_8$ was reported by E. N. Horsford, but there is no evidence of the formation of chemical individuals. The alloys, said N. A. Puschin, are isomorphous mixtures; and no evidence of the formation of chemical compounds can be obtained from the microstructure.

A. Battelli said that amalgams with more mercury than the atomic proportion $Hg_4 : Sn$ are liquid at ordinary temp., and those with more tin than $Hg_2 : Sn$ are solid. The amalgam $Hg_2 : Sn$ is very soft, and at 100° is quite fluid. According to S. Lucas, the amalgam with one part of mercury and 4 parts of tin gives a kind of mosaic silver when pulverized, and it acquires a metallic lustre when rubbed with a polishing stone. According to L. J. M. d'Aubenton, tin amalgam has the colour of tin if the mercury be not in excess, and it then crystallizes in cubes. F. Hauser studied the microstructure. H. Behrens found that an amalgam with 10 per cent. of mercury is harder than tin, and can be filed; and when broken the fractured surface shows under the microscope stumpy six-sided prisms; under similar conditions, an amalgam with 20 per cent. of mercury shows octahedral crystals. C. von Simson studied the X-radiograms of the tin-amalgams, and found they gave hexagonal space-lattices. G. Tammann and Q. A. Mansuri measured the hardness of tin amalgams. Observations on the fracture were made by N. A. Puschin, J. Schumann, J. P. Joule, F. C. Calvert and R. Johnson, J. H. Croockewit, and J. P. Joule. The sp. gr. of some amalgams measured by R. H. Weber at 17°/17° were:

Tin (per cent.)				37·141	49·873	71·987	82·560	100
Sp. gr.				10·475	9·684	8·418	7·959	7·390

and, according to T. W. Richards and J. H. Wilson, at 20°, amalgams with 0·21, 0·30, and 0·45 per cent. of tin had the respective sp. gr. 13·529, 13·519, and 13·513. Observations on the sp. gr. were also made by A. T. Kupffer, F. C. Calvert and R. Johnson, J. P. Joule, P. I. Bachmetéeff, F. C. Henrici, J. H. Croockewit, A. Matthiessen, and C. Cattaneo. In most cases, said A. T. Kupffer, condensation occurs when the amalgam is formed. E. von Maey represented the sp. vol. of an amalgam with p per cent. of mercury $0·07366 + 0·0006345p$. G. Tammann and K. Dahl measured the vol. changes with ageing. N. A. Puschin said that amalgams with a small proportion of mercury are harder than tin, but with increasing proportions of mercury they become softer. G. Tammann and co-workers measured the hardness of tin amalgams. Rods with 30 at. per cent. of mercury break very easily. L. Schüz also found that rods with between the at. proportions $Hg : Sn$ $= 2 : 1$ and $1 : 5$ fracture readily. W. C. Roberts-Austen, and W. J. Humphreys studied the diffusion of tin in mercury. H. Feninger measured the viscosity of the tin amalgams; and E. von Schweidler found the viscosity coeff. for an amalgam with one per cent. of tin to be $0·01630 - 0·01658$ at 20°. G. Meyer found the surface tension of an amalgam with 0·0796 per cent. of tin, in the presence of sulphuric acid of sp. gr. 1·0559, to be 47·8 dynes per cm. F. Schmidt also measured this constant; and C. Cattaneo, and C. Köller, the thermal expansion of tin amalgams. L. Schüz gave for the sp. ht. of the amalgams with the at. ratio:

Hg : Sn			2 : 1	1 : 1	1 : 2	1 : 3	1 : 4	1 : 5
Sp. ht.			0·03940	0·04083	0·04218	0·04605	0·04800	0·05039
Temp. to 15°			−23°	−30°	−24°	−23°	−30°	−16°

J. Marttinen and J. R. Tiihonen, and H. V. Regnault also measured the sp. ht. of tin amalgam. Observations on the m.p. of tin amalgams have been indicated in connection with Fig. 56; similarly also on the mol. lowering of the f.p. C. Barfoed noted that the tin amalgams on old mirrors give off mercury vap. E. de Souza found that the mercury is not expelled at 360°, but is driven off at 440°; and

V. Merz and W. Weith found the mercury is expelled in 6 hrs. at 445° ; in 15 hrs. at 357° ; and in 92 hrs. at 310°. A. Sieverts and H. Oehme measured the vap. press. in mm. of mercury for a number of amalgams with

Per cent. Hg				0·84	1·30	2·43	4·97	8·00	10·0
At 305°				4	11	14	31	50	—
At 345°				14	20	38	81	119	—
At 358°				—	25	—	90	136	—
At 528°				—	—	—	—	—	886

W. Ramsay also measured the mol. raising of the vap. press. and obtained numbers corresponding with a monatomic mol. J. H. Hildebrand and co-workers found the vap. press., p, of tin amalgams with n mols of mercury per mol of tin, at 324°, $\log (p/p_0) = \log N + 0.220/(0.26 + 0.26n)^2$, where N denotes the molar fraction of mercury, and p_0, the vap. press. of mercury at 324°. A. Coehn and A. Lotz found tin amalgam to be electronegative towards glass. G. Tammann and E. Ohler found that the at. heat of soln. of tin in mercury is -2541 cals. at 14°, and -3148 cals at 97°. For the soln. of tin in dil. gold amalgam the at. heat of soln. is 12,090 cals. greater than in mercury alone. G. Tammann and E. Ohler measured the heat of soln. of tin in mercury. A. Matthiessen and co-workers measured the electrical conductivity of tin amalgams at 18°. R. H. Weber gave for the sp. resistance, R, at 16° referred to that of mercury unity :

Sn			0	1·399	16·805	24·057	49·873	71·987	82·560	100	per cent.
R			1	0·880	0·581	0·479	0·285	0·230	0·195	0·123	

He also measured the resistance at 275°, and found :

Sn			0	4·606	9·292	17·89	43·75	68·81	84·74	100	per cent.
R			1	0·698	0·614	0·550	0·478	0·434	0·419	0·394	

Measurements were also made by G. G. Gerosa, H. Feninger, A. Battelli, G. Tammann and K. Dahl, F. C. Calvert and R. Johnson, C. Michaelis, R. Sabine, W. Siemens, R. S. Willows, A. Larsen, A. Lohr, C. L. Weber, G. Vicentini, and R. S. Willows. The e.m.f. of the cell Sn | N-SnCl$_2$.2H$_2$O | Hg.Sn$_n$ was measured by N. A. Puschin, but no evidence of the existence of chemical individuals was obtained. H. P. Cady measured the electrolytic potential of tin amalgams in soln. of potassium stannate ; V. Rothmund, in 0·01N-SnCl$_2$ and N-HCl ; W. J. van Heteren found that the difference of potentials between mercury and tin amalgam at 25° is 556·5 millivolt ; and C. Hockin and H. A. Taylor measured the e.m.f. of HgSn$_n$|ZnSO$_4$|HgZn. Observations on this subject were made by J. H. Hildebrand, S. Lindeck, W. J. van Heteren, F. Haber, A. Oberbeck and J. Edler, T. W. Richards and J. H. Wilson, G. Meyer, and G. Gore. R. Kremann and A. Kapaun studied the electrolysis of the tin amalgams, and found the tin accumulates about the cathode. L. Arons found the tension of the electric arc with tin amalgam is greater than with mercury alone. The thermoelectric properties were measured by A. Battelli.

According to W. Ramsay, tin amalgams are stable in air ; but S. Lucas said that if a soln. of one part of tin in 6000 of mercury be shaken in air, the liquid becomes covered with a black film. C. F. Schönbein showed that no hydrogen dioxide is formed when a liquid amalgam is shaken for a long time with water and oxygen or air ; but the dioxide is formed rapidly if water acidified with sulphuric acid be employed. According to C. Brame, if sulphur be allowed to stand a few cm. above tin amalgam, some mercuric sulphide is formed ; L. Brault and A. B. Poggiale showed that when tin amalgam is heated with sulphuric acid, the whole of the tin is dissolved and the mercury remains unattacked. G. S. Sérullas found that potassium amalgam and water separate tin from tin amalgam. A. S. Russell and D. C. Evans studied the efficiency of tin-amalgam in reducing soln. of ferric sulphate, potassium permanganate, and uranyl sulphate, and interpreted the results in terms of the overvoltages.

Tin amalgam is used for silvering mirrors. G. Harrison said that the ordinary amalgam used for this purpose has 83·78 per cent. of tin. J. C. Bull and R. E. M. Lagerwall recommended alloying a little mercury with some of the white metals—Pb–Sb–Sn alloys—*vide supra*, Sn–Ag alloys. R. A. Joyner and W. A. Knight made a partial study of the ternary system Ag–Sn–Hg at 63°, 90°, 166°, and 214°. They said there is no eutectic since the solubilities of tin and silver both become immeasurably small well above the f.p. of mercury. There is a sharp transition point near 70° corresponding with the formation of **mercury hexargentodistannide**, $HgAg_6Sn_2$, or $Hg(Ag_3Sn)_2$. The results at 63° and 214° are shown in Figs. 57 and 58. The field A includes liquids; B, liquids

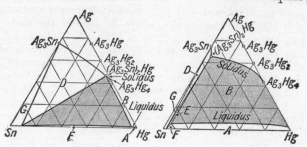

FIG. 57.—Equilibrium Diagram of the Ternary System Ag–Sn–Hg at 63°.
FIG. 58.—Equilibrium Diagram of the Ternary System Ag–Sn–Hg at 214°.

and solid soln. represented by a corresponding point on the solidus curve; D, a sol of the substances represented by the angular points of the triangle D; E, a sat. soln. of tin and silver in mercury; F, a soln. of the substances represented by the angular points of the triangle F; and G, a solid soln. of tin and silver in mercury—*vide* tin-silver alloys. G. Tammann and K. Dahl also studied the ternary system. The volume and other changes which accompany the amalgamation of the tin-silver alloys have been discussed by A. W. Gray, G. Tammann and K. Dahl, G. V. Black, J. W. McBain and R. A. Joyner, W. A. Knight and R. A. Joyner, A. Fenchel, and C. Köller. G. Tammann and Q. A. Mansuri studied the hardness of the ternary alloys. G. Tammann and W. Jander measured the tension for the magnesium-tin and cerium-tin amalgams. R. Kremann and co-workers studied the electrolytic potential of the ternary system: Hg–Cd–Sn.

REFERENCES.

[1] J. L. Gay Lussac and L. J. Thénard, *Recherches physicochimiques*, Paris, 1811; H. Caron. *Compt. Rend.*, 48. 440, 1859; H. Moissan, *ib.*, 127. 584, 1898; R. Kremann, H. Wostall, and H. Schöpfer, *Zeit. Metallkunde*, 5, 1922; K. Jellinek and J. Wolff, *Zeit. anorg. Chem.*, 146. 329, 1925; B. Setlik, *Chem. Ztg.*, 29. 218, 1905; L. Donsky, *Zeit. anorg. Chem.*, 58. 185, 1908; C. T. Heycock and F. H. Neville, *Journ. Chem. Soc.*, 57. 384, 1890; C. G. Carroll and W. H. Adams, *U. S. Pat. No.* 906383, 1907; O. Ruff and H. Hartman, *Zeit. anorg. Chem.*, 121. 167, 1922; W. Biltz and W. Holverscheit, *ib.*, 140. 261, 1924; C. A. Kraus and H. F. Kurtz, *Journ. Amer. Chem. Soc.*, 47. 43, 1925; W. Hume-Rothery, *Journ. Inst. Metals*, 35. 295, 1926; E. Kordes, *Zeit. anorg Chem.*, 154. 97, 1926; M. Chikashige, *ib.*, 154. 333, 1926.
[2] J. Parkinson, *Journ. Chem. Soc.*, 20. 117, 1867; C. T. Heycock and F. H. Neville, *ib.*, 57. 381, 656, 1890; T. L. Phipson, *Proc. Roy. Soc.*, 13. 217, 1864; G. Grube, *Zeit. anorg. Chem.*, 46. 76, 1905; N. S. Kurnakoff and N. J. Stepanoff, *ib.*, 46. 177, 1905; N. J. Stepanoff, *ib.*, 78. 1, 1912; A. von Vegesack, *ib.*, 54. 367, 1907; G. Masing, *ib.*, 62. 273, 1909; E. Beck, *Met.*, 5. 504, 1908; R. Kremann and H. Ruderer, *Zeit. Metallkunde*, 12. 358, 1920; W. Borchers and E. Beck, *German Pat.*, *D.R.P.* 196323, 1906; A. E. Smith, *Journ. Franklin Inst.*, 192. 69, 157, 1921; L. Pauling, *Journ. Amer. Chem. Soc.*, 45. 2777, 1923; C. A. Kraus, *ib.*, 44. 1216, 1922; G. Tammann, *Zeit. anorg. Chem.*, 118. 92, 1921; G. Tammann and W. Jander, *ib.*, 124. 105, 1922; W. Biltz and W. Holverscheit, *ib.*, 140. 261, 1924; E. Kordes, *ib.*, 154. 93, 1926; W. Hume-Rothery, *Journ. Inst. Metals*, 35. 295, 1926; C. H. Green, *Trans. Amer. Inst. Min. Met.*, 71. 651, 1925.

³ F. Rudberg, *Pogg. Ann.*, **18**. 240, 1830 ; A. Matthiessen, *ib.*, **103**. 428, 1858 : **110**. 190, 1860 ; **130**. 50, 1866 ; *B.A. Rep.*, **37**, 1863 ; *Phil. Trans.*, **148**. 383, 1858 ; **150**. 161, 1860 ; **156**. 861, 1866 ; *Journ. Chem. Soc.*, **20**. 201, 1867 ; A. Matthiessen and C. Vogt, *Pogg. Ann.*, **122**. 19, 1864 ; G. Wiedemann and R. Franz, *Phil. Trans.*, **154**. 167, 1864 ; *ib.*, **89**. 498, 1853 ; T. Thomson, *Proc. Glasgow Phil. Soc.*, **1**. 77, 1844 ; C. M. Marx, *Schweigger's Journ.*, **60**. 1, 1830 ; D. Mazzotto, *Mem. Ist. Lombardo*, (2), **16**. 29, 1883 ; (2), **18**. 165, 1885 ; (2), **19**. 458, 1886 ; *Mem. Ist. Lombardo*, (3), **16**. 1, 1891 ; H. Behrens, *Das mikroskopische Gefüge der Metalle und Legierungen*, Hamburg, 56, 1894 ; C. Karmarsch, *Dingler's Journ.*, **129**. 438, 1853 ; A. Guettier, *ib.*, **114**. 199, 1849 ; J. H. Croockewit, *Specimen chemicum de conjunctionibus chemicis metallorum*, Amsterdam, 1848 ; *Journ. prakt. Chem.*, (1), **45**. 87, 1848 ; M. Levi-Malvano and O. Ceccarelli, *Gazz. Chim. Ital.*, **41**. ii, 269, 314, 1911 ; N. W. Taylor, *Journ. Amer. Chem. Soc.*, **45**. 2865, 1923 ; B. E. Curry, *Journ. Phys. Chem.*, **13**. 597, 1909 ; S. D. Muzaffar, *Journ. Chem. Soc.*, **123**. 2341, 1923 ; F. C. Calvert and R. Johnson, *Phil. Mag.*, (4), **18**. 354, 1859 ; *Mem. Manchester Lit. Phil. Soc.*, **15**. 113, 1860 ; E. von Maey, *Zeit. phys. Chem.*, **38**. 289, 292, 1901 ; M. Herschkowitsch, *ib.*, **27**. 161, 1898 ; J. W. Richards, *Journ. Franklin Inst.*, **140**. 351, 1895 ; A. W. Smith, *ib.*, **192**. 69, 157, 1921 ; J. Habermann, *Zeit. anal. Chem.*, **28**. 88, 1889 ; C. di Capua, *Atti Accad. Lincei*, (5), **33**. i, 141, 1924 ; G. Charpy, *Bull. Soc. Enc. Nat. Ind.*, (5), **3**. 670, 1898 ; C. T. Heycock and F. H. Neville, *Journ. Chem. Soc.*, **55**. 666, 1889 ; **57**. 382, 1890 ; **71**. 392, 1897 ; **A**. P. Laurie, *ib.*, **53**. 111, 1888 ; H. E. Armstrong, *Chem. News*, **53**. 211, 1886 ; H. von Jüptner, *Stahl Eisen*, **19**. 23, 1899 ; J. Taylor, *Phil. Mag.*, (5), **50**. 37, 1900 ; R. H. Thurston, *Non-ferrous Metals and Alloys*, New York, 1884 ; G. Wertheim, *Ann. Chim. Phys.*, (3), **12**. 581, 1848 ; F. Wiedemann, *Wied. Ann.*, **3**. 237, 1878 ; A. W. Smith, *Phys. Rev.*, (2), **23**. 307, 1924 ; W. B. Brown, *ib.*, (2), **22**. 171, 1923 ; C. R. A. Wright, *Journ. Soc. Chem. Ind.*, **13**. 1016, 1894 ; *Proc. Roy. Soc.*, **48**. 25, 1890 ; **50**. 372, 1891 ; **52**. 11, 1892 ; G. Vicentini and C. Cattaneo, *Atti Accad. Lincei*, (5), **1**. i, 383, 1892 ; C. Montemartini and E. Colonna, *L'Ind. Chim.*, **7**. 293, 1907 ; F. A. Schultze, *Ann. Physik*, (4), **9**. 565, 583, 1902 ; G. C. Lowe, F. C. Calvert, and R. Johnson, *Chem. News*, **3**. 315, 357, 371, 1861 ; L. Guillet, *Bull. Soc. Enc. Nat. Ind.*, **101**. 240, 1902 ; N. S. Kurnakoff and S. F. Schemtschuschny, *Zeit. anorg. Chem.*, **64**. 149, 1909 ; P. Fuchs, *ib.*, **109**. 80, 1919 ; W. Guertler, *Metallographie*, Berlin, **1**. i, 706, 1912 ; G. H. Wiedemann, *Wied. Ann.*, **2**. 304, 1877 ; E. Rudolfi, *Zeit. anorg. Chem.*, **67**. 65, 1910 ; R. Lorenz and D. V. Plumbridge, *ib.*, **83**. 228, 1913 ; D. V. Plumbridge, *Ueber die binären und ternären Legierungen des Aluminiums, Zinks, Cadmiums, und Zinns*, Edinburgh, 1911 ; H. Gautier, *Bull. Soc. Enc. Nat. Ind.*, (5), **1**. 1293, 1896 ; *Contribution à l'étude des alliages*, Paris, 93, 1901 ; H. le Chatelier, *ib.*, 441, 1901 ; *Rev. Gén. Sciences Pure App.*, **6**. 529, 1895 ; W. S. Harris, *Phil. Trans.*, **117**. 18, 1827 ; W. Rollmann, *Pogg. Ann.*, **83**. 77, 1851 ; **84**. 275, 1851 ; **89**. 90, 1855 ; A. M. Portevin, *Journ. Inst. Metals*, **29**. 239, 1923 ; S. L. Hoyt, *ib.*, **10**. 235, 1913 ; **14**. 178, 1915 ; W. Campbell, *Journ. Franklin Inst.*, **154**. 1, 131, 201, 1902 ; *Journ. Amer. Chem. Soc.*, **26**. 1312, 1904 ; E. Crepaz, *Giorn. Chim. Ind. Appl.*, **5**. 115, 285, 1923 ; H. B. Lambert, *U.S. Pat. No.* 906637, 1908 ; P. T. Arnemann, *Met.*, **7**. 201, 1910 ; L. Losana, *Gazz. Chim. Ital.*, **53**. ii, 539, 1923 ; L. Losana and E. Carozzi, *ib.*, **53**. ii, 546, 1923 ; G. Sachs, *Zeit. Metallkunde*, **17**. 85, 1925 ; O. F. Hudson and R. M. Jones, *Journ. Inst. Metals*, **14**. 98, 1915 ; D. H. Andrews and J. Johnston, *ib.*, **32**. 385, 1924 ; L. Guillet, *Rev. Mét.*, **18**. 445, 1921 ; H. L. Reason, *Metal. Ind.*, **12**. 325, 1918 ; G. Tammann and M. Hansen, *Zeit. anorg. Chem.*, **138**. 137, 1924 ; P. Rosbaud and E. Schmid, *Zeit. Physik*, **32**. 197, 1925 ; P. G. J. Gueterbock and G. N. Nicklin, *Journ. Soc. Chem. Ind.*, **44**. 370, T, 1925 ; R. Kremann and O. Baukovac, *Monatsh.*, **45**. 379, 1925 ; A. Batelli, *Mem. Accad. Torino*, (2), **36**. 487, 1884 ; C. H. Green, *Trans. Amer. Inst. Min. Met.*, **76**. 651, 1925 ; E. Kordes, *Zeit. anorg. Chem.*, **154**. 97, 1926 ; A. Magnus and M. Mannheimer, *Zeit. phys. Chem.*, **121**, 267, 1926.

⁴ W. Campbell, *Journ. Amer. Chem. Soc.*, **26**. 1313, 1904 ; B. Wood, *Chem. News*, **6**. 135, 1862 ; *Journ. Franklin Inst.*, **40**. 113, 1860 ; F. Rudberg, *Pogg. Ann.*, **18**. 240, 1830 ; **71**. 460, 1847 ; A. Matthiessen, *Phil. Trans.*, **150**. 111, 161, 1860 ; *B.A. Rep.*, **37**, 1863 ; *Journ. Soc. Chem.*, **20**. 201, 1867 ; **110**. 21, 190, 1860 ; A. Matthiessen and C. Vogt, *ib.*, **110**. 206, 1860 ; *Phil. Trans.*, **154**. 167, 1864 ; A. Stoffel, *Zeit. anorg. Chem.*, **53**. 137, 1907 ; R. Lorenz and D. V. Plumbridge, *ib.*, **83**. 237, 1913 ; P. Fuchs, *ib.*, **109**. 80, 1919 ; E. Rudolfi, *ib.*, **67**. 65, 1910 ; A. Bucher, *ib.*, **98**. 106, 1916 ; L. Schüz, *Wied. Ann.*, **46**. 177, 1892 ; E. Schrader, *Studien über die Struktur der Legierungen*, Insterburg, 1890 ; H. Behrens, *Das mikroskopische Gefüge der Metalle und Legierungen*, Hamburg, 52, 1894 ; M. Herschkowitsch, *Zeit. phys. Chem.*, **27**. 163, 1898 ; E. von Maey, *ib.*, **38**. 290, 1901 ; C. T. Heycock and F. H. Neville, *Chem. News*, **59**. 175, 1889 ; *Journ. Chem. Soc.*, **55**. 666, 1889 ; **57**. 383, 656, 1890 ; **61**. 895, 1892 ; A. P. Laurie, *ib.*, **53**. 111, 1888 ; C. R. A. Wright, *Journ. Soc. Chem. Ind.*, **13**. 1016, 1894 ; A. W. Kapp, *Ueber vollständige Gefrierpunktskurven binärer Metallverbindungen*, Konigsberger, 1901 ; *Ann. Physik*, (4), **6**. 771, 1901 ; A. Schulze, *Zeit. Metallkunde*, **31**. 321, 1924 ; A. Gawalowsky, *Zeit. Apoth. Ver.*, **43**. 451, 1905 ; W. Spring, *Ber.*, **15**. 595, 1882 ; A. Räder, *German Pat. D.R.P.* 72683, 1891 ; A. W. Smith, *Journ. Franklin Inst.*, **192**. 69, 157, 1921 ; A. W. Portevin, *Journ. Inst. Metals*, **29**. 239, 1923 ; A. Battelli, *Mem. Accad. Torino*, (2), **36**. 487, 1884 ; H. le Chatelier, *Bull. Soc. Enc. Nat. Ind.*, (4), **10**. 192, 1895 ; *Rev. Gén. Sciences Pure App.*, **6**. 529, 1895 ; *Contribution à l'étude des alliages*, 441, 1901 ; *Compt. Rend.*, **121**. 325, 1895 ; W. Guertler, *Metallurgie*, Berlin, **1**. i, 709, 1912 ; *Zeit. anorg. Chem.*, **51**. 420, 1906 ; G. Vicentini and C. Cattaneo, *Atti Accad. Lincei*, (5), **1**. i, 386, 1894 ; A. P. Schleicher, *Internat. Zeit. Metallog.*, **2**. 76, 90, 1912 ; D. Mazzotto, *ib.*, **4**. 13, 1913 ; *Rend. Ist. Lombardo*, (2), **18**. 165, 1885 ; E. Schrader, *Program. Realgymnas Insterburg*, 1, 1889 ; **1**, 1890 ; N. W. Taylor, *Journ. Amer. Chem. Soc.*, **45**. 2865,

1923 ; B. H. Andrews and J. Johnston, *Journ. Inst. Metals*, **32**. 385, 1924 ; R. Kremann and K. Thomis, *Forsch. Metallkunde*, **6**, 1922 ; D. V. Plumbridge, *Ueber die binären und ternären Legierungen des Aluminiums, Zinks, Cadmiums, und Zinns*, Edinburgh, 1911 ; K. Honda and T. Ishigaki, *Scien e Rep. Tohoku Univ.*, **14**. 219, 1925 ; C. H. Green, *Trans. Amer. Inst. Min. Met.*, **71**. 65 , 1925 ; A. Magnus and M. Mannheimer, *Zeit. phys. Chem.*, **121**. 267, 1926.

⁵ N. A. Puschin, *Zeit. anorg. Chem.*, **36**. 207, 1903 ; *Journ. Russ. Phys. Chem. Soc.*, **32**. 635, 1900 ; **34**. 856, 1902 ; P. I. Bachmetéeff, *ib.*, **25**. 219, 1893 ; L. J. M. d'Aubenton, *Tableau méthodique de minéraux*, Paris, 1784 ; H. Behrens, *Das mikroskopische Gefüge der Metalle und Legierungen*, Hamburg, 53, 1894 ; J. H. Croockewit, *Specimen chemicum de conjunctionibus chemicis metallorum*, Amsterdam, 1848 ; *Journ. prakt. Chem.*, (1), **45**. 87, 1848 ; R. Böttger, *ib.*, (1), **3**. 278, 1834 ; (1), **12**. 350, 1837 ; C. Barfoed, *ib.*, (2), **38**. 464, 1888 ; J. Schumann, *Untersuchungen von Amalgamen*, Erlangen, 1891 ; *Wied. Ann.*, **43**. 113, 1891 ; R. H. Weber, *ib.*, **68**. 719, 1899 ; A. Oberbeck and J. Edler, *ib.*, **42**. 209, 1891 ; C. L. Weber, *ib.*, **23**. 470, 1884 ; **31**. 243, 1887 ; G. Meyer, *Zeit. phys. Chem.*, **7**. 477, 1891 ; *Wied. Ann.*, **53**. 848, 867, 1894 ; L. Arons, *ib.*, **58**. 93, 1896 ; E. Wiedemann, *ib.*, **3**. 249, 1878 ; S. Lindeck, *ib.*, **35**. 328, 1888 ; L. Schüz, *ib.*, **46**. 196, 1892 ; W. J. Humphreys, *Journ. Chem. Soc.*, **69**. 250, 1896 ; W. Ramsay, *ib.*, **55**. 533, 1889 ; C. T. Heycock and F. H. Neville, *Chem. News*, **59**. 175, 1889 ; *Journ. Chem. Soc.*, **55**. 666, 1889 ; **57**. 376, 1890 ; **61**. 888, 1892 ; R. A. Joyner, *ib.*, **99**. 195, 1911 ; E. N. Horsford, *Amer. Journ. Science*, (2), **13**. 305, 1852 ; J. F. Daniell, *Journ. Roy. Inst.*, **1**. 1, 1831 ; J. Nicklès, *Compt. Rend.*, **36**. 154, 1853 ; J. Regnauld, *ib.*, **52**. 534, 1861 ; A. C. Becquerel, *ib.*, **75**. 1729, 1872 ; *Mém. Acad.*, **38**. 499, 1873 ; H. W. B. Roozeboom, *Verh. Akad. Amsterdam*, **420**, 1902 ; H. W. B. Roozeboom and W. J. van Heteren, *Arch. Néerl.*, (2), **8**. 260, 1903 ; W. J. van Heteren, *Die Zinnamalgame*, Amsterdam, 1901 ; *Zeit. anorg. Chem.*, **42**. 153, 1904 ; C. Köller, *Zeit. Metallkunde*, **13**. 1, 1921 ; G. Tammann and Q. A. Mansuri, *Zeit. anorg. Chem.*, **132**. 65, 1923 ; G. Tammann and W. Jander, *ib.*, **124**. 105, 1922 ; A. Gouy, *Journ. Phys.*, (3), **4**. 320, 1895 ; D. Mazzotto, *Atti Ist. Lombardo*, (2), **18**. 165, 1884 ; *Atti Ist. Veneto*, (7), **4**. 1311, 1527, 1893 ; R. S. Willows, *Phil. Mag.*, (5), **48**. 433, 1899 ; F. C. Calvert and R. Johnson, *ib.*, (4), **17**. 114, 1859 ; (4), **18**. 354, 541, 1859 ; *Phil. Trans.*, **148**. 349, 1858 ; C. F. Schönbeim, *Pogg. Ann.*, **112**. 445, 1861 ; W. Siemens, *ib.*, **113**. 91, 1861 ; F. C. Henrici, *ib.*, **58**. 376, 1843 ; F. C. Poggendorff, *ib.*, **50**. 255, 1840 ; A. Matthiessen, *ib.*, **110**. 21, 190, 1860 ; *Phil. Trans.*, **150**. 111, 161, 1860 ; *Phil. Mag.*, (4), **22**. 195, 1861 ; *Pogg. Ann.*, **114**. 310, 1861 ; **124**. 318, 1861 ; A. Matthiessen and C. Vogt, *ib.*, **116**. 374, 1862 ; *Phil. Mag.*, (4), **23**. 171, 1862 ; F. Guthrie, *ib.*, (5), **16**. 321, 1883 ; R. Sabine, *ib.*, (4), **23**. 457, 1862 ; R. S. Willows, *ib.*, (5), **48**. 433, 1899 ; A. T. Kupffer, *Ann. Chim. Phys.*, (2), **40**. 293, 1829 ; G. S. Sérullas, *ib.*, (2), **34**. 129, 1827 ; H. V. Regnault, *ib.*, (3), **1**. 129, 1841 ; C. Cattaneo, *Atti Accad. Torino*, **25**. 342, 1890 ; J. P. Joule, *Chem. Gaz.*, **8**. 339, 1850 ; *B.A. Rep.*, 55, 1850 ; *Mem. Manchester Lit. Phil. Soc.*, (3), **2**. 115, 1865 ; *Journ. Chem. Soc.*, **16**. 378, 1863 ; R. A. Joyner, *ib.*, **99**. 195, 1911 ; W. A. Knight, *ib.*, **105**. 639, 1914 ; W. A. Knight and R. A. Joyner, *ib.*, **103**. 2247, 1913 ; J. W. McBain and R. A. Joyner, *Dental Cosmos*, **54**. 641, 1912 ; **57**. 630, 1915 ; A. Fenchel, *Oester.-ungar. Viertelj Zahnheilkunde*, **26**. 394, 1910 ; *Dental Cosmos*, **50**. 553, 1908 ; **52**. 30, 1910 ; G. V. Black, *ib.*, **37**. 353, 469, 553, 571, 637, 737, 1895 ; **38**. 43, 965, 982, 1896 ; *A Work on Operative Dentistry*, Chicago, 2. 309, 1914 ; A. W. Gray, *Trans. Amer. Inst. Min. Met. Eng.*, **60**. 684, 693, 1919 ; **64**. 507, 1920 ; *Journ. Nat. Dental Assoc.*, **6**. 913, 918, 1919 ; **8**. 491, 1921 ; **9**. 324, 1922 ; *Oral Topics*, London, **2**. 24, 33, 1922 ; *Phys. Rev.*, (2), **18**. 108, 1921 ; (2), **19**. 405, 1922 ; *Journ. Inst. Metals*, **29**. 139, 1923 ; R. Kremann, H. Prammer, and L. Helly, *Zeit. anorg. Chem.*, **127**. 295, 1923 ; G. McP. Smith, *Amer. Chem. Journ.*, **36**. 135, 1906 ; J. H. Hildebrand, *Journ. Amer. Chem. Soc.*, **35**. 511, 1913 ; A. Battelli, *Atti Ist. Veneto*, (6), **5**. 1137, 1887 ; *Atti Accad. Lincei*, (4), **4**. 206, 1887 ; G. G. Gerosa, *ib.*, (4), **2**. 344, 1887 ; G. Vicentini, *ib.*, (4), **7**. 258, 1891 ; G. Vicentini and C. Cattaneo, *ib.*, (5), **1**. i, 343, 1892 ; T. W. Richards and J. H. Wilson, *Zeit. phys. Chem.*, **72**. 141, 1910 ; G. Tammann, *ib.*, **3**. 445, 1889 ; V. Rothmund, *ib.*, **15**. 18, 1894 ; E. von Maey, *ib.*, **38**. 295, 1901 ; F. Haber, *ib.*, **41**. 399, 1902 ; J. Marttinen and J. R. Tiihonen, *Comment. Phys. Math. Soc. Fennica*, **1**. 11, 1922 ; A. Larsen, *Ann. Physik*, (4), **1**. 128, 1900 ; H. V. Regnault, *Mém. Acad.*, **26**. 525, 1862 ; F. Schmidt, *Ann. Physik*, (4), **39**. 1108, 1912 ; E. von Schweidler, *Sitzber. Akad. Wien*, **104**. 280, 1895 ; A. Lohr, *Ueber Wilderstandsänderungen von Amalgamen und einigen leichtschmelzbaren Legierungen mit der Temperatur und der Zeit.*, Erlangen, 1914 ; H. P. Cady, *Journ. Phys. Chem.*, 2. 551, 1898 ; G. Harrison, *Amer. Chem. Journ.*, **8**. 430, 1886 ; C. Hockin and H. A. Taylor, *Journ. Soc. Tel. Eng.*, **8**. 282, 1879 ; L. Brault and A. B. Poggiale, *Journ. Pharm. Chim.*, (2), 21. 140, 1835 ; (L. Gmelin, *Handbook of Chemistry*, London, 61. 125, 1851, showed that there is a misprint in the original memoir, mercury being put for tin) ; H. Feninger, *Die elektrische Leitfähigkeit und innere Reibung verdünnter Amalgame*, Freiburg, 1914 ; J. C. Bull and R. E. M. Lagerwall, *Brit. Pat. No.* 8430, 1886 ; V. Merz and W. Weith, *Ber.*, **14**, 1441, 1881 ; E. de Souza, *ib.*, **9**. 1050, 1876 ; A. Sieverts and H. Oehme, *ib.*, **46**. 1238, 1913 ; S. Lucas, *Trommsdorff's Journ. Pharm.*, **10**. 195, 1825 ; C. Brame, *L'Institut*, **17**. 403, 1849 ; G. Gore, *Chem. News*, **61**. 40, 1890 ; K. Bornemann, *Met.*, **7**. 108, 1910 ; P. Köller, *Zeit. Metallkunde*, **13**. 1, 1921 ; C. Michaelis, *Ueber die elektrische Leitfähigkeit verunreinigten Quecksilbers und die Methoden zur Reinigung desselben*, Berlin, 1883 ; W. C. Roberts-Austen, *Phil. Trans.*, **187**. A, 383, 1896 ; F. Hauser, *Zeit. Physik*, **13**. 1, 1923 ; G. Tammann and K. Dahl, *Zeit. anorg. Chem.*, **126**. 113, 1923 ; **144**. 16, 1925 ; G. Tammann and E. Ohler, *ib.*, **135**. 118, 1924 ; R. Kremann and A. Kapaun, *ib.*, **140**. 183, 1924 ; R. Kremann, H. Prammer, and L. Helly, *ib.*, **127**. 295, 1923 ;

C. von Simson, *Zeit. phys. Chem.*, **109**. 183, 1924 ; A. Coehn and A. Lotz, *Zeit. Physik*, **5**. 242, 1921 ; J. H. Hildebrand, A. H. Foster, and C. W. Beebe, *Journ. Amer. Chem. Soc.*, **42**. 545, 1920 ; A. S. Russell and D. C. Evans, *Journ. Chem. Soc.*, **127**. 2221, 1925.

§ 10. Alloys of Tin with Aluminium, Indium, Thallium, and Cerium

Tin and aluminium readily form alloys ; and small amounts of either metal profoundly modify the properties of the other. H. Debray [1] found that aluminium is hardened but made brittle by alloying with a little tin. E. Wetzel showed that tin alloyed with up to 1 per cent. of aluminium becomes brittle in a few days and can be crumbled into fragments. W. C. Anderson and G. Lean found that molten tin and aluminium can be mixed in all proportions. The alloy should be made in fireclay crucibles, but carbon crucibles are suitable. E. Self, A. Riche, and H. Moissan made these alloys. C. R. A. Wright said that when the molten metals have been well mixed by stirring, there is no noticeable tendency for them to separate. L. Guillet made the alloys by reducing stannic oxide with aluminium ; and J. Walter electrolyzed molten sodium aluminium chloride using a carbon anode and a tin cathode. The fusion curves have been studied by C. T. Heycock and F. H. Neville, R. Lorenz and D. V. Plumbridge, A. G. C. Gwyer, L. Losana and E. Carozzi, H. Gautier, W. Campbell and J. A. Mathews, L. Guillet, E. S. Shepherd, E. Kordes, and E. Crepaz. The general result is indicated in Fig. 59, showing that the result is comparatively simple. H. Gautier, and L. Guillet give a curve with a maximum corresponding with *aluminum stannide*, AlSn. As A. W. Smith has shown, the electrical conductivity curves for other physical properties give no indication of this compound ; but A. Saposhnikoff found a maximum in the hardness curve corresponding with AlSn. H. Gautier considered that the f.p. curve indicates the existence of *aluminium hemitristannide*, Al_2Sn_3 ; and F. Guillet claimed to have made *aluminium tetritastannide*, Al_4Sn. The chemical individuality of these products has not been established. E. S. Shepherd gave for the sp. gr. of the aluminium-tin alloys when that of aluminium alone is 2·68 :

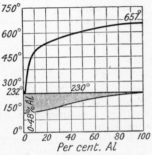

FIG. 59.—Fusion Curves of the Binary System : Al–Sn.

Al	90	80	70	60	50	40	30	20	10	5 per cent.
Sp. gr.	2·845	3·001	3·211	3·489	3·829	4·199	4·671	5·306	6·176	6·679

C. H. Hirzel, and K. Bornemann and F. Sauerwald also made observations on the sp. gr. A. Saposhnikoff gave for the hardness, H, of these alloys :

Sn	0	10	20	30	40	50	60	70	80	90
H	21·7	21·0	18·2	15·8	17·7	16·5	15·4	15·0	18·0	16·3

H. Schirmeister measured the tensile strength ; A. W. Smith, the thermal conductivity ; and A. Matthiessen, and W. Broniewsky, the electrical conductivities of these alloys, and his results are indicated in Fig. 59 ; M. Herschkowitsch made observations on the electrode potential ; R. Kremann and J. Dellacher, on the electrolysis of these alloys ; H. Pécheux, on the thermoelectric force as plotted in Fig. 60.

H. St. C. Deville stated that alloys containing a small proportion of tin can be used for soldering aluminium ; M. Bourbouze recommended an alloy with 9–10 per cent. of tin for the interior parts of optical instruments in place of brass. L. Schlieffarth said that this alloy had a tensile strength of 14 kgrms. per sq. mm., and an elongation of 6 per cent. C. and A. Tissier said that an alloy with over

7 per cent. of aluminium is not homogeneous. The uses and properties of the aluminium-tin alloys have been discussed by J. W. Richards, C. Margot, and W. Campbell and J. A. Mathews. According to A. Riche, alloys with 15-50 per cent. aluminium are attacked by water at ordinary temp. with the evolution of

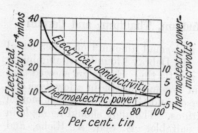

hydrogen; H. Moissan could not confirm this; but W. C. Anderson and G. Lean found that the statement is correct, and if the alloy has stood for some time at a high temp., the speed of attack is reduced. H. Péchaux said that when fresh filings of tin-aluminium alloy are immersed in cold distilled water hydrogen is evolved, the oxygen of the water oxidizes the aluminium. With distilled water, 2 c.c. of an alloy $Al_3 : Sn$ produce 5-6 c.c. of hydrogen in 20 mins.; and with a soln. of copper sulphate of sp. gr. 1·1, 5 c.c. of hydrogen are evolved in 20 mins. Old filings are not

FIG. 60.—The Electrical Conductivity and Thermoelectric Power of the Tin-Aluminium Alloys.

so active. He said that the phenomenon is due to the juxtaposition of the mols. of each metal; the sp. hts. of aluminium and tin are very different, and the action of the file raises the mols. of each metal to different temp., a series of thermoelectric-couples is accordingly formed when the filings are placed in water. For the change which occurs on ageing, *vide supra*, the tin-silver alloys. J. W. Richards described a strong malleable alloy with 10 per cent. aluminium, which, after standing for a few months, lost all its malleability and became as rotten as dried clay; annealing did not restore its strength. If the temp. of a piece of alloy in the form of sheet be gradually raised, small globules sprout out in all directions, but these have the same composition as the alloy. E. Heyn and E. Wetzel found that the length of a sample of tin with 0·5 per cent. of aluminium decreased for 28 days after quenching and then increased, but at a slower rate, for the next 150 days.

M. Wählert,[2] D. Stockdale, and A. A. Read and R. H. Greaves studied the Cu–Sn–Al alloys. E. S. Shepherd studied the ternary alloy Au–Sn–Al; and C. T. Heycock and F. H. Neville, E. S. Shepherd, and W. C. Geer, the ternary

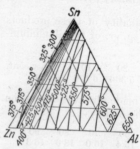

alloys: Au–Sn–Cd. Evidence of *gold cadmium distannide*, $AuCdSn_2$, and of *gold dicadmium stannide*, $AuCd_2Sn$, was obtained by C. T. Heycock and F. H. Neville; but no evidence of $AuCdSn_3$ or of $AuCdSn_4$ was obtained by E. S. Shepherd. The ternary alloys Al–Zn–Sn were studied by E. Crepaz, and L. Losana and E. Carozzi. The fusion curves are shown in Fig. 61. C. R. A. Wright investigated the Sn–Cd–Al alloys; W. Campbell, the Sn–Al–Sb alloys; and C. R. A. Wright, the Sn–Al–Bi alloys.

FIG. 61.—Fusion Curves of the Ternary System: Sn–Al–Zn.

Indium rapidly dissolves in molten tin. C. T. Heycock and F. H. Neville[3] measured the f.p. of *tin-indium alloys* with only small proportions of indium; and similarly also with the *tin-thallium alloys*. W. Crookes, and E. Carstanjen made alloys of tin and thallium, and found them to be fusible and ductile. C. T. Heycock and F. H. Neville measured the effect of thallium on the f.p. of tin; and the subject was discussed by K. Bornemann. N. S. Kurnakoff and N. A. Puschin gave 170·2° for the eutectic temp. when $Sn : Tl = 2·2 : 1$. P. Fuchs found the eutectic to be at 166° with 30 at. per cent. of thallium, Fig. 62. The eutectic line extends from 0 to 73 at. per cent. of thallium; with a greater proportion of thallium the alloy forms homogeneous, solid soln. Alloys with less than 73 per cent. of thallium show, on cooling, in addition to the arrest point at the eutectic temp., a second arrest at

144·5°. This arrest point represents the transition point of thallium, lowered through the influence of the tin from about 231°, the transition point of pure thallium. In the solid soln. region, that is, from 73 to 100 per cent. of thallium, the transition point is lowered approximately in proportion to the amount of tin present. The arrest point at 144·5° is the transition point of solid soln. containing 73 at. per cent. of thallium. A. Matthiessen and C. Vogt measured the electrical conductivity of these alloys. The e.m.f. of tin-thallium alloys was found by R. Kremann and A. Lobinger to show no signs of a compound. D. Omodei found an alloy with 30 per cent. of thallium melted at 186°; it had

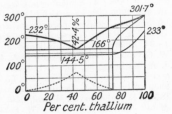

FIG. 62.—Fusion Curves of the Thallium-Tin Alloys.

a sp. gr. 8·054 when solid and 7·786 when molten; and a coeff. of thermal expansion of 0·0001184. E. Carstanjen studied ternary mixtures of tin, thallium, and bismuth.

R. Vogel [4] prepared *cerium-tin alloys* by heating the mixed metals in a carbon tube previously heated to 1400° without any protecting gas. E. Kordes studied the eutectic mixtures. The f.p. curve, Fig. 63, rises with increasing amount of tin, reaching a maximum at 1400° and 30 per cent. Sn, corresponding with **cerium hemistannide**, Ce_2Sn. There is a second maximum at 1165° and 56 per cent. Sn, corresponding with **cerium hemitristannide**, Ce_2Sn_3, and a third at 1135° and 64 per cent. Sn, due to **cerium distannide**, $CeSn_2$. G. Tammann and W. Jander measured the surface tension of cerium-tin amalgams. R. Vogel found that the alloys rapidly tarnish even when polished and examined under petroleum, but it is possible to recognize the compounds as homogeneous and to detect the eutectic structure in other alloys of the series. All the alloys containing less than 80 per cent. Sn are pyrophoric, especially those containing the hemistannide, mere scratching with a hard object producing a shower of sparks. This compound has also the maximum hardness, of about 6, is very unstable in air, and reacts very vigorously with water. The Kemet Laboratories found that *tin-zirconium alloys* were pyrophoric.

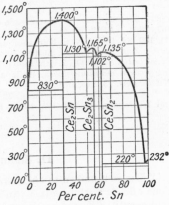

FIG. 63.—Freezing-point Curves of Tin-Cerium Alloys.

REFERENCES.

[1] H. Debray, *Compt. Rend.*, **43**. 925, 1856; M. Bourbouze, *ib.*, **98**. 1490, 1884; **102**. 1317, 1886; H. Moissan, *Ann. Chim. Phys.*, (7), **9**. 337, 1896; *Compt. Rend.*, **121**. 794, 1895; H. Péchaux, *ib.*, **138**. 1170, 1904; **140**. 1535, 1905; L. Guillet, *ib.*, **133**. 935, 1901; *Génie Civil*, **41**. 139, 156, 169, 188, 1902; *Bull. Soc. Enc. Nat. Ind.*, **101**. 240, 1902; H. Gautier, *ib.*, (5), **1**. 1311, 1896; (5), **1**. 1293, 1896; *Contribution à l'étude des alliages*, Paris, 93, 1901; *Bull. Soc. Enc. Nat. Ind.*, (5), **1**. 1293, 1896; *Compt. Rend.*, **123**. 109, 1896; C. and A. Tissier, *Guide pratique de la recherche, de l'extraction, et de la fabrication de l'aluminium et des métaux alcalins*, Paris, 1858; J. W. Richards, *Aluminium*, Philadelphia, 525, 1896; A. Matthiessen, *Pogg. Ann.*, **110**. 190, 1860; *Phil. Trans.*, **150**. 161, 1860; A. Riche, *Journ. Pharm. Chim.*, (6), **1**. 5, 1895; E. S. Sperry, *Trans. Amer. Inst. Min. Eng.*, **29**. 280, 1029, 1899; A. W. Smith, *Phys. Rev.*, (2), **23**. 307, 1924; C. R. A. Wright, *Journ. Soc. Chem. Ind.*, **13**. 1016, 1894; A. H. Sexton, *Mech. Eng.*, **19**. 865, 1907; J. Walter, *Zeit. Elektrochem.*, **3**. 387, 1897; W. Broniewsky, *Ann. Chim. Phys.*, (8), **25**. 66, 1912; A. Saposhnikoff, *Journ. Russ. Phys. Chem. Soc.*, **40**. 665, 1908; C. T. Heycock and F. H. Neville, *Chem. News*, **59**. 175, 1889; *Journ. Chem. Soc.*, **55**. 666, 1889; **57**. 386, 1890; **65**. 65, 1894; A. W. Smith, *Journ. Franklin Inst.*, **192**. 69, 157, 1921; C. H. Hirzel,

Zeit. Pharm., 10. 145, 177, 1858; E. S. Shepherd, Journ. Phys. Chem., 8. 233, 1904; W. C. Anderson and G. Lean, Proc. Roy. Soc., 72. 277, 1903; B.A. Rep., 606, 1901; Chem. News, 84. 63, 1901; E. Wetzel, Zeit. Metallkunde, 14. 335, 1922; M. Herschkcwitsch, Zeit. phys. Chem., 27. 123, 1898; L. Schlieffarth, Chem. Ztg., 14. 1409, 1890; A. G. C. Gwyer, Zeit. anorg. Chem., 49. 311, 1906; R. Lorenz and D. V. Plumbridge, ib., 83. 243, 1913; D. V. Plumbridge, Ueber die binären und ternären Legierungen des Aluminiums, Zinks, Cadmiums, und Zinns, Edinburgh, 1911; A. Riche, Journ. Pharm. Chim., (6), 1. 5, 1895; C. Margot, Arch. Sciences Genève, (4), 1. 34, 1896; W. Campbell and J. A. Mathews, Journ. Amer. Chem. Soc., 24. 253, 1902; W. Campbell, Journ. Franklin Inst., 154. 1, 131, 201, 1902; E. Self, ib., 123. 209, 313, 388, 1887; J. A. Mathews, ib., 153. 1, 119, 221, 1901; Eng. Min. Journ., 72. 819, 855, 1901; L. Losana and E. Carozzi, Gazz. Chim. Ital., 53. ii, 546, 1923; E. Crepaz, Giorn. Chim. Ind. Appl., 5. 115, 285, 1923; H. St. C. Deville, L'aluminium, ses propriétés, sa fabrication, et ses applications, Paris, 1859; E. Heyn and E. Wetzel, Mitt. Kaiser Wilhelm Inst. Metallfors., 1. 19, 1922; M. Wahlert, M tall Erz, 18. 298, 1921; H. Schirmeister, Beiträge zur Kenntnis der binären Aluminium-legierungen hinsichtlich ihrer technischen Eigenschaften, Düsseldorf, 1914; K. Bornemann and F. Sauerwald, Zeit. Metallkunde, 14. 145, 1922; R. Kremann and J. Dellacher, Monatsh., 45. 385, 1924; E. Kordes, Zeit. anorg. Chem., 154. 97, 1926.
    ² E. S. Shepherd, Journ. Phys. Chem., 8. 114, 1904; W. C. Geer, ib., 8. 285, 1904; C. T. Heycock and F. H. Neville, Journ. Chem. Soc., 59. 953, 1891; E. Crepaz, Giorn. Chim. Ind. Appl., 5. 115, 285, 1923; L. Losana and E. Carozzi, Gazz. Chim. Ital., 53. ii, 546, 1923; M. Wählert, Metall. Erz, 18. 298, 1921; C. R. A. Wright, Journ. Soc. Chem. Ind., 13. 1017, 1894; W. Campbell, Journ. Amer. Chem. Soc., 26. 1311, 1904; M. Levi-Malvano and M. Marantonio, Gazz. Chim. Ital., 41. ii, 282, 1911; A. A. Read and R. H. Greaves, Journ. Inst. Metals, 15. 264, 1916; D. Stockdale, ib., 35. 181, 1926.
    ³ C. T. Heycock and F. H. Neville, Chem. New-, 59. 175, 1889; Journ. Chem. Soc., 55. 666, 1889; 57. 385, 1890; A. Matthiessen and C. Vogt, Pogg. Ann., 122. 19, 1864; Phil. Trans., 154. 167, 1864; A. W. Smith, Phys. Rev. (2), 23. 307, 1924; E. Carstanjen, Journ. prakt. Chem., (1), 102. 83, 1867; N. S. Kurnakoff and N. A. Puschin, Journ. Russ. Phys. Chem. Soc., 33. 565, 1901; Zeit. anorg. Chem., 30. 101, 1902; P. Fuchs, ib., 107. 308, 1919; D. Omodei, Atti Accad. Fisico critici Siena. (4), 2. 515, 1890; W. Crookes, On Thallium, London, 1863; K. Bornemann, Die binären metallegierungen, Halle a. S., ii, 84, 1912; R. Kremann and A. Lobinger, Zeit. Metallkunde, 12. 246, 1920.
    ⁴ R. Vogel, Zeit. anorg. Chem., 72. 319, 1911; E. Kordes, ib., 154. 97, 1926; G. Tammann and W. Jander, ib., 124. 105, 1922; Kemat Laboratories, U.S. Pat. No. 1562540, 1925.

§ 11. Stannous Oxide and Hydroxide

" 'Tis well known to chymists," said Robert Boyle,[1] " that tin calcined by fire alone affords a white calx." In 1792, B. Pelletier first showed that tin forms two oxides with different proportions of oxygen—**stannous oxide, or tin monoxide,** SnO ; and *stannic oxide*, or *tin dioxide*, SnO_2—and the conclusion was subsequently confirmed by the work of J. L. Proust. A third oxide intermediate between these two oxides—namely, *tin sesquioxide, tin hemitrioxide,* Sn_2O_3, or *stannous stannate,* $Sn(SnO_3)$—was reported by J. J. Berzelius. A. Ditte reported *tin tritatetroxide,* Sn_3O_4 ; H. Schiff, $Sn_7O_{13}.H_2O$; and E. Frémy, and G. Tschermak, $Sn_8O_{15}.$ W. Spring obtained *tin peroxide*, $2SnO_3.H_2O$, or $H_2Sn_2O_7$. S. Tanatar reported the peroxides $H_2Sn_2O_7.3H_2O$, and $HSnO_4.2H_2O$. J. Cameron also reported four-sided, prismatic crystals of *tin tetroxide,* SnO_4, occurring in the slag of a copper furnace. Their sp. gr. was 2·8–3·0. There is no confirmation of this oxide as a chemical individual.

The preparation of stannous oxide.—Stannous oxide is obtained by adding an alkali to a soln. of a stannous salt, and boiling the mixture so as to convert the hydroxide into crystalline oxide. For example, J. J. Berzelius prepared the oxide by adding an excess of potassium carbonate to a soln. of stannous chloride ; quickly washing the precipitate with thoroughly boiled water so that as little air as possible comes in contact with the precipitate ; drying the product below 80° ; and dehydrating the oxide by heating it in an atm. of carbon dioxide or hydrogen. J. L. Gay Lussac added an excess of ammonia to a soln. of stannous chloride and boiled the mixture until the stannous hydroxide was transformed into black stannous oxide which was rapidly washed and dried. According to A. Ditte, ammonia does not cause the dehydration of the hydroxide, but actually prevents it taking place. If the anhydrous oxide be formed, it is only after the ammonia has been expelled by boiling; and if the ammonia be replaced as it is given off by the soln., and the soln. be kept alkaline, no dehydration occurs, however long the soln. be boiled. E. Frémy used a modification of this process; and A. E. Nordenskjöld boiled potassium hydroxide with an excess of a soln. of stannous chloride until the precipitate passed into crystalline anhydrous stannous oxide—*vide infra*. E. Frémy obtained a reddish-brown oxide by precipitating stannous chloride with ammonia and boiling some time; but F. W. Bury and J. R. Partington were unable to obtain the coloured product. If an excess of alkali is used to precipitate the hydroxide, the colour darkens, becoming almost black. O. W. Brown and C. O. Henke made observations on this subject. W. G. Mixter added sodium hydroxide to a soln. of 400 grms. of stannous chloride in 4 litres of hot water, and heated the mixture many days on a water-bath. The precipitate was washed, dried at 100°, and heated to 400° in an atm. of carbon dioxide until no more water was given off. W. Fränkel and K. Snipischsky dissolved stannous chloride in the least amount of hot conc. hydrochloric acid, and gradually added a soln. of sodium hydroxide until the soln. reacted alkaline towards phenolphthalein; the resulting milky liquid was then kept boiling in a bath of sat. sodium chloride soln. In a few hours a blue, lustrous powder was obtained; this was then washed and dried.

S. A. Sandall triturated in a mortar a mixture of a mol of fused stannous chloride and more than a mol of hydrated sodium carbonate; and heated the fluid mass in a basin with constant stirring until it became black. The sodium chloride was washed out with boiling water, and the product dried at a gentle heat. R. Böttger obtained good results and A. Wagner poor results by this process. R. Roth recommended transforming the hydrated stannous oxide into reddish crystalline anhydrous oxide by digesting it with an excess of acetic acid of sp. gr. 1·06 at 56°. J. von Liebig made the anhydrous oxide by calcining stannous oxalate out of contact with air; A. Vogel emphasized the necessity for strongly heating the salt, otherwise up to about 4 per cent. of carbon dioxide may be retained. L. Varenne added potassium cyanide to a soln. of a stannous salt, and boiled the mixture many days to convert the precipitate into crystalline stannous oxide. E. J. Maumené found that when powdered or granular tin is treated with nitric acid corresponding with $HNO_3 \cdot 4H_2O$, ammonia, and stannous oxide are formed, and that most of the latter remains undissolved.

The properties of stannous oxide.—The appearance of stannous oxide varies with the mode of the preparation. The **colour** may be black, bluish-black, slate-grey, red, green, or greenish-brown. According to E. Frémy, when the hydrate is boiled with a quantity of potassium hydroxide not sufficient to dissolve it, the undissolved portion is converted into small, hard, shining, black crystals of the anhydrous oxide. When heated to 200°, these crystals are converted into an olive-green powder of the anhydrous oxide; when a dil. soln. of ammonium chloride in which hydrated stannous oxide is suspended is evaporated until the ammonium salt crystallizes, the anhydrous oxide furnishes a cinnabar-red powder, which, by friction with a hard body immediately passes into stannic oxide. Hence, added E. Frémy, there are three modifications of stannous oxide, the black crystals, the olive-green, and the red. The red oxide quickly turns black when exposed to sunlight. The olive-green form seems to be the most stable. According to A. E. Nordenskjöld, and L. Varenne, the **crystals** are singly refracting. The hexahedral and octahedral forms belong to the cubic system. G. R. Levi said that stannous oxide has really a tetragonal structure isomorphous with red plumbous oxide, and having the axial ratio $a : c = 1 : 0.895$. The **X-radiogram** corresponds with a lattice having $a = 5.33$ A., and $c = 4.77$ A. J. J. Berzelius and J. Herapath gave 6·666 at 16·5° for the **specific gravity** of stannous oxide; E. Frémy, 6·11; and A. E. Nordenskjöld, 6·04–6·16 at 16°. G. R. Levi gave 6·53 for the sp. gr. According to A. Ditte, the small black crystals obtained by using a very dil. potash-lye have a sp. gr. 6·600 at 0° ; if conc. potash-lye is used, the deep bluish-black crystals have a sp. gr. 6·3254 at 0°, and the dark green plates from a hot soln. of ammonium chloride have a sp. gr. 5·979–6·1083 at 0° ; the oxide which has been calcined at 300° has a sp. gr. 6·4465 at 0°. E. Tiede and E. Birnbräuer observed no fusion or volatilization in the cathode rays. W. R. Mott estimated the b.p. to be 1000° ; but this is much too low. T. Maeda found that at 700°–950°, stannous oxide is unstable ; and decomposes into tin and stannic oxide. W. G. Mixter gave for the heat of formation : $Sn_{cryst.} + O = SnO_{cryst.} + 66·8$ Cals. ; T. Andrews, 67·6 Cals. ; M. Delépine and L. A. Hallopeau, 70·7 Cals. ; and G. Chaudron, 69 Cals. E. Friederich found the electrical conductivity of stannous oxide to be 150×10^{-6} mho. J. Ewles observed a whitish cathodoluminescence with stannous oxide. S. Meyer gave for the magnetic susceptibility $-0·158 \times 10^{-6}$ units per gram, or $-0·012 \times 10^{-6}$ units per mol.

J. J. Berzelius found that when heated in an atm. of hydrogen, stannous oxide is reduced to the metal. According to A. Ditte, stannous oxide is not changed in air at ordinary temp. Stannous oxide is very readily oxidized to stannic oxide. According to R. Weber, when heated in air, or brought in contact with a red-hot substance, stannous oxide glows like tinder, forming a fine, amorphous, pulverulent stannic oxide. A. Ditte showed that stannous oxide is not changed when heated to 300°–310° in the absence of air, but the sp. gr. rises from 6·3254–6·4465. At a red heat, in vacuo or in an atm. of an indifferent gas, a greenish-grey powder is formed with the composition Sn_3O_4. According to L. Wöhler and O. Balz, the equilibrium constant for $[SnO]/[Sn] = 10·6$ at 800° ; and for $[SnO]/[SnO_2] = 18·7$. H. Rose reported stannous oxide to be insoluble in water. A. Ditte showed that with water vapour at a red heat, stannous oxide forms stannic oxide. R. Weber found that when heated in chlorine, stannic oxide and chloride are formed. M. Berthelot said an oxychloride may also be produced. Stannous oxide is soluble in acids, forming stannous salts. J. B. Senderens said that when boiled with water containing sulphur in suspension, stannous oxide is not changed ; but when stannous oxide is melted with sulphur, stannic sulphide and sulphur dioxide are formed. According to D. L. Hammick, when stannous oxide is heated in an atm. of sulphur dioxide, the interaction is attended by incandescence, and clouds of sulphur are formed : $18SnO + 7SO_2 = 16SnO_2 + 2SnS + 5S$; and the pale brown mixture of stannic oxide and stannous sulphide passes into stannic oxide, oxide and stannous sulphide. There is probably a secondary reaction $SnS + 3SnO_2 = 4SnO + SO_2$, but no sulphur trioxide was formed. R. Weber said that nitric acid converts stannous oxide into metastannic acid ; L. H. Milligan and G. R. Gillette examined the reduction of nitric acid by stannous salts. P. Sabatier and J. B. Senderens showed that at 400° stannous oxide burns in an atm. of nitrous oxide, forming stannic oxide ; and at 500°, nitrogen peroxide also forms stannic oxide. H. Rose found stannous oxide is slowly dissolved by a boiling soln. of ammonium chloride. According to J. J. Berzelius, when heated with strong reducing agents—with carbon, or potassium, for example—stannous oxide furnishes the metal. H. Moissan also found that boron reduces stannous oxide to the metal. L. Kahlenberg and W. J. Trautman, and E. Vigouroux found stannous oxide is reduced by silicon : $2SnO + Si = 2Sn + SiO_2$. According to A. Wagner, when stannous oxide is heated in a stream of carbon dioxide, carbon monoxide, and stannic oxide are formed ; this reaction also occurs in the presence of sodium carbonate, and it is of importance in view of some of the methods used in preparing stannous oxide. P. Sabatier and A. Mailhe found that when heated in alcohol vapour to 340°–350°, it is slowly reduced, forming carbon dioxide and aldehyde. J. N. Pearce and A. M. Alvarado also discussed the catalytic activity of stannous oxide on alcohol vapour. F. de Carli found that stannous oxide reacts with molybdic oxide at 400° ; with tungstic oxide at 265° ; and with vanadic oxide at 250°. A. Wagner found that when stannous oxide and potassium nitrate are heated together in a stream of carbon dioxide, both the carbon dioxide and the nitrate are reduced. H. Rose said that stannous oxide is not soluble in a dil. soln. of **potassium hydroxide ;** but when boiled with a conc. soln. of potassium hydroxide, J. J. Berzelius, and A. Ditte found that the stannous oxide is partly converted into a stannate, and partly reduced to the metal.

The preparation of stannous hydroxide.—This hydroxide is obtained as a white powder by adding an excess of ammonia, or alkali carbonate to a soln. of stannous chloride, the slimy precipitate filters badly, and is washed by suction or decantation. The proportion of contained water depends on the mode of drying. J. L. Proust found 5 per cent. of water in his preparation ; but, according to J. J. Berzelius, the precipitate gives up water when gently heated or boiled with water. L. Schaffner found that the precipitate produced by ammonia contained 6·46 per cent. of water —*i.e.* $2SnO.H_2O$—when dried at 80° ; and A. Ditte found that when dried in vacuo over sulphuric acid at 14°, the yellowish-brown powder contained 22·94 per cent. of water—*i.e.* $Sn(OH)_2.H_2O$—and when heated in thin layers in a porcelain dish at 110°, the hydrate contained 8·87 per cent. of water—*i.e.* $3SnO.2H_2O$. L. Schaffner regarded the precipitate produced in a soln. of stannous chloride by ammonia as a basic chloride. F. W. Bury and J. R. Partington examined the precipitates obtained by different methods, and inferred that the products are all essentially the same, approximating $3SnO.2H_2O$. No sample was free from chlorine, though in most cases the amount was negligible. S. Ghosh and N. R. Dhar prepared negatively charged colloidal stannous hydroxide. According to H. T. S. Britton, stannous hydroxide begins to precipitate from soln. of stannous chloride, on the addition of alkali hydroxide, when the H·-ion conc. is $p_H=1·9$.

The properties of stannous hydroxide.—The composition of the hydrate of stannous oxide has been previously discussed. Freshly precipitated stannous hydroxide is white ; but when dried in vacuo at 110°, it appears as a yellowish-brown powder which becomes reddish-yellow when rubbed. J. Thomson gave for the heat of formation of stannous hydroxide (Sn, O, H_2O)=68·09 Cals. J. L. Proust said that the moist hydroxide absorbs oxygen from the air, and is gradually converted into hydrated stannic oxide. The oxidation must be slow because, as F. W. Bury and J. R. Partington stated, no reaction occurs between the moist hydroxide and atm. air at ordinary temp. It is readily dehydrated when heated in vacuo, or in a non-oxidizing gas ; or when boiled with water, dil. acids, dil. alkali-lye, etc., as indicated above. F. W. Bury and J. R. Partington said that when stannous hydroxide stands under water, it slowly passes to stannous oxide ; but stannous hydroxide does not lose all its water at 160°. A. Ditte found that stannous hydroxide is converted into crystalline stannous oxide by traces of any acid which is capable of forming a stannous salt which, in turn, is capable of being decomposed by boiling water into free acid and oxide. It is therefore assumed that with hydrochloric acid, a little stannous chloride is formed ; this reacts with the excess of stannous hydroxide, forming an oxychloride which is decomposed by water into anhydrous stannous oxide less soluble in hydrochloric acid. The regenerated acid commences anew, and the cyclic reactions continue until the dehydration is complete. Hydrobromic, hydriodic, and acetic acids behave like hydrochloric acid, but the conversion of the hydroxide into oxide is not effected by acids which form stable stannous salts—*e.g.* nitric acid—nor by those giving stable basic salts in contact with water—*e.g.* sulphuric acid. The dehydration occurs in the presence of salts like stannous chloride, ammonium chloride, etc., which are partly decomposed by water with the liberation of an acid which can then react cyclically as just indicated.

F. W. Bury and J. R. Partington found the undried hydroxide slowly blackens when kept under water and exposed to light. When suspended in water and two or three crystals of stannous chloride are added, the hydroxide becomes grey, and an olive-green oxide is slowly deposited. When the dried hydroxide is boiled with water and one or two crystals of stannous oxide, a faint salmon-pink colour developed, but this did not darken with further boiling. An excess of stannous chloride restored the white colour. A. Ditte stated that red, green, and black colours are developed. H. Goldschmidt and M. Eckardt found stannous hydroxide to be sparingly soluble in water; a litre of water dissolves 0·0000135 mol. J. L. Proust found the hydroxide to be readily soluble in acids, forming stannous salts. F. W. Bury and J. R. Partington observed no change when stannous hydroxide is boiled with very dil. hydrochloric acid. A. Ditte reported several modifications of stannous oxide to be formed by boiling stannous hydroxide with ammonium chloride soln. of different conc. F. W. Bury and J. R. Partington found the product in all cases to be the same, namely, dark grey stannous oxide which is formed slowly when the white hydroxide is kept under water. The various reagents described by A. Ditte are considered to be catalytic agents accelerating the passage of the unstable hydroxide to the oxide. Undried stannous oxide in excess was digested with dil. acetic acid, and the soln. in a desiccator formed a yellow crystalline solid, and is probably stannous acetate containing a little water ; A. Ditte regarded it as a basic acetate. When the undried hydroxide is boiled with water containing a few drops of acetic acid, the colour darkens, and a black precipitate is formed ; the liquid remains yellow. The black precipitate becomes yellowish-white with an excess of acetic acid. There was no sign of the red form described by R. Roth. When undried stannous hydroxide is treated with dil. nitric acid, a soln. is obtained which, when evaporated in a desiccator, furnishes a white porcelain-like mass—probably a basic stannic nitrate—it did not detonate when heated ; was insoluble in cold water ; not completely soluble in boiling water ; and gave no precipitate with mercuric chloride. J. L. Proust showed that when stannous hydroxide is treated with a soln. of an alkali hydroxide, it forms soln. of the **stannites;** but it is insoluble in aq. ammonia, or soln. of alkali carbonates. A. Ditte found that potassium and sodium hydroxides act on stannous hydroxide both in the cold and when heated, but the reaction in complicated, and the resulting product varies according to the temp. and conc. of the soln. According to circumstances, an alkali stannate, a mixture of alkali stannate and stannous oxide or metallic tin, may be produced. When a little potassium hydroxide is added to a mixture of water and stannous hydroxide at ordinary temp., crystals of stannous oxide are formed, and these increase in size until all the hydroxide is transformed. Under these conditions, a little potassium stannite is formed, and this is hydrolyzed by water into stannous oxide, less soluble in the alkali-lye, and potassium hydroxide is regenerated to begin the reaction anew. The cyclic reactions continue until all the stannous hydroxide is transformed into the oxide. Sodium hydroxide acts similarly ; aq. ammonia, as previously indicated, does not dehydrate the hydroxide. J. L. Proust said that when stannous hydroxide is mixed with water and cupric carbonate, carbon dioxide is given off, while stannic oxide and crystals of copper are formed. C. Reichard showed that when warmed with a soln. of arsenious oxide in aq. ammonia or sodium hydroxide, the colour becomes brown owing to the formation of stanniferous arsenic : $3Sn(OH)_2 + As_2O_3 + 6NaOH = 3Na_2SnO_3 + 2As + 6H_2O$. F. Feigl showed that a soln. of potassium stannite is partly oxidized to stannate by filtration through blood charcoal.

According to A. Hantzsch, the formation of stannites by the dissolution of stannous hydroxide in a not too conc. soln. of alkali hydroxide, corresponds with the presence of monobasic **hydrostannous acid,** $H.SnO.OH$, *stannoformic acid,* analogous to formic acid, $H.CO.OH$. This means that in the stannites, tin is quadrivalent. This conclusion is based on measurements of the electrical conductivities of the hydroxides of beryllium, zinc, germanium, tin, and lead in alkaline soln., and the rates at which these soln. hydrolyze ethyl acetate. The sodium salt thus becomes $H.SnO.ONa$, or **sodium hydrostannite.** Although there is no confirmatory evidence of the direct union of the atom of hydrogen to tin, there are analogous acids—*e.g.* $H.SO_2.OH$, $H_2.PO.OH$, and $H.PO(OH)_2$. H. Goldschmidt and M. Eckardt studied the reducing action of soln. of the alkali stannites, and they agree with A. Hantzsch's view of the constitution of these salts in dil. alkaline soln., but with conc. soln., they state that normal sodium stannite, Na_2SnO_2, is formed. P. Pfeiffer found that when an aq. alcoholic soln., of the alleged **potassium hydrostannite,** $H.SnO.OK$, is treated with ethyl iodide, the product is not $C_2H_5.SnO.OK$ as would be expected, but *stannyl diethide,* $(C_2H_5)_2SnO$, is formed. According to J. Rubenbauer, soln. of stannous hydroxide in alkali-lye do not contain stannites, but rather a sol. of colloidal hydroxide. The amount dissolved depends on the conc. of the alkali-lye and reaches a minimum when the ratio $Sn : Na = 1 : 7.7$. The minimum is attributed to the dehydration of the hydroxide by the alkali in conc. soln. whereby the hydroxide becomes less soluble. N. R. Dhar and S. Ghosh found that tin hydroxide is peptized by alkali-lye with glycerol, starch, or sugar. W. Herz observed that when an alkaline soln. of stannous hydroxide is dialyzed, the hydroxide passes through without being precipitated on the parchment. This is taken to agree with A. Hantzsch's view that stannous hydroxide is a weak acid. N. R. Dhar found that the oxidation of stannous salts is hindered by the presence of easily oxidized substances like sodium arsenite, quinol, glycerol, and sugars. According to A. Gutmann, sodium or potassium stannite reacts with sodium thiosulphate at ordinary temp. with the formation of stannous sulphide, sodium stannate, sulphite, and sulphostannate. Potassium stannite reacts with sulphur, forming stannous sulphide, which unites with the alkali stannite, forming octahedral crystals of potassium metasulphostannite, $K_2SnS_3.3H_2O$; sodium tetrathionate reacts with a stannite at ordinary temp. forming stannous sulphide, and alkali stannate, sulphite, and sulphostannate ; while sodium dithionate has no action at ordinary temp., or in boiling soln.

The stannites are known only in soln. J. L. Proust made a soln. of **potassium stannite** by dissolving stannous hydroxide in a soln. of potassium hydroxide ; and a soln. of **sodium stannite** in an analogous manner. G. Lunge made a soln. of potassium stannite by adding solid potassium hydroxide to a mixture of water and washed, freshly precipitated stannous hydroxide. H. Goldschmidt and M. Eckardt obtained a soln. of sodium stannite free from sodium chloride by electrolyzing a conc. soln. of soda-lye with a rotating tin anode, and a platinum cathode, working with a low current density, and protecting the soln. from oxidation in an atm. of hydrogen. According to E. Frémy, if a soln. of potash-lye be sat. with stannous hydroxide and evaporated in vacuo, stannic oxide is precipitated. M. H. Klaproth found that laminæ of tin are precipitated when the soln. of potassium stannite is treated with zinc. According to A. Ditte, the stannites are not stable in conc. soln. of the alkali hydroxides, but are decomposed with the separation either of stannous oxide or of tin, and the formation of the alkali stannate. When stannous hydroxide is dissolved to saturation in a 39 per cent. soln. of potassium hydroxide, stannous oxide separates out, and on standing, oxygen is absorbed and potassium stannate is formed ; with a 39-50 per cent. soln., the stannate is rapidly formed owing to the reduction of part of the stannous oxide to tin ; when the soln. is allowed to stand both products—potassium stannate, and tin—appear in well-formed crystals. When the soln. of alkali stannate is evaporated these two products are always formed. A. Ditte has discussed the thermochemistry of the change. J. A. Hedvall and N. von Zweigburgk did not observe any reaction between stannous oxide and barium dioxide when a mixture of the two was heated.

Soln. of the alkali stannites are readily oxidized, and the soln. therefore act chemically as reducing agents. Thus, A. Terreil found that Fehling's soln. furnishes a precipitate of cuprous oxide ; M. C. Harding, that an alkali soln. of **antimonious oxide** gives a greyish-black precipitate of antimony ; and L. Vanino and F. Treubert, that lead is precipitated from soln. of **lead salts ;** and bismuth, bismuth trioxide, and bismuth oxychloride from soln. of **bismuth salts**—R. Schneider reported that bismuth monoxide is also formed. E. Divers and T. Haga found that **nitrogen peroxide** is reduced by soln. of alkali stannites to a hyponitrite ; and that **nitric oxide** also forms hyponitrite : $K_2SnO_2 + 2KOH + 2NO = K_2SnO_3 + 2KNO + H_2O$; and there is an intermediate formation of a nitrostannate, $K_2SnO_2 + 2NO = K_2(NO)_2SnO_2$. Alkali stannites do not reduce **nitrites** and **nitrates**. A. Gutmann observed that **sodium tetrathionate** is reduced to sodium sulphide, and sulphite, and sodium thiostannate and stannate are formed, while **dithionates** are not changed. H. Goldschmidt and M. Eckardt studied the reduction of **aromatic nitro-compounds** by alkali stannites; and R. Böttger found a conc. soln. of potassium stannite dissolves **gun cotton** but not **cellulose**.

A number of oxides intermediate between stannous and stannic oxides has been reported. A. Ditte heated to redness crystals of stannous oxide in an atm. of carbon dioxide and obtained a pale greyish powder mixed with small globules of tin. The powder had a composition; **tin tetritoxide**, Sn_3O_4, or $Sn(SnO_2)_2$, stannic stannite. It was slowly attacked by cold hydrochloric acid, and rapidly attacked by hot acid leaving a residue containing stannic oxide and tin. There is no evidence supporting the view that this oxide is a chemical individual. According to J. N. von Fuchs,[2] when a slight excess of a soln. of stannous oxide is boiled with freshly precipitated ferric or manganic hydroxide, **hydrated tin sesquioxide,** or *tin hemitrioxide*, $Sn_2O_4.nH_2O$, is formed : $Fe_2O_3 + 2SnCl_2 = 2FeCl_2 + Sn_2O_3$. The action takes place less quickly in the cold ; and with dried ferric hydroxide the boiling must be prolonged. The precipitate, said J. J. Berzelius, is frequently mixed with ferric hydroxide even after a prolonged washing. J. N. von Fuchs said that if the stannous chloride contains no free acid, a small quantity of iron is dissolved at the beginning of the reaction before any tin sesquioxide is precipitated ; and if the ferric hydroxide be boiled briskly with an excess of stannous chloride, the precipitate which forms at first is redissolved, but reappears on the addition of water, and is then contaminated with a basic chloride. J. N. von Fuchs made the hydrated sesquioxide by mixing soln. of ferric and stannous chlorides, and as soon as the mixture becomes green, adding an excess of calcium carbonate, applying a gentle heat. J. J. Berzelius also made the hydrated sesquioxide by mixing soln. of ferric and stannous chlorides each mixed with as much ammonia as possible without precipitation. The mixture gradually loses its colour, and the sesquioxide is precipitated. When heated in an atm. of carbon dioxide, brownish-black anhydrous **tin sesquioxide**, Sn_2O_3, is formed. The hydrated sesquioxide forms a yellowish-white precipitate which is gelatinous and difficult to wash. J. N. von Fuchs said that with auric chloride it forms a fine purple of Cassius ; and, according to J. J. Berzelius, it dissolves completely in ammonia, and is therefore not merely a mixture of stannous and stannic oxides—the latter does not dissolve in ammonia. L. Gmelin suggested that the sesquioxide is *stannous stannate*, $Sn(SnO_3)$. S. Meyer gave for the magnetic susceptibility -0.614×10^{-6} units per gram, -0.076×10^{-6} units per mol of Sn_2O_3. L. Wöhler and O. Balz found no evidence of the formation of a sesquioxide in their study of the formation and reduction of stannic oxide.

A number of **stannous stannates** has been reported. E. Frémy digested the so-called metastannic acid for some hours with a soln. of stannous chloride at 40°–50°, and obtained an orange-yellow, insoluble substance with the composition $Sn_4O_7.3H_2O$, or $SnO.3SnO_2.3H_2O$, or *stannous tristannate*. In air or when treated with nitric acid, it forms stannic acid ; with hydrochloric acid, it forms stannous and metastannic chlorides ; and when heated with a soln. of potassium hydroxide, it forms alkali stannite and stannate. It loses its water at 140° in a current of carbon dioxide or nitrogen. E. Frémy said that an excess of metastannic acid will remove all the tin from a soln. of stannous chloride ; but G. Tschermak was unable to confirm this. H. Schiff reported an orange-yellow hydrated oxide with the composition $Sn_7O_{13}.5H_2O$, or $SnO.6SnO_2.5H_2O$, or *stannyl hexastannate*, to be formed when stannous hydroxide is digested for some hours with a soln. of stannous chloride. E. Frémy heated stannic acid with stannous chloride, and obtained a brown powder with the composition $Sn_8O_{15}.nH_2O$, or $SnO.7SnO_2.nH_2O$, or *stannyl heptastannate*. By working at 50°–60°, H. Schiff obtained a chocolate-brown product with the composition $SnO.20SnO_2.nH_2$, or *stannyl icosistannate*. There is no evidence establishing the chemical individuality of these products; and variation in the composition rather indicates that mixtures are in question.

According to P. Schützenberger, when the product obtained by heating with hydrochloric acid an **alloy** of platinum with five times its weight of tin in an inert atm., is treated with **warm** dil. aq. ammonia, the whole of the combined chlorine is removed, and a hydrated oxide is obtained resembling the chloride in appearance, but with a slight brown colour. When dried in a vacuum over sulphuric acid, it has the composition $Pt_2Sn_3O_4H_2$, or *platinum distannyl stannous hydroxide*, $Pt_2(SnO)_2Sn(OH)_2$, and on reduction by hydrogen it yields a greyish-white, pulverulent, almost fusible alloy of the composition Pt_2Sn_3, identical with that obtained by H. St. C. Deville and H. Debray by melting 1 part of platinum with 6 parts of tin, and treating the cold alloy with hydrochloric acid. In this latter case, it is probable that the large crystals in which the alloy Pt_2Sn_4 was obtained, were only superficially attacked by the hydrochloric acid. If the pulverulent alloy be heated to dull redness in oxygen, combination takes place with incandescence, and the oxide formed has the composition $Pt_2Sn_3O_3$, or *platinum tristannyl*, $Pt_2(SnO)_3$. The reduction and reproduction of this oxide can be repeated any number of times. If the hydrated oxide is heated in a current of dry oxygen, water is given off, but is replaced by oxygen, and an oxide of the composition $Pt_2Sn_3O_4$, or **platinum distannyl stannic oxide**, $Pt_2(SnO)_2SnO_2$, is formed. If, however, this compound is reduced by hydrogen, and the residue reoxidized, the oxide $Pt_2Sn_3O_3$ is alone obtained. These stanno-platinic compounds have considerable catalytic power. They oxidize alcohol into aldehyde, and when the hydrated oxide is brought in contact with hydrogen, there is a considerable development of heat. When the pulverulent alloy Pt_2Sn_3 is brought in contact with chlorine, a large amount of heat is developed, and stannous chloride volatilizes. P. Schützenberger represented these products graphically :

$$OSn=Pt-Pt=SnO$$
$$\diagdown\diagup$$
$$SnO$$

$$OSn=Pt-Pt=SnO$$
$$\diagdown\diagup$$
$$HO-Sn-OH$$

$$OSn=Pt-Pt=SnO$$
$$\diagdown\diagup$$
$$Sn$$
$$\diagup\diagdown$$
$$O-O$$

$Pt_2(SnO)_3$ $Pt_2(SnO)_2Sn(OH)_2$ $Pt_2(SnO)_2SnO_2$

REFERENCES.

[1] R. Boyle, *Experiments and Observations upon Colours*, London, 1670 ; J. L. Proust, *Journ. Phys.*, **51**. 173, 1800 ; **61**. 338, 1804 ; *Ann. Chim. Phys.*, (1), **28**. 213, 1798 ; *Nicholson's Journ.*, (1), **2**. 515, 1798 ; (2), **14**. 38, 1806 ; E. Frémy, *Compt. Rend.*, **14**. 442, 1842 ; **15**. 1107, 1842 ; **16**. 187, 1843 ; *Ann. Chim. Phys.*, (3), **12**. 460, 1844 ; (3), **23**. 385, 1848 ; J. L. Gay Lussac, *ib.*, (2), **1**. 40, 1816 ; M. Berthelot, *ib.*, (5), **15**. 185, 1878 ; (5), **16**. 442, 1878 ; B. Pelletier, *ib.*, (1), **12**. 225, 1792 ; *Crell's Ann.*, i, 46, 1797 ; J. N. von Fuchs, *Kastner's Arch.*, **5**. 368, 1832 ; *Journ. prakt. Chem.*, (1), **5**. 318, 1835 ; J. J. Berzelius, *Schweigger's Journ.*, **6**. 284, 1812 ; *Ann. Chim. Phys.*, (1), **87**. 50, 1813 ; (2), **5**. 149, 1817 ; *Pogg. Ann.*, **28**. 443, 1833 ; G. Chaudron, *ib.*, (9), **16**. 220, 1921 ; A. Ditte, *ib.*, (5), **27**. 145, 1882 ; *Compt. Rend.*, **94**. 792, 864, 1882 ; L. Varenne, *ib.*, **89**. 361, 1879 ; E. J. Maumené, *Chem. News.* **44**. 59, 1881 ; A. Terreil, *ib.*, (1), **4**. 64, 1862 ; W. Spring, *ib.*, (3), **1**. 180, 1889 ; *Bull. Soc. Chim.*, (2), **35**. 598, 1881 ; J. B. Senderens, *ib.*, (3), **6**. 805, 1891 ; P. Sabatier and J. B. Senderens, *Compt. Rend.*, **114**. 1429, 1892 ; **120**. 619, 1895 ; *Ann. Chim. Phys.*, (7), **7**. 348, 1896 ; J. von Liebig, *Liebig's Ann.*, **15**. 116, 1855 ; R. Roth, *ib.*, **60**. 214, 1846 ; *Journ. prakt. Pharm.*, **10**. 381, 1845 ; R. Böttger, *Dingler's Journ.*, **209**. 315, 1873 ; *Liebig's Ann.*, **29**. 87, 1839 ; L. Schaffner, *ib.*, **51**. 168, 1844 ; A. Vogel, *Jahrb. Pharm.*, **4**. 193, 1855 ; A. Wagner, *Zeit. anal. Chem.*, **18**. 559, 1879 ; S. A. Sandall, *Phil. Mag.*, (3), **12**. 216, 1838 ; H. Rose, *Pogg. Ann.*, **75**. 1, 1848 ; A. E. Nordenskjöld, *ib.*, **114**. 612, 1861 ; *Œfvers. Akad. Stockholm*, **17**. 439, 1860 ; W. G. Mixter, *Amer. Journ. Science*, (4), **27**. 229, 1909 ; M. Delépine and L. A. Hallopeau, *Compt. Rend.*, **129**. 600, 1899 ; P. Sabatier and A. Mailhe, *ib.*, **147**. 18, 106, 1908 ; G. Viard, *ib.*, **135**. 242, 1902 ; M. Mouraour, *ib.*, **130**. 141, 1900 ; H. Moissan, *ib.*, **114**. 617, 1892 ; J. Thomsen, *Journ. prakt. Chem.*, (2), **14**. 429, 1876 ; E. Divers and T. Haga, *Journ. Chem. Soc.*, **47**. 361, 1885 ; A. Piccini and L. Marino, *Zeit. anorg. Chem.*, **32**. 55, 1902 ; W. Herz, *ib.*, **31**. 454, 1902 ; J. Rubenbauer, *ib.*, **30**. 331, 1902 ; A. Hantzsch, *ib.*, **30**. 289, 1902 ; M. C. Harding, *ib.*, **20**. 239, 1899 ; W. Fränkel and K. Snipischsky, *ib.*, **125**. 235, 1922 ; E. Vigouroux, *Compt. Rend.*, **120**. 367, 1895 ; J. Cameron, *Chem. Gaz.*, **9**. 125, 1851 ; S. Tanatar, *Ber.*, **38**. 1184, 1905 ; H. Schiff, *Liebig's Ann.*, **120**. 53, 1861 ; G. Tschermak, *Sitzber. Akad. Wien*, **44**. 734, 1862 ; H. Goldschmidt and M. Eckardt, *Zeit. phys. Chem.*, **56**. 385, 1906 ; C. Reichard, *Ber.*, **30**. 1915, 1897 ; P. Pfeiffer, *ib.*, **35**. 3303, 1902 ; L. Vanino and F. Treubert, *Ber.*, **31**. 1118, 2267, 1898 ; A. Gutmann, *ib.*, **38**. 1733, 3280, 1905 ; R. Schneider, *Pogg. Ann.*,

88. 55, 1853 ; *Journ. prakt. Chem.*, (2), **58.** 562, 1988 ; J. Herapath, *Phil. Mag.*, **64.** 321, 1824 ; T. Andrews, *ib.*, (3), **32.** 321, 1848 ; J. Ewles, *ib.*, (6), **45.** 957, 1923 ; F. Feigl, *Zeit. anorg. Chem.*, **119.** 305, 1922 ; W. R. Mott, *Trans. Amer. Electrochem. Soc.*, **34.** 266, 1918 ; L. Kahlenberg and W. J. Trautman, *ib.*, **39.** 377, 1921 ; S. Meyer, *Wied. Ann.*, **69.** 236, 1899 ; G. Lunge, *Ber.*, **18.** 1391, 1885 ; G. R. Levi, *Nuovo Cimento*, (7), **1.** 335, 1924 ; J. N. Pearce and A. M. Alvarado, *Journ. Phys. Chem.*, **29.** 256, 1925 ; L. H. Milligan and G. R. Gillette, *ib.*, **28.** 744, 1924 ; E. Friederich, *Zeit. Physik*, **31.** 813, 1925 ; S. Ghosh and N. R. Dhar, *Journ. Phys. Chem.*, **29.** 435, 1925 ; N. R. Dhar, *Zeit. anorg. Chem.*, **144.** 289, 1925 ; A. Gutmann, *Ueber den Abbau der Thiosulfate und einiger Polythionate zu Sulfiten durch reducierende Salze in alkalischer Lösung und über einige Monosulfoxyarsenate*, München, 1897 ; M. H. Klaproth, *Beiträge zur chemischen Kenntniss der Mineralkörper*, Berlin, **2.** 245, 1797 ; T. Maeda, *Bull. Japan. Inst. Phys. Chem. Research*, **2.** 350, 1923 ; F. W. Bury and J. R. Partington, *Journ. Chem. Soc.*, **121.** 1998, 1922 ; D. L. Hammick, *ib.*, **111.** 379, 1917 ; O. W. Brown and C. O. Henke, *ib.*, **27.** 739, 1923 ; L. Wöhler and O. Balz, *Zeit. Elektrochem.*, **27.** 406, 1921 ; E. Tiede and E. Birnbräuer, *Zeit. anorg. Chem.*, **87.** 129, 1914 ; J. A. Hedvall and N. von Zweigburgk, *ib.*, **108.** 119, 1919 ; F. de Carli, *Atti Accad. Lincei*, (6), **1.** 533, 1925 ; H. T. S. Britton, *Journ. Chem. Soc.*, **127.** 2110, 1925 ; R. Weber, *Pogg. Ann.*, **112.** 619, 1861 ; N. R. Dhar and S. Ghosh, *Zeit. anorg. Chem.*, **152.** 409, 1926.

  ² J. N. von Fuchs, *Kastner's Arch.*, **23.** 368, 1832 ; *Journ. prakt. Chem.*, (1), **5.** 318, 1832 ; J. J. Berzelius, *Pogg. Ann.*, **28.** 443, 1833 ; G. Tschermak, *Sitzber. Akad Wien* **44.** 734, 1862 ; H. Schiff, *Liebig's Ann.*, **120.** 53, 1861 ; E. Frémy, *Ann. Chim. Phys.*, (3), **12.** 478, 1844 ; A. Ditte, *ib.*, (5), **27.** 170, 1882 ; L. Wöhler and O. Balz, *Zeit. Elektrochem.*, **27.** 406, 1921 ; L. Gmelin, *Handbook of Chemistry*, London, **5,** 71, 1851 ; S. Meyer, *Wied. Ann.*, **69.** 236, 1899 ; P. Schützenberger, *Compt. Rend.*, **98.** 985, 1884 ; H. St. C. Deville and H. Debray, *Ann. Chim. Phys.* (3), **56.** 430, 1859.

§ 12. Stannic Oxide

The ancients no doubt obtained tin from the native form of **stannic oxide**, or **tin dioxide**, SnO_2. This ore is the *stannum calciforme* of T. Bergman,[1] and the *Zinnstein* of J. G. Wallerius. It is the *tin ore*, or *tinstone* of various mineralogists, *e.g.* C. C. von Leonhard, etc. F. S. Beudant called it *cassiterite*.

The brown ore. found in botryoidal and reniform shapes concentric in structure and with a radiating fibrous structure, was called by R. Kirwan, *wood-tin*, owing to its external resemblance to wood. This was shown by R. J. Haüy, and J. F. L. Hausmann to be a form of tinstone. Wood tin in the upper part of tin lodes and gravel deposits is considered to be an alteration product of stannite or tin pyrites, or bell-metal ore. A Cornish name for small spherical nodules of wood-tin is *toad's-eye tin.* Acute pyramidal crystals of cassiterite are called *needle tin ore ;* and acute crystals from Camborne, Cornwall, are called *sparable tin* in allusion to their resemblance to the so-called sparable nails. The German miner's names for the twinned crystals are *Zwitter*, and *Zinngraupen*. The so-called *stream tin* is cassiterite occurring in the form of sand or pebbles in the beds of streams or in the adjoining gravel ; cassiterite occurring in the soil formed by the disintegration of stanniferous rocks is called *float tin*. The *stannite* of A. Breithaupt is an amorphous, yellowish-white substance from Cornwall, and is a mixture of stannic oxide and other minerals. The *ainalite* of A. E. Nordenskjöld is a cassiterite containing about 9 per cent. of tantalic oxide, found at Pennikoja, Finland ; W. T. Schaller proposed calling it *tantalum cassiterite*.

Analyses have been made by T. Bergman,[2] M. H. Klaproth, F. Gmelin, J. J. Berzelius, E. Charlon, C. Bergemann, J. D. Bruce, A. E. Nordenskjöld, R. J. Meyer, J. W. Mallet, D. Forbes, P. Kröber, F. A. Genth, F. P. Dunnington, W. G. Brown, F. Becke, W. Kohlmann, W. R. Dunstan, T. Petersen, E. S. Simpson, T. Liebisch, A. Breithaupt, J. Königsberger and O. Reichenheim, etc. The results are in agreement with the formula SnO_2. T. Liebisch found the spectroscopic evidence of the presence in cassiterites of copper, calcium, aluminium, silicon, titanium, columbium, tungsten, and iron to be very clear ; that of potassium, strontium, manganese, chromium, molybdenum, tantalum, zirconium, and gallium, more or less clear ; and indium was observed in cassiterite from Zinnwald. G. Eberhardt observed scandium in some samples of cassiterite.

There is evidence that in some cases cassiterite has been formed in nature by crystallization from soln. ; and in other cases by the infiltration of vap. from below. C. Doelter [3] found the oxide is appreciably soluble in water at 80°, particularly if sodium fluoride be present. S. Meunier, for example, found 0·5 per cent. in an opaline deposit like geyserite, from a thermal spring at Selangor. J. H. Collins observed cassiterite as a cement in some Cornish conglomerates ; as an impregnation in the long-buried horns of a deer ; as pseudomorphs after felspar ; as cappings on crystals of quartz ; as a lining in fissures of quartz ; as an incrustation on an ingot of ancient tin having been formed by slow oxidation ; and as crystals on reniform masses of wood-tin. F. A. Genth observed pseudomorphs of cassiterite after hæmatite ; L. V. Pirsson, as enclosures in crystals of hæmatite ; and E. Wittich, as stalactitic masses at Sierra de Guanajacato, Mexico. This subject has been also discussed by C. Reid and J. B. Scrivener, and J. B. Hill and D. A. MacAlister. The formation of cassiterite veins as a result of the infiltration of stanniferous soln. has been noted by L. K. Ward, F. Sandberger, G. Bischof, W. von Fircks, C. W. Kempton, W. R. Ingalls, E. Halse, J. Nevius, A. H. Bromly, R. A. F. Penrose, R. Beck, etc.

Cassiterite occurs in lodes connected with granite intrusions, or with the volcanic equivalents of granite. The lodes penetrate the granite and surrounding rocks, and mark a late phase in the consolidation of the intrusion, when the fluoriferous and boriferous exhalations altered the granite into *griesen*, and formed minerals like tourmaline, fluorite, etc. Tin commonly occurs in quartz veins in granite, and the felspar of the granite has been transformed into mica (generally lepidolite and zinnwaldite). The boriferous and fluoriferous minerals topaz and tourmaline are also present. These facts agree with the assumption that the ordinary type of tin deposits has been formed by the injection of vapour carrying boron, fluorine, and tin. This hypothesis is confirmed by the syntheses of cassiterite by processes involving the use of boric oxide and of tin fluoride or chloride. Usually the boron forms tourmaline and tin cassiterite, but in the rare mineral nordenskjöldine, the tin and boron occur together. The fluorine is represented by topaz, fluorite, apatite, axinite, triphylite, and amblygonite. This subject has been discussed by A. Daubrée, J. H. L. Vogt, W. Lindgren, H. Schröder, A. W. Stelzner, K. Dalmer, R. Recknagel, F. Gautier, F. Beyschlag and co-workers, G. Steinmann, A. Bergeat, G. Tschermak, J. F. W. Charpentier, K. Dalmer, W. R. Jones, etc. Wolframite and the secondary minerals scheelite and stolzite are commonly associated with cassiterite. Copper sulphides, arsenopyrite, pyrite, and ores of bismuth, uranium, and iron are also found in cassiterite lodes.

When tin is heated nearly to its b.p. in air, it burns with a white luminous flame, and the stannic oxide so formed is in a very fine state of subdivision, and was formerly known as *flores jovis* or *flores stannic—flowers of tin*. When the metal is fused in the presence of air, the surface soon becomes covered with a grey pellicle, which passes into a grey powder known as *tin-ash*, and this consists of a mixture of finely divided metal and oxide which with a prolonged roasting is converted into white stannic oxide. The oxide obtained at a high temp., and in a very finely divided state, is less soluble in fused silicates, and is preferred when stannic oxide is used as an opacifying agent in glazes and enamels ; this form of oxide has also a greater opacifying power than the oxide made by many other processes. C. P. Bary [4] recommended blowing heated air over the surface of tin at a high temp. ; the Elektrizitäts-Gesellschaft Gelnhausen heated the metal electrically to about 1700° and burnt the tin vap. in air or oxygen ; H. Försterling, E. Dechert, M. Wassermann and M. Jäger, etc., also devised analogous processes. V. Kohlschütter and J. L. Tüscher obtained **colloidal stannic oxide** by making tin one electrode of an arc, and oxidizing its vap. by air. In this way, stannic oxide dispersed in a gaseous medium is obtained.

J. L. Gay Lussac, and H. V. Regnault found that amorphous stannic oxide is formed when tin is heated in a current of water vapour. J. L. Proust showed that the lower oxide and hydroxide are transformed, by roasting, into stannic oxide ; and that moist stannous oxide is transformed into stannic oxide when exposed to the air for a year. J. J. Berzelius made analogous observations, and he found that stannic oxide is formed by roasting the sulphide, or by heating a mixture of tin and mercuric oxide. The dioxide is also obtained by treating tin with nitric acid; the reaction is vigorous and the resulting hydrate is a white powder which is washed and ignited. When a soln. of a stannic salt is treated with aq. ammonia, a gelatinous precipitate is obtained which is difficult to wash; but if the mixture be warmed with a conc. soln. of sodium sulphate, the dense precipitate is easily washed, and it furnishes the dioxide on ignition. P. T. Austen made the amorphous dioxide by passing carbon dioxide into a boiling soln. of sodium stannate, or by heating the soln. with sodium hydrocarbonate; and roasting the washed product— *vide infra*, alkali stannates. A. Vogel made finely divided stannic oxide by heating to redness stannous oxalate in thin layers; and S. J. Lubowsky, by heating tin hydroxide to 1040° sufficiently long to produce the required colour.

M. H. Klaproth [5] melted brown cassiterite from Schlaggenwald in a clay crucible, and observed that pale brown acicular crystals were formed on the inner wall of the crucible. Crystals of stannic oxide of the cassiterite type have been frequently observed among furnace products—*e.g.* in the scoriæ of brass furnaces—by J. Törmer, W. P. Headden, G. vom Rath, F. A. Abel, K. N. Spallart, A. Arzruni, J. H. L. Vogt, L. Bourgeois, etc. The first synthesis of crystalline stannic oxide was made by A. Daubrée by passing a mixture of steam and stannic chloride vap., or of dry carbon dioxide and, stannic chloride vap., through a red-hot porcelain tube. He also made it by passing the vap. of stannic chloride over red-hot calcium oxide. H. St. C. Deville and H. Caron obtained the crystals by passing stannic fluoride and water vap. through a red-hot tube; and H. St. C. Deville, by passing a slow current of hydrogen chloride over red-hot amorphous stannic oxide. H. de Sénarmont obtained crystals of stannic dioxide by heating in a sealed tube a soln. of stannic acid in hydrochloric acid. A. Knop, and G. Wunder observed that a phosphate is formed when a soln. of stannic oxide in microcosmic salt at a white heat is cooled, but with molten borax, crystalline stannic oxide is formed. A. Michel-Lévy and L. Bourgeois obtained the crystals by melting at a white heat a mixture of sodium carbonate and stannic oxide; H. Traube melted the oxide with sodium tungstate along with ferric, manganese, chromic, nickel, or cobalt oxide, and obtained coloured crystals of cassiterite. L. Bourgeois obtained crystals by melting silica, stannic oxide, and calcium chloride at a red heat; and by melting a mixture of tin or stannic oxide with an excess of cupric oxide at a red heat, cooling the mixture slowly, and dissolving out the cuprous oxide with aqua regia; A. Ditte, by heating a mixture of amorphous stannic oxide, calcium chloride, and ammonium chloride; and L. Grandeau, by heating a mixture of tin phosphate and potassium sulphate.

The physical properties of stannic oxide.—Artificial preparations of stannic oxide are white, greyish-white, or colourless; but colourless cassiterite is very rarely found in nature. The colour is often yellow, red, or grey; and commonly yellowish- or reddish-brown to black. In some places the red ore is called *ruby tin;* and the yellow ore, *resin tin.* The dark colour is almost always due to the presence of ferric oxide; but F. Becke [6] found only 0·12 per cent. of ferric oxide in the dark brown crystals of Schlaggenwald. J. W. Retgers found that neither ferric oxide nor manganese dioxide forms isomorphous mixtures with stannic oxide, and he called the mixture *eine anomale Mischung.* H. Traube noted that stannic oxide can dissolve a number of colouring oxides—*vide supra*—and obtained peach-red crystals when chromic oxide is present. W. Kohlmann attributed the colour of the crystals from Perak to the presence of 0·11 per cent. of tungstic oxide, and 0·12 per cent. of ferrous oxide. E. Weinschenk observed the effect of calcination on the colour of the crystals of cassiterite. A. Dittmann found cassiterite from Ehrenfriedersdorf was decolorized at a red heat; and concluded that the pigment was not ferrous oxide; no organic matter distilled off. Thin sections may be colour- less or tinged yellow, brown, or red. The colour may be irregularly distributed in streaks or spots, and sometimes zonally. The lustre is adamantine.

The crystals of cassiterite were early described by J. B. L. Romé de l'Isle,[7] R. J. Haüy, W. Phillips, F. Mohs, C. F. Naumann, and W. H. Miller. The crystals are rarely simple and euhedral, and when such crystals do occur, they may be either stout square prisms, or slender prisms terminated by acute pyramid faces— *needle tin*. Both forms belong to the tetragonal system, and, according to F. Becke, have the axial ratio $a : c = 1 : 0.67232$; S. Stevanovic gave $a : c = 1 : 0.6726$; and L. H. Borgström, $1 : 0.6722$. Cassiterite is usually found in irregularly shaped anhedral crystals ; and, as indicated above, it may occur in divergent fibrous masses. Contact and penetration twins are common ; the **twinning** and composition plane is (101) ; repeated twinning may produce complex forms giving a succession of knee-shaped corners in which two striated prism zones meet at angles of 67° 50′. The crystals of cassiterite have been described by P. Groth, A. W. Stelzner, H. von Foullon, A. Arzruni, F. Hessenberg, W. Haidinger, A. Sadebeck, R. Hörnes, A. Pelikan, V. von Zepharovich, A. Lacroix, R. P. Greg and W. G. Lettsom, C. Busz, R. H. Solly, W. Kohlmann, A. Lévy, A. E. Nordenskjöld, M. Bentivoglio, G. Cesaro, H. Baumhauer, A. Gadolin, L. H. Borgström, P. von Jeremejeff, G. vom Rath, A. von Groddeck, W. T. Schaller, S. Stevanovic, E. Artini, etc. G. Rose showed that rutile, zircon, and cassiterite appear to be isomorphous, and P. Groth attributes this to the similarity in their constitutions supposed to be respectively $Ti(TiO_4)$, $Zr(SiO_4)$, and $Sn(SnO_4)$. L. V. Pirsson described pseudomorphs of cassiterite after hæmatite, and J. A. Phillips, after orthoclase. The **cleavage** parallel to (100) is imperfect ; that parallel to (111) is less so ; and that parallel to (110) is scarcely distinct. F. Becke, and W. E. Hidden observed parting planes or lamellar separations in some crystals. H. Traube studied the **corrosion figures** with molten potassium fluoride or potassium hydrofluoride and obtained results similar to those with rutile and zircon. G. A. Dima studied the **photoelectric effect.** The **X-radiograms** of cassiterite, analogous with those of rutile, have been made by W. P. Davey, L. Vegard, H. Haga and F. M. Jäger, C. M. Williams, N. Yamada, P. F. Kerr, M. L. Huggins, and J. A. Hedvall.

A. Daubrée's artificial crystals [8] were stated to be *rhombic* like brookite, but H. St. C. Deville could not confirm this, and P. Groth also doubted the inference. A. Michel-Lévy, and L. Bourgeois' preparation—*vide supra*—was stated to be *hexagonal* like tridymite, but this lacks confirmation. A. Arzruni observed in furnace slags from Talgau, besides cassiterite some small, colourless crystals which he considered to be a *monoclinic* modification of stannic oxide, but P. Groth said that these crystals were probably twinned tetragonal crystals.

R. Boyle [9] gave 4·18–5·00 for the **specific gravity** of tin-ore. Numerous observations have been made on the sp. gr. of cassiterite, and stannic oxide. The values range from D. Forbes' value 7·021 for a sample from Bolivia to F. A. Genth's value 6·160 for a sample from Durango—J. W. Mallet found 6·753 ; C. Bergemann, 6·862 ; P. Kröber, 6·4 ; J. Herapath, 6·639 at 16·5° ; P. Boullay, 6·90 ; F. E. Neumann, 6·952 ; W. G. Brown, 6·609 ; E. P. Dunnington, 6·956 ; F. A. Genth, 6·160–6·911 ; W. R. Dunstan, 6·91 ; H. Rose, 6·849–6·978 ; E. Weinschenk, 6·65 ; A. E. Nordenskjöld, 6·6–6·8 ; and L. Playfair and J. P. Joule, 6·1722 at 4°. H. Schröder gave 6·85–6·98 ; and after calcination, 6·89–7·18. The best representative value is 6·95. D. Forbes reported 6·8432–6·8439 at 15·5° for the sp. gr. of colourless cassiterite from Bolivia, 6·704 at 15·5° for a yellow specimen, and 6·7021 at 15·5° for a black specimen. For artificial crystals, A. Daubrée gave 6·72 ; and A. Michel-Lévy and L. Bourgeois, 6·70. S. Stevanovic gave 6·992–7·044 for the sp. gr. of artificial crystals at 16°. J. J. Berzelius gave 6·64 for the sp. gr. of amorphous stannic oxide, and F. Emich for stannic oxide made by calcining the metal, 7·0096 at 0°/4°. The **hardness** on Mohs' scale is 6–7. Artificially prepared stannic oxide is used as a polishing powder for metals, etc. The hardness was discussed by A. Reis and F. Zimmermann. E. Madelung and R. Fuchs found the coeff. of **compressibility** of cassiterite to be $3·38 \times 10^{-12}$ dynes per sq. cm.

The coeff. of **thermal expansion** of cassiterite found by H. Kopp [10] is

$a=0.000004$ between 16° and 46°, and for the coeff. of cubical expansion 0·000016. L. Playfair and J. P. Joule gave 0·0000172 for the coeff. of cubical expansion of stannic oxide between 0° and 100°. F. Pfaff gave for the coeff. of linear expansion in the direction of the a-axis, 0·000004526, and in the direction of the c-axis, 0·000004860 ; or, for the coeff. of cubical expansion, 0·00001389. H. Fizeau gave for the coeff. of linear expansion at 40° parallel to the c-axis, $0·0_5392$, and $0·0_5321$ vertical to that axis. For the coeff. of cubical expansion at 40° he gave $0·0_41034$. F. E. Neumann gave 0·0931 for the **specific heat** of cassiterite between 0° and 100° ; H. V. Regnault, 0·09326 between 16° and 98° ; and H. Kopp, 0·0894 between 16° and 47°. E. Jannettaz found that if the **thermal conductivity** in the direction of the chief axis is unity, that in a vertical direction is 0·79. H. de Sénarmont made some observations on this subject. E. J. Housten found that when the temp. of white amorphous stannic oxide is gradually raised, it becomes pale green, then yellowish-green, and passes through a chromatic scale to orange or reddish-orange ; on cooling, the order is reversed. E. D. Clarke melted cassiterite in the oxy-hydrogen blowpipe flame, and G. Spezia found that cassiterite was fused when the ordinary blowpipe flame was fortified by using hot air, or oxygen. R. Cusack gave 1127° for the **melting point** of cassiterite ; and A. L. Fletcher, 1177°. O. Ruff and co-workers gave 1625° for the m.p. of stannic oxide contained in a zirconia crucible ; a pyramidal cone of the oxide squats at 1625°. E. Tiede and E. Birn-bräuer observed no fusion or volatilization in the cathode rays. H. Moissan found that in the electric arc furnace cassiterite is fused and volatilized. O. Ruff and co-workers found that at the m.p. stannic oxide decomposes, and at 2250°, the vap. of tin is present. W. Fränkel and K. Snipischky gave 1·66 Cals. for the latent **heat of fusion** of a mol of stannic oxide. T. Maeda found the **dissociation pressure** of the oxygen by stannic oxide at 927° is $4·47 \times 10^{-15}$; and the heat of formation $(Sn_{liquid}, O_2) = 130·26$ Cals. at 800° ; W. Fränkel and K. Snipischsky gave 135·8 Cals. from solid tin and 137·46 from molten tin. W. Rosenhain gave 2350 cals. per gram for the **heat of formation** of stannic oxide from tin-foil ; W. G. Mixter gave $(Sn, O_2) = 137·8$ Cals. for the crystalline oxide ; T. Andrews obtained a similar number ; and J. E. Moose and S. W. Parr gave 138·2 Cals. L. Vignon found the **heat of neutralization** with potassium hydroxide to be 1·0 Cal. for stannic oxide which has been calcined at a red heat, and 4 Cals. for the oxide obtained by boiling a stannic salt with a soln. of sodium sulphate.

The **index of refraction** and **birefringence** of cassiterite are strong. T. Liebisch[11] observed that the index of refraction of the strongly coloured parts of a crystal is greater than in the feebly coloured parts. H. Rosenbusch gave for the indices of refraction of a crystal from Schlaggenwald :

	Red.	Yellow.	Green.
ω	1·9793 (1·9765)	1·9966 (1·9923)	2·0115
ε	2·0799 (2·0748)	2·0934 (2·0911)	2·1088

The bracketed numbers refer to a crystal from Zinnwald. A. Arzruni found for artificial violet crystals $\omega = 1·9850$ and $\epsilon = 2·0817$ for the red ray ; $\omega = 1·9965$ and $\epsilon = 2·0991$ for the yellow ray ; and $\omega = 2·0093$ and $\epsilon = 2·1045$ for the green ray. The **optical character** is positive. A. Ehringhaus and H. Rose studied the relation between the mol. wt. and the dispersion or birefringence. A. Madelung observed that crystals from Breitenbrunn appeared to be biaxial, and are therefore **optically anomalous.** The **pleochroism** of the crystals of cassiterite is usually feeble, and has been observed by H. Traube, H. von Foullon, A. Lacroix, A. Pelikan, and E. Weinschenk. E. Richat observed the action of **N-rays.** J. Ewles studied the **cathode ray** luminescence of tin oxide. V. von Agafonoff said that cassiterite is transparent for **ultra-violet light** as far as the cadmium line. J. O. Perrine found no fluorescence in the ultra-violet rays. A. de Gramont found that all the tin lines show clearly in the **spark spectrum** of cassiterite. W. W. Coblentz found small absorption bands in the **ultra-red transmission spectrum** of cassiterite at

$1·3\mu$, 3μ, $5·8\mu$, $6·6\mu$, $7·3\mu$, $8·25\mu$, $9·7\mu$, and $10·4\mu$. He also found that stannic oxide emits a continuous spectrum, with a small band at $3·2\mu$. G. A. Dima studied the **photoelectric effect** with tin oxide. W. Crookes found that stannic oxide does not show an appreciable phosphorescence in **cathode rays**.

According to F. von Kobell,[12] cassiterite is a non-conductor of electricity; while F. Beijerinck, and G. Cesaro found that it is a conductor, and, according to the former, the **electrical conductivity** is less in the direction of the c-axis than it is perpendicular to that axis. J. Königsberger and O. Reichenheim, however, showed that transparent colourless cassiterite is a non-conductor, and that the dark-coloured crystals are conductors. G. Tammann and H. Bredmeier measured the conductivity of thin films of the oxide. C. Doelter measured the **electrical resistance** of a plate cut parallel to the c-axis, and found the sp. resistance, R ohms, to be on a rising temp. :

	360°	500°	700°	900°	1060°	1200°	1430°
R . . .	3550	1060	1050	29	5·0	1·2	0·85

and on a falling temp.,

	1270°	1200°	1080°	1010°	930°	780°
R . . .	0·980	1·105	1·488	1·6888	2·677	55·80

No polarization phenomena were observed, and it was inferred that the conductivity is not due to ionization. According to T. Liebisch, sections of cassiterite cut parallel to the basal plane and parallel to the principal axis of crystals of cassiterite show a well-marked zonal structure. The dark kernel of these crystals is strongly negative thermo-electrically with respect to copper, whilst the paler coloured shell is inactive. When placed between the electrodes of an electric wave detector the dark kernel reacts strongly, whilst the paler shell is inactive. For this reason crystals of cassiterite only act in the detector when the darker coloured pyramid faces, and not the paler prism faces, are in contact with the electrodes. B. Saklatwalla recommended stannic oxide as a resistance medium for electrical heating. K. Fischbeck studied the electrochemical reduction of cassiterite. W. Schmidt could not determine the **dielectric constant** of a crystal of cassiterite from Altenberg, on account of its great electrical conductivity. E. T. Wherry found that cassiterite showed no evidence of the rectification required by a radio-detector. According to V. von Lang, cassiterite is paramagnetic, and it is greater in the direction of the c-axis than it is perpendicular thereto. S. Meyer gave for the **magnetic susceptibility** $-0·082 \times 10^{-6}$ units per gram, and $-0·006 \times 10^{-6}$ per mol.

The chemical properties of stannic oxides.—W. A. Tilden[13] found that cassiterite from the Straits Settlements occludes 1·3 parts of gas, 45·4 per cent. of which is carbon dioxide. C. M. Despretz showed that stannic oxide is reduced when heated in a current of **hydrogen** at the temp. at which tin decomposes steam. W. Müller found the reduction begins at about 170°. W. Hampe, H. Haas, and A. E. Arnold employed this method for breaking down cassiterite to a state where the contained tin can be dissolved in acids and analyzed. L. Wöhler and O. Balz studied the reduction of stannic oxide, and the oxidation of stannous oxide (q.v.). J. C. S. Wells, and H. Mennicke showed that when stannic oxide is treated with a mixture of zinc and hydrochloric acid, the oxide is reduced to tin which dissolves in the acid. E. D. Clarke, and C. H. Pfaff observed the reduction of cassiterite in the oxy-hydrogen flame. Cassiterite or stannic oxide is very resistant towards chemical agents. The oxide is not affected when heated in **air** or **oxygen ;** nor has **water** any action. This is illustrated by the water-worn granules which occur as stream tin in alluvial deposits ; it seems to survive indefinitely in detrital deposits. A. Kenngott observed no reaction when the moist powder is tested with litmus, but after it has been calcined in a reducing flame, it does show an **alkaline reaction.**

When heated in a current of **chlorine,** R. Weber found that stannic chloride is formed ; and A. E. Arnold found that by heating cassiterite in a stream of **hydrogen chloride,** or digesting the mineral in conc. **hydrochloric acid** at 100°, most of the stannic oxide dissolves. The stannic oxide in a few rare minerals is also extracted by digestion with this acid. In general, however, aq. soln. of acids scarcely affect cassiterite or calcined stannic oxide. F. de Lalande and M. Prud'homme heated stannic oxide and an alkali chloride in a current of air, and they found that the reaction can be symbolized : $SnO_2+2NaCl+O=Na_2SnO_3+Cl_2$. According to E. Stelling, if the oxide be digested in sulphurous acid, it afterwards dissolves readily in hot hydrochloric acid. Fused **potassium hydrofluoride** was found by W. Gibbs to dissolve stannic oxide. C. Matignon and F. Bourion found that when cassiterite is heated in chlorine charged with the vapour of **sulphur chloride,** SCl_2, stannic chloride is formed. R. Weber found that when stannic oxide and **sulphur** are heated together, stannic sulphide is formed ; and, according to H. Rose, a molten mixture of sulphur and sodium carbonate transforms stannic oxide into sodium thiostannate. D. L. Hammick said stannic oxide remains unchanged by **sulphur dioxide** at a red heat ; and E. Stelling also found that it is not reduced by sulphurous acid. H. Rose found that when a mixture of conc. **sulphuric acid** is heated, a syrupy liquid is formed from which water precipitates all the stannic oxide ; and that molten **potassium hydrosulphate** dissolves stannic oxide, but when the cold mass is treated with water, the stannic oxide is precipitated completely.

P. Sabatier and J. B. Senderens showed that at temp. below 500° stannic oxide is not affected by **nitrous oxide, nitric oxide,** or **nitrogen peroxide.** C. T. Barfoed showed that **phosphorus trichloride** reacts with stannic oxide at 160°, forming a mixture of stannous and stannic chlorides. A. Michaelis also studied the reaction. D. B. Dott found that stannic oxide is reduced to tin by **hypophosphorous acid.** Stannic oxide is reduced to the metal when heated with **carbon ;** and, according to F. O. Döltz and C. A. Graumann, the reaction begins between 800° and 810°. R. E. Slade and G. I. Higson found that the equilibrium press. of the oxide with carbon is over 760 mm. at 750°. H. Moissan said that stannic oxide is reduced when heated with **calcium carbide,** forming the metal but not a tin carbide. F. von Kügelgen found that the reaction begins at a dull red heat, and that it proceeds smoothly at a bright red heat if calcium chloride be used as a flux. The tin retains about 0·4 per cent. of calcium. C. M. Despretz, and P. G. F. Leplay and A. Laurent observed the reduction of stannic oxide by **carbon monoxide.** According to I. L. Bell, the stannic oxide is not attacked at a dull red heat. F. Schlagdenhauffen and C. Pagel said that no reduction occurs below 300° ; but K. Stammer said that at a higher temp. stannic oxide is first reduced to stannous oxide and then to tin. R. E. Slade and G. I. Higson found that equilibrium occurs at 750°, when stannic oxide and carbon are heated in a closed vessel and the press. is over 760 mm. ; and at 753°, when the press. is 670° mm. T. Maeda found, at 700°–950°, the state of equilibrium : $SnO_2+2CO \rightleftharpoons Sn +2CO_2$, where the equilibrium constant, K, is given by log $K=-641\cdot8T^{-1}+1\cdot084$; and the thermal value of the reaction $SnO_2+2CO=Sn +2CO_2-5\cdot87$ Cals. at 80°. The kinetics of the reduction was also studied by W. Fränkel and K. Snipischsky ; they gave 1·46 Cals. for the heat of the reaction ; and found equilibrium was attained in a few weeks at 500° ; in a few days at 600° ; at 670°, in about 2½ hrs. ; and at 755°, in half an hour. The results at 670°, 720°, and 755° are illustrated in Fig. 64, where the lower

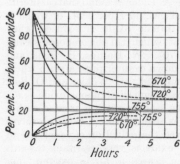

FIG. 64.—Equilibria in the Reaction $Sn+2CO_2 \rightleftharpoons SnO_2+2CO$.

curves refer to the oxidation of tin by carbon dioxide, and the upper to the reduction of stannic oxide by carbon monoxide : $Sn+2CO_2 \rightleftharpoons SnO_2+2CO$. For the constant $C_{CO_2}K=C_{CO}$:

K	$600°$	$700°$	$800°$	$900°$	$1000°$	$1100°$	$1200°$
	0·28	0·27	0·25	0·22	0·13	0·07	0·05

S. Medsforth examined the effect of stannic oxide on the catalytic action of nickel in the reduction of carbon monoxide and dioxide by hydrogen. W. Müller said stannic oxide is not altered when heated in a current of **methane,** or **ethylene ;** but W. Ipatieff showed that the vap. of **alcohol** forms acetaldehyde and ethylene when passed through a tube packed with stannic oxide and heated to 650° ; metallic tin is formed. A. Mailhe said that ethyl alcohol vap. rapidly reduces stannic to stannous oxide at 340°, and the reduction of the stannous oxide to the metal proceeds rather slowly ; acetaldehyde and hydrogen are formed. According to J. von Liebig, stannic oxide is quickly reduced to the metal by molten **potassium cyanide.** According to L. Hackspill and R. Grandadam, while fused **alkali cyanides** reduce the oxide under ordinary atm. conditions to metal and alkali carbimide, yet, at 570°–750°, in vacuo, sodium cyanide yields eq. proportions of sodium and tin, along with nitrogen, carbon monoxide and dioxide, and carbon. Sodium carbimide is probably first formed, and it decomposes under the reduced press. J. Milbauer found that molten **potassium thiocyanate** reacts vigorously with stannic oxide, forming stannous sulphide and then potassium thiostannate. According to C. W. Watts and C. A. Bell, and C. Renz, **carbon tetrachloride** reacts with red-hot stannic oxide, forming stannic chloride. N. P. Peskoff found that the presence of colloidal stannic oxide facilitated the action of X-rays on organic compounds. G. Rauter found that **silicon tetrachloride** reacts between 350° and 360°, forming stannic chloride and silica. C. H. Burgess and A. Holt said that stannic oxide is quite insoluble in fused **boric oxide.** A. Lomax showed that the solubility of stannic oxide in fused **silicates** increases with the proportion of con-tained alkali. The insolubility of the oxide in fused silicates determines its utility as an opacifying agent in glasses, glazes, and enamels. The subject has been investigated by R. R. Danielson and M. K. Frehafer. K. B. Lehmann has examined the dissolution of tin oxide by hot acetic acid from enamels opacified with this oxide.

Stannic oxide is reduced to the metal by **potassium** or **sodium** at a gentle heat ; and the reaction is accompanied by incandescence. C. Winkler showed that the reduction of stannic oxide heated with **magnesium** occurs with explosive violence ; H. Goldschmidt reduced stannic oxide by heating it with **aluminium.** W. O. Snell-ing showed that cassiterite in contact with **zinc** and hydrochloric acid is reduced by cathodic action. According to A. E. Arnold, aq. soln. of the **alkali hydroxides** have very little action on cassiterite ; H. D. Rankin said that after heating to redness, stannic oxide dissolves in alkali-lye when the mixture is heated in an autoclave. H. Rose found that the oxide is completely dissolved by fused **alkali hydroxides,** while it is scarcely attacked by molten **alkali carbonates.**

REFERENCES.

1 T. Bergman, *De minerarum docimasia humida,* Upsala, 1780 ; J. G. Wallerius, *Mineralogia,* Stockholm, 303, 1747 ; C. C. von Leonhard, *Handbuch der Oryktognosie,* Heidelberg, 218, 1821 ; F. S. Beudant, *Traité élémentaire de minéralogie,* Paris, 2. 618, 1832 ; R. Kirwan, *Elements of Mineralogy,* London, 2. 198, 1794 ; R. J. Haüy, *Traité de minéralogie,* Paris, 4. 147, 1801 ; J. F. L. Hausmann, *Handbuch der Mineralogie,* Göttingen, 1. 316, 1873 ; A Breithaupt, *Voll-ständiges Handbuch der Mineralogie,* Dresden, 3. 772, 1847 ; A. E. Nordenskjöld, *Beskrifning öfver de i Finland funna Mineralier,* Helsingfors, 162, 1855 ; 26, 1863 ; W. T. Schaller, *Journ. Washington Acad.,* 1. 177, 1911 ; *Bull. U.S. Geol. Sur.,* 509, 1912.

2 T. Bergman, *De minerarum docimasia humida,* Upsala, 1780 ; F. Gmelin, *Crell's Ann.,* ii, 126, 1786 ; M. H. Klaproth, *Beiträge zur chemischen Kenntniss der Mineralkörper,* Berlin,

2. 245, 1797; J. J. Berzelius, *Afhand. Fis. Kemi Min.*, 4. 164, 1815; C. Bergemann, *Neues Jahrb. Min.*, 395, 1857; J. Königsberger and O. Reichenheim, *ib.*, ii, 31, 1906; A. Breithaupt, *ib.*, 820, 1872; J. W. Mallet, *Journ. Geol. Soc. Dublin*, 4. 272, 1850; *Edin. Phil. Journ.*, (2), 56. 103, 1884; *Phil. Mag.*, (3), 37. 394, 1850; D. Forbes, *ib.*, (4), 30. 141, 1865; P. Kröber, *ib.*, (4), 30. 141, 1865; *Berg. Hütt. Ztg.*, 23. 131, 1864; F. A. Genth, *Proc. Amer. Phil. Soc.*, 24. 29, 1887; F. P. Dunnington, *Chem. News*, 50. 208, 1884; W. G. Brown, *Amer. Chem. Journ.*, 6. 185, 1883; F. Becke, *Tschermak's Mitt.*, (1), 7. 260, 1877; W. Kohlmann, *Zeit. Kryst.*, 24. 363, 1895; T. Liebisch, *Sitzber. Akad. Berlin*, 422, 1911; G. Eberhardt, *ib.*, 851, 1908; 404, 1910; W. R. Dunstan, *Bull. Imp. Inst.*, 3. 41, 1905; T. Petersen, *Pogg. Ann.*, 134. 64, 1868; 136. 499, 1869; A. E. Nordenskjöld, *Beskrifning öfver de i Finland funna Mineralier*, Helsingfors, 162, 1855; 26, 1863; E. S. Simpson, *Rep. Geol. Sur. West Australia*, 52, 1899; R. J. Meyer, *Sitzber. Akad. Berlin*, 414, 1911; E. Charlon, *Ann. Mines* (7), 9. 119, 1876; *Dingler's Journ.*, 224. 653, 1877; J. D. Bruce, *Chem. News*, 50. 209, 1884.

³ C. Doelter, *Tschermak's Mitt.*, (2), 11. 325, 1890; S. Meunier, *Compt. Rend.*, 110. 1083, 1890; J. H. Collins, *Min. Mag.*, 4. 1, 103, 1880; 5. 121, 1883; J. B. Hill and D. A. MacAlister, *Geology of Falmouth*, London, 167, 1906; D. A. MacAlister, *Journ. Geol. Soc.*, 59. 53, 1905; C. Reid and J. B. Scrivener, *Geology of the Country near Newquay*, London, 39, 1906; F. A. Genth, *Proc. Amer. Phil. Soc.*, 24. 23, 1887; L. V. Pirsson, *Amer. Journ. Science*, (3), 42. 407, 1891; E. Wittich, *Zeit. prakt. Geol.*, 18. 121, 1910; A. W. Stelzner, *Die Erzlargerstätten*, Leipzig, 2. 918, 1906; *Zeit. prakt. Chem.*, 4. 377, 1896; R. Beck, *Lehre von den Erzlagerstätten*, Berlin, 220, 1901; *Zeit. prakt. Geol.*, 6. 121, 1898; J. H. L. Vogt, *ib.*, 3. 145, 1895; *Trans. Amer. Inst. Min. Eng.*, 31. 125, 1901; W. Lindgren, *ib.*, 30. 578, 1900; H. Schröder, *Sitzber. Leipzig Naturforsch. Ges.*, 70. 1883; W. von Fircks, *Zeit. deut. geol. Ges.*, 51. 431, 1899; A. Bergeat, *ib.*, 49. 51, 1897; G. Steinmann, *ib.*, 59. 7, 1907; C. W. Kempton, *Trans. Amer. Inst. Min. Eng.*, 25. 997, 1896; W. Ingalls, *ib.*, 25. 147, 1896; E. Halse, *ib.*, 29. 502, 1900; A. H. Bromly, *ib.*, 36. 227, 1906; J. N. Nevius, *Eng. Min. Journ.*, 75. 920, 1903; R. A. F. Penrose, *Journ. Geol.*, 11. 135, 1903; L. K. Ward, *Bull. Geol. Sur. Tasmania*, 6, 1909; F. Gautier, *Actes Soc. Scient. Chili*, 5. 92, 1895; R. Recknagel, *Trans. Geol. Soc. South Africa*, 12. 128, 1910; A. Daubrée, *Études synthétiques de géologie expérimentale*, Paris, 28, 1879; *Compt. Rend.*, 29. 227, 1849; E. de Beaumont and A. Daubrée, *Ann. Mines*, (3), 20. 65, 1841; F. W. Clarke, *The Data of Geochemistry*, Washington, 683, 1916; F. Sandberger, *Untersuchungen über Erzgänge*, Wiesbaden, 2. 167, 1885; F. Beyschlag, P. Krusch, and J. H. L. Vogt, *Die Lagerstätten der nutzbaren Mineralien und Gesteine nach Form, Inhalt, and Entstehung*, Stuttgart, 1. 414, 1910; G. Tschermak, *Sitzber. Akad. Wien*, 49. 377, 1864; G. Bischof, *Lehrbuch der chemischen und physikalischen Geologie*, Bonn, 3. 811, 1866; J. F. W. Charpentier, *Mineralogische Geographie der chursächsischen Lande*, Leipzig, 101, 1778; W. R. Jones, *Geol. Mag.*, (6), 3. 255, 1916; K. Dalmer, *Erlauterungen zur geologischen Specialkarte des Königsreichs Sachsen*, Altenberg-Zinnwald, 119. 108, 1890.

⁴ A. Vogel, *Journ. prakt. Chem.*, (1), 14. 107, 1838; *Kunst-Gewerbe-batt. Bayern*, 85, 1855; M. Wassermann and M. Jäger, *German Pat.. D.R.P.* 34653, 1885; H. Försterling, *ib.*, 173774, 1905; E. Dechert, *ib.*, 180692, 1905; Elektrizitäts-Gesellschaft Gelnhausen, *ib.*, 116758, 1898; C. P. Bary, *Brit. Pat. No.* 9231, 1900; V. Kohlschütter and J. L. Tüscher, *Zeit. Elektrochem.*, 27. 225, 1921; A. G. Goldschmidt and V. Kohlschütter, *Brit. Pat. No.* 189706, 1922; S. J. Lubowsky, *U.S. Pat. Nos.* 1529260, 1529261, 1925; P. T. Austen, *Chem. News*, 47. 286, 1882; *Journ. Amer. Chem. Soc.*, 4. 285, 1882; J. J. Berzelius, *Pogg. Ann.*, 28. 443, 1833; *Schweiger's Journ.*, 6. 284, 1812; *Ann. Chim. Phys.*, (1), 87. 50, 1813; (2), 5. 149, 1817; J. L. Gay Lussac, *ib.*, (2), 1. 40, 1816; H. V. Regnault, *ib.*, (2), 62. 337, 1836; J. L. Proust, *Journ. Phys.*, 51. 173, 1800; 61. 338, 1804; *Ann. Chim. Phys.*, (1), 28. 213, 1798; *Nicholson's Journ.*, 2. 515, 1799; 14. 38, 1806.

⁵ A. Arzruni, *Zeit. Kryst.*, 25. 467, 1896; J. H. L. Vogt, *ib.*, 31. 279, 1899; K. N. Spallart, *Œster. Chem. Ztg.*, 23. 44, 1920; L. Bourgeois, *Bull. Soc. Min.*, 11. 58, 1888; *Compt. Rend.*, 104. 231, 1887; A. Michel-Lévy and L. Bourgeois, *ib.*, 94. 1365, 1882; H. de Sénarmont, *ib.*, 32. 762, 1854; H. St. C. Deville, *ib.*, 53. 161, 1861; H. St. C. Deville and H. Caron, *ib.*, 46. 746, 1858; F. Lenarmont, *ib.*, 32. 762, 1851; A. Ditte, *ib.*, 96. 701, 1883; A. Daubrée, *ib.*, 29. 227, 1849; 39. 153, 1854; 53. 161, 1854; *Ann. Mines*, (4), 16. 129, 1849; *Bull. Soc. Géol.*, 7. 267, 1849; L. Grandeau, *Ann. Chim. Phys.*, (6), 8. 230, 1886; F. A. Abel, *Proc. Roy. Soc.*, 10. 119, 1859; J. Törmer, *Journ. prakt. Chem.*, (1), 37. 380, 1846; G. Wunder, *ib.*, (2), 2. 206, 1870; (2), 4. 340, 1871; A. Knop, *Liebig's Ann.*, 157. 363, 1871; M. H. Klaproth, *Beiträge zur chemischen Kenntniss der Mineralkörper*, Berlin, 2. 249, 1797; G. vom Rath, *Ber. Niederrh. Ges. Bonn*, 283, 1887; W. P. Headden, *Amer. Journ. Science*, (4), 5. 96, 1896; H. Traube, *Neues Jahrb, Min. B.B.*, 10. 474, 1895.

⁶ F. Becke, *Tschermak's Mitt.*, (1), 7. 260, 1877; W. Kohlmann, *Zeit. Kryst.*, 24. 364, 1895; H. Traube, *Neues Jahrb. Min. B.B.*, 10. 474, 1895; J. W. Retgers, *Zeit. phys. Chem.*, 16. 622, 1895; E. Weinschenk, *Zeit. anorg. Chem.*, 12. 384, 1896; A. Dittmann, *Ueber die durch Zin- nerzpneumatolyse aus Granit entstehenden Umwandlungsgesteine*, Heidelberg, 1909.

⁷ F. Becke, *Tschermak's Mitt.*, (1), 7. 244, 1877; A. Pelikan, *ib.*, (2), 16. 27, 1897; G. Cesaro, *Bull. Soc. Min.*, 8. 102, 1885; 9. 220, 1886; H. Haga and F. M. Jäger, *Versl. Akad. Amsterdam*, 24. 400, 443, 1012, 1135, 1403, 1410, 1916; W. Phillips, *Journ. Geol. Soc.*, 2. 336, 1814; J. B. L. Romé de l'Isle, *Cristallographie*, Paris, 3. 416, 1783; R. J. Haüy, *Traité de minéralogie*, Paris, 4. 140, 1801; 4. 166, 1822; F. Mohs, *Grundriss der Mineralogie*, Dresden, 2. 446, 1824; C. F. Naumann, *Lehrbuch der Krystallographie*, Leipzig, 514, 1829; W. H. Miller, *Introduction*

to *Mineralogy*, London, 230, 1852 ; P. Groth, *Die Mineral-Sammlung der Universität Strassburg*, Strassburg, 105, 1878 ; M. Bentivoglio, *Proc. Roy. Soc. New South Wales*, **55**. 65, 1922 ; A. W. Stelzner, *Zeit. Kryst.*, **14**. 398, 1888 ; W. Kohlmann, *ib.*, **24**. 351, 1895 ; V. von Zepharovich, *ib.*, **6**. 319, 1882 ; C. Busz, *ib.*, **15**. 623, 1889 ; L. H. Borgström, *ib.*, **40**. 1, 1905 ; S. Stevanovic, *ib.*, **37**. 255, 1903 ; H. von Foullon, *ib.*, **10**. 429, 1885 ; A. Arzruni, *ib.*, **9**. 73, 1884 ; H. Baumhauer, *ib.*, **47**. 1, 1908 ; F. Hessenberg, *Mineralogische Notizen*, Frankfurt, **1**. 29, 1856 ; **6**. 18, 1864 ; W. Haidinger, *Handbuch der bestimmenden Mineralogie*, Wien, 266, 1845 ; A. Sadebeck, *Zeit. deut. geol. Ges.*, **21**. 251, 1869 ; A. von Groddeck, *ib.*, **36**. 642, 1884 ; **38**. 370, 1886 ; **39**. 78, 1887 ; R. Hörnes, *Neues Jahrb. Min.*, 870, 1846 ; P. F. Kerr, *Econ. Geol.*, **19**. 1, 1924 ; G. vom Rath, *Ber. Niederrh. Ges. Bonn.*, 66, 1877 ; 7, 1878 ; *Pogg. Ann.*, **144**. 596, 1871 ; A. Lacroix, *Minéralogie de la France et ses colonies*, Paris, **3**. 227, 1901 ; *Bull. Soc. Min.*, **24**. 353, 1901 ; R. P. Greg and W. G. Lettsom, *Manual of the Mineralogy of Great Britain and Ireland*, London, 355, 1858 ; R. H. Solly, *Min. Mag.*, **9**. 201, 1891 ; A. Lévy, *Description d'une collection de minéraux formée par H. Heuland*, Londres, **3**. 190, 1837 ; A. Gadolin, *Proc. Russ. Min. Soc.*, 184, 1856 ; P. von Jeremejeff, *ib.*, **23**. 368, 1886 ; **33**. 38, 1895 ; A. E. Nordenskjöld, *Pogg. Ann.*, **101**. 637, 1857 ; G. Rose, *ib.*, **107**. 602, 1859 ; W. T. Schaller, *Bull. U.S. Geol. Sur.*, 262. 1905; W. E. Hidden, *Amer. Journ. Science*, (4), **20**. 410, 1905 ; L. V. Pirsson, *ib.*, (3), **42**. 405, 1891 ; L. Vegard, *Phil. Mag.*, (6), **31**. 83, 1916 ; (6), **32**. 65, 1916 ; (7), **1**. 1151, 1926 ; C. M. Williams, *Proc. Roy. Soc.*, **93**. A, 418, 1917 ; J. A. Hedvall, *Zeit. anorg. Chem.*, **120**. 327, 1922 ; J. A. Phillips, *Journ. Chem. Soc.*, **28**. 684, 1875 ; P. Groth, *Tabellarische Übersicht der Mineralien*, Braunschweig, 43, 1898 ; H. Traube, *Neues Jahrb. Min. B.B.*, **10**. 411, 1895 ; N. Yamada, *Journ. Chem. Soc. Japan*, **44**. 210, 1923 ; M. L. Huggins, *Phys. Rev.*, (2), **21**. 719, 1923 ; W. P. Davey, *ib.*, (2), **23**. 763, 1924 ; E. Artini, *Atti Accad. Lincei*, (5), **29**. ii, 13, 1920 ; G. A. Duma, *Bull. Soc. Stiinte Cluj*, **1**. 321, 1922.

8 A. Daubrée, *Ann. Mines*, (4), **16**. 137, 1849 ; P. Groth, *Chemische Krystallographie*, Leipzig, **1**. 84, 96, 1906 ; A. Michel-Lévy and L. Bourgeois, *Compt. Rend.*, **94**. 1365, 1882 ; H. St. C. Deville, *ib.*, **53**. 161, 1861 ; A. Arzruni, *Zeit. Kryst.*, **25**. 467, 1896.

9 R. Boyle, *Hydrostatic Balance*, London, 1690 ; J. Herapath, *Phil. Mag.*, **64**. 321, 1824 ; D. Forbes, *ib.*, (4), **30**. 139, 1865 ; P. Boullay, *Ann. Chim. Phys.*, (2), **43**. 266, 1830 ; F. E. Neumann, *Pogg. Ann.*, **23**. 1, 1831 ; L. Playfair and J. P. Joule, *Journ. Chem. Soc.*, **1**. 137, 1847 ; J. W. Mallet, *Journ. Geol. Soc. Dublin*, **4**. 272, 1850 ; *Edin. Phil. Journ.*, (2), **56**. 103, 1854 ; *Phil. Mag.*, (3), **37**. 394, 1850 ; P. Kröber, *ib.*, (4), **30**. 141, 1865 ; *Berg. Hütt. Ztg.*, **23**. 131, 1864 ; F. A. Genth, *Proc. Amer. Phil. Soc.*, **24**. 29, 1887 ; F. P. Dunnington, *Chem. News*, 50. 208, 1884 ; W. G. Brown, *Amer. Chem. Journ.*, 6. 185, 1883 ; E. Madelung and R. Fuchs, *Ann. Physik*, (4), **65**. 289, 1921 ; C. Bergemann, *Neues Jahrb. Min.*, 395, 1857 ; W. R. Dunstan, *Bull. Imp. Inst.*, **3**. 41, 1905 ; E. Weinschenk, *Abhand. Bayern Akad.*, **21**. ii, 351, 1901 ; *Zeit. Kryst.*, **38**. 193, 1904 ; S. Stevanovic, *ib.*, **37**. 255, 1903 ; A. E. Nordenskjöld, *Pogg. Ann.*, **122**. 614, 1864 ; H. Rose, *ib.*, **75**. 1, 1848 ; A. Daubrée, *Ann. Mines*, (4), **16**. 137, 1849 ; A. Michel-Lévy and L. Bourgeois, *Compt. Rend.*, **94**. 1365, 1882 ; H. Schröder, *Pogg. Ann.*, **107**. 113, 1859 ; *Dichtigkeitsmessungen*, Heidelberg, 1873 ; A. Reis and L. Zimmermann, *Zeit. phys. Chem.*, **102**. 298, 1922 ; J. J. Berzelius, *Schweigger's Journ.*, **6**. 284, 1812 ; *Ann. Chim. Phys.*, (1), **87**. 50, 1813 ; (2), **5**. 149, 1817 ; F. Emich, *Monatsh.*, **14**. 345, 1893 ; S. Rideal, *Ber.*, **19**. 589, 1886 ; G. A. Dima, *Bul. Soc. Stiinte Cluj*, **1**. 321, 1922 ; W. G. Woolnough, *Proc. Roy. Soc. New South Wales*, **35**. 332, 1901.

10 L. Playfair and J. P. Joule, *Journ. Chem. Soc.*, **1**. 121, 1849 ; H. Kopp, *Liebig's Ann. Suppl.*, **3**. 1, 1864 ; *Liebig's Ann.*, **81**. 1, 1852 ; *Pogg. Ann.*, **86**. 156, 1852 ; F. Pfaff, *ib.*, **107**. 148, 1859 ; F. E. Neumann, *ib.*, **23**. 1, 1831 ; H. V. Regnault, *Ann. Chim. Phys.*, (3), **1**. 129, 1841 ; H. Fizeau, *ib.*, (4), **8**. 335, 1866 ; *Compt. Rend.*, **62**. 1101, 1133, 1866 ; E. Jannettaz, *ib.*, **75**. 1501, 1872 ; *Bull. Soc. Min.*, **15**. 138, 1892 ; H. de Sénarmont, *Compt. Rend.*, **25**. 459, 1847 ; *Ann. Chim. Phys.*, (3), **21**. 457, 1847 ; (3), **22**. 179, 1847 ; G. Spezia, *Atti Accad. Torino*, **22**. 419, 1887 ; J. E. Moose and S. W. Parr, *Journ. Amer. Chem. Soc.*, **46**. 2656, 1924 ; R. Cusack, *Proc. Inst. Acad.*, (3), **4**. 399, 1896 ; A. L. Fletcher, *Scient. Proc. Roy. Dublin Soc.*, (2), **13**. 443, 1913 ; E. D. Clarke, *The Gas Blowpipe*, London, 84, 1819 ; H. Moissan, *Le four électrique*, Paris, 1897 ; London, 30, 1904 ; E. J. Housten, *Chem. News*, **24**. 177, 1871 ; O. Ruff, H. Seiferheld, and J. Suda, *Zeit. anorg. Chem.*, **82**. 373, 1913 ; L. Vignon, *Compt. Rend.*, **108**. 1049, 1889 ; T. Maeda, *Bull. Japan. Inst. Phys. Chem. Research*, **2**. 350, 1923 ; W. Rosenhain, *Journ. Soc. Chem. Ind.*, **25**. 239, 1906 ; W. G. Mixter, *Amer. Journ. Science*, (4), **27**. 231, 1909 ; T. Andrews, *Phil. Mag.*, (3), **32**. 321, 1848 ; W. Fränkel and K. Snipischsky, *Zeit. anorg. Chem.*, **125**. 235, 1922 ; E. Tiede and E. Birnbräuer, *ib.*, **87**. 129, 1914 ; K. B. Lehmann, *München. Med. Wochschr.*, **49**. 340, 1902.

11 T. Liebisch, *Sitzber. Akad. Berlin.* 416, 1911 ; H. Rosenbusch, *Mikroskopische Physiographie der Mineralien und Gesteine*, Stuttgart, **1**. 309, 1885 ; 1. b, 55, 1905 ; A. Arzruni, *Zeit. Kryst.*, **25**. 470, 1896 ; A. Ehringhaus and H. Rose, *ib.*, **58**. 472, 1923 ; A. Madelung, *ib.*, **7**. 75, 1883 ; H. Traube, *Neues Jahrb. Min. B.B.*, **10**. 475, 1895 ; H. von Foullon, *Verh. Geol. Reichsanst. Wien*, 144, 1884 ; A. Pelikan, *Tschermak's Mitt.*, (2), **16**. 28, 1897 ; V. von Agafonoff, *Proc. Russ. Min. Soc.*, **39**. 497, 1902 ; *Neues Jahrb. Min.*, ii, 342, 1904 ; A. Lacroix, *Minéralogie de la France et ses colonies*, Paris, **3**. 219, 1901 ; E. Weinschenk, *Zeit. anorg. Chem.*, **12**. 384, 1896 ; E. Richat, *Compt. Rend.*, **138**. 1396, 1904 ; G. A. Dima, *Bul. Soc. Stiinte Cluj*, **1**. 321, 1922 ; J. Ewles, *Phil. Mag.*, (6), **45**. 957, 1923 ; A. de Gramont, *Bull. Soc. Min.*, **78**. 233, 1895 ; W. W. Coblentz, *Investigations of Infra-red Spectra*, Washington, **3**. 32, 70, 1906 ; *Bull. Bur*

Standards, **5.** 176, 1908; *Journ. Franklin Inst.*, **174.** 549, 1912; J. O. Perrine, *Phys. Rev.*, (2), **22.** 54, 1923; W. Crookes, *Chem. News*, **43.** 237, 1881.

[12] F. von Kobell, *Ber. München. Acad.*, 89, 1850; E. T. Wherry, *Amer. Min.*, **10.** 28, 1925; B. Saklatwalla, *Zeit. Elektrochem.*, **13.** 589, 1907; F. Beijerinck, *Neues Jahrb. Min. B. B.*, **11.** 461, 1897; J. Königsberger and O. Reichenheim, *Neues Jahrb. Min.*, i, 5, 1906; O. Reichenheim, *Ueber die Elektrizitätsleitung einiger natüralichkristallisierten Oxyde und Sulfide und des Graphits*, Freiburg i. B., 25, 1906; G. Cesaro, *Bull. Acad. Belg.*, 115, 1904; V. von Lang, *Sitzber. Akad. Wien*, **108.** 557, 1901; C. Doelter, *ib.*, **119.** 70, 1910; *Zeit. anorg. Chem.*, **67.** 392, 1910; G. Tammann and H. Bredmeier, *ib.*, **144.** 64, 1925; T. Liebisch, *Sitzber. Akad. Berlin*, 414, 1911; S. Meyer, *Wied. Ann.*, **69.** 236, 1899; W. Schmidt, *Ann. Physik*, (4), **9.** 934, 1902; E. Friederich, *Zeit. Physik*, **31.** 813, 1925; K. Fischbeck, *Zeit. anorg. Chem.*, **148.** 97, 1925.

[13] W. A. Tilden, *Proc. Roy. Soc.*, **60.** 453, 1896; A. Kenngott, *Neues Jahrb. Min.*, 437, 1867; L. Kahlenberg and W. J. Trautman, *Trans. Amer. Electrochem. Soc.*, **39.** 377, 1921; C. M. Despretz, *Ann. Chim. Phys.*, (2), **43.** 222, 1830; P. G. F. Leplay and A. Laurent, *ib.*, (2), **65.** 404, 1837; W. O. Snelling, *U.S. Pat. No.* 917176, 1909; *Met. Chem. Engg*, **8.** 347, 1910; E. D. Clarke, *The Gas Blowpipe*, London, 84, 1819; C. H. Pfaff, *Handbuch der analytischen Chemie*, Altona, **2.** 336, 1822; W. Müller, *Pogg. Ann.*, **136.** 51, 1869; R. Weber, *ib.*, **112.** 619, 1861; K. Stammer, *ib.*, **82.** 135, 1851; *Liebig's Ann.*, **80.** 243, 1851; H. Rose, *ib.*, **91.** 104, 1853; **112.** 163, 1861; A. E. Arnold, *Chem. News*, **36.** 238, 1877; **40.** 25, 1879; J. S. C. Wells, *ib.*, **64.** 294, 1891; I. L. Bell, *ib.*, **23.** 258, 1871; C. W. Watts and C. A. Bell, *Journ. Chem. Soc.*, **33.** 442, 1878; W. Hampe, *Chem. Ztg.*, **11.** 19, 1887; A. Mailhe, *ib.*, **33.** 30, 1909; H. Haas, *Ueber die quantitative Trennung des Zinns und Titans*, Erlangen, 1890; C. Matignon and F. Bourion, *Compt. Rend.*, **138.** 761, 1904; H. Moissan, *ib.*, **125.** 839, 1898; F. Schlagdenhauffen and C. Pagel, *ib.*, **128.** 309, 1899; E. Stelling, *Journ. Ind. Eng. Chem.*, **16.** 346, 1924; C. T. Barfoed, *Danske Vid. Selskr. Skr.*, (5), **7.** 236, 1866; *Journ. prakt. Chem.*, (1), **101.** 369, 1867; A. Michaelis, *ib.*, (2), **4.** 455, 1871; R. E. Slade and G. I. Higson, *B.A. Rep.*, 450, 1913; W. Fränkel and K. Snipischsky, *Zeit. anorg. Chem.*, **125.** 235, 1922; W. Fränkel, *Festschrift zur Jahrhundertfeier des physikalischen Vereins*, Frankfurt a. M., 136, 1924; G. Rauter, *Liebig's Ann.*, **270.** 249, 1892; H. Goldschmidt, *ib.*, **301.** 21, 1898; J. von Liebig, *ib.*, **38.** 31, 1841; R. R. Danielson and M. K. Frehafer, *Journ. Amer. Cer. Soc.*, **6.** 634, 1923; C. H. Burgess and A. Holt, *Proc. Chem. Soc.*, **19.** 221, 1903; *Trans. Cer. Soc.*, **5.** 163, 1906; A. Lomax, *ib.*, **11.** 118, 1912; H. Mennicke, *Zeit. öffentl. Chem.*, **6.** 190, 204, 1900; P. Sabatier and J. B. Senderens, *Compt. Rend.*, **120.** 619, 1895; F. de Lalande and M. Prud'homme, *Bull. Soc. Chim.*, (2), **17.** 290, 1872; F. O. Döltz and C. A. Graumann, *Met.*, **4.** 421, 1907; F. von Kügelgen, *Zeit. Elektrochem.*, **7.** 566, 1901; L. Wöhler and O. Balz, *ib.*, **27.** 406, 1921; D. B. Dott, *Pharm. Journ.*, (4), **27.** 585, 1908; C. Renz, *Ber.*, **39.** 249, 1906; W. Ipatieff, *ib.*, **35.** 1051, 1902; C. Winkler, *ib.*, **24.** 892, 1891; S. Medsforth, *Journ. Chem. Soc.*, **123.** 1452, 1923; W. Gibbs, *Amer. Journ. Science*, (2), **37.** 355, 1864; J. Milbauer, *Zeit. anorg. Chem.*, **42.** 337, 1904; T. Maeda, *Bull. Japan. Inst. Phys. Chem. Research*, **2.** 350, 1923; H. D. Rankin, *U.S. Pat. No.* 1471751, 1923; D. L. Hammick, *Journ. Chem. Soc.*, **111.** 379, 1917; N. P. Peskoff, *Bull. Inst. Polyt. Ivanovo-Voznesensk*, **7.** 119, 1923; L. Hackspill and R. Grandadam, *Compt. Rend.*, **180.** 930, 1925; K. B. Lehmann, *Arch. Hyg.*, **63.** 67, 1907; R. E. Slade and G. I. Higson, *B.A. Rep.*, 450, 1913; F. von Kügelgen, *Chem. Ztg.*, **24.** 1060, 1900; *Zeit. Elektrochem.*, **7.** 541, 557, 573, 1901; **8.** 781, 1902.

§ 13. The Stannic Hydroxides ; and the Stannic and Perstannic Acids

In 1716, J. Kunckel studied the action of nitric acid on tin and showed that it can be dissolved only when a small proportion is added to the acid, and that heat must be avoided because the white tin calx is thrown down when the acid is hot. Robert Boyle [1] made several references to the action of nitric acid upon tin. He said that the acid eats up or destroys more tin than it dissolves ; and in his *Experiments and Observations upon Colours* (London, 1670), he said :

Tin, corroded by aqua fortis, till the menstruum will work no farther on it, becomes exceedingly white ; and easily, of itself, acquires the consistence not of a metalline calx, but of a coagulated matter, so like either to curdled milk, or curdled white of eggs, that a person unacquainted with such soln. might easily be mistaken in it.

These statements mean that with dil. nitric acid, tin forms stannous or stannic nitrate according to the conc. of the acid ; and that the salts readily decompose with the separation of gelatinous stannic acid. With conc. nitric acid, much heat is evolved, and a white insoluble powder, the so-called metastannic acid, is formed. In 1811, J. J. Berzelius showed that tin hydroxide prepared by the action of nitric acid on tin possesses properties which are not found in the hydroxide precipitated from tin chloride by an alkali like ammonia. At that time, it was assumed that the two hydrates represented different stages of oxidation, but J. Davy, and J. L. Gay Lussac, and, later, J. J. Berzelius showed that this was not the case. Both hydroxides contain the same proportion of oxygen, but possess different properties; and J. J. Berzelius thus regarded them as isomeric modifications. The hydroxide obtained from stannic chloride contains $SnO_2.nH_2O$, which saturates three times as much base as the hydroxide obtained by the action of nitric acid on tin. He likened the latter to metaphosphoric acid, and called it *oxidum stannicum*, and the former to ordinary phosphoric acid, and called it *oxidum parastannicum ;* E. Frémy designated the latter *acide metastannique*, and the former *acide stannique*. J. J. Berzelius also called the acid derived from the action of nitric acid on tin, β-stannic acid, and that obtained by precipitation from a soln. of stannic chloride, α-stannic acid. Both acids dissolve in aq. soln. of alkali hydroxides or carbonates, and when reprecipitated by acids they retain the properties they had before they were dissolved in the alkali-lye. Either modification can be transformed into the other. J. J. Berzelius contrasted the more salient differences :

α-STANNIC ACID	β-STANNIC ACID
This acid is the more basic one and furnishes salts which are readily soluble in water without decomposition. The moist acid is easily soluble in nitric acid ; it is also soluble in dil. sulphuric acid, and the soln. does not gelatinize when boiled. It dissolves easily in hydrochloric acid, and when boiled the soln. remains clear.	This acid is the less basic one, and furnishes salts which are sparingly soluble in water, and are. hydrolyzed into an insoluble basic salt and acid The acid is insoluble in nitric acid ; and it is insoluble even in conc. sulphuric acid. It unites with hydrochloric acid, forming a substance insoluble in an excess of the acid, and soluble in water. The aq. soln. gelatinizes when boiled.

The cause of these differences has not been clearly established. Investigations are difficult because the characteristic properties are not very pronounced, and they readily change, one into the other, so that some contradictory reports are based on observations with mixtures of the two isomers, and not with homogeneous substances. Two types of hypotheses have been devised to explain the differences ; one set assumes that one of the alleged stannic acids is a colloidal form of the other ; and the other set assumes that, as J. J. Berzelius supposed, the one acid is an isomeric form of the other ; and, as E. Frémy assumed, that one acid is a polymeric form of the other.

1. *Polymerization or condensation hypotheses.*—It is here assumed that two distinct and definite substances are capable of existence, and that the one is a polymerized form of the other. E. Frémy first regarded the β-acid as a polymerized form of the α-acid. Using the prefixes with the same meaning as employed in dealing with the carbonic, silicic, tannic, and zirconic acids, the α-acid was assumed to be metastannic acid, H_2SnO_3, and the β-acid, a polymerized form. E. Frémy at first represented the β-acid by the formula $H_2Sn_3O_7.2H_2O$, or $H_6Sn_3O_9$, *i.e.* $(H_2SnO_3)_3$, but later adopted the formula $H_2Sn_5O_{11}.4H_2O$, or $H_{10}Sn_5O_{15}$, *i.e.* $(H_2SnO_3)_5$. This view was supported by H. Rose, H. Schiff, and C. T. Barfoed, but H. Rose gave for the formula $H_{14}Sn_7O_{21}$; H. Schiff, $H_{10}Sn_6O_{17}$; and C. T. Barfoed, $H_{18}Sn_9O_{27}$. F. Musculus concluded that there is a whole series of polymerized forms between H_2SnO_3 and E. Frémy's $(H_2SnO_3)_5$, but R. Weber said that the constancy of the composition of the alkali salts lends no support to this hypothesis. J. M. Ordway's products with $Na_2O : SnO_2=1 : 3$, 1 : 5, 1 : 7, etc., were probably so-called adsorption compounds. From his observations on the thermal value of the reaction between alkali-lye and various modifications of stannic acid, L. Vignon inferred that a whole series of stannic acids exists, the extremes being the acid completely soluble in water and ignited stannic oxide. The composition of metastannic acid indicates that condensation does not take place by elimination of water, but is the result of mol. rearrangement which

produces a gradual diminution of the activity of the acid function. The polymerization may be regarded as due to the energetic acid function of the simple acid, which unites with a number of its own mols. which play the part of a base. J. Biron also assumed that by condensation an uninterrupted series between α- and β-acids could be obtained. R. Lorenz compared the rates at which the α- and β-stannic acids are dehydrated under similar conditions, and inferred that their composition is identical, and that both exist in all stages of hydration between H_4SnO_4 and H_3SnO_3. The compounds retain their characteristic properties after repeated precipitation from salts or soln., and the salts are different. R. C. Engel suggested that the so-called intermediate acids are not homogeneous substances, but mixtures, α-stannic acid or orthostannic acid, β-stannic acid or metastannic acid, and a third acid which he called *parastannic acid*. He represented the composition of these acids, their potassium salts, and their chlorides,

TABLE VI.—THE COMPOSITION OF R. C. ENGEL'S STANNIC ACIDS.

Stannic acids.	Dried in air.	Dried at 100°.	Potassium salts.	Chlorides.
Ortho-	$H_2SnO_3.H_2O$	H_2SnO_3	$K_2SnO_3Aq.$	$SnCl_4Aq.$
Meta-	$H_2Sn_5O_{11}.9H_2O$	$H_2Sn_5O_{11}.4H_2O$	$K_2Sn_5O_{11}.4H_2O$	$Sn_5O_9Cl_2.4H_2O$
Para-	$H_2Sn_5O_{11}.7H_2O$	$H_2Sn_5O_{11}.2H_2O$	$K_2Sn_5O_{11}.2H_2O$	$Sn_5O_9Cl_2.2H_2O$

by Table VI. The parastannic acid of R. C. Engel was made by boiling the ordinary β-acid, or metastannic acid with water. A. Kleinschmidt, however, showed that this product is nothing but ordinary β-stannic acid ; and his examination of the stannic acids led him to conclude that both α- and β-stannic acids are colloidal substances capable of reversible transformation. The change from the α- to the β-acids occurs more readily than the reverse action. The behaviour of these compounds towards acids is in harmony with the assumption that α-stannic acid has the composition H_2SnO_3, that is, stannyl hydroxide, $O{=}Sn{=}(OH)_2$, and β-stannic acid, $(H_2SnO_3)_5$, or

$$\begin{matrix} & & (OH)_2 & & \\ & & O.Sn.O & & \\ (OH)_2{=}Sn & & & & Sn{=}(OH)_2 \\ & O & & O & \\ (OH)_2{=}Sn.O.O.Sn{=}(OH)_2 & & \end{matrix}$$

β-stannic acid.

in which only two of the hydroxyl groups are replaced by Cl-, NO_3-, SO_4-, or (ONa)-radicles. This makes the formula $Sn_5O_5(OH)_8(OH)_2$. With the previously used nomenclature, α-stannic acid is **metastannic acid**, H_2SnO_3, or stannyl hydroxide, $SnO(OH)_2$; and β-stannic acid is **pentametastannic acid**, $(H_2SnO_3)_5$, or $H_{10}Sn_5O_{15}$, or **pentastannyl decahydroxide**, $(SnO)_5(OH)_{10}$. On the other hand, N. Yamada found no difference in the X-radiograms of the stannic acids prepared by different processes, and hence inferred that the difference is not due to chemical differences, but rather to the way the water adheres to the surface of the oxide granules. P. Pascal's observations on the magnetic susceptibility of the stannic acids indicate that they are not definite compounds, but mixtures of stannic oxide and water ; while R. Willstätter, H. Kraut, and W. Fremery's experiments on the dehydration indicates that definite hydrates are formed. Thus, stannic hydroxide gels prepared by the action of ammonia and ammonium chloride on stannic chloride under conditions which ensure a low hydroxyl-ion conc. and great rapidity of experiment, and subsequently dried by acetone at $-35°$ to $-10°$, have the composition, $Sn(OH)_4.H_2O$, whereas after similar treatment at the atmospheric temp. they have the composition of the ortho compound, $Sn(OH)_4$. Monostannic acid becomes transformed in an aq. medium into a more feebly basic acid which appears to be the first member of a series of α-stannic acids (previously designated α'-acids). When dried by the acetone process at 0°–10°, the product has approximately the composition of an orthodistannic acid, $(OH)_3Sn.O.Sn(OH)_3$, whereas after treatment at 30°–56° or prolonged heating with acetone, it has exactly the composition of an *orthotetrastannic acid*, $(OH)_3Sn.O.Sn(OH)_2.O.Sn(OH)_2.O.Sn(OH)_3$. The union of several mols. of stannic hydroxide with loss of water appears to yield a series of polyorthostannic acids with diminishing basic properties.

2. *Colloidal hypotheses.*—G. C. Wittstein assumed that the α-acid is amorphous, and the β-acid is crystalline; but this view is untenable, for, as just indicated, both stannic acids are colloidal. J. M. van Bemmelen investigated the dehydration and rehydration of the stannic acid gels, and failed to obtain any evidence of the existence of definite hydrates of stannic oxide, and he considered both the stannic acids to be colloids, and the β-stannates were considered to be " adsorption compounds." According to W. Mecklenburgh, *the difference in the behaviour of the different stannic acids is due to differences in the sizes of the particles ;* the modifications with the most highly developed β-characteristics were supposed to have the largest primary particles. R. Zsigmondy, and H. B. Weiser accepted this hypothesis, and R. R. Franz said that the primary particles are of amicronic dimensions, and that in sol-systems there is a gradual transition from the mol. to the primary particles and onwards, by complex formation, to secondary particles. W. Pauli also expressed the view that many sols of metallic compounds contain complex mols. due to the union of, for example, some of the simple mols. of the original substance with mols. formed by the hydrolysis of the original compound. The particular properties of a given stannic acid are thus assumed to be dependent on the grain-size, and that the grain-size is determined by the temp. of preparation, etc. A. Tian assumed that the coalescence of particles reducing the degree of dispersion is due to the operation of capillary forces ; and G. E. Collins and J. K. Wood inferred that the difference in the character of α- and β-stannic acids depends on the extent to which a process of condensation between mols. of stannic hydroxide has taken place, the cause of this condensation being the amphoteric nature of the hydroxide. The first step in this process of condensation was considered to be the formation of α-stannic acid, H_2SnO_3, from a single mol. of stannic hydroxide ; the gradual conversion of the α-acid into the β-modification, which takes place slowly at the ordinary temp. and more rapidly on boiling, is due to the continuation of the process of condensation, thus leading, by the loss of water from several mols., to the production of mols. of gradually increasing complexity and of increasing β-character ; thus, $SnO(OH)_2$ with one mol. ; and $(OH)_3Sn.O.Sn(OH)_3$ with two mols. ; and so on, even to A. Kleinschmidt's formula. This form of the colloidal hypothesis reinstates the polymerization or condensation hypotheses.

The preparation of α-stannic acid.—J. J. Berzelius made α-stannic acid by treating a soln. of stannic chloride with alkali hydroxide, and washing the precipitate ; if potassium carbonate is used as precipitant, a sparingly soluble stannate is formed. R. Lorenz used stannic bromide in place of the chloride. A. Ditte used alkali hydrocarbonate, and E. Frémy, and H. Schiff used calcium or barium carbonate as precipitant. E. Frémy treated alkali stannate with acid; P. T. Austen passed carbon dioxide into the soln., or boiled it with a hydrocarbonate. H. Rose boiled a dil. aq. soln. of stannic chloride, but R. Engel found the precipitate so obtained is a mixture of α- and β-stannic acids. G. Neumann treated a soln. of stannic chloride and an excess of ammonium sulphate with a little hydrogen sulphide ; alkali sulphates, without hydrogen sulphide, precipitate α-stannic acid from the soln., but alkali chlorides or nitrates do not do so. R. Lorenz electrolyzed a soln. of alkali chloride, nitrate, or sulphate, using a platinum cathode, and a tin anode.

J. Löwenthal found that β-stannic acid is transformed into the α-acid by treatment with conc. hydrochloric acid ; and, added C. T. Barfoed, the transformation is proportional to the temp., the time, and the proportion of hydrochloric acid employed. The hydrate dried above 100° is less easily transformed than that dried at a lower temp. H. Allen found that conc. sulphuric acid transforms β-stannic acid to stannic sulphate which, when treated with cold water, precipitates the α-acid. L. Vignon boiled for 4 hrs. a mol of the β-acid with 20 mols of potassium chloride and as much water, and obtained the α-acid. A. Moberg, and H. Rose melted the β-acid with potassium hydroxide, or boiled an alkaline soln. of the alkali stannate, and E. Frémy found that potassium β-stannate in contact with a conc. soln. of potassium hydroxide gives a precipitate of the α-acid in a few days at ordinary temp. A soln. of colloidal α-stannic acid is produced by the method used for silicic acid. T. Graham dialyzed a soln. of stannic chloride mixed with alkali-lye, or a soln. of potassium stannate mixed with hydrochloric acid.

In both cases a gelatinous mass forms on the dialyzer, but as the salts diffuse away, the jelly is again peptized by the small proportion of free alkali remaining. The alkali itself may be removed by continued diffusion, a drop or two of the tincture of iodine facilitating the separation. The liquid α-stannic acid is converted, on heating, into liquid β-stannic acid. Both liquid acids are remarkable for the facility with which they are peptized by a minute addition of hydrochloric acid, as well as by salts.

T. Graham also dialyzed a soln. of freshly precipitated gelatinous stannic acid in one of stannic chloride and obtained stannic hydroxide as a gelatinous mass. Whatever the conc. of the soln. submitted to dialysis, the product was always the same, viz., α-stannic acid. E. A. Schneider poured a dil. soln. of stannic chloride into dil. aq. ammonia until the precipitate dissolved ; more water was added, and the soln. dialyzed. The product is transformed by dil. acids, other than nitric acid, into a hydrogel ; conc. sulphuric or hydrochloric acid forms the corresponding salt. The hydrosol and stannous chloride produce a yellow liquid, probably colloidal tin sesquioxide : $SnO_2 + SnCl_2 + H_2O = 2HCl + Sn_2O_3$. J. M. van Bemmelen made colloidal stannic acid by dialyzing hydrochloric acid or alkaline soln. of stannic acid ; by the action of calcium carbonate on an aq. soln. of the chloride ; by the action of carbon dioxide or air on a soln. of an alkali stannate. W. Biltz dialyzed the filtered soln., obtained by mixing eq. proportions of stannic chloride and lead nitrate in dil. aq. soln. The product was contaminated with lead nitrate. R. Zsigmondy made stannic acid by dissolving 3 grms. of tin in hydrochloric acid, and the soln. of stannous chloride diluted with 4 litres of water ; air was passed through the liquid for 5 days, and the gelatinous precipitate washed by decantation. The product is not soluble in conc. acids, but it is soluble in dil. hydrochloric, sulphuric, or nitric acid ; dil. potash-lye dissolves the colloid more readily than does soda-lye, and the α-stannic acid passes into the β-form. W. A. Patrick made hydrogels by the action of acids on a soln. of stannic chloride. According to J. Bellucci and N. Parravano, when a soln. of potassium stannate, cooled with ice, is treated with a small proportion of hydrochloric acid, the precipitate, after being washed repeatedly with cold water, has the same composition—$H_2SnO_3.H_2O$, or $Sn(OH)_4$, **stannic hydroxide,** or **orthostannic acid**—after 6 days' drying in air as it has after 30 days' similar drying.

The properties of α-stannic acid.—As J. J. Berzelius, E. Frémy, and others have shown, α-stannic acid is a white, voluminous, amorphous or colloidal precipitate which when dried looks like bits of glass. The moist product reddens blue litmus, and is dissolved or rather peptized by water. J. Thomsen gave for the heat of formation $(Sn,O_2,2H_2O) = 133\cdot49$ Cals., and for the heat of neutralization, with hydrochloric acid, $(H_4SnO_4,4HCl) = 3\cdot11$ Cals. ; and with sodium hydroxide, $(H_4SnO_4,4NaOH) = 9\cdot56$ Cals. L. Vignon found for $(H_2SnO_3,4KOH)$ numbers varying from $21\cdot3$ to $32\cdot7$ Cals. dependent on the mode of preparation. According to R. C. Engel, there is a tendency for the α-acid on drying to pass into the β-acid so that the product is a mixture of both acids. When dried rapidly in air, R. Engel's α-acid had $32\cdot7$ per cent. of water ; and the air-dried α-acid was found by E. Frémy to contain $22\cdot5$ per cent. of water, and by R. Weber, $22\cdot73$ per cent. When dried over conc. sulphuric acid, E. Frémy found the α-acid contained $11\cdot2$ per cent.

of water; R. Weber, 12·45 per cent.; and R. Lorenz, 12·6 per cent. T. Graham, R. C. Engel, and L. Schaffner found that when dried at 100°, the composition corresponded with H_2SnO_3. R. Lorenz found that when dried at 130°, 7·5–7·6 per cent. of water was present; and when dried at 140°, 7·4 per cent. After drying at 170°, H. Rose said that it no longer loses weight when heated, but J. B. A. Dumas said that a red heat is necessary to drive off all the water. T. Carnelley and J. Walker observed no signs of the formation of a definite hydrate in their observations on the drying of α-stannic acid at different temp. According to C. T. Barfoed, the hydrate dried at 100° gradually absorbs moisture from the air, and, according to J. M. van Bemmelen, a mol of stannic acid in a moist atm. absorbs 2·7–3·0 mols of water, and when dried over sulphuric acid, 2–2·3 mols are lost; at 100°, 1·7–1·8 mols; and at a red heat, 0·8 mol. He also found that a sample with $1·07H_2O$ after drying many days in dry air at ordinary temp., contained:

95° (½ hr.)	105° (1¼ hrs.)	110° (4 hrs.)	120° (3 hrs.)	145° (3 hrs.)	165° (4 hrs.)
$0·99H_2O$	$0·88H_2O$	$0·74H_2O$	$0·72H_2O$	$0·60H_2O$	$0·56H_2O$

S. Glixelli studied the electro-osmosis of stannic acid. Freshly precipitated α-stannic acid readily dissolves in mineral acids. According to J. Bellucci and N. Parravano, the soln. in nitric acid gradually gelatinizes on standing, and becomes clear again when ammonium nitrate is added. The soln. in nitric acid coagulates at 50°; the soln. in sulphuric acid is stable; and the soln. in hydrochloric acid is not precipitated by an excess of hydrogen chloride. H. Kühl found that the stannic acid obtained by treating a hot soln. of sodium stannate with sulphuric acid, when freshly prepared, is completely soluble in 5 per cent. hydrochloric acid and conc. sulphuric acid; the soln. in the latter deposits prismatic crystals when heated. The stannic acid, kept as a paste for ten days, is soluble in 5 per cent. hydrochloric acid only on boiling, and is only partly soluble in conc. sulphuric acid; the insoluble gelatinous portion is not completely soluble in conc. hydrochloric acid, neither is the gelatinous stannic acid precipitated on heating the sulphuric acid soln. The stannic acid, obtained by carefully adding dil. sulphuric acid to a cold soln. of sodium stannate when freshly prepared, is readily soluble in 2 per cent. hydrochloric acid and conc. sulphuric acid; the soln. in sulphuric acid gives no deposit when heated. The acid loses its solubility in sulphuric acid, but not in hydrochloric acid, when kept for some time in a pasty condition. The stannic acid, obtained from a freshly prepared soln. of sodium stannate, is readily soluble in 2 per cent. hydrochloric acid and 2 per cent. potassium hydroxide, whereas that obtained from the same soln. after being kept for 12 days is not soluble in soln. containing less than 6 per cent. of potassium hydroxide and 5 per cent. of hydrogen chloride. F. Hein and H. Meininger observed that stannous hydroxide is a feeble base, but when all the hydroxyl radicles except one are replaced by ethyl or phenyl radicles, strong bases are formed. J. Bellucci and N. Parravano showed the α-acid is soluble in or peptized by soln. of alkali hydroxides, and the soln. does not give a precipitate when treated with an excess of the alkali-lye. The α-acid is also dissolved by soln. of alkali carbonates, and ammonia. The soln. in alkali-lye furnish salts in which the α-characteristics persist, and in the salts α-stannic acid behaves as if it were dibasic $K_2SnO_3.3H_2O$. The water is expelled only at a high temp., and the salts are isomorphous with *potassium hexahydroxyplatinate*, and hence it was suggested that the α-stannates are salts of an unknown dibasic *hydrohexahydroxystannic acid*, $H_2[Sn(OH)_6]$. W. Herz found that stannic hydroxide, $Sn(OH)_4$, diffuses in alkaline soln. like stannous hydroxide, $Sn(OH)_2$. According to A. Moberg, and H. Rose, the α-stannates are obtained by heating the β-stannates with an excess of alkali-lye. W. Biltz and F. Zimmermann observed no coloration when the freshly precipitated hydroxide is treated with $0·1N$-silver nitrate; nor did J. Löwenthal observe any such coloration with α-stannic acid and stannous chloride as occurs with β-stannic acid. Colour reactions with phenols were indicated by L. Vignon, and L. Levy. A. M. Morley and J. K. Wood found that like titanic acid, α-stannic acid precipitated from alkaline soln. absorbs basic dyes, and α-stannic acid precipitated from slightly acid soln. adsorbs acid dyes. G. E. Collins and J. K. Wood measured the isotherms of the adsorption by different forms of stannic acid, and found that more tin than chlorine is taken up by the colloidal acid. The adsorptive power does not depend wholly on size of grain, and it is less in the presence of hydrochloric acid. H. B. Weiser studied the precipitation of sols of α-stannic acid by electrolytes; and R. Schwarz and H. Stock, the coagulation of silver bromide emulsion by α-stannic acid. H. Zocher showed that the low crystallization velocity of stannic oxide, resulting from its slight solubility, facilitates its assumption of the colloidal state. The "ageing" of the colloid is accelerated or retarded by various influences, particularly by accompanying salts in soln. Coagulation, that is, the coalescence of the bounding surfaces of the colloidal particles in soln., is retarded by the electrostatic charge on the particles. A. Stiegler studied the gradual change in the electrical conductivity of colloidal stannic acid after peptization with an alkali, and he attributed the increase to the gradual break-down of stannyl stannate complexes, especially in dil. soln.

P. Pfeiffer and R. Lehnardt, and J. G. F. Druce have prepared *methyl stannonic acid*, $CH_3.SnO.OH$; *potassium methyl stannonate*, $CH_3.SnO.OK$; and *dimethyl stannone*, $(CH_3)_2SnO$. H. Lambourne represents the constitution of methyl stannonic acid as

$$\begin{matrix} CH_3 \\ HO \end{matrix} > Sn < \begin{matrix} O.Sn(CH_3)(OH) \\ O.Sn(CH_3)(OH) \end{matrix} > O$$

J. G. F. Druce also made *ethyl stannonic acid*, $C_2H_5.SnO.OH$; *ethyl stannone*, $(C_2H_5)_2SnO$; *isopropyl stannonic acid*, $C_3H_7.SnO.OH$; *diisopropyl stannone*, $(C_3H_7)_2SnO$; and normal *propyl stannonic acid*, $C_3H_7.SnO.OH$; their potassium salts ; and *dipropyl stannone*, $(C_3H_7)_2SnO$. He also made *sodium isopropyl stannonate*, as well as basic salts of calcium, barium, and strontium ; and basic ethyl stannonates of silver, zinc, mercury, cobalt, nickel, and manganese.

The preparation of β-stannic acid.—The observations of C. T. Barfoed, E. Frémy, T. Graham, and J. Löwenthal show that α-stannic acid has a strong tendency to pass into the β-acid. This transformation sets in during the drying of the α-acid at ordinary temp., and also when it stands under water for some time. The change is faster when the liquid is warmed. H. Rose obtained the β-acid by boiling a soln. of stannic chloride with nitric acid until the hydrochloric acid is almost all expelled ; and by allowing a soln. of stannic chloride to stand for a couple of years ; by boiling a soln. of stannic chloride for a long time with an excess of conc. hydrochloric acid ; and by allowing a soln. of stannous chloride in potassium hydroxide to stand exposed to the air—the β-stannic acid is precipitated gradually as the alkali hydroxide passes into carbonate. According to J. Löwenthal, and R. Lorenz, dil. soln. of stannic chloride form β-stannic acid more rapidly than conc. soln. ; the transformation is hastened by potassium ferrocyanide, and retarded by tartaric acid. J. J. Berzelius prepared β-stannic acid by completely oxidizing tin with moderately conc. nitric acid, and washing the white powder with water until the wash-liquor no longer reddens blue litmus. D. B. Dott obtained the acid in a similar manner. According to R. Engel, the nature of the product of the action of nitric acid on tin depends on the conditions under which it is formed. If nitric acid of sp. gr. 1·42 is diluted with different proportions of water, kept at 0°, and a stick of tin immersed in 200 c.c. of the liquid, the products are (*a*) with 1 vol. of nitric acid and 2 vols. or more of water, stannous nitrate ; (*b*) with equal vols. of water and acid, stannic nitrate, the liquid finally becoming syrupy ; and (*c*) with undiluted acid, stannic nitrate, which, however, is precipitated, because it is insoluble in moderately conc. nitric acid. Stannic nitrate is, however, readily decomposed by water or by a rise of temp., the first product being stannic acid mixed with a small proportion of β-stannic acid, the proportion of the latter increasing, however, if the substance remains in contact with water, or if it is dried. The limiting compound in the cold is metastannyl stannate. When metastannyl stannate is boiled with water, the conversion into β-stannic acid proceeds further, and parastannic acid is also formed in gradually increasing quantity. Pure meta-stannic acid yields parastannic acid when boiled with water; the latter may perhaps be regarded as an internal anhydride of the former. β-stannic acid is not formed by the direct action of nitric acid on tin; the substance described by J. J. Berzelius was in reality parastannic acid. G. Jörgensen recommended wash-ing the precipitate with conc. hydrochloric acid and showed that a large proportion of water is required to wash the product free from nitric acid. H. Rose showed that if the tin is alloyed with more feebly basic metals—e.g. bismuth—the β-stannic acid which is formed will be contaminated with considerable proportions of the oxides of these metals. If iron be present, the precipitated β-stannic acid contains iron and some iron and tin remain in soln. C. Lepéz and L. Storch, and F. H. van Leent studied the action of nitric acid on stanniferous alloys with the object of separating the tin as insoluble β-stannic acid for analytical purposes. Chromium behaves like iron; only a trace of tin passes into soln. if cerium is present, and none in the presence of aluminium, cobalt, nickel, copper, and uranium. J. Hood and A. G. Salmon obtained β-stannic acid by heating tin with a mixture of sulphuric acid and sodium nitrate. E. Frémy, and H. Rose prepared β-stannic acid by treating potassium β-stannate with acid; and R. Engel hydrolyzed sodium β-stannate, or metastannyl chloride by digestion in water at 60°. T. Graham obtained colloidal β-stannic acid by hydrolysis as in the case of the α-acid; and also by boiling a colloidal soln. of the α-acid. The aq. soln. of the product obtained by treating β-stannic with a little hydrochloric acid when dialyzed leaves a semi-transparent gelatinous mass of β-stannic acid. T. Graham added that there appears to be no soluble form of either α- or β-stannic acid, although they are colloidal substances. A. Dumansky and co-workers studied the formation of complexes as an intermediate stage in the synthesis of colloids.

The properties of β-stannic acid.—According to J. J. Berzelius, the product of the action of nitric acid on tin is a white, amorphous powder of sp. gr. 4·933; whilst that precipitated from α-stannates is gelatinous. The moist product reddens blue litmus, even though when calcined, water free from nitric acid is alone given off; but C. T. Barfoed always found some nitric acid was retained by the washed precipi-tate. L. Vignon found the heat of neutralization with air-dried β-stannic acid, $(H_2Sn_5O_{11}.9H_2O,2KOH)=11\cdot5$ Cals.; that dried at 100°, $(H_2Sn_5O_{11}.4H_2O,2KOH)$ $=10\cdot8$ Cals.; and that which has been heated to 250°, 5·3 Cals. R. Weber found the air-dried acid contained 21·3 per cent. of water; E. Frémy, that dried in air, 19·5 per cent.; and T. Thomson, that dried at 55°, 19·36 per cent.; when dried over sulphuric acid, or in vacuo, R. Weber, and E. Frémy found 11·3 per cent. water—nearly $SnO(OH)_2$. When dried at 100°, L. Schaffner found 8 per cent.; at 930°, E. Frémy, 8·75 per cent., and R. Lorenz, 8·6 per cent.; at 140°, E. Frémy, 7·9 per cent.; and at 150°, L. Schaffner, 5·2 per cent. T. Carnelley and J. Walker observed no signs of the formation of a definite hydrate in their experiments on the dehydration of β-stannic acid at different temp. According to J. M. van Bemmelen, a mol. of β-stannic acid absorbs from moist air 2·3 mols. of water; when dried over sulphuric acid, 1·07 mols.; when dried at 100°, 1·5 mols.; and at red heat, 0·65 mol. A sample with nearly a mol of H_2O after drying several days in a dry atm. at 15°, contained:

100° (1 hr.)	145° (5 hrs.)	165°	175° (4 hrs.)	185° (4 hrs.)
$0\cdot68H_2O$	$0\cdot60H_2O$	$0\cdot56H_2O$	$0\cdot53H_2O$	$0\cdot487H_2O$

According to J. J. Berzelius, β-stannic acid is sparingly soluble in acids, and insoluble in nitric acid; it takes up a small proportion of some acids—e.g. sulphuric or hydrochloric acid—and when washed with a large proportion of water, the acid is removed; the product obtained with hydrochloric acid is soluble in water, and is precipitated from the soln. by acids. H. Rose added that the soln. obtained by using the smallest possible proportion of hydrochloric acid gives a precipitate when more of that acid is added. F. P. Treadwell represented the reaction with hydrochloric acid by the equations : $Sn_5O_5(OH)_{10}+10HCl=10H_2O+Sn_5O_5Cl_{10}$, when the product is insoluble in water : $Sn_5O_5Cl_{10}+8H_2O \rightleftharpoons 8HCl+Sn_5O_5Cl_2(OH)_8$, where the product is soluble in water; and $Sn_5O_5Cl_2(OH)_8+2HCl \rightleftharpoons 2H_2O$ $+Sn_5O_5Cl_4(OH)_6$, where the product is insoluble in water. When the aq. soln. is boiled, hydrolysis is complete : $Sn_5O_5Cl_2(OH)_8+2H_2O=Sn_5O_5(OH)_{10}+2HCl$. According to J. J. Berzelius, the β-acid is less basic than the α-acid, and dil. alkali-lye dissolves β-stannic acid, forming β-stannates $M'_2Sn_5O_{11}.4H_2O$, which do not readily crystallize ; and excess of alkali-lye reprecipitates β-stannic acid. The β-acid is not dissolved by aq. soln. of ammonia or the alkali carbonates.

G. Varga, and J. N. Mukherjee studied the peptization of stannic acid by alkalies. R. Wintgren calculated from the transport numbers and electrical conductivities the proportion due to the micellar portion of the sol. In agreement with G. Varga, a measurable portion of the alkali is enclosed in the micellæ. J. M. van Bemmelen and E. A. Klobbie found that β-stannic acid has a very considerable power of absorbing hydrogen chloride from aq. soln. ; when equilibrium has been established, the conc. of the hydrogen chloride in the colloid is often greater than that in the aq. soln. The absorption factor $k=$(conc. in colloid)/(conc. in soln.) is not constant, but is dependent on the conc. at the point of equilibrium. β-stannic acid has an appreciable power of adsorbing potassium sulphate. From soln. of potassium chloride and potassium nitrate, the same colloid absorbs as much salt as makes the conc. in the colloid and in the soln. approximately equal. C. Lepéz and L. Storch found that when an acid soln. of ferric sulphate is mixed with β-stannic acid, no tin passes into soln. ; but if a mixture of β-stannic acid, ferric sulphate, and sulphuric acid be heated, and, when cold, poured into cold water, some tin remains in soln., but not if the cold mixture were to be poured into hot water. J. Löwenthal found β-stannic acid acquires a yellow colour in contact with a soln. of stannous chloride. H. Kreis showed that ferric hydroxide acts as a protective colloid on the peptized stannic acid. A mixture of the hydrated oxides of iron and tin in certain proportions is soluble in dil. ammonia. H. B. Weiser explained this by showing that hydrated stannic oxide is peptized by hydroxyl ion whilst hydrated ferric oxide is not. However, colloidal stannic oxide adsorbs ferric oxide and carries it into colloidal soln. as long as tin is present in excess. At the same time, hydrated ferric oxide adsorbs stannic oxide and tends to take it out of colloidal soln., so that when the former is present in large excess none of the latter remains peptized. Again, stannic oxide does not precipitate in the usual way from a soln. of tin in nitric acid containing a suitable amount of iron. H. B. Weiser explained this by showing that stannic oxide peptized by nitric acid coagulates spontaneously since the aged oxide is neither peptized nor dissolved by this acid. Ferric nitrate peptizes the oxide when newly formed and when aged. Accordingly, if freshly prepared stannic oxide is peptized either by ferric nitrate or by a suitable mixture of ferric nitrate and nitric acid, coagulation does not take place on standing or boiling on account of the stabilizing action of the strongly adsorbed ferric ion ; but if the concentration of ferric ion in the nitric acid soln. is too low, complete or partial coagulation takes place on standing or boiling. S. Ghosh and N. R. Dhar found soln. with 2·71 grms. of stannic oxide per litre were coagulated by electrolytes in accord with Hardy's rule—3. 23, 8. The precipitating conc. being $0·1167N$-K_2SO_4 ; $0·1083N$-KCl ; $0·0020N$-$MgCl_2$; $0·0012N$-$BaCl_2$; $0·0012N$-$Th(NO_3)_4$; and $0·0009N$-$Al_2(CO_4)_3$. R. Wintgen, and J. Löwenthal investigated the mutual precipitation of tin oxide and chromic oxide gels, and found maximum precipitation occurred on mixing equi-normal conc. of the two soln. T. R. Briggs and W. J. Bartlett studied the adsorption of arsenious acid by metastannic acid. R. Weinland and M. Maier prepared complex salts with pyrogallol and pyrocatechol.

The perstannic acids and perstannates.—According to W. Spring,[2] when hydrated barium dioxide is added in excess to a hydrochloric acid soln. of stannous chloride, and the turbid liquid thus produced is dialyzed until barium chloride no longer passes through the membrane, the colloid residue, after evaporation on the water-bath, yields a white mass whose formula is $H_2Sn_2O_7$, **perdistannic acid**, which may be regarded as the derivative of **stannic trioxide**, SnO_3, resulting from the following reactions: $SnCl_2 + BaO_2 = SnOCl_2 + BaO$; $SnOCl_2 + BaO_2 = SnO_3 + BaCl_2$. When stannous acid precipitated from a soln. of stannous chloride by sodium carbonate was triturated with an excess of 30 per cent. hydrogen dioxide, and the mixture heated to 70°, S. Tanatar found that the product after drying for some days in a desiccator gave white, pulverulent **permonostannic acid**, $HSnO_4.3H_2O$. When this product was further dried in a desiccator, it slowly lost water and oxygen; it also undergoes partial decomposition in water, forming stannic acid and hydrogen dioxide. When dried at 100°, its composition is trihydrated perdistannic acid, $H_2Sn_2O_7.3H_2O$. S. Tanatar also prepared **potassium permonostannate**, $KSnO_4.2H_2O$, by the action of hydrogen dioxide on potassium stannate; it is a white, amorphous powder, which, when heated, parts with oxygen and water. Its aq. soln. has an alkaline reaction; on the addition of sulphuric acid, it decolorizes permanganate. When heated, it is converted into **potassium perdistannate**, $K_2Sn_2O_7.3H_2O$. **Sodium permonostannate**, $NaSnO_4.2H_2O$, was prepared in a similar manner, and is sparingly soluble in water, by which it is readily decomposed; it is a white, amorphous powder. S. Tanatar said that a soln. of potassium permonostannate gives with platinic salt soln. a precipitate which is a mixture of platinic hydroxide and *platinic perstannate*.

According to A. Coppadoro, when conc. alkali stannate soln. are electrolyzed at low temp. and with low current densities, perstannates are formed, owing to anodic oxidation. The proportion of perstannate formed is only small, a condition of equilibrium being soon reached between the perstannate formed and decomposed. The addition of alkali fluoride to the electrolyte increases the rate of formation of the perstannate, but does not change the final equilibrium, so that the yield of perstannate remains unaltered. The presence of fluorine-ions does not increase the anodic potential during electrolysis, and it appears to form either a stable fluorine persalt or an intermediate compound which favours the oxidation of the stannate. The fact that perstannates are formed even at low current densities shows that their formation is due to secondary oxidation of the stannate by the nascent oxygen rather than by the union of two stannic anions. The yield of perstannate diminishes rapidly as the temp. of electrolysis rises. In soln. at the ordinary temp., the perstannates undergo gradual decomposition, yielding stannates.

REFERENCES.

[1] Robert Boyle, *Reflections on the Hypotheses of Alkali and Acidum*, London, 1670; *Experiments and Observations upon Colours*, London, 1670; E. Frémy, *Compt. Rend.*, **14**. 442, 1842; **15**. 1106, 1842; **16**. 187, 1843; *Ann. Chim. Phys.*, (3), **12**. 460, 1844; (3), **23**. 385, 1848; J. J. Berzelius, *ib.*, (1), **87**. 50, 1813; (2), **5**. 149, 1817; *Berzelius' Jahresber.*, **25**. 172, 1845; J. L. Gay Lussac, *Ann. Chim. Phys.*, (2), **1**. 40, 1816; F. Musculus, *Compt. Rend.*, **65**. 961, 1867; *Ann. Chim. Phys.*, (4), **13**. 95, 1867; A. Ditte, *ib.*, (6), **30**. 282, 1893; H. Demarçay, *ib.*, (2), **55**. 398, 1833; R. Engel, *Compt. Rend.*, **124**. 765, 1897; **125**. 464, 651, 709, 1897; L. Vignon, *ib.*, **108**. 1049, 1889; **109**. 372, 1889; P. Pascal, *ib.*, **175**. 1063, 1922; L. Levy, *ib.*, **103**. 1074, 1886; A. Tian, *ib.*, **172**. 1402, 1921; J. B. A. Dumas, *ib.*, **45**. 409, 1857; J. Kunckel, *Vollständiges laboratorium chymicum*, Berlin, 1716; J. Davy, *Phil. Trans.*, **102**. 169, 1812; W. Biltz, *Ber.*, **35**. 4431, 1902; H. Rose, *Journ. prakt. Chem.*, (1), **45**. 76, 1847; *Pogg. Ann.*, **75**. 1, 1848; **112**. 164, 1861; R. Weber, *ib.*, **122**. 358, 1864; N. W. Fischer, *ib.*, **9**. 255, 1827; **10**. 603, 1827; J. Löwenthal, *Journ. prakt. Chem.*, (1), **77**. 321, 1859; J. Thomsen, *ib.*, (2), **14**. 429, 1876; A. Moberg, *ib.*, (1), **28**. 230, 1843; *Liebig's Ann.*, **44**. 261, 1842; J. Bellucci and N. Parravano, *Atti Accad. Lincei*, (5), **13**. ii, 307, 1904; *Zeit. anorg. Chem.*, **45**. 142, 1905; W. Herz, *ib.*, **32**. 357, 1902; G. C. Wittstein, *Repert. Pharm.*, (3), **5**. 313, 1850; C. T. Barfoed, *Danske Vid. Selskr. Skr.*, (5), **7**. 236, 1866; *Journ. prakt. Chem.*, (1), **101**. 369, 1867; J. M. Ordway, *Amer. Journ. Science*, (2), **40**. 173, 1865; R. Ruer, *Zeit. anorg. Chem.*, **43**. 282, 1905; R. Lorenz, *ib.*, **9**. 369, 1895; **12**. 436, 1896; E. A. Schneider, *ib.*, **5**. 83, 1894; H. Zocher, *ib.*, **112**. 1, 1920; G. Jörgensen, *ib.*, **28**. 140, 1901; **57**. 353, 1908; W. Mecklenburgh, *ib.*, **64**. 368, 1909; **74**. 207, 1912; **84**. 121, 1914; H. Kühl, *Pharm. Ztg.*, **53**. 49, 1908; T. Graham, *Proc. Roy. Soc.*, **13**. 335, 1864; *Journ. Chem. Soc.*, **17**. 318, 1864; *Phil. Trans.*, **156**. 399, 1866; *Phil. Mag.*.

(4), **32**. 401, 503, 1866 ; *Liebig's Ann.*, **13**. 146, 1835 ; H. Schiff, *ib.*, **120**. 47, 1861 ; R. Zsigmondy, *ib.*, **301**. 368, 1898 ; L. Schaffner, *ib.*, **51**. 168, 1844 ; J. M. van Bemmelen and E. A. Klobbie, *Zeit. anorg. Chem.*, **23**. 111, 1900 ; J. M. van Bemmelen, *Rec. Trav. Chim. Pays-Bas*, **7**. 37, 1888 ; *Die Absorption*, Dresden, 54, 393, 1910 ; *Arch. Néerl.*, **15**. 321, 1881 ; *Zeit. anorg. Chem.*, **23**. 111, 1900 ; *Ber.*, **13**. 1466, 1880 ; R. Willstätter, H. Kraut, and W. Fremery, *ib.*, **57**. B, 63, 1491, 1924 ; W. Biltz and F. Zimmermann, *ib.*, **40**. 4979, 1907 ; W. Biltz, *ib.*, **35**. 4431, 1902 ; E. Knövengel and E. Ebler, *ib.*, **35**. 3066, 1902 ; P. T. Austen, *Journ. Amer. Chem. Soc.*, **4**. 285, 1882 ; *Chem. News*, **46**. 286, 1882 ; N. Yamada, *Journ. Chem. Soc. Japan*, **44**. 210, 1923 ; G. Neumann. *Monatsh.*, **12**. 518, 1891 ; C. Lepéz and L. Storch, *ib.*, **10**. 283, 1889 ; A. Kleinschmidt, *ib.*, **39**. 149, 1918 ; C. L. Wagner, *ib.*, **34**. 95, 931, 1913 ; *Koll. Zeit.*, **14**. 149, 1914 ; G. E. Collins and J. K. Wood, *Journ. Chem. Soc.*, **123**. 452, 1923 ; F. H. van Leent, *Monit. Scient.*, (4), **12**. 866, 1899 ; H. Rose, *Pogg. Ann.*, **75**. 1, 1848 ; D. B. Dott, *Pharm. Journ.*, (4), **27**. 486, 1908 ; R. Wintgen, *Zeit. phys. Chem.*, **103**. 238, 1922 ; H. Allen, *Journ. Chem. Soc.*, **25**. 274, 1872 ; G. E. Collins and J. K. Wood, *ib.*, **121**. 441, 1122, 1922 ; T. Carnelley and J. Walker, *ib.*, **53**. 59, 1888 ; J. Biron, *Journ. Russ. Phys. Chem. Soc.*, **36**. 933, 1904 ; 37. 963, 1905 ; J. Hood and A. G. Salmon, *Brit. Pat. No.* 12110, 1886 ; T. Thomson, *Ann. Phil.*, (1), **10**. 149, 1817 ; R. Schwarz and H. Stock, *Zeit. wiss. Photochem.*, **22**. 26, 1922 ; A. Stiegler, *Zeit. Koll.*, **29**. 65, 1921 ; G. Varga, *Koll. Beihefte*, **11**. 26, 1919 ; J. R. Mukherjee, *Phil. Mag.*, (6), **44**. 321, 1922 ; H. Kreis, *Schweis. Chem. Ztg.*, 389, 1919 ; T. R. Briggs and W. J. Bartlett, *Trans. Amer. Electrochem. Soc.*, **37**. 723, 1920 ; W. A. Patrick, *Brit. Pat. Nos.* 136543, 1919 ; 212065, 1923 ; F. P. Treadwell, *Kurzes Lehrbuch der analytischen Chemie*, Leipzig, **1**. 215, 1907 ; London, **1**. 220, 1903 ; W. Pauli, *Trans. Faraday Soc.*, **16**. 15 (app.), 1921 ; *Zeit. Koll.*, **28**. 49, 1921 ; M. C. Lea, *Amer. Journ. Science*, (2), **33**. 80, 1862 ; F. Faktor, *Pharm. Post*, **28**. 53, 1905 ; R. R. Franz, *Beiträge zur Chemie der Zinnsäuren vom Kolloidchemischen Standpunkt*, Göttingen, 1913 ; A. M. Morley and J. K. Wood, *Journ. Soc. Dyers Col.*, **39**. 105, 1923 ; P. Pfeiffer, *Zeit. anorg. Chem.*, **68**. 106, 1910 ; P. Pfeiffer and R. Lehnardt, *Ber.*, **36**. 1054, 3027, 1903 ; J. G. F. Druce, *Chem. News*, **120**. 229, 1920 ; **125**. 327, 1922 ; **127**. 306, 1923 ; *Journ. Chem. Soc.*, **119**. 758, 1921 ; *ib.*, **121**. 1859, 1922 ; H. Lambourne, *ib.*, **121**. 2533, 1922 ; S. Glixelli, *Anz. Akad. Krakau*, 102, 1917 ; H. B. Weiser, *Journ. Phys. Chem.*, **26**. 654, 1922 ; **28**. 232, 1924 ; *Colloid Symposium Monograph*, Wisconsin, 38, 1923 ; F Hein and H. Meininger, *Zeit. anorg. Chem.*, **145**. 95, 1925 ; R. Weinland and M. Maier, *ib.*, **150**. 217, 1926 ; S. Ghosh and N. R. Dhar, *Journ. Phys. Chem.*, **29**. 435, 1925 ; A. Dumansky, A. P. Buntin, S. J. Dijatschkowsky, and A. G. Kriga, *Koll. Zeit.*, **38**. 208, 1926.
    ² W. Spring, *Bull. Soc. Chim.*, (3), **1**. 180, 1889 ; S. Tanatar, *Ber.*, **38**. 1184, 1905 ; A. Coppadoro, *Gazz. Chim. Ital.*, **38**. i, 489, 1908.

§ 14. The Stannates

H. Rose[1] obtained what he regarded as **potassium α-stannate,** $K_2SnO_3.3H_2O$, or according to J. Bellucci and N. Parravano, $K_2Sn(OH)_6$, by fusing stannic oxide or one of its hydrates with potassium hydroxide or carbonate. If the fusion with potassium carbonate be interrupted before the carbon dioxide is all expelled, the gas still evolved from the interior of the cooling mass forces its way through the hardening crust with a crackling noise, and makes the surface uneven. J. C. G. de Marignac dissolved the cold soln. of stannic oxide in molten potassium hydroxide in water, and evaporated the soln. to allow the stannate, which is only sparingly soluble in a conc. soln. of potassium hydroxide, to crystallize. J. M. Ordway ignited a mixture of tin, potassium nitrate, and hydroxide ; dissolved the cold cake in water ; added an equal vol. of alcohol, of sp. gr. 0·84 ; purified the syrupy liquid by repeated soln. in water and reprecipitation with alcohol ; and finally evaporated the liquid in vacuo. E. Frémy dissolved α- or β-stannic acid in hot conc. potash-lye, and treated the soln. as just indicated. A. Moberg, and A. Ditte dissolved the stannic oxide or hydrate in hot conc. potash-lye and evaporated the sat. soln. over conc. sulphuric acid. J. Bellucci and N. Parravano washed the stannate rapidly with a little cold water ; then with alcohol ; and dried the product at 100°. They obtained it by adding an excess of potassium hydroxide to a soln. of stannic chloride or hydrochlorostannic acid. G. E. Collins and J. K. Wood recommended the following process :

Thirty grams of α-stannic acid prepared by the action of calcium carbonate on a soln. of stannic chloride was washed and dried in air. The product was fused with 80 grms. of potassium hydroxide, and the cold mass extracted with hot water and filtered. The filtered soln. was evaporated until sat., and placed in vacuo over sulphuric acid as recommended by F. Musculus ; the acid being subsequently replaced by sodium hydroxide. The small, clear crystals obtained were filtered off, rapidly washed once with distilled water, then several times with alcohol; and finally with ether.

H. Zocher prepared the *trihydrate*, $K_2Sn(OH)_6$; *tetrahydrate*, $K_2Sn(OH)_6.H_2O$; and the *pentahydrate*, $K_2Sn(OH)_6.2H_2O$. The potassium salts are more soluble than the sodium and lithium salts (*q.v.*). According to the analyses of A. Moberg, J. C. G. de Marignac, and J. Bellucci and N. Parravano, the composition agrees with $K_2SnO_3.3H_2O$, but E. Frémy considered the composition to be $K_2SnO_3.4H_2O$. The colourless, shining, oblique, rhombic prisms often have the acute lateral edges truncated. According to J. Bellucci and N. Parravano, the crystals belong to the trigonal system, and have the axial ratio $a:c=1:1.9588$. The crystals are often twinned about the (100)-plane ; and the cleavage parallel to (111) is perfect. The crystals are isomorphous with potassium hydroxyplatinate, $K_2Pt(OH)_6$. The birefringence is positive. F. Zambonini made observations on this subject. J. M. Ordway found the sp. gr. to be 3·197. According to J. L. Proust, the crystals turn red when heated, but they do not fuse. J. Bellucci and N. Parravano said that the crystals at 100° lose only traces of water, but at 140° water is copiously evolved. When the dehydrated stannate is heated, it no longer forms the original α-stannate when treated with water. They infer that the contained water is not present as water of crystallization, but, as indicated above, the water is an intrinsic part of the mol. The dehydrated salt is hygroscopic, and takes up water with the evolution of heat. The stannate appears to decompose into tin oxide and alkali on dehydration. According to A. Moberg, the salt does not deliquesce in air, and it is readily soluble in hot or cold water. J. M. Ordway found that 100 parts of water dissolve 106·7 parts of salt at 10°, and the sp. gr. of the soln. is 1·628; at 20°, 110·5 parts of salt are dissolved, and the sp. gr. of the soln. is 1·627. J. Bellucci and N. Parravano gave for the electrical conductivity, λ, of soln. containing half a mol of the salt in v litres of water at 25° :

v	32	64	128	256	512	1024
λ	97·5	105·6	113·2	122·8	134·9	155·8

and for the first two soln. the conductivity increases with time :

Time in hours	24	72	120	168
$\lambda\{v=32$	108·0	114·0	119·5	119·7
$\{v=64$	115·8	130·5	136·5	136·4

G. E. Collins and J. K. Wood found the velocity constant of the reaction $K_2Sn(OH)_6+2H_2O=H_2Sn(OH)_6+2KOH$ to be $k=0.0188$, and the amount of free alkali present in a 0·128N-soln. corresponds with a 13 per cent. hydrolysis. With a similar soln. of stannic chloride the hydrolysis was 94 per cent. This shows that stannic hydroxide is stronger as an acid than as a base. E. Frémy found that the aq. soln. gives a precipitate with soluble salts ; and acids added to the soln. precipitate α-stannic acid soluble in nitric acid; J. M. Ordway showed that with dil. acids about one-fourth of the potash is precipitated, and that which remains in soln. is precipitated by alcohol as acid stannate which dries to a gummy mass. P. T. Austen made stannic oxide by passing carbon dioxide into an aq. soln. of an alkali stannate containing an excess of alkali ; and, according to A. Ditte, when some bubbles of carbonic anhydride are allowed to fall on the surface of a dil. soln. of an alkali stannate, a cloudy separation of gelatinous stannic oxide rises to the surface, and, as it increases in amount, the carbon dioxide ceases to be absorbed. When, however, the carbon dioxide is introduced very slowly in contact with crystals of stannate, a dense monohydrated stannic oxide is formed, which seems to be amorphous. If carbon dioxide is passed into a mixture of stannate and carbonate, stannic oxide falls to the bottom of the liquid. Alkali carbonate free from the acid salt does not give rise to the production of stannic oxide when added to a stannate ; stannic oxide is formed in amount proportional to the quantity of acid salt present. N. W. Fischer found that if lead be immersed in the aq. soln., all the tin is precipitated ; and R. Böttger, that copper in contact with tin is quickly plated with tin by the soln.

When an aq. soln. of this salt is treated with alcohol, J. J. Berzelius said that an acid salt is precipitated, while J. M. Ordway obtained the normal salt under this condition, J. J. Berzelius added that when a soln. of a salt is treated with potassium carbonate, hydrated stannic oxide is precipitated, and this, after the saline soln. has been removed by decantation, dissolves in water, forming a turbid liquid which gives a precipitate with potassium carbonate. R. Weber made an acid salt approximating $K_2O.5SnO_2$ by evaporating over sulphuric acid a soln. of potassium stannate sat. with stannic hydroxide ; and, as indicated above, J. M. Ordway also obtained an acid stannate which varied in composition between $K_2O : SnO_2 = 1 : 5$ and $1 : 7$. These products appear to be mixtures of stannic acid with more or less adsorbed alkali, or alkali stannate.

A. Moberg prepared **sodium α-stannate**, $Na_2SnO_3.3H_2O$, or, according to J. Bellucci and N. Parravano, and H. Zocher, $Na_2Sn(OH)_6$, by saturating a soln. of sodium hydroxide with stannic hydroxide, and evaporating the soln. for crystallization. E. Frémy fused stannic acid with sodium hydroxide, dissolved the product in water, boiled the soln., and the sparingly soluble salt which was deposited was purified by recrystallization. R. Lüpke roasted cassiterite, and fused 6 grms. of the powdered product with 4 grms. of sodium hydroxide for 15 mins. in an electric furnace ; the sodium stannate can be isolated as before. J. M. Ordway purified commercial sodium stannate by adding barium acetate to the soln., and treating the filtered soln. with alcohol. The salt is used in calico-printing under the name *preparing salts*. Technical processes have been described by R. E. Brown, E. Schunck, E. Haeffely, P. A. Bolley, T. Roberts and J. Dale, etc. Analyses by A. Moberg, J. C. G. Marignac, J. M. Ordway, R. F. Weinland and A. Gutmann, and J. Bellucci and N. Parravano gave $Na_2SnO_3.3H_2O$; while E. Frémy, and W. Prandtl gave $Na_2SnO_3.4H_2O$. H. Zocher said that while the trihydrate is formed at ordinary temp., the *tetrahydrate*, $Na_2Sn(OH)_6.H_2O$, is formed at 0°, or by alcohol at 0° or ordinary temp. A. Scheurer-Kestner said that at a low temp. a conc. soln. of sodium stannate, free from alkali hydroxide, furnishes long, prismatic crystals of the *decahydrate*, $Na_2SnO_3.10H_2O$; while E. Haeffely reported an *octohydrate* ; and H. Jonas, an *enneahydrate*. The two latter are probably partly effloresced specimens of the decahydrate. The crystals, said A. Moberg, form six-sided tablets belonging, according to J. C. G. de Marignac, to the trigonal system and have the axial ratio $a : c = 1 : 1.447$. W. G. Mixter gave for the heat of formation $2Na_2O_2 + Sn = Na_2SnO_3 + Na_2O + 138$ Cals.; $(Na_2O, Sn, O_2) = 172.6$ Cals. ; with crystalline stannic oxide, $(Na_2O, SnO_2) = 35.4$ Cals., and with the amorphous oxide, 37.1 Cals. E. Frémy, and E. Haeffely said the salt is more soluble in cold than in hot water ; J. C. G. de Marignac said that 100 parts of water at 20° dissolve 50 parts of salt, and the same amount is dissolved by hot water ; while, according to J. M. Ordway, 100 parts of water at 0° dissolve 67.4 parts of salt, and the sp. gr. of the soln. is 1.472 at 15.5° ; whilst at 20°, 61.3 parts of salt are dissolved and the sp. gr. of the soln. is 1.438 at 15.5°. H. Zocher represented the percentage solubilities of the tri- and tetra-hydrates by the curves shown in Fig. 65. The transition point is near −5°. The trihydrate forms a eutectic with water at −11°. and the tetrahydrate at −7°. The *henicosihydrate*, $Na_2Sn(OH)_6.18H_2O$, has a transition point to the anhydrous salt $Na_2Sn(OH)_6$ at 1°. In normal soln., about 2.7 per cent. is hydrolyzed and the reaction is complete with $\frac{1}{3000}N$-soln. The hydrolysis increases with time, as is also the case with some other colloidal soln.—*e.g.* stannic chloride. There was no evidence of an adsorption of alkali by sodium stannate. J. Bellucci and N. Parravano

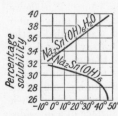

FIG. 65.—Solubility of Sodium Stannates.

said that the trihydrate gives off no water at 100°, but at 140°, it is decomposed. The contained water is assumed to be constitutional, forming $Na_2Sn(OH)_6$. The action of carbon dioxide is similar to the action of that gas on potassium α-stannate—*vide supra*. The salt dehydrated at 140° is a white powder which does not evolve heat when mixed with water at room temp., and shows no tendency to dissolve in that menstruum. H. Zocher prepared trihydrated **lithium stannate**, $Li_2SnO_3.3H_2O$, or $Li_2Sn(OH)_6$, and the pentahydrate, $Li_2Sn(OH)_6.2H_2O$, and the solubilities of the two hydrates are indicated in Fig. 66.

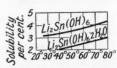

FIG. 66.—Solubilities of Lithium Stannates.

β-stannic acid is insoluble in ammonia, and *ammonium* β-*stannate* has not been made. E. Frémy obtained a number of β-**stannates** with varying proportions of $K_2O : SnO_2$. They have not been obtained in the crystalline state, and J. M. van Bemmelen regards them as adsorption products. J. J. Berzelius, and H. Rose reported $K_2O.10SnO_2$ to be formed by the action of very dil. potash-lye on β-stannic acid; H. Rose, and R. Weber made $K_2O.7SnO_2.3H_2O$, by the action of potassium hydroxide on a soln. of β-stannic acid; and E. Frémy, and R. Weber, $K_2O.6SnO_2.5H_2O$, by the action of much water on $K_2O.3SnO_2.3H_2O$, or by the action of dil. potash-lye on β-stannic acid; E. Frémy added potassium hydroxide to a soln. of β-stannic acid in potash-lye, and obtained what R. Engel regarded as the normal salt, **potassium β-stannate**, $K_2O.5SnO_2.4H_2O$. The product, dried on a porous tile, appears as a horny, translucent colloid. It is quite soluble in water, but cannot be crystallized. When heated with conc. alkali-lye, it forms the α-stannate. It is dehydrated at 130°, and is then completely soluble in water. It is decomposed at a red heat. E. Frémy reported $K_2O.3SnO_2.3H_2O$ to be formed as a gummy precipitate by adding alcohol to a conc. soln. of β-stannic acid in potash-lye. R. Engel reported *potassium parastannate*, $K_2Sn_5O_{11}.2(or 3)H_2O$, to be formed by the action of potassium hydroxide or parastannic acid (*q.v.*). E. Frémy reported the formation of **sodium β-stannate**, $Na_2O.5SnO_2.8H_2O$, by treating β-stannic acid with a conc. aq. soln. of sodium hydroxide. The sparingly soluble, crystalline powder is decomposed at 60°, or when boiled, forming β-stannic acid and sodium hydroxide. The salt was also prepared by E. Haeffely. R. Engel took advantage of the insolubility of sodium β-stannate in an excess of potash-lye to prepare pure β-stannic acid. C. T. Barfoed reported the formation of $Na_2O.9SnO_2.8H_2O$, by adding an excess of sodium hydroxide to a clear soln. of β-stannyl chloride; and washing the gummy mass with dil. aq. alcohol. It is insoluble in alcohol, and in sodium hydroxide.

C. Zulkowsky melted stannic oxide and potassium carbonate in the proportions $2SnO_2 : K_2CO_3$, and obtained what he regarded as $K_2Sn_2O_5$, or $KO.SnO.O.SnO.OK$, *i.e.* **potassium mesodistannate,** and said that the opacity produced by stannic oxide in glasses and enamels depends on the formation of this compound. A. Moberg prepared **ammonium α-mesodistannate,** $(NH_4)_2Sn_2O_5.nH_2O$, as a viscid mass, by evaporating over sulphuric acid a sat. soln. of stannic hydroxide in aq. ammonia; and J. J. Berzelius obtained a similar product by adding ammonium chloride to an aq. soln. of potassium stannate, and evaporating the soln. spontaneously. A. Ditte also obtained a hard, bony mass by evaporating the ammoniacal soln. of stannic hydroxide.

According to T. Leykauf, when a soln. of cupric nitrate is treated with a soln. of stannous chloride in potassium hydroxide, a yellowish-green precipitate is formed, which, if kept out of contact with air, becomes yellow, and then forms hydrated **cuprous α-stannate**—possibly $Cu_2SnO_3.nH_2O$—and on exposure to air forms a mixture of cupric hydroxide and stannic acid.

The dark green mineral called by T. Ulke *cuprocassiterite*, supposed to be produced by the oxidation of stannite, was regarded as having the composition $4SnO_2+Cu_2Sn(OH)_2$, and sp. gr. 4·534; W. P. Headden, however, showed that its composition varies widely.

According to E. Lenssen, if soln. of stannous and cupric oxides in potassium hydroxide be mixed, with the former in excess, cuprous oxide is deposited if the liquid be allowed to stand ; but if boiled, *stannous cuprous stannate*, $3SnO.Cu_2O.SnO_2.5H_2O$, is deposited as a black or greenish-black powder. It loses 4·73 per cent. of water at 100°, and at a higher temp. is oxidized to cuprous stannate. Aq. ammonia, and dil. acids decompose it slowly ; and with conc. hydrochloric acid, metallic copper, as well as cuprous, stannous, and stannic chlorides are formed.

A. Moberg mixed a soln. of a cupric salt and potassium stannate, and obtained green **cupric α-stannate**, $CuSnO_3.3H_2O$; L. Elsner described the preparation of a blue pigment on these lines. A. Ditte obtained small, pale blue crystals by adding a soln. of potassium stannate to an ammoniacal soln. of a cupric salt so long as the precipitate redissolves, and evaporating the liquid over sulphuric acid. He supposed the product to be the *tetrahydrate*. It dissolved readily in aq. ammonia. By treating the crystals with a conc. ammoniacal soln. of the mother-liquid at ordinary temp., dark blue crystals were obtained which were assumed to be **ammonium cupric α-stannate**, $(NH_4)_2O.CuO.SnO_2.2H_2O$. The crystals were sparingly soluble in cold water, and formed a green soln. with acids.

According to A. Ditte, soluble silver salts form with soluble stannous salts, characteristic, highly-coloured precipitates, the composition of which varies with the relative proportions of the reacting bodies. When the stannous salt is added to an excess of silver nitrate, a white precipitate is formed which rapidly becomes red, and eventually deep red, almost black. The filtrate is colourless, but after a short time deposits the same precipitate. Several hours are required for complete precipitation. The dark red precipitate is well washed and dried in a vacuum. It is **silver α-stannate**, $SnO_2.Ag_2O+2H_2O$, soluble in dil. nitric acid, but insoluble in ammonia. When heated, it loses water without detonation or incandescence, and becomes insoluble in dil. acids. J. Bellucci and N. Parravano also prepared the α-stannate. A. Ditte also found that when silver nitrate is added to an excess of stannous nitrate, a white precipitate is produced, which when dry forms a grey powder readily soluble in dil. nitric acid, insoluble in ammonia, but turned deep red by a trace of this reagent. If the white precipitate is left in the original liquid, it becomes red after some time. When suspended in a large quantity of water, it is converted into a deep red powder, which, when dried in a vacuum, is insoluble in ammonia, but soluble in dil. nitric acid. This red compound is **silver β-stannate**, $5SnO_2.Ag_2O$. If slowly formed in the original liquid, it contains the *heptahydrate*, but if formed by suspension in water, the *trihydrate*. Dried at 80°, it has a deep blue-black colour. When heated, it loses water and detonates, with development of heat and light. This detonation is transmitted along a train of the compound, as in the case of gunpowder. The anhydrous metastannate is insoluble in dil. acids, but warm conc. nitric acid dissolves out silver, leaving metastannic acid. When dil. stannous nitrate in slight excess is added little by little to silver nitrate, a deep reddish-purple precipitate is deposited after some time. This dissolves in nitric acid, forming a clear yellow soln., and also in ammonia, forming an intensely red liquid. When exposed to the air, the dil. ammoniacal soln. is completely decolorized after some time, but if it contains a moderate quantity of the silver salt, it deposits on evaporation a purple precipitate having all the properties of the original substance. When this precipitate is washed and dried, either in vacuum or at 30°, it forms small friable masses with a vitreous fracture, entirely soluble in cold dil. ammonia. In the formation of this compound, $5SnO_2.Ag_4O.2n(SnO_2,Ag_2O)+nH_2O$, a portion of the stannous salt is oxidized to stannic acid, and a portion of the silver salt is reduced to suboxide. The compound loses water when heated, and becomes insoluble in ammonia. The so-called *silver-purple* analogous to purple of Cassius was examined by G. F. C. Frick, H. Schulz, G. T. Fechner, N. W. Fischer, J. J. Berzelius, etc.—*vide* **3**. 23, 1i. Similarly also for *gold purple*.

G. Tschermak obtained needle-like crystals of anhydrous **calcium α-stannate**, $CaSnO_3$, by melting together molar proportions of calcium and stannic oxides

A. Ditte melted a mixture of stannic and calcium oxides and calcium chloride. The cold mass was treated with dil. hydrochloric acid, and the residue contained small transparent crystals—plates, and cubes of more or less altered octahedra. The salt is not attacked by dil. acids or by molten sodium hydroxide. According to A. Moberg, a hydrated form is slowly precipitated by adding a calcium salt to a soln. of potassium stannate; according to A. Ditte, the precipitate is transformed into well-formed crystals at 100°. A. Moberg regarded the salt as a *tetrahydrate*; A. Ditte, as a *pentahydrate*; and J. Bellucci and N. Parravano, as a *trihydrate* with a constitution $CaSn(OH)_6$ in conformity with the corresponding alkali salts (*q.v.*). The hydrate is stable in vacuo over sulphuric acid; it loses the following percentage amounts of water at the given temp. :

	100°	120°	140°	160°	200°
Loss	0·36	2·50	2·84	3·00	4·63

A prolonged heating to redness is needed to remove the water completely. A. Ditte said that the hydrate is insoluble in water, but soluble in nitric acid. C. Zulkowsky prepared what he regarded as a **calcium orthostannate,** Ca_2SnO_4, by heating at a pale yellow heat a mixture of the two oxides in the required proportions. The mass so produced hardens under water with a feeble evolution of heat. D. Balareff found that tin dioxide does not react with calcium oxide at 950°, but it does so rapidly with barium and strontium oxides. G. Aminoff represented *nordenskjöldine,* $Ca(BO)_2SnO_4$—*calcium diborylstannate*—as having crystals with the axial ratio $a:c=1:1·6442$—*vide* **5.** 32, 14.

J. Bellucci and N. Parravano prepared **strontium α-stannate,** $SrSnO_3.3H_2O$, or $SrSn(OH)_6$, by adding a sat. soln. of strontium hydroxide or chloride to a soln. of potassium stannate, and warming the gelatinous mass on the water-bath. The white crystalline powder is stable in vacuo over sulphuric acid; it loses 0·33 per cent. of water at 100°, and 0·97 per cent. at 140°. All three mols of water are completely expelled only at a red heat. A. Ditte obtained a similar substance by an analogous process and assigned to it the composition $3SrO.2SnO_2.10H_2O$. It was possibly the α-stannate contaminated with a little strontium hydroxide A. Moberg, J. J. Berzelius, and A. Ditte mixed a soln. of a barium hydroxide or chloride with a soln. of potassium stannate, and obtained a heavy white powder. J. Bellucci and N. Parravano washed the precipitate with water at ordinary temp. and dried it first in air, and then over calcium chloride to a constant weight. J. J. Berzelius represented it by $BaO.4SnO_2.nH_2O$; A. Ditte, by $2BaO.SnO_2.10H_2O$; A. Moberg, by $BaSnO_3.6H_2O$; and J. Bellucci and N. Parravano, by $BaSn(OH)_6$. $4H_2O$, or **heptahydrated barium α-stannate,** $BaSnO_3.7H_2O$. At 100°, it loses 17·17 per cent. of water, forming the *trihydrate;* at 120°, it loses 19·29 per cent.; at 140°, 20·85 per cent.; at 160°, 21·62 per cent.; at 180°, 22·55 per cent.; at 200°, 23·80 per cent. It is sparingly soluble in water, and readily soluble in nitric acid. J. A. Hedvall and N. von Zweigbergk did not observe any reaction between barium dioxide and stannic oxide when a mixture of the two was heated, but D. Balareff found a slight heat effect when a mixture of barium and stannic oxides was heated. H. Zocher examined some properties of barium stannate.

A. Moberg added a magnesium salt soln. to one of potassium stannate and obtained a slimy precipitate—probably **magnesium α-stannate,** $MgSnO_3.nH_2O$. A. Ditte reported **zinc** α-stannate, $ZnSnO_3.2H_2O$, to be formed when a soln. of a zinc salt is added to one of potassium stannate; and $3ZnO.2SnO_2.10H_2O$, by treating an ammoniacal soln. of zinc sulphate with one of potassium stannate. The small, clear, colourless crystals are soluble in dil. acids; but after dehydration they are insoluble. A. Moberg added a soln. of mercurous nitrate to one of potassium stannate, and obtained a yellow precipitate of **mercurous α-stannate,** with the composition $Hg_2SnO_3.5H_2O$ when dried over sulphuric acid; it soon turned green. By using mercuric nitrate in a similar way, he obtained white mercuric α-**stannate,** $HgSnO_3.6H_2O$, which soon became dark green.

J. J. Berzelius found that when an alloy of lead and tin is drossed in air, it oxidizes much more readily than either metal alone, " the change being accelerated by the affinity which the two oxides have for one another." An alloy of tin with 4 or 5 times its weight of lead burns in air like charcoal, the combustion afterwards proceeds spontaneously like low-grade peat. According to R. W. Fox, the presence of platinum retards the oxidation, but gold has no adverse effect and is at the same time oxidized, forming purple of Cassius. The product of the oxidation of the tin-lead alloy was once called **lead stannate,** but it is probably only a mixture. That obtained from an alloy approximating solder in composition is called *tin-ash*, *putty-powder*, or *potée d'etain*, and the commercial product approximates 30 per cent. stannic oxide and 70 per cent. lead oxide. The powder is used for polishing and as an opacifying agent in enamels. A. Moberg said that when a lead salt is added to a soln. of potassium stannate, there is but a slight precipitation of lead stannate owing to the solubility of that salt.

A. Moberg, and J. J. Berzelius obtained white, pulverulent **manganese α-stannate** by mixing soln. of manganese salt and potassium stannate. The white colour changes to dark brown on exposure to air. According to C. Fromherz, potassium permanganate gives no precipitate with stannous chloride. J. J. Berzelius mixed soln. of potassium stannate and of a cobalt salt, and obtained a blue precipitate which, when washed and dried, became dark brown. After heating white hot, the colour was blue. A. Ditte mixed a soln. of potassium stannate with an ammoniacal soln. of a cobalt salt and obtained a pulverulent precipitate which redissolved in the ammoniacal liquor. If the stannate is added until the precipitate no longer dissolves, and the clear soln. be evaporated, rose-red crystals of **cobalt α-stannate,** $CoSnO_3.6H_2O$, are formed. A. Ditte obtained pale green cubic crystals of **nickel α-stannate,** $NiSnO_3.5H_2O$, by an analogous process. J. A. Hedvall prepared green **cobalt orthostannate,** Co_2SnO_4, by heating a mixture of the constituent oxides; and likewise also **nickel orthostannate,** Ni_2SnO_4. M. Rüger also made some observations on this subject.

According to N. W. Fischer, the precipitate which is produced when soln. of stannous chloride and hydrochloroplatinic acid are mixed is probably **platinous α-stannate.** According to R. Schneider, **platinum distannyl α-stannate,** $Pt(SnO)_2SnO_3$, is formed by mixing soln. of hydrochloroplatinic acid and a soln. of stannous chloride in dil. hydrochloric acid ; and also by the action of stannous chloride on a soln. of platinic chloride which has been decolorized with sulphur dioxide. The washed precipitate appears as a black powder when dried. It loses water when heated. It is decomposed by alkali-lye, forming stannic oxide and an alkali platinate. A dil. soln. of sodium hydroxide extracts some tin oxide and leaves residual sodium platinic stannyl stannate, $Na_2O.2PtO.SnO.SnO_2$. L. Wöhler considers that the assumed platinum distannyl α-stannate is nothing but *platinum purple*, an adsorption product of stannic hydroxide and colloidal platinum—*vide* 3. 23, 11. Platinum purple has been studied by L. Wöhler, and B. Delachanal and A. Mermet. According to A. Ditte, palladium nitrate, added to an excess of stannous salt, forms very deep brown **palladium β-stannate,** $5SnO_2.PdO.4H_2O$, insoluble in ammonia, but soluble in hydrochloric acid, forming a deep brown soln., and in nitric acid, forming a reddish-yellow soln. Platinum chloride under similar conditions forms a blood-red **platinum β-stannate,** $5SnO_2.PtO+4H_2O$, insoluble in ammonia, but soluble in hydrochloric acid, forming a beautiful red soln., and in nitric acid, forming a yellowish soln. Both these compounds when heated lose their water with detonation and incandescence, and become insoluble in dil. acids. If the palladium or platinum salt is in excess, highly coloured stannates, soluble in dil. acids, are formed. When heated, these lose their water without deflagration, and become insoluble in dil. acids. A. Michel-Lévy and L. Bourgeois obtained a product with a composition approaching $PtO_2.4SnO_2$, in yellow hexagonal plates resembling muscovite gold, and sp. gr. 6·70, by melting at a white heat in a platinum crucible a mixture of precipitated stannic acid and sodium carbonate for 15 mins. The cold mass is lixivated with water, washed with water acidified by nitric acid, and dried. Boiling conc. acids attack the product with difficulty. At a dull red heat, hydrogen reduces it to Pt_4Sn_3.

A fine pink colour [2]—*chrome-tin pink*—is developed when a mixture of stannic oxide and a very small proportion of chromic oxide is calcined at a high temp. in an oxidizing atm. ; at a lower temp. the colour is lilac. If some calcium carbonate is present, the pink colour develops at a lower temp. The cause of the coloration has been the subject of much speculation ; *chromium stannates*, and stannic chromates with the required properties have been invented. The coloration probably is related to the chrome-alumina crimson of the ruby, and purple of Cassius in that finely divided chromic oxide is deposited on the stannic oxide.

REFERENCES.

[1] A. Moberg, *Dissertatio de Stannatibus*, Helsingfors, 1838 ; *Liebig's Ann.*, 44. 261, 1842 ; *Journ. prakt. Chem.*, (1), 28. 231, 1843 ; T. Leykauf, *ib.*, (1), 19. 129, 1840 ; E. Lenssen, *ib.*, (1), 79. 90, 1860 ; J. M. Ordway, *Amer. Journ. Science*, (2), 40. 173, 1865 ; W. G. Mixter, *ib.*, (4), 27. 229, 1909 ; W. P. Headden, *ib.*, (3), 45. 107, 1893 ; J. C. G. de Marignac, *Ann. Mines*, (5), 15. 278, 1859 ; E. Frémy, *Ann. Chim. Phys.*, (3), 12. 484, 1844 ; (3), 23. 399, 1847 ; A. Ditte, *ib.*, (5), 27. 167, 1882 ; (6). 30. 282, 1893 ; *Compt. Rend.*, 94. 1114, 1882 ; 96. 702, 1883 ; 104. 172, 1887 ; F. Musculus, *ib.*, 65. 961, 1867 ; *Ann. Chim. Phys.*, (4), 13. 95, 1867 ; R. Engel, *Compt. Rend.*, 125. 466, 709, 1897 ; A. Michel-Lévy and L. Bourgeois, *ib.*, 94. 1365, 1882 ; P. Schützenberger, *ib.*, 98. 985, 1884 ; B. Delachanal and A. Mermet, *ib.*, 81. 370, 1875 ; *Bull. Soc. Chim.*, (2), 24. 435, 1875 ; L. Wöhler, *Zeit. Koll.*, 7. 244, 1910 ; *Zeit. anorg. Chem.*, 40. 439, 1904 ; J. M. van Bemmelen, *ib.*, 23. 124, 1900 ; J. Bellucci and N. Parravano, *Atti Accad. Lincei*, (5), 13. ii, 307, 1904 ; *Zeit. anorg. Chem.*, 45. 151, 1905 ; R. F. Weinland and A. Gutmann, *ib.*, 17. 418, 1898 ; *Ber.*, 38. 1734, 1905 ; N. W. Fischer, *Schweigger's Journ.*, 55. 361, 1829 ; *Pogg. Ann.*, 9. 263, 1827 ; R. Weber, *ib.*, 122. 364, 1864 ; H. Rose, *ib.*, 75. i, 1847 ; G. T. Fechner, *ib.*, 47. 1, 1829 ; G. F. C. Frick, *ib.*, 12. 258, 1828 ; R. Schneider, *ib.*, 136. 105, 1869 ; A. Scheurer-Kestner, *Bull. Soc. Chim.*, (2), 8. 289, 1867 ; R. Böttger, *Liebig's Ann.*, 39. 171, 1841 ; J. G. F. Druce, *Journ. Chem., Soc.*, 119. 758, 1921 ; H. Jonas, *Chem. Centr.*, (2), 36. 607, 1865 ; C. Zulkowsky, *Chem. Ind.*, 22. 280, 1899 ; 24. 422, 1901 ; F. Zambonini, *Zeit. Kryst.*, 41. 53, 1906 ; J. J. Berzelius, *Schweigger's Journ.*, 6. 284, 1912 ; *Ann. Chim. Phys.*, (2), 5. 141, 1817 ; J. L. Proust, *ib.*, (1), 28. 213, 1798 ; *Journ. Phys.*, 51. 173, 1800 : 61. 338, 1804 ; R. Lüpke, *Zeit. phys, Chem. Unterr.*, 6. 176, 1893 ; R. E. Brown, *Chem. Gaz.*, 5. 60, 1847 ; E. Schunck, *ib.*, 7. 327, 1849 ; *Brit. Pat. No.* 12345, 1848 ; E. Haeffely, *ib.*, 603, 1854 ; *Chem. Gaz.*, 13. 59, 1855 ; *Phil. Mag.*, (4), 10. 290, 1855 ; P. A. Bolley, *Dingler's Journ.*, 145. 313, 1857 ; *Schweiz. Polyt. Ztg.*, 2. 92, 1857 ; T. Roberts and J. Dale, *Brit. Pat. No.* 2242, 1858 ; W. Prandtl, *Ber.*, 40. 2129, 1907 ; C. T. Barfoed, *Danske Vid. Selsks. Forh.*, (5), 7. 449, 1868 ; G. Tschermak, *Sitzber. Akad. Wien*, 44. 738, 1862 ; P. T. Austen, *Chem. News*, 46. 286, 1882 ; *Journ. Amer. Chem. Soc.*, 4. 285, 1882 ; G. E. Collins and J. K. Wood, *Journ. Chem. Soc.*, 121. 441, 1122, 1922 ; T. Ulke, *Proc. Amer. Inst. Min. Eng.*, 21. 240, 1892 : L. Elsner, *Chem. Tech. Mitt.*, 9. 44, 1860 ; *Polyt. Centrb.*, 494, 1891 ; H. Schulz, *Ueber eine den Goldpurpur analoge Verbindungen*, Göttingen, 1857 ; C. Fromherz, *Schweigger's Journ.*, 41. 257, 1824 ; *Pogg. Ann.*, 31. 677, 1834 ; R. W. Fox, *Journ. Roy. Inst.*, 1. 626, 1918 ; *Ann. Phil.*, 13. 467, 1819 ; J. A. Hedvall, *Journ. Phys. Chem.*, 28. 1316, 1924 ; J. A. Hedvall and N. von Zweigbergk, *Zeit. anorg. Chem.*, 108. 119, 1919 ; D. Balareff, *ib.*, 136. 216, 1924 ; 145. 117, 1925 ; J. A. Hedvall and J. Heuberger, *ib.*, 140. 243, 1924 ; M. Rüger, *Ker. Rund.*, 31, 79, 87, 99, 110, 1923 ; G. Aminoff, *Zeit. Kryst.*, 60, 262, 1924 ; H. Zocher, *ib.*, 112. 1, 1920.

[2] J. Malaguti, *Ann. Chim. Phys.*, (2), 61. 435, 1836 ; T. Leykauf, *Journ. prakt. Chem.*, (1), 19. 127, 1840 ; A. J. Fairie, *Journ. Chem. Soc.*, 4. 301, 1852 ; A. Maus, *Pogg. Ann.*, 11. 82, 1827 ; C. W. Eliott and F. H. Storer, *Proc. Amer. Acad.*, 5. 192, 1862 ; *Chem. News*, 6. 121, 136, 145, 157, 169, 182, 207, 217, 1862 ; E. Fleischer, *Arch. Pharm.*, (3), 2. 300, 1873 ; A. Leopold, *Magyar Chem. Foly.*, 11. 21, 1905 ; 12. 186, 1906 ; L. Petrik, *ib.*, 12. 100, 1906 ; *Centr. Glass. Ind.*, 6. 31, 1891 ; 21. 1729, 1906 ; *Sprech.*, 40. 361, 1907 ; W. A. Lethbridge, *Trans. Cer. Soc.*, 3. 9, 1903 ; C. E. Ramsden, *ib.*, 11. 29, 196, 1912 ; 12. 239, 1913 ; J. W. Mellor, *ib.*, 9. 79, 1910 ; R. H. H. Jones, *ib.*, 1. 1, 1901 ; F. J. Rogers and J. W. Mellor, *ib.*, 4. 66, 1905 ; H. Stein, *Sprech.*, 21. 825, 1888 ; 22. 706, 1889 ; A. Steinbrach, *ib.*, 24. 123, 1891 ; E. Meyer, *Trans-Amer. Cer. Soc.*, 1. 56, 1900 ; S. Geysbeak, *ib.*, 1. 62, 1900 ; W. A. Hull, *ib.*, 4. 231, 1902 ; 6. 148, 1904 ; R. Carter, *ib.*, 5. 242, 1903 ; O. Hensel, *ib.*, 5. 245, 1903 ; R. C. Purdy, *ib.*, 5. 249, 1903 ; 14. 178, 1912 ; R. C. Purdy and G. H. Brown, *ib.*, 11. 228, 1909 ; R. C. Purdy and A. S. Rea, *ib.*, 12. 518, 1911 ; H. A. Seger, *Gesammelte Schriften*, Berlin, 541, 1908 ; Easton, Pa., 2. 663, 1902 ; T. Deck, *La Faience*, Paris, 358, 1888 ; A. Brongniart, *Traité des arts ceramiques*, Paris, 2. 581, 1844 ; M. Rüger, *Ker. Rund.*, 31. 79, 87, 99, 110, 1923 ; J. A. Hedvall, *Arkiv Kemi Min. Geol.*, 5. 16, 1914 ; *Ueber Reaktionprodukte von Kobaltoxyden mit anderen Metalloxyden bei hohen Temperaturen*, Upsala, 110, 1915.

§ 15. The Fluorides of Tin and the Fluostannates

C. W. Scheele [1] found that aq. hydrofluoric acid has no sensible action on tin even when warmed, while a soln. of stannous oxide dissolves in that acid ; and J. L. Gay Lussac and L. J. Thénard, that when evaporated out of contact with air, it yields small white crystals of **stannous fluoride,** SnF_2. E. Frémy obtained the salt by the action of hydrogen fluoride, or of hydrofluostannous acid on stannous oxide. O. Unverdorben added a soln. of ammonium fluoride to one of stannous chloride, and found that lamellar plates of stannous fluoride were precipitated. J. J. Berzelius also obtained opaque prisms of the salt, which, according to J. C. G. de Marignac, belong to the monoclinic system, and have axial ratios $a : b : c = 2\cdot7204 : 1 : 1\cdot4078$, and $\beta = 109° \ 24'$. The salt has an acid taste. J. J. Berzelius said that when exposed to air, the salt is transformed into **stannic oxyfluoride,** $SnOF_2$. J. L. Gay Lussac and L. J. Thénard said it is easily soluble in water ; and O. Unverdorben, in an aq. soln. of potassium hydroxide. According to L. R. W. McCay, when hydrogen sulphide is passed into a soln. of stannous fluoride containing free acid, stannous sulphide is formed in the presence of much free sodium acetate ; stannic fluoride under similar conditions gives no precipitate. E. Frémy said that an excess of hydrofluoric acid and stannous oxide react, forming **hydrofluostannous acid,** H_2SnF_4, or $2HF.SnF_2$. According to R. Wagner, a soln. of stannous hydroxide in one of ammonium hydrofluoride furnishes crystals of **ammonium fluostannite,** $(NH_4)_2SnF_4.2H_2O$; and with potassium hydrofluoride, crystals of **potassium fluostannite,** $K_2SnF_4.2SnF_2.H_2O$, are formed.

According to J. L. Gay Lussac and L. J. Thénard,[2] when a soln. of stannic oxide in hydrofluoric acid is evaporated, an insoluble basic fluoride is formed ; and, according to J. J. Berzelius, when the soln. of stannic oxide in hydrofluoric acid is boiled, it coagulates like the white of an egg. H. Moissan said that at low temp., tin is not attacked by fluorine, but at 100°, white stannic fluoride is formed with incandescence. O. Ruff and W. Plato prepared **stannic fluoride,** SnF_4, by adding stannic chloride to anhydrous hydrofluoric acid, when a vigorous reaction occurs. The mixture was allowed to stand over-night in a vessel cooled by ice, and at room temp. for 4 hrs. It was then kept at 100° for a couple of days or until no more hydrogen chloride was given off. The temp. of the mixture was kept between 130° and 220°, to drive off stannic chloride. The residue has the composition $SnCl_4.SnF_4$, and it decomposes at a red heat with the evolution of stannic chloride. At 750°, the stannic fluoride sublimes. Thirty grams of stannic chloride gave 17 grms. of the fluoride. According to O. Ruff and W. Plato, stannic fluoride forms a snow-white crystalline mass of sp. gr. 4·780, and b.p. 705°. The salt is very hygroscopic, and dissolves in water with a hissing noise. When the soln. is boiled, or allowed to stand for some days, it deposits hydrated stannic oxide. N. H. Furman found stannic fluoride is more resistant than stannic chloride towards hydrolysis. The presence of hydrofluoric acid and of alkali fluorides hinders the precipitation of tin by hydrogen sulphide. J. J. Berzelius said that it reacts with silicon tetra-fluoride, forming the complex $SiF_4.SnF_4$, **silicon tin octofluoride.** O. Ruff and C. Albert found that it reacts with silicon hydrotrichloride at 200°, forming tin tetrachloride and silicon hydrotrifluoride, $SiHF_3$.

J. C. G. de Marignac showed that it forms a number of complex **fluostannates** isomorphous with the corresponding fluosilicates and fluotitanates, being salts of the hypothetical hydrofluostannic acid, H_2SnF_6. R. D. Hall and E. F. Smith found that when dissolved in sulphuric acid, the fluostannates do not react with morphine, codeine, resorcine, etc., like the fluotitanates. J. C. G. de Marignac prepared **ammonium fluostannates,** $(NH_4)_2SnF_6$, by treating ammonium stannate with hydrofluoric acid ; but it is much easier to make the salt by the action of ammonium fluoride or sulphate on silver or lead fluostannate. The salt seldom forms good crystals. The crystals belong to the trigonal system and have the axial ratio $a:c=1:0.8062$. The birefringence is negative. By adding ammonia and hydrofluoric acid to a soln. of the normal fluostannate, **tetrammonium octo-fluostannate,** $4NH_4F.SnF_4$, is formed. This salt loses ammonium fluoride below $100°$; and the soln. does not effervesce with ammonium carbonate. J. C. G. de Marignac made **lithium fluostannate,** $Li_2SnF_6.2H_2O$, by the action of hydrofluoric acid on lithium stannate. The monoclinic prisms have the axial ratios $a:b:c$ $=1.235:1:2.160$, and $\beta=118°\ 0'$. He obtained normal **sodium fluostannate,** Na_2SnF_6, as a crystalline crust by evaporating a soln. of the alkali stannate neutralized with hydrofluoric acid. The salt is probably isomorphous with the fluotitanate. 100 parts of water dissolve about 5·5 parts of salt at $20°$. J. C. G. de Marignac made **potassium fluostannate,** $K_2SnF_6.H_2O$, in an analogous way, the white crystalline plates resembling talc. These monoclinic crystals—the α-**salt**—have the axial ratios $a:b:c=0.9924:1:1.0520$, and $\beta=98°\ 42'$. H. Töpsöe gave 3·053 for the sp. gr. ; 100 parts of water at $18°$ dissolve 6·7 parts of salt, and 100 parts of boiling water, 43·9 parts of salt. At the same time, rhombic octa-hedral crystals—the β-**salt**—having the same composition are formed ; 100 parts of water dissolve 3·7 parts of salt at $18°$, and 100 parts of boiling water, 33·3 parts of salt. If the α-salt be digested at a gentle heat with insufficient water for com-plete soln., and preferably in the presence of a few drops of hydrofluoric acid, it passes into the β-salt. The latter is the stable form. The β-salt crystallizes unchanged on evaporating the soln. at a gentle heat ; but if a little potassium hydroxide is present, the α-salt is formed. According to F. Emich, the β-salt is obtained by mixing soln. of 27 grms. of stannic chloride in 270 c.c. of water and of 57 grms. of potassium fluoride in 170 c.c. of water. The dry crystals do not attack glass. J. C. G. de Marignac said the salt loses all its water at a little over $100°$, and that it melts at a red heat with the loss of hydrogen fluoride. He also obtained monoclinic prisms of potassium hydrohexafluostannate, $3KF.SnF_4.HF$, or $K_2SnF_6.KHF_2$, with the axial ratios $a:b:c=0.6277:1:0.4928$, and $\beta=93°\ 0'$. They lose very little weight at $100°$; at $250°$–$300°$, 5·40 per cent. is lost. The soln. effervesces with ammonium carbonate, but no precipitate is formed until the soln. is quite neutralized. A. Skrabel and J. Gruber prepared **rubidium fluo-stannate,** Rb_2SnF_6, by adding a soln. of the carbonate to a soln. of stannic acid in 40 per cent. hydrofluoric acid, and allowing the salt to crystallize. The hexagonal plates are optically negative and uniaxial; they made **cæsium fluostannate,** Cs_2SnF_6, in a similar manner. The hexagonal plates are optically uniaxial and negative.

J. C. G. de Marignac made blue, monoclinic, prismatic crystals of **copper fluostannate,** $CuSnF_6.4H_2O$, with axial ratios $a:b:c=0.7535:1:0.5591$, and $\beta=104°\ 10'$. The crystals of the corresponding **silver fluostannate,** $Ag_2SnF_6.4H_2O$, are so deliquescent that crystallographic data were not obtained. He made **calcium fluostannate,** $CaSnF_6.2H_2O$, by treating calcium stannate with hydro-fluoric acid, or potassium fluostannate with calcium chloride, and evaporating the soln. at a gentle heat. The badly formed crystals belong to the monoclinic system having the axial ratios $a:b:c=1.236:1:$ —, $\beta=110°\ 54'$. The crystals are not altered at $100°$, but lose water and hydrogen fluoride at a higher temp., forming a mixture of stannic oxide and calcium fluoride. The corresponding **strontium fluostannate,** $SrSnF_6.2H_2O$, forms small monoclinic crystals with the axial ratios $a:b:c=1.22:1:$ —, and $\beta=111°\ 9'$. They are isomorphous with the corre-sponding fluosilicate ; they do not lose water at $100°$, but are decomposed at a higher temp. At $18°$, 100 parts of water dissolve 18·2 parts of salt. Small crystals of anhydrous **barium fluostannate,** $BaSnF_6$, were obtained in an analogous manner ; they resemble barium fluosilicate. If a dil. aq. soln. of the anhydrous salt be slowly cooled, or spontaneously evaporated, plates of the *trihydrate,* $BaSnF_6.3H_2O$, are formed, resembling boric acid. F. Emich obtained the salt by mixing aq. soln. of stannic chloride and barium fluoride. According to J. C. G. de Marignac, the monoclinic crystals have the axial ratios $a:b:c=0.739:1:0.834$, and $\beta=105°\ 30'$.

At 18°, 100 parts of water dissolve 5·6 parts of salt. F. Emich said the crystalline salt attacks glass.

J. C. G. de Marignac obtained trigonal crystals of **magnesium fluostannate**, $MgSnF_6.6H_2O$, which were stable in air. The corresponding crystals of **zinc fluostannate**, $ZnSnF_6.6H_2O$, had the axial ratio $a : c = 1 : 0.5190$, and $a = 112° 7'$. The cleavage was perfect. B. Gossner gave 2·445 for the sp. gr., and he measured the sp. gr. of mixtures with the isomorphous molybdenato-fluoride, $ZnMoO_2F_4.6H_2O$. When heated, the salt loses water and hydrofluoric acid. Trigonal crystals of **cadmium fluostannate**, $CdSnF_6.6H_2O$, were obtained in an analogous manner. The trigonal crystals of **manganese fluostannate**, $MnSnF_6.6H_2O$, obtained in an analogous way, have the axial ratio $a : c = 1 : 0.5161$, and $a = 111° 12'$. They gradually effloresce in air. The corresponding **nickel fluostannate**, $NiSnF_6.6H_2O$, forms trigonal crystals with the axial ratio $a : c = 1 : 0.5245$, and $a = 112° 14'$. By treating lead stannate with hydrofluoric acid, J. C. G. de Marignac obtained thin 4- or 8-sided plates of **lead fluostannate**, $PbSnF_6.3H_2O$, corresponding with the barium salt. The monoclinic prisms have the axial ratios $a : b : c = 0.7485 : 1 : 0.8549$, and $\beta = 104° 18'$.

REFERENCES.

[1] C. W. Scheele, *Svenska Akad. Handl.*, **33.** 120, 1771 ; J. L. Gay Lussac and L. J. Thénard, *Mém. Soc. Arcueil*, **2.** 317, 1809 ; E. Frémy, *Ann. Chim. Phys.*, (3), **47.** 37, 1856 ; O. Unverdorben, *Trommsdorff's Journ. Pharm.*, **9.** 22, 1824 ; J. J. Berzelius, *Pogg. Ann.*, **1.** 34, 1824 ; J. C. G. de Marignac, *Ann. Mines*, (5), **12.** 20, 1857 ; L. R. W. McCay, *Journ. Amer. Chem. Soc.*, **31.** 373, 1909 ; N. H. Furman, *ib.*, **40.** 906, 1918 ; R. Wagner, *Ber.*, **19.** 896, 1886.

[2] J. J. Berzelius, *Pogg. Ann.*, **1.** 34, 1824 ; J. L. Gay Lussac and L. J. Thénard, *Mém. Soc. Arcueil*, **2.** 317, 1809 ; N. H. Furman, *Journ. Amer. Chem. Soc.*, **40.** 906, 1918 ; A. Skrabel and J. Gruber, *Monatsh.*, **38.** 19, 1917 ; O. Ruff and W. Plato, *Ber.*, **37.** 681, 1904 ; O. Ruff and C. Albert, *ib.*, **38.** 55, 1905 ; B. Gossner, *ib.*, **40.** 2373, 1907 ; *Zeit. Kryst.*, **42.** 481, 1907 ; R. D. Hall and E. F. Smith, *Proc. Amer. Phil. Soc.*, **44.** 177, 1905 ; H. Moissan, *Ann. Chim. Phys.*, (6), **24.** 224, 1891 ; J. C. G. de Marignac, *Ann. Mines*, (5), **15.** 221, 1859 ; F. Emich, *Monatsh.*, **25.** 907, 1904 ; H. Töpsöe, *Arch. Sciences Genève*, (2), **45.** 223, 1872.

§ 16. The Stannous Chlorides

Tin furnishes two types of chloride corresponding with the oxides—stannous chloride, $SnCl_2$, and stannic chloride, $SnCl_4$. Each of these forms hydrates, and hydrochlorides. The two chlorides were not clearly distinguished until B. Pelletier's [1] investigation : *Sur plusiers propriétés du muriate d'étain*, in 1792. The so-called *tin trichloride* obtained by J. N. von Fuchs, and J. J. Berzelius, by dissolving tin sesquioxide in hydrochloric acid, is probably a mixture of stannous and stannic chlorides. Anhydrous **stannous chloride**, $SnCl_2$, was formerly called *butter of tin*, and it was made by gradually heating tin or tin amalgam with mercurous or mercuric chloride, when the mercury volatilizes ; it was also made by heating tin in a stream of hydrogen chloride : $Sn + 2HCl = SnCl_2 + H_2$; and A. Ditte [2] made it by heating stannous sulphide under similar conditions : $SnS + 2HCl = SnCl_2 + H_2S$. According to J. Kelley and E. F. Smith, the continued action of the hydrogen chloride in the cold completely converts stannous sulphide into chloride without any volatilization. It is, however, impossible to separate stannous and stannic sulphides by this method, as heat is necessary to drive out the stannic salt, and this causes a partial volatilization of the stannous salt. Stannous chloride can be made by heating the dihydrated $SnCl_2.2H_2O$ in a closed vessel, gradually to redness ; the anhydrous chloride distils over after the water has been expelled. H. Capitaine gently heated the dihydrate in a capacious crucible until frothing ceased. The molten mass remaining was poured into a small crucible and the cold mass coarsely powdered and heated in a glass retort. The first fraction which distils over is stannous chloride, and the last fraction may contain iron chloride, and requires a second distillation to free it from that impurity. T. Rondelli heated the ore with carbonaceous matter and chlorine; with carbon monoxide and chlorine or hydrogen chloride; or with carbonyl chloride.

If a soln. of tin in warm hydrochloric acid, or if a soln. of stannous chloride in dil. hydrochloric acid be evaporated and cooled, crystals of **dihydrated stannous chloride**, $SnCl_2.2H_2O$, also called *tin salt*, are formed. C. Nöllner, and E. Bérard described the preparation on a large scale in copper or stoneware vessels. A. Scheurer-Kestner described the preparation of the salt from a soln. of stannous hydroxide or sulphide in hydrochloric acid. The dihydrate was analyzed by J. C. G. de Marignac, F. Penny, and T. H. Henry. The analysis of commercial tin salt was discussed by W. Minor, and F. Dietze. A. Ditte reported that small crystals of **monohydrated stannous chloride**, $SnCl_2.H_2O$, are formed by the action of hydrogen chloride on crystals of the dihydrate, and afterwards fusing and cooling the product. A. Scheurer-Kestner said that **tetrahydrated stannous chloride**, $SnCl_2.4H_2O$, is formed when a mol of stannous hydroxide is dissolved in a mol of stannic chloride of sp. gr. 1·8, and the soln. cooled in ice-water; if more stannous hydroxide is used, the dihydrate is produced. C. T. Gerlach could not make the tetrahydrate.

The physical properties of the stannous chlorides.—Anhydrous stannous chloride appears as a white or greyish-white translucent mass with a conchoidal fracture; and when cooled after fusion, C. M. Marx found that it becomes syrupy and then solidifies. According to A. E. Nordenskjöld, the sublimed **crystals** are colourless and belong to the rhombic system, with axial ratios $a : b : c = 0·7366 : 1 : 1·0680$. The crystals of the dihydrate are transparent colourless prisms, which were found by J. C. G. de Marignac to belong to the monoclinic system, and to have the axial ratios $a : b : c = 1·2888 : 1 : 1·2452$, and $\beta = 114° \ 58'$. The anhydrous salt was analyzed by J. Davy, and V. and C. Meyer; and the dihydrate by J. C. G. Marignac, F. Penny, and T. H. Henry. J. J. Berzelius' analysis made the dihydrate a mono-hydrate, and E. Turner's, a trihydrate.

F. Penny found the **specific gravity** of the dihydrate to be 2·710 at 15·5°, and F. W. Clarke, 2·634 at 24°. According to A. Michel and L. Kraft, the sp. gr. of a sat. aq. soln. at 15° is 1·827, and C. T. Gerlach found the sp. gr. of soln. containing ω per cent. of $SnCl_2.2H_2O$, at 15°.

ω	2	10	20	30	40	50	60	70	75
Sp. gr.	1·013	1·068	1·144	1·230	1·330	1·445	1·582	1·745	1·840

W. Biltz and E. Birk gave 3·952 for the sp. gr. of fused stannous chloride at 25°/4°, and 47·98 for the mol. vol. W. Klemm and W. Biltz gave for the sp. gr., D, of the molten chloride at $\theta°$, $D = 3·394 - 0·00120(\theta - 245°)$ between 278° and 556°; and for the vol., v, at $\theta°$ when v_m is the vol. at the m.p., $v = v_m\{1 + 0·00036(\theta - 245)\}$; the mol. vol. at the m.p. is 55·9 and at 25°, 48·00. R. Lorenz and W. Herz gave 3·367 for the sp. gr. and 56·31 for the mol. vol. at the m.p. F. Ephraim studied the vol. contraction attending the formation of the tin halides; and I. I. Saslawsky found 0·98 for the ratio of the mol. vol. to the sum of the at. vol. of the constituents. S. Motylewsky found the **drop-weight** of stannous chloride to be 111 mgrms. when that of water at 0° is 100 mgrms. The **vapour density** of stannous chloride was found by R. Rieth to be variable; V. and C. Meyer gave 12·96 at 619°–697° when referred to air, and this agrees with the formula Sn_2Cl_4; T. Carnelley said the temp. at which vap. density was made was here too close to the b.p., and other observations by V. Meyer and H. Züblin, and H. Biltz and V. Meyer gave:

—	639°	678°	699°	759°	790°	113°
Vap. density	8·85	8·57	8·49	8·26	7·7	7·08

This makes it probable that Sn_2Cl_4 does not represent the mol. state of the vap., although the numbers are a little high for the normal $SnCl_2$ mol. A. Werner found from the raising of the b.p. of pyridine, the mol. wt. in that solvent is 202·89, and in ethyl sulphide, 176—the calculated value for $SnCl_2$ is 189. J. Schröder and H. Steiner found the mol. wt. is half the normal value with very dil. soln. of stannous chloride in boiling methyl acetate. N. Castoro found the mol. wt. is normal for $SnCl_2$ during the freezing of soln. in urethane.

According to R. Lorenz and W. Herz, the coeff. of **thermal expansion**, a, of the molten salt is 0·000319 ; and the relation $aT_m=0.166$ is in line with that for related chlorides. According to W. D. Bancroft and H. B. Weiser, stannous chloride is decomposed in the bunsen flame furnishing a deposit of metallic tin. A. Juliusberger measured the **vapour pressure**, p mm., of stannous chloride ; and C. G. Maier found :

	372·7°	447·8°	499·4°	536·2°	563·1°	596·6°	617·5°	633·9°	641·0°
p	10·2	56·4	116·6	205·3	346·9	537·5	706·3	882·0	972·4

According to J. Davy, anhydrous stannous chloride boils at a red heat with partial decomposition ; T. Carnelley and W. Williams gave 617°–628° for the **boiling point** ; H. Biltz and V. Meyer, 606·1° ; C. G. Maier, 622·8° ; F. Freyer and V. Meyer, 606° ; T. Karantassis, 245° ; J. McCrae, 603·25° ; and A. Helfenstein, 606°. T. H. Henry found that the dihydrate loses water over sulphuric acid in vacuo. A. Vogel found that when the anhydrous chloride is strongly heated, stannic chloride is given off, then stannous chloride, and a black mass remains which dissolves in hydrochloric acid, forming stannous chloride and hydrogen ; when the hydrated salt is heated it gives off water and hydrogen chloride, and a little chlorine ; while an oxychloride remains. If air be excluded, the salt can be dehydrated with but little hydrolysis. C. T. Gerlach found a sat. aq. soln. boils at 121·7°. J. A. Muller calculated the degree of polymerization in the critical state to be 1·404. L. Graetz gave 250° for the **melting point** of stannous chloride ; O. Menge, 245° ; G. Hermann, 247·2° ; and J. Kendall and co-workers, 246·8° ; while F. Penny gave 37·7° to 40·5° for the dihydrate. H. V. Regnault found the **heat of vaporization** of stannous chloride to be 46·84 Cals. C. G. Maier gave for the mol. heat of vaporization, 21,100 cals. at 622·8° and at 371·4°. H. V. Regnault found the **specific heat** between 20° and 99° to be 0·10162. J. Thomsen found the **heat of formation.** $(Sn,2HCl_{gas})=36.4$ Cals., and $(Sn,Cl_2)=80.79$ Cals. with solid stannous chloride ; $(SnCl_2,2H_2O)=5.72$ Cals. at 18° ; and for the **heat of solution,** $SnCl_2.2H_2O+Aq.$, 53·7 Cals., and $(SnCl_2,Aq.)=350$ Cals. T. H. Henry found that the dissolution of the dihydrate in 100 c.c. of water lowers the temp. from 14·4° to −2·8°. W. Biltz and W. Fischer found the heat of soln. of stannous chloride in one per cent. hydrochloric acid to be 0·9 Cal. G. P. Drossbach investigated the ultra-red **absorption spectrum ;** and W. Jevons, the band spectrum. J. O. Perrine found no **fluorescence** in the ultra-violet rays. S. W. Young measured the **electrical conductivity** of hydrochloric acid soln. of stannous chloride. L. Graetz gave for the electrical conductivity of stannous chloride k, referred to mercury=1 :

	140°	160°	190°	200°	240°	250°	260°	300°	350°
$k \times 10^8$	6	12·5	60	360	5500	6650	7600	9600	10320

W. Klemm and W. Biltz gave 0·002 to 0·014 mho for the conductivity of the solid chloride between 222° and 244° ; and for the molten chloride, 0·89 mho at 263° ; 1·12, at 302° ; 1·18, at 314° ; 1·42, at 353° ; and 1·72, at 411° ; and the mol. conductivity, μ, at $\theta°$ is $\mu=43.8+0.350(\theta-245)$. Contrasted with stannic chloride, the electrical conductivity of stannous chloride is very high ; and G. von Hevesy noted in general a marked change in the b.p. and conductivity when an element changes its valency. K. F. Ochs measured the oxidation potential of hydrochloric acid soln. of stannous chloride. G. Tammann studied the electrode potential of magnesium, manganese, aluminium, thallium, zinc, cadmium, lead, and iron in contact with fused stannous chloride. S. Meyer found the **magnetic susceptibility** of stannous chloride to be -0.334×10^{-6} per gram, or -0.055×10^{-6} per mol., or -0.29×10^{-6} mass units at 18° ; and G. Quincke, -0.07×10^{-6} mass units.

The **solubility** of anhydrous stannous chloride in water is high, and the dihydrate is formed ; the dihydrate is also readily dissolved by water. According to R. Engel, 100 parts of water at 0° dissolve 83·9 parts of stannous chloride, while A. Michel and L. Kraft found that at 15°, 100 c.c. of a sat. soln. contain 133·3 grms. of $SnCl_2$, and 49·4 grms. of water. R. Engel found that the solubility in water is diminished by the presence of a small proportion of *hydrochloric acid*, but increased by a large proportion ; H. Capitaine found the anhydrous salt is readily dissolved by *alcohol ;* and M. de Jong, by *ether.* According to A. Naumann, at 18°, a sat. soln. of stannous chloride in *acetone* contains 1·8 grms. of acetone for every gram of stannous chloride, and the soln. has a sp. gr. 1·6 at 18°. Stannous chloride is also soluble in *pyridine,* and *acetic ether.* A. Werner investigated the solubility in pyridine. Boiling *methyl acetate* was found by J. Schröder and H. Steiner to dissolve 15·7 per cent. of stannous chloride. F. L. Shinn said the salt is insoluble in *ethylamine.* V. Meyer found the dihydrate is easily soluble in alcohol, and J. Thiele and O. Dimrot, in glacial *acetic acid.* O. Aschan found 100 grms. of 95 per cent. *formic acid* dissolve 4·1 grms. of stannous chloride at 19°. S. von Laszczynsky found 100 parts of *ethyl acetate* dissolve 31·2 grms. of the dihydrate at −2° ; 35·5 grms. at 22° ; and 73·4 grms. at 82°.

The chemical properties of the stannous chlorides.—F. de Carli studied the reduction of stannous chloride by **hydrogen**. H. Capitaine said that anhydrous stannous chloride is fairly stable in air ; only a little oxidation could be detected in 3 weeks, and the product was quite soluble in water. When heated to its b.p., a mixture of stannic and stannous chlorides is distilled over, and a yellow oxy-chloride remains ; H. Schulze also found that when stannous chloride is heated in **oxygen,** stannic chloride and oxide are formed. According to M. Berthelot, when stannous chloride and oxygen are heated in a sealed tube to 500°, the reaction can by symbolized $SnCl_2 + O = SnOCl_2 + 50·4$ Cals. N. W. Fischer found that hydrated stannous chloride absorbs atm. oxygen and forms an oxychloride. If the aq. soln. be exposed to the air, the turbid soln. becomes clear, and acquires a yellow colour. The reaction is slower the more conc. the soln. H. Capitaine made observations on this subject, and J. W. Mallet said that a fairly conc. soln. of stannous chloride when kept over a year became turbid, and deposited a transparent gelatinous colloid of a yellowish colour, which, when washed, and dried at atm. temp., had a composition corresponding with what he called *chlorostannic acid*, $HO.SnO.Cl$. To preserve the aq. soln. from oxidation, C. F. Mohr recommended keeping some tin immersed in the liquid ; or protecting it from air—say, by covering the liquor with a layer of petroleum ; or, according to H. Morgan, keeping it in an atm. of coal-gas. J. Löwenthal found that an aq. soln. of stannous chloride was not oxidized when oxygen was passed through the liquid, or by a soln. of oxygen in water ; but it was oxidized in the presence of a little potassium permanganate or dichromate. A. Scheurer-Kestner showed that oxygen is absorbed by dil. soln. of stannous chloride, forming stannic chloride, and stannic acid ; but with conc. soln. oxygen is not absorbed. S. W. Young showed that the oxidation of aq. soln. of stannous chloride is promoted by caoutchouc, sulphur, ferrous sulphate, and cupric sulphate ; and retarded by manganous salts, some alkaloids, and potassium cyanide. The first stage of the process of oxidation involves the formation of stannic chloride, and this is then hydrolyzed, forming an oxychloride. Strongly alkaline soln. of stannous chloride are oxidized by atm. oxygen in a normal way without showing any signs of the activation of the oxygen. M. C. Boswell and J. V. Dickson found that fused sodium hydroxide oxidizes stannous chloride with the evolution of hydrogen. A. W. Francis measured the velocity of oxidation of stannous chloride. N. R. Dhar found that the oxidation of stannous chloride simultaneously induces the oxidation of soln. of sodium arsenite, formate and oxalate ; and that the oxidation of stannous salts by air is retarded by easily oxidizable substances like hydroquinone, sugars, glycerol, sodium arsenite, and some organic substances. N. N. Mittra and N. R. Dhar found the oxidation of a soln. of stannous chloride in air favours the simultaneous oxidation of ferrous ammonium sulphate, and is favoured by the simultaneous oxidation of sulphurous acid.

The solubility of stannous chloride in **water,** and the formation of hydrated stannous chlorides have been previously discussed. According to N. W. Fischer, when stannous chloride is dissolved in a little air-free water, the soln. remains clear, but becomes turbid when dil. owing to the formation of an oxychloride. The soln. remains clear in the presence of hydrochloric or tartaric acid, or ammonium chloride ; and N. W. Fischer showed that the aq. soln. is hydrolyzed when heated to 200° in a sealed tube, and a yellow flocculent oxychloride is produced. J. L. Proust reported stannous oxychloride to be formed by treating a soln. of stannous chloride with insufficient potash-lye for complete precipitation. J. Davy used a similar process, and his analysis of the washed and dried product corresponded with **stannous oxychloride,** $SnO.SnCl_2.3H_2O$, or $Sn_2OCl_2.3H_2O$. A. Ditte obtained crystals of what was regarded as the same salt, but with four mols of water, $Sn_2OCl_2.4H_2O$, by treating the $3SnO.SnCl_2.6H_2O$ salt with a soln. of stannous chloride. According to J. Davy, this compound decomposes when heated, forming water, hydrochloric acid, stannous chloride and its hydrate, and stannous oxide. It froths vigorously when treated with conc. nitric acid ; it gives off hydrogen chloride when treated with conc. sulphuric acid ; and it dissolves without effervescence, forming stannous salts when treated with hydrochloric, acetic, dil. nitric or dil. sulphuric acid. H. F. Keller found small acicular or tabular crystals of stannous oxychloride, Sn_2OCl_2, lining the cavities in some metal objects in the aboriginal cemetery, Hogtown Bayou, Florida. A. Ditte emphasized that in preparing stannous oxychloride by the hydrolysis of stannous chloride, the soln. should be protected from air. He reported that **stannous tetraoxydichloride,** $4SnO.SnCl_2.6H_2O$, is produced as a gelatinous precipitate from an aq. soln. of stannous chloride ; and when digested in an aq. soln. of stannous chloride, it furnishes a white crystalline powder of **stannous trioxytetrachloride,** $3SnO.2SnCl_2.6H_2O$. This product is sparingly soluble in water, and readily soluble in dil. acids. All the stannous oxychlorides are decomposed by hot water, forming stannous oxide. According to C. M. Carson, **stannous tetradecahydroxytetrachloride,** $2SnCl_2.7Sn(OH)_2$, is the most basic of all the basic stannous chlorides. A slightly variable, crystalline material of approximately **trihydrated stannous pentoxyhexachloride,** $3SnCl_2.5SnO.3H_2O$, is the precipitate commonly formed by the action of boiling potassium hydroxide on an excess of stannous chloride, and there is no compound of intermediate composition. The precipitates usually formed by the action of water on stannous chloride contain such a large proportion of stannic compound that the analyses are of no value in ascertaining the composition of the basic stannous chlorides.

According to M. Berthelot, **chlorine** converts stannous chloride into stannic chloride, $SnCl_2+Cl_2=SnCl_{4liq.}+48\cdot8$ Cals. ; and in aq. soln., $SnCl_{2aq.}+Cl_2$ $=SnCl_{4aq}+72-78\cdot2$ Cals. A. Ladenberg found that with **bromine,** anhydrous stannous chloride forms the dichlorodibromide ; while in aq. soln., S. W. Young and M. Adams found that stannic salts are formed. A. W. Francis studied the speed of the reaction. C. Lenormand showed that **iodine** has no perceptible action at ordinary temp. on stannous chloride, but when the two substances are in contact, the stannous chloride gradually becomes pale red. V. Thomas showed that anhydrous stannous bromide decolorizes a soln. of iodine in carbon disulphide, and on evaporation a mixture of stannic iodide and iodine trichloride is formed, but no dichlorodiiodide is produced. In aq. soln., S. W. Young and M. Adams found that a mixture of iodine and stannous chloride furnishes mixed crystals of stannous chloride and iodide. M. C. Schuyten said that when iodine or bromine are triturated with a soln. of stannous chloride, the halogen is greedily absorbed, the mixture becomes turbid, and finally clear. For the solubility of stannous chloride in **hydrochloric acid,** vide supra. A. Ditte observed no formation of a *stannous hydrochloride* when **hydrogen chloride** is passed over crystals of hydrated stannous chloride. According to R. Engel, when hydrogen chloride is passed into a sat. aq. soln. of stannous chloride in water, a part of the salt is at first precipitated, but later on is dissolved. If the soln. sat. with hydrogen chloride at 0° is cooled to −40°, crystals of trihydrated **hydrotrichlorostannous acid,** $HSnCl_3$, are formed. The salt melts at −27° to −28°. This acid furnishes **trichlorostannites** of the type $MSnCl_3$. S. W. Young measured the electrical conductivity of soln. of stannous chloride in hydrochloric acid, and inferred that hydrotrichlorostannous acid, $HSnCl_3$, and **hydrotetrachlorostannous acid,** H_2SnCl_4, are formed. He also found that potassium chloride and potassium iodide have a marked tendency to form complexes with stannous chloride. J. C. G. de Marignac obtained a series of **tetrachlorostannites ;** and A. B. Poggiale reported a series of **hexachlorostannites,** but G. M. Richardson could not verify this result—*vide infra.* According to A. J. Balard, a soln. of stannous chloride reduces **hypochlorous acid** to chlorine. A. Naumann and co-workers found the oxidation of stannous chloride by a mixture of **potassium chlorate** is much accelerated by a trace of vanadic oxide. F. Jean showed that with **antimony pentachloride,** stannous chloride forms a mixture of stannic and antimonous chlorides.

If a soln. of stannous chloride be boiled with **sulphur,** G. Vortmann and C. Padberg found that half the tin is precipitated as stannous sulphide, and half remains in soln. as stannic chloride. If much free hydrochloric acid be present, all the tin is converted into stannic chloride, and hydrogen sulphide is evolved—*vide* sulphur— and E. Trautmann said that a hydrochloric acid soln. of stannous chloride acts on sulphur or **selenium,** forming respectively hydrogen sulphide or selenide. Stannous sulphide is precipitated when **hydrogen sulphide** is passed into a soln. of stannous chloride. E. Hering found that a soln. of stannous chloride becomes turbid when treated with **sulphur dioxide,** especially when heated, forming stannic chloride and sulphide : $6SnCl_2 + 2SO_2 + 8HCl = 5SnCl_4 + SnS_2 + 4H_2O$. M. M. P. Muir observed the separation of sulphur when a hot soln. of stannous chloride is treated with sulphur dioxide. R. G. Durrant found that the result of the action of sulphur dioxide on stannous chloride depends on the relative proportions of the components of the reaction. The primary reaction is $3SnCl_2 + 6HCl + H_2SO_3 = 3SnCl_4 + H_2S + 3H_2O$, and this is accompanied by the three consecutive reactions : $2H_2S + H_2SO_3 = 3H_2O + 3S$; $2H_2S + SnCl_4 = SnS_2 + 4HCl$; and $H_2S + SnCl_2 = SnS + 2HCl$. There is a slight reversion of the oxidation process : $SnCl_4 + H_2SO_3 + H_2O = SnCl_2 + 2HCl + H_2SO_4$. For complete oxidation, the stannous chloride, sulphur dioxide, and hydrochloric acid must be approximately in the proportions 3 : 1·55 : 6. The speed of the reaction in the presence of hydrochloric acid is bimolecular—*vide* sulphur dioxide. J. Girardin found that the dissolution of hydrated stannous chloride in hydrochloric acid containing a trace of sulphurous acid furnishes a yellow turbid liquid, which, when diluted with water, evolves a little hydrogen sulphide, and precipitates a brown mixture of stannic oxide and sulphide. N. S. von Fedoroff showed that sulphides of other metals—copper, arsenic, antimony, bismuth, and platinum—are formed when their salts are treated with hydrochloric acid soln. of stannous chloride and sulphur dioxide, while all the tin remains in soln. as stannic chloride. A. Vogel found that conc. **sulphuric acid** and a cold soln. of stannous chloride produce only a little hydrogen chloride, a little stannic sulphate, stannic chloride, sulphur dioxide, hydrogen sulphide, and free sulphur. R. G. Durrant said that the action of an excess of conc. sulphuric acid on hydrated stannic chloride tak-s p ace in three consecutive stages : (i) dehydration ; (ii) the liberation of hydrogen chloride between 20° and 90° ; and (iii) the liberation of sulphur dioxide between 130° and 200° with the formation of stannic sulphate : $SnSO_4 + 2H_2SO_4 = Sn(SO_4)_2 + 2H_2O + SO_2$. If water be present, a number of secondary reactions occur owing to the action of the sulphurous acid and the hydrogen chloride in soln. According to C. C. Persoz, a hot soln. of stannous chloride gives a precipitate of stannic sulphide when treated with **trithionic acid.**

The behaviour of **ammonia** towards aq. soln. of stannous chloride is indicated in connection with the analytical reactions of tin. F. Friedrichs found that stannous chloride forms a yellow compound of low solubility when treated with liquid ammonia; the soln. separates into two phases at 120°. C. C. Persoz found that warm stannous chloride absorbs gaseous ammonia, forming **stannous amminochloride,** $SnCl_2.NH_3$. J. J. Berzelius added ammonia to a soln. of stannous chloride until the precipitate first formed redissolved, and obtained crystals—supposed to be ammonium chlorostannite—by evaporating the soln. in vacuo. W. Biltz and W. Fischer found for the temp. at which the vap. press. is 100 mm., and for the heat of dissociation in Cals. per mol of NH_3, for **stannous enneamminochloride,** $SnCl_2.9NH_3$, —55°, and 7·6 respectively; **stannous tetramminochloride,** $SnCl_2.4NH_3$, +15°, and 9·3. G. L. Clark examined the relative stability of these and the corresponding ammines of the other halides. H. Franzen and O. von Mayer added **hydrazine hydrate** drop by drop to a clear alcoholic soln. of stannous chloride, separated the precipitate by suction; washed it with alcohol, and ether, and the product, dried in vacuo, corresponded with **stannous dihydrazinochloride,** $Sn(N_2H_4)_2Cl_2$. The compound is brownish-white; insoluble in aq. ammonia, easily decomposed by water; and when heated decomposes explosively. O. von Dumreicher found that at 100°, **hydroxylamine** is rapidly reduced to ammonia by stannous chloride. According to A. Scheurer-Kestner, **nitric acid** acts on a soln. of stannous chloride, forming stannic chloride, β-stannic acid, and red oxides of nitrogen. A. Naumann and coworkers found that the oxidation of stannous chloride by nitric acid is much accelerated by a trace of vanadic oxide. In the presence of hydrochloric acid, the nitric acid is reduced to ammonia: $8SnCl_2+18HCl+2HNO_3=7SnCl_4+(NH_4)_2SnCl_6 +6H_2O$; and in the absence of hydrochloric acid, the nitric acid is reduced to nitric oxide: $6SnCl_2+4HNO_3=3SnCl_4+3SnO_2+4NO+2H_2O$. E. Divers and T. Haga found that with dil. nitric acid in the presence of hydrochloric acid, stannous oxide furnishes hydroxylamine, etc.; and with nitric oxide, hydroxylamine, nitrogen, etc. F. Raschig said a cold conc. soln. of stannous chloride does not alter nitric acid; and O. von Dumreicher, that a cold soln. of stannous chloride reduces nitric acid, and nitric oxide to hydroxylamine; while with a hot soln. ammonia is formed. M. Coblens and J. K. Bernstein found that a drop of ferrous sulphate soln. in one of stannous chloride reduces nitric acid to nitric oxide; L. H. Milligan and G. R. Gillette obtained a 90 per cent. yield of hydroxylamine by the action of stannous chloride on nitric acid provided the temp. is kept low; and M. Coblens and J. K. Bernstein obtained hydroxylamine when **sodium nitrate** or **silver hyponitrite** is added slowly to a soln. of stannous chloride. F. Raschig observed that **nitric oxide** is not reduced by a cold conc. soln. of stannous chloride and that an aq. soln. of **nitrous acid** furnishes nitrous oxide, and the red oxides of nitrogen. O. von Dumreicher obtained a similar result, and found that **nitrous oxide** is not reduced by stannous chloride. H. Wölbling found that stannous chloride does **not** unite with **nitrogen sulphide,** N_4S_4, but reduces that compound to NSH. H. Schiff found **arsenic oxide** is reduced to arsenious oxide; and, according to P. Woulfe, to arsenic if it be digested for a long time in soln. of stannous chloride in hydrochloric acid; and A. Bettendorf employed the reaction as distinguishing test for arsenic. M. de Jong used an ethereal soln. of stannous chloride as a test for arsenic. P. Woulfe also reduced **antimonous oxide** to antimony in a similar way. A. Vogel found **bismuth nitrate** is reduced by stannous chloride to black bismuth monoxide.

According to F. von Kügelgen, a mixture of stannous chloride and **calcium carbide** can be inflamed with a match, and the reaction proceeds with incandescence and the production of pulverulent tin. H. Goldschmidt and E. Sunde showed that stannous chloride reduces many organic compounds—e.g. nitro-compounds to amides, etc. Reactions with organic compounds were also studied by O. von Dumreicher, F. Uty, P. Soltsien, G. Gimel, P. Pfeiffer, H. Goldschmidt and co-workers, etc. B. Köhnlein found that **propyl iodide** readily reacts with stannous chloride.

In the general case, tin is precipitated from soln. by the more electropositive metals in the electrochemical series—**1**. 16, 2. Tin can be precipitated from soln. of stannous salts by many metals—*e.g.* **magnesium, zinc, cadmium, aluminium,** etc. H. Mouraour found that with magnesium powder there is a brisk evolution of hydrogen when tin is precipitated from soln. of stannous chloride. N. W. Fischer found that **iron** precipitates tin from soln. of stannous chloride, but not from boiling soln. ; H. Schulze said that the soln. must be neutral ; and J. Thiele, that electrolytic iron gives the best result, for iron which has been heated to redness does not precipitate the tin. A. M. Pleischel found that **lead** precipitates tin quantitatively from soln. of stannous chloride or nitrate. The reaction $Pb+SnCl_2 \rightleftharpoons Sn+PbCl_2$ was studied by R. Lorenz and M. Mannheimer. H. Reinsch found that **copper** precipitates tin as greyish-black powder from a soln. strongly acid with hydrochloric acid, especially in the presence of air and from boiling soln.

The behaviour of stannous chloride towards **alkali hydroxides,** and **alkali carbonates** is indicated in connection with the analytical reactions of tin, and the action of water on this chloride. E. Lenssen showed that in the presence of tartaric acid, soln. of stannous chloride remain clear when treated with sodium hydroxide or carbonate. The oxidation of stannous chloride by fusion with sodium hydroxide is supposed by M. C. Boswell and J. V. Dickson to be due to the decomposition of the water, and the escape of hydrogen. When stannous chloride is heated with **sodium nitrate** or **potassium chlorate,** H. Schulze found that stannic chloride and oxide are formed. R. Brönner found that potassium chlorate energetically oxidizes stannous to stannic chloride. In general, stannous chloride acts as a strong reducing agent, and it is itself simultaneously oxidized to stannic chloride. According to R. E. Liesegang, the oxidation of the stannous salts is accelerated by exposure to light—stannous bromide is quite sensitive to light, while stannous chloride is but slightly affected. Many salts are reduced to a lower stage of oxidation or to the metal. Thus, **chromic acid** is reduced to a chromic salt ; and, according to H. Schiff, **tungstic acid,** and **molydic acid** form the blue lower oxides. T. Warynsky and M. Mdivani showed that **vanadium pentoxide** is quantitatively reduced to the tetroxide, V_2O_4. J. N. von Fuchs studied the reduction of **manganic salts** by stannous chloride. A. V. Harcourt showed that the greater the amount of water employed in the soln. of a given amount of stannous chloride, the greater the amount of a standard soln. of **potassium permanganate** required for the titration. If air-free water be employed this phenomenon is not observed. The same amount of permanganate is required, however much water be employed. It was hence inferred that the oxygen dissolved in the water as well as the permanganate oxidizes the stannous salt ; but oxygen dissolved in water has no perceptible action on the stannous salt alone. Air can oxidize the stannous chloride only simultaneously with the permanganate. W. Ostwald called such reactions *coupled reactions.* **Cupric oxide** and **cupric salts** are reduced to cuprous chloride ; the reaction was studied by G. Viard. According to A. Vogel, **mercuric oxide, mercuric chloride,** and **mercuric cyanide** are reduced to mercurous chloride ; and **mercurous chloride,** in turn, is reduced to mercury. The reaction : $SnCl_2+2HgCl_2=SnCl_4+2HgCl$, was studied by N. A. Tananaeff. A. Lottermoser found that when a dil. soln. of **mercurous nitrate** is treated with a soln. of stannous chloride containing but a trace of free hydrochloric acid, colloidal mercury is formed. With **silver salts,** metallic silver is precipitated ; according to A. Ditte, the reaction is very sensitive for a purple precipitate is produced by silver nitrate when only 0·001 grm. of stannous chloride is contained in a litre of water. When a **gold salt** is added to a soln. of stannous chloride, purple of Cassius is precipitated. A. Vogel found that red or brown lead dioxide is reduced to lead chloride ; while M. de Jong found that lead sulphate is dissolved by a hydrochloric acid soln. of stannous chloride. J. N. von Fuchs, J. Löwenthal, L. V. Pissarjewsky, and L. Blum studied the reduction of **ferric salts** to ferrous salts by stannous oxide or chloride. L. Kahlenberg indicated that the reaction between stannous and ferric chlorides is bimolecular ; while A. A. Noyes represented it as termolecular : $2FeCl_3+SnCl_2=SnCl_4+2FeCl_2$, or $dx/dt=k(a-x)(b-x)^2$, where a represents the initial conc. of the stannous chloride, and b that of ferric chloride; x represents the amount of substance changed in the time t; and k the affinity constant dependent on conc., temp., etc. In the presence of acid, the reaction appears to approximate to the bimolecular reaction of L. Kahlenberg. According to F. L. Kortright, the ferric chloride is hydrolyzed in soln., and only the non-hydrolyzed portion takes part in the reaction. The effect of neutral salts on the reaction was investigated by W. F. Timoféeff and co-workers. S. W. Young studied the oxidation of stannous chloride by various reagents.

Complex salts of stannous chloride.—J. L. Proust, and J. J. Berzelius, found on evaporating a soln. of tin-filings in one of ammonium chloride, whereby ammonia and hydrogen are evolved, crystals of a salt which, according to the analyses of J. Apjohn, is **ammonium tetrachlorostannite**, $(NH_4)_2SnCl_4.H_2O$, are obtained; but the analyses of C. F. Rammelsberg, and G. M. Richardson make it a dihydrate, $(NH_4)_2SnCl_4.2H_2O$. The last-named said that the salt is easily obtained by crystallization from a soln. of the component salts. The rhombic bipyramidal crystals have the axial ratios $a:b:c=0.6789:1:0.7522$. A. Johnsen gave $0.67686:1:0.74525$; and he considered this salt to be isomorphous with the corresponding ammonium tetrachloromercuriate, $(NH_4)_2HgCl_4.H_2O$. L. Playfair and J. P. Joule gave 2.104 for the sp. gr. at 3.9°, and A. Johnsen, 2.11. According to C. F. Rammelsberg, the octahedral crystals reported by J. Apjohn were not this salt, but the corresponding stannate. G. M. Richardson reported that **ammonium trichlorostannite**, $NH_4SnCl_3.H_2O$, crystallizes from a soln. of ammonium chloride mixed with a large excess of stannous chloride. E. Rimbach and K. Fleck made this salt by mixing equimolar proportions of soln. of the component salts, allowing the solid phase to separate, saturating with the same mixture while hot, and allowing to cool. The needle-like crystals readily lose their water. The solubility, S, in grams of anhydrous salt in 100 grms. of soln. is given by $S=57.374+0.35098\theta$, between 16° and 81°. E. Rimbach and K. Fleck made mono- and di-hydrated **ammonium tetrachlorostannite**, $(NH_4)_2SnCl_4$. The solubility, S, in grams of anhydrous salt per 100 grms. of soln. is $S=27.479+0.58168\theta$, between 1.6° and 79.0°. G. M. Richardson could not prepare **ammonium hexachlorostannite**, $(NH_4)_4SnCl_6.3H_2O$, reported by A. B. Poggiale to be formed from a soln. of stannous chloride mixed with an excess of ammonium chloride, but E. Rimbach and K. Fleck obtained the monohydrated salt. Stannous amminochloride has been previously described. T. Curtius and F. Schrader evaporated an aq. soln. containing eq. proportions of hydrazine and stannous chlorides and obtained a syrupy mass which when crystallized from absolute alcohol furnished white tabular crystals of hydrazine trichlorostannite, $(N_2H_5)SnCl_3$. The crystals are not hygroscopic; they melt at 105°, and the m.p. is lowered when the tetrachlorostannite is present. The two salts can be separated by fractional crystallization. The salt is easily soluble in water, and less soluble in alcohol. The residue obtained by extracting with a small proportion of alcohol the syrupy liquid obtained in preparing the preceding salt consists mainly of colourless crystals of **hydrazine tetrachlorostannite**, $(N_2H_5)_2SnCl_4$. This salt is hygroscopic; it melts at 55°–60°; and is sparingly soluble in absolute alcohol. Stannous hydrazine chloride, $Sn(N_2H_4)_2Cl_2$, has been previously described. J. G. F. Druce, and P. Pfeiffer studied the complex salts with organic bases.

I. Remsen and G. M. Richardson,[3] and E. Rimbach and K. Fleck prepared white hair-like crystals of **potassium trichlorostannite**, $KSnCl_3.H_2O$, by evaporating a soln. of potassium chloride mixed with a large excess of stannous chloride. The crystals are stable in air; they do not lose water when confined over conc. sulphuric acid, but they do so when heated to 100°; and at a higher temp., both water and hydrogen chloride are evolved. E. Rimbach and K. Fleck represented the solubility, S, in grams of anhydrous salt per 100 grms. of soln., by $S=23.186+0.830630\theta$, between 3.2° and 71°. According to I. Remsen and G. M. Richardson, the salt is soluble in hot hydrochloric acid, or in a soln. of potassium chloride, and the evaporation of these soln. furnishes crystals of **potassium tetrachlorostannite,** $K_2SnCl_4.2H_2O$. According to C. F. Rammelsberg, J. A. Streng, and J. C. G. de Marignac, the crystals have only one mol of water. According to I. Remsen and G. M. Richardson, the dihydrate is produced from a mixture of the component salts in nearly equal proportions or with an excess of potassium chloride. E. Rimbach and K. Fleck made the mono- and di-hydrates, and they found that the solubility, S, in grams of anhydrous salt per 100 grms. of soln. is $S=26·705+0·48290$, between 35·6° and 77·3°. The white crystals belong to the rhombic system, and have the axial ratios $a:b:c=0·6852:1:0·7586$. L. Playfair and J. P. Joule ,ave 2·514 for the sp. gr. They are stable in air, and crystallize unchanged from aq. soln., but L. Peetz said that salt is partially decomposed in aq. soln. The crystals melt when heated, and lose water and hydrogen chloride ; they are more stable than stannous chloride when heated, and at a red heat some stannous chloride is volatilized. I. Remsen and G. M. Richardson made crystals of the *monohydrate* by rapidly cooling a soln. of the salt in hot hydrochloric acid. A. B. Poggiale reported *potassium hexachlorostannite,* $K_4SnCl_6.3H_2O$, from a mixed soln. of the component salts. E. Rimbach and K. Fleck said the salt is monohydrated. E. H. Ducloux prepared **cæsium trichlorostannite,** $CsSnCl_3$.

G. Hermann showed that the fusion curves of mixtures of *stannous and cuprous chlorides* form a simple **V**, with the eutectic at 172° and 77·5 per cent. $SnCl_2$, Fig. 69. I. Remsen and G. M. Richardson could not confirm this. L. Peetz could not obtain

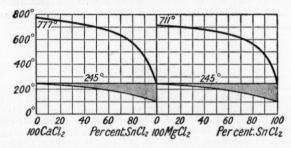

Fig. 67.—Fusion Curve of the System : $CaCl_2–SnCl_2$.

Fig. 68.—Fusion Curve of the System : $MgCl_2–SnCl_2$.

calcium chlorostannite by melting a mixture of the component chlorides at a red heat ; and O. Menge found that the thermal diagram of calcium and stannous chlorides showed a continuous series of mixed crystals with no evidence of chemical com-

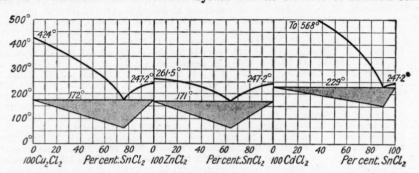

Fig. 69.—Fusion Curves of the System : $Cu_2Cl_2–SnCl_2$.

Fig. 70.—Fusion Curves of the System : $ZnCl_2–SnCl_2$.

Fig. 71.—Fusion Curves of the System : $CdCl_2–SnCl_2$.

bination, Fig. 67.   A. B. Poggiale reported needle-like crystals of **strontium tetra-chlorostannite**, $SrSnCl_4.4H_2O$, to be formed by evaporating a soln. of the component salts ; and prismatic crystals of **barium tetrachlorostannite**, $BaSnCl_4.4H_2O$, were made in a similar way.   O. Menge found no evidence of the formation of *magnesium chlorostannite* on the fusion curve of the component

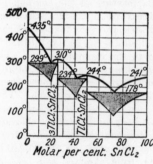

FIG. 72.—Freezing-point Curves of Mixtures of Thallous and Stannous Chlorides.

salts, Fig. 68 ; there is a continuous series of mixed crystals.   G. Hermann measured the fusion curves of *zinc and stannous chlorides* which have a simple V-eutectic at 171°, and 64 per cent. $SnCl_2$, Fig. 70 ; and *cadmium and stannous chlorides*, with a simple V-eutectic at 229°, and 90 per cent. $SnCl_2$, Fig. 71. J. Kendall and co-workers found that with mixtures of stannous and aluminium chlorides there is a two-liquid layer with between 1·5 and 14·3 per cent. of stannous chloride in equilibrium with the solid phase $xAlCl_3.ySnCl_2$ at 192°.   There are the compounds **aluminium octochlorostannite**, $2AlCl_3.SnCl_2$, melting at 209·3° ; and **aluminium pentachloro-stannite**, $AlCl_3.SnCl_2$, melting at 158·5°.   According to E. Korreng, fused mixtures of thallous and stannous chlorides furnish **thallous pentachlorostannite**, Tl_3SnCl_5, melting at 310°, and **thallous trichlorostannite**, $TlSnCl_3$, melting at 244°.   The f.p. curves are shown in Fig. 72.   C. D. Braun made **cobalt hexamminochlorostannite**, $2[Co(NH_3)_6]Cl_3.3SnCl_2.8(or\ 10)H_2O$, by the action of stannic chloride on cobalt hexamminochloride.   *Vide* the stannous chloroplatinites.

REFERENCES.

[1] B. Pelletier, *Ann. Chim. Phys.*, (1), 12. 225, 1792 ; J. N. von Fuchs, *Kastner's Arch.*, 23. 368, 1832 ; *Journ. prakt. Chem.*, (1), 5. 318, 1832 ; J. J. Berzelius, *Pogg. Ann.*, 28. 443, 1833.
[2] A. Ditte, *Ann. Chim. Phys.*, (5), 27. 146, 1882 ; *Compt. Rend.*, 94. 1114, 1882 ; 97. 42, 1883 ; V. Thomas, *ib.*, 122. 1539, 1896 ; A. Scheurer-Kestner, *ib.*, 52. 531, 1861 ; *Ann. Chim. Phys.*, (3), 58. 471, 1860 ; J. J. Berzelius, *Gilbert's Ann.*, 40. 235, 1812 ; *Pogg. Ann.*, 8. 184, 1826 ; M. Berthelot, *Thermochimie*, Paris 2. 154, 1897 ; A. B. Poggiale, *Compt. Rend.*, 20. 1180, 1845 ; G. Gimel, *ib.*, 147. 1324, 1908 ; H. Mouraour, *ib.*, 130. 141, 1900 ; G. Viard, *ib.*, 135. 242, 1902 ; J. C. G. de Marignac, *Ann. Mines*, (5), 9. 6, 1856 ; E. Turner, *Elements of Chemistry*, London, 550, 1834 ; A. E. Nordenskjöld, *Svenska Akad. Handl.*, 2. 2, 1874 ; F. von Kügelgen, *Zeit. Elektrochem.*, 7. 567, 1901 ; R. E. Liesegang, *Phot. Arch.*, 34. 161, 1893 ; A. M. Pleischel, *Sitzber. Akad. Wien*, 43. 555, 1861 ; O. W. Brown and C. O. Henke, *Journ. Phys. Chem.*, 27. 739, 1923 ; H. Capitaine, *Journ. Pharm. Chim.*, (2), 25. 552, 1840 ; C. Lenormand, *ib.*, (6), 8. 249, 1898 ; J. Kelley and E. F. Smith, *Journ. Amer. Chem. Soc.*, 18. 1096, 1896 ; L. Kahlenberg, *ib.*, 16. 314, 1894 ; F. L. Kortright, *ib.*, 17. 116, 1895 ; G. M. Richardson, *ib.*, 14. 89, 1892 ; S. W. Young, *ib.*, 23. 21, 450, 1901 ; S. W. Young and M. Adams, *ib.*, 19. 515, 1897 ; J. Davy, *Phil. Trans.*, 102. 169, 1912 ; T. H. Henry, *ib.*, 135. 367, 1845 ; J. Thomsen, *Journ. prakt. Chem.*, (2), 14. 429, 1876 ; (2), 18. 1, 1878 ; J. Schröder and H. Steiner, *ib.*, (2), 79. 63, 1909 ; T. Curtius and F. Schrader, *ib.*, (2), 50. 339, 1893 ; A. Naumann, L. Möser, and E. Lindebaum, *ib.*, (2), 75. 150, 1907 ; H. Reinsch, *ib.*, (1), 24. 248, 1841 ; H. Schulze, *ib.*, (2), 21. 407, 1880 ; J. Löwenthal, *ib.*, (1), 60. 267, 1853 ; (1), 79. 473, 1860 ; E. Lenssen, *ib.*, (1), 79. 90, 1860 ; T. Carnelley and W. Williams, *Journ. Chem. Soc.*, 85. 568, 1879 ; F. Penny, *ib.*, 4. 239, 1851 ; J. W. Mallet, *ib.*, 35. 524, 1879 ; E. Divers and T. Haga, *ib.*, 47. 623, 1885 ; R. G. Durrant, *ib.*, 107. 622, 1915 ; T. Carnelley, *Ber.*, 12. 1836, 1879 ; H. Biltz and V. Meyer, *Zeit. phys. Chem.*, 2. 184, 1888 ; *Ber.*, 21. 22, 1888 ; V. and C. Meyer, *ib.*, 12. 1195, 1879 ; V. Meyer and H. Züblin, *ib.*, 13. 813, 1880 ; F. Freyer and V. Meyer, *ib.*, 25. 622, 1892 ; A. Naumann, *ib.*, 37. 3601, 4336, 4609, 1905 ; G. P. Drossbach, *ib.*, 35. 1487, 1902 ; R. Rieth, *ib.*, 3. 666, 1870 ; A. Ladenberg, *ib.*, 3. 353, 1870 ; G. Vortmann and C. Padberg, *ib.*, 22. 2642, 1889 ; S. von Laszczynsky, *ib.*, 27. 2285, 1894 ; H. Schulze, *ib.*, 23. 974, 1890 ; C. M. Marx, *Schweigger's Journ.*, 60. 1, 1830 ; *Journ. prakt. Chem.*, (1), 22. 143, 1841 ; M. M. P. Muir, *Monit. Scient.*, 12. 783, 1882 ; *Chem. News*, 45. 69, 1882 ; M. Berthelot, *Ann. Chim. Phys.*, (5), 15. 200, 1878 ; C. C. Persoz, *ib.*, (2), 44. 315, 1830 ; A. Michel and L. Kraft, *ib.*, (3), 41. 471, 1854 ; R. Engel, *ib.*, (6), 17. 338, 1889 ; *Compt. Rend.*, 106. 1398, 1888 ; J. Girardin, *Ann. Chim. Phys.*, (2), 61. 286, 1836 ; H. V. Regnault, *ib.*, (3), 1. 129, 1841 ; *Relation des expériences entrepris pour déterminer les principales lois physiques et les données numériques qui entrent dans le calcul des machines à vapeur*, Paris, 1847 ; N. Castoro, *Gazz. Chim. Ital.*, 28. ii, 317, 1898 ; A. Vogel,

Schweigger's Journ., 21. 66, 1817; *Kastner's Arch.*, 23. 78, 1832; J. McCrae, *Wied. Ann.*, 55. 95, 1895; L. Graetz, *ib.*, 40. 28, 1890; G. Quincke, *ib.*, 24. 347, 1885; 34. 401, 1888; M. de Jong, *Zeit. anal. Chem.*, 41. 596, 1902; C. F. Mohr, *ib.*, 8. 113, 1869; H. Morgan, *ib.*, 27. 164, 1888; L. Blum, *ib.*, 44. 11, 1905; S. Motylewsky, *Zeit. anorg. Chem.*, 38. 410, 1904; A. Werner, *ib.*, 15. 1, 1897; F. Ephraim, *ib.*, 44. 185, 1905; F. Jean, *ib.*, 9. 297, 1893; O. Menge, *ib.*, 72. 162, 1911; G. Hermann, *ib.*, 71. 257, 1911; L. A. Voutz, *ib.*, 35. 55, 1903; E. Rimbach and K. Fleck, *ib.*, 94. 139, 1915; A. Helfenstein, *ib.*, 23. 255, 1900; R. Ehrenfeld, *ib.*, 59. 161, 1908; H. Franzen and O. von Mayer, *ib.*, 60. 286, 1909; W. Biltz and W. Fischer, *ib.*, 129. 1, 1923; W. Biltz, *ib.*, 130. 93, 1923; P. Pfeiffer, *ib.*, 133. 91, 1924; K. F. O. Seubert and A. Schmidt, *Liebig's Ann.*, 267. 235, 1892; C. Nöllner, *ib.*, 63. 120, 1847; 115. 233, 1860; E. Hering, *ib.*, 29. 90, 1839; H. Schiff, *ib.*, 120. 47, 1861; V. Meyer, *ib.*, 264. 131, 1891; J. Thiele and O. Dimrot, *ib.*, 305. 114, 1899; J. Thiele, *ib.*, 263. 361, 1891; E. Bérard, *Chem. Ztg.*, 5. 869, 1885; M. C. Schuyten, 32. 619, 1908; F. W. Clarke, *Amer. Journ. Science*, (3), 14. 281, 1877; C. T. Gerlach, *Zeit. Chem.*, (2), 4. 306, 1868; *Dingler's Journ.*, 186. 131, 1867; R. Brönner, *ib.*, 209. 77, 1873; H. W. Fischer, *Untersuchungen über Metallhydroxyde*, Breslau, 1908; N. W. Fischer, *Pogg. Ann.*, 9. 263, 1827; 10. 603, 1827; *Kastner's Arch.*, 13. 225, 1828; J. N. von Fuchs, *ib.*, 23. 368, 1823; *Journ. prakt. Chem.*, (1), 5. 318, 1832; M. C. Boswell and J. V. Dickson, *Journ. Amer. Chem. Soc.*, 40. 1773, 1918; J. Kendall, E. D. Crittenden, and H. K. Miller, *ib.*, 45. 963, 1923; C. M. Carson, *ib.*, 41. 1969, 1919; H. F. Keller, *ib.*, 39. 2354, 1917; J. O. Perrine, *Phys. Rev.*, (2), 22. 54, 1923; N. R. Dhar, *Journ. Asiatic Soc. Bengal*, 17. 130, 1921; *Proc. Acad. Amsterdam*, 23. 1074, 1921; *Versl. Akad. Amsterdam*, 29. 1023, 1921; J. A. Muller, *Compt. Rend.*, 175. 740, 1922; F. Raschig, *Zeit. angew. Chem.*, 20. 720, 1907; W. Minor, *ib.*, 3. 26, 1890; O. von Dumreicher, *Sitzber. Akad. Wien*, 82. 560, 1880; *Monatsh.*, 1. 724, 1880; N. Fedoroff, *Zeit. Chem.*, (2), 5. 15, 1869; A. Bettendorff, *ib.*, (2), 5. 492, 1869; P. Woulfe, *Phil. Trans.*, 61. 114, 1771; *Crell's Chem. Journ.*, i, 155, 1778; F. L. Shinn, *Journ. Phys. Chem.*, 11. 537, 1907; A. A. Noyes, *Tech. Quart.*, 8. 90, 1895; *Zeit. phys. Chem.*, 16. 546, 1895; 21. 16, 1896; W. Ostwald, *ib.*, 34. 248, 1900; H. Goldschmidt and E. Sunde, *ib.*, 56. 1, 1906; H. Goldschmidt, E. Storm, and O. Hassel, *ib.*, 100. 197, 1922; W. D. Bancroft and H. B. Weiser, *Journ. Phys. Chem.*, 18. 211, 1914; G. Tammann, *Zeit. anorg. Chem.*, 133. 267, 1924; R. Lorenz and W. Herz, *ib.*, 145. 88, 1925; I. I. Saslawsky, *ib.*, 146. 315, 1925; H. Goldschmidt, *Natur. Rund.*, 20. 365, 1905; F. Dietze, *Pharm. Ztg.*, 42. 191, 1897; A. Lottermoser, *Therapeut. Monatsh.*, 13. 159, 1899; T. Warynsky and M. Mdivani, *Bull. Soc. Chim.*, (4), 3. 626, 1908; F. Uty, *Chem. Rev. Fett. Harz Ind.*, 14. 183, 1907; P. Soltsien, *ib.*, 14. 242, 1907; E. Trautmann, *Bull. Soc. Mulhouse*, 61. 87, 1891; A. Johnsen, *Neues Jahrb. Min.*, ii, 117, 1903; L. Playfair and J. P. Joule, *Mem. Chem. Soc.*, 2. 401, 1845; C. F. Rammelsberg, *Pogg. Ann.*, 94. 507, 1855; J. Apjohn, *Dublin Phil. Journ.*, 1. 387, 1825; J. L. Proust, *Journ. Phys.*, 61. 338, 1804; *Ann. Chim. Phys.*, (1), 28. 213, 1798; *Nicholson's Journ.*, (1), 2. 515, 1799; (2), 14. 38, 1806; P. Juliusberger, *Ann. Physik*, (4), 3. 618, 1900; F. Ephraim, *Helvetica Chim. Acta*, 7. 298, 1924; N. A. Tananaeff, *Zeit. anorg. Chem.*, 133. 372, 1924; F. Friedrichs, *ib.*, 84. 373, 1913; N. R. Dhar, *ib.*, 144. 289, 1925; R. Lorenz and W. Herz, *ib.*, 147. 135, 1925; G. von Hevesy, *Danske Vid. Medd.*, 3. 13, 1921; F. de Carli, *Atti Accad. Lincei*, (5), 33. ii, 94, 1924; W. F. Timoféeff, G. E. Muchin, and W. G. Gurewitsch, *Zeit. phys. Chem.*, 115. 161, 1925; J. G. F. Druce, *Chem. News*, 130. 385, 1925; C. G. Maier, *Vapor Pressures of the Common Metallic Chlorides*, Washington, 38, 1925; L. H. Milligan and G. R. Gillette, *Journ. Phys. Chem.*, 28. 744, 1924; M. Coblens and J. K. Bernstein, *ib.*, 29. 752, 1925; A. J. Balard, *Ann. Chim. Phys.*, (2), 57. 225, 1834; *Taylor's Scientific Memoirs*, 1. 269, 1837; A. V. Harcourt, *B.A. Rep.*, 43, 1863; H. Wölbling, *Zeit. anorg. Chem.*, 57. 281, 1908; G. Tammann, *ib.*, 133. 267, 1924; P. Pfeiffer, *ib.*, 71. 97, 1911; 133. 91, 1924; O. Aschan, *Chem. Ztg.*, 37. 1117, 1913; W. Biltz and W. Fischer, *Zeit. anorg. Chem.*, 129. 1, 1923; W. Biltz and E. Birk, *ib.*, 134. 125, 1924; R. Lorenz and M. Mannheimer, *ib.*, 150. 343, 1926; 152. 314, 1926; W. Klemm, *ib.*, 152. 235, 295, 1926; W. Klemm and W. Biltz, *ib.*, 152. 225, 267, 1926; N. N. Mittra and N. R. Dhar, *ib.*, 122. 146, 1922; K. F. Ochs, *Ueber Oxydations- und Reduktionsketten*, Göttingen, 1895; M. C. Boswell and J. V. Dickson, *Journ. Amer. Chem. Soc.*, 40. 1773, 1918; A. W. Francis, *ib.*, 48. 655, 1926; E. Karantassis, *Compt. Rend.*, 182. 134, 1926; W. Jevons, *Proc. Roy. Soc.*, 110. A, 365, 1926; T. Rondelli, *Brit. Pat. No.* 229359, 232281, 1923; L. V. Pissarjewsky, *Journ. Russ. Phys. Chem. Soc.*, 54. 798, 1924; B. Köhnlein, *Liebig's Ann.*, 225. 171, 1884; A. W. Francis, *Journ. Amer. Chem. Soc.*, 48. 655, 1926; G. L. Clark, *Amer. Journ. Science*, (5), 7. 1, 1924; E. H. Ducloux, *Anal. Asoc. Quim. Argentina*, 9. 215, 1921.

[3] I. Remsen and G. M. Richardson, *Amer. Chem. Journ.*, 14. 89, 1895; L. Peetz, *Met.*, 1. 280, 1904; J. C. G. de Marignac, *Ann. Mines*, (5), 12. 52, 1857; A. B. Poggiale, *Compt. Rend.*, 20. 1182, 1845; C. F. Rammelsberg, *Handbuch der krystallographischen Chemie*, Berlin, 211, 1855; C. D. Braun, *Liebig's Ann.*, 125. 181, 1863; G. Hermann, *Zeit. anorg. Chem.*, 71. 257, 1911; O. Menge, *ib.*, 72. 162, 1911; J. A. Streng, *Neues Jahrb. Min.*, ii, 143, 1888; L. Playfair and J. P. Joule, *Mem. Chem. Soc.*, 2. 401, 1845; E. Rimbach and K. Fleck, *Zeit. anorg. Chem.*, 94. 139, 1915; E. Korreng, *Kristallographische und thermische Untersuchungen von binären Systemen aus Thallochlorid und Chloriden zweiwertiger Metalle*, Stuttgart, 1913; *Neues Jahrb. Min. B.B.*, 37. 76, 1914; E. H. Ducloux, *Anal. Asoc. Quim. Argentina*, 9. 215, 1921; J. Kendall, E. Crittenden, and H. K. Miller, *Journ. Amer. Chem. Soc.*, 45. 963, 1923.

§ 17. The Stannic Chlorides

In 1605, A. Libavius [1] described a fuming liquid which he called *liquor argenti vivi sublimati* or *spiritus argenti vivi sublimati;* he obtained it by distillation from a mixture of tin or tin amalgam and mercuric chloride. The liquid was afterwards called *spiritus fumans Libavii.* According to H. Peters, the preparation of the liquor from tin amalgam and mercuric chloride was described in a circular of the Nürnberg Museum nearly 300 years before A. Libavius' time. R. Boyle thus described its preparation:

If from good Cornish tin, you warily distil an equal or double weight of Venetian sublimate, into a very large receiver, very well luted on to the retort, you will obtain a spirituous liquor, which, as soon as the free air comes to touch it, will, before very long, send up abundance of white exhalations in the form of thick smoak.

The composition of the liquid was shown by J. L. Proust, J. J. Berzelius, and J. Davy to correspond with **stannic chloride, or tin tetrachloride,** $SnCl_4$. Chlorine unites directly with heated tin ; the reaction is attended by the development of much heat and light, and the formation of stannic chloride. Tin-foil catches fire after being in the gas a little while and burns with the emission of red sparks, and the formation of stannic chloride ; and R. Cowper [2] found that tin-foil is attacked by chlorine which has been so thoroughly dried that it does not attack sodium. R. Lorenz also based a method of preparing stannic chloride on the reaction between chlorine and tin at ordinary temp.

The most suitable apparatus is a wide tube closed at one end. 5 to 6 cm. wide, and 75 to 100 cm. long, fitted with a condenser and a tube, by means of which dry chlorine can be passed to the bottom of the vessel, where it bubbles through a little tin tetrachloride. The tube is filled nearly to the top with granulated tin. $1\frac{1}{2}$ to 2 kgrms. of the tetrachloride are easily prepared in about one hour. The product boils at 114°.

H. J. Taverne, and P. S. Brallier used a modification of this process ; and E. A. Sperry made stannic chloride on a large scale by the action of dry chlorine on tin contained in a cast-iron vessel. Liquid chlorine was found by E. Beckmann and P. Geib to dissolve tin, forming the tetrachloride. W. Coldridge purified stannic chloride prepared by the chlorine process by allowing it to stand over granulated tin for some days, and fractionally distilling the product. P. Heermann used a similar process. E. Kotzur purified impure material by distilling it in a stream of hydrogen chloride at as low a press. as possible. The tetrachloride is also formed by the action of chlorine on stannous chloride at ordinary temp. J. Davy heated a conc. aq. soln. of stannous chloride with conc. sulphuric acid and obtained stannic chloride ; and by the rectification of stannic chloride with sulphuric acid, the iron can be removed when present as an impurity. As indicated above, stannic chloride is formed when a mixture of tin and mercuric chloride is heated ; R. Schneider said that when a mixture of sulphur or selenium and stannous chloride is heated, some stannic chloride is produced ; and if an aq. soln. of stannous chloride is heated with sulphur, G. Vortmann and C. Padberg obtained some stannic chloride. J. von Kraskowitz made this compound by distilling from a mixture of sodium chloride and stannic sulphate. K. Heumann and P. Köchlin obtained stannic chloride by the action of chlorosulphonic acid on tin, $Sn+4HClSO_3=SnCl_4+2SO_2+2H_2SO_4$; but with sulphuryl chloride, SO_2Cl_2, and tin only a small proportion of stannic chloride is formed. H. Goldschmidt found that phosphorus pentachloride converted tin into the tetrachloride.

C. Matignon and F. Bourion converted stannic oxide into the chloride, by passing chlorine mixed with the vap. of sulphur chloride, SCl_2, over the heated oxide. B. H. Jacobson used chlorine mixed with a little bromine. A. Michaelis formed a mixture of stannous and stannic chlorides by the action of phosphorus trichloride on stannic oxide at 160° ; G. Rauter, by the action of silicon tetrachloride on stannic oxide at 350°–360° ; C. W. Watts and C. A. Bell, and C. Renz, by the action of carbon tetrachloride vap. on red-hot stannic oxide ; C. Renz, by the action of chloroform on stannic oxide ; and J. Kelley and E. F. Smith, by the action of hydrogen chloride on heated stannic sulphide.   L. Czimatis obtained stannic chloride on a large scale by heating a mixture of stannic oxide and magnesium or calcium chloride ; F. Meilly, by dissolving stannic hydroxide in hydrochloric acid, and heating the product with magnesium chloride, magnesia, and sand.

In 1770, J. F. Demachy [3] found that when *liquor fumans ex stanno* is treated with a little water, it forms a crystalline mass called *butter of tin*.   The union of stannic chloride with water is attended by the development of much heat.   According to G. T. Gerlach, when equimolar proportions of stannic chloride and water are mixed, two-thirds of the chloride remains unchanged, and **trihydrated stannic chloride,** $SnCl_4.3H_2O$, is formed.   W. T. Casselmann prepared crystals of this same hydrate by exposing stannic chloride to moist air ; A. Scheurer-Kestner, by oxidizing stannous chloride with nitric acid, potassium chlorate, or chromic acid, and evaporating the liquid for crystallization, or by evaporating a soln. of stannic hydroxide in an aq. soln. of stannic chloride ; and T. Scheerer, by passing moist chlorine over warm tin and stannic chloride.   W. Meyerhoffer gave 64°–83° as the limiting range of temp. for the existence of the trihydrate.   A. Scheurer-Kestner reported the formation of **dihydrated stannic chloride,** $SnCl_4.2H_2O$, by drying the trihydrate ; and B. Lewy, by drying the pentahydrate over sulphuric acid in vacuo.   G. T. Gerlach, however, was unable to prepare the dihydrate by the action of water on stannic chloride ; and W. Meyerhoffer observed no evidence of its formation in his work on the hydrates of stannic chloride.   G. T. Gerlach made **tetrahydrated stannic chloride,** $SnCl_4.4H_2O$, by mixing four mols of water with one mol of stannic chloride ; W. Meyerhoffer said that the limits of existence of this hydrate are between 56° and 63°.   In 1789, P. A. Adet reported the formation of a crystalline mass of **pentahydrated stannic chloride,** $SnCl_4.5H_2O$, by mixing 22 parts of stannic chloride with 7 parts of water.   This hydrate is the easiest to prepare, and it is commercially known as *oxymuriate of tin*, being used in the textile industries ; and, according to M. Taufflieb, as a preservative for anatomical specimens.   W. Meyerhoffer gave 19°–56° for the limiting range of temp. within which the pentahydrate exists.   B. Lewy obtained it by evaporating a soln. of stannic chloride in water ; H. Rose, by saturating a soln. of stannous chloride with water ; R. Brönner, and M. Rössler, by oxidizing a hydrochloric acid soln. of stannous chloride with nitric acid or potassium chlorate, and evaporating for crystallization ; and J. Bellucci and N. Parravano, by keeping the hydrochloride, $SnCl_4.2HCl.6H_2O$, for several days over alkali hydroxide at ordinary temp. and under reduced press.   G. T. Gerlach made **octohydrated stannic chloride,** $SnCl_4.8H_2O$, by crystallizing an aq. soln. of stannic chloride at a low temp. C. Nöllner regarded the product as **enneahydrated stannic chloride**, $SnCl_4.9H_2O$. W. Meyerhoffer gave 19° as the upper limit of temp. at which the octohydrate can exist.   No *tin-chloroform*, $SnHCl_3$, has been made.   According to J. Beckmann, the Dutch alchemist C. Drebbel discovered in 1630 that a soln. of tin in aqua regia with cochineal furnishes a permanent scarlet dye.

The physical properties of the stannic chloride.—Stannic chloride is a colourless fuming liquid, and below −33°, it furnishes white **crystals.**   The trihydrate furnishes monoclinic crystals which were examined by W. T. Casselmann ; [4] the tetrahydrate was found by G. T. Gerlach to form opaque crystals ; and the pentahydrate, monoclinic crystals.   J. I. Pierre gave 2·2671 for the **specific gravity** of stannic chloride at 0° ; G. T. Gerlach, 2·234 at 5° ; P. Heermann, 2·26 ; A. Stiefelhagen, 2·279 at 16·2° ; and T. E. Thorpe, 2·27875 at 0°, 2·2328 at 20°, and 1·97813 at 1 : 4°.   I. I. Saslawsky found the ratio of the mol. vol. to the sum of the at. vol. of the constituent elements to be 1·40; and he calculated the density, D, from the critical density, $D_k=0·7419$ $D=D_k(1+2·73\sqrt{T/T_0})$. R. Lorenz and W. Herz made observations of the sp. vol. F. Schuster gave 1184 atms. for the **internal pressure** of the liquid; W. Herz studied this subject. J. I. Pierre gave 0·00129977 for the coeff. of **cubical expansion** between 0° and 100°; and for the vol., v, assumed by a vol. v_0 when raised to $\theta°$ between $-19·1°$ and 112·6°, $v=v_0(1+0·0011328\theta+0·0_69170\theta^2+0·0_87579808\theta^3)$, whilst T. E. Thorpe gave $v=v_0(1+0·0011605\theta+0·0_6646167\theta^2+0·0_8772710\theta^3)$; and for the **specific volume**, 131·07. When stannic chloride is mixed with water, there is a marked contraction; and G. T. Gerlach gave for the sp. gr. of aq. soln. at 15°:

SnCl$_4$	10	20	30	40	50	60	70	100 per cent.
Sp. gr.	1·082	1·174	1·279	1·404	1·556	1·743	1·943	2·234

For the sp. gr. of soln. with different proportions of the pentahydrate, at 15°, he also gave:

SnCl$_4$.5H$_2$O	1	10	15	20	40	60	80	95 per cent.
Sp. gr.	1·006	1·0593	1·0905	1·1236	1·2755	1·4684	1 7271	1·9881

A table of observations on this subject was also compiled by P. Heermann; he also said that when the octohydrate is melted, the liquid has a sp. gr. 1·836 at 17·5°. E. Rabinowitsch, O. Masson, and J. A. Groshaus compared the mol. vol. and b.p. of the family of tetrachlorides. J. B. A. Dumas found that the **vapour density** at 124° is 9·18 when the value calculated for SnCl$_4$ is 9·04; and H. V. Regnault found a litre of the vap. under standard conditions weighs 11·9514 grms. S. Young gave for the **vapour pressure**, p mm., at temp. below the b.p.:

	$-10°$	0°	10°	20°	40°	60°	80°	100°	120°
p	2·78	5·53	10·33	18·58	50·82	122·2	256·7	496·0	895·4

and for the temp. above the b.p. up to near the critical temp.:

	130°	150°	200°	250°	280°	310°	319·35
$p\times10^{-3}$.	1·171	1·895	5·145	11·514	17·454	25·079	28·079

H. von Jüptner, and R. Lorenz and W. Herz studied this subject. J. B. A. Dumas gave 120° at 767 mm. for the **boiling point**; J. I. Pierre, 115·4° at 753 mm.; T. Andrews, 112·5° at 752 mm.; J. Bongartz and A. Classen, 120°; W. Coldridge, 112°; G. Neumann, 113·5°–114°; A. Haagen, 112° at 755 mm.; J. Kendall and co-workers, 114° at 760 mm.; F. W. Schmidt, 117° at 708·5 mm.; E. Beckmann and P. Geib, 114·5°; P. Walden, 114° at 757 mm.; P. A. Bond and H. T. Beach, 112·1° at 750 mm.; and T. E. Thorpe, 113·89° at 760 mm. S. Young gave 0·000121 $(760-p)$ $(273+\theta)$ for the correction to be added to the observed b.p. θ, at the barometric press. p corrected to 0°. N. de Kolossowsky gave 0·515 to 0·65 for the **ebullioscopic constant.** S. Young gave 318·7° for the **critical temperature;** 28,080 mm. for the **critical pressure;** 0·732–0·743 for the **critical density** calculated from the formula of R. O. Herzog; and 1·347 for the **critical volume.** Observations were also made by P. Walden, F. Schuster, E. Mathias, and G. Rudorf. E. E. Walker found the association factor at the critical point to be 1·011. W. Herz studied the relations of the critical constants, and of the co-volume.

A. Besson said that stannic chloride is still liquid at $-29°$, and at the **freezing point,** $-33°$, it forms a white crystalline solid if free chlorine be absent, but if chlorine be present, the f.p. is lower. J. Kendall and co-workers gave $-30·2°$ for the f.p., and W. M. Latimer gave $-33·1°$ for the **melting point;** A. Besson, $-33°$; and P. A. Bond and H. T. Beach, $-32·7°$. W. H. Latimer found the **heat of fusion** at the m.p. to be 8·42 cals. per gram. A. Hantzsch and H. Carlsohn found that the m.p. of the halides of silicon, titanium, germanium, and tin can be calculated from the empirical relation: m.p. of halide=(m.p. of n-valent element

$+n \times$ m.p. of halogen$)/(n+1)$. He therefore inferred that the atoms can be little changed by union to form molecules; and inference which directly contradicts the deformation theory of K. Fajans and G. Joos. J. E. Mills and P. K. Smith, and E. Ariès calculated values for the internal **heat of vaporization** at different temp. T. Andrews gave 30·5 cals. for the latent heat of vaporization per gram, or 253·5 cals. per litre; D. L. Hammick, 32·6 cals.; W. Herz, 21·49 cals.; and H. V. Regnault gave 46·838 Cals. per kilogram for the total heat of vaporization from 0° to the temp. of vaporization. According to W. Meyerhoffer, if the tri-hydrate be heated above 83° it forms two non-miscible liquids—the one is a soln. of stannic chloride sat. with water, and the other, a soln. of water sat. with stannic chloride. G. T. Gerlach gave about 60° for the m.p. of the pentahydrate. H. V. Regnault gave for the **specific heat** of the vapour of stannic chloride 0·0939 for equal weights and 0·8416 for equal vols.; for the liquid between 14° and 98°, 0·1476; and for the aq. soln. between 10° and 15°, 0·1402. W. M. Latimer gave for the sp. ht. C_p per mol. wt. $\div 5$ (when the * refers to the liquid state):

	$-184°$	$-178°$	$-111·8°$	$-72·5°$	$-45·7°$	$-6·1°$	$21°$
C_p .	4·59	47·3	5·89	6·32	6·62	7·56*	7·86*

T. Andrews gave for the **heat of formation** of stannic chloride, $(Sn,2Cl_2)=127·0$ Cals.; M. Berthelot, 129·8 Cals.; and J. Thomsen, 127·25 Cals. M. Berthelot gave $(SnCl_{2aq.},Cl_2)=77·0$ Cals.; and J. Thomsen, 76·03 Cals. The last-named gave for the oxidation $SnCl_2.2HCl_{aq.}$ to $SnCl_4.Aq.$, 65·7 Cals., and 29·92 Cals. for the **heat of solution** of stannic chloride in water. G. T. Morgan and co-workers found the heat of soln. of stannic chloride in 200 parts of carbon tetrachloride to be 0·87 Cal. W. Herz gave 2·66 for the **chemical constant.**

A. Haagen found for the **index of refraction** of stannic chloride at 20°, 1·5070 for the H_a-line; 1·5225 for the H_β-line; and 1·5318 for the H_γ-line; while the **refraction equivalent** $(\mu_a-1)/D=0·2271$. J. H. Gladstone gave for the index of refraction 1·512 for $\lambda=0·589\mu$, and 1·503 for $\lambda=0·759\mu$. W. J. Pope gave 86·5 for the refraction eq. of the $SnCl_6$-radicle. J. H. Gladstone made some observa-tions on the index of refraction of stannic chloride, and A. Stiefelhagen found for rays of wave length $\lambda=262$, 394, and $768\mu\mu$, the indices of refraction $\mu=1·678$, 1·54720, and 1·50689 respectively, and $\mu^2=1·63524+0·60045\lambda(\lambda^2-180·38)^{-1}$. F. F. Martens gave 1·544 for $\lambda=0·434\mu$; 1·530 for $\lambda=0·486\mu$; and 1·523 for $\lambda=0·535\mu$. W. Herz, and H. H. Marvin discussed the **optical dispersion,** etc. E. Bichat found that the vap. of stannic chloride rotates the plane of polarization of light. C. Sheard and C. S. Morris measured the **emission spectrum** of stannic chloride between 5800 and 4400.

L. Bleekrode found that stannic chloride is a very poor conductor of electricity; and W. Coldridge said that both at ordinary temp. and at the b.p. the **electrical conductivity** is nil or very small, the resistance at 112° being more than 1600 megohms; the liquid becomes a conductor if alcohol or hydrogen chloride is added, but not with chloroform, hydrogen sulphide, or chlorine. G. von Hevesy said it is as bad a conductor as benzene. As W. Madelung said, the salt is non-ionized. According to W. von Kowalewsky, the conductivity of stannic chlorides and of the liquid hydrates up to the enneahydrate is negligibly small. In dil. soln., the salt is hydrolyzed: $SnCl_4+4H_2O \rightleftharpoons 4HCl+Sn(OH)_4$; and some *hydrochlorostannic acid*, H_2SnCl_6, appears to be formed. The low velocity of the hydrolysis proves that few ions are present in the soln. The electrical conductivity increases with time; and equilibrium is attained before the hydrolysis is complete. The degree of hydrolysis is diminished by raising the temp. An excess of Cl'-ions hinders the hydrolysis, and the conductivity of a soln. of stannic chloride and hydrochloric acid may be less than that of the acid alone, owing, presumably, to the formation of a complex acid. The tendency of the tetrachlorides of tin, tita-nium, and silicon decreases in this order; and the same remark applies to the tendency to form complex salts. W. Foster, and A. Heydweiller made observations on this subject. Stannic acid separates from soln. of stannic chloride between 0·01N- and 0·5N-soln. ; above and below these limits, the soln. remains clear. F. Kohlrausch traced the change in the conductivity with time, and it becomes less rapid as hydrolysis proceeds. Light has no hydrolyzing influence. The rate of hydrolysis increases at higher temp. The differences in the results with platinic and stannic chlorides show that these two salts are essentially different in type. The increase in the conductivity k per degree, dk/dt, is:

Conc.	0·001N	0·01N	0·02N	0·5N	N	2N	5N	17·7N
At 16°	—	—	—	0·0163	0·0163	0·0168	—	—
At 22°	0·0163	0·0162	0·0162	—	0·0160	0·0167	0·0225	0·0636

W. Dittenberger and R. Dietz observed that in the electrolysis of aq. soln. of stannic chloride, some tin is deposited at the cathode, but this is due to secondary reactions since it is improbable that the salt is resolved into Sn···· and 4Cl'-ions. P. Walden found that the conductivity of soln. of stannic chloride in liquid sulphur dioxide is very small, but is raised considerably by the addition of triphenylmethylchloride ; D. Helbig and G. Fausti showed that soln. in liquid hydrogen chloride conduct like liquid hydrogen chloride alone ; and W. von Kowalewsky showed that when a soln. of stannic chloride in a sat. soln. of sodium chloride is dil. with water, the sp. conductivity increases to a certain point with dilution. H. Schlundt gave 3·2 for the **dielectric constant** at 22° ; and J. H. Mathews gave 2·0. The latter also gave 3·15 for the dielectric constant of a soln. of stannic chloride sat. with hydrogen chloride. W. Herz discussed the relation to the critical temp. G. Quincke gave $-0·18 \times 10^{-6}$ mass units for the **magnetic susceptibility** of stannic chloride.

The stannic oxychlorides.—If a mixture of the vapours of stannic chloride and water be passed through a red-hot tube, crystalline stannic oxide is formed (q.v.). The hydrolysis of the aq. soln. has been traced by the electrical conductivity of the soln. (q.v.). The aq. soln. is produced by the soln. of stannic chloride in water ; of tin in aqua regia ; of α-stannic acid in hydrochloric acid ; or by the oxidation of a soln. of stannous chloride. H. Rose [5] showed that the soln. of stannic chloride in water gradually changes, and the change depends on the temp. and conc. of the soln. A conc. soln. is stable, while a dil. soln. deposits stannic acid ; and, according to W. T. Casselmann, a very dil. soln. deposits stannic acid in the cold. C. E. Carstanjen observed that the hydrolysis of the aq. soln. is favoured by the presence of the sulphates of the alkalies, alkaline earths, ammonium, and aluminium. J. de la Puente directed attention to the possibility of a complete series of compounds, H_2SnCl_6, $H_2Sn(OH)Cl_5$, . . . $H_2Sn(OH)_6$. J. Löwenthal showed that the older an aq. soln. of stannic chloride, the greater the quantity required to unite with potassium ferrocyanide ; the change is faster the more dil. the soln. ; and it is hindered when tartaric acid is present. R. Lorenz supposed that with the ageing of the soln., the proportion of tin-ions gradually decreases, and E. H. Loomis showed that the mol. depression of the f.p. is greater than corresponds with ionization into five ions Sn···· and 4Cl' ; and he assumed that the soln. contained H_2SnCl_4. W. O. de Coninck, and P. Geiseler showed that charcoal accelerates the separation of stannic acid or an oxychloride from the aq. soln. L. Vignon regarded the soln. of stannic chloride in water as a mixture of stannic hydroxide and aq. hydrochloric acid ; and at ordinary temp., the product is partially polymerized and α- and β-stannic acids are formed. If an excess of potassium hydroxide be added to the soln. of stannic chloride, the clear liquid becomes turbid in a few hours owing to the formation of a polystannate, $K_2Sn_nO_{2n}\cdot(n-1)H_2O$. According to E. Biron, when α-stannic acid undergoes change, it yields an uninterrupted series of varieties of β-stannic acid, differing as regards their degree of condensation, which becomes greater as the temp. rises. The action of hydrochloric acid on these various β-stannic acids gives rise to oxychlorides which have an indefinite composition and contain a larger or smaller proportion of chlorine according as the condensation of the β-acid is small or great.

The reverse reactions, by which the oxychlorides are converted into a derivative of the α-acid, namely, stannic chloride, proceed the more readily the less the condensation. W. Smirnoff showed that when the tri-, tetra-, and penta-hydrates of stannic chloride are shaken up with xylene at various temp. between 60° and 111°, the value C_1/C_2 gradually changes, where C_1 denotes the percentage of the chloride in water, and C_2, the percentage in xylene. With the pentahydrate, the ratio falls from 504·4 at 66° to 59·3 at 111°; with the tetrahydrate, the ratio falls from 45·3 at 66° to 12·9 at 111°; and with the trihydrate, the ratio is independent of temp. It is assumed that the hydrates are readily dissociated into their components, that only free stannic chloride is soluble in xylene, and that the degree of dissociation of the hydrate increases with rising temp. and diminishing content of water; even at 66°, the trihydrate is completely dissociated.

As in the case of the stannic acids (q.v.), there are two views as to the nature of the chlorides of the stannic acids. The work of J. M. van Bemmelen, and G. Jörgensen shows that the first action of hydrochloric acid on the stannic acids is an absorption process. The products of definite composition obtained by R. Engel, and A. Kleinschmidt were the result of using stannic acid of practically the same degree of condensation, and absorption products of similar composition were obtained. F. Musculus, H. Kühl, and R. Zsigmondy consider that α-stannic acid passes into soln. on treatment with dil. or conc. hydrochloric acid, the β-acid is considered to be insoluble, although D. B. Dott held the contrary view. According to W. Mecklenburgh, once the β-acid is formed it can furnish a soln. only by peptization with conc. hydrochloric acid for a definite time, followed by dilution. G. E. Collins and J. K. Wood obtained stable sols by the direct action of dil. hydrochloric acid on β-stannic acid, provided the action be continued for a longer time. They showed that the first of the reactions between hydrochloric acid and stannic acid is probably simple absorption; and other things being constant, the amount of hydrochloric acid adsorbed by a given weight of stannic acid will depend on the surface exposed by the particles of the latter; and this will be smaller with a sample of β-stannic acid than with one of the α-acid. In agreement therewith a larger weight of the β-acid than of α-acid is needed to adsorb a given weight of hydrochloric acid. The adsorption may be followed by a chemical reaction between adsorbent and some of the adsorbed acid owing to the neutralization of the latter by some of the basic affinities of the original stannic hydroxide still possessed by the condensed acid; this will result in the formation of a certain amount of salt on the surface of the particle. Such a salt would be capable of ionization, and would then yield a complex positive ion and chloride ion. It will depend primarily on the conc. of hydrochloric acid still remaining in soln. whether or not this ionization actually occurs; the salt and the acid give rise to a common ion, and in view of this fact and the small solubility product which the salt will have, at any rate in the case of a highly condensed stannic acid, a small conc. of acid will be sufficient to repress almost entirely the ionization of the salt. If the ionization of the salt is not prevented, the complex particles will acquire a positive charge, and it will depend on the ratio between its mass and the charge it carries, whether or not a particle can separate itself from adjacent ones and thus acquire a greater degree of dispersion. Owing to the greater degree of condensation and therefore the greater mass and smaller adsorptive power of the β-stannic acid, it follows that this variety will not be so readily peptized as the α-acid. The latter modification will the more easily be brought into a state of true soln.; with an acid of β-character, however, it may easily arise that the ratio of mass to charge is of such dimensions that the particle is not raised to the potential which will enable it to lead a separate existence, in which case the substance will not peptize but will remain in the condition of a gel. Conversely, sols of β-stannic acid will be more readily coagulated than sols of the α-modification, as the particles in the former sol are, for a given charge, less dispersed than those in the latter sol; this is in agreement with the observations of W. Mecklenburgh. Another kind of reaction may occur, for, continued G. E. Collins and J. K. Wood, the more the character of the acid approaches that of the β-acid, the greater is the extent to which salt formation between acidic and basic stannic hydroxide has taken place. If a highly condensed stannic acid, therefore, be in the presence of hydrochloric acid, there will be a tendency for this salt-like complex to be decomposed by the stronger acid, and by this reaction there will be formed a less condensed stannic acid. This decomposition or reversal of the α-β change will, for a given preparation, take place to a greater degree the higher the conc. of the hydrochloric acid, the longer the time of contact, and the more elevated the temp. This view is supported by the observations of C. T. Barfoed, F. Musculus, and W. Mecklenburgh. The formation of a less condensed acid results in an increase in the surface area of the particles, thus changing the adsorptive power and chemical affinity, which, in turn, changes the amount of hydrochloric acid remaining in soln., and in the degree of dispersion of the stannic acid. Hence, G. E. Collins and J. K. Wood concluded that a degree of condensation of the stannic acid is eventually arrived at, which is in equilibrium with the free hydrochloric acid and with the substance which has been dispersed, so that no further peptization or coagulation takes place. Such a state of equilibrium is attained only after the lapse of a very considerable time, for certain of the reactions involved are taking place in a solid medium. During the period of attainment of this equilibrium, the liquid manifests continual change of composition, and the amount of tin existing in true and in colloidal soln. is continually changing.

According to W. T. Casselmann, when a soln. of stannous chloride is treated with chlorine, and evaporated, hydrogen chloride is evolved ; and after several evaporations from aq. soln., the soluble product has the composition, $SnOCl_2$, **stannyl chloride,** or **tin oxydichloride.** A. Scheurer-Kestner obtained it by oxidizing a soln. of stannous chloride with nitric acid in the presence of an excess of hydrochloric acid, or by means of chromic acid. J. M. Ordway used potassium chlorate as the oxidizing agent. A. Scheurer-Kestner also obtained the salt from a filtered soln. of stannic hydroxide in a not too dil. soln. of stannic chloride. M. Berthelot obtained it by heating stannous chloride and oxygen in a sealed tube at 500° : $SnCl_2+O=SnOCl_2+50.4$ Cals. ; and by heating stannous oxide and chlorine : $SnO+Cl_2=SnOCl_2+62.2$ Cals. J. W. Mallet reported **stannyl hydroxy-chloride,** $SnO(OH)Cl$, to be formed when a conc. aq. soln. of stannous chloride is kept for a couple of years in an incompletely stoppered glass bottle. It decomposes when heated, forming hydrogen chloride and stannic oxide ; sodium hydroxide precipitates stannic hydroxide ; and with ammonia it forms **stannyl ammonium chloride,** $SnO(ONH_4)Cl$. P. Pfeiffer reported **tin hydroxytrichloride,** $Sn(OH)Cl_3$, to be formed by the hydrolysis of stannic chloride, for if a 50 per cent. soln. of stannic chloride, freshly prepared by dissolving the salt in water externally cooled by ice, is shaken with ether and the ethereal soln. dried and evaporated, 29 per cent. of the salt is obtained as the hydroxytrichloride, $SnCl_3.OH,H_2O,Et_2O$. Only traces of this are obtained from stannic chloride soln. which have been prepared some hours before extraction. On soln. in ether and precipitation with light petroleum, it forms colourless, deliquescent crystals melting and decomposing at 160°, and decomposing when dissolved in water.

J. J. Berzelius obtained a β-**stannic chloride** corresponding with the β-stannic acid which is formed by the action of nitric acid on tin. When this compound is boiled with hydrochloric acid, the stannic acid does not dissolve, but it takes up some hydrochloric acid, forming a yellow mass which can be dried on filter-paper. The product is soluble in water, but the soln. coagulates when boiled ; it gives a precipitate with conc. hydrochloric acid, and the precipitate dissolves in water after the acid has been removed. When distilled, hydrochloric acid is evolved, then hydrogen chloride mixed with a little stannic chloride, and stannic oxide remains. According to C. T. Barfoed, the aq. soln. contains the eq. of $8HCl+9SnO_2$.

R. Weber reported *tin hexoxytetrachloride*, $Sn_4O_6Cl_4.5H_2O$, to be formed by evaporating a hydrochloric acid soln. of stannic acid ; the product is soluble in a small proportion of water but is precipitated when more water is added. He also reported *tin octoxytetrachloride*, $Sn_5O_8Cl_4.7H_2O$, to be precipitated by adding conc. hydrochloric acid to a hydrochloric acid soln. of stannic acid. There is nothing to establish these products as chemical individuals.

According to R. Engel, when 400 grms. of air-dried β-stannic acid, obtained by the action of nitric acid of sp. gr. 1·3–1·4, on tin, are digested in 100 c.c. of hydrochloric acid, of sp. gr. 1·18, for 15 mins., the gummy mass diluted with water, and the filtered soln. treated with an equal vol. of hydrochloric acid, a white amorphous precipitate is formed which settles very slowly. The precipitate, after washing with hydrochloric acid of sp. gr. 1·18, and dilution with its own vol. of water, can be dried first on porous tiles, and afterwards in vacuo over sulphuric acid and potassium hydroxide. The composition corresponds with β-**stannic dichloride**, $Sn_5O_9Cl_2.4H_2O$, analogous with β-stannic acid, $Sn_5O_9(OH)_2.4H_2O$. According to E. Biron's analysis, the product has twice this amount of chlorine. R. Engel reported this chloride to form a translucent deliquescent mass which dissolves in a small proportion of water or alcohol. The conc. aq. soln. can be diluted with water if a small proportion of hydrochloric acid has been added previously ; an excess of hydrochloric acid gives a precipitate. The addition of water to the soln. without acid gives a gelatinous precipitate of β-stannic acid which, after being washed and dried, will recombine with hydrochloric acid to form the original compound.

According to R. Engel, when a soln. of β-stannic dichloride in dil. hydrochloric acid is heated to 100° for some time, it rapidly acquires the property of giving a precipitate with dil. sulphuric acid which is characteristic of J. J. Berzelius' β-stannic chloride. No compound of definite composition could be isolated from the soln., but the composition of the solute approximates to that of β-stannyl chloride. R. Engel found that although parastannic acid is insoluble in hydrochloric acid, combination occurs, and, when dried, the resulting **parastannic dichloride**, $Sn_5O_9Cl_2.2H_2O$, dissolves in a small proportion of water, but with an excess of water furnishes a precipitate of parastannic acid. The opalescent soln. in water gives a precipitate with sulphuric acid, and is slowly precipitated by hydrogen sulphide.

G. Tschermak obtained a soln. of β-stannic acid in a hot hydrochloric acid soln. of stannous chloride. When the brownish-yellow liquid was cooled it furnished yellow lustrous plates difficult to obtain free from the mother-liquor. The composition approximated $(SnO)_4Cl_7.5H_2O$, *stannyl heptachloride*, and it was considered to be a *stannostannic* or *stannosic chloride* because it gives reactions characteristic of stannous chloride and β-stannic chloride. The salt is readily soluble in water and in alcohol, but it cannot be crystallized from the former without decomposition.

F. de Carli [6] studied the reducing action of **hydrogen** on stannic chloride. The action of water has just been discussed. A. Besson showed that stannic chloride at a low temp. absorbs large quantities of **chlorine,** with a considerable increase in vol., and a lowering of the f.p. W. Biltz and E. Meinecke found the f.p. curve of mixtures of chlorine and stannic chloride to have a eutectic at −106° and 80 at. per cent. of chlorine as indicated in Fig. 73. There is no evidence of the existence of complex salts. According to J. Girardin, **sulphur** may be crystallized unchanged from stannic chloride. H. Rose said that when stannic chloride is warmed with **hydrogen sulphide,** hydrogen chloride and stannic sulphide are formed ; in the cold, W. Coldridge observed the formation of white crystals of a complex **stannic chloropentasulphohydrate,** $SnCl_4.5H_2S$, or, according to J. B. A. Dumas, liquid **stannic disulphotetrachloride,** $SnCl_4.SnS_2$. W. Biltz and E. Keunecke found

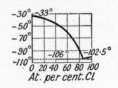

Fig. 73. — Freezing-point Curves of Cl–SnCl₄ Mixtures.

that a *disulphohydrate*, $SnCl_4.2H_2S$, and a *tetrasulphohydrate*, $SnCl_4.4H_2S$, are formed respectively with heats of formation 6·98 Cals. and 6·60 Cals., and at −58° and −81°, the dissociation press. is 100 mm. H. Rose made stannic sulphochloride, $SnCl_4.2SCl_4$, by the action of dry chlorine on stannic sulphide ; the reaction is slow in the cold, but fine crystals were obtained under these conditions by W. T. Cassel-mann. H. Rose also obtained it by the action of chlorine on stannous sulphide and from a cold mixture of stannic chloride and **sulphur monochloride,** S_2Cl_2, and W. T. Casselmann said that if the mixture is sealed in a glass tube, rhombohedral crystals are produced by spontaneous sublimation. O. Ruff and G. Fischer obtained it by a modification of this process. The yellow crystals, according to H. Rose, melt at a summer's heat, and, according to O. Ruff and G. Fischer, at 37°. W. T. Cas-selmann said that when heated above 40° the compound is decomposed, chlorine is evolved, and a mixture of sulphur monochloride and stannic chloride is produced. At 30°, the compound sublimes with very little decomposition, especially in a current of hydrogen chloride. The compound fumes in air more strongly than stannic chloride. W. T. Casselmann said that the compound slowly decomposes at 0° in moist air, forming a white mass impregnated with an acid liquid. The mass dissolves in water without the separation of sulphur. The soln. contained stannic chloride, and hydrochloric and sulphuric acids, but no thiosulphuric or sulphurous acid. According to H. Rose, the salt attracts moisture from the atm., and with water forms a turbid liquid owing to the separation of sulphur ; when the aq. soln. is boiled, stannic oxide and chloride, and sulphuric, thiosulphuric, and hydrochloric acids are formed. The crystals dissolve completely in dil. nitric acid evolving nitrogen oxides, and the soln. contains stannic oxide and sulphuric acid. Fuming nitric acid forms a white mass which is soluble in water. Aq. ammonia separates sulphur and part of the stannic oxide, but dissolves a large proportion of the stannic oxide, and there are formed thiosulphuric, sulphuric, and hydrochloric acids. The crystals absorb ammonia with a great evolution of heat, forming a yellowish-brown mass, which, when digested with water, forms undissolved stannic oxide and sulphur, and the filtrate, which is neutral at first, becomes acidic, and contains ammonium thiosulphate, sulphate, and chloride. O. Ruff and G. Fischer found that the compound $SnCl_4.2SCl_4$ is soluble in chloroform, carbon disulphide, phosphoryl chloride, benzene, ether, acetic ether, and sulphur chloride. The soln. in phosphoryl chloride was found by W. T. Casselmann to form crystals of the complex $SnCl_4.POCl_3$. P. A. Bond and H. T. Beach observed that no compound is formed with **sulphur dioxide** above the m.p., $-72°$; and they found a percentage solubility curve :

SnCl$_4$	.	100·00	86·16	71·75	58·54	31·96	11·78	5·40 per cent.
M.p.	.	$-32·7°$	42·6°	43·7°	44·0°	47·1°	63·0°	72·7°

They also obtained an unstable binary liquid system below the solubility curve. According to H. Rose, stannic chloride absorbs much **sulphur trioxide** without giving off sulphur dioxide, and a white mass is produced which dissolves in a small proportion of water, forming a clear soln., and with an excess of water, a turbid soln. When distilled, a brittle colourless mass collects in the receiver, and is decomposed by water ; a white sublimate collects in the neck of the retort ; and the residue in the retort contains stannic oxide and sulphate. O. C. M. Davis, and H. Wölbling obtained **stannic nitrogen chlorosulphide,** $SnCl_4.2N_4S_4$, by mixing dry chloroform soln. of **nitrogen sulphide,** N_4S_4, and stannic chloride. The red crystals are decomposed at 165°, and by exposure to moist air. R. Weber made **stannic selenoxychloride,** $SnCl_4.2SeOCl_2$, by dropping **selenium oxychloride** into stannic chloride. If the latter be in excess, two immiscible liquids are formed, and when slowly cooled, the lower layer furnishes white fusible crystals which are rapidly decomposed by water. H. Friedrich found that **sulphuric acid** does not react with stannic chloride. According to R. G. Durrant, **sulphur dioxide** has a slight reducing action on stannic chloride : $SnCl_4+H_2SO_3+H_2O \rightleftharpoons SnCl_2+2HCl +H_2SO_4$—vide stannous chloride. F. Clausnitzer showed that **chlorosulphonic acid,** HSO_3Cl, does not react with stannic chloride ; the two liquids are not com-pletely miscible.

J. Davy [7] found that at ordinary temp. stannic chloride absorbs dry **ammonia** with the development of heat, forming a white solid. H. Rose showed that the product should be repeatedly ground and exposed to the gas in order to saturate it completely. J. Davy said that the product can be sublimed without decomposition, and the sublimate appears in the form of yellowish-white acicular crystals. H. Rose's analysis of the sublimate corresponds with stannic diamminochloride, $SnCl_4.2NH_3$; both P. Grouvelle, and J. Persoz consider the unsublimed product is stannic tetramminochloride, $SnCl_4.4NH_3$. W. G. Mixter found the vap. density of the diammine to be 46·45, when the calculated value is 44·5; and it is inferred that there is some dissociation in the vaporous state. H. Rose said that it can be sublimed in hydrogen gas without decomposition, but, when it is heated in air, J. Davy said that it gives off white, pungent fumes. P. Grouvelle, and H. Rose said that the salt dissolves completely in cold water; only that which has not been sublimed forms a turbid soln.; the aq. soln. reddens litmus. According to H. Rose, when the aq. soln. is evaporated in vacuo over sulphuric acid, a mass of crystals of the undecomposed salt is obtained; but if the cold soln. which gives no turbidity with ammonia, be heated or left standing for a few days, it deposits a gelatinous precipitate. Sulphuric acid gives a gelatinous precipitate when added to the aq. soln. Similar characteristics are shown by an aq. soln. of stannic chloride to which a little ammonia has been added. The diammine is not altered by phosphine in the cold, but when heated it gives off ammonia and becomes superficially red. When heated with sodium, it emits a brilliant violet light, and forms tin, sodium chloride, and ammonia gas. P. P. Dehérain said that hydrochloric acid transforms the diammine into ammonium chlorostannate. P. Fireman observed no reaction between stannic chloride and **ammonium chloride** after heating for several days at 400°.

J. L. Gay Lussac [8] found that when stannic chloride is treated with **nitric acid,** chlorine and nitrogen oxides are evolved, and β-stannic acid is formed. According to F. Kuhlmann, stannic chloride unites with **nitric oxide,** forming crystals of *stannic nitrosyl chloride,* $SnCl_4.NO$, but neither W. Hampe nor R. Weber could confirm this; the latter obtained a lemon-yellow crystalline mass of *stannic nitrogen trioxychloride,* $SnCl_4.N_2O_3$, by the action of dry **nitrogen trioxide** on stannic chloride. V. Thomas passed **nitrogen peroxide** into a chloroform soln. of stannic chloride, and obtained a white crystalline mass with the composition of *stannic nitrogen oxychloride,* $SnOCl_2.3SnCl_4.N_2O_5$. R. Weber obtained a product corresponding with **stannic dinitroxylchloride,** $SnCl_4.2NOCl$, by the action of the vap. from aqua regia on stannic chloride; a similar result was obtained by A. Baeyer, and S. M. Jörgensen. W. Hampe represented the composition $3SnCl_4.4NOCl$. V. Thomas obtained a white crystalline mass purporting to be $3SnCl_4.4NOCl$, by sublimation from the stannic nitrogen oxychloride, $SnOCl_2.3SnCl_4.N_2O_5$, cited above. J. J. Sudborough obtained a like product by the action of **nitrosyl chloride** on tin. W. J. van Heteren obtained it by the action of a large excess of nitrosyl chloride on stannic chloride, distilling off the nitrosyl chloride, and subliming the product. W. Hampe prepared this compound by the action of nitrogen trioxide on stannic chloride, and subliming the product: $3SnCl_4+2N_2O_3=SnO_2+2SnCl_4(NOCl)_2$. The pale yellow octahedral crystals were found by S. M. Jörgensen to have the sp. gr. 2·60; W. J. van Heteren said that they melt in a sealed tube at 180°, and volatilize without decomposition. According to R. Weber, and W. Hampe, the crystals fume in air, and are easily decomposed by water with the evolution of nitric oxide. S. M. Jörgensen said the compound attacks benzene and chloroform, but not carbon disulphide.

According to H. Rose,[9] stannic chloride absorbs **phosphine,** forming a yellow solid with the composition **stannic ditritaphosphinochloride,** $3SnCl_4.2PH_3$. The solid fumes in air and absorbs moisture with avidity; when heated out of contact with air it forms stannous chloride, hydrogen chloride, and phosphorus. R. Mahn found it decomposes in carbon dioxide at 100°, forming hydrogen chloride and *chlorophosphorzinn,* $Sn_3P_2Cl_6$, **tin diphosphohexachloride** : $3SnCl_4.2PH_3=6HCl$ $+Sn_3P_2Cl_6$. Stannic ditritaphosphinochloride is coloured black by ammonia gas ; with water, or aq. soln. of alkali hydroxide or carbonate, or of ammonium carbonate. Phosphine is evolved and tin phosphide is precipitated. W. T. Casselmann found that while stannic chloride mixes with **phosphorus trichloride** without union, it combines directly with **phosphorus pentachloride**, forming **stannic phosphoric chloride**, $SnCl_4.PCl_5$. If a mixture of the component chlorides be heated in a retort, stannic chloride distils over between $120°-130°$; phosphoric chloride between $140°-160°$; and the compound sublimes between $200°-230°$. E. Baudrimont found that phosphorus pentachloride reacts with tin, $3PCl_5+Sn=SnCl_4.PCl_5$ $+2PCl_3$; it was also made by heating a mixture of stannic disulphochloride and phosphorus trichloride : $SnCl_4.2SCl_2+PCl_3=S_2Cl_2+SnCl_4.PCl_5$, or by the action of chlorine and phosphorus pentachloride on the same compound. The white product has a penetrating odour, and at about $200°$ sublimes, forming colourless crystals which, in a hermetically sealed vessel, soon disintegrate into a white powder ; the compound fumes in air and attracts moisture, forming colourless monoclinic crystals of what may be a hydrate. The compound is decomposed by water, forming stannic chloride, hydrochloric and phosphoric acids, and what appears to be stannic phosphate. According to W. T. Casselmann, **phosphoryl chloride** unites directly with stannic chloride, forming **stannic phosphoryl chloride**, $SnCl_4.POCl_3$; he also made it by heating in a sealed tube a mixture of phosphoryl chloride and stannic sulphochloride, $SnCl_4.2SCl_4$. A. W. Cronander prepared it by the action of phosphoric oxide on $SnCl_4.PCl_5$. According to W. T. Casselmann, the crystals melt at $58°$, forming a clear liquid which may remain for days in an undercooled state and then suddenly crystallize. It boils at $180°$ without decomposition. It fumes in air and attracts moisture, forming crystals of hydrated stannic chloride, stannous chloride, and hydrochloric and phosphoric acids. With a large excess of water it forms stannic phosphate. According to E. and P. Fireman, stannic chloride reacts slowly with **phosphonium iodide** at $90°-160°$: $4SnCl_4$ $+4PH_4I=SnI_4+3SnCl_2+10HCl+2PH_3+2P$; and at $250°-260°$: $6SnCl_4$ $+6PH_4I=3SnCl_2+3SnI_2+18HCl+2PH_3+4P$. For the action of **sodium hypophosphite**, *vide* the hypophosphites. R. Mahn observed no reaction between stannic chloride and **stibine**.

J. Davy [10] found that stannic chloride decomposes **alcohol**, forming stannous oxychloride and ethyl chloride ; C. Girard and P. Chapoteaut, J. H. Mathews, H. Goldschmidt and H. Larsen, G. Gustavson, H. Meyer and R. Turnau, E. Besthorn, B. Holmberg, A. Bauer and E. Klein, and A. Rosenheim and R. Schnabel prepared complex compounds of stannic chloride and alcohol. B. Lewy, and F. Kuhlmann prepared an addition product with **ether,** namely, $SnCl_4.2(C_2H_5)_2O$. According to J. Davy, stannic chloride reacts with **turpentine ;** and, at the same time, the mixture becomes strongly heated, sometimes inflaming the mass and forming stannic oxide. F. Wöhler observed no reaction with **ethylene ;** A. Bertrand found that stannic chloride decomposes **acetic acid,** and **acetic anhydride.** N. Trifonoff examined the magnetic susceptibility of mixtures with **ethyl acetate,** and found a maximum corresponding with $SnCl_4.3C_4H_8O_2$. G. N. Antonoff studied the f.p. curve of mixtures of stannic chloride and **methyl oxalate.** L. Klien obtained an addition product with **hydrogen cyanide,** namely, $SnCl_4.HCy$. P. Pfeiffer and R. Lehnardt, and J. G. F. Druce prepared *methyl stannic chloride,* $Sn(CH_3)Cl_3$; and various other substitution products and complex salts. J. G. F. Druce also made *ethyl stannic chloride,* $Sn(C_2H_5)Cl_3$; *isopropyl stannic chloride,* $Sn(C_3H_7)Cl_3$; as well as complex salts of these compounds, and *diisopropyl stannic dibromide,* $(C_3H_7)_2SnBr_2$; G. Scagliarini complexes with organic bases; and G. T. Morgan and H. D. K. Drew made chloro-derivatives of the β-ketones. P. Pfeiffer represented tin hexavalent in the compounds of stannic chloride with two mols. of a ketone ; and on the co-ordinate valency theory the co-ordination number of tin is 6, *e.g.* $SnCl_4(\cdot O : CR_2)_2$. N. S. Kurnakoff and co-workers measured the viscosity and f.p. of mixtures of stannic chloride with various esters ; N. S. Kurnakoff and co-workers, prepared other organic compounds. B. Köhnlein found that

propyl iodide reacts nearly completely with stannic chloride. F. Fichter and co-workers hold that in weighting silk with stannic chloride, the process begins with the formation of an additive compound of the two. E. Elöd doubted this. W. Anosoff studied the refractive index of mixtures of benzene and stannic chloride.

A. C. Vournasos [11] found that **potassium** reduced tin tetrachloride in boiling toluene soln., forming fine particles of tin. According to J. B. A. Dumas, stannic chloride reacts with **mercury**, forming mercurous and stannous chlorides. A. Levallois studied the action of stannic chloride on **lead sulphide**. A number of complex salts with the metal chlorides have been prepared. Many of these are to be regarded as chlorostannates or stannichlorides, derivatives of **hydrochloro-stannic acid**, H_2SnCl_6. E. Biron [12] prepared chlorostannates of the alkalies, calcium, strontium, beryllium, magnesium, manganese, iron, nickel, cobalt, and zinc, but not of barium, cadmium, silver, copper, lead, and thallium. He found that the chlorides of the elements which furnish chlorostannates retard the speed of hydrolysis of stannic chloride to about the same extent. The increase in the conductivity of the soln. with time and the change in the absorption of light enable the affinity constants, k, of the respective chlorides for stannic chloride to be calculated with the results :

	LiC	NaCl	KCl	NH_4Cl	$MgCl_2$	$ZnCl_2$	$CdCl_2$
k . .	1·00	0·62	0·48	0·59	0·80	0·16	0·06
	$CaCl_2$	$SrCl_2$	$BaCl_2$	$MnCl_2$	$CoCl_2$	$NiCl_2$	$FeCl_2$
k . .	0·71	0·75	0·80	0·62	0·80	0·76	0·48

R. Engel prepared hexahydrated hydrochlorostannic acid, $H_2SnCl_6.6H_2O$, by the action of dry hydrogen chloride on pentahydrated stannic chloride. The crystals form a homogeneous liquid which when sat. has a sp. gr. 1·971 at 28° ; the liquid solidifies at 0° to tabular crystals which melt at 20°. K. Seubert and E. Schürmann prepared similar crystals by the following process :

Stannic chloride is mixed with conc. hydrochloric acid in such proportions that the water in the acid shall be in relation to the stannic chloride as $SnCl_4 : 6H_2O$. 100 parts of stannic chloride require 62·15 parts of 33 per cent. hydrochloric acid. Combination ensues, the mass becomes hot and softens, and hydrogen chloride is evolved. About 8 parts more of dry hydrogen chloride are then slowly passed into the mixture, which is then cooled. The whole solidifies to a scaly crystalline mass of hydrochlorostannic acid.

K. Seubert and E. Schürmann gave 19·2° for the m.p. The crystals lose hydrogen chloride in air ; they are very deliquescent ; but can be preserved in sealed tubes. According to J. Bellucci and N. Parravano, when kept in air or in vacuo, over potassium hydroxide, pentahydrated stannic chloride is formed ; and dil. aq. soln. at ordinary temp. deposit stannic acid.

According to P. A. Bolley,[13] when conc. soln. of stannic chloride and ammonium chloride are mixed, or when a mixture of the dil. soln. is evaporated, octahedral crystals of **ammonium chlorostannate**, $(NH_4)_2SnCl_6$, are deposited. J. G. F. Druce also prepared this salt. It was formerly used by the calico printer under the name *pink-salt* in allusion to its use as a mordant for madder-red colours. G. C. Wittstein made it by mixing a soln. of 40 parts of tin in aqua regia and 35 parts of ammonium chloride at 100°, evaporating the soln. to dryness, and recrystallizing from its aq. soln. H. Silbermann, and E. Biron used a modification of these processes. L. Gmelin obtained it as a sublimate during the preparation of stannic sulphide from a mixture of tin, sulphur, and ammonium chloride. The salt furnishes octahedral crystals belonging to the cubic system; the cleavage is also octahedral. R. G. Dickinson studied the X-radiogram of this salt, and the result is indicated in connection with potassium chlorostannate. E. Carozzi gave 1·677 for the index of refraction with the D-line at 18°. He found the crystals form isomorphous mixtures with those of the corresponding lead and platinum compounds, but in the latter case there is a gap in the miscibility curve with between 22 and 74·5 per cent. of the chlorostannate. S. M. Jörgensen gave 2·390 for the sp. gr. ; H. G. F. Schröder, 2·387 ; E. Carozzi, 2·39 ; and R. Romanis, 2·511. The last-named gave 146·1 for the mol. vol.   P. A. Bolley found that 100 parts of water at 14·5° dissolve 33·3 parts of salt ; the conc. aq. soln. is not decomposed by boiling, but the dil. soln. may form flocculent stannic hydroxide.   A. Gutbier and co-workers prepared a number of organic ammonium chlorostannates.

A. Chassevant [14] prepared **lithium chlorostannate,** $Li_2SnCl_6.8H_2O$, by oxidizing a mixed aq. soln. of stannous and lithium chlorides.   The soln. becomes turbid if it is allowed to stand for some time owing to the formation of stannous hydroxide, but if evaporated over sulphuric acid, small, colourless, octahedral crystals are formed. J. G. F. Druce also prepared this salt.   The salt easily decomposes, and is deliquescent in air ; it is easily soluble in water, but is hydrolyzed by an excess of water. It loses hydrogen chloride and chlorine at 140°–150°.   E. Biron prepared this salt but regarded it as a hexahydrate.   G. C. Wittstein, and J. G. F. Druce prepared **sodium chlorostannate,** $Na_2SnCl_6.6H_2O$, by evaporating a mixed soln. of stannic and sodium chlorides, and they described the product as forming anhydrous cubes ; P. A. Bolley said rhombic laminæ ; and B. Lewy, small prisms.   The evidence is not clear that the salts obtained by P. A. Bolley, and G. C. Wittstein had the same crystalline form.   The analysis of B. Lewy corresponded with a pentahydrate ; S. M. Jörgensen's, E. Biron's, and H. Töpsöe and C. Christiansen's analyses, with a hexahydrate.   The last-named said that the ignition of the complex furnishes sodium chloride and stannic chloride ; P. A. Bolley added that 12·13 per cent. of water is lost during ignition, and stannic chloride is evolved at a red heat.   The crystals are permanent in cold air, but effloresce in warm air.   W. von Kowalewsky found that when a soln. of stannic chloride is added to a sat. soln. of sodium chloride, the sp. conductivity of the mixed soln. increases to a certain point with dilution. J. de la Puente found a mol of stannic chloride reacts with 4 mols of sodium hydroxide, forming **sodium dihydroxydichlorostannate,** $Na_2Sn(OH)_2Cl_2$, and the same product is obtained by the action of a mol of orthostannic acid and 2 mols of hydrogen chloride and sodium hydroxide.

V. A. Jacquelin evaporated an aq. soln. of equimolar parts of potassium and stannic chlorides and obtained crystals of **potassium chlorostannate,** K_2SnCl_6 ; P. A. Bolley found that the same salt is produced if the potassium chloride be in large excess.   The salt was made by E. Biron and J. A. Streng.   J. G. F. Druce made it by oxidizing with chlorine a conc. soln. of potassium chlorostannite, or an acid soln. of stannous chloride in a conc. soln. of potassium chloride.   V. A. Jacquelin said the crystals are rhombohedral ; P. A. Bolley, G. C. Wittstein, B. Lewy, and C. F. Rammelsberg said that the crystals are octahedral.   The X-radiograms of the isomorphous ammonium and potassium chlorostannates were shown by R. G. Dickinson to be in agreement with the space lattice of calcium fluoride in which the calcium atoms are replaced by the chlorostannate radicle $SnCl_6$, and this group, A, Fig. 74, is represented by ● in the lattice diagram, Fig. 74.   The lattice of the potassium salt is a system of potassium atoms and $SnCl_6$-groups ; similarly with the ammonium salt.   The potassium atoms K, or NH_4-radicles, are represented by ○ in the diagram.   Each potassium atom has four tin atoms equidistant from it ; and each tin atom has eight potassium atoms equidistant from it ; each chlorine atom has four potassium atoms equidistant from it ; and each chlorine

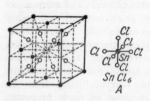

FIG. 74.—Space Lattice of the Alkali Chlorostannates.

atom is at a shorter distance from one tin atom than from any other ; and each tin atom has six chlorine atoms at this distance from it.   The distance between the atoms in the ammonium and potassium chlorostannates are :

	Sn Cl	K—Sn, or NH_4—Sn	K—Cl, or NH_4—Cl
K_2SnCl_6	2·44 A.	4·31 A.	3·52 A.
$(NH_4)_2SnCl_6$	2·46 A.	4·35 A.	3·55 A.

S. M. Jörgensen gave 2·70 for the sp. gr.; H. G. F. Schröder, 2·687; and R. Romanis, 2·948. A. E. van Arkel and J. H. de Boer examined the at. vol. J. Thomsen's value for the heat of formation from the component salts is 34·16 Cals.; and the heat of soln. in water, —3·38 Cals. H. Töpsöe and C. Christiansen found for the refractive index 1·6517 with the C-line; 1·6574 with the D-line; and 1·6717 with the F-line. The crystals are permanent in air, and decrepitate when heated giving off stannic chloride and leaving a residue of potassium chloride mixed with a little stannic chloride, according to G. C. Wittstein, or stannic oxide, according to P. A. Bolley. J. Bellucci and N. Parravano saw that this salt is less stable than the isomorphous potassium chloroplatinate; it is hydrolyzed in hot conc. soln., and in cold dil. soln. with the separation of stannic hydroxide. They were unable to make other complex salts by the double decomposition of conc. soln. of potassium chlorostannate and soln. of the metal salts. J. Morel obtained **monohydrated potassium chlorostannate,** $K_2SnCl_6.H_2O$, by crystallization from an aq. soln. at a temp. below 25°. The rhombic crystals have the axial ratios $a:b:c=0·6843:1:0·7588$. The crystals are colourless and transparent; they are stable in air and in a moist atm. They lose 4–5 per cent. in weight at 110°–120°; and the loss is not attended by a change in the crystalline form. R. Godeffroy deposited octahedral crystals of **rubidium chlorostannate,** Rb_2SnCl_6, from a mixed hydrochloric acid soln. of rubidium chloride and stannic chloride. The octahedral crystals, said E. Biron, are isomorphous with those of the corresponding potassium salt. J. G. F. Druce also made this salt. It is the basis of a method for separating rubidium from other alkali chlorides. F. Stolba, E. H. Ducloux, and J. G. F. Druce obtained **cæsium chlorostannate,** Cs_2SnCl_6, from a mixed aq. soln. of the component salts. The microscopic crystals are octahedral and cubic. The sp. gr. is 3·3308 at 20·5°. They are virtually insoluble in conc. hydrochloric acid; they are decomposed by heating with ammonium chloride; by sulphuric acid; and by hydrofluosilicic acid. E. Biron also prepared this salt. H. Behrens used the salt as a means of recognizing cæsium microscopically. E. Biron did not succeed in making *copper and silver chlorostannates.*

H. Töpsöe and C. Christiansen, E. Biron, F. de la Provostaye, and B. Lewy prepared crystals of **calcium chlorostannate,** $CaSnCl_6.6H_2O$, by evaporating a mixed soln. of the component chlorides over sulphuric acid. The rhombohedral crystals are very deliquescent. B. Lewy regarded the crystals as pentahydrated. J. G. F. Druce obtained anhydrous crystals. H. Töpsöe and C. Christiansen, E. Biron, and B. Lewy made prismatic crystals of **strontium chlorostannate,** $SrSnCl_6.6H_2O$. B. Lewy regarded the salt as pentahydrated; J. G. F. Druce, as tetrahydrated; and H. Töpsöe and C. Christiansen, as octohydrated. E. Biron also reported **tetrahydrated strontium chlorostannate,** $SrSnCl_6.4H_2O$. B. Lewy reported crystals of **barium chlorostannate,** $BaSnCl_6.5H_2O$, but E. Biron could not make this salt, and J. G. F. Druce obtained it only in an impure form. A. Atterberg, and E. Biron obtained a white powder of **beryllium chlorostannate,** $BeSnCl_6.8H_2O$, by evaporating a soln. of the component salts. B. Lewy, J. G. F. Druce, and E. Biron made **magnesium chlorostannate,** $MgSnCl_6.6H_2O$, by evaporating a soln. of the component salts. S. M. Jörgensen evaporated the soln. at 45°–50°, and, on slowly cooling, obtained deliquescent rhombohedral crystals belonging to the trigonal system with the axial ratio $a:c=1:0·508$. The crystals were optically positive. The sp. gr. is 2·08. B. Lewy regarded the salt as a pentahydrate. H. Töpsöe and C. Christiansen also examined the optical properties of the crystals, and gave for the indices of refraction for the D-line, $\omega=1·5885$ and $\epsilon=1·597$; and for the C-line, $\omega=1·5715$, and $\epsilon=1·583$. At 100°, they lose water and stannic chloride. E. Biron, and J. G. F. Druce made crystals of **zinc chlorostannate,** $ZnSnCl_6.6H_2O$, by evaporating a mixed soln. of the component salts; but he could not obtain *cadmium chlorostannate* in this way.

J. Kendall and co-workers found evidence of no compound on the f.p. curve of mixtures of *aluminium and stannic chlorides.* The m.p. falls from 188·6° with

6·8 per cent. of $SnCl_4$ to 65·7° with 99·6 per cent. E. Biron could not prepare *thallous chlorostannate;* nor *lead chlorostannate.* S.M.Jörgensen reported **manganese chlorostannate,** $MnSnCl_6.6H_2O$, to be formed in pale red rhombohedra belonging to the trigonal system, and with the axial ratio $a : c = 1 : 0.5194$. The sp. gr. is 2·215. The crystals are optically positive; they deliquesce in moist air, and effloresce in dry air, losing at 100°, water and stannous chloride. E. Biron made the same salt, S. M. Jörgensen, and J. G. F. Druce made **nickel chlorostannate,** $NiSnCl_6.6H_2O$, in greenish rhombohedra belonging to the trigonal system with the axial ratio $a : c = 1 : 0.5048$, and $a = 112° 30'$. The sp. gr. is 2·699. H. Töpsöe and C. Christiansen found that the double refraction is feeble and positive. S. M. Jörgensen, and J. G. F. Druce made the corresponding **cobalt chlorostannate,** $CoSnCl_6.6H_2O$, in rhombohedral crystals belonging to the trigonal system with the axial ratio $a : c = 1 : 0.5103$. The sp. gr. is 2·699. The crystals effloresce in dry air and at 100° lose water and stannic chloride. E. Biron studied the hydrolysis of the salt. E. Biron studied the **ferrous chlorostannate** in soln. *Vide* the stannic chloroplatinites and chloroplatinates.

REFERENCES.

¹ A. Libavius, *Praxis alchymiæ,* Francofurti, 1605 ; *Syntagma selectorum arcanorum,* Francofurti, 1615 ; R. Boyle, *Causes of the Wholesomeness and Unwholesomeness of the Air,* London, 1674 ; H. Peters, *Mitt. Museum Nürnberg,* 98, 1893 ; *Chem. Ztg.,* 32. 754, 1908 ; J. J. Berzelius, *Schweigger's Journ.,* 6. 284, 1812 ; *Ann. Chim. Phys.,* (2), 5. 141, 1817 ; J. Davy, *Phil. Trans.,* 102. 169, 1812 ; J. L. Proust, *Journ. Phys.,* 51. 173, 1802 ; 61. 338, 1804 ; *Ann. Chim. Phys.,* (1), 28. 213, 1798 ; *Nicholson's Journ.,* (1), 2. 515, 1799 ; (2), 14. 38, 1806.

² R. Cowper, *Journ. Chem. Soc.,* 43. 153, 1883 ; C. W. Watts and C. A. Bell, *ib.,* 33. 442, 1878 ; W. Coldridge, *Phil. Mag.,* (5), 29. 383, 1890 ; K. Heumann and P. Köchlin, *Ber.,* 15. 416, 1736, 1882 ; G. Vortmann and C. Padberg, *ib.,* 22. 2642, 1889 ; C. Renz, *ib.,* 39. 249, 1906 ; R. Lorenz, *Zeit. anorg. Chem.,* 10. 44, 1895 ; E. Beckmann and P. Geib, *ib.,* 51. 96, 1906 ; J. von Kraskowitz, *Liebig's Ann.,* 16. 195, 1835 ; *Pogg. Ann.,* 35. 518, 1835 ; R. Schneider, *ib.,* 127. 624, 1866 ; H. Goldschmidt, *Chem. Centr.,* (3), 12. 489, 1881 ; C. Matignon and F. Bourion, *Compt. Rend.,* 138. 761, 1904 ; H. J. Taverne, *Chem. Weekkbl.,* 17. 610, 1920 ; A. Michaelis, *Journ. prakt. Chem.,* (2), 4. 449, 1871 ; J. Davy, *Phil. Trans.,* 102. 169, 1812 ; G. Rauter, *Liebig's Ann.,* 270. 249, 1892 ; L. Czimatis, *German Pat., D.R.P.* 51550, 1884 ; F. Meilly, *ib.,* 33925, 1883 ; E. Kotzur, *ib.,* 85567, 1894 ; B. H. Jacobson, *Brit. Pat. Nos.* 181385, 190688. 1922 ; E. A. Sperry, *Journ. Soc. Chem. Ind.,* 27. 312, 1908 ; P. Heermann, *Färber Ztg.,* 34, 1904 ; *Zeit. angew. Chem.,* 20. 1373, 1907 ; J. Kelley and E. F. Smith, *Journ. Amer. Chem Soc.,* 18. 1096, 1896 ; P. S. Brallier, *Trans. Amer. Electrochem. Soc.,* 49. 65, 1926.

³ J. F. Demachy, *Nova Acta Acad. Nat. Cur.,* 4. 60, 1770 ; G. T. Gerlach, *Dingler's Journ.,* 178. 49. 1865 ; R. Brönner, *ib.,* 209. 77, 1873 ; M. Rössler, *ib.,* 186. 38, 1867 ; W. Meyerhoffer, *Bull. Soc. Chim.,* (3), 6. 85, 1891 ; B. Lewy, *Compt. Rend.,* 21. 369, 1845 ; *Ann. Chim. Phys.,* (3), 16. 304, 1846 ; P. A. Adet, *ib.,* (1), 1. 10, 1789 ; A. Scheurer-Kestner, *ib.,* (3), 58. 471, 1860 ; *Compt. Rend.,* 52. 531, 1861 ; *Chem. News,* 4. 101, 192, 1861 ; W. T. Casselmann, *Liebig's Ann.,* 83. 257, 1852 ; T. Scheerer, *Journ. prakt. Chem.,* (2), 3. 472, 1871 ; C. Nöllner, *Zeit. Chem.,* (1), 1. 445, 1865 ; P. Heermann, *Chem. Ztg.,* 21. 680, 1907 ; M. Taufflieb, *Journ. Chem. Méd.,* 4. 116, 1832 ; H. Rose, *Pogg. Ann.,* 75. 4, 1848 ; J. Bellucci and N. Parravano, *Zeit. anorg. Chem.,* 45. 143, 1905 ; *Atti Accad. Lincei,* (5), 13. ii, 307, 1904 ; J. Beckmann, *Beyträge zur Geschichte der Erfindungen.* Leipzig, 3. 43, 1792 ; London, 1. 402, 1846.

⁴ G. T. Gerlach, *Dingler's Journ.,* 178. 49, 1865 ; E. Mathias, *Le point critique,* Paris, 1904 ; H. H. Marvin, *Phys. Rev.,* (2), 17. 412, 1921 ; J. I. Pierre, *Ann. Chim. Phys.,* (3), 19. 193, 1847 ; (3), 20. 1, 1847 ; J. B. A. Dumas, *ib.,* (2), 33. 385, 1826 ; W. Meyerhoffer, *Bull. Soc. Chim.,* (3), 6. 85, 1891 ; A. Besson, *Compt. Rend.,* 109. 940, 1889 ; E. Bichat, *ib.,* 88. 712, 1879 ; R. O. Herzog, *Zeit. Elektrochem.,* 15. 345, 1909 ; G. Rudorf, *ib.,* 15. 746, 1909 ; T. E. Thorpe. *Proc. Roy. Soc.,* 24. 283, 1876 ; *Journ. Chem. Soc.,* 37. 331, 1880 ; T. Andrews, *ib.,* 1. 27, 1847 ; S. Young, *ib.,* 59. 911, 1891 ; *Fractional Distillation,* London, 12, 1903 ; *Proc. Dublin Scient. Soc.,* (2), 12. 428, 1910 ; *Phil. Mag.,* (5), 34. 505, 1902 ; H. V. Regnault, *Relations des expériences entrepis, pour déterminer les principales lois et les données numériques qui entrent dans le calcul des machines a vapeur,* Paris, 203, 1862 ; *Mém. Acad.,* 21. 1, 1847 ; *Ann. Chim. Phys.,* (3), 9. 322, 1843 ; F. W. Schmidt, *Zeit. Koll.,* 1. 129, 1906 ; J. Thomsen, *Journ. prakt. Chem.,* (2), 14. 429, 1876 ; *Thermochemische Untersuchungen.* Leipzig, 3. 327, 1883 ; E. Beckmann and P. Geib, *Zeit. anorg. Chem.,* 51, 96, 1906 ; R. Lorenz, *ib.,* 138. 104, 1924 ; R. Lorenz and W. Herz. *ib.,* 135. 372, 1924 ; 143. 337, 1925 ; W. Herz, *ib.,* 124. 56, 1922 ; 144. 40, 1925 ; 145, 378, 1925 ; 150. 336, 1926 ; *Zeit. Elektrochem.,* 27. 323, 1921 ; *Zeit. angew. Chem.,* 37. 453, 1924 ; *Zeit. phys. Chem.,* 103. 269, 1923 ; R. Lorenz, *Zeit. anorg. Chem.,* 10. 46, 1895 ; W. von Kowalewsky, *ib.,* 23, 1, 1899 ; 25. 189. 1900 ; W. Coldridge, *Phil. Mag.,* (5), 29. 383, 1890 ; E. E. Walker, *ib.,* (6), 47. 111,

1924 ; L. Bleekrode, *Wied. Ann.*, 3. 161, 1878 ; W. Dittenberger and R. Dietz, *ib.*, 68. 858, 1899 ; W. M. Latimer, *Journ. Amer. Chem. Soc.*, 44. 90, 1922 ; J. Kendall, E. D. Crittenden, and H. K. Miller, *ib.*, 45. 963, 1923 ; J. E. Mills and P. K. Smith, *Journ. Phys. Chem.*, 27. 301, 1923 ; D. L. Hammick. *Phil. Mag.*, (6), 44. 590, 1922 ; E. Ariès, *Compt. Rend.*, 163. 204, 444, 1919 ; G. von Hevesy, *Danske Vid Medd.*, 3. 13, 1921 ; H. von Jüptner, *Zeit. phys. Chem.*, 85. 1, 1913 ; W. J. Pope, *Journ. Chem. Soc.*, 69. 1530, 1896 ; A. Stiefelhagen, *Dispersion flüssiger Tr´chloride und Tetrachloride für ultraviolette Strahlen*, Berlin, 1905 ; A. Heydweiller, *Zeit. Physik*, 4. 442, 1921 ; *Zeit. anorg. Chem.*, 116. 42, 1921 ; F. Schuster, *ib.*, 146. 299, 1925 ; I. I. Saslawsky, *ib.*, 146. 315, 1925 ; *Zeit. phys. Chem.*, 109. 111, 1924 ; P. Heermann, *Farber Ztg.*, 18. 34, 1907 ; *Chem. Ztg.*, 21. 680, 1907 ; A. Haagen, *Pogg. Ann.*, 131. 117, 1867 ; G. Neumann, *Monatsh.*, 12. 515, 1891 ; H. Schlundt, *Journ. Phys. Chem.*, 5. 503, 1901 ; J. H. Mathews, *ib.*, 9. 641, 1905 ; W. T. Casselmann, *Liebig's Ann.*, 83. 257, 1852 ; M. Berthelot, *Thermochimie*, Paris, 2. 154, 1897 ; D. Helbig and G. Fausti, *Atti Accad. Lincei*, (5), 13. 30, 1904 ; F. Kohlrausch, *Zeit. phys. Chem.*, 33. 270, 1900 ; P. Walden, *ib.*, 43, 385, 1903 ; 66. 385, 1909 ; 70. 581, 1910 ; *Ber.*, 35. 2024, 1902 ; J. Bongartz and A. Classen, *ib.*, 21. 2900, 1888 ; W. Madelung, *Liebig's Ann.*, 427. 35, 1922 ; C. Sheard and C. S. Morris, *Thio Journ. Science*, 16. 113, 1916 ; J. H. Gladstone, *Journ. Chem. Soc.*, 59. 290, 1891 ; *Phil. Trans.*, 160. 28, 1870 ; F. F. Martens, *Verh. deut. phys. Ges.*, 4. 138, 1902 ; W. Foster, *Phys. Rev.*, (1), 45. 41, 1899 ; G. Quincke, *Wied. Ann.*, 24. 347, 1885 ; 34. 401, 1888 ; A. Hantzsch and H. Carlsohn, *Ber.*, 58. B, 1741, 1925 ; K. Fajans and G. Joos, *Zeit. Physik*, 23. 1, 1924 ; P. A. Bond and H. T. Beach, *Journ. Amer. Chem. Soc.*, 48. 348, 1926 ; W. Herz, *Zeit. anorg. Chem.*, 153. 269, 1926 ; N. de Kolossowsky, *Journ. Chim. Phys.*, 23. 353, 1926 ; E. Rabinowitsch, *Ber.*, 58. B, 2790, 1925 ; G. T. Morgan, S. R. Carter, and W. F. Harrison, *Journ. Chem. Soc.*, 127. 1917, 1925 ; O. Masson, *Phil. Mag.*, (5), 30. 412, 1890 ; J. A. Groshans, *ib.*, (5), 20. 197, 1885 ; *Ber.*, 19. 974, 1886 ; W. Herz, *Zeit. Elektrochem.*, 32. 31, 210, 1926 ; F. Schuster, *ib.*, 32. 191, 1926.

⁵ W. Smirnoff, *Zeit. phys. Chem.*, 58. 373, 1907 ; E. Biron, *Journ. Russ. Phys. Chem. Soc.*, 37. 933, 963. 994, 1906 ; H. Rose, *Pogg. Ann.*, 75. 1, 1847 ; R. Weber, *ib.*, 122, 368, 1864 ; J. J. Berzelius, *Schweigger's Journ.*, 6. 284, 1812 ; *Ann. Chim. Phys.*, (2), 5. 141, 1817 ; L. Vignon, *Compt. Rend.*, 109. 372, 1889 ; W. O. de Coninck, *ib.*, 130. 1627, 1900 ; R. Engel, *ib.*, 103. 213, 1886 ; 124. 765, 1897 ; 125. 464, 651, 709, 1897 ; W. T. Casselmann, *Liebig's Ann.*, 85. 257, 1852 ; R. Zsigmondy, *ib.*, 301, 361, 1898 ; J. Löwenthal, *Journ. prakt. Chem.*, (1), 77. 321, 1859 ; C. T. Barfoed, *ib.*, (1), 101. 368, 1867 ; *Danske Vid. Selsk. Forh.*, (5), 7. 236, 1866 ; E. H. Loomis, *Wied. Ann.*, 60. 523, 1897 ; G. Tschermak, *Sitzber. Akad. Wien*, 44. 736, 1862 ; R. Lorenz, *Zeit. anorg. Chem.*, 9. 376, 1895 ; G. Jörgensen, *ib.*, 57. 353, 1908 ; N. N. Mittra and N. R. Dhar, *ib.*, 122. 146, 1922 ; W. Mecklenburgh, *ib.*, 74. 207, 1912 ; 84. 121, 1914 ; J. M. van Bemmelen, *ib.*, 23. 111, 1900 ; *Die Absorption*, Dresden, 393, 1910 ; *Rec. Trav. Chim. Pays-Bas*, 7. 37, 1888 ; A. Kleinschmidt, *Monatsh.*, 39. 149, 1918 ; H. Kühl, *Pharm. Ztg.*, 53. 49, 1908 ; D. B. Dott, *Journ. Pharm.*, (4), 27. 486, 1908 ; P. Geiseler, *Arch. Pharm.*, (1), 7. 148, 1833 ; *Liebig's Ann.*, 20. 155, 1836 ; C. E. Carstanjen, *German Pat.*, *D.R.P.* 163322, 1902 ; J. W. Mallet, *Journ. Chem. Soc.*, 35. 524, 1879 ; G. E. Collins and J. K. Wood, *ib.*, 121. 441, 1122, 1922 ; M. Berthelot, *Ann. Chim. Phys.*, (5), 15. 185, 1878 ; (5), 16. 442, 1879 ; F. Musculus, *ib.*, (4), 13. 95, 1868 ; *Compt. Rend.*, 65. 961, 1867 ; A. Scheurer-Kestner, *ib.*, 52. 531, 1861 ; *Chem. News*, 4. 101, 192, 1861 ; *Ann. Chim. Phys.*, (3), 58. 471, 1860 ; J. M. Ordway, *Amer. Journ. Science*, (2), 23. 220, 1857 ; P. Pfeiffer, *Ber.*, 38. 2466, 1905 ; J. de la Puente, *Anales Soc. Espan. Fis. Quim.*, 20. 486, 1922.

⁴ W. Coldridge, *Phil. Mag.*, (5), 29. 480, 1890 ; J. B. A. Dumas, *Journ. Chim. Méd.*, 8. 748, 1832 ; O. C. M. Davis, *Proc. Chem. Soc.*, 22. 261, 1906 ; R. G. Durrant, *Journ. Chem. Soc.*, 107. 622, 1915 ; F. de Carli, *Atti Accad. Lincei*, (5), 33. ii, 94, 1924 ; H. Rose, *Pogg. Ann.*, 16. 339, 1829 ; 24. 339, 1832 ; 42. 517, 1837 ; 44. 320, 1838 ; R. Weber, *Sitzber. Akad. Berlin*, 154, 1865 ; W. Biltz and E. Meinecke, *Zeit. anorg. Chem.*, 131. 1, 1923 ; W. Biltz and E. Keunecke, *ib.*, 147. 171, 1925 ; W. T. Casselmann, *Liebig's Ann.*, 83. 267, 1852 ; O. Ruff and G. Fischer, *Ber.*, 37. 4517, 1904 ; H. Friedrich, *ib.*, 26. 1434, 1893 ; F. Clausnitzer, *ib.*, 11. 2012, 1878 ; J. Girardin *Ann. Chim. Phys.*, (2), 61. 286, 1836 ; H. Wölbling, *Zeit. anorg. Chem.*, 57. 281, 1908 ; P. A. Bond and H. T. Beach, *Journ. Amer. Chem. Soc.*, 40. 348, 1926 ; A. Besson, *Compt. Rend.*, 124. 683, 1897.

⁷ J. Davy, *Phil. Trans.*, 102. 169, 1812 ; H. Rose, *Pogg. Ann.*, 16. 63, 1829 ; 24. 163, 1832 ; W. G. Mixter, *Amer. Chem. Journ.*, 2. 153, 1881 ; P. Grouvelle, *Ann. Chim. Phys.*, (2), 44. 322, 1830 ; J. Persoz, *ib.*, (2), 44. 315, 1830 ; P. P. Dehérain, *Bull. Soc. Chim.*, (1), 3. 51, 1861 ; P. Fireman, *Journ. Amer. Chem. Soc.*, 26. 741, 1904.

⁸ J. L. Gay Lussac, *Ann. Chim. Phys.*, (2), 1. 40, 1816 ; F. Kuhlmann, *ib.*, (3), 2. 118, 1841 ; V. Thomas, *ib.*, (7), 13. 145, 1897 ; *Compt. Rend.*, 122. 32, 1896 ; R. Weber, *Pogg. Ann.*, 118. 471, 1863 ; 123. 347, 1864 ; S. M. Jörgensen, *Danske Vid. Selsk. Forh.*, (5), 6. 499, 1867 ; W. J. van Heteren, *Zeit. anorg. Chem.*, 22. 277, 1899 ; W. Hampe, *Liebig's Ann.*, 126. 43, 1863 ; A. Baeyer, *Ber.*, 7. 1639, 1874 ; J. J. Sudborough, *Journ. Chem. Soc.*, 59. 655, 1891 ; O. C. M. Davis, *ib.*, 89. 1575, 1906.

⁹ R. Mahn, *Jena Zeit.*, 5. 160, 1870 ; H. Rose, *Pogg. Ann.*, 24. 159, 1832 ; E. and P. Fireman, *Journ. Amer. Chem. Soc.*, 30. 116, 1903 ; E. Baudrimont, *Ann. Chim. Phys.*, (4), 2. 5, 1864 ; W. T. Casselmann, *Liebig's Ann.*, 83. 257, 1852 ; 91. 242, 1854 ; 98. 213, 1856 ; A. W. Cronander, *Ber.*, 4. 753, 1871.

¹⁰ J. Davy, *Phil. Trans.*, 102. 169, 1812 ; L. Klien, *Liebig's Ann.*, 74. 85, 1850 ; A. Bauer and

E. Klein, *ib.*, 147. 249, 1868; *Sitzber. Akad. Wien*, 57. 92, 1868; F. Wöhler, *Pogg. Ann.*, 13. 297, 1828; C. Girard and P. Chapoteaut, *Compt. Rend.*, 64. 1252, 1867; A. Rosenheim and R. Schnabel, *Ber.*, 38. 2777, 1905; E. Besthorn, *ib.*, 41. 2003, 1908; H. Meyer and R. Turnau, *ib.*, 42. 1163, 1909; H. Goldschmidt and H. Larsen, *Zeit. phys. Chem.*, 48. 424, 1904; G. Gustavson, *Journ. Russ. Phys. Chem.*, 23. 253, 1891; B. Holmberg, *Zeit. anorg. Chem.*, 56. 385, 1908; J. H. Mathews, *Journ. Phys. Chem.*, 9. 658, 1905; P. Pfeiffer and R. Lehnardt, *Ber.*, 36. 1054, 3027, 1903; P. Pfeiffer, *Zeit. anorg. Chem.*, 71. 97, 1911; 112. 81, 1920; 133. 91, 1924; J. G. F. Druce, *Chem. News*, 120. 229, 1920; 125. 327, 1922; 127. 306, 1923; 130. 385, 1925; *Journ. Chem. Soc.*, 119. 758, 1921; 121. 859, 1922; G. T. Morgan and H. D. K. Drew, *ib.*, 125. 372, 1924; N. S. Kurnakoff, *Zeit. anorg. Chem.*, 135. 81, 1924; G. N. Antonoff, *Phil. Mag.*, (7), 1. 1121, 1926; N. S. Kurnakoff, S. L. Perlmutter, and F. P. Kanoff, *Journ. Russ. Phys. Chem. Soc.*, 48. 1658, 1916; N. S. Kurnakoff and N. N. Beketoff, *ib.*, 48. 1694, 1916; B. Köhnlein, *Liebig's Ann.*, 225. 171, 1884; N. Trifonoff, *Mitt. Wiss. Tech. Russ.*, 13. 10, 1924; W. Anosoff, *ib.*, 13. 10, 1924; G. Scagliarini, *Atti Accad. Lincei*, (6), 2. 269, 1925; F. Kuhlmann, *Ann. Chim. Phys.*, (3), 2. 118, 1841; B. Lewy, *ib.*, (3), 16. 303, 1846; A. Bertrand, *Bull. Soc. Chim.*, (2), 33. 252, 1880; F. Fichter and E. Müller, *Farber-Ztg.*, 26. 253, 274, 289, 1915; F. Fichter and F. Reichardt, *Helvetica Chem. Acta*, 7. 1078, 1924; E. Elöd, *Chem. Ztg.*, 46. 597, 1922; *Koll. Beihefte*, 19. 298, 1924.

[11] J. B. A. Dumas, *Ann. Chim. Phys.*, (2), 33. 385, 1826; A. Levallois, *Compt. Rend.*, 96. 1666, 1883; A. C. Vournasos, *ib.*, 81. 364, 1913.

[12] R. Engel, *Compt. Rend.*, 103. 213, 1886; K. Seubert and E. Schürmann, *Ber.*, 20. 793, 1887; E. Biron, *Journ. Russ. Phys. Chem. Soc.*, 36. 489, 1904; 37. 994, 1036, 1905; J. Bellucci and N. Parravano, *Atti Accad. Lincei*, (5), 13. ii, 307, 1904; *Zeit. anorg. Chem.*, 45. 150, 1905.

[13] P. A. Bolley, *Liebig's Ann.*, 39. 100, 1841; J. G. F. Druce, *Chem. News*, 117. 193, 1918; *Journ. Chem. Soc.*, 111. 418, 1917; E. Carrozzi, *Gazz. Chim. Ital.*, 54. i, 556, 1924; G. C. Wittstein, *Repert. Pharm.*, (3), 4. 7, 1850; E. Biron, *Journ. Russ. Phys. Chem. Soc.*, 36. 439, 1904; 37. 994, 1036, 1905; H. Silbermann, *Tärber Ztg.*, 8. 34, 1897; R. Romanis, *Chem. News*, 49. 273, 1884; L. Gmelin, *Handbook of Chemistry*, London, 5. 94, 1851; S. M. Jörgensen, *Danske Vid. Selsk. Forh.*, (5), 6. 499, 1865; R. G. Dickinson, *Journ. Amer. Chem. Soc.*, 44. 276, 1922; H. G. F. Schröder, *Dichtigkeitsmessungen*, Heidelberg, 1873; A. Gutbier, G. Kunze, and E. Gühring, *Zeit. anorg. Chem.*, 128. 169, 1923.

[14] V. A. Jacquelin, *Ann. Chim. Phys.*, (2), 66. 130, 1837; H. Töpsöe and C. Christiansen, *ib.*, (4), 31. 1, 1873; *Danske Vid. Selsk. Forh.*, (5), 4. 246, 1869; B. Lewy, *Ann. Chim. Phys.*, (3), 16. 308, 1846; F. de la Provostaye, *ib.*, (3), 6. 47, 1842; A. Chassevant, *ib.*, (6), 30. 42, 1903; E. Biron, *Journ. Russ. Phys. Chem. Soc.*, 36. 489, 1904; 37. 994, 1036, 1905; G. C. Wittstein, *Repert. Pharm.*, (3), 4. 7, 1850; P. A. Bolley, *Liebig's Ann.*, 39. 100, 1841; A. Atterberg, *Svenska Vet. Akad. Handl.*, 12. 5, 1873; J. de la Puente, *Anal. Soc. Espan. Fis. Quim.*, 20. 486, 1922; J. Kendall, E. D. Crittenden, and H. K. Miller, *Journ. Amer. Chem. Soc.*, 45. 963, 1923; A. E. van Arkel and J. H. de Boer, *Physica*, 4. 392, 1924; W. von Kowalewsky, *Zeit. anorg. Chem.*, 23. 1, 1900; R. Romanis, *Chem. News*, 49. 273, 1884; J. G. F. Druce, *ib.*, 117. 193, 1918; S. M. Jörgensen, *Danske Vid. Selsk. Forh.*, (5), 6. 499, 1865; H. G. F. Schröder, *Dichtigkeitsmessungen*, Heidelberg, 1873; F. Capitaine, *Journ. Pharm. Chim.*, 25. 549, 1839; J. Morel, *Bull. Soc. Min.*, 13. 339, 1891; C. F. Rammelsberg, *Handbuch der krystallographisch-physikalischen Chemie*, Leipzig, 1. 468, 1881; J. Thomsen, *Journ. prakt. Chem.*, (2), 14. 429, 1876; J. Bellucci and N. Parravano, *Atti Accad. Lincei*, (5), 13. ii, 307, 1904; *Zeit. anorg. Chem.*, 45. 150, 1905; J. A. Streng, *Neues Jahrb. Min.*, ii, 143, 1888; R. Godeffroy, *Ber.*, 7. 376, 1874; H. Behrens, *Zeit. anal. Chem.*, 30. 137, 1891; F. Stolba, *Dingler's Journ.*, 198. 225, 1870; R. G. Dickinson, *Journ. Amer. Chem. Soc.*, 44. 276, 1922; E. H. Ducloux, *Anal. Asoc. Quim. Argentina*, 9. 215, 1921.

§ 18. The Stannous Bromides

A. J. Balard[1] prepared stannous bromide, $SnBr_2$, by heating tin in an atm. of hydrogen bromide. An oily liquid condenses close to the hot zone, and it freezes on cooling to a grey mass. B. Rayman and K. Preis purified the product of this operation by fractional distillation. A. E. Nordenskjöld treated tin with dry hydrogen bromide, and sublimed the white product in a sealed tube. C. Löwig made stannous bromide by heating a mixture of tin and mercurous bromide; J. Nicklès, by heating stannic ethoxybromide, $SnBr_4.2(C_2H_5)_2O$; and F. Freyer and V. Meyer, by dissolving powdered tin in hot hydrobromic acid, and gently evaporating the soln. Stannous bromide forms a pale yellow crystalline mass, consisting, according to J. Nicklès, of hexagonal columns, which A. E. Nordenskjöld said belong to the rhombic system and have the axial ratios $a:b:c = 0.5735:1:0.5305$. S. Motylewsky found 75 for the drop weight of stannous bromide with respect to water at $0° = 100$. B. Rayman and K. Preis found the sp. gr. at 17° to be 5·117 ; W. Beltz and E. Birk gave 4·923 for the sp. gr. of fused stannous bromide at 25°/4°, and 56·57 for the mol. vol. I. I. Saslawsky gave 1·03 for the ratio of the mol. vol. to the sum of the at. vols. of the constituent elements. B. Rayman and K. Preis found that stannous bromide melts to a pale yellow liquid at 215·5° ; J. Kendall and co-workers gave 232° for the m.p. ; and T. Karantassis, 226·7° ; T. Carnelley and W. C. Williams found the b.p. to be 617°–634° ; and F. Freyer and V. Meyer, 619°. M. Berthelot gave for the heat of formation $(Sn,Br_2)=71·4$ Cals., or with solid bromine 68·8 Cals. ; and for the heat of soln. in water, 16·0 Cals. ; W. Biltz and W. Fischer gave −1·6 cals. for $SnBr_2$. R. E. Liesegang showed that stannous bromide is sensitive to light. A. Naumann and J. Schröder found stannous bromide is soluble in pyridine ; and A. Werner found a mol. wt. of 268·35 in boiling pyridine : and 257 in boiling ethyl sulphide when the value calculated for $SnBr_2$ is 278. When stannous bromide is heated in air or with potassium nitrate, stannic bromide and oxide are formed ; when heated in dry oxygen, M. Berthelot found that it catches fire at a red heat, forming bromine and stannic oxide. T. Karantassis could not obtain **stannous chlorobromide**, SnClBr, by the action of bromine on a soln. of stannous chloride in hydrochloric acid, and reducing the product with an excess of tin. The mixed chloride and bromide has a eutectic at 213° and 62·8 molar per cent. of stannous chloride.

B. Rayman and K. Preis said that the salt is hydrolyzed by water, forming a white **stannous oxybromide**. A **stannosic oxybromide**, or **stannostannic oxybromide**, $Sn_3OBr_6.12H_2O$, was also obtained in colourless prismatic crystals, by B. Rayman and K. Preis, by placing tin in a soln. of barium bromostannate. A. J. Balard evaporated an aq. soln. of stannous bromide, and found that while part of the salt is decomposed, colourless crystals of **monohydrated stannous bromide**, $SnBr_2.H_2O$, are formed. C. Löwig showed that tin dissolves very slowly in cold hydrobromic acid, and rapidly when boiled. The evaporation of the soln. gave a gelatinous mass without crystallization, and hydrogen bromide was produced on heating the product. B. Rayman and K. Preis showed that if the soln. be evaporated until a drop on a cold slab shows signs of crystallization and the liquid be then seeded with ready-formed crystals, the monohydrate forms needle-like or prismatic crystals. A. J. Balard also obtained the monohydrate from a soln. of stannous hydroxide in hydrobromic acid, or by reducing an aq. soln. of stannic bromide with tin. W. Biltz and W. Fischer found the heat of soln. of stannous bromide in one per cent. hydrochloric acid to be −1·6 Cals. They also found the temp. at which the vap. press. of the ammines is 100 mm., and the heats of dissociation in Cals. per mol. of NH_3 to be respectively for **stannous enneamminobromide**, $SnBr_2.9NH_3$, −57°, and 7·55 ; **stannous pentamminobromide**, $SnBr_2.5NH_3$, −2°, and 9·8 ; **stannous triamminobromide**, $SnBr_2.3NH_3$, 66°, and 12·4 ; and for **stannous diamminobromide**, $SnBr_2.2NH_3$, 102°, and 13·6. G. L. Clark also made observations on this subject. P. Pfeiffer studied the dialkyl stannous bromides ; and H. Goldschmidt and co-workers, the reduction of organic nitro-compounds by stannous bromide.

B. Rayman and K. Preis found that stannous bromide unites with metal bromides, forming **bromostannites**. A conc. soln. of stannous bromide and ammonium bromide, for example, deposits colourless, needle-like crystals of **ammonium tetrabromostannite**, $(NH_4)_2SnBr_4.H_2O$. E. Rimbach and K. Fleck made the same salt, and also **ammonium tribromostannite**, $NH_4SnBr_3.H_2O$, by the method employed for the corresponding chlorostannite ; while E. Rimbach and K. Fleck, and I. Remsen and G. M. Richardson obtained **potassium tribromostannite**, $KSnBr_3.H_2O$, from a soln. of potassium bromide containing a large excess of stannous bromide ; and a soln. of the component salts in equimolar proportions yields **potassium tetrabromostannite**, $K_2SnBr_4.H_2O$, in rhombic bipyramids with axial ratios $a : b : c$ $=0·6828 : 1 : 0·7467$. A. C. Vournasos made **sodium dichlorodibromostannate**, $Na_2[SnCl_2Br_2]$. E. Rimbach and K. Fleck obtained **ammonium hexabromo-**

stannite, $(NH_4)_4SnBr_6.H_2O$, in stable crystals. B. Rayman and K. Preis reported ammonium dibromodichlorostannite, $2NH_4Cl.SnBr_2.H_2O$, or $(NH_4)_2SnBr_2Cl_2.H_2O$, to be formed in prismatic crystals by cooling a soln. of stannous bromide. The crystals belong to the rhombic system and have the axial ratios $a : b : c$ $=0.6959 : 1 : 0.7724$. If a larger proportion of stannous bromide is used, the product contains more bromine, $2NH_4(Cl,Br).SnBr_2.H_2O$. J. Kendall and co-workers found that with mixtures of aluminium and stannous bromides there is a two-liquid region extending from 1·8 to 14·2 per cent. $SnBr_2$ in equilibrium with aluminium octobromostannite, $2AlBr_3.SnBr_2$, at 161·1° ; the critical soln. temp. being 204·5° with 8·4 per cent. $SnBr_2$; the octobromostannite melts at 205°, and aluminium pentabromostannite, $AlBr_3.SnBr_2$, melts at 183°.

REFERENCES.

1 I. Remsen and G. M. Richardson, *Amer. Chem. Journ.*, 14. 89, 1892 ; C. G. Cook, *ib.*, 22. 435. 1899 ; *Some Double Halides of Tin with the Aliphatic Amines and with Tetramethylammonium*, Easton, Pa., 1898 ; J. Kendall, E. D. Crittenden, and H. K. Miller, *Journ. Amer. Chem. Soc.*, 45. 963, 1923 ; I. I. Saslawsky, *Zeit. anorg. Chem.*, 146. 315, 1925 ; A. J. Balard, *Ann. Chim. Phys.*, (2), 32. 337, 1826 ; M. Berthelot, *ib.*, (5), 15. 185, 1878 ; (5), 16. 442, 1878 ; (5), 21. 389, 1880 ; B. Rayman and K. Preis, *Liebig's Ann.*, 223. 324, 1884 ; C. Löwig, *Pogg. Ann.*, 14. 485, 1828 ; G. L. Clark, *Amer. Journ. Science*, (5), 7. 1, 1924 ; J. Nicklès, *Compt. Rend.*, 52. 869, 1861 ; F. Freyer and V. Meyer, *Zeit. anorg. Chem.*, 2. 1, 1892 ; W. Biltz and W. Fischer, *ib.*, 129. 1, 1923 ; W. Biltz, *ib.*, 130. 93, 1923 ; S. Motylewsky, *ib.*, 38. 410, 1904 ; A. Werner, *ib.*, 15. 1, 1897 ; E. Rimbach and K. Fleck, *ib.*, 94. 139, 1915 ; P. Pfeiffer, *ib.*, 133. 91, 1924 ; A. Naumann and J. Schröder, *Ber.*, 37. 4609, 1904 ; R. E. Liesegang, *Phot. Arch.*, 34. 161, 1893 ; T. Carnelley and W. C. Williams, *Journ. Chem. Soc.*, 35. 563, 1879 ; A. E. Nordenskjöld, *Danska Vet. Akad. Handl.*, 2. 2, 1874 ; H. Goldschmidt, E. Storm, and O. Hassel, *Zeit. phys. Chem.*, 100. 197, 1922 ; T. Karantassis, *Compt. Rend.*, 182. 134, 1926 ; A. C. Vournasos, *Zeit. anorg. Chem.*, 150. 147, 1926 ; W. Biltz and E. Birk, *ib.*, 127. 34, 1923.

§ 19. The Stannic Bromides

A. J. Balard [1] found that tin burns in an atm. of bromine, forming stannic bromide, $SnBr_4$. T. Carnelley and L. T. O'Shea, and A. E. Nordenskjöld also prepared the bromide by the action of bromine on tin ; C. G. Cook added bromine drop by drop to granulated tin contained in a hot retort ; and R. Lorenz carried on the process as follows :

Tin, in pieces 2–3 cms. long, is placed in a distillation flask, closed at the top with a cork fitted with a separating funnel drawn out to a capillary point ; the funnel is filled with bromine, which is added to the tin so slowly that the temp. remains at 35°–59°, and the side tube does not become filled with bromine vap. ; the action proceeds quietly. When the greater portion of the tin has disappeared, the contents of the flask are distilled ; the first few drops contain a little bromine, but that which subsequently passes over is pure stannic bromide. It boils at 201°, is colourless, readily forms crystals, and fumes slightly on exposure to moist air. The bromide may be stored in a corked flask ; if this is heated to about 40°, the bromide readily melts, and can be withdrawn in any desired quantity.

B. Rayman and K. Preis purified the product from chlorides by fractional distilla-tion. C. Löwig obtained the same salt by the action of bromine on stannous bromide ; J. Personne, by the action of metallic tin on a soln. of bromine in carbon disulphide, or, according to J. Bongartz and A. Classen, in chloroform, distilling off the solvent, and purifying the product by fractional distillation ; and A. L. Poti-lizin, by the action of bromine on stannic chloride in a glass tube at about 420°.

According to A. J. Balard, stannic bromide is a white crystalline substance which, according to B. Rayman and K. Preis, can be obtained from its soln. in stannic chlorobromide in fine crystals ; the bromide sublimed in a sealed glass vessel also appears in well-developed crystals. A. E. Nordenskjöld showed that the crystals form rhombic pyramids with axial ratios $a : b : c=0.556 : 1 : 1.487$. The crystals were also examined by J. W. Retgers. The sp. gr. given by C. H. D. Boedeker is 3·322 at 39°, and by B. Rayman and K. Preis, 3·340 at 35°. I. I. Saslawsky gave 1·40 for the ratio of the mol. vol. to the sum of the at. vols. of the constituent elements. The vap. density determined by T. Carnelley and L. T. O'Shea corresponds with the formula $SnBr_4$. The m.p. is near 30°; J. Kendall and co-workers gave 31·0; F. Garelli, 29·45; P. A. Bond and H. T. Beach, 29·45°; and B. Rayman and K. Preis gave 33°, and said that the molten bromide is a colourless, strongly refracting liquid—*vide supra*, stannic chloride. F. M. Raoult gave 26·4° for the m.p., and 243 for the mol. lowering of the f.p. R. Lorenz found that during the solidification of the molten bromide, an increase in vol. occurs often resulting in the fracture of the glass containing vessel. T. Carnelley and L. T. O'Shea gave 201° for the b.p.; B. Rayman and K. Preis, 203·3°; P. A. Bond and H. T. Beach, 205·05° and 734 mm.; and R. Lorenz, 201°. M. Berthelot gave for the heat of formation, $(Sn, 2Br_2) = 11·54$ Cals. for the crystalline salt, and 11·24 Cals. for the melted bromide; and $(SnBr_2, Br_{2solid}) = 32·2$ Cals. S. U. Pickering gave 0·007169 cal. per gram for the latent heat of fusion; 18·6 Cals. for the heat of soln. in water; and for the heat of hydration, $(SnBr_4, 8H_2O) = 14·906$ Cals. for the liquid, and 9·748 for the solid. G. T. Morgan and co-workers gave −3·15 Cals. for the heat of soln. of stannic bromide in 200 parts of carbon tetrachloride. S. Tolloczko studied the ionizing power of stannic bromide as a solvent.

B. Rayman and K. Preis found that stannic bromide is fairly stable when heated; very little decomposition occurs when the vap. is passed through a red-hot tube. M. Berthelot showed that when stannic bromide is heated in oxygen, bromine is evolved and stannic oxide formed without incandescence. According to R. Lorenz, when stannic bromide is exposed to air, it absorbs water; and when the aq. soln. is evaporated over sulphuric acid, colourless crystals of **tetrahydrated stannic bromide**, $SnBr_4.4H_2O$, are produced. The crystals fume a little on exposure to air. The aq. soln. of stannic bromide becomes turbid faster than is the case with stannic chloride. The clear aq. soln. soon becomes opalescent, and it deposits α-stannic acid which soon forms the β-acid. One c.c. of a $\frac{1}{10}N$-soln. of stannic bromide contained after

0	1010	1430	1490	2510	2870	3890	7590 min.
Sn . 0·01180	0·0₃9676	0·0₃9027	0·0₃8614	0·0₄590	0·0₄295	0·0₄177	0·0₄177 grm

B. Rayman and K. Preis obtained colourless, needle-like crystals of a **stannic oxybromide**, $Sn_3O_2Br_8.10H_2O$; and A. J. Balard reported one to be formed by the action of bromine on stannous oxide; he added that bromine has no action on stannic oxide. P. Pfeiffer obtained a complex of **stannic hydroxytribromide**, $Sn(OH)Br_3$, with ether, namely, $Sn(OH)Br_3.H_2O.(C_2H_5)_2O$, analogous to the corresponding hydroxychloride. P. Pfeiffer and R. Lehnardt, and J. G. F. Druce prepared *methyl stannic bromide*, $Sn(CH_3)Br_3$; *ethyl stannic bromide*, $Sn(C_2H_5)Br_3$; *isopropyl stannic bromide*, $Sn(C_3H_7)Br_3$; and normal *propyl stannic bromide*, $Sn(C_3H_7)Br_3$, as well as some complex salts. G. T. Morgan and H. D. K. Drew made complexes with the β-ketones. J. Nicklès obtained a complex of ether with stannic bromide, $SnBr_4.(C_2H_5)_2O$. W. Biltz and E. Keunecke observed no reaction or dissolution of stannic bromide and liquid hydrogen sulphide at −78·5°; and P. A. Bond and H. T. Beach found that stannic bromide does not form a compound with sulphur dioxide below the m.p., −72°; but there is a critical soln. temp. in the binary system at 48·6°. There is a eutectic at 16·3° on the stannic bromide side of the percentage solubility in sulphur dioxide curve:

SnBr₄ .	100	94·12	78·97	21·67	16·55	9·45	6·29	1·88	0·39
m.p. .	29·45°	16·60°	47·70°	16·3°	13·2°	3·25°	−3·5°	−24·0°	53·05°

The reducing action of hydrogen was studied by F. de Carli. Molten stannic bromide was found by B. Rayman and K. Preis to dissolve iodine readily, and sulphur, and P. Walden found the soln. in liquid sulphur dioxide is not a good electrical conductor. A. J. Balard said that stannic bromide dissolves in sulphuric acid, without perceptible decomposition, forming an oily liquid. B. Rayman and K. Preis found that stannic bromide absorbs ammonia with avidity, forming white **stannic diamminobromide,** $SnBr_4.2NH_3$. V. Thomas found that with nitrogen peroxide, a compound $3SnOBr_2.SnO_2.N_2O_5$ is formed ; and A. J. Balard, that with nitric acid, the vap. of bromine is vigorously given off. P. Walden found stannic bromide is soluble in arsenic tribromide.

B. Rayman and K. Preis dissolved stannic bromide in a very small proportion of water, sat. the soln. with hydrobromic acid, and obtained fine colourless prisms or needle-like crystals of what was regarded as **hydrobromostannic acid,** $H_2SnBr_6.8H_2O$. They obtained the same product by the action of bromine on a soln. of stannic bromide in amyl alcohol. K. Seubert and E. Schürmann made a similar substance by the method employed for hydrochlorostannic acid, using 100 parts of molten stannic bromide and 74·1 parts of 50 per cent. hydrobromic acid. The product was regarded as a heptahydrate ; but the analysis was difficult on account of the deliquescence of the salt, and the ease with which it gave off hydrogen bromide. The acid occurs in amber-yellow, needle-like crystals ; or if a conc. soln. is cooled it occurs in plates which are probably triclinic. The crystals fume in air. G. N. Antonoff studied the f.p. curves of mixtures of stannic bromide and methyl oxalate.

B. Rayman and K. Preis prepared a number of **bromostannates.** When ammonium bromide is added to a conc. soln. of hydrobromostannic acid, **ammonium bromostannate,** $(NH_4)_2SnBr_6$, is precipitated in pale yellow or colourless crystals. H. Töpsöe found the octahedral crystals have a sp. gr. 3·505 ; E. Carozzi gave 3·51 ; and F. Leteur added that they are inactive in polarized light, and stable in air. B. Rayman and K. Preis found ammonium chloride reacts with a soln. of stannic bromide, forming *ammonium chlorobromostannate.* They prepared **cæsium bromostannate,** Cs_2SnBr_6, and **rubidium bromostannate,** Rb_2SnBr_6, in a similar manner. They prepared **potassium bromostannate,** K_2SnBr_6, by pouring a soln. of hydrobromostannic acid on solid potassium bromide. H. Töpsöe said the octahedral crystals are easily soluble in water, and have a sp. gr. 3·783 ; F. Leteur added that the crystals are stable in air. B. Rayman and K. Preis obtained **sodium bromostannate,** $Na_2SnBr_6.6H_2O$, by evaporating over conc. sulphuric acid an aq. soln. of stannic bromide with the calculated quantity of sodium bromide ; K. Seubert and E. Schürmann obtained it by evaporating a soln. of hydrobromostannic acid sat. with sodium carbonate. The pale yellow prismatic or acicular crystals belong, according to F. Leteur, to the monoclinic system, and have a strong double refraction. They are very soluble in water ; and, according to K. Seubert and E. Schürmann, they effloresce in air. At 90°, water and stannic bromide are given off. It is supposed to correspond with the sodium bromoplatinate, $Na_2PtBr_6.6H_2O$. B. Rayman and K. Preis, and F. Leteur prepared **lithium bromostannate,** $Li_2SnBr_6.6H_2O$, in small, yellow, hygroscopic plates which have a strong double refraction. They lost a mol of water over sulphuric acid.

B. Rayman and K. Preis obtained slender, needle-like, deliquescent crystals of **calcium bromostannate,** $CaSnBr_6.6H_2O$, by evaporating over conc. sulphuric acid a mixed soln. of the component bromides. The corresponding **strontium bromostannate,** $SrSnBr_6.6H_2O$, could be obtained only in admixture with tetrahydrated stannic bromide as a pale yellow, deliquescent, crystalline mass. They obtained pale yellow tabular crystals of **magnesium bromostannate,** $MgSnBr_6.10H_2O$. J. Kendall and co-workers obtained no evidence of a compound on the f.p. curves of mixtures of *stannic and aluminium bromides.* F. Leteur said that the crystals are monoclinic ; very deliquescent ; and when heated give off water and stannic bromide. B. Rayman and K. Preis used a similar process to prepare **manganese bromostannate,** $MnSnBr_6.6H_2O$, in large, pale yellow, deliquescent crystals, **ferrous bromostannate,** $FeSnBr_6.6H_2O$, in greenish-yellow, granular crystals ; **cobalt bromostannate,**

$CoSnBr_6.10H_2O$, in yellowish-red, tabular, deliquescent crystals; and **nickel bromo-stannate**, $NiSnBr_6.8H_2O$, in apple-green, granular, deliquescent crystals.

A number of mixed salts containing both chlorine and bromine have been reported—**stannic bromochlorides**. J. W. Retgers doubted whether these products are chemical individuals, but A. Besson considered the individuality of some of them to be established. A. Ladenburg dropped bromine into cooled stannous chloride, and found that much heat is developed, and that two gram-atoms of bromine are fixed by a mol of stannous chloride. The yellow fuming liquid was quickly decomposed by water; and it boiled between 130° and 190°. The fractions with the lower b.p. were richer in bromine. B. Rayman and K. Preis obtained a chlorobromide by the action of chloriferous bromine on tin, and it boiled between 170° and 196°. A. Besson prepared a mixture of the chloro-bromides by the slow action of dry hydrogen bromide on stannic chloride at a temp. below 0°; by the action of dry hydrogen bromide on a carbon tetra-chloride soln. of anhydrous stannous chloride. The constituents were separated by fractional distillation in vacuo. They fume in air and are soluble in water, being at the same time decomposed. A. Besson found the **stannic tribromo-chloride**, $SnClBr_3$, is a liquid with a sp. gr. 3·12 at 13°; m.p. 1°; and b.p. 73° at 30 mm. press. It corresponds with the fraction obtained by A. Ladenburg boiling between 170° and 190°, and with the product prepared by B. Rayman and K. Preis. A. Besson found that **stannic dibromodichloride**, $SnBr_2Cl_2$, had a sp. gr. 2·82 at 13°; m.p., −20°; and b.p., 65° at 30 mm. press. It corresponds with the fraction obtained by A. Ladenburg, boiling between 160° and 170°. A. Besson obtained **stannic bromotrichloride**, $SnBrCl_3$, as a colourless liquid of sp. gr. 2·51 at 13°; m.p.−1°; and b.p. 50° at 30 mm. press. or 45° at 20 mm. press.

REFERENCES.

[1] A. J. Balard, *Ann. Chim. Phys.*, (2), **32**. 337, 1826; V. Thomas, *ib.*, (7), **13**. 145, 1898; M. Berthelot, *ib.*, (5), **15**. 185, 1878; (5), **16**. 442, 1878; J. Personne, *Compt. Rend.*, **54**. 216, 1862; J. Nicklès, *ib.*, **52**. 869, 1861; F. Leteur, *ib.*, **113**. 540, 1891; A. Besson, *ib.*, **124**. 683, 1897; R. Lorenz, *Zeit. anorg. Chem.*, **9**. 366, 1895; W. Biltz and E. Birk, *ib.*, **134**. 125, 1924; J. Kendall, E. D. Crittenden, and H. K. Miller, *Journ. Amer. Chem. Soc.*, **45**. 963, 1923; F. de Carli, *Atti Accad. Lincei*, (5), **33**. ii, 94, 1924; E. Carozzi, *Gazz. Chim. Ital.*, **54**. i, 556, 1924; I. I. Saslawsky, *Zeit. anorg. Chem.*, **146**. 315, 1925; C. Löwig, *Pogg. Ann.*, **14**. 485, 1828; P. Pfeiffer, *Ber.*, **38**. 2466, 1905; A. L. Potilizin, *Ber.*, **9**. 1025, 1876; J. Bongartz and A. Classen, *ib.*, **21**. 2900, 1888; K. Seubert and E. Schürmann, *ib.*, **20**. 794, 1887; T. Carnelley and L. T. O'Shea, *Journ. Chem. Soc.*, **33**. 55, 1878; *Chem. News*, **36**. 264, 1877; B. Rayman and K. Preis, *Liebig's Ann.*, **223**. 326, 1884; H. Töpsöe, *Tids. Phys. Kemi*, **8**. 326, 1869; A. E. Nordenskjöld, *Svenska Vet. Akad. Handl.*, **2**. ?, 1874; J. W. Retgers, *Zeit. Kryst.*, **22**. 270, 1903; *Zeit. phys. Chem.*, **16**. 577, 1895; M. Herschkowitsch, *ib.*, **27**. 123, 1898; P. Walden, *ib.*, **43**. 385, 1903; *Zeit. anorg. Chem.*, **29**. 377, 1902; C. H. D. Boedeker, *Die Beziehungen zwischen Dichte und Zusammen-setzung bei festen und liquiden Stoffen*, Leipzig, 1860; F. Garelli, *Atti Accad. Lincei*, (5), **7**. 27, 1898; S. U. Pickering, *Phil. Mag.*, (5), **39**. 510, 1895; A. Ladenburg, *Liebig's Ann. Suppl.*, **8**. 60, 1870; C. G. Cook, *Some Double Halides of Tin with the Aliphatic Amines and with Tetra-methylammonium*, Easton, Pa., 1898; *Amer. Chem. Journ.*, **22**. 435, 1899; F. M. Raoult, *Sur les progrès de la cryoscopie*, Paris, 1889; P. Pfeiffer and R. Lehnardt, *Ber.*, **36**. 1054, 3027, 1903; J. G. F. Druce, *Chem. News*, **120**. 229, 1920; **125**. 327, 1922; **127**. 306, 1923; *Journ. Chem. Soc.*, **119**. 758, 1921; **121**. 1859, 1922; G. T. Morgan and H. D. K. Drew, *ib.*, **125**. 372, 1924; G. N. Antonoff, *Phil. Mag.*, (7), **1**. 1121, 1926; P. A. Bond and H. T. Beach, *Journ. Amer. Chem. Soc.*, **48**. 348, 1926; T. Karantassis, *Compt. Rend.*, **182**. 134, 699, 1926; G. T. Morgan, S. R. Carter, and W. F. Harrison, *Journ. Chem. Soc.*, **127**. 1917, 1925; W. Biltz and E. Keunecke, *Zeit. anorg. Chem.*, **147**. 171, 1925; S. Tolloczko, *Bull. Acad. Cracovie*, **1**, 1901.

§ 20. The Stannous Iodides

Tin forms two iodides, **stannous iodide**, SnI_2, and stannic iodide, SnI_4. According to H. Davy,[1] C. F. Rammelsberg, and J. L. Gay Lussac, when a mixture of tin-filings with twice its weight of iodine is heated, brownish-red translucent stannous iodide is formed, but W. C. Henry showed that the product really contains both stannous and stannic iodides which can be separated by sublimation, for stannic iodide volatilizes at 180°, and stannous iodide remains fixed at a red heat ; and he added that if the product be mixed with finely divided tin, stannous iodide alone is obtained. J. Personne said that only stannic iodide can be prepared by the direct union of iodine and tin. W. Reinders and S. de Lange found that while it is true that stannic iodide is the first product of the action of iodine on tin, stannous iodide can be made by the prolonged heating of tin and stannic iodide in a sealed tube at 360°, by the reaction indicated by W. C. Henry : $Sn+SnI_4=2SnI_2$; and that the failure of J. Personne to obtain a partial conversion was due to his having failed to accelerate the reaction by the use of an excess of finely powdered tin which was done by W. C. Henry. If a soln. of stannous chloride be treated with iodine, stannous iodide is precipitated, and a mixture of stannous iodide and chloride, and stannic chloride remains in soln. P. Boullay found that if potassium iodide be added to a soln. of stannous chloride, the liquid soon deposits yellowish-red crystalline tufts of stannous iodide, and, if the mixture be warm, the iodide is deposited in yellowish-red needles. With eq. quantities of stannous chloride and potassium iodide, B. Köhnlein found that the stannous iodide is mixed with potassium iodostannite ; but if half the calculated potassium iodide be employed, stannous iodide alone is formed. J. Personne obtained similar results. J. L. Gay Lussac added that if tin is heated with an excess of iodine and a large proportion of water, a violent reaction occurs, the tin is rapidly oxidized, and a soln. of hydriodic acid is formed. J. Personne prepared stannous iodide by adding hydriodic acid to a soln. of stannous chloride; and also by the action of hydriodic acid on pulverulent tin. F. Wöhler and F. Dünhaupt obtained stannous iodide by the action of boiling hydriodic acid on tin-foil for a day ; or by heating the mixture for an hour in a sealed tube at 120°–150°. A. E. Nordenskjöld used the latter process, and afterwards sublimed the product. F. Wöhler and F. Dünhaupt also obtained the iodide as sulphur-yellow prisms by heating tin-foil with amyl iodide in a sealed tube at 180°. When crystallized from its aq. soln., *dihydrated* stannous iodide, $SnI_2.2H_2O$, is formed in yellowish-red needles, and one mol. of the water is lost on drying the hydrate over sulphuric acid. P. Freundler and Y. Laurent said that when prepared from soln. of stannous chloride and potassium iodide the product is a mixture of red and yellow modifications—an excess of stannous chloride favouring the red form, and an excess of potassium iodide the yellow form. Exposure to sunlight changes the yellow to the red form, and conversely in darkness. With potassium iodide the red form is at once produced if the mixture is heated on the water-bath ; but with sodium iodide, and an excess of stannous chloride, the yellow form is produced. The yellow form is considered to be the stable modification at 100°. P. Freundler and Y. Laurent obtained the *monohydrate*, $SnI_2.H_2O$, by mixing cold, conc. soln. of sodium iodide and stannous chloride ; it is dehydrated by drying in the cold.

C. J. H. Warden said that if the moist precipitated iodide in a glass vessel be exposed to light, ruby-red crystals are formed on the side exposed directly to light, while the salt on the other side remains amorphous. A. E. Nordenskjöld said that the sublimed anhydrous salt furnishes colourless rhombic crystals with the axial ratios : $a:b:c=0.5638:1:0.4993$. H. S. van Klooster stated that the crystals are monoclinic prisms $a:b:c=1:-:0.5911$, and $\beta=82°$ 55'. C. H. D. Boedeker gave 4.696 for the sp. gr. ; J. W. Retgers, 4.7 ; and H. S. van Klooster, 5.21 at 15°/15°. S. Motylewsky gave 46 mgrms. for the drop-weight of stannous iodide when that of water at 0° is 100. J. Personne said that the crystals melt at a dull red heat, and, added W. C. Henry, the mass freezes to a dark red crystalline mass. J. Personne found that the salt sublimes at the temp. of melting glass, forming bright red crystals. W. Biltz and co-workers found 5.283–5.287 for the sp. gr. of crystalline stannous iodide at 25°/4°, and 70.48 for the mol. vol. T. Karantassis gave 320° for the m.p., while W. Reinders and S. de Lange gave 320°, and 720°

tor the b.p. of stannous iodide. When heated in air, P. Boullay found that stannous iodide furnishes stannic oxide and a substance which is broken down by water into stannic acid and hydriodic acid. W. Biltz and W. Fischer gave -5.8 cals. for the heat of soln. of stannous iodide. G. T. Morgan and co-workers gave -3.81 for the heat of soln. of stannous iodide in 200 parts of carbon tetrachloride.

C. A. Kraus and H. F. Kurtz studied the reduction by sodium of stannous iodide dissolved in liquid ammonia. C. F. Rammelsberg found that stannous iodide is decolorized by ammonia, the gas is absorbed with the evolution of heat, and stannous tetramminoiodide, $SnI_2.4NH_3$, is formed. F. Ephraim and T. Schmidt add that this tetrammine was probably a stannic salt because, with dry ammonia and dry stannous iodide they could prepare only stannous diamminoiodide, $SnI_2.2NH_3$, which is white with a faint yellow tinge. W. Biltz and W. Fischer gave for the temp. at which the vap. press. of the amminoiodides is 100 mm. and the heats of dissociation in Cals. per mol of NH_3 respectively stannous enneammino-iodide, $SnI_2.9NH_3$, $-48°$, and 7.9; stannous pentamminoiodide, $SnI_2.5NH_3$, $10°$, and 10.2; stannous triamminoiodide, $SnI_2.3NH_3$, $55°$, and 11.9; stannous diamminoiodide, $SnI_2.2NH_3$, $94°$, and 13.3; and stannous monamminoiodide, $SnI_2.NH_3$, $157°$, and 16. G. L. Clark also made observations on this subject. P. Pfeiffer studied the dialkyl stannous iodides; and T. Karantassis, complexes with organic bases.

The stannous iodide prepared by J. L. Gay Lussac, and C. F. Rammelsberg was said to be easily decomposed by water, especially by hot water, forming stannous hydroxide and an aq. soln. of hydriodic acid; the hydrolysis is the more complete the greater the proportion of water; and J. Personne reported a number of stannous oxyiodides. which he obtained by the action of water either on stannous iodide, or on potassium iodostannite. The analyses made of the products he obtained corresponded with the molar ratios $SnO:SnI_2=1:2$, $2:3$, $1:1$, and $2:1$, but there is no evidence to determine whether the products are chemical individuals or different stages in the progressive hydrolysis of stannous iodide. W. C. Henry, and P. Boullay said that the salt dissolves sparingly in water without decomposition, and the solubility is greater in hot than in cold water. The discrepancy in the results may be due to the contamination of J. Personne's stannous iodide with some stannic iodide. S. W. Young gave for the percentage solubility in water:

	20·8°	30·5°	41·0°	51·5°	60·1°	73·9°	84·9°	98·5°
Per cent. SnI_2 . .	1·30	1·21	1·50	1·79	2·09	2·56	3·05	3·43

P. Boullay added that the salt is soluble in a soln. of stannous chloride so that no precipitation occurs if only a small proportion of potassium iodide is added to the stannous salt soln. J. Personne found that stannous iodide is soluble in soln. of the alkali chlorides, in benzene, chloroform, and carbon disulphide. P. Boullay also showed that it combines with the more basic metal iodides, forming complex salts.

S. W. Young measured the solubility of stannous iodide in aq. soln. of hydriodic acid at $23.5°$, and, expressing the results in percentages, he found:

HI . . .	0	3	4	6	8	10	12	14	15
SnI_2 . . .	1·0	0·26	0·22	0·16	0·17	0·26	0·45	0·62	0·81

The solubility of stannous iodide in water increases as the temp. rises. In hydriodic acid soln. containing 3 to 8 per cent. of acid, the solubility is less than in water, increasing with the temp. and diminishing with the conc. of the acid. With soln. of 9 to 15 per cent., the solubility is still less than in water, and increases with the temp., but it now also increases with the conc. When the soln. contain 25 per cent. and upwards, the solubility is greater than in water, and as the temp. rises the solubility at first diminishes until a point of minimum solubility is reached lying between $30°$ and $40°$; beyond this, the solubility again increases. A sat.

soln. of stannous iodide in hydriodic acid—25 per cent. and upwards—when cooled by ice-cold water, deposits pale yellow needles quite different in appearance from the red needles of stannous iodide. This yellow substance readily decomposes, giving the red iodide, and is so unstable that its composition could only be obtained by indirect methods. The yellow solid is **hydroiodostannous acid,** $HSnI_3$, which P. Pfeiffer called *stannoiodoform*. From 0° to 15° the solubility in hydriodic acid of 39·6 per cent. strength increases ; and from 15° to 20°, it still increases, but much more slowly ; on allowing the mixture to remain for some hours at 20°, the undissolved yellow hydroiodostannous acid changes to red stannous iodide, and this change is accompanied by a marked decrease in solubility ; from 20° to 30°, the solubility diminishes gradually, and from 30° upwards it increases regularly. With a similar soln. in 30 per cent. acid, the rapid decomposition of hydroiodostannous acid occurs at 1·5 , and in this case the change is accompanied by an increase in solubility. When in contact with stronger hydriodic acid, the hydroiodostannous acid is stable at higher temp. The peculiarities observed in the curves of solubility are due to the gradual decomposition of solid and dissolved hydroiodostannous acid over a considerable range of temp. T. Karantassis observed that no compound of sulphur and stannous iodide could be prepared. B. Köhnlein found that stannous iodide scarcely reacts with propyl chloride.

A number of **iodostannites** have been obtained from mixtures of the metal iodide with a soln. of stannous chloride, or from a soln. containing the component iodides. The iodostannites are usually hydrolyzed by water. P. Boullay said that **ammonium iodostannite** is precipitated when ammonium iodide is added to a conc. soln. of stannous chloride ; or, according to J. Personne, when iodine acts on powdered tin in a conc. soln. of ammonium chloride. The greenish-yellow needles were found by P. Boullay to be readily decomposed by water. He showed that when a soln. of sodium iodide in one of conc. stannous chloride is allowed to stand for a few hours, it deposits crystals of stannous iodide followed by pale yellow crystals of **sodium iodostannite** which are decomposed by water. He also observed that when conc. soln. of stannous chloride and potassium iodide are mixed, there is deposited a mass of yellow silky needles of **enneahydrated potassium hexaiododistannite,** $2KI.2SnI_2.9H_2O$. The salt can be recrystallized from alcohol. J. Personne obtained the salt by the action of iodine on powdered tin, in a conc. soln. of potassium chloride. When the enneahydrate is confined in vacuo over sulphuric acid, or heated to 110°, six mols of water are given off and the *trihydrate* is formed ; between 140° and 150°, hydrogen iodide is given off. When chlorine gas is passed over the salt, the tin burns with the emission of light, forming stannous and potassium chlorides. When the salt is treated with a small proportion of water, potassium iodide is removed, and the residue dissolves when more water is added. Hot alcohol dissolves the complex salt leaving a little stannous iodide, and the soln. furnishes crystals of the salt on cooling. V. Auger and T. Karantassis found that when stannous iodide is added to warm aq. soln. of rubidium iodide containing hydriodic acid, the liquid turns brown and deposits stannic iodide ; but if tin be present, and air absent, **rubidium triiodostannite,** $RbSnI_3$, is formed in yellow needles ; and if an excess of stannous iodide be present, orange-yellow, cubic crystals of **rubidium pentaiododistannite,** $RbSn_2I_5$, are formed. Similarly also with **cæsium triiodostannite,** $CsSnI_3$, and **cæsium pentaiododistannite,** $CsSn_2I_5$. The dry salts are fairly stable, they oxidize rapidly in air, forming in part iodostannates, and hence they do not correspond with the reaction products of stannous halides with potassium and ammonium halides. P. Boullay obtained **barium iodostannite** from a soln. of stannous and barium iodides ; and **strontium iodostannite** from a soln. of stannous and strontium iodides.

W. C. Henry reported that if soln. of stannous chloride and iodine be mixed, either stannous or stannic iodide is deposited according to the proportion of iodine employed ; and when the mother-liquor is evaporated and cooled, yellow crystals of **stannous chloroiodide,** $SnClI$, are formed. The salt is decomposed by water into soluble stannous chloride and sparingly soluble stannous iodide. S. W. Young and M. Adams regard the salt as a solid soln. of stannous chloride and iodide which may be obtained in isomorphous admixture in various proportions. S. W. Young also prepared yellowish-red prisms of **stannostannic tetrachlorodiiodide,** $SnCl_4.SnI_2$, by the action of iodine chloride on stannous chloride. T. Karantassis prepared **stannous chloroiodide,** $SnICl$, by dissolving iodine in a soln. of stannous chloride and hydrochloric acid, and reducing the red liquid by addition of excess of tin : $2SnCl_2+4I=SnCl_4+SnI_4$; $SnI_4+Sn=2SnI_2$ and $SnCl_4+Sn=2SnCl_2$; $2SnCl_2+2SnI_2=4SnClI$. If the original soln. contains an excess of iodine, red crystals of stannous iodide are first deposited, and these are slowly converted in the cold into white needles of the chloroiodide. With a large excess of stannous chloride, white crystals of the chloroiodide are deposited at once. The existence of the chloroiodide is further confirmed by thermal analysis of mixtures of the chloride and iodide. The f.p. curve falls from 320°, the m.p. of the pure iodide, to a eutectic at 244° and 52·4 molar per cent. of stannous iodide; it then rises to a maximum 259° corresponding with $SnI_2.SnBr_2$; it then falls to a second eutectic at 221° and 84·5 molar per cent. of $SnCl_2$; and finally rises to 254°, the m.p. of the pure chloride. A soln. of **stannous bromoiodide,** $SnIBr$, was prepared in an analogous manner. The pale yellow needles deposited in presence of an excess of stannous bromide consist of a solid soln. of the iodide in the bromoiodide. Thermal analysis confirms the existence of mixed crystals with a tendency to form the bromoiodide. The f.p. curve falls from 326·7°, the m.p. of the pure bromide, to a eutectic at 220°, and it then rises to a maximum of 240° with between 42·8 and 62·7 molar per cent. of the stannous iodide; and then rises to 320°, the m.p. of the pure iodide. A. C. Vournasos prepared **potassium dibromodiiodostannite,** $Na_2[SnBr_2I_2]$. P. Freundler and Y. Laurent said that sodium iodide and stannous chloride do not form a complex, a mixture of conc. soln. of the two yields the monohydrate ; stannous chloride and potassium iodide form yellow needles of **potassium triiodostannite,** $KSnI_3.3H_2O$, in neutral soln., and in the cold (22°), warm (45°), and hot acidic soln., **potassium hydrodiiodotrichlorostannite,** $K_2HSnI_2Cl_3$, or $2KI.HCl.SnCl_2$, and **potassium hydrotriiodotrichlorostannite,** $K_3HSnI_3Cl_3$, or $3KI.HCl.SnCl_2$, and anhydrous stannous iodide are formed. These complex salts are stable in neutral soln., but oxidize in acidic soln. especially in sunlight, forming deep brown soln. It is argued that the colloidal complex of iodine, sodium, and rubidium is contained in some marine plants. The existence of rubidium and iodine in association with protoplasm is further supported by the presence of rubidium and iodine in the eq. proportions, by the absence of iodine and rubidium from the salts resulting from spontaneous desiccation, and by the similar behaviour of the compound obtained from *Laminaria flexicaulis* and the rubidium-stannous iodide complex, $2SnI_2,RbI$, on exposure to sunlight.

REFERENCES.

[1] H. Davy, *Phil. Trans.*, **104.** 74, 1814 ; *Ann. Chim. Phys.*, (1), **88.** 271, 1813 ; J. L. Gay Lussac, *Ann. Chim. Phys.*, (2), **1.** 40, 1816 ; P. Boullay, *ib.*, (2), **34.** 372, 1827 ; C. F. Rammelsberg, *Pogg. Ann.*, **48.** 169, 1839 ; J. Personne, *Compt. Rend.*, **54.** 216, 1862 ; F. Wöhler and F. Dünhaupt, *Liebig's Ann.*, **85.** 374, 1853 ; B. Köhnlein, *ib.*, **225.** 184, 1884 ; C. A. Kraus and H. F. Kurtz, *Journ. Amer. Chem. Soc.*, **47.** 43, 1925 ; C. J. H. Warden, *Pharm. Journ.*, (4), **4.** 61, 1897 ; S. W. Young, *Journ. Amer. Chem. Soc.*, **19.** 845, 851, 1897 ; S. W. Young and M. Adams, *ib.*, **19.** 515, 1897 ; P. Pfeiffer, *Ber.*, **37.** 4618, 1904 ; C. H. D. Boedeker, *Die Beziehung zwischen Dichte und Zusammensetzung*, Leipzig, 1860 ; F. Ephraim and T. Schmidt, *Ber.*, **42.** 3856, 1909 ; A. E. Nordenskjöld, *Bihang. Svenska Akad. Handl.*, **2.** 2, 1874 ; W. Biltz and W. Fischer, *Zeit. anorg. Chem.*, **129.** 1, 1923 ; W. Biltz, *ib.*, **130.** 93, 1923 ; W. Biltz and E. Birk, *ib.*, **134.** 125, 1924 ; P. Pfeiffer, *ib.*, **133.** 91, 1924 ; H. S. van Klooster, *ib.*, **79.** 223, 1913 ; J. W. Rotgers, *ib.*, **3.** 343, 1893 ; S. Motylewsky, *ib.*, **38.** 410, 1904 ; W. Reinders and S. de Lange, *ib.*, **79.** 230, 1923 ; *Proc. Acad. Amsterdam*, **21.** 474, 1912 ; G. L. Clark, *Amer. Journ. Science*, (5), **7.** 1, 1924 ; W. C. Henry, *Phil. Mag.*, (3), **5.** 354, 1845 ; *Phil. Trans.*, **135.** 363, 1845 ; P. Freundler and Y. Laurent, *Bull. Soc. Chim.*, (4), **37.** 1133, 1925 ; *Compt. Rend.*, **179.** 1049, 1924 ; V. Auger and T. Karantassis, *ib.*, **181.** 665, 1925 ; T. Karantassis, *ib.*, **182.**

462   INORGANIC AND THEORETICAL CHEMISTRY

134, 699, 1926 ; *Bull. Soc. Chim.*, (4), **37**. 854, 1925 ; (4), **39**. 43, 1926 ; B. Köhnlein, *Liebig's Ann.*, **225**. 171, 1884 ; A. C. Vournasos, *Zeit. anorg. Chem.*, **150**. 147, 1926 ; G. T. Morgan, S. R. Carter, and W. F. Harrison, *Journ. Chem. Soc.*, **127**. 1917, 1925.

§ 21. The Stannic Iodides

J. L. Gay Lussac[1] prepared **stannic iodide**, SnI_4, by heating a mixture of tin and iodine ; J. Personne found that in a sealed tube the reaction begins at 50°, and is attended by incandescence. The excess of tin remains unaffected without producing stannous iodide. A. E. Nordenskjöld melted a mixture of iodine and tin, and obtained stannic iodide by the sublimation of the product. J. Personne, and E. R. Schneider allowed a warm soln. of iodine in carbon disulphide to act on tin. E. R. Schneider obtained it by mixing conc. soln. of stannic chloride and potassium iodide ; and by the action of iodine on stannous or stannic selenide. J. J. Berzelius prepared it from a soln. of stannic hydroxide in hydriodic acid ; and W. C. Henry obtained it by sublimation from stannous iodide, heated in air—stannic oxide remains. He also found that stannic iodide is formed by mixing a conc. soln. of stannous chloride with an equal proportion of iodine.

P. Groth said that crystals obtained from carbon disulphide are red and singly refracting, belonging to the cubic system ; but A. E. Nordenskjöld showed that they belong to the rhombic system. J. W. Retgers obtained octahedral crystals by evaporating a soln. of the salt in an excess of hydriodic acid, in carbon disulphide, methylene iodide, and other solvents. R. G. Dickinson found the X-radiograms corresponded with a mol. of $(SnI_4)_8$ per unit cube with edge 12·23 A. The iodine atoms are not all in eq. positions, and are probably at points eq. to (vvv) and (xyz), while the tin atoms are at points (uuu). The arrangement is illustrated by Fig. 75, where the cube has been divided along the plane $ABCD$

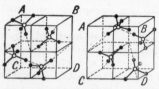

FIG. 75.—Arrangement of the Atoms in the Space Lattice of Stannic Iodide.

for convenience in drawing. Measurements were also made by H. Ott, and H. Mark and K. Weissenberg. E. Beckmann and P. Geib found the raising of the b.p. of stannic chloride by stannic iodide corresponded with only one-third the normal mol. wt. ; but E. Beckmann and F. Junker found the lowering of the b.p. of antimonic chloride by the dissolved stannic iodide does not agree with the normal mol. wt. C. H. D. Boedeker gave 4·696 for the sp. gr. at 11° ; J. Personne said the crystals melt at 160°, and the molten liquid freezes at 142° ; F. Emich gave 160°, and W. Reinders and S. de Lange, 143·5° for the m.p. W. C. Henry said the salt sublimes at 180°, forming reddish-yellow needles. J. Personne could not measure the b.p., but he found a thermometer near the surface of the boiling liquid registered 295° ; F. Emich gave 341° for the b.p. W. Reinders and S. de Lange found the m.p. of

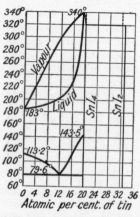

Atomic per cent. of tin

FIG. 76.—Fusion and Boiling Curves of Mixtures of Tin and Stannic Iodide.

mixtures of stannic iodide and iodine consists of two branches with a eutectic at 79·6°, and 12·06 at. per cent. or 60 per cent. by weight of tin, Fig. 76—*vide supra*, stannic chloride. The b.p. curve follows the normal course, and the curves indicated. A fused mixture of stannous and stannic iodides forms two liquid layers. At 350°, the one layer consists of stannic iodide with traces of stannous iodide ; and the other, of stannous iodide with a maximum of 6 per cent. stannic iodide. Tin is not perceptibly soluble in molten stannous iodide, and there is a very narrow line of homogeneous mixing which, at 350°, extends from pure stannous iodide to stannous iodide with 6 per cent. by weight of stannic iodide. Similar results were obtained by H. S. van Klooster, and A. M. Vasiléeff. The latter found the eutectic at 77·8° and $SnI_4+3·257I$. A. H. Chapman measured the emission spectrum of stannic iodide. F. de Carli studied the reducing action of hydrogen.

The salt is hydrolyzed in aq. soln., as noted by J. L. Gay Lussac, C. F. Rammelsberg, W. C. Henry, and J. Personne; but no definite stannic oxyiodide was observed. E. R. Schneider said that 100 parts of carbon disulphide at ordinary temp. dissolve 145 parts of stannic iodide; and J. Personne noted that it is soluble in chloroform, alcohol, ether, and benzene, forming compounds with all but the first of these four solvents. J. W. Retgers found that methylene iodide at 10° dissolves 22·9 per cent. of stannic iodide, and the sp. gr. of the soln. is 3·481 at 10°. W. Biltz and E. Kuenecke observed no reaction or dissolution with liquid hydrogen sulphide at $-78·5°$. Arsenic tribromide dissolves the salt; the sp. gr. of the sat. soln. is 3·73 at 15°, and, according to P. Walden, the soln. is a poor electrical conductor. J. H. Mathews found the salt is soluble in allylthiocarbamide, and the sp. conductivity of the soln. is $4·08\times10^{44}$ mhos at 25°. A. Rosenheim and H. Aron prepared complexes with pyridine and quinoline. There is evidence of the formation of *hydroiodostannic acid* by the union of stannic iodide and hydrogen iodide. The soln. is readily hydrolyzed. V. Auger and T. Karantassis observed that stannic iodide is gradually hydrolyzed in dil. hydriodic acid soln. and more readily in aq. soln. The addition of sodium, potassium, or ammonium iodide to these soln. does not modify their properties, but the addition of rubidium or cæsium iodides or of the hydriodides of strong bases leads to the formation of stable complex salts; *e.g.* **rubidium iodostannate,** Rb_2SnI_6, by adding rubidium iodide to a soln. of stannic iodide in hydriodic acid; and similarly with **cæsium iodostannate,** Cs_2SnI_6; but *ammonium, potassium, and sodium iodostannates* could not be made. They also prepared mixed crystals of **potassium bromoiodostannate,** $K_2Sn(Br_{5·75}I_{0·25})$, and **ammonium bromoiodostannate,** $(NH_4)_2Sn(Br_{5·35}I_{0·65})$, as well as of *tetramethylarsonium iodostannate.* J. G. F. Druce made *methyl stannic iodide,* $Sn(CH_3)I_3$; and normal *propyl stannic iodide,* $Sn(C_3H_7)I_3$. M. Wildermann studied the reaction with several organic bromides. V. Auger and T. Karantassis studied some complexes with organic compounds. J. Personne said that dry ammonia reacts with stannic iodide dissolved in carbon disulphide or ether, forming **stannic triamminoiodide,** $SnI_4.3NH_3$; **stannic tetramminoiodide,** $SnI_4.4NH_3$, and **stannic hexamminoiodide,** $SnI_4.6NH_3$. F. F. Fitzgerald showed that in liquid ammonia it reacts with potassium amide, forming potassium stannic tetramminoimide, $Sn(NK)_2.4NH_3$. F. Ephraim and T. Schmidt prepared **stannic octamminoiodide,** $SnI_4.8NH_3$, by passing ammonia into a soln. of stannic iodide in carbon disulphide and evaporating off the solvent on a bath of warm water; also by passing ammonia over the solid iodide, when much heat is evolved. Evidence of higher ammines was obtained, but they were not stable. Stannic iodide dissolves in stannic chloride, and antimonic chloride as indicated above. A. Ditte noted the formation of a basic nitrate, $4SnO_4.N_2O_5.4H_2O$, by reaction with nitrogen peroxide. Stannic iodide was found by H. Moissan to be reduced when heated with boron. G. Scagliarini studied complexes with organic bases.

C. Lenormand heated a mixture of stannous chloride and iodine in a flask or in a sealed tube at 100°, and obtained **stannic dichlorodiiodide,** $SnCl_2I_2$, as a red mobile liquid of sp. gr. 3·287 at 15°. The liquid fumes in air, and it begins to distil at 190°, and the b.p. during distillation remains stationary at 297°. It is decomposed by repeated distillation. The dichlorodiiodide is soluble in water with the development of much heat; with a small proportion of water, a hydrate is formed which is soluble in an excess of water. The dil. soln. at 65° is quantitatively decomposed into stannic hydroxide, and hydrochloric and hydriodic acids. The dichlorodiiodide is soluble in benzene, chloroform, and carbon disulphide. It yields complexes with ether, and with ethyl, propyl, butyl, and amyl alcohols. If this liquid be fractionally distilled, substances corresponding with **stannic trichloro-iodide**, $SnCl_3I$, and **stannic chlorotriiodide**, SnI_3Cl,

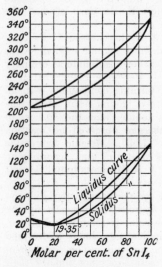

Molar per cent. of $Sn I_4$

Fig. 77.—Freezing- and Boiling-point Curves of Mixtures of Stannic Iodide and Bromide.

as well as stannic chloride, and stannic dichloro-diiodide are formed. C. Lenormand also found that iodine is without action on stannous bromide in the cold, but when the mixture is heated in a sealed tube at 100° an orange-red, crystalline mass of hexagonal plates is produced, consisting of **stannic dibromodiiodide**, $SnBr_2I_2$. The compound begins to melt at 50°, and forms a ruby-red liquid which does not fume in the cold. The sp. gr. is 3·631 at 15°; it boils at 225°, or at 130° in vacuo. It is soluble in cold water, and the soln. decomposes at 80° into stannic oxide, and hydrogen iodide and bromide. When this compound is fractionally distilled, **stannic tribromoiodide**, $SnBr_3I$, passes over at 230°–250° and condenses as a mass of yellowish-red crystals and of undecomposed stannic dibromodiiodide; and **stannic bromotriiodide**, $SnBrI_3$, remains as a residue. If the dibromodiiodide be distilled in vacuo, the undecomposed salt passes over at 130°; the tribromo-iodide, at 180°, and the bromotriiodide remains as a residue. M. G. Räder said the method of preparation of the dibromodiiodide really gives a mixture of the two salts; and there is no evidence on the f.p. or b.p. curves, Fig. 77, to show the existence of salts of the mixed acids; with stannous bromide and iodine, the reaction is symbolized: $2SnBr_2 + 2I_2 = SnBr_4 + SnI_4$.

REFERENCES.

[1] J. L. Gay Lussac, *Ann. Chim. Phys.*, (2), **1**. 40, 1816; J. J. Berzelius, *ib.*, (1), **87**. 50, 1873; (2), **5**. 149, 1817; J. Personne, *Compt. Rend.*, **54**. 216, 1862; H. Moissan, *ib.*, **114**. 617, 1891; E. R. Schneider, *Pogg. Ann.*, **127**. 624, 1866; C. F. Rammelsberg, *ib.*, **48**. 169, 1839; F. de Carli, *Atti Accad. Lincei*, (5), **33**. ii, 94, 1924; H. Mark and K. Weissenberg, *Zeit. Physik*, **16**. 1, 1923; A. M. Vasiléeff, *Journ. Russ. Phys. Chem. Soc.*, **49**. 88, 1917; W. C. Henry, *Phil. Mag.*, (3), **5**. 354, 1845; *Phil. Trans.*, **135**. 363, 1845; A. H. Chapman, *Phys. Rev.*, (2), **4**. 28, 1914; J. W. Retgers, *Zeit. Kryst.*, **22**. 270, 1894; *Zeit. anorg. Chem.*, **3**. 343, 1843; E. Beckmann and P. Geib, *ib.*, **51**. 96, 1906; E. Beckmann and F. Junker, *ib.*, **55**. 175, 1907; A. Rosenheim and H. Aron, *ib.*, **39**. 170, 1904; H. S. van Klooster, *ib.*, **79**. 223, 1913; P. Walden, *ib.*, **29**. 377, 1902; W. Biltz and W. Fischer, *ib.*, **129**. 1, 1923; M. G. Räder, *ib.*, **130**. 325, 1923; W. Reinders and S. de Lange, *Proc. Acad. Amsterdam*, **21**. 474, 1912; *Zeit. anorg. Chem.*, **79**. 230, 1913; S. W. Young and G. L. Thomas, *Journ. Amer. Chem. Soc.*, **19**. 515, 1897; F. F. Fitzgerald, *ib.*, **29**. 1693, 1907; R. G. Dickinson, *ib.*, **45**. 958, 1923; *Phys. Rev.*, (2), **22**. 199, 1923; C. Lenormand, *Journ. Pharm. Chim.*, (6), **8**. 249, 1898; (6), **10**. 114, 1899; V. Auger and T. Karantassis, *Compt. Rend.*, **180**. 1845, 1925; A. E. Nordenskjöld, *Bihang. Svenska Akad. Handl.*, **2**. 2, 1874; J. H. Mathews, *Journ. Phys. Chem.*, **9**. 647, 1905; M. Wildermann, *Zeit. phys. Chem.*, **9**. 12, 1892; F. Ephraim and T. Schmidt, *Ber.*, **42**. 3856, 1909; E. and P. Fireman, *Amer. Chem. Journ.*, **30**. 127, 1903; F. Emich, *Monatsh.*, **25**. 907, 1904; C. H. D. Boedeker, *Die Beziehung zwischen Dichte und Zusammensetzung*, Leipzig, 1860; P. Groth, *Chemische Krystallographie*, Leipzig, i, 231, 1906; A. Ditte, *Ann. Chim. Phys.*, (5), **27**. 159, 1882; J. G. F. Druce, *Chem. News*, **120**. 229, 1920; **127**. 306, 1923; V. Auger and T. Karantassis, *Compt. Rend.*, **180**. 1845, 1925; G. Scagliarini, *Atti Accad. Lincei*, (6), **1**. 582, 1925; W. Biltz and E. Kuenecke, *Zeit. anorg. Chem.*, **147**. 171, 1925; H. Ott, *Zeit. Kryst.*, **63**. 222, 1926.

§ 22. Stannous Sulphides

Estimates of the affinity of sulphur for tin were made by K. Jellinek and J. Zakowsky. Tin forms two well-established sulphides, **stannous sulphide**, SnS, and stannic sulphide, SnS_2 ; and a less well established *tin sesquisulphide*, Sn_2S_3. There are also hydrated forms of these sulphides, and a series of sulpho-derivatives. J. Kunckel, in his *Völlstandiges Laboratorium chymicum* (Berlin, 1767), described the product obtained by fusing tin with sulphur. J. L. Proust [1] supposed that when molten stannous chloride is treated with sulphur, stannic chloride and sulphide are formed, but E. R. Schneider showed that stannic chloride and stannous sulphide are formed, and that the latter dissolves in the excess of molten stannous chloride from which it crystallizes on cooling. According to G. C. Winkelblech, narrow strips of tin-foil catch fire in sulphur vapour. Stannous sulphide is formed when a mixture of sulphur and tin is heated above the m.p. of the metal ; and since the product still contains uncombined tin, it is pulverized, mixed with fresh sulphur, and again heated in a closed vessel. This method of preparation was used by P. Berthier, and E. R. Schneider. W. Biltz and W. Mecklenburg said that the yield of stannous sulphide obtained by fusing tin and sulphur is poor because of the volatilization of most of the latter ; they made it by heating to 900° a mixture of tin with twice the calculated quantity of sulphur in a tube ; and repeating the operation with the resulting product. A. Ditte sublimed the stannous sulphide from the product obtained by the repeated fusion of a mixture of sulphur and tin.

J. L. Gay Lussac found that at a red-heat stannic sulphide decomposes into stannous sulphide and sulphur ; and F. Damm and F. Kraft, that when heated in vacuo in the cathode rays, stannic sulphide, even at 250°, gives off half its sulphur and passes into the more stable stannous sulphide. According to H. Pélabon, the f.p. curve for mixtures of tin and sulphur rises rapidly from 232°, the f.p. of tin, to 840°, the f.p. of the mixture containing 5 per cent. of sulphur, and then rises more gradually to the maximum point 880°, the f.p. of stannous sulphide ; beyond this point the mixtures lose sulphur on being heated, but their m.p. are lower than 880°. W. Biltz and W. Mecklenburg found that with mixtures containing over 23·4 per cent. of sulphur, the sulphur is lost by volatilization. The compound melts at 881°, and the eutectic at 232° is almost pure tin. The sulphide passes into a viscous liquid at 950° and becomes limpid again at near 1100°, Fig. 78. W. Spring obtained stannous sulphide by compressing a mixture of powdered sulphur and tin. O. B. Kühn obtained stannous sulphide

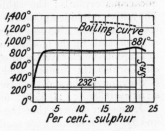

FIG. 78.—The Fusion Curve of Some Mixtures of Sulphur and Tin.

by melting a mixture of tin and sodium pentasulphide ; J. Milbauer, by melting stannic oxide mixed with potassium thiocyanate ; and G. Tocco and N. Jacob, by the alternating current electrolysis of soln. of sodium thiosulphate using tin electrodes.

According to A. Ditte, when tin is heated to 100° in a stream of hydrogen sulphide, it acquires a coating of stannous sulphide ; and when the tin melts, the formation of the sulphide proceeds more quickly. Above the decomposition temp. of hydrogen sulphide, the production of stannous sulphide is due to the direct union of sulphur and tin. K. Jellinek and J. Zakowsky studied the reaction between 500° and 1100°. When hydrogen sulphide is passed into a neutral or feebly acid soln. of stannous chloride, dark brown or black stannous sulphide is precipitated ; and A. Ditte added that it is necessary to exclude air because, otherwise, the stannous chloride would be partially oxidized, and therefore some stannic chloride formed. H. Reinsch found that if a soln. of one part of stannous chloride in 100 parts of water and 15 parts of hydrochloric acid, of sp. gr. 1·168, be treated with hydrogen sulphide, all the tin is precipitated at once, but if 25 parts of acid be used, a precipitate appears only after some time, and if 40 parts of acid be used, no tin sulphide is precipitated, although it is if some water be added. The meaning of H. Reinsch's crude data is represented diagrammatically, Fig. 79. Fig. 79 means that there is a state of equilibrium in the system: $H_2S+SnCl_2 \rightleftharpoons 2HCl+SnS$. A. Ditte found that 8·3 per cent. hydrochloric acid at ordinary temp. begins to act on stannous sulphide, forming a soln. of stannous chloride, and giving off hydrogen sulphide. The formation of stannous chloride is faster the greater the conc. of the acid, and the higher the temp. According to A. Ditte, the precipitate dried in vacuo at 20° has the composition **trita-hydrated stannous sulphide**, $3SnS.H_2O$, with a sat. soln. of stannous chloride ; the first product of the action of hydrogen sulphide appears as an orange-red crystalline separation, the colour then changes to brown and finally to black ; the brownish-red crystals are formed if an acid soln. of stannous chloride be treated with a small proportion of hydrogen sulphide, or if water be added to an acid soln. of stannous chloride sat. with hydrogen sulphide. These coloured crystals are considered to be **stannous hydrosulphochloride,** $Sn(HS)Cl$, which is transformed by hydrogen sulphide into stannous sulphide ; the intermediate hydrosulphochloride was not isolated because it is decomposed when washed with water. When the hydrated stannous sulphide is thoroughly dried, it passes into the anhydrous sulphide. Stannous sulphide appears as a dark brown crystalline powder when the tritahydrate is dissolved to saturation in molten stannous chloride, and the cold product washed with dil. hydrochloric acid.

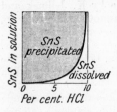

FIG. 79.—Effect of the Acidity of Solution on the Precipitation of Stannous Sulphide.

The physical properties of stannous sulphide.—The product obtained by the direct union of molten sulphur and tin is a dark lead-grey mass of lamellar, micaceous crystals ; the sublimed product appears in long, needle-like crystals. The native sulphide appears in thin scales, plates, or blades, which are pliable but not elastic, and resemble flaky graphite. A. C. Becquerel claimed to have obtained cubic crystals by the method indicated above ; but W. P. Headden found iron-black or graphite-black crystals of stannous sulphide as a deposit on some slags from an old Cornish tin furnace, and he considered the crystals to be monoclinic ; but S. Stevanovic showed that the crystals are rhombic bipyramids with axial ratios $a:b:c=0·3883:1:0·3566$; or, according to C. O. Trechmann, $0·3874:1:0·3558$. L. J. Spencer showed that the crystals of rhombic tin reported by C. O. Trechmann, and H. von Foullon, were really crystals of stannous sulphide. Owing to the thinness of the plates—$\frac{1}{20}$ mm.—it was not possible to determine if there is any cleavage parallel to the surface. There is often a repetition of parallel growths giving rise to comb-like and feathery forms and also to plates with serrated edges. L. J. Spencer gave illustrations of the twinning of these crystals. W. P. Davey discussed the sizes of the tin atoms in stannous sulphide. C. J. B. Karsten gave 4·852 for the sp. gr. of stannous sulphide ; P. A. Boullay, 5·267 ; E. R. Schneider, 4·973 ; and A. Ditte, 5·0802 at 0°. The hardness is 2. When molten stannous sulphide freezes, A. Ditte said that there is a considerable dilation ; and that it melts at a red heat. J. Guinchant gave 950°-1000° for the m.p. ; H. Pélabon, 880° ; and W. Biltz and co-workers, 882°—Fig. 78. As indicated above, W. Biltz and co-workers found that stannous sulphide has two m.p. The lower m.p is at 882°, and as the temp. is raised quickly from 1000° to 1100°, the viscosity increases very quickly, so that at the latter temp. the sulphide has the properties of a solid. At about 1200°, liquefaction again occurs. A. Ditte said that stannous sulphide begins to give off greenish vap., and to sublime close to its m.p. ; and

A. Mourlot found that it volatilizes unchanged in the electric furnace. J. Guinchant said that stannous sulphide boils at about 1090°, and W. Biltz and W. Mecklenburg found the b.p. of mixtures with different proportions of sulphur to be 1293° with 11·5 per cent. of sulphur; 1276°, with 15·6 per cent.; 1266°, with 17·9 per cent.; and 1240°, with 20·3 per cent., Fig. 78. W. Spring said that stannous sulphide is decomposed when heated in vacuo, forming stannic sulphide and tin; *au contraire*, A. Mourlot found that it can be distilled unchanged in the electric furnace, although there is evidence of a partial dissociation at very high temp. N. R. Campbell found that stannous sulphide exhibits a feeble radioactivity (induced). B. Aulenkamp, and W. W. Coblentz, studied the photoelectric sensitivity. K. Bädeker studied the electrical conductivity; and A. C. James, the effect of stannous sulphide on galena as a rectifier of alternating currents. F. Trey said that the electrical conductivity is electrolytic.

The chemical properties of stannous sulphide.—H. Rose found that when stannous sulphide is heated in a stream of hydrogen, some hydrogen sulphide is formed; and L. Elsner showed that if the hydrogen be passed a long enough time, nothing but tin remains. A. Ditte, however, said that stannous sulphide can be sublimed in a stream of hydrogen without forming hydrogen sulphide, provided the temp. does not exceed dark redness; at a cherry-red heat, a trace of hydrogen sulphide is formed; at a bright red heat, the issuing hydrogen has 1·8 to 2·0 per cent. of hydrogen sulphide; and at a white heat, 4·7 per cent. hydrogen sulphide; and, as observed by L. Elsner, tin alone remains. It is inferred that only the vap. of the stannous sulphide is decomposed by the hydrogen, for at lower temp., stannous sulphide is produced by the action of hydrogen sulphide on tin: $Sn + H_2S \rightleftharpoons SnS + H_2$. C. J. Brookes found that when roasted in air or oxygen, stannous sulphide is converted into stannic oxide, with a loss of some of the tin. E. Pollacci found that moist stannous sulphide is gradually oxidized by exposure to air. P. B. Ganguly and N. R. Dhar found a colloidal soln. of stannous sulphide is oxidized in sunlight and air, forming colloidal sulphur. O. Weigel showed that stannous sulphide is very sparingly soluble in water, for a litre of water at 18° dissolves 0.14×10^{-6} mol. H. Rose found that in a stream of water-vapour, red-hot stannous sulphide forms hydrogen sulphide and stannic oxide. F. M. Perkin showed that stannous sulphide is readily oxidized by hydrogen dioxide in alkaline soln., forming a sulphostannate.

According to H. Rose, stannous sulphide reacts with chlorine at ordinary temp., forming a compound of stannic chloride and sulphur tetrachloride, but at a higher temp. stannic chloride is produced. A. Ditte said that dried hydrogen chloride does not attack stannous sulphide at ordinary temp., but at a higher temp. hydrogen sulphide and stannous chloride are formed, and this the more rapidly the higher the temp. J. Kelley and E. F. Smith found that at ordinary temp. hydrogen chloride completely transforms stannous sulphide into the chloride. The action of hydrochloric acid has been indicated above in connection with the reversible reaction: $SnS + 2HCl \rightleftharpoons SnCl_2 + H_2S$. The solubility of stannous sulphide in this acid was utilized by L. Loviton in the separation of antimony and tin. A. Ditte found that hydrochloric acid attacks hydrated stannous sulphide more readily than it does the anhydrous salt, for 8·3 per cent. hydrochloric acid attacks the anhydrous sulphide at ordinary temp., while a 4 per cent. acid attacks the hydrated sulphide in the cold and one per cent. acid attacks it at 100°; while W. R. Lang and C. M. Carson found that stannous sulphide is soluble in hydrochloric acid of sp. gr. 1·16 diluted with about half its weight of water.

P. Berthier found that stannous sulphide is not dissolved by sulphurous acid. A. Ditte compared the action of alkali sulphides on stannous sulphide with the action of alkali hydroxides on stannous oxide. An aq. soln. with less than 20 per cent. potassium sulphide does not attack the sulphide at ordinary temp., but more conc. soln. gradually form metallic tin, and sulphostannates—*confer*, the action of potassium hydroxide on stannous oxide. Its reaction also accounts for the reprecipita-

tion of tin as stannic sulphide after the addition of an acid to the alkaline soln.
The action is faster the more conc. the soln., and the higher the temp. ; and with
very conc. soln. the separated tin is attacked, forming potassium sulphostannate
(q.v.). Dil. soln. of the alkali sulphide in the presence of air gradually transform
stannous sulphide into the alkali sulphostannate. The sulphide is not attacked by
cold or hot soln. of **ammonium sulphide,** but in the presence of air, ammonium
sulphostannate is slowly formed. Stannous sulphide is soluble in soln. of **alkali or
ammonium polysulphide.** According to O. Ruff, **sulphuryl chloride** transforms
stannous sulphide into the chloride which passes into soln., and sulphur is separated.
A. Ditte showed that stannous sulphide is but slightly attacked by aq. **ammonia,**
but in the presence of air, ammonium stannate and sulphostannate are slowly
formed. E. R. Schneider said that **nitric acid** readily oxidizes amorphous stannous
sulphide to stannic oxide, but the crystalline sulphide is but slowly attacked.
H. Rose found that **phosphine** is reduced by warm stannous sulphide, forming
hydrogen sulphide and phosphorus.

According to J. L. Proust, stannous sulphide is not attacked by **potassium
hydroxide** soln., but F. M. Perkin found that some preparations of precipitated
stannous sulphide readily dissolve in the alkali-lye. A. Ditte showed that stannous
sulphide suspended in water reacts with potassium hydroxide : $SnS+2KOH$
$=SnO+K_2S+H_2O$; the reaction is considered to be reversible, and the equilibrium
to be dependent on the temp. and conc. of the soln. ; with conc. alkali-lye, however,
tin and alkali stannate and sulphostannate are formed. O. Materne said that a
boiling 10 per cent. soln. of sodium hydroxide readily dissolves stannous sulphide,
and that brownish-red sulphide is precipitated from the soln. by acids, ammonium
chloride, or hydrogen sulphide. According to P. Berthier, when a mixture of
stannous sulphide and **sodium carbonate** is heated in a carbon crucible to a white
heat, about three-fourths of the tin is reduced to metal ; the slag contains some tin
sulphide ; at a red-heat, sodium carbonate decomposes part of the sulphide.
A. Höring found that when a mixture of stannous sulphide, sulphur, carbon, and
sodium carbonate is fused, the tin is converted into alkali sulphostannate which is
soluble in water. H. Rose found that fused **potassium cyanide** reduces stannous
sulphide to tin. E. Schürmann showed that stannous sulphide is completely converted into the sulphate when heated with soln. of **copper sulphate** or **cadmium
sulphate,** but not by soln. of **zinc sulphate, lead nitrate,** or **potassium antimonyl
tartrate ;** and F. Raschig found that with a soln. of **cuprous chloride** in one of
sodium chloride, cuprous sulphide and stannous chloride are formed ; and with a
boiling dil. soln. of **cupric chloride,** cuprous sulphide and stannic chloride are
formed. J. B. Cammerer found that the hydrated sesquioxide reduces a soln.
of **ferric chloride** to ferrous chloride, with the formation of stannic chloride and the
separation of sulphur. A. Mourlot showed that when mixed with **magnesium
chloride,** and heated in the electric furnace, stannous chloride is volatilized
and magnesium sulphide remains. R. Zsigmondy and C. Haller showed that
stannous sulphide dissolves in molten **glass,** with scarcely any effect on the colour
of the glass.

According to J. J. Berzelius,[2] when stannic sulphide is digested with a sat. soln. of
potassium sulphostannate, **hydrated tin sesquisulphide,** $Sn_2S_3.nH_2O$, is formed which
is reconverted to stannous sulphide by digestion with alkali-lye. When an intimate
mixture of stannous sulphide and 25 per cent. of sulphur is heated in a retort a greyish-
yellow mass of what J. J. Berzelius regarded as **tin sesquisulphide,** Sn_2S_3, is formed.
H. Pélabon found that a mixture of tin and sulphur, in the proportion required for the
sesquisulphide, decomposes on fusion, yielding a sublimate of sulphur and a residue of
stannous sulphide. J. J. Berzelius said that when tin sesquisulphide is strongly ignited in
a closed vessel, two-thirds of the contained sulphur is volatilized ; digestion with potash-
lye converts it into potassium stannate and sulphostannate and stannous sulphide ; and
conc. hydrochloric acid converts it into stannic sulphide and stannous oxide. U. Antony
and L. Niccoli dissolved the sesquisulphide in hydrochloric acid. The available evidence
is not satisfactory proof of the chemical individuality of this product.

REFERENCES.

[1] C. J. B. Karsten, *Schweigger's Journ.*, 65. 394, 1832 ; J. L. Proust, *Ann. Chim. Phys.*, (1). 28. 213, 1798 ; *Nicholson's Journ.*, (1), 2. 515, 1798 ; (2), 1. 109, 1802 ; *Journ. Phys.*, 53. 89, 1801 ; 59. 260, 1804 ; *Phil. Mag.*, 21. 208, 1805 ; E. R. Schneider, *Pogg. Ann.*, 95. 169, 1855 ; 127. 624, 1866 ; 138. 604, 1869 ; 139. 661, 1870 ; H. Rose, *ib.*, 24. 335, 1832 ; 42. 517, 1837 ; 106. 652, 1859 ; J. Kelley and E. F. Smith, *Amer. Chem. Journ.*, 18. 1096, 1896 ; O. B. Kühn, *Liebig's Ann.*, 86. 110, 1852 ; E. Schürmann, *ib.*, 249. 341, 1888 ; G. C. Winkelblech, *ib.*, 21. 34, 1837 ; *Journ. prakt. Chem.*, (1), 10. 237, 1837 ; H. Reinsch, *ib.*, (1), 13. 132, 1838 ; L. Elsner, *ib.*, (1), 17. 233, 1839 ; F. Damm and F. Kraft, *Ber.*, 40. 4778, 1907 ; O. Ruff, *ib.*, 34. 1752, 1901 ; F. Raschig, *ib.*, 17. 697, 1884 ; *Liebig's Ann.*, 228. 19, 1885 ; J. Milbauer, *Zeit. anorg. Chem.*, 42. 440, 1904 ; K. Jellinek and J. Zakowsky, *ib.*, 142. 1, 1925 ; J. Zakowsky, *Ueber die Affinität der Metalle zum Schwefel*, Danzig, 1904 ; W. Biltz and W. Mecklenburg, *Zeit. anorg. Chem.*, 64. 226, 1909 ; W. Biltz, *ib.*, 59. 281, 1908 ; J. L. Gay Lussac, *Ann. Chim. Phys.*, (2), 1. 44, 1816 ; W. W. Coblentz, *Bur. Standards Scient. Paper*, 18. 585, 1922 ; W. R. Lang and C. M. Carson, *Journ. Soc. Chem. Ind.*, 21. 1018, 1902 ; H. V. Regnault, *ib.*, (3), 1. 129, 1841 ; P. A. Boullay, *ib.*, (2), 43. 266, 1830 ; P. Berthier, *ib.*, (2), 3. 169, 1826 ; A. Ditte, *ib.*, (8), 12. 236, 1907 ; *Compt. Rend.*, 94. 1419, 1882 ; 96. 1790, 1883 ; 97. 42, 1883 ; H. Pélabon, *ib.*, 142. 1147, 1906 ; *Ann. Chim. Phys.*, (8), 17. 526, 1909 ; E. Pollacci, *Boll. Chim. Farm.*, 47. 363, 1908 ; J. B. Cammerer, *Berg. Hütt. Ztg.*, 50. 284, 1891 ; A. C. Becquerel, *Ann. Chim. Phys.*, (2), 42. 225, 1829 ; S. Stevanovic, *Zeit. Kryst.*, 40. 321, 1905 ; W. P. Headden, *Amer. Journ. Science*, (4), 5. 93, 1898 ; *Proc. Colorado Scient. Soc.*, 6. 74, 1901 ; C. O. Trechmann, *Min. Mag.*, 3. 186, 1879 ; L. J. Spencer, *ib.*, 19. 113, 1921 ; P. B. Ganguly and N. R. Dhar, *Zeit. Koll.*, 31. 16, 1922 ; H. von Foullon, *Verh. Geol. Reichanst. Wien*, 237, 1881 ; *Jahrb. Geol. Reichsanst Wien*, 34. 367, 1884 ; O. Weigel, *Zeit. phys. Chem.*, 58. 293, 1907 ; W. Spring, *ib.*, 18. 553, 1895 ; N. R. Campbell, *Proc. Cambridge Phil. Soc.*, 13. 282, 1906 ; J. Guinchant, *Compt. Rend.*, 142. 1147, 1902 ; A. Mourlot, *ib.*, 124. 768, 1897 ; *Ann. Chim. Phys.*, (7), 17. 537, 1899 ; B. Aulenkamp, *Zeit. Physik*, 18. 70, 1923 ; C. J. Brookes, *Chem. News*, 73. 218, 1896 ; F. M. Perkin, *Journ. Soc. Chem. Ind.*, 20. 425, 1901 ; L. Loviton, *Journ. Pharm. Chim.*, (5), 17. 361, 1888 ; O. Materne, *Bull. Soc. Chim. Belg.*, 20. 46, 1906 ; R. Zsigmondy and C. Haller, *Dingler's Journ.*, 273. 29. 1889 ; A. Höring, *Pharm. Ztg.*, 3. 120, 1851 ; W. Spring, *Bull. Acad. Belg.*, (3), 5. 492, 1883 ; *Ber.*, 16. 1002, 1883 ; G. Tocco and N. Jacob, *Gazz. Chim. Ital.*, 54. i, 32, 1924 ; W. P. Davey, *Phys. Rev.*, (2), 19. 249, 1922 ; K. Bädeker, *Ueber die elektrische Leitfahigkeit und die thermoelektrische Kraft einiger Schwermetallverbindungen*, Leipzig, 1906 ; A. C. James, *Phil. Mag.*, (6), 49. 681, 1925 ; F. Trey, *Phys. Zeit.*, 26. 849, 1925.

[2] J. J. Berzelius, *Schweigger's Journ.*, 6. 284, 1812 ; *Pogg. Ann.*, 28. 443, 1833 ; *Ann. Chim. Phys.*, (2), 5. 141, 1817 ; U. Antony and L. Niccoli, *Gazz. Chim. Ital.*, 22. 408, 1892 ; H. Pélabon, *Ann. Chim. Phys.*, (8), 17. 543, 1909.

§ 23. Stannic Sulphide

Mosaic gold was in use in the eighteenth century as a pigment for painting, and it was called *aurum mosaicum*—*mosaic gold*—or *aurum musioum*—*muscovite gold*. It was prepared by heating a mixture of tin, sulphur, ammonium chloride, and mercury. Owing to the use of mercury in its preparation, it was at one time supposed to contain that element, and was used medicinally in venereal diseases. P. Woulfe[1] showed that it can also be obtained by omitting the mercury and ammonium chloride. B. Pelletier regarded it as a sulphuretted oxide of tin. J. L. Proust showed that mosaic gold contained very little oxygen ; and J. Davy, and J. J. Berzelius proved that it is stannic sulphide. Mosaic gold is now used as a bronzing powder for wood, metals, wall-paper, etc., although its application is being displaced by cheaper bronze powders.

Stannic sulphide cannot be obtained by direct fusion of the constituents at ordinary press. ; but W. Spring[2] obtained it by compressing an intimate mixture of the constituents at 6500 atm. ; and J. L. Proust, by heating a mixture of stannous chloride or ammonium chlorostannite and sulphur. E. R. Schneider said that only stannous sulphide, and not stannic sulphide, can be produced in this way. B. Pelletier, L. J. Thénard, J. Lagutt, J. B. van Mons, H. Hadert, and P. Woulfe have recommended various recipes—*e.g.* (i) heating a mixture of sulphur, tin filings, and ammonium chloride ; (ii) tin, mercury, sulphur and ammonium chloride ; (iii) tin amalgam, sulphur and ammonium chloride ; (iv) stannic oxide, sulphur and ammonium chloride ; (v) stannous oxide, and sulphur ; (vi) stannous sulphide, sulphur, and ammonium chloride; (vii) stannous sulphide, chloride and sulphur; etc. For a pale yellow mosaic gold, J. Lagutt recommended heating an intimate mixture of stannous chloride with half its weight of flowers of sulphur; and for reddish-yellow mosaic gold, 50 parts of tin amalgam (1 : 1), 25 of flowers of sulphur, and 25 of ammonium chloride. The heating was done in a retort, and the temp. was slowly raised during $3-3\frac{1}{2}$ hrs. On account of the poor thermal conductivity of the mixture only small quantities were made at a time. L. Gmelin assumed that in the preparation of mosaic gold from sulphur, ammonium chloride, and tin, the first stage of the reaction involves the formation of ammonium chlorostannite : $Sn+4NH_4Cl=(NH_4)_2SnCl_4+H_2+2NH_3$; and afterwards, as the temp. rises higher, the sulphur reacts with the ammonium chlorostannite, forming stannic sulphide, and ammonium chloride and chlorostannate which sublime : $2(NH_4)_2SnCl_4+2S=SnS_2+(NH_4)_2SnCl_6+2NH_4Cl$. According to J. Lagutt, ammonium bromide can be used in place of the chloride, but ammonium sulphate or thiocyanate do not furnish mosaic gold. The halogen of the ammonium halide is considered to be the active agent. If tin amalgam is used mercuric sulphide also sublimes. J. L. Proust said that he obtained stannic sulphide by heating stannous or stannic oxides with sulphur. J. B. Senderens found that tin oxide is not affected by boiling with water in which sulphur is suspended. B. Pelletier said that stannic sulphide is produced by heating a mixture of stannous and mercuric sulphides, but J. L. Proust denied this. P. Woulfe obtained stannic sulphide by heating a mixture of stannous sulphide and mercuric chloride; or a mixture of stannous sulphide, sulphur, and ammonium chloride. H. Rose obtained stannic sulphide by passing a mixture of the vap. of stannic chloride and hydrogen sulphide through a red-hot tube. V. Kletzinsky obtained an amorphous precipitate by boiling a soln. of stannous chloride and a little sulphuric acid or hydrochloric acid and sulphur dioxide; the sublimation of the washed and dried product furnishes crystals of mosaic gold. According to L. Dede and T. Becker, with a $0.001N$-soln. of stannic chloride the normality of the hydrochloric acid required for the appearance of a precipitate, by treatment with hydrogen sulphide, was $2.28N$-, or $2.06N$- in 5 hrs.; $1.87N$- in 9 hrs.; and $1.38N$- in 24 hrs.; and in the presence of potassium chloride, the following proportions of hydrochloric acid completely hindered precipitation :

KCl	.	0	$0.3N$-	$0.6N$-	$1.0N$-	$1.5N$-	$2.0N$-	$2.6N$-
HCl	.	$2.28N$-	$1.95N$-	$1.80N$-	$1.59N$-	$1.40N$-	$1.17N$-	$1.06N$-

Amorphous or **colloidal stannic sulphide** is produced when hydrogen sulphide is passed into an acidified soln. of stannic chloride, or into water in which freshly precipitated stannic hydroxide is suspended; it is also precipitated when hydrochloric or sulphuric acid is added to an aq. soln. of a sulphostannate. L. Storch said that the precipitate obtained by hydrogen sulphide in a soln. of a stannic salt contains no stannous sulphide; and T. Scheerer found the product obtained by the action of the gas on the hydroxide has the composition $SnS_2.2H_2O$ when undried and $SnS_2.H_2O$ when dried at 140°. C. T. Barfoed said that the pale yellow or reddish-yellow stannic sulphide precipitated from freshly prepared soln. of stannic chloride contains sulphur, and this the more the greater the dilution; no chlorine is present; but some stannic hydroxide is formed. The precipitate obtained with a hydrochloric acid soln. of β-stannic acid is mainly white β-stannic acid which is slowly converted into brown stannic sulphide. According to F. W. Schmidt, the egg-yellow precipitate obtained by the action of hydrogen sulphide on stannic chloride when moist contains SnS_2, but during the drying it decomposes giving off hydrogen sulphide and becomes dark brown. A dil. acid soln. of stannic chloride gives a precipitate with hydrogen sulphide which, when washed by suction, treated with alcohol to remove water, and with carbon disulphide to remove sulphur, and then washed with alcohol and finally with water, gave $Sn : S=1 : 1.946$, very nearly SnS_2; but when dried in air, the composition was $Sn : S=1 : 1.638$, owing to the loss of hydrogen sulphide. A neutral dil. soln. of stannic chloride gives at first a white precipitate which contains chlorine—stannic chlorosulphide—and which passes into the disulphide by the continued action of the hydrogen sulphide. G. Jörgensen found that the precipitate produced by hydrogen sulphide with hydrochloric acid soln. of metastannic acid has a sulphur content which varies with the conc. of the acid and the salt, with time, and with temp. W. Spring showed that during the washing of the precipitated stannic sulphide, it is peptized forming a colloidal hydrosol. E. R. Schneider obtained a colloidal hydrosol by passing hydrogen sulphide into a hydrosol of metastannic acid, and heating the mixture. The addition of an acid flocculates the hydrosol into hydrogel. N. R. Dhar and S. Ghosh found that stannic sulphide and the complex stannates are peptized by alkali-lye, yellow aluminium sulphide, and sodium arsenite. W. Biltz studied the colour changes of colloidal stannic sulphide.

The properties of stannic sulphide.—Crystalline stannic sulphide furnishes golden-yellow plates which are soft and feel like graphite. C. J. B. Karsten gave 4·600 for the sp. gr., and P. A. Boullay, 4·425. H. V. Regnault gave 0·11932 for the sp. ht. between 12° and 95°. H. J. Houston found that the colour passes to dark red and finally black when heated; the reverse changes occur on cooling. According to J. J. Berzelius, when heated, stannic sulphide sublimes, but at a higher temp. it decomposes into stannous sulphide and sulphur; and if the action of heat has not been too prolonged, stannous sulphide will be found at the bottom of the mass, stannic sulphide at the top, and tin sesquioxide in between. According to J. L. Gay Lussac, and J. J. Berzelius, the sulphur dioxide reported by J. L. Proust is not evolved unless air be present. Stannic sulphide was found by W. W. Coblentz not to be appreciably photoelectric. O. Stelling studied the X-ray absorption spectrum of stannic sulphide.

When heated in **air**, stannic sulphide furnishes sulphur dioxide and stannic oxide; and, added P. Jannasch and O. Heydenreich, the reaction is much more rapid and complete in **oxygen.**

According to F. W. Schmidt, when stannic sulphide obtained by the action of hydrogen sulphide on a soln. of stannic chloride, is allowed to remain in contact with ammonia, it dissolves, forming a soln., which, on acidification, yields a very voluminous white precipitate. The same substance may be obtained by digesting stannic sulphide with ammonium carbonate soln., filtering, and acidifying; about 10 per cent. of the stannic sulphide is dissolved. This compound, when freed from sulphur by treatment with carbon disulphide, corresponds with **stannic oxytrisulphide,** $Sn_2S_2O.11\frac{1}{2}H_2O$; it is easily and completely soluble in ammonium carbonate, and is also slowly soluble in water. When dried, the white mass gradually loses its property of dissolving in ammonium carbonate soln., and becomes amber-yellow. The solubility of the substance in ammonia is not affected by keeping for a long time. It is assumed, therefore, that the decrease of solubility in ammonium carbonate soln. is not due to polymerization, but to loss of water and to a gradual change from a voluminous colloidal condition to an amorphous state in which the composition varies from $Sn_2S_3O.11\frac{1}{2}H_2O$ to $Sn_2S_3O.5H_2O$, according to the time of drying. Stannous sulphide dissolves in ammonia, forming an orange-red soln., which behaves like a colloidal soln. of stannic sulphide; the sulphide, SnS_2, is precipitated by acids from freshly-prepared soln. The soln. loses its colour on exposure to air for four to five days, ammonium sulphide being first formed and then ammonium thiosulphate; the oxysulphide and sulphur are precipitated by acids, but neither hydrogen sulphide nor sulphur dioxide is formed. The oxysulphide may be purified and any tin sulphide removed by dissolving in ammonium carbonate. The oxysulphide is not precipitated from very dil. soln. in ammonium carbonate until carbon dioxide has been liberated, and it then separates as a very fine, flocculent, white mass which has a blue tinge; the precipitate after washing three or four times with water forms colloidal soln. which have an acid reaction and from which the colloid is precipitated by neutral salts, but not by acids. These soln. are assumed to contain the acid, $S(SnS.OH)_2$, whilst the composition of the original precipitate is regarded as $HO.SnS.S.SnS.ONH_4$; and that of the oxysulphide, which is soluble in ammonium carbonate as

$$S:Sn{<}{\overset{S}{\underset{O}{}}}{>}Sn:S$$

W. Skey said that stannic sulphide is not soluble **in water;** but O. Weigel found the solubility of stannic sulphide in water to be $1·13\times10^{-6}$ mol per litre at 18°. P. de Clermont and J. Frommel, and A. Classen and O. Bauer found that hydrogen dioxide forms stannic oxide and sulphuric acid. H. Rose showed that when stannic sulphide is treated at ordinary temp. with chlorine, a brown liquid is formed which solidifies to yellow crystals of $SnCl_4.2SCl_4$. W. T. Casselmann obtained a similar result. E. R. Schneider found that with iodine, stannic disulpho-tetraiodide, SnS_2I_4, is formed. J. Kelley and E. F. Smith found that hydrogen chloride or bromide converts heated stannic sulphide into the stannic halide which volatilizes. H. Rose said that crystallized stannic sulphide is not attacked by conc. hydrochloric acid ; the amorphous sulphide is insoluble in dil. acids, but is dissolved by the hot acid ; W. R. Lang and C. M. Carson also found that the amorphous sulphide is dissolved by the hot acid of sp. gr. 1·16. W. T. Casselmann found that at a red heat stannic sulphide reacts with phosphorus pentachloride, producing stannic chloride and sulphophosphide, and phosphorus sulphide and sulphochloride. O. Ruff showed that sulphuryl chloride converts stannic sulphide into stannic chloride and sulphur—the presence of aluminium chloride accelerates the reaction. A. Guéront said that stannic sulphide is dissolved with difficulty by sulphurous acid. H. Rose found stannic sulphide is not dissolved by nitric acid, but boiling aqua regia converts it into sulphuric acid and stannic oxide. H. Rose said that stannic sulphide is dissolved by aq. ammonia only with difficulty. Aq. soln. of alkali hydroxides dissolve stannic sulphide, forming stannates and sulphostannates ; with alkali carbonates, a similar result is obtained, but carbon dioxide is at the same time evolved. O. Materne also showed that precipitated stannic sulphide is soluble in a soln. of sodium carbonate ; and sparingly soluble in one of sodium hydroxide. Soln. of alkali sulphides and of ammonium sulphide dissolve stannic sulphide, forming sulphostannates—vide infra. According to A. Classen and O. Bauer, the dissolution with sodium sulphide is faster than with ammonium sulphide. P. de Clermont showed that when stannic sulphide is boiled with soln. of ammonium salts, it forms stannic oxide ; and F. W. Schmidt showed that under certain conditions it is slightly soluble in soln. of ammonium carbonate. F. Raschig showed that with a soln. of cuprous chloride in one of sodium chloride, cuprous sulphide and stannic chloride are formed. J. B. Cammerer found that with a soln. of ferric chloride, stannic and ferrous chlorides are formed. H. Rose found that fused potassium nitrate converts stannic sulphide into potassium sulphate and stannate ; fused lead oxide converts it into stannic oxide and lead sulphide ; and molten potassium cyanide forms a sulphostannate. O. Materne found stannic sulphide to be insoluble in a cold soln. of borax, but soluble in a hot soln. C. Pertusi found that when stannic sulphide is suspended in water and mixed with an excess of powdered magnesium, it is reduced to tin and to stannous sulphide with the evolution of hydrogen sulphide.

The sulphochlorides have been discussed in connection with stannic chloride. E. R. Schneider [3] obtained stannic sulphoiodide, SnS_2I_4, by crystallization from the brown liquid obtained by melting together a mol of stannic sulphide and two mols of iodine, and subliming the product in a current of carbon dioxide. While mosaic gold does not dissolve in a soln. of iodine in carbon disulphide, dry precipitated stannic sulphide dissolves slowly in the liquid, and on evaporating the soln., crystals of the sulphoiodide are formed. The crystals are coloured like potassium dichromate, and they are probably rhombic. Water decomposes the compound into sulphur, stannic oxide, and hydriodic acid. The salt is decomposed by hydrochloric acid with the separation of sulphur, iodine and tin passing into soln. Aqua regia acts similarly ; and nitric acid forms sulphur, iodine, stannic oxide and some soluble stannic nitrate. A cold soln. of potassium hydroxide forms stannic oxide and sulphur ; the iodine passes into soln. ; a boiling soln. of the lye dissolves the compound completely ; soln. of sodium carbonate and ammonia act likewise but more slowly. Ammonia gas is absorbed, forming a white powder. Stannic sulphoiodide is soluble in carbon disulphide, or chloroform ; alcohol separates sulphur, and the tin and iodine dissolve as stannic iodide.

REFERENCES.

[1] P. Woulfe, *Phil. Trans.*, **61**. 114, 1771 ; J. Davy, *ib.*, **102**. 169, 1812 ; J L. Proust, *Journ. Phys.*, **53**. 89, 1801 ; **59**. 260, 1803 ; **61**. 338, 1803 ; *Nicholson's Journ.*, (1), **2**. 515, 1798 ; (2), **1**. 109, 1802 ; (2), **14**. 38, 1806 ; *Phil. Mag.*, **21**. 208, 1805 ; *Ann. Chim. Phys.*, (1), **28**. 213, 1798 ; B. Pelletier, *ib.*, (1), **13**. 280, 1792 ; J. J. Berzelius, *ib.*, (2), **5**. 141, 1817 ; (2), **22**. 138, 1822 ; (2), **32**. 60, 1826 ; *Schweigger's Journ.*, **6**. 284, 1812 ; E. J. B. de Bullion, *Journ. Savans*, 598, 1792 ; *Crell's Ann.*, i, 437, 1803.

[2] L. J. Thénard, *Traité de chimie élémentaire*, Paris, **1**. 507, 1824 ; P. Woulfe, *Phil. Trans.*, **61**. 114, 1771 ; J. J. Berzelius, *Schweigger's Journ.*, **6**. 284, 1812 ; *Ann. Chim. Phys.*, (2), **5**. 141, 1817 ; (2), **20**. 138, 1822 ; (2), **32**. 60, 1826 ; J. L. Proust, *Journ. Phys.*, **51**. 173, 1802 ; **61**. 338, 1803 ; L. Gmelin, *Handbook of Chemistry*, London, **5**. 79, 1851 ; W. Biltz, *Nach. Gött.*, 1, 1904 ; J. Lagutt, *Zeit. angew. Chem.*, **11**. 557, 1897 ; J. B. van Mons, *Conspectus mixtionum chemicarum*, Louvain, 1827 ; V. Kletzinsky, *Dingler's Journ.*, **174**. 245, 1864 ; J. Kelley and E. F. Smith, *Amer. Chem. Journ.*, **18**. 1096, 1896 ; H. J. Houston, *Chem. News*, **24**. 177, 1871 ; W. Skey, *ib.*, **23**. 291, 1871 ; J. B. Cammerer, *Berg. Hütt. Ztg.*, **50**. 284, 1891 ; C. J. B. Karsten, *Schweigger's Journ.*, **65**. 394, 1832 ; P. A. Boullay, *Ann. Chim. Phys.*, (2), **43**. 266, 1830 ; J. L. Gay Lussac, *ib.*, (2), **1**. 40, 1816 ; H. Pélabon, *ib.*, (8), **17**. 543, 1909 ; H. V. Regnault, *ib.*, (3), **1**. 129, 1841 ; B. Pelletier, *ib.*, (1), **13**. 280, 1792 ; P. de Clermont and J. Frommel, *ib.*, (5), **18**. 189, 1879 ; P. de Clermont, *Bull. Soc. Chim.*, (2), **31**. 483, 1879 ; O. Weigel, *Zeit. phys. Chem.*, **58**. 293, 1907 ; H. Rose, *Handbuch der analytischen Chemie*, Berlin, **1**. 412, 1867 ; *Pogg. Ann.*, **91**. 104, 1853 ; **106**. 652, 1859 ; E. R. Schneider, *ib.*, **95**. 165, 1855 ; **138**. 604, 1869 ; **139**. 661, 1870 ; *Journ. prakt. Chem.*, (1), **79**. 419, 1860 ; C. T. Barfoed, *ib.*, (1), **101**. 369, 1867 ; T. Scheerer, *ib.*, (2), **3**. 472, 1871 ; J. B. Senderens, *Bull. Soc. Chim.*, (3), **6**. 805, 1891 ; L. Storch, *Monatsh.*, **10**. 260, 1889 ; W. Spring, *Bull. Acad. Belg.*, (3), **5**. 492, 1883 ; *Ber.*, **16**. 1002, 1883 ; F. Raschig, *ib.*, **17**. 697, 1884 ; O. Ruff, *ib.*, **34**. 1752, 1901 ; A. Classen and O. Bauer, *ib.*, **16**. 1063, 1883 ; F. W. Schmidt, *ib.*, **27**. 2739, 1894 ; *Koll. Zeit.*, **1**. 131, 1907 ; P. Jannasch and O. Heydenreich, *Zeit. anorg. Chem.*, **12**. 358, 1896 ; E. A. Schneider, *ib.*, **5**. 83, 1894 ; G. Jörgensen, *ib.*, **28**. 140, 1901 ; W. T. Casselmann, *Liebig's Ann.*, **83**. 267, 1852 ; A. Guéront, *Compt. Rend.*, **75**. 1276, 1872 ; A. Verneuil, *ib.*, **103**. 600, 1886 ; *Bull. Soc. Chim.*, (2), **46**. 302, 1886 ; O. Materne, *Bull. Soc. Chim. Belg.*, **20**. 46, 1906 ; W. R. Lang and C. M. Carson, *Journ. Soc. Chem. Ind.*, **21**. 1018, 1902 ; W. W. Coblentz, *Scient. Papers Bur. Standards*, **18**. 585, 1922 ; L. Dede and T. Becker, *Zeit. anorg. Chem.*, **152**. 191, 1926 ; N. R. Dhar and S. Ghosh, *ib.*, **152**. 408, 1926 ; C. Pertusi, *Ann. Chim. Anal.*, **20**. 229, 1915 ; O. Stelling, *Zeit. phys. Chem.*, **117**. 175, 1925 ; H. Hadert, *Chem. Ztg.*, **50**. 7, 1926.

[3] E. R. Schneider, *Pogg. Ann.*, **111**. 249, 1860.

§ 24. The Sulphostannates or Thiostannates

J. J. Berzelius [1] showed that stannic sulphide unites with the more basic sulphides of the other elements, forming a series of **sulphostannates** or **thiostannates**. These salts can usually be referred to **sulphometastannic acid**, H_2SnS_3 ; and some-times to **sulphorthostannic acid**, H_4SnS_4. O. B. Kuhn reported the formation of the former, as an olive-green precipitate, when a conc. soln. of sodium thiostannate is decomposed by hydrochloric or acetic acid. L. Storch was unable to obtain anything other than a mixture of the acid with tin sulphide by this process. He added various acids to a soln. of sodium thiostannate, prepared by saturating a soln. of sodium stannate with hydrogen sulphide. Hydrochloric, sulphuric, and dichloracetic acids cause an immediate precipitation of yellow stannic sulphide, but oxalic, phosphoric, monochloracetic, tartaric, citric, succinic, and acetic acids produced brownish-yellow soln., from which reddish-brown precipitates separated more or less slowly. These results showed that this reaction was dependent on the affinity (avidity) of the acid. The brown precipitates contained only slightly more sulphur than corresponded with the formula SnS_2, and did not appear to be homogeneous. Attempts to isolate the compound formed proved unavailing. When a dil. soln. of oxalic acid is added to a soln. of sodium thiostannate in quantity only just sufficient to neutralize the sodium, a deep yellow soln. is produced which gradually changes to reddish-brown, but remains clear for hours, and may be partially conc. before separation of the reddish-brown precipitate occurs. Acetic and oxalic acids produce no immediate precipitates from this soln. Ammonia and potash gradually decolorize it, as do sodium and ammonium carbonates, ammonium chloride, and

sodium acetate, although more slowly.   Many salts and strong acids cause pre·
cipitation.   As the substance formed could not be isolated, the author estimated
the ratio of sulphur to tin in this soln. after the free hydrogen sulphide had
been removed by a current of air.   The result showed the presence of three atoms
of sulphur to one of tin.   Hence, it is probable that sulphostannic acid, H_2SnS_3,
is present in this soln.   It is also probably present in small quantities in the
brown precipitate.

The general methods of preparing the sulphostannates are as follow : A. Berg
melted a mixture of metallic tin and 6 to 8 times its weight of a mixture of equal
parts of sulphur and sodium carbonate at a dark red heat.   H. Rose used stannic
oxide in place of tin ; and A. Höring used stannous sulphide.   A. Ditte melted tin
with the alkali or ammonium polysulphides ; and he dissolved stannic sulphide
in soln. of the sulphides of the alkalies, alkaline earths, or ammonium sulphide.
Precipitated stannic sulphide dissolves more readily when in the amorphous state,
and requires a boiling liquid for complete soln.   A. Ditte also dissolved stannous
sulphide in a soln. of a polysulphide.   J. Milbauer melted stannic oxide with
potassium thiocyanate.   R. F. Weinland and A. Gutmann made the sulphortho-
stannates by the action of a thiosulphate on alkali stannite.   The sulphostannates
of the heavy metals are precipitated when a soln. of a salt of the heavy metal is
treated with potassium sulphostannate.

As L. Storch has shown, the analytical separation of tin from copper, mercury,
and cadmium rests on the formation of the sulphostannates.   The sulphostannates
are well-defined compounds which can usually be obtained in a crystalline form.
The sulphostannates of ammonium, the alkalies, and alkaline earths are colourless
or yellow ;   and readily soluble in water.   The alkali salts are stable at a dull
red heat.   Mineral acids precipitate stannic sulphide from the soln.   A. Classen and
O. Bauer showed that the soln. is oxidized by hydrogen dioxide, and when the soln.
is boiled, A. Kolb found that stannic hydroxide is precipitated.

V. Stanek reported **trihydrated ammonium sulphostannate,** $(NH_4)_2SnS_3.3H_2O$,
in thin yellow plates, by saturating a soln. of colourless ammonium sulphide with
stannic sulphide, diluting the soln. with an equal vol. of ammonium sulphide, and
adding alcohol.   He also obtained **heptahydrated ammonium sulphostannate,**
$(NH_4)_2SnS_3.7H_2O$, if alcohol be added to the preceding soln. until a small pre·
cipitate appears, the soln. filtered, and alcohol be poured over the filtrate.   Long
needle-like crystals are formed.   E. Priwoznik obtained what was regarded as
ammonium heptasulphotristannate, $(NH_4)_2Sn_3S_7.6H_2O$, by the action of ammonium
sulphide on metallic tin.   A. Ditte made it by dissolving tin-foil in yellow ammonium
sulphide ;   in the cold the reaction is slow and ceases before the ammonium sulphide
has all reacted ;   if the soln. be warmed much ammonium sulphide is volatilized.
If the soln. be evaporated over sulphuric acid and potassium hydroxide in vacuo,
yellow plates are produced which readily decompose.   When exposed to air, the
crystals lose water and become superficially violet.   When treated with a large
proportion of water, or acids, stannic sulphide is precipitated.   When the temp.
is gradually raised, water is given off, then ammonium sulphide, then sulphur,
and finally stannous sulphide is formed.

O. B. Kuhn melted a mixture of sodium sulphide, stannous sulphide and sulphur,
and obtained a black crystalline mass which gave a dark soln. with hot water.   On
cooling, the soln. deposited colourless monoclinic crystals of **sodium sulphorthostannate,** $Na_4SnS_4.12H_2O$—when dried over sulphuric acid ; before drying $15H_2O$
are present.   The salt is precipitated from its aq. soln. by alcohol.   R. F. Weinland
and A. Gutmann obtained it by the action of sodium thiosulphate on sodium
stannite, or of sodium tetrathionate on a soln. of sodium stannite.   Stannous
sulphide is first deposited, and on evaporation sodium stannite separates out, and
finally the salt in question.   The yield is small.   The yellow monoclinic prisms were
found by H. Zirngiebl to have the axial ratios $a : b : c = 0.9030 : 1 : 0.3652$, and
$\beta = 92° 5'$.   O. B. Kuhn said that when the salt is heated, it melts in its water of

crystallization. R. F. Weinland and A. Gutmann prepared **potassium sulphortho-stannate**, $K_4SnS_4.12H_2O$, in a similar manner. They represented the crystals as monoclinic prisms with the axial ratios $a:b:c=0.90304:1:0.36520$, and $\beta=92°\ 5'$. O. B. Kuhn obtained dihydrated **sodium sulphometastannate**, $Na_2SnS_3.2H_2O$, by the action of tin or molten sodium pentasulphide. When the product is extracted with water, tin and stannous sulphide remain undissolved; and the soln. deposits yellow octahedral crystals of the salt. The crystals become matted when exposed to air; and melt at a temp. approaching redness. A. Höring made it by the action of tin on a molten mixture of sodium carbonate and sulphide, sulphur, and carbon; extracting the product with water; and evaporating the soln., when dirty white needles of sodium and stannic sulphides first separate, and finally colourless, octa-hedral crystals of the sulphometastannate. The aq. soln. is pale green, and on evapo-ration furnishes a mixture of sodium and stannic sulphides. A. Ditte made this salt and also **potassium sulphometastannate**, $K_2SnS_3.3H_2O$, by analogous processes. Both these salts were made by J. J. Berzelius. As indicated in connection with stan-nous sulphide, A. Ditte found that the reaction between stannous sulphide and 20 per cent. potassium sulphide can be represented: $2SnS+K_2S=Sn+K_2SnS_3$; and with a very conc. soln. of potassium sulphide, the metallic tin is attacked, forming potassium sulphostannate and hydroxide, and hydrogen: $Sn+3K_2S+4H_2O$ $=K_2SnS_3+4KOH+2H_2$. The evolution of hydrogen also takes place when tin is heated with potassium sulphide. In the presence of air, potassium sulphide is decomposed with the formation of potassium hydroxide, the sulphur uniting with the stannous sulphide, forming stannic sulphide, which is dissolved by the potassium sulphide. Stannous oxide is also formed by the action of potassium hydroxide on the stannous sulphide. In conc. soln., the stannous sulphide is decomposed, with the formation of potassium sulphostannate and tin, whilst the potassium hydroxide formed holds the stannous oxide in soln. as potassium stannate; but the presence of a sufficient quantity of potassium sulphide prevents the forma-tion of stannous oxide. A soln. of stannous sulphide in one of potassium poly-sulphide, or of tin in a boiling conc. soln. of potassium sulphide, furnishes, on evapora-tion, colourless transparent prisms of this salt. If evaporated in vacuo, the soln. becomes supersaturated, and finally congeals to a crystalline mass. The salt is sparingly soluble in water, and a strongly diluted soln. is decomposed with the precipitation of stannic sulphide; this substance is also precipitated by acids. When the yellow soln. is treated with alcohol, a conc. soln. of the sulphostannate is precipitated as a yellow liquid, which, according to O. B. Kuhn, has the composition K_2SnS_3+9 or $10H_2O$.

P. Niggli and K. Faesy,[2] J. T. Singewald, W. Davy, G. M. Schwartz, W. Lindgren, C. Hartwell, A. Knopf, etc., studied the complex mineral sulphides. W. Guertler and K. L. Meissner made a partial study of the ternary system Cu–Sn–S, and found two sulphides of tin, and three intermetallic compounds. In 1787, M. H. Klaproth analyzed a mineral from Cornwall which he stated to be *das erstes und bisher einziges Bespiel eines naturlichen geschwefelten Zinnerzes;* and A. G. Werner named it *Zinnkies;* A. Breithaupt, *Zinnkupferglanz;* R. Kirwan, *tin-pyrites;* R. J. Haüy, *étain sulfuré;* F. S. Beudant, *stannin;* and J. D. Dana, **stannite.** It was at first obtained from Wheal Rock, and Carn Brea, Cornwall, where there is an extended vein. It has since been found in several other localities. The colour of the mineral is steel-grey to iron-black. In some parts it has the appearance of bronze or bell-metal, and is then called *bell-metal ore.* Analyses have been reported by M. H. Klaproth, J. Kudernatsch, C. F. Rammelsberg, L. J. Spencer, H. T. de la Beche, J. W. Mallet, J. B. Adger, I. Domeyko, A. Stelzner, W. P. Headden, etc. J. Kudernatsch represented its composition by the formula $2FeS.SnS_2+2Cu_2S.SnS_2$; C. F. Rammelsberg, by $(RS.Cu_2S).SnS_2$; and L. J. Spencer, $CuFeS_2.CuSnS_2$, **cuprous ferrous stannic sulphide,** in agreement with the crystallographic analogies of the mineral with copper pyrites. G. A. Kenngott and G. Delafosse also favoured a formula showing its analogy with copper pyrites.

S. Reinheimer regarded tin pyrites as a mixture of $m\mathrm{Cu_2FeSn_4}+n\mathrm{Cu_2ZnSnS_4}$. Observations on the crystals were made by R. J. Häuy, W. Haidinger, A. Breithaupt, G. vom Rath, and A. Stelzner. L. J. Spencer showed that the crystals are tetragonal, sphenoidal, but pseudocubic owing to twinning. The axial ratios $a : c = 1 : 0.98270$. The twinning is always interpenetrating. The microscopic structure, and the corrosion figures, were examined by H. Schneiderhöhn, G. M. Schwartz, and S. Reinheimer. The sp. gr. given by A. Breithaupt is 4.371–4.454; M. H. Klaproth gave 4.350; J. W. Mallet, 4.522; J. B. Adger, 4.46; A. Stelzner, 4.495; and L. J. Spencer, 4.45–4.52. The hardness is 3 to 4. A. Sella gave 0.1088 for the sp. ht. A. de Gramont examined the spark spectrum of the mineral. It is decomposed by nitric acid with the separation of sulphur and stannic oxide.

According to T. Ulke, a greenish earthy mass from Dakota is an alteration product of stannite with the composition $4\mathrm{SnO_2.Cu_2Sn.(OH)_2}$, and he called it *cuprocassiterite*. W. P. Headden showed that the composition is very variable. A. Daubrée obtained a substance, with a composition approaching that of stannite, as an incrustation on an old bronze coin found in a sulphate spring in Corsica.

J. J. Berzelius [3] prepared **calcium sulphometastannate** by adding potassium sulphostannate to a soln. of calcium chloride. A. Ditte prepared **calcium sulphorthostannate,** $\mathrm{Ca_2SnS_4.14H_2O}$, by boiling milk of lime with sulphur and tin. As the soln. cools, sulphur and calcium sulphide are deposited, and when the filtrate is evaporated in vacuo, the given salt is obtained; it can be purified by repeated crystallization from water. The lemon-yellow crystals are very soluble in water; and acids precipitate stannic sulphide from the aq. soln. A. Ditte obtained **strontium sulphometastannate,** $\mathrm{SrSnS_3.12H_2O}$, in thick colourless prisms by the action of a soln. of sulphur on one of strontium sulphide, and evaporating the liquor in vacuo. J. J. Berzelius obtained it by adding a soln. of potassium sulphometastannate to one of strontium chloride; he also obtained **barium sulphometastannate** in a similar way; and A. Ditte prepared this salt, $\mathrm{BaSnS_3.8H_2O}$, by a process analogous to that employed for the strontium salt. The lemon-yellow crystals dissolve in cold water without decomposition.

According to L. F. Hawley, **thallous sulphorthostannate,** $\mathrm{Tl_2SnS_4}$, is quantitatively precipitated by adding sodium sulphostannate to a hot, slightly acid soln. of a thallous or thallic salt, and then adding a soln. of sodium sulphide until the liquid is more than neutralized. The mixture is boiled for about 5 mins., diluted with water, and allowed to stand. J. Loczka showed that when thallium sulphide and stannic sulphide are precipitated together, a solid is obtained which is only partially soluble in either dil. acids or alkaline sulphides, and which varies in colour from an orange-yellow when rich in stannic sulphide through a bright red to a very dark red when rich in thallium sulphide. L. F. Hawley examined the precipitates and found that over the range of conc. from thallous sulphide to a point corresponding to thallous sulphorthostannate, $\mathrm{Tl_4SnS_4}$, there were distinguishable two phases, a black and a red, both with a tendency toward crystalline structure and both opaque; at the point thallous sulphorthostannate, $2\mathrm{Tl_2S.SnS_2}$, only one phase was present, the red crystalline opaque phase. From this point to 76 mol. per cent. stannic sulphide two phases were present, the red crystalline opaque phase and an orange-yellow amorphous translucent phase; from 76 mol. per cent. stannic sulphide to pure stannic sulphide the solid is entirely homogeneous and changes gradually in colour from orange-yellow to the light yellow of pure stannic sulphide. These observations show that besides the pure components two other phases are present in the series, a compound thallous sulphorthostannate and a series of solid soln. running from 76 per cent. stannic sulphide to pure stannic sulphide. Another indication of the formation of the compound thallous sulphorthostannate occurs when precipitates containing an excess of stannic sulphide are treated with sodium sulphide soln. Stannic sulphide is dissolved until the residue has the composition thallous sulphorthostannide, and then no more will be dissolved even on increasing the conc. of sodium

sulphate to 4 mols. per litre and boiling. The compound thallous sulphorthostannate is decomposed, however, by a boiling soln. of sodium sulphide when the
conc. of the latter is about 5 mols. per litre.

G. T. Prior [4] described a greyish-black mineral, which, according to R. Köchlin,
came from Santa Rosa, Bolivia. It was called **teallite**—after J. J. H. Teall. The
analysis corresponds with **lead sulphometastannate,** $PbS.SnS_2$, or $PbSnS_3$. The
thin flexible folia belong to the rhombic system having the axial ratios $a : b : c$
$=0.93 : 1 : 1.31$. The (001)-cleavage is perfect. G. T. Prior compared the
analogies between teallite, franckeite, and cylindrite. The hardness is 1 to 2 ; and
the sp. gr. 6·36. It is readily decomposed by hot hydrochloric or nitric acid.
M. Ahlfeld reported a related mineral, *pufahlite*, from Oruro, Bolivia. Its sp. gr. is
5·4; and its composition : Sn, 41·9 ; Sb, 37·4 ; Zn, 6·3 ; and S, 13·5 per cent.

REFERENCES.

[1] J. J. Berzelius, *Schweigger's Journ.*, **6.** 284, 1812 ; *Ann. Chim. Phys.*, (2), **5.** 141, 1817 ;
(2), **20.** 138, 1822 ; (2), **32.** 60, 1826 ; A. Ditte, *ib.*, (8), **12.** 236, 1907 ; *Compt. Rend.*, **94.** 1470,
1882 ; **95.** 641, 1882 ; A. Höring, *Pharm. Ztg.*, **3.** 120, 1851 ; J. Milbauer, *Zeit. anorg. Chem.*, **42.**
440, 1904 ; R. F. Weinland and A. Gutmann, *ib.*, **17.** 418, 1898 ; R. F. Weinland and R. F. Kühn,
ib., **54.** 244, 1907 ; H. Rose, *Pogg. Ann.*, **112.** 163, 1861 ; H. Zirngiebl, *ib.*, **17.** 416, 1898 ;
V. Stanek, *ib.*, **17.** 124, 1898 ; A. Classen and O. Bauer, *Ber.*, **16.** 1061, 1883 ; L. Storch, *ib.*, **16.**
2015, 1883 ; *Monatsh.*, **10.** 255, 1889 ; A. Berg. *Bull. Soc. Chim.*, (4), **1.** 905, 1907 ; A. Kolb,
Zeit. angew. Chem., **16.** 1054, 1903 ; O. B. Kühn, *Liebig's Ann.*, **84.** 110, 1852 ; E. Priwoznik,
ib., **164.** 51, 1872.
[2] M. H. Klaproth, *Schrift. Ges. Natur. Freunde*, **7.** 155, 169, 1787 ; *Beiträge zur chemischen
Kenntniss der Mineralkörper*, Berlin, **2.** 257, 1797 ; **5.** 228, 1810 ; R. Kirwan, *Elements
of Mineralogy*, London, **2.** 300, 1796 ; J. T. Singewald, *Econ. Geol.*, **7.** 263, 1912 ; W. Davy, *ib.*, **15.**
463, 1920 ; W. Lindgren, *ib.*, **19.** 223, 1924 ; G. M. Schwartz, *Amer. Min.*, **8.** 162, 1923 ; C. Hartwell, *Australian Min. Standard*, **10.** 577, 1908 ; A. Knopf, *Bull. U.S. Geol. Sur.*, 358, 1908 ;
H. Schneiderhöhn, *Anleitung zur mikroskopischen Bestimmung und Untersuchung von Erzen und
Aufbreitungsprodukten*, Berlin, 89, 96, 1922 ; W. Haidinger, *Treatise on Mineralogy*, Edinburgh, **3.**
163, 1825 ; R. J. Haüy, *Traité de minéralogie*, Paris, **2.** 170. 1822 ; A. Breithaupt, *Uebersicht des
Mineralsystems*, Freiberg, 75, 1830 ; *Vollständige Charakteristik der Mineralsystems*, Dresden,
125, 1823 ; 275, 1832 ; *Die Paragenesis der Mineralien*, Freiberg, 146, 1849 ; *Mineralogische
Studien*, Leipzig, 103, 1866 ; A. G. Werner, *Berg. Journ.*, 385, 397, 1789 ; C. F. Rammelsberg,
Handbuch der Mineralchemie, Leipzig, **2.** 297, 1841 ; **1.** 160, 1843 ; **2.** 178, 1845 ; **5.** 267, 1853 ;
2. 271, 1886 ; *Pogg. Ann.*, **68.** 518, 1846 ; **88.** 603, 1853 ; J. Kudernatsch, *ib.*, **39.** 146, 1836 ;
I. Domeyko, *Elementos de mineralojia*, Santiago, 224, 1879 ; J. W. Mallet, *Amer. Journ. Science*,
(2), **17.** 33, 1854 ; W. P. Headden, *ib.*, (2), **45.** 106, 1893 ; J. B. Adger, *Chem. News*, **25.** 259, 1872 ;
A. Stelzner, *Zeit. deut. geol. Ges.*, **49.** 97, 131, 1897 ; H. T. de la Beche, *Report on the Geology of
Cornwall, Devon, and West Somerset*, London, 1839 ; L. J. Spencer, *Min. Mag.*, **13.** 61, 1901 ;
W. Guertler and K. L. Meissner, *Metall Erz*, **18.** 466, 1921 ; J. L. C. Schröder van der Kalk,
Centr. Min., 79, 1901 ; S. Reinheimer, *Neues Jahrb. Min. B.B.*, **49.** 179, 1923 ; T. Ulke, *Trans.
Amer. Inst. Min. Eng.*, **21.** 240, 1892 ; F. S. Beudant, *Traité élémentaire de minéralogie*, Paris, **2.**
416, 1832 ; J. D. Dana, *A System of Mineralogy*, New York, 68, 1868 ; C. A. Kenngott, *Mineralogische Untersuchungen*, Breslau, **1.** 41, 1849 ; G. Delafosse, *Nouveau cours de minéralogie*,
Paris, **2.** 416, 1860 ; G. vom Rath, *Verh. Ver. Rheinl.*, 296, 1884 ; A. Daubrée, *Compt. Rend.*,
92. 57, 1881 ; A. Sella, *Zeit. Kryst.*, **22.** 180, 1894 ; *Nachr. Gött.*, 311, 1891 ; P. Niggli and K. Faesy,
ib., **60.** 477, 1924 ; A. de Gramont, *Bull. Soc. Min.*, **18.** 275, 1895 ; G. M. Schwartz, *Amer. Min.*,
8. 162, 1923 ; S. Reinheimer, *Neues Jahrb. Min. B.B.*, **49.** 159, 1924.
[3] J. J. Berzelius, *Schweigger's Journ.*, **6.** 284, 1812 ; *Ann. Chim. Phys.*, (2), **5.** 141, 1817 ;
(2), **20.** 138, 1822 ; (2), **32.** 60, 1826 ; A. Ditte, *Compt. Rend.*, **95.** 641, 1882 ; L. F. Hawley,
Journ. Amer. Chem. Soc., **29.** 1011, 1907 ; *Journ. Phys. Chem.*, **10.** 654, 1906 ; J. Loczka, *Magyar
Chem. Foly.*, **3.** 1, 1899.
[4] G. T. Prior, *Min. Mag.*, **14.** 21, 1904 ; R. Köchlin, *Tschermak's Mitt.*, (2), **24.** 114, 1905 ;
M. Ahlfeld, *Metall Erz*, **22.** 135, 1925.

§ 25. The Tin Sulphates

The action of sulphuric acid on tin has been previously discussed, one product
of the action of this acid or of pyrosulphuric acid on the metal is **stannous sulphate,**
$SnSO_4$. J. J. Berzelius [1] obtained the anhydrous sulphate by heating a mixture of
stannous sulphide and mercuric oxide : **or a mixture of** stannous chloride and

sulphuric acid.   J. P. Bouquet obtained it as a white pulverulent precipitate by adding sulphuric acid or ammonium sulphate to a conc. soln. of stannous chloride. Freshly precipitated stannous hydroxide readily dissolves in dil. sulphuric acid, and when the soln. is filtered and evaporated over sulphuric acid, J. P. Bouquet, A. Longi, J. C. G. de Marignac, and A. Ditte found that the crystalline sulphate is formed.   J. C. G. de Marignac could not prepare the crystals by cooling a boiling sat. soln. as recommended by J. P. Bouquet.   According to R. G. Durrant, when stannous chloride is heated with sulphuric acid at temp. between $20°$ and $90°$, stannous sulphate is formed, and hydrogen chloride liberated: $SnCl_2+H_2SO_4 =SnSO_4+2HCl$; if the temp. rises between $130°$ and $200°$, stannic sulphate is formed and sulphur dioxide is evolved: $SnSO_4+2H_2SO_4=Sn(SO_4)_2+2H_2O+SO_2$. If the sulphuric acid is dil., some hydrogen sulphide is evolved before the sulphur dioxide appears; the hydrogen sulphide is formed by the reduction of the sulphur dioxide, which, along with hydrogen chloride, is dissolved in the liquid. J. P. Bouquet was unable to measure the crystallographic constants of the crystals obtained by evaporating the aq. soln. in vacuo.   A. B. Berthollet said that the crystals are acicular.   According to J. J. Berzelius, the salt could be heated to dark redness without decomposition, but at a higher temp. it forms stannic oxide. J. L. Gay Lussac, and J. P. Bouquet obtained similar results.   J. A. Arfvedson said that when heated in hydrogen, some sulphur and stannous sulphide are formed. J. C. G. de Marignac found that 100 parts of water at $19°$ dissolve $18·8$ parts of salt; and 100 parts of a boiling soln., $18·2$ parts.   The difference is too small to enable crystals to be prepared by cooling a hot sat. soln.   A. Longi said that a clear soln. is produced with a small proportion of water, and a turbid soln., with a large proportion.   The aq. soln. was found by J. P. Bouquet, and A. Ditte to be soon hydrolyzed with the deposition of a basic salt.   The turbid soln. clears when sulphuric acid is added.   According to E. Divers and T. Haga, stannous sulphate in the presence of sulphuric acid does not reduce nitric acid to ammonia or to hydroxylamine.   Vide the action of sulphuric acid on stannous chloride: $SnSO_4+2H_2SO_4=Sn(SO_4)_2+2H_2O+SO_2$.   R. G. Durrant said that when stannic sulphate is heated alone, sulphur dioxide is given off between $360°$ and dull redness: $SnSO_4=SnO_2+SO_2$.

A. B. Berthollet said that a basic salt is precipitated when a soln. of the normal salt is treated with alkali.   As just indicated, an aq. soln. of the normal sulphate slowly deposits a basic sulphate in the cold, and rapidly when heated; according to A. Ditte, its composition corresponds with **stannous dioxysulphate,** $3SnO.SO_3.\frac{3}{2}H_2O$, $SnSO_4.2SnO.3H_2O$, or $2Sn_3O_2.SO_4.3H_2O$.   He also made this compound by the action of hot dil. sulphuric acid on stannous oxide; some stannous sulphate simultaneously passes into soln.—the amount depends on the conc. of the acid.   Cold water does not alter this basic salt, but when heated with water, a pale red crystalline powder of the anhydrous salt is formed.   It is easily soluble in hot water.   C. M. Carson found that by gradually adding sodium hydroxide to a soln. of stannous sulphate at $100°$, the composition of the precipitates in two regions remained fairly constant.   The one corresponds with s annous **oxysulphate,** $SnSO_4.SnO$; and the other with A. Ditte's stannous dioxysulphate, $SnSO_4.2SnO.nH_2O$.

J. P. Bouquet prepared **ammonium sulphostannite,** by the union of the component sulphates in aq. soln., and A. Longi, by the action of ammonia on stannous sulphate; the composition of the product was not constant.   J. P. Bouquet prepared **potassium sulphostannite** by the union of the component sulphates, and J. C. G. de Marignac found the analyses of two preparations obtained by evaporating mixed soln. of potassium and stannous sulphates to be $K_2Sn_2(SO_4)_3$, and $K_2Sn(SO_4)_2$.   A warm conc. soln. of potassium sulphate and stannous chloride gave J. C. G. de Marignac, and C. F. Rammelsberg hexagonal prisms of **potassium chlorosulphatostannite,** $4K_2Sn(SO_4)_2.SnCl_2$, with axial ratios $a : c=1 : 0·7485$.

H. Rose found that when stannic oxide is digested with hot conc. sulphuric acid, the syrupy liquid deposits stannic hydroxide when diluted with water; a similar product was obtained when a soln. of stannic oxide in fused potassium hydrosulphate was diluted with water. J. J. Berzelius made a soln. of **stannic sulphate** by dissolving stannic hydroxide in dil. sulphuric acid; and J. von Kraskowitz, by heating tin with an excess of conc. or fuming sulphuric acid. According to A. Ditte, stannic hydroxide produced by the action of alkalies on a soln. of stannic chloride, dissolves readily in warm dil. sulphuric acid (1 : 8), forming a limpid soln., which when conc. until it contains not more than 3 or 4 vols. of water to 1 vol. of sulphuric acid, deposits at first colourless, radiating needles, then rhombohedral lamellæ, and eventually hexagonal prisms with two parallel faces largely developed; and corresponded with **dihydrated stannic sulphate**, $SnO_2.2H_2SO_4$, or $Sn(SO_4)_2.2H_2O$. The same compound is obtained by the action of sulphuric acid of suitable conc. on the hard, vitreous hydroxide, $Sn(OH)_4$, obtained by dissolving gelatinous stannic hydroxide in ammonia, and evaporating the liquid; on metastannic acid obtained by treating the metal by nitric acid; and on strongly heated anhydrous stannic oxide. In the last case, the rate of soln. is very slow. The form of the crystals varies with the relative proportions of acid and water in the liquid, as just indicated. The crystals are decomposed by water, but the stannic oxide is kept in soln. by the sulphuric acid which is liberated, and a precipitate is only obtained when water is added in such quantity that the liquid does not contain more than about 43 grms. of sulphuric acid per litre. The crystals are very deliquescent, and form a colourless, transparent liquid when exposed to the air; this soln. does not crystallize on evaporation, but forms a hard, vitreous mass. If, however, some sulphuric acid is added to the liquid, crystals of the dihydrate are readily obtained. They dissolve readily in dil. sulphuric acid, especially on heating, are not affected by ether, but are decomposed by alcohol with removal of sulphuric acid. If the sulphuric acid is not in large excess but has dissolved a considerable proportion of stannic oxide, it forms a transparent jelly on cooling, which is sometimes opalescent. This liquefies when heated, but gelatinizes again when cooled. The jelly is strongly acid, and does not become crystalline even after several weeks. If, however, it is mixed with an excess of ether, it yields a precipitate of slender, white needles of **stannic dihydroxy-sulphate**, $SnO_2.H_2SO_4$, or $Sn(OH)_2SO_4$. This compound dissolves in cold water, and the soln. is at first limpid, but soon becomes turbid, owing to the separation of gelatinous stannic hydroxide.

J. G. F. Druce made the potassium salt from a soln. of potassium chlorostannate and sulphuric acid. R. F. Weinland and H. Kühl reported **potassium sulphato-stannate**, $K_2Sn(SO_4)_3$, to be formed in needle-like crystals by evaporating a soln. of a mol of α-stannic acid and 1 to 1·5 mols of potassium sulphate in conc. sulphuric acid; they prepared in a similar manner six-sided leaflets of **rubidium sulphatostannate**, $Rb_2Sn(SO_4)_3$; slender needles of **silver sulphatostannate**, $Ag_2Sn(SO_4)_3.3H_2O$; colourless cubes of **calcium sulphatostannate**, $CaSn(SO_4)_3.3H_2O$; J. G. F. Druce also made this salt by the method he used for the potassium salt. R. F. Weinland and H. Kühl made **strontium sulphatostannate**, $SrSn(SO_4)_3.3H_2O$; **barium sulphatostannate**, $BaSn(SO_4)_3.3H_2O$; **lead sulphatostannate**, $PbSn(SO_4)_3.3H_2O$; **cerium hydrosulphatostannate**, $CeHSn(SO_4)_4$, as a colourless, microcrystalline powder; **lanthanum hydrosulphatostannate**, $LaHSn(SO_4)_4$, in small six-sided plates; **yttrium sulphatostannate**, $Y_2Sn(SO_4)_6$, as a microcrystalline powder; **thorium sulphatostannate**, $ThSn(SO_4)_4.2H_2O$, in slender needles; and **bismuth hydroxysulphatostannate**, $Bi(OH)Sn(SO_4)_3$, in rhombic leaflets. J. G. F. Druce made aniline, m-phenylenediamine, and quinoline sulphatostannates.

REFERENCES.

[1] J. J. Berzelius, *Schweigger's Journ.*, **6**. 284, 1812; *Ann. Chim. Phys.*, (?), **5**. 141, 1817; J. L. Gay Lussac, *Journ. Mines*, **22**. 325, 1807; *Nicholson's Journ.*, **33**. 44, 1812; *Ann. Chim. Phys.*, (2), **1**. 40, 1816; A. Ditte, *ib.*, (5), **27**. 159, 1882; *Compt. Rend.*, **104**. 172, 1887; J. P. Bou-

quet. *Journ. Pharm. Chim.*, (3), **11**. 459, 1847 ; C. F. Rammelsberg, *Handbuch der krystallographischen Chemie*, Leipzig, **1**. 468, 1881 ; A. B. Berthollet, *Mém. d'Arcueil*, **1**. 161, 1807 ; J. C. G. de Marignac, *Ann. Mines*, (5), **22**. 1, 1857 ; R. G. Durrant, *Journ. Chem. Soc.*, **107**. 622, 1915 ; J. A. Arfvedson, *Pogg. Ann.*, **1**. 74, 1824 ; J. von Kraskowitz, *ib.*, **35**. 518, 1835 ; H. Rose, *ib.*, **112**. 163, 1861 ; A. Longi, *L'Orosi*, 253, 1885 ; *Arch. Pharm.*, **223**. 811, 1885 ; E. Divers and T. Haga, *Journ. Chem. Soc.*, **47**. 623, 1885 ; R. F. Weinland and H. Kühl, *Zeit. anorg. Chem.*, **54**. 244, 1907 ; *Ber.*, **39**. 2951, 1906 ; J. G. F. Druce, *Chem. News*, **128**. 33, 1924 ; C. M. Carson, *Journ. Amer. Chem. Soc.*, **48**. 906, 1926.

§ 26. Tin Carbonates

According to K. Seubert and M. Elten,[1] when a soln. of sodium carbonate is poured into one of stannous chloride, carbon dioxide is evolved, and stannous hydroxide precipitated—*vide* analytical reactions of tin. H. St. C. Deville, left a conc. soln. of sodium hydrocarbonate and crystals of stannous chloride in a corked flask for some days, and obtained a crystalline powder of **stannous oxycarbonate,** Sn_2OCO_3, or $SnO.SnCO_3$, which decomposed rapidly, becoming black under a soln. of sodium hydrocarbonate, and yellow in air. G. C. Wittstein found that a boiling soln. of ammonium carbonate dissolves stannous hydroxide ; and H. St. C. Deville left a conc. soln. of ammonium hydrocarbonate and crystals of stannous chloride in a corked flask, and in 24 hrs. obtained white, hexagonal prisms of **ammonium carbonatostannite,** $(NH_4)_2Sn_2(CO_3)_3.3H_2O$. The salt is decomposed by water, forming black stannous oxide ; and when rapidly heated, it furnishes olive-green stannous oxide. White needles of **potassium carbonatostannite,** $K_2Sn_2(CO_3)_3.2H_2O$, were prepared in a similar manner. T. Leykauf reported a *sodium carbonatostannite* to be formed by adding an excess of sodium carbonate to a soln. of stannous chloride because the washed precipitate effervesced with acids. The phenomenon may have been due to the adsorbed alkali carbonate.

REFERENCES.

[1] H. St. C. Deville, *Ann. Chim. Phys.*, (2), **35**. 456, 1852 ; G. C. Wittstein, *Repert Pharm.*, **63**. 334, 1838 ; K. Seubert and M. Elten, *Zeit. anorg. Chem.*, **4**. 69, 1893 ; T. Leykauf, *Journ. prakt. Chem.*, (1), **21**. 317, 1840.

§ 27. Tin Nitrates

J. L. Proust[1] found that at ordinary temp. dil. nitric acid dissolves tin, and the reaction is attended not with the evolution of nitrous gases, but with the formation of ammonia, and of a soln. of **stannous nitrate.** The action of nitric acid on tin has been previously discussed. J. J. Berzelius added that the salt obtained by the action of dil. nitric acid on stannous hydroxide is free from ammonium nitrate. N. W. Fischer added lead nitrate to a soln. of stannous chloride and filtered off the lead chloride. R. Weber obtained stannous nitrate, $Sn(NO_3)_2.20H_2O$, by adding freshly prepared stannous hydroxide to nitric acid of sp. gr. 1·20, so long as the liquid remains clear ; when the soln. is cooled to −20°, the salt is deposited in thin, transparent, colourless leaflets, resembling potassium chlorate. The crystals melt very quickly after their removal from the cold liquid. J. J. Berzelius, J. L. Proust, and R. Weber found that the soln. of stannous nitrate soon decomposes and deposits hydrated stannous oxide ; and if heated with fresh acid it deposits all the tin as β-stannic acid. A. Ditte said that when the soln. is evaporated, there is a sudden evolution of nitrous gases, and the deposition of basic stannic nitrate.

According to R. Weber, **stannous oxynitrate,** $Sn_2O(NO_3)_2$, or $SnO.Sn(NO_3)_2$, is formed (i) when a soln. of stannous hydroxide in nitric acid of sp. gr. 1·20 is mixed with excess of the oxide at 30°–35°, the basic salt is deposited as a greyish-white coherent crystalline mass, which is dried in the air and recrystallized from water ;

prepared in this way, however, it is generally mixed with oxide. (ii) It can be obtained pure by adding sodium carbonate, with constant shaking, to the freshly-made nitric acid soln. of stannous oxide ; the precipitate of the basic salt thus obtained forms snow-white granular aggregations of rectangular prisms. (iii) When nitric acid, sp. gr. 1·20, is spread over sheets of tin-foil or of an alloy of tin and lead by means of a spray producer, the metallic surface becomes coated with this basic salt, which, when dry, burns with scintillation, or explodes when struck. (iv) It is also formed when tin acts on metallic nitrates, e.g., tin-foil and copper nitrate react ; the tin speedily becomes covered with a mixture of precipitated copper and the basic salt ; the final product, when dry, burns with scintillation, or, when suddenly heated or struck, explodes. The basic nitrate is partially decomposed by water, and gradually oxidizes and changes in the air. It can be heated to $100°$; at a higher temp. it is decomposed with explosion, the product being nitrous fumes and finely-divided stannic oxide. It also detonates strongly either by concussion or friction. R. Weber attributed some explosions which have occurred during the mixing and pressing of the damp constituents of gunpowder to the formation of this nitrate by the action of the nitre and sulphur of the gunpowder on the solder of the rollers. He reproduced the conditions by placing a piece of tin-foil in a dish with a damp mixture of nitre and sulphur, which was covered by a piece of copper, so that only a thin film of the mixture was between the two metals ; in a short time a considerable quantity of the basic tin nitrate had formed. The use of tin in rollers for gunpowder mills at Spandau was therefore abandoned.

According to J. J. Berzelius, stannic hydroxide dissolves copiously in nitric acid, and neutralizes it completely, forming a soln. which, if conc., deposits silky needles of **stannic nitrate.** At $50°$, nearly all the stannic oxide is deposited in the hydrated β-form ; at ordinary temp., the soln. deposits stannic hydroxide which redissolves in the presence of ammonium nitrate. Possibly *ammonium nitratostannate* is formed, which is more stable than stannic nitrate. J. B. A. Dumas said that the first action of cold conc. nitric acid on tin is the production of a basic nitrate. A. Ditte obtained **stannic trioxydinitrate,** $Sn_2S_3(NO_3)_2.6H_2O$, by the evaporation of an aq. soln. of stannous nitrate—*vide supra*. V. Thomas poured a chloroform soln. of nitrogen peroxide into a dil. chloroform soln. of stannic iodide, and obtained a violet precipitate, which, when washed with chloroform, became white. The composition $Sn_5N_2O_{17}.4H_2O$ is represented as β-**stannic dinitrate,** $Sn_5(NO_3)_2O_{11}.4H_2O$, analogous with $Sn_5K_2O_{11}.4H_2O$—*vide* β-stannic chlorides.

REFERENCES.

[1] J. L. Proust, *Journ. Phys.*, **51.** 173, 1802 ; **61.** 338, 1803 ; N. W. Fischer, *Schweigger's Journ.*, **56.** 360, 1829 ; J. J. Berzelius, *ib.*, **6.** 284, 1812 ; *Ann. Chim. Phys.*, (2), **5.** 141, 1817 ; A. Ditte, *ib.*, (5), **27.** 159, 1882 ; J. B. A. Dumas, *ib.*, (3), **55.** 154, 1859 ; *Compt. Rend.*, **45.** 409, 1857 ; V. Thomas, *ib.*, **122.** 32, 1896 ; *Bull. Soc. Chim.*, (3), **15.** 312, 1896 ; R. Weber, *Journ. prakt. Chem.*, (2), **26.** 123, 1882.

§ 28. The Tin Phosphates

E. Lenssen [1] found that when a neutral soln. of stannous chloride is added to a conc. soln. of sodium hydrophosphate, acidified with acetic acid, a white, voluminous precipitate is produced which soon becomes crystalline. It appears to be a **stannous tetraphosphate,** $5SnO.2P_2O_5.4H_2O$, or **stannous dihydrotetraphosphate,** $Sn_5H_2(PO_4)_4.3H_2O$. If the soln. of sodium hydrophosphate be added to the stannous chloride soln., the precipitate contains a chloride. The stannous hydrophosphate is insoluble in water ; it is not changed at $100°$; and when ignited, it forms stannic oxide and metallic tin. K. Jablczynsky and W. Wieckowsky prepared **stannous orthophosphate,** $Sn_3(PO_4)_2$, by pouring a ten per cent. soln. of sodium hydrophosphate into a sat. soln. of stannous sulphate (1 : 10), acidified with sulphuric acid, with constant stirring. The precipitate was washed with hot water; boiled with water; washed with alcohol, and ether; and dried over phosphorous pentoxide. If stannous chloride be used, the precipitate always contains a chloride. If the stannous sulphate soln. be poured into the hydrophosphate soln., a yellow basic salt is formed owing to hydrolysis. Stannous orthophosphate is a white amorphous solid with a sp. gr. 3·823 at 17·4°/4°. It is stable in air; insoluble in water, but soluble in dil. mineral acids and alkali-lyes. By dissolving 5 grms. of tin in 22 c.c. of warm phosphoric acid of sp. gr. 1·23, and adding water from time to time so that the soln. is not too viscid, and slowly cooling the resulting liquid, there are deposited six-sided plates of **stannous hydrophosphate,** $SnHPO_4$, of sp. gr. 3·476 at 15·5°/4°. If 13 grms. of tin be dissolved in 35 c.c. of warm phosphoric acid, and 15 c.c. of hot water be added to the hot soln., the hydrophosphate is precipitated in narrow, pointed crystals. If 10 grms. of the hydrophosphate be dissolved in 10 grms. of phosphoric acid of sp. gr. 1·7, heated to 140°, and the liquid cooled slowly in a desiccator with phosphorous pentoxide. rhombic crystals of **stannous dihydrophosphate,** $Sn(H_2PO_4)_2$, are formed. Their sp. gr. is 3·167 at 22·8°/4°. By heating the hydrophosphate to 350°–400°, in an atm. of carbon dioxide, **stannous pyrophosphate,** $Sn_2P_2O_7$, is formed as an amorphous powder, of sp. gr. 4·009 at 16·4°/4°. If the dihydrophosphate be similarly heated, **stannous metaphosphate,** $Sn(PO_3)_2$, is formed as an amorphous, glassy mass of sp. gr. 3·380 at 22·8°/4°. These phosphates resemble those of lead except that lead orthophosphate is not altered by dil. phosphoric acid, while stannous orthophosphate forms the hydrophosphate; that lead hydrophosphate in boiling water easily forms the orthophosphate but not so with the tin salt; and that lead dihydrophosphate is fairly stable in air, but not so with the tin salt. The stannous salts are more readily hydrolyzed than the lead salts.

According to E. Haeffely, when stannic oxide is treated with phosphoric acid, **stannic oxydiphosphate,** $Sn_2O(PO_4)_2.10H_2O$, or $2SnO_2.P_2O_5.10H_2O$, is formed; P. Hautefeuille and J. Margottet found that orthophosphoric acid, at a temp. below that at which water is given off, dissolves stannic hydroxide, and on cooling furnishes octahedral crystals of the anhydrous salt $Sn_2O(PO_4)_2$; and H. Kopp melted stannic oxide with microcosmic salt, and obtained two kinds of crystals, *viz.*, pyramidal crystals of the oxydiphosphate, and cubic crystals of **stannic pyrophosphate,** SnP_2O_7. L. Ouvrard obtained the pyrophosphate but not the oxydiphosphate by fusing stannic oxide with sodium metaphosphate. G. Bornemann obtained a precipitate of variable composition: 22·21–29·53 per cent. P_2O_5 and 70·47–77·8 per cent. SnO_2, by adding an excess of sodium phosphate to a soln. of a sodium stannate; and W. T. Casselmann obtained a gelatinous mass of stannic phosphate by the decomposition of $2SnCl_4.PCl_5$ with an excess of water. The very sparing solubility of stannic phosphate in dil. nitric acid was utilized by A. Reynoso, W. Reissig, and A. Girard for the determination of phosphoric acid in nitric acid soln. free from chlorine. U. Antony and G. H. Mondolfo examined the insoluble compound obtained by adding a phosphate to a metastannic acid. P. Heermann, and H. Silbermann used stannic phosphate as a filling for silk.

L. Ouvrard fused stannic oxide with a large excess of potassium metaphosphate, and obtained **potassium triphosphatostannate,** $K_2O.4SnO_2.3P_2O_5$, or $KSn(PO_4)_3$, isomorphous with the corresponding titanium salt; no cassiterite was formed. If potassium pyro- or ortho-phosphate be employed, **potassium oxyphosphatostannate,** $K_2O.2SnO_2.P_2O_5$, or $KSnOPO_4$, analogous with the corresponding titanium compound, is formed. According to G. Wunder, when a mixture of stannic oxide. microcosmic salt, and borax or sodium pyroborate is fused in a crucible; the clear molten liquid poured into another crucible and slowly cooled; the product washed with dil. hydrochloric acid; and the residue separated by elutriation, the tetragonal prisms, resembling anatase, which are obtained have the composition $Na_2Sn(PO_4)_2$, or **sodium diphosphatostannate;** and the rhombohedral crystals, almost cubic, have the composition $NaSn_2(PO_4)_2$, or $Na(SnPO_4)_2$, **sodium diphosphatodistannate.**

These salts were also obtained by H. Knop in an analogous manner. L. Ouvrard prepared sodium diphosphatostannate, and **sodium triphosphatostannate**, $Na_2O.4SnO_2.3P_2O_5$, or $NaSn(PO_4)_3$. W. Prandtl and O. Rosenthal mixed sodium phosphate and stannate in alkaline soln., or dissolved stannic phosphate in sodium hydroxide and obtained complex salts or mixed crystals with the composition $Na_2SnO_3.4Na_3PO_4.48H_2O$; $Na_2SnO_3.5Na_3PO_4.60H_2O$; $Na_2SnO_3.6Na_3PO_4.72H_2O$; and $Na_2SnO_3.4Na_3(P,V)O_4.48H_2O$. H. Zocher showed that the alleged complex phosphatostannates are not chemical individuals because they form a continuous series whose composition depends on the stannate conc. of the mother liquid. G. Saring also reported **potassium calcium phosphatostannate**, $Ca_3(PO_4)_2(CaO)_2(K_2O)_2SnO_2$, analogous with the corresponding phosphato-silicate, titanate, zirconate, cerate, thorate, and plumbate.

REFERENCES.

[1] E. Lenssen, *Liebig's Ann.*, **114**. 113, 1860 ; H. Kopp, *ib.*, **159**. 39, 1871 ; W. Reissig, *ib.*, **98**. 339, 1856 ; W. T. Casselmann, *ib.*, **83**. 257, 1852 ; H. Silbermann, *Färber Ztg.*, **8**. 34, 51, 68, 1897 ; P. Heermann, *ib.*, **16**. 353, 1905 ; *Zeit. angew. Chem.*, **20**. 416, 485, 1907 ; G. Bornemann. *ib.*, **12**. 635, 1899 ; A. Reynoso, *Journ. prakt. Chem.*, (1), **54**. 261, 1851 ; G. Wunder, *ib.*, (2), **2**. 206, 1870 ; (2), **4**. 339, 1871 ; A. Girard, *Chem. News*, **5**. 281, 1862 ; **6**. 99, 1862 ; *Bull. Soc. Chim.*, (1), **4**. 20, 1862 ; *Compt. Rend.*, **54**. 468, 1862 ; P. Hautefeuille and J. Margottet, *ib.*, **102**. 1017, 1886 ; L. Ouvrard, *ib.*, **111**. 177, 1890 ; E Haeffely, *Phil. Mag.*, (4), **10**. 290, 1855 ; U. Antony and G. H. Mondolfo, *Gazz. Chim. Ital.*, **28**. ii, 142, 1898 ; W. Prandtl and O. Rosenthal, *Ber.*, **40**. 2125, 1907 ; W. Prandtl, *Verbindungen höherer Ordnung zwischen den Oxyden RO₂ und R₂O₃ Ein Beitrag zur Systematik anorganischer Verbindungen*, München, 1906 ; G. Saring, *Versuche über von Aufschluss von Phosphaten durch Kieselsäure bei hohen Temperaturen*, Dresden. 1906 ; H. Zocher, *Zeit. anorg. Chem.*, **112**. 1, 1920 ; E. Jablczynsky and W. Wieckowsky, *ib.*, **152**. 207, 1926.

CHAPTER XLVII

LEAD

§ 1. The History of Lead

THE metal lead is one of the seven metals known to man from the earliest times. The Egyptians must have been familiar with the metal at the time of Rameses III. (1200 B.C.), since lead plates and small statues, chiefly of Osiris and Anubis, have been found in the tombs of that period. M. Berthelot[1] showed that lead was used by the Egyptians in making jewellery, mirrors, etc. ; and R. Lepsius reported that lead is mentioned in Egyptian hieroglyphics, 1515–1461 B.C. The British Museum has a lead figure found in the temple of Osiris at Abydos, and which probably dates from 3000 B.C. Old Egyptian pottery has also been found covered with plumbiferous glazes (**6**. 40, 36). According to Numbers (**31.** 32), lead was included in the spoil taken from the Midianites by the Israelites. The *opheret* of the Hebrews, Phœnicians, and Egyptians was rendered μόλυβδος, *molybdos*, in the earliest Greek translations of the Old Testament, and as *lead* in the English version ; while *bedil* was generally translated κασσίτερος, and later tin (*q.v.*). F. Hoefer's suggestion that the term *opheret* should be rendered *copper* is not generally accepted. According to Ezekiel (**27.** 12), the Carthaginians traded in silver, iron, tin, and lead. The Israelites do not appear to have made a clear distinction between lead and tin, and their *bedil* is sometimes translated *tin*, and sometimes *lead*. Lead is mentioned by Homer. As indicated in connection with tin, Pliny, in his *Historia naturalis* of the first century, distinguished the two metals by calling tin *plumbum candidum*, and lead *plumbum nigrum*. The use of lead among the ancients was discussed by Theophrastus, in his Περὶ Λίθων (**2.** 8, 56) in the third century B.C. ; by Pliny, *Historia naturalis* (**34.** 173), Dioscorides, *De materia medica* (**5.** 100), and Vitruvius, *De architectura* (**7.** 12), all in the first century of our era ; Strabo, *Geographica* (**3.** 148), in the first century B.C. ; and Gahlen, *De simplicium medicamentorum temperamentis* (**9.** 22 ; **12.** 230), in the second century ; and by the later writers : K. B. Hofmann, H. Blümmer, A. Gobantz, C. G. Fiedler, H. Faure, E. O. von Lippmann, A. Rössing, B. Neumann, A. F. von Pauly and G. Wissowa, J. A. Overbeck, A. Baumeister, H. Droysen, G. Bapst, H. Faure, L. Guillaume, and F. X. M. Zippe. Lead was used for sling-bolts, tipping arrows, coffins, tablets, toys, vases, tokens, weights, net-sinkers, plummets, seals, water-pipes, backing glass mirrors, and Pliny (**33.** 19) referred to the use of lead discs for drawing lines on parchment. Several of the literary men—Catullus, Herodotus, Thucydides, and Cicero—made allusions to lead. Cicero, for instance, humorously emphasized the feeble character of a man by saying that he could be slain with a *plumbo gladio*, or leaden sword ; and stupid people were called *plumbei*.

Lead was mined in considerable quantities by the Greeks and Romans. Polybius, in his *Historia*, in the second century B.C., said that the mines at Carthagena employed 40,000 men ; Xenophon, in his treatise on the revenues of Athens—Πόροι ἤ περὶ προσόδων—written in the fourth century B.C., stated that the mines at Laurium were worked in ancient times, and he advocated the better management of the mines **as a means** of improving the revenue. For three hundred years these mines were a source of revenue to Athens. The mines at Linares were worked in turn by the Phœnicians, Carthaginians, and Romans. Some old shafts in the neighbourhood are still known as *Los Pozos de Anibal*—Hannibal's Wells. According to Pliny, *Historia naturalis* (**34**. 138, 164), and Strabo, *Geographica* (**3**. 148), the Romans obtained large amounts of lead from South-Eastern Spain. These mines were opened in the twelfth century B.C. The mines in Crete were described by A. Mosso. The early Spanish mines were described by K. B. Hofmann, H. Blümmer, etc., and they form the main lead district in Spain to-day. The Phœnicians bartered earthenware, salt, and copper with Britain in exchange for lead, tin, and hides—*vide* history of tin. Cicero, in his *Epistolæ ad Atticum*, said that there was no silver in Britain ; but he must have been misinformed, because Strabo, Pliny, and others mention it. This shows that cupellation must have been in operation, because the only source of the silver was the lead ore. According to Pliny, the Romans also carried on mining operations in various parts of Britain (Somersetshire, Shropshire, Yorkshire, Derbyshire, Durham, Cumberland, Northumberland, and Scotland), and the British mines have been described by G. Chalmers, H. Blümmer, R. I. Murchison, J. Childrey, J. C. Bruce, and K. B. Hofmann. The lead industry in Scotland dates from a very early period. According to G. V. Wilson and J. S. Flett, there is no evidence that the Romans worked lead in Scotland, although J. R. S. Hunter reported the finding of bronze and stone implements in some old surface workings at Leadhills and Wanlockhead, and D. Wilson, the finding of some pigs of Roman lead. According to T. Pennant, the mines of Islay were worked by the Norwegian invaders when they occupied the country. G. V. Irving, R. W. C. Patrick, J. Leslie, and S. Atkinson have referred to the mining of lead during the Middle Ages in Scotland. J. A. Phillips has suggested that the great wall of Hadrian (A.D. 117–138) was built partly with a view of enclosing and protecting the lead mines of Northumberland and Cumberland. There are ingots in existence to-day with the inscription : *Britannicus ad Verum.* A. Way has given a list of known ingots, and they range from the time of Claudius (A.D. 44–48) to the reign of Hadrian (A.D. 117–138). Many examples are in the British Museum. Lead mining in England may have been restricted, but there is nothing to show that it stopped after the Roman withdrawal. Lead coffins of Saxon age are known. There is a reference in the Doomsday Book of the eleventh century to a lead mine at Crice, and there are records of grants to miners dating from the thirteenth century. The furnaces, etc., were described by J. Glanvil, G. Plattes, T. Houghton, R. Watson, J. Martyn, J. Farey, W. Wallace, and P. A. Dufrénoy. The mining in the Mendip Hills probably dates from pre-Roman times, and has been described by R. Hunt, J. McMurtrie, and T. Morgan. The Roman mines in Gaul, along the Rhine from Bâle to Cologne, have been described by A. Daubrée, and H. Blümmer. Blocks of lead have been found with inscriptions : Nero, Hadrian, and Septimus Severus. The Roman mines in Germany have been described by H. Blümner, A. Frantz, T. Haupt, A. Daubrée, and K. B. Hofmann. The mines of Saxony, Silesia, and the Harz Mountains, as well as the Austrian mines, were discovered about A.D. 1000. The history of the German mines has been discussed by G. Agricola, P. Bech, P. Albinus, H. Ermisch, C. Blömeke, etc. Lead was smelted in the United States at the beginning of the seventeenth century, and this subject has been discussed by H. R. Schoolcraft, C. L. Henning, H. Garlichs, W. H. Pulsifer, etc. According to W. Gowland, although galena is common in Japan, the early Japanese rarely used the metal, copper being usually employed where Europeans use lead. In the ninth and tenth centuries, lead or pewter coins were employed. According to W. H. Adolph, in China, lead was used as a substitute for tin from very early times. The Chinese and Japanese bronzes were discussed by H. Morin, P. Christofle and H. Bouilhet, and S. Kalischer.

The alchemists of the Middle Ages represented lead by ♄ the symbol for

Saturn. It has been suggested that this symbolizes the scythe of Saturn—Father Time—but, according to J. Beckmann,[2] the imaginary scythe has been really formed from the first two letters of his name κρόνος, which transcribers, for the sake of dispatch, made more convenient for use, but at the same time less perceptible. In the Latin work, *Summa prefectionis magisterii*, of Geber, probably of the twelfth century, lead is thus described :

Lead is a metal which is livid, dull, and white ; it is heavy ; not sonorous ; extensible under the hammer ; and easily fused. When exposed to the vapour of vinegar, it forms white lead, and when roasted, red lead. Although lead scarcely resembles silver, it can be easily converted into silver *per nostrum artificium*. It does not maintain its weight during calcination, but acquires a new weight by this operation. Lead is employed in cupellation.

REFERENCES.

[1] F. Hoefer, *Histoire de la chimie*, Paris, 1. 47, 1842 ; A. Rössing, *Geschichte der Metalle*, Berlin, 1901 ; F. X. M. Zippe, *Geschichte der Metalle*, Wien, 1857 ; L. Guillaume, *La métallurgie du plomb au Laurium*, Paris, 1909 ; R. Lepsius, *Sitzber. Akad. Berlin*, 112, 1871 ; *Die Metalle in den ägyptischen Inschriften*, Berlin, 1872 ; K. B. Hofmann, *Das Blei bei den Völkern des Altertums*, Berlin, 1885 ; H. Blümmer, *Technologie und Terminologie der Gewerbe und Künste bei Griechen und Römern*, Leipzig, 4. 89, 290, 1887 ; C. G. Fiedler, *Reise durch alle Theile des königreichs Griechenland in den Jahren 1834 bis 1837*, Leipzig, 2. 111, 336, 557, 1841 ; L. Gouïn, *Notice sur les mines de l'île de Sardegna*, Cagliari, 1869 ; A. Daubrée, *Rev. Archéol.*, (2). 17. 300, 1868 ; G. Bapst, *ib.*, (3), 1. 100, 1883 ; A. Frantz, *Œsterr. Zeit. Berg. Hütt.*, 28. 450, 1880 ; A. Gobantz, *ib.*, 42. 123, 1894 ; T. Haupt, *Berg. Hütt. Ztg.*, 42. 290, 1883 ; C. Blömeke, *ib.*, 48. 15, 1889 ; J. A. Overbeck, *Pompeji in seinem Gebäuden Altertümern und Kunstwerken*, Leipzig, 4. 621, 1875 ; A. Baumeister, *Denkmäler des klassischen Altertums*, München, 1884 ; H. Droysen, *Heerwesen und Kriegsführung der Griechen*, Freiburg, 20, 1888 ; A. F. von Pauly and G. Wissowa, *Real-Encyclopädie der classischen Altertumsarrenschaft*, Stuttgart, 5. 561, 1893 ; B. Neumann, *Metalle, Geschichte, Vorkommen, und Gewinnung*, Halle a. S., 1904 ; H. Ermisch, *Das sächsische Bergrecht*, Leipzig, 1887 ; P. Albinus, *Commentarius novus de Mysnia*, Wittenberg, 1580 ; C. A. Schlüter, *Gründlicher Unterricht von Hüttenwerken*, Braunschweig, 110, 1738 ; G. Agricola, *Bermannus, sive de re metallica*, Basileæ, 1546 ; P. Bech, (G. Agricola) *Vom Bergkwerck*, Basel, 1557 ; H. R. Schoolcraft, *Narrative Journal of Travels through the North-Western Regions of the United States*, Albany, 348, 1821 ; C. L. Henning, *Die Erzlagerstätte der Vereinigten Staaten von Nordamerika*, Stuttgart, 200, 1911 ; G. Chalmers, *Caledonia*, London, 1. 55, 1824 ; E. O. von Lippmann, *Entstehung und Ausbreitung der Alchemie*, Berlin, 574, 1919 ; W. H. Pulsifer, *Notes for a History of Lead and the Manufacture of White Lead and Lead Oxides*, New York, 1888 ; W. H. Adolph, *Chem. Met. Engg.*, 26. 914, 1922 ; *Scient. Monthly*, 14. 441, 1922 ; H. Faure, *Histoire de la céruse suivie d'un essai sur l'histoire du plomb*, Lille, 1889 ; W. Gowland, *The Early Metallurgy of Silver and Lead*, London, 1901 ; *Archæologia*, 57. 1, 1901 ; *Trans. Japan Soc. London*, 13. 20, 1915 ; *Journ. Ind. Metals*, 4. 4, 1910 ; M. Berthelot, *Ann. Chim. Phys.*, (6), 30. 285, 1893 ; (7), 12. 451, 1897 ; (7), 15. 433, 1898 ; *Compt. Rend.*, 127. 259, 1898 ; H. Morin, *ib.*, 78. 811, 1874 ; P. Christofle and H. Bouilhet, *ib.*, 78. 1019, 1874 ; S. Kalischer, *Ber.*, 7. 1114, 1874 ; J. A. Phillips, *On the Metallurgy of Lead*, London, 1859 ; *Proc. Yorkshire Phil. Soc.*, 1. 77, 1848 ; *Archæol. Journ.*, 16. 7, 1859 ; R. Watson, *Chemical Essays*, London, 3. 273, 1782 ; W. Wallace, *Alston Moor, its Pastoral People, its Mines and Miners, from the Earliest Periods to Recent Times*, Newcastle-on-Tyne, 1890 ; R. I. Murchison, *The Silurian System*, London, 279, 1839 ; J. C. Bruce, *The Roman Wall*, Newcastle-on-Tyne, 433, 1851 ; A. Way, *Journ. Arch, Soc.*, 16. 22, 1859 ; 23. 277, 1866 ; J. Childrey, *Britannia Baconia*, London, 112, 1660 ; J. Glanvil, *Phil. Trans.*, 2. 525, 770, 1668 ; J. Martyn, *ib.*, 36. 22, 1729 ; J. Farey, *General View of the Agriculture and Minerals of Derbyshire*, London, 382, 1815 ; P. A. Dufrénoy, *Voyage métallurgique en Angleterre*, Paris, 1839 ; H. Garlichs, *Min. Scient. Press.*, 115. 315, 1917 ; G. Plattes, *A Discovery of Subterranean Treasure*, London, 1679 ; T. Houghton, *Rara avis in terris, or The Compleat Miner*, London, 1681 ; A. Mosso, *Atti Accad. Lincei*, (5). 19. ii, 225, 1910 ; *Excursioni nel Mediterraneo e gli scavi di Creta*, Milano, 117, 1910 ; R. Hunt, *British Mining*, London, 31, 131, 230, 1884 ; J. McMurtrie, *Trans. Inst. Min. Eng.*, 20. 528, 1902 ; T. Morgan, *ib.*, 20. 478, 1902 ; G. V. Wilson and J. S. Flett, *The Lead, Zinc, Copper and Nickel Ores of Scotland*, Edinburgh, 1921 ; J. R. S. Hunter, *Trans. Geol. Soc. Glasgow*, 7. 376, 1884 ; D. Wilson, *Prehistoric Annals of Scotland*, London, 2. 64, 1863 ; T. Pennant, *A Tour of Scotland*, London, 2. 250, 1790 ; G. V. Irving, *The Upper Ward of Lanarkshire*, Glasgow, 1. 50, 1864 ; R. W. C. Patrick, *Early Records relating to Mining in Scotland*, Edinburgh, 34, 1878 ; J. Leslie, *De origine moribus et rebus gestis Scotorum*, Romæ, 1578 ; Amsterdam, 11, 1675 ; S. Atkinson, *Discovery and Historie of the Gold Mynes in Scotland*, Edinburgh, 47, 1825.

[2] J. Beckmann, *Beyträge zur Geschichte der Erfindungen*, Leipzig, 3. 373, 1792 ; London, 2. 29, 1846.

§ 2. The Occurrence of Lead

According to the estimates of J. H. L. Vogt,[1] and F. W. Clarke and H. S. Washington, lead is less commonly distributed than some of the elements usually regarded as rarer and scarcer—*e.g.* zirconium, vanadium, cerium, and yttrium. The average composition of the ten-mile crust, the hydrosphere, and atm. is $n \times 10^{-6}$ per cent. lead, according to J. H. L. Vogt ; 0·0005 per cent., according to A. E. Fersmann ; and 2×10^{-5} per cent., according to F. W. Clarke and H. S. Washington. A. M. Finlayson estimated in British areas an average of 0·0024 per cent. of lead in granite, diabase, shale, and limestone ; the granites contained most—0·002–0·004 per cent. ; and the limestones least—0·0005–0·0015 per cent. In the workable deposits, however, the lead occurs in a much greater proportion owing to the natural concentration of the material. The presence of lead in the sun has been demonstrated by the spectral observations of J. N. Lockyer,[2] H. Rowland, C. C. Hutchins and E. L. Holden. According to E. Cohen, the occurrence of lead in meteorites has been reported.

Lead occurs chiefly as sulphide, galena, which is one of the most widely distributed of the metal sulphides. Cerussite and anglesite occur in quantities sufficiently large to be mined ; and plumbojarosite, a rare mineral, is mined at Utah. Lead ores occur in veins and lodes or in fissures which have served as channels for the circulation of lead-bearing soln. from magmatic and other sources. The general opinion is that galena is usually of hydrochemical origin. G. Bischof [3] mentions its occurrence in stalactitic form, and as an incrustation on fossil bones

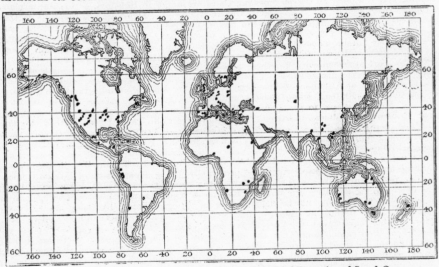

Fig. 1.—The Geographical Distribution of the Chief Deposits of Lead Ore.

in an old mine. A. Russell observed its formation from lead and sea-water in contact with charcoal—*vide* lead sulphide. In the so-called metasomatic deposits, the ore has been formed by a replacement of dolomite or limestone by galena, and some of the most important deposits have been produced in this manner. In the contact deposits the ore occurs in the zone of contact of intrusive igneous masses. Ores of lead usually associated with those of copper and vanadium, are sometimes found disseminated in sandstones and shales. Galena occurs in both crystalline and non-crystalline rocks. It is commonly associated with pyrites, sphalerite, chalcopyrite, arsenopyrite, etc., in the gangue of quartz, calcite barytes, or fluorspar, etc. Many other salts of lead have been formed by the alteration of galena. All galena is more or less argentiferous. The silver follows the metal when lead is extracted from galena, and many alchemists thought that the processes they used for extracting the silver were veritable transmutations of lead into silver. Lead is also commonly associated with zinc, and their primary or sulphide ores were brought together probably owing to the similarity in the properties of the sulphides. In the zone of oxidation the zinc sulphate is more soluble than lead sulphate, and consequently the alteration products of the zinc sulphide have been frequently leached away, leaving the lead ore practically free from zinc. A general idea of the distribution of the lead ores will be obtained from Fig. 1.

The occurrence of lead ore in **Europe**. The lead ore of the *British Isles* is generally obtained from veins in carboniferous rocks ; and the ore is galena generally associated with some zinc blende, and on the average with about 3 ozs. of silver per ton. About the middle of last century, the industry was very prosperous, over 1,000,000 tons of dressed ore were obtained from about 350 mines. Scarcely one-tenth of this amount is now obtained, and the industry in many counties, formerly big producers, is now almost extinct owing to the exhaustion and impoverishment of the deposits ; and the increase in the mining costs, and transport. Under these circumstances, the ores cannot compete success-fully against richer ores or ores obtained under more favourable conditions. Between 1848 and 1884, Cornwall and Devon had an average yearly output of nearly 1800 tons ; in 1917, it was 2 tons. In England, lead ore occurs in Cheshire, Cornwall, Cumberland, Derbyshire, Durham, Northumberland, Shropshire, Westmoreland, and Yorkshire ; in Wales, in Cardigan, Carmarthen, Carnarvon, Denbigh, Flint, and Montgomery ; in Scotland, in Dumfries and Lanark ; in Ireland, in Sligo and Wicklow ; and in the Isle of Man. In *Austria*, there are large deposits in the Triassic limestones and dolomites of Carinthia. In *Belgium*, the deposit of the Moresnet district extends into Luxembourg and Prussia ; the Vieille Montagne Mine is here worked. There is also ore at Bleyberg, Liège, and Verviers. In *Bulgaria*, there are mines at Blagodal near Kustendil, at Sedmilchi-sleniza, and Roupio. In *Czecho-Slovakia*, there are mines in Bohemia, at Prizibram near Prague ; near Piken ; at Kuttenberg, and at Budeweis. There are also deposits in the north-west which are extensions of the Saxon Erzegebirge. In the past, *Germany* has occupied a foremost place in the production of lead ore. The most productive deposits are in Upper Silesia. These deposits occur in the south-eastern corner of the province, on the borders of Russia and Austria extending across into Galicia and Russian Poland. The mines are at Miechowitz, Beuthen, Scharly, and Dombrowka. The mining is said to date from the sixteenth century. There are deposits in Saxony in the mining region of the Erzegebirge, at Altenberg, Schneeberg, etc. In the Harz Mountains there are deposits at the Clausthal Plateau, Rammelsberg, and at St. Andreasberg. There are the deposits of Ems, and Holzappel in the Lahn Valley, Nassau ; in Westphalia there are deposits near Coblenz, Armsberg, Gladbach, Dusseldorf, Iserlohn, and Brilon. Near Aix-la-Chapelle there are deposits at Commern, and Mechernich. The gypsum beds of Bavaria and Würtemberg contain galena ; also the Voltzia sandstone of Rheinish Prussia and Lorraine ; the assemblage of veins of the Kinzig Valley, the Black Forest, Baden ; and the beds at Munsterthal, and at Wiesloch. The chief deposits of *France* are situated in the meta-morphic and igneous rocks of Auvergne principally in the departments of Puy-de-Dôme, Cantal, and Haute-Loire ; and southwards in the departments of Gard, Lozere, and Lot. The chief mining localities are Malines, Bleymard, Vialas, and Planioles. The lead ores of the Pyrénées, occur in the departments of Ariège, Hautes Pyrénées, and Basses Pyrénées ; and mines at Boulard de Sentein St. Lary, and Girons. There are lodes in the department of Var, Provence ; and in *Brittany* the most important mine is at Pontpéan, Rennes, in the department of Ille-et-Vilaine. There are lodes near Oporto, *Portugal*. Formerly *Spain* was the largest producer in Europe, and ranked second to the United States in the world's production. The chief deposits are near Linares, in the Sierra Morena, and at Ciudad Real ; in the south-east of Province of Murcia, about Carthagena, etc. There are lodes north of Almeria, South Spain ; and at Guadalajara, Central Spain. The chief deposits in *Italy* are in Sardinia—Iglesais, Montevecchio, Monte-poni, Malafatano, etc. It is said that the Romans worked lead-mines in Sardinia which had been opened up by the Phœnicians, and worked by the Carthaginians. In the Cam-piglia Marittima district of Tuscany the lodes are mined at Bottino. There are many lead and zinc veins near Trent, Pfundererberg, and other places in the Tyrol. The silver-lead mines of the Laurium, *Greece*, were worked before 560 B.C., and flourished one hundred years later ; they were supposed to have been worked out by the beginning of our era, but were re-opened in 1863. Argentiferous ores have long been worked in the islands of Milos, Pharos, and Santorin in the Ægean Sea. The volcanic rocks of the Carpathian Mountains, *Hungary*, have mines dating from the eleventh century or earlier. The chief mining districts are those of Schemnitz-Kremnitz, Nagybunya-Felsobanya-Kapnik, and the Transylvanian Erzegebirge. The deposits of *Poland* at Boleslaw, Szakowa, Trzebinia and Olkusz are an extension of those in Upper Silesia. The deposits in *Yugo-Slavia* are represented by mines at Cerveni Brey, Kosmaj, and Babe in Serbia ; in Bosnia ; and at

Laibach in Carniola. In *Russia*, lead ores have been mined in the Caucasus and in Siberia. In *Norway*, lead ores occur near Vefsen and other places; and in *Sweden*, at Sala, Ammeberg, etc.

The occurrence of lead ore in **Asia.** The principal argentiferous lead mines in *Asia Minor* are those of Balia-Karaidin in Brusa, and Bulgar-Maden in Konia of Anatolia. There are veins about Karahussa, Swas; Bulgar-Dagh, Konia; Arden near Sokia; Angora; at Karalar, Kastamuni; and Keban Maden, Mamuret. In *India*, there are many deposits of galena. Those at Bawdwin, Upper Burma, are being worked on a big scale. From 1910–1916, a large quantity of slag worked by the old Chinese was treated for lead. The largest mine in *China* is that of Shui-ko-shan, in the Hunan Province, Central China. According to A. S. Wheler and S. Y. Li,[4] these mines had been worked spasmodically by the Chinese for the past three hundred years before being taken over by a European company in 1902. There are other mines in the same province at Kianghua, Pinghsien, Liangsiang, Kueiyang, Liling, Lingwu, Liuyang, Hengyang, Suikouling, and Chowkiagang. There are also mines in the province of Chi-li. In *Indo-China* there are lead ores in Annam and Tonkin—Bong-Mieu, Quan-Son, Moa-Ha, Trang-Da, Lang-Hit, and Pia-Ka. In *Japan* there is an important deposit at Kamioka, in the province of Hida, at Akita on the Island of Sado, and near Tokyo.

The occurrence of lead ores in **Africa.** In *Egypt*, the ancient mines at Gebel Rosas were reopened by a European company in 1913. Lead ores occur in Jebel Kutum in the Soudan. Lead is mined in several places in *Algeria*, notably at Oued Moziz. There are also important deposits in *Tunis*. In *Nigeria* lead and zinc ores occur in the Abakaliki district. A lode at Alusi Hill, Ifotta, has been worked by the natives. There are deposits at Broken Hill, North-Western *Rhodesia*. In the *South-West Protectorate*, lead ores have been mined in the Otavi Mountains. In the *Union of South Africa* there are pockets of galena in the dolomite rocks of the Transvaal in the Malmani district; at Leeuwkloof, Broederstroom, Dwarfontein, and Roodekrans in the Pretoria district, and at Rhenosterhoek, Witkop, Bokkraal, Buffelshoek, Rietspruit, and Doornhoek, in the Marico district; and Windhuk, in the Pietersburg district. There is a vein of lead ore at Argent, and others in Northern Transvaal, Gordonia, and Potgietersrust. In Cape Province there are deposits near Port Elizabeth; Banghoek; Knysna; Richmond in the Beaufort West, Victoria West, and Van Rhysndorp districts. Deposits are known in Bechuanaland, Damaraland, and in the Caledon and Swellendam districts. In Natal, galena has been found at Umsingi, in Umvoli Country; and in the Mfongosi and Ngobeon Valleys, Zululand.[5]

The occurrence of lead ore in **America.** In the *British West Indies* and in *British Guiana*, there are lead ores which have been worked on a very small scale. Large quantities are mined in Mexico—Sierra Madre, Sierra Mojada, Zimapan, Santa Barbara, Cuatro Cienegas, Santa Eulalia, and Michoacan. The *United States* is the world's largest producer. The Mississippi Valley deposits include: (i) the south-eastern district of Missouri—Potosi, Palmer, Valle, etc. (ii) South-western Missouri, including neighbouring portions of Kansas and Oklahoma or the Joplin district—Aurora, Granby, Webb City, Alba, Neck, Joplin, Galena, Badger, Quapaw, and Miami; and (iii) the Upper Mississippi Valley, including the Wisconsin, Iowa, and Illinois districts—Mineral Point, Platteville, Dubuque, etc. The Atlantic coast deposits include the deposits near Rossie, Guymard, Ellenville, Wurtsboro, and in Wythe Co., Virginia; in New England, North Carolina, and Tennessee. The Rocky Mountains and Pacific Slope deposits—in Arizona—Mowry, Eureka, Castle Dome, Tombstone, and the Hualpai district; in California—Cerro Gordo, Inyo Co., and the Darwin district; in Colorado—Leadville, Aspen, Monarch, Redcliff, Ten Mile, Silver Cliff, and San Juan; in Idaho—Cœur d'Alene, Bunker Hill, Sullivan, Standard-Mammoth, Morning, Hercules, Minnie Moore, Crœsus, Bullion, Red Elephant, and Red Cloud; in Montana—Alta, Elkhorn, etc.; in Nevada—Eureka, Pioche, Yellow Pine, and Cherry Creek; in New Mexico—Magdalena Mine, and the Grant and Cook districts; in Maine[6]—Portland; in Utah—Salt Lake City, Bingham, Park City, Tintic, and Frisco districts, and in Beaver Co. There are several important deposits of lead in *Canada.*[7] In British Columbia—Slocan, East Kootenay, Ainsworth, and the Nelson districts, and in the Yukon territory. In Ontario there are several occurrences in Frontenac Co., and Hastings Co., and near Sault Sainte Marie. In Quebec—Notre-Dame-des-Anges in Portneuf Co., and on Calumet Island, Pontiac Co. In Nova Scotia deposits have been located in Inverness Co. Lead ores have been found in several places in Newfoundland. In Central America there is a small production of lead ore near Guatemala. In South America, *Peru* produces a few thousand tons per annum; there are small quantities of argentiferous galena in the Colquechaca district, *Bolivia;* about 100 or 200 tons of ore are produced per annum in *Chile;* and in the *Argentine* Andes, there are extensive deposits of galena.

The occurrence of lead ore in **Australasia.** Australia is the largest producer of lead ore in the British Empire. In *New South Wales*, the famous deposit at Broken Hill, discovered in 1883, was first worked for silver, then for silver and lead, and later largely for zinc. In *Queensland*, there are several groups of claims in the Barketown district, and in the Eungella Goldfield. No important deposits have been discovered in *South Australia*, and the occurrences in *Victoria* have not been worked. The chief occurrences in *West Australia* are in the Northampton district. There are several important deposits in *Tasmania*. The chief deposits are in the Mount Read and Rosebery areas. There are also important deposits in the Zeehan district, the Dundas region, and the Waratah district. In *New Zealand*, lead ores occur in the Hauraki Peninsula.

The World's production [8] of lead in metric tons is :

1867	1877	1887	1897	1907	1917	1924
157,885	322,910	564,194	721,167	1,011,397	1,107,153	1,302,000

The production in 1924, in the different countries is :

Australia	12.843	Italy	21,706
Austria	4.904	Japan	2,500
Belgium	(64,624)	Mexico	132,000
India	51,759	Rhodesia, etc.	6,631
Canada	74,500	Spain	139,569
France	20,500	Sweden and Norway	1,208
Germany	49,000	United Kingdom	5,303
Greece	5,000	United States	561,058
Czechoslovakia	2,229	Tunis	15,483
Jugoslavia	11,300	Argentina	8,000
Turkey	5,100	Rumania	139,569

For China, the production in 1924 was 1116 metric tons. The extreme prices of soft foreign lead in 1917 were £29 10s. and £30 10s. per ton ; and in 1921, £16 10s. and £26 per ton.

Lead occurs in nature rarely in the metallic form, and when it does, it is always on a secondary formation, having been reduced from some pre-existing lead compound. Many of the reputed occurrences are doubtful. J. J. Nöggerath,[9] in his *Ueber gediegen Blei natürliche Bleiglatte und Mennige*, made a critical study of the evidence. In 1750, J. G. Wallerius mentioned the occurrence of *plumbum nativum*, both massive—*plumbum nativum sodidum*—and granular—*plumbum nativum in granulis*. J. B. L. Romé de l'Isle considered the evidence somewhat problematic ; L. A. Emmerling, and A. Breithaupt also doubted the occurrence ; while A. G. Werner, and A. Estner did not mention it. R. J. Haüy obtained a specimen of native lead from some lava on Madeira, and he called it *plomb natif volcanique amorphe*. J. F. L. Hausmann considered this the only reliable evidence of the occurrence of native lead, but P. A. Dufrénoy regarded the Madeira lead as doubtful, and believed the only reliable find to be that reported by W. Haidinger at Alston Moor, Cumberland. Concerning this, R. P. Greg and W. G. Lettsom say that the Romans worked lead ore in this locality. Other reputed finds in England and Ireland are mentioned by T. Austin, and H. J. Brooke and W. H. Miller. J. J. Nöggerath considered an occurrence reported at Vera Cruz, Mexico, to be satisfactory, but J. D. Dana considered it to be doubtful. The Mexican finds were also considered by G. A. Stein, A. Breithaupt, R. P. Greg and W. G. Lettsom, and J. L. Comte de Bournon. L. J. Igelström described eight occurrences of metallic lead at Pajsberg, Sweden.

The occurrence of metallic lead in Sweden, in addition to those mentioned above, include deposits at Harstigen, Langban, Oerebro, and Sjögrufvan, described by L. J. Igelström, A. Hamberg, G. Flink, and A. W. Tamm. The occurrence of metallic lead in France was discussed by M. de Gensanne and C. Coquebert ; in Italy, by J. J. Nöggerath ; in Hungary, by S. R. I. E. à Born ; in Poland, by J. G. Wallerius ; in Carinthia, by J. G. Wallerius ; in Spain, by J. C. Ullmann, A. Orio, and C. C. von Leonhard ; in Stavonia and Siebenbürgen, by G. Zerrenner ; in Moravia, by C. F. von Reichenbach ; in Bohemia, by S. R. I. E. à Born ; in Silesia, by L. D. Hermann, G. A. Volkmann, J. G. Lehmann, C. C. Bienert, and H. R. Göppert ; in Saxony, by G. Jenzsch ; in Hesse, by G. Gautieri and J. Schaub ; in the Urals, by P. von Jeremejeff, A. Erman, M. von Tscheffkin, G. Zerrenner, N von Kokscharoff, E. S. von Fedoroff, J. J. Nöggerath, O. von Hingenau, and C. C. von Leonhard ; in Dutch East Indies, by R. Ewerwijn ; in Burma, by F. R. Mallet ; in Australia, by A. Liversidge, G. H. F. Ulrich, and W. F. Petterd ; in Chile, by E. Cohen, and R. P. Greg ; in New Zealand, by J. Park ; in Peru, by A. Raimondi, and I. Domeyko ; in Mexico, by C. W. Kempton ; in the United States, Colorado, by J. D. Dana, and R. N. Clark ; Idaho, by W. P. Blake ; Montana, by F. A. Genth ; North Carolina, by F. A. Genth ; New Jersey, by W. M. Foote, S. L. Penfield, and C. W. Kempton ; and New York, by J. D. Dana ; and in Canada, by E. J. Chapman.

The following list includes most of the plumbiferous minerals. Galena, cerussite, anglesite, plumbojarosite, and mimetesite, are of interest as sources of lead. The other minerals may be useful as sources of other elements, but, owing to their sparsity or to their unsuitability for metallurgical purposes, not as sources of lead. Many can be regarded only as mineralogical curiosities.

The **oxides**: *Corodanite*, $(Pb,Mn'')Mn_3O_7$; *hydroplumbite*, $3PbO.H_2O$; *mennige*, Pb_3O_4; *miriquidite*, $PbO.Fe_2O_3.As_2O_5.P_2O_5.H_2O$; *nivenite*, $UO_2.UO_3.PbO.ThO_2$, with iodates; *phœnicite*, $Pb_2Cr_2O_9$; *plumboferrite*, $(PbO,FeO,CuO)Fe_2O_3$; and *uraninite*, $(U,Pb_2)_3(UO_6)_2$; *curite*, $PbO.5UO_3.4H_2O$; *pilbarite*, $PbO.UO_3.ThO_2.2SiO_2.2H_2O$; *dewindtite*, $4PbO.8UO_3.3Pb_2O_5.12H_2O$; *plumbocolumbite*, a complex plumbiferous mineral, $R''_2Cb_2O_7.R'''_4(Cb_2O_7)_3$, where $R''_2=Pb$, UO, Fe, or Cu, and $R'''_4=Al$ and rare earth metals. The **chlorides, oxychlorides, and chlorocarbonates**: *Phosgenite*, or *cromfordite*, $PbCl_2.PbCO_3$; *boleite*, $3\{Pb(OH)Cl.Cu(OH)Cl\}AgCl$; *chubutite*, $Pb_{16}O_{14}Cl_4$; *laurionite*, $Pb(OH)Cl$; *lorettoite*, $Pb_{15}O_{13}Cl_4$; *matlockite*, Pb_5OCl_2; *mendipite*, $Pb_3O_4Cl_4$; *pseudomendipite*, $Pb_8O_6Cl_4$; *mimetesite*, $Pb_5Cl(AsO_4)_3$; *nadorite*, $PbClSbO_2$; *ochrolite*, $Pb_6Cl_4Sb_2O_7$; *paralaurionite*, $Pb(OH)Cl$; *penfieldite*, $PbO.2PbCl_2$; *percylite*, $PbOH.CuOH.Cl$; *polysphaerite*, $(Ca,Pb)Cl(PO_4)_3$; *pseudoboleite*, $5PbCl_2.4CuO.6H_2O$; *pseudocotunnite*, $2KCl.PbCl_2$; *rafaelite*, $Pb(OH)Cl$; and *schwartzembergite*, $Pb_3O_2(I,Cl)_2$. The **sulphides, and oxysulphides; selenides, and tellurides**: *Alaskaite*, $Bi_2S_3.(Cu_2,Ag_2,Pb)S$; *alisonite*, $PbS.3Cu_2S$; *baumhauerite*, $4PbS.3As_2S_3$; *beegerite*, $Pb_6Bi_2S_9$; *bismuthplagionite*, $5PbS.4Bi_2S_3$; *bjelkite*, $Bi_2Pb_2S_5$; *nagyagite*, $Pb_{10}Au_2Sb_2Te_6S_{15}$ (variable); *zinkenite*, $PbSb_2S_4$; *bismuthoplagionite*, $Pb_8Bi_8S_{17}$; *galena*, PbS; *boulangerite*, $Pb_5Sb_4S_{11}$; *bournonite*, $Pb_2Cu_2Sb_2S_6$; *brongniartite*, $2(Pb,Ag_2)S.Sb_2S_3$; *chiviatite*, $2PbS.3Bi_2S_3$; *cosalite*, $2PbS.Bi_2S_3$; *domingite*, $3PbS.2Sb_2S_3$; *dufrenoysite*, $Pb_2As_2S_5$; *dürfeldite*, $3(Pb,Ag_2)S.Sb_2S_3$; *embrithite*, $Pb_3Sb_2S_6$ or $Pb_{10}Sb_6S_{19}$; *epiboulangerite*, $Pb_3Sb_2S_8$; *teallite*, PbSnS$_2$; *cylindrite*, $3PbSnS_2+SnFeSb_4S_9$; *franckeite*, $Sn_2Pb_5Sb_2S_{12}$, or $3PbSnS_2+PbFeSb_2S_6$; *galenobismuthite*, $PbBi_2S_4$; *geocronite*, $Pb_5Sb_2S_8$; *guitermanite*, $10PbS.3As_2S_3$; *heteromorphite*, $Pb_7Sb_8S_{19}$; *hutchinsonite*, $PbS.As_2O_4$ with $(Tl,Cu,Ag)_2S.As_2S_3$; *jamesonite*, $Pb_2Sb_2S_5$; *jordanite*, $Pb_4Sb_2S_7$; *kilbrickenite*, $Pb_6Sb_2S_9$; *kobellite*, $2PbS.(Bi,Sb)_2S_3$; *cuproplumbite*, $2PbS.Cu_2S$; *lengenbachite*, $6PbS(Cu,Ag)_2S.2As_2S_3$; *lillianite*, $Pb_3Bi_2S_6$; *aikinite*, $PbCuBiS_3$; *liveingite*, $Pb_5As_4S_{17}$; *meneghinite*, $Pb_4Sb_2S_7$; *mullanite*, $5PbS_2Sb_2S_3$; *plagionite*, $Pb_5Sb_8S_{17}$; *plumbostannite*, $Pb_2(Fe,Zn)_2Sn_2Sb_2S_{11}$; *plumosite*, $Pb_2Sb_2S_5$; *plumbostibnite*, $Pb_3Sb_2S_6$, see boulangerite; *plumbobismuth glance*, $Pb_2Bi_2S_5$; *polytelite*, $(Pb,Ag_2)_4Sb_2S_7$, with $(Zn,Fe)_4Sb_2S_7$; *quirogite*, $Pb_8Sb_6S_{32}$; *rathite*, or *wiltshireite*, $3PbS.2As_2S_3$; *rezbanyite*, $Pb_4Bi_{10}S_{19}$; *sartorite*, $PbAs_2S_4$; *schapbachite*, $(Pb,Ag_2)_2Bi_2S_5$; *freieslebenite*, $(Pb,Ag_2)_5Sb_4S_{11}$; *schirmerite*, $(Pb,Ag_2)_2Bi_4S_9$; *seligmannite*, $3(Pb,Cu_2)S.As_2S_3$; *semseyite*, $Pb_7Sb_8S_{16}$; *teallite*, PbSnS$_2$; *tinder ore*, or *Zundererz*, $Pb_7Sb_8S_{19}$; *weibullite*, $2PbS.Bi_4S_3Se_3$; *clausthalite*, PbSe; *zorgite*, $(Pb,Cu_2)Se$; *kerstenite*, $PbSeO_4$; *lehrbachite*, HgSe with $(Pb,Cu_2)Se$; and *altaite*, PbTe. The **sulphates**: *Caledonite*, $(Pb,Cu)_2(SO_4)CO_3$; *caracolite*, $Na_2Pb(OH)SO_4Cl$; *hinsdalite*, $3Al_2O_3.2PbO.2SO_3.P_2O_5.6H_2O$; *johnstonite*, mixture PbS, PbSO$_4$, and S; *lanarkite*, Pb_2SO_5; *leadhillite*, or *susannite*, $4PbSO_4.2CO_2.H_2O$; *linarite*, $(Pb,Cu)(OH)_2.(Pb,Cu)SO_4$; *palmierite*, $K_4Na_2Pb_4(SO_4)_7$; *anglesite*, PbSO$_4$; and *plumbojarosite*, $PbFe_6(OH)_{12}(SO_4)_4$. The **carbonates**: *Beresowite*, $2PbO.PbCO_3.3PbCrO_4$; *cerussite*, PbCO$_3$; *hydrocerussite*, $Pb\{(PbOH)_2CO_3\}_2$; *iglesiasite* isomorphous mixtures of lead and zinc carbonates, *plumbonacrite*, $2PbO.Pb(OH)_2.PbCO_3$; and *roeblingite*, $5CaH_2SiO_4.2(Pb,Ca)SO_4$. The **phosphates, arsenates, antimonates, bismuthates, and vanadates**: *Araeoxene*, $(Zn,Pb)_3(V,As)_2O_8$; *arsenomelane*, $2PbS.As_2O_3$; *bayldonite*, $(Cu,Pb)AsO_4.CuOH.\frac{1}{2}H_2O$; *beudantite*, $(AsO_4)(SO_4)Pb\{Fe(OH)_2\}_3$; *bindheimite* or *bleiniëre*, $PbO.Sb_2O_5.H_2O$; *brackebuschite*, $(Cu,Pb,Fe,Zn,Mn)_3V_2O_8.H_2O$; *cuprodescloizite*, $(PbOH)(Pb,Cu,Zn)VO_4$; *dechenite*, $Pb(VO_3)_2$; *descloizite*, $(PbOH)(Pb,Zn)VO_4$, and the related *pyrobelonite*; *ecdemite*, or *ekedemite*, $2PbCl_2.Pb_2As_2O_7$; *endlichite*, $Pb_5Cl\{(As,V)O_4\}_3$; *eusynchite*, $(Pb,Zn)(VO_4)_2$; *ferrazite*, $3(Pb,Ba)O.2P_2O_5.8H_2O$; *hedyphane*, $(Pb,Ca,Ba)Cl(AsO_4)$; *hügelite*, zinc lead vanadate; *kampylite*, $Pb_5Cl\{(As,P)O_4\}_3$; *carminite*, $Pb_3(AsO_4)_2.10FeAsO_4$; *karyinite* or *caryinite*, $(Na_2,Ca,Mg,Mn,Pb)_3(AsO_4)_2$; *lossenite*, $9Pb(FeOH)(AsO_4)_6SO_4.12H_2O$; *mimetesite*, $PbCl_2.3Pb_3(AsO_4)_2$; *mottramite*, $5(Pb,Cu)O.V_2O_5.2H_2O$; *parsonsite*, $2PbO.P_2O_5.UO_3.H_2O$; *pyrobenolite*, $7MnO.4PbO.2V_2O_5.3H_2O$; *stasite*, $4PbO.3P_2O_5.8UO_3.12H_2O$; *trigonite*, $Pb_3MnH(AsO_3)_3$; and *vanadinite*, $Pb(VO_3)_2$ or $PbCl_2.3Pb_3(VO_4)_2$. The **chromates, molybdates, tungstates, and uranates**: *Beresowite* or *beresovite*, $Pb_2.2Pb_2O.3CrO_4.CO_3$; *chillagite*, $Pb(W,Mo)O_4$; *wulfenite*, $PbMoO_4$; *phönicite*, $Pb_3Cr_2O_9$; *crocoite*, $PbCrO_4$; *curite*, and *dewindite* —*vide supra*, oxides; *stolzite*, or *raspite*, $PbWO_4$; and *vauquelinite*, $2(Pb,Cu)CrO_4.(Pb,Cu)_3(PO_4)_2$. The plumbiferous **silicates** are : *Alamosite*, PbSiO$_3$; *barysilite*, $Pb_3Si_2O_7$; *ganomalite*, $Ca_4Pb_4(PbOH)_2(Si_2O_7)_3$; *gummite*, $(Pb,Ca,Ba)SiCl_3O_{12}.5H_2O$; *hancockite*, $(Ca,Pb)_4(Al,Fe)_6H_2Si_6O_{24}$; *hyalotekite*, barium calcium lead silicate; *kasolite*, $3PbO.3SiO_2.3UO_3.4H_2O$; *kentrolite*, $Mn_4Pb_3Si_3O_{16}$; *melanotekite*, $Pb_3Fe_4Si_3O_{15}$; *margarosanite*, $PbCa_2Si_3O_9$; *molybdophyllite*, $PbMgSiO_4.H_2O$; and *nasonite*, $Ca_4Pb_6Cl_2(Si_2O_7)_3$.

Lead occurs as a more or less accidental impurity in many minerals. C.W. Cross,[10]

W. H. Emmons, R. N. Clark, B. Lotti, J. Strischoff, P. L. Burthe, and A. W. Stelzner and A. Bergeat found it in some auriferous and other alluvial sands ; A. Raimondi, A. d'Achiardi, M. Fort, and A. W. Stelzner and A. Bergeat, in silver ores, and in copper ores ; K. Nenadkewitsch, in zinc ores ; R. Krzizan, in limestone, also in the Jura bone-earths ; H. Lange, in a red fluorspar from Greenland ; A. Piutti and E. Stoppani, and D. Playfair, in pyrites ; A. Lacroix, and F. Zambonini in Vesuvian fumaroles as lead sulphide, and A. Scacchi, in Vesuvian lavas as lead sulphate and basic chloride. The occurrence of lead in uranium minerals was discussed by A. Becker and P. Jannasch, A. L. Davis, M. Muguet, etc.—*vide infra.*

There are reports of *waters* containing plumbiferous salts. Thus, P. Laur, J. A. Phillips, C. F. Becker, and A. W. Stelzner and A. Bergeat, found lead in the sinter from the hot springs of California ; F. A. Quenstedt, in the ochre from a spring at Cannstatt, Stuttgart ; L. Darapsky, in the calcareous tuff of the spring at Cachapoal, Chile ; R. Fresenius, in the spring at Pyrmont ; F. Garrigou, in the springs of Beaucens ; E. Carstens, 0·000011 grm. PbO per litre in the spring-water at Alexandro-Jormoloff, Caucasus ; W. F. Hillebrand, Joplin, Missouri ; L. Dede, in the sinter at Nauheimer Sprudels ; A. Daubrée, and J. Roth, in a spring at Vichy ; and F. J. Malaguti and co-workers, in sea-water.

The ashes of *grasses*, etc., growing on plumbiferous soils were found by E. Lidgey,[11] R. Beck, and G. Hattensaus to contain lead ; and F. Malaguti and co-workers found lead in the ash of some *sea-weeds*. A. Devergie, M. J. B. Orfila, J. Barse, and A. Chevallier regarded lead as normally present in the internal organs of *man*. V. Legrip said that the ash of the liver and milk of human beings contains 0·0818 per cent. of lead ; and the ash of various organs of a cow, 0·0367 per cent. E. Heubel reported 0·18–0·27 part lead in 1000 parts of bone ; 0·17–0·20 in kidneys ; 0·10–0·33 in the liver ; 0·06–0·11 in the spinal cord ; 0·04–0·05 in the brain ; 0·02–0·04 in the muscles ; 0·01–0·02 in the intestines ; and only traces in the spleen, blood, and bile. H. Oidtmann reported 1 mgrm. per kgrm. in the liver of a man fifty-six years of age, and 3 mgrms. per kgrm. in the spleen. N. A. E. Millon also found lead in the blood of soldiers whose food was cooked in metal vessels. A. Béchamp, L. H. F. Melsens, E. Cottereau, and B. du Buisson found no lead in blood ; and H. W. F. Wackenroder said that the presence of a trace of lead in blood is an accidental circumstance, for the lead is derived from contaminated food. E. Heubel found in a dog killed by chronic lead-poisoning 0·018–0·027 per cent. of lead—in the kidneys, 0·017–0·020 ; in the liver, 0·010–0·033 ; spinal cord, 0·006–0·011 ; brain, 0·004–0·005 ; muscles, 0·002–0·004 ; intestine, 0·001–0·002 ; and traces in the spleen, blood, and bile. The presence of lead in the organs of lead-workers, and of *animals* and man poisoned with lead, has been discussed by A. W. Blyth, E. Brumpt, W. Ebstein, W. Ellenberger and V. Hofmeister. H. Greven, L. Hugounenq, H. Oidtmann, H. Legrand and L. Winter, V. Lehmann, L. G. Maillard, A. Marie and P. Requier, G. Meillère, F. Shufflebotham and J. W. Mellor, C. Oppenheimer, K. Stockmann and F. J. Charteris, etc. The general results show that lead is not a natural constituent of the body, but it may be found in healthy persons who have been quite free from symptoms of lead-poisoning. A. Thiergardt found 0·0031–0·0557 per cent. of lead in *fish* poisoned by water containing a soluble lead salt ; and T. W. Hogg found 0·35–0·52 per cent. of lead in the bodies of earth *worms* which lived in the plumbiferous *débris* of a white-lead works.

Lead occurs normally in many industrial products—alloys, enamels, glazes, glasses, paints, etc. J. Boes[12] indicated its presence in rubber goods, where it was used to accelerate vulcanization ; K. Endell, A. Micault, P. Carles, J. Grünwald, G. Giusti, N. P. Marasneff, etc., in the glazes and enamels of cooking vessels ; O. Megger and K. Fuchs, in dolls' tea-services ; and H. Stockmeier, in children's tin soldiers ; A. Vogel, and A. Seyda, lead in tin-foil ; A. Barillé, in the tin fittings of mineral water syphons ; F. M. Litterscheid, in the tinning of copper vessels ; E. Junker, and K. Neukam in preparations—tooth-pastes, etc.—in metal tubes; C. H. la Wall, and W. D. Collins and W. F. Clarke, in the zinc oxide of commerce; S. de Luca, in the platinum sparking tips; O. F. Lubatti, in cassia oil, E. Rieter, in stearin; N. T. Fox, in calcium phosphate; A. Vogel, in red wafers; A. Classen, A. Carnot, and A. Hilger, in bismuth preparations; E. Schering, in potassium iodide; A. Geheel, in formic acid; E. Klingelhöffer, and R. R. Tatlock and R. T. Thomson, in tartaric and citric acids; W. Wicke, in filter-paper; and H. Lührig, and R. Weber, in transfers.

Lead was also reported by A. R. Leeds,[13] R. Roth, A. Cutolo, L. Stefanowicz, M. Klostermann and K. Scholta, E. Spaeth, P. Carles, F. Wirthle and K. Amberger, and P. Schindler, in foodstuffs which had been contained in tinned vessels; J. A. F. Ballard also found it in extract of meat; A. F. Canelli, and H. Baum and R. Seeliger, in milk; H. Roos, beet-sugar; G. Sonntag, F. Muttelet and F. Touplain, L. Moreau and E. Vinet, L. Nathan and A. Schmidt, A. Hubert and F. Alba, and F. H. Storer, wines, yeast, and beer; and A. Stadler, in snuff.

REFERENCES.

[1] F. W. Clarke and H. S. Washington, *Proc. Nat. Acad. Sciences*, **8**. 108, 1922; *The Composition of the Earth's Crust*, Washington, 1924; A. E. Fersmann, *Bull. Acad. St. Petersburg*, (6), **6**. 367, 1912; F. W. Clarke, *Bull. U.S. Geol. Sur.*, 78, 1891; J. H. L. Vogt, *Zeit. prakt. Geol.*, **6**. 225, 314, 377, 413, 1898; 7. 10, 274, 1899; A. M. Finlayson, *Journ. Geol. Soc.*, **66**. 281, 1910.

[2] J. N. Lockyer, *Proc. Roy. Soc.*, **27**. 279, 1878; *Compt. Rend.*, **86**. 317, 1878; C. C. Hutchins and E. L. Holden, *Amer. Journ. Science*, (3), **34**. 451, 1883; *Phil. Mag.*, (5), **24**. 325, 1883; H. Rowland, *Preliminary Table of Solar Spectrum Wave-Lengths*, Chicago, 1898; *Johns Hopkins Univ. Circ.*, 85, 1891; *Amer. Journ. Science*, (3), **41**. 243, 1891; *Chem. News*, **63**. 133, 1891; E. Cohen, *Meteoritenkunde*, Stuttgart, **1**. 33, 1894.

[3] G. Bischof, *Elements of Chemical and Physical Geology*, London, **1**. 43, 1854; A. Russell, *Min. Mag.*, **19**. 64, 1920; A. Lodin, *Ann. Mines*, (9), **1**. 389, 1892; R. Hunt, *British Mining*, London, 836, 1884; F. Beyschlag, J. H. L. Vogt, and P. Krusch, *Die Lagerstätten der nutzbaren Mineralien und Gesteine nach Form Inhalt und Entstehung*, Stuttgart, **2**. 656, 1913.

[4] A. S. Wheler and S. Y. Li, *Min. Mag.*, **16**. 91, 1917.

[5] S. J. Speak, *Mining Mag.*, **21**. 203, 1921.

[6] G. R. MacCarthy, *Amer. Min.*, **10**. 332, 1925.

[7] F. J. Alcock, *Canadian Min. Journ.*, **47**. 448, 1926; *Min. Ind.*, **28**. 521, 1926.

[8] R. Hunt, *Mem. Geol. Survey*, 703, 1848; *British Mining*, London, 1884; T. E. C. Hall, *Lead Ores*, London, 1921; Imperial Mineral Resources Bureau, *Lead*, 1922; G. V. Wilson and J. S. Flett, *Mineral Resources of Great Britain*, London, 1921; L. H. Quin, *Metal Handbook and Statistics*, London, 1922; H. B. Pulsifer, *The Mineral Industry*, New York, 417, 1923; J. Czochralsky, *Zeit. Metallkunde*, **18**. 43, 1926.

[9] M. de Gensanne, *Histoire naturelle de la province de Languedoc*, Montpellier, **3**. 186, 208, 1777; C. Coquebert, *Journ. Mines*, **9**. 317, 1799; A. W. Tamm, *Analyser af svenska mineralier*, Upsala, 1869; P. A. Dufrénoy, *Traité de minéralogie*, Paris, **3**. 1, 1847; W. Haidinger, *Treatise on Mineralogy*, Edinburgh, **3**. 129, 1825; A. Estner, *Versuch einer Mineralogie*, Wien, 1804; L. A. Emmerling, *Lehrbuch der Mineralogie*, Giessen, 1796; R. J. Haüy, *Traité de minéralogie*, Paris, **3**. 451, 1801; **3**. 334, 1822; J. F. L. Hausmann, *Handbuch der Mineralogie*, Göttingen, 1847; A. Orio, *Elementos de mineralogia*, Madrid, 275, 1882; G. Ferrenner, *Jahrb. Geol. Reichsanst. Wien*, **4**. 497, 1853; *Sitzber. Akad. Wien*, **11**. 262, 1853; J. G. Wallerius, *Mineralogia*, Stockholm, 375, 1750; J. B. L. Romé de l'Isle, *Cristallographie*, Paris, **3**. 361, 1783; A. G. Werner, *Letztes Mineralsystem*, Freiberg, 1817; A. Erman, *Archiv für wissenschaftliche Kunde von Russland*, Berlin, **2**. 763, 1842; F. A. Walchner, *Handbuch für die gesammte Mineralogie*, Carlsruhe, **1**. 464, 1829; J. C. W. Voigt, *Mineralogische Reise nach den Braunkohlenwerken und Basalten in Hessen*, Weimar, 117, 1802; G. A. Volkmann, *Silesia subterranea*, Frankfort, 1729, P. von Jeremejeff, *Gornyi Journ.*, **3**. 263, 1887; C. C. von Leonhard, *Handbuch der Oryktogonosie*, Heidelberg, 224, 1821; *Taschenbuche für die gesammte mineralogie*, Frankfurt a. M., **3**. 19, 1847; G. Jenzsch, *Neues Jahrb. Min.*, 805, 1855; J. G. Lehmann, *Versuch einer Geschichte von Flötz Gebürgen, betreffend deren Entstehung, Lage, darinne befindliche Metallen, Mineralien, und Fossilien*, Berlin, 211, 1756; L. D. Hermann, *Maslographie*, Brieg, 194, 1711; C. C. Bienert, *Kastner's Arch.*, **17**. 387, 1843; H. R. Göppert, *ib.*, **18**. 538, 1843; G. Gautieri and J. Schaub, *Moll's Jahrb. Berg. Hütt.*, **5**. 434, 1801; A. Liversidge, *Minerals of New South Wales*, Sydney, 1882; W. F. Petterd, *Catalogue of the Minerals of Tasmania*, Launceston, 55, 1896; A. Raimondi, *Les Minéraux du Pérou*, Paris, 145, 1878; 1. Domeyko, *Elementos de mineralojia*, Santiago, 316, 1879; J. L. Comte de Bournon, *Catologue de la collection minéralogique particulière du roi*, Paris, 333, 1817; C. F. de Landero, *Sinopsis mineralogica*, Mexico, 405, 1888; F. A. Genth, *Ann. Phil. Soc. Philadelphia*, **11**. 443, 1870; *The Minerals and Mineral Localities of North Carolina,*

Rayleigh. 20, 1870; H. Steffens, *Handbuch der Oryktognosie*. Halle. 3. 51, 1819; F. L. Sonnenschein, *Zeit. deut. geol. Ges.*, 7. 664, 1855; M. von Tscheffkin, *Isis*, 434, 1837; *Jahrb. Min.*, 59, 1838; S. R. I. E. à Born, *Catalogue méthodique et raisonné de la collection des fossiles de Mlle. Eléonore de Raab*, Vienna, 2. 353, 1790; M. Tondi, *Elementi di orittognosia*, Napoli, 1. 128, 1817; J. J. Nöggerath, *Zeit. deut. geol. Ges.*, 6. 678, 1854; *Neues Jahrb. Min.*, 129, 1861; R. P. Greg, *Phil. Mag.*, (4), 10. 12, 1855; T. Austin, *ib.*, (3), 22. 234, 1843; C. W. Kempton, *Science*, (1), 21. 345, 1893; J. Park, *Trans. New Zealand Inst.*, 35. 403, 1902; W. M. Foote, *Amer. Journ. Science*, (4), 6. 187, 1898; W. P. Blake, *ib.*, (3), 25. 161, 1883; S. L. Penfield and C. H. Warren, *ib.*, (4), 8. 339, 1899; E. J. Chapman, *ib.*, (2), 41. 254, 1866; *Phil. Mag.*, (4), 31. 176, 1866; F. Wöhler, *Liebig's Ann.*, 100. 127, 1856; C. F. von Reichenbach, *Verh. Geol. Reichsanst. Wien*, 53, 1855; L. J. Igeström, *Œfvers. Akad. Handl. Stockholm*, 417, 1864; *Berg. Hütt. Ztg.*, 25. 21, 1866; *Geol. För. Forh. Stockholm*, 11. 36, 1889; *Bull. Soc. Min.*, 12. 22, 1889; O. von Hingenau, *Œsterr. Zeit. Berg. Hütt.*, 2. 413. 1854; N. von Kokscharoff, *Materialien zur Mineralogie Russlands*, St. Petersburg, 6. 236, 1874; R. Ewerwijn, *Jahrb. Mijwezen Neder. Oost-Indie*, 1, 1872; F. R. Mallet, *Min. Mag.*, 5. 336, 1884; G. Flink, *Ark. Fysik. Kemi Min.*, 3. 11, 1908; A. Hamberg, *Zeit. Kryst.*, 17. 253, 1890; W. C. Brögger, *ib.*, 3. 492, 1879; R. P. Greg and W. G. Lettsom, *Manual of the Mineralogy of Great Britain and Ireland*, London, 387, 1858; H. J. Brooke and W. H. Miller, *An Elementary Introduction to the Knowledge of Mineralogy*, London, 127, 1852; J. D. Dana, *A System of Mineralogy*, New York, 488, 1850; 17, 1855; 17, 1868; 24, 1892; A. Breithaupt, *Berg. Hütt. Ztg.*, 15. 114, 1856; *Handbuch der Mineralogie*. Freiberg, 4. a, 1. 1817; J. C. Ullmann, *Systematisch-tabellarische Uebersicht der mineralogisch-einfachen Fossilien*. Cassel, 224, 1821; E. von Fedoroff, *Tschermak's Mitt.*, (2), 14. 88, 1895; G. H. F. Ulrich, *Contributions to the Mineralogy of Victoria*, Melbourne, 48, 1866; E. Cohen, *Meteoritenkunde*, Stuttgart, 34, 1894; R. N. Clark, *Trans. Amer. Inst. Min. Eng.*, 7. 21, 1879; G. A. Stein, *Liebig's Ann.*, 100. 127, 1856; G. Zerrenner, *Jahrb. Geol. Reichsanst. Wien*, 4, 497, 1853; *Sitzber. Akad. Wien*, 11. 262, 1853.

        [10] P. L. Burthe, *Ann. Mines*, (7), 5. 717, 1874; P. Laur, *ib.*, (6), 3. 423, 1863; A. Raimondi, *Memoire sobre el Cerro de Pasco*, Lima, 1885; *Les minéraux de Pérou*, Paris, 1878; B. Lotti, *I depositi dei minerali metalliferi*, Torino, 116, 1903; *Zeit. prakt. Geol.*, 9. 281, 1901; *Rass. Min.*, 14. 16, 1901; A. d'Achiardi, *I metalli*, 1. 182, 1883; D. Playfair, *Chem. News*, 39. 243, 1879; C. W. Cross, *Ann. Rep. U.S. Geol. Sur.*, 17, 1896; W. H. Emmons, *Trans. Amer. Inst. Min. Eng.*, 26. 733, 1896; R. N. Clark, *ib.*, 7. 21, 1879; A. Becker and P. Jannasch, *Jahrb. Rad. Elektron.*, 12. 1, 1915; M. Fort, *Ann. Constr. Civ. Min. Ind. Peru*, (2), 1. 1, 1901; A. Piutti and E. Stoppani, *Rend. Accad. Lincei*, (3), 10. 362, 1904; F. Zambonini, *Atti Accad. Lincei*, (5), 15. ii, 235, 1906; *Compt. Rend.*, 143. 921, 1906; A. Lacroix, *ib.*, 143. 723, 1906; M. Muguet, *ib.*, 174, 172, 1922; J. Strischoff, *Neues Jahrb. Min.*, i, 233, 1904; A. Scacchi, *Rend. Accad. Napoli*, (2), 16. 226, 1877; H. Lange, *Zeit. Naturwiss.*, 82. 23, 1910; A. L. Davis, *Journ. Phys. Chem.*, 22. 631, 1918; A. W. Stelzner and A. Bergeat, *Die Erzlagerstätten*, Leipzig, 2. 984, 1906; F. A. Quenstedt, *Geologische Ausflüge in Schwaben*, Tübingen, 154, 1864; A. Daubrée, *Les eaux souterraines aux époques anciennes et actuelles*, Paris, 2. 3, 1887; J. Roth, *Allgemeine und chemische Geologie*, Berlin, 1. 567, 1879; F. J. Malaguti, J. Durocher, and M. Sarzeaud, *Ann. Chim. Phys.*, (3), 28. 129, 1850; L. Darapsky, *Rev. Marina*, 5. 27, 1887; J. A. Phillips, *Journ. Geol. Soc.*, 35. 390, 1879; R. Fresenius, *Journ. prakt. Chem.*, (1), 95. 151, 1865; C. F. Becker, *Monog. U.S. Geol. Sur.*, 13. 331, 1888; E. Carstens, *Proc. Assoc. Russ. Med.*, 1, 1901; F. Garrigou, *Compt. Rend.*, 161. 144, 1915; W. F. Hillebrand, *Amer. Journ. Science*, (3), 43. 418, 1892; L. Dede, *Zeit. anal. Chem.*, 62. 342, 1923; P. Schmidt, *Arch. Hyg.*, 80. 62, 1913; R. Krzizan, *Œster. Chem. Ztg.*, 8. 173, 1905; K. Nenadkewitsch, *Trav. Mus. géol. St. Petersburg*, 5. 37, 1914.

        [11] G. Hattensaus, *Sitzber. Akad. Wien*, 99. 29, 1889; *Monatsh.*, 11. 19, 1890; E. Lidgey, *Trans. Anstral. Inst. Min. Eng.*, 4. 116, 1843; R. Beck, *ib.*, 4. 695, 1843; H. W. F. Wackenroder, *Arch. Pharm.*, (2), 75. 140, 257, 1853; (2), 76. 1, 1853; G. Meillère, *Le saturnisme*, Paris, 1903; *Journ. Pharm. Chim.*, (7), 7. 26, 1913; *Compt. Rend. Soc. Biol.*, 55, 517, 1903; A. Marie and P. Requier, *ib.*, 62. 675, 1907; L. G. Maillard, *ib.*, 64. 473, 1908; E. Brumpt, *ib.*, 64. 953, 1908; H. Legrand and L. Winter, *ib.*, 41. 46, 1889; A. Béchamp, *Compt. Rend.*, 49. 895, 1859; V. Schwarzenbach, *Verh. Ges. Wärzburg*, 7. 19, 1857; W. Ebstein, *Arch. Anat. Physiol.*, 134. 541, 1893; A. W. Blyth, *Chem. News*, 55. 222, 1887; T. W. Hogg, *ib.*, 71. 223, 1895; F. Muttelet and F. Touplain, *Ann. Falsif.*, 5. 9, 1912; W. Ellenberger and V. Hofmeister, *Ber. Veter. Sachsen*, 2, 1883; *Arch. Tierheilkunde*, 10. 216, 1884; L. Hugounenq, *Journ. Pharm. Chim.*, (6), 8. 529, 1898; V. Lehmann, *Zeit. physiol. Chem.*, 6. 528, 1882; K. Stockmann and F. J. Charteris, *Journ. Pathol. Bakter.*, 9. 202, 1903; G. Sonntag, *Arb. Kaiser Ges. Amt*, 49. 502, 1914; H. Oidtmann, *Die anorganischen Bestandtheile der Leber und Milz und der meisten anderen thierischen Drüsen*, Linnich, 1858; E. Heubel, *Pathogenese und Symptome der chronischen Bleivergiftung*, Berlin, 1871; A. Devergie, *Bull. Thérap.*, 15. 259, 1840; *Ann. Hyg. Publ.*, 180. 1840; M. J. B. Orfila, *ib.*, 149, 1839; J. Antschul, *Pharm. Centrh.*, 16. 707, 1895; A. Chevallier, *Journ. Chim. Méd.*, (3), 3. 375, 1847; V. Legrip, *ib.*, (3), 3. 251, 1847; E. Cottereau, *ib.*, (3), 5. 179, 1849; J. Barse, *ib.*, (2), 9. 571, 1843; N. A. E. Millon, *Compt. Rend.*, 26. 41, 1848; *Ann. Chim. Phys.*, (3), 23. 372, 508, 1848; (3), 24. 255, 1848; L. H. F. Melsens, *ib.*, (3), 23. 358, 1848; *Journ. Chim. Méd.*, (3), 4. 486, 1848; B. du Buisson, *Sur l'existence du manganèse dans le sang humain*, Lyon, 1852; A. Thiergardt, *Ueber Aufnahme und Ansammlung von Arsen und Blei in Körper der Fische*, Wärzburg, 184, 1897; *Jahresb. Tierchem.*, 30. 524, 1900; C. Oppenheimer, *ib.*, 29. 82, 1899; *Zur Kenntnis der experimentellen Bleivergiftung*, Berlin, 1899; H. Greven,

Versuchungen über chronische Bleivergifterung beim Kaninchen, Born, 1900 ; Jahresb. Tierchem.,
30. 880, 1900 ; F. Shufflebotham and J. W. Mellor, Lancet, 165. 746, 1903.
   [12] J. Boes, Apoth. Ztg., 22. 1105, 1907 ; R. Weber. Zeit. öffent. Chem., 12. 108, 1906 ; A. Seyda,
ib., 3. 364, 1897 ; H. Stockmeier, ib., 14. 208, 1908 ; Zeit. angew. Chem., 21. 1453, 1908 ;
O Megger and K. Fuchs, ib., 21. 1556, 1908 ; W. Wicke, Liebig's Ann., 112. 122, 1859 ;
R. R. Tatlock and R. T. Thomson, Analyst, 33. 173, 1908 ; N. T. Fox, ib., 47. 468, 469, 1922 ;
A. Geheel, Arch. Pharm., (3), 10. 41, 1877 ; A. Hilger, ib., (3), 6. 391, 1875 ; P. Carles, Rev.
Internat. Falsif., 20. 162, 1908 ; A. Vogel, Repert Pharm., (2), 19. 348, 1870 ; (2), 22. 394, 1873 ;
J. Grünwald, Œster. Chem. Ztg., 11. 271, 1908 ; N. P. Marasneff, Zeit. Unters. Nahr. Genuss.,
15. 388, 1908 ; E. Schering, Ber., 12. 156, 1879 ; A. Classen, ib., 23. 938, 1890 ; G. Giusti, Staz.
Sperim. Agrav. Ital., 37. 352, 1904 ; E. Klingelhöffer, Jahrb. Pharm., 39. 86, 1873 ; K. Endell,
Ueber den Bleigehalt glasierter Thongeschirre, Tübingen, 1915 ; H. Lührig, Pharm. Centrh., 46.
835, 1905 ; A. Barillé, Compt. Rend., 153. 351, 1911 ; A. Carnot, ib., 86. 718, 1878 ; A. Riche,
ib., 86. 1502, 1878 ; S. de Luca, ib., 82. 1187, 1876 ; F. M. Litterscheid, Zeit. unters. Nahr,
Genuss., 23. 440, 1912 ; E. Junker, Pharm. Centrh., 62. 271, 1921 ; K. Neukam, Chem. Ztg.
45. 301, 1921 ; W. D. Collins and W. F. Clarke, Journ. Ind. Eng. Chem., 11. 138,
1919 ; C. H. la Wall, Amer. Journ. Pharm., 89. 353, 1917 ; O. F. Lubatti, Journ. Soc. Chem.
Ind., 39. 36, 1920 ; E. Rieter, Mitt. Lebensm. Hyg. Schweiz. Gesundh., 3. 11, 1912 ; V. Micault,
Bull. Soc. Min., 4. 83, 1881.
   [13] J. A. F. Ballard, Compt. Rend., 111. 895, 1890 ; L. Moreau and E. Vinet, ib., 150. 787,
1910 ; L. Nathan, Centrb. Bakter., 14. 289, 1905 ; L. Nathan and A. Schmidt, ib., 15. 349, 1905 ;
F. Spaeth, Pharm. Centrb., 53. 703, 1912 ; F. H. Storer, Viertelj. prakt. Pharm., 19. 496, 1870 ;
A. Hubert and F. Alba, Ann. Chim. Anal. App., 12. 230, 1907 ; A. R. Leeds, Journ. Amer.
Chem. Soc., 3. 60, 1881 ; Chem. News, 44. 244, 1881 ; H. Baum and R. Seeliger, Arch. Tierheilk ,
21. 297, 1895 ; A. Stadler, Schweiz. Wochschr. Pharm., 50. 202, 1912 ; G. Sonntag, Arb. Kaiser
Ges. Amt., 49. 502, 1914 ; H. Roos, Rev. Int. Falsif., 3. 43, 1889 : A. F. Canelli, Riv. Clin. Pediatr.,
18. 473, 1920 ; R. Roth, Umschau, 366, 1916 ; M. Klostermann and K. Scholta, Zeit. Unters
Nahr. Gernuss., 33. 304, 1907 ; F. Wirthle and K. Amberger, ib., 44. 89, 1922 ; L. Stefanowicz,
Wien Klin. Wochschr., 29. 1531, i916 ; A. Cutolo, Boll. Chim. Farm., 53. 692, 1914 ; P. Carles,
Ann. Falsif, 10. 484, 1917 ; F. Muttelet and F. Touplain, ib., 5. 9, 1912 ; P. Schindler, Zeit.
öffent. Chem., 19. 132, 1913.

§ 3. The Extraction of Lead

Copper and gold and iron were discovered and at the same time weighty silver and the substance of lead when fire with its heat had burnt up vast forests on the great hills, . . . and had thoroughly baked the earth, there would collect in the hollows of the ground a stream of silver and gold as well as of copper and lead.—Lucretius (5. 1241).

The available lead ores are divided into *sulphide ores* which include galena generally mixed with more or less pyrites and other sulphides ; and *oxidized ores* which include the carbonates, anglesite, and pyromorphite. They all contain silver, and when that element is present in amounts sufficient to pay for its extraction they are designated *argentiferous*, and if in less quantity, *non-argentiferous*. During the smelting of the ore, the silver follows the lead, although a small proportion may remain with the slag, or in a regulus or speise which accompanies the reduced lead. The lead is usually desilverized to recover the silver. There are many monographs, etc., on the different phases of the metallurgy of lead.[1]

The lead content of the ore as mined varies within wide limits, being upwards of about 5 per cent. Occasionally the sulphide ores are so free from extraneous matters that a preliminary dressing or concentration is unnecessary ; usually, the sulphide ore is crushed and concentrated on jigs and buddles so as to yield a concentrate containing over 70–85 per cent. of lead.   J. Percy showed that it is not necessarily true that the fine-grained galenas are richer in silver than the coarse-grained ore ; the more complex sulphide ores, however, are usually richer in silver than simple galena ore.   Particular attention is paid to the silver content of the slimes because with some ores the associated argentiferous mineral may be more brittle and more easily crushed than the galena and so accumulate in the slimes. F. Clark discussed the concentration of lead ores by flotation.

When the ore is associated with much zinc blende, the concentration is difficult. At Broken Hill, New South Wales, the ordinary process of concentration is supplemented by the flotation process so as to procure the zinc blende free from objectionable lead, and the galena free from the objectionable zinc. E. W. Mayer and R. Schön [2] have described the flotation process at Steiermark. The concentration of oxidized ores is more difficult because of the losses of lead and silver with the slime. These ores are usually smelted as they come direct from the mine.

Lead is usually extracted from its ores by dry processes ; the wet processes are more elaborate and their cost too high for successful competition with the dry processes. Lead ores are usually so easily smelted by ordinary furnace methods that the many wet processes which have been suggested have no chance of success. In exceptional cases, lead may be economically extracted from plumbiferous residues by wet processes. Electrolytic methods are not employed in the treatment of the ores, though they may be used to some extent when dealing with certain alloys.

In the first century B.C., the poet Lucretius speculated how lead and other metals were discovered by man. According to R. H. Lamborn, the early settlers in Missouri made lead for their bullets by smelting pieces of galena in a fire built in the hollow of a tree stump. The allusions in Strabo's *Geographica* (**3**. 2), and in Pliny's *Historia naturalis* (**34**. 22), to the ancient lead furnaces give very little information. A reference in Jeremiah (**6**. 29) shows that bellows were probably used in smelting lead. The primitive smelting of lead in Britain appears to have been done in wind-furances—*boles*—built in a favourable position with respect to the prevailing winds. Thus, J. Childrey [3] said :

The lead-stones in the Peak lye but just within the ground next to the upper crust of the earth. They melt the lead upon the top of the hills that lye open to the west ; making their fires to melt it as soon as the west wind begins to blow ; which wind by long experience they find holds longest of all others.

R. Watson described the *boles* of Derbyshire where lead was smelted in former times ; J. Farey gave a list of the sites of the ancient boles ; and A. Barba described similar furnaces used by the Peruvians. W. Forster said that the boles were simply piles of stone placed around a fire and arranged to leave openings for the admission of air and the escape of gaseous products of combustion. These were supplanted by hearth-furnaces built on the plan of a smith's forge as described by J. Martyn, and J. Glanvil. In 1678, G. L. Grandison obtained a patent for the use of coal in place of wood for smelting lead in reverberatory furnaces ; and J. Hodges, a patent for a similar purpose in 1690. J. J. Becher claimed to have introduced coal as a fuel for smelting tin ores in Cornwall, but J. Percy doubted the validity of the claim. According to C. A. Schlüter, the reverberatory furnace for melting lead was invented by a Mr. Wright in co-operation with two others. A. Barba in 1640 described a *hornos de reberberacion* or reverberatory furnace for roasting ores using wood as a fuel. According to J. Farey, cupola, or low-arched reverberatory furnaces were used at Kalstedge, Derbyshire, in 1747 ; and, according to A. P. Dufrénoy, at Alston, Northumberland, in 1810. These furnaces were very similar to those now in use.

The processes for smelting lead may be classified according to the type of furnace —reverberatory, hearth, or shaft furnace—or they may be classified according to the way the lead is obtained from the sulphide :

(1) In the so-called *air reduction process, or the roasting process*, the galena is roasted so as to form a mixture of the sulphide, sulphate, and oxide in approximately definite proportions, and when the temp. is raised, the lead sulphide reacts with the sulphate and oxide, forming sulphur dioxide and lead : $2PbS+PbSO_4+2PbO$ $=5Pb+3SO_2$.

(2) In the *reduction process*, the galena is roasted until it is all converted into oxide admixed with a little sulphate which is then reduced to lead by carbonaceous matters. The sulphate is either converted into silicate by fusion with silica at the end of the roasting, and the silicate reduced to metal by subsequently smelting with carbon and iron oxide, or it can be reduced to the sulphide.

(3) In the so-called *iron reduction process*, or the *precipitation process*, the galena

is decomposed by heating it with metallic iron, lead is set free, and *lead matte*, a complex of iron and lead sulphides, is formed. The processes may not be kept entirely separate, but combined as when the residues from the first process are reduced with carbon or with iron ; or when the product of the second process is worked up by either of the other two.

Some chemical changes occurring during the reduction of lead sulphide.— Finely divided and precipitated lead sulphide was found by G. F. Rodwell [4] to absorb oxygen at 50°, and to smell of sulphur dioxide at 125°–150° According to E. F. Anthon, lead sulphide precipitated from a soln. of the nitrate by strontium sulphide, and dried between 40° and 50°, takes fire when nearly dry and continues to burn for about an hour, when it is all converted into lead sulphate. When lead sulphide is gently ignited in air, H. V. Collet-Descotils found that the greater part of the sulphur is given off as sulphur dioxide, while about half the contained lead separates as metal, and the remainder is converted into lead sulphate. This is a very curious reaction. F. Dempwolff found that when air is passed over lead sulphide, warmed in a boat at 250°, and not over 450°, almost all is converted into lead sulphate when the surface exposed is sufficiently great ; with a rising temp., the velocity of the reaction increases and likewise also the amount of sulphur dioxide evolved. Some sulphur trioxide is also given off, and at 750° the ratio of the $SO_2 : SO_3$ from the burnt sulphur is 65 : 35. A reaction between the lead oxide and sulphate then begins. The reaction was studied by F. Janda, P. Berthier, and J. B. Hannay. K. Friedrich found that galena resembles the precipitated sulphide in giving evidence of oxidation at a low temp., namely, 90°. The temp. at which galena begins to glow varies with the size of grain and rate of heating. For grains approximating 0·1–0·2 mm. diameter, the initial glow occurred at 847° when the temp. is raised slowly, and at 646° when the temp. is raised quickly from ordinary temp. The glow occurred at 554° when the mineral is put directly into a furnace at that temp. The product of the oxidation of galena in air is a mixture of lead oxide and sulphate. C. F. Rammelsberg supposed that the sulphide is directly oxidized to sulphate, $PbS+2O_2=PbSO_4$; it is, however, possible that during the roasting some of the sulphur dioxide given off is oxidized to sulphur trioxide and that this unites with the lead oxide, forming the sulphate. This agrees with the observation that the factors which favour the oxidation of sulphur dioxide increase the relative proportions of sulphate and oxide in the roasted mass. C. F. Plattner found that in the roasting of a sample of galena, the product contained 66·3 per cent. of oxide and 36·7 per cent. of sulphate, or twice as much oxide as sulphate.

When lead is extracted from galena by roasting in air, the process is not carried to completion ; for at a certain stage the temp. of the partially roasted ore is raised. A new set of reactions is inaugurated between the unaltered lead sulphide and its partially roasted products. The fundamental reactions involve the oxidation of galena to sulphate *viâ* the intermediate formation of sulphur trioxide as indicated above. These processes furnish the summation equation $PbS+2O_2=PbSO_4$. If two-fifths of the galena is converted to oxide : $2PbS+3O_2=2PbO+2SO_2$, the two products, lead oxide and sulphate, react with the unchanged galena, forming the metal $PbS+PbSO_4=2Pb+2SO_2$, and $PbS+2PbO=3Pb+SO_2$. H. C. Jenkins and E. A. Smith showed that these reactions are reversible, and this was established by the work of W. Reinders, and of R. Schenck and fellow-workers. When the conditions are such that sulphur dioxide is continuously removed, A. Lodin showed that these two reactions may be made quantitative ; such a condition is obtained by heating a mixture of the necessary amounts of sulphide and oxide or sulphide and sulphate in a stream of carbon dioxide or nitrogen. The conc. of the sulphur dioxide is thus negligibly small. C. O. Bannister gives 730°–745° for the temp. of the reaction between sulphide and sulphate, and A. Lodin gave 670° for $PbS+PbSO_4$ $=2Pb+2SO_2$; 820° for $PbS+3PbSO_4=4PbO+4SO_2$; and 720° for $PbS+2PbO$ $=3Pb+SO_2$, and C. O. Bannister gives 800°–810° for this reaction. The temp. in any particular case must naturally depend on the conditions. According to

J. W. Döbereiner, lead oxide and sulphide can be melted together without decomposition ; but P. Berthier, and J. Percy have shown that the reaction proceeds as just indicated. If the litharge already has another metal sulphide in soln.—*e.g.* zinc or iron sulphide—the lead sulphide can be dissolved without decomposition. The summation of these equations furnishes : $PbS+O_2=Pb+SO_2$, which shows only the initial and end-products of the remarkable sequence of oxidizing and reducing reactions. In confirmation of the production of lead by a reaction between lead sulphide and oxide, P. Berthier found that lead is obtained by heating galena with strong oxidizing agents like potassium nitrate, or manganese dioxide. J. B. Hannay also obtained a 50 per cent. yield of lead by blowing air through molten galena. The reactions, however, are even more complex than is here indicated. There is no evidence of any appreciable reaction between lead and its sulphide or oxide, but P. Berthier, and J. Percy showed that at a fairly high temp., lead reacts with the sulphate $Pb+PbSO_4=2PbO+SO_2$, so that when this equation is combined with : $PbS+PbSO_4=2Pb+2SO_2$, there remains $PbS+3PbSO_4=4PbO+4SO_2$ to represent the end-products of this side-reaction. There is nothing to show that sulphur dioxide reacts with lead sulphide or sulphate, but when lead oxide is heated in the gas, C. F. Plattner said that it glows, forming lead sulphide and sulphate. D. L. Hammick found that the reaction occurs just below visible redness—400°–500°. This therefore reverses the reaction $Pb+PbSO_4 =2PbO+SO_2$, and $PbS+3PbSO_4=4PbO+4SO_2$. Given the three components, lead, sulphur, and oxygen, there may be the gaseous phase, sulphur dioxide, as well as the solid phases lead, lead sulphate, lead sulphide, lead oxide, as well as the three basic sulphates, making three components, and seven possible phases ; giving thirteen possible univariant systems each consisting of three solid phases in equilibrium with the gaseous phase. These form three groups. *Group I* has four systems in which lead sulphide is in equilibrium with solid phases containing oxygen: (1) $7PbSO_4+PbS \rightleftharpoons 4Pb_2OSO_4+4SO_2$; (2) $10Pb_2OSO_4+PbS \rightleftharpoons 7Pb_3O_2SO_4+4SO_2$; (3) $13Pb_3O_2SO_4+PbS \rightleftharpoons 10Pb_4O_3SO_4+4SO_2$; and (4) $3Pb_4O_3SO_4+PbS \rightleftharpoons 13PbO+4SO_2$. *Group II* has five systems in which lead and lead sulphide are in equilibrium with one solid phase containing oxygen: (5) $PbSO_4+PbS=2Pb+2SO_2$; (6) $2Pb_2OSO_4+3PbS \rightleftharpoons 7Pb+5SO_2$; (7) $Pb_3O_2SO_4 +2PbS \rightleftharpoons 5Pb+3SO_2$; (8) $2Pb_4O_3SO_4+5PbS=13Pb+7SO_2$; and (9) $2PbO+PbS =3Pb+SO_2$. *Group III* has four systems with metallic lead and two solid phases containing oxygen: (10) $3PbSO_4+Pb \rightleftharpoons 2Pb_2OSO_4+SO_2$; (11) $4Pb_2OSO_4+Pb \rightleftharpoons 3Pb_3O_2SO_4+SO_2$; (12) $5Pb_3O_2SO_4+Pb \rightleftharpoons 4Pb_4O_3SO_4+SO_2$; and (13) $Pb_4O_3SO_4+Pb \rightleftharpoons 5PbO+SO_2$. The vap. press. of the systems in groups I and II have been investigated.

For univariant equilibrium in a three component system, four phases are required, and one of these is the gas sulphur dioxide. Measurable equilibria were found to occur with some systems, and the press. of the gas was independent of the direction from which equilibrium was approached. For the system $PbS+PbSO_4 \rightleftharpoons 2Pb+2SO_2$, the reaction goes appreciably at 550° as shown by the evolution of sulphur dioxide, and measurable press. are attained at 600°.

	600°	615°	635°	665°	695°	713°	723°
Pressure SO_2 .	39	61	98	201	402	590	735 mm.

The sulphide and oxide begin to react : $PbS+2PbO \rightleftharpoons 3Pb+SO_2$ at about 650°–660°, and provided the temp. does not exceed 800°, the reaction is reversible.

	692°	712°	733°	751°	776°	800°	824°
Pressure SO_2 .	6	14	23	39	60	99	276 mm.

If the mixture of solids be heated to a higher temp., and then cooled, the press. of the sulphur dioxide does not return to its original value, but is much higher than those just indicated. This was traced to the formation of the basic sulphate

PbO.PbSO$_4$, and the system in equilibrium is represented by 2Pb$_2$OSO$_4$+3PbS
$\rightleftharpoons$7Pb+5SO$_2$, and the partial press. of the sulphur dioxide was :

	681°	716°	759°	780°	795°	821°	830°
Pressure SO$_2$.	16	42	130	217	306	548	710 mm.

These partial press. curves are plotted in Fig. 2 ; and there is also included
in the same diagram observations by W. Reinders, and R. Schenck and A. Albers.
The curve Aa refers to system (1) ; Bb to (2) ; Cc
to (3) ; Dd to (4) ; OA to (5) ; AB to (6) ; BC to (7) ;
CD to (8) ; and De to (9). At the invariant point
A, 567°, the phases PbSO$_4$, Pb$_2$OSO$_4$, PbS, and Pb
are in equilibrium with the gas phase ; at B, 706°,
Pb$_2$OSO$_4$, Pb$_3$O$_2$SO$_4$, PbS, and Pb ; at C, 770°,
Pb$_3$O$_2$SO$_4$, Pb$_4$O$_3$SO$_4$, PbS, and Pb ; and at D, 784°,
Pb$_4$O$_3$SO$_4$, PbO, PbS, and Pb. Lead sulphide is a
solid phase in all the zones, and in addition PbSO$_4$
in OAa ; Pb$_2$OSO$_4$ in aABb ; Pb$_3$O$_2$SO$_4$ in bBCc ;
Pb$_4$O$_3$SO$_4$ in cCDd ; PbO in dDe ; and finally, below
the line OABCDe there is metallic lead. The most
stable phases are those in group II, where both lead
and lead sulphide are present as solid phases, these

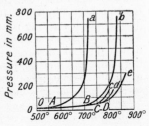

FIG. 2.—Partial Pressures of
Sulphur Dioxide in Various
Systems, PbO, PbS, PbSO$_4$,
etc.

systems being in equilibrium with a lower press. of sulphur dioxide than those of
group I. The vapour phase always contains lead sulphide. In systems of group
III, where lead sulphide is not present as a solid phase, the vapour must be sat.
with respect to lead sulphide. A diagram for group III must therefore be in three
dimensions, one of which represents the vapour press. of lead sulphide. The
systems of group III were found to be too unsuitable to realize experimentally.
R. Schenck studied the action of sulphur dioxide on metallic lead in a closed vessel.
The press. of the gas diminishes to a constant value representing the equilibrium
of sulphate with sulphide and metal as in the field OAa, Fig. 2. The values 101
mm. at 653°, and 240 mm. at 690°, fall exactly on the sulphate curve. In all the
above systems of equilibria, the metal phase is not
really lead, but a soln. of lead sulphide in lead. If
the metal is not sat. with sulphide, the system will
be bivariant, not univariant, since the press. of the
sulphur dioxide will depend on the conc. of the
sulphide in the lead. W. Reinders investigated the
ternary system with lead, sulphur, and oxygen as
components by gradually removing sulphur dioxide
from a mixture of lead sulphide and sulphate, and observed the five univariant systems : I. PbS–PbSO$_4$–
Pb$_2$OSO$_4$; II. Pb$_a$–PbS–Pb$_2$OSO$_4$; III. Pb$_b$–Pb$_2$OSO$_4$–
Pb$_3$O$_2$SO$_4$; IV. Pb$_c$–Pb$_3$O$_2$SO$_4$–Pb$_4$O$_3$SO$_4$; and V.
Pb$_d$–Pb$_4$O$_3$SO$_4$–PbO. The proportion of lead sulphide dissolved in the lead probably varies with

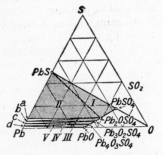

FIG. 3.—Equilibria in the Ternary Systems : Pb–S–O.

the different equilibria, and the amounts are diagrammatically represented by the points a, b, c, d, Fig. 3. The diagram
represents the regions corresponding with the five systems just indicated.
K. Jänecke applied the phase rule to the roasting of the sulphide ore.

Carbon dioxide exerts a slight oxidizing action on galena, and A. Lodin
found that at 860°, sulphur dioxide is formed, and lead remains—being
formed, presumably, by the reaction between lead oxide and sulphide. The
effect of carbon on the reduction of lead sulphate and sulphide was studied
by P. Berthier, J. L. Gay Lussac, J. Fournet, etc. Galena may contain sulphides
other than iron pyrites, and the sulphides of copper, silver, zinc, manganese,
and bismuth, which are all oxidized during the roasting, and oxides or basic

sulphates are formed. Arsenic and antimony sulphides form volatile oxides. The products of the reactions of the roasting of these sulphides were considered by C. F. Plattner, G. Keppeler, D. L. Hammick, H. Schiff, W. Mostowisch, and J. Uhl. J. Percy, and C. F. Plattner studied the behaviour of the pyrites present during the roasting of galena, while C. O. Bannister studied the effect of silica ; ferric oxide ; calcium oxide, sulphate, hydroxide and carbonate ; magnesia ; and lead oxide. Silica and calcium sulphate were found to act as inactive diluents opening up the ore and allowing a freer penetration of the air ; ferric oxide reduced the temp. at which roasting begins by about 100°, and at the same time reduced the interval of temp. during which roasting is active. The proportion of lead sulphate in the product was augmented presumably by the catalytic oxidation of sulphur dioxide. Strongly basic oxides like litharge, magnesia, and lime cause exothermal reactions—due to the combination of the base with the sulphur oxide gases—evidenced by glowing, when the oxidation of the galena occurs between 500° and 550° ; with calcium carbonate the effect is similar between 550° and 600°.

In T. Huntington and F. Heberlein's process of high temp. blast-roasting, a mixture of 6 to 15 parts of alkaline earth per 100 parts of ore, is heated to 700° in a reverberatory furnace with the free admission of air, and the temp. allowed to fall to about 500°, and not below 450°. The hot mass is transferred to converters where it is subjected to an air-blast and the temp. is raised ; sulphur dioxide is copiously evolved, and the mass becomes viscous as the reactions are completed. It is generally admitted that the mechanical effect of the lime is to prevent premature agglomeration of the charge, and, as emphasized by G. Rigg, to ventilate the ore so that there is a rapid circulation of air about the charge. J. Percy, however, showed that the action of lime is not exclusively mechanical, and is distinctly chemical. There are many differences of opinion as to the chemical actions involved. P. Berthier showed that calcium oxide and galena react when strongly heated, forming calcium sulphide and lead oxide. Some metallic lead, and a slag of sulphide and sulphate, are produced, making it probable that the lead oxide is reduced by lead or calcium sulphides with the formation of an equivalent quantity of sulphate. It has not been proved that reactions between calcium oxide and lead sulphate ; calcium sulphate and lead oxide ; calcium sulphide and lead sulphate : or calcium sulphate and lead sulphide, if they occur at all, have any influence on the roasting process. T. Huntington and F. Heberlein assumed that the action of the lime is catalytic involving the cyclic formation and reduction of calcium dioxide : $4CaO_2+PbS$ $=PbSO_4+4CaO$; while the reactions in the converter were assumed to be PbS $+3PbSO_4=4PbO+4SO_2$ and $PbS+PbSO_4+O_2=2PbO+2SO_2$. W. Borchers, W. M. Hutchings, F. Richter, and C. Guillemain doubt if calcium dioxide is formed under the conditions which obtain in the furnace, although W. Borchers believes that a calcium plumbite or plumbate, $CaPbO_3$, is produced by the action of air and lime on the litharge produced from the lead sulphide, and that the oxidation of the galena involves the cyclic formation and reduction of calcium plumbate : $3CaPbO_3$ $+PbS=4PbO+3CaO+SO_2$. D. Clark, W. Borchers, and A. D. Carmichael found calcium plumbate among the products of the action, but T. Richter found none, and he believed that although a little may be produced, it plays only a secondary part in the roasting process. W. M. Hutchings suggested that calcium sulphate is formed by the action of sulphur dioxide and oxygen on lime, and this product is the catalytic agent ; indeed, in A. D. Carmichael's modification, calcium sulphate is employed in place of lime. H. F. Collins pointed out that as emphasized by W. C. Roberts-Austen, the reaction $PbS+CaSO_4=PbSO_4+CaS-28$ cals., being endothermal, is probably impossible in a neutral atm., but may be possible if the calcium sulphate can be oxidized by air : $CaS+2O_2=CaSO_4+226\cdot4$ cals., for the calcium sulphate can give up oxygen to lead sulphide, forming calcium sulphide, which is reoxidized in the act of being formed, so that the net result is the exothermal reaction : $PbS+CaSO_4$ $+2O_2=PbSO_4+CaSO_4+198\cdot4$ cals. It therefore seems probable, added H. F. Collins, that the addition of lime to the converter charge does facilitate the oxidation of lead sulphide, yet, as pointed out by C. Guillemain, the addition is by no means essential and the result of eliminating the sulphur and converting the lead into oxide can be obtained by a combination of the exo- and endo-thermal reactions: $2PbS+3O_2$ $=2PbO+2SO_2+199\cdot6$ cals., and $PbS+3PbSO_4=4PbO+4SO_2-187$ cals.; and the premature sintering of the charge prevented by the addition of fine iron flux. quartz ore, or other inert substance. Arguments are frequently based on the thermo-chemical data obtained at comparatively low temp., but it is probable the data are quite inapplicable at higher temp., and the conclusions are therefore *non sequitur.*

P. Weiller represents the reaction $PbS+2O_2=PbSO_4$; $2PbS+2O_2=2PbO+2SO_2$: $PbS+CaO=CaS+PbO$; and $CaS+PbSO_4=CaSO_4+PbS$, and the latter reacts with oxygen as before. D. Clark, A. D. Carmichael, F. O. Doeltz, W. Mostowisch, W. M. Hutchings, C. Guillemain, and F. Richter have also studied these reactions. R. Tandler represents the main reaction as involving the oxidation of lead sulphide to sulphate by the irreversible reaction: $PbS+2O_2=PbSO_4$; and the balanced reaction $PbSO_4+CaO\rightleftharpoons CaSO_4+PbO$. The important part played by silica in the reactions in the formation of slag in the converter has been emphasized by A. Savelsberg, W. M. Hutchings, etc. According to P. Richter, the silica acts by decomposing the objectionable sulphates, forming a readily fusible silicate. According to H. O. Hofmann and W. Mostowisch, the silica begins to decompose calcium sulphate at about 1000°, and decomposition is complete at 1250°. C. Dörschel studied the effect of zinc blende and of barytes on the roasting of galena.

Dry processes for the extraction of lead.—G. Agricola, in his *De re metallica* (Basel, 1556), gave a description of the methods of smelting lead ores in vogue among the Saxons, Poles, and Westphalians in the sixteenth century. Alternate layers of fuel (wood) and ore were piled on a " hearth of bricks—four feet high—with sloping sides," so as to form a kind of basin. When the fuel burnt, the ore was reduced, and the resulting metal collected in the basin of the hearth. The lead basin was either tipped like a crucible, or the lead was allowed to flow over the edge at one corner. The extraction of lead from the rich galenas by partially roasting the ore followed by the reduction through the interaction of the products of oxidation is generally con-ducted in **reverberatory furnaces** of the type of the so-called *Flintshire furnace.*[5]

The hearth of the furnace is built over a vault to avoid the loss of lead in the foundations. The modification of the Flintshire furnace used at Couëron, Loire Inférieure, France, is illustrated by the longitudinal section, Fig. 4. Here *A* represents the fireplace; the hearth, *B*, is trapezoidal in shape, and is about 100 sq. ft. in area, sloping towards the tapping-hole *C*. The working doors are shown at *D*; the feeding hopper at *E*. The working-bed *B* is made of grey slag from the smelting. The slag is broken into pieces, thrown into the red-hot furnace, and, when melted, is worked by rabbles over the firebrick bottom into the required shape. About 30 cwts. of ore are spread on the bottom of the red-hot furnace; it is then stirred and worked over with rabbles at a temp. as high as possible without sintering the ore. The sul-phide is partly oxidized to sulphate and oxide. The temp. is then raised, and reduced lead accumulates in the well, from which it is tapped at inter-

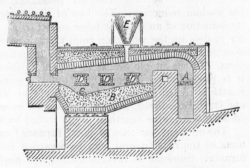

FIG. 4.—Flintshire Reverberatory Lead Furnace.

vals. Lime is then thrown in to thicken the slag. The unreduced ore floats on the surface, and the operations of roasting and smelting are repeated until the flow of lead slackens. The residual slags are raked out, and the lead is tapped again. The skimmings from the lead pot are returned to the furnace. Three charges are worked off in about 24 hrs., and each charge yields about a ton of lead. The metal is cast in ingots or pigs—*pig-lead.*

There are several modifications of the process arranged to suit peculiarities in the local ores. The *Silesian process* is similar in principle to the above, but the furnace is larger, and the temp. is lower. Oxidizing materials—works residues, consisting of lead, etc.—are added to assist the reaction with unoxidized sulphide. The *Corinthian process* was formerly worked at Bleiberg, Corinthia, and in some other countries—Belgium, Missouri, etc. The *French process*, or *le procédé breton* —*Brittany process*—of this process was formerly used at Poullaouen, Brittany, and in other parts of France and in other countries. The *Cornish process*, or *flowing furnace process*, was once used for impure galenas in Cornwall. Here the lead is partially reduced by the Flintshire process, and partly by iron and culm (small coal or anthracite). This process is also used for recovering lead from slags and other refuse in the Flintshire process. The product is called *slag lead*, and is contaminated with more antimony, copper, and other impurities than is the case with the lead from the Flintshire process.

The method of smelting in the **ore hearth** or **ore-hearth furnace** preceded the use of the reverberatory furnace. The ore hearth is really a small rectangular blast-furnace of a primitive type. Early in the eighteenth century, nearly all the lead-smelting in Derbyshire was conducted in the ore hearth, charcoal or dried wood being used as a fuel, and the blast was supplied by bellows worked with a water-wheel. Towards the end of the eighteenth century, said R. Watson,[6] there were only one or two such furnaces in the whole country. The ore hearth is still considered to be useful for ores rich in lead, and the residues and slags with a high lead-content require separate treatment in a flowing furnace or in a cupola. The illustration, Fig. 5, resembles in a general way one employed by Keld Head Co., Yorkshire. In the ore hearth the charge of ore, mixed with fuel A, Fig. 5, floats on a bath of molten lead, B, in a sump or cast-iron dish set in masonry. The air is supplied by a blast C. The reduced lead trickles through the charge into the bath and overflows down a sloping plate, D, into an iron pot, E, outside the furnace. The lumps of slag are picked out and removed as they are formed, and fresh quantities of ore and fuel added in small charges as required. The reactions are similar to those in the reverberatory furnace process, but the oxidation and reduction stages occur simultaneously; the air reduction, however, is here supplemented by the carbon reduction. The loss of silver, etc., by volatilization necessitates the introduction of an efficient fume collector, F. The fume collector is indispensable for protecting the workmen from the injurious action of lead vapour and sulphur dioxide fumes which ascend copiously from the hearth. There are many modifications. In the simple *Scotch hearth*, the furnace gets very hot in about 6 hrs., and it is then allowed to cool for about the same time. In the *Rossie furnace*, the hearth is cooled by air; in another type at Missouri, described by C. P. Williams, and G. C. Broadhead, the hearth is cooled by water; in the *Moffet hearth* or *Jumbo furnace*, the double hearth is partly cooled by water and partly by air.

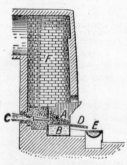

FIG. 5.—Ore Hearth.

The different varieties of **blast furnace**[7] or **shaft furnace** used for the reductions of the roasted ores, can be regarded as a highly developed form of hearth furnace. Smelting in reverberatories and hearths is confined to ores and concentrates with over 60 per cent. of lead and less than 5 per cent. of silica. Ores with a lower proportion of lead, plumbiferous slags, roasted matters, and furnace products rich in lead are smelted in blast furnaces. Ores free from sulphur can be heated in blast furnaces after being mixed with lime, silica, or other fluxes so as to form a slag with the gangue of the ore, and the ash of the fuel. The carbonaceous matters in the fuel reduce the lead.

Sulphide ores are subjected to a preliminary roasting. There may be the simple heap roasting for ores in lumps, and roasting in reverberatory furnaces suitable for powdered ore. In sinter roasting, the charge is heated sufficiently to agglomerate or sinter the ore into masses which are afterwards broken up for the blast furnace. Ores which do not sinter well may be made into briquettes with a suitable bond—milk of lime, or clay— and afterwards roasted. In lime roasting, the ore is mixed with limestone, or silica and limestone and roasted in the usual way. This process was used by T. Huntington and F. Heberlein; in the A. D. Carmichael process the ore is mixed with calcium sulphate and roasted. L. S. Austin used a specially designed pot for roasting. There are roasting furnaces with fixed hearths and immovable rabbles—*e.g.* the furnace of Wethey, A. von der Ropp, and E. Keller; in another type, the hearth rotates and the rabble is fixed—*e.g.* the furnaces of Brunton, F. Heberlein, etc. Some roasting is also done in shaft furnaces.

There are many types of blast furnace, and in the earlier types, the furnace linings were so quickly destroyed by the corrosive action of the plumbiferous slags, etc., that they were not a commercial success. It was only after B. Pilz had designed the water-jacketing of these furnaces in 1863, that blast furnace processes for lead smelting became a practical success. The many types now used are either circular—*e.g.* the *Pilz furnace*—or rectangular—*e.g.* the *Raschette furnace*. A furnace used at Freiberg, Fig. 6, illustrates the circular type. There is a wrought-iron water-cooled jacket in the tuyère zone. This is arranged in segments. Cold water enters at the bottom of each segment and flows away in a pipe leading from the top. The lead is tapped from N into the basin O; and the slag is tapped from M into P; T, T represent tuyères. The furnace may or may not be fitted with automatic charging devices. The blast, hot or cold, is delivered near the base of the furnace through tuyères. The products obtained are (i) the *lead* or *base bullion;* (ii) the *matte*, or *Bleistein*, or regulus, which is a mixture of sulphides of copper, nickel, zinc, iron, etc. The proportion of matte depends on the proportion of sulphur left in the roasted ore. If the matte is cupriferous, it may be used by the copper smelter; if not, it is roasted, and returned to the lead smelting furnace. Analyses of mattes were reported by H. Weidmann, R. Vambera, A. Streng, A. Schertel, A. Zdrahal, N. von Jossa and N. S. von Kurnakoff, etc. (iii) Ores carrying arsenic furnish a *speiss* which is essentially an iron arsenide, and if nickel is also present, nickel arsenide. If the speiss contains enough lead to be worth retreatment, it is roasted and re- turned to the furnace; if not, it is thrown away. Analyses were reported by C. Guillemain, A. Schertel, F. A. Hübner, etc. (iv) The *slag* is a complex silicate of iron, calcium, etc. It is usually black and should not contain enough lead to be of value—usually 1–2 per cent. is present. The slag is usually thrown away on the slag-tip. Analyses of the slags were reported by C. F. Plattner, C. Mann, P. Heberdey, A. Zdrahal, A. Schertel, R. Vambera, F. von Lipp, C. Ernst, N. von Jossa and N. S. von Kurnakoff, L. Dietz. (v) Much lead is volatilized during the smelting, and some material is carried away mechanically by blast or draught. The material recovered is called *flue-dust* or *fume*. Formerly no effort was made to collect the finely divided material carried along with the waste gases from the smelting furnaces. Much valuable material was lost, and damage done to the vegetation, etc., in the surrounding country owing to the poisonous nature of the *smelter's smoke*. The fume is condensed in settling chambers or settling flues just as suggested by R. Watson in 1778; [8] by washing with water as suggested by R. Watson and applied by J. D. Stagg; by allowing the coarser dust to settle in chambers, and then collecting the finer dust in filtering bags as first suggested by J. Percy; and by passing an electric discharge through the fume as applied by F. G. Cotterell. The fume collected from blast furnaces in bags is usually com- bustible and is ignited on the floor of the bag-house and returned to the furnace with the flue-dust collected by the other methods. Analyses of flue-dust and fume were reported by M. A. Fallize, F. Moldenhauer, J. Hannay, K. Friedrich, C. Schiffner,

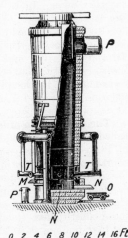

0 2 4 6 8 10 12 14 16 Ft.

FIG. 6.—Blast Furnace.

B. Kosmann, N. W. Iles. E. F. Côte and P. R. Pierron tried the so-called electro-thermal process for reducing galena by iron and fluxes.

Wet processes for the extraction of lead.—In the treatment of lead sulphide ores containing zinc, the zinc may be volatilized, as in Bartlett's process; or else it is slagged by treatment with suitable fluxes, as in *H. E. Fry's process* with alkaline fluxes. In the wet processes for the treatment of these ores, the ore is roasted so as to convert the zinc into oxide or sulphate as in the processes of E. A. Parnell,[9] E. A. Ashcroft, E. Ellershausen, W. West, and C. F. Croselmere; or the zinc may be roasted with salt—*chloridizing roast*, so as to convert it into a mixture of chloride and sulphate as in E. H. Russell's process. In each case the zinc is converted into a soluble salt; the product is leached; the iron and other metals removed if necessary; and the zinc precipitated, and smelted for zinc, or employed in other ways. In E. W. von Siemens and J. G. Halske's process, the unroasted ore is treated with chlorine, and leached. The insoluble residues are smelted for lead, and the soln. electrolyzed for zinc. The chlorine which is liberated is used over again. The lead residues are treated for metal. N. C. Christensen, H. and P. Faivre, and F. E. Elmore treated the ore with a chloride soln., and electrolyzed the soln. A. Nathansohn also extracted the lead with chlorine or hypochlorites in the presence of dissolved chlorides; H. Hey, with hydrogen chloride gas. Lead is a by-product in the extraction of vanadium from vanadite at Santa Marta, Spain.

The purification of lead.—The lead received from the smelting operations is called *base-bullion*—the *work-lead* or *Werkblei* of the Germans, and the *stannous* of Pliny's *Historiæ naturalis* (**34**. 47, *c.* 77 A.D.). Base-bullion is generally so contaminated with antimony, arsenic, sulphur, copper, tin, etc., that it is unsuitable for treatment by the desilverization processes, and it is also too hard and deficient in malleability to admit of its application to various manufacturing operations. Hence its name *hard lead*. The first process of purification is intended to separate those constituents, chiefly antimony, which make the lead hard. The quality of the base-bullion, said J. Percy, depends less on the mode of smelting than on the nature of the ore from which it is derived. Analyses of work-lead and of hard lead have been reported by A. Streng and E. Overbeck,[10] W. Hampe. H. Jäger, A. Schertel, S. Mitteregger, L. Schneider, E. Priwoznik, F. Moldenhauer, E. Dietz, L. F. Emmons, W. Mrazek, C. Balling, H. Dietrich, F. von Lill, etc. Analyses of impure lead derived from drosses, slags, etc., were reported by F. Reich,[11] H. Jäger, A. D. Machatti, etc. The **softening of lead** may involve two operations—liquation, and oxidation. In the **liquation of lead,** the metals and their compounds held in soln. by the lead are separated when the metal is melted slowly at a low temp. The *dross* consists of a mixture of lead, copper, sulphur, arsenic, etc. Analyses before and after liquation have been made by W. Hampe,[12] A. Schertel, etc. *E.g.*

	Pb	Ag	Cu	Bi	Sb	As	Sn	Fe	S	Ni+Co
Before	96·667	0·549	0·940	0·066	0·820	0·449	0·212	0·027	0·200	0·055
After	97·830	0·536	0·042	0·066	0·771	0·333	0·210	0·006	0·180	0·001

In some cases the liquated lead is desilverized, in other cases, a further softening is needed. This is effected by exposing the molten metal to an oxidation process —say, by melting it on the bed of a reverberatory furnace exposed to a current of atm. air. The dross is skimmed off from time to time, until the residual lead, on trial, has the required degree of softness. The rapidity of the operation depends on exposing fresh surfaces to oxidation. W. Hall found that in the process of making red-lead, the residual lead becomes soft. The softening has also been conducted in kettles or cast-iron dishes holding, say, 15 tons of lead. Steam may or may not be blown through the molten metal. The reverberatory furnace process is slower, but cheaper. Oxidizing agents of various kinds have been suggested by E. A. Pontifex and C. Glassford, T. Richardson, A. H. Johnson, H. Harris, A. Warner, B. George, American Metal Co., and W. Baker. A combined liquation and poling process was described by H. W. Kachelmann. Analyses of softened and purified lead were reported by R. Fresenius,[13] H. Jäger, F. von Lill, E. Dietz, A. Eschka, P. Beck, A. Mosso, American Metal Co., O. Herting, P. N. Degens, F. Mylius, L. Schneider, E. Priwoznik, A. Zdrahal, A. Exeli, etc.

The desilverization of lead.—Lead obtained by smelting contains variable proportions of silver and gold, and the separation of these metals is usually economically profitable. The desilverization of lead [14] has been considered in connection with silver—3. 22, 4. There are (i) *Pattinson's process* and *L. Rozan's modification* in which steam under press. is forced into the molten argentiferous lead, so as to promote uniformity of temp. in the crystallizing metal, and prevent the formation of crusts. This gives small crystals of lead which can be readily drained from the mother-liquor. Analyses of *pattinized lead* were made by A. Streng, W. Mrazek, H. Hahn, etc. (ii) *Parkes's process* based on the discovery of C. J. B. Karsten that zinc extracts silver from molten argentiferous alloys. Analyses of *parkesized lead* were made by W. Mrazek, etc. The silver and gold are separated from the products of Pattinson's or Parkes' process by *cupellation*—a process known to Biblical writers, and frequently mentioned in the Bible in order to accentuate moral lessons.

Electrolytic process for the purification of lead.—A. C. Becquerel [15] made some early observations on the electrodeposition of lead, and N. S. Keith tried to refine base-bullion by using as electrolyte a soln. of lead sulphate in one of sodium acetate, using anodes of the base-bullion. D. Tommasi tried a modification of this process, but neither was a commercial success. A. G. Betts employed as electrolyte a soln. of lead fluosilicate which is free from polarization effects due to the formation of lead dioxide on the anode. The anode is placed in bags to collect the slimes. When about 0·1 grm. of galena is present per litre of electrolyte, the lead deposited on the cathode is smooth, lustrous, and so coherent as to permit bending without breaking. E. W. von Siemens and J. G. Halske consider that a soln. of lead perchlorate with some free perchloric acid gives even better results than the fluosilicate. R. Saxon found poor deposits of lead were obtained by the electrolysis of galena in various salt soln. or in hydrochloric or nitric acid. The following analyses illustrate the results obtained with A. G. Betts's process :

	Pb	Ag	Au	Cu	Fe	Sn	Sb	As
Hard lead .	98·1014	0·8934	0·0122	0·1800	0·0140	0·0289	0·6076	0·1693
Refined . .	—	0·0009	—	0·0066	0·0012	0·0059	0·0043	0·0001

G. Titschak examined the electrodeposition of lead from soln. of lead chloride in magnesium chloride dissolved in dil. hydrochloric acid ; and from soln. containing α-naphthalenemonosulphonic acid or hydrofluotitanic acid. Analyses of electrolytic lead have also been reported by N. S. Keith, W. Hampe, K. Pietrusky, C. F. Mathers, E. W. von Siemens and J. G. Halske, etc.

There are many grades of lead on the market. The basis of most transactions on the London Metal Exchange is soft-foreign lead ; but there is *double-refined lead, super-refined lead, chemical-assay lead,* or *granulated lead.* The so-called *soft lead* is the product of a non-argentiferous ore which has been refined in the ordinary way, or else softened lead ; it is less pure than the so-called *desilvered lead.* The *chemical hard lead* contains a rather higher proportion of copper and antimony than ordinary soft-lead, and owing to its higher resistance to corrosion by acids is preferred more in chemical industries. The so-called *antimonial lead,* or *hard-lead,* is really an alloy with 15–20 per cent. of antimony. The composition of some varieties is indicated in Tables I and II. The ordinary English brand had 0·0026 per cent. of cadmium and no tin ; the best English brand had no cadmium, no tin, and no nickel, but the ordinary English and the chemical lead had traces of nickel, the electrolytic tin had 0·0025 per cent. of arsenic, the good chemical lead had a trace of arsenic, and the two brands of English lead had no arsenic, no manganese, and no cobalt. F. Mylius found the purest obtainable commercial samples of lead

TABLE I.—COMPOSITION OF SOME VARIETIES OF HARD LEAD.

	Per cent.						Ozs. per ton.	
	Pb	Cu	Sb	As	Bi	S	Ag	Au
Hard Weardale (English) .	99·87	0·015	0·05	0·01	0·001	0·015	7	—
„ Freiberg (German) .	96·67	0·94	0·82	0·28	0·066	0·200	180	—
„ Orcellitana (Spain) .	98·92	0·15	0·40	0·21	0·005	0·100	45	—
„ Laurium (Greece) .	98·27	0·75	0·55	0·10	0·010	0·080	45	0·07
„ Tombstone (Arizona) .	98·50	0·22	0·32	0·28	0·013	—	100	0·10
„ Magapil (Mexico). .	95·72	0·09	2·50	0·90	0·030	0·32	105	0·42

TABLE II.—COMPOSITION OF SOME COMMERCIAL VARIETIES OF LEAD.

	Pb	Cu	Sb	Bi	Ag	Fe	Zn
English (best) . .	99·992	0·0003	0·004	0·0005	0·0003	0·0015	0·0015
English (ordinary) .	99·9655	0·0019	0·0132	0·0124	0·0007	0·0031	0·0026
Chemical (good) . .	99·985	0·022	0·033	0·001	0·002	0·003	0·0015
Australian special .	99·9977	0·0003	0·0005	0·0006	0·0002	—	0·0007
Australian ordinary .	99·9917	0·0001	0·006	—	0·0012	—	0·0001
Electrolytic (Trail) .	99·9861	0·0027	nil	0·0037	0·001	0·0022	0·0018

contained 0·0006 per cent. of iron, 0·001 per cent. of copper, and a trace of oxide. W. Stahl said that the best refined lead made by the dry process contains 0·001–0·0015 per cent. of tin derived from the original ores, the fluxes used in smelting, or from the zinc used in desilverization.

The metallic precipitation of lead.—T. Bergman [16] was not right in stating that the metals precipitate one another after a certain order, which is the same in nearly all acid menstrua ; in spite of some anomalous circumstances the order is constant, and never inverted. Zinc prevails over iron ; iron over lead ; lead over tin ; tin over copper; copper over silver; silver over mercury; etc. Rather did O. Sackur show that tin is precipitated by lead from soln. of tin in nitric acid ; and, on the other hand, that lead is precipitated by tin from soln. of lead acetate—*vide infra*. C. A. Kraus and H. F. Kurtz found salts of lead dissolved in liquid ammonia are reduced by **sodium** and **calcium**. H. Reinsch found that **copper** precipitates lead as a black powder from soln. of lead acetate acidified with hydrochloric acid provided air has free access to the soln.; if air be excluded, no precipitation of lead occurs. According to A. Roussin, **magnesium** precipitates lead from soln. of its salts, and, according to H. Mouraour, and E. G. Bryant, the reaction is accompanied by the evolution of hydrogen. S. Kern said that if a soln. of lead nitrate is used, the finely divided lead is covered by a film of lead hydroxide ; and A. Commaille showed that with lead chloride gas is evolved and some lead oxychloride is formed. Lead is precipitated by **zinc** from soln. of lead nitrate, and, according to N. W. Fischer, if a zinc rod be suspended in a soln. containing one part of a lead salt, 1½ parts of acetic acid, and 100 parts of water, the so-called *arbor saturni* is formed ; A. Simon also found that the lead-tree is formed if the zinc is suspended in silicic hydrogel containing some lead acetate. E. Giurgea obtained lead crystals by placing a porous pot containing a zinc rod in a soln. of lead acetate. The crystals of lead appear on the outside of the pot. H. N. Warren also obtained octahedral crystals by wrapping asbestos paper about a zinc rod which was then dipped in a soln. of lead salt. Neither N. W. Fischer, nor A. M. Pleischl obtained a deposition of lead when zinc is placed in an alcoholic soln. of lead acetate. The precipitation of lead by zinc was examined from an analytical point of view by F. Stolba, A. Gawlowsky, L. T. Merrill, A. Eckenroth, F. Mohr, and C. Rössler. L. T. M. Gray, and H. Freundlich and J. Fischer examined the effect of gelatin, gum, and glue on the precipitation of lead from soln. of its salts by zinc and found that finer deposits are obtained with special conc. of the colloid. Both N. W. Fischer, and A. M. Pleischl found that **cadmium** precipitates lead rapidly and quantitatively from soln. of lead salts—*vide* lead chloride. A. M. Pleischl observed no deposition of lead when a **tin** rod is placed in a soln. of a lead salt, but O. Sackur found that while no lead is obtained from neutral and acid soln. of lead nitrate, with a sat. soln. of lead sulphate in sulphuric acid, or of lead chloride in hydrochloric acid, tin passes into soln. as a stannous salt, and lead is deposited. A state of equilibrium is established between the lead, tin, and the salts of these metals. The equilibrium ratio Sn : Pb in dil. soln. of the two chlorides in the presence of solid tin and lead : $Sn+PbCl_2 \rightleftharpoons Pb+SnCl_2$ at 25° varies from 3·09 to 3·45 when the acidity ranges from N- to $0·2N$-HCl. The results were affected by hydrolytic phenomena. The conditions agree with those deduced from the law of mass action and the theory of soln. press. It was also found that lead is almost completely precipitated by tin from soln. of lead acetate, and this the more rapidly the greater the acidity of the soln. O. Sackur explains the behaviour of tin and lead towards different acids on the assumption that lead has a greater soln. tension than tin, and that the stannous salts, with the exception of the nitrate, are only very slightly dissociated into ions. Measurements of the *E.M.F.* of a voltaic element of the form $Pb \,|\, Pb(NO_3)_2 \,|\, Sn(NO_3)_2 \,|\, Sn$ showed that the electrolytic soln. tension of lead is about 17·2 times as great as that of tin. A. A. Noyes and K. Toabe found that lead is precipitated by tin from soln. of lead perchlorate in dil. perchloric acid ; they found that the equilibrium ratio of Sn : Pb in dil. soln. of lead and tin perchlorates ranged from 3·080 : 1 with soln. containing $0·475N$-$HClO_4$ to 3·011 : 1 with $0·959N$-$HClO_4$ at 25°. The reaction $Sn+PbCl_2 \rightleftharpoons Pb+SnCl_2$ was studied by R. Lorenz and co-workers ; F. Wöhler found that a **lead** rod in a soln. of lead nitrate or acetate forms crystals of lead ; J. B. Senderens found the same thing with neutral soln. of lead nitrate with the exclusion of air, and basic lead nitrite is formed—*vide infra*, allotropic lead. According to G. von Hevesy, the measurement of the rate of exchange between lead and the lead in a soln. of lead nitrate was made possible by adding a trace of thorium-B to the latter. He found the rate of exchange at the surface of metallic lead in contact with such a soln. of lead nitrate is of such magnitude as to suggest that the exchange is not solely due to thermodynamic equilibrium, but rather to the action of local currents. At some points lead passes into soln., at others lead is precipitated. A. Cossa found that **aluminium** readily precipitates lead from soln. of its salts, and A. H. Low, and J. E. Williams employed the reaction in analytical work. W. C. Reid showed that **thallium** precipitates lead from soln. of its salts. N. W. Fischer found that **manganese** precipitates lead from soln. of lead acetate as a brown powder, and O. Prelinger found that lead is also precipitated from (previously warm) soln. of lead salts. N. W. Fischer, and A. Payen found that **iron** slowly precipitates lead from soln. of lead acetate in the presence of air ; and from soln. of lead nitrate by a process analogous to that used by E. Giurgea—*vide supra.*

For the electrodeposition of lead, *vide infra*, the electrical properties of lead. G. Shimazu [17] described the preparation of reactive *powdered lead*. B. de Rostaing prepared powdered lead by pouring the molten metal on a sieve rotating in a horizontal plane 2000 revolutions per minute. The rain of lead is received into a vessel of water. L. Creveling and others obtained finely divided lead by driving a blast of warm air or superheated steam on to a fine stream of molten lead. J. Ohshima electrolyzed a dil. soln. of lead benzene sulphonate or lead naphthalene sulphonate, and pulverized the deposited lead. Pulverulent lead was made by P. Schützenberger, A. Thiel, H. Luggin, G. Bredig, and W. A. Tichomiroff and P. Lidoff. O. Ohmann [18] made *lead-wool;* V. G. Yourieff, and O. W. Brown and A. R. Nees, *spongy-lead;* H. I. Hannover, and L. Höpfner, *porous lead;* G. F. Taylor, *lead-filaments;* and F. Paneth and O. Nörring, and P. Schützenberger, *lead-films.* H. N. Ridyard described the deposition of lead-films on glass, porcelain, etc., so that joints can be soldered.

Lead of a high degree of purity.—Lead of a high degree of purity can be obtained in many ways. The following process was employed by J. S. Stas : [19]

A soln. of lead acetate was digested with lead-foil at 40°–50° in order to precipitate copper and silver. The soln. was filtered into sulphuric acid, and the lead sulphate was washed and digested in an ammoniacal soln. of ammonium carbonate ; and the resulting carbonate washed free from ammonium salts. To eliminate iron, part of the carbonate was heated in a platinum dish to convert it into oxide, and the remainder was converted into neutral nitrate. The latter was dissolved in boiling water, and the oxide added in small portions at a time. The iron was thus precipitated as hydroxide, and the soln. of basic lead nitrate was filtered into a soln. of ammonium carbonate. The precipitated carbonate was washed, dried, and reduced to lead by adding it to molten potassium cyanide contained in an unglazed porcelain crucible. The button of lead was remelted under fused cyanide, and if the metal is free from traces of sulphate or oxide it furnishes a convex button resembling mercury.

B. Lambert and H. E. Cullis distilled in vacuo at 1200° the lead prepared by J. S. Stas' process, using quartz tubes divided into three compartments by constrictions. The first fraction was collected in the 1st compartment ; the middle fraction in the 2nd compartment ; and the residue remained in the 3rd compartment. They found that the globules of lead obtained in this way adhered very closely on the under side to the quartz, producing a very fine reflecting surface. It was found that if the distilled lead was exposed to air a short time after distillation, but when quite cold, the brilliant surface was quickly dimmed by a film of oxide. If, however, the metal was kept in the vacuous tube for several months, exposure to the air did not then cause any appreciable decrease in its brilliant lustre for several days. The purification of lead by the repeated crystallization of the nitrate, and the subsequent reduction of the nitrate to metallic lead, has been discussed by G. P. Baxter and F. L. Grover, and T. W. Richards and C. Wadsworth.

Colloidal lead.—According to G. Bredig and F. Haber,[20] and R. Lorenz and co-workers, when dil. mineral acids are electrolyzed with a bright lead plate or wire as cathode, and a platinum anode, with a current at 24–72 volts, a momentary pulverization of the lead occurs, and a fine, metallic powder of **colloidal lead** or **lead hydrosol** falls through the liquid. This takes place at isolated spots on the surface of the metal, bright indentations being left with rounded edges. A similar phenomenon takes place in alkaline soln., but in this case is continuous and much more energetic. The metallic lead thrown down is peculiarly susceptible to chemical change, and can readily be converted into white lead by the simultaneous action of air and carbonic anhydride. The addition of small quantities of a chromate or chromium salt prevents the occurrence of the phenomenon. Colloidal lead was also made by T. Svedberg, and S. Bodforss and P. Frölich by forming a direct current arc, or a high frequency arc, or an oscillatory Leyden jar discharge between lead electrodes under a given medium. A. Gutbier made the colloid by reducing a cold dil. soln. of lead chloride with hydrazine ; and R. Furth, by dusting the metals in air by means of the electric arc. E. F. Burton gave for the rate of migration of the particles in an electric field towards the negative pole was $12 \cdot 0 \times 10^{-5}$ for a fall of potential of 1 volt per cm. at 18°. The potential difference between the lead particles and water was 0·018 volt. J. Billitzer obtained the colloidal metal in a similar manner ; he found that the action is facilitated by using a roughened surface, and a loose superficial aggregation. C. J. Reed obtained the colloid by cathodic spluttering in a borax soln. D. Zavrieff, and G. Börjeson and T. Svedberg studied the production of colloidal lead by the oscillatory discharge. F. Bayer used caoutchouc as a protective colloid. O. Ruff and R. Wallstein made colloidal lead by the action of zirconium trichloride on a soln. of lead chloride ; and L. Gurvich, by shaking the powder in a liquid for a few hours. H. Nordenson, and F. Haber doubted if the colloid is really metallic lead—it may be a hydroxide or hydride.

According to T. Svedberg, when a clean surface of lead is placed in a flat dish covered with a dispersion medium, and exposed to ultra-violet light, a colloidal soln. of lead is produced. With water, the particles are probably those of the colloidal hydroxide; with methyl alcohol, ethyl alcohol, isobutyl alcohol, ethyl ether, acetone, and ethyl or amyl acetate as dispersion media, the size and number of the particles vary very much; and the disintegration of the lead depends on the nature of the dispersion medium. E. F. Burton, and T. Svedberg prepared lead methylalcosol, which was deep brown in transmitted light, and bluish-black in reflected light. They also made lead ethylalcosol, and lead isobutylalcosol in an analogous way. C. H. Hall [21] found that suspensions of finely divided lead in lubricating oil are not precipitated by alternating or direct currents at 10^4 to 2×10^5 volts.

REFERENCES.

[1] A. Arche, *Die Gewinnung und Darstellung des Bleies und seiner Produkte*, Leipzig, 1888; R. H. Lamborn, *A Rudimentary Treatise on the Metallurgy of Silver and Lead*, London, 1861; M. Cahen, *Métallurgie du Plomb*, Paris, 1863; H. F. Collins, *The Metallurgy of Lead*, London, 1910; H. O. Hofmann, *The Metallurgy of Lead*, New York, 1908; W. R. Ingalls, *Lead Smelting and Refining*, New York, 1906; C. W. Hixon, *Notes on Lead and Copper Smelting*, New York, 1898; M. W. Iles, *Lead Smelting*, New York, 1902; L. E. Rivot, *Exploitation et traitement des minérais de plomb*, Paris, 1868; L. E. Gruner, *État actuel de la métallurgie du plomb*, Paris, 1870 ; J. Percy, *The Metallurgy of Lead*, London, 1870 ; A. Ronna, *État actuel de la métallurgie du plomb en Angleterre*, Paris, 1871 ; A. Eilers, *Contributions to the Records of Lead Smelting in Blast-furnaces*, Washington, 1873 ; O. Pütz, *Metall Erz*, **10**. 41, 1913 ; K. Friedrich, *ib.*, **16**. 21, 1919 ; F. Peters, *Glückauf*. **45**. 554, 1909 ; **51**. 1190, 1215, 1915 ; **55**. 796, 1919 ; G. H. Clevenger, *Met. Chem. Engg.*, **11**. 447, 1913 ; J. W. Richards, *ib.*, **6**. 8, 63, 1908 ; H. K. Picard, *Chem. Trade Journ.*, **54**. 475, 1919 ; D. A. Lyon and O. R. Ralston, *Innovations in the Metallurgy of Lead*, Washington, 1918 ; O. H. Hahn, *Eng. Min. Journ.*, **91**. 1106, 1911 ; M. S. y Massia, *Metalurgia del plomo*, Madrid, 1893 ; C. C. Longbridge, *A Précis of Lead Smelting*, London, 1901; T. A. Lambert, *Lead and its Compounds*, London, 1902 ; J. A. Smythe, *Lead*, London, 1920; *Lead, its Occurrence in Nature—The Modes of its Extraction, Its Properties and Uses with some Account of its Principal Compounds*, London, 1923 ; K. Richter, *Zink, Zinn, und Blei*, Wien, 1909 ; J. A. Phillips, *On the Metallurgy of Lead*, London, 1859 ; L. Guillaume, *La métallurgie du plomb au Laurium*, Paris, 1909 ; B. Kerl, *Die Oberharzer Hüttenprozesse*, Clausthal, 1852 ; C. Schnabel, *Handbuch der Metallhüttenkunde*, Berlin, **1**. 399, 1901 ; London, **1**. 371, 1905 ; A. G. Betts, *Lead Refining by Electrolysis*, New York, 1908 ; L. F. Clark, *U.S. Pat. No.* 1548351, 1925.

[2] E. W. Mayer and R. Schön, *Metall Erz*, **20**. 385, 1923 ; L. E. Rivot, *Ann. Mines*, (4), **19**. 463, 1851 ; L. E. Rivot and A. Lejeune, *ib.*, (4), **12**. 271, 1848 ; R. H. Lamborn, *A Rudimentary Treatise on the Metallurgy of Silver and Lead*, London, 1861.

[3] J. Martyn, *Phil. Trans.*, **36**. 22, 1729 ; J. Glanvil, *ib.*, **2**. 525, 1688 ; J. Farey, *General View of the Agriculture and Minerals of Derbyshire*, London, 382, 1815 ; A. P. Dufrénoy, *Voyage métallurgique en Angleterre*, Paris, **2**. 662, 1839 ; G. L. Grandison, *Brit. Pat. No.*, 206, 1678 ; J. Hodges, *ib.*, 264, 1690 ; J. J. Becher, *Alphabetum minerale*, Truro, 1682 ; J. Percy, *The Metallurgy of Lead*, London, 213, 1870 ; R. H. Lamborn, *A Rudimentary Treatise on the Metallurgy of Silver and Lead*, London, 132, 1861 ; J. Childrey, *Britannia Baconia*, London, 112, 1661 ; R. Watson, *Chemical Essays*, London, **3**. 273, 1782 ; A. Barba. *Arte de los metales*, Madrid, 79, 1640 ; W. Forster, *A Treatise on a section of the Strata from Newcastle-on-Tyne to the Mountain of Cross Fell in Cumberland ; with remarks on Mineral Veins in General*, Newcastle, 364, 1821 ; C. A. Schlüter, *Gründlicher Unterricht von Hüttenwerken*, Braunschweig, 110, 1738.

[4] R. Schenck, *Physikalische Chemie der Metalle*, Halle a. S., 182, 1909 ; London, 216, 1919 ; *Zeit. anorg. Chem.*, **148**. 351, 1925 ; **153**. 149, 1926 ; R. Schenck and W. Borkenstein, *ib.*, **142**. 143, 1925 ; R. Schenck and W. Rassbach, *Ber.*, **40**. 2185, 2947, 1907 ; **41**. 947, 1908 ; *Met.*, **4**. 455, 1907 ; R. Schenck and A. Albers, *Zeit. anorg. Chem.*, **105**. 145, 1919 ; W. Reinders, *ib.*, **93**. 213, 1915 ; **109**. 52, 1919 ; *Proc. Acad. Amsterdam*, **17**. 703, 1914 ; G. Keppeler, *Zeit. angew. Chem.*, **15**. 809, 1902 ; **21**. 579, 1908 ; H. F. Collins, *The Metallurgy of Lead*, London, 1910 ; C. O. Bannister, *Trans. Inst. Min. Met.*, **21**. 346, 1912 ; G. Rigg, *ib.*, **29**. 1, 1920 ; H. C. Jenkins and E. A. Smith, *Journ. Chem. Soc.*, **71**. 666, 1897 ; F. Richter, *Beiträge zur Theorie des Huntington-Heberlein Prozesses und der ihm verwandten Verblaseverfahren*, Dresden, 1909 ; *Chem. Ztg.*, **32**. 632, 1908 ; T. Huntington and F. Heberlein, *Brit. Pat. No.* 13454, 1903 ; A. Germot, *ib.*, 23014, 1899 ; A. D. Carmichael, *ib.*, 17580, 1901 ; *Eng. Min. Journ.*, **79**. 421, 1902 ; Anon., *Engg. Min. Journ.*, **80**. 778, 1905 ; D. Clark, *ib.*, **78**. 603, 1903 ; W. R. Ingalls, *ib.*, **80**. 726, 1905 ; W. M. Hutchings, *ib.*, **80**. 726, 1905 ; H. O. Hofmann, R. P. Reynolds, and A. E. Wells, *Trans. Amer. Inst. Min. Met.*, **33**. 37, 1907 ; G. A. Puchard, *ib.*, **34**. 603, 1908 ; H. O. Hofmann and W. Mostowisch, *ib.*, **34**. 503, 1908 ; W. Mostowisch, *Journ. Russ. Met. Soc.*, **1**. 303, 1915 ; *Met.*, **4**. 647, 1907 ; F. O. Doeltz, *ib.*, **2**. 640, 1905 ; C. Guillemain, *ib.*, **2**. 433, 1905 ;

W. Borchers, *ib.*, **2**. 6, 1905 ; *Electrometallurgie*, 467, 1903 ; *Engg. Min. Journ.* **80** 398, 1905
W. C. Roberts-Austen, *An Introduction to the Study of Metallurgy*, London, 419, 1902 ; P. Weiller
Chem. Ztg., **32**. 342. 1908 ; R. Tandler, *ib.*, **32**. 437, 1908 ; Gesellschaft der Emser Blei- und Silber-
werke, *German Pat.*, *D.R.P.* 142932, 1903 ; A. Savelsberg, *ib.*, 171215, 1906 ; *French Pat. No*
336540, 1903 ; *Met.*, **2**. 5, 1905 ; A. Birnbaum, *Zeit. Berg. Hütt. Sal.*, **53**. 219, 1905 ; *Œster. Zeit
Berg. Hütt.*, **53**. 541, 1905 ; G. Kroupa, *ib.*, **53**. 251, 1905 ; F. Janda, *ib.*, **53**. 234, 1905 ;
E. F. Anthon, *Repert. Pharm.*, **59**. 250, 1832 ; J. W. Döbereiner, *Schweigger's Journ.*, **17**. 248
1816 ; K. Friedrich, *Met.*, **6**. 169, 1909 ; C. F. Plattner, *Die metallurgischen Röstprozesse theoretisch
behandelt*, Freiburg, 145, 1865 ; P. Richter, *Min. Ind.*, **19**. 443, 1910 ; P. Berthier, *Traité de
essais par la voie sèche*, Paris, 1834 ; *Ann. Chim. Phys.*, (2), **20**. 275, 1822 ; (2), **33**. 156, 1826 ;
(2), **39**. 262, 1828 ; J. L. Gay Lussac, *ib.*, (2), **63**. 435, 1836 ; H. V. Collet-Descotils, *ib.*, (2), **55**.
441, 1833 ; *Journ. Mines*, **27**. 469, 1810 ; F. Dempwolff, *Metall Erz*, **11**. 622, 1914 ;
C. F. Rammelsberg, *Lehrbuch der chemischen Metallurgie*, Berlin, 221, 1850 ; G. F. Rodwell,
Journ. Chem. Soc., **16**. 42, 1863 ; J. Percy, *The Metallurgy of Lead*, London, 45, 1870 ;
J. B. Hannay, *Proc. Chem. Soc.*, **10**. 113, 151, 1894 ; *Chem. News*, **70**. 43, 1894 ; H. J. Jenkins
and E. A. Smith, *Journ. Chem. Soc.*, **71**. 666, 1897 ; D. L. Hammick, *ib.*, **111**. 379, 1917 ; J. Uhl,
Ber., **23**. 2151, 1890 ; A. Lodin, *Compt. Rend.*, **120**. 1164, 1895 ; A. Mailfert, *ib.*, **94**. 1186, 1882 ;
H. Schiff, *Liebig's Ann.*, **67**. 94, 1861 ; J. Fournet, *Ann. Mines*, (2), **1**. 503, 1827 ; (2), **4**. 465,
1828 ; C. Dörschel, *Metall Erz*, **19**. 29, 57, 1922 ; E. Jänecke, *Zeit. phys. Chem.*, **151**. 289, 1926.
⁵ M. Cahen, *Métallurgie du plomb*, Paris, 1863 ; *Rev. Univ. Mines*, **13**. 1, 1863 ; E. Petitgand,
ib., **9**. 362, 1861 ; A. Paillette, *Ann. Mines*, (3), **19**. 239, 1841 ; L. E. Gruner, *ib.*, (6), **13**. 335, 1868 ;
M. M. Replat, *ib.*, (3), **18**. 161, 1840 ; C. Boulanger, *ib.*, (3), **7**. 167, 1835 ; E. M. Phillips, *ib.*, (4), **8**.
239, 1845 ; L. E. Gruner, *ib.*, (6), **13**. 325, 1868 ; V. Bouhy, *ib.*, (6), **17**. 178, 1870 ; J. F. L. Hausmann,
Gött. Ver. Berg. Freunde, **5**. 221, 1849 ; *Beiträge zur metallurgischen Krystallkunde*, Göttingen, 9,
1850 ; L. E. Rivot, *Ann. Mines*, (4), **19**. 465, 1860 ; *Principes généraux du traitement des minérais
métalliques*, Paris, 310, 1871 ; L. E. Rivot and M. Zeppenfeld, *Description des gites métallifères
de la préparation mécanique et du traitement métallurgique des minérais de plomb argentifères de
Pontgibaud*, Paris, 1850 ; *Ann. Mines*, (4), **18**. 137, 1850 ; C. J. B. Karsten, *System der Metallurgie*, Berlin, **5**. 100, 1832 ; H. Wedding, *Zeit. Berg. Hütt. Sal.*, **14**. 139, 1866 ; A. Pleischl,
Karsten's Arch., **6**. 177, 1825 ; J. C. Zimmermann, *ib.*, **10**. 27, 1837 ; A. Mentzel, *ib.*, **8**. 103,
1835 ; W. J. Cookson, *Brit. Pat. No.* 553, 1854 ; C. Löwig, *Zeit. Berg. Hütt. Sal.*, **14**. 84, 1866 ;
B. Kerl, *Die oberharzer Hüttenprocesse*, Clausthal, 48, 1860 ; A. Habets, *Rev. Univ. Mines*, (2),
1. 79, 1877 ; *Industrie Belge*, Liège, 1878 ; C. F. Plattner, *Berg. Hütt. Ztg.*, **14**. 128, 1855 ; *Die
metallurgische Röstprozesse*, Freiburg, 201, 1856 ; T. Fischer, *Leitfaden der Metallurgie*, Leipzig,
232, 1904 ; F. Wüst and W. Borchers, *Eisen- und Metallhüttenkunde*, Leipzig, 507, 1900 ;
K. Waldeck, *Streifzüge durch die Blei- und Silberhütten des Oberharzes*, Halle a. S., 20, 1907 ;
O. Säger, *Hygiene der Hüttenarbeiter*, Jena, 1895 ; W. R. Ingalls, *Eng. Min. Journ.*, **80**. 1067,
1111, 1905 ; G. C. Broadhead, *Rep. Geol. Sur. Missouri*, 492, 1874 ; C. P. Williams. *ib.*, 8, 1877 ;
Trans. Amer. Inst. Min. Eng., **5**. 324, 1876 ; D. A. Lyon and O. C. Ralsou, *Bull. U.S. Bur.
Mines*, 157, 1919 ; A. Germot, *Brit. Pat. No.* 23014, 1899 ; G. L. Clark, *Proc. Australasian
Inst. Min. Met.*, 27, 1924.
⁶ R. Watson, *Chemical Essays*, London, **3**. 273, 1782 ; H. L. Pattinson, *Trans. Nat. Hist.
Soc. Newcastle-on-Tyne*, **2**. 152, 1832 ; C. F. Plattner, *Berg. Hütt. Ztg.*, **13**. 22, 1854 ; F. Köller,
Œster. Zeit. Hütt., **4**. 341, 1856 ; W. Forster, *Treatise on a Section of the Strata from Newcastle-
on-Tyne to the Mountain of Cross Fell, Cumberland*, Newcastle, 1821 ; E. Pettigand, *Rev. Univ.
Mines*, **9**. 94, 1861 ; A. H. Sexton, *Eng. Min. Journ.*, **59**. 175, 1895 ; K. W. M. Middleton, *ib.*,
80. 11, 1905 ; G. C. Broadhead, *Geol. Sur. Missouri*, 492, 1874 ; C. P. Williams, *ib.*, 36, 1877 ;
Trans. Amer. Min. Eng., **5**. 324, 1876 ; F. P. Dewey, *ib.*, **18**. 674, 1890 ; F. L. Clerc, *Eng. Min.
Journ.*, **40**. 4, 1885 ; W. E. Newman, *ib.*, **106**. 101, 1918 ; A. St. Moses, *German Pat.*, *D.R.P.*
317903, 1916.
⁷ C. F. Plattner, *Vorlesungen über allgemeine Hüttenkunde*, Freiberg, **2**. 196, 1860 ; *Die
metallurgische Röstprozesse*, Freiberg, 205, 1856 ; *Berg. Hütt. Ztg.*, **13**. 81, 1854 ; K. A. Winkle,
Beschreibung der Freiberger Schemlzhütten prozesse, Freiberg, 1837 ; A. Carnot, *Ann. Mines*,
(6), **6**. 1, 1864 ; L. Guillaume, *ib.*, (10), **15**. 1, 1909 ; W. Mrazek, *Berg. Hütt. Jahrb.*, **16**. 392,
1867 ; C. F. Rammelsberg, *Lehrbuch der chemischen Metallurgie*, Berlin, 247, 1865 ; A. W. Hahn,
Met. Chem. Engg., **8**. 686, 1910 ; A. Lange, *Karsten's Arch.*, **24**. 430, 1851 ; H. Wedding, *Zeit.
Berg. Hütt. Sal.*, **14**. 157, 1866 ; O. Pufahl, *ib.*, **53**. 439, 1905 ; *Eng. Min. Journ.*, **81**. 889, 1906 ;
H. O. Hofmann and W. Mostowisch, *Bull. Amer. Inst. Min. Eng.*, 688, 1906 ; 869, 1909 ; *Trans.
Amer. Inst. Mem. Eng.*, **90**. 317, 1910 ; *ib.*, **29**. 683, 1899 ; **39**. 628, 1908 ; *Journ. Amer. Chem.
Soc.*, **28**. 1089, 1906 ; A. Gurlt, *Uebersicht der pyrogenneten künstlichen Mineralien*, Freiberg,
22, 1857 ; R. Pumpelly, *Across America and Asia*, New York, 145, 1870 ; A. Streng, *Zeit.
Berg. Hütt. Sal.*, **15**. 61, 1867 ; E. Strauch, *ib.*, **15**. 323, 1867 ; L. A. Palmer, *Mines Minerals*,
30. 496, 513, 1910 ; J. M. Turnbull, *ib.*, **31**. 121, 1910 ; J. Grimm, *Berg. Hütt. Ztg.*, **23**. 315,
1864 ; *Berg. Hütt. Jahrb.*, **5**. 93, 1856 ; **7**. 326, 1857 ; A. Eschka, *ib.*, **13**. 47, 1864 ; C. Balling,
ib., **16**. 409, 1867 ; W. Mrazek, *ib.*, **13**. 360, 393, 1864 ; F. Köller, *Œster. Zeit. Berg. Hütt.*, **4**.
322. 341, 1856 ; A. Cap, *ib.*, **48**. 231, 1900 ; **50**. 147, 1902 ; A. Schertel, *Jahrb. Berg. Hütt.*, **37**.
1880 ; *Œster. Zeit. Berg. Hütt.*, **28**. 501, 1880 ; G. Kroupa, *ib.*, **53**. 251, 1905 ; A. Birnbaum,
ib., **53**. 241, 1905 ; *Zeit. Berg. Hütt. Sal.*, **53**. 219, 1905 ; E. Ferraris, *ib.*, **53**. 455. 1905 ; *Eng.
Min. Journ.*, **80**. 781, 1905 ; A. Eilers, *Contributions to the Records of Lead-smelting in Blast-
furnaces*, Washington. 1873 ; *Eng. Min. Journ.*, **31**. 246. 1881 ; R. Pearce, *Trans. Amer. Inst.*

Min. Eng., **11**. 59, 1875; **18**. 62, 1882; **H.** M. Howe, W. Campbell, and C. **W.** Knight, *ib.*, **38**. 170, 1907; A. F. Wendt, *ib.*, **19**. 100, 1890; E. L. Newhouse, *ib.*, **22**. 657, 1891; R. H. Terhune, *School Mines Quart.*, **15**. 108, 1893; *Trans. Amer. Inst. Min. Eng.*, **15**. 92, 1886; **16**. 19, 1887; W. R. Ingalls, *ib.*, **37**. 627, 1906; *Bull. Amer. Inst. Min. Eng.*, 688, 1906; *Eng. Min. Journ.*, **80**. 778, 1067, 1905; **84**. 575, 1907; *Mineral Ind.*, **16**. 656, 1907; M. W. Iles, *School Mines Quart.*, **17**. 19, 1895; **21**. 341, 695, 1899; D. Clark, *ib.*, **78**. 630, 708, 1904; G. D. Delprat, *Trans. Austr. Inst. Min. Eng.*, **12**. 1, 1907; *Eng. Min. Journ.*, **83**. 321, 516, 1907; H. F. Brown, *ib.*, **57**. 441, 1894; W. Hutchings, *ib.*, **80**. 726, 1905; A. S. Dwight and R. L. Lloyd, *ib.*, **85**. 650, 1908; S. E. Bretherton, *ib.*, **55**. 196, 393, 1893; C. Cochrane, *ib.*, **65**. 760, 1898; *Smelting Furnace*, **53**. i, 69, 1898; A. von der Ropp, *U.S. Pat. No.* 532013, 1895; *Trans. Amer. Inst. Min. Eng.*, **20**. 171, 1891; *Min. Scient. Press.*, **85**. 308, 1902; **97**. 364, 1908; L. S. Austin, *ib.*, **90**. 511, 1906; *Eng. Min. Journ.*, **58**. 558, 1894; **97**. 364, 525, 1895; 525, 1908; C. Henrich, *ib.*, **50**. 744, 1890; **51**. 651, 1891; R. C. Canby, *ib.*, **68**. 3, 1899; **V.** H. Croll, *ib.*, **65**. 639, 1898; H. Harris, *ib.*, **81**. 178, 1906; H. W. Hixon, *ib.*, **82**. 553, 1906; **J.** C. Bennett, *ib.*, **86**. 83, 1908; O. H. Hahn, *ib.*, **89**. 1111, 1910; C. T. Rice, *ib.*, **106**. 649, 1918; J. F. Kemp, *School Mines Quart.*, **9**. 215, 1888; T. Egelston, *ib.*, **12**. 112, 1891; E. L. Newhouse, *ib.*, **9**. 373, 1888; J. Douglas, *Journ. Soc. Arts*, **43**. 821, 1895; W. Blackmore, *Trans. Inst. Min. Met.*, **7**. 324, 1899; H. F. Collins, *ib.*, **12**. 410, 1903; *Eng. Min. Journ.*, **87**. 882, 1909; *Proc. Inst. Civ. Eng.*, **112**. 151, 1893; *Trans. Amer. Inst. Min. Eng.*, **8**. 303, 1900; J. W. Neill, *ib.*, **13**. 634, 1885; **20**. 165, 1891; C. H. Fulton and I. E. Goodner, *ib.*, **39**. 584, 1908; A. F. Schneider, *ib.*, **11**. 58, 1882; O. H. Hahn, A. Eilers, and R. W. Raymond, *ib.*, **1**. 91, 1871; F. R. Carpenter, *ib.*, **30**. 764, 1906; A. S. Dwight, *ib.*, **32**. 353, 1901; **39**. 812, 1908; G. F. Beardsley, *ib.*, **21**. 575, 1892; H. A. Keller, *ib.*, **22**. 574, 1893; E. Keller, *Eng. Min. Journ.*, **60**. 465, 1895; *Bull. Amer. Inst. Min. Eng.*, 282, 1906; *Trans. Amer. Inst. Min. Eng.*, **21**. 71, 1892; W. Braden, *ib.*, **26**. 38, 1896; H. F. Collins, *Proc. Inst. Civ. Eng.*, **114**. 171, 1893; C. H. Mathewson, *Colorado School Mines Quart.*, **2**. 40, 1893; *Mineral Ind.*, **3**. 436, 1894; F. A. Hübner, *Glückauf*, **41**. 6, 1905; L. Schneider, *Berg. Hütt. Jahrb.*, **26**. 203, 1878; G. Kroupa, *Œster. Zeit. Berg. Hütt.*, **60**. 513, 539, 1912; W. K. Mallette, *Chem. Met. Engg.*, **21**. 67, 1919; G. Rigg, *ib.*, **22**. 518, 1920; *Trans. Inst. Min. Met.*, **29**. 1, 1920; C. O. Bannister, *ib.*, **21**. 346, 1912; M. Moslard, *Monit. Scient.*, (4), **20**. 789, 1906; F. Chaine, *ib.*, (4), **21**. 102, 1907; B. Naumann, *Glückauf*, **44**. 1631, 1908; R. Wüster, *ib.*, **57**. 69, 93, 1921; C. Dörschel, *Metall Erz*, **19**. 29, 57, 1922; C. Offerhaus, *ib.*, **18**. 591, 1921; **19**. 19, 1922; A. Goldmann, *ib.*, **16**. 41, 1919; W. Metzel, *ib.*, **10**. 193, 1913; W. Borchers and W. Metzel, *German Pat.*, *D.R.P.* 275904, 1913; W. Schütz, *Met.*, **8**. 228, 1911; F. Bennitt, *German Pat.*, *D.R.P.* 204082, 1907; R. von Zelewsky, *ib.*, 256083, 1912; S. Huldt, *ib.*, 325897, 1918; J. Asbeck, *ib.*, 218839, 1908; Helfenstein Elektroöfen Gesellschaft, *ib.*, 297872, 1918; P. A. Mackay, *ib.*, 340423, 1920; W. Witter, *ib.*, 232097, 1908; 240365, 1909; K. Recke, *ib.*, 325971, 325972, 1917; E. H. Shortman, *ib.*, 261187, 1907; E. Langguth, *ib.*, 273483, 1913; C. A. Dinsmore, *Min. World*, **34**. 691, 1911; E. H. Hamilton, *Min. Met.*, **25**, 1922; *U.S. Pat. No.* 1404714, 1919; E. F. Kern, *ib.*, 885761, 1906; A. S. Auerbach, *ib.*, 941904, 1909; *Eng. Min. Journ.*, **89**. 715, 1910; L. Devaucelle, *French Pat. No.* 532389, 1920; E. Villejean, *Journ. Pharm. Chim.*, (6), **13**. 97, 1901; E. F. Elmore, *Brit. Pat. No.* 162026, 1919; E. A. Ashcroft, *ib.*, 200701, 1922; S. Ganelin, *ib.*, 135968, 1918; O. C. Ralston, C. E. Williams, M. J. Udy, and G. J. Holt, *Trans. Amer. Inst. Min. Eng.*, **57**. 634, 1917; *Bull. Amer. Inst. Min. Eng.*, 1205, 1917; *Chem. Met. Engg.*, **17**. 437, 1917; L. F. Emmons, *Monograph U.S. Geol. Sur.*, **12**. 724, 1886; J. S. Curtis, *ib.*, **7**. 160, 1884; J. Farbakij, *Berg. Hütt. Ztg.*, **53**. 177, 1894; F. Heberlein, *ib.*, **58**. 189, 1899; N. von Jossa and N. S. von Kurnakoff, *ib.*, **45**. 548, 1886; A. Streng, *ib.*, **23**. 88, 1864; L. Dietz, *ib.*, **34**. 119, 1875; **45**. 272, 1886; L. W. Davies, *U.S. Pat. No.* 384682, 1888; W. Brückner, *Eng. Min. Journ.*, **43**. 37, 1887; C. H. Fulton and I. E. Goodner, *Bull. Amer. Inst. Min. Eng.*, 960, 1908; *Trans. Amer. Inst. Min. Eng.*, **39**. 584, 1908; T. Huntington and F. Heberlein, *Brit. Pat. No.* 13454, 1903; A. D. Carmichael, *ib.*, 17580, 1902; P. Heberdey, *Zeit. Kryst.*, **21**. 56, 1893; H. A. Evans, *Proc. Australasian Inst. Min. Met. Eng.*, 31, 1923; A. Firket, *Ann. Mines Belg.* **6**. 237, 1901; W. Hampe, *Chem. Ztg.*, **16**. 2028, 1892; C. H. Fulton and T. Knutze, *Trans. Amer. Inst. Min. Eng.*, **35**. 336, 1904; M. H. Bolles, *ib.*, **35**. 674, 1904; J. A. Church, *ib.*, **24**. 561, 1894; W. Braden, *ib.*, **26**. 51, 1896; C. Ernst, *Œster. Zeit. Berg. Hütt.*, **34**. 221, 1886; C. Mann, *Œster. Jahrb.*, 15, 1890; C. A. Hering, *Die Verdichtung des Hüttenrauches*, Stuttgart, 34, 1888; H. Weidmann, *Met.*, **3**. 660, 1906; C. Guillemain, *ib.*, **7**. 595, 1910; R. Vambera, *Berg. Hütt. Jahrb.*, **48**. 1, 1900; A. Zdrahal, *ib.*, **38**. 24, 1890; F. von Lipp, *ib.*, **33**. 193, 1885; A. Schertel, *Jahrb. Sachsen*, 13, 1887; *Berg. Hütt. Jahrb.*, 37, 1880.

* E. F. Côte and P. R. Pierron, *German Pat.*, *D.R.P.* 206472, 1907; N. W. Iles, *Lead Smelting and the Scientific Handling of Smoke*, New York, 1902; *School Mines Quart.*, **17**. 97, 1896; *Eng. Min. Journ.*, **68**. 729, 1899; R. Watson, *Chemical Essays*, London, **3**. 240, 282, 1782; J. D. Stagg, *Brit. Pat. No.* 9920, 1843; W. and H. B. Young, *ib.*, 12256, 1848; A. Courage, *ib.*, 959, 1859; J. Neville, *ib.*, 4746, 1823; M. A. Fallize, *Rev. Univ. Mines*, **11**. 367, 1862; L. E. Rivot, *Description des gîtes métallifères de la préparation mécanique et du traitement métallurgique des minérais de plomb argentifères de Pontgibaud*, Paris, 142, 1851; P. Berthier, *Traité des essais par la voie sèche*, Paris, **2**. 744, 1834; F. Moldenhauer, *Schweiz. Polyt. Ztg.*, **8**. 186, 1863; *Zeit. Berg. Hütt.*, **22**. 89, 1863; A. P. Dufrénoy, *Voyage métallurgique en Angleterre*, Paris, **2**. 658, 1839; H. L. Pattinson, *Trans. Nat. Hist. Soc. Newcastle-on-Tyne*, **2**. 166, 1832; J. A. Phillips, *Journ. Soc. Arts*, **7**. 413, 1859; W. E. Newman, *Trans. Amer. Inst. Min. Eng.*,

54. 485, 1916; C. B Sprague, *Eng. Min. Journ.*, **89**. 519, 1910; C. T. Rice, *ib.*, **106**. 771, 1918; J. Aitken, *Proc. Roy. Soc. Edin.*, **12**. 440, 1884; O. J. Lodge and J. W. Clark, *Nature*, **28**. 297, 1883; O. J. Lodge, *ib.*, **71**. 582, 1905; *Phil. Mag.*, (5), **17**. 214, 1884; *Electrician*, **93**. 523, 1924; *B.A. Rep.*, 743, 1895; *Journ. Soc. Chem. Ind.*, **5**. 572, 1886; *Brit. Pat. No.* 24355, 1903; E. Walker, *ib.*, 24355, 1903; K. Friedrich, *Met.*, **3**. 747, 1906; C. Schiffner, *ib.*, **5**. 169, 1908; F. G. Cotterell, *Smithsonian Rep.*, 653, 1913; *Eng. Min. Journ.*, **86**. 375, 1908; *Brit. Pat. No.* 227022, 1924; *Journ. Ind. Eng. Chem.*, **3**. 542, 1911; *Trans. Amer. Inst. Min. Eng.*, **43**. 512, 1912; H. C. Weber, *Journ. Ind. Eng. Chem.*, **16**. 1239, 1924; W. G. Smith and A. A. Heimrod, *Chem. Met. Engg.*, **21**. 360, 1919; M. Hohlfeld, *Kastner's Arch.*, **2**. 205, 1824; L. A. Palmer, *Mines Minerals*, **30**. 496, 543, 1910; B. Kosmann, *Zeit. Berg. Hütt. Sal.*, **31**. 233, 1883; C. A. Hering, *Die Verdichtung des Hüttenrauches*, Stuttgart, 1888; C. F. Shelby, *Eng. Min. Journ.*, **85**. 205, 1908; J. B. Wynne, *ib.*, **88**. 602, 1910; T. J. Greenway, *ib.*, **79**. 73, 1905; J. C. Bennett, *ib.*, **86**. 456, 1908; E. Ferraris, *ib.*, **80**. 783, 1905; *Œster. Zeit. Berg. Hütt.*, **53**. 455, 1905; H. W. Edwards, *Trans. Amer. Inst. Min. Eng.*, **35**. 60, 1904; T. Egelston, *ib.*, **11**. 404, 1883; J. A. Church, *ib.*, **15**. 611, 1887; F. R. Carpenter, *ib.*, **30**. 764, 1900; K. H. Bauer, *Jahrb. Berg. Hütt.*, **39**, 1894; *Œster. Zeit. Berg. Hütt.*, **53**. 347, 1905; O. Säger, *Berg. Hütt. Ztg.*, **53**. 299, 1894; *Hygiene der Hüttenarbeiter*, Jena, 1895; J. Hannay, *German Pat.*, *D.R.P.* 151863, 1904; The Sulphides Reduction Co., *ib.*, 128534, 1902; J. Percy, *The Metallurgy of Lead*, London, 1870; N. H. Gellert, *Iron Age*, **113**. 422, 1924; A. Dahlgren, *Teknisk Tids.*, **54**. 34, 1924.

* P. Spence, *Brit. Pat. No.* 997, 1867; A. G. Betts, *Trans. Amer. Inst. Min. Eng.*, **34**. 175, 1904; *The Refining of Lead by Electrolysis*, New York, 1908; *U.S. Pat. No.* 713277, 1902; G. Mardus, *Elektrolytische Raffination von Blei aus borfluorwasserstoffsauer Lösung*, Berlin, 1908; J. F. Miller, *Met. Chem. Engg.*, **11**. 463, 1913; J. Percy, *The Metallurgy of Lead*, London, 1870; W. R. Ingalls, *Lead Smelting and Refining*, New York. 270, 1906; W. R. Ingalls and F. Wyatt, *U.S. Pat. No.* 516016, 1884; F. C. Mathers, *ib.*, 931944, 1909; *Met. Chem. Engg.*, **8**. 347, 1910; *Trans. Amer. Electrochem. Soc.*, **26**. 99, 1914; C. Blas and E. Miest, *Essai d'application de l'électrolyse*, Paris, 1882; *Berg. Hütt. Ztg.*, **41**. 328, 1882; **42**. 37, 1883; M. Kiliani, *ib.*, **44**. 252, 1885; E. Ellershausen, *Eng. Min. Journ.*, **70**. 52, 1900; A. Neuburger, *Handbuch der praktischen Elektrometallurgie*, München, 300, 1907; P. Salom, *Elektrochem. Zeit.*, **10**. 82, 1902; *Electrochem. Ind.*, **1**. 18, 1902; *Trans. Amer. Electrochem. Soc.*, **1**. 87, 1902; J. C. Claney and L. W. Marsland, *U.S. Pat. No.* 715023, 715024, 1902; C. P. Townsend, *ib.*, 867320, 1907; H. S. Auerbach, *ib.*, 941904, 1909; *Eng. Min. Journ.*, **89**. 715, 1910; U. Coppa, *ib.*, **85**. 943, 1908; B. Mohr, *Brit. Pat. No.* 13169, 1896; E. A. Ashcroft, *ib.*, 13850, 1894; *Trans. Inst. Min. Met.*, **6**. 282, 1899; E. A. Ashcroft and J. Swinburne, *ib.*, **9**. 378, 1901; *Brit. Pat. No.* 14278, 1899; J. Swinburne, *ib.*, 10829, 10829A, 1897; A. Nathansohn, *ib.*, 187195, 1921; F. E. Elmore, *ib.*, 127641, 1917; S. O. Cowper-Coles, *ib.*, 5943, 1898; H. E. Fry and R. Addie, *ib.*, 4911, 1898; H. E. Fry, J. David, and C. le Doux, 12452, 1895; P. C. C. Isherwood, *ib.*, 16364, 1906; A. Stansfield and L. B. Reynolds, *Canadian Pat. No.* 102311, 1906; M. G. Platten, *U.S. Pat. No.* 1480110, 1924; N. C. Christensen, *ib.*, 1441064, 1441065, 1923; H. Hey, *ib.*, 1432858, 1922; S. Ganelin, *German Pat.*, *D.R.P.* 97943, 1897; 124846, 1899; E. W. von Siemens and J. G. Halske, *ib.*, 92023, 1896; H. Neuendorf, *ib.*, 403934, 1898; A. H. Imbert, *ib.*, 195793, 1906; 208403, 1907; E. Vaigner, *ib.*, 203518, 1906; M. Liebig, *ib.*, 196284, 1904; J. Asbeck, *ib.*, 223667, 1909; C. Höpfner, *ib.*, 126396, 1895; J. de Coppet, *ib.*, 246973, 1910; G. de Bechi, *ib.*, 266219, 1913; R. Hesse, G. von Rauschenplat, and T. Schmidt, *ib.*, 277241, 1913; A. Wiedemann, *ib.*, 240366, 1913; A. B. Stoddart, *ib.*, 326596, 1913; C. Schnabel, *Handbuch der Metallhüttenkunde*, Berlin, **1**. 564, 1901; London, **1**. 712, 1921; W. West, *Proc. Inst. Civ. Eng.*, **104**. 407, 1891; *Eng. Min. Journ.*, **51**. 321, 1891; C. F. Croselmere, *ib.*, **46**. 240, 1888; **47**. 135, 1889; E. H. Russell, *U.S. Pat. No.* 295815, 1887; R. Gahl, *ib.*, **115**. 119, 1923; E. A. Parnell, *German Pat.*, *D.R.P.* 1351, 1897; *B.A. Rep.*, 544, 1880; F. L. Bartlett, *Brit. Pat. No.* 12322, 1889; F. T. Snyder, *Mining Mag.*, **1**. 220, 1909; *U.S. Pat. No.* 933133, 1909; T. L. Greenway, *Brit. Pat. No.* 1027, 1886; W. R. Ingalls and F. Wyatt, *Mineral Ind.*, **3**. 432, 1894; *U.S. Pat. No.* 516016, 1894; S. H. Emmens, *ib.*, 513490, 1894; *Min. Ind.*, **3**. 431, 1894; W. Borchers, *ib.*, **9**. 622, 1902; L. Létrange, *Réduction des minérais de zinc par l'électricité*, Paris, 1892; *Dingler's Journ.*, **245**. 455, 1882; F. M. Lyte, *Brit. Pat. No.* 15813, 1896; F. E. Elmore, *ib.*, 162026, 1919; 187313, 1921; *German Pat.*, *D.R.P.* 343076, 343077, 1920; E. A. Ashcroft, *Brit. Pat. No.* 198024, 1922; W. G. Rumbold, *ib.*, 135052, 1919; J. J. Collins, *ib.*, 166929, 1920; H. L. Sulman and H. F. K. Picard, *ib.*, 109817, 1916; W. H. Hannay, *U.S. Pat. No.* 1456798, 1920; N. C. Christensen, *ib.*, 1390603, 1919; 1415796, 1434087, 1434088, 1435891, 1441063, 1919; 1572268, 1926; H. Hay, *ib.*, 1572388, 1926; D. F. Harbaugh, *ib.*, 1306479, 1306480, 1918; F. N. Flynn and S. D. van Arsdale, *ib.*, 1448923, 1919; G. Battelli, *ib.*, 1430270, 1921; A. Nathansohn and F. Leyser, *Zeit. Elektrochem.*, **28**. 310, 1922; A. Nathansohn, *German Pat.*, *D.R.P.* 362909, 1921; 366483, 366484, 366485, 1923; O. C. Ralston, *Trans. Amer. Inst. Min. Met. Eng.*, **70**. 447, 1924; C. E. Sims and O. L. Ralston, *Trans Amer. Electrochem. Soc.*, **30**. 242, 1917; D. A. Lyon, O. C. Ralston, and J. F. Cullen, *Met. Chem. Engg.*, **14**. 32, 1916; O. C. Ralston, C. E. Williams, M. J. Udy, and J. Holt, *Bull. Amer. Inst. Min. Eng.*, 1205, 1917; *Trans. Amer. Inst. Min. Eng.*, **57**. 634, 1917; *Chem. Met. Engg.*, **17**. 437, 1917; J. E. Conley, *ib.*, **20**. 514, 1919; E. L. Blossom, *ib.*, **17**. 456, 1917; *Trans. Amer. Inst. Min. Eng.*, **57**. 645, 1917; R. Hesse, *Met.*, **8**. 321, 365, 1911; K. Wagemann, *ib.*, **9**. 537, 1912; W. Menzel, *Metall. Erz.*, **10**. 193, 230, 1913; *Studien zur Frage der Verhüttung*

der sogenamsten melierten Erze, Kupfer, Blei, und Zink führender Sulfidischer Erze, Halle a. S., 1915; W. Borchers and W. Menzel, *German Pat.*, *D.R.P.* 275904, 1913; H. and P. Faivre, *French Pat. No.* 596147, 1924.

[10] A. Streng, *Berg. Hütt. Ztg.*, **20**. 384, 1861; **21**. 125, 1860; **22**. 30, 1861; **23**. 134, 1864; A. Streng and E. Overbeck, *ib.*, **16**. 203, 1857; H. Jäger, *ib.*, **34**. 129, 1875; F. von Lill, *ib.*, **26**. 371, 1867; **36**. 81, 1877; C. Balling, *ib.*, **26**. 419, 1867; L. F. Emmons, *ib.*, **45**. 57, 82, 1886; E. Dietz, *ib.*, **45**. 263, 1886; L. Schneider, *Berg. Hütt Jahrb.*, **24**. 331, 1876; *Berg. Hütt. Ztg.*, **36**. 81, 1877; W. Hampe, *ib.*, **30**. 144, 1871; *Zeit. Berg. Hütt. Sal.*, **18**. 195, 1870; A. Schertel, *Jahrb. Sachsen*, 13, 1882; F. Moldenhauer, *Schweiz. Polyt. Jahrb.*, 118, 1863; *Zeit. Berg. Hütt.*, **22**. 89, 1863; W. Mrazek, *ib.*, **26**. 419, 1867; S. Mitteregger, *ib.*, **30**. 292, 1871; *Zeit. Berg. Hütt. Ver. Rürrithen*, 7, 1871; H. Dietrich, *Œster. Zeit. Berg. Hütt.*, **28**. 489, 1880; E. Priwoznik, *Berg. Hütt. Jahrb.*, **28**. 41, 1880; J. Percy, *The Metallurgy of Lead*, London, 1870.

[11] F. Reich, *Jahrb. Sachsen*, 37, 1860; A. D. Machatti, *Chem. News*, **10**. 193, 1864; H. Jäger, *Berg. Hütt. Ztg.*, **21**. 231, 1876.

[12] A. Schertel, *Berg. Hütt. Ztg.*, **41**. 293, 1822; C. Rössler, *ib.*, **49**. 248, 1890; C. F. Plattner, *ib.*, **42**. 417, 1883; *Vorlesungen über allgemeine Hüttenkunde*, Freiberg, **12**. 137, 1860; W. Hampe, *Zeit. Berg. Hütt. Sal.*, **18**. 203, 1870; J. Percy, *The Metallurgy of Lead*, London, 458, 1870; J. A. Phillips, *The Mining and Metallurgy of Gold and Silver*, London, 482, 1867; H. O. Hofman, *The Metallurgy of Lead*, New York, 445, 1906; C. Schnabel, *Handbuch der Metallhüttenkunde*, Berlin, **1**. 431, 1901; London, **1**. 580, 1921; *Zeit. Berg. Hütt. Sal.*, **28**. 262, 1880; E. Ferraris, *Œster. Zeit. Hütt. Berg.*, **53**. 455, 1905; *Eng. Min. Journ.*, **80**. 781, 1905; W. M. Hutchings, *ib.*, **59**. 171, 1895; **80**. 726, 1905; T. Huntington, *ib.*, **59**. 291, 1895; G. D. Delprat, *ib.*, **83**. 518, 1907; O. Pufahl, **81**. 718, 1906; *Œster. Zeit. Berg. Hütt.*, **53**. 400, 1905; B. B. Bayly, *Trans. Austr. Inst. Min. Eng.*, **12**. 80, 1907; W. Poole, *Queensland Min. Journ.*, **10**. 117, 1909; A. Firket, *Ann. Mines Belg.*, **6**. 237, 1901; H. Harris, *Brit. Pat. No.* 189013, 1922; 217391, 1923; *Canadian Pat. No.* 242735, 1924; W. Hall, *Brit. Pat. No.* 4085, 1816; E. A. Pontifex and C. Glassford, *ib.*, 1644, 1854; T. Richardson, *ib.*, 14093, 1852; A. H. Johnson, *ib.*, 11872, 1847; A. Warner, *ib.*, 2363, 1860; W. Baker, *ib.*, 1507, 1860; *Mining Journ.*, **31**. 130, 1861; H. W. Kachelmann, *Berg. Hütt. Jahrb.*, **11**. 198, 1862; B. George, *Metall Erz*, **22**. 27, 1925; American Metal Co., *U.S. Pat. No.* 1548852, 1548853, 1924.

[13] H. Jäger, *Berg. Hütt. Ztg.*, **34**. 129, 1875; *ib.*, **25**. 433, 1886; F. von Lill, *ib.*, **26**. 371, 1867; E. Dietz, *ib.*, **47**. 263, 1886; R. Fresenius, *ib.*, **16**. 147, 1870; *Zeit. anal. Chem.*, **8**. 148, 1869; **9**. 242, 1870; A. Eschka, *Berg. Hütt. Jahrb.*, **22**. 389, 1874; L. Schneider, *ib.*, **26**. 203, 1878; *Berg. Hütt. Ztg.*, **36**. 81, 1877; E. Priwoznik, *Berg. Hütt. Jahrb.*, **27**. 188, 1879; **28**. 41, 1880; A. Zdrahal, *ib.*, **29**. 485, 1881; *Œster. Zeit. Berg. Hütt.*, **38**. 497, 1890; A. Exeli, *ib.*, **29**. 568, 1881; **30**. 15, 186, 302, 520, 1882; **32**. 45, 489, 1884; P. N. Degens, *Zeit. anorg. Chem.*, **63**. 209, 1909; F. Mylius, *ib.*, **74**. 407, 1912; O. Herting, *Chem. Ztg.*, **27**. 923, 1903; A. Mosso, *Atti Accad. Lincei*, (5), **19**. ii, 225, 1910; P. Beck, *Chem. Ind.*, **30**. 272, 1907; American Metal Co., *U.S. Pat. No.* 1583495, 1926.

[14] J. A. Müller, *Versuch eines hüttenmännischen Berichts über einen Prczess Silber und Blei aus ihren Erzen trocken zu scheiden*, Leipzig, 1825; P. F. G. le Play, *Description de l'affinage par cristallisation*, Paris, 1837; *Ann. Mines*, (3), **10**. 381, 1836; L. Rozan, *ib.*, (7), 3. 160, 1873; H. O. Hofman, *Min. Resources U.S Geol. Sur.*, 462, 1884; *The Metallurgy of Lead and the Desilverization of Base Bullion*, New York, 1899; 430, 504, 1906; M W. Iles, *Eng. Min. Journ.*, **70**. 186, 1900; G. G. Griswold, *ib.*, **112**. 978, 1921; L. S. Austin, *Min. Scient. Press.*, **94**. 89, 1907; *Trans. Amer. Inst. Min. Eng.*, **12**. 185, 1883; **13**. 41, 1884; O. F. Pfordte, *ib.*, **21**. 25, 1892; H. F. Collins, *ib.*, **31**. 446, 1901; C. E. Wait, *ib.*, **15**. 463, 1886; F. C. Blake, *ib.*, **10**. 220, 1881; F. C. Newton, *ib.*, **51**. 786, 1915; *Met. Chem. Engg.*, **13**. 181, 1915; L. Addicks, *ib.*, **23**. 110, 1920; C. Schnabel, *Dingler's Journ.*, **228**. 186, 1878; *Zeit Berg Hütt Sal.*, **28**. 296, 1880; *Handbuch der Metallhüttenkunde*, Berlin, **1**. 576, 1901; London, **1**. 624, 1905; F. L. Piddington, *Journ. Chem Met. Min. Soc. South Africa*, **4**. 232, 389, 1904; K. L. Graham, *ib.*, **5**. 315, 1904; J. S. Curtis, *Monograph U.S. Geol. Sur.*, **7**. 160, 1884; H. F. Collins, *The Metallurgy of Lead*, London, 360, 1910; F. von Schlippenbach, *Metall Erz.*, **15**. 323, 1918; H. Harris, *Brit. Pat. Nos.* 189013, 199660, 1922; C. Roswag, *Metallurgie de la désargentation des minérais du plomb*, Paris, 1884; M. Eisler, *The Metallurgy of Argentiferous Lead*, London, 251, 1891; H. L. Pattinson, *B.A. Rep.*, 30, 1838; *Brit. Pat. No.* 6487, 1833; A. Parkes, *ib.*, 13118, 1850; 13675, 13746, 1851; 13997, 1852; N. C. Cookson, *Trans. Newcastle Chem. Soc.*, **4**. 171, 1877; T. A. Rickard, *Min. Scient. Press*, **112**. 505, 1916; **113**. 941, 1916; C. J. B. Karsten, *Karsten's Arch.*, **16**. 597, 1829; (2), **26**. 295, 1834; O. Pufahl, *Zeit. Berg. Hütt. Sal.*, **53**. 400, 1905; E. J. Kohlmeyer, *Chem. Ztg.*, **36**. 1079, 1912: P. Berthier, *Traité des essais par la voie sèche*, Paris, **2**. 725, 1834; F. Reich, *Berg. Hütt. Ztg.*, **21**. 251, 1862; W. Mrazek, *ib.*, **26**. 419, 1867; **33**. 413, 1874; A. Streng, *Zeit. Ges. Naturw.*, **12**. 10, 1859; *Berg. Hütt. Ztg.*, **20**. 348, 1861; **23**. 88, 1864; H. Hahn, *ib.*, **23**. 88, 1864; J. Asbeck, *German Pat.*, *D.R.P.* 218839, 1908; F. Roderbourg, *ib.*, 241483, 1910; C. F. Föhr, *Chem. Tech. Zentr. Anz.*, 687, 1887; *Berg. Hütt. Ztg.*, **47**. 28, 1888; C. Rössler, *ib.*, **48**. 387, 1889; B. Rösing, *ib.*, **49**. 369, 1890; F. Heberlein, *ib.*, **54**. 41, 1895; C. F. Plattner, *ib.*, **48**. 117, 1889; *Œster. Zeit. Berg. Hütt.*, **35**. 421, 1887; C. Kirchoff, *Mét. Rev.*, 1. 224, 1878; E. Ferraris, *Eng. Min. Journ.*, **80**. 781, 1905; H. Rössler and B. Edelmann, *ib.*, **51**. 404, 582, 1891; **56**. 245, 568, 1893; A. Raht, *U.S. Pat. No.* 826114, 1906; W. T. Davis, *ib.*, 1452364, 1921; R. Spicer, *ib.*, 1285511, 1917; G. P. Hulst,

ib., 1001525, 1920 ; G. D. Delprat, *Trans. Austr. Inst. Min. Eng.*, **12.** 1, 1907 ; B. B. Bayly, *ib.*, **12.** 80, 1907 ; G. H. Blakemore, *ib.*, **5.** 221, 1898 ; E. A. Weinberg, *ib.*, **7.** 167, 1901 ; A. Firket, *Ann. Mines Belg.*, **6.** 237, 1901.

[15] A. C. Becquerel, *Compt. Rend.*, **38.** 1095, 1854 ; *Traité expérimental de l'électricité et du magnétisme*, Paris, **2.** 276, 1855 ; N. S. Keith. *Eng. Min. Journ.*, **26.** 26, 1878 ; *Trans. Amer. Inst. Min. Eng.*, **13.** 310, 1884 ; C. Blas and E. Miest, *Essai d'application de l'électrolyse*, Paris, 1882 ; *Berg. Hütt. Ztg.*, **41.** 328, 1882 ; **42.** 37, 1883 ; G. Titschak, *Mitt. Materialprüf.*, **41.** 89, 1923 ; *Beiträge zur elektrolytischen Abscheidung und Raffination von Blei*, Berlin, 1924 ; C. Balling, *Die Metallhüttenkunde*, Berlin, 160. 1885 ; W. Borchers, *Electrometallurgie*, Leipzig, 476, 1903 ; D. Tommasi, *Compt. Rend.*, **122.** 1476, 1896 ; *Zeit. Elektrochem.*, **3.** 92, 310, 341, 1896 ; H. Senn, *ib.*, **11.** 229, 1905 ; F. Haber, *ib.*, **9.** 23, 39, 390, 1903 ; W. Hampe, *Zeit. Berg. Hütt. Sal.*, **30.** 81, 1882 ; R. S. Snowdon, *Trans. Amer. Electrochem. Soc.*, **9.** 221, 1906 ; K. Pietrusky, *Œster. Chem. Ztg.*, **7.** 32, 1904 ; W. Stahl, *Metall Erz*, **20.** 117, 1923 ; M. Altmayer, *Journ. Four. Élect.*, **32.** 66, 1923 ; A. Watt and A. Philip, *Electroplating and Electrorefining*, London, 1902 ; A. G. Betts, *Lead Refining by Electrolysis*, New York, 1908 ; *Trans. Amer. Inst. Min. Eng.*, **34.** 175, 1904 ; *Electrochem. Met. Ind.*, **3.** 272, 1905 ; *U.S. Pat. Nos.* 679357, 679824, 1901 ; *Trans. Amer. Electrochem. Soc.*, **8.** 83, 1905 ; *Met.*, **6.** 234, 1909 ; R. L. Whitehead, *ib.*, **2.** 163, 1905 ; *Mines Minerals*, **25.** 285, 1905 ; *Mineral Ind.*, **14.** 425, 1905 ; T. Ulke, *Eng. Min. Journ.*, **74.** 475, 1902 ; F. Mylius, *Zeit. anorg. Chem.*, **74.** 407, 1912 ; R. Wintgen and H. Löwenthal, *Zeit. phys. Chem.*, **109.** 391, 1924 ; E. Kraynik, *Glückauf*, **45.** 1004, 1905 ; A. Neuburger, *Handbuch der praktischen Elektrometallurgie*, München, 305, 1907 ; E. W. von Siemens and J. G. Halske, *German Pat.*, *D.R.P.* 223688, 1909 ; C. F. Mathers, *Met. Chem. Engg.*, **8.** 347, 1910 ; **12.** 351, 1914 ; *Trans. Amer. Electrochem. Soc.*, **17.** 267, 1910 ; **26.** 99, 1914 ; E. A. Ashcroft, *Electrochem. Ind.*, **4.** 357, 1906 ; G. P. Baxter and F. L. Grover, *Journ. Amer. Chem. Soc.*, **37.** 1031, 1915 ; A. J. Hale, *Journ. Soc. Chem. Ind.—Chem. Ind.*, **43.** 1224, 1250, 1291, 1924 ; F. Peters, *Glückauf*, **51.** 1194, 1915 ; T. K. Rose, *ib.*, **47.** 97, 1911 ; V. Engelhardt, *Trans. Amer. Electrochem. Soc.*, **21.** 332, 1912 ; E. M. Chance, *ib.*, **17.** 235, 1910 ; E. M. Chance and E. Kent, *U.S. Pat. No.* 948681, 1910 ; M. Turnbull, *Mines Min.*, **31.** 121, 1910 ; *Chem. Met. Engg.*, **8.** 642, 1910 ; J. F. Miller, *ib.*, **11.** 463, 1913 ; E. Jacobs, *ib.*, **9.** 30, 1911 ; W. J. Jordan, *Journ. prakt. Chem.*, (1), **9.** 84, 1836 ; R. Saxon, *Chem. News*, **131.** 324, 1925.

[16] A. Roussin, *Journ. Pharm. Chim.*, (4), **3.** 413, 1866 ; *Chem. News*, **14.** 27, 1866 ; H. Mouraour, *Compt. Rend.*, **130.** 140, 1900 ; A. Commaille, *ib.*, **63.** 1356, 1866 ; T. Bergman, *De attractionibus electivis*, Upsala, 1775 ; *De præcipitatis Metallicis*, Upsala, 1780 ; S. Kern, *Chem. News*, **33.** 112, 1876 ; E. G. Bryant, *ib.*, **79.** 75, 1899 ; H. N. Warren, *ib.*, **61.** 183, 1890 ; W. C. Reid, *ib.*, **12.** 242, 1865 ; A. Cossa, *Nuovo Cimento*, (2), **3.** 75, 1870 ; *Zeit. Chem.*, (2), **6.** 380, 1870 ; *Bull. Soc. Chim.*, (2), **14.** 199, 1870 ; J. B. Senderens, *ib.*, (3), **11.** 424, 1894 ; O. Prelinger, *Monatsh.*, **24.** 353, 1893 ; A. H. Low, *Journ. Anal. App. Chem.*, **4.** 12, 1891 ; **6.** 664, 1892 ; J. E. Williams, *Eng. Min. Journ.*, **53.** 641, 1892 ; L. T. Merrill, *ib.*, **91.** 56, 1911 ; A. Eckenroth, *Pharm. Ztg.*, **40.** 528, 1895 ; F. Mohr, *Zeit. anal. Chem.*, **12.** 142, 1873 ; C. Rössler, *ib.*, **24.** 1, 1885 ; F. Wöhler, *Liebig's Ann.*, **85.** 253, 1853 ; A. Simon, *Zeit. Koll.*, **12.** 171, 1913 ; L. T. M. Gray, *Journ. Chem. Soc.*, **127.** 776, 1925 ; A. Gawlowsky, *Œster. Chem. Ztg.*, **19.** 150, 1916 ; C. A. Kraus and H. F. Kurtz, *Journ. Amer. Chem. Soc.*, **47.** 43, 1925 ; A. M. Pleischl, *Sitzber. Akad. Wien*, **43.** 555, 1861 ; N. W. Fischer, *Gilbert's Ann.*, **72.** 289, 1822 ; *Pogg. Ann.*, **9.** 262, 1827 ; **10.** 603, 1827 ; *Das Verhältniss der chemischen Verwandtschaft zur galvanischen Elektricität in Versuchen dargestellt*, Berlin, 137, 1830 ; O. Sackur, *Zeit. Elektrochem.*, **10.** 523, 1904 ; *Arb. Kais. Ges. Amt.*, **20.** 512, 1903 ; E. Giurgea, *Bull. Soc. Stiinte Bucuresti*, **21.** 192, 1912 ; A. A. Noyes and K. Toabe, *Journ. Amer. Chem. Soc.*, **39.** 1537, 1917 ; G. von Hevesy, *Phys. Zeit.*, **16.** 52, 1915 ; A. Payen, *Ann. Chim. Phys.*, (2), **54.** 273, 1833 ; H. Reinsch, *Journ. prakt. Chem.*, (1), **24.** 248, 1841 : F. Stolba, *ib.*, (1), **101.** 150, 1867 ; *Chem. News*, **17.** 2, 1868 ; H. Freundlich and J. Fischer, *Zeit. Elektrochem.*, **8.** 885, 1912 ; R. Lorenz, W. Fränkel, and M. Ganz, *Zeit. anorg. Chem.*, **153.** 281, 1926.

[17] J. Ohshima, *Japan Pat. No.* 41177, 1921 ; G. Shimazu, *ib.*, 42562, 42563, 42564, 1922 ; *French Pat. No.* 549209, 1922 ; *U.S. Pat. No.* 1584149, 1926 ; W. A. Tichomiroff and P. Lidoff, *Wied. Ann.*, **37.** 443, 1889 ; G. Bredig, *Zeit. angew. Chem.*, **11.** 953, 1898 ; P. Schützenberger, *Compt. Rend.*, **86.** 1398, 1878 ; A. Thiel, *Ber.*, **53.** 1066, 1920 ; S4. 2757, 1921 ; *Ber. Ges. Marburg*, 1, 1920 ; B. de Rostaing, *Bull. Soc. Enc. Nat. Ind.*, (2), **6.** 730, 1859 ; *Repert. Chim. Appl.*, 1. 91, 1858 ; Elektrizitätsgesellschaft Gelnhausen, *German Pat.*, *D.R.P.* 70348, 1892 ; Union Lead and Oil Co., *ib.*, 152695, 1902 ; L. Creveling, *U.S. Pat. No.* 665827, 1900 ; H. Luggin, *Zeit. phys. Chem.*, **16.** 683, 1895.

[18] G. F. Taylor, *Phys. Rev.*, (2), **23.** 655, 1924 ; O. Ohmann, *Ber.*, **45.** 2973, 1912 ; F. Paneth and O. Nörring, *ib.*, **53.** 1706, 1920 ; P. Schützenberger, *Compt. Rend.*, **86.** 1398, 1878 ; H. I. Hannover, *ib.*, **154.** 1594, 1912 ; O. W. Brown and A. R. Nees, *Journ. Ind. Eng. Chem.*, **4.** 870, 1912 ; V. G. Yourieff, *Brit. Pat. No.* 123587, 1918 ; L. Höpfner, *German Pat.*, *D.R.P.* 87430, 1895 ; 91848, 1896 ; H. N. Ridyard, *Journ. Amer. Chem. Soc.*, **46.** 287, 1924.

[19] J. S. Stas, *Bull. Acad. Belg.*, (2), **10.** 295, 1860 ; *Chem. News*, **4.** 307, 1861 ; B. Lambert and H. E. Cullis, *Journ. Chem. Soc.*, **107.** 210, 1915 ; G. P. Baxter and F. L. Grover, *Journ. Amer. Chem. Soc.*, **37.** 1027, 1915 ; T. W. Richards and C. Wadsworth, *ib.*, **38.** 221, 1916 ; A. R. Andrew, *Bull. Inst. Min. Met.*, **19.** 276, 1910.

[20] H. Nordenson, *Koll. Beihefte*, **7.** 91, 1915 ; D. Zavrieff, *Zeit. phys. Chem.*, **87.** 507, 1914 ;

F. Bayer, *German Pat.*, *D.R.P.* 260470, 1912 ; C. J. Reed, *Journ. Franklin Inst.*, **140**. 68, 1895 ; *Trans. Amer. Electrochem. Soc.*, **2**. 194, 1902 ; F. Haber, *ib.*, **2**. 190, 1902 ; G. Bredig and F. Haber, *Ber.*, **31**. 274, 1898 ; J. Billitzer, *ib.*, **35**. 1933, 1902 ; T. Svedberg, *ib.*, **38**. 3617, 3620, 1905 ; **39**. 1712, 1906 ; **42**. 4376, 1909 ; *Ark. Kem. Min.*, **2**. 14, 21, 1906 ; G. Börjeson and T. Svedberg, *Koll. Zeit.*, **25**. 154, 1919 ; R. Furth, *ib.*, **34**. 224, 1924 ; E. F. Burton, *Phil. Mag.*, (6), **11**. 425, 1906 ; A. Gutbier, *Zeit. anorg. Chem.*, **31**. 448, 1902 ; O. Ruff and R. Wallstein, *ib.*, **128**. 111, 1923 ; R. Lorenz and W. Eitel, *ib.*, **91**. 46, 1915 ; R. Lorenz, *Phys. Zeit.*, **16**. 204, 1915 ; H. Finger, *Zeit. wiss. Photochem.*, **7**. 351, 1909 ; S. Bodforss and P. Frölich, *Koll. Beihefte*, **16**. 301, 1922 ; L. Gurvich, *Koll. Zeit.*, **33**. 321, 1923 ; C. H. Hall, *Journ. Amer. Chem. Soc.*, **44**. 1246, 1922.

[11] C. H. Hall, *Journ. Amer. Chem. Soc.*, **44**. 1246, 1922.

§ 4. The Physical Properties of Lead

Lead belongs to the white metals, but ordinary lead has a decided bluish-grey colour ; and the term lead-grey is used to indicate a specific colour. Lead has a much darker colour than tin, and this was emphasized when Pliny, in his *Historiæ naturalis* (**35**. 16, c. 77 A.D.), called lead *plumbum nigrum*, and tin, *plumbum album*. The colour of lead of a high degree of purity, distilled in vacuo, resembles that of mercury or silver, and B. Lambert and H. E. Cullis [1] found the bluish tint, usually associated with lead, to be entirely absent. According to M. Faraday, a very thin layer of lead appears brown by transmitted light, and after the film had been pressed with agate it appeared blue ; according to A. W. Wright, thin films of lead are brown or olive-green. W. L. Dudley found that the vapour of lead is blue. W. Spring and C. van Aubel, and F. Mylius and O. Fromm obtained *black lead* by dissolving zinc containing lead in an acid. They said that the black substance may be finely divided lead or an allotropic modification of lead. If zinc be rubbed with this lead-black by means of a spatula, it becomes more soluble in acids. Mercury amalgamates and dissolves the lead-black, and this is probably the reason why amalgamated zinc is not soluble in acids. F. Wöhler showed that if a soln. of lead nitrate is electrolyzed the tabular crystals which deposit on the cathode are coloured *copper-red*. F. Stolba attributed the colour to a surface film of a foreign substance. The lustre of a freshly cut surface of lead is bright, but it quickly tarnishes on exposure to air.

According to J. B. L. Romé de l'Isle,[2] R. J. Haüy, L. L. Pajot, G. R. Levi, J. A. Mongez, H. Behrens, and J. Braunsdorf, lead crystallizes from the molten state in octahedral crystals. C. M. Marx showed that on allowing molten lead to cool slowly and partially to solidify without being disturbed, when a hole is made in the surface crust and the still liquid portion is poured off, the remaining solid portion will be found in skeleton octahedral crystals belonging to the cubic system. The fern-like forms were said to recall those formed when ammonium chloride crystallizes. Fig. 7 shows the appearances of some well-developed dendritic forms reported by W. Campbell.

F. Stolba obtained crystals, 4 mm. long, by pouring lead into one corner of a tilted cardboard box, and as soon as solidification began tilting the box so that the still molten metal ran to another corner. F. M. Ihle found distinct octahedral crystals of lead in a cavity in a pig of lead, and crystals in furnace products have been reported by J. J. Nöggerath, J. Percy, F. Sandberger, J. F. L. Hausmann, and C. C. von Leonhard. G. W. A. Kahlbaum and co-workers found that when lead condenses from the vaporous state, cubes and octahedra are formed. The formation of lead crystals was also described by R. Gross, A. Thiel, J. B. Senderens, E. Giurgea, O. Rothe, J. H. Bowman, A. Stock and F. Gomolka, P. Schützenberger, E. Cohen and W. D. Heldermann, etc. H. A. Miers acted on lead for 24–48 hrs. with 5–10 per cent. nitric acid, and obtained small crystals. J. Durocher prepared small crystals by reducing lead chloride at a red heat with hydrogen sulphide. F. Wöhler poured water into a vessel to form a layer above the surface of a soln. of lead nitrate or acetate, and a piece of lead was dipped in both liquids. Small crystals of lead were formed. J. B. Senderens made a similar observation with neutral soln. of lead nitrate when air is excluded—*vide supra*, metallic precipitation of lead. The subject was also discussed by G. von Hevesy, and A. Thiel. The production of the lead-tree—*arbor saturni*—was discussed by R. Lüpke. O. Lehmann considers that the electrolytic formation of crystals may be compared with ordinary crystallization on the assumption that the metal which separates out at first remains dissolved in the electrolyte, and that, when the latter becomes sat., it crystallizes out in the ordinary manner. When the strength of the current is increased until

Fig. 7.—Dendritic Crystals of Lead.

the metal no longer forms a uniform deposit on the surface of the electrode, the crystals that are deposited arrange themselves into a skeleton-like structure, and that further increase in the current strength will only alter the mass of the structure, but not its form. Lead is an exception, because with a weak current it separates out in leafy crystals which appear to belong to the monoclinic system, and are similar to those forming the ordinary lead-tree; whilst with a strong current the crystals obtained are those of the cubic system and, under favourable circumstances, well-formed octahedra. He assumes that the rate at which the lead-atoms separate out being far less in the first than in the second case, different mol. are formed in the soln., and that since the metal separates out from the soln. in crystalline form, the one set of mols. will form crystals which are distinct from those of the other. The lead-tree, said J. Schildowsky, always grows towards the anode. E. Cohen and K. Inouye's measurements of the e.m.f. of the supposed monoclinic and cubic forms of lead showed that the crystals are identical, and not allotropic forms. According to C. Elbs and F. W. Rixon, lead is sometimes deposited in large shining plates, and sometimes in the form of a sponge, the difference is due to the presence or absence of a plumbic salt in the electrolyte; if present, a spongy deposit is always obtained. F. Haber found that a layer of spongy lead is formed on the cathode during the electrolysis of sulphuric acid with lead electrodes. B. Wäser and R. Kühnel, P. K. Frölich and co-workers, and V. Kohlschütter and F. Uebersax investigated the cathode deposits of lead obtained under different conditions. A. Günther-Schulze examined the rate of growth of the deposit and the current strength. In the growth of the lead-tree which occurs when a rod of zinc is immersed in a soln. of lead acetate or nitrate, the separation of the plates is frequently followed by a spongy deposit. H. N. Warren found that when litharge or lead sulphate is introduced into canvas bags, through which is inserted a lead sheet, and the bags immersed in dil. sulphuric acid, then when the lead is connected with sheets of iron, immersed in the acid, the sulphate or other lead compound contained therein is speedily and completely reduced to the spongy metal— *vide* the metallic precipitation of lead. N. A. Puschin obtained crystals of lead from amalgams rich in lead. As in the case of tin, I. V. Obreimoff and L. V. Shubnikoff prepared large single crystals of lead.

Like most metals, lead crystallizes in the cubic system. Octahedral crystals occur in nature (*vide supra*), and they are produced when the metal crystallizes in Pattinson's desilverization process, and by the methods indicated above. The etching of the surface of lead shows that the octahedral crystals are sometimes in combination with the cube. A. Hamberg, and G. Flink examined crystals of native lead (*q.v.*). L. Vegard's **X-radiogram** shows that the space-lattice is a face-centred cube, with the edge of length $a=4\cdot91$ A.; E. C. Bain gave $4\cdot92\times10^{-8}$ cm.; W. P. Davey, $a=4\cdot920\pm0\cdot005$ A.; W. C. Phebus and F. C. Blake, $a=4\cdot92$ A.; and M. Levi, $4\cdot93$ A. R. Vogel, and E. A. Owen and G. D. Preston also examined the X-radiogram of lead; and K. Weissenberg, the structure of the crystals. P. Scherrer said that the crystals are isomorphous with those of aluminium, copper, silver, and gold. R. J. Anderson and J. T. Norton examined the effect of cold work on the X-radiogram of lead; and A. E. van Arkel found that the lattice of the stressed metal could suffer a maximum distortion of $0\cdot15$ per cent. According

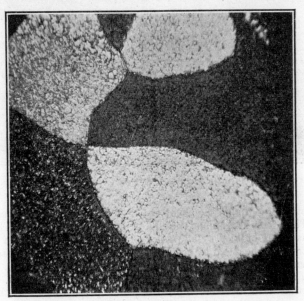

Fig. 8.—Lead etched with Acetic Acid ($\times$ 33).

to J. C. W. Humfrey, the **corrosion figures** produced by 5 per cent. nitric acid are of the cubo-octahedral form. J. Czochralsky gave the **velocity of crystallization** of lead as 140 at 320° when that of tin at 232° is 90, and of zinc at 416°, 100. A. Günther-Schulze studied the speed at which lead crystals grow during electro-deposition; V. Kohlschütter and F. Uerbersax examined this subject. J. Czochralsky found the velocities of crystallization of tin, lead, and zinc to be related as 90 : 140 : 100. N. I. Nikitin showed that finely divided lead prepared by reduction at 125° is non-pyrophoric because the metal crystallizes at this low temp.

Ordinary lead usually presents no evidence of a crystalline structure to the eye, although it is certain that the metal is an aggregate of polyhedral crystals. The crystalline structure is usually shown on the surface of pigs (ingots) of market lead. According to R. Vogel, N. S. von Kurnakoff and N. A. Puschin, F. Robin, etc., the crystalline structure appears on the surface of lead cast on a smooth surface—say glass. G. Cartaud etched the polished surface with a soln. of picric acid in acetone. If ordinary rolled sheet lead be etched, the structure appears like Fig. 8, which W. Campbell obtained by etching the metal with acetic acid. After annealing for a week at 200°, a coarse, irregular, crystalline structure was developed. A crystal 2·5 cms. long and 1·25 cms. broad was grown in 5 days at 180°. Some of the crystals show twinning. E. Cohen and K. Inouye said that if lead with the crystalline surface exposed by etching be pressed against rolled lead at or about 100°, the strained metal is rendered crystalline by contact. A. L. Norbury studied the spontaneous annealing of lead. H. Baucke found the crystallization at ordinary temp. of cold-worked lead is accelerated by the presence of an electrolyte—say dil. acid. Figs. 9 and 10, by J. A. Ewing and

FIGS. 9 and 10.—Slip-bands in Lead Crystals (×100 and ×1000 respectively).

W. Rosenhain, show the development of **slip-bands** which occur when a crystal is strained. These slips occur along the gliding planes of the crystal. Those shown in the diagrams were obtained by allowing molten lead to solidify on a smooth glass plate, and straining the metal by bending. The slip-bands with lead are particularly straight even under extreme magnification, as shown in Fig. 10. P. Gaubert observed no twinning of the crystals to be produced by press. J. C. W. Humfrey found that lead tends to slip along planes perpendicular to the octahedral axes of the crystals. Some slight differences of orientation of the slip lines may occur after a single crystal has been strained, but this is not due to recrystallization, but to the fact that the strain was not homogeneous; when a slip has occurred in a certain part, it tends to go on there rather than in other parts of the crystal. After straining, the lead recrystallizes, and the recrystallization is not a direct and instantaneous effect of the strain, but severe strain and high temp. both tend to increase the subsequent rate of change of structure. The patches of new orientation probably start from a cleavage plane, and this gives rise to the formation of twin crystals.

According to J. A. Ewing and W. Rosenhain, although twinned crystals are rarely, if ever, found in cast metal, they are frequently developed by strain, and are commonly found in metal which has been annealed after severe strain. This is explained as follows :

When the metal solidifies from the liquid state, it does so by the formation of skeleton crystals, starting from a great number of centres, and the arms of these skeletons continue to grow until arrested by meeting with other growths. From these arms, other arms again shoot out, and so on until the entire metal is solidified ; but each crystalline element as it settles into place on any of these arms must assume the proper orientation to enable it to fit in, and in the process of filling space by means of such a system of many meeting and interlacing arms, the formation of a twin would be almost impossible. But when the metal recrystallizes after severe strain, it does so by the growth of skeleton arms that must often start from a cleavage plane of an actual solid crystal, and probably the new elements deposited upon such a plane would find it as easy to assume the twin orientation as the normal. The idea that twin crystals are formed in annealed metal by growth starting from cleavage planes which have been sheared across in the process of compression is suggested by the very straight boundaries observed as a characteristic feature of twin lamellæ.

J. A. Ewing and W. Rosenhain made observations between 100° and 300°, and concluded :

In lead which has been severely strained, recrystallization goes on at all temp. from that of an ordinary room up to the m.p. The higher the temp. the more rapid are the changes in the crystalline structure. The rate of change varies with different specimens, probably depending upon the nature and quantity of impurities present, and upon the severity of the strain to which the metal has been subjected. The size of the crystals ultimately produced does not vary appreciably between 100° and 300°. In lead annealed at the temp. of the air, very large crystals have not yet been obtained, but this is probably only a question of time. The phenomena of growth of crystals occur in lead only when the metal has previously been subjected to severe plastic strain. The structure of a cast specimen remains unaltered at temp. which cause a strained specimen to show rapid change. By casting in a mould arranged to cause rapid cooling, specimens of lead can be obtained having a minute crystalline structure, whose scale is not very different from that of severely crushed lead ; such a specimen was exposed to 200° for nearly seven days, but no visible change of structure occurred. A piece of this specimen was then strained by severe crushing, and on further exposure to 200° vigorous growth took place. The rate at which a lead specimen is cooled down to ordinary temp. has no visible effect on the structure. Even " quenching " in liquid air has no visible effect ; quenching in water, cooling in air, and slow cooling in the oven, were all tried on a number of specimens without in any way affecting them. Lead is mechanically hardened to a small extent by severe strain, and the subsequent effect of annealing in restoring softness is correspondingly small. In one of the experiments a specimen of lead was crushed under a given load in the testing machine, and the load was left on until no further creeping occurred. The specimen was then annealed and again placed under the same load, when a distinct amount of further crushing was seen to take place.

F. C. Thompson and W. E. Millington found that with cast and slowly cooled lead, slip-bands appear at 25 kgrms. per sq. cm. when the elastic limit is 102 kgrms. per sq. cm. **R. S. Dean and W. E. Hudson** found the velocity, V, of grain growth in lead with 1 per cent. antimony is represented by $V=ae^{b/T}$, where a and b are constants. **G. Tammann** said that after cold working, annealing begins at 45°, and at 150°, the new crystals formed are rather small. The annealing of mechanically worked lead, even at ordinary temp.. is illustrated by the gradual loss in the mechanical hardening occasioned by rolling ; and to coarse crystalline character of old roofing lead. Unlike tin, lead does not emit a *cry* when bent. **G. T. Beilby** showed that during hammering lead is converted from the crystalline to the amorphous state. The recrystallization of lead during annealing was also studied by **H. Baucke, R. Vogel, G. Tammann and co-workers, O. Bauer, F. Robin, W. Rosenhain and S. L. Archbutt, M. Cook and U. R. Evans, etc.**

There are passages in Theophrastus' Περὶ Πυρός, in the third century before our era, and in Plutarch's *Symposiaka* (**6.** 8), towards the end of the first century of this era, which refer to the change which occurs in lead and tin during the cold of the wintry season. It must be remembered that at this time the distinction between lead and tin was not clearly marked. **H. St. C. Deville** [3] showed that the sp. gr.

of lead is affected by the thermal history of the metal, and U. J. J. le Verrier found that the same thing applied to the sp. ht. As indicated above, the dimorphic forms of lead reported by O. Lehmann were shown by E. Cohen and K. Inouye, to be the same thing. According to C. Jeantaud, when a soln. of mixed alkali plumbate and plumbite is electrolyzed, using a current density not less than 2 amps. per sq. dcm. of cathode surface, dull grey crystals of lead are obtained which have a smaller electrochemical eq. than ordinary lead, and give an e.m.f. about 5 per cent. higher than ordinary lead, and have double the capacity of the ordinary metal. G. Rosset, and C. Jeantaud claimed special advantages for this form of lead in the construction of accumulators, but this has been denied.

E. Cohen and W. D. Helderman inferred that lead furnishes at least two **allotropic forms**, for, as shown by H. Heller, when the metal is suspended in a 40 per cent. soln. of lead acetate containing 10 per cent. of nitric acid of sp. gr. 1·16, the metal shows marked signs of structural change ; the surface becomes wrinkled, and in three weeks this becomes so pronounced as to suggest complete disintegration of the metal as when white tin passes into grey tin. H. J. M. Creighton confirmed H. Heller's experiment by the following experiment :

A current of 2 amps. at 6 volts was passed through an electrolyte consisting of nitric acid, sp. gr. 1·42, using as cathode a piece of sheet lead 2 cms. wide, 2 mm. thick, and 10 cms. long, and a thin piece of platinum foil as anode. At the end of 8 hrs., the cathode had increased slightly in vol., its colour had changed to grey ; it lost its former malleability and firmness ; and when the lower part was rubbed between the fingers, it furnished small particles which could easily be rubbed to a fine powder, or pressed into a soft mass.

F. H. Getman found the potential of lead to be 0·4121 volt against the normal calomel electrode, whether the lead be cast in sticks, electrolytically deposited, or used as an amalgam. Lead which has been immersed in a soln. of lead acetate and nitric acid gives higher values, which increase with the time of immersion ; the lead at the same time becomes brittle. E. Cohen and W. D. Helderman found that the sp. gr. of the metal changed from 11·3299 at 25°/4° to respectively 11·3415, 11·3283, and 11·3129 when kept for some time at 15°, 25°, and 50°, in the soln. just indicated. They estimate that the **transition temperature** is near 50°, above which lead is stable without a tendency to disintegration. E. Jänecke measured the pressure-temperature cooling and heating curves of the metal and found evidence of a break or transition point between 59° and 62°. E. Cohen and A. L. T. Moesveld say that the failure of P. W. Bridgman to find polymorphic forms is due to his use of compact masses of metal. The changes are so slow that it is necessary to accelerate the change by working with finely-powdered metals in a soln. of an electrolyte. B. Lambert and H. E. Cullis inferred that the corrosion of pure lead is due to electrolytic action between electrically different parts of the mass of lead. P. W. Bridgman observed no signs of allotropism in his observations of the thermo-electric properties of lead. The assumed physical heterogeneity is due to the presence of different allotropes in the mass of metal causing parts to be electrically different from other parts ; these differences persist for a long time after the metal has been prepared. On the other hand, A. Thiel concluded that the phenomenon observed by H. Heller is not due to an allotropic change but is an effect of chemical action. The disintegration is observed only with a soln. containing nitrates, and does not occur with lead acetate and acetic acid ; lead chloride and hydrochloric acid ; lead fluosilicate and hydrofluosilicic acid ; or lead perchlorate and per-chloric acid. Disintegration which has started in H. Heller's soln. is arrested when the metal is transferred to a soln. free from nitrates. The metal is slowly attacked by Heller's soln. with the evolution of nitrogen and nitric oxide, and much is dis-solved before disintegration occurs. The metal is similarly attacked by soln. of nitrates free from lead, but the reaction is faster if a trace of lead nitrate or nitrite is present. The disintegrated metal has not the appearance to be expected if an allotrope were formed consisting, as it does, of irregular, polyhedral grains, with more or less rounded edges, and free from small crystals. The lead supposed to be stable above 50°–60° readily disintegrates under soln. containing nitrates at 100°, though unaffected by soln. free from nitrates. There is only a very slight difference of potential between compact and disintegrated lead immersed in a soln. of lead perchlorate. A. Thiel explains what he calls the *disglomeration of lead* in the following manner :

Compact lead is composed of crystallites, the crevices of which are filled by a finely granular eutectic, which is present even in " pure " metals (a similar structure must be assumed for all metals which have solidified from the molten state). This eutectic is more readily attacked by the suitable agent when the impurities are more chemically active than the metal itself ; in consequence, cavities are formed around the crystallites, which finally become so deep that the latter are completely detached from the main mass.

The disintegration can be effected by other agents—*e.g.* when a lead anode slowly dissolves in a soln. of perchloric acid. Copper can be similarly disintegrated in an ammoniacal soln. of persulphate.

Lead is the densest of the common base metals. The Arabic manuscript of Abu-r-Rarhan, *The Book of the Best Things*, written about the tenth century, and described by H. C. Bolton,[4] and J. J. C. Mullet, gave 11·33 for the specific gravity of lead, and this value is very near that accepted to-day ; and in the Arabian manuscript, *Book of the Balance of Wisdom* of Al-Khazini, written about 1122 A.D., and described by H. C. Bolton, and N. Khanikoff, 11·32 is given for the sp. gr. of lead. D. G. Fahrenheit gave 11·35 ; R. Boyle, 11·325 ; P. van Muschenbrock, 11·445 ; and L. B. Guyton de Morveau, 11·358 to 11·388. Collections of data were made by R. Böttger,[5] and F. W. Clarke. J. J. Berzelius gave 11·445 for the best representative value ; 11·35 is perhaps nearer the mark. M. J. Brisson gave 11·352 ; R. Böttger, 11·207 ; A. T. Kupffer, 11·3338 at 14°, 11·3299 at 15°, and 11·3303 at 17° ; J. Crichton, 11·346 at 15·5° ; A. Baudrimont, 11·3775 ; W. Herapath, 11·352 ; C. J. B. Karsten, 11·3888 ; G. Timoféeff, 11·349 at 15°/4°, and 11·331 at 25°/4° ; H. Tomlinson, 11·193 at 20°/4° ; L. H. Adams and co-workers, 11·336 at 20° ; J. J. van Laar, 11·4 at 0° ; A. Streng, 11·395 at 4° ; A. Hamberg, 11·372 at 15°/18° ; A. Matthiessen and M. Holzmann, 11·376 at 14°/0° ; P. Schweitzer found 11·344 at 4° and 11·352 at 23° for a sample cut from the end of a cast ingot, and 11·358 at 4°, 11·359 at 18°, and 11·366 at 23° for a piece cut from the middle of the bar. W. Herz calculated the sp. gr. at absolute zero to be 12·880, and the at. vol. 16·09. C. J. St. C. Deville found that when lead is slowly cooled from a fused state, the sp. gr. is 11·254, and when rapidly cooled 11·363 ; and that electrolytic lead has a sp. gr. 11·542, and if fused and cooled quickly, 11·225. W. Herz estimated that the sp. gr. of lead at absolute zero is 12·88. E. Cohen and W. D. Heldermann's observations on the sp. gr. of the allotropic forms of lead are indicated above.

The differences in the results of different observers in what appears to be one of the simplest of observations are somewhat remarkable, and emphasize how little reliance can be placed in the agreement or disagreement of determinations on different samples. J. Percy observed that the sp. gr. of lead is usually diminished if sensible proportions of the usual impurities are present, so that other things being equal, the greater the purity the higher the sp. gr. of lead. C. J. B. Karsten's sample was reduced from the nitrate by carbon. A. Streng's sample was stated to be the purest pattinsonized lead, but it was really somewhat impure and contained 0·02 per cent. of copper and 0·04 per cent. of antimony. F. Reich gave for the cast lead 11·352 at 0°/4°, and 11·372 at 24°/24° ; for rolled lead, 11·358–11·365 at 0°/4°, and 11·376–11·383 at 24°/24°. The sp. gr. of pattinsonized lead with less than 0·1 per cent. of copper and iron was 11·363–11·374 at 0°/4° ; lead prepared from the acetate with 0·007 per cent. of iron had a sp. gr. 11·3683–11·3695 at 0°/4°, and after hammering between paper and the surface cleaned, 11·3675 at 0°/4°. F. Kick examined the sp. gr. in different parts of a lead cylinder. J. Percy reported a sample of highly purified lead, after melting under potassium cyanide, to have a sp. gr. 11·358 at 15·5° ; a piece chiselled out from the pig had a sp. gr. 11·382, and, after

hammering, a sp. gr. of 11·387.   F. Reich found the sp. gr. of lead after rolling into
thin sheet rose from 11·354 to 11·356 ; and L. Knab found that rolling cast lead
raised the sp. gr. from 11·352 to 11·358.   G. W. A. Kahlbaum found the sp. gr. of
lead distilled in vacuo was 11·3415 at 20°/4° ; and after compression at 10,000 atm.,
11·3470.   W. Spring said that like all bodies which expand during fusion, lead
expands when subjected to high press., for the sp. gr. of cast lead was 11·3351, rolled
lead 11·3348, and drawn lead 11·3410—the presence of gas inclusions interfere
with the results.   He also found that lead with a sp. gr. 11·350 at 14° had a sp. gr.
11·501 at 14° after pressing at 20,000 atm., and 11·492 at 16° after another treatment at 20,000 atm. press.   G. Spezia obtained a decrease in the sp. gr. at high
press., but regarded this as an effect of the elasticity of the metal.   F. W. Clarke,
and S. P. Howell reported that the sp. gr. of lead is materially decreased when
distorted quickly as by an explosion—the latter observed a drop from 11·403 to
10·996, and from 11·376 to 11·156 ; and the former from 11·510 to 11·268.
T. M. Lowry and R. G. Parker found the density of lead *en masse* to be 11·3368, and
of the same sample as filings, 11·3337.   The annealing of lead at 100°, produced
an expansion.   F. Nies and A. Winkelmann said that the sp. gr. of lead must be
increased during fusion because solid lead floats on molten lead, but E. Wiedemann
said that this is a mistaken inference, for the result is an effect of convection in the
molten metal—lead expands on melting.   R. Hoffmann and W. Stahl gave for
99·98 per cent. lead, 11·371 at 0°/4° ; 11·379 at 4°/4° ; 11·364 at 20°/4° ; and
11·358 at 600°/4°.   W. C. Roberts-Austen and R. Wrightson found the sp. gr. of
solid lead at the m.p. to be 11·40, and that of the liquid, 10·37 ;   G. Vicentini and
D. Omedei gave 11·359 for the sp. gr. at 0° ;   11·005 for the sp. gr. of the solid at
325°, and 10·645 for the liquid.   L. Playfair and J. P. Joule gave 11·231 at 4°
and 10·509 for the molten metal ;   G. Quincke gave 11·335 at 0° and 10·952 for the
molten metal ;   R. Hoffmann and W. Stahl, 10·358 at 600°/4° ;   M. Plüss, 10·896 at
340° ;   C. E. Fawsitt found 10·65 at 330° and 10·63 at 347°.   C. Benedicks also
measured the sp. gr. of molten lead.   A. L. Day and co-workers found at

	327°	350°	450°	550°	650°	750°	850°
Sp. gr. . .	10·686	10·658	10·536	10·418	10·302	10·188	10·078

P. Pascal and J. Jouniaux obtained rather higher values, namely, 10·875 at the
m.p. ;   10·85 at 400° ;   10·71 at 600° ;   10·49 at 800° ;   and 10·15 at 1000°, so that
there is a 4·3 per cent. increase in vol. when lead at 20° is converted into liquid at
the m.p.   M. Toepler found 3·7 per cent. expansion during melting.   H. Endo found
a change in vol. of 3·44 per cent. during the melting of lead.   R. Arpi, and C. Cattaneo measured the effect of temp. on the sp. gr. of lead.   T. R. Hogness gave
10·65 for the sp. gr. of molten lead at 366° ;   10·55 at 444° ;   and 10·44 at 522° ;
and he represented the sp. gr. of molten lead at $\theta°$ by $10·71 - 0·00139(\theta - 327)$.   For
the sp. gr. of lead from radioactive sources, *vide* at. wt. of lead ;   A. C. Egerton
and W. B. Lee gave 11·3437 for the sp. gr. of ordinary lead at 20°, and 11·2960
for that of uranium-lead at 16° ;   and B. Perrette obtained respectively 11·3363
and 11·2784 at 0°.   The at. vol. of the isotopes are the same.   T. W. Richards
and C. Wadsworth prepared samples of lead of a very high degree of purity from
different sources, and found that while ordinary lead has a sp. gr. 11·337 at
20°/4° (at. wt. 207·2), that derived from a radioactive Australian one had a sp. gr.
11·288 (at. wt. 206·3), and that from Norwegian cleveite, 11·273 (at. wt. 206·09).
F. Soddy observed no appreciable difference in the at. vol. of the two forms
of lead.   J. Joly and J. H. J. Poole did not get any appreciable separation
by centrifuging molten lead.   W. L. Bragg calculated the **atomic radius** to
be 1·90 A.   A. Groh and G. von Hevesy computed the radius of the lead-ions
to be three times as great as that of the atoms.   W. P. Davey, and W. J. Sollas
made calculations on the dimensions of the atoms of lead.   J. J. van Laar
calculated b of J. D. van der Waals' equation to be $b = 0·00320$; for a, $\sqrt{a} = 0·11$.

and for the valency attraction A, $\sqrt{A}=40$. H. H. Potter compared the gravitational attraction of brass and lead but detected no difference.

Lead is the softest of the common base metals—thallium, calcium, potassium, and sodium are softer than lead. It can be easily cut with a knife, and scratched with the finger nail. It makes a grey streak on paper, and was formerly used as a pencil for writing on paper.[6] Lead clogs an ordinary file, but it can be worked with a rasp. P. Nicolardot[7] showed that lead is hardened by hammering. J. R. Rydberg gave for the **hardness** of lead on Moh's scale 1·5, when that of tin is 2·5 ; zinc, 6 ; and copper, 8. The softness of the metal is utilized in modelling for artistic purposes, as described by W. R. Lethaby, and L. Weaver. For lead containing less than one per cent. of silver, copper, and antimony, F. Auerbach represented what he called the absolute hardness by 10, which is nearly the same as that of gypsum (14)—the value obtained for cast tin was 11, gold 97, and the diamond 2500. F. C. Calvert and R. Johnson gave 16 when that of iron is 1000 ; H. Gollner gave 3 for the hardness of hard-lead when that of tin is 2 ; T. Turner gave 1·0 when that of copper is 8·0 ; and C. A. Edwards, 6·95 when that of copper is 53. **H. J. Coe** gave 11·355 for Brinell's hardness of cast lead. F. Sauerwald and K. Knehans gave 7·44 for Brinell's hardness at 25° ; 6·93 at 73° ; 6·62 at 122° ; 5·68 at 170° ; 4·93 at 219° ; and 4·24 at 267°. K. Ito, and A. L. Norbury also measured the hardness of lead at different temp. G. Coriolis found that after repeated melting in air, lead becomes harder and more brittle owing to the formation of the oxide which mixes with the metal. The effect of impurities was examined by C. O. Thieme, A. Bencke, and P. Ludwik. W. Baker showed that the hardness of lead is largely conditioned by the proportion of sulphur, antimony, arsenic, copper, and iron it contains. P. Duhem, S. Bottone, and A. Kürth made some observations on the hardness of lead. K. Honda and R. Yamada measured the abrasive hardness of lead. P. Ludwik measured Brinell's hardness of lead with loads continuous **for** 5 and 300 secs., and the results are plotted in Fig. 11. A. Kürth measured the effect of temp. on the hardness. A. L. Norbury found the results for the Brinell's hardness depend on the time of application of the load ; tests were also made by J. Okubo. Tests on the effect of cold-work on hardness showed that lead is hardened by cold-work to an extent depending on the amount of work done ; and that the metal is annealed spontaneously at room temp. at a rate which increases with the amount of deformation. In severely cold-worked specimens, this annealing is so rapid that 20 secs. after hammering the metal is dead soft. Related observations were made by T. K. Rose, P. Nicolardot, N. S. von Kurnakoff and S. F. Schemtschuschny, M. Levi-Malvano and O. Ceccarelli, A. Saphoshnikoff and J. Kaniewsky, G. Moreau, W. Herold, and M. Hanriot. P. P. Lazareff discussed the relation between the hardness and other physical properties of lead ; and K. Ito, the relation between the temp. coeff. and the m.p. C. A. Edwards and A. M. Herbert gave 3·2 for the **plasticity** number of lead when that of copper is 49·3. The flowing press. of lead was measured by N. S. von Kurnakoff and S. F. Schemtschuschny, A. Geller, and D. Saito and K. Hayashi. G. Subrahmanian measured the **viscosity** of lead; and E. E. Walker, the resistance offered by powdered lead to compression.

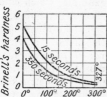

FIG. 11.—The Effect of Temperature on the Hardness of Lead.

The **surface tension,** σ, of lead at the m.p., 327°, found by G. Quincke[8] is 535·9 dynes per cm. ; by H. Siedentopf, 509·5 dynes per cm. ; by L. L. Grünmach, 482 mgrms. per mm. ; by S. W. Smith, 424·5 dynes per cm. ; and T. R. Hogness, 444 dynes per cm. G. Tammann, and W. Hagemann made observations on this subject. T. R. Hogness also gave :

	327°	350°	400°	450°	500°
Surface tension . .	444	442	438	438	431 dynes per cm.

and at θ, for molten lead, $\sigma=444-0 \cdot 077(\theta-327)$. For the capillary constant, a^2, G. Quincke gave 9·98 ; H. Siedentopf, 9·778 ; L. L. Grünmach, 9·060 ; G. Tammann, 9·778 ; S. W. Smith, 8·12–8·36. R. Lorenz and A. Liebmann observed that the surface tension of molten lead in contact with molten lead chloride increases if potassium chloride is present, and this the more the higher the temp. T. K. Rose found that tellurium lowers the surface tension of gold so that the bead of gold is flattened during cupellation, and absorbed by the cupel. Hence the loss of telluriferous gold on cupellation. I. Traube gave for the **internal pressure** of lead 51,500 megabars or $51,500 \times 10^{-6}$ dynes per sq. cm.; and T W. Richards, 53,000 megabars. J. H. Hildebrand and co-workers calculated relative values for the internal press. of the metals. J. J. van Laar showed that the mol. attraction is probably very strong. M. von Wogau [9] found the coeff. of **diffusion** of lead in mercury at 9·4° to be 1·50 per sq. cm. per day, and at 99·2°, 1·92 per sq. cm. per day ; G. Meyer gave 1·37 per sq. cm. per day at 15·6°; and R. Kremann and A. Hrasovec made some observations on this subject. W. C. Roberts-Austen gave for lead in tin at 500°, 3·18 per sq. cm. per day ; for gold in lead, 490°, 3·03, and at 500°, 3·19 per sq. cm. per day ; for platinum in lead at 490°, 1·69 per sq. cm. per day, and for rhodium in lead at 500°, 3·04 per sq. cm. per day ; and G. von Hevesy and co-workers gave 2·22 per sq. cm. per day for the diffusion of thorium-B in lead at 343°. According to W. C. Roberts-Austen, gold diffused in a cylinder of lead to a height of 7·65 cm. in 4 years at 18°; and C. S. van Orstrand and F. P. Dewey found that while the diffusion of gold into lead (both solid) could be traced a distance of 2·4 cm., that of lead into gold did not exceed 0·2 mm. G. von Hevesy and A. Obrutsheva calculated that the rate of self-diffusion of lead increased from 6×10^{-7} sq. cm. per day at 260° to $1 \cdot 4 \times 10^{-4}$ sq. cm. per day at 324°.

Lead emits a peculiar odour when rubbed between the fingers ; the smell is probably not due to the metal, but to the organic substances—the fingers, for example, which come in contact with it. According to J. Percy,[10] lead is feebly elastic or sonorous, and it furnishes a dull sound when struck with a hard substance ; and the dullness of the sound, the " leaden-ring," is proportionate to the purity of the metal. R. A. F. de Réaumur reported that in 1726, L. Lemery discovered *par un pur hazard*, that if lead be cast into the shape of a segment of a sphere—*i.e.* mushroom-shaped—it has the novel and remarkable property of emitting sharp notes when struck with another piece of lead. The sonorous lead is rendered dull by hammering. C. Neumann also stated that lead cast into the form of a hollow spherical or elliptical segment, is very sonorous. R. A. F. de Réaumur attributed the sonorous quality to the shape of the grains and to the way they touch one another. If the rounded grains are flattened by hammering, the elongated grains fill the interstitial spaces, and the particles are no longer free to vibrate, and the lead then emits a dull sound when struck. The **velocity of sound** in lead, according to G. Wertheim, is 1320 metres per second ; and, according to A. Masson, and W. Herz, in soft-lead at 15°–20°, 1227·4 metres per second.

D. Saito and K. Hayashi [11] measured the fluidity of molten lead. According to C. E. Fawsitt, molten lead is about three times as viscous as water ; at 330°, the viscosity of lead was 0·0320, and at 347°, 0·0293. A. Mesnager obtained 0·029 for the viscosity. M. Plüss made observations on some alloys of lead. R. Arpi found the **viscosity,** η, of molten lead, in an atm. of hydrogen, to be

	340°	376°	419°	470°	550°
Viscosity	0·0189	0·0167	0·0160	0·0144	0·0144

The **malleability** of lead at ordinary temp. is large, and the metal may be rolled into thin sheets. Sheet-lead was formerly made by casting, but the resulting sheets were often defective owing to blow-holes, sand-holes, and uneven thickness. The manufacture of sheet-lead by rolling dates from about 1670, and was not adopted without strong opposition. Lead is flexible and pliable. It becomes harder with mechanical work—rolling, hammering, etc.—but acquires its original softness by annealing. H. S. Rawdon [12] and co-workers examined the brittleness of lead produced by stress and corrosion. As shown by J. Percy, Z. Jeffries, P. Ludwick, and G. W. A. Kahlbaum and E. Sturm, the **ductibility** of lead is not so marked as its malleability, and it cannot be drawn into fine wire, although lead wire about $\frac{1}{16}''$ diameter is manufactured and used by gardeners in fixing trees to walls, etc. When at the right temp. lead may be worked in the same way as macaroni and squeezed into solid or hollow cylinders. Lead-piping, for instance, is made by squirting, a process in which lead is forced by hydraulic press. through the annular space between a die and a mandrel. [13] If the temp. be near the m.p. of lead, the metal becomes brittle, and an ingot can be broken to pieces by striking with a hammer. The fracture is then columnar.

J. Percy [14] reported the accidental formation of a fine hair-like mass of lead—*lead-moss* or *lead-wool*—on the outside of a pot of lead when the lead after desilverization was left to solidify. The liquid lead appeared to have been forced through a minute hole in the pot.

When two plane and clean surfaces of lead are pressed together, they adhere with great tenacity. Such surfaces are produced by cutting, say, a leaden bullet in half with a knife, and pressing, with a screwing or twisting movement, the halves together on their cut surfaces. In T. Dobbs' patent, [15] adhesion is effected between tin and lead by passing superimposed ingots of these metals through a rolling machine. J. Fournet considers this kind of cohesion as true welding, being dependent on the softness of the metal at ordinary temp. As indicated by J. Percy, the requisite softness for welding iron is induced only at a high temp.; so that the heat acts on iron by producing the necessary softness which in the case of lead exists at ordinary temp. According to P. A. Bolley, lead in a fine state of subdivision can by press. be made into a solid mass. W. Spring also claimed that at 2000 atm. press., plates of lead form a compact mass. On the contrary, W. Hallock said that not the slightest change occurs even at 6000 atm. press., and no signs of melting were observed. The increase in vol. which occurs when lead is melted is cited in evidence that lead cannot be liquefied simply by increasing the press. (**1**, 9, 4; and **1**. 13, 18); but the m.p. of a solid is always lowered when the press. acts on the solid, but not on the liquid. W. Rosenhain and P. A. Tucker could obtain only a conglomeration of tin and lead by compression at 35 tons per sq. in. H. S. Rawdon studied the intercrystalline brittleness of lead.

In 1830, G. Coriolis [16] gave an account of some *expériences sur la résistance du plomb à l'écrasement* made with the quaint object of finding if the resistance which lead offers to crushing under pressure could be utilized to make a simple machine to act as a substitute for the weigh-bridge used for weighing carts, waggons, etc. The great influence of the duration of the press. on the resistance of the lead showed the idea to be impracticable. T. W. Richards and co-workers gave $2·33 \times 10^{-6}$ for the coeff. of **compressibility** of lead at 20°, between 100 and 500 megabars press. when that of mercury is $3·95 \times 10^{-6}$. L. H. Adams and co-workers gave $2·21 \times 10^{-6}$ at 0 megabar and at 10,000 megabars $2·16 \times 10^{-6}$, corresponding with a 2 per cent. decrease of compressibility when the press. changes from 0 to 10,000 megabars; and for the volume change δv when the press. changes $p - p_0$, $\delta v = 0·8 \times 10^{-4} + 2·202 \times 10^{-6}(p - p_0) + 0·24 \times 10^{-11}(p - p_0)^2$. P. W. Bridgman found rather higher values for the coeff. of compressibility; and gave for $\delta v/v$, for cast rods, $-10^{-7}(23·73 - 17·25 \times 10^{-5}p)p$ at 30°, and $-10^{-7}(24·33 - 17·7 \times 10^{-5}p)p$ at 75°; while for an extruded sample, $-10^{-7}(23·05 - 12·3 \times 10^{-5}p)p$ at 30°, and $-10^{-7}(23·63 - 12·3 \times 10^{-5}p)p$ at 75°. E. H. Amagat gave $2·761 \times 10^{-6}$ for the compressibility coeff. H. J. Coe found the break-down press. of lead to be $1·12$–$1·17$ tons per sq. in., and the elastic limit 0·05 ton per sq. in. Observations were also made by J. Johnston. E. Grüneisen measured the compressibility between the temp. of liquid air and 165°. W. Hallock found no flow of the metal under a press. of 6000 atm.

B. B. Lera found lead agreed with the relation $\frac{4}{5}aD/\beta A=$ constant, where a denotes the coeff. of expansion, β the coeff. of compressibility, D the density, and A the at. wt. of the metal.

The **tensile strength** of lead is small. J. J. Berzelius [17] found the breaking load to be 14·75 kgrms. for a wire 0·3 mm. diam. ; P. Berthier gave 9 kgrms. with a wire 0·2 mm. diam. ; A. Baudrimont, 6·5 kgrms. with a wire 1·8755 mm. diam. G. Wertheim, working with lead reduced from the nitrate, found that, between 15° and 20°, cast lead broke with a load of 1·25 kgrms. per sq. mm. when applied slowly, and with 2·21 kgrms. per sq. mm. when applied quickly ; for drawn lead, 2·07 kgrms. per sq. mm. when applied slowly, and 2·36 kgrms. per sq. mm. when applied quickly ; and for annealed lead, 1·80 kgrms. per sq. mm. when applied slowly, and 2·04 kgrms. per sq. mm. when applied quickly. At 100°, annealed lead broke with a load of 0·54 kgrm. per sq. mm. C. Bach found 0·635–1·26 kgrm. per sq. mm. for cast lead ; 0·835–2·735 for rolled lead ; and 2·13–2·325 for lead wire. H. J. Coe found the maximum load in tension for lead annealed at 100° to be 1·17 tons per sq. in. ; the elastic limit, 0·05 ton per sq. in. ; and the elongation in length, 67·3 per cent. ; and the metal was reduced to a point. G. Lunge and E. Schmid said that the presence of 0·02 per cent. of copper raised the tenacity of lead. K. Karmarsch found that lead elongates considerably before it breaks. Thus a wire 42·15 cms. long and 1·6 mm. diameter extended to 213·1 cms. before it broke. Much, however, depends on the time during which rupture is effected. According to J. Dewar, cast lead rods, 0·2 in. in diameter, broke under a load of 77 lbs. at 15°, and 172 lbs. at −182°. Thus, the cooling raised the tenacity to twice its usual value. The elongation at −182° was found to be equal to that at 15°. P. Ludwik, and D. H. Ingall studied the relation between tensile strength and temp. P. Ludwik investigated the action of alternating stresses on the mechanical properties of lead. G. Respondek used X-rays to detect pores and flaws in the metal. H. S. Rawdon and co-workers found that the metal under tension is more easily attacked by acids. Observations were made by H. S. Rawdon, L. Archbutt, and Z. Jeffries. H. L. Heathcote and co-workers found the **tearing test** is 220 lbs. per linear inch on a thickness 0·075 in., meaning the load required to tear the metal apart. R. H. Greaves and J. A. Jones measured the notched **bar impact test**— *vide* Fig. 14, **7**. 46, 4.

According to P. Lagerhjelm, the **elasticity** of lead is about one-tenth that of wrought iron. J. Thoulet made some observations by means of pendulums. J. Dewar found that the elasticity of the metals cooled to −182° is markedly greater than at ordinary temp. The flattened surface produced by dropping a leaden sphere at −182° on an iron anvil is one-third the diameter of that produced under similar conditions with a leaden sphere at 15°. G. Wertheim found the **modulus of elasticity,** or **Young's modulus,** for cast lead is 1803 kgrms. per sq. mm., and for annealed lead, 1727 kgrms. per sq. mm. E. H. Amagat gave 1556 ; C. Schäfer, 1493 ; E. Grüneisen, 1656–1786 ; and A. H. Stuart, 1800 kgrms. per sq. mm. G. Wertheim found the elastic modulus of annealed lead fell from 1727 to 1630 kgrms. per sq. mm. by raising the temp. from 15° to 1000°. W. Sutherland gave 1900 (extremes 1490–2550) kgrms. per sq. mm. at 0°, and estimated 2700 kgrms. per sq. mm. at −273°, absolute zero. A. Mallock gave 1·80 for the ratio of Young's modulus at −273° to that at 0°. A. Kürth, A. Mallock, and C. Schäfer measured the effect of temp. on the elasticity of lead ; and K. R. Koch and C. Dannecker found a steady fall in the elasticity as the temp rises to 220°. G. Wertheim gave 2500 kgrms. per sq. mm. for the **elastic limit** of drawn lead, and 2000 kgrms. per sq. mm. for annealed lead. O. Faust and G. Tammann gave 2500 kgrms. per sq. mm. for drawn lead ; and they measured the elastic limit as evidenced by the appearance of slip-bands in the crystals. K. R. Koch and R. Dieterle found for the elastic modulus, in kgrms. per sq. mm. :

	13°	89°	150°	198°	250°
Elastic modulus.	2010	1930	1790	1685	1560

T. Kikuta measured the logarithmic decrement of wires of the metal. For **Poissan's ratio,** A. Mallock gave 0·375; E. H. Amagat, 0·428; and C. Schäfer, 0·431. H. Shoji studied the elastic after-effect. For the **rigidity** or **torsion modulus,** C. Schäfer gave 550; H. Tomlinson, 740; W. Sutherland, 840; and F. Horton, 814 kgrms. per sq. mm.; K. R. Koch and C. Dannecker gave for the torsion modulus in kgrms. per sq. mm. :

	20°	50°	100°	150°	200°	235°
Torsion modulus . . .	780	743	667	597	539	244

For the temp. coeff., C. Schäfer gave 78·7, and N. Katzenelsohn, 80. W. Sutherland gave 0·773 for the ratio of the rigidity at 100° to that at zero; T. Kikuta found the rigidity of lead at 12·5° is $7·098 \times 10^{10}$, and remains constant up to 100°; at 122°, $5·64 \times 10^{10}$; at 258°, $3·485 \times 10^{10}$, and it continues decreasing until it vanishes at the m.p., 327°. P. P. Lazareff discussed the relation between the elastic constants and the hardness of lead.

The linear coeff. of **thermal expansion** of lead was determined by P. S. Laplace and A. L. Lavoisier,[18] who gave $0·0_4 2848$; A. Matthiessen gave $0·0_4 2799$ between 0° and 100°; F. C. Calvert and R. Johnson, $0·0_4 3005$; P. Glatzel, $0·0_4 2936$ between 16° and 100°; H. Fizeau, $0·0_4 2924$ at 40°, and $0·0_4 2918$ at 50°; and G. Vicentini and D. Omodei, $0·0_4 295$ at about 320°. E. Grüneisen gave $0·0_4 293$ between 17° and 100°, and $0·0_4 270$ between −190° and 17°; J. N. Friend and R. H. Vallance gave $0·0_4 295$ between 10° and 100°; and R. Hoffmann and W. Stahl, 0·000168 (cubic) between 0° and 600°. C. H. Lindemann found between 19° and −190°, $0·0_4 265$; between −83° and −190°, $0·0_4 196$; and between −192° and −253°, $0·0_4 188$. H. Kopp found the coeff. of cubical expansion between 0° and 100° to be $0·0_5 89$; and A. Matthiessen gave for the vol., v at θ, $v = v_0(1 + 0·0_4 81770 + 0·0_5 222\theta^2)$, where v_0 represents the vol. at 0°. G. Vicentini and D. Omodei gave for the coeff. of cubical expansion of liquid tin between 325° and 357°, $0·0_3 129$. P. W. Bridgman found the proportional change of the coeff. of linear expansion, a, with press., p, to be $-da/adp = 1·51 \times 10^{-5}$ for cast lead, and $1·46 \times 10^{-5}$ for extruded lead. The relations between the coeff. of thermal expansion and other physical properties have been discussed by H. Buff, E. M. Lémeray, P. Frenchen and V. Poulsen, T. Carnelley, E. Grüneisen, J. Kleiber, and C. H. Lindemann. H. Buff calculated what he called the heat of expansion from the relation for that of expansion $= DSa/\beta$, where D denotes the sp. gr.; S, the sp. ht.; a, the coeff. of linear expansion; and β, the coeff. of cubical expansion.

According to C. M. Despretz,[19] if the **thermal conductivity** of silver be 100, that of lead is 14; G. Wiedemann and R. Franz gave 8·1; and F. C. Calvert and R. Johnson, 28·7. R. Schott working with commercial and purified samples obtained with the former respectively 0·114 cal. per cm. per sec. at −252·6°; 0·108 at −246·8°; 0·095 at −187·3°, and 0·079 at 0°; and with the latter, 0·138 at −252·4°; 0·117 at −247·1°; 0·092 at −187°; and 0·089 at 0°. The first, and the last two of the following determinations are by W. Meissner, and the others are by P. Macchia :

	−252·8°	−183°	−12°	25°	43°	80°	100°	200°
Conductivity .	0·116	0·1080	0·0921	0·0825	0·0795	0·0782	0·084	0·084

Other determinations were made by C. H. Lees, L. Lorenz, H. F. Weber, G. Kirchhoff and G. Hansemann, T. Peczalsky, A. Berget, C. D. Bidwell, M. F. Angell, and W. Jäger and H. Diesselhorst. M. O'Day gave 0·0877 at 0°; 0·0920 at 26·5°; and 0·0955 at 53·1°. G. Glage gave 0·244 for the temp. coeff. of the conductivity at 40°. M. Jakob gave 0·095 at −180°; 0·085 at 0°; 0·080 at 100° and at 200°; and 0·075 at 300°. S. Konno's observations over a range beyond the m.p. (327°) are :

	0°	100°	200°	300°	400°	500°	600°	700°
Conductivity . .	0·083	0·081	0·077	0·074	0·038	0·037	0·036	0·036

These results show that the thermal conductivity of lead decreases with a rise of temp. up to the m.p., and there is an abrupt decrease at the m.p. According to S. Lussana, the thermal conductivity is 2·04 per cent. greater at 1300 atm. press., and 3·60 per cent. greater at 2600 atm. press. than it is at one atm. ; while P. W. Bridgman found a 20·7 per cent. linear increase at a press. of 12,000 kgrms. per sq. cm., and an average press. coeff. of $0·0_4173$; S. Lussana gave for the average press. coeff. $0·0_4134$ at 2600 kgrms. per sq. cm.—the initial value was $0·0_4164$, and the final value $0·0_4116$. C. H. Lees and J. E. Calthorp found the thermal conductivity is decreased by twisting lead wires—approximately proportionally with the twist per unit length.

P. L. Dulong and A. T. Petit [20] gave 0·0293 for the **specific heat** of lead ; H. V. Regnault, 0·0314 ; H. Kopp, 0·0315 between 19° and 48° ; L. Lorenz, 0·0308 at 0° and at 100° ; H. Tomlinson, 0·03151 from 0° to 100° ; H. E. Schmitz, 0·03046 from 20° to 100° ; C. I. Burton and W. Marshall, 0·0320 ; H. Schimpff, 0·0297 ; L. Schütz, 0·03171 ; A. Bartoli and E. Stracciati, 0·030887 ; and W. Spring, 0·03050 from 17° to 108° ; 0·03195 from 13° to 191° ; 0·03437 from 16° to 292°. A. Naccari gave

	15°	50°	100°	150°	200°	250°	300°
Sp. ht. .	0·02993	0·03040	0·03108	0·03176	0·03243	0·03312	0·03380

U. J. J. le Verrier, and E. Cohen showed that the sp. ht. depends on the thermal history of the metal ; thus, G. W. A. Kahlbaum and co-workers found the sp. ht. of the unpressed metal to be 0·03033, and of metal which had been exposed to a press. of 10,000 atm., 0·03083. F. Glaser gave 0·031708 for the sp. ht. of hard-lead containing 0·3 per cent. of antimony, and for purified lead, 0·047063. P. Schübel gave 0·0318 between 18° and 200°, and 0·0326 between 18° and 300°. E. Bède represented the effect of temp. by $c=0·0286+0·0000019\theta$; A. Naccari, by $c=0·0297+0·000013358\theta$; and E. H. and E. Griffiths, by $c=0·03020(1+0·0_3400\theta -0·0_636\theta^2)$. Low temp. observations were made by W. Nernst and co-workers, U. Behn, H. Barschall, F. Koref, T. W. Richards and F. G. Jackson, E. H. and E. Griffiths, J. Dewar, C. Forch and P. Nordmeyer, etc. A. Eucken and F. Schwers gave for the sp. ht. and the **atomic heat** :

	2·0°	−187·0°	−218·6°	−225·7°	−232·9°	−247·6°	−258·9°
Sp. ht. . .	0·0307	0·0279	0·0257	0·0248	0·0232	0·0169	0·0075
At. ht. . .	6·365	5·790	5·333	5·131	4·801	3·510	1·56

The last datum is by W. H. Keesom and H. K. Onnes. For the formulæ relating the sp. ht. with temp. in the vicinity of the absolute zero, *vide* 1. 13, 15. W. R. Fielding estimated that the sp. ht. is zero at −267°. H. Schimpff found the sp. ht. of lead and bismuth decreases with rise of temp., whilst that of the other metals tried increases. The relation of the sp. ht. to other constants has been discussed by C. H. Lindemann, W. Nernst and co-workers, J. Kleiber, etc. F. Glaser found that whilst the sp. ht. at 18°–198° is 0·0317, that between 18° and 380° is 0·0471 (m.p. 327°) ; W. Spring gave 0·03556 for the sp. ht. at 310°, and 0·04096 at 360°. I. Iitaka found that the sp. ht. of lead decreases during its passage through the liquid state, being 0·0358 at 327° with solid lead, and 0·0340 at 327° with molten lead. W. M. Latimer studied the relation between the sp. ht. and the thermoelectric force ; and F. Michaud compared the ratio of the sp. ht. to the absolute temp. for a number of metals. L. H. Adams calculated the thermal capacity of lead vapour at different press. E. D. Eastman, and G. N. Lewis and co-workers gave 15·53 for the **entropy** of lead at 25° and 1 atm. W. M. Latimer gave 0·03–0·04 for the change of entropy in passing from 200° to 300°. H. Tetrode predicted 41·9 for the entropy of lead vapour at 25° ; and W. H. Rodebush and A. L. Dixon found 41·8. A. L. Bernouilli discussed the relation between the sp. ht. and the elastic constants of lead and some other metals. E. D. Eastman and co-workers made estimates of the thermal energy of the electrons in lead.

Lead is very fusible, and it might be anticipated that the discrepancies, so common in the determination of the **melting points** of the less fusible elements by the early observers, would not be so marked. The accurate determination of the higher melting-points became possible only with the comparatively recent development of pyrometry. The results with lead are often wide of the mark, and show that sufficient care was not taken to purify the metal under observation. Among the earlier data may be quoted 260° by J. B. Biot [21]; 282° by I. Newton; 296·2° by A. V. Tidblom; 312° by L. B. G. de Morveau; and 322° by J. Dalton, J. F. Daniell, L. B. G. de Morveau, and J. Crichton. F. Rudberg came very near the value accepted at the present day with his 325°, and later 326°, likewise also A. von Riemsdijk with 326°, C. C. Person with 326·2°. The two last-named results are too high, and likewise also A. T. Kupffer with 334°, and G. Brigel with 330°–335°. A large number of determinations have been made in connection with the study of binary and ternary systems of lead with other elements. Thus, K. Friedrich and co-workers, G. J. Petrenko, A. G. C. Gwyer, J. Czochralsky and E. Rassoff. W. E. Barlow, K. Lewkonja, E. Isaac and G. Tammann, N. S. Kurnakoff and N. A. Puschin, E. Jänecke, D. P. Smith, G. Grube, N. S. Kurnakoff and N. J. Stepanoff, G. Voss, R. Ruer, F. Dörinckel, S. Tamaru, and W. Spring and L. Romanoff gave 327°; R. S. Dean, 327·1°; C. H. Mathewson, 326·9°; R. Vogel, A. Stoffel, R. S. Williams, K. Friedrich and A. Leroux, F. Wüst, A. Ledebur, W. Gontermann, and P. N. Degens, 326°; G. Vicentini and D. Omodei, H. Siedentopf, and G. Hindrichs, 325°; A. Stoffel, 321·5°; H. Fay and C. B. Gillson, 322°; and N. Baar, and L. Donsky, 330°. C. T. Heycock and F. H. Neville gave 327·60°; L. J. Dana and P. D. Foote, 327·4°; H. L. Callendar, 327·7°; H. L. Callendar and E. H. Griffiths, 327·69°; W. R. Mott, 327·4°; L. Holborn and A. L. Day, 326·9°; C. W. Waidner and G. K. Burgess, 327·43°; E. H. Griffiths gave 328·78°; H. Tsutsumi, 328·4°; A. L. Day and R. B. Sosman, 327·3°; L. H. Adams and J. Johnston, 327·3°. The best representative value is 327·4°, in agreement with W. Guertler and M. Pirani. C. W. Waidner and G. K. Burgess found evidence of a slight undercooling during the freezing. C. T. Heycock and F. H. Neville measured the effect of small additions of various metals on the f.p. of lead, and applied F. M. Raoult's law to the results. A. Wertheimer, and T. Carnelley found the m.p. of lead, fitted with the application of the periodic law to the m.p. of the elements. G. von Hevesy discussed the break-down of the space-lattice during melting. The effect of press. on the m.p. of lead is in harmony with Clapeyron's equation (1. 9, 4), there is the rise in the m.p. of about 0·008026° per atm. J. Johnston and L. H. Adams found:

Press.	1	150	250	350	500	1000	1490	2000 atm.
M.p.	325·35°	326·53°	327·46°	328·12°	329·26°	333·38°	337·35°	341·38°

The results agree very well with the formula $\theta_m - 327·3 = 0·008026p$, showing that the change is a linear function of the press. The change $\delta\theta$ per 1000 atm. is 8·03°, or $d\theta/dp = 0·00803°$ per atm., in agreement with 0·00832° calculated from C. C. Person's datum for the heat of fusion (5·37 cals. per gram), and G. Vicentini and D. Omodei's value 0·003076 c.c. per gram for the change in vol. on melting. According to E. Hagenbach, lead can be melted by *un choc violent*. W. H. Preece found the melting of a wire d mm. diameter by a current of intensity I, occurs when $I = 10·8d^{1·5}$. A. Jouniaux studied the variation of the mol. wt. of lead with temp. calculated from cryoscopic results.

L. Lewin [22] could detect no vapour at all from lead at 500°–520°. According to J. Percy, when lead is heated in air, fumes of lead monoxide are evolved at a bright red-heat, and appear to have a well-marked odour which can be imitated by shaking finely divided litharge in the air of a room. In the absence of air, lead is not sensibly volatilized below a white heat. Lead boils rapidly before the oxyhydrogen blowpipe, but it cannot be distilled like zinc *per se* in closed vessels. In the extraction of zinc from plumbiferous ores, the vapour of zinc is mixed with that of lead. In the process of smelting and cupelling lead, there is an evaporation of lead or of its compounds. In practice, lead is therefore regarded as a volatile metal, and K. Sander, C. W. Hixon, etc., have cited cases where large proportion of the lead in a charge passed into the flues—*vide supra*, fume-collectors. H. Enge and V. Froboese found that the volatilization of lead during lead burning, etc., is favoured by an excess of oxygen.

P. Berthier reported that when lead is heated in a brasqued crucible to about 1060° there is a 0·5 per cent. loss in weight, and a 9 per cent. loss when heated to 1400°. J. W. Richards calculated values for the **vapour pressure** of lead from those of mercury. J. Johnston represented the vap. press. of lead at $T°$ K. by log $p=8·0$ —9900T^{-1}. He thence computed :

	620°	710°	820°	960°	1130°	1290°	1360°	1640°
p mm.	0·001	0·01	0·1	1	10	50	100	750

H. von Wartenberg gave $1·05 \times 10^{-4}$ atm. at 808° ; $2·30 \times 10^{-3}$ at 996° ; and $2·20 \times 10^{-2}$ at 1178°. J. H. Hildebrand gave log $p=7·85-10362T^{-1}+$log $3·3$ .J. A. M. van Liempt found $\log_{10} p=5·05-9521T^{-1}$; and for the sublimation curve $\log_{10} p=5·54-10030T^{-1}$; W. H. Rodebush and A. L. Dixon gave log $p=-10100T^{-1}$ $-0·65$ log $T+10·05$ mm. between 600° and 900° K. They also calculated values for the entropy of the vapour. A. C. Egerton gave for the vap. press. of molten lead at temp. ranging from 600° K. to 1200° K. log $p=7·908-9923T^{-1}$, and C. K. Ingold found that an equation of the type $\log_{10} p=4·818$ $-11160T^{-1}$ $+1·750 \log_{10} T-0·000982T'$ in mm. of mercury, represented the results of his observations up to 1130°, but it diverged more and more as the temp. exceeded this limit ; the equation $T_{Pb}/T'_{Hg}=3·244-0·00038T_{Hg}$ gave results in close agreement with observations over the whole range ; here, T'_{Hg} refers to the absolute b.p. of mercury when under the same pressure as the lead whose absolute b.p. is T'_{Pb}. The observed results are :

	920°	950°	1000°	1050°	1100°	1150°	1200°	1250°	1300°	1340°
p mm.	0·49	0·86	1·77	3·69	4·87	12·8	23·2	37·5	62·0	90·3

O. Ruff and B. Bergdahl gave 73 mm. at 1275° and 758 mm. at 1555°. W. H. Rode bush measured the vap. press. between 1118° **and** 1235°, and W. H. Rodebush and A. L. Dixon gave log $p=-10372T^{-1}-$log $T-11·35$, when the press. are expressed in mm. The **boiling point** of lead deduced from these results is 1619° J. Johnston computed 1640° ; O. Ruff and B. Bergdahl, 1555° ; T. Carnelley and W. C. Williams, 1600° ; W. R. Mott, 1525° ; J. J. van Laar, 1870° H. von Wartenberg, 1580° $\pm20°$; and H. C. Greenwood obtained

	105 mm.	266 mm.	760 mm.	6·3 atm.	12·7 atm.
Boiling point	1315°	1410°	1525°	1870°	2100°

L. H. Borgström gave 2870° at 93 atm. press. F. Krafft and co-workers observed at a low press. a reduction of 30° in the b.p. of lead corresponding with a change of 45 mm. mercury press. ; and in the vacuum of a cathode light, the b.p. was 1144° at 70 mm. They also found that under these conditions lead is distinctly volatile at 335°. P. Walden calculated the b.p. in the cathode vacuum to be 1140°, and at 760 mm., 1700°. According to W. J. Russell, and C. Zenghelis, lead volatilizes at ordinary temp. because a thin plate of silver hanging in a moist atm. over powdered lead, is perceptibly attacked in 24 hrs. W. N. Hartley mentioned the volatilization of lead in the induction sparks ; and R. J. Strutt, in the cathode ray vacuum A. Schuller, and G. W. A. Kahlbaum and co-workers found that lead distils with difficulty under reduced press., and E. Tiede and F. Fischer showed that although tin melts at a lower temp. than lead, its b.p. is much higher, and it is possible to separate the two elements quantitatively by fractional distillation in a cathode light vacuum with the metal contained in a porcelain boat at a bright red heat H. Moissan and co-workers also made some observations on this subject—*vide* tin No trace of tin was carried by the vap. of lead. W. Crookes found the rate of volatilization of tin and lead from a negative electrode in vacuo is as 57 : 75 when the value for gold is 100. W. G. Duffield measured the velocity of evaporation of molten lead. H. F. Wiebe deduced a relation between the b.p., m.p., at. wt., and coeff. of thermal expansion of a number of metals. W. Herz studied some regularities in the vap. press. of lead and other elements; and E. D. Eastman, the heat capacity of the electrons.

J. J. van Laar estimated the **critical temperature** of lead to be 3000°, and the **critical pressure**, 370 atm. C. M. Guldberg gave 2000° for the critical temp. if that of mercury is 1000°; P. Walden gave 3598°; and W. Herz, 2696°. F. Rudberg gave 5·86 cals. per gram for the latent **heat of fusion**; C. C. Person, and D. Mazzotto, 5·37 cals.; E. Glaser, 4·78 cals.; W. Spring, 5·320 cals.; P. W. Robertson, 6·45 cals.; and I. Iitaka, 5·53 cals. per gram. A. C. Egerton gave 47000 ± 1000 cals. for the latent heat of vaporization of solid lead at absolute zero; that of molten lead which varies a little with the temp. up to 1200° is about 45,350 cals. The so-called radioactive lead has a slightly higher value than ordinary lead. H. C. Greenwood gave 45,500 cals. per mol. for the **heat of vaporization** of lead; J. Tate, 175 cals. per gram at 1170°; W. H. Rodebush and A. L. Dixon, 46,300 cals.; and J. A. M. van Liempt, 43,590 cals. per mol. For **Trouton's constant,** the last-named found 23·12. A. Henglein gave 0·174 Cal. for the mol. heat of evaporation. H. von Wartenberg calculated 44,000 cals. for the inner heat of vaporization, and from the **vapour density** he inferred the molecule to be monatomic at 1870°. F. Simon gave 2·66 for the **chemical constant** of lead; and W. H. Rodebush and A. L. Dixon gave —1·40 in agreement with —1·588 required by the quantum theory.

According to S. Haughton,[23] the **index of refraction** of lead for red light is 2·2; P. Drude gave for rays of wave length 0·589μ, 2·01 for the index of refraction; 3·48 for the **absorption index**; and the **reflecting power,** 62 per cent. H. von Wartenberg gave 2·01 for the index of refraction of lead for light of wave-length 0·589μ; 3·48 for the absorption coeff.; and 62 per cent. for the reflecting power. A. K. Aster found the index of refraction of molten lead to be 0·415, and the absorption coeff. 1·76; and that both were independent of the temp. L. Austin and H. Starke said that the reflecting power of lead is 63 per cent. of that of copper. M. A. Schirmann studied the polarization of light by the colloidal particles of lead. J. H. Gladstone found the **specific refraction** of lead to be 0·117–0·129; and 24·5–26·7 for the **atomic refraction;** E. Krause and co-workers gave 18·89; and W. J. Pope gave 30·02 for the at. refraction. P. Niggli studied this subject. C. A. Valson examined the refractive power of lead in soln. of its salts; G. Grüttner and E. Krause, the refractive power of quadrivalent lead in the lead tetralkyl compounds; and H. Grossmann, the effect of lead salts on the refractive index of sugar. M. Faraday found thin films of lead depolarized and rotated a ray of polarized light as in the case of thin films of gold.

The ultra-violet **fluorescence** of lead compounds was studied by E. Wiedemann and G. C. Schmidt,[24] and of the vapour by H. Kopfermann; the **cathode ray** luminescence, by P. Schuhknecht; and the effect of lead salts on the luminescence of calcium sulphide, by P. Lenard and V. Klatt. P. Lewis examined the spectrum of the vapour luminescent in the cathode rays; and V. Carlheim-Gyllensköld, the luminescence in the **canal rays.** G. Dima[25] studied the **photoelectric effect** of lead oxide and lead halides. W. Ramsay and J. F. Spencer placed lead after cadmium and before bismuth in the order of their photoelectric effect; K. Herrmann placed it after cadmium and before copper; and R. A. Millikan and G. Winchester placed it after zinc. O. Stuhlmann found 1·12 for the ratio of the photoelectric effect on two sides of a lead film in air. The phenomenon was studied by G. Reboul. The limiting frequency of the photoelectric effect is $\lambda=2980\pm50$. S. Maracineanu reported that lead may be excited by solar radiations and, for a few months, shows slight ionizing properties; causes scintillations on a screen of zinc sulphide; and darkens a photographic plate provided water vapour is present. The subject was discussed by A. Kufferath and W. Merckens, and G. L. Keenan.

A magnetic field, heat, pressure, and friction may also be used to excite lead. N. Piltschikoff found that lead emits positive Moser rays.

J. A. McClelland [26] studied the effect of **radium radiations** on lead; and showed that the intensity of the secondary radiation invoked increases with the at. wt. of the elements. W. H. Bragg measured the stopping powers of various substances for the **α-rays**, and found the stopping power of lead to be 4·27 (air unity). The subject was studied by Y. Tuomikoski, M. Ishino, J. Thibaud, C. D. Ellis, A. H. Compton, H. A. Bumstead and A. G. McGougan, N. R. Campbell, etc. H. R. von Traubenberg gave $24 \cdot 1 \times 10^{-4}$ cm. for the range of the α-rays in lead. J. A. Crowther found for the ratio of the coeff. of absorption, μ, and the density, for the **β-rays**, $\mu/D = 10 \cdot 8$ when that of copper is 6·8. Further observations were made by W. Wilson, W. B. Huff, J. S. Latès and G. Fournier, etc. J. Thibaud studied the β-rays of lead. A. S. Russell and F. Soddy found the coeff. of absorption, μ, for the **γ-rays** of radium 0·495 per cm.; γ-rays of uranium, 0·725 per cm.; thorium-D, 0·462 per cm.; and for mesothorium, 0·620 per cm. The subject was studied by Y. Tuomikoski, M. Ishino, J. Thibaud, C. D. Ellis, A. H. Compton, M. Baltruschat and H. Starke, N. Ahmad, B. Keetman, H. Richardson, E. Rutherford and co-workers, etc. The **δ-rays** from lead were studied by N. R. Campbell. A. T. Waterman observed the emission of no characteristic positive ions from heated lead halides. The **radioactivity of lead** was examined by J. Elster and H. Geitel, E. Rutherford, K. A. Hofmann and co-workers, H. Geitel, M. Levin and R. Ruer, J. Danysz, B. B. Boltwood, C. S. Wright, C. Winkler, H. Herchfinkel, A. Debierne, A. Korn and E. Strauss, J. C. McLennan, etc. According to M. Muguet, the radioactivity of lead from the uranium ores of Madagascar increased 12-fold during six months.

The absorption of **X-rays** by lead was studied by T. E. Aurén,[27] W. Duane and co-workers, E. A. Owen and co-workers, K. W. F. Kohlrausch, J. C. Chapman, K. A. Wingardh, D. Hurmuzescu, G. Fournier, H. S. Read, S. J. M. Allen, F. P. Slater, G. Holtsmark, F. K. Richtmyer, L. Benoist, E. Rutherford and co-workers, C. D. Cooksey, G. W. C. Kaye and R. A. Houstoun—*vide* 4. 25, 6. For rays of wave-length λ Angström units, the ratio of absorption coeff., μ, and the density, D, is, according to A. W. Hull and M. Rice, for wave-lengths greater than 0·149 A., the

λ			0·294	0·245	0·221	0·196	0·184	0·160	0·147
μ/D			11·10	6·70	4·63	3·40	2·71	1·82	1·50

The absorption is given by $\mu/D = 430\lambda^3 + 0 \cdot 12$; below 0·149 A., there is a sudden increase in the values of μ/D, owing to the presence of a characteristic absorption band, which was also observed by L. de Broglie. E. Rutherford found that the thickness of lead through which the radiation was measureable increased with the voltage applied, being 3·1 mm. with a voltage of 79,000; 4·6 mm. with a voltage of 10,500; 7·0 mm. with a voltage of 183,000; and 10·0 mm. with a voltage of 196,000. W. E. Williams and B. L. Worksop found the critical frequency for the K-absorption $21 \cdot 58 \times 10^{18}$ per sec. H. S. Read studied the effect of temp. on the X-ray absorption. G. W. C. Kaye and E. A. Owen examined the absorption of the rays by various substances. Injurious effects—X-ray burns—are produced by the absorption of very soft X-rays by the skin. Most of the protective devices— gloves, aprons, spectacles, etc.—depend on the absorption properties of lead salts. C. G. Barkla and J. G. Dunlop studied the scattering of X-rays by lead, and found for the ratio of the scattering coeff., σ, and the density, D, referred to that for aluminium to be for

σ			0·63	0·52	0·43	0·316	0·314	0·305
Pb/Al			11·2	9·0	4·4	2·65	2·1	1·7

K. E. F. Schmidt studied the refraction of the X-rays by lead; J. Herweg, the polarization of these rays; G. Shearer, the emission of electrons; P. D. Innes, the velocity of the electrons emitted by lead under the influence of X-rays;

W. Seitz, the asymmetry of the X-rays from lead; C. G. Bedreag, electrification by the X-rays; H. A. Blumstead, the heating effects of X-rays; K. W. F. Kohlrausch, and P. Curie and G. Saynac, J. C. Chapman, the secondary radiations from different metals; J. Cluzet and T. Kofman, the effect of lead on the action of X-rays on colloidal metals; and M. Wolfke, the production of X-rays by the action of canal rays on lead.

The **X-ray spectrum** was examined by M. and L. de Broglie,[28] B. B. Ray, E. C. Stoner, D. Coster, H. Robinson, G. Kettmann, P. A. Ross, H. Hirata, G. Réchou, K. Lang, J. Laub, H. Küstner, E. Hjalmar, H. G. J. Moseley, C. G. Barkla, H. Robinson and W. F. Rawlinson, E. Rutherford and co-workers, M. Siegbahn and co-workers, W. Stenström, E. G. Taylor, etc. The K-series were reported on by W. Duane and co-workers, A. Leide, B. R. Stephenson and J. M. Cork, M. Siegbahn and E. Jönsson. M. de Broglie, C. D. and D. Cooksey, D. Coster, W. Duane and co-workers, and M. Siegbahn found for the L-series in Angström units, 10^{-8} cm., $a_2a'=1{\cdot}18352$, $a_1a=1{\cdot}17202$; $\beta_1\beta=0{\cdot}97990$; $\beta_2\gamma=0{\cdot}97990$, $\gamma_1\delta=0{\cdot}83708$; $\epsilon=1{\cdot}34662$; $\eta=10902$; $\beta_6=1{\cdot}0188$; $\beta_7=0{\cdot}9590^2$; $\beta_8=0{\cdot}9735$; $\beta_5\zeta=0{\cdot}9452$; $\gamma_2\theta=0{\cdot}8182$; $\beta_4v=1{\cdot}00469$; $\beta_3\phi=0{\cdot}96602$; $\gamma_5=0{\cdot}8639$; $\gamma_6=0{\cdot}81370$; $\gamma_3\chi=0{\cdot}8379$; and $\gamma_4\psi=0{\cdot}8100$. G. Wentzel, G. Kettmann, F. K. Richtmyer, and M. Siegbahn reported for the K-series, $a_1=5{\cdot}290$; $a'=5{\cdot}287$; $a=5{\cdot}2851$; $\beta=5{\cdot}0648$; $\beta_1=5{\cdot}078$; $\gamma=4{\cdot}6637$; $\gamma_1=4{\cdot}534$; $\gamma_2=4{\cdot}073$. S. J. M. Allen, and F. W. Warburton and F. K. Richtmyer studied the adsorption coeff. for the X-rays.

Lead salts impart to Bunsen's flame a bluish tinge, and give a **flame spectrum** of what is presumably the oxide, and show some bands. The flame spectrum was studied by H. Auerbach,[29] R. Böttger, L. de Boisbaudran, E. Diaçon, J. M. Eder and E. Valenta, A. Gouy, A. Hagenbach and H. Konen, A. Harnack, W. N. Hartley, O. Vogel, and C. de Watteville. The band spectra, and the spectra of lead compounds were examined by G. Ciamician, E. Diaçon, W. N. Hartley and H. Ramage, H. Lamprecht, A. R. Leeds, A. Mitscherlich, and E. Wiedemann.

The spectrum obtained by heating lead in an electric furnace was examined by A. S. King. The **spark spectrum** of lead was examined by C. Wheatstone in 1835. A flame fed with oxygen playing on lead resting on charcoal gave a continuous spectrum. Numerous records of the spark spectrum have been made—D. Alter, A. J. Angström, L. and E. Bloch, W. von Bolton, L. de Boisbaudran, R. Capron, R. J. Lang, E. Demarçay, J. M. Eder and co-workers, F. Exner and E. Haschek, H. Finger, C. E. Gissing, A. de Gramont, A. Hagenbach and H. Konen, W. N. Hartley and co-workers, J. Hartmann, G. A. Hemsalech, A. C. Jones, A. Kalähne, G. Kirchhoff, J. N. Lockyer, O. Lohse, A. Masson, J. C. McLennan and co-workers, W. A. Miller, S. R. Milner, H. W. Morse, J. Parry and A. E. Tucker, J. Plücker and J. W. Hittorf, F. R. Robinson, T. Royds, J. A. Carroll, and J. Wilsing. The most intense lines are 2802·10; 2833·12; 3573·03; 3639·72; 3682·64; 3740·28; 4058·00 (violet) a, Fig. 12; 4167 (violet); 4245·42; 4387·11 (indigo); 5005 (green)β; 5045

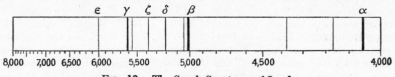

FIG. 12.—The Spark Spectrum of Lead.

(green); 5201 δ; 5373 (green) ζ; 5547 (green), 5609·00 (green),γ; and 6002 (orange-yellow). E. O. Hulbert examined the spark spectrum in water and in aq. soln. of lead salts. The **arc spectrum** was examined by A. S. C. Dunstan and B. A. Wooten, J. C. McLennan and co-workers, M. Kimura, J. M. Eder and E. Valenta, K. W. Meissner, F. Exner and E. Haschek, W. Gallenkamp, W. Grotrian, A. Hagenbach and H. Konen, J. Hartmann, A. de Gramont and G. A. Hemsalech,

H. Hertenstein, T. Royds, W. B. Huff, W. Huppers, H. Kayser and C. Runge, H. Könemann, J. C. McLennan and co-workers, N. K. Sur, T. R. Merton, W. R. Mott, H. A. Rowland, J. Stark and R. Küch, and V. Thorsen. The more intense lines in the arc spectrum are 2539·92, 2577·39, 2614·39, 2614·26, 2663·27, 2802·10, 2828·31, 2833·21, 2873·48, 3572·95, 3639·72, 3671·80, 3683·52, 3740·20, 4019·80, 4058·00, and 5005·63. B. E. Moore studied the excitation stages in the arc spectrum. The effect of *pressure* was examined by W. J. Humphreys; the effect of the *oscillating discharge*, by P. Joye, G. A. Hemsalech, G. Berndt, and E. Néculcea; the effect of a *magnetic field*, the **Zeeman effect**, by J. E. Purvis, E. Back, P. A. van der Harst, and H. Lunelund; the **Stark effect**, by H. Nagaoka and Y. Sugiura; the *reversed lines*, by A. Cornu; the *enhanced lines*, by M. Kimura and G. Nakamura, and J. Steinhausen; the *variability* of the spectrum, by L. de Boisbaudran; and the *sensitiveness*, by F. Brasack, W. N. Hartley and H. W. Moss, and A. de Gramont. The **ultra-violet spectrum** was investigated by L. and E. Bloch, R. J. Lang, F. Exner and E. Haschek, J. M. Eder and E. Valenta, G. D. Liveing and J. Dewar, J. C. McLennan and co-workers, W. A. Miller, A. de Gramont, R. V. Zumstein, V. Schumann, and G. G. Stokes; and the **ultra-red spectrum**, by H. Becquerel, A. Bergmann, H. Lehmann, V. P. Lubovich and E. M. Pearen, R. J. Lang, and H. M. Randall. The structure of the spectrum, or the **series spectrum**, was studied by R. V. Zumstein, P. G. Nutting, K. W. Meissner, W. N. Hartley, J. A. Carroll, F. Hund, A. E. Ruark and R. L. Chenault, H. Gieseler and W. Grotrian, H. Sponer, L. Janicki, V. Thorsen, and H. Lunelund. H. Kayser and C. Runge found constant difference groups in the spectrum of lead, and these were verified by F. Klein, and R. Arnolds; otherwise A. Fowler reported that no typical series have been discovered in the spectral lines of lead. The **absorption spectrum** of lead vapour was examined by J. N. Lockyer and W. C. Roberts-Austen, N. K. Sur and R. K. Sharma, J. C. McLennan and co-workers, W. Grotrian, R. V. Zumstein, E. O. Hulburt, W. Friederichs, J. G. Frayne and A. W. Smith, A. L. Narayan and K. R. Rao, and H. Geiseler. Both ends of the spectrum are said to be absorbed. L. Janicki and R. Seliger, and B. Reismann examined the spectrum of the vapour of lead at the anode of a discharge tube. Soln. of lead salts are colourless, and give no absorption spectrum. They have been examined by C. Schäfer, W. N. Hartley, W. W. Coblentz, and T. Retschinsky, and absorption bands beyond the visible spectrum have been observed. T. R. Merton, E. S. Bieler, L. Grebe and H. Konen, and W. D. Harkins and L. Aronberg compared the spectra of ordinary lead, and lead from radioactive sources. According to J. Formanek, no characteristic absorption spectrum is given by a soln. of a lead salt and alkanna. A. P. Weber, and B. R. Stephenson and J. M. Cork measured the **K-series** in the **X-ray spectrum** of lead; and S. J. M. Allen, and F. K. Richtmyer, the L-series. F. L. Mohler and co-workers found 1·26 volts for the **resonance potential** and 7·93 volts for the **ionization potential** of lead vapour. P. A. Ross found the critical potentials of the M-line $\lambda=5·2751$ to be 2·5 kvolts; the $\lambda=5·0648$ line, 2·7 kvolts; the $\lambda=4·6637$ and 4·073 lines, 3·1 kvolts; and $\lambda=3·94$, and 4·0 kvolts. B. E. Moore examined the excitation stages in the arc-spectrum of lead. J. E. P. Wagstaff calculated the **vibration frequency** of lead to be $1·84 \times 10^{-12}$. A. Terenin studied the fluorescence and resonance spectra. A. T. Waterman calculated the conc. of free electrons in lead to be $1·1 \times 10^{17}$ per c.c. at 0°, and the value decreases with rise of temp. The electronic structure with respect to the spectrum of lead was studied by S. Goudsmit. The cathodic spectrum of lead in a vacuum tube with an aluminium anode was studied by M. Kimura and G. Nakamura. A. Nodon found that the photogenic radiations from the sun can penetrate lead, but not metals of lower valency. H. Könemann examined the spectrum of fluorescent lead vapour; and S. Smith, that of electrically exploded lead wire.

Determinations of the **electrical conductivity** of lead were reported by A. C. Bequerel,[30] A. Matthiessen and co-workers, J. R. Benoit, A. Arndtsen,

R. Clausius, J. Bergmann and co-workers, H. F. Weber, A. Berget, L. Lorenz, G. Kirchhoff and G. Hansemann, C. Vicentini and D. Omodei, J. Dewar and J. A. Fleming, H. Dickson, L. de la Rive, A. Eucken, etc. The results show that if the conductivity of silver at 0° be 100, that of lead is 8·277 at 0°, 8·245 at 12°, and 5·761 at 100°. J. Dewar and J. A. Fleming, and H. Dickson gave $4·91 \times 10^4$, G. Niccolai, $5·05 \times 10^4$, and J. Bergmann, $5·18 \times 10^4$ mhos at 0°; and W. Jäger and H. Diesselhorst, $4·80 \times 10^4$; W. Meissner, $5·19 \times 10^4$ mhos at 0°, and $4·83 \times 10^4$ mhos at 18°; C. H. Lees gave $5·19 \times 10^4$ mhos at 0°, and $4·84 \times 10^4$ mhos at 18°. G. Kirchhoff and G. Hansemann, and W. Herold traced variations in the conductivity of a lead wire to its heterogeneous structure. The sp. **electrical resistance,** R, given by G. Niccolai is:

	−189°	−150°	−125°	−50°	0°	25°	50°	100°	200°	300°
R . .	6648	9253	10975	16190	19803	22047	23663	27844	38047	49932

A. Schulze gave $0·0_42038$ for the sp. resistance of lead. For the *temperature* coeff. of the resistance, a, in $R=R_0(1+a\theta)$; for temp., $\theta°$, between 0° and 100°, J. Dewar and J. A. Fleming gave 0·0411 ; W. Jäger and H. Diesselhorst, 0·0428 ; G. Niccolai, 0·0406 ; L. Holborn, and F. Henning, 0·0422 ; C. Cattaneo, −0·00065 between 226·5° and 325° ; and P. W. Bridgman, 0·0421 ; for the molten metal, G. Vicentini and D. Omodei gave $a=0·00052$, and P. Müller gave $a=488$ for the temp. coeff. of the conductivity from 327° to 1000°. S. Konno gave for the sp. resistance R,

	20°	100°	220°	302°	327°	329°	331°	338°	345°	450°	551°	577°
$R \times 10^{-4}$ . .	21·0	25·6	34·1	40·8	43·4	50·8	67·6	81·5	83·0	87·4	91·8	93·0

The change in the electrical resistance of lead on fusion was measured by C. Benedicks, L. de la Rive, A. Schulze, P. Müller, G. Vicentini and D. Omodei, etc. H. Tsutumi found 3·27 for the ratio of the sp. resistance of liquid and solid lead at the m.p. E. F. Northrup and co-workers found the electrical resistance is nearly doubled when the metal melts. The results are graphed in Fig. 13. Expressing the resistance R in microhms per c.c., they found :

	319°	333°	400°	500°
R . . .	50·00	95·00	98·30	102·85

	600°	700°	800°
	107·25	111·75	116·20

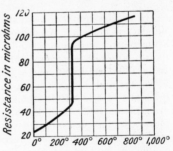

FIG. 13.—Electrical Resistance of Lead at Different Temperatures.

The curve of the variation of the electrical resistance of lead with temp., Fig. 13, is slightly convex towards the temp. axis; and for the liquid state, a straight line. The highest value for the resistance of the solid before fusion was 49·2 microhms, and 94·7 after fusion. A. Schulze gave 49×10^{-6} for the sp. resistance of the solid at the m.p., and $94·6 \times 10^{-6}$ for that of the liquid. The resistance of lead becomes smaller and smaller as the temp. is reduced ; H. K. Onnes and co-workers found the following values referred to lead unity at 0°,

	16·33°	−103·63°	−195·15°	−216·61°	−252·78°	−255·07°	−258·70°
R . .	0·0652	0·59548	0·25257	0·17129	0·03032	0·02314	0·01311

At the temp. of liquid helium, said F. B. Silsbee, or, according to C. A. Crommelin, at 7·3° K., lead becomes a super conductor. W. Tuyn and H. K. Onnes found ordinary lead and radioactive lead behave similarly. Observations at low temp. were also made by E. Grüneisen, H. Schimank, L. Holborn, etc. H. K. Onnes and co-workers stated that the great change in the temp. coeff. exhibited by lead at low temp. in the presence of a small amount of *impurity* must be attributed to the transition of the admixture to a state of solid soln. N. S. Kurnakoff, and S. F. Schemtschuschny found the lowering of the electrical conductivity of lead by equi-atomic proportions of other metals to be the same. W. Meissner and H. Schimank computed values for the ratio of the resistance at absolute zero to that at $T°$ K. S. Smith measured the electrical resistance of lead vapour. Working with lead containing not more than 1 part of silver and copper in 300.000, and no trace of any other metal, P. W. Bridgman found, for the effect of *pressure* on the electrical resistance,

		0°	25°	50°	75°	100°
Resistance .	. . .	1·0000	1·1022	1·2065	1·3127	1·4207
Press. coeff.	0 kgrm. .	-0.0_41442	-0.0_41452	$+0.0_41462$	-0.0_41473	-0.0_41483
	12,000 kgrms.	-0.0_41044	-0.0_41045	-0.0_41047	-0.0_41049	-0.0_41051
	Average .	-0.0_41212	-0.0_41222	-0.0_41232	-0.0_41243	-0.0_41253

E. Lisell gave for the press. coeff. at 0°, -0.0_4144 ; and W. F. Williams, -0.0_4138. H. K. Onnes and B. Beckman gave for the press. coeff. at $-183°$, -0.0_4225, and at $-252.7°$, -0.0_4170. Interpolating the observed values, it was found that the decrease in the resistance per 100 atm. approximates to zero on approaching the absolute zero of temp. E. D. Williamson also studied this subject. Z. A. Epstein examined the relation of the electrical conductivities of the metals to the *periodic law*. H. Tomlinson noted that the resistance of a lead wire was increased when the metal is in *torsion;* L. Guillet and M. Ballay found that cold-hammering raised the resistance very little. C. H. Lees and J. E. Calthrop found the change to be less than in the case of thermal conductivity, but it is approximately proportional to the square of the twist per unit length. O. Chwolson found the resistance increased by *annealing*; and L. L. Grunmach and F. Weidert found a slight increase in the resistance when the metal is transversely *magnetized*. P. W. Bridgman found that the differences in the electrical resistance, and the temp. and press. coeff. of ordinary lead and that from radioactive sources lie within the limits of experimental error. A. Stein discussed the relation between the m.p. and electrical resistance of tin and other metals ; and A. T. Waterman, the theory of electrical conduction.

N. A. Hesehus [31] showed that in a closed circuit with hot and cold lead there is no electric current. According to A. Matthiessen, lead stands in the thermoelectric series between magnesium and tin. The **Seebeck effect,** or the **thermoelectric force** of the *platinum-lead* couple at 100°, was found by W. Jäger and H. Diesselhorst to be 0·041 millivolt where the current flows from the lead to the platinum ; J. Dewar and J. A. Fleming gave 0·44 millivolt at 100° and 0·21 at $-190°$, and 0·12 at $-100°$; H. Pélabon gave 5·14 microvolts at 100° ; K. Noll gave 0·41 millivolt at 100° ; and E. Wagner, and E. Rudolfi, 0·46 millivolt. H. Pélabon found the e.m.f. rises linearly with the temp. up to the m.p. of lead. W. M. Latimer studied the thermoelectric force of the *silver-lead couple.* For the *lead-mercury* couple, K. Noll gave 0·41 millivolt at 100°, and 1·03 millivolts at 200°. For the *lead-copper* couple, W. Jäger and H. Diesselhorst gave 2·9 millivolts at 18°, and 3·4 at 100° ; E. Wagner gave 3·09 millivolt at 49·2° and 3·23 millivolts at 70·5°. C. Benedicks gave -2.8 microvolts. H. K. Onnes and G. Holst gave 0·457 millivolt for the lead-copper couple at $-192°$; 0·553 at $-253°$; and 0·559 at 270·74°. P. G. Tait, and H. Pécheux measured the e.m.f. of the lead-copper couple. F. G. Wick gave for the *lead-silicon* couple at $-185°$, 63 millivolts ; at 0°, zero ; at 100°, -42 ; at 200°, -77 ; and at $-300°$, -112 millivolts. For the *lead-constantin* couple P. Cermak gave 0·4 millivolt at 17·4° ; 90·2 millivolts at 254° ; 118·3, at 325° ; 141 at 365° ; 147·2 at 383° ; and 173·3 at 445°—there is no abrupt change when the lead fuses. K. Siebel measured the values for liquid and solid lead at the m.p. According to G. Wietzel, the thermoelectric force approximates to zero at the absolute zero of temp. Table III was compiled by F. E. Fowle from the results of E. Becquerel, A. Matthiessen, P. G. Tait, and W. Haken. The thermoelectric power, $dE/d\theta$, in microvolts is defined as the e.m.f., E, produced by one degree difference of temp. between the junctions, so that $dE/d\theta = E_0 + a\theta$, where E is the thermoelectric power at 0°, a is a con-

TABLE III.—THE THERMOELECTRIC POWER OF DIFFERENT ELEMENTS AGAINST LEAD.

Substance.	E_0	a	$dE/d\theta$		Neutral temp., E_0/a
			20°	50°	
Aluminium . . .	−0·76	+0·0039	−0·68	−0·56	+195°
Antimony commercial . .	—	—	+6·0	—	—
„ axial . . .	—	—	+22·6	—	—
„ equatorial . .	—	—	+26·4	—	—
„ ordinary . .	—	—	+17·0	—	—
Argentan	−11·94	−0·0506	−12·95	−14·47	−236
„	—	—	—	−12·7	—
Arsenic	—	—	−13·56	—	—
Bismuth, comm'l pressed wire	—	—	−97·0	—	—
„ pure . . .	—	—	−89·0	—	—
„ crystal, axial .	—	—	−65·0	—	—
„ „ equatorial .	—	—	−45·0	—	—
Cadmium	+2·63	+0·0424	+3·48	+4·75	−62
„ fused . . .	—	—	—	+2·45	—
Calcium	—	—	—	+8·9	—
Cobalt	—	—	−22	—	—
Constantin	—	—	—	−19·3	—
Copper	+1·34	+0·0094	+1·52	+1·81	−143
„ commercial . .	—	—	+0·10	—	—
„ galvanoplastic .	—	—	+3·8	—	—
Gallium	—	—	−0·2	—	—
Gold	+2·80	+0·0101	+3·0	+3·30	[−277]
Iron	+17·15	−0·0482	+16·2	+14·74	+356
„ pianoforte wire . .	—	—	+17·5	—	—
„ commercial . . .	—	—	—	+12·10	—
„ „ . .	—	—	—	+9·10	—
Lead	—	0·0000	−0·00	0·00	—
Magnesium . . .	+2·22	−0·0094	+2·03	+1·75	+236
Molybdenum . . .	—	—	+5·9	—	—
Mercury	—	—	−0·413	−3·30	—
Nickel	—	—	—	−15·50	—
„ (−18° to 175°) . .	−21·8	−0·0506	−22·8	−24·33	[−431]
„ (250° to 300°) . .	−83·57	+0·2384	—	—	—
„ (above 340°) . .	−3·04	−0·0506	—	—	—
Palladium . . .	−6·18	−0·0355	−6·9	−7·96	−174
Phosphorus (red). . .	—	—	+29·9	—	—
Platinum	—	—	+0·9	—	—
„ (hardened) . .	+2·57	−0·0074	+2·42	+2·20	347
„ (malleable) . .	−0·60	−0·0109	−0·818	−1·15	−55
„ wire . . .	—	—	—	+0·94	—
„ another specimen .	—	—	—	+2·14	—
Platinum-iridium alloys :					
85Pt+15Ir . . .	+7·90	+0·0062	+8·03	+8·21	[−1274]
90Pt+10Ir . . .	+5·90	−0·0133	+5·63	+5·23	444
95Pt+5Ir . . .	+6·15	+0·0055	+6·26	+6·42	[−1118]
Selenium	—	—	+807	—	—
Silver	+2·12	+0·0147	+2·41	+2·86	−144
„ (pure hard) . .	—	—	+3·00	—	—
„ wire . . .	—	—	—	+2·18	—
Steel	+11·27	−0·0325	+10·62	+9·65	347
Tantalum	—	—	−2·6	—	—
Tellurium β . . .	—	—	+500	—	—
„ a . . .	—	—	+160	—	—
Thallium	—	—	+0·8	—	—
Tin (commercial) . . .	—	—	—	+0·33	—
„	—	—	+0·1	—	—
„	+0·43	+0·0055	−0·33	−0·16	78
Tungsten	—	—	−2·0	—	—
Zinc	+2·32	+0·0238	+2·79	+3·51	−98
„ pure pressed . .	—	—	+3·7	—	—

stant, and θ, the mean temp. of the junctions. G. Borelius examined the effect of mechanical work on the thermoelectric power of lead ; and E. Wagner examined the effect of press. on the copper-lead couple. H. Pélabon measured the thermoelectric power of molten lead against solid metals. The **Peltier effect** was measured by E. Edlund, A. Battelli, H. Jahn, P. Cermak, and K. Bädeker. The effect of press. on a couple of compressed and uncompressed lead was measured by P. W. Bridgman, and the results are shown in Table IV. The **Thomson effect**

TABLE IV.—THE EFFECT OF PRESSURE ON THE SEEBECK, PELTIER, AND THOMSON EFFECTS.

Temp.	Seebeck effect. Volts $\times 10^6$			Peltier effect. Joules per coulomb $\times 10^6$			Thomson effect. Joules per coulomb $\times 10^6$		
	Press. kgrms. per sq. cm.			Press. kgrms. per sq. cm.			Press. kgrms. per sq. cm.		
	2000	6000	12000	2000	6000	12000	2000	6000	12000
10°	+0·08	+0·25	+0·52	+2·4	+6·6	+13·8	+1·4	+2·2	+6·0
40°	0·36	1·08	2·20	3·0	9·3	18·6	1·6	5·0	7·5
60°	0·57	1·71	3·44	3·6	11·0	21·6	1·7	6·7	9·3
100°	1·05	3·19	6·33	4·7	15·7	30·2	1·9	10·4	20·1

was examined by P. Cermak, O. Berg, and A. Battelli. G. Borelius and F. Gunneson found that at $-153°$ the Thomson effect is -0.19 ; at $-120°$, -0.30 ; at $-73°$, -0.45 ; at $27°$, -0.68 ; and at $127°$, 0.85. P. W. Bridgman's observations on the effect of press. with compressed and uncompressed lead are shown in Table IV. The **Corbino effect** was studied by O. M. Corbino, and E. P. Adams and A. K. Chapman. The **Hall effect** was studied by A. von Ettinghausen and W. Nernst, H. Zahn, and P. Drude. H. K. Onnes and co-workers examined the influence of a very low temp. on the Hall effect.

According to W. M Jones,[32] when lead is rubbed with silk it becomes positively electrified. H. F. Vieweg studied the frictional electricity of lead. S. Procopiu showed that if two lead wire electrodes be in circuit and in water, and one be stirred, it becomes positively electrified ; and R. D. Kleeman and W. Fredrickson, that lead acquires a positive charge when immersed in distilled water, and A. Coehn and A. Lötz said that when shaken in an evacuated glass tube, it acquires a positive charge. A. Coehn and A. Curs studied the contact electricity of lead for quartz, and glass. J. Erskine-Murray measured the contact potential of lead and gold alone or in the presence of water or alcohol. The **Volta difference of potential** of two metals in contact in air varies with the condition of the metal surface and the nature of the surrounding atm. W. E. Ayrton and J. Perry gave for ordinary commercial metals at 18° in volts,

	C	Pt	Cu	Brass	Fe	Sn	Zn	Zn–Hg
Pb .	−0·858	−0·771	−0·542	−0·472	−0·401	−0·099	0·210	0·357

Observations were also made by W. Hankel, H. Pellat, and F. Exner and J. Tuma, A. Volta, J. W. Ritter, T. Seebeck, J. C. E. Péclet, P. S. Munk af Rosenschöld, J. M. Gaugain, J. C. Poggendorff, and C. H. Pfaff placed lead near the middle of the **electrochemical series:**

K, Ba, Mg, Al, Mn, Zd, Cd, Fe, Co, Ni, Sn, **Pb**, H, Cu, Bi, Sb, Hg, Ag, Pd, Pt, Au.

A. Coehn and A. Lotz found lead to be electropositive towards glass. G. T. Fechner measured the series obtained, using water and a soln. of sodium chloride as electrolytes ; H. Davy, M. Faraday, and J. C. Poggendorff, dil. sulphuric acid ; A. de la Rive, M. Faraday, and A. Avogadro and V. Michelotti, dil. and conc. nitric acid ; M. Faraday, hydrochloric acid ; P. Marianini, sea-water ; J. C. Poggendorff, soln. of ammonium chloride, potassium cyanide, and potassium ferrocyanide ; and H. Davy, and M. Faraday, soln. of potassium hydroxide and sulphide.

F. W. Bergstrom found the electrochemical series in liquid ammonia : Pb, Bi, Sn, Sb, As, P, Te, Se, S, I. A. Naccari and M. Bellat found for carbon and lead in an aq. soln. of chromic acid, 83·7 when the e.m.f. of a normal Daniell's cell is taken as 100. C. Hocken and H. A. Taylor observed 0·559–0·627 volt with the zinc-lead couple in dil. sulphuric acid ; and 0·509–0·510 volt, with a conc. soln. of zinc sulphate. S. P. Thompson found respectively 0·64, 0·609, and 0·44 volt for the lead-carbon couple in aq. soln. containing 99·4, 19·4, and 1·18 grms. of potassium cyanide per litre. A. Overbeck and J. Edler observed the effect with the mercury-lead couple with soln. of the hydroxides, carbonates, nitrates, chlorides, bromides, iodides, and sulphates of potassium, sodium, zinc, and cadmium, and with sulphuric, nitric, and hydrochloric acids, and with aq. ammonia. R. H. Gerke studied the e.m.f. of cells with lead, lead acetate soln., and lead amalgam ; lead, lead chloride soln., and silver or mercury ; lead, lead iodide soln., and silver. W. E. Henderson and co-workers studied the possibility of making standard cells of the type PbHg | PbSO$_4$ | Na$_2$SO$_4$.10H$_2$O (sat. soln.) Hg$_2$SO$_4$ | Hg with soln. of the sulphates of potassium lithium, copper, magnesium, zinc, cadmium, manganese, nickel, or cobalt in place of the sodium salt. G. Tammann discussed the potential difference of lead and cadmium in their fused chlorides ; and C. Krahmer, of cells with lead and a lead halide in sat. soln. against another electrode. According to J. N. Frers, an examination of the system lead anode | lead chloride-silver chloride | lead chloride-platinum cathode at 210° shows that only the silver ion of silver chloride wanders. Similarly, in the system lead anode | lead chloride-platinum cathode, migration is confined to the chlorine ion of the lead chloride. This shows that certain ions are retained with extraordinary firmness in the lattice, whereas others are much more readily removed from the positions which they occupy in the lattice system. H. von Steinwehr gave 6·3×10^{-5} atm. for the **electrolytic solution pressure** : Pb→Pb″.

The **electrode potential** of lead can be obtained by using lead electrodes, or, according to P. Günther,[33] a film of lead deposited on platinum. G. N. Lewis and T. B. Brighton found the electrode did not alter with the ageing of the lead, cast lead six years old gave the same value as a freshly deposited lead-tree. J. Brown found the potential of lead in molten lead chloride, or potassium chloroplumbite is nearly the theoretical value. B. Neumann obtained −0·079 volt in soln. of lead acetate ; −0·095 volt in soln. of lead chloride ; and −0·115 volt in soln. of lead nitrate. G. Grube, in potassium plumbite ; A. von Oettingen, in lead acetate ; W. Ostwald found with soln. of lead sulphate in sulphuric acid, 0·001 volt with the eq. conc. of the acid 1·04, and 0·041 volt with the acid conc. 6·4. B. Neumann found 0·182 volt against a normal hydrogen electrode in soln. of the chloride ; and 0·162 volt in soln. of the nitrate. Measurements were also made by A. C. Cumming, S. Procopiu, W. K. Lewis, O. Sackur, and N. T. M. Wilsmore, with soln. of lead nitrate. O. P. Watts and N. D. Whipple used N-NaOH ; P. P. Lebedeff, and C. Immerwahr, N-NaHS ; S. B. Christy, soln. of potassium cyanide ; W. D. Bancroft, soln. of alkali halides, and of sodium sulphide ; and G. Trümpler, and L. Rolla, soln. of sodium sulphides ; C. Zenghelis, soln. of potassium chloride, bromide, hydrotartrate, iodide, ferrocyanide, cyanide, chromate, sulphide, and hydroxide ; sodium thiosulphate, phosphate, and carbonate ; ammonia ; and ammonium carbonate. S. Labendzinsky used mixed soln. of alkali nitrate, chloride, and acetate ; M. G. Mellon and W. E. Henderson, soln. of sodium sulphate and sulphates of nickel, cobalt, manganese, or zinc. F. H. Getman gave 0·1293 volt, and H. Gordon, 0·108 volt, for the potential of lead against a normal hydrogen electrode ; and 0·4121 volt against the normal calomel electrode ; G. N. Lewis and T. B. Brighton gave 0·4125 volt ; W. E. Henderson and G. Stegeman, 0·4696 at 25° ; and P. Günther 0·4916–0·000132θ in a sat. soln. of lead chloride. W. Ostwald measured the electrode potential of lead in hydrochloric, hydrobromic, hydriodic, nitric, sulphuric, orthophosphoric, formic, acetic, propionic, oxalic, and benzene-sulphonic acids. A. L. Clark examined the polarization capacity of the acid : lead surfaces. A. A. Noyes and K. Toabe found that dil. perchloric acid referred to the hydrogen electrode 0·132 volt at 25°. G. N. Lewis and T. B. Brighton measured the potential of the lead electrode in sat. soln. of lead chloride, bromide, and iodide. From the results obtained with the iodide soln., the normal potential is found to be 0·4125 against the normal calomel electrode and 0·1295 against the normal hydrogen electrode. H. Hock and F. Klawitter studied the behaviour of lead anodes in the electrolysis of zinc sulphate soln. S. Procopiu noted that agitation, and illumination raise the electrode potential; and W. Spring, that hard lead (rolled) is more negative than soft lead by 0·12 millivolt at 20°. G. Athanasiu ascribed the e.m.f. generated when lead plates are immersed in a soln. of a salt of the metal, and one plate is illuminated, to the heating effect of the radiation. W. Löb and R. W. Moore measured the electrode potential of lead in a soln. of sodium hydroxide and nitrobenzene; L. Kahlenberg, in a soln. of lithium chloride in pyridine; and F. M. G. Johnson and N. T. M. Wilsmore, in a soln. of lead nitrate in liquid ammonia. J. Neustadt and R. Abegg said that the position of lead in the electrochemical series is not materially affected in the presence of non-aqueous solvents. G. Tammann measured the potential of lead against fused silver and cuprous chlorides.

C. R. A. Wright and C. Thompson, and N. T. M. Wilsmore measured the potential difference between *zinc* and lead in a soln. of zinc sulphate; C. R. A. Wright and C. Thompson, N. T. M. Wilsmore, and J. B. Baille and C. Féry, in soln. of zinc chloride; C. R. A. Wright and C. Thompson, in soln. of zinc iodide; W. D. Bancroft, in soln. of potassium chloride, bromide, and iodide, and sodium chloride, bromide, and iodide; and C. R. A. Wright and C. Thompson, in soln. of zinc acetate.

G. Magnanini found for the potential difference in centivolts between zinc in N-H_2SO_4 and lead in different soln. : 0·5H_2SO_4, 51·3; N-NaOH, 31·8; N-KOH, 32·0; 0·5N-Na_2SO_4, 50·8; N-$Na_2S_2O_3$, 45·3; N-KNO_3, 42·6; N-$NaNO_3$, 51·0; 0·5N-K_2CrO_4, 41·2; 0·5N-$K_2Cr_2O_7$, 78·4; 0·5N-K_2SO_4, 51·0; 0·5N-$(NH_4)_2SO_4$, 53·2; 0·25N-K_4FeCy_6, 50·7; 0·167N-K_3FeCy_6, 81·2; N-KCyS, 52·8; 0·5N-$Sr(NO_3)_2$, 50·6; 0·125N-$Ba(NO_3)_2$, 51·7; 0·2N-$KClO_3$, 53·8; 0·167N-$KBrO_3$, 51·3; N-NH_4Cl, 51·3; N-KF, 41·1; N-NaCl, 51·2; N-KBr, 47·2; N-KCl, 51·6; 0·5N-Na_2SO_3, 41·0; NaOBr (using bromine eq. to NaOH unity), 73·1; N-tartaric acid, 61·3; 0·5N-tartaric acid, 61·6; and 0·5N-potassium tartrate, 51·5.

C. R. A. Wright and C. Thompson, N. T. M. Wilsmore, H. Jahn, and F. Braun measured the potential difference of lead against *cadmium* in soln. of the nitrate; C. R. A. Wright and C. Thompson, N. T. M. Wilsmore in soln. of the chloride, and bromide; and W. D. Bancroft, in soln. of potassium chloride, bromide, sulphate, and nitrate. F. M. G. Johnson and N. T. M. Wilsmore measured the e.m.f. of the cell Pb | 0·1N-$Pb(NO_3)_2$, sat. soln. $Cd(NO_3)_2$ | Cd, and found —0·515 volt, and with 0·01N-$Pb(NO_3)_2$, —0·495 volt. J Oblata measured the e.m.f. of cells with $Cd_{amalgam}$ | $CdCl_{2aq.}$ | $PbCl_{2aq.}$ | $Pb_{amalgam}$ = 0·14186 volt; and with soln. of the iodides in place of the chloride, 0·09825 volt. G. Tammann measured the e.m.f. of a kind of Daniell's cell with fused chlorides and lead in contact with cuprous or silver chloride. C. Christiansen measured the potential difference of lead against *mercury* in moist and dry oxygen; and C. R. A. Wright and C. Thompson, and N. T. M. Wilsmore in soln. of the nitrate. W. E. Henderson and G. Stegeman found the e.m.f. of the cell lead amalgam | $PbSO_4$,$NaSO_4$.$10H_2O$,Hg_2SO_4 | Hg to be 0·96343 volt at 18°; and at $\theta°$, $E = 0.96463 + 0.0_3174(\theta - 25) + 0.0_638(\theta - 25)^2$. C. R. A. Wright and C. Thompson, and N. T. M. Wilsmore measured the potential difference of lead against *copper* in soln. of the nitrate, and acetate. H. Jahn also worked with the acetate. C. R. A. Wright and C. Thompson, N. T. M. Wilsmore, J. N. Brönsted, and P. Günther measured the potential difference between lead and silver in soln. of the chloride. W. D. Bancroft measured the difference of potential between lead and *bismuth* in soln. of potassium or sodium chloride, bromide, or iodide. C. R. A. Wright and C. Thompson, and N. T. M. Wilsmore measured the difference of potential between lead and *iron* in soln. of the sulphate. H. Götz and A. Kurz gave 0·93 volt for the difference of potential of lead against *graphite* in water. O. Sackur's measurements of the e.m.f. of the cell Pb | Pb(NO₃)₂,Sn(NO₃)₂ | Sn show that the electrolytic **solution pressure** of lead is about 17·2 times that of tin.

According to C. M. van Deventer, if the lead in sulphuric acid becomes covered with a film of lead sulphate, it may appear to become more electronegative than hydrogen. J. Tafel showed that polished and prepared lead electrodes have nearly the same polarization values. The cathode process may produce mechanical and chemical changes at the surface of the cathode, and these changes influence the potential values, so that the latter are more or less dependent on the previous history of the cathode. Lead exhibits two distinct polarization states when the anode liquid has access to the cathode, a state of " elevation " and a state of " depression." The change from the one to the other takes place during electrolysis, and often occurs suddenly. Cathode process and anode process are opposed to each other, and what leads to the state of depression is some change in the cathode surface induced by an unknown product of the anode process. When the cathode is protected from the anode liquid, the maximum **polarization** value is attained in a short time—say half an hour. He does not consider that the varying polarization is due to varying thicknesses of the gaseous layer on the cathode, but rather to the cathode surfaces having different effects on the process of forming hydrogen gas. The polarization of lead electrodes in soln. of lead nitrate was studied by H. Jahn ; in soln. of lead iodide, or bromide, by A. Gockel, and V. Czepinsky. A. L. Clark, J. T. Burt-Gerrans and H. R. Hugill, H. D. Holler, and M. Dresbach and H. R. Hosmer also investigated the subject. A. Günther-Schulze [34] discussed the **electrolytic valve action** of lead in conc. sulphuric acid ; and W. Winter, the anodic valve action in potash-lye.

According to W. Hittorf,[35] lead does not assume a **passive state** in the same sense that iron becomes passive, but it behaves as if it were passive in soln. of some oxy-salts. For instance, the e.m.f. of the cell Pb | Na₂SO₄,H₂CrO₄ | Pt is at first 1·78 volts, but quickly falls below one volt. F. Förster, W. R. Dunstan and J. R. Hill, W. J. Müller, O. Sackur, G. C. Schmidt, G. Grube, P. P. Lebedeff, and M. le Blanc agree that the passivity of lead is produced by a film on the surface of the metal. C. W. Bennett and W. S. Burnham showed that a lead anode in dil. sulphuric acid becomes covered with lead dioxide, in quantities such that there is no question about the film. The combination is noble, but the film is destroyed by hydrochloric acid. When thus protected by oxide, the lead dissolves only slowly in sulphuric or nitric acid. They were unable to induce the passivity of lead without a visible film. K. Elbs and F. Fischer showed that with conc. sulphuric acid, at a high current density, and low temp., lead as anode dissolves as quadrivalent lead, and thus is regarded as a case of retarded dissolution analogous to the case of chromium. According to E. Newbery, both in acid and in alkali, a lead anode rapidly becomes coated with dioxide at moderate current densities, but at all current densities it shows a strong positive potential to an oxygen electrode after the dioxide coating has formed. While the coating is forming, the overvoltage rises steadily and remains very constant at a high value when the coating attains a thickness approaching 0·1 mm. Lead is therefore a very suitable electrode for very powerful oxidation in dil. sulphuric acid electrolytes. In alkali its use is attended with certain disadvantages owing to the formation of plumbates which may inter- fere with the course of a reaction. The solubility of the dioxide in alkali prevents the formation of the protective coating at low current densities, and hence under these conditions lead behaves as an active metal. With a current density of 100 milliampères per sq. cm. the metal becomes passive in about forty seconds, whilst it requires about fifteen minutes with a current density of 10 milli- ampères per sq. cm. Lead is the only electrode so far examined which is passivated more easily in acid than in alkali. U. Sborgi and P. Marchetti found that anodes of lead show a partial mechanical passivity in acetone soln. of silver nitrate.

The **overvoltage** of hydrogen on polished lead electrodes was found by W. A. Caspari to be 0·631 volt ; on etched electrodes, 0·631 volt ; on electrolytic spongy lead, 0·628 volt ; and on amalgamated lead, 0·540 volt. C. Hambuechen gave 0·50 volt for the overvoltage of hydrogen on lead. The subject was investigated by E. Newbery, W. Löb and R. W. Moore, T. Ericson-Aurén and W. Palmaer, P. Fischer, J. Tafel and co-workers, A. Coehn and K. Dannenberg, S. Dunnill, F. Meunier, A. Sieverts and P. Lueg, M. Knobel, A. Thiel and W. Hammerschmidt, S. Glasstone, etc.

W. Ostwald [36] gave −10 Cals. for the **heat of ionization** of lead, Pb··, from metallic lead. L. Boltzmann measured the thermal value of the electrolysis of soln. of lead salts when gas is developed. A. A. Noyes, and K. G. Falk gave 0·487 for the **transport number** at 25° ; while A. A. Noyes and E. H. Woodworth gave 68·3 for the **speed of migration** ; H. F. Fernau, 66·1 ; and F. Kohlrausch, 61·10– 61·15 at 18°. He also gave 0·0244 for the temp. coeff. C. L. von Ende found that disturbances were produced when mercury amalgam is used as an electrode owing to the formation of lead dioxide. M. le Blanc [37] found the **decomposition voltage** of N-Pb(NO$_3$)$_2$ to be 1·52 ; H. Jahn gave 1·96. Observations were also made by K. Elbs and J. Forssell, J. E. Root, H. W. Gillett, and W. D. Bancroft. G. Bödländer found for

PbSO$_4$	Pb(OH)$_2$	PbS	PbF$_2$	PbCl$_2$	PbBr$_2$	PbI$_2$
4·70	1·10	0·40	2·27	1·80	1·40	0·86

The electrodeposition of lead.—Metallic lead can be readily and quantitatively obtained by cathodic deposition from alkaline electrolytes containing phosphates, oxalates, cyanides, plumbates, etc., and this process is used in electro-analysis [38] ; but the drying of the lead without oxidation is considered so difficult that it is usual to take advantage of the fact that lead is deposited as lead dioxide on the anode during the electrolysis of acidulated soln. V. Kohlschütter and F. Ubersax studied the electrodeposition of lead crystals from soln. of lead nitrate. H. Freundlich and J. Fischer examined the influence of a number of colloids on the quality of the lead deposited from soln. by electrolysis, as well as when precipitated by zinc. C. Marie and G. Lejeune found the energy required to liberate lead is increased when a colloid, like gelatin, is added to the soln. The colloid reduces the amount of metal deposited by a given current. The **electrolysis** of neutral soln. of *lead nitrate* was investigated by E. Becquerel [39] ; soln. of *lead nitrate* in acid or neutral soln., by F. Wöhler,[40] C. Luckow, etc. ; *lead chloride*, by L. Glaser ; *lead cyanide*, by J. Haas,[41] *lead acetate*, by F. C. Mathers,[42] E. P. Clark, etc. ; by A. G. Betts [43] ; in *sulphuric acid* soln., by F. Haber,[44] L. Glaser, etc. ; in *hydrochloric acid* soln. by K. Elbs,[45] E. P. Schoch and D. J. Brown, etc. ; in *hydrobromic acid* and *hydriodic acid* soln., by K. Elbs and R. Nübling ; in *fluorides*, by F. Fischer and K. Thiele [46] ; in *perchloric acid* soln., by F. C. Mathers,[47] H. Freundlich and J. Fischer, etc. ; in *hypophosphorous acid*, and *phosphorous acid* soln., by K. Elbs and F. W. Rixon [48] ; in *phosphoric acid* soln., by A. F. Linn,[49] F. Fischer, etc. ; in *pyrophosphoric acid*, by A. Brand [50] ; in *fluoborates*, by G. Mardus,[51] W. Blum and co-workers, etc. ; in *fluosilicates*, by A. G. Betts,[52] H. Senn, etc. ; in *fluotitanates*, by G. Titschack ; in *chromic acid* soln., by C. Luckow,[53] and M. le Blanc and E. Bindschedler ; in *formic acid* soln., by R. Marc,[54] H. S. Warwick, etc. ; in *acetic acid* soln., by W. Hartmann,[55] R. C. Snowdon, etc. ; in *lactic acid* soln., by F. C. Mathers and B. W. Cockrum,[56] and E. Jordis ; in *benzoic acid* soln., and *salicylic acid* soln., by R. Marc [57] ; in soln. of organic *sulphonates*, by A. G. Betts,[58] G. Titschack, and F. Fischer and co-workers ; in *oxalic acid* soln., by A. Riche,[59] A. Classen, etc. ; and in soln. of *sodium hydroxide*, by P. Schützenberger,[60] A. G. Betts, etc.

The electrolysis of the *fused lead halides* furnishes a conductivity curve with two breaks which, on the ionic theory, are interpreted to mean that the dissociation occurs in two stages, $PbX_2 \rightleftharpoons PbX^\cdot + X'$, and $PbX^\cdot \rightleftharpoons Pb'' + X'$. The subject has been investigated by R. Lorenz,[61] C. C. Garrard, etc. The electrolysis of *non-aqueous soln.* has not been extensively studied; L. Kahlenberg,[62] and A. W. Speransky and E. G. Goldberg worked with soln. of lead nitrate in *pyridine;* and H. Röhler, with soln. of lead chloride, or nitrate in *formamide.* Electrolysis using a *rotating anode* was examined by A. Fischer and R. J. Boddaert,[63] F. M. Perkin, etc.; and using an *alternating current,* by P. Vaillant,[64] E. Wilson, etc. The *anodic behaviour of lead* has been investigated by W. Lust,[65] E. Newbery, etc.; the *cathodic behaviour of lead,* by J. Tafel and co-workers,[66] etc.; the *anodic behaviour of lead sulphide,* by I. Bernfeld,[67] and P. P. Lebedeff; the *cathodic behaviour of lead sulphide,* by I. Bernfeld,[68] H. Danneel, etc.; and the *anodic behaviour of lead dioxide,* by A. Hollard,[69] H. J. S. Sand, S. Glasstone, etc.

Accumulators.—In 1801, N. Gautherot [70] showed that the recently invented voltaic pile when at work seemed to develop a resisting or opposing force which tended to choke the flow of the electric current; and that if the current be sent through a pair of plates dipping in a saline liquid, the latter give a transient current immediately after disconnection with the pile. J. W. Ritter also used this result to make what he called a *secondary pile* which when charged by a primary battery could give transitory currents of considerable intensity. In 1842, W. R. Grove made his gas cell (**1.** 16, 7) in which the hydrogen and oxygen liberated in separate tubes fitted with platinized electrodes by the action of the primary current can on a closed circuit re-form water and generate a small current reproducing the original conditions. The reactions in this cell have been closely investigated by K. Siegl. E. J. Wade said: " No storage cell presents the principle of reversibility in a more simple or striking form than does the gas-cell of W. R. Grove." W. J. Sinsteden investigated the subject in 1854. G. Planté placed rods of various metals in an acid and passed a current through the soln.; on cutting the battery out of the circuit, he found momentary secondary currents were given by all the metals he tried, but that obtained with lead electrodes in dil. sulphuric acid, exceeded all others in duration and intensity. G. Planté developed this observation and showed how cells could be constructed for " storing electricity." Two coils of lead wire were dipped in dil. sulphuric acid; and a current was sent through the liquid from one plate to the other. The metal at one pole became covered with lead dioxide, and hydrogen was given off at the other pole. The lead cell came to be variously called an accumulator, secondary cell, or storage cell. G. Planté's cell was a little in advance of its time, but as soon as the evolution of the dynamo had advanced far enough to enable currents of high potential to be produced cheaply, the possibilities of the mysterious storage cells began to be recognized. The peroxide of G. Planté's cell was prepared from the electrode itself. C. A. Faure patented a method of preparing the peroxide from lead oxides as salts mechanically applied at the surface of the electrode. The results were so good that numerous inventors were attracted, and many modifications of G. Planté's and C. A. Faure's cells were worked out and patented. Cells based on that of G. Planté are called *formed cells;* those on that of C. A. Faure, *pasted cells.* Various forms of " paste " were described, and numerous forms of grids, lattices, etc., were devised for supporting the active material. Descriptions of the different types of cell, the design of cells, and working details will be found in books specially devoted to this subject.

P. Schoop, *Die Sekundärelemente,* Halle a. S., 1895; H. W. Morse, *Storage Batteries,* New York, 1912; E. J. Wade, *Secondary Batteries , their Theory, Construction, and Use,* London, 1902; H. G. Brown, *The Lead Storage Battery,* London, 1922; D. Salomons, *Complete Handbook on the Management of Accumulators,* London, 1887; H. H. U. Cross, *The Care and Management of Ignition Accumulators,* London, 1910; W. Bermbach, *Die Akkumulatoren, ihre Theorie, Herstellung, Behandlung, Verwendung mit Berückdichtigung der neuerer Sammler,* Leipzig, 1905; B. E. Jones, *Electric Accumulators,* London, 1911; L. Lyndon, *Storage Battery Engineering,* New York, 1903; F. Dolezalek, *Die Theorie des Bleiaccumulators,* Halle, 1901; L. Jumau, *Accumulateurs électriques,* Paris, 1907.

G. Planté recognized that the high e.m.f. of the cell is a result of the deoxidation of the lead dioxide at the anode, and the oxidation of lead at the cathode, but he wrongly assumed that the dioxide was reduced to metallic lead, and that the lead at the other electrode was oxidized nearly up to the dioxide state. He did not consider the chemical function of the sulphuric acid, although he knew that lead sulphate could be produced during the working of the cell. Later, it was assumed that the function of the acid was merely to make the electrolyte conducting, and that in charging the cell the hydrogen and oxygen were occluded at the respective electrodes, part of the oxygen forming lead dioxide. The working of the cell was considered to be analogous to the working of the ordinary gas-cell; and the large capacity of the accumulator was attributed to the enormous surface of the absorption of gases produced by the porous mass of reduced oxides. O. J. Lodge ascribed the activity of the negative electrode to occluded hydrogen, but at the positive pole the reduction of the dioxide to monoxide was noted. The union of the monoxide with the acid to form lead sulphate was considered as a secondary reaction which was considered to be an unmitigated evil. J. H. Gladstone and A. Tribe showed that at the negative electrode only a mere trace of hydrogen is absorbed. This was confirmed by J. Shields. J. H. Gladstone and A. Tribe showed that in the regular discharge of the cell lead sulphate is the normal product; similarly at the peroxide plate, lead sulphate is normally formed at the expense of the sulphuric acid electrolyte. As a result lead sulphate is formed on both electrodes during the discharge. This, the so-called *double sulphate theory*, gave rise to some controversy since it seemed highly improbable that large quantities of non-conducting insoluble lead sulphate could be produced under normal conditions, especially when it is remembered that attempts to reduce lead sulphate by electrolysis in dil. sulphuric acid failed, and that it could be peroxidized only with some difficulty. E. Frankland obtained a number of basic sulphates, $3PbSO_4.2PbO$, and $PbSO_4.PbO_2$, by the action of dil. sulphuric acid on litharge and red-lead respectively, and suggested that these may be formed during the discharge of the cell; but G. H. Robertson, and J. H. Gladstone and W. Hibbert showed that these sulphates are probably only mixtures. Hence, E. Frankland's results mean that lead sulphate is truly produced at both electrodes during the discharge of the cell, and that appreciable quantities neither of oxygen nor hydrogen are occluded by the electrodes during the charging of the cell. S. Schenck and S. Farbaky found that the change in the conc. of the sulphuric acid in a cell during the discharge was 3·6 grms. when the double sulphate theory required 2·24 grms. A. Pfaff also discussed the changes in the conc. of the acid during the discharge of the cell.

G. Planté noted that an unstable oxygenated compound—possibly hydrogen dioxide—is formed during the charging of the cell, and he knew that persulphuric acid is a direct product of the electrolysis of dil. sulphuric acid. J. H. Gladstone and A. Tribe detected persulphuric acid in the charged cell, and H. E. Armstrong and G. H. Robertson said that this acid probably plays an important rôle in the cell. The presence of persulphuric acid was also discussed by G. Darrieus, and P. Schoop. M. Mugdan showed that the addition of persulphuric acid to the cell reduces its e.m.f. K. Elbs and co-workers suggested that during the charging, lead persulphate is first formed, and that this breaks down into lead dioxide and sulphuric acid. W. Nernst showed that the decomposition of lead persulphate is an irreversible process, and since the reactions in the accumulator are reversible, F. Dolezalek maintained that this interpretation of the function of the persulphate cannot be correct. W. Esch regarded the hydrotrisulphatometaplumbic acid, $H_2Pb(SO_4)_3$, as the intermediate compound. The double sulphate theory was accepted by E. N. Reynier, A. Crova and P. Garbe, H. Aron, A. Gérard, W. Kohlrausch and C. Heim, F. Streintz, M. Mugdan, A. Jouve, etc. The double sulphate hypothesis thus takes on the following form:

If two corrugated lead plates be covered with a paste of litharge, PbO, and dipped in a 20 per cent. soln. of sulphuric acid, the litharge on the plates is converted into lead sulphate, $PbSO_4$. If an electric current be passed through the cell, hydrogen is evolved at the cathode, and oxygen at the anode during the electrolysis of the sulphuric acid. The hydrogen at the cathode reduces the lead sulphate producing a grey film of "spongy" metallic lead: $PbSO_4+H_2=H_2SO_4+Pb$; and at the anode, the oxygen transforms the lead sulphate directly into lead dioxide or maybe into lead persulphate: $2PbSO_4+2H_2SO_4+O_2=2Pb(SO_4)_2 +2H_2O$; the persulphate is at once hydrolyzed into lead peroxide and sulphuric acid: $Pb(SO_4)_2+2H_2O=PbO_2+2H_2SO_4$. In either case, a dark brown film of lead peroxide is formed on the lead plate. The current may then be stopped. If the terminals of the cell be then connected with a suitable resistance, a current at nearly two volts press. can be obtained, and this continues for about twelve hours. The cell is then said to be "discharged." The brown film of lead dioxide on the anode gradually disappears during the discharge of the cell, and a white film of lead sulphate takes its place. The reaction on the anode during the discharge of the cell is $PbO_2+Pb+2H_2SO_4=2PbSO_4+2H_2O$. When the cell is being charged, the reaction can be represented by the same equation taken from right to left:

$$2PbSO_4+2H_2O \rightleftharpoons Pb+PbO_2+2H_2SO_4$$

Charge→ ←Discharge.

As soon as the dioxide has disappeared, the electromotive force of the cell drops rapidly, although the voltage keeps remarkably constant as long as any dioxide remains on the plate. This is illustrated by the curve, Fig. 14. The curve from B to C shows that the voltage remains nearly constant for ten to twelve hours while the cell is discharging; the curve from C to D represents the drop in voltage when the dioxide is almost all gone. The cell should be recharged before it has reached this condition, otherwise the efficiency of the plates may be reduced. An accumulator may thus be regarded as a cell with metallic lead plates, or with lead plates specially designed to hold as large an amount of litharge or lead oxide as possible. The plates dip in dil. sulphuric acid. When charged, the accumulator acts as if it were a primary cell $PbO_2 \mid H_2SO_4aq. \mid Pb$. To summarize, the changes at the electrodes during charge and discharge are:

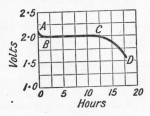

Fig. 14.—Voltage Drop of Accumulator.

	CHARGING.	DISCHARGING.
Cathode	$PbSO_4 \rightarrow Pb$	$Pb \rightarrow PbSO_4$
Anode	$PbSO_4 \rightarrow PbO_2$	$PbO_2 \rightarrow PbO \rightarrow PbSO_4$

During the discharge, the surface of both plates becomes covered with a film of white lead sulphate, and hydrogen is evolved at the cathode: $Pb+H_2SO_4 =PbSO_4+H_2$. The hydrogen is partly absorbed by the lead which has not been converted into sulphate. The presence of the absorbed gas raises the electromotive force of the cell during discharge until it is all consumed. This occupies but a few minutes; during this time, the voltage is represented by the curve AB.

The hypothesis just indicated can be translated into the language of the ionic hypothesis. In the charged cell, we have a liquid containing $H^·$ and SO''_4 ions, with lead and lead dioxide electrodes. When the cell is discharging, the $H^·$ ions travel towards the PbO_2 plate and reduce the lead dioxide to lead monoxide: $2H^·+PbO_2=H_2O+PbO$; and this plate accordingly receives a positive charge, owing to the de-electrification of the $H^·$ ions. The SO''_4 ions simultaneously travel to the lead plates converting the lead at the surface of the plate into lead sulphate: $SO''_4+Pb \rightarrow PbSO_4$, and the plates are at the same time charged negatively. In consequence, a positive current of electricity travels from the "peroxide" plate to the "lead" plate outside the cell, and from the "lead" to the "peroxide" plate in the liquid. A secondary reaction between the sulphuric acid and the lead monoxide of the "peroxide" plate leads to the formation of lead sulphate, and consequently the consumption of the sulphuric acid in the liquid in the cell is relatively large during discharge. When the cell is to be re-charged, the "peroxide" plate is connected with the positive pole of the dynamo, and the "lead" plate with the negative pole of the dynamo. The H· ions of the cell travel to the negatively charged plate, an *equivalent* number of SO''_4 ions pass into the soln. and metallic lead remains on the plate. The effect is to reduce the lead sulphate back to metallic lead. The SO''_4 ions travel to the positively charged "peroxide" plate and form lead persulphate : $2SO''_4 + 2PbSO_4 = 2Pb(SO_4)_2$. The lead persulphate is immediately hydrolyzed to lead peroxide as indicated above. Sulphuric acid is thus regenerated, and the cell is brought back to its original condition. According to M. le Blanc, the active ion in the charged cell is quadrivalent Pb····, which during discharge changes to Pb·· ; C. Liebenoff's theory assumes that the active ion in the charged cell is PbO''_2. These two modifications of the ion theory have been discussed by E. Abel, F. Förster, W. Löb, etc.

There is no fundamental difference in the principles of action between the lead accumulator and other combinations, only the chemical characters of lead and its compounds are peculiarly suited for the purpose to be achieved. Primary and secondary cells can both be regarded as machines for converting chemical into electrical energy. It will be observed that if electrolytically prepared lead dioxide be packed about a core of lead, and put in dil. sulphuric acid along with a similar electrode about which is packed electrolytic spongy lead, the cell would be called a primary one although it possesses all the chief characteristics of a lead accumulator. Every secondary cell can thus be regarded as a primary cell, and every primary cell a potential secondary cell. In charging the lead accumulator, electrical energy is converted into chemical energy, and in discharging, as with primary cells generally, chemical energy is converted into electrical energy. The energy changes in the cell have been discussed by A. Lottermoser and M. Grützner, and I. M. Tscheltzoff, and F. Dolezalek. The result of the calculation has been cited in support of the assumed theory of the reactions in the lead accumulator.

The thermal values of the reactions, so far as are known, are $2(Pb,SO_4) = 225,940$ cals. ; $2(H_2,O) = 136,720$ cals. ; $2(H_2,SO_4) = 179,360$ cals. ; $2(H_2,SO_4,Aq.) = 215,060$ cals. ; and $(Pb,O_2) = 62,300$ cals. This gives 121,000 cals. for the thermal value of the reaction with undiluted sulphuric acid ; and 85,300 cals. with very dil. acid. If the acid has a sp. gr. 1·160, corresponding with $2(H_2,SO_4,19H_2O) = 211,870$ cals., the heat of the reaction is 88,490 cals. From Gibbs-Helmholtz's equation (**1**. 16, 8), the o.m.f., E, is given by $E = Q/C + T(dE/dT)$, where dE/dT represents the observed temp. coeff. of the reaction, namely $0·4 \times 10^{-3}$; at 17°, $T = 290°$ K. The heat of the reaction $Q = 88,490$ cals. $= 88,490 \div 0·24$ joules ; and $C = 2 \times 96,540$; hence $E = 2·03$ volts. This agrees closely with the observed values 1·99–2·01 volts.

While J. H. Gladstone and A. Tribe's double sulphate theory assumes that the positive active material combines with as much sulphuric acid as the negative material : $PbO_2 + H_2 + H_2SO_4 = PbSO_4 + 2H_2O$, G. Darrieus maintained that it is merely reduced to the monoxide : $PbO_2 + H_2 = PbO + H_2O$; D. G. Fitzgerald, that it is reduced to the sesquioxide : $2PbO_2 + H_2 = Pb_2O_3 + H_2O$; and S. Drzewiecky, and C. Féry assumed Pb_2O_5 was formed :

$$2PbO_2 + Pb_2SO_4 + H_2O \rightleftharpoons Pb_2O_5 + H_2SO_4 + 2Pb$$
$$\text{Charge} \longrightarrow \qquad \longleftarrow \text{Discharge.}$$

C. Féry's argument that the oxide on the plate is Pb_2O_5 and that during the discharge this changes to PbO_2, and on the negative plate the active lead becomes Pb_2SO_4 not $PbSO_4$, is based on (i) the colour of the oxide on the one plate is darker than PbO_2, and on the other plate is darker than $PbSO_4$; (ii) the active oxide in a stream of hydrogen becomes warm, gives off water, and forms ordinary lead dioxide ; (iii) if the active polyoxide is used as one plate in all with dil. sulphuric acid and zinc, the e.m.f. is 2·4 volts, whereas with ordinary lead dioxide

0·7 volt is obtained—this statement does not agree with the observations of F. Streintz—and (iv) the analyses correspond with Pb_2O_5 rather than with PbO_2. The analyses of the active materials are open to many sources of error, and are not conclusive. G. Crut supported C. Féry's hypothesis. The work of D. A. MacInnes and co-workers, A. Pfaff, H. Cassel and F. Todt, W. Kohlrausch and C. Heim, shows that C. Féry's claims are not well-founded ; and M. Knobel found that the acid consumption in the cell is in harmony with the double sulphate theory of J. H. Gladstone and A. Tribe. The bulk of the evidence from the chemical characteristics of the compounds involved, and the electrical properties of the cell also favours the double sulphate theory. M. Hartenheim found that the effect of radium is to decrease the internal resistance of the cell.

A number of combinations other than the Pb–PbO_2 cell have been proposed—e.g. E. Thomson and E. J. Houston [71] (1879) proposed a reversible Daniell's cell ; H. Sutton (1881) proposed a Cu–H_2SO_4–PbO_2 cell ; E. Reynier (1883) proposed a somewhat similar arrangement ; A. d'Arsonval (1879), J. Carpentier (1879), K. E. Böttcher (1882), and C. H. Cathcart (1882), Zn–H_2SO_4–PbO_2 ; W. Main (1887–92), A. V. Meserole (1887), L. Epstein (1894), H. Leitner (1895), and E. Julien (1885) proposed forms of the Zn–PbO_2 cells; A. E. Peyrusson (1887), C. E. Lee (1897), and E. Commetin and R. Viau (1904), Cd–PbO_2 cells ; F. de Lalande and G. Chaperon (1881–4) used the Zn–KOH–CuO cell reversibly as an accumulator; E. Commetin, G. Bailhache, A. de Virloy and L. de Bousignac (1884), J. B. Entz and W. A. Phillips (1889–91), and C. Desmazures (1886–7) proposed modifications of this cell ; A. Dun and F. Hasslacher, and T. de Michalowsky (1899), Zn–NiO cell ; H. Aron (1886), the Zn–KOH–HgO cell ; T. A. Edison (1900), Cd–CuO cell with an alkaline electrolyte ; and a Fe–NiO cell with an alkaline liquid.

G. von Hevesy and R. Lorenz [72] found the **electrocapillary phenomenon** with fused salts in the systems $Pb : KCl$; $Pb : KI,KCl$; and $Pb : NaI,NaCl$ closely resembled that with mercury-sulphuric acid electrometer. W. Crookes noted the spluttering of lead cathodes in the **discharge tube** in attenuated air. W. B. Nottingham studied the characteristic curves of the normal lead arc. F. Fischer and co-workers noted the disintegration of lead in liquid argon ; and studied the volatilization of lead from cathodes in various attenuated gases ; V. Kohlschütter and co-workers also made observations on this subject. For the spluttering of lead in the arc discharge under liquids, vide colloidal metals. G. A. Helmsalech investigated the electric discharge from lead electrodes ; F. W. Aston, the effect of the lead cathode on the width of Crookes' dark space (**4. 25, 4**) ; and E. Rumpf, the polarization which occurs with lead cathodes in vacuum tubes with air and hydrogen. J. Lavaux, and J. Lifschitz observed no luminous phenomena— **volta-luminescence**—with lead anodes such as are shown by bismuth, and some other metals. G. Hoffmann found that two lead plates separated a distance of the order $400\mu\mu$ produce a current with a critical field strength of $2·2 \times 10^6$ volts per cm.

According to M. Faraday,[73] lead is diamagnetic. K. Honda found that lead which has crystallized from the metallic state has a **magnetic susceptibility** ten times greater than hammered or drawn lead. M. Loutschinsky gave for the magnetic susceptibility of crystalline lead $-2·4 \times 10^{-6}$ mass units, and of hammered lead, $-0·2 \times 10^{-6}$ mass units. Hence, the magnetic susceptibility of the normal crystalline metal is ten times higher than when it has been hammered, rolled, or drawn. K. Honda gave $-0·12 \times 10^{-6}$ mass units between 18° and 330°, and $-0·08 \times 10^{-6}$ mass units between 330° and 600°. There is therefore not much change, and M. Owen observed very little change between $-170°$ and 327°. J. Königsberger found $-1·4 \times 10^{-6}$ vol. units for the magnetic susceptibility ; and L. Lombardi, $-0·84 \times 10^{-6}$. G. Borelius applied the electron theory to explain the magnetic properties of lead. W. Voigt and S. Kinoshita, and S. Meyer examined the magnetic properties of a number of lead compounds ; and S. Meyer gave $-0·025 \times 10^{-6}$ for the **atomic magnetism ;** and P. Pascal gave $-295·0 \times 10^{-7}$ for lead in aliphatic organometallic compounds, and $+66·0 \times 10^{-7}$ in aromatic organometallic compounds ; and $-45·8 \times 10^{-6}$ for ordinary lead. The **magnetic moment** of lead was studied by W. Gerlach and A. C. Cilliers. E. H. Williams observed that compounds with an odd mol. number are paramagnetic, and those with an even mol. number, diamagnetic.

REFERENCES.

¹ W. Spring and C. van Aubel, *Zeit. phys. Chem.*, **1.** 479, 1887; F. Stolba, *Journ. prakt. Chem.*, (1), **94.** 113, 1865; (1), **96.** 178, 1865; B. Lambert and H. E. Cullis, *Journ. Chem. Soc.*, **107.** 210, 1915; F. Mylius and O. Fromm, *Ber.*, **27.** 647, 1894; F. Wöhler, *Pogg. Ann. Ergbd.*, **135**, 1862; M. Faraday, *Phil. Trans.*, **147.** 145, 1857; *Phil. Mag.*, (4), **14.** 512, 1857; A. W. Wright, *Amer. Journ. Science*, (3), **13.** 49, 1877; (3), **14.** 169, 1877; W. L. Dudley, *Amer. Chem. Journ.*, **14.** 185, 1892; *Chem. News*, **66.** 163, 1892.

² J. B. L. Romé de l'Isle, *Cristallographie*, Paris, **3.** 363, 1783; R. J. Haüy, *Traité de minéralogie*, Paris, **3.** 453, 1801; J. Czochralsky, *Zeit. phys. Chem.*, **92.** 219, 1918; C. M. Marx, *Schweigger's Journ.*, **57.** 193, 1829; J. J. Nöggerath, *ib.*, **44.** 252, 1875; J. B. Senderens, *Bull. Soc. Chim.*, (3), **11.** 424, 1894; J. Braunsdorf, *Journ. prakt. Chem.*, (1), **1.** 120, 1834; F. Stolba, *ib.*, (1), **96.** 180, 1865; *Dingler's Journ.*, **164.** 371, 1862; J. Durocher, *Compt. Rend.*, **32.** 823, 1851; P. Berthier, *Ann. Chim. Phys.*, (2), **43.** 285, 1830; F. Wöhler, *Liebig's Ann.*, **85.** 253, 1853; G. von Hevesy, *Phys. Zeit.*, **16.** 52, 1915; O. Lehmann, *Zeit. Kryst.*, **17.** 277, 1890; A. Hamberg, *ib.*, **17.** 253, 1890; C. Elbs and F. W. Rixon, *Zeit. Elektrochem.*, **9.** 267, 1903; J. A. Mongez, *Journ. Phys.*, **18.** 74, 1781; L. L. Pajot, *ib.*, **38.** 52, 1791; H. A. Miers, *Min. Mag.*, **12.** 111, 1899; F. M. Ihle, *Berg. Hütt. Ztg.*, **17.** 123, 1858; R. Lüpke, *Grundzüge der Elektrochemie auf experimenteller Basis*, Berlin, 1907; London, 12, 1903; E. Cohen and K. Inouye, *Chem. Weekbl.*, **7.** 454, 1910; *Zeit. phys. Chem.*, **71.** 301, 1910; **74.** 202, 1910; J. F. L. Hausmann, *Beiträge zur metallurgischen Krystallkunde*, Göttingen, 9, 1850; *Ges. Wiss. Göttingen*, 217, 1851; F. Sandberger, *Jahrb. Ver. Nat. Nassau*, **9.** 40, 1854; C. C. von Leonhard, *Hüttenerzeugnisse und andere Künstliche Minerale, als Stützpunkte geologischer Hypothesen*, Stuttgart, 343, 1858; *Studien Gött. Ver. Berg. Freunde*, **7.** 65, 1856; G. W. A. Kahlbaum, K. Roth, and P. Siedler, *Zeit. anorg. Chem.*, **29.** 177, 278, 1902; F. Haber, *ib.*, **16.** 438, 1889; H. N. Warren, *Chem. News*, **74.** 144, 1897; J. Percy, *The Metallurgy of Lead*, London, 1, 1870; A. Thiel, *Ber.*, **53.** B, 1066, 1920; B. Wäser and R. Kühnel, *Elektrochem. Zeit.*, **18.** 151, 211, 1912; **19.** 36, 63, 1912; W. Campbell, *Met.*, **4.** 329, 1907 (I am greatly indebted to Prof. W. Campbell for permission to publish Figs. 7–10); *Journ. Franklin Inst.*, **154.** 1, 131, 201, 1902; J. A. Mathews, *ib.*, **153.** 1, 119, 221, 1902; H. Behrens, *Das mikroskopische Gefüge der Metalle und Legierungen*, Hamburg, 58, 1894; G. Flink, *Ark. Kemi Min.*, **3.** 11, 1908; H. Baucke, *Zeit. Internat. Metallog.*, **2.** 243, 1912; C. Brigel, *Ber.*, **6.** 192, 1873; J. A. Ewing, *Journ. Inst. Metals*, **8.** 4, 1912; W. Rosenhain, *ib.*, **20.** 151, 1918; W. Rosenhain and S. L. Archbutt, *Proc. Roy. Soc.*, **96.** A, 55, 1919; J. A. Ewing and W. Rosenhain, *ib.*, **67.** 112, 1901; *Phil. Trans.*, **193.** A, 353, 1899; **195.** A, 279, 1900; J. C. W. Humfrey, *ib.*, **200.** A, 225, 1902; J. A. Ewing and J. C. W. Humfrey, *ib.*, **200.** A, 241, 1902; N. A. Puschin, *Zeit. anorg. Chem.*, **36.** 244, 1903; N. S. Kurnakoff and N. A. Puschin, *ib.*, **92.** 440, 1907; W. Baker, *Pract. Mech. Journ.*, (2), **9.** 7, 1864; G. T. Beilby, *Phil. Mag.*, (6), **8.** 258, 1904; J. Schildowsky, *Journ. Russ. Phys. Chem. Soc.*, **9.** 50, 1877; L. Vegard, *Phil. Mag.*, (6), **32.** 65, 1916; W. P. Davey, *Phys. Rev.*, (2), **23.** 292, 1924; (2), **25.** 753, 1925; *Zeit. Kryst.*, **63.** 316, 1926; E. C. Bain, *Trans. Amer. Inst. Min. Met.*, **68.** 625–639, 1922; *Chem. Met. Engg.*, **25.** 657, 1921; E. Cohen and W. D. Heldermann, *Zeit. phys. Chem.*, **89.** 737, 1915; R. Gross, *Jahrb. Rad. Elektron.*, **15.** 270, 1918; J. H. Bowman, *Journ. Amer. Chem. Soc.*, **38.** 1469, 1915; A. Stock and F. Gomolka, *Ber.*, **42.** 4516, 1909; P. Schützenberger, *Compt. Rend.*, **86.** 1398, 1878; O. Rothe, *Apot. Ztg.*, **34.** 437, 1919; E. Giurgea, *Bull. Soc. Roma*, **21.** 192, 1912; A. Thiel, *Ber. Ges. Marburg*, 1, 1920; *Ber.*, **53.** 1066, 1920; **54.** 2757, 1921; J. Czochralsky, *Zeit. phys. Chem.*, **92.** 219, 1917; J. B. Senderens, *Bull. Soc. Chim.*, (3), **11.** 424, 1894; K. Weissenberg, *Zeit. Kryst.*, **61.** 58, 1925; V. M. Goldschmidt, *Zeit. Metallkunde*, **19.** 23, 1918; P. Scherrer, *Phys. Zeit.*, **19.** 23, 1918; A. Günther-Schulze, *Zeit. Elektrochem.*, **28.** 119, 221, 1922; V. Kohlschütter and F. Uerbersax, *ib.*, **30.** 72, 1924; R. Vogel, *ib.*, **29.** 301, 1923; *Zeit. anorg. Chem.*, **116.** 21, 1921; **126.** 2, 1923; G. Tammann and Q. A. Mansuri, *ib.*, **126.** 122, 1923; G. Tammann, *ib.*, **113.** 171, 1920; *Nachr. Gött.*, 1, 1918; A. W. Porter, *Nature*, **111.** 362, 1923; F. Robin, *Rev. Mét.*, **11.** 491, 1914; *Compt. Rend.*, **155.** 586, 718, 1912; G. Cartaud, *ib.*, **139.** 429, 1904; P. Gaubert, *ib.*, **159.** 680, 1914; O. Bauer, *Mitt. Materialprüf.*, **31.** 357, 1914; S. Nishikawa and G. Asahara, *Phys. Rev.*, (2), **15.** 38, 1890; W. C. Phebus and F. C. Blake, *ib.*, (2), **25.** 107, 1925; R. J. Anderson and J. T. Norton, *Trans. Amer. Inst. Min. Met.*, **71.** 720, 1925; M. Cook and U. R. Evans, *ib.*, **71.** 627, 1924; E. A. Owen and G. D. Preston, *Proc. Phys. Soc.*, **35.** 101, 1923; R. Vogel, *Zeit. anorg. Chem.*, **126.** 1, 1923; G. R. Levi, *Nuovo Cimento*, (7), **1.** 137, 1924; F. C. Thompson and W. E. Millington, *Journ. Iron Steel Inst.*, **109.** i, 67, 1924; **110.** ii, 61, 1924; *Journ. Inst. Metals*, **31.** 81, 1924; R. S. Dean and W. E. Hudson, *Journ. Amer. Chem. Soc.*, **46.** 1778, 1924; A. L. Norbury, *Trans. Faraday Soc.*, **19.** 140, 1923; P. K. Frölich, G. L. Clark, and R. H. Aborn, *Trans. Amer. Electrochem. Soc.*, **49.** 239, 1926; *Zeit. Elektrochem.*, **32.** 295, 1926; M. Levi, *Nuovo Cimento*, (7), **1.** 137, 1924; A. E. van Arkel, *Physica*, **5.** 208, 1925; *Naturwiss.*, **13.** 662, 1925; N. I. Nikitin, *Journ. Russ. Phys. Chem. Soc.*, **56.** 120, 1925; I. V. Obriemoff and L. V. Shubnikoff, *Trans. Phys. Lab. Leningrad*, **100.** 21, 1925.

⁹ O. Lehmann, *Zeit. Kryst.*, **17.** 277, 1890 ; E. Cohen and K. Inouye, *Chem. Weekbl.*, **7.** 454, 1910 ; *Zeit. phys. Chem.*, **74.** 202, 1910 ; H. Heller, *ib.*, **89.** 735, 761, 1915 ; E. Jänecke, *ib.*, **90.** 336, 1915 ; E. Cohen and W. D. Helderman, *ib.*, **89.** 733, 1915 ; *Proc. Acad. Amsterdam*, **17.** 822, 1914 ; E. Cohen and A. L. T. Moesveld, *Versl. Akad. Amsterdam*, **28.** 762, 1920 ; P. W. Bridgman, *Proc. Amer. Acad.*, **52.** 269, 1918 ; *Proc. Nat. Acad. Washington*, **3.** 10, 1917 ; C. Jeantaud, *Brit. Pat. No.* 52, 1906 ; G. Rosset, *Centrb. Accumul.*, **6.** 75, 1905 ; Anon., *ib.*, **7.** 305, 1906 ; **8.** 61, 1907 ; H. St. C. Deville, *Compt. Rend.*, **40.** 769, 1855 ; U. J. J. le Verrier, *ib.*, **114.** 907, 1892 ; H. J. M. Creighton, *Journ. Amer. Chem. Soc.*, **37.** 2064, 1915 ; F. H. Getman, *ib.*, **38.** 792, 1916 ; **40.** 611, 1918 ; B. Lambert and H. E. Cullis, *Journ. Chem. Soc.*, **107.** 210, 1915 ; A. Thiel, *Ber.*, **53.** B, 1052, 1066, 1920 ; **54.** 2757, 1921 ; *Sitzber. Ges. Marburg*, 1, 1920 ; H. S. Rawdon, *Min. Met.*, 158, 1920 ; H. S. Rawdon and S. C. Sangdon, *Trans. Amer. Inst. Min. Eng.*, **64.** 443, 1920 ; *Chem. Met. Engg.*, **22.** 346, 1920.

⁴ J. J. C. Mullet, *Journ. Asiatique*, (5), **11.** 379, 1876 ; N. Khanikoff, *Journ. Amer. Oriental Soc.*, **6.** 1, 1859 ; H. C. Bolton, *Quart. Journ. Science*, **13.** 494, 1876 ; R. Boyle, *Hydrostatic Balance*, London, 1690 ; *Medicina hydrostatica*, London, 1690 ; D. G. Fahrenheit, *Phil. Trans.*, **33.** 114, 1726 ; P. van Muschenbrock, *ib.*, **33.** 357, 1732 ; *Introductio ad philosophiam naturalem*, Lugduni Batavorum, **2.** 540, 1762 ; L. B. Guyton de Morveau, *Ann. chim. Phys.*, (1), **21.** 3, 1797.

⁵ F. Reich, *Jahrb. Berg. Hütt.*, 180, 1860 ; *Journ. prakt. Chem.*, (1), **78.** 330, 1859 ; A. Baudrimont, *ib.*, (1), **7.** 278, 1856 ; *Ann. chim. Phys.*, (3), **30.** 304, 1850 ; L. Knab, *Traité de métallurgie des métaux autres que le fer*, Paris, 1891 ; W. Spring, *Bull. Acad. Belg.*, (3), **6.** 507, 1883 ; 1066, 1903 ; *Ber.*, **16.** 2724, 1883 ; G. W. A. Kahlbaum, K. Roth, and P. Siedler, *Zeit. anorg. Chem.*, **29.** 238, 1902 ; F. Nies and A. Winkelmann, *Sitzber. Akad. München*, **11.** 63, 1881 ; E. Wiedemann, *Wied. Ann.*, **20.** 228, 1883 ; F. Soddy, *Nature*, **107.** 41, 1922 ; W. C. Roberts-Austen and R. Wrightson, *ib.*, **24.** 470, 1881 ; *Phil. Mag.*, (5), **13.** 360, 1881 ; W. Herapath, *ib.*, (1), **64.** 321, 1824 ; J. Crichton, *ib.*, (1), **16.** 48, 1803 ; C. J. St. C. Deville, *ib.*, (4), **11.** 144, 1856 ; *Compt. Rend.*, **20.** 1453, 1845 ; **40.** 769, 1855 ; B. Perrette, *ib.*, **180.** 1589, 1925 ; M. Toepler, *Wied. Ann.*, **53.** 343, 1894 ; C. E. Fawsitt, *Journ. Chem. Soc.*, **93.** 1299, 1908 ; T. M. Lowry and R. G. Parker, *ib.*, **107.** 1005, 1915 ; P. Schweitzer, *Amer. Chem.*, **7.** 174, 1877 ; G. Quincke, *Pogg. Ann.*, **97.** 396, 1856 ; **135.** 642, 1868 ; A. Matthiessen and M. Holzmann, *ib.*, **110.** 21, 1860 ; C. J. B. Karsten, *Schweigger's Journ.*, **65.** 413, 1832 ; F. Kick, *Dingler's Journ.*, **229.** 559, 1878 ; H. Tomlinson, *Proc. Roy. Soc.*, **37.** 109, 1884 ; A. C. Egerton and W. B. Lee, *ib.*, **103.** A, 487, 1923 ; G. Vicentini and D. Omedei, *Atti Accad. Torino*, **23.** 8, 1887 ; G. Spezia, *ib.*, **45.** 525, 1911 ; C. Cattaneo, *ib.*, **27.** 698, 1892 ; J. W. Mallet, *Amer. Journ. Science*, (3), **8.** 212, 1874 ; L. Playfair and J. P. Joule, *Mem. Chem. Soc.*, **3.** 74, 1848 ; A. Streng, *Berg. Hütt. Ztg.*, **19.** 125, 1860 ; A. T. Kupffer, *Ann. Chim. Phys.*, (2), **40.** 289, 1829 ; *Kastner's Arch.*, **8.** 340, 1831 ; M. J. Brisson, *Pesanteur spécifique des corps*, Paris, 1787 ; R. Böttger, *Tabellarische Uebersicht der specifischen Gewichte der Körper*, Frankfurt, 1837 ; J. Percy, *The Metallurgy of Lead*, London, 3, 1870 ; J. J. Berzelius, *Traité de chimie*, Paris, **2.** 576, 1846 ; F. W. Clarke, *A Table of Specific Gravities for Solids and Liquids*, London, 5, 1888 ; F. Wust, *Met.*, **6.** 769, 1909 ; W. Herz, *Zeit. anorg. Chem.*, **105.** 171, 1909 ; M. Plüss, *ib.*, **93.** 29, 1915 ; *Zur Kenntnis der Viskosität und Dichte geschmolzener Metalle und Legierungen*, Leipzig, 1915 ; J. J. van Laar, *Zeit. anorg. Chem.*, **104.** 134, 1918 ; *Proc. Amsterdam Akad.*, **20.** 492, 1917 ; C. Benedicks, *Compt. Rend.*, **179.** 389, 1924 ; P. Pascal and J. Jouniaux, *ib.*, **158.** 414, 1914 ; *Bull. Soc. Chim.*, (4), **15.** 312, 1912 ; *Zeit. Elektrochem.*, **22.** 71, 1916 ; G. Timoféeff, *Zeit. phys. Chem.*, **78.** 308, 1911 ; E. Cohen and W. D. Heldermann, *ib.*, **89.** 733, 1915 ; L. H. Adams, E. D. Williamson, and J. Johnston, *Journ. Amer. Chem. Soc.*, **41.** 12, 1919 ; T. W. Richards and C. Wadsworth, *ib.*, **38.** 221, 1658, 1916 ; T. R. Hogness, *ib.*, **43.** 1621, 1921 ; A. L. Day, R. B. Sosman, and J. C. Hostetter, *Neues Jahrb. Min. B.B.*, **40.** 132, 1915 ; H. Endo, *Science Rep. Tohoku Univ.*, **13.** 193, 1924 ; *Journ. Inst. Metals*, **30.** 121, 1923 ; W. L. Bragg, *Phil. Mag.*, (6), **40.** 169, 1920 ; J. Joly and J. H. J. Poole, *ib.*, (6), **39.** 372, 1920 ; R. Hoffmann and W. Stahl, *Metall Erz.* **18.** 547, 1921 ; J. Groh and G. von Hevesy, *Ann. Physik*, (4), **63.** 85, 1920 ; W. P. Davey, *Phys. Rev.*, (2), **17.** 402, 1921 ; W. J. Sollas, *Proc. Roy. Soc.*, **63.** 270, 1898 ; A. Hamberg, *Zeit. Kryst.*, **17.** 253, 1890 ; R. Arpi, *Internat. Zeit. Metallog.*, **5.** 162, 1914 ; S. P. Howell, *Journ. Franklin Inst.*, **188.** 567, 1919 ; F. W. Clark, *Trans. Amer. Inst. Min. Eng.*, **18.** 526, 1889 ; H. H. Potter, *Proc. Roy. Soc.*, **104.** A, 588, 1923 ; J. J. van Laar, *Die Zustandsgleichung von Gasen und Flussigkeiten*, Leipzig, 1924 ; *Proc. Acord. Amsterdam*, **18.** 1220, 1915 ; **19.** 2, 1916.

⁶ C. A. Mitchell, *Nature*, **105.** 12, 1920 ; **109.** 516, 1912.

⁷ W. R. Lethaby, *Lead Work : Old and Ornamental and for the most part English*, London, 1893 ; *Journ. Soc. Arts*, **45.** 452, 1897 ; L. Weaver, *ib.*, **58.** 1054, 1910 ; W. Baker, *Prat. Mech. Journ.*, (2), **9.** 7, 1864 ; P. P. Lazareff, *Bull. Acad. Russ.*, 1259, 2241, 1918 ; 1005, 1919 ; G. Coriolis, *Ann. Chim. Phys.*, (2), **44.** 103, 1830 ; F. Auerbach, *Ann. Phys.*, (4), **3.** 108, 1900 ; A. Kürth, *Phys. Zeit.*, **8.** 417, 1907 ; *Zeit. Ver. deut. Ing.*, **53.** 85, 209, 1909 ; J. R. Rydberg, *Zeit. phys. Chem.*, **33.** 353, 1900 ; P. Duhem, *ib.*, **34.** 312, 1900 ; P. Ludwik, *ib.*, **91.** 232, 1916 ; *Zeit. anorg. Chem.*, **94.** 161, 1915 ; *Die Kugeldruck probe*, Berlin, 1908 ; *Zeit. Ver. deut. Ing.*, **59.** 657, 1915 ; A. Kürth, *ib.*, **53.** 85, 1909 ; F. C. Calvert and R. Johnson, *ib.*, (4), **17.** 114, 1859 ; *Mem. Manchester Lit. Phil. Soc.*, (2), **15.** 113, 1858 ; *Dingler's Journ.*, **152.** 130, 1859 ; K. Ito, *Science Rep. Tohoku Univ.*, (1), **12.** 137, 1923 ; H. Gollner, *Kick's Tech. Blatt.*, 181, 1882 ; S. Bottone, *Chem. News*, **28.** 215, 1873 ; Z. Jeffries, *Journ. Amer. Inst. Metals*, **11.** 300, 1918 ; C. A. Edwards, *Proc. Manchester Assoc. Eng.*, 225, 1919 ; *Engg.*, **106.** 285, 1918 ; *Journ. Inst. Metals*, **20.** 61, 1918 ;

C. A. Edwards and A. M. Herbert, *ib.*, 25. 175, 1921 ; T. K. Rose, *ib.*, 8. 123, 1912 ; H. J. Coe, *ib* , 30. 309. 1923 ; *Metal Ind.*, 23. 245, 1923 ; T. Turner, *Journ. Iron Steel Inst.*, 75. i, 434. 1909 ; P. Nicolardot, *Compt. Rend.*, 168. 558, 1919 ; M. Hanriot. *ib.*, 155. 971, 1913 ; A. L. Norbury, *Trans. Faraday Soc.*, 19. 140, 1923 ; *Metal Ind.*, 22. 504, 1923 ; A. Saphoshnikoff and J. Kaniewsky, *Journ. Russ. Phys. Chem. Soc.*, 39. 901, 1907 ; N. S. Kurnakoff and S. F. Schemt-schuschny, *ib.*, 41. 1182, 1909 ; *Zeit. anorg. Chem.*, 64. 174, 1909 ; W. Herold, *ib.*, 112. 145, 1920 ; F. Sauerwald and K. Knehans, *ib.*, 140. 227, 1924 ; G. Moreau, *Journ. Phys.*, (5). 14. 306. 1920 ; A. Geller, *Zeit. Kryst.*, 62. 395, 1925 ; G. Subrahmanian, *Phil. Mag.*, (7), 1. 1074, 1926 ; A. Bencke, *Giessztg.*, 17. 351, 1920 ; C. O. Thieme, *Journ. Ind. Eng. Chem.*, 12. 446, 1920 ; E. E. Walker, *Trans. Faraday Soc.*, 19. 73, 1923 ; M. Levi-Malvano and O. Ceccarelli, *Gazz. Chim. Ital.*, 41. ii, 317, 1911 ; D. Saito and K. Hayashi, *Mem. Coll. Engg. Kyoto Univ.*, 2. 83, 1919 ; K. Honda and R. Yamada, *Science Rep. Tohoku Univ.*, 14. 63, 1925 ; J. Okubo, *ib.*, 11. 455, 1922.

⁸ W. Hagemann, *Ueber die Oberflächenspannung geschmolzener Metalle*, Freiburg i. Br., 1914 ; G. Quincke, *Pogg. Ann.*, 135. 642, 1868 ; 138. 141, 1869 ; H. Siedentopf, *Wied. Ann.*, 61. 235, 1897 ; *Ueber Kapillaritatserscheinungen geschmolzener Metalle*, Göttingen, 35. 1897 ; S. W. Smith, *Journ. Inst. Metals*, 12. 168, 1914 ; 17. 65, 1917 ; W. R. Fielding, *Chem. News*, 123. 97, 1921 ; L. L. Grünmach, *Ann. Physik;* (4), 3. 660, 1900 ; D. Saito and K. Hayashi, *Mem. Coll. Eng. Kyoto Univ.*, 2. 83, 1919 ; T. R. Hogness, *Journ. Amer. Chem. Soc.*, 43. 1621, 1921 ; *Phil. Mag.*, (4). 36. 267, 1868 ; (4), 38. 78, 1869 ; *Wied. Ann.*, 52. 1, 1894 ; 61. 267, 1897 ; J. H. Hildebrand, T. R. Hogness, and N. W. Taylor, *ib.*, 45. 2828, 1923 ; T. W. Richards, *ib.*, 46. 1419, 1924 ; 47. 731, 1925 ; I. Traube, *Ber. deut. phys. Ges.*, 11. 231, 1909 ; *Ber.*, 42. 86, 1909 ; G. Tammann, *Zeit. phys. Chem.*, 3. 442, 1889 ; R. Lorenz and A. Liebmann, *ib.*, 83. 459, 1913 ; J. J. van Laar, *ib.*, 194. 134, 1918 ; T. K. Rose, *Journ. Chem. Soc.*, 62. 72, 1893 ; *Trans. Inst. Min. Met.*, 17. 463, 1918.

⁹ M. von Wogau, *Ann. Physik*, (4), 23. 345, 1907 ; G. Meyer, *Wied. Ann.*, 61. 225, 1897 ; 64. 752, 1898 ; W. C. Roberts-Austen, *Proc. Roy. Soc.*, 58. 281, 1896 ; 67. 101, 1900 ; *Phil. Trans.*, 187. A, 383, 1896 ; *Chem. News*, 74. 289, 1896 ; G. von Hevesy and A. Obrutsheva, *Nature*, 115. 675. 1925 ; J. Groh and G. von Hevesy, *Ann. Physik*, (4), 63. 85, 1920 ; G. von Hevesy, *Zeit. Elektrochem.*, 26. 363, 1920 ; C. S. van Orstrand and F. P. Dewey, *Prof. Paper U.S. Geol. Sur.*, 95, 1915 ; R. Kremann and A. Hrasovec, *Monatsh.*, 46. 409, 1926.

¹⁰ C. Neumann, *Chymia medica*, Züllichau, 1749 ; London, 54, 1759 ; J. Percy, *The Metallurgy of Lead*, London, 2, 1870 ; G. Wertheim, *Ann. Chim. Phys.*, (3), 12. 385, 1844 ; A. Masson, *Cosmos*, 10. 425, 1858 ; *Pogg. Ann.*, 103. 272, 1858 ; W. Herz, *Zeit. anorg. Chem.*, 94. 21, 1916 ; R. A. F. de Réaumur, *Mém. Acad.*, 243, 1726.

¹¹ R. Arpi, *Internat. Zeit. Metallog.*, 5. 142, 1914 ; C. E. Fawsitt, *Journ. Chem. Soc.*, 93. 1299, 1908 ; M. Plüss, *Zeit. anorg. Chem.*, 93. 1, 1915 ; *Zur Kenntnis der Viskosität und Dichte geschmolzener Metalle und Legierungen*, Leipzig, 1915 ; A. Mesnager, *Compt. Rend.*, 126. 517, 1898 ; D. Saito and K. Hayashi, *Mem. Coll. Eng. Kyoto Univ.*, 2. 83, 1919.

¹² J. Percy, *The Metallurgy of Lead*, London, 2, 1870 ; Z. Jeffries, *Trans. Amer. Inst. Min. Met. Eng.*, 67. 509, 1920 ; *Chem. Met. Engg.*, 22. 394, 1920 ; H. S. Rawdon, A. I. Krynitsky, and J. F. T. Berliner, *ib.*, 26. 109, 1922 ; E. N. da C. Andrade, *Proc. Roy. Soc.*, 84. A, 1, 1910 ; P. Ludwik, *Stahl Eisen*, 40. 1547, 1920 ; G. W. A. Kahlbaum and E. Sturm, *Zeit. anorg. Chem.*, 46. 237, 1905.

¹³ E. Sheldon, *Amer. Machinist*, 51. 909, 1920.

¹⁴ J. Percy, *The Metallurgy of Lead*, London, 2, 1870.

¹⁵ T. Dobbs, *Brit. Pat. No.* 4515, 1820 ; J. Fournet, *Ann. Chim. Phys.* (2), 75. 435, 1840 ; G. Coriolis, *ib.*, (3), 44. 103, 1855 ; W. Spring, *ib.*, (5), 22. 181, 1881 ; J. Dewar, *Chem. News.* 91. 206, 1905 ; W. Hallock, *Amer. Chem. Journ.*, (3), 34. 277, 1887 ; W. Rosenhain and P. A. Tucker, *Phil. Trans.*, 209. A, 89, 1909 ; J. Percy, *The Metallurgy of Lead*, London, 9, 1870 ; P. A. Bolley, *Jahrb. prakt. Pharm.*, 18. 380, 1849 ; H. S. Rawdon, *Metal Ind.*, 19. 171, 1921 ; *Intercrystalline Brittleness of Lead*, Washington, 1920.

¹⁶ T. W. Richards, *Zeit. Elektrochem.*, 13. 519, 1907 ; T. W. Richards and W. H. Stull, *Zeit. phys. Chem.*, 51. 196, 1908 ; T. W. Richards and E. P. Bartlett, *Journ. Amer. Chem. Soc.*, 37. 470, 1643, 1915 ; L. H. Adams, E. D. Williamson, and J. Johnston, *ib.*, 41. 12, 1919 ; E. H. Amagat, *Ann. Chim. Phys.*, (6), 22. 95, 1891 ; *Compt. Rend.*, 108. 1199, 1889 ; *Journ. Phys.*, (2), 8. 192, 358, 1889 ; B. B. Lera, *Rend. Accad. Lincei*, (4), 6. 165, 1890 ; P. W. Bridgman, *Proc. Amer. Acad.*, 58. 197, 1923 ; *Proc. Washington Acad.*, 8. 361, 1922 ; J. Johnston, *ib.*, 1. 260, 1915 ; *Journ. Amer. Chem. Soc.*, 34. 788, 1912 ; G. Coriolis, *Ann. Chim. Phys.*, (3), 44. 103, 1830 ; H. J. Coe, *Metal Ind.*, 23. 245, 1923 ; *Journ. Inst. Metals*, 30. 309, 1923 ; W. Hallock, *Amer. Journ. Science*, (3), 34. 277, 1887 ; E. Grüneisen, *Ann. Physik*, (4), 33. 65, 1239, 1910.

¹⁷ J. J. Berzelius, *Traité de chimie*, Paris, 2. 576, 1846 ; P. Berthier, *Traité de essais par la voie sèche*, Paris, 2. 662, 1834 ; T. Kikuta, *Science Rep. Tohoku Univ.*, 10. 139, 1921 ; A. Baudrimont, *Traité de chimie générale*, Paris, 2. 179, 1846 ; G. Wertheim, *Ann. Chim. Phys.*, (3), 12. 409, 1844 ; (3), 23. 52, 1849 ; K. Karmarsch, *Jahrb. Polyt. Inst. Wien*, 18. 54, 1834 ; C. Bach, *Zeit. Ver. deut. Ing.*, 29. 629, 1885 ; J. Dewar, *Chem. News*, 71. 192, 199, 1895 ; G. Lunge and E. Schmid, *Zeit. angew. Chem.*, 5. 650, 1892 ; A. Ledebur, *Die Verarbeitung der Metalle auf mechanischen Wege*, Braunschweig, 20, 326, 1877 ; A. H. Stuart, *Proc Inst. Mech. Eng.*, 1155, 1912 ; C. Schäfer, *Zeit. Physik*, 17. 152, 1923 ; *Verh. deut. phys. Ges.*, 2. 122, 1900 ; *Ann. Physik*, (4), 5. 220, 1901 ; (4), 9. 665, 1124, 1902 ; E. Grüneisen, *ib.*, (4), 22. 801, 1907 ; J. Thoulet, *Compt. Rend.*, 96. 1373, 1883 ; E. H. Amagat, *ib.*, 108. 1199, 1889 ; *Journ. Phys.*, (2), 8. 197,

358, 1889 ; *Ann. Chim. Phys.*, (6), 22. 94, 1891 ; N. Katzenelsohn, *Ueber den Einfluss der Temperatur auf die Electricität der Metalle*, Berlin, 1887 ; P. Ludwik, *Zeit. Metallkunde*, 11. 157, 1919 ; *Zeit. Ver. deut. Ing.*, 59. 657, 1915 ; A. Mallock, *Proc. Roy. Soc.*, 29. 157, 1879 : 46 283, 1889 ; 40. 380, 1891 ; 95. A, 429, 1919 ; H. Tomlinson, *ib.*, 42. 362, 1887 ; 43. 88, 1887 ; F. Horton, *ib.*, 73. 334, 1904 ; 74. 401, 1905 : *Phil. Trans.*, 204. A, 1, 1905 ; W. Sutherland, *Phil Mag.*, (5), 32. 31, 215, 524, 1891 ; O. Faust and G. Tammann, *Zeit. phys. Chem.*, 75. 118, 1911 ; H. Buff, *Pogg. Ann. Jubelld.*, 349, 1874 ; P. Lagerhjelm, *Jerncontorets Ann.*, 10. 2. 1826 ; *Dingler's Journ.*, 30. 97, 1828 ; *Quart. Journ. Science*, 1. 393, 1829 ; H. J. Coe, *Metal Ind.*, 23. 245, 1923 ; *Journ. Inst. Metals*, 30. 309, 1923 ; K. R. Koch and C. Dannecker, *Ann. Physik.*, (4), 47. 197, 1915 ; H. L. Heathcote, *Iron Coal Trades Rev.*, 103. 693, 1921 ; H. L. Heathcote and C. G. Whinfrey, *Chem. Met. Engg.*, 27. 310, 1922 ; P. P. Lazareff, *Bull. Acad. Russ.*, 1259, 2241, 1918 ; 1005, 1919 ; F. A. and C. L. Lindemann, *Nernst's Festschrift*, 264, 1912 ; G. Respondek, *Stahl Eisen*, 38. 837, 872, 1918 ; Z. Jeffries, *Trans. Amer. Inst. Min. Eng.*, 67. 509, 1920 ; *Chem. Met. Engg.*, 22. 347, 1920 ; H. S. Rawdon, A. I. Krynitsky, and J. F. T. Berliner, *ib.*, 26. 109, 1922 ; H. S. Rawdon, *Metal Ind.*, 19. 171, 1921 ; L. Archbutt, *ib.*, 18. 241, 1921 ; *Trans. Faraday Soc.*, 17. 22, 1921 ; K. R. Koch and R. Dieterle, *Ann. Physik*, (4), 47. 217, 1915 ; (4), 68. 457, 1922 ; T. Kikuta, *Science Rep. Tohoku Univ.*, 10. 150, 1922 ; D. H. Ingall, *Metal Ind.*, 25. 371, 1924 ; H. Shoji, *Bull. Phys. Chem. Research Japan*, 2. 334, 1923 ; R. H. Greaves and J. A. Jones *Journ. Inst. Metals*, 35. 34, 1925 ; A. Kürth, *Zeit. Ver. deut. Ing.*, 53. 85, 1909.

18 A. Matthiessen, *Proc. Roy. Soc.*, 15. 220, 1866 ; *Pogg. Ann.*, 130. 50, 1864 ; *Phil. Trans.*, 156. 231, 1866 ; *Phil. Mag.*, (4), 32. 472, 1866 ; F. C. Calvert and R. Johnson, *ib.*, (4), 17. 114, 1859 ; *B.A. Rep.*, 46, 1858 ; *Phil. Trans.*, 148. 349, 1858 ; 149. 831, 1859 ; *Mem. Manchester Lit. Phil. Soc.*, (2), 15. 113, 1858 ; H. Fizeau, *Compt. Rend.*, 68. 1125, 1869 ; E. M. Lémeray, *ib.*, 131. 1291, 1900 ; P. Glatzel, *Pogg. Ann.*, 160. 497, 1877 ; H. Buff, *ib.*, 145. 629, 1872 ; G. Vicentini and D. Omodei, *Atti Accad. Torino*, 23. 38, 1888 ; P. Frenchen and V. Poulsen, *Tids. Phys. Kem.*, 45, 1896 ; T. Carnellev, *Ber.*, 12. 439, 1879 ; C. H. Lindemann, *Phys. Zeit.*, 12. 1197, 1911 ; E. Grüneisen, *Ann. Physik*, (4), 33. 33, 1910 ; J. Kleiber, *ib.*, (4), 46. 1054, 1915 ; P. W. Bridgman, *Proc. Amer. Acad.*, 58. 165, 1923 ; P. S. Laplace and A. L. Lavoisier, *Mém. Acad.*, 355, 1780 ; *Recueil des mémoires de chimie de Lavoisier*, Paris, 1. 121, 1805 ; H. Kopp, *Liebig's Ann.*, 81. 29, 1851 ; 93. 129, 1855 ; J. N. Friend and R. H. Vallance, *Metal Ind.*, 24. 275, 1924 ; *Journ. Inst. Metals*, 31. 75, 1924 ; R. Hoffmann and W. Stahl, *Metall Erz*, 18. 547, 1921.

19 G. Wiedemann and R. Franz, *Pogg. Ann.*, 89. 497, 1853 ; C. M. Despretz, *ib.*, 12. 281, 1828 ; *Ann. Chim. Phys.*, (2), 19. 97, 1822 ; *Compt. Rend.*, 35. 540, 1842 ; F. C. Calvert and R. Johnson, *Phil. Trans.*, 148. 349, 1858 ; 149. 831, 1859 ; *Compt. Rend.*, 47. 1069, 1858 ; A. Berget, *ib.*, 105. 224, 1884 ; T. Peczalsky, *ib.*, 160. 766, 1915 ; L. Lorenz, *Danske Vid. Selsk. Skr.* (6), 2. 37, 1886 ; *Wied. Ann.*, 13. 422, 582, 1881 ; G. Kirchhoff and G. Hansemann, *ib.*, 13. 406, 1881 ; P. Macchia, *Atti Accad. Lincei*, (5), 15. ii, 620, 1906 ; (5), 16. i, 507, 1907 ; W. Jäger and H. Diesselhorst, *Abhand. Phys. Tech. Reichsanst.*, 3. 269, 1900 ; M. Jakob, *Zeit. Metallkunde*, 16. 353, 1924 ; G. Glage, *Ann. Physik*, (4), 18. 904, 1905 ; W. Meissner, *ib.*, (4). 47. 1001, 1915 ; M. O'Day, *Phys. Rev.*, (2), 23. 245, 1924 ; S. Konno, *Phil. Mag.*, (6), 40. 542, 1920 ; *Science Rep. Tohoku Univ.*, 8. 169, 1919 ; P. W. Bridgman, *Proc. Amer. Acad.*, 57. 77, 1922 ; *Phys. Rev.*, (-), 18. 115, 1921 ; H. F. Weber, *Sitzber. Akad. Berlin*, 457, 1880 ; *Zürich Vierteljahr.*, 25. 184, 1880 ; S. Lussana, *Nuovo Cimento*, (6), 15. 130, 1918 ; R. Schott, *Ver. deut. phys. Ges.*, 18. 27, 1916 ; C. H. Lees, *Phil. Trans.*, 208. 381, 1908 ; C. H. Lees and J. E. Calthorp, *Proc. Phys. Soc.*, 35. 225, 1923 ; P. G. Tait, *B.A. Rep.*, 175, 1869 ; *Phil. Mag.*, (5), 12. 147, 1881 ; *Trans. Roy Soc. Edin.*, 28. 717, 1879 ; A. C. Mitchell, *ib.*, 33. 535, 1887 ; 35. 947, 1890 ; *Proc. Roy. Soc. Edin.*, 17. 300, 1890 ; W. M. Latimer, *Journ. Amer. Chem. Soc.*, 44. 2136, 1922 ; C. D. Bidwell, *Phys. Rev.*, (2), 27. 819, 1926 ; M. F. Angell, *ib.*, (2), 27. 820, 1926.

20 P. L. Dulong and A. T. Petit, *Ann. Chim. Phys.*, (2), 10. 395, 1819 ; C. C. Person, *ib.*, (3), 24. 136, 1848 ; H. V. Regnault, *ib.*, (2), 73. 42, 1840 ; J. Pionchon, *ib.*, (6), 11. 33, 1887 ; *Compt. Rend.*, 102. 675, 1454, 1886 ; 103. 1122, 1886 ; U. J. J. le Verrier, *ib.*, 114. 907, 1892 ; F. Michaud, *ib.*, 171. 241, 1920 ; W. R. Fielding, *Chem. News*, 123. 97, 1921 ; H. Kopp, *Liebig's Ann. Suppl.*, 3. 75, 1865 ; A. L. Bernouilli, *Helvetica Chim. Acta*, 1. 278, 1918 ; E. Bède, *Mém. Acad. Belg.*, (2), 27. 1, 1855 ; A. Naccari, *Rend. Accad. Torino*, 23. 107, 1887 ; *Gazz. Chim. Ital.*, 18. 30, 1888 ; A. Bartoli and E. Stracciati, *ib.*, 25. i, 389, 1895 ; *Rend. Ist. Lombardo*, 2. 28, 1895 ; U. Behn, *Wied. Ann.*, 66. 235, 1898 ; L. Schütz, *ib.*, 46. 184, 1892 ; L. Lorenz, *ib.*, 13. 422, 1881 ; L. H. Adams, *Journ. Washington Acad.*, 12. 407, 1922 ; H. Schimpff, *Zeit. phys. Chem.*, 71. 257, 1910 ; E. Cohen, *ib.*, 89. 489, 1915 ; T. W. Richards and F. G. Jackson, *ib.*, 70. 414, 1910 ; P. Schübel, *Zeit. anorg. Chem.*, 87. 100, 1914 ; G. W. A. Kahlbaum, K. Roth, and P. Siedler, *ib.*, 29. 248, 1902 ; E. H. and E. Griffiths, *Phil. Trans.*, 213. A, 119, 1913 ; 214. A, 319, 1914 ; *Proc. Roy. Soc.*, 88. A, 549, 1913 ; 90. A, 557, 1914 ; H. Tomlinson, *ib.*, 37. 109, 1884 ; H. E. Schmitz, *ib.*, 72. 177, 1903 ; C. I. Burton and W. Marshall, *ib.*, 50. 130, 1892 ; J. Dewar, *ib.*, 89. A, 158, 1913 ; R. C. Tolman, *Journ. Amer. Chem. Soc.*, 42. 1185, 1920 ; G. N. Lewis and G. E. Gibson, *ib.*, 39. 2555, 1917 ; G. N. Lewis, G. E. Gibson, and W. M. Latimer, *ib.*, 44. 1008, 1922 ; W. M. Latimer, *ib.*, 44. 2136, 1922 ; E. D. Eastman, *ib.*, 45. 80, 1923 ; E. D. Eastman, G. M. Williams, and T. F. Young, *ib.*, 46. 1184, 1924 ; W. H. Rodebush and A. L. Dixon, *ib.*, 47. 1036, 1925 ; C. Forch and P. Nordmeyer, *Ann. Physik*, (4), 20. 423, 1906 ; F. Koref, *ib.*, (4), 36. 49, 1911 ; H. Tetrode, *ib.*, (4), 38. 434, 1912 ; J. Kleiber, *ib.*, (4), 46. 1054, 1915 ; A. Magnus, *ib.*, (4), 31. 597, 1910 ; W. Nernst, *ib.*, (4), 36. 395, 1911 ; *Sitzber. Akad. Berlin*, 262, 1910 ; 306, 1911 ; W. Nernst, F. Koref, F. A. Lindemann, *ib.*, 247, 1910 ; W. Nernst and F. A. Lindemann, *Zeit. Elektrochem*

17. 821, 1911; *Sitzber. Akad. Berlin*, 494, 1911; C. H. Lindemann, *Phys. Zeit.*, 12. 1197, 1911; F. Glaser, *Met.*, 1. 121, 1904; I. Iitaka, *Science Rep. Tohoku Univ.*, 8. 99, 1919; W. Spring, *Bull. Acad. Belg.*, (3), 11. 355, 1886; *Bull. Soc. Chim.*, (2), 46. 255, 1886; H. Barschall, *Zeit. Elektrochem.*, 17. 341, 1911; A. Eucken and F. Schwers, *Verh. deut. phys. Ges.*, 15. 578, 1913; W. H. Keesom and H. K. Onnes, *Proc. Acad. Amsterdam*, 17. 894, 1914; *Comm. Phys. Leb. Leiden Univ.*, 143, 1914.

²¹ J. B. Biot, *Traité de physique expérimentale et mathématique*, Paris, 1. 534, 1816; I. Newton, *Philosophiæ naturalis principia mathematica*, London, 354, 1726; J. Dalton, *A New System of Chemical Philosophy*, Manchester, 1. 248, 1808; C. C. Person, *Ann. Chim. Phys.*, (3), 24 136, 156, 1848; *Compt. Rend.*, 23. 162, 336, 1853; J. F. Daniell, *Phil. Trans.*, 120. 257, 1830; 121. 443, 1831; *Phil. Mag.*, (3), 11. 191, 268, 350, 1830; J. Crichton, *ib.*, (1), 15. 147, 1803; (1), 16. 48, 1803; A. von Riemsdijk. *Chem. News*. 20. 32, 1869; *Arch. Néerl.*, 3. 357, 1868; W. Guertler and M. Pirani, *Zeit. Metallkunde*, 11. 1, 1919; J. Czochralsky and E. Rassoff, *ib.*, 12. 337, 1920; L. B. G. de Morveau, *Ann. Chim. Phys.*, (1), 90. 236, 1814; *Mém. l'Inst.*, 12. ii, 89, 1811; W. R. Mott, *Trans. Amer. Electrochem. Soc.*, 34. 255, 1918; C. W. Waidner and G. K. Burgess, *Bull. Bur. Standards*, 6. 163, 1909; C. T. Heycock and F. H. Neville, *Journ. Chem. Soc.*, 59. 154, 1889; 62. 1888, 1892; 65. 65, 1894; 71. 394, 1897; *Phil. Trans.*, 189. A, 37, 1897; H. L. Callendar and E. H. Griffiths, *Chem. News*, 63. 1, 1891; H. L. Callendar, *Phil. Trans.*, 178. 161, 1888; *Phil. Mag.*, (5), 48. 519, 1899; F. Rudberg, *Pogg. Ann.*, 19. 133, 1830; M. Roland-Gosselin. *Bull. Soc. Enc. Nat. Ind.*, (5). 1. 1301, 1896; J. E. Stead, *Journ. Soc. Chem. Ind.*, 16. 202, 505, 1897; K. Friedrich and M. Wählert, *Metall Erz*, 10. 578, 1913; A. T. Kupffer, *Ann. Chim. Phys.*, (2), 40. 289, 1829; *Kastner's Arch.*, 8. 340, 1831; G. Brigel, *Ber.*, 6. 191, 1873; T. Carnelley, *Phil. Mag.*, (5), 18. 1, 1884; T. Carnelley and W. C. Williams, *Journ. Chem. Soc.*, 35. 563, 1879; E. Hagenbach, *Pogg. Ann.*, 140. 486, 1870; A. V. Tidblom, *Acta Lund.*, 10. 6, 1874; E. H. Griffiths, *Proc. Roy. Soc.*, 48. 223, 1890; W. H. Preece, *ib.*, 44. 109, 1888; A. W. Kapp, *Ueber vollständige Gefrierpunktkurven binärer Metallegierungen*, Königsberg. 1901; W. Guertler, *Zeit. Elektrochem.*, 15. 129, 1909; J. Johnston and L. H. Adams, *Amer. Journ. Science*, (4), 31. 501, 1911; (4), 33. 534, 1912; J. Johnston, *Journ. Amer. Chem. Soc.*, 34. 788, 1912; R. S. Dean, *ib.*, 45. 1683, 1923; G. Vicentini and D. Omodei, *Atti Accad. Torino*, 23. 38, 1888; H. Siedentopf, *Ueber Kapillaritätserscheinungen geschmolzener Metalle*, Göttingen, 35, 1897; *Wied. Ann.*, 61. 235, 1897; L. J. Dana and P. D. Foote, *Trans. Faraday Soc.*, 15. 186, 1920; L. Holborn and A. L. Day, *Ann. Physik*, (4), 2. 505, 1900; A. L. Day and R. B. Sosman, *Amer. Journ. Science*, (4), 33. 517, 1912; H. Fay and C. B. Gillson, *Amer. Chem. Journ.*, 27. 81, 1902; R. Edler and R. Schuster, *Mett. Tech. Gewerbe Mus.*, (2), 19. 143, 1910; W. C. Roberts-Austen, *Engg.*, 63. 223, 1897; F. Wüst, *Met.*, 6. 769, 1909; K. Friedrich and A. Leroux, *ib.*, 2. 536, 1905; 4. 300, 1907; 5. 355, 1908; K. Friedrich, *ib.*, 3. 46, 398, 1906; P. T. Arnemann, *ib.*, 7. 201, 1910; E. Glaser, *ib.*, 1. 121, 1904; E. Jänecke, *Zeit. phys. Chem.*, 60. 399, 1907; G. von Hevesy, *ib.*, 101. 337, 1922; F. M. Raoult, *Compt. Rend.*, 95. 1030, 1882; A. Jouniaux, *Bull. Soc. Chim.*, (4), 35. 696, 1924; A. Ledebur, *Metallarb.*, 202, 210, 1881; A. Wertheimer, *Chem. News*, 80. 265, 1899; G. A. Gozdorf, *ib.*, 54. 232, 1886; D. Mazzotto, *Mem. Ist. Lombardo*, 16. 1, 1891; *Internat. Zeit. Metallog.*, 1. 289, 1911; W. Spring, *Bull. Acad. Belg.*, (3), 11. 355, 1886; I. Iitaka, *Science Rep. Tohoku Univ.*, 8. 99, 1919; H. Tsutsumi, *ib.*, 7. 93, 1918; P. N. Degens, *Zeit. anorg. Chem.*, 63. 212, 1900; A. Stoffel, *ib.*, 53. 139, 1907; S. Tamaru, *ib.*, 61. 43, 1909; W. Gontermann, *ib.*, 55. 421, 1907; F. Dörinckel, *ib.*, 54. 361, 1907; R. Ruer, *ib.*, 52. 347, 1907; G. Voss, *ib.*, 57. 47, 1908; K. Lewkonja, *ib.*, 52. 454, 1907; 59. 314, 1908; N. S. Kurnakoff and N. A. Puschin, *ib.*, 52. 435, 1907; W. Spring and L. Romanoff, *ib.*, 13. 29, 1897; C. H. Mathewson, *ib.*, 50. 175, 1906; R. S. Williams, *ib.*, 55. 32, 1907; G. Grube, *ib.*, 44. 124, 1905; N. S. Kurnakoff and N. J. Stepanoff, *ib.*, 46. 184, 1905; D. P. Smith, *ib.*, 56. 137, 1908; E. Isaac and G. Tammann, *ib.*, 55. 59, 1907; G. Hindrichs, *ib.*, 59. 429, 1908; N. Baar, *ib.*, 70. 375, 1911; L. Donsky, *ib.*, 57. 210, 1908; W. Herold, *ib.*, 112. 131, 1920; R. Vogel, *ib.*, 45. 17, 1905; A. G. C. Gwyer, *ib.*, 57. 149, 1908; G. J. Petrenke, *ib.*, 53 202, 1907; W. E. Barlow, *ib.*, 70. 178, 1911; *Journ. Amer. Chem. Soc.*, 32. 1394, 1910.

²² J. Percy, *The Metallurgy of Lead*, London, 9, 1870; P. Berthier, *Ann. Chim. Phys.*, (3), 17. 254, 1846; C. W. Hixon, *Notes on Lead and Copper Smelting*, New York, 47, 1898; F. Krafft, *Ber.*, 36. 1690, 1903; F. Krafft and P. Lehmann, *ib.*, 38. 253, 1905; F. Krafft, R. Küch, and E. Haagn, *ib.*, 36. 1690, 1903; H. F. Wiebe, *ib.*, 12. 788, 1879; F. Krafft and L. Bergfeld, *ib.*, 38. 254, 1905; E. Tiede and F. Fischer, *ib.*, 44. 1712, 1911; O. Ruff and B. Bergdahl, *Zeit. anorg. Chem.*, 106. 76, 1919; G. W. A. Kahlbaum, K. Roth, and P. Siedler, *ib.*, 29. 278, 1902; P. Walden, *ib.*, 112. 231, 1920; T. Carnelley and W. C. Williams, *Journ. Chem. Soc.*, 35. 563, 1879; *Ber.*, 12. 1360, 1879; W. Crookes, *Proc. Roy. Soc.*, 50. 102, 1891; H. C. Greenwood, *ib.*, 82. A, 396, 1909; 83. A, 482, 1910; *Zeit. phys. Chem.*, 76. 484, 1911; *Engg.*, 91. 418, 1911; *Zeit. Elektrochem.*, 18. 319, 1912; H. von Wartenberg, *ib.*, 19. 484, 1913; *Zeit. anorg. Chem.*, 56. 370, 1908; J. A. M. van Liempt, *ib.*, 114. 105, 1920; W. Herz, *Zeit. Elektrochem.*, 24. 49, 1918; 25. 45, 1919; J. H. Hildebrand, *Journ. Amer. Chem. Soc.*, 40. 45, 1918; K. Sander, *Berg. Hütt. Ztg.*, 61. 561, 1902; C. M. Guldberg, *Zeit. phys. Chem.*, 1. 231, 1887; C. Zenghelis, *ib.*, 50. 222, 1905; L. Lewin, *Zeit. Hyg.*, 73. 154, 1913; R. J. Strutt, *Le Radium*, 11. 260, 1919; L. H. Adams, *Journ. Washington Accad.*, 12. 407, 1922; W. H. Rodebush and A. L. Dixon, *Journ. Amer. Chem. Soc.*, 47. 1036, 1925; L. H. Borgström, *Œfvers. Finska Soc. Förh.*, 59. A, 16, 1917; A. Henglein, *Zeit. Elektrochem.*, 26. 431, 1920; J. Johnston, *Journ. Ind. Eng. Chem.*, 9. 873, 1917; J. W. Richards, *Electrochem. Ind.*, 6. 115, 1908; *Journ. Franklin*

Inst., **187**. 581, 1919 ; W. R. Mott, *Trans. Amer. Electrochem. Soc.*, **34**. 255, 1918 ; J. J. van Laar, *Proc. Acad. Amsterdam*, **18**. 1220, 1916 ; **20**. 138, 492, 1918 ; A. Schuller, *Wied. Ann.*, **18**. 319, 1883 ; A. C. Egerton, *Proc. Roy. Soc.*, **103**. A, 469, 1923 ; W. N. Hartley, *ib.*, **46**. 88, 1889 ; W. J. Russell, *ib.*, **63**. 106, 1898 ; *Chem. News*, **77**. 167, 1898 ; C. K. Ingold, *Journ. Chem. Soc.*, **121**. 2419, 1922 ; H. Moissan and A. J. P. O'Farrelley, *Compt. Rend.*, **138**. 1659, 1904 ; H. Moissan and P. Watanabe, *ib.*, **144**. 18, 1907 ; C. C. Person, *ib.*, **23**. 162, 336, 1853 ; *Ann. Chim. Phys.*, (3), **24**. 136, 156, 1848 ; F. Rudberg, *Pogg. Ann.*, **19**. 133, 1830; E. Glaser, *Met.*, **1**. 121, 1904 ; W. Spring, *Bull. Acad. Belg.*, (3), **11**. 355, 1886 ; D. Mazzotto, *Mem. 1st. Lombardo*, **16**. 1, 1891 ; I. Iitaka, *Science Rep. Tohoku Univ.*, **8**. 99, 1919 ; P. W. Robertson, *Journ. Chem. Soc.*, **81**. 1233, 1902 ; W. G. Duffield, *Phil. Mag.*, (6), **45**. 1104, 1923 ; F. Simon, *Zeit. phys. Chem.*, **110**. 572, 1924 ; H. Engel and V. Froboese, *Arch. Heyg.*, **93**. 69, 1925 ; W. H. Rodebush, *Phys. Rev.*, (2), **26**. 251, 1925 ; W. H. Rodebush and A. L. Dixon, *ib.*, (2), **26**. 851, 1925 ; E. D. Eastman, *ib.*, **48**. 552, 1926 ; W. Herz, *Zeit. Elektrochem.*, **25**. 45, 1919 ; J. Tate, *Die experimentelle Bestimmung der Verdampfungswärme einiger Metalle*, Berlin, 46, 1914.

[23] P. Drude, *Wied. Ann.*, **39**. 481, 1890 ; **42**. 186, 1891 ; **64**. 159, 1898 ; S. Haughton, *Phil. Trans.*, **153**. 81, 1863 ; W. J. Pope, *Journ. Chem. Soc.*, **69**. 1530, 1896 ; J. H. Gladstone, *Proc. Roy. Soc.*, **16**. 439, 1867 ; **60**. 140, 1897 ; C. A. Valson, *Compt. Rend.*, **76**. 224, 1873 ; P. Niggli, *Zeit. Kryst.*, **60**. 249, 1924 ; G. Grüttner and E. Krause, *Liebig's Ann.*, **415**. 338, 1918 ; H. Grossmann, *Ber.*, **38**. 1711, 1905 ; *Zeit. Ver. Zuckerind.*, **55**. 650, 941, 1905 ; A. K. Aster, *Phys. Rev.*, (2), **20**. 349, 1922 ; M. A. Schirmann, *Phys. Zeit.*, **23**. 441, 1923 ; E. Krause and M. Schmitz, *Ber.*, **52**. 2150, 1919 ; G. Grüttner and E. Krause, *Liebig's Ann.*, **415**. 338, 1918 ; L. Austin and H. Starke, *Ann. Physik*, (4), **9**. 292, 1902 ; M. Faraday, *Phil. Trans.*, **147**. 145, 1857 ; H. von Wartenberg, *Verh. deut. phys. Ges.*, **12**. 105, 1910.

[24] E. Wiedemann and G. C. Schmidt, *Wied. Ann.*, **56**. 205, 1895 ; P. Lenard and V. Klatt, *Ann. Physik*, (4), **15**. 231, 1904 ; P. Schuhknecht, *ib.*, (4), **17**. 720, 1905 ; *Untersuchungen über ultraviolette Fluoreszenz durch Röntgen- und Kathodenstrahlens*, Leipzig, 1905 ; *Ann. Physik*, (4), **17**. 717, 1915 ; P. Lewis, *Astrophys. Journ.*, **16**. 27, 1902 ; V. Carlheim-Gyllensköld, *Ark. Mat. Astron. Fys.*, **4**. 33, 1908 ; H. Kopfermann, *Zeit. Physik*, **21**. 316, 1924.

[25] G. Dima, *Compt. Rend.*, **156**. 1366, 1913 ; **157**. 590, 736, 1913 ; J. Thibaud, *ib.*, **179**. 1052, 1924 ; S. Maracineanu, *Compt. Rend.*, **181**. 774, 1925 ; *Bull. Acad. Roumania*, **9**. 3, 1924 ; W. Ramsay and J. F. Spencer, *Phil. Mag.*, (6), **12**. 397, 1906 ; R. A. Millikan and G. Winchester, *ib.*, (6), **14**. 188, 1907 ; O. Stuhlmann, *ib.*, (6), **20**. 331, 1910 ; (6), **22**. 854, 1911 ; K. Herrmann, *Beiträge zum Hallwachseffekt*, Berlin, 1908 ; *Ann. Physik*, (4), **23**. 481, 1907 ; *Verh. deut. phys. Ges.*, **14**. 638, 1912 ; G. Reboul, *Compt. Rend.*, **158**. 477, 1914 ; R. Hamer, *Phys. Rev.*, (2), **20**. 198, 1922 ; *Journ. Amer. Opt. Soc.*, **9**. 251, 1924 ; G. Kufferath and W. Merckens, *Zeit. angew. Chem.*, **17**. 1095, 1904 ; W. Merckens, *Ann. Physik*, (4), **16**. 667, 1906 ; G. L. Keenan, *Chem. Rev.*, **3**. 95, 1926 ; N. Piltschikoff, *Phys. Zeit.*, **7**. 69, 1906.

[26] W. H. Bragg, *Phil. Mag.*, (6), **11**. 617, 1906 ; E. Rutherford, *ib.*, (6), **28**. 305, 1914 ; (6), **34**. 153, 1917 ; E. Rutherford and E. N. da C. Andrade, *ib.*, (6), **28**. 263, 1914 ; H. Robinson and W. F. Rawlinson, *ib.*, (6), **28**. 285, 1914 ; E. Rutherford and H. Robinson, *ib.*, (6), **26**. 717, 1913 ; J. A. McClelland, *Trans. Roy. Soc. Dublin*, (2), **9**. 1, 1905 ; *Phil. Mag.*, (6), **9**. 230, 1905; J. A. Crowther, *ib.*, (6), **12**. 379, 1906 ; N. R. Campbell, *ib.*, (6), **11**. 206, 1906 ; (6), **24**. 527, 1912 ; M. Ishino, *ib.*, (6), **33**. 129, 1917 ; A. T. Watermann, *ib.*, (6), **33**. 225, 1916 ; A. S. Russell and F. Soddy, *ib.*, (6), **21**. 130, 1911 ; A. H. Compton, *ib.*, (6), **41**. 749, 1921 ; *Chem. News*, **122**. 133, 1921 ; H. A. Bumstead and A. G. McGougan, *Phil. Mag.*, (6), **24**. 462, 1912 ; *Amer. Journ. Science*, (4), **34**. 309, 1912 ; H. Richardson, *Proc. Roy. Soc.*, **91**. A, 396, 1915 ; W. Wilson, *ib.*, **87**. A, 100, 1912 ; C. D. Ellis, *ib.*, **99**. A, 261, 1921 ; R. D. Kleeman, *ib.*, **82**. A, 358, 1909 ; N. Ahmad, *ib.*, **105**. A, 508, 1924 ; Y. Tuomikoski, *Phys. Zeit.*, **10**. 372, 1909 ; J. Elster and H. Geitel, *ib.*, **7**. 841, 1906 ; **8**. 273, 1907 ; **9**. 289, 1908 ; H. Geitel, *ib.*, **8**. 776, 1907 ; M. Levin and R. Ruer, *ib.*, **10**. 576, 1909 ; J. C. McLennan, *ib.*, **8**. 556, 1907 ; **9**. 440, 1908 ; M. Baltruschat and H. Starke, *ib.*, **23**. 403, 1922 ; B. Keetman, *Ann. Physik*, (4), **52**. 709, 1917 ; W. B. Huff, *Ion*, **2**. 360, 1910 ; H. Herchfinkel, *Radium*, **7**. 198, 1910 ; K. A. Hofmann, K. L. Gonder, and V. Wölfl, *Ann. Physik*, (4), **15**. 615, 1904 ; K. A. Hofmann and E. Strauss, *Ber.*, **33**. 3126, 1900 ; **34**. 8, 903, 3033, 1901 ; K. A. Hofmann, *ib.*, **35**. 1453, 1902 ; **37**. 2193, 1904 ; K. A. Hofmann and V. Wölfl, *ib.*, **35**. 692, 1902 ; **36**. 1040, 1903 ; C. Winkler, *ib.*, **37**. 1657, 1904 ; K. A. Hofmann, V. Wölfl, and G. Ebert, *ib.*, **40**. 2425, 1907 ; F. Giesel, *ib.*, **33**. 3569, 1900 ; **35**. 105, 1902 ; A. Korn and E. Strauss, *Compt. Rend.*, **136**. 1312, 1903 ; A. Debierne, *ib.*, **139**. 281, 1904 ; M. Muguet, *ib.*, **174**. 172, 1922 ; J. Danysz, *ib.*, **143**. 232, 1906 ; E. Rutherford, *Phil. Mag.*, (6), **8**. 636, 1904 ; B. B. Boltwood, *ib.*, (6), **9**. 599, 1905 ; C. S. Wright, *ib.*, (6), **17**. 295, 1905 ; H. R. von Traubenberg, *Zeit. Physik*, **2**. 268, 1920 ; J. S. Lates and G. Fournier, *Compt. Rend.*, **181**. 895, 1926 ; J. Thibaud, *Journ. Phys. Rad.*, **6**. 82, 1925.

[27] T. E. Aurén, *Phil. Mag.*, (6), **33**. 471, 1917 ; (6), **37**. 165, 1919 ; C. G. Barkla and J. G. Dunlop, *ib.*, (6), **31**. 222, 1916 ; E. Rutherford, J. Barnes, and H. Richardson, *ib.*, (6), **30**. 339, 1915 ; H. A. Blumstead, *ib.*, (6), **11**. 292, 1906 ; A. H. Compton, *ib.*, (6), **46**. 897, 1923 ; E. Rutherford, *ib.*, (6), **34**. 153, 1917 ; E. Rutherford and E. N. da C. Andrade, *ib.*, (6), **28**. 263, 1914 ; F. P. Slater, *ib.*, (6), **42**. 904, 1921 ; (6), **44**. 300, 1922 ; G. Shearer, *ib.*, (6), **44**. 793, 1922 ; E. Rutherford and H. Richardson, *ib.*, (6), **26**. 717, 1913 ; R. A. Houstoun, *ib.*, (7), **2**. 512, 1926 ; J. C. Chapman, *Proc. Roy. Soc.*, **86**. A, 439, 1912 ; H. Richardson, *ib.*, **91**. A, 396, 1915 ; P. D. Innes, *ib.*, **79**. A, 442, 1907 ; E. A. Owen, N. Fleming, and W. E. Fage, *Proc. Phys. Soc.*, **36**. 355, 1924 ; W. Duane and T. Shimizu, *Proc. Washington Acad.*, **5** 198, 1919 ; W. Duane,

H. Fricke, and W. Stenström, *Proc. Nat. Acad. Science*, **6**. 607, 1920 ; K. W. F. Kohlrausch, *Sitzber. Akad. Wien*, **126**. 683, 1917 ; G. W. C. Kaye, *Proc. Cambridge Phil. Soc.*, **14**. 236, 1917 ; J. C. Chapman, *ib.*, **16**. 399, 1912 ; C. D. Cooksey, *Amer. Journ. Science*. (4), **24**. 285, 1917 ; F. K. Ricchtmyer, *Phys. Rev.*, (2), **17**. 264, 1921 ; (2), **18**. 13, 1921 ; (2), **27**. 1, 1926 ; A. W. Hull and M. Rice, *ib.*, (2). **8**. 326, 1916 ; D. Hurmuzescu, *Ann. Science Jassy*. **3**. 258, 1906 ; L. de Broglie, *Compt. Rend.*, **158**. 1493, 1914 ; **162**. 596, 1916 ; **163**. 87, 1916 ; **169**. 962, 1919 ; G. Fournier, *ib.*, **180**. 1490, 1925 ; K. A. Wingardh, *Zeit. Physik*, **8**. 363, 1922 ; L. Benoist, *Journ. Phys.*, (3), **10**. 653, 1901 ; *Compt. Rend.*, **124**. 146, 1897 ; **132**. 325, 545, 772, 1901 ; J. Herweg, *Ann. Physik*, (4), **29**. 398, 1909 ; G. Holtsmark, *ib.*, (4), **10**. 522, 1903 ; M. Wolfke, *Phys. Zeit.*, **18**. 479, 1917 ; K. W. F. Hohlrausch. *ib.*, **21**. 193, 1920 ; W. E. Williams and B. L. Worksop, *Nature*, **108**. 306, 1922 ; C. G. Bedreag, *Ann. Science Jassy*, **10**. 235, 1920 ; G. W. C. Kaye and E. A. Owen, *Chem. News*, **127**. 122, 1923 ; P. Curie and G. Saynac, *Compt. Rend.*, **130**. 1013, 1900 ; J. Cluzet and T. Kofman, *Compt. Rend. Soc. Biol.*, **86**. 49, 1922 ; H. S. Read, *Phys. Rev.*, (2), **27**. 373, 795, 1926 ; S. J. M. Allen, *ib.*, (2), **27**. 266, 1926 ; K. E. F. Schmidt, *Phys. Zeit.*, **17**. 554, 1916 ; W. Seitz, *Phys. Zeit.*, **26**. 6'0, 1925.

[26] M. and L. de Broglie, *Compt. Rend.*, **158**. 1493, 1914 ; **162**. 596, 1916 ; **163**. 87, 1916 ; **169**. 962, 1919 ; **173**. 1157, 1921 ; **174**. 939, 1922 ; M. Siegbahn, *ib.*, **162**. 787, 1896 ; *Jahrb. Rad. Elektron.*, **13**. 296, 1916 ; M. Siegbahn and E. Friman, *Phys. Zeit.*, **17**. 17, 1916 ; M. Siegbahn and E. Jönsson, *ib.*, **20**. 251, 1919 ; E. G. Taylor, *ib.*, **17**. 316, 1916 ; J. Laub, *ib.*, **15**. 732, 844, 1914 ; H. Küstner, *ib.*, **23**. 257, 1922 ; W. Stenström, *Ann. Physik*, (4). **57**. 347, 1918 ; J. Laub, *ib.*, (4), **46**. 785, 1915 ; G. Wentzel, *Zeit. Naturwiss.*, **10**. 369, 1922 ; H. Robinson and W. F. Rawlinson, *Phil. Mag.*, (6), **28**. 277, 1914 ; E. Rutherford, H. Robinson, and W. F. Rawlinson, *ib.*, (6), **28**. 281, 1914 ; C. G. Barkla, *ib.*, (6), **49**. 1033, 1925 ; S. J. M. Allen, *Phys. Rev.*, (2), **23**. 291, 1924 ; F. W. Warburton and F. K. Richtmyer, *ib.*, (2), **23**. 291, 1924 ; F. K. Richtmyer, *ib.*, (2), **27** 1, 1926 ; H. G. J. Moseley, *ib.*, (6), **26**. 1024, 1913 ; (6), **27**. 703, 1914 ; W. Duane, H. Fricke, and W. Senström, *Proc. Washington Acad.*, **6**. 607, 1920 ; W. Duane and T. Shimizu, *Phys. Rev.*, (2), **14**. 522, 1919 ; *Proc. Washington Acad.*, **5** 189, 1919 ; W. Duane and R. A. Patterson, *ib.*, **6**. 509, 1920 ; C. D. and D. Cooksey, *ib.*, (2). **16**. 327, 1920 ; P. A. Ross, *Proc. Nat. Acad. Science*, **10**. 304, 1924 ; *Phys. Rev.*, (2), **18**. 336, 1922 ; (2), **22**. 524, 1923 ; (2), **25**. 235, 1925 ; D. Coster, *ib.*, (2), **18**. 218, 1921 ; (2), **19**. 20, 1922 ; *Zeit. Physik*, **4**. 178, 1920 ; **6**. 185, 1921 ; E. Hjalmar, *ib.*, **15**. 65, 1923 ; G. Kettmann, *ib.*, **18**. 359, 1923 ; E. C. Stoner and L. H. Martin, *Proc. Roy. Soc.*, **107**. A, 312, 1925 ; E. C. Stoner, *Phil. Mag.*, (6), **48**. 719, 1924 ; B. B. Ray, *ib.*, (6), **48**. 707, 1924 ; M. and L. de Broglie, *Compt. Rend.*, **173**. 527, 1921 ; G. Réchou, *ib.*, **180**. 1107, 1925 ; K. Lang, *Ann. Physik*, (4), **75**. 489, 1924 ; M. Kimura and G. Makamura, *Japan. Journ. Phys.*, **3**. 29, 1924 ; P. A. Ross, *Proc. Nat. Acad. Science*, **10**. 304, 1924 ; *Phys. Rev.*, (2), **18**. 336, 1921 ; (2), **22**. 524, 1923 ; (2), **25**. 235, 1925 ; H. Hirata, *Proc. Roy. Soc.*, **105**. A, 40, 1924 ; H. Robinson, *ib.*, **104**. A, 455, 1923 ; A. Nodon, *Compt. Rend.*, **174**. 1061, 1922 ; A. Leide, *ib.*, **180**. 1203, 1925 ; A. T. Waterman, *Phys. Rev.*, (2), **24**. 366, 1924 ; J. E. P. Wagstaff, *Phil. Mag.*, (6), **47**. 84, 1924 ; H. Koffermann, *Zeit. Physik*, **21**. 316, 1924 ; B. Walter, *ib.*, **30**. 357, 1924 ; B. R. Stephenson and J. M. Cork, *Phys. Rev.*, (2), **27**. 138, 1926.

[29] C. Wheatstone, *Phil. Mag.*, (3), **7**. 299, 1835 ; *Chem. News*, **3**. 198, 1861 ; R. Böttger, *Journ. prakt. Chem.*, (1), **65**. 392, 1862 ; T. Royds, *Phil. Mag.*, (6), **19**. 285, 1910 ; *Phil. Trans.*, **208**. A, 333, 1908 ; R. J. Lang, *ib.*, **224**. A, 371, 1924 ; D. Alter, *Amer. Journ. Science*, (2), **18**. 55, 1854 ; A. Masson, *Ann. Chim. Phys.*, (3), **31**. 295, 1851 ; E. Diaçon, *ib.*, (4), **6**. 5, 1865 ; P. Joye, *ib.*, (8), **21**. 148, 1910 ; J. C. McLennan and R. V. Zumstein, *Trans. Roy. Soc. Canada*, (3), **14**. 9, 1920 ; V. Thorsen, *Naturwiss.*, **11**. 78, 1923 ; A. J. Angström, *Svenska Akad. Handl.*, 229, 1853 ; *Pogg. Ann.*, **94**. 141, 1855 ; A. Mitscherlich, *ib.*, **121**. 459, 1864 ; A. de Gramont, *Compt. Rend.*, **144**. 1101, 1907 ; **145**. 231, 1907 ; **170**. 31, 1920 ; *Analyse spectrale directe des minéraux*, Paris, 1895 ; *Bull. Soc. Min.*, **18**. 214, 1895 ; A. de Gramont and G. A. Hemsalech, *Compt. Rend.*, **173**. 278, 1921 ; *Phil. Mag.*, (6), **43**. 287, 1922 ; G. Kirchhoff, *Sitzber. Akad. Berlin*, 63, 1861 ; 227, 1863 ; H. Kayser and C. Runge, *ib.*, 3, 1893 ; *Wied. Ann.*, **52**. 93, 1894 ; A. C. Jones, *ib.*, 62, 30, 1897 ; A. Kalähne, *ib.*, **65**. 815, 1898 ; G. G. Stokes, *Phil. Trans.*, **152**. 599, 1862 ; F. R. Robinson, *ib.*, **152**. 939, 1862 ; W. A. Miller, *ib.*, **152**. 861, 1862 ; S. R. Milner, *ib.*, **209**. A, 71, 1908 ; W. Huggins, *Phil. Mag.*, (4), **48**. 471, 1874 ; *Phil. Trans.*, **154**. 139, 1864 ; J. Plücker and J. W. Hittorf, *ib.*, **155**. 1, 1865 ; J. N. Lockyer, *ib.*, **163**. 253, 639, 1873 ; J. N. Lockyer and W. C. Roberts-Austen, *Proc. Roy. Soc.*, **23**. 344, 1875 ; **27**. 279, 1878 ; *Compt. Rend.*, **86**. 317, 1878 ; J. Parry and A. E. Tucker, *Engg.*, **27**. 127, 429, 1879 ; **28**. 141, 1879 ; F. Brasack, *Abhand. Nat. Ges. Halle*, **9**. 1, 1864 ; R. Thalén, *Nova Acta Soc. Upsala*, (3), **6**. 9, 1868 ; *Om Spectralanalyse*, Upsala, 1866 ; A. R. Leeds, *Quart. Journ. Science*, **8**. 59, 1871 ; J. Stark and B. Küch, *Phys. Zeit.*, **6**. 438, 1905 ; L. Grebe and H. Konen, *ib.*, **22**. 546, 1921 ; A. Cornu, *Compt. Rend.*, **73**. 332, 1871 ; L. and E. Bloch, *Journ. Phys. Rad.*, (6), **2**. 229, 1921 ; *Compt. Rend.*, **172**. 803, 1921 ; **178**. 472, 1924 ; M. de Broglie, *ib.*, **174**. 939, 1922 ; L. de Boisbaudran, *ib.*, **77**. 937, 1152, 1873 ; *Spectres lumineux*, Paris, 1874 ; R. Capron, *Photographed Spectra*, London, 1877 ; E. Demarçay, *Spectres électriques*, Paris, 1895 ; C. E. Gissing, *Spark Spectra of the Metals*, London, 1910 ; G. Ciamician, *Sitzber. Akad. Wien*, **76**. 499, 1877 ; F. Exner and E. Haschek, *ib.*, **106**. 54, 1897 ; *Wellenlängentabellen zu spectralanalytischen Untersuchungen auf Grund der ultravioletten Funkenspectren der Elemente*, Leipzig, 1902 ; *Wellenlängentabellen zu spectralanalytischen Untersuchungen auf Grund der ultravioletten Bogenspectren der Elemente*, Leipzig, 1904 ; *Die Spectren der Elemente bei normalen Druck*, Leipzig, 1911 ; A. Harnack, *Vergleichende Unter-*

suchungen über Spectren in der Sauerstoff-Wasserstoff und in der Chlor-Wasserstoff-Knallgasflamme,
Leipzig, 1911 ; H. Lamprecht, *Das Bandenspectrum des Bleis,* Bonn, 1911 ; *Zeit. wiss. Photo-*
chem., 10. 16, 33, 1911 ; J. Steinhausen, *ib.,* 3. 45, 1905 ; *Ueber " enhanced lines,"* Bonn, 1904 ;
G. Berndt, *Ueber den Einfluss von Selbstinduction auf die durch den Inductionsfunken erzeugten,*
Metallspectren im Ultraviolett, Halle, 1901 ; A. Hagenbach and H. Konen, *Atlas der Emissions-*
spectra, Jena, 1905 ; E. Néculcéa, *Recherches théoretiques et expérimentales sur la constitution*
des spectres ultraviolettes d'étincelles oscillantes, Paris, 1906 ; *Compt. Rend.,* 134. 1572, 1902 ;
G. A. Hemsalech, *ib.,* 132. 959, 1901 ; *Journ. Phys.,* (3), 8. 652, 1899 ; *Recherches expérimentales*
sur les spectres d'étincelles, Paris, 1901 ; C. de Watteville, *Spectres de flammes,* Evreux, 1904 ;
Phil. Trans., 204. A, 139, 1904 ; J. Formanek, *Die Qualitative Spektralanalyse anorganischer und*
organischer Körper, Berlin, 156, 1905 ; H. Kayser, *Handbuch der Spectroscopie,* Leipzig, 6. 256,
1912 ; A. Fowler, *Report on Series in Line Spectra,* London, 163, 1922 ; M. Kimura, *Japan.*
Journ. Phys., 3. 217, 1924 ; L. Grebe and H. Konen, *Phys. Zeit.,* 22. 546, 1921 ; F. L. Mohler,
P. D. Foote, and H. F. Stimson, *Phil. Mag.,* (6), 40. 73, 1920 ; A. Gouy, *Compt. Rend.,* 84. 231,
1877 ; H. Becquerel, *ib.,* 97. 71, 1883 ; 99. 374, 1884 ; *Ann. Chim. Phys.,* (5), 30. 5, 1883 ;
W. D. Harkins and L. Aronberg, *Journ. Amer. Chem. Soc.,* 42. 1328, 1920 ; W. N. Hartley,
Trans. Roy. Soc. Dublin, (2), 1. 231, 1883 ; (2), 9. 85, 1908 ; *Journ. Chem. Soc.,* 41. 84, 1882 ;
101. 820, 1912 ; *Phil. Trans.,* 175. 325, 1884 ; 185. 161, 1894 ; *Proc. Roy. Soc.,* 54. 5, 1893 ;
W. N. Hartley and H. W. Moss, *ib.,* 87. A, 38, 1912 ; W. N. Hartley and H. Ramage, *ib.,* 60.
393, 1896 ; W. N. Hartley and W. E. Adeney, *Phil. Trans.,* 175. 63, 1884 ; R. J. Lang, *ib.,* 224.
A, 371, 1925 ; G. D. Liveing and J. Dewar, *ib.,* 174. 187, 1883 ; *Proc. Roy. Soc.,* 36. 471, 1884 ;
C. J. Lundström, *ib.,* 59. 76, 1895 ; J. C. McLennan, D. S. Ainslie, and D. S. Fuller, *ib.,* 85. A,
316, 1919 ; T. R. Merton, *ib.,* 91. A, 198, 1915 ; 96. A, 388, 1920 ; 100. A, 84, 1921 ; T. Royds,
ib., 107. A, 560, 1925 ; J. C. McLennan, J. F. T. Young, and H. J. C. Ireton, *ib.,* 98. A, 95, 1920 ;
Trans. Roy. Soc. Canada, (3), 13. 7, 1919 ; R. V. Zumstein, *ib.,* (3), 12. 59, 1918 ; J. C. McLennan,
J. F. T. Young, and A. B. McLay, *ib.,* (3), 18. 77, 1924 ; W. R. Mott, *Trans. Amer. Electrochem.*
Soc., 31. 369, 1917 ; V. Schumann, *Phot. Rund.,* 41. 71, 1890 ; J. M. Eder, *Denks. Akad. Wien,*
60. 1, 1893 ; J. M. Eder and E. Valenta, *ib.,* 68. 531, 1899 ; *Sitzber. Akad. Wien,* 118. 511, 1077,
1909 ; 119. 519, 1910 ; *Atlas typischer Spectren,* Wien, 1911 ; H. A. Rowland, *Astron. Astrophys.*
Journ., 12. 321, 1893 ; *Preliminary Table of Solar Spectrum Wave-lengths,* Chicago, 1898 ;
O. Vogel, *Zeit. anorg. Chem.,* 5. 42, 1894 ; W. J. Humphreys, *Astrophys. Journ.,* 6. 169, 1897 ;
B. E. Moore, *ib.,* 58. 86, 104, 1923 ; J. Wilsing, *ib.,* 10. 112, 1899 ; *Sitzber. Akad. Berlin,* 426,
1899 ; J. Hartmann, *ib.,* 234, 1903 ; *Astrophys. Journ.,* 17. 270, 1903 ; H. W. Morse, *ib.,* 19.
162, 1904 ; A. S. King, *ib.,* 21. 236, 1905 ; *Ann. Physik,* (4), 16. 360, 1905 ; K. W. Meissner, *ib.,*
(4), 71. 135, 1923 ; L. Janicki, *ib.,* (4), 29. 833, 1909 ; L. Janicki and·R. Seliger. *ib.,* (4), 44.
1151, 1914 ; H. Lunelund, *ib.,* (4), 34. 505, 1911 ; T. Retschinsky, *ib.,* (4), 27. 105, 1908 ; H. Lehmann, *ib.,* (4), 39. 78, 1912 ; O. Lohse, *Pub. Astrophys. Obs. Potsdam,* 12. 109, 1902 ; E. Wiedemann, *Boltzmann's Festschrift,* 826, 1904 ; W. von Bolton, *Zeit. Electrochem.,* 9. 913, 1903 ;
W. B. Huff, *Astrophys. Journ.,* 16. 27, 1902 ; P. Lewis, *ib.,* 16. 31, 1902 ; H. M. Randall, *Ann.*
Physik, (4), 33. 730, 1910 ; *Astrophys. Journ.,* 34. 1, 1911 ; P. G. Nutting, *ib.,* 23. 64, 1906 ;
A. S. C. Dunstan and B. A. Wooten, *ib.,* 54. 65, 1921 ; P. A. van der Harst, *Proc. Acad. Amster-*
dam, 20. 170, 1919 ; 22. 300, 1920 ; W. W. Coblentz, *Bull. Bur. Standards,* 2. 469, 1906 ; W. Gallenkamp, *Zeit. wiss. Photochem.,* 5. 299, 1907 ; H. Auerbach, *Spektroskopische Untersuchungen*
über das Verhalten der Metallsalze in Flammen von verschiedener Temperaturen, Berlin, 1907 ;
Zeit. wiss. Photochem., 7. 30, 41, 1909 ; H. Geisler, *ib.,* 7. 89, 1909 ; H. Finger, *ib.,* 7. 329, 369,
1909 ; F. Klein, *ib.,* 12. 16, 1913 ; R. Arnolds, *ib.,* 13. 313, 1914 ; H. Könemann, *ib.,* 12. 65,
1913 ; H. Hertenstein, *ib.,* 11. 69, 119, 1912 ; W. Huppers, *ib.,* 13. 16, 1913 ; C. Schäfer, *ib.,*
8. 212, 1910 ; B. Reismann, *ib.,* 13. 269, 301, 1914 ; A. Bergmann, *ib.,* 6. 113, 145, 1908 ;
Beiträge zur Kenntniss der ultrarothen Emissionspectren der Alcalien, Jena, 1907 ; A. Terenin,
Zeit. Physik, 31. 26, 1925 ; R. V. Zumstein, *ib.,* (2), 26. 189, 1925 ; H. Nagaoka and Y. Sugiura,
Science Papers Inst. Phys., 2. 139, 1924 ; J. E. Purvis, *Prov. Cambridge Phil. Soc.,* 13. 82, 1905 ;
14. 216, 1907 ; V. Carlheim-Gyllensköld, *Ark. Mat. Astron. Fysik,* 4. 33, 1908 ; V. Thorsen,
Naturwiss., 11. 78, 255, 1923 ; W. Grotrian, *ib.,* 11. 255, 1923 ; *Zeit. Physik,* 18. 169, 1923 ;
H. Sponer, *ib.,* 32. 19, 1925 ; S. Goudsmit, *ib.,* 32. 794, 1925 ; F. L. Mohler, P. D. Foote, and
H. F. Stimson, *Phil. Mag.,* (6), 40. 73, 1920 ; D. W. Jones, *Journ. Soc. Chem. Ind.,* 39. 221, T,
1920 ; E. O. Hulburt, *Phys. Rev.,* (2), 24. 129, 1924 ; (2), 25. 888, 1925 ; P. A. Ross, *ib.,* (2), 17.
336, 1921 ; V. Thorsen, *Naturwiss.,* 12. 705, 1924 ; N. K. Sur and R. K. Sharma, *Journ. Science*
Assoc. Vizianagaram., 1. 121, 1924 ; V. P. Lubovich and E. M. Pearen, *Trans. Roy. Soc. Canada,*
(3), 16. 195, 1922 ; B. E. Moore, *Astrophys. Journ.,* 58. 86, 104, 1923 ; E. S. Bieler, *Nature,* 115.
980, 1925 ; J. G. Frayne and A. W. Smith, *Phil. Mag.,* (7), 1. 732, 1926 ; J. E. P. Wagstaff,
ib., (6), 47. 84, 1924 ; F. K. Richtmyer, *Phys. Rev.,* (-), 27. 1, 1926 ; S. J. M. Allen, *ib.,* (-), 27.
266, 1926 ; B. R. Stephenson and J. M. Cork, *Phys. Rev.,* (2), 27. 138, 1926 ; W. Friederichs,
Ueber Absorptionsspektra von Dämpfen, Bonn, 1905 ; F. Hund, *Zeit. Physik,* 33. 658, 1925 ;
H. Giesler and W. Grotrian, *ib.,* 34. 374, 1925 ; E. Back, *ib.,* 37. 193, 1926 ; J. A. Carroll,
Phil. Trans., 225. A, 357, 1926 ; A. L. Narayan and K. R. Rao, *Phil. Mag.,* (6), 50. 645, 1925 ;
A. E. Ruark and R. L. Chenault, *ib.,* (6), 50. 951, 1925 ; N. K. Sur, *ib.,* (7), 2. 633, 1926 ;
S. Smith, *Atrop ys. Journ.,* 61. 186, 1925 ; M. Kimura and G. Nakamura, *Science Papers*
Japan. Inst. Phys. Chem. Research, 3. 51, 1925 ; A. P. Weber, *Zeit. Wiss. Photochem.,* 23. 149,
1925 ; R. V. Zumstein, *Phys. Rev.,* (2), 26. 189, 1925 ; A. T. Waterman, *ib.,* (2), 22. 259, 1923 ;
A. Nodon, *Compt. Rend.,* 174. 1061, 1922.

[30] A. Matthiessen, *Pogg. Ann.*, 103. 428, 1858; A. Matthiessen and A. von Bose, *Proc. Roy. Soc.*, 11. 516, 1862; *Phil. Trans.*, 152. 1, 1862; *Pogg. Ann.*, 115. 393, 1862; A. Arndtsen, *ib.*, 104. 1, 1858; R. Clausius, *ib.*, 104. 650, 1858; J. Bergmann, *Wied. Ann.*, 42. 90, 1891; A. Overbeck and J. Bergmann, *ib.*, 31. 792, 1887; L. Lorenz, *ib.*, 13. 422, 582, 1881; G. Kirchhoff and G. Hansemann, *ib.*, 13. 406, 1881; E. D. Williamson, *Journ. Franklin Inst.*, 193. 491, 1922; C. Benedicks, *Ark. Mat. Astron. Fys.*, 6. 24, 1910; *Rev. Mét.*, 8. 20, 1911; P. Müller, *Met.*, 7. 730, 769, 1910; W. Jäger and H. Diesselhorst, *Abhand. Phys. Tech. Reichsanst.*, 3. 269, 1900; W. Herold, *Zeit. anorg. Chem.*, 112. 141, 1920; H. F. Weber, *Sitzber. Akad. Berlin*, 476, 1880; J. R. Benoit, *Arch. Sciences Genève*, (2), 51. 284, 1874; *Études expérimentales sur la résistance électrique des métaux et sa variation sous l'influence de la température*, Paris, 1873; *Compt. Rend.*, 76. 342, 1873; L. de la Rive, *ib.*, 57. 698, 1863; A. Berget, *ib.*, 76. 342, 1873; L. Guillet and M. Ballay, *ib.*, 176. 1800, 1923; *Rev. Mét.*, 20. 398, 1923; A. Schulze, *Zeit. Metallkunde*, 15. 33, 155, 1923; 16. 48, 1924; E. F. Northrup, *Trans. Amer. Electrochem. Soc.*, 25. 388, 1914; *Journ. Franklin Inst.*, 179. 621, 1915; E. F. Northrup and V. A. Suijdam, *ib.*, 175. 153, 1913; H. Dickson, *Phil. Mag.*, (5), 45. 525, 1898; J. Dewar and J. A. Fleming, *ib.*, (5), 36. 271, 1893; W. E. Williams, *ib.*, (6), 13. 635, 1907; A. Stein, *Phys. Zeit.*, 13. 267, 1912; A. C. Becquerel, *Ann. Chim. Phys.*, (3), 17. 242, 1846; G. Vicentini and D. Omodei, *Atti Accad. Torino*, 25. 30, 1889; C. Cattaneo, *ib.*, 27. 698, 1892; G. Niccolai, *Atti Accad. Lincei*, (5), 16. i, 757, 909, 1907; *Phys. Zeit.*, 9. 367, 1908; E. Grüneisen, *ib.*, 19. 382, 1918; F. B. Silsbee, *Journ. Washington Accad.*, 6. 597, 1916; H. Schimank, *Ann. Physik*, (4), 45. 706, 1914; L. Holborn, *ib.*, (4), 59. 158, 1919; *Zeit. Physik*, 8. 58, 1922; F. Henning, *Ann. Physik*, (4), 40. 635, 1913; *Zeit. Instr.*, 34. 116, 1914; *Zeit. Physik*, 5. 264, 1921; P. W. Bridgman, *Proc. Amer. Acad.*, 52. 573, 1917; *Proc. Nat. Acad.*, 3. 10, 1917; 5. 351, 1919; *Journ. Washington Acad.*, 11. 455, 1921; S. Lussana, *Nuovo Cimento*, (4), 10. 771, 1899; N. S. Kurnakoff and S. F. Schemtschuschny, *Zeit. anorg. Chem.*, 64. 157, 1909; E. Lisell, *Om Tryckets Inflytande pa det elektriska Ledningsmotständet hos Metaller samt en ny Metod att Mäta Höga Tryck*, Upsala, 1902; O. Chwolson, *Bull. Acad. St. Petersburg*, (4), 10. 379, 1877; (4), 11. 353, 1878; H. K. Onnes and B. Beckman, *Versl. Akad. Amsterdam*, 21. 263, 888, 1912; *Comm. Phys. Lab. Leiden*, 132, b, 1913; H. K. Onnes and J. Clay, *ib.*, 99, c, 1907; *Versl. Akad. Amsterdam*, 16. 169, 1907; W. Tuyn and H. K. Onnes, *Arch. Néerl.*, (3), 6. 293, 1923; *Journ. Franklin Inst.*, 201. 379, 1926; *Proc. Acad. Amsterdam*, 26. 504, 1923; W. H. Keesom and H. K. Onnes, *ib.*, 17. 894, 1914; C. A. Crommelin, *Jahrb. Rad. Elektron.*, 19. 38, 1922; *Comm. Phys. Lab. Leiden*, Suppl. 44, 1921; H. Tomlinson, *Proc. Roy. Soc.*, 26. 401, 1877; L. L. Grunmach and F. Weidert, *Ber. deut. phys. Ges.*, 4. 359, 1907; W. Meissner, *Verh. deut. phys. Ges.*, 16. 262, 1914; *Ann. Physik*, (4), 47. 1001, 1915; H. Tsutsumi, *Science Rep. Tohoku Univ.*, 7. 93, 1918; S. Konno, *ib.*, 10. 60, 1922; C. H. Lees and J. E. Calthrop, *Proc. Phys. Soc.*, 35. 225, 1923; C. H. Lees, *Phil. Trans.*, 208. A, 426, 1908; A. T. Waterman, *Phys. Rev.*, (2), 22. 259, 1923; S. Smith, *Astrophys. Journ.*, 61. 186, 1925; A. Eurken, *Zeit. Metallkunde*, 18. 182, 1926; Z. A. Epstein, *Zeit. Physik*, 32. 620, 1925.

[31] F. E. Fowle, *Smithsonian Physical Tables*, Washington, 208, 1916; (I am indebted to the Smithsonian Institute for permission to use Table III); R. D. Kleeman and W. Fredrickson, *Phys. Rev.*, (2), 22. 134, 1923; E. Becquerel, *Ann. Chim. Phys.*, (4), 8. 415, 1866; P. G. Tait, *Trans. Roy. Soc. Edin.*, 27. 125, 1872; C. Benedicks, *Internat. Zeit. Metallog.*, 7. 225, 1915; P. W. Bridgman, *Proc. Amer. Acad.*, 53. 259, 1918; W. Jäger and H. Diesselhorst, *Abhand. Phys. Tech. Reichsanst.*, 3. 269, 1900; H. Pélabon, *Ann. Phys.*, (9), 13. 169, 1920; H. K. Onnes and B. Beckman, *Versl. Akad. Amsterdam*, 21. 263, 888, 1913; H. K. Onnes and G. Holst, *Proc. Acad. Amsterdam*, 17. 760, 1914; E. Wagner, *Ann. Physik*, (4), 27. 992, 1908; P. Cermak, *ib.*, (4), 26. 523, 1908; (4), 33. 1195, 1910; P. Cermak and H. Schmidt, *ib.*, (4), 36. 575, 1911; G. Wietzel, *ib.*, (4), 43. 605, 1914; G. Borelius and F. Gunneson, *ib.*, (4), 65. 520, 1921; G. Borelius, *ib.*, (4), 60. 381, 1919; W. Haken, *ib.*, (4), 32. 291, 1910; P. Drude, *ib.*, (4), 3. 392, 1900; O. Berg, *ib.*, (4), 32. 477, 1910; K. Siebel, *ib.*, (4), 45. 839, 1914; *Das thermoelektrische Verhalten einiger Metalle*, Kiel, 1914; J. Dewer and J. A. Fleming, *Phil. Mag.*, (5), 40. 118, 1895; H. Dickson, *ib.*, (5), 45. 527, 1898; E. P. Adams and A. K. Chapman, *ib.*, (6), 28. 692, 1914; E. Edlund, *Pogg. Ann.*, 143. 404, 534, 1871; A. Matthiessen, *ib.*, 103. 412, 1858; H. Zahn, *Jahrb. Rad. Elektron.*, 5. 178, 200, 1887; K. Noll, *Wied. Ann.*, 53. 874, 1894; N. A. Hesehus, *Journ. Russ. Phys. Chem. Soc.*, 39. 1, 1907; H. Pélabon, *Ann. Physique*, (9), 13. 169, 1920; *Compt. Rend.*, 176. 1305, 1923; A. von Ettinghausen and W. Nernst, *Sitzber. Akad. Berlin*, 560, 1886; H. Jahn, *Zeit. phys. Chem.*, 18. 422, 1895; K. Bädeker, *Die elektrischen Erscheinungen in metallischen Leitern*, Braunschweig, 73, 1911; A. Battelli, *Atti 1st. Veneto*, (7), 4. 1452, 1893; *Atti Accad. Lincei*, (4), 3. 404, 1887; (5), 2. ii, 162, 1893; O. M. Corbino, *Phys. Zeit.*, 12. 561, 1911; H. K. Onnes and K. Hof, *Comm. Phys. Lab. Leiden Univ.*, 142, 1914; 142, b, 1914; E. Rudolfi, *Zeit. anorg. Chem.*, 67. 65, 1910; F. G. Wick, *Phys. Rev.*, (2), 25. 382, 1907; H. Pécheux, *Compt. Rend.*, 139. 1203, 1904; Z. A. Epstein, *Zeit. Physik*, 32. 620, 1925; W. M. Latimer, *Journ. Amer. Chem. Soc.*, 44. 2136, 1922.

[32] H. Davy, *Phil. Trans.*, 116. 408, 1826; M. Faraday, *ib.*, 123. 675, 1833; W. E. Ayrton and J. Perry, *ib.*, 171. 1, 1880; *Proc. Roy. Soc.*, 27. 196, 1878; S. P. Thompson, *ib.*, 42. 387, 1887; J. Erskine-Murray, *ib.*, 63. 129, 1898; W. M. Jones, *Phil. Mag.*, (6), 29. 261, 1915; A. Coehn and A. Curs, *Zeit. Physik*, 29. 186, 1924; W. Hankel, *Ber. Sächs. Ges.*, 6. 1, 1861; 7. 385, 1865; *Pogg. Ann.*, 115. 57, 1862; 126. 286, 1865; J. C. Poggendorff, *ib.*, 50. 263, 1840; 66. 597, 1845; 73. 619, 1848; P. S. Munk af Rosenschöld, *ib.*, 35. 55, 1835; C. H. Pfaff, *ib.*, 51. 209, 1840; *Journ. Phys.*, 8. 196, 1794; *De electricitate sic dicta animali*, Stuttgart, 1793;

R. H. Gerke, *Journ. Amer. Chem. Soc.*, **44**. 1684, 1922 ; **F.** W. Bergstrom, *ib.*, **47**. 1503, 1925 ; W. E. Henderson and G. Stegeman, *ib.*, **40**. 84, 1918 ; M. G. Mellon and W. E. Henderson, *ib.*, **42**. 676, 1920 ; G. Tammann, *Zeit. anorg. Chem.*, **133**. 267, 1924 ; J. N. Frers, *Ber.*, **57**. B, 1693, 1924 ; F. Exner and J. Tuma, *Sitzber. Akad. Wien*, **97**. 917, 1888 ; H. Pellat, *Compt. Rend.*, **80**. 990, 1880 ; *Difference de potential des couches électriques qui recouvert deux métaux au contact*, Paris, 1881 ; *Journ. Phys.*, (1), **10**. 68, 1881 ; A. Volta, *Gilbert's Ann.*, **10**. 421, 1802 ; T. Seebeck, *Sitzber. Akad. Berlin*, 295, 1822 ; J. C. E. Péclet, *Ann. Chim. Phys.*, (3), **2**. 243, 1841 ; J. M. Gaugain, *Compt. Rend.*, **59**. 493, 1864 ; J. W. Ritter, *Beiträge zur Kenntniss des Galvanismus*, Jena, **1**. 47, 1800 ; A. Coehn and A. Lotz, *Zeit. Physik*, **5**. 242, 260, 1921 ; G. T. Fechner, *Schweigger's Journ.*, **53**. 129, 1828 ; P. Marianini, *ib.*, **49**. 52, 1827 ; A. Avogadro and V. Michelotti, *Ann. Chim. Phys.*, (2), **22**. 364, 1823 ; A. de la Rive, *ib.*, (2), **37**. 225, 1828 ; C. Krahmer, *Zeit. Elektrochem.*, **26**. 97, 1920 ; G. Athanasiu, *Compt. Rend.*, **178**. 561, 1924 ; A. L. Clark, *Trans. Roy. Soc. Canada*, (3), **18**. 275, 1924 ; H. von Steinwehr, *Zeit. Instrk.*, **33**. 321, 1913 ; A. Naccari and M. Bellati, *Nuovo Cimento*, (2), **11**. 120, 1872 ; C. Hocken and H. A. Taylor, *Journ. Soc. Tel. Eng.*, **8**. 282, 1879 ; A. Overbeck and J. Edler, *Wied. Ann.*, **42**. 209, 1891 ; S. Procopiu, *Bull. Soc. Rom.*, **3**. 187, 1915 ; R. D. Kleeman and W. Fredrickson, *Phys. Rev.*, (2), **22**. 134, 1923 ; H. F. Vieweg, *Journ. Phys. Chem.*, **30**. 865, 1926.

33 G. Magnanini, *Atti Accad. Lincei*, (4), **6**. 182, 1890 ; *Gazz. Chim. Ital.*, **20**. 308, 1890 ; L. Rolla, *ib.*, **43**. ii, 545, 1913 ; C. R. A. Wright and C. Thompson, *Phil. Mag.*, (5), **17**. 188. 1884 ; (5), **19**. 1, 1885 ; J. Brown, *Proc. Roy. Soc.*, **52**. 80, 1923 ; P. Günther, *Zeit. Elektrochem.*, **23**. 97, 1917 ; P. P. Lebedeff, *ib.*, **18**. 893, 1912 ; C. Immerwahr, *ib.*, **7**. 477, 1901 ; J. Oblata, *Proc. Japan. Phys. Math. Soc.*, (3), **3**. 64, 1921 ; S. B. Christy, *Trans. Amer. Inst. Min. Eng.*, **27**. 354, 1902 ; *Amer. Chem. Journ.*, **37**. 345, 1902 ; *Zeit. Elektrochem.*, **8**. 198, 1902 ; S. Labendzinsky, *ib.*, **10**. 78, 1904 ; *Ueber die Konstitution gelösten Schwermetallsalze auf Grund von Potentialmessungen*, Breslau, 1904 ; J. N. Brönsted, *Zeit. Elektrochem.*, **19**. 754, 1913 ; G. Grube, *ib.*, **28**. 289, 1922 ; J. Tafel, *ib.*, **12**. 118, 1906 ; *Zeit. phys. Chem.*, **50**. 641, 1905 ; C. Zenghelis, *ib.*, **12**. 309, 1893 ; W. D. Bancroft, *ib.*, **12**. 289. 1893 ; W. Ostwald, *ib.*, **1**. 601, 1887 ; **35**. 338, 1900 ; B. Neumann, *ib.*, **14**. 212, 1894 ; W. Löb and R. W. Moore, *ib.*, **47**. 434, 1904 ; J. Neustadt and R. Abegg, *ib.*, **69**. 486, 1909 ; G. Trümpler, *ib.*, **99**. 9, 1921 ; W. K. Lewis, *ib.*, **63**. 171, 1908 ; *Die Komplexbildung zwischen Bleinitrat und Kalumnitrat*, Breslau, 155, 1908 ; N. T. M. Wilsmore, *Zeit. phys. Chem.*, **35**. 314, 1900 ; F. M. G. Johnson and N. T. M. Wilsmore, *Trans. Faraday Soc.*, **3**. 77, 1907 ; A. C. Cumming, *ib.*, **2**. 207, 1907 ; G. N. Lewis and T. B. Brighton, *Journ. Amer. Chem. Soc.*, **39**. 1906, 1907 ; A. A. Noyes and K. Toabe, *ib.*, **39**. 1537, 1907 ; F. H. Getman, *ib.*, **38**. 792, 1916 ; **40**. 611, 1918 ; W. E. Henderson and G. Stegeman, *ib.*, **40**. 84, 1918 ; S. B. Christy, *Amer. Chem. Journ.*, **27**. 369, 1902 ; O. Sackur, *Arb. Kaiser Ges. Amt.*, **20**. 512, 1904 ; O. P. Watts and N. D. Whipple, *Trans. Amer. Electrochem. Soc.*, **32**. 276, 1918 ; L. Kahlenberg, *ib.*, **6**. 57, 1904 ; *Journ. Phys. Chem.*, **3**. 379, 1899 ; C. M. van Deventer, *Chem. Weekbl.*, **13**. 472, 1916 ; Z. Klemensiewicz, *Compt. Rend.*, **158**. 1889, 1904 ; C. Christiansen, *Wied. Ann.*, **69**. 661, 1899 ; F. Braun, *ib.*, **16**. 562, 1882 ; **17**. 592, 1882 ; H. Jahn, *ib.*, **28**. 498, 1886 ; *Zeit. phys. Chem.*, **16**. 52, 1895 ; **26**. 400, 1898 ; A. Gockel, *ib.*, **34**. 544, 1900 ; H. Götz and A. Kurz, *Elektrotech. Zeit.*, **11**. 30, 1890 ; J. B. Baille and C. Féry, *ib.*, **11**. 154, 1890 ; V. Czepinsky, *Zeit. anorg. Chem.*, **19**. 257, 1899 ; G. Tammann, *ib.*, **133**. 267, 1924 ; S. Procopiu, *Journ. Chim. Phys.*, **19**. 121, 1921 ; W. Spring, *Bull. Acad. Belg.*, 1074, 1903 ; M. G. Mellon and W. E. Henderson, *Journ. Amer. Chem. Soc.*, **42**. 476, 1920 ; A. von Oettingen, *Journ. Chem. Met. Soc. South Africa*, **2**. 9, 21, 1899 ; A. L. Clark, *Trans. Roy. Soc. Canada*, (3), **18**. 275, 1924 ; M. Dresbach and H. R. Hosmer, *Amer. Journ. Physiol.*, **68**. 122, 1924 ; H. Hock and F. Klawitter, *Metall Erz*, **22**. 377, 1925 ; J. T. Burt-Gerrans and H. R. Hugill, *Trans. Roy. Soc. Canada*, (3), **19**. 26, 1925 ; H. D. Holler, *Science Papers Bur. Standards*, **20**. 153, 1925 ; H. Gordon, *Ueber die Komplextät verschiedener Metalltartrationen und die Löslichkeit verschiedener Metallhydroxyde und Sulfide*, Danzig, 1924 ; H. Jellinek and H. Gordon, *Zeit. phys. Chem.*, **112**. 207, 1924 ; G. Athanasiu, *Compt. Rend.*, **178**. 567, 1924.

34 A. Günther-Schulze, *Ann. Physik*, (4), **65**. 223, 1921 ; W. Winter, *Phys. Zeit.*, **14**. 1823, 1913.
35 W. Hittorf, *Zeit. phys. Chem.*, **34**. 401, 1900 ; G. C. Schmidt, *ib.*, **106**. 105, 1923 ; W. J. Müller, *ib.*, **48**. 577, 1904 ; W. A. Caspari, *ib.*, **30**. 931, 1899 ; W. Löb and R. W. Moore, *ib.*, **47**. 421, 1904 ; T. Ericson-Aurén and W. Palmaer, *ib.*, **45**. 194, 1903 ; J. Tafel and B. Emmert, *ib.*, **52**. 373, 1905 ; J. Tafel, *ib.*, **34**. 197, 1900 ; **50**. 712, 1906 ; *Zeit. Elektrochem.*, **12**. 118, 1906 ; A. Sieverts and P. Lueg, *Zeit. anorg. Chem.*, **126**. 219, 1923 ; S. Dunnill, *Journ. Chem. Soc.*, **119**. 1081, 1921 ; S. Glasstone, *Trans. Faraday Soc.*, **21**. 36, 1925 ; *Journ. Chem. Soc.*, **123**. 2926, 1923 ; **124**. 2414, 1924 ; **127**. 1824, 1925 ; A. Coehn and K. Dannenberg, *Zeit. phys. Chem.*, **38**. 618, 1901 ; F. Förster, *ib.*, **22**. 101, 1916 ; P. P. Lebedeff, *ib.*, **18**. 895, 1912 ; M. le Blanc, *ib.*, **11**. 8, 1905 ; **16**. 33, 1910 ; P. Fischer, *ib.*, **113**. 326, 1924 ; G. Grube, *ib.*, **18**. 211, 1912 ; K. Elbs and F. Fischer, *ib.*, **7**. 343, 1900 ; C. W. Bennett and W. S. Burnham, *Trans. Amer. Electrochem. Soc.*, **29**. 217, 1916 ; W. R. Dunstan and J. R. Hill, *Journ. Chem. Soc.*, **99**. 1853, 1911 ; E. Newbery, *ib.*, **105**. 2419, 1914 ; **109**. 1073, 1916 ; **125**. 511, 1924 ; O. Sackur, *Chem. Ztg.*, **28**. 954, 1904 ; C. Hambuechen, *Chem. Met. Engg.*, **8**. 634, 1910 ; A. Thiel and W. Hammerschmidt, *Zeit. anorg. Chem.*, **132**. 15, 1923 ; F. Meunier, *Bull. Acad. Belg.*, (4), **9**. 300, 1923 ; *Journ. Chim. Phys.*, **22**. 595, 1925 ; C. Marie and G. Lejeune, *Compt. Rend.*, **179**. 679, 1924 ; U. Sborgi and P. Marchetti, *Nuovo Cimento*, (6), **22**. 151, 1921 ; M. Knobel, *Journ. Amer. Chem. Soc.*, **46**. 2751, 1924.
36 W. Ostwald, *Zeit. phys. Chem.*, **11**. 501, 1893 ; F. Kohlrausch, *ib.*, **43**. 511, 1903 ; *Sitzber. Akad. Berlin*, 1026, 1901 ; E. Grüneisen, *ib.*, 1215, 1904 ; K. G. Falk, *Journ. Amer. Chem. Soc.*,

32. 1555, 1910 ; **A.** A. Noyes and E. H. Woodworth, *Zeit. phys. Chem.*, **26**. 156, 1898 ; **C. L.** von Ende, *Ueber das Verhalten von Bleisalzen in Lösungen*, Göttingen, 1899 ; *Zeit. anorg. Chem.*, **26**. 157, 1901 ; H. F. Fernau, *ib.*, **17**. 327, 1898 ; G. van Dyk, *Ann. Physik*, (4), **14**. 569, 1904 ; L. Boltzmann, *Monatsh.*, **8**. 230, 1887.

³⁷ M. le Blanc, *Zeit. phys. Chem.*, **8**. 299, 1891 ; H. Jahn, *ib.*, **26**. 385, 1898 ; G. Bodländer, *ib.*, **27**. 57, 1898 ; W. D. Bancroft, *Trans. Amer. Electrochem. Soc.*, **3**. 86, 1903 ; K. Elbs and J. Forssell, *Zeit. Elektrochem.*, **8**. 760, 1902 ; J. E. Root, *Journ. Phys. Chem.*, **7**. 428, 1902 ; H. W. Gillett, *ib.*, **13**. 338, 1909.

³⁸ E. F. Smith, *Electroanalysis*, Philadelphia, 100, 1907 ; *Proc. Amer. Phil. Soc.*, **24**. 428, 1887 ; R. O. Smith, *Journ. Amer. Chem. Soc.*, **27**. 1287, 1905 ; F. F. Exner, *ib.*, **25**. 904, 1903 ; A. F. Linn, *ib.*, **24**. 435, 1902 ; W. Hampe, *Zeit. anal. Chem.*, **13**. 183, 1874 ; C. Luckow, *ib.*, **19**. 215, 1880 ; L. Schucht, *ib.*, **21**. 488, 1882 ; M. Kiliani, *Berg. Hütt. Ztg.*, **42**. 253, 1883 ; J. G. Fairchild, *Journ. Ind. Eng. Chem.*, **3**. 902, 1911 ; R. C. Benner, *ib.*, **2**. 348, 1910 ; A. Classen, *ib.*, **21**. 257, 1888 ; *Ber.*, **27**. 163, 2060, 1894 ; A. Riché, *Ann. Chim. Phys.*, (5), **13**. 508, 1878 · W. C. May, *Amer. Journ. Science*, (3), **6**. 255, 1873 ; F. A. Gooch and H. E. Medway, *ib.*, (4), **15**. 320, 1903 ; G. Parodi and A. Mascazzini, *Gazz. Chim. Ital.*, **8**. 169, 1878 ; G. Vortmann, *Ber.*, **24**. 2749, 1891 ; *Liebig's Ann.*, **351**. 283, 1907 ; A. Kreichgauer, *Ber.*, **27**. 315, 1894 ; *Zeit. anorg. Chem.*, **9**. 89, 1895 ; B. S. Summers, *U.S. Pat. No.* 1475973, 1923 ; F. Fenny, *Amer. Chem. Journ.*, **5**. 413, 1883 ; F. Rüdorff, *Zeit. angew. Chem.*, **5**. 198, 1892 ; H. S. Warwick, *Chem. News*, **66**. 275, 1892 ; *Zeit. anory. Chem.*, **1**. 258, 1892 ; F. Henz, *ib.*, **37**. 2, 1903 ; M. G. Mellon and H. F. Reinhard, *Proc. Indiana Acad.*, 181, 1921 ; W. E. Hughes, *Beama*, **9**. 555, 1921 ; L. Medicus, *Ber.*, **95**. 2490, 1892 ; V. Kohlschütter and F. Uebersax, *Zeit. Elektrochem.*, **30**. 72, 1924 ; H. Freundlich and J. Fischer, *ib.*, **18**. 885, 1912 ; H. Nissenson and B. Neumann, *Chem. Ztg.*, **19**. 1142, 1895 ; B. Neumann, *ib.*, **20**. 381, 1896 ; F. Utz, *ib.*, **36**. 1788, 1912 ; A. Hollard, *Bull. Soc. Chim.*, (3), **19**. 911, 1898 ; (3), **29**. 151, 1903 ; (3), **31**. 239, 1904 ; *Compt. Rend.*, **136**. 229, 1904 ; *Chem. News*, **79**. 122, 1899 ; H. J. S. Sand, *Journ. Chem. Soc.*, **91**. 373, 1907 ; *Chem. News*, **100**. 269, 1909 ; C. Marie, *ib.*, **82**. 51, 1900 ; *Bull. Soc. Chim.*, (3), **23**. 563, 1900 ; *Compt. Rend.*, **130**. 1032, 1900 ; C. Marie and G. Lejeune, *ib.*, **179**. 679, 1924 ; G. Meillére, *Journ. Pharm. Chim.*, (6), **16**. 465, 1902 ; H. A. Guess, *Eng. Min. Journ.* **81**. 328, 1906 ; A. Fischer, and R. J. Boddaert, *Zeit. Elektrochem.*, **10**. 949, 1904 ; K. Elbs and F. W. Rixon, *ib.*, **9**. 267, 1903 ; H. Danneel and H. Nissenson, *Ber. Internat. Cong. Appl. Chem.*, **4**. 677, 1902 ; M. le Blanc, *Zeit. phys. Chem.*, **8**. 299, 1891 ; H. Jahn, *ib.*, **26**. 385, 1898 ; G. Bodländer, *ib.*, **27**. 57, 1898 ; W. D. Bancroft, *Trans. Amer. Electrochem. Soc.*, **3**. 86, 1903 ; K. Elbs and J. Forssell, *Zeit. Elektrochem.*, **8**. 760, 1902 ; J. E. Root, *Journ. Phys. Chem.*, **7**. 428, 1903 ; H. W. Gillett, *ib.*, **13**. 338, 1909.

³⁹ E. Becquerel, *Ann. Chim. Phys.*, (3), **13**. 216, 1845 ; A. Günther-Schulze, *Zeit. Elektrochem.*, **28**. 119, 1922 ; W. H. Creutzfeldt, *Zeit. anorg. Chem.*, **121**. 25, 1922 ; O. Lehmann, *Zeit. phys. Chem.*, **4**. 525, 1889 ; S. Glasstone, *Journ. Chem. Soc.*, **119**. 1915, 1921.

⁴⁰ F. Wöhler, *Liebig's Ann. Suppl.*, **2**. 135, 1862 ; F. Rüdorff, *Zeit. angew. Chem.*, **5**. 198, 1892 ; C. Luckow, *ib.*, **3**. 345, 1890 ; *Zeit. anal. Chem.*, **19**. 15, 1880 ; L. Schucht, *ib.*, **22**. 486, 1883 ; C. Marie, *Bull. Soc. Chim.*, (3), **23**. 563, 1900 ; *Compt. Rend.*, **130**. 1032, 1900 ; F. C. Mathers, *Trans. Amer. Electrochem. Soc.*, **24**. 328, 1913 ; S. A. Tucker and E. G. Thomssen, *ib.*, **15**. 477, 1909 ; *Electrochem. Ind.*, **7**. 273, 1909 ; E. F. Kern, *ib.*, **7**. 272, 1909 ; *Trans. Amer. Electrochem. Soc.*, **15**. 453, 1909 ; F. C. Mathers and A. McKinney, *ib.*, **27**. 133, 1915 ; L. Glaser, *Zeit. Elektrochem.*, **7**. 365, 381, 1900 ; H. Senn, *ib.*, **11**. 235, 1905 ; R. Marc, *ib.*, **19**. 434, 1913 ; H. Nissenson, *ib.*, **9**. 760, 1903 ; O. von Giese, *ib.*, **2**. 588, 1896 ; A. Classen, *ib.*, **1**. 229, 287, 1894 ; *Quantitative Analyse durch Elektrolyse*, Berlin, 127, 1908 ; *Ber.*, **27**. 163, 2060, 1894 ; A. Classen and J. Messinger, *ib.*, **21**. 368, 1888 ; E. F. Smith and J. B. Moyer, *Journ. Anal. Appl. Chem.*, **7**. 252, 1893 ; G. Vortmann, *Liebig's Ann.*, **351**. 283, 1907 ; I. H. Buckminster and E. F. Smith, *Journ. Amer. Chem. Soc.*, **32**. 1471, 1910 ; P. Ferchland, *German Pat., D.R.P.* 140317, 1902 ; A. G. Betts, *Lead Refining by Electrolysis*, New York, 1908 ; H. Jervis and E. F. Kern, *School Mines Quart.*, **30**. 100, 1909 ; H. J. S. Sand, *Journ. Chem. Soc.*, **91**. 373, 1907 ; R. Gartenmeister, *Chem. Ztg.*, **37**. 1281, 1913 ; B. Neumann and H. Nissenson, *ib.*, **19**. 49, 1895 ; B. Neumann, *ib.*, **20**. 381, 1896 ; *Zeit. Elektrochem.*, **2**. 253, 1896 ; W. C. May. *Amer. Journ. Science*, (3), **6**. 255, 1873 ; F. A. Gooch and F. B. Beyer, *ib.*, (4), **25**. 249, 1908 ; (4), **27**. 59, 1909 ; *Zeit. anorg. Chem.*, **58**. 65, 1908 ; **61**. 286, 1909 ; F. Tenny, *Amer. Chem. Journ.*, **5**. 413, 1883.

⁴¹ J. Haas, *Metal Ind.*, **14**. 12, 140, 1919.

⁴² E. P. Clark, *U.S. Pat. No.* 598313, 1898 ; J. W. Richards and C. W. Roepper, *ib.*, ⁶44779, 1898 ; E. Becquerel, *Compt. Rend.*, **18**. 197, 1844 ; *Ann. Chim. Phys.*, (3), **13**. 216, 1845 ; F. C. Mathers, *Trans. Amer. Electrochem. Soc.*, **23**. 172, 1913 ; F. C. Mathers and A. B. Leible, *ib.*, **31**. 271, 1917 ; C. F. Carrier, *ib.*, **5**. 229, 1904 ; S. A. Tucker and E. G. Thomssen, *ib.*. **15**. 477, 1909 ; *Electrochem. Ind.*, **7**. 273, 1909 ; L. Glaser, *Zeit. Elektrochem.*, **7**. 365, 381, 1900 ; H. Senn, **11**. 235, 1905.

⁴³ A. G. Betts, *Lead Refining by Electrolysis*, New York, 1908.

⁴⁴ F. Haber, *Zeit. anorg. Chem.*, **16**. 438, 1898 ; F. W. Rixon, *Zeit. Elektrochem.*, **9**. 267, 1903 ; L. Glaser, *ib.*, **7**. 365, 381, 1902 ; **A.** Brochet and J. Petit, *ib.*, **11**. 449, 1905 ; *Compt. Rend.*, **138**. 359, 419, 1904 ; *Bull. Soc. Chim.*, (3), **31**. 359, 1904 ; W. W. Taylor and J. K. H. Inglis, *Proc. Roy. Soc.*, **18**. 301, 1902 ; *Chem. News*, **88**. 265, 1902 ; W. E. Hughes, *Journ. Phys. Chem.*, **26**. 316, 1922 ; A. G. Reeve, *Trans. Amer. Electrochem. Soc.*, **35**. 389, 1920.

45 K. Elbs, *Zeit. Elektrochem.*, **8**. 512, 1902 ; K. Elbs and R. Nübling, *ib.*, **9**. 776, 1903 ; E. P. Schoch and D. J. Brown, *Journ. Amer. Chem. Soc.*, **38**. 1660, 1916.
46 F. Fischer and K. Thiele, *Zeit. anorg. Chem.*, **67**. 302, 1910.
47 F. C. Mathers, *Trans. Amer. Electrochem. Soc.*, **23**. 160, 1913 ; F. C. Mathers and A. B. Lieble, *ib.*, **31**. 271, 1917 ; F. C. Mathers and O. R. Overman, *ib.*, **21**. 313, 1912 ; *Met. Chem. Engg.*, **10**. 298, 1912 ; W. E. Hughes, *Journ. Phys. Chem.*, **26**. 316, 1922 ; K. Freundlich and J. Fischer, *Zeit. Elektrochem.*, **18**. 889, 1812 ; R. Marc, *ib.*, **19**. 433, 1913.
48 K. Elbs and F. W. Rixon, *Zeit. Elektrochem.*, **9**. 267, 1903.
49 A. F. Linn, *Journ. Amer. Chem. Soc.*, **24**. 435, 1902 ; F. Fischer, *Zeit. Elektrochem.*, **8**. 398, 1902 ; K. Elbs and R. Nübling, *ib.*, **9**. 776, 1903 ; H. W. Gillett, *Journ. Phys. Chem.*, **13**. 338, 1909 ; J. E. Root, *ib.*, **7**. 428, 1903 ; H. Alders and A. Stähler, *Ber.*, **42**. 2685, 1909.
50 A. Brand, *Zeit. anal. Chem.*, **28**. 595, 1889.
51 F. Fischer, K. Thiele, and E. B. Maxted, *Zeit. anorg. Chem.*, **67**. 347, 1910 ; W. Blum, F. J. Liscomb, Z. Jencks, and W. E. Bailey, *Trans. Amer. Electrochem. Soc.*, **34**. 101, 1919 ; W. Blum and H. E. Haring, *ib.*, **40**. 287, 1921 ; G. Mardus, *Elektrolytische Raffination von Blei aus borfluorwasserstoffsauer Lösungen*, Berlin, 1908.
52 A. G. Betts, *Lead Refining by Electrolysis*, New York, 1908 ; *Trans. Amer. Electrochem. Soc.*, **8**. 69, 83, 1905 ; A. G. Reeve, *ib.* **35**. 389, 1919 ; *Chem. Met. Engg.*, **20**. 388, 1919 ; H. Jarvis and E. F. Kern, *School Mines Quar.*, **30**. 100, 1909 ; E. F. Kern, *Trans. Amer. Electrochem. Soc.*, **15**. 441, 1909 ; O. P. Watts, *Metal Ind.*, **17**. 166, 1919 ; *Trans. Amer. Electrochem. Soc.*, **35**. 279, 1919 ; A. G. Betts and E. F. Kern, *ib.*, **6**. 67, 1904 ; F. C. Mathers and A. B. Lieble, *ib.*, **31**. 271, 1917 ; H. Freundlich and J. Fischer, *Zeit. Elektrochem.*, **18**. 888, 1912 ; H. Senn, *ib.*, **11**. 232, 1905 ; R. Marc, *ib.*, **19**. 433, 1913 ; K. Elbs and R. Nübling, *ib.*, **9**. 776, 1903 ; W. Thum, *Metal Ind.*, **17**. 220, 1919 ; E. L. Andersen, *U.S. Pat. No.* 862871, 1907 ; G. Titschack, *Mitt. Materialprüf.*, **41**. 89, 1923.
53 M. le Blanc and E. Bindschedler, *Zeit. Elektrochem.*, **8**. 255, 1902 ; K. Elbs and R. Nübling, *ib.*, **9**. 776, 1903 ; C. Luckow, *Brit. Pat. No.* 14801, 1895.
54 R. Marc, *Zeit. Elektrochem.*, **19**. 433, 1913 ; F. C. Mathers and B. W. Cockrum, *Trans. Amer. Electrochem. Soc.*, **26**. 117, 1915 ; *Met. Chem. Engg.*, **12**. 714, 1914 ; H. S. Warwick, *Chem. News*, **66**. 275, 1892 ; *Zeit. anorg. Chem.*, **1**. 307, 1892.
55 R. C. Snowdon, *Journ. Phys. Chem.*, **10**. 500, 1906 ; W. Hartmann, *German Pat., D.R.P.* 139068, 1900 ; L. Glaser, *Zeit. Elektrochem.*, **7**. 365, 381, 1900 ; R. Marc, *ib.*, **19**. 433, 1913 ; O. W. Brown ,and A. R. Nees, *Journ. Ind. Eng. Chem.*, **4**. 870, 1912 ; S. Glasstone, *Journ. Chem. Soc.*, **119**. 1915, 1921 ; W. D. Bancroft, *Trans. Amer. Electrochem. Soc.*, **21**. 333, 1912 ; F. C. Mathers, *ib.*, **24**. 317, 1913 ; **26**. 99, 1915 ; *Met. Chem. Engg.*, **12**. 714, 1914 ; F. C. Mathers and A. McKinney, *ib.*, **13**. 328, 1915 ; *Trans. Amer. Electrochem. Soc.*, **27**. 131, 1915 ; F. C. Mathers and B. W. Cockrum, *ib.*, **26**. 117, 1915 ; *Met. Chem. Engg.*, **12**. 714, 1914.
56 F. C. Mathers and B. W. Cockrum, *Trans. Amer. Electrochem. Soc.*, **26**. 117, 1915 ; *Met. Chem. Engg.*, **12**. 714, 1914 ; E. Jordis, *Zeit. Elektrochem.*, **2**. 140, 1896.
57 R. Marc, *Zeit. Elektrochem.*, **19**. 433, 1913.
58 F. Fischer, K. Thiele, and E. B. Maxted, *Zeit. anorg. Chem.*, **67**. 347, 1910 ; A. G. Betts, *Lead Refining by Electrolysis*, New York, 1908 ; G. Titschack, *Mitt. Mat. Prufungsamts*, **41**. 89, 1923.
59 A. Riche, *Ann. Chim. Phys.*, (5), **13**. 508, 1878 ; A. Classen and M. A. von Reiss, *Ber.*, **14**. 1627, 1881 ; A. Classen, *German Pat., D.R.P.* 17864, 1881 ; A. Pertsch, *ib.*, 66185, 1892 ; L. Wolman, *Zeit. Elektrochem.*, **3**. 538, 1897 ; C. A. Kohn, *Journ. Soc. Chem. Ind.*, **10**. 327, 1891 ; J. E. Root, *Journ. Phys. Chem.*, **7**. 428, 1903.
60 P. Schützenberger, *Compt. Rend.*, **86**. 1387, 1878 ; A. G. Betts, *Lead Refining by Electrolysis*, New York, 1908 ; K. Elbs and J. Forssell, *Zeit. Elektrochem.*, **8**. 760, 1902 ; L. Glaser, *ib.*, **7**. 383, 1900 ; E. Becquerel, *Ann. Chim. Phys.*, (3), **8**. 405, 1843 ; W. Beetz, *Pogg. Ann.*, **61**. 209, 1844 ; F. C. Mathers, *Trans. Amer. Electrochem. Soc.*, **38**. 121, 1920 ; *Metal Ind.*, **18**. 467, 1920 ; W. Wernicke, *ib.*, **139**. 143, 1870 ; **141**. 111, 1870 ; L. Schucht, *Zeit. anal. Chem.*, **22**. 488, 1883 ; A. Brand, *ib.*, **28**. 595, 1889 ; C. Luckow, *ib.*, **19**. 15, 1880 ; C. H. Burleigh, *Electrochem. Ind.*, **2**. 355, 1904 ; E. F. Smith, *Proc. Amer. Phil. Soc.*, **24**. 428, 1887 ; O. W. Brown and A. R. Nees, *Journ. Ind. Eng. Chem.*, **4**. 870, 1912 ; G. Parodi and A. Marcazzini, *Gazz. Chim. Ital.*, **8**. 169, 1878 ; J. E. Root, *Journ. Phys. Chem.*, **7**. 428, 1903 ; T. P. McCutcheon, *Journ. Amer. Chem. Soc.*, **29**. 1446, 1907 ; Q. Marino, *Brit. Pat. No.* 130302, 130446, 1918 ; J. Matuschek, *German Pat., D.R.P.* 239222, 1910.
61 A. Helfenstein, *Zeit. anorg. Chem.*, **23**. 255, 1900 ; A. Appelberg, *ib.*, **36**. 36, 1903 ; G. Auerbach, *ib.*, **28**. 1, 1901 ; F. Quincke, *Zeit. Elektrochem.*, **4**. 52, 1898 ; *Zeit. anorg. Chem.*, **24**. 220, 1900 ; R. Lorenz, *ib.*, **23**. 99, 1900 ; **24**. 222, 1900 ; *Zeit. Elektrochem.*, **7**. 284, 1900 ; K. Arndt and H. Probst, *ib.*, **29**. 323, 1923 ; C. C. Garrard, *ib.*, **6**. 214, 1899 ; *Zeit. anorg. Chem.*, **25**. 273, 1890 ; J. F. Sacker, *ib.*, **28**. 385, 1901 ; O. H. Weber, *ib.*, **21**. 305, 1899 ; V. Czepinsky, *ib.*, **19**. 246, 1899 ; R. Lorenz, G. von Hevesy, and E. Wolff, *Zeit. phys. Chem.*, **76**. 732, 1911 ; R. Lorenz and A. Liebmann, *ib.*, **83**. 459, 1913.
62 L. Kahlenberg, *Journ. Phys. Chem.*, **4**. 349, 1900 ; A. W. Speransky and E. G. Goldberg, *Journ. Russ. Phys. Chem. Soc.*, **32**. 797, 1900 ; H. Röhler, *Zeit. Elektrochem.*, **16**. 425, 1910.
63 A. Fischer and R. J. Boddaert, *Zeit. Elektrochem.*, **10**. 553, 1904 ; R. Amberg, *ib.*, **10**.

853, 1904 ; F. F. Exner, *Journ. Amer. Chem. Soc.*, 25. 896, 1903 ; D. S. Ashbrook *,ib.*, 26. 1283. 1904 ; F. M. Perkin, *Electrochemist*, 3. 22, 1903 ; *Chem. News*, 88. 102, 1903.
⁶⁴ P. Vaillant, *Compt. Rend.*, 168. 768, 1919 ; F. Pearce and C. Conchet, *ib.*, 138. 361, 1904 ; A. Brochet and J. Petit, *ib.*, 138. 359, 419, 1904 ; *Bull. Soc. Chim.*, (3), 31. 359, 1904 ; *Zeit. Elektrochem.*, 11. 449, 1905 ; R. G. von Name and L. Gräfenberg, *ib.*, 10. 305, 1904 ; E. Wilson, *Chem. News*, 92. 198, 1905 ; C. G. Schluederberg, *Journ. Phys. Chem.*, 12. 623, 1908 ; J. A. Wilkinson, *ib.*, 13. 695, 1909.
⁶⁵ E. Newbery, *Journ. Chem. Soc.*, 109. 1051, 1916 ; W. Lust, *Ueber das anodische Verhalten von Blei und Wismuth in verscheidenen Elektrolyten*, Nürnberg, 1919 ; G. Just, *Zeit. Elektrochem.*, 9. 275. 547, 1903 ; K. Elbs and E. Stohr, *ib.*, 9. 531, 1903 ; G. Grube, *ib.*, 28. 275, 1922 ; O. W. Brown, C. O. Henke and L. J. Smith, *Journ. Phys. Chem.*, 24. 367, 1920 ; G. R. White, *ib.*, 15. 763, 1911 ; N. M. Bell, *Trans. Faraday Soc.*, 11. 79, 1915 ; *Met. Chem. Engg.*, 13. 500, 1915 ; S. Glasstone, *Journ. Chem. Soc.*, 121. 2092, 1922.
⁶⁶ W. Thomson, *Chem. News*, 99. 157, 1909 ; C. F. Burgess and C. Hambuechen, *Journ. Phys. Chem.*, 7. 409, 1903 ; E. Merck, *German Pat.*, *D.R.P.* 113719, 1899 ; C. N. Otin and G. Wäser, *ib.*, 235955, 1910 ; K. Elbs, *Zeit. Elektrochem.*, 7. 644, 1901 ; W. Löb, *ib.*, 7. 300, 1901 ; *Zeit. phys. Chem.*, 34. 641, 1909 ; J. Tafel, *ib.*, 34. 187, 1900 ; 50. 619, 1905 ; *Ber.*, 32. 2209, 1900 ; 39. 3626, 1907 ; *Zeit. Elektrochem.*, 12. 120, 1906 ; J. Tafel and K. Schmitz, *ib.*, 8. 281, 1902 ; J. Tafel and B. Emmert, *Zeit. phys. Chem.*, 52. 349, 1905 ; 54. 433, 1906 ; J. Tafel and K. Naumann, *ib.*, 50. 750, 1905.
⁶⁷ I. Bernfeld, *Zeit. phys. Chem.*, 25. 49, 1898 ; P. P. Lebedeff, *Zeit. Elektrochem.*, 18. 894, 1912.
⁶⁸ I. Bernfeld, *Zeit. phys. Chem.*, 25. 49, 1898 ; A. T. Weightman, *Journ. Phys. Chem.*, 7. 18, 1903 ; E. L. Anderson, *U.S. Pat. No.* 862871, 1907 ; H. Danneel, *Zeit. Elektrochem.*, 9. 256, 1903.
⁶⁹ A. Hollard, *Compt. Rend.*, 136. 142, 229, 1903 ; *Bull. Soc. Chim.*, (3), 31. 239, 1904 ; H. J. S. Sand, *Chem. News*, 100. 264, 1909 ; *Journ. Chem. Soc.*, 91. 373, 1907 ; K. Elbs and E. Stohr, *Zeit. Elektrochem.*, 9. 531, 1902 ; A. Panchaud de Bottens, *ib.*, 8. 673, 1901 ; R. Lorenz and E. Lauber, *ib.*, 15. 157, 1909 ; H. Trog, *ib.*, 15. 255, 1909 ; E. Müller and M. Soller, *ib.*, 11. 863, 1905 ; E. Müller and O. Freidberger, *Ber.*, 35. 2652, 1902 ; A. Classen, *ib.*, 27. 163, 1894 ; H. Bardt, *German Pat.*, *D.R.P.* 325154, 1919 ; F. Kreiger, *ib.*, 207706, 1908 ; *Zeit. Elektrochem.*, 16. 28, 1910 ; H. Nissenson and H. Danneel, *ib.*, 9. 760, 1903 ; P. Ferchland, *ib.*, 15. 554, 666, 1909 ; *German Pat.*, *D.R.PP.* 206329, 1905 ; 207257, 1906 ; M. Stefani, *ib.*, 231583, 1909 ; W. Böttger, *Zeit. angew. Chem.*, 22. 1548, 1909 ; F. Peters, *Die angewandte Elektrochemie*, Leipzig, 2. 176, 1898 ; S. Glasstone, *Journ. Chem. Soc.*, 121. 2092, 1922.
⁷⁰ D. G. Fitzgerald, *Electrician*, 15. 136, 1885 ; *Journ. Inst. Elect. Eng.*, 16. 168, 1887 ; E. J. Wade, *ib.*, 29. 460, 1900 ; *Secondary Batteries, their Theory, Construction and Use*, London, 2, 1902 ; G. Darrieus, *Bull. Soc. Internat. Electriciens*, 9. 205, 1892 ; S. Drzewiecky, *ib.*, 6. 414, 1890 ; F. Dolezalek, *Die Theorie des Bleiaccumulators*, Halle, 1901 ; *Zeit. Elektrochem.*, 4. 349, 1898 ; 5. 533, 1899 ; *Wied. Ann.*, 65. 894, 1898 ; W. Nernst, *ib.*, 3. 78, 1897 ; K. Elbs, *ib.*, 3. 70, 1897 ; 6. 46, 1900 ; K. Elbs and O. Schönherr, *ib.*, 1. 473, 1895 ; M. Mugdan, *ib.*, 6. 309, 1900 ; E. Abel, *ib.*, 7. 732, 1901 ; F. Förster, *ib.*, 3. 525, 1897 ; C. Liebenoff, *ib.*, 2. 420, 653, 1896 ; W. Löb, *ib.*, 2. 495, 1896 ; M. le Blanc, *Lehrbuch der Elektrochemie*, Leipzig, 223, 1896 ; H. Aron, *Elektrotech. Zeit.*, 4. 58, 100, 1885 ; W. Kohlrausch and C. Heim, *ib.*, 10. 327, 1889 ; H. Strecker, *ib.*, 12. 435, 513, 524, 1891 ; A. Gérard, *Lumière Elect.*, 27. 387, 1887 ; *L'électricité a l'exposition universelle d'Anvers*, Bruxelles, 58, 1885 ; S. Schenck and S. Farbaky, *ib.*, 28. 295, 1888 ; *Dingler's Journ.*, 257. 357, 1885 ; *Brit. Pat. No.* 13697, 1885 ; F. Streintz and G. Neumann, *Wied. Ann.*, 41. 97, 1890 ; F. Streintz, *ib.*, 38. 344, 1889 ; 46. 449, 1892 ; 53. 698, 1894 ; A. Jouve, *Rev. Gén. Chim. Pure Appl.*, 6. 95, 1903 ; A. Pfaff, *Centrb. Accumul.*, 11. 73, 173, 1901 ; J. Shields, *Chem. News*, 65. 195, 1892 ; W. Esch, *Chem. Ztg.*, 27. 297. 1903 ; C. Féry, *Bull. Soc. Chim.*, (4), 25. 223, 1919 ; *Bull. Soc. Enc. Nat. Ind.*, 131. 92, 1919 ; 138. 49, 1926 ; *Bull. Soc. Française Elect.*, 9. 85, 1919 ; *Journ. Phys.*, (5), 5. 187, 1917 ; (5), 8. 161, 1919 ; P. Schoop, *Zeit. Elektrochem.*, 1. 293, 1895 ; N. Gautherot, *Journ. Phys.*, 56. 429, 1803 ; *Mém. Soc. Française*, 1. 471, 1802 ; K. Siegl, *Elektrotech. Zeit.*, 34. 1317, 1913 ; W. R. Grove, *Phil. Mag.*, (3), 21. 417, 1842 ; *Phil. Trans.*, 133. 91, 1843 ; M. Hartenheim, *Elektrotech. Zeit.*, 45. 41, 1924 ; W. J. Sinsteden, *Pogg. Ann.*, 92. 1, 1854 ; G. Planté, *Compt. Rend.*, 49. 402, 1859 ; 60. 640, 1860 ; 66. 1255, 1869 ; 74. 592, 1872 ; 95. 480, 1882 ; *Recherches sur l'électricité*, Paris, 1879 ; J. W. Ritter, *Voigt's Mag.*, 6. 105, 1803 ; C. A. Faure, *Compt. Rend.*, 92. 951, 1881 ; O. J. Lodge, *Engineer*, 53. 365, 373, 439, 457, 1882 ; 54. 11, 30, 230, 249, 1882 ; *Electrician*, 9. 92, 130, 157, 207, 590, 1882 ; J. H. Gladstone and W. Hibbert, *Proc. Phys. Soc.*, 10. 448, 1890 ; 11. 44, 1891 ; *Journ. Inst. Elect. Eng.*, 21. 12, 1892 ; J. H. Gladstone and A. Tribe, *Journ. Chem. Soc.*, 43. 345, 1883 ; *Nature*, 25. 221, 461, 1882 ; 26. 251, 342, 602, 1882 ; *The Chemistry of Secondary Batteries*, London, 1883 ; E. Frankland, *Proc. Roy. Soc.*, 35. 67, 1883 ; 46. 304, 1889 ; *Chem. News*, 60. 160, 1889 ; P. Bary, *Rev. Gén. Coll.*, 2. 33, 1924 ; J. Grant, *Journ. Soc. Chem. Ind.* —*Chem. Ind.*, 44. 502, 1925 ; H. Cassel and F. Todt, *Zeit. angew. Chem.*, 36. 227, 1923 ; E. N. Reynier, A. Crova, and P. Garbe, *Compt. Rend.*, 100. 1340, 1885 ; I. M. Tscheltzoff, *ib.*. 100. 1458, 1885 ; M. Knobel, *Trans. Amer. Electrochem. Soc.*, 43. 98, 1923 ; D. A. MacInnes, L. Alder, and D. B. Joubert, *ib.*, 37. 641, 1920 ; B. Drake and J. M. Gorham, *B.A. Rep.*, 813, 1886 ; *Electrician*, 17. 384, 1886 ; W. E. Aryton, *Journ. Inst. Elect. Eng.*, 19. 660, 1890 ; H. E. Armstrong and G. H. Robertson, *ib.*, 50. 105, 1891 ; G. H. Robertson, *Journ. Soc. Arts*, 40. 44.

1891 ; L. Duncan and H. Wiegand, *Elect. World*, 13. 347, 1889 ; A. Lottermoser and M. Grützner, *Zeit. anorg. Chem.*, 140. 93, 1924 ; G. Crut, *Journ. Pharm. Chim.*, (8), 3. 15, 1926.

71 E. Thomson and E. J. Houston, *Brit. Pat. No.* 4400, 1879 ; A. V. Meserole, *ib.*, 4311, 1887 ; T. A. Edison, *ib.*, 20960. 1900 ; 2490, 20072, 1901 ; 26948, 1904 ; H. Sutton, *ib.*, 3464, 1882 ; K. E. Böttcher, *ib.*, 5938, 1890 ; W. Main, *ib.*, 6112, 1889 ; 1646, 1892 ; L. Epstein, *ib.*, 17369, 1894 ; H. Leitner, *ib.*, 24473, 1896 ; E. Julien, *ib.*, 8881, 1885 ; A. E. Peyrusson, *ib.*, 8226, 1886 ; C. E. Lee, *ib.*, 10439, 1897 ; E. Commetin and R. Viau, *ib.*, 6619, 1904 ; E. Commetin, G.Bailhache. A. de Virloy, and L. de Bousignac, *ib.*, 7966, 1886 ; J. B. Entz and W. A. Phillips, *ib.*, 18365, 1889 ; 1484, 1892 ; C. Desmazures, *ib.*, 4219, 1889 ; 1887, 1892 ; A. Dun and F. Hasslacher, *ib.*, 14612, 1885 ; 5731, 1886 ; C. H. Cathcart, *ib.*, 2068, 3107, 1882 ; F. de Lalande and G. Chaperon, *ib.*, 1464, 1882 ; 4475, 1884 ; H. Aron, *German Pat.*, *D.R.P.* 38220, 1886 ; A. d'Arsonval, *Compt. Rend.*, 90. 166, 1880 ; 91. 284, 1880 ; *French Pat. Nos.* 132842, 1879 ; 148264, 152348, 1882 ; J. Carpentier, *ib.*, 1306060, 1880 ; A. d'Arsonval and J. Carpentier, *ib.*, 133884, 1879 ; 135651, 1880 ; 141388, 1881 ; E. Reynier, *ib.*, 150558, 1882 ; 153915, 155752, 1883 ; T. de Michalowsky, *U.S. Pat. No.* 714201, 1902.

72 G. von Hevesy and R. Lorenz, *Zeit. phys. Chem.*, 74. 443, 1910 ; W. Crookes, *Proc. Roy. Soc.*, 50. 88, 1891 ; F. W. Aston, *ib.*, 87. A, 437, 1912 ; F. Fischer and F. Schrötter, *Ber.*, 43. 1442, 1910 ; F. Fischer and G. Iliovici, *ib.*, 41. 4449, 1908 ; F. Fischer and O. Hähnel, *Zeit. Elektrochem.*, 14. 366, 433, 1908 ; V. Kohlschütter, *ib.*, 12. 869, 1906 ; 14. 417, 437, 1908 ; V. Kohlschütter and T. Goldschmidt, *ib.*, 14. 221, 1908 ; V. Kohlschütter and R. Müller, *ib.*, 12. 365, 1906 ; G. A. Helmsalech, *Compt. Rend.*, 154. 767, 1912 ; E. Rumpf, *Ann. Physik*, (4), 59. 1, 1919 ; J. Lavaux, *Compt. Rend.*, 169. 180, 1919 ; G. Hoffmann, *Zeit. Physik*, 4. 363, 1921 ; J. Lifschitz, *Proc. Acad. Amsterdam*, 26. 561, 1923 ; W. B. Nottingham, *Phys. Rev.*, (2), 27. 806, 1926.

73 M. Faraday, *Phil. Trans.*, 136. 21, 1846 ; K. Honda, *Ann. Physik*, (4). 32. 1027, 1046, 1062, 1910 ; M. Owen, *ib.*, (4), 37. 657, 1912 ; G. Borelius, *ib.*, (4), 58. 489, 1919 ; J. Königsberger, *ib.*, (4), 6. 506, 1901 ; *Wied. Ann.*, 66. 698, 1898 ; S. Meyer, *ib.*, 68. 325, 1899 ; 69. 236, 1899 ; *Ann. Physik*, (4), 1. 664, 1900 ; W. Voigt and S. Kinoshita, *ib.*, (4), 24. 492, 1907 ; M. Loutschinsky, *Rev. Mét.*, 6. 986, 1909 ; *Compt. Rend.*, 148. 1759, 1909 ; P. Pascal, *ib.*, 156. 1904, 1913 ; 158. 1895, 1914 ; 159. 129, 1914 ; L. Lombardi, *Mem. Accad. Torino*, (2), 47. 1, 1897 ; W. Gerlach and A. C. Cilliers, *Zeit. Physik*, 26. 106, 1924 ; W. Gerlach, *Phys. Zeit.*, 23. 618, 1924 ; E. H. Williams, *Phys. Rev.*, (2), 28. 167, 1926.

§ 5. The Chemical Properties of Lead

The chemical properties of lead present some strange and peculiar contrasts which at first sight seem inconsistent. For example, the metal resists the action of sulphuric and hydrochloric acids much better than iron, zinc, or tin, and yet it is readily attacked by weak organic acids ; it is slowly dissolved even by water, and is very susceptible to corrosion by the action of moist air. O. Sackur [1] has compared the chemical properties of lead and tin. The position of lead in the electrochemical series is close to that of tin, and not far from that of hydrogen, both metals being slightly more electropositive than hydrogen. Consequently, lead will have little tendency to displace hydrogen from aq. soln. of the acids, even when this tendency is not interfered with by the insolubility of the products of the reaction. Thus, lead has a greater soln. press. than tin, but it dissolves in hydrochloric acid less readily than tin. The greater soln. press. of lead in comparison with that of tin is partly explained by the feeble ionization of the stannous salts, and the stronger basic properties of lead oxide as exemplified by the stability of its oxysalts. Owing to the low tendency exerted by lead to displace hydrogen from the acids, its ready dissolution by the feebler acids, say acetic acid, is attributed to the accelerating influence of atm. oxygen. Tin is not so readily oxidized as lead, and hence it is not attacked by, say, acetic acid. The difference in the action of aerated water on the two metals is attributed to the same cause—the strong basic properties of lead.

B. Hodgson [2] referred to the absorption of gas by lead electrodes in vacuum tubes ; and M. Guichard found that after lead had been heated for 11 hrs. at 750° and 8 hrs. at 550° under reduced press., it still evolved gas at the rate of 0·1 c.c. per 100 grms. per hour. G. Neumann and F. Streintz said that fused lead absorbed 0·11–0·15 vol. of hydrogen, and P. Schoop, E. Rumpf, and S. Drzewiecky also said that lead absorbs hydrogen. On the other hand, E. Frankland, M. Cantor,

G. Meyer, A. M. Scott, W. Stahl, and J. H. Gladstone and A. Tribe were quite unable to detect any absorption of hydrogen either by molten lead, or by lead made the negative electrode in the electrolysis of dil. sulphuric acid. J. Shields confirmed these results, and showed that G. Neumann and F. Streintz's report was due to a mal-observation; if any gas is absorbed it is purely a surface effect and plays no essential part in the working of the lead accumulator. M. Guichard said that the hydrogen absorbed by lead is only slowly expelled by heat. F. H. Newman, and A. Sieverts also included lead among the metals which do not dissolve hydrogen—the former worked with lead electrodes in a discharge tube. H. G. Deming and B. C. Hendrichs found hydrogen diffuses through lead at 265° at the rate of 0·001 mgrm. per hour per sq. cm. per mm. thickness. N. S. Kurnakoff and N. J. Stepanoff inferred that lead may form a hydride of the type : PbH_2, viz. PbH_4; S. Drzewiecky assumed that Pb_2H_2 exists. D. P. Smith, and F. Paneth considered that the position of lead in the periodic table is not incompatible with the existence of a hydride. E. Newbery found that an unstable **lead hydride**—or overvoltage compound—is formed when hydrogen is liberated at a lead electrode. F. Paneth and O. Nörring activated magnesium powder with thorium-B and thorium-C in a desiccator for half an hour, and dissolved the product in 0·1–0·2N-HCl. The resulting gases were carried in a stream of hydrogen through a cotton-wool filter to a heated Marsh tube. The radioactivity of the metallic deposit, consisting chiefly of thorium-C (bismuth), was then examined. For the first few hours its behaviour was indistinguishable from that of thorium-C, but after 24 hrs., by which time the thorium-C should have disappeared, a notable activity remained, the rate of disappearance of which corresponded with that of thorium-B (lead). The " yield " of lead obtained, however, was only about one-hundredth that of the bismuth. The lead hydride appeared to be stopped or decomposed more readily by a thick cotton-wool filter than bismuth hydride. Attempts to prepare the hydride by the action of acids on ordinary lead-magnesium alloys were unsuccessful, and so were numerous attempts by electric methods—for example, induction sparks or an arc in an atmosphere of hydrogen. Success was eventually attained by a combined electrolysis-spark process. Using dil. sulphuric acid as electrolyte and a lead-glycerol cement cathode, with an e.m.f. of 220 volts, the apparatus was so arranged that intermittent sparking at high frequency occurred between the cathode and the electrolyte. The cathode gases were passed to a condensing tube immersed in liquid air where any lead-dust was deposited, whilst the hydride was liquefied. On allowing the temp. to rise, the hydride was again vaporized and passed through a cotton-wool filter to a heated Marsh tube, where it was decomposed and lead deposited. The deposit had a dull grey colour, and was close to the flame, but not so close as a tin deposit. The lead was identified by a number of chemical tests which distinguished it from arsenic, antimony, tin, tellurium, or bismuth. A number of modifications of the experiment indicated that the hydrogen required for the formation of the hydride is not derived from the electrolysis of the electrolyte, but probably through the action of the spark, positive hydrogen ions combining directly with negative lead ions. F. Paneth and E. Rabinovitsch calculate the b.p. of lead hydride to be −13°; the composition corresponds with **lead tetrahydride,** PbH_4. E. J. Weeks prepared **lead dihydride,** Pb_2H_2, as a grey powder, by the action of aluminium foil on a soln. of an alkali plumbite. It does not form the tetrahydride when heated in the absence of air, b ,t if heated in hydrogen, it is probably reduced to the tetrahydride : $Pb_2H_2+3H_2=2PbH_4$. The dihydride oxidizes rapidly in air ; it is vigorously attacked by fused potassium nitrate under conditions where finely divided lead is only slowly attacked.

A. Sieverts and W. Krumbhaar observed no sign of the dissolution of **nitrogen** in lead at 600°. F. H. Newman found that nitrogen is not absorbed by lead electrodes in the electric discharge. F. Fischer and G. Iliovici observed no sign of the combination of lead with argon when the arc or spark discharge between lead electrodes is passed beneath liquid **argon.** G. Lunge and E. Schmid [3] found that lead usually contains but a minute trace of **oxygen**—about 0·0025 per cent.—but when the lead is contaminated with from 0·01 to 1 per cent. of copper, the quantity of oxygen is much increased. W. Stahl showed that the dissociation of lead oxide occurs over 2075°, and the oxygen absorbed by lead is probably chemically combined. Lead reduced from the tartrate at as low a temp. as possible was found by W. van Rijn to be *pyrophoric ;* and G. C. Winkelblech found that lead reduced by hydrogen from gently heated lead oxide remains unaltered in **air** at ordinary temp., but takes fire when heated, burning with a feeble glow and forming lead oxide. P. A. von Bonsdorff showed that dried lead and oxygen or air suffer no change at ordinary temp., but if moisture be present, the metal becomes tarnished owing to the formation of a surface film of oxide ; in an atm. sat. with moisture, this oxidation takes place in a few days, and the bright surface of the metal acquires in succession all the colours of the rainbow before it becomes dull grey. The action is hastened by a gentle heat. G. Tammann and co-workers estimated that it would take 90 years to produce a visible film on polished lead in an atm. of dry air at 15°. W. Müller considered that pure oxygen has a smaller affinity for lead than atm. air. B. Lambert and H. E. Cullis showed that lead distilled in vacuo, and kept for some months, can be exposed to ordinary air for many days without any appreciable diminution of its brilliant metallic lustre, but more prolonged exposure causes the gradual formation of a surface-film of a dark-coloured oxide. When lead near its m.p. is kept exposed to air, its surface becomes covered with a grey powder which J. J. Berzelius supposed to be a suboxide, Pb_2O ; at its m.p., the lead forms the yellow oxide, PbO, and afterwards gradually passes into the red oxide, Pb_3O_4. J. Percy added that " the surface of the metal after fusion becomes beautifully iridescent, and the superficial film thus coloured may be removed and permanently preserved." The atm. corrosion is facilitated by the presence of carbon dioxide. G. Jung studied the optical properties of tarnish films. C. L. Bloxam has said that " in breach-loading cartridges where grease is employed as a lubricator, the bullets have sometimes become partly converted into white-lead, and thus increased so much in bulk as to burst open the copper case of the cartridges and render them useless." If the grey film be skimmed from molten lead so that the clean surface is continually renewed, the metal is ultimately all converted into *lead-ash,* a yellowish-grey mixture of lead and its oxide. At a bright red heat, the oxidation of the metal is rapid, and, at that temp., the resulting oxide is molten. At a still higher temp. the lead volatilizes and burns with a white light, forming flocculent lead oxide called *flores plumbi,* or *flowers of lead.* Oxygen, according to W. Manchot, shows a slight action on lead at 132° in 5 mins. ; the action is more pronounced at 180°–197° ; and at 227°, the action is very marked. N. B. Pilling and R. E. Bedworth found that at 300°, the oxidation of lead proceeds with comparative rapidity in air, forming a reddish-brown oxide, smooth and adherent to the metal. The quantity of oxygen, W, forming the oxide in the time, t, is given by $W^2=kt$, where k is the constant of proportion.

C. Engler and W. Wild found that the mist which is produced when **ozone** acts on clear filings of moist lead is lead oxide. W. Manchot found that in an atm. containing one per cent. ozone there is the faintest sign of reaction at 100°, one minute's exposure at 132° produces a golden yellow film, and in 5 mins. a steel-blue film ; as the temp. rises further the action becomes faster ; at 180°, the steel-blue film appears in $\frac{1}{2}$ min. ; at 197°, in 5 secs. ; and at 227°, immediately. Lead which has been rendered passive by immersion in nitric acid, and well washed, reacts with ozone, producing in 10 secs. a golden-yellow colour.

The atmospheric oxidation is complicated by the presence of **water ;** as just indicated, if moisture be absent, neither oxygen nor air attack lead. W. G. Whitman and R. P. Russell studied the effect of dissolved **oxygen** on the rate of attack of lead by acids. F. Clowes said that in an atm. of hydrogen or in vacuo, air-free water dissolved 0·3 part of lead per million; F. C. Calvert and R. Johnson said that 200 litres of air-free distilled water dissolved 1·529 grms. of lead per sq. metre in 8 weeks; H. Heap, J. I. Pierre, and W. C. Parsons observed very little action. A. Traube-Mengarini and A. Scala said that lead yields a colloidal soln. of the metal when treated with distilled water free from oxygen and in vacuo : the particles show the Brownian movement. According to C. D. Bengough and J. M. Stuart, the surface attack of lead by water produces a film of the colloidal gel lead hydroxide, but this film soon crystallizes, and no longer protects the metal from further attack. In contact with oxygen from the air the colloidally dissolved metal is rapidly transformed into the colloidal hydrated oxide, the particles of which slowly aggregate to form crystals of various forms. Electrolytes, above a conc. characteristic for each, prevent the corrosion of lead; below this conc. corrosion continues, but the colloid is coagulated and deposited on the surface of the metal. It is considered that the colloidal state is an ionized combination of a colloid with water. On the other hand, if the water be thoroughly purified and free from dissolved gases, and the lead be thoroughly purified, and confined in quartz vessels, it is probable that there will be no reaction with the metal, for B. Lambert and H. E. Cullis, W. R. Nichols, W. van Rijn, R. Phillips, E. N. Horsford, C. Stalmann, P. Yorke, U. Antony and T. Benelli, G. Wolffhügel, and M. Müller were unable to detect any reaction between lead and air-free water at ordinary temp. J. C. Thresh also found that water alone has no action on lead.

L. B. G. de Morveau, A. Baumé, N. C. de Milly, M. Luzuriaga, and M. Delaville observed that when in contact with lead, water acquires *un aspect laiteux ;* and P. A. von Bonsdorff, and G. Wetzlar showed that in the presence of air freed from carbon dioxide lead is attacked by water, forming white flakes of lead hydroxide, and the water becomes sat. with that compound. Confirmatory observations have been reported by A. Scala, J. C. Thresh, W. R. Nichols, and H. Heap. O. Bauer and E. Wetzel showed that the attack on lead by distilled-water in air is less than by rain-water ; and, according to R. Christison, the attack by distilled-water alone is greater than when salts are present in soln. ; and L. B. G. de Morveau, and M. E. Chevreul, greater than hard-water. J. F. Liverseege and A. W. Knapp found that exposure to light increases the action of water on lead; and that the nearer the lead is to the surface of the water, the greater the corrosion ; that the differences in the corrosive action of different waters are not due to the difference in the contained oxygen, but in opposition to E. Reichardt, the volume of oxygen in soln. limits the amount of lead eroded, if no more oxygen be admitted : and that in closed tubes the amount of lead eroded only corresponds to the maximum amount of plumbous oxide or salt that could be produced by the oxygen present (thus 7·8 c.c. per litre of oxygen give 14 parts of plumbous lead per 100,000). N. W. Fischer found that if a platinum wire be wound about the lead, the oxidation by air and water is accelerated. P. Yorke found that a clean iron nail driven through the lead plate produces a quicker attack, and the nail does not rust in the vicinity of the lead. M. Pettenkofer said that lead soldered with tin is less rapidly attacked than before, while F. J. Otto, and A. Smith said it is more quickly attacked. L. Besnou, G. Wolffhügel, and F. E. Wynne noted the rapid attack on tinned lead tubes. F. Malméjac showed that lead strips in the mineral water of Sétif lost 0·20 grm. in 20 days under conditions where a similar strip wrapped with iron wire lost 0·04 grm., and with copper wire 0·10 grm. A. Scala found that the solubility of lead in water is not hastened by alloying the metal with tin, or using Pb-Zn, Pb-Sn, Pb-C, or Pb-Cu couples. P. Carles observed that the presence of foreign metals may hasten the corrosion by forming sacrificial couples (1. 16, 3).

B. Lambert and H. E. Cullis showed that the corrosion of lead proceeds very quickly even when the metal, the oxygen, and water are of the highest attainable degree of purity ; if the lead be kept a long time in vacuo before it is exposed to the oxygen, the rate of corrosion is enormously decreased. M. Berthelot found the corrosion is accelerated in the presence of acids. C. F. Schönbein raised the question : Does all the oxygen concerned in the corrosion of the metal actually unite with the metal ? and returned the answer : No ! He called that part of the oxygen which unites with the metal the *bound oxygen*, and the other part which he found to produce hydrogen dioxide, he called active oxygen. The oxygen is said to be *activated* during the oxidation. C. Engler called the substance undergoing oxidation the *auto-oxidizer*, and the substance which simultaneously unites with the active oxygen, the *acceptor*. C. F. Schönbein showed that just so much oxygen is rendered active or consumed in the formation of hydrogen dioxide as is consumed by the oxidizing metal. An exact proof is not always possible because some hydrogen dioxide may be due to a secondary reaction.

A gram of lead was mixed with 200 grms. of mercury, and shaken with 300 c.c. of standardized sulphuric acid (1 : 55) in the presence of oxygen. The lead sulphate which formed was filtered off, and the amount of sulphate still remaining was determined by the titration of an aliquot part of the filtrate. The reactions were presumably Pb(auto-oxidizer)$+H_2O$(acceptor)$+O_2=PbO+H_2O_2$; and then $PbO+H_2SO_4=H_2O+PbSO_4$. The amount of bound oxygen consumed in the primary formation of lead monoxide was then computed. The amount of active oxygen was obtained by titrating an aliquot portion of the soln. with standard potassium permanganate soln. It was found that the ratio bound oxygen : active oxygen$=1\cdot46 : 1\cdot39$. This is in agreement with C. F. Schönbein's hypothesis.

M. Traube confirmed these results. W. Merckens said that the tendency of metals to form hydrogen dioxide in moist air is smaller the higher the metal stands in Volta's electrochemical series—Mg, Al, Zn, Cd, Ni, and Co. C. F. Schönbein considered that the mercury acted by amalgamating with the lead, and by keeping it in a clean finely divided condition for the attack by water and oxygen. Lead alone gives less hydrogen dioxide than lead amalgam. M. Traube represented the reaction :

$$Pb+O\!<\!\begin{array}{c} H \\ H \end{array} + \begin{array}{c} O \\ O \end{array} = PbO + \begin{array}{c} H-O \\ H-O \end{array}$$

followed by $PbO+H_2O=Pb(OH)_2$. C. F. Schönbein assumed that the oxygen itself is compounded of a negatively and a positively charged atom. The former united with water producing hydrogen dioxide, and the latter united with lead to produce lead monoxide. Various modifications of these hypotheses have been discussed by J. W. Mellor.

In the *hydrogen dioxide theory of corrosion* advocated by W. R. Dunstan and co-workers it is assumed that the formation of hydrogen dioxide is directly concerned in the wet oxidation of the metals : $Pb+H_2O+O_2=PbO+H_2O_2$; and $PbO+H_2O$ $=Pb(OH)_2$, and $Pb+H_2O_2=Pb(HO)_2$. An opposing hypothesis assumes that the hydrogen dioxide is a secondary product of the reaction formed by the action of ordinary molecular oxygen on nascent hydrogen, after, and not during, the actual corrosion. The hydrogen dioxide can convert the lead hydroxide produced by the reaction into a higher stage of oxidation ; and B. Lambert and H. E. Cullis found that if the oxidation is allowed to proceed for many months, lead dioxide, and possibly the sesquioxide and tritatetraoxide are formed. J. W. Shipley also attributed the formation of the higher oxides of lead to the hydrogen dioxide produced as just indicated.

In the *electrolytic theory of corrosion*, advocated by W. R. Whitney, J. W. Shipley, and B. Lambert and H. E. Cullis, it is assumed that the pure metal is not homogeneous, for it contains at least two allotropic forms. The resulting differences in the physical character produce electrolytic action between the different parts of the metal. The resulting film of hydrogen protects the metal from further attack by offering an enormous resistance to the passage of the current. If oxygen is present, the film of hydrogen is oxidized, the polarization is destroyed, and water and hydrogen dioxide are produced. The theory can also be expressed in the language of the ionic hypothesis. L. A. Stenger believed that the varying conc.

of the salt soln. in contact with the lead produced concentration-cells which caused electrolytic action. H. S. Rawdon referred the "perishing" of the metal to the electrolytic dissolution of its intergranular impurities with the resulting isolation of the crystallites. A. Scala found that the solubility of lead in distilled water is not appreciably affected by connecting the lead with zinc, tin, or copper.

According to H. V. Regnault,[4] lead at a white heat is decomposed by water-vapour forming lead oxide : $Pb+H_2O \rightleftharpoons PbO+H_2$, but, according to P. A. von Bonsdorff, the decomposition does not occur at a red heat. Lead monoxide is reduced by hydrogen, so that the reaction, as symbolized, is reversible. A. S. Taylor, G. Wolffhügel, and J. C. Lermer observed that steam attacks lead, and particularly so in the presence of air and carbon dioxide. The last-named found that by alloying the lead with increasing proportions of tin, the corrosion becomes less and less. According to F. Stolba, boiling water decomposes lead with the evolution of hydrogen, and the formation of soln. of lead hydroxide with an alkaline reaction. J. Percy reported that if the boiling water be quite free from atm. air, it has no action on lead ; but if air has access to the boiling water, or if the water has not been de-aerated, the lead is attacked and the metal can be detected in the water. An alloy of lead with 2 per cent. of antimony was not attacked by boiling water deprived of air, and even if air had access the action was very slow. Neither an alloy of lead with 5 per cent. of zinc nor one with 5 per cent. of zinc and 5 per cent. of antimony was attacked by boiling water freed from air. S. Zinberg found that the addition of a trace of copper to lead causes a turbidity in water in contact with the lead, while adding less than 0·25 per cent. of lead to brass or bronze makes it corrodible by water. Adding tin to lead makes it less corrodible by water. The opposite effect is explained by the potential of tin in the lead-tin alloys, which being higher than that of lead, prevents the formation of hydrated lead oxide, whilst the potential of copper being lower than that of lead cannot protect the lead from the action of water.

At the beginning of our era, Pliny, in his *Historia naturalis* (31, 19), mentioned the corrosive action of natural waters on metals ; and he also referred to the use of lead in making pipes. Near the beginning of our era, T. Varro, in his *Rerum rusticarum*, stated that lead conduits were used in Rome to distribute the water from the Appian Way ; and although Vitruvius in his *De architectura* mentioned the danger attending the use of lead pipes for the water supply of Rome, it was only during the Middle Ages that the corrosive action of water on lead began to attract serious attention, and systematic observations were inaugurated near the beginning of the nineteenth century. Since that time, the action of atmospheric agents— water, carbon dioxide, and oxygen—and of natural waters containing the two gases in soln. has attracted numerous investigators chiefly on account of the extensive use of lead-piping for leading water-supplies into houses ; and of sheet-lead for lining cisterns for storing water. The subject is of particular importance in view of the toxic properties of water contaminated with lead compounds in soln. As indicated above, the dissolution of lead by water is largely conditioned by the presence of oxygen or air. This has been demonstrated by the observations [5] of A. J. Balard, L. Besnou, A. Bobierre, P. A. von Bonsdorff, F. C. Calvert and R. Johnson, R. Christison, A. Faiszt, M. J. Fordos, P. Fortner, E. N. Horsford, R. Kersting, H. Klut, B. Lambert and H. E. Cullis, M. Müller, M. Pettenkofer, R. Phillips, M. Pleissner, J. Rodenburg, S. Ruzicka, J. Smith, G. Wetzlar, G. Wolffhügel, and P. Yorke. Owing to the action of potable water on lead, it is often recommended that the water which has been standing in the pipes overnight should be run off in the morning.

Increasing the proportion of oxygen dissolved in the water was found by T. Paul and co-workers to hasten the corrosion of lead. The soln. is sat. with lead oxide or hydroxide which is formed when it contains 110 mgrms. PbO per litre. F. Clowes found that by passing oxygen into 100 grms. of distilled water, 0·013 grm. of lead dissolved in 24 hrs., 0·023 in 48 hrs., and 0·029 in 72 hrs. The speed of corrosion was diminished in the presence of carbon dioxide, sulphuric acid, carbonates, sulphates, or lime-water.   P. F. Frankland found that water containing oxygen is less active when the water is compressed, while the activity of water containing carbon dioxide is not materially affected by increasing the press. J. H. Marais said that water saturated with carbon dioxide will dissolve 0·012 grm. of lead per litre.

F. Clowes found that water containing **carbonic acid** alone corrodes lead far more slowly than water with oxygen in soln.; thus, under similar conditions, as in the experiments with oxygen alone, he found 0·005 grm. of lead was dissolved in 24 hrs., 0·008 grm. in 48 hrs., and 0·017 grm. in 72 hrs.   Observations were also made by M. M. P. Muir, J. Milne, S. Ruzicka, J. Rodenburg, and C. Umney. L. Bourgeois found the crystalline deposit sometimes formed has the composition $3PbO.2CO_2.H_2O$.   According to J. F. Liverseege and A. W. Knapp (expressing the alkalinity of water as parts of $CaCO_3$ per 100,000 parts of water, and the erosion in terms of parts of lead per 100,000 parts of water dissolved when $\frac{1}{2}$ sq. in. of lead is immersed in 10 c.c. of the liquid per day), for waters of low alkalinity (0·4) the increase of carbon dioxide produces little effect until as much as 1 per cent. is present (Fig. 15), so that in all probability with our ordinary treated and untreated waters carbon dioxide is not an important factor in erosion.   From 1 to 2 per cent. of carbon dioxide causes a sudden change, for this quantity is sufficient to prevent "erosion" and to cause "plumbo-solvency," i.e., the lead precipitate ceases to appear, lead hydrocarbonate being soluble.   Carbon dioxide is not necessary for the corrosion, for lead is attacked in the absence of free carbon dioxide.   E. Gudeman showed how carbonated water will attack the solder used in sealing fruits, etc., in tins.

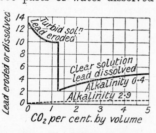

FIG. 15.—The Effect of Carbon Dioxide on the Corrosion of Lead.

The effect of the dissociation or ionization of the carbonic acid in soln. was worked out by T. Paul and co-workers, on the basis of J. Walker and W. Cormack's and G. Bodländer's results : $[H^{.}][HCO_3{}'] = k_1[H_2CO_3]$, and $[H^{.}][CO''_3] = k_2[HCO']$, where $k = 3·04 \times 10^{-7}$, and $k_2 = 1·3 \times 10^{-11}$.   Assuming the lead carbonate is present as a solid phase, and that the lead carbonate in soln. ionizes $PbCO_3 \rightleftharpoons Pb^{..} + CO_3''$, it follows that $[Pb^{..}][CO''_3] = k$; and from these equations, $[Pb^{..}] = (kk_1[H_2CO_3])/(K_2[HCO_3'])$; meaning that the concentration of the lead ions in soln. is directly proportional to the conc. of the free carbonic acid, and inversely proportional to the square of the conc. of the hydrocarbonate ions.   M. M. P. Muir found that by increasing the press. of the dissolved carbon dioxide up to 6 atm. the solvent action of water on lead was increased.   The joint action of air and carbon dioxide has been investigated by R. Christison, T. Graham and co-workers, L. B. G. de Morveau, M. Müller, M. M. P. Muir, T. Paul and co-workers, E. Reichardt, M. Traube-Mengarini and A. Scala, R. Wagner, G. Wölffhügel, P. Yorke, etc. F. Clowes noted that the rate of corrosion is retarded by the presence of carbonic acid, thus, under the same conditions as in the previously described experiments but in the presence of 8 vols. of oxygen to one vol. of carbon dioxide, 0·015 grm. of lead was dissolved in 24 hrs., and 0·018 grm. in 48 hrs.   T. Graham and co-workers showed that while small proportions of carbon dioxide in water decreased its corrosive action, larger proportions increased the effect.   P. F. Frankland, and A. Wagner thus found that carbon dioxide is more active than oxygen in accelerating the corrosion of lead by water.   H. Heap, and F. Clowes showed that the oxygen first attacks the lead, $2Pb + O_2 = 2PbO$; the oxide is hydrated $PbO + H_2O = Pb(OH)_2$; and the hydroxide is attacked by the carbonic acid, $2Pb(OH)_2 + CO_2 = H_2O + CO_3(Pb.OH)_2$, and $Pb(OH)_2 + CO_2 = PbCO_3 + H_2O$; and the lead carbonate passes into the hydrocarbonate, $PbCO_3 + CO_2 + H_2O \rightleftharpoons Pb(HCO_3)_2$.   H. Heap found that the corrosive action of natural water increased with rise of temp. up to 100°, while with distilled water, the activity increased from 5° to 50°, and thereafter decreased as the temp. rose from 50° to 100°.

A. Barillé found that the action of Seltzer water on the syphon of the metal container—an alloy of lead and tin or antimony—for 6 months dissolved the eq. of 0·0905 grm. of lead sulphate, and 0·0381 grm. of stannic acid per litre; and that the alloys were more readily attacked than the individual metals. J. Attfield, G. Brownen, A. Chevallier, J. M. Cyrnos, A. Gautier, J. Steiner, W. Thomson, and A. F. Wilson have discussed the solvent action of soda-water, and other mineral-waters on lead, and plumbiferous alloys. C. H. Crowe, and H. F. Whittaker discussed the general subject of the corrosion of lead.

If clean strips of lead are immersed in distilled-water and ordinary tap-water contained in stoppered bottles, and allowed to stand for some months, the distilled-water will contain basic lead carbonate in suspension while the tap-water will be clear. In the latter case, the action has been stopped by the formation of a coherent, protective crust of salt on the metal. The phosphates, carbonates, and hydrocarbonates in water are the most efficacious, and the sulphates and chlorides are also good. One part of calcium hydrocarbonate in 50,000 parts of water affords a protective coating ; so does lime when present in amounts below 1 : 10,000 ; if more than this amount of lime is present, the lead is attacked. Owing to the solvent action of the water supply on lead pipes in some towns in Lancashire and Yorkshire lead poisoning was prevalent for a considerable period before its real nature was recognized, and the cause discovered. Lead, being a cumulative poison, may produce serious results if regularly taken in very minute quantities over long periods of time. The softest and purest water and peaty waters often act most readily on lead, so that lead has always been considered a more or less dangerous metal in connection with the supply of potable water. These waters are treated with limestone to make them safe. The subject has therefore attracted a great deal of attention. The results of the various observations show that water of a moderate degree of temporary and permanent hardness, and containing but little dissolved nitrates and inappreciable quantities of ammonium salts, may be safely conveyed in lead pipes. L. Greenburg traced the lead in some cistern-water to the flashing on the roofs of buildings which collected the rain-water.

Observations on the solvent action of rain and other natural waters on lead have been made by A. H. Allen, U. Antony and T. Benelli, A. J. Balard, H. Bamberger, O. Bauer and E. Wetzel, E. de Beaumont, E. Belgrand, A. Bellocq, M. Berthelot, L. Besnou, C. H. Bisserié, A. Bobierre, C. Bouillaud, A. C. Brown, F. C. Calvert and R. Johnson, P. Carles, M. Champouillon, M. E. Chevreul, H. W. Clark, F. Clowes, J. B. A. Dumas, G. Flögel, M. J. Fordos, F. Fischer, P. F. Frankland, R. H. Gaines, J. H. Garrett, H. Heap, E. N. Horsford, A. C. Houston, W. P. Jorissen, W. Kaiser, H. Klut, G. Kühnemann, C. G. de Laval, J. H. Marais, M. Mayençon and M. Bergeret, H. Medlock, M. Müller, W. R. Nichols, J. Rodenburg, P. Schmidt, C. Schneider, P. Schweitzer, J. C. Thresh, E. Vandevyverre, A. Wagner, W. C. Williams, G. Wolffhügel, and H. W. Woudstra and C. J. Snuif.

C. H. Crowe, M. M. P. Muir, and S. Ruzicka said that the presence of soluble *chlorides* diminished the magnitude of the attack, and M. Traube-Mengarini and A. Scala said that the chlorides decrease the formation of hydroxide in a marked manner. On the other hand, J. C. Thresh, A. J. Balard, M. J. Fordos, T. Graham and co-workers, C. H. Bisserié, E. N. Horsford, H. Letheby, A. Mailhe, J. B. Nevins, R. Phillips, and C. Reichel found the presence of chlorides raised the solvent action of water on lead. Table V contains some results selected from S. Ruzicka's observations. Pieces of lead, obtained by cutting longitudinally pieces of tubing 11·5 cms. long, and 2 cms. external diameter and 1·3 cms. internal diameter, were exposed for 24 hrs. to water of different degrees of hardness, and the results are expressed in mgrms. of lead dissolved at ordinary temp. Numbers in brackets are doubtful. The salts marked with an asterisk were employed with air-free water.   J. A. N. Friend and J. S. Tidmus found after 200 days' exposure to 99·9 per cent. lead at a mean temp. of 8·5°, with sodium chloride soln. :

NaCl	.	0	2·5	5·0	7·5	10·0	15	30	60 grms. per litre
Loss	.	0·0334	0·2331	0·2626	0·4003	0·6982	0·5670	0·2425	0·1267 grm.

and with potassium chloride soln. under the same conditions for 201 days :

KCl	.	.	0	2·5	5·0	8·0	15·0	40	80 grms. per litre
Loss	.	.	0·0315	0·5006	0·3747	0·5056	0·2453	0·0574	0·0496

J. A. N. Friend and R. H. Vallance found that the presence of colloids retards the corrosive action.   The effect of chlorides in the presence of sulphates, nitrates, and carbonates was examined by C. H. Bisserié, C. H. Crowe, R. Christison, S. Ruzicka, A. Mailhe, and P. Yorke.   C. Reichel found that when soln. of *sodium chloride* are in contact with lead, in air, a crust of lead chloride, oxide, and carbonate is formed, and some lead passes into soln.   Common salt is more active than purified sodium chloride.   Moist sodium chloride in contact with lead, or plumb-iferous tin, soon takes up appreciable amounts of lead.   A. J. Hale and H. S. Foster found 0·02N-NaCl dissolved 0·02 grm. per sq. dm. per day in 7 days, and 0·08 grm. per day in 28 days at 17°–20°.   A. Wagner, and G. Lunge and L. Weibel measured the corrosive action of these soln. on lead—a sat. soln. of sodium chloride in 8 days at 20° dissolved 0·010 grm. per sq. dm., and 0·015 in 2 hrs. at 100°.   M. M. P. Muir found a soln. of 0·250 grm. of *calcium chloride* in a litre of water dissolved 0·5 mgrm. of lead from 5600 sq. mm. of lead in 72 hrs.   A. J. Hale and H. S. Foster found 0·2N-CaCl$_2$ dissolved 0·40 grm. per sq. dm. per day in 7 days at 17°–20° and 0·15 grm. per sq. dm. per day in 28 days ; while a 0·2N-soln. of *magnesium chloride* dissolved 0·55 grm. per sq. dm. per day in 7 days and 0·12 grm. per day in 28 days.   The action of *sea-water* on lead was investigated by O. Bauer and E. Wetzel, and R. Kaiser.   The lead from the fire-ship, *Firebrand*, sunk in Falmouth Harbour in 1780, and raised in 1846, was examined by A. Russell.   The lead from the pump was melted, and cavities in the metal contained crystals of cotunnite, PbCl$_2$; anglesite, PbSO$_4$; and leadhillite, PbSO$_4$.2PbCO$_3$.Pb(OH)$_2$.   C. Matignon observed that the powder obtained by the disintegration of lead objects in museums consists of lead carbonate and chlorides.   He found that a piece of lead dipped in a 30 per cent. soln. of sea-salt, and then dried so as to become coated with salt crystals, progressively disintegrated in 3 years, while a piece of similar lead, not so treated, was not destroyed.   Lead oxychloride, and sodium hydrocarbonate are formed. He attributed the effect to the cyclic effect of the catalytic agent—sodium chloride : 2NaCl+Pb+O+CO$_2$=Na$_2$CO$_3$+PbCl$_2$;   and Na$_2$CO$_3$+PbCl$_2$=PbCO$_3$+2NaCl.

According to S. Ruzicka, the presence of *sulphates* hinders the attack of water on lead (Table V), and M. Traube-Mengarini and A. Scala said that sodium sulphate acts by preventing the formation of lead hydroxide.   J. A. N. Friend and J. S. Tidmus found after 192 days' exposure of 99·9 per cent. lead at a mean temp. of 8°, with sodium sulphate soln. :

Na$_2$SO$_4$.10H$_2$O	.	0	2·5	5	10	20	50	100	200 grms. per litre
Loss	.	.	0·0428	0·0215	0·0198	0·0518	0·0170	0·0028	0·0015	0·0015

and with potassium sulphate soln. under the same conditions for 192 days :

K$_2$SO$_4$	.	.	0	2·5	5·0	8·0	15	40	80 grms. per litre
Loss	.	.	0·0379	0·0183	0·0331	0·0373	0·0574	0·0110	0·0079

Water containing aluminium and calcium sulphates was found by H. Heap to dissolve much lead, but if calcium sulphate and hydrocarbonate are present, M. Müller found that very little is dissolved.

The effect of various sulphates in natural waters was studied by A. J. Balard, P. A. von Bonsdorff, C. H. Bisserié, E. Belgrand, M. J. Fordos, T. Graham and co-workers, G. Kühne-mann, A. Mailhe, and E. Solly ; and the effect in the presence of chlorides and nitrates,

TABLE V.—THE CORROSIVE ACTION OF SALT SOLUTIONS ON LEAD.

Salt	Degrees of hardness.						
	1¼°	2½°	5°	10°	20°	40°	100°
NH₄Cl*	5·0	4·0	3·5	2·5	1·6	1·8	—
NH₄Cl	9·0	7·0	6·0	4·0	3·0	0·8	—
KCl	4·6	3·3	2·4	2·0	1·0	0·6	0·5
NaCl	4·5	4·0	2·8	2·2	1·6	0·6	0·8
CaCl₂	5·4	3·4	3·2	2·2	1·7	0·5	0·1
MgCl₂	5·0	3·6	2·5	2·4	1·5	1·2	0·8
(NH₄)₂SO₄*	1·0	1·0	1·0	1·0	0·8	0·8	—
(NH₄)₂SO₄	2·0	1·5	1·5	1·5	1·6	1·8	—
K₂SO₄	1·0	1·0	1·0	1·3	—	1·5	1·4
Na₂SO₄	1·4	1·0	0·9	1·2	0·8	0·6	0·3
CaSO₄	1·75	1·3	0·25	1·1	0·9	0·6	—
MgSO₄	1·4	0·8	0·8	0·3	0·4	0·7	0·8
KNO₃	7·0	10·0	14·5	15·0	8·0	6·0	—
NaNO₃	5·0	6·0	10·0	7·5	9·5	5·5	3·0
Ca(NO₃)₂	7·4	6·2	7·2	16·3	13·5	7·5	5·5
Mg(NO₃)₂	8·0	7·5	16·0	17·0	13·0	13·0	10·0
(NH₄)₂CO₃	0·05	0·05	0·05	0·13	0·15	2·25	—
K₂CO₃	0·06	0·14	0·13	—	—	0·2	0·12
Na₂CO₃	0·13	(0·40)	0·13	0·13	0·13	0·13	0·10
CaCO₃	0·08	0·06	—	—	—	—	—
MgCO₃	0·10	0·13	0·12	—	—	—	—
Salt	¼	½	⅝	¾	1	1¼	—
K₂CO₃	6·0	4·5	0·9	0·15	0·13	0·13	—
Na₂CO₃	5·5	4·5		0·10	0·10	0·13	

by T. Paul and co-workers, and S. Ruzicka. A. Wagner said that a soln. of *potassium sulphate* had no action on lead, and that the lead suffered no loss of weight in a soln. containing a gram of that salt in 100 c.c. of water although traces of lead were present in the liquid, and G. Lunge and L. Weibel found 100 grms. of *sodium sulphate* in a litre of water dissolved 0·0076 grm. of lead from a sq. dm. surface in 7 days at 20°, and 0·0058 grm. in 2 hrs. at 100°. M. M. P. Muir found 0·200 grm. of sodium sulphate in a litre of water dissolved 0·8 mgrm. of lead from a 5600 sq. mm. surface in 72 hrs. Under similar conditions, a soln. of 0·252 grm. of *calcium sulphate* in a litre dissolved 0·4 mgrm. in 24 hrs. and 0·8 mgrm. in 72 hrs. The presence of carbonates was found by T. Carnelley and W. Frew, P. F. Frankland, H. Heap, H. Klut, G. Kühnemann, M. T. Lecco, A. Leonhardt, M. Müller, M. M. P. Muir, M. Neisser, W. R. Nichols, R. Proskauer, S. Ruzicka, J. C. Thresh, etc., to retard the action of water on lead (Table V). J. C. Thresh found that the precipitation of lead carbonate is hindered by citric, tartaric, or quinic acid, while formic, acetic, or benzoic acid has very little effect. The effect in the presence of chlorides, nitrates, and sulphates was studied by M. J. Fordos, and S. Ruzicka. According to P. Carles, the presence of *nitrites* favours the attack of water on lead. C. H. Crowe, and S. Ruzicka said that the presence of *nitrates* favours more or less the action of water on lead. Similar results were obtained by A. J. Balard, P. A. von Bonsdorff, C. H. Bisserié, J. B. J. D. Boussingault, T. Carnelley and W. Frew, M. J. Fordos, P. Fortner, T. Graham and co-workers, E. N. Horsford, R. Kersting, H. Letheby, C. Stahlmann, J. C. Thresh, M. Traube-Mengarini and A. Scala, etc. (Table V). A. Wagner found that a soln. containing a gram of *potassium nitrate* in 100 c.c. of water in a week removed 14 mgrms. of lead per 11·831 sq. cm. of lead when carbon dioxide was removed from the air, and 20 mgrms. when the carbon dioxide was not removed—the filtered liquid was plumbiferous. T. Carnelley and W. Frew found the attack is very much hindered if air be excluded. M. M. P. Muir observed the solvent action of soln. of potassium nitrate on lead. C. F. Schönbein, and P. Fortner showed that lead reduces the alkali nitrates to nitrites and some metal passes into solution. J. Kliatchko and C. Binggely found that with lead electrodes soln. of potassium and lithium nitrates are reduced more rapidly than with copper electrodes and more slowly than with cadmium

electrodes. J. L. Proust found that a warm aq. soln. of lead nitrate dissolves some lead.
J. A. N. Friend and J. S. Tidmus found that 99·9 per cent. lead at a mean temp. of 8·0°
after 189 days' exposure to soln. of potassium nitrate, lost

KNO$_3$	0	5	10	15	50	100 grms. per litre.
Loss	0·0393	0·8156	1·0902	1·7188	0·8692	0·5342

S. Ruzicka studied the joint effect of nitrates, chlorides, sulphates, and carbonates.
A. Wagner detected no action on lead by a soln. of a gram of *sodium carbonate* in 100 c.c.
of water; M. M. P. Muir found a soln. of 0·310 grm. of *potassium carbonate* in a litre of
water dissolves 0·2 mgrm. of lead from 5600 sq. mm. cross-section in 72 hrs. A. J. Hale
and H. S. Foster found 0·2N-Na$_2$CO$_3$ dissolved 0·10 grm. per sq. dm. in 28 days, and
0·00 grm. in 7 days at 17°–20°. The presence of *phosphates* in the water favours the
formation of a protective film on the surface of the metal as shown by R. Christison,
A. Gautier, W. R. Nichols, J. C. Thresh, A. Parkes, E. Reichardt, G. Wölffhügel, and
P. Yorke. According to K. Scheringa, if a plumbiferous water be kept some time in a
glass vessel, some of the lead compound is deposited on the glass. The presence of *sili-
cates* in the water retards the action of water on glass. This was shown by the work of
R. Böttger, T. Carnelley and W. Frew, F. Clowes, J. C. Thresh, P. F. Frankland, and
W. Crookes and co-workers. W. Crookes and co-workers showed that 0·5 grain of dissolved silica per gallon will render water " lead-proof." According to T. Carnelley and
W. Frew, M. J. Fordos, R. Kersting, H. Medlock, M. M. P. Muir, C. Stahlmann, and
G. Wölffhügel, the presence of even small traces of *ammonium salts* favours the corrosion
of lead (Table V). H. Heap said that this action depends on the ready dissociation of
the salts in soln., so that they behave rather like dil. acids than like neutral salts. According
to T. Carnelley and W. Frew, *slaked lime* acts more energetically than water alone, either
with or without the exclusion of air. G. A. Stutterheim found that the presence of calcium
hydroxide per litre lowered the attack in 24 hrs. from 3·7 mgrms. to 0·2–0·3 mgrm. of
dissolved lead per litre. Sand, calcium carbonate, old mortar, and calcium silicate exert
a protective action. L. Besnou, H. Endemann, and M. Müller also observed that lime-
water exerts a corrosive action; and E. J. Kohlmeyer, cement-water. G. von Knorre
found that lime-water does not attack lead if air be carefully excluded, but the action is
energetic in the presence of air. The retarding action of calcium carbonate on the
corrosive action of lead was discussed by M. Neisser, P. F. Frankland, T. Graham and
co-workers, F. le Blanc, M Champouillon, H. Letheby, U. Antony and T. Benelli,
M. Müller, H. Heap, C. G. Egeling, etc. According to J. F. Liverseege and A. W. Knapp,
the erosion, expressed as the amount of lead in parts per 100,000 parts of water, dissolved, removed from ½ sq. in. of lead exposed to 10
c.c. of water for one day. The results are plotted in
Fig. 16. They found that as the amount of *calcium
hydroxide* present in the water increases, the amount of
lead eroded falls to a minimum when there is present
about 7 to 10 parts of calcium hydroxide per 100,000.
After this point, an increase in the proportion of calcium
hydroxide causes an increase in the erosion, which gradually approaches its original value. As the amount of
calcium carbonate and *hydrocarbonate* present in the water
increases, the amount of lead eroded continually falls.
Calcium hydrocarbonate is by far the most effective pre-
venter of erosion. Only about half the quantity of bicarbonate is required to form a protective coating as compared with carbonate. This would receive a theoretical
explanation if, as seems probable, the coating is a car-

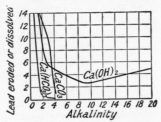

FIG. 16.—Corrosion of Lead by
Calcium Hydroxide and Carbonate.

bonate of lead. As little as two parts per 100,000 of calcium bicarbonate is generally
sufficient to form a plumbo-protective coating on the lead. Assuming that the actual
coating is lead carbonate, it would form a layer only 0·000016 cm. thick. As suggested
above, the irregularities that are observed in the erosion with water about this alkalinity may be due to the fact that the deposit does not quite cover the lead surface and
leaves a little bright lead open to the ordinary erosive action. The *alkalinity* of the
water (the total alkalinity expressed as parts of CaCO$_3$ per 100,000 parts of water) is
an important factor in the corrosion of lead; J. F. Liverseege and A. W. Knapp found
that with waters of alkalinity 0·2–0·6, and generally with treated waters the alkalinity
of which does not exceed 1·5, *the whole of the surface of the lead is eroded*. A flocculent
precipitate forms, which falls to the bottom of the tube and leaves the lead surface quite
bright but mottled.

With treated water of alkalinity 1·5–2·5, the action is usually one of *corrosion* rather than
of erosion; a loosely-held, opaque, white crust forms here and there irregularly on the lead
surface. This crust appears on the upper surface of the inclined lead in an ordinary erosion
test, on the under surface if the lead is placed horizontally and almost touching the glass,
and on both sides if the lead stands vertically. With waters of alkalinity 2·5 and over

the lead almost invariably becomes covered with a dull whitish film, which appears to act as a *protective coating*. J. C. Thresh also discussed this question. F. Varrentrapp, and G. A. Stutterheim noted the retarding influence of soluble *iron salts*, and E. N. Horsford, of iron rust on the corrosion of lead. H. Medlock patented a process for purifying plumbiferous waters by iron. The influence of *organic matters* in water was investigated by H. M. Noad, J. C. Thresh, E. N. Horsford, T. Graham and co-workers, M. Müller, H. Medlock, T. Carnelly and W. Frew, etc. The results show that when the organic matter is oxidized to ammonium salts, the action may be accelerated. J. A. N. Friend and R. H. Vallance found that the presence of colloids—dextrin, gum, or agar-agar—reduces the corrosive action of water. S. Ruzicka found that a decoction of peat increased the corrosion, but decoctions of radish-leaves, grass, or fish reduced the attack. The activity of many natural waters, said H. Heap, is to be explained by the presence of varying amounts of ammonium nitrate, and he added : " Moorland streams are generally very pure waters and contain small amounts of saline matter, thus approaching in character very nearly to distilled water. Thus, as one would expect, the amounts of lead they dissolve are very similar ; but river waters, having transversed stretches of rocky beds and dissolved appreciable amounts of mineral matter, behave more like dil. saline soln. and exert much milder action upon lead than the purer waters."

According to A. C. Houston, " Neutral waters sometimes erode lead in the presence of oxygen. Neutral moorland waters are not erosive unless they have been previously in contact with lead. Acid moorland waters, so-called peaty waters, are apt to possess erosive properties, but the action is not so rapid as that of distilled water. They may erode not only bright but also old coated lead. Rain-water after stagnating in peaty, boggy, or marshy places becomes acid ; this acidity is greater than that which rain-water may acquire before falling on the ground. During storms, and when wet succeeds dry weather, moorland water becomes very acid and acts strongly on lead. During dry weather the water draining from moorlands is generally neutral and does not attack lead. Water draining from formations rich in iron pyrites may be acid and act on lead ; the acidity of moorland waters is seldom attributable to this cause. Acid-producing bacteria are found in peat. Neutral sterile decoctions of peat inoculated with fresh peat became acid and acquired the power of attacking lead."

J. I. Crabtree and co-workers [6] studied the action of *photographic solutions* on leaden vessels. Lead is but slowly corroded in contact with some soils, while in others active deterioration occurs. Antique objects of lead always have a white appearance due to the formation of a basic lead carbonate. According to J. H. Pepper, and C. L. Bloxam, the lead of old coffins is sometimes found to have become entirely converted into an earthy-looking mass of basic carbonate of lead. T. Carnelley and W. Frew found that a peaty soil protected lead piping from corrosion ; blue clay was highly corrosive ; chalk protected the lead, likewise also magnesium oxide, calcium carbonate, old mortar, calcium silicate, sand or a mixture of sand and calcium carbonate. The action of soils was also examined by L. A. Stenger, and J. W. Shipley. In some soils considerable damage to lead pipes is produced by electrolysis, and the electrolysis may be due to the escape of current from electric railway lines, etc. The corrosion of lead by stray currents has been discussed by O. Hähnel, R. H. Gaines, E. R. Shepard, H. Michalke, F. O. Anderegg and R. V. Achatz, W. N. Smith and J. W. Shipley, E. F. Petritsch and A. H. de Vogt, H. F. Zangger, S. C. Bartholomew, J. Chapuis and H. Deprez, M. Remaugé, M. Girousse, B. McCollum and G. H. Ahlborn, etc. Although T. Carnelley and W. Frew showed that old mortar has a protective action on lead pipes, it is well known to plumbers that lead pipes laid on new mortar are liable to corrosion. G. von Knorre showed that when lead pipes come in contact with mortar or cement where air has easy access, corrosion frequently occurs. This is attributed to the action of air and moisture ; similar observations were made by O. Bauer and E. Wetzel. According to W. Vaubel, the attack is due to the formation of a calcium peroxyhydrate, but H. Ditz and co-workers do not accept this view. R. H. Gaines studied the corrosion of lead in damp concrete for two months, and found with lead a loss of about 12 grms. per sq. ft., whereas with steel, the highest loss observed was 2·48 grms. per sq. ft., with copper 1·04 grms. per sq. ft., and with manganese bronze, 0·30 grm. per sq. ft. The corrosive action of cement, or of water seeping through concrete, was also noted by E. J. Kohlmeyer, and G. C. Bunker and A. H. Khachadoorian.

In 1787, R. Watson [7] commented on the corrosion of roofing lead.   He said :

When plumbers strip the roofs of churches, or other buildings covered with lead, which has lain undisturbed for many years, they usually find that side of the lead which is contiguous to the boards, covered with a white pellicle, as thick sometimes as a half-crown ; this pellicle is corroded lead, and is as useful for painting, and other purposes, as the best white lead.   The lead on the south side of any building is found to abound most with this white crust ; that on the north side having very little, or none at all of it.   It is believed, also, that lead which lies on deal boards is not so apt to be covered with this white incrustation, as that which lies upon oak : if there be any truth in this observation, it may, perhaps, be explained from hence, that oak contains a much stronger acid than deal, and this strong acid being distilled, as it were, by the heat of the sun in summer, attaches itself to the lead, and corrodes it : or this corrosion may be the effect of the sun and air, which, by their constant action, calcine or corrode the lead ; and this calcined lead not being washed off by the rain, may, in the course of a great many years, form the crust here spoken of.

J. S. S. Brame also observed the corrosion of lead in contact with oak, and F. Southerden said that the roofing of Axminster church laid on deal in 1833 was sound 85 years afterwards, but the portion laid on oak in 1909, was thickly encrusted with white lead after nine years.   P. Dunsheath noted the corrosion of lead pipes in contact with oak.   C. E. Cresse noted the perforation of sheet lead by a wood borer—Capricorn beetle, Goat beetle, or Sawyer worm.

H. Moissan [8] found that at ordinary temp. **fluorine** slowly transforms lead into lead fluoride ; if the lead be warm, it burns in that gas.   According to J. B. A. Dumas, **chlorine** slowly transforms lead into chloride without incandescence, and A. Classen and B. Zahorsky showed that in the absence of hydrogen chloride, liquid chlorine has no action on lead.   J. A. Wilkinson showed that there is a flash of light when chlorine comes in contact with molten lead, and a feeble luminescence occurs when lead is heated in chlorine or **bromine** vapour and lead chloride or bromide is formed ; and J. Nicklès showed that in the presence of a soln. of bromine in dry ether, lead is rapidly converted into the bromide. E. Beckmann said that **iodine** does not dissolve lead.   G. Tammann and co-workers found that with air containing 0.0003 mol. Cl_2 per litre the film of chloride at $225°$ is $245\mu\mu$ thick in 20 secs., and $490\mu\mu$ in 90 secs.   At $290°$, with air carrying 0.0033 mol Br_2 per litre, the film thickens from $300\mu\mu$ in 20 secs. to $700\mu\mu$ in 115 secs. ; and air with 0.06 mol I_2 per litre, at $15°$, produces a film $164\mu\mu$ thick in 4 mins. ; and $409\mu\mu$ in 25 mins. at $167°$.   J. L. Gay Lussac and L. J. Thénard found that **hydrofluoric acid** does not attack lead below the b.p. of the acid ; a protective film of insoluble lead fluoride is formed.   T. E. Thorpe and W. Kirman found that **fluosulphonic acid**, $HFSO_3$, rapidly attacks lead, forming lead sulphate and fluoride.   M. Berthelot found that **hydrogen chloride** is decomposed when heated with lead, and the reaction is irreversible ; he also showed that in the cold, dry **hydrogen chloride** does not attack lead, but if a little oxygen or water, or, according to E. Salkowsky, hydrogen dioxide, be present, the metal is slowly attacked.   Lead is so very slightly soluble in **hydrochloric acid** that it is sometimes stated to be insoluble.   F. Stolba showed that lead is very slowly attacked by hydrochloric acid in the presence of air ; an acid of sp. gr. 1.12 attacks purified lead with the production of small bubbles of hydrogen.   A. J. Hale and H. S. Foster found that $0.2N$-HCl dissolves 0.06 grm. of lead per day in 4 hrs., 1.20 grms. per day in 7 days, and 0.69 grm. per day in 28 days per sq. cm. at $17°–20°$.   J. P. Sharples said that the cold acid slowly attacks lead vessels, and that the hot acid attacks the lead rapidly.   A. J. Hale and H. S. Foster found that hydrochloric acid attacks lead much more rapidly than does sulphuric acid—*vide* acetic acid.   W. G. Whitman and R. P. Russell observed that the presence of oxygen favoured the attack.   In a general way, H. J. Prinz found that the presence of nitrobenzene accelerated the attack of lead by acids.   Hydrochloric acid in the presence of hydrogen dioxide was found by E. Salkowsky to dissolve finely divided lead.   Molten **lead chloride** dissolves very little lead, but as the temp. rises the percentage solubility increases being 0·000154 at 550°, 0·000374 at 610°, 0·000410 at 615°, and 0·000746 at 640°. The solubility is reduced if alkali chlorides are present. The solubility in aq. soln. of the chlorides of the alkalies and alkaline earths has already been discussed. **Hydrogen iodide** and **hydriodic acid** were found by H. St. C. Deville to attack lead vigorously. A soln. of **sodium hypochlorite** was found by H. P. Pearson to attack lead vigorously, forming lead dioxide ; J. H. Gladstone and A. Tribe showed that a soln. of **potassium chlorate** is not reduced by spongy lead, but in the presence of dil. sulphuric acid, potassium chloride is slowly formed. Boiling soln. of potassium chlorate were found by G. Lunge and A. Deggeler to be slowly reduced in lead vessels. A. Ditte said that a hot or cold soln. of **hydriodic acid** does not attack lead.

L. Franck [9] found that if a clean surface of lead be rubbed with **sulphur,** the metal is blackened owing to the formation of lead sulphide. F. Knapp also found lead is tarnished in contact with sulphur. K. Jellinek and J. Zabowsky discussed the affinity of lead for sulphur. W. Spring said that if a mixture of lead and sulphur be greatly compressed, 6500 atm., it forms a black graphitic mass with a crystalline fracture. E. Jannettaz obtained no sign of the crystalline sulphide (**1.** 13, 18). Lead unites directly with molten sulphur ; and, according to G. C. Winkelblech, if combination be started in a mixture of finely divided lead and sulphur contained in a test tube by heating one end, the reaction does not of itself proceed through the mass unless the tube and contents have been pre-heated in boiling water ; strips of lead take fire in sulphur vapour burning with a vivid glow, and depositing half-fused globules of lead sulphide. M. Chavastelon found lead is dissolved when placed near a fragment of sulphur even though not in actual contact. G. Little found that a reaction attended by incandescence occurs when **selenium** is heated in contact with lead, and a grey, porous, silver-white mass is formed. According to G. Rose, molten lead readily dissolves **tellurium,** and H. Fay and C. B. Gillson found that the m.p. of the metal is thereby raised. According to G. Tammann and W. Köster, air containing **hydrogen sulphide** acts very slowly on lead. H. Schiff, and C. Geitner noticed that **sulphur dioxide** is decomposed when heated with lead, forming lead sulphide, etc. H. C. Jenkins and E. A. Smith found that lead reacts with sulphur dioxide at about 300° : $Pb+3SO_2=PbS+2SO_3$; and between 327° and 400°, some lead sulphate is formed, $Pb+2SO_3=PbSO_4+SO_2$; the summation equation is $2Pb+2SO_2=PbSO_4+PbS$—R. Schenck and co-workers made observations on this subject—*vide supra*, the theory of the extraction of lead. C. Geitner found that when a mixture of **sulphurous acid** and lead is heated in a sealed tube at 200°, lead sulphate, but no sulphide, is formed. W. G. Smith and A. A. Heimrod showed that gases containing **selenium dioxide,** SeO_2, and **selenium trioxide,** SeO_3, readily attack lead containing only 0·1 per cent. of antimony. G. Rose said that molten lead easily unites with **tellurium,** and H. Fay and C. B. Gillson added that the f.p. of lead is raised by a little tellurium.

Cold conc. **sulphuric acid** was found by G. Lunge and L. Weibel to **attack** lead—the 99·8 per cent. acid dissolved 1·790 grms. of lead per sq. dm. surface in 6 days at 20°, and 847 grms. in 2 hrs. at 100°. A. J. Hale and H. S. Foster observed that with 500 c.c. of $0·2N\text{-}H_2SO_4$, 0·00 grm. of commercial, cold hard-rolled, and polished lead per sq. dm. per day was dissolved in 4 days at 17°–20° ; 0·01 grm. per day in 7 days ; and 0·02 grm. per day in 28 days. W. G. Whitman and R. P. Russell found that the presence of oxygen favoured the attack of lead by sulphuric acid. G. Lunge and E. Schmid found that sulphuric acid of sp. gr. 1·8 dissolves 128·1 grms. per sq. metre in 8 days at ordjnary temp. ; an acid of sp. gr. 1·84 in 6 days at 100° dissolved 86·8 grms. per sq. m. ; and 79·1 grms. in 10 hrs. at 100° ; 277·6 grms. in 3 hrs. at 200° ; 565·4 grms. in 4 hrs. at 100° ; and acid of sp. gr. 1·725 dissolved 47·0 grms. in 6 hrs. at 100° ; 51·4 grms. in 10 hrs. at 100° ; and 191·9 grms. in 6 hrs. at 200°. The purest soft lead is less acted on by sulphuric acid or nitrated sulphuric acid than any other kind of lead at temp. up to 200°, and if the temp. does not rise beyond that point, it can be safely used in the construction of vitriol chambers ;

tanks, and towers; and for concentrating pans. The presence of oxygen (oxides) in the lead is always very small and has no appreciable effect on the resistance of lead to sulphuric acid. The presence of 0·2 per cent. of antimony does little or no harm, and since it increases the hardness and tensile strength of the lead it can be used for work in contact with the cold acid. Higher proportions of antimony are inadmissible particularly if the acid be hot. More than 0·2 per cent. of copper is injurious, but between 0·1 and 0·2 per cent. has no appreciable influence with the cold acid, but above 200° has a protective action on lead and reduces its chance of being converted to the sulphate at about 240°. With more conc. sulphuric acid, and 10 hrs.' exposure, the following amounts of lead in grams per sq. metre, dissolved in the acid at 50°:

Nordhausen acid.

SO₃			79·30	80·69	81·63	83·49	87·10	88·92	89·90 per cent
Loss	.	.	64·0	867·5	1300	1899·6	2008·8	1801·5	1649·7 grms.

The attack thus increases with conc. slowly up to an acid of sp. gr. 1·843, and very rapidly beyond this point. An acid with 99 per cent. H_2SO_4 should not be in contact with lead, the same remark applies to the fuming acid. A. Frisak's results for the attack on lead by sulphuric acid at different temp. and different conc. of acid are shown in Figs. 17 and 18. F. Kuhlmann said that the attack by conc. sulphuric

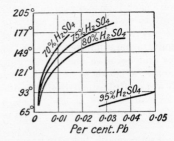

FIG. 17.—Solubility of Lead (per cent. Pb) in Sulphuric Acid. (Temperature variable.)

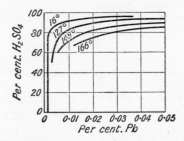

FIG. 18.—Solubility of Lead in Sulphuric Acid. (Concentration Variable.)

acid is imperceptible if the temp. does not exceed 200°–205°. A. Ditte showed that with the hot acid, sulphur dioxide is given off, and R. Hasenclever, and A. Bauer and P. von Mertens observed that by warming 0·2 grm. of lead with 50 c.c. of sulphuric acid of sp. gr. 1·843, at 175°, some gas is given off which increases in amount as the temp. rises to 190°; at 230°–240°, sulphur dioxide and hydrogen are given off, and there is a separation of sulphur, while the lead is completely transformed into sulphate which dissolves in the acid. Observations were also made by R. R. Tatlock, H. de Hemptinne, A. A. Mallard, A. Lassieur, J. Napier, and F. C. Calvert and R. Johnson. G. Lunge and E. Schmid found that the sudden action of sulphuric acid is slightly retarded by one per cent. of antimony in the lead, and inhibited by 0·2 per cent. of copper. If dil. sulphuric acid be boiled with lead, the acid is concentrated, and the b.p. gradually rises—the sudden conversion of the lead into sulphate occurs at about 280°. H. C. Lancaster found electrolytic lead of 99·998 per cent. purity resists the action of conc. sulphuric acid at 310°. E. Salkowsky found that in the presence of hydrogen dioxide and dil. sulphuric acid, lead is insoluble, and powdered lead is partly converted into lead sulphate. The effect of various foreign metals in lead on its corrosion by sulphuric acid has been studied by F. C. Calvert and R. Johnson, R. Hasenclever, N. Cookson and A. Sanderson, R. W. Hochstetter, L. Pitkin, A. Bauer and P. von Mertens, W. B. Hart, E. L. Rhead, D. W. Jones, W. G. McKellar, J. Mactear, H. van der Planitz, etc. The observations of G. Lunge and E. Schmid on the effect of copper and antimony have been previously discussed. These confirmed the work of J. Glover, who showed that with each of these metals

Per cent. addition		0·1	0·2	0·3	0·4	0·5
Per cent. loss {Cu		7·1	7·1	7·5	9·1	8·5
{Sb		8·1	9·2	10·9	11·6	11·8

C. E. Barrs found that small proportions of silver, arsenic, sulphur, and tin lessen the action of the acid on lead. H. W. Rowell said that a little zinc in lead accelerates the action of the acid more than is the case with other metals. C. E. Barrs found that zinc and bismuth favour the corrosion. If bismuth and antimony are present together they neutralize one another's activity. Comparing the action of the lead alone and with 0·2 per cent. of different metals, by taking the temp. of the " first action " to be that at which a continuous stream of bubbles rose from the metal, and as temp. of " vigorous action " that at which excessive frothing occurred and the lead was converted to sulphate, C. E. Barrs found

	Pb	Cu	Bi	As	Sb	Zn	Sn	Ag	Te	S
First action	150°	210°	70°	213°	150°	160°	156°	200°	190°	142°
Vigorous	220°	315°	135°	260°	220°	200°	232°	262°	316°	238°

D. W. Jones examined the effect with lead containing different proportions of these metals. He found that 0·2 per cent. of copper neutralizes the baneful effect of 0·05 per cent. of bismuth; mercury alloyed with lead has a deleterious effect on its resistance to the acid; sodium and copper were each found to exert a beneficial influence. The subject of lead for making plant to resist sulphuric acid, etc.—the so-called *chemical lead*—was also investigated by T. French. J. A. Wilkinson found that when molten lead is oxidized with **sodium persulphate,** $Na_2S_2O_8$, there is a vigorous reaction, and the whole mass fuses and becomes cherry red, but no luminescence occurs; with **ammonium persulphate,** a bluish-white light appears as the mass becomes solid. M. G. Levi and co-workers obtained lead disulphate by the action of a soln. of alkali persulphate on lead; and F. J. Faktor showed that when a soln. of **sodium thiosulphate** is heated with lead, lead sulphide is formed.

According to L. Arons,[10] when an electric arc is made between lead electrodes in **nitrogen** gas, the metal acquires a film which is probably **lead nitride.** W. R. E. Hodgkinson and N. E. Bellairs found that aq. **ammonia** slowly dissolves lead, and after long contact some lead hydroxide is produced, but no nitrites. H. Endemann found that conc. aq. ammonia dissolved 0·0139 per cent. of lead in three days. A. J. Hale and H. S. Foster observed that a 0·2N-soln. dissolved 0·02 grm. per sq. dm. per day in 7 days and 0·01 grm. per day in 28 days. The solvent action of soln. of ammonium salts has been previously indicated. According to A. Wagner, a soln. of a gram of **ammonium chloride** in 100 c.c. of water dissolved 12 mgrms. from a surface of lead of 11·831 sq. cm. when air free from carbon dioxide was used, and 5 mgrms. with ordinary air. G. Lunge and L. Weibel made observations on this subject. W. G. Whitman and R. P. Russell found that the presence of oxygen favoured the attack of lead by nitric acid. W. R. E. Hodgkinson and A. M. Coote found that molten **ammonium nitrate** attacks lead giving off ammonia and forming lead nitrate; the hydrogen given off at the same time reduces the nitrate to nitrite, and this in contact with the ammonium salt produces nitrogen; an ice-cold soln. of ammonium nitrate attacked lead, forming lead nitrite, and M. M. P. Muir made observations on the solvent action of soln. of this salt—*vide supra*. J. W. Turrentine noted that lead anodes are attacked during the electrolysis of a soln. of **sodium azide,** NaN_3. According to P. Sabatier and J. B. Senderens, **nitrous oxide** slowly oxidizes lead at 300°, and is reduced to nitrogen—no nitrous vapours were observed. They also found that with nitric oxide lead oxide is formed. The production of films on heated lead by nitrous and nitric oxides was studied by E. Schröder and G. Tammann; while E. Müller and H. Barck found that nitric oxide slowly attacks the metal. B. B. Adhikary showed that with a mixture of nitric oxide and hydrogen (1 : 3) lead acts catalytically, forming ammonia. P. Sabatier and J. B. Senderens showed that **nitrogen peroxide** slowly oxidizes lead at 200°, forming a basic nitrate. R. Weber said that **nitrogen pentoxide** is not decomposed by lead. J. J. Sudborough found that when lead is heated many days in contact with **nitrosyl chloride**, at 100°, a nitrosochloride is formed.

Dil. **nitric acid** is the best solvent for lead, the action of the conc. acid was found by G. Lunge and E. Schmid to be hindered by the formation of a protective film of lead nitrate which is soluble in water and dil. acid but not in conc. acid. According to C. Montemartini, below 15°, nitric acid of all conc. attacks purified lead very slowly, but is quickest with dil. acid. Small quantities of ammonia are formed in amounts which are greatest with the dil. acid. J. J. Acworth and H. E. Armstrong found that comparatively large amounts of nitrous oxide and nitrogen are contained in the gases ; thus, with acid 1 : 2 at 14°, the 10·56 c.c. gas obtained from 0·381 grm. of metal, contained 51·23 per cent. of nitric oxide, 41·47 per cent. nitrous oxide, and 7·30 per cent. of nitrogen. G. O. Higley made observations on this subject. E. Divers said that it is doubtful if hydroxylamine is formed during the action of nitric acid on lead, although a small proportion was once detected, but ammonia was always produced. G. Lunge and E. Schmid found the loss of lead in grams per sq. metre during 30 days at ordinary temp. in acids of different sp. gr., or per cent. HNO_3 :

Sp. gr.	1·210	1·262	1·305	1·350	1·365	1·371	1·404	1·425	1·458	1·480	1·498	
HNO_3	33·82	41·64	48·26	52·37	53·45	59·57	65·09	79·98	79·33	86·05	93·10	per cent.
Loss	3710	1803	900	552	398	261	195	196	516	733	378	

A. J. Hale and H. S. Foster found that $0.2N$-HNO_3 dissolves lead at the rate of 0·36 grm. per sq. dm. per day in 4 hrs., 9·8 grms. per day in 7 days, and 6·3 grms. per day in 28 days. B. C. Banerji and N. R. Dhar found that the presence of ferric chloride or nitrate favours the attack of lead by nitric acid. F. Kuhlmann observed that in the manufacture of sulphuric acid, where the acid vapours pass from one lead chamber to another, when nitric or nitrous acids are present, the lead plates are rapidly corroded. G. Lunge and E. Schmid measured the effect of the nitrous vitriol of different degrees of conc. and with varying proportions of nitric acid on lead. Mixtures of nitric and sulphuric acids vigorously attack lead. They stated that conc. nitrous acid acts more strongly than sulphuric acid at all temp. and upon all descriptions of lead. In the case of dil. acids, say sp. gr. 1·72–1·76, the action of nitrous vitriol is rather less than with sulphuric acid, owing to the formation of a crust of lead sulphate. With still more dil. acids, where the nitroso-sulphuric acid is partly changed into free nitrous and nitric acids, the action is again stronger. If these acids are compared among each other, it is found that those acids act least upon lead at 65°–70°, whose conc. is between sp. gr. 1·6 and 1·5, that is, between the limits which are mostly observed for "chamber acids"; both more highly conc., and more dil. acids act more upon the lead in the latter case in proportion to the nitric acid present (or formed). P. Sabatier, and P. Pascal and co-workers studied the attack on lead by nitrated sulphuric acid, and found pure lead resists attack provided less than 30 per cent. water is present. H. Braconner attributed the sluggish action of the conc. acid on lead to the formation of a protective film of lead nitrate. V. H. Veley found that at a constant temp. the rate at which lead dissolves increases as the conc. of the acid is increased up to a maximum, and thereafter decreases. This result is unlike that obtained with copper, mercury, and bismuth ; and it is dependent on the decreasing solubility of the lead nitrate with increasing conc. of the acid. Nitrous acid is produced during the reaction, and the amount of metal dissolved in unit time is correlated with the amount of nitrous acid in the soln. The amount of nitrous acid produced is much less than is the case with copper ; the amount increases gradually to a maximum and constant value ; the amount of metal dissolved in unit time is reduced by the presence of substances like potassium chloride and hydrogen dioxide which destroy nitrous acid. A. Quartaroli added that if the nitric acid be perfectly free from nitrous acid it does not attack lead ; the presence of urea in nitric acid, by inhibiting the formation of nitrous acid, slows down the reaction. Lead is attacked to a less degree by **nitrous acid** or nitric acid taken separately than when mixed together. Expressing the amount of lead dissolved in decimilligrams per sq. mm. per hour, and the conc. of the acids in grams per 15 c.c. at 15°–18°, V. H. Veley found

HNO$_3$.	. 4·5286	14·122	0·8562	1·7062	4·2407	4·1721	0·6840	trace
HNO$_2$.	. 0	0	0·122	0·2219	0·1704	0·5089	0·2754	0·158
Pb dissolved .	2·22	0·015	3·05	2·64	3·67	4·52	15·01	0·8

B. Pelletier [11] found that when **phosphorus** is projected on molten lead, or when lead films are fused with an equal w..ight of glacial **phosphoric acid,** or lead chloride

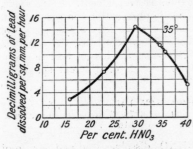

FIG. 19.—Velocity of the Reaction between Lead and Nitric Acid of Different Concentrations.

is treated with phosphorus, a lead phosphide is formed containing less than 15 per cent. of phosphorus. The subject is discussed in connection with lead phosphide. J. Heimann found lead to be soluble in a soln. of **metaphosphoric acid,** B. Reinitzer and H. Goldschmidt found that at 250°, **phosphoryl chloride** is only slightly affected by lead ; and C. Poulenc said that at 180°, **phosphorus trifluochloride** forms phosphorus trifluoride and lead chloride.

T. Bergman [12] found that when lead is fused with **arsenic,** the lead takes up one-sixth of its weight of arsenic. P. A. Bolley said that when arsenic is alloyed with lead, the union occurs without incandescence, and the product is brittle. W. Spring made the alloys by compressing a mixture of the powdered elements at 65·00 atm. A. Descamps made the alloy by melting arsenic and lead with boric oxide ; W. Heike, with animal charcoal in an evacuated vessel ; K. Friedrich melted the elements together in an atm. of carbon dioxide ; and A. Descamps, and G. A. Koenig, passed the vapour of arsenic into molten lead. J. Fournet reduced lead arsenate in a carbon crucible, and A. Descamps reduced it by fusion with potassium cyanide. The fusion curves of the alloys with 0·34 per cent. of arsenic, by K. Friedrich, are shown in Fig. 20. There is a partial separation of the arsenic as the liquid alloy cools. The fusion curve has two branches

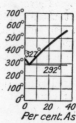

FIG. 20.—Fusion Curves of As–Pb Alloys.

with a eutectic at 292° and 2·5–3 per cent. of arsenic. The solid metal contains lead, arsenic, and the eutectic. The fusion curves were also studied by W. Heike, S. F. Schemtschuschny, W. Guertler, and C. T. Heycock and F. H. Neville. K. Friedrich found no sign of the compounds Pb : As=3 : 4, 1 : 1, 4 : 3, and 2 : 1 reported by A. Descamps, or of 3 : 2 reported by W. Spring. I. P. Göbel, and C. O. Thieme discussed the hardening of lead by arsenic ; and I. P. Göbel, the hardness and sp. gr. N. A. Puschin studied the electrical potential of the alloys. A. Descamps preserved the alloys under air-free water, or under a hydrocarbon, since they are quickly attacked in air. A. Bauer and P. von Mertens found that the alloys are slowly decomposed by sulphuric acid—*vide* lead arsenides. Lead alloyed with a small proportion of arsenic is used to form *shot-metal*. J. Fournet represented the reaction between **arsenic sulphide,** as realgar, and lead by the equation : $2Pb+AsS_2=2PbS+As$; and J. Percy likewise treated **antimony sulphide** with lead.

J. F. Gmelin [13] prepared some alloys of antimony and lead. G. Karsten found prismatic crystals of an alloy of lead and **antimony** in the hearth of a smelting furnace at Mulden; the composition approximated $Pb_{18}Sb$. A. Brand found the two elements in isomorphous mixture with lead and cuprous sulphides, and with nickel and copper antimonides in the hearth of a lead smelting furnace. Lead and antimony unite when mixed in different proportions and melted. According to W. Spring, the two elements unite even at 265°. Alloys were made by H. Gautier, A. Matthiessen, R. Durrer, M. Kühnel and M. Marzahn, F. de Jussieu, J. E. Stead, C. Pack, Q. Marino and C. Bowen, E. Heyn, A. Riche, R. H. Thurston, W. G. Knox, etc. The equilibrium diagram was studied by H. Gautier, R. Loebe, M. le Gris, C. R. A. Wright and co-workers, A. Saposhnikoff and J. Kaniewsky, G. Charpy, J. E. Stead, A. Gorbow, L. J. Gurevich and J. S. Hromatko, W. Gontermann, M. Wählert, W. Campbell, K. Honda and T. Ishigaki, O. Bertoya, C. C. Bissett, etc. R. S. Dean's, and W. Gontermann's curves are summarized in Fig. 21; the curves are of the V-type with the eutectic at 246° and 87 per cent. of lead, with the possible existence of *lead tetritantimonide*, Pb_4Sb. S. D. Muzaffar could find no compound and no solid soln. in the antimony-lead alloys. V. Fischer studied the equilibrium relations of the liquid alloy.

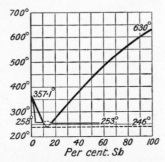

FIG. 21.—Freezing-point Curves of Mixtures of Antimony and Lead.

The structure of the alloys was investigated by A. Riche, J. Fournet, G. Karsten, A. M. Portevin, H. Behrens, D. Ewen and T. Turner, H. Fowler, F. L. Brady, J. E. Stead, C. C. Bissett, F. de Jussieu, G. Charpy, W. Campbell, P. Siedler, etc.; the grain-growth, by R. S. Dean and W. E. Hudson; the sp. gr., by A. Matthiessen, I. P. Göbel, A. Riche, J. A. Linnavuori, F. C. Calvert and R. Johnson, G. Faunce, E. Maey, J. E. Stead, etc.; A. Matthiessen's results are:

Lead	0	45·9	62·9	77·3	83·6	89·5	94·5	97·7	100 per cent.
Sp. gr.	6·713	8·201	8·989	9·811	10·144	10·586	10·930	11·194	11·376

E. Maey measured the sp. vol. D. Ewen and T. Turner found that the shrinkage of the alloys on cooling diminishes from a maximum with 15 per cent. of antimony to a minimum with 30 per cent. of antimony. M. Dubosc, R. S. Dean and co-workers, and L. Gillet, found that the alloys could be hardened by quenching. The hardness was measured by H. Behrens, E. Heyn and O. Bauer, F. C. Calvert and R. Johnson, C. O. Thieme, I. P. Göbel, P. Ludwik, D. Ewen and T. Turner, A. Saposhnikoff and J. Kaniewsky, L. J. Gurevich and J. S. Hromatko, G. K. Burgess and R. W. Woodward, H. M. Waring, M. Wählert, F. de Jussieu, etc.; the tenacity, by E. Heyn and O. Bauer, H. Behrens, and L. J. Gurevich and J. S. Hromatko, etc.; the elastic constants, by G. Wertheim;

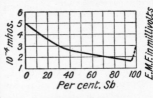

FIG. 22.—The Electrical Conductivity of the Sb–Pb Alloys.

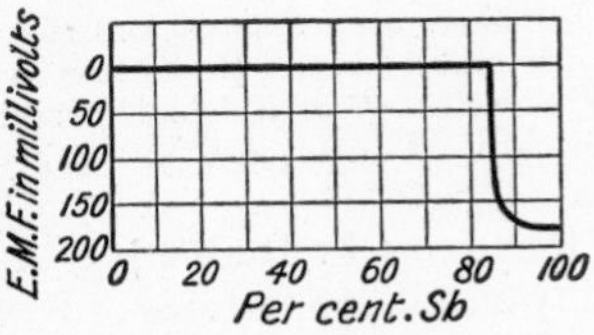

FIG. 23.—The Electromotive Force of Solution of Sb–Pb Alloys.

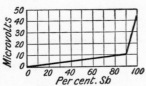

FIG. 24.—The Thermoelectric Force of Sb–Pb Alloys.

the thermal expansion, by G. Vicentini and D. Omodei; the thermal expansion and the heat conductivity, by F. C. Calvert and R. Johnson; the thermal conductivity, by W. B. Brown; the sp. ht., by H. V. Regnault, H. Kopp.

J. A. Linnavuori, R. Durrer, etc.; the viscosity, by M. Plüss; the shrinkage on solidification, by F. Wüst; the fusion curves, by C. T. Heycock and F. H. Neville, P. Müller, T. Thomson, H. Gautier, etc.—*vide supra*, Fig. 21; F. de Jussieu, the liquation and surfusion, and J. Kallir, the disintegration of these alloys; M. Plüss, the viscosity and sp. gr. of the liquid alloy; the magnetization, by H. Leroux

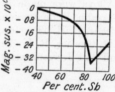

FIG. 25.—The Magnetic Susceptibility of Sb–Pb Alloys.

(Fig. 25), E. Becquerel, W. Rollmann, T. J. Seebeck, E. Rudolfi, A. Naccari and M. Bellati, A. Bettalli, H. Endo, etc.; the thermoelectromotive force, by H. Pélabon, E. Rudolfi, Fig. 24. The curve for the thermal e.m.f. is a straight line for alloys with up to 90 per cent. antimony; and there is then a rapid rise up to the value for antimony alone. The electric conductivity and resistance were measured by A. Matthiessen (Fig. 22), P. Müller, W. Guertler, E. Elsässer, G. Vicentini and C. Cattaneo, etc. The curve has a singular point for alloys with about 90 per cent. antimony. The electric potential was measured by N. A. Puschin, and S. D. Muzaffar; the e.m.f., by A. P. Laurie, H. le Chatelier, etc.; and the e.m.f. of dissolution by N. A. Puschin, Fig. 23. The curve is singular for alloys with over 90 per cent. of antimony.

According to S. Zinberg, the greater the proportion of lead in the alloys the more readily are they attacked by air and moisture; and R. Meyer and S. Schuster showed that the mode of casting and subsequent treatment of the alloys affect their tendency to oxidize. B. Kohlmann noted that the white oxide found on type-metal is mostly basic lead carbonate; and R. Moscheles, that the grey film sometimes present is organic matter. W. G. Knox tried covering iron with a protective layer of antimony-lead alloy in place of zinc, but the results were not so good. H. Leroux found that on the oxidation of the alloy the lead oxidizes first and then the antimony; the lead oxide first formed acts as an oxygen carrier to oxidize more antimony. The use of the alloy as anode in the electrodeposition of colloidal clay was patented by the Gesellschaft für Elektro-Osmose. The action of nitric acid was discussed by H. Behrens; of sulphuric acid, by L. Pitkin, H. von der Planitz, and A. Bauer and P. von Mertens; and of hydrochloric acid, by H. Behrens, and H. von der Planitz. J. O. Johnstone found that in contact with lead nitrate, some basic lead nitrite is formed; and C. W. Proctor showed that in acidified soln. of copper sulphate, or sodium cupricyanide, the alloy is coated with copper, and on this, brass or silver can be deposited. J. W. Richards discussed the valuation of these alloys.

Alloys of lead with about 15 per cent. of antimony furnish the so-called *type-metal*. This alloy is fairly fusible, expands on cooling, and is hard, but it does not resist the action of the press, and of the scouring liquids employed in cleaning the type. To overcome these defects, tin or bismuth is also added: in rarer cases, zinc or copper is added. S. Zinberg found type-metal is not attacked by ordinary water, but is readily attacked by distilled water. The alloys are less attacked the more antimony they contain. Analogous alloys are also used for candlesticks, statuettes, and other decorative articles. The keys for flutes and similar parts of other musical instruments are made from a lead alloy with approximately 33 per cent. of antimony.

Lead and **bismuth** were found by F. Rudberg,[14] A. Riche, F. G. A. Wright, H. Endemann, to unite readily in all proportions; W. Spring made the alloy by compressing an intimate mixture of the powders. According to F. Rudberg, the alloy with 40 per cent. of bismuth has only one solidifying temp., 129°, while alloys with other proportions have two solidifying temp. This is very near the result accepted to-day. The f.p. curve, Fig. 26, examined by G. Charpy, D. Mazzotto, W. Herold, A. W. Kapp, A. Gorboff, W. E. Barlow, C. di Capua, A. Stoffel, C. P. Steinmetz, G. Tammann, K. Bornemann, E. S. Shepherd, N. A. Puschin, P. Ludwik, C. T. Heycock and F. H. Neville, E. Dippel, L. Losana, A. Matthiessen

and co-workers, and K. Honda and T. Ishigaki, has a eutectic at 1245°, and
56·5° per cent. bismuth. According to W. Herold, solid soln. are formed, but the
region over which these extend is not clearly de-
fined; otherwise the alloys are mechanical mixtures of two crystalline phases. The structure of the alloys was examined by K. Bux,
J. Ewing and W. Rosenhain, A. M. Portevir
F. L. Brady, W. Herold. R. Arpi measured the
viscosity; G. Wertheim, the elastic constants;
C. di Capua and M. Arnone, the hardness;
G. Vicentini and D. Omodei, and A. Matthiessen, the thermal expansion of these alloys;
M. Jakob, and W. B. Brown, the thermal conductivity; C. C. Person, and D. Mazzotto, the
heat of fusion; J. Taylor, the heat of formation;
the m.p. of specific alloys were reported by
J. W. Döbereiner, C. T. Heycock and F. H. Neville,
E. S. Shepherd, I. P. Göbel, E. Wiedemann,
C. C. Person, F. Rudberg, F. Guthrie, P. Berthier,

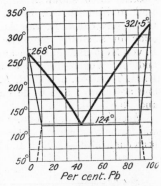

FIG. 26.—Freezing-point Curves
of Bismuth-Lead Alloys.

and T. Thomson. The sp. gr. was measured by P. van Musschenbroek, A. Riche,
T. Thomson, A. Matthiessen, and C. M. Marx. A. Matthiessen's results are :

Lead .	0	4·8	11·2	33·4	66·6	80·0	92·3	100 per cent.
Sp. gr. .	9·823	9·893	10·048	10·538	11·141	11·188	11·280	11·376

The last-named reported that the Pb : Bi=1 : 2 alloy does not expand on solidification : the 1 : 3 alloy expands slightly ; while the 1 : 8 alloy expands markedly on
solidifying. E. Wiedemann measured the changes of vol. on melting. E. von Maey
studied the sp. vol. The hardness curve, Fig. 27, by W. Herold shows an increase
in hardness for low and high conc. of bismuth,
and this indicates that solid soln. are formed
at the beginning and end of the series—otherwise the curve is a straight line. J. Goebel, and
P. Ludwik also measured the hardness of these
alloys. F. Sauerwald studied the viscosity ;
R. Arpi, the thermal expansion ; and O. Richter,
A. Levi, F. A. Schulze, G. Tammann, and
E. Dippel, the sp. ht. of lead-bismuth alloys.

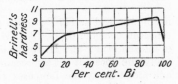

FIG. 27.—The Hardness of Alloys
of Lead and Bismuth.

The sp. ht. curve has a maximum, thought to
indicate the formation of a compound or aggregate. The m.p. also depends on
whether the alloy is over-heated before cooling, or merely heated a few degrees above
the m.p. The sp. ht. is also smaller where the cooling is slower. All these phenomena are supposed to depend on the formation of mol. complexes. A. Magnus
and M. Mannheimer observed that cooling occurs when molten lead and bismuth
are mixed. E. S. Shepherd, W. Herold, R. Schenck, A. Matthiessen, P. Müller,
E. F. Northrup and R. G. Sherwood, R. Kremann and A. Brodar, and W. Guertler,
measured the electrical conductivity. F. A. Schulze's values for the thermal and
electrical conductivities, Fig. 28, have minima for alloys containing 4–5 per cent.
of lead ; this, as well as the initial falls in the curves for alloys with from 0 to 15 per
cent. bismuth, also indicates that solid soln. are formed. A. Leduc measured the
conductivity of bismuth-lead alloys ; A. Matthiessen and C. Vogt, the effect of
temp. and of impurities on the conductivity; R. Kremann and co-workers found
that on electrolysis, the lead accumulates at the cathode, the bismuth at the anode ;
C. R. Darling and R. H. Rinaldi, the thermoelectric properties of the alloys against
copper; E. van Aubel, the effect of a magnetic field on the electrical resistance ;
A. P. Laurie, R. Kremann and A. Langbauer, H. le Chatelier, and E. S. Shepherd,
the e.m.f. of the alloys in a voltaic cell; S. D. Muzaffar, the electrode

potential; and E. Becquerel, W. Broniewsky, W. Rollmann, and T. J. Seebeck
the thermoelectric properties; A. Battelli's values, Fig. 29, for the thermoelectric force shows a rapid decrease for the addition of small quantities of
lead to bismuth. J. Beattie, P. Senepa, H. Endo, W. Rollmann, A. Battelli
G. Spadavecchia, E. van Aubel, and H. Zahn investigated the behaviour of the
alloy in a steady magnetic field; T. French, L. Pitkin, and A. Bauer and
P. von Mertens studied the action of sulphuric acid ; A. Riche, the action of water
and A. Vogel discussed the spontaneous disintegration of these alloys
R. H. Thurston, and C. R. A. Wright studied the ternary alloys of lead, bismuth
and antimony; and C. de Capua, the hardness of the ternary alloys Pb–Bi–Sn
and Pb–Bi–Cd.

According to J. F. John,[15] when lead is heated with **carbon,** the metal volatilizes
and forms a sublimate of lead carbide in black lustrous crystals ; but this has not
been confirmed—O. Ruff and B. Bergdahl could get only 0·024 per cent. of carbon

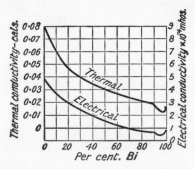

FIG. 28.—The Thermal and Electrical Conductivities of Alloys of Lead and Bismuth.

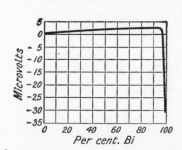

F.G. 29.—The Thermoelectric Force of.
Alloys of Lead and Bismuth.

in soln. in lead at 1170° ; 0·046 per cent. at 1415° ; and 0·094 per cent. at 1555°—
vide lead carbide, **6.** 39, 18. W. Stahl found that the **hydrocarbons** are insoluble
in molten lead ; and H. Reckleben and J. Scheiber showed that purified and dried
acetylene does not act appreciably on lead during 20 months' exposure, while crude
and moist acetylene increases the weight of lead less than 1 per cent. Type-
metal and lead-antimony solder are scarcely affected by the gas. W. R. E. Hodgkinson found that acetylene does not change the properties of lead at temp. up to the
m.p. of the metal. According to W. Stahl, neither **carbon monoxide** nor **carbon
dioxide** is dissolved by molten lead. M. Berthelot found that when lead is heated
with carbon monoxide in a sealed tube at 550°, carbon dioxide is formed. A
mixture of carbon monoxide and dioxide passed into milk of lime contained
in a leaden vessel was found by G. Gore to produce red-lead. The action of
aq. soln. of carbon dioxide, or of the moist gas, on lead has been previously
discussed. M. Berthelot examined the action of **cyanogen** on lead; and
F. H. Rhodes and J. T. Carty, the action of carbon tetrachloride, which
produces a slight white film on the metal. G. A. Goyder found that
an aq. soln. of **potassium cyanide** acts very slowly on lead without the
evolution of gas. The action was examined by A. Brochet and J. Petit
S. G. Sastry said that lead acts on many **chlorinated hydrocarbons**—CCl_4
$CHCl_3$, $C_2H_2Cl_4$, and C_2HCl_5—but not on $C_2H_2Cl_2$. The vapours of the **fatty acids**
were shown by A. Mailhe to react with finely divided, reduced lead, forming first a
salt of the acid, and then a ketone and carbon dioxide ; the reaction is slow at 300°
but fast at 350°. F. P. Hall showed that lead is attacked by **acetic acid, tartaric
acid,** and **citric acid** more strongly when exposed to air than when air is absent
W. G. Whitman and R. P. Russell found that the presence of oxygen favoured the
attack on lead by acetic acid. F. Auerbach and H. Weber examined the effect

of the fruit acids, citric and tartaric acids, as well as of malic, succinic, and benzoic acids. H. C. Bolton found lead to be attacked by a soln. of citric acid mixed with sodium nitrate. J. C. Thresh examined the action of citric, acetic, benzoic, and tartaric acids, and also of quinic and formic acids. O. Sackur said that lead is attacked by dil. acids—acetic acid, lactic acid, and hydrochloric acid—only in the presence of oxygen; the velocity of the reaction is nearly independent of the strength and conc. of the acid, but it is dependent on the conc. of the dissolved oxygen, and on the velocity of stirring; otherwise expressed, the rate of reaction is determined by the diffusion velocity of the dissolved oxygen. E. Salkowsky found that in the presence of hydrogen iodide the attack by acetic acid is greatly hastened. H. S. Rawdon said the attack on commercial lead is largely conditioned by intercrystalline impurities which resist attack, and set up electrolytic action—vide supra. According to O. P. Watts and N. D. Whipple, with 190 c.c. of N-acetic acid at 37·5° and 60 sq. cms. of metal during 45 hrs., the loss was 0·2019–0·2143 grm.; if 5 c.c. hydrogen dioxide were present, the loss was 6·4026 grms.; with 2 grms. of mercuric chloride and 5 c.c. of hydrogen dioxide present, 6·5596 grms.; with 2 grms. mercuric chloride, 0·8529 grm.; and with 0·25 grm. of sodium arsenate, 0·0490 grm. I. L. C. Eckelt found lead is attacked by ethylsulphuric acid, and, added O. Schaal, the more the lead is purified, the slower the reaction. M. Schirmonsky also reported that lead is strongly attacked by naphthenic acid—vide the electrolysis of soln. of lead salts in organic acids. H. J. Prins studied the action of nitrobenzene in acetic acid soln. on lead. The speed of the action is determined by the rate of diffusion of the products of the reaction. C. O. Henke and O. W. Brown, and W. Falta and M. Richter-Quittner found that the reduction of nitrobenzene by hydrogen is catalyzed by lead; J. Tafel, that ketones are reduced to hydrocarbons by electrolysis with lead electrodes; V. Thomas, that methylene iodide reacts with lead giving off a gas; and F. F. Rupert, that the reaction between hydrogen is accelerated by the presence of lead-foil. L. T. O'Shea studied the adsorption of lead salts by filter-paper. O. Schmidt studied the catalytic action of lead in the hydrogenation of organic compounds.

F. Rathgen mentioned that lead medallions were attacked by the organic acid in the sweat of the hand; and F. Southerden, by tanning soln. H. Baum and R. Seeliger,[16] and T. Sudendorf found that milk dissolves lead; D. Klein and A. Berg observed no reaction between lead and soln. of sugar, and L. Lindet noticed that lead accelerates the inversion of sugar. J. Aub gave 0·578 grm. per litre for the solubility of lead in blood serum. A. Gautier, G. Wölffhügel, P. Schützenberger and E. Boutmy, A. Sander, A. Meyer, A. S. Taylor, N. N. Banerjee, E. Gudeman, T. Sudendorf, M. Rjältschewsky, and E. Spaeth detected the contamination of various foodstuffs by contact with lead, and A. Beythein, in cosmetics. H. Riesenfeld and F. Taurke noted that when a soln. of cellulose in an ammoniacal soln. of copper carbonate is treated with lead, cellulose and copper are precipitated. J. Tafel observed that succinimide is not reduced by contact with spongy lead and dil. sulphuric acid. A. Gawalowsky found that mash-wort attacks lead very little. T. Sudendorf examined the solvent action of wine on lead, but this fact has been known since the beginning of our era—vide infra. P. Grélot found wine which has been treated with sulphur dioxide is particularly liable to attack lead. G. Steifler also found fermenting cider develops acids which attack lead. F. Malmejac found that 95 per cent. alcohol in contact with lead in a closed vessel slowly dissolves some lead; but G. Heinzelmann could not detect any reaction between lead and 95–96 per cent. pure or denatured alcohol, although the 90 per cent. alcohol did attack the metal; pyridine was found to be without influence. M. Traube found that the oxidation of lead under absolute alcohol does not occur; oxidation is slow with 90 per cent. alcohol; and in 50 per cent. alcohol it is as fast as in water alone. F. M. Perkin showed that when a current of ozonized air is passed into ether containing strips of lead, yellow lead ethoxide, $Pb(OC_2H_5)_2$, is formed. F. C. Mathers and A. B. Leible found that lead adsorbs ethereal oils when an aq. soln. of the oil is shaken with lead.   J. Merrick found that lead is quickly attacked by **turpentine ;** and C. Engler and E. Kneis showed that freshly distilled turpentine dissolved in 2 days, 0·085 per cent. Pb ; in 8 days, 0·265 per cent. ; and in 14 days, 0·715 per cent. ; while old turpentine in the same time dissolved respectively 0·578, 0·982, and 1·851 per cent. Pb ; and **oil of resin** at ordinary temp. dissolved traces of lead in 8 days and 0·024 per cent. in 14 days, and on a water-bath, respectively 0·380 and 0·880 per cent.   W. Fox, A. Gawalowsky, and G. Engler and E. Kneis found that lead is quickly attacked by **petroleum,** and J. Schiel showed that a piece of lead ribbon 1 mm. thick was wholly converted into a yellow oxide when kept 8 weeks under petroleum.   A. Gawalowsky also found that lead is attacked by mineral lubricating oils.   S. Macadam showed that by prolonged contact with **paraffin oils,** lead is considerably attacked.   A. Schneider and F. Jenniger found that **benzene** wash oils corrode lead.   P. Schindler observed that lead is attacked by **oil of sesame,** and **olive oil ;** and A. Livache, by **linseed oil.**   According to I. J. Redwood, with a **mineral oil** lubricant, for a year, sheet lead lost 0·05607 per cent. ; with olive oil, 0·04243 per cent. ; with **rape oil,** 0·19716 per cent. ; with **tallow oil,** 0·16782 per cent. : with **lard oil,** 0·28000 per cent. ; with **cotton seed oil,** 0·07113 per cent. ; with **sperm oil,** 0·28241 per cent. ; with **whale oil,** 0·29502 per cent. ; with **seal oil,** 0·14198 per cent.   U. Ehrhardt and G. Pfeiderer showed that crude **tar oils** containing phenol dissolved 1·1 mgrm. of lead per sq. cm. in four weeks.   C. O. Henke and O. W. Brown studied the catalytic activity of lead in reducing organic compounds ; and A. Benedicenti and S. Rebello-Alves, the effect of lead on soln. of egg-albumen or blood serum.

For the action of **silicon** and **boron** on lead, *vide* borides (**5.** 32, 4), and silicides (**6.** 40, 11).   F. Damm and F. Krafft [17] showed that vitreous **quartz** is attacked by lead vapour.   For the action of the **metals** on lead, *vide infra;* and for salt solutions, *vide supra.*   E. B. Maxted noted the presence of lead reduces the catalytic activity of **platinum ;** and that platinum black adsorbs lead ions from soln. of lead salts.   W. Venator found that a soln. of **sodium hydroxide** quickly corrodes lead, but many plumbiferous alloys are not attacked.   G. Lunge and L. Weibel found that 102·5 grms. of sodium hydroxide in a litre of water dissolve 0·2957 grm. of lead per sq. metre in 7 days at 20°, and 0·1489 grm. in 2 hrs. at 100° ; with 205 grms. of sodium hydroxide per litre, 0·0560 grm. in 7 days at 20°, and 0·0375 grm. in 2 hrs. at 100° ; and with 510 grms. of sodium hydroxide per litre, 0·03004 grm. in 7 days at 20°, and 0·0333 grm. in 2 hrs. at 100°.   Observations were also made by A. Wagner, and R. H. Gaines. A. J. Hale and H. S. Foster found that between 17° and 20°, 0·2N-NaOH dissolved 1·0 grm. of lead per sq. dm. per day during 7 days, and 0·69 grm. per day during 28 days.   According to O. P. Watts and N. D. Whipple, with 190 c.c. of N-NaOH for 45 hrs. at 37·5°, and 60 sq. cm. of metal the loss was 0·1101 grm. ; with 0·25 grm. of sodium arsenate also present the loss was 0·1026 ; with 5 grms. potassium permanganate, 0·0978 grm. ; with 5 grms. **potassium** nitrate, 0·0938 grm. ; and with 5 grms. sodium chlorate, 0·0942 grm.   O. W. Brown and co-workers, K. Elbs and J. Forssell, and F. Jirsa studied the anodic corrosion of lead during the electrolysis of soln. of sodium hydroxide.   When lead is mixed with an alkali hydroxide and carbon, and heated, carbon dioxide and hydrogen are formed ; similar results were obtained with **alkaline earth hydroxides**—*vide supra*, water. F. Jirsa and J. Fabinger studied the dissolution of lead by alkali-lye during the passage of sinusoidal alternating currents.   G. Lunge and L. Weibel found 4·4 grms. of **sodium sulphide** in a litre of water dissolve 0·0082 grm. of lead per sq. metre in 7 days at 20°, and 0·017 in 2 hrs. at 100°.   P. P. Lebedeff said that a piece of lead wrapped round with platinum wire does not give off hydrogen from a soln. of sodium sulphide.   P. Wenger and D. Midhat studied the electro-reduction of soln. of **potassium dichromate** with lead electrodes ; E. A. von der Burg, the solvent action of soln. of potassium dichromate on cupriferous and ferruginous lead.   Soln. of **molybdates** in hydrochloric acid were found by W. D. Treadwell to be reduced quantitatively by lead to tervalent molybdenum salts. J. F. Liverseege and A. W. Knapp recommended treating lead pipes with a soln. of **potassium permanganate** whereby they resist better the action of alkaline water. F. Mylius and O. Fromm found copper is precipitated by lead from soln. of **copper salts.** J. B. Senderens found that lead precipitates copper from aq. soln. of cupric nitrate, chloride, or acetate ; but a soln. of cupric sulphate does not give copper because of the formation of a film of lead sulphate on the lead. H. W. Gillett found copper is precipitated from acid soln. of copper phosphate, and of silver phosphate. Molten silver chloride was found by C. Tubandt and S. Eggert to convert lead into lead chloride. F. Mylius and O. Fromm found dil. soln. of **silver salts** precipitate silver when treated with lead. Silver nitrate and acetate, for instance, were found by J. B. Senderens to give a precipitate of silver, whilst a silver sulphate soln. behaves like one of copper sulphate. W. W. Strong found lead gives an imprint on the photographic plate. R. H. Gerke gave for the free energy of the reaction $Pb+2AgCl=PbCl_2+2Ag$, 22,612 cals., and for the thermal value, 25,170 cals. ; with $Pb+2AgI=PbI_2+2Ag$, the numbers are respectively 9852 cals. and 12,231 cals. ; and for $Pb+2HgCl=PbCl_2+2Hg$, 24,717 cals and 22,720 cals. L. Peetz found lead precipitates tin from fused **stannous chloride ;** and W. D. Treadwell, that lead reduces **stannic chloride** to stannous chloride. R. Lorenz and M. Mannheimer studied the equilibrium conditions in the reaction $Pb+SnCl_2 \rightleftharpoons PbCl_2+Sn$. R. Lorenz and co-workers found that when lead, cadmium, and cadmium and lead chlorides are fused together at 600°–700°, equilibrium in the balanced reaction $Cd+PbCl_2 \rightleftharpoons CdCl_2+Pb$, is attained in 10 mins. The system consists of three phases, and with each salt phase of given composition there corresponds a whole series of metal phases. The composition of the equilibrium mixture was independent of the absolute quantities of the phases present and of the direction of the reaction according to the above equation, and nearly independent of the temperature over the interval 600°–700°. The value of $[Pb]/[Cd].[CdCl_2]/[PbCl_2]$ at constant temperature decreased steadily as the cadmium content decreased. Addition of lithium chloride and of mixtures of sodium and potassium chlorides favour the forward reaction in the above equation. Bismuth has no influence on the equilibrium, but antimony favours the reaction from right to left in the equation above. E. B. Spear and K. D. Kahn, and F. Mylius and O. Fromm found **gold or platinum** soln. are precipitated by lead.

Reactions of analytical interest.—A soln. of a soluble **chloride** or of **hydrochloric acid** precipitates lead chloride from moderately conc. soln. of lead nitrate ; about one part of lead chloride per 135 parts of water remains in soln. The precipitate is much more soluble in hot water and crystals of lead chloride separate on cooling the hot soln. Lead chloride is more soluble in conc. hydrochloric acid than it is in water because a soluble complex salt is formed. The complex is decomposed by water so that lead chloride is precipitated by diluting the soln. According to T. G. Wormley,[18] hydrochloric acid enables one part of lead in 500 parts of soln. to be detected ; C. H. Pfaff said that a soln. of one part of lead nitrate in 100 parts of water is the most dil. one in which hydrochloric acid will give a precipitate ; and E. Eegriwe said that a gram of lead in 400 c.c. of water can be detected by hydrochloric acid. The precipitation of orange-yellow lead iodide by **potassium iodide** is a more delicate reaction than is the case with the chloride. According to T. G. Wormley, one part of lead in 21,540 parts of water can be recognized, and F. Jackson said 1 in 8000. E. Eegriwe detected a gram of lead in 85,500 c.c. of water by potassium iodide. The iodide is fairly soluble in hydriodic acid or in a soln. of the alkali iodide, forming complex salts decomposed by water with the deposition of lead iodide. Alkaline, neutral or slightly acid soln. of a lead salt, give with **hydrogen sulphide** a black precipitate of lead sulphide ; with hydrochloric acid soln., an orange-red precipitate of *lead sulphochloride,* $PbCl.S.PbCl$, is first formed, and this is decomposed by more hydrogen sulphide into black lead sulphide. If the soln. contains much free hydrochloric acid, the red sulphochloride may alone be formed. F. Parmentier studied the phenomenon in the presence of lead bromide, and V. Lehner, with lead iodide. According to M. Martin, if the soln. contains 2·4 per cent. hydrogen chloride, 2·9 per cent. $PbCl_2$ remains in soln. The reaction between lead chloride and hydrogen sulphide is reversible : $H_2S+PbCl_2 \rightleftharpoons 2HCl+PbS$, because lead sulphide is soluble in conc. hydrochloric acid. L. Bruner and J. Zawadsky gave for the equilibrium constant, $K=[Pb''][H_2S]/[H·]^2=3·1\times10^{-6}$. A study of the action of hydrogen sulphide on a 0·001 molar soln. of lead chloride in water at 20° in the presence of hydrochloric acid and of neutral chlorides, by L. Dede and P. Bonin, showed that the precipitation of lead sulphide is completely inhibited by hydrochloric acid alone if present in a concentration of 1·4N. In the presence of increasing quantities of calcium, ammonium, or potassium chloride, decreasing conc. of hydrochloric acid are sufficient to prevent precipitation entirely. The conc. of hydrochloric acid required completely to prevent the precipitation of lead sulphide from a soln. containing 20·7 mgrms. of lead per 100 c.c. with different proportions of these three chlorides, are as follow :

Conc. of lead chloride					0	0·8	2·8
Conc. HCl $\begin{cases} CaCl_2 \\ NH_4Cl \\ KCl \end{cases}$					1·40	0·90	0·20
					1·40	1·00	0·15
					1·40	1·00	0·15

The results with calcium chloride are graphed in Fig. 30. In the presence of considerably smaller conc. of hydrochloric acid, the precipitation of lead sulphide is incomplete. At higher temp., the effect of hydrochloric acid in the presence of neutral chlorides is still more marked. L. Dede and P. Becker found that magnesium and ammonium chlorides also retard the precipitation of lead sulphide from soln. of lead chloride. The precipitation of lead sulphide is also hampered, although to a less degree, by the presence of perchloric acid. In this case, however, the addition of sodium perchlorate favours precipitation, presumably by depressing the ionization of the acid. The precipitation of lead chromate in acetic acid soln. is not quantitative in the presence of much chloride ;

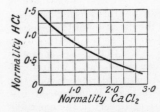

FIG. 30.—Concentration of Hydrochloric Acid required to prevent the Precipitation of Lead Sulphide.

in ammoniacal soln. this is not the case. Lead sulphide is decomposed by nitric acid, $3PbS+8HNO_3=3Pb(NO_3)_2+4H_2O+2NO+3S$, but some of the sulphur is at the same time oxidized to sulphuric acid, forming insoluble lead sulphate, and this the more the greater the conc. of the nitric acid. According to C. H. Pfaff, the brown coloration with hydrogen sulphide is visible when one part of lead nitrate is present in 100,000 parts of water ; J. L. Lassaigne said 1 in 200,000 ; and P. Harting, 1 in 350,000. I. M. Kolthoff found that the brown colour of lead sulphide is produced in acetic or phosphoric acid soln. when 0·2 mgrm. per litre is present ; and with oxalic acid soln., when 100 mgrms. per litre is present ; N. Schoorl, a milligram per litre. According to G. Chesneau, a soln. containing eq. proportions of lead and cupric nitrates furnishes more copper than lead when treated with an amount of a one per cent. soln. of hydrogen sulphide insufficient to precipitate both the copper and the lead—vide infra, lead sulphide. M. Berthelot showed that solid lead acetate is not decomposed by dry hydrogen sulphide. H. Reinsch found that a soln. containing one part of normal lead acetate in 200 parts of water mixed with 5 parts of hydrochloric acid, sp. gr. 1·168, gives with hydrogen sulphide a brown precipitate which soon turns black ; with 10 parts of hydrochloric acid, the precipitate is first red, then brown, and finally black ; with 20 parts of hydrochloric acid, the carmine-red precipitate is gradually formed which retains its colour ; and with 30–50 parts of hydrochloric acid, a slight precipitate is formed only after the addition of water. If one part of normal lead acetate be dissolved in 112 parts of water and 14 parts of hydrochloric acid, a yellow precipitate is produced by the gas. E. A. Parnell observed that paper saturated with a lead salt and thoroughly dried is not blackened by dried hydrogen sulphide. **Alkali sulphides** precipitate lead sulphide from a soln. of a lead salt, and the black precipitate is insoluble in an excess of the reagent. E. F. Anthon also showed that the sulphides of cadmium, manganese, iron, cobalt, and nickel precipitate lead sulphide from a soln. of lead salts; and, added E. Schürmann, the precipitation by cobalt, nickel, thallium (ous), and zinc sulphides is complete, but with arsenious sulphide only under press. in an autoclave. E. Eegriwe detected one gram of lead in 2,840,000 c.c. of water by means of sodium sulphide.

According to G. S. Jamieson, aq. soln. of **sulphurous acid** or an **alkali sulphite**—$NaHSO_3$, $(NH_4)HSO_3$, etc.—precipitates lead sulphate, the sensitiveness of the reaction is said by W. N. Iwanoff to be $1 : 20,000,000$, and he added that with one part of lead in $1,000,000$ a turbidity is produced in a few minutes—barium, and tin should be absent, copper, silver, nickel, iron, aluminium, magnesium, and calcium may be present. When a soln. of a lead salt is treated with **sulphuric acid,** or a soluble **sulphate,** sparingly soluble lead sulphate is precipitated. According to C. H. Pfaff, and P. Harting, one part of lead nitrate in $200,000$ parts of water can be detected by sulphuric acid; T. G. Wormley said $1 : 21,540$, and F. Jackson, $1 : 16,000$. J. L. Lassaigne observed an opalescence with one part of lead nitrate in 25,000 parts water, 15 mins. after treatment with sodium sulphate. E. Eegriwe detected a gram of lead in 24,900 c.c. of water by means of sulphuric acid. Lead sulphate is very slightly soluble in water, less so if the water be acidulated with sulphuric acid, and still less so in alcohol. The sulphate is perceptibly soluble in nitric and sulphuric acids; and is readily dissolved by hot conc. hydrochloric acid. Lead sulphate is readily soluble in soln. of the alkali hydroxides, and in the ammonium salts of many organic acids; this latter property enables lead sulphate to be separated from barium sulphate, silica, etc. Ammonium acetate or tartrate is generally used as solvent. N. Tarugi found that **ammonium thioacetate** in cold hydrochloric acid soln. of lead salts gives a reddish precipitate of lead sulphochloride which becomes black when boiled. H. Vohl found that hot conc. soln. with **sodium thiosulphate,** in the presence of ammonium chloride, precipitate lead sulphide quantitatively. The reaction was studied by J. Girard, F. Faktor, and K. A. Hofmann and V. Wölfl.

When a lead salt soln. is treated with **aq. ammonia,** white lead hydroxide is precipitated, insoluble in excess. L. J. Curtman and A. D. St. John detected $1 : 6500$ by this reaction. A similar precipitate is obtained with **alkali hydroxides,** but with an excess of the reagent, soluble alkali plumbite, say, $Pb(OK)_2$, is formed. The **alkali carbonates** precipitate a basic lead carbonate; and the **alkali hydrocarbonates,** normal lead carbonate. According to J. L. Lassaigne, a soln. of one part of lead nitrate in $50,000$ parts of water becomes turbid when treated with sodium carbonate; and $1 : 100,000$ becomes opalescent in 5 mins.; and $1 : 200,000$ opalescent in 10 mins. E. Eegriwe detected one gram of lead in $152,000$ c.c. of water by means of sodium carbonate. A white lead phosphate, $Pb_3(PO_4)_2$, is precipitated when a lead salt is treated with **sodium phosphate.** E. Eegriwe detected a gram of lead in 284,000 c.c. of water by means of sodium hydrophosphate. The precipitate is insoluble in acetic acid, but soluble in nitric acid or alkali-lye; **sodium arsenate** likewise precipitates lead arsenate; **potassium cyanide** gives a white precipitate which is insoluble in an excess of the reagent; and **oxalic acid** and **alkali oxalates** precipitate lead oxalate which, according to H. W. F. Wackenroder, is produced in soln. containing an excess of acid provided they are dilute. C. H. Pfaff detected one part of lead nitrate in 100,000 parts of water by means of oxalic acid. E. Eegriwe detected a gram of lead in 30,400 c.c. of water by means of ammonium oxalate. A yellow precipitate of lead chromate,

$PbCrO_4$, is produced when an **alkali chromate** is added to a lead salt; the precipitate is insoluble in acetic acid, but soluble in nitric acid and alkali-lye. P. Harting gave 1 : 70,000 for the limits of this test; T. G. Wormley, 1 : 107,700; S. Harvey, 1 : 350,000; and F. Jackson, 1 : 32,000. E. Eegriwe detected a gram of lead in 1,050,000 c.c. of water by potassium chromate, and in 2,100,000 c.c. of water by potassium dichromate. The reaction was studied by C. Reichard, M. Gröger, and O. Mayer. A white precipitate is produced in a soln. of a lead salt by **potassium ferrocyanide**, according to C. H. Pfaff, when one part of lead salt is present in 8000 parts of water. E. Eegriwe detected a gram of lead in 56,800 c.c. of water by the ferrocyanide reaction. **Potassium ferricyanide** gives no precipitate except, according to E. Müller and O. Diefenthäler, in nitrate soln. red crystals of a nitrato-ferricyanide are formed. J. von Liebig, and R. D. Hall obtained a precipitate with a soln. of **potassium thiocyanate.** No precipitates are produced with soln. of **potassium chlorate** or **bromate.** Lead dioxide is precipitated from soln. of lead salts by **hydrogen dioxide,** by **persulphates,** or by **hypochlorites.** E. Eegriwe detected a gram of lead in 714,000 c.c. of water by the hydrogen dioxide reaction. According to A. Trillat, an acetic acid soln. of **tetramethyldiamidodiphenylmethane** gives an intense blue coloration with lead dioxide, but not with lead salts. The reaction is very sensitive in the absence of other oxidizing substances. E. Eegriwe detected one gram of lead in 8,000,000 parts of water by the blue coloration produced with **ammonium molybdate ;** one gram of lead in 171,000 c.c. of water by a soln. of **cochineal ;** and a gram of lead in 200,000 c.c. of water by a soln. of **hæmatoxyline.**

Physiological action of lead.—There is a reference to the poisonous effects of lead in the medical portion of that collection of writings attributed to Hippocrates of the fifth century before our era. Dioscorides, in his second-century *De materia medica,* mentioned the delirium produced by lead. He said:

The drinking of "lead" causes oppression to the stomach, belly, and intestines, with wringing pains; sometimes it even wounds the intestines by its severe pressure; it suppresses the urine, while the body swells and acquires an unsightly leaden hue.

Pliny, in his first-century *Historia naturalis,* mentioned colic as an effect of lead poisoning; Aretæus, in his first-century *De causis et signis acutorum et diuturnorum morborum,* epilepsy; and Paul of Ægina, in his seventh-century *De re medica,* epilepsy and convulsions. Vitruvius, in his *De architectura,* written near the beginning of our era, condemned the use of lead pipes for the water supply of Rome because of the risk of poisoning. Pliny also described how the Romans tested the harshness of wine by immersing in it a sheet of lead, and marking the corrosive action; they also sweetened some wine by boiling it in leaden vessels. Pliny does not seem to have thought the practice was attended by any danger. In the preparation of wine, if the fermentation process be carried too far, the liquor becomes charged with acid. The ancients probably knew that lead rendered harsh wine milder, and preserved it from acidity. The process was long used with confidence because the toxic effects were not ascribed to the metal but to some other cause. The deleterious result of sweetening wine with lead compounds was mentioned by M. Citois [19] in 1616, and M. Delamarc in 1696; and J. Zeller and J. Weismann said that the practice was invented in France. After the poisonous effects of this addition had been recognized, it required the severest of punishments—torture and death—before the use of litharge for this purpose could be stopped. Even in the eighteenth century, the improvement of wines by litharge was in some quarters taught as a method free from danger—*e.g.* by W. Graham—although J. Beckmann has cited a number of cases near the end of the seventeenth century, where those who treated the wines with lead compounds were very severely punished. The litharge or white-lead was singularly efficacious in renovating spoilt wine, but its effect on the consumer was disastrous. According to J. Beckmann,

No adulteration of any article has ever been invented so pernicious to the health, and at the same time so much practised as that of wine with preparations of lead ; and as the inventor must have been acquainted with its destructive effects, he deserves, for making it known, severer execration than Berthold Schwartz, the supposed inventor of gunpowder. . . . The wine occasions, according as it is used in a great or small quantity, and according to the constitution of the consumer, a speedy or a lingering death, violent colics, obstructions, and other maladies ; so that one may justly doubt whether, at present, Mars, Venus, or Saturn is most destructive to the human race.

Although the noxious character of the fumes given off during the smelting of lead was mentioned by many ancient writers, it was not until 1656 that S. Stockhusen established a definite relation between lead and the so-called colic ; early in the sixteenth century, A. Aetius described the colic frequently associated with the use of certain wines, and in 1757, T. Tronchin discovered that many wines could dissolve the plumbiferous glaze from the earthenware vessels in which the wine was stored. In 1788, J. Hunter described the " dry belly ache " prevalent in the garrison of Jamaica caused by the consumption of rum contaminated with lead. The historical side of lead poisoning has been discussed by G. Meillère, J. Alderson, and by L. Tanqueril des Planches ; and the physiological and pathological effects —*plumbism* or *saturnism*—have been the subject of an extraordinary number of reports and memoirs.[20]

Poisoning by lead compounds may be acute or chronic. Acute poisoning is produced by comparatively large doses of a soluble salt of lead. Recovery has followed after swallowing an ounce, and cases of death are comparatively rare. An astringent metallic taste is perceived ; there is a feeling of constriction in the œsophagus ; and a hot sensation which extends to the stomach. Within half an hour vomiting occurs ; there is a great thirst, and colicky pains in the abdomen which come on in paroxysms. There are prostration, vertigo, numbness, and pains in the head and limbs. There may be a state of drowsiness or one of excitability, and death occurs on the second or third day. There is a sub-acute form in which small but not minute doses of a soluble salt of lead are administered. Chronic lead poisoning is produced by the introduction into the system of minute doses of a lead compound, or lead itself. The sources from which the lead may be derived in chronic lead poisoning are numerous and diverse. There are the so-called *occupational risks* which attend the use of lead or lead compounds in many trades such as painting, plumbing, pottery glazing, glass working, making lead compounds—*e.g.* litharge, red-lead, white-lead, etc.—printing, cutlers, file cutting, making accumulators, making sheet lead and lead piping, smelting metals, enamelling iron, litho-transferring, etc. There are also the so-called *accidental risks* where people in ordinary avocations are in danger from negligence or ignorance owing to the extensive employment of plumbiferous materials for so many purposes in everyday life. Lead is a cumulative poison, and the absorption of a minute quantity at a time but extended over long periods may produce disastrous results. It may be a long time before symptoms of chronic poisoning appear, and in some cases it would require a Dupin to detect the source of the trouble as a preliminary to its elimination.

As indicated previously, lead has been detected in most of the ordinary foods—flour, bread, beer, wines, spirits, cider, tea, vinegar, sugar, confectionery, etc.—in numerous drugs made by the aid of sulphuric acid which, when manufactured by the chamber process, nearly always contains lead ; or in drugs made in leaden vessels—*e.g.* the crystallization of tartaric or citric acid in leaden pans. Lead colic has been reported in a cabman whose first glass of beer every morning at a public house was drawn from that which had been standing in pipes overnight. The use of old painted wood in a baker's oven, and the subsequent adherence of a film of lead oxide to the outside of the loaves is reported to have caused the illness of 66 people. G. Marmisse mentioned the gate-keeper of a grave-yard at Bordeaux who continually used the remnants of crosses, etc., covered with lead paint to replenish his fires, and who was suffering from lead poisoning. A trace of lead tetraethyl, $Pb(C_2H_5)_4$, in motor spirit prevents " knocking." If carelessly used, accidents may occur owing to the toxic qualities of the exhaust vapours. This was discussed by E. Behrle, and T. Midgley. T. Bancks and R. L. Freer reported that in 1840 about 500 non-fatal cases of acute poisoning were caused by 30 lbs. of sugar of lead having been accidentally mixed with 80 sacks of flour. S. J. Knott mentioned a case of chronic poisoning due to the cleaning of pewter pots; G. H. Allden, G. A. E. Roberts, and D. Campbell, to the drinking of home-made wine fermented in lead-glazed pans; H. Pillaud, to the use of food prepared in glazed earthenware vessels; E. V. Raumer and E. Spaeth, to the consumption of whortle-berries stored in large glazed earthenware pots; A. S. Taylor, to the wrapping of foods in tin-foil, and the fingering by fishmongers of lead counters covered with brine; G. Johnson, to the handling of vulcanized rubber, etc.—*vide supra*, the action of water, etc., on lead. Chronic lead poisoning has been reported owing to the use of wine bottles cleaned by shaking lead-shot in them; tinned foods; confectionery coloured with lead chromate; tea, and snuff packed in lead-foil; hair-dyes; cosmetics; soda-water syphons with pewter or lead-valves; etc. According to G. Stiefler, the lead poisoning common among the peasants in Lower Austria is due to the cider having dissolved some lead from the containing vessels during its fermentation. There are many other strange reports although in some cases the assigned cause is not the real one, for the lead may have entered the system through another unsuspected channel. H. Masters, G. W. Monier-Williams, and others have discussed the solubility of lead from glazed pottery and enamelled iron. F. H. de Balsac and co-workers reported on lead poisoning in the accumulator industry.

Some people are particularly susceptible to the influence of lead poisoning, while others seem to resist the action of or to tolerate the poison to a marked degree. The possible channels for the *ingestion* of lead are cutaneous absorption, intestinal, and respiratory. The possibility of the cutaneous absorption of lead through the unbroken skin has provoked much controversy; but, in spite of the observations of T. Canuet, M. Drouet, and A. Maneuvrier, T. M. Legge and K. W. Goadby consider that the possibility of the cutaneous absorption has no practical significance. Industrial lead poisoning may occur through compounds of lead finding their way into the alimentary canal *via* the mouth mainly by un-washed hands, by food contaminated with lead dust, and the deposition of lead dust, suspended in air, upon the mucous membrane of the mouth and pharynx, and then swallowed. T. M. Legge and K. W. Goadby consider that this source of contamination is far less dangerous than is that due to the inhalation of dust or fume suspended in air, and that the lung rather than the stomach is the chief channel through which lead finds its way into the system. As a result, the pro-tection of the operatives from dust and fumes by exhaust ventilation and cleanli-ness have produced an extraordinary decrease in occupational plumbism. The *storage* of lead in the system is illustrated by T. Oliver in Table VI, representing

TABLE VI.—THE DISTRIBUTION OF LEAD IN THE VARIOUS ORGANS OF THE BODY.

Organ.	A.	B.	Organ.	A.	B.
Large intestine	26·1	—	Spleen	21·9	0·0462
Small intestine	9·2	—	Liver	42·4	0·8820
Muscle	3·1	—	Cerebellum	36·9 ⎫	
Lung	4·9	—	Grey matter (basal ganglia)	53 ⎪	
Heart	5·3	0·0199	Brain-grey matter cortex	40·9 ⎬	0·7070
Mamma	4·8	—	Brain-white matter	18·9 ⎭	—
Kidney	12·9	0·0253	Spinal cord	1·2	—

the mean analyses of various organs of three lead-workers who had succumbed to lead poisoning. The amount of lead obtained is expressed *A* in parts per million, and *B* in grains calculated on the total weight of the organ. Lead is also stored in the bones. The *excretion* of lead from the system is mainly through the kidneys; and lead is often found in the urine of those suffering from lead poisoning. Accord-ing to T. M. Legge and K. W. Goadby, lead is more commonly present in the fæces of lead-workers than in the urine.

The chief symptoms of chronic lead poisoning are general ill-health usually referred to as indigestion; the appetite is lessened; and the bowels constipated. There is a disagreeable taste in the mouth, and the breath is offensive. The skin acquires an unhealthy colour, being at first yellowish and subsequently anæmic. The gums often show a bluish-black line—the *Burtonian line*—produced by lead sulphide, and first described by H. Burton.[21] The pulse is slow, and secretions are diminished. The sexual functions are weakened, and pregnant women have a tendency to abortion. In addition, there may be lead colic due to recurrent abdominal pains ; pains in the joints ; partial paralysis so that when the arms are held out horizontally, palms downwards, the hands drop and cannot be raised—wrist-drop ; the organs of sight may degenerate, inducing partial or total blindness ; and there may be psychical disturbances commencing by head-ache, dizziness, and sleeplessness which may further develop to drowsiness or to excitability or insanity accompanied by hallucinations and wild deliria. In 1831, R. T. H. Laennec described the pallor of the tissues, and the thinness of the blood in cases of plumbism ; and in 1840, G. Andral and J. Gavarret found that the proportion of red blood corpuscles during lead poisoning is lower than normal. To-day, an erythrocite count is a routine clinical procedure in lead poisoning. The subject has been studied by J. C. Aub and many others. P. Orfila made experiments on the action of lead compounds on animals ; and numerous other experiments have since been reported. R. V. Tuson stated that seven cows and one bull had died by eating lead paint ; and cattle have been poisoned by eating grass which has been splashed by the spray from bullets in pastures in the vicinity of rifle butts. Many observations [22] have also been made on the toxic effects of lead compounds on plants, yeast, and bacteria.

Some uses of lead.—The pliability of lead and the ease with which it can be moulded, and soldered or united by autogenous welding have resulted in the metal being largely used for gutters, spouts, and roofing in buildings ; as lead piping for conveying water, and gases in chemical manufacture, and in the construction of vessels or plant where resistance to many corrosive acids is needed—*e.g.* evaporating pans, sulphuric acid chambers, etc.[23] It is also used largely in making accumulators. A great many alloys of lead are used in the arts—shot, solders, pewters, etc.—*vide infra.* There are methods [24] for coating steel and iron with lead for pipes and vessels in contact with corrosive liquids—*e.g.* S. Cowper-Coles's electrolytic process, or M. A. Schoop's spraying process—earthenware and wood may also be coated with the metal. The acetate of lead—*liquor plumbi subacetatis*—is employed medicinally as an astringent in diarrhœa, in gastric ulcers, and in hæmorrhage of the intestines. The acetate, iodide, and carbonate are used in conjunction with the oleate for ointments and plasters—*unguentum plumbi acetatis ; unguentum plumbi iodidi ; unguentum plumbi carbonatis ; diachylon* or *lead oleate* or *lead soap ;* etc. The basis of Ledoyen's disinfecting fluid is lead nitrate, and the same salt is used in calico printing ; *lead pyrolignite* is used in dyeing. There are numerous lead pigments, mainly white, yellow, and red. Lead is used in the preparation of flint glass, pottery glazes, enamels, etc. The oxide is used to accelerate the hot vulcanization of rubber ; and the ethide, as an anti-knocking agent in explosion engines, etc.[25] The presence of as little as one mol of lead tetraethide in 200,000 mols of a combustible mixture of petrol and air exerts a marked effect in the suppression of detonation. Sodium plumbite is used in the sweetening of gasoline, by removing the sulphides as lead sulphide.[26]

REFERENCES.

[1] O. Sackur, *Arb. Kaiser. Ges. Amt.*, **20**. 512, 1904.
[2] A. Sieverts, *Zeit. phys. Chem.*, **60**. 129, 1907 ; **77**. 591, 1911 ; A. Sieverts and W. Krumbhaar, *ib.*, **74**. 277, 1910 ; *Ber.*, **43**. 893, 1910 ; W. Krumbhaar, *Ueber die Löslichkeit von Gasen Metallen und Legierungen*, Leipzig, 1910 ; J. Shields, *Chem. News*, **65**. 195, 1892 ; M. Guichard, *Bull. Soc. Chim.*, (4), **11**. 49, 1912 ; M. Cantor, *Monatsh.*, **11**. 444, 1890 ; G. Neumann and F. Streintz, *ib.*, **12**. 642, 1891 ; *Wied. Ann.*, **38**. 355, 1889 ; **41**. 97, 1890 ; F. Streintz, *ib.*, **38**. 355, 1889 ; G. Meyer, *ib.*, **33**. 278, 1888 ; A. M. Scott, *ib.*, **67**. 388, 1899 ; B. Hodgson, *Phys. Zeit.*, **13**. 595, 1912 ; F. H. Newman, *Proc. Phys. Soc.*, **33**. 73, 1921 ; S. Drzewiecky, *Lumière Élect.*, **35**. 290, 1890 , *Bull. Soc. Internat. Electriciens*, **6**. 414, 1890 ; E. Frankland, *Proc. Roy. Soc.*, **35**. 67, 1883 ; J. H. Gladstone and A. Tribe, *The Chemistry of Secondary Batteries*, London, **48**, 1883 ; *Journ. Chem. Soc.*, **43**. 345, 1883 ; *Nature*, **25**. 221, 461, 1882 ; **26**. 602, 1882 ;

F. Paneth, *Ber.*, 53. B, 1710, 1920 ; F. Paneth, M. Matthies, and E. Schmidt-Hebbel, *ib.*, 55. B, 775, 1922 ; F. Paneth and O. Nörring, *ib.*, 53. B, 1693, 1920 ; F. Paneth and E. Rabinovitsch, *ib.*, 58. B, 1138, 1925 ; F. Fischer and G. Iliovici, *ib.*, 41. 4449, 1908 ; N. S. Kurnakoff and N. J. Stepanoff, *Zeit. anorg. Chem.*, 46. 191, 1905 ; D. P. Smith, *Journ. Phys. Chem.*, 23. 186, 1919 ; (1. 7, 8) ; E. Newbery, *Journ. Chem. Soc.*, 125. 511, 1924 ; P. Schoop, *Electrician*, 24. 44, 1889 ; E. Rumpf, *Zeit. Electrochem.*, 16. 163, 1910 ; W. Stahl, *Chem. Ztg.*, 39. 885, 1915 ; M. Guichard, *Bull. Soc. Chim.*, (4), 11. 49, 1912 ; H. G. Deming and B. C. Hendrichs, *Journ. Amer. Chem. Soc.*, 45. 2857, 1923 ; E. J. Weeks, *Journ. Chem. Soc.*, 127. 2845, 1925.

³ W. van Rijn, *Chem. Weekbl.*, 5. 1, 1908 ; P. A. von Bonsdorff, *Repért. Chim.*, 3. 42, 1838 ; *Pogg. Ann.*, 41. 385, 1837 ; J. Percy, *The Metallurgy of Lead*, London, 10, 1870 ; M. Berthelot, *Compt. Rend.*, 91. 871, 1880 ; J. I. Pierre, *ib.*, 78. 1265, 1874 ; M. E. Chevreul, *ib.*, 77. 1137, 1873 ; L. Besnou, *ib.*, 78. 322, 1874 ; B. Lambert and H. E. Cullis, *Journ. Chem. Soc.*, 105. 210, 1915 ; W. R. Dunstan and J. R. Hill, *ib.*, 99. 1835, 1911 ; W. R. Dunstan, H. A. D. Jowett, and E. Goulding, *ib.*, 87. 1548, 1905 ; F. C. Calvert and R. Johnson, *Journ. Soc. Arts*, 13. 378, 1865 ; *Journ. Chem. Soc.*, 19. 434, 1866 ; *Chem. News*, 11. 161, 1865 ; *Proc. Manchester Lit. Phil. Soc.*, 4. 115, 1866 ; C. F. Schönbein, *Verh. Basel. Nat. Ges.*, (2), 1. 432, 1864 ; *Journ. prakt. Chem.*, (1), 93. 35, 1864 ; M. Müller, *ib.*, (2), 36. 317, 1887 ; G. C. Winkelblech, *ib.*, (1), 10. 227, 1837 ; *Liebig's Ann.*, 21. 21, 1837 ; N. B. Pilling and R. E. Bedworth, *Journ. Inst. Metals*, 29. 529, 1923 ; *Chem. Trade Journ.*, 72. 319, 1923 ; P. Yorke, *Phil. Mag.*, (3), 5. 82, 1834 ; W. Merckens, *Ann. Physik*, (4), 16. 667, 1905 ; *Zeit. angew. Chem.*, 18. 489, 1905 ; G. Lunge and E. Schmid, *ib.*, 5. 665, 1892 ; *Zeit. anorg. Chem.*, 2. 451, 1892 ; E. Gademan, *Met. Chem. Engg.*, 8. 680, 1910 ; U. Antony and T. Benelli, *Gazz. Chim. Ital.*, 26. ii, 333, 1896 ; H. Heap, *Journ. Soc. Chem. Ind.*, 32. 771, 811, 1913 ; G. Wolffhügel, *Arb. Kaiser. Ges. Amt.*, 2. 135, 1887 ; W. Stahl, *Chem. Ztg.*, 39. 885, 1915 ; R. Phillips, *Chem. Gaz.*, 3. 7, 1845 ; *Dingler's Journ.*, 45. 386, 1845 ; C. Stalmann, *ib.*, 180. 366, 1866 ; E. N. Horsford, *ib.*, 114. 299, 1849 ; *Chem. Gaz.*, 7. 295, 1849 ; W. R. Nichols, *Journ. Gaslight.*, 42. 1051, 1883 ; W. Manchot, *Ber.*, 42. 3942, 1909 ; M. Müller, *ib.*, 3. 84, 1870 ; C. Engler, *ib.*, 30. 2358, 1897 ; 36. 2642, 1903 ; C. Engler and W. Wild, *ib.*, 29. 1929, 1896 ; M. Traube, *ib.*, 15. 2428, 1882 ; *Zeit. phys. Chem.*, 32. 137, 1900 ; W. C. Parsons, *Chem. News*, 32. 82, 1875 ; R. Christison, *ib.*, 28. 15, 1873 ; F. Clowes, *ib.*, 86. 168, 1902 ; *Proc. Chem. Soc.*, 18. 46, 1902 ; N. W. Fischer, *Kastner's Arch.*, 17. 382, 1829 ; M. Traube-Mengarini and A. Scala, *Zeit. Koll.*, 6. 240, 1910 ; *Mem. Acad. Lincei*, (5), 8. 576, 1911 ; *Atti Accad. Lincei*, (5), 19. ii, 505, 1910 ; A. Scala, *ib.*, (5), 22. i, 155, 1913 ; G. Wetzlar, *Schweigger's Journ.*, 54. 324, 1828 ; J. J. Berzelius, *ib.*, 7. 71, 1813 ; *Gilbert's Ann.*, 40. 166, 186, 1812 ; 46. 131, 1814 ; W. R. Whitney, *Journ. Amer. Chem. Soc.*, 25. 394, 1903 ; J. W. Shipley, *Journ. Soc. Chem. Ind.*, 41. 314, T, 1922 ; L. A. Stenger, *Chem. Met. Engg.*, 22. 965, 1920 ; H. S. Rawdon, *Bull. U.S. Bur. Standards*, 377, 1920 ; H. S. Rawdon, A. I. Krynitzky, and J. F. T. Berliner, *ib.*, 26. 109, 1922 ; *Trans. Amer. Inst. Min. Met. Eng.*, 64. 443, 1920 ; J. W. Mellor, *Chemical Statics and Dynamics*, London, 307, 1904 ; O. Bauer and E. Wetzel, *Mitt. Materialprüf.*, 34. 333, 1917 ; P. Carles, *Journ. Pharm. Chim.*, (6), 12. 517, 1900 ; F. Malméjac, *ib.*, (6), 13. 365, 1901 ; E. A. van der Burg, *Nieuw Tijds. Pharm. Nederl.*, 65, 97, 1878 ; L. B. G. de Morveau, *Ann. Chim. Phys.*, (1), 71. 191, 1809 ; A. Baumé, *Chimie expéri-mentale et raisonée*, Paris, 1773 ; C. L. Cadet de Gassicourt, *La chimie domestique*, Paris, 1801 ; F. E. Wynne, *Brit. Med. Journ.*, ii, 267, 1911 ; G. Tammann, *Rec. Trav. chim. Pays-Bas*, 42. 547, 1923 ; G. Tammann and W. Köster, *Zeit. anorg. Chem.*, 123. 217, 1922 ; M. Pettenkofer, *Bayer. Ind. Gewerb.*, 682, 1864 ; F. J. Otto, *Lehrbuch der Chemie*, Braunschweig, 2. iii, 312, 1853 ; A. Scala, *Atti Accad. Lincei*, (5), 22. i, 155, 1913 ; *Ann. d'Igiene*, 30. 35, 1921 ; G. D. Bengough and J. M. Stuart, *Journ. Inst. Metals*, 28. 108, 1922 ; A. Smith, *Pharm. Journ.*, (2), 3. 283, 1861 ; *Chem. News*, 4. 172, 1861 ; F. C. Calvert, *ib.*, 4. 172, 1861 ; F. J. Liverseege and A. W. Knapp, *Journ. Soc. Chem. Ind.*, 39. 27, T, 1920 ; E. Reichardt, *Arch. Pharm.*, (3), 25. 858, 1887 ; C. L. Bloxam, *Metals, their Properties and Treatment*, London, 1888 ; W. G. Whitman and R. P. Russell, *Journ. Ind. Eng. Chem.*, 17. 348, 1925 ; N. C. de Milly, *Journ. Phys.*, 13. 145, 1779 ; M. Luzuriaga, *ib.*, 25. 252, 1784 ; M. Delaville, *Ann. Chim. Phys.*, (1), 58. 92, 1806 ; C. Engler and W. Wild, *Ber.*, 29. 1929, 1896 ; W. Manchot, *ib.*, 42 3942, 1909 ; J. C. Thresh, *Analyst*, 46. 270, 1921 ; G. Jung, *Zeit. phys. Chem.*, 119. 111, 1926.

⁴ H. V. Regnault, *Ann. Chim. Phys.*, (2), 62. 363, 1836 ; A. S. Taylor, *On Poisons in relation to Medical Jurisprudence and Medicine*, London, 510, 1859 ; G. Wolffhügel, *Arb. Kaiser. Ges. Amt.*, 2. 135, 1887 ; J. C. Lermer, *Dingler's Journ.*, 167. 348, 1863 ; P. A. von Bonsdorff, *Repért. Chim.*, 3. 42, 1838 ; *Pogg. Ann.*, 41. 385, 1837 ; J. Percy, *The Metallurgy of Lead*, London, 10, 1870 ; F. Stolba, *Journ. prakt. Chem.*, (1), 94. 113, 1865 ; *Quart. Journ. Science*, 2. 457, 1867 ; S. Zinberg, *Mess. Ind. Mét. Russ.*, 1, 2, 3, 1923 ; *Rev. Mét.*, 21. ii, 62, 1924.

⁵ R. Christison, *Trans. Roy. Soc. Edin.*, 15. 265, 1844 ; *Chem. News*, 28. 15, 1873 ; M. Traube-Mengarini and A. Scala, *Zeit. Koll.*, 6. 240, 1910 ; *Mem. Accad. Lincei*, (5), 8. 576, 1911 ; *Atti Accad. Lincei*, (5), 19. ii, 505, 1910 ; A. Scala, *ib.*, (5), 22. i, 155, 1913 ; *Ann. d'Igiene*, 30. 35, 1920 ; U. Antony and T. Benelli, *Gazz. Chim. Ital.*, 26. ii, 97, 1896 ; G. Wetzlar, *Schweigger's Journ.*, 54. 324, 1828 ; M. Müller, *Journ. prakt. Chem.*, (2), 36. 317, 1887 ; P. A. von Bonsdorff, *Repért. Chim.*, 3. 42, 1838 ; *Pogg. Ann.*, 41. 385, 1837 ; J. C. Thresh, *Analyst*, 46. 270, 1921 ; A. Faiszt, *Württemberg. Gewerbebl.*, 6, 1853 ; *Dingler's Journ.*, 127. 317, 1853 ; R. Kersting, *ib.*, 169. 183, 1863 ; M. Pettenkofer, *ib.*, 175. 283, 1865 ; *Bayer. Ind. Gewerbebl.*, 682, 1864 ; L. Bourgeois, *Bull. Soc. Min.*, 11. 224, 1888 ; G. Flögel, *Chem. Ztg. Rep.*, 11. 210, 1887 ; M. T. Lecco, *ib.*, 17. 1431, 1897 ; E. J. Kohlmeyer, *ib.*, 36. 993, 1912 ; E. N. Horsford.

Dingler's Journ., **114**. 299, 1849 ; *Chem. Gaz.*, **7**. 295, 1849; R. Phillips, *ib.*, **3**. 7, 1845 ; *Dingler's Journ.*, **45**. 386, 1845 ; C. Stahlmann, *ib.*, **180**. 366, 1866 ; R. Kersting, *ib.*, **169**. 197, 1863 ; A. Leonhardt, *Jahrb. Geb. Hyg.*, **7**. 51, 1889 ; M. Neisser, *Gesundheits Ing.*, **36**. 920, 1913 ; F. Clowes, *Chem. News*, **85**. 130, 1902 ; **86**. 168, 1902 ; *Proc. Chem. Soc.*, **18**. 46, 1902 ; B. Lambert and H. E. Cullis, *Journ. Chem. Soc.*, **105**. 210, 1915 ; J. Smith, *ib.*, **4**. 123, 1851 ; F. C. Calvert and R. Johnson, *ib.*, **19**. 434, 1866 ; *Proc. Manchester Lit. Phil. Soc.*, **4**. 115, 1866 ; *Journ. Soc. Arts*, **13**. 296, 1865 ; *Chem. News*, **11**. 161, 1865 ; J. Milne, *ib.*, **31**. 77, 1875 ; M. M. P. Muir, *ib.*, **25**. 294, 1874 ; **33**. 102, 125, 1876 ; **34**. 223, 224, 1876 ; S. Ruzicka, *Arch. Hyg.*, **41**. 23, 1902 ; P. Fortner, *ib.*, **54**. 325, 1906 ; P. Schmidt, *ib.*, **80**. 62, 1913 ; G. Wolffhügel, *Arb. Kaiser Ges. Amt.*, **2**. 135, 1887 ; T. Paul, W. Ohlmüller, R. Heise, and F. Auerbach, *ib.*, **23**. 377, 1906 ; M. Pleissner, *ib.*, **26**. 392, 1907 ; M. Müller, *Journ. prakt. Chem.*, (2), **36**. 317, 1887 ; A. Bobierre, *Compt. Rend.*, **77**. 1277, 1873 ; **78**. 317, 1874 ; L. Besnou, *ib.*, **78**. 322, 1874 ; A. J. Balard, *ib.*, **78**. 392, 1874 ; M. J. Fordos, *Bull. Soc. Chim.*, (2), **21**. 439, 1874 ; *Compt. Rend.*, **77**. 1099, 1873 ; **78**. 1108, 1874 ; J. B. A. Dumas, *ib.*, **77**. 1054, 1873 ; M. E. Chevreul, *ib.*, **77**. 1137, 1873 ; F. le Blanc, *ib.*, **77**. 1063, 1873 ; C. Belgrand, *ib.*, **77**. 1054, 1873 ; A. Barillé, *ib.*, **153**. 351, 1911 ; E. de Beaumont, *ib.*, **77**. 1055, 1873 ; E. Bouillaud, *ib.*, **77**. 1062, 1873 ; M. Berthelot, *ib.*, **77**. 1063, 1873 ; C. G. de Laval. *ib.*, **77**. 1271, 1873 ; M. Champouillon, *ib.*, **77**. 1273, 1873 ; J. H. Marais, *ib.*, **77**. 1529, 1873 ; M. Mayençon and M. Bergeret, *ib.*, **78**. 484, 1874 ; E. Solly, *ib.*, **78**. 395, 1874 ; J. B. J. D. Boussingault, *ib.*, **78**. 395, 1874 ; H. Letheby, *ib.*, **78**. 319, 1874 ; C. Matignon, *ib.*, **154**. 1609, 1912 ; P. Carles, *Journ. Pharm. Chim.*, (6), **12**. 517, 1900 ; A. Bellocq, *ib.*, (6), **13**. 56, 1901 ; A. Mailhe, *Bull. Soc. Chim.*, (4), **5**. 616, 1919 ; A. Russell, *Min. Mag.*, **19**. 64, 1920 ; J. Kliatchko and C. Binggely, *Ann. Chim. Anal.*, **22**. 81, 1917 ; C. Reichel, *Neues Jahrb. prakt. Pharm.*, **21**. 150, 1864 ; J. B. Nevins, *Pharm. Journ.*, **10**. 595, 1851 ; A. Parkes, *Brit. Pat. No.* 12534, 1849 ; J. L. Proust, *Journ. Phys.*, **56**. 206, 1803 ; J. C. Thresh, *Analyst*, **47**. 459, 1922 ; P. F. Frankland, *Journ. Soc. Chem. Ind.*, **8**. 241, 247, 1889 ; H. Heap, *ib.*, **32**. 771, 811, 847, 1913 ; T. Carnelley and W. Frew, *ib.*, **7**. 15, 1888 ; W. C. Williams, *ib.*, **6**. 111, 1887 ; J. F. Liverseege and A. W. Knapp, *ib.*, **39**. 27, T, 1920 ; *Chem. News*, **108**. 136, 1913 ; A. H. Allen, *ib.*, **46**. 88, 145, 1882 ; P. Schweitzer, *Amer. Chemist*, **6**. 456, 1876 ; R. H. Gaines, *Journ. Ind. Eng. Chem.*, **5**. 766, 1913 ; O. Bauer and E. Wetzel, *Mitt. Materialprüfung*, **34**. 333, 1917 ; W. Crookes, W. Odling, and C. M. Tidy, *Report on the Action of Water on Lead made to the Water Committee of the Corporation of Huddersfield*, Huddersfield, 1886 ; *Industries*, **1**. 306, 1886 ; R. Kaiser, *Arch. Pharm.*, (3), **6**. 405, 1875 ; F. Varrentrapp, *Mitt. Gewerb Ver. Braunschweig*, **27**. 1864 ; *Dingler's Journ.*, **175**. 286, 1865 ; H. Bamberger, *ib.*, **245**. 35, 1882 ; G. von Knorre, *ib.*, **266**. 220, 1888 ; A. C. Houston, *Ann. Rep. M.O.H. to the Local Government Board*, London, 1903 ; J. H. Garrett, *Trans. 7th Internat. Congress Hyg.*, **5**. v, 75, 1891 ; H. W. Clark, *Rep. Massachusetts State Board of Health*, 541, 1898 ; A. C. Brown, *Journ. Iron Steel Inst.*, **32**. ii, 129, 1888 ; G. Lunge and L. Weibel, *Chem. Ind.*, **9**. 47, 1886 ; *Dingler's Journ.*, **261**. 133, 1886 ; C. H. Crowe, *Canadian Chem. Met.*, **6**. 151, 1922 ; J. A. N. Friend and J. S. Tidmus, *Journ. Inst. Metals*, **31**. 177, 1924 ; J. A. N. Friend and R. H. Vallance, *Journ. Chem. Soc.*, **121**. 466, 1922 ; H. Endemann, *Amer. Chem. Journ.*, **19**. 1890, 1897 ; H. C. C. Maisch, *Amer. Journ. Pharm.*, **56**. 91, 1884 ; *Arch. Pharm.*, (3), **22**. 672, 1884 ; H. Marais, *Compt. Rend.*, **77**. 1529, 1873 ; A. J. Hale and H. S. Foster, *Journ. Soc. Chem. Ind.*, **34**. 464, 1915 ; C. F. Schönbein, *Verh. Nat. Ges. Basel*, **3**. 188, 1863 ; T. Graham, A. W. Hofmann, and W. A. Miller, *Report by the Government Commission on the Chemical Quality of the Supply of Water to the Metropolis*, London, 1851 ; *Journ. Chem. Soc.*, **4**. 75, 1852 ; J. Walker and W. Cormack, *ib.*, **77**. 5, 1900 ; H. M. Noad, *ib.*, **4**. 20, 1851 ; A. Wagner, *Bayer Ind. Gewerbebl.*, **8**. 1, 1876 ; *Dingler's Journ.*, **221**. 259, 1876 ; F. Fischer, *ib.*, **219**. 454, 522, 1876 ; R. Wagner, *Zeit. anal. Chem.*, **6**. 170, 1867 ; G. Bodländer, *Zeit. phys. Chem.*, **35**. 23, 1900 ; P. Yorke, *Phil. Mag.*, (3), **5**. 82, 1854 ; E. Reichardt, *Grundlagen der Beurteilung des Trinkwassers*, Halle a. S., 107, 1880 ; *Arch. Pharm.*, (3), **12**. 1, 1878 ; L. Greenburg, *U.S. Public Health Rep.*, **37**. 1825, 1922 ; L. B. G. de Morveau, *Ann. Chim. Phys.*, (1), **71**. 191, 1809 ; H. Medlock, *Brit. Pat. No.* 186, 1857 ; *Phil. Mag.*, (4), **14**. 202, 1857 ; J. Rodenburg, *Chem. Weekbl.*, **12**. 494, 1915 ; H. W. Woudstra and C. J. Snuif, *ib.*, **9**. 540, 1912 ; K. Scheringa, *ib.*, **6**. 15, 1909 ; C. Umney, *Pharm. Journ.*, (3), **5**. 583, 1875 ; C. G. Egeling, *Pharm. Weekbl.*, **41**. 561, 1904 ; G. A. Stutterheim, *ib.*, **57**. 530, 1920 ; G. Kühnemann, *Vierteljahr. Ger. Med.*, (3), **27**. 310, 1904 ; C. H. Bisserié, *Bull. Sci. Pharmacol.*, **1**. 271, 1900 ; A. F. Wilson, *Brit. Med. Journ.*, ii, 322, 1874 ; G. Brownen, *ib.*, i, 789, 1874 ; J. Attfield, *ib.*, i, 340, 1874 ; R. Proskauer, *Zeit. Hyg.*, **14**. 292, 1893 ; J. M. Cyrnos, *Journ. Hyg.*, **6**. 235, 1881 ; A. Chevallier, *Ann. Hyg.*, (1), **50**. 327, 1853 ; A. Gautier, *ib.*, (3), **7**. 5, 1882 ; *Le cuivre et le plomb*, Paris, 1883 ; J. Steiner, *Arch. Hyg.*, **2**. 436, 1884 ; P. Fortner, *ib.*, **54**. 325, 1906 ; W. Thomson, *Proc. Manchester Lit. Phil. Soc.*, **21**. 84, 1882 ; H. F. Whittaker, *Chem. Met. Engg.*, **31**. 74, 1924 ; J. S. Thomson, *Pharm. Journ.*, (3), **8**. 353, 1877 ; *Chem. News*, **45**. 116, 1882 ; W. P. Jorissen, *ib.*, **111**. 56, 1915 ; W. R. Nichols, *Journ. Gaslight.*, **42**. 1051, 1883 ; H. Klut, *Mitt. Wasserversorg.*, **13**. 96, 1910 ; *Viertelj. Ger. Med.*, **40**. 330, 1910 ; *Das Wasser*, **16**. 151, 1920 ; E. Vandevyverre, *Journ. Méd. Bruxelles*, **58**. 545, 1874 ; *Arch. Pharm.*, (3), **7**. 39, 1875 ; C. Schneider. *ib.*, (3). **22**. 185, 1884 ; *Ind. Blatt.*, **21**. 213, 1884 ; E. Gudeman, *Met. Chem. Engg.*, **8**. 680, 1910 ; R. Böttger, *Jahresb. Phys. Ver. Frankfurt*, **58**, 1866.

⁶ J. I. Crabtree, H. A. Hartt, and G. E. Matthews, *Journ. Ind. Eng. Chem.*, **16**. 13, 1924 ; C. L. Bloxam, *Metals, their Properties and Treatment*, London, 1888 ; J. H. Pepper, *The Playbook of Metals*, London, 250, 1866 ; R. H. Gaines, *Journ. Ind. Eng. Chem.*, **5**. 766, 1913 ;

J. W. Shipley, *ib.*, **41**. 311, T. 1922 ; M. Girousse, *Compt. Rend.*, **157**. 705, 1913 ; L. Besnou, *ib.*, **78**. 323, 1874 ; B. McCollum and G. H. Ahlborn, *Journ. Franklin Inst.*, **182**. 108, 1916 ; G. von Knorre, *Dingler's Journ.*, **266**. 220, 1888 ; H. Ditz and F. Kanhäuser, *Journ. prakt. Chem.*, (2), **88**. 456, 1913 ; H. Ditz, *ib.*, (2), **87**. 208, 1912 ; *Zeit. angew. Chem.*, **26**. 596, 1913 ; W. Vaubel, *ib.*, **25**. 2300, 1912 ; **26**. 423, 1913 ; E. J. Kohlmeyer, *Chem. Ztg.*, **36**. 993, 1912 ; O. Bauer and E. Wetzel, *Mitt. Materialprüf.*, **34**. 333, 1917 ; *Metall Erz*, **16**. 128, 1919 ; T. Carnelley and W. Frew, *Journ. Soc. Chem. Ind.*, **7**. 15, 1888 ; J. W. Shipley, *ib.*, **41**. 311, 1922 ; L. A. Stenger, *Chem. Met. Engg.*, **22**. 965, 1920 ; E. R. Shepard, *Trans. Amer. Electrochem. Soc.*, **39**. 239, 1921 ; S. C. Bartholomew, *Elect. Rev.*, **92**. 432, 1923 ; O. Hähnel, *Centr. Min.*, **25**, 1920 ; *Zeit. Fernemeldetechn.*, **94**. 715, 1923 ; W. N. Smith and J. W. Shipley, *Engg. Journ.*, **5**. 291, 359, 1922 ; G. C. Bunker and A. H. Khachadoorian, *Journ. Worcester. Polyt. Inst.*, 11, 1922 ; H. F. Zangger, *Schweiz. Elektrotech. Ver.*, **13**. 485, 529, 1922 ; E. F. Petritsch and A. H. de Vogt, *De Ing.*, **37**. 98, 1922 ; H. Michalke, *Elektrotech. Zeit.*, **42**. 1451, 1921 ; *Verkehrstechnik*, **39**. 114, 1922 ; J. Chapuis and H. Deprez, *Compt. Rend.*, **173**. 1344, 1921 ; M. Remaugé, *Ann. Postes Télég. Télép.*, **11**. 1290, 1922 ; *Journ. Télégr.*, **46**. 141, 1922 ; F. O. Anderegg and R. V. Achatz, *Bull. Eng. Station Purdue Univ.*, 18, 1924.

ᵛ R. Watson, *Chemical Essays*, London, **3**. 366, 1787 ; J. S. S. Brame, *Journ. Soc. Chem. Ind.*, **37**. 39, 1918 ; F. Southerden, *ib.*, **37**. 85, 1918 ; C. E. Cresse, *Chem. Met. Engg.*, **26**. 111, 1922 ; P. Dunsheath, *Elect. Rev.*, **90**. 690, 1922.

⁸ A. Ditte, *Compt. Rend.*, **70**. 621, 1870 ; *Ann. Chim. Phys.*, (4), **21**. 5, 1870 ; H. Moissan, *ib.*, (6), **24**. 224, 1891 ; J. B. A. Dumas, *ib.*, (3), **55**. 129, 1859 ; J. L. Gay Lussac and L. J. Thénard, *ib.*, (1), **69**. 204, 1809 ; M. Berthelot, *ib.*, (5), **23**. 91, 1889 ; (7), **13**. 73, 1898 ; *Compt. Rend.*, **125**. 746, 1897 ; J. Nicklès, *ib.*, **52**. 869, 1861 ; H. St. C. Deville, *ib.*, **42**. 894. 1856 ; W. G. Whitman and R. P. Russell, *Journ. Ind. Eng. Chem.*, **17**. 348, 1925 ; E. Salkowsky, *Chem. Ztg.*, **40**. 448, 1916 ; E. Beckmann, *Zeit. anorg. Chem.*, **77**. 200, 1912 ; A. Classen and B. Zahorsky, *ib.*, **4**. 102, 1893 ; *Rev. Trav. Chim. Pays-Bas*, **42**. 547, 1923 ; G. Tammann and W. Köster, *Zeit. anorg. Chem.*, **123**. 217, 1922 ; G. Tammann, *ib.*, **111**. 176, 1920 ; *Stahl Eisen*, **42**. 615, 1922 ; A. J. Hale and H. S. Foster, *Journ. Soc. Chem. Ind.*, **34**. 464, 1915 ; H. P. Pearson, *ib.*, **22**. 731, 1903 ; G. Lunge and A. Deggeler, *ib.*, **4**. 32, 1885 ; J. H. Gladstone and A. Tribe, *Journ. Chem. Soc.*, **43**. 347, 1883 ; T. E. Thorpe and W. Kirman, *ib.*, **61**. 921, 1892 ; *Zeit. anorg. Chem.*, **3**. 63, 1892 ; *Chem. News*, **66**. 276, 1892 ; J. P. Sharples, *ib.*, **50**. 126, 1884 ; F. Stolba, *Journ. prakt. Chem.*, (1), **94**. 114, 1865 ; R. Lorenz, G. von Hevesy. and E. Wolff, *Zeit. phys. Chem.*, **76**. 732, 1911 ; J. A. Wilkinson, *Journ. Phys. Chem.*, **13**. 691, 1909 ; O. P. Watts and N. D. Whipple, *Trans. Amer. Electrochem. Soc.*, **32**. 267, 1918 ; H. J. Prinz, *Proc. Acad. Amsterdam*, **23**. 1449, 1922.

⁹ L. Franck, *Bull Soc. Chim.*, (3), **17**. 506, 1897 ; E. Jannettaz, *ib.*, (2), **40**. 427, 1883 ; W. Spring, *ib.*, (2), **39**. 644, 1883 ; (2), **41**. 492, 1884 ; *Ber.*, **16**. 1001, 1883 ; **17**. 1218, 1884 ; *Bull Acad. Belg.*, (3), **5**. 492, 1883 ; G. C. Winkelblech, *Liebig's Ann.*, **20**. 37, 1836 ; H. Schiff, *ib.*, **117**. 95. 1861 ; G. Little, *ib.*, **112**. 211, 1859 ; C. Geitner, *ib.*, **129**. 350, 1864 ; H. C. Jenkins and E. A. Smith, *Journ. Chem. Soc.*, **71**. 666, 1897 ; A. Lassieur, *Recherches Inventions*, **4**. 254, 1923 ; K. Jellinek and J. Zabowsky, *Zeit. anorg. Chem.*, **142**. 1, 1925 ; R. Schenck, *Physikalische Chemie der Metalle*, Halle, 181, 1909 ; **New York**, 227, 1919 ; R. Schenck and W. Rassbach, *Ber.*, **40**. 2185, 1917 ; W. G. Smith and A. A. Heimrod, *Chem. Met. Engg.*, **21**. 360, 1919 ; J. Glover, *Trans. Newcastle-on-Tyne Chem. Soc.*, **5**. 132, 1882 ; *Chem. News*, **45**. 105, 1882 ; F. Knapp, *Journ. prakt. Chem.*, (2), **43**. 305, 1891 ; G. Rose, *Pogg. Ann.*, **18**. 68, 1830 ; M. Chavastelon, *Compt. Rend.*, **177**. 1040, 1923 ; H. Fay and C. B. Gillson, *Amer. Chem. Journ.*, **27**. 81, 1902 ; F. Kuhlmann, *Dingler's Journ.*, **93**. 131, 1844 ; R. Hasenclever, *ib.*, **205**. 125, 1877 ; H. van der Planitz, *ib.*, **215**. 442, 1875 ; H. de Hemptinne, *ib.*, **205**. 419, 1872 ; *Chronique de l'industrie*, Bruxelles, 206, 1872 ; A. Bauer and P. von Mertens, *Ber.*, **8**. 210, 1875 ; *Dingler's Journ.*, **216**. 328, 1875 ; G. Lunge and L. Weibel, *ib.*, **261**. 132, 1886 ; *Chem. Ind.*, **9**. 47, 1886 ; G. Lunge and E. Schmid, *Zeit. angew. Chem.*, **5**. 663, 1892 ; E. Schmid, *Ueber die Einwirkung von reiner, nitroser, und rauchender Schwefelsäure und Salpetersäure, auf reines Blei und Legierungen von Blei mit Antimon und Kupfer. Ueber die Bestimmung des Sauerstoffs im Weichblei und dessen Einfluss auf die Angriefbarkeit durch Schwefelsäure*, Basel, 1892 ; A. A. Mallard, *Bull. Soc. Chim.*, (2), **22**. 114, 1874 ; P. Pascal and M. Garnier, *ib.*, (4), **29**. 701, 1921 ; P. Sabatier, *ib.*, (3), **17**. 787, 1897 ; *Compt. Rend.*, **123**. 255, 1896 ; R. R. Tatlock *Chem. News*, **42**. 314, 1880 ; J. Napier, *ib.*, **42**. 314, 1880 ; J. Mactear, *ib.*, **41**. 236, 1880 ; N. Cookson and A. Sanderson, *ib.*, **45**. 105, 1882 ; *Trans. Newcastle-on-Tyne Chem. Soc.*, **5**. 133, 1882 ; A. Ditte, *Ann. Chim. Phys.*, (6). **19**. 69, 1890 ; C. E. Barrs, *Journ. Soc. Chem. Ind.*, **38**. 407, T, 1919 ; W. G. McKellar, *ib.*, **40**. 137, 1921 ; H. W. Rowell, *ib.*, **38**. 407, T, 1919 ; D. W. Jones, *ib.*, **39**. 221, T, 1920 ; H. C. Lancaster, *ib.*, **38**. 408, 1919 ; D. W. Jones, *ib.*, **39**. 221, T, 1920 ; A. J. Hale and H. S. Foster, *ib.*, **34**. 464 1915 ; E. L. Rhead, *ib.*, **39**. 128, R, 1920 ; W. B. Hart, *ib.*, **26**. 504, 1907 ; L. Pitkin, *ib.*, **4**. 460, 1885 ; *Journ. Amer. Chem. Soc.*, **5**. 228, 1883 ; R. W. Hochstetter, *Bull. Soc. Ind. Nord France*, 231, 1890 ; F. C. Calvert and R. Johnson, *Proc. Manchester Lit. Phil. Soc.*, **4**. 115, 1865 ; *Chem. News*, **11**. 171, 1865 ; *Journ. Chem. Soc.*, **16**. 66, 1863 ; **19**. 434, 1866 ; *Compt. Rend.*, **56**. 140, 1863 ; F. J Faktor, *Pharm. Post.*, **38**. 219, 1905 ; J. A. Wilkinson, *Journ. Phys. Chem.*, **13**. 691, 1909 ; T. French, *Chem. Met. Engg.*, **27**. 219, 1922 ; E. Salkowsky, *Chem. Ztg.*, **40**. 449, 1916 ; W. J. Jordan, *Journ. tech. ökon. Chem.*, **11**. 333, 1831 ; A. Frisak, *Metall Erz*, **19**. 200, 1922 ; G. Tammann and W. Köster, *Zeit. anorg. Chem.*, **123**. 217, 1923 ; J. A. N. Friend and R. H. Vallance, *Journ. Chem. Soc.*, **121**. 466, 1922 ; W. G. Whitman and R. P. Russell, *Journ. Ind. Eng. Chem.*, **17**. 348, 1925 ; M. G. Levi, E. Migliorini, and E. Ercolini, *Gazz. Chim. Ital.*

38. i, 598, 1908 ; C. Geitner, *Ueber das Verhalten des Schwefels und der schwefligen Säure zu Wasser bei hohen Druck und hohen Temperatur*, Göttingen, 1863 ; *Liebig's Ann.*, **129.** 359, 1864.
¹⁰ L. Arons, *Naturwiss. Rund.*, **14.** 453, 1899 ; G. C. Schmidt, *Zeit. phys. Chem.*, **106.** 105, 1923 ; V. H. Veley, *Journ. Soc. Chem. Ind.*, **10.** 206, 1891 ; A. Wagner, *Bayer. Ind. Gewerbebl.*, 1, 1876 ; *Dingler's Journ.*, **221.** 260, 1876 ; G. Lunge and L. Weibel, *ib.*, **261.** 132, 1886 ; *Chem. Ind.*, **9.** 47, 1886 ; E. Schmid, *Ueber die Einwirkung von reiner, nitroser und rauchender Schwefelsäure und Salpetersäure auf reines Blei und Legierungen von Blei mit Antimon und Kupfer. Ueber die Bestimmung des Sauerstoffs im Weichblei und dessen Einfluss auf die Angreifbarkeit Schwefelsäure*, Basel, 1892 ; G. Lunge and E. Schmid, *Zeit. angew. Chem.*, **5.** 666, 1892 ; W. G. Whitman and R. P. Russell, *Journ. Ind. Eng. Chem.*, **17.** 348, 1925 ; A. J. Hale and H. S. Foster, *Journ. Soc. Chem. Ind.*, **34.** 464, 1915 ; F. Kuhlmann in A. W. Hofmann, *Bericht über die Entwicklung der chemischen Industrie*, Braunschweig, **1.** 274, 1875 ; *Dingler's Journ.*, **93.** 131, 1844 ; A. Quartaroli, *Gazz. Chim. Ital.*, **53.** i, 345, 1923 ; M. M. P. Muir, *Chem. News*, **25.** 294, 1872 ; W. R. E. Hodgkinson and A. M. Coote, *ib.*, **90.** 142, 1904 ; W. R. E. Hodgkinson and N. E. Bellairs, *ib.*, **71.** 73, 1895 ; H. J. Prins, *Proc. Acad. Amsterdam*, **23.** 1449, 1922 ; C. Montemartini, *Gazz. Chim. Ital.*, **22.** 397, 1892 ; A. Quartaroli, *ib.*, **53.** i, 345, 1923 ; J. J. Acworth and H. E. Armstrong, *Journ. Chem. Soc.*, **32.** 54, 1877 ; E. Divers, *ib.*, **43.** 443, 1883 ; J. J. Sudborough, *ib.*, **59.** 655, 1891 ; G. O. Higley, *Amer. Chem. Journ.*, **17.** 18, 1895 ; H. Endemann, *ib.*, **19.** 1890, 1897 ; P. Sabatier and J. B. Senderens, *Bull. Soc. Chim.*, (3), **13.** 870. 1895 ; *Compt. Rend.*, **114.** 1419, 1892 ; **115.** 236, 1892 ; **120.** 618, 1895 ; P. Sabatier, *ib.*, **123.** 255, 1896 ; *Bull. Soc. Chim.*, (3), **17.** 787, 1897 ; P. Pascal and M. Garnier, *ib.*, (4), **29.** 701, 1921 ; P. Pascal, C. Garnier, and M. Labourrasse, *Mém. Poudres*, **20.** 21, 1923 ; B. C. Banerji and N. R. Dhar, *Zeit. anorg. Chem.*, **122.** 73, 1922 ; N. R. Dhar, *Journ. Phys. Chem.*, **29.** 142, 1925 ; J. W. Turrentine, *Journ. Amer. Chem. Soc.*, **33.** 822, 1911 ; B. B. Adhikary, *Chem. News*, **112.** 163, 1915 ; R. Weber, *Sitzber. Akad. Berlin*, 545, 1872 ; *Pogg. Ann.*, **147.** 113, 1872 ; *Journ. prakt. Chem.*, (2), **6.** 142, 1872 ; E. Schröder and G. Tammann, *Zeit. anorg. Chem.*, **128.** 201, 1923 ; E. Müller and H. Barck, *ib.*, **129.** 313, 1923 ; H. Braconnet, *Pogg. Ann.*, **29.** 174, 1823.
¹¹ B. Pelletier, *Ann. Chim. Phys.*, (1), **13.** 114, 1792 ; A. Granger, *ib.*, (7), **14.** 74, 1898 ; *Contribution à l'étude des phosphures métalliques*, Paris, 1898 ; J. Heimann, *Beiträge zur Kenntnis der Ortho- and Metaphosphorsäure*, Heidelberg, 1902 ; A. C. Vournasos, *Ber.*, **44.** 3269, 1911 ; A. Stock and F. Gomolka, *ib.*, **42.** 4510, 1909 ; G. Linck and P. Möller, *ib.*, **41.** 1404, 1908 ; R. Bossuet and E. Hackspill, *Compt. Rend.*, **157.** 721, 1913 ; H. Rose, *Pogg. Ann.*, **24.** 326, 1832 ; C. F. Rammelsberg, *ib.*, **132.** 489, 1867 ; P. S. Braucher, *U.S. Pat. No.* 1304849, 1919 ; P. Hautefeuille and A. Perrey, *Compt. Rend.*, **98.** 1378, 1884 ; C. Poulenc, *Bull. Soc. Chim.*, (3), **5.** 458, 1891 ; B. Reinitzer and H. Goldschmidt, *Sitzber. Akad. Wien*, **81.** 820, 1880 ; *Ber.*, **13.** 845, 1880.
¹² T. Bergman, *De arsenico*, Stockholm, 1777 ; J. B. Messrschmitt, *Wied. Ann.*, **34.** 883, 1888 ; P. A. Bolley, *Dingler's Journ.*, **129.** 438, 1853 ; W. Spring, *Bull. Acad. Belg.*, (3), **5.** 229, 1883 ; *Ber.*, **16.** 324, 1883 ; A. Bauer and P. von Mertens, *ib.*, **8.** 211, 1875 ; *Dingler's Journ.*, **216.** 322, 1875 ; W. Heike, *Zeit. Internat. Metallog.*, **6.** 50, 1914 ; K. Friedrich, *Met.*, **3.** 42, 1906 ; G. A. Koenig, *Proc. Amer. Phil. Soc.*, **42.** 219, 1903 ; *Zeit. Kryst.*, **38.** 544, 1904 ; N. A. Puschin, *Journ. Russ. Phys. Chem. Soc.*, **39.** 869, 1907 ; S. F. Schemtschuschny, *ib.*, **37.** 1283, 1905 ; W. Guertler, *Metallographie*, Berlin, **1.** 863, 1912 ; C. T. Heycock and F. H. Neville, *Journ. Chem. Soc.*, **57.** 376, 656, 1890 ; **61.** 888, 1892 ; *Chem. News*, **62.** 280, 1890 ; A. Descamps, *Compt. Rend.*, **86.** 1065, 1878 ; J. Fournet, *Ann. Mines*, (3), **4.** 3, 235, 1833 ; C. O. Thieme, *Journ. Ind. Chem.*, **12.** 446, 1920 ; I. P. Göbel, *Zeit. Metallkunde*, **14.** 357, 1922 ; J. Percy, *The Metallurgy of Lead*, London, 63, 1870 ; J. Fournet, *Ann. Mines*, (3), **4.** 15, 1833.
¹³ G. Karsten, *Pogg. Ann.*, **55.** 118, 1842 ; A. Matthiessen, *Phil. Trans.*, **150.** 161, 171, 1860 ; *Pogg. Ann.*, **110.** 22, 190, 195, 1860 ; T. J. Seebeck, *ib.*, **6.** 148, 1826 ; W. Rollmann, *ib.*, **83.** 77, 1851 ; A. Saposhnikoff and J. Kaniewsky, *Journ. Russ. Phys. Chem. Soc.*, **39.** 901, 1907 ; A. Gorbow, *ib.*, **41.** 1241, 1909 ; N. A. Puschin, *ib.*, **39.** 869, 1907 ; *Rev. Met.*, **4.** 933, 1907 ; M. le Gris, *ib.*, **8.** 614, 1911 ; J. F. Gmelin, *Comment. Gött.*, **10.** 28, 1790 ; W. Campbell, *Journ. Franklin Inst.*, **154.** 1, 131, 201, 1902 ; S. R. Dean, *Journ. Amer. Chem. Soc.*, **45.** 1683, 1923 ; A. Brand, *Zeit. Kryst.*, **17.** 266, 1890 ; J. Fournet, *Ann. Mines*, (3), **4.** 235, 1833 ; W. Spring, *Zeit. Phys. Chem.*, **15.** 74, 1894 ; E. Maey, *ib.*, **38.** 295, 1901 ; R. H. Thurston, *Non-ferrous Metals and Alloys*, New York, 1884 ; W. Gontermann, *Zeit. anorg. Chem.*, **55.** 420, 1907 ; M. Plüss, *ib.*, **93.** 35, 1915 ; E. Rudolfi, *ib.*, **67.** 85, 1910 ; G. Tammann, *ib.*, **53.** 454, 1907 ; E. Rudolfi, *ib.*, **67.** 65, 1910 ; P. Ludwik, *ib.*, **94.** 168, 1916 ; W. Guertler, *ib.*, **51.** 415, 1906 ; *Metallurgie*, Berlin, **1.** 795, 1909 ; R. Durrer, *Phys. Zeit.*, **19.** 86, 1918 ; H. Gautier, *Contribution à l'étude des alliages*, Paris, 93, 1901 ; *Bull. Soc. Enc. Nat. Ind.*, (5), **1.** 1306, 1896 ; H. le Chatelier, *Rev. Gén. Sciences Pure Appl.*, **6.** 529, 1895 ; *Contribution à l'étude des alliages*, Paris, 441, 1901 ; *Bull. Soc. Enc. Nat. Ind.*, (4), **10.** 195, 1895 ; G. Charpy, *ib.*, (5), **2.** 384. 1897 ; (5), **3.** 670, 1898 ; *Contribution à l'étude des alliages*, Paris, 119, 201, 1901 ; C. R. A. Wright and C. Thompson, *Proc. Roy. Soc.*, **48.** 25, 1890 ; C. R. A. Wright, *Journ. Soc. Chem. Ind.*, **13.** 1016, 1894 ; J. E. Stead, *ib.*, **16.** 201, 506, 1897 ; F. Wüst, *Met.*, **6.** 769, 1909 ; E. Elsässer, *Wied. Ann.*, **8.** 455, 1879 ; F. de Jussieu, *Ann. Chim. Phys.*, (5), **18.** 138, 1879 ; H. V. Regnault, *ib.*, (3), **1.** 129, 1841 ; E. Becquerel, *ib.*, (4), **8.** 408, 1866 ; *Arch. Sciences Genève*, (2), **26.** 239, 1866 ; Q. Marino and C. Bowen, *Brit. Pat. No.* 130302, 1918 ; I. P. Göbel, *Zeit. Metallkunde*, **14.** 357, 1922 ; W. G. Knox, *Metal Ind.*, **18.** 264, 1920 ; C. Pack, *ib.*, **18.** 410, 1920 ; C. C. Bissett, *ib.*, **17.** 182, 441, 1920 ; C. W. Proctor, *ib.*, **18.** 414, 1920 ; R. Loebe, *Met.*, **8.** 8, 1911 ; M. Wählert, *ib.*

17. 182, 231, 1920; W. Kaiser, *ib.*, **8.** 260, 307, 1911; F. Wüst, *ib.*, **6.** 769, 1909; P. Müller, *ib.*, **7.** 769, 1910; K. Friedrich, *ib.*, **7.** 98, 1910; I. Hall, *German Pat.*, *D.R.P.* 334806, 1914; Gesellschaft für Elektro-Osmose, *ib.*, 251098, 1911; L. J. Gurevich and J. S. Hromatko, *Chem. Met. Engg.*, **25.** 62, 1921; G. K. Burgess and R. W. Woodward, *ib.*, **19.** 669, 1918; H. M. Waring, *ib.*, **19.** 657, 1918; M. L. Lissberg, *ib.*, **19.** 658, 1918; A. Riche, *Compt. Rend.*, **55.** 143, 1862; H. Pélabon, *ib.*, **176.** 1305, 1923; P. Leroux, *ib.*, **156.** 1765, 1913; J. A. Linnavuori, *Comment. Soc. Scient. Fenn.*, **1.** 10, 1922; H. Kopp, *Liebig's Ann. Suppl.*, **3.** 289, 1864; A. P. Laurie, *Journ. Chem. Soc.*, **65.** 1035, 1894; *Chem. News*, **69.** 310, 1894; C. O. Thieme, *Journ. Ind. Eng. Chem.*, **12.** 446, 1920; H. Behrens, *Das mikroskopische Gefüge der Metalle und Legierungen*, Hamburg, 59, 1894; F. C. Calvert and R. Johnson, *Phil. Mag..* (4), **17.** 114, 1859; (4), **18.** 354, 1859; *Phil. Trans.*, **148.** 349, 1858; *Chem. News*, **3.** 315, 357, 371, 1861; D. Ewen and T. Turner, *Journ. Inst. Metals*, **4.** 128, 1910; F. L. Brady, *ib.*, **28.** 397, 1922; H. Fowler, *ib.*, **28.** 138, 1922; A. M. Portevin, *ib.*, **29.** 239, 1923; *Engg.*, **115.** 478, 1923; M. Plüss, *Zur Kenntnis der Viskosität und Dichte geschmolzener Metalle und Legierungen*, Leipzig, 1915; *Zeit. anorg. Chem.*, **93.** 1, 1915; E. Heyn, *Zeit. Ver. deut. Ing.*, **44.** 137, 175, 1900; E. Heyn and O. Bauer, *Untersuchungen über Lagermetalle—Sb-Pb-Sn Legierungen*, Berlin, 1914; O. Bauer, *Stahl Eisen*, **35.** 554, 1915; S. D. Muzaffar, *Trans. Faraday Soc.*, **19.** 56, 1923; H. Nissenson and P. Siedler, *Berg. Hütt. Ztg.*, **62.** 421, 1903; K. Peters, *Einige Produkte die durch Einwirkung von Blei und von KNO_2 auf $Pb(NO_3)_2$ entstehen*, Basel, 1893; *Zeit. anorg. Chem.*, **11.** 145, 1896; G. Faunce, *Journ. Anal. Chem.*, **1.** 121, 1897; M. Halfmann, *Metall Erz*, **17.** 11, 1920; H. Leroux, *ib.*, **21.** 421, 1924; M. Kühnel and M. Marzahn, *Zeit. Metallkunde*, **16.** 278, 1924; C. T. Heycock and F. H. Neville, *Journ. Chem. Soc.*, **57.** 376, 656, 1890; **61.** 888, 1892; *Chem. News*, **62.** 280, 1890; A. Naccari and M. Bellati, *Elettricista*, **1.** 329, 1877; A. Battelli, *Mem. Accad. Torino*, (2), **36.** 487, 1884; S. Zinberg, *Zeit. angew. Chem.*, **27.** 436, 1914; R. Meyer and S. Schuster, *ib.*, **27.** 121, 1914; R. Moscheles, *Chem. Ztg.*, **16.** 1395, 1892; B. Kohlmann, *ib.*, **16.** 1560, 1892; J. Kallir, *ib.*, **16.** 1378, 1892; J. O. Johnstone, *U.S. Pat. No.* 1389511, 1920; T. Thomson, *Proc. Phil. Soc. Glasgow*, **1.** 77, 1844; H. von der Planitz, *Dingler's Journ.*, **215.** 442, 1875; *Ber.*, **7.** 1664, 1874; A. Bauer and P. von Mertens, *ib.*, **8.** 210, 1875; *Dingler's Journ.*, **216.** 328, 1875; H. Pélabon, *Compt. Rend.*, **176.** 1305, 1923; L. Pitkin, *Journ. Amer. Chem. Soc.*, **5.** 228, 1883; R. S. Dean, *ib.*, **45.** 1683, 1923; R. S. Dean and W. E. Hudson, *ib.*, **46.** 1178, 1924; R. S. Dean, W. E. Hudson, and M F. Fogler, *Journ. Ind. Eng. Chem.*, **17.** 1246, 1925; R. S. Dean, L. Zicheick, and F. C. Nix, *Min. Met.*, **7.** 76, 1926; *Trans. Amer. Inst. Min. Met. Eng.*, 1534, 1926; J. W. Richards, *Journ. Amer. Chem. Soc.*, **16.** 541, 1894; I. Moser, *Sitzber. Akad. Wien*, **2.** 85, 1849; M. von Schwarz, *Legierungen*, Stuttgart, 76, 1920; C. R. McCabe, *Journ. Ind. Eng. Chem.*, **9.** 42, 1917; G. Vicentini and C. Cattaneo, *Rend. Accad. Lincei*, (5), **1.** i, 419, 1892; G. Vicentini and D. Omodei, *ib.*, (4), **3.** i, 235, 294, 321, 1887; G. Wertheim, *Ann. Chim. Phys.*, (3), **12.** 581, 1848; H. Endo, *Science Rep. Tohoku Univ.*, **14.** 479, 1925; K. Honda and T. Ishigaki, *ib.*, **14.** 219, 1925; W. B. Brown, *Phys. Rev.*, (2), **22.** 171, 1923; V. Fischer, *Zeit. Tech. Phys.*, **6.** 146, 1925; O. Bertoya, *ib.*, **17.** 141, 1900; P. Siedler, *Berg. Hütt. Ztg.*, **62.** 421, 1903; M. Dubosc, *Réunion de l'Assoc. Internat. pour l'essai des matériaux de construction*, Paris, 18, 1905; L. Guillet, *Chim. Ind.*, **5.** 371, 1921; *Compt. Rend.*, **182.** 1362, 1926.

[14] O. Richter, *Untersuchungen der spezifischen Wärme von Legierungen*, Marburg, 1908; *Ann. Physik*, (4), **36.** 590, 1912; (4), **42.** 793, 1913; E. Dippel, *ib.*, (4), **42.** 894, 1913; *Abhängigkeit der spezifiischen Wärme und des Schmelzpunktes gewisser Legierungen von der thermischen Vorgeschichte*, Marburg, 1910; T. Thomson, *Proc. Glasgow Phil. Soc.*, **1.** 77, 1844; E. F. Northrup and R. G. Sherwood, *Journ. Franklin Inst.*, **182.** 477, 1916; C. M. Marx, *Schweigger's Journ.*, **58.** 463, 1830; **60.** 1, 1830; J. W. Döbereiner, *ib.*, **42.** 182, 1824; A. Vogel, *Repert. Pharm.*, **22.** 471, 1872; F. Rudberg, *Pogg. Ann.*, **18.** 240, 1830; **71.** 460, 1847; W. Rollmann, *ib.*, **83.** 77, 1851; **84.** 275, 1851; **89.** 90, 1853; C. C. Person, *Compt. Rend.*, **23.** 926, 1846; *Ann. Chim. Phys.*, (3), **24.** 129, 1848; R. Kremann and A. Brodar, *Monatsh.*, **44.** 383, 1923; R. Kremann, *ib.*, **44.** 401, 1923; **45.** 133, 1924; *Zeit. phys. Chem.*, **110.** 559, 1924; A. F. V. Guettier, *Guide pratique des alliages métalliques*, Paris, 1865; P. Berthier, *Traité des essais par la voie sèche*, Paris, **2.** 613, 1834; E. Wiedemann, *Wied. Ann.*, **20.** 236, 1883; A. W. Kapp, *Ann. Physik*, (4), **6.** 771, 1901; *Ueber vollständige Gefrierpunktskurven binärer Metallegierungen*, Königsberg, 1901; A. M. Portevin, *Journ. Inst. Metals*, **29.** 239, 1923; *Engg.*, **115.** 478, 1923; W. Herold, *Zeit. anorg. Chem.*, **112.** 131, 1920; F. Sauerwald, *ib.*, **135.** 255, 1924; A. Stoffel, *ib.*, **53.** 150, 1907; R. Kremann and A. Langbauer, *ib.*, **127.** 240, 1923; W. E. Barlow, *ib.*, **70.** 183, 1911; *Journ. Amer. Chem. Soc.*, **32.** 1390, 1910; C. P. Steinmetz, *ib.*, **40.** 100, 1918; L. Pitkin, *ib.*, **5.** 228, 1883; F. A. Schulze, *Ueber das Verhalten einiger Legierungen zum Gesetz von Wiedemann und Franz*, Berlin, 1902; *Ann. Physik*, (4), **9.** 564, 1902; R. Schenck, *ib.*, (4), **32.** 264, 1910; G. Spadavecchia, *Nuovo Cimento*, (4), **10.** 161, 1899; A. Battelli, *Atti 1st. Veneto*, (6), **5.** 1137, 1887; A. Levi, *ib.*, (8), **18.** 627, 1916; G. Charpy, *Contribution à l'étude des alliages*, Paris, 200, 1901; O. Richter, *Ann. Physik*, (4), **39.** 1590, 1912; (4), **42.** 779, 1913; E. Dippel, *ib.*, (4), **42.** 889, 1913; F. A. Schulze, *Phys. Zeit.*, **13.** 425, 1912; R. H. Thurston, *Non-ferrous Metals and Alloys*, New York, 1884; A. Bauer and P. von Mertens, *Ber.*, **8.** 210, 1875; J. Goebel, *Zeit. Metallkunde*, **14.** 357, 388, 425, 1922; J. Beattie, *Proc. Roy. Soc. Edin.*, **20.** 481, 1895; E. van Aubel, *Arch. Sciences Genève*, (3), **19.** 103, 1888; *Bull. Acad. Belg.*, (3), **15.** 198, 1888; *Phil. Mag.*, (5), **25.** 191, 1888; *Compt. Rend.*, **136.** 1131, 1903; E. Becquerel, *Ann. Chim. Phys.*, (4), **8.** 389, 1866; W. Guertler, *Metallographie*, Berlin, **1.** 549, 1912; *Zeit. anorg. Chem.*, **51.** 404, 1906; *Jahrb. Rad. Elektron.*, **5.** 61, 1908; H. Zahn, *ib.*, **5.** 201, 1908; J. Ewing and W. Rosen-

hain, *Phil. Trans.*, 193. A. 370. 1900 ; P. Senepa, *Arch. Sciences Genève*, (4), 35. 63, 1913 ; *Atti Accad. Lincei*, (5), 21. ii, 53. 1912 ; F. Guthrie, *Phil. Mag.*, (5), 17. 462, 1884 ; J. Taylor, *ib.*, (5), 50. 37, 1900 ; C. T. Heycock and F. H. Neville, *Chem. News*, 62. 280, 1890 ; *Journ. Chem. Soc.*, 57. 376, 656, 1890 ; 61. 888, 1892 ; 62. 280, 1890 ; A. P. Laurie, *ib.*, 65. 1031, 1894 ; H. Endemann, *Amer. Chemist*, 6. 457, 1876 ; W. Broniewsky, *Rev. Mét.*, 7. 352, 1910 ; H. le Chatelier, *Bull. Soc. Enc. Nat. Ind.*, (4), 10. 192, 1895 ; *Rev. Gén. Sciences Pure Appl.*, 6. 529, 1895 ; *Contribution à l'étude des alliages*, Paris, 441, 1901 ; G. Charpy, *ib.*, 220, 1901 ; E. S. Shepherd, *Journ. Phys. Chem.*, 6. 519, 1902 ; 7. 15, 1903 ; A. Leduc, *Journ. Phys.*, (2), 3. 362, 1884 ; A. Gorboff, *Journ. Russ. Phys. Chem. Soc.*, 41. 1241, 1910 ; N. A. Puschin, *ib.*, 39. 869, 1907 ; E. von Maey, *Zeit. phys. Chem.*, 38. 292, 1901 ; 50. 216, 1905 ; W. Spring, *ib.*, 15. 74, 1894 ; G. Tammann, *Zeit. Elektrochem.*, 18. 595, 1912 ; A. Matthiessen, *Pogg. Ann.*, 110. 21, 190, 1860 ; 130. 50, 1867 ; *Phil. Trans.*, 150. 161, 177, 1860 ; 156. 861, 1866 ; *B.A. Rep.*, 37, 1863 ; *Journ. Chem. Soc.*, 20. 201, 1867 ; A. Matthiessen and C. Vogt, *Pogg. Ann.*, 116. 369, 1862 ; 122. 19, 1864 ; *Phil. Mag.*, (4), 23. 171, 1862 ; *Phil. Trans.*, 154. 167, 1864; D. Mazzotto, *Rend. Ist. Lombardo*, (2), 18. 165, 1885 ; (2), 19. 458, 1886 ; *Mem. Ist. Lombardo*, (3), 16. 1, 1886 ; *Nuovo Cimento*, (5), 18. 180, 1909 ; *Internat. Zeit. Metallog.*, 1. 346, 1911 ; C. R. Darling and R. H. Rinaldi, *Proc. Phys. Soc.*, 36. 281, 1924 ; L. Losana, *Gazz. Chim. Ital.*, 53. i, 393, 1923 ; G. Wertheim, *Ann. Chim. Phys.*, (3), 12. 581, 1848 ; A. Riche, *Compt. Rend.*, 55. 143, 1862 ; T. French, *Metal Ind.*, 21. 196, 1922 ; *Met. Chem. Engg.*, 27. 219, 1922 ; W. Spring, *Bull. Acad. Belg.*, (3), 28. 23, 1894 ; *Zeit. phys. Chem.*, 15. 65, 1894 ; G. Vicentini and D. Omodei, *Rend. Accad. Lincei*, (4), 4. i, 718, 805, 1888 ; C. di Capua, *ib.*, (5), 31. i, 162, 1922 ; 55. ii. 582, 594, 1925; C. di Capua and M. Arnone, *ib.*, (5), 33. i, 28, 1924 ; A. Vogel, *Sitzber. Akad. München*, 2, 1872 ; *Repert. Pharm.*, 22. 471, 1873 ; C. R. A. Wright, *Journ. Soc. Chem. Ind.*, 13. 1014, 1894 ; P. Ludwik, *Zeit. anorg. Chem.*, 94. 161, 1916 ; K. Bux, *Zeit. Physik*, 14. 316, 1923 ; I. P. Göbel, *Zeit. Metallkunde*, 14. 391, 1922 ; F. L. Brady, *Journ. Inst. Metals*, 28. 383, 1922 ; R. Arpi, *Internat. Zeit. Metallog.*, 5. 157, 1914 ; P. van Musschenbroek, *Introductio ad philosophiam naturalem*, Lugduni Batavorum, 1. 454, 1762 ; J. T. Seebeck, *Pogg. Ann.*, 6. 148. 1826 ; P. Muller, *Met.*, 7. 769, 1910 ; H. Endo, *Science Rep. Tohoku Univ.*, 14. 479, 1925 ; A. Magnus and M. Mannheimer, *Zeit. phys. Chem.*, 121. 267, 1926 ; M. Jakob, *Zeit. Metall..unde*, 16. 353, 1924; K. Honda and T. Ishigaki, *ib.*, 14. 219, 1925 ; S. Muzaffar, *Trans. Faraday Soc.*, 19. 56, 1923 ; W. B. Brown, *Phys. Rev.*, (2), 22. 171, 1923.

   [14] J. F. John, *Berlin Jahrb. Pharm.*, 21. 365, 1820 ; W. Stahl, *Chem. Ztg.*, 39. 885, 1915 ; H. Reckleben and J. Scheiber, *ib.*, 39. 42, 1915 ; L. Bleckrode, *Phil. Mag.*, (5), 38. 81, 1894 ; S. G. Sastry, *Journ. Soc. Chem. Ind.*, 35. 94, 1916 ; W. R. E. Hodgkinson, *ib.*, 37. 86, 1918 ; F. Southerden, *ib.*, 37. 86, 1918 ; O. Ruff and B. Bergdahl, *Zeit. anorg. Chem.*, 106. 76, 1919 ; M. Berthelot, *Ann. Chim. Phys.*, (7), 22. 305, 1901 ; E. Gudeman, *Met. Chem. Engg.*, 8. 680, 1910 ; G. Gore, *Chem. News*, 48. 295, 1883 ; G. A. Goyder, *ib.*, 69. 262, 1894 ; F. P. Hall, *ib.*, 47. 290, 300, 1883 ; *Amer. Chem. Journ.*, 4. 440, 1883 ; M. Traube, *Ber.*, 18. 1877, 1885 ; V. Thomas, *ib.*, 174. 465, 1922 ; H. C. Bolton, *ib.*, 13. 730, 1880 ; J. Tafel, *ib.*, 42. 3146, 1909 ; L. T. O'Shea, *Chem. News*, 53. 260, 1886 ; *Proc. Chem. Soc.*, 2. 206, 1886 ; F. F. Rupert, *Journ. Amer. Chem. Soc.*, 42. 407, 1920 ; W. Falta and M. Richter-Quittner, *Biochem. Zeit.*, 115. 39, 1921 ; A. Mailhe, *Bull. Soc. Chim.*, (4), 5. 616, 1919 ; L. Lindet, *ib.*, (3), 31. 476, 1904 ; A. Brochet and J. Petit, *ib.*, (3), 31. 366, 1904 ; J. C. Thresh, *Analyst*, 47. 459, 1922 ; W. G. Whitman and R. P. Russell, *Journ. Ind. Eng. Chem.*, 17. 348, 1925 ; F. Auerbach and H. Weber, *Zeit. anorg. Chem.*, 147. 68, 1925 ; C. O. Henke and O. W. Brown, *Journ. Phys. Chem.*, 26. 324, 1922 ; O. Sackui, *Arb. Kaiser Ges. Amt.*, 22. 205, 1904 ; G. Stiefler, *Zeit. Neurologie Psychiatrie*, 77. 25, 1922 ; O. P. Watts and N. D. Whipple, *Trans. Amer. Electrochem. Soc.*, 32. 267, 1918 ; A. Beythein, *Zeit. Unters. Nachr. Genuss.*, 43. 47, 1922 ; H. S. Rawdon, *Trans. Amer. Inst. Min. Eng.*, 64. 443, 1920 ; *Chem. Met. Engg.*, 22. 346, 1920 ; *Bull. U.S. Bur. Standards*, 377, 1920 ; F. Rathgen, *Chem. Ztg.*, 27. 825, 1903 ; I. L. C. Eckelt, *ib.*, 35. 1131, 1911 ; O. Schaal, *ib.*, 44. 741, 1920 ; E. Salkowsky, *ib.*, 40. 449, 1916 ; M. Schirmonsky, *Nephtanoje Djelo*, 6, 1912 ; O. Schmidt, *Zeit. phys. Chem.*, 118. 193, 1925 ; F. H. Rhodes and J. T. Carty, *Journ. Ind. Eng. Chem.*, 17. 905, 1925 ; H. J. Prins, *Rec. Trav. Chim. Pays-Bas*, 44. 876, 1925.

   [16] T. Sudenforf, *Zeit. Unters. Nahr. Genussm.*, 24. 386, 1912 ; E. Spaeth, *ib.*, 18. 650, 1910 ; A. Schneider and F. Jenniger, *Gas. Wasserfach.*, 66. 369, 1923 ; N. N. Banerjee, *Zeit. anorg. Chem.*, 83. 113, 1913 ; A. Benedicenti and S. Rebello-Alves, *Arch. Intern. Pharm.*, 26. 297, 1922 ; M. Rjältschewsky, *Die hygienische Bedeutung des in Speisekammern enthaltenan Bleies*, St. Petersburg, 1887 ; *Deut. Med. Ztg.*, 932, 1886 ; G. Stiefler, *Zeit. Neurologie Psychiatrie*, 77. 25, 1922 ; E. Gudemann, *Met. Chem. Engg.*, 8. 680, 1910 ; L. Lindet, *Bull. Soc. Chim.*, (3), 31. 476, 1904 ; A. Beythein, *Zeit. Unters. Nachr. Genuss.*, 43. 47, 1902 ; J. Tafel and B. Emmert, *Zeit. phys, Chem.*, 54. 433, 1916 ; J. Tafel, *Zeit. Elektrochem.*, 12. 120, 1906 ; H. Baum and R. Seeliger, *Milch Ztg.*, 25. 87, 1897 ; *Arch. Tierheilk.*, 21. 297, 1895 ; A. Gautier, *Bull. Acad. Méd.*, 10. ii, 1825, 1881 ; *Le cuivre et plomb*, Paris, 132, 1883 ; P. Schützenberger and E. Boutmy, *Ann. Hyg.*, (4), 5. 209, 1881 ; D. Klein and A. Berg, *Bull. Soc. Chim.*, (2), 45. 854, 1886 ; *Compt. Rend.*, 102. 1170, 1886 ; A. Livache, *ib.*, 124. 1520, 1897 ; H. Riesenfeld and F. Taurke, *Ber.*, 38. 2798, 1905 ; J. Schiel, *ib.*, 12. 507, 1879 ; G. Wölffhügel, *Arb. Kaiser Ges. Amt.*, 2. 135, 1887 ; A. Sander, *Deut. Med. Wochschr.*, 4. 46, 1878 ; P. Schindler, *Zeit. öffentl. Chem.*, 19. 132, 1913 ; A. S. Taylor, *On Poisons in relations to Medical Jurisprudence and Medicine*, London, 510, 1859 ; A. Meyer, *Landswirtschaflt. Ztg.*, 71, 1880 ; A. Gawalowsky, *Zeit. anal. Chem.*, 38. 769, 1899 ; C. Engler and E. Kneis, *Dingler's Journ.*, 263. 193, 1887 ; J. Merrick, *Amer. Chemist*

4. 289, 1874; F. C. Mathers and A. B. Leible, *Trans. Amer. Electrochem. Soc.*, 31. 271, 1917; *Met. Chem. Engg.*, 16. 587, 1917; G. Heinzelmann, *Zeit. Spiritusind.*, 27. 399, 1904; F. M. Perkin, *Proc. Chem. Soc.*, 24. 179, 1909; S. Macadam, *Pharm. Trans.*, (3), 8. 463, 1878; I. J. Redwood, *Journ. Soc. Chem. Ind.*, 5. 362, 1886; F. Malmejac, *Journ. Pharm. Chim.*, (6), 13. 169, 1901; W. Fox, *Chem. News*, 58. 39, 1888; P. Grélot, *Ann. Falisfications Fraudes*, 15. 326, 1923; U. Ehrhardt and G. Pfeiderer, *Gesammelte Abh. Kennt. Kohle*, 5. 576, 1920: C. O. Henke and O. W. Brown, *Journ. Phys. Chem.*, 28. 71, 1924; J. Aub, *Lead Poisoning*, Baltimore, 19, 1926; M. Traube, *Ber.*, 18. 1877, 1885.

¹⁷ F. Damm and F Krafft, *Ber.*, 40. 4775, 1907; F. Mylius and O. Fromm, *ib.*, 27. 639, 1894; F. Jirsa, *Zeit. phys. Chem.*, 94. 1, 1920; P. P. Lebedeff, *Zeit. Elektrochem.*, 18. 895, 1912; K. Elbs and J. Forssell, *ib.*, 8. 760, 1902; G. Lunge and L. Weibel, *Chem. Ind.*, 9. 47. 1886; *Dingler's Journ.*, 261. 133, 1886; W. Venator, *ib.*, 261. 133, 1886; A. Wagner, *ib.*, 221. 260, 1876; *Bayer, Ind. Gewerbebl.*, 1, 1876; O. P. Watts and N. D. Whipple, *Trans. Amer. Electrochem. Soc.*, 32. 275, 1918; H. Endemann, *Amer. Chem. Journ.*, 19. 1890, 1897; W. W. Strong, *ib.*, 42. 147, 1909; R. H. Gaines, *Journ. Ind. Eng. Chem.*, 5. 766, 1913; E. Hlavati, *German Pat.*, *D.R.P.* 250128, 1911; P. Wenger and D. Midhat, *Ann. Chim. Anal.*, 17. 321, 1912; E. B. Spear and K. D. Kahn, *Journ. Amer. Chem. Soc.*, 46. 181, 1918; R. H. Gerke, *ib.*, 44. 1684, 1922; E. A. von der Burg, *Nieuw Tijdschr. Pharm. Nederl.*, 65, 97, 1878; J. F. Liverseege and A. W. Knapp, *Chem. News*, 108. 136, 1913; *Journ. Soc. Chem. Ind.*, 39. 27, T. 1920; A J. Hale and H. S. Foster, *ib.*, 34. 465, 1915; E. B. Maxted, *Journ. Chem. Soc.*, 117. 1501, 1920; 119. 225, 1921; 127. 73, 1925; O. W. Brown, C. O. Henke, and L. T. Smith, *Journ. Phys. Chem.*, 24. 367, 1920; H. W. Gillett, *ib.,* 13. 338, 1909; C. Tubandt and S. Eggert, *Zeit. anorg. Chem.*, 110. 230, 1920; R. Lorenz, W. Fraenkel, and J. Silberstein, *ib.*, 131. 247, 1923; R. Lorenz and M. Mannheimer, *ib.*, 150. 343, 1926; J. B. Senderens, *Bull. Soc. Chim.*, (3). 15. 211, 1896; (3), 17. 272, 1897; *Compt. Rend.*, 104. 504, 1887; W. D. Treadwell, *Helvetica Chim. Acta*, 5. 806, 1922; L. Peetz, *Met.*, 1. 287, 1904; F. Jirsa and J. Fabinger, *Zeit. phys. Chem.*, 109. 260, 1924.

¹⁸ T. G. Wormley, *Microchemistry of Poisons*, New York, 1867; V. Lenher, *Journ. Amer. Chem. Soc.*, 17. 511, 1895; R. D. Hall, *ib.*, 24. 570, 1902; F. Jackson, *Journ. Amer. Chem. Soc.*, 25. 992, 1903; L. J. Curtman and A. D. St. John, *ib.*, 34. 1679, 1912; L. Bruner and J. Zawadsky, *Bull. Acad. Cracow*, 267, 1909; *Zeit. anorg. Chem.*, 65. 145, 1910; 67. 454, 1910; P. Harting, *Journ. prakt. Chem.*, (1), 22. 52, 1841; *Bull. Sciences Neerl.*, 2. 164, 1841; J. L. Lassaigne, *Journ. Chim. Méd.*, 8. 583, 1832; C. H. Pfaff, *Handbuch der analytischen Chemie*, Altona, 2. 287, 1821; H. W. F. Wackenroder, *Repert. Pharm.*, 46. 225, 1833; H. Reinsch, *ib.*, 56. 183, 1836; *Journ prakt. Chem.*, (1), 13. 130, 1838; H. Vohl, *Liebig's Ann.*, 96. 242, 1858; *Journ. prakt. Chem.*, (1), 67. 177, 1856; E. F. Anthon, *ib.*, (1), 10. 353, 1837; E. A. Parnell, *B.A. Rep.*, 51, 1841; M. Berthelot, *Compt. Rend.*, 78. 1247, 1874; F. Parmentier, *ib.*, 114. 298, 1892; G. Chesneau, *ib.*, 111. 269, 1890; A. Trillat, *ib.*, 136. 1205, 1903; J. L. Breton, *Ann. Chim. Phys.*, (7), 30. 554, 1903; S. Harvey, *Analyst.*, 15. 68, 1890; N. Schoorl, *Pharm. Weekbl.*, 44. 121, 1907; M. Martin, *Journ. prakt. Chem.*, (1), 67. 374, 1856; E. Schürmann, *Liebig's Ann.*, 249. 326, 1888; G. S. Jamieson, *Amer. Journ. Science*, (4), 40. 157, 1915; W. N. Iwanoff, *Journ. Russ. Phys. Chem. Soc.*, 46. 418, 1914; K. A. Hofmann and V. Wölfl, *Ber.*, 32. 249, 1904; E. Müller and O. Diefenthäler, *ib.*, 43. 2321, 1901; O. Mayer, *ib.*, 36. 1740, 1903; L. Dede and P. Bonin, *ib.*, 55. B, 2327, 1922; L. Dede and T. Becker, *Zeit. anorg. Chem.*, 152. 185, 1926; N. Tarugi, *Gazz. Chim. Ital.*, 45. 341, 1895; J. Girard, *Ann. Chim. Anal.*, 5. 56, 1900; F. Faktor, *Pharm. Post*, 33. 355, 1900; J. von Liebig, *Pogg. Ann.*, 25. 546, 1832; M. Gröger, *Zeit. anorg. Chem.*, 58. 412, 1908; C. Reichard, *Chem. Ztg.*, 27. 924, 1903; E. Eegriwe, *Zeit. anal. Chem.*, 53. 420, 1914; *Fest. Riga Polyt. Inst.*, 103, 1912; I. M. Kolthoff, *Pharm. Weekbl.*, 53. 1739, 1916.

¹⁹ J. Beckmann, *Beyträge zur Geschichte der Erfindungen*, Leipzig, 1. 179, 1786; London, 1. 245, 1846; L. Tanqueril des Planches, *Traité des maladies de plomb ou saturnines*, 1839; G. Meillère, *Le Saturnisme*, Paris, 1903; T. Tronchin, *De colica pictorium*, Genevæ, 1757; London, 1764; A. Aetius, *Tomus primus liborum medicinalium*, Venetiis, 1534; J. Hunter, *Observations on the Diseases of the Army in Jamaica*, London, 1788; S. Stockhusen, *De lithargyri famo noxio morbifico ejusque metallico frequentiori morbo vulgo dicto Hüttenkatze*, Goslariæ, 1656; M. Delamarc, *Traité de la police*, Paris, 1. 615, 1713; J. Zeller and J. Weismann, *De docimasia sini lithargyrio mangonisati, experimentis illustratio*, Tubingæ, 1707; W. Graham, *Art of making Wines from Fruits, Flowers, and Herbs*, London, 1770; J. Hardy, *A Candid Examination of what has been aavanced on the Colic of Poitou and Devonshire*, London, 1. 84, 1778; M. Citois, *De novo et populari apud pictores dolore colico bilioso diatriba*, Potiers, 1616; J. Alderson, *Lancet*, ii, 73, 95, 1852.

²⁰ T. M. Legge and K. W. Goadby, *Lead Poisoning and Lead Absorption*, London, 1912; T. M. Legge, *Report on the Manufacture of Paints and Colours containing Lead*, 1905; *The Health of Brass Workers*, London, 1905; K. W. Goadby, *Journ. Hyg.*, 9. 122, 1909; *Lancet*, 180. 639, 1911; *Report of the Committee on Lead in Potteries*, London, 3. 478, 1910; K. W. Goadby and F. W. Goadby, *Lancet*, 177. 988, 1909; D. Campbell, *Lancet*, ii, 836, 1886; i, 728, 1889; *Practitioner*, 37. 477, 1886; J. D. Mann, *Forensic Medicine and Toxicology*, London, 487, 1908; *Brit. Med. Journ.*, i, 401, 1893; A. W. and M. W. Blyth, *Poisons—their Effects and Detection*, London, 616, 1906; J. Carlès, F. Leuret, and H. Blanc, *Compt. Rend. Soc. Biol.*, 87. 521, 1922; A. Borrel, A. de Coulon, and L. Boez, *ib.*, 87. 1118, 1922; P. Girard, *ib.*, 88. 487, 1923; O. Ferrier, *Journ.*

Pharm. Chim., (6). **13**. 407, 1901 ; M. Guerbet, *ib.*, (7), **18**. 291, 1918 ; J. B. Charcot and P. Yvon, *ib.*, (6), **5**. 375, 1897 ; L. Hugounecq, *ib.*, (6), **8**. 529, 1898 ; M. Neisser, *Gesund. Ing.*, **36**. 920, 1913 ; J. Drost, *ib.*, **38**. 37, 1915 ; L. Morveau and E. Vinet, *Compt. Rend.*, **151**. 1068, 1147, 1910 ; **152**. 1057, 1911 ; F. Heim, E. Agasse-Lafont, and A. Feil, *ib.*, **173**. 270, 1923 ; A. Gautier, *ib.*, **152**. 1060, 1911 ; A. Livache, *ib.*, **132**. 1230, 1902 ; J. L. Breton, *ib.*, **136**. 1446, 1904 ; *Ann. Chim. Phys.*, (7), **30**. 554, 1904 ; A. S. Taylor, *On Poisons in Relation to Medical Jurisprudence and Medicine*, London, 1859 ; P. Carles and L. Barthe, *Bull. Soc. Chim.*, (4), **11**. 413, 1912 ; T. Bancks and R. L. Freer, *Lancet*, 478, 1849 ; *ib.*, **169**. 1033, 1905 ; F. Muttelet and F. Touplain, *Ann. Falsif.*, **5**. 9, 1912 ; F. Bordas, *ib.*, **6**. 566, 1913 ; H. Trillich, *Zeit. öffentl. Chem.*, **11**. 419, 1905 ; R. Krzizan, *ib.*, **17**. 31, 1911 ; *Oester. Chem. Ztg.*, **8**. 173, 1905 ; J. Grünwald, *ib.*, **12**. 146, 214, 1909 ; M. Ragg, *ib.*, **12**. 62, 212, 1909 ; A. Beythein, *Zeit. Unters. Nahr. Genuss.*, **3**. 221, 1900 ; T. Oliver, *Lead Poisoning*, London, 1891 ; *Diseases of Occupation*, London, 139, 1908 ; *Brit. Med. Journ.*, i, 1096, 1911 ; O. Mezger and W. Fuchs, *Zeit. angew. Chem.*, **21**. 1556, 1908 ; F. Koelsch, *ib.*, **33**. 2, 1920 ; *Chem. Ind.*, **43**. 200, 1920 ; L. Bronn, *ib.*, **29**. 105, 1906 ; P. Beck, *ib.*, **30**. 270, 305, 1907 ; P. Stegmüller, *Arb. Kaiser. Ges. Amt.*, **34**. 446, 1910 ; F. Auerbach and H. Pick, *ib.*, **45**. 191, 1913 ; H. Lührig, *Pharm. Centrb.*, **46**. 845, 1905 ; T. Canuet, *Essai sur la plomb*, Paris, 1825 ; M. Drouet, *Recherches expérimentales sur la rôle de l'absorption cutanée dans la paralyse saturnine*, Paris, 1875 ; F. Wiedemann, *Chem. Ztg.*, **27**. 299, 1903 ; A. Martin, *ib.*, **45**. 953, 1921 ; E. Brezina, *ib.*, **45**. 600, 1921 ; H. Pick, *ib.*, **45**. 865, 1921 ; Anon., *ib.*, **45**. 865, 1921 ; A. Maneuvrier, *Intoxication par absorption cutanée*, Paris, 1873 ; M. Habersang, *Berlin. Tierärztl. Wochschr.*, 383, 1918 ; E. O. Rasser, *Chem. Tech. Wochschr.*, **3**. 335, 1919 ; S. Miall, *Journ. Soc. Chem. Ind.*, **40**. 140, R, 1921 ; R. Meneguzzi, *Arch. Farmacol.*, **20**. 67, 1915 ; B. Rassow, *Zeit. angew Chem.*, **34**. 490, 1921 ; J. Schönfeld, *ib.*, **27**. 313, 1914 ; J. T. Cash, *Arch. Exp. Path.*, **93**, 1908 ; E. Erlenmeyer, *Zeit. Exp. Path.*, **14**. 310, 1913 ; J. Rambousek, *ib.*, **7**. 686, 1910 ; A. Chyzer, *Des intoxications par le plomb*, Budapest, 1908 ; D. J. Gilbert, *Le saturnisme expérimental*, Bruxelles, 1906 ; G. Quarghali and P. Albertoni, *Ann. Chimica*, **19**. 257, 1894 ; F. Zanardi, *Boll. Chim. Farm.*, **35**. 289, 1896 ; L. Santi, *ib.*, **43**. 748, 1904 ; O. Schumm, *Zeit. physiol. Chem.*, **119**. 139, 1922 ; A. Fedeli, *Arch. Farm. Sperim.*, **22**. 184, 1916 ; G. Marmisse, *Gaz. Hopit.*, 98, 1866 ; H. Rauch and V. Schilling, *Zeit. Ges. Exp. Med.*, **28**. 50, 1920 ; **30**. 446, 1922 ; C. Pedrazzini, *La chimie e la médicina moderna*, Milano, **1**. 5, 1921 ; V. Fici, *Folia Med.*, **6**. 587, 1920 ; **7**. 82, 1921 ; R. Kobert, *Lehrbuch der Intoxikation*, Stuttgart, **2**. 353, 1906 ; H. Eichhorst, *Virchow's Arch.*, **120**. 217, 1890 ; W. Rosenstein, *ib.*, **39**. 1, 174, 1897 ; *Arch. Path. Pharm.*, **40**. 363, 1898 ; H. Curschmann, *Therap. Monatsh.*, **34**. 108, 1920 ; P. J. Hanzlik, M. McIntyre, and E. Presho, *Proc. Soc. Exp. Biol. Med.*, **19**. 192, 1922 ; E. Harnack, *Deut. Med. Wochschr.*, **23**. 8, 1897 ; A. Schnitter, *ib.*, **45**. 711, 1919 ; N. Welwart, *ib.*, **45**. 939, 1919 ; C. Neuberg and W. Caspari, *ib.*, **38**. 375, 1912 ; L. Schwarz and H. Hefke, *ib.*, **49**. 212, 1923 ; L. Schwarz, *Med. Klinik*, **17**. 659, 1921 ; A. Gärtner, *Viertelj. Ger. Med.*, **40**. 105, 1910 ; F. Helwes, *ib.*, **31**. 408, 1906 ; L. Stieglitz, *Arch. Psychiat.*, **24**. 1, 1892 ; A. Westphal, *ib.*, **19**. 620, 1888 ; F. Quensel, *ib.*, **35**. 612, 1902 ; G. Diesselhorst, *Berlin. Klin. Wochschr.*, **45**. 1404, 1906 ; W. Erb, *ib.*, **21**. 110, 1884 ; O. Seifert, *ib.*, **21**. 555, 1884 ; W. Zinn, *ib.*, **36**. 1093, 1899 ; G. Diesselhorst, *ib.*, **45**. 1404, 1908 ; A. Glaser, *ib.*, **58**. 152, 1921 ; P. O. Süssmann, *München. Med. Wochschr.*, **65**. 1407, 1918 ; G. Seiffert, *ib.*, **68**. 1580, 1921 ; **69**. 1595, 1922 ; A. Kutschera, *Wien Klin. Wochschr.*, **29**. 135, 1916 ; F. Blum, *ib.*. **17**. 538, 1904 ; A. Schiff, *ib.*, **32**. 387, 1919 ; F. Nissl, *Allgem. Zeit. Psychiat.*, **45**. 675, 1892 ; **54**. 1, 1897 ; A. Niemann, *Arch. Hyg.*, **69**. 223, 1909 ; C. Vogt and J. L. Burckhardt, *ib.*, **85**. 323, 1916 ; P. Schmidt, *ib.*, **63**. 1, 1908 ; **80**. 62, 1913 ; **82**. 351, 1914 ; *Sprech.*, **47**. 57, 1914 ; F. W. Mott, *Arch. Neurol. Psychiat.*, **4**. 117, 1909 ; W. Pritzkoff, *Zeit. Hyg.*, **17**. 164, 1894 ; L. Lewin, *Apoth. Ztg.*. **31**. 19, 1916 ; *Journ. Hyg.*, **73**. 161, 1913 ; H. W. Armit, *ib.*, **8**. 565, 1908 ; H. Hüttmann, *Deut. Tierärztl. Wochschr.*, **30**. 313, 1922 ; H. Baum and R. Seeliger, *Arch. Tierheilk.*, **21**. 297, 1895 ; *Milch. Ztg.*, **25**. 87, 1897 ; G. A. E. Roberts, *Brit. Med. Journ.*, ii, 1291, 1893 ; E. V. Raumer and E. Spaeth, *Zeit. Nahr. Genuss.*, **5**. 414, 1902 ; H. Masters, *Analyst*, 44, 164, 1919 ; *Lancet*, i, 1394, 1920 ; G. H. Allden, *ib.*, i, 728, 1889 : H. Pillaud, *Quelques considerations sur differents cas d'intoxication saturnine causes par le vernis des potières communes*, Paris, 1893 ; G. W. Monier-Williams, *The Solubility of Glazes and Enamels used in Cooking Utensils*, London, 1925 ; T. Midgley, *Journ. Ind. Eng. Chem.*, **17**. 827, 1925 ; A. W. Annert, *U.S. Pat. No* 1439596, 1922 ; L. Baillard, *French. Pat. No* 523050, 1920 ; H. Klut, *Journ. Gasbeleucht.*, **54**. 409, 1911 ; R. Jones, *Brit. Med. Journ.*, ii, 794, 1900 ; M. Mackenzie, *ib.*, ii, 1202, 1893 ; L. Gibson, *ib.*, ii. 1488, 1908 ; F. C. Eve, *ib.*, i, 103, 170, 1923 ; W. Thomason, *Trans. Cer. Soc.*, **9**. 198, 1910 ; *Journ. Soc. Chem. Ind.*, **23**. 470, 1904 ; L. Preti, *Biochem. Zeit.*, **21**. 551, 1909 ; E. L. Collis, *Special Report on Dangerous or Injurious Processes in the Smelting of Materials containing Lead, and in the Manufacture of Red and Orange Litharge and Flaked Litharge*, London, 1910 ; C. Jones, *Report on the Draft Regulations for File Cutting by Hand*, London, 1903 ; C. Oppenheimer, *Zur Kenntniss der experimentellen Bleivergiftung Harnsäureausscheidung*, Berlin, 1898 ; *Zeit. Klin. Med.*, **29**. 266, 1896 ; H. Lüthje, *Ueber Bleigicht und den Einfluss der Bleiintoxication auf die Harnsaureausscheidung*, Berlin, 1896 ; L. Teleky, H. Gerbis, and P. Schmidt, *Die Frühdiagnose der Bleivergiftung*, Berlin, 1919 ; G. Nistico, *Il Lavoro*, **5**. 234, 1912 ; A. Tedeschi, *ib.*, **5**. 217, 1912 ; L. Preti, *ib.*, **5**. 307, 1912 ; *Biochem. Zeit.*, **45**. 488, 1912 ; *Zeit. physiol. Chem.*, **58**. 539, 1909 ; F. Pancier, *Bull. Science. Pharmacol.*, **20**. 261, 1913 ; G. Stiefler, *Zeit. Neurol. Psych.*, **77**. 25, 1922 ; R. Apt, *Sozial Techn.*, **11**. 446, 1912 ; A. M. Anderson, *Special Report on Dangerous or Injurious Processes in the Coating of Metal with Lead or a Mixture of Lead and Tin*, London, 1907 ; T. M. Legge and

A. M. Anderson, *Special Report on Dangerous and Injurious Processes in the Enamelling and Tinning of Metals*, London, 1902 ; G. van Eijk, *Chem. Weekbl.*, **2**. 541, 1905 ; T. E. Thorpe and T. Oliver, *Lead Compounds in Pottery*, London, 1899 ; T. E. Thorpe, *Report of the Government Laboratory on the Question of the Employment of Lead Compounds in Pottery*, London, 1901 ; L. Spiegel, *Naturwiss.*, **1**. 374, 1913 ; E. Wutzdorff, *Die in elektrischen Akkumulatoren Fabriken beobachteten Gesundheits schädigunge und die zur Verhüting derselben erforderlichen Massnahmen*, Berlin, 1898 ; *Arb. Kaiser. Gesundheitsamte*, **15**. 154, 1898 ; L. Petrik, *Sprech.*, **47**. 1, 1914 ; **53**. 405, 1920 ; R. Berge, *ib.*, **47**. 99, 113, 1914 ; J. Dorfner, *ib.*, **47**. 390, 1914 ; L. J. Boyd, *Journ. Amer. Inst. Homeopathy*, **14**. 1001, 1922 ; M. Willenz, *Bull. Assoc. Belg.*, **15**. 230, 1901 ; G. E. Duckering, *The Cause of Lead Poisoning in the Tinning of Metals*, London, 1908 ; A. Sellers, *Journ. Ind. Hyg.*, **2**. 361, 1921 ; J. Grönberg, *Finsk. Läkaresällskapets Handl.*, **63**. 429, 1922 ; R. Franz, *Ker. Rund.*, **31**. 219, 1923 ; L. Petri, *Biochem. Zeit.*, **21**. 551, 1909 ; S. J. Knott, *Chem. News*, **34**. 196, 1876 ; *Lancet*, ii, 531, 1876 ; G. Johnson, *Pharm. Journ.*, (3), **1**. 426, 1870 ; *Brit. Med. Journ.*, ii, 325, 1870 ; E. Behrle, *Zeit. angew. Chem.*, **37**. 1023, 1924 ; F. H. de Balsac, A. Lafont, and A. Feil, *Bull. Méd.*, **3**, 1925 ; *Chim. Ind.*, **15**. 225, 1926 ; J. C. Aub, *Lead Poisoning*, Baltimore, 1926 ; Anon., *Bleivergiftungen in hüttenmännischen und gewerblichen Betrieben Ursachen und Bekämpfung*, Wien, 1905; R. Fischer, *Mitt. Inst. Gew. Hyg.*, 169, 1912 ; P. Schmidt, *Bleivergiftungen und ihre Erkennung*, Berlin, 1907 ; J. F. Sacher, *Der Völkerbund gegen die Bleiindustrie*, Dusseldorf, 1921 ; J. Rambousek, *Chem. Ztg.*, **37**. 181, 1913 ; *Zentr. Gew. Hyg.*, **2**. 87, 121, 233, 1914 ; L. Teleky, *ib.*, **2**. 161, 193, 1913 ; 225, 1914 ; S. Böttrich. *ib.*, **1**. 158, 1913 ; **4**. 58, 1916 ; J. Schönfeld, *ib.*, **9**. 3, 256, 1921 ; *Farbe Lack*, 297, 1925 ; A. Müller, *Zentr. Gew. Hyg.*, **1**. 529, 1913 ; **2**. 223, 1914 ; L. Grobe, *ib.*, **9**. 52, 1921 ; F. Koelsch, *ib.*, **1**. 156, 1913 ; K. B. Lehmann, *ib.*, **10**. 46, 1922 ; *Die deutsche Bleifarbenindustrie vom Standpunkte der Hygiene*, Berlin, 1925 ; K. Hamel, *Deut. Arch. Klin. Med.*, **67**. 357, 1900 ; A. Trautmann, *Münch. Med. Wochschr.*, 1371, 1909.

²¹ P. Orfila, *Heller's Arch.*, 376, 1847 ; R. V. Tuson, *Veterinarian*, **38**. 6, 217, 220, 421, 1865 ; E. Harnack, *Deut. Med. Wochschr.*, **23**. 8–10, 1897 ; A. Gusserow, *Virchow's Arch.*, **21**. 443, 1861 ; W. Rosenstein, *ib.*, **39**. 1, 174, 1867 ; *Arch. Path. Pharm.*, **40**. 363, 1898 ; E. Heubel, *Pathogenese und Symptome der chronischen Bleivergiftung*, Berlin, 1871 ; R. Stockman and F. J. Charteris, *Journ. Path. Bact.*, **9**. 202, 1903 ; R. T. H. Laennec, *Traité de l'auscultation médiate*, Paris, 1831 ; G. Andral and J. Gavarret, *Ann. Chim. Phys.*, (2), **75**. 309, 1840 ; J. C. Aub, P. Reznikoff, and D. E. Smith, *Journ. Exp. Med.*, **40**. 151, 173, 1924 ; J. C. Aub and P. Reznikoff, *ib.*, **40**. 189, 1924 ; J. C. Aub, A. S. Minot, L. T. Fairhall, and P. Reznikoff, *Journ. Amer. Med. Assoc.*, **83**. 588, 1924 ; H. Burton, *Gaz. Méd. Paris*, (2), **8**. 470, 1840.

²² H. Devaux, *Compt. Rend.*, **133**. 58, 1901 ; J. Stoklasa, *ib.*, **156**. 153, 1913 ; A. Lumière and J. Chevrotin, *Bull. Gén. Thérap.*, **165**. 959, 1913 ; T. Messerschnidt, *Zeit. Hyg.*, **82**. 289, 1916 ; L. Bitter, *ib.*, **69**. 483, 1912 ; G. Sonntag, *Arb. Kaiser. Ges. Amt.*, **49**. 502, 1914 ; R. Klein, *Dingler's Journ.*, **221**. 287, 1876 ; *Chem. Ackersmann*, **21**. 248, 1875 ; U. Varvaro. *Staz. Sperim. Agrar. Ital.*, **45**. 917, 1912 ; A. Stutzer, *Journ. Landw.*, **64**. 1, 1916 ; R. Stockmann and F. J. Charteris, *Journ. Rath. Bact.*, **9**. 202, 1903 ; A. Stockhardt, *Arch. Pharm.*, **200**. 170, 1872 ; A. Schmidt, *Centrb. Bakteriol.*, **12**. 93, 1904 ; **14**. 289, 1905 ; **15**. 349, 1906 ; T. Bokorny, *ib.*, **35**. 118, 1912 ; P. Eisenberg, *ib.*, **82**. 69, 1918.

²³ G. O Hiers, *Journ. Ind. Eng. Chem.*, **15**. 467, 1923.

²⁴ S. Cowper-Coles, *Metal Ind.*, **4**. 308, 1912 ; M. A. Schoop, *Met. Chem. Engy.*, **11**. 89, 1913.

²⁵ J. H. Frydlender, *Rev. Prod. Chim.*, **23**. 685, 1925 ; G. L. Clark and W. C. Thee, *Journ. Ind. Eng. Chem.*, **17**. 1219, 1915 ; G. L. Clark, E. W. Brugmann, and W. C. Thee, *ib.*, **17**. 1226, 1925 ; G. L. Wendt and F. V. Grimm, *ib.*, **16**. 890, 1924 ; Anon., *ib.*, **18**. 432, 1926 ; T. Midgley, *ib.*, **17**. 752, 1925.

²⁶ A. Kinsel, *Chem. Met. Engg.*, **32**. 873, 1925.

§ 6. The Valency and Atomic Weight of Lead

According to H. E. Roscoe and A. Harden,[1] in a note-book dated March, 1804, J. Dalton wrote 105 for the at. wt. of lead when that of oxygen is 5·5 ; and this number becomes 305 when the at. wt. of oxygen is 16. In his later work, J. Dalton adopted 90 for the at. wt. of lead when that of oxygen is 7, or 206 if oxygen is 16. In 1811, J. J. Berzelius calculated from the ratio Pb : PbO, the at. wt. 206·5 when the at. wt. of oxygen is 16 ; from the ratio PbS : PbSO₄, 209·9 ; from the ratio Pb : PbSO₄, 207·6 ; and from the ratio PbO : PbSO₄, 207·98. At first he was not very clear whether to represent what is now called lead monoxide, PbO, by the formula PbO, Pb₂O₃, PbO₂, PbO₃, or PbO₄. After the sp. ht. rule, and the isomorphism rule had been developed, he adopted the now accepted formula PbO. This made the at. wt. of lead approximate 207. Lead ordinarily behaves as a *bivalent element* giving salts isomorphous with those of the bivalent alkaline earth metals. So much do the normal lead salts resemble those of the alkaline earths that A. Baudrimont suggested that lead should be included in that family. For the genetic connection of lead with radium which in turn belongs to the alkaline earth family of metals, *vide infra*. Lead can also behave as a *quadrivalent element* as is evidenced by the higher oxide, PbO_2 ; *lead tetramethide*, $Pb(CH_3)_4$, which has a vap. density of 9·52 (air unity) in agreement with the calculated value 9·25 ; and the isomorphism of the complex fluorides and chlorides—$3KF.HF.PbF_4$ and $3KF.HF.SnF_4$; and R_2PbCl_6 and R_2SnCl_6, where R represents NH_4 or Cs. These observations agree with the position of lead in the tin family in the periodic table. G. Oddo also emphasized the family relations of lead, tin, and germanium. E. W. Wetherell discussed the position of lead in the periodic table.

There is some evidence of *univalent lead*—*vide* lead suboxide and the subsalts of lead. According to H. G. Denham and A. J. Allmand, in attempting to measure the hydrolysis of lead salts by the hydrogen electrode, abnormally high values are obtained. This is not due to the separation from the soln. of a metal, say silver, more noble than hydrogen ; nor to the deposition of lead on the electrode in such a way that the hydrogen electrode acted as a cathode, nor to the formation of a lead-platinum alloy. The potential depended on the rate at which hydrogen was bubbled through the soln. and it was assumed that the action on the surface film involves a reduction of bivalent lead : $PbCl_2+H \rightleftharpoons PbCl+HCl$; the faster the stream of hydrogen, the more quickly was the free acid so produced carried into the main bulk of the liquid, and the lower the potential. E. Bose attributed a discrepancy in the silver voltameter to the formation of subvalent ions ; and T. W. Richards and co-workers, in the copper voltameter, to the formation of cuprous salts in soln. A hot soln. of a lead salt can dissolve the metal, and give it up again on cooling. A piece of lead in a soln. of lead acetate, maintained at two different temp., forms a thermo-cell ; the current flows from the hot soln. to the cold one, and causes a deposition of spongy lead at the cold end of the piece of lead. There is also a series of compounds in which lead appears to act as a *tervalent element*, judging by the analogy of the products prepared by E. Krause, with triphenylmethyl—*vide* valency of carbon. Thus, E. Krause made *lead tricyclohexyl*, $Pb(C_6H_{11})'_3$, by the action of lead chloride on a soln. of magnesium cyclohexyl bromide in dry ether. The corresponding *lead triphenyl*, $Pb(C_6H_5)_3$; *lead tri-o-tolyl*, $Pb(C_7H_7)_3$; *lead tri-p-tolyl*, $Pb(C_7H_7)_3$; and *lead tri-p-xylyl*, $Pb(C_8H_9)_3$, have been examined by E. Krause and G. G. Reissaus. According to W. Esch, lead exhibits a still higher valency in the acid sulphate, $H_2Pb(SO_4)_3$, which may be regarded as *hydrotrisulphatometaplumbic acid*.

The at. wt. of lead calculated from J. J. Berzelius' values for the ratio Pb : PbO, obtained by converting the metal to the nitrate, and calcining the product for the oxide, is 206·5 ; from the ratio PbO : Pb obtained by reducing the heated oxide in hydrogen, 207·06–207·14 ; and from the ratio PbS : $PbSO_4$, obtained by treating the sulphide with aqua regia, he obtained 209·9. T. Anderson's values for $Pb(NO_3)_2$: PbO give 207·360. J. J. Berzelius converted the metal into sulphate, and his values for the ratio Pb : $PbSO_4$, furnish the at. wts. 206·97 and 207·6 ; T. Turner's values, 207·05 ; and J. S. Stas, 206·93. J. J. Berzelius also converted the oxide into sulphate and from the ratio PbO : $PbSO_4$, it follows that the at. wt. is 207·5–207·98 ; and T. Turner's values gave 207·64. The values of the last-named for the ratio $Pb(NO_3)_2$: $PbSO_4$ gave 204·2, and J. S. Stas', 206·46. From J. S. Stas' value for the ratio Pb : $Pb(NO_3)_2$, the at. wt. is 206·80–206·82. J. J. Berzelius measured the ratio PbO : CO_2, and the results correspond with the at. wt. 206·98. T. Thomson made some observations on the at. wt. of lead. J. C. G. de Marignac converted lead into the chloride, and obtained the ratio Pb : $PbCl_2$, from which the at. wt. is 206·87 ; he also analyzed the chloride for the ratio $PbCl_2$: 2AgCl, and the results give 206·85, while G. P. Baxter and J. H. Wilson's results give 207·103 ; and G. P. Baxter and F. L. Grover's gave 207·23. From the ratio

$PbBr_2 : 2AgBr$, G. P. Baxter and T. Thorvaldson obtained 207·19. J. C. G. de Marignac's value for the ratio $PbCl_2 : 2Ag$ furnishes the at. wt. 206·80 ; J. B. A. Dumas' value, 206·88 ; G. P. Baxter and J. H. Wilson's value, 207·103 ; and O. Hönigschmid and M. Steinheil, 207·23. From the ratio 2Ag : Pb, obtained by the electrolysis of a soln. of a lead fluosilicate in hydrofluosilicic acid, while a silver voltameter was in circuit, A. G. Betts and E. F. Kern's data gave 206·73. G. van Dyk obtained 0·0111823 for the electrochemical equivalent of lead ; H. Pécheux obtained 206·86–207·09 for the at. wt. by electrolysis. From the ratio 2Ag : Pb, which L. Meaglia obtained by precipitating silver from a soln. of silver nitrate by lead, 206·866–206·935. J. Thomsen calculated 206·904 for the best representative value of the at. wt. of lead ; W. A. Noyes, and J. D. van der Plaats, 206·91 ; L. Dubreuil, 206·919 ; F. W. Clarke, 206·970 ±0·0017 ; T. W. Richards and co-workers, 207·217 ; and B. Brauner, 207·10. The International Table for 1924 gives 207·20. The **atomic number** is 82. The **electronic structure** on N. Bohr's[2] scheme is (2) (4,4) (6,6,6) (8,8,8,8) (6,6,6) (2,2). J. Beckenkamp, and H. Collins made some speculations on this subject.

The at. wt. problem has assumed another aspect since the study of the end-products of the radioactive degradation of uranium and radium led F. Soddy[3] to question as to whether the lead found in association with uranium is the same as that of ordinary lead.

W. F. Hillebrand noticed the association of lead with uranium in some minerals, and numerous observations have since been made on this subject and on the induced radioactivity of lead. The metal itself is not primarily radioactive. B. B. Boltwood found the ratio of uranium to lead in primary minerals from the same locality to be so nearly constant as to suggest that lead may be the end-product of the degradation of uranium. The rate of radioactive change is so slow that a direct proof of the degradation of uranium to lead cannot be expected. It has been calculated that a gram of uranium yields $1·25 \times 10^{-10}$ grm. of radium-G per annum ; and if the gram of uranium be constantly replenished to make up the loss, a gram eq. of radium-G would require 8000 million years for its formation. A. Holmes has shown that with stable minerals of primary origin, where there is no geological or petrological evidence of the presence of lead as a primary product, and no evidence of the loss of any of the constituents by weathering, the age of the mineral can be estimated from the ratio Pb : U. The result shows that the age of some precambrian Norwegian minerals, in which this ratio is 0·013, approximates 1000 million years. The trustworthiness of the evidence was discussed by G. Kirsch.

The so-called displacement rule—4. 26, 11—enabled F. Soddy, and K. Fajans to calculate the at. wt. of radium-G from that of uranium (238·2) or of radium (226). The result shows that the at. wt. of radium-G is 206·2 or 206·0, while that of ordinary lead approximates 207. R. de M. de Ballore proposed 206·5 for the best representative value of the at. wt. of lead derived from the radioactive uranium minerals. The at. wt. of lead in 24 of the determinations indicated above varies from 206·8 to 207·6. The results of various determinations[4] of the at. wt. of the lead in radioactive minerals, recorded in Table VII, show that the at. wt. of the lead from various uranium minerals approximates 206, and it resembles ordinary lead in all its known chemical reactions. The evidence that lead is accumulating in minerals at the expense of the uranium is purely circumstantial and is as follows : (i) The constancy of the ratio Pb : U in minerals of the same geological age, and its variation in those of different geological age ; and (ii) the close approximation of the calculated to the observed values for the at. wt. of lead derived from uranium minerals. R. de Montessus de Ballore proposed 206·5 ±0·05 for the at. wt. of radio-lead.

The genetic connection between thorium and lead is founded on more slender evidence ; both B. B. Boltwood,[5] and A. Holmes did not consider it probable that thorium should give lead. The displacement rule gives 208·4 for the at. wt. of thorium-D assumed to be lead produced by the radioactive degradation of uranium ;

TABLE VII.—ATOMIC WEIGHT OF LEAD FROM DIFFERENT SOURCES.

Sources of lead.	At. wt.	Observers.
Radioactive mineral of Ceylon . .	208·40	F. Soddy and H. Hyman
Radioactive mineral of Colorado .	207·00	T. W. Richards and C. Wadsworth
Radioactive minerals of Australia .	206·34	,, ,,
Bröggerite	206·12	,, ,,
Cleveite of Langesund . . .	206·08	,, ,,
Uraninite, North Carolina . .	206·46	T. W. Richards and M. E. Lambert
Pitchblende, Joachimstahl . .	206·57	,, ,,
Carnotite, Colorado . . .	206·59	,, ,,
Thorianite, Ceylon . . .	206·82	,, ,,
Pitchblende, England . . .	206·86	,, ,,
Ordinary lead as control . . .	(207·15)	
Spring water of Japan . . .	207·13	T. W. Richards and J. Sameshima
Mixed mineral, Belgian Congo .	206·20	T. W. Richards and P. Putzevs
Uraninite, South Dakota . . .	203·07	T. W. Richards and L. P. Hall
Uranium mineral	206·98	F. W. O. de Coninck and P. Gérard
Ordinary lead as control . . .	(206·71)	,, ,,
Uranium mineral	206·36	M. Curie
Monazite	207·08	,,
Ordinary lead as control . . .	(207·01)	,,
Thorianite, Ceylon	206·88	O. Hönigschmid
Thorite, Norway	207·92	,,
Pitchblende	206·736	O. Hönigschmid and S. Horovitz
Pitchblende, Joachimstahl . .	206·405	,, ,,
Uranium mineral, East Africa . .	206·046	,, ,,
Bröggerite, Norway . . .	206·063	,, ,,
Ordinary lead as control . . .	(207·180)	,, ,,
Uranium ore, Katanga, Congo . .	206·048	O. Hönigschmid and L. Birchenbach
Tamarskite	206·300	A. L. Davis
Cotunnite, Vesuvius . . .	206·14	B. Perrette
Norwegian clevite	207·050	A. Piutti and D. Migliacci
Uranium lead	206·17	E. Gleditsch, M. Dorenfeldt, and O. W. Berg

at. wt. 232·4 ; and H. N. McCoy's estimate of the ratio of the rates of change makes the production of lead by uranium about three times as fast as would be the case if it were produced by thorium. The observations in Table VII show that the lead derived from thorium minerals has the necessary high at. wt. According to F. W. Clarke, the variations in the at. wt. of different varieties of lead derived from radioactive minerals may be due to the admixture of ordinary lead and an isotopic form of lead, or ordinary lead may be a distinct variety, or a balanced mixture of isotopes derived from uranium and thorium, or an unknown degradation from some lighter parent element. A. Bull ascribed the difference in the at. wts. of different forms of lead to the gravitational attraction being dependent on the electrons which are strained in the radioactive atoms, and the strain becomes less and less as the end-product is approached.

A. S. Russell's analysis of the complexity of the elements gives him the hypothetical conclusion that lead consists of isotopes of at. mass 204, 205, 206, 207, 208, and 210, but F. W. Aston failed to get isotopes by using lead ethide, etc. The attempt by J. Joly and J. H. J. Poole to separate lead isotopes by centrifuging the molten metal was nugatory. T. Dillon and co-workers attempted to separate the isotopes of lead by treating the chlorides with magnesium ethyl halide : $2PbCl_2 + 4MgRX = PbR_4 + 2MgCl_2 + 2MgX_2 + Pb$. The lead and lead ethide so obtained were regarded as two fractions and the whole repeated a number of times on each of the two products separately. The relative values for the at. wts. were 207·1 and 207·4, which shows that there may be here a partial separation of isotopic forms. R. F. Atkinson reported that by melting and cooling about 300 grms. of lead assay foil, fractional crystallization furnished two end-fractions each weighing about 60 grms. after the purification of each by J. S. Stas' process; the sp. gr. of the fraction at the crystals end was $11\cdot345 \pm 0\cdot005$, and at the mother-liquid end, $11\cdot313 \pm 0\cdot005$. Another sample of lead not fractioned, gave, after purification, an intermediate sp. gr. This may have no reference to the isotopes of lead, but may be an effect of purification *per se.* According to T. W. Richards and co-workers, the m.p. of two varieties of lead differing 0·8 in their at. wt. agreed within 0·05°, and the thermoelectric force in the Seebeck effect was zero ; the index of refraction, and the solubility of the nitrates of ordinary lead and of lead of at. wt. 206·42 were virtually the same. The sp. gr. of ordinary lead at 20° was 11·377, which is higher than 11·288, that of the lead extracted from Australian radioactive minerals —Table VII. Since at. wts. vary proportionally with densities, the at. vols. of the two forms of lead were the same. M. E. Lembert observed no difference in the m.p. of the chlorides. C. D. and D. Cooksey compared the spectra of lead isotopes. The electrical resistance and the temp. and press. coeff. of the resistance of ordinary and radioactive lead were found by P. W. Bridgman to be the same. The superconductivity of both varieties of lead was found by W. Tuyn and H. K. Onnes to begin at $-265\cdot8°$, and to be the same down to $-258\cdot8°$. As indicated (**4.** 26, 11), the spectra of the different varieties of lead were shown by F. Soddy and H. Hyman, O. Hönigschmid and S. Horovitz, B. Perrette, W. D. Harkins and L. Aronberg, and T. R. Merton, to be the same. E. S. Bieler observed a shift of the 4270 band towards the violet in passing from ordinary lead to uranium-lead. O. Hönigschmid and M. Steinheil failed to obtain a separation by fractional distillation; and H. Brennen, by Grignard's reaction : $4(C_2H_5)MgI + 2PbCl_2 = Pb + 4MgICl + Pb(C_2H_5)_4$. T. W. Richards and co-workers observed that no separation of the isotopes could be made with Grignard's reaction or by irreversible volatilization. H. Pettersson and G. Kirsch [6] discussed the **atomic disintegration** of lead atoms when bombarded by α-rays.

L. Naudin [7] reported experiments by P. Schützenberger on the conversion of lead into silver, but there is no confirmation of this statement. W. Ramsay and F. L. Usher's conversion of lead chlorate into carbon monoxide and dioxide by exposing a soln. of that salt to radium emanation has not been confirmed. A. Smits discussed the possibility of transmuting lead into some other metal—mercury and thallium—when used as electrode in a quartz vacuum tube on 30–35 amps. and 80 volts.

REFERENCES.

[1] H. E. Roscoe and A. Harden, *A New View of the Origin of Dalton's Atomic Theory*, London, 1896 ; J. Dalton, *A New System of Chemical Philosophy*, Manchester, 2. 352, 1810 ; J. J. Berzelius, *Gilbert's Ann.*, **37**. 252, 1811 ; *Pogg. Ann.*, **19**. 314, 1830 ; *Lehrbuch der Chemie*, Leipzig, **3**. 1187, 1218, 1842 ; J. W. Döbereiner, *Schweigger's Journ.*, **17**. 241, 1816 ; T. Thomson, *Ann. Phil.*, (1), **16**. 327, 1820 ; T. Turner, *Phil. Trans.*, **123**. 527, 1833 ; J. B. A. Dumas, *Ann. Chim. Phys.*, (3), **55**. 129, 1859 ; G. Longchamp, *ib.*, (2), **34**. 105, 1827 ; J. D. van der Plaats, *ib.*, (6), **7**. 499, 1886 ; *Chem. News*, **54**. 52, 1886 ; T. Anderson, *ib.*, (3), **9**. 254, 1843 ; *Journ. prakt. Chem.*, (1), **27**. 381, 1843 ; O. Hönigschmid and M. Steinheil, *Ber.*, **56**. B, 1831, 1923 ; H. Pécheux, *Compt. Rend.*, **154**. 1419, 1912 ; G. P. Baxter and J. H. Wilson, *Proc. Amer. Acad.*, **43**. 365, 1907 ; *Zeit. anorg. Chem.*, **57**. 174, 1908 ; *Journ. Amer. Chem. Soc.*, **30**. 187, 1908 ; G. P. Baxter and F. L. Grover, *ib.*, **37**. 1027, 1915 ; G. P. Baxter and T. Thorvaldson, *ib.*, **37**. 1020, 1915 ; J. C. G. de Marignac, *Liebig's Ann.*, **59**. 284, 1846 ; *Arch. Sciences Genève*, (1), **1**. 53, 1846 ; (2), **1**. 209, 1858 ; *Journ. prakt. Chem.*, (1), **74**. 218, 1858 ; G. Oddo, *Gazz. Chim. Ital.*, **50**. ii, 213, 1920 ; J. Thomsen, *Danske Vid. Selsk. Forh.*, 328, 1894 ; W. A. Noyes, *Journ. Anal. App. Chem.*, **5**. 36, 1891 ; L. Dubreuil, *Bull. Soc. Chim.*, (4), **5**. 341, 1909 ; F. W. Clark, *Chem. News*, **63**. 76, 1891 ; *A Recalculation of the Atomic Weights*, Washington, 199, 1910 ; B. Brauner and R. Abegg, *Handbuch der anorganischen Chemie*, Leipzig, **3**. ii, 613, 1909 ; J. S. Stas, *Bull. Acad. Belg.*, (2), **10**. 208, 1860 ; *Chem. News*, **4**. 181, 206, 215, 228, 243, 257, 270, 282, 294, 307, 324, 335, 1861 ; **5**. 1, 15, 29, 1862 ; J. Beckenkamp, *Verh. Würzberg*, (2), **45**. 135, 1918 ; P. Walden, *Zeit. Elektrochem.*, **14**. 720, 1908 ; H. Siedentopf, *Wied. Ann.*, **61**. 265, 1897 ; L. Meaglia, *Sur quelques essais de determination des poids atomiques de plomb, de cadmium et de zinc*, Grenoble, 1907 ; A. G. Betts and E. F. Kern, *Trans. Amer. Electrochem. Soc.*, **6**. 67, 1904 ; A. Baudrimont, *Compt. Rend.*, **48**. 594, 1859 ; E. W. Wetherell, *Chem. News*, **90**. 271, 1904 ; E. Krause, *Ber.*, **54**. B, 2060, 1921 ; E. Krause and G. G. Reissaus, *ib.*, **55**. B, 888, 1922 ; G. van Dyk, *Ann. Physik*, (4), **14**. 569, 1904 ; E. Bose, *Zeit. Elektrochem.*, **13**. 477, 1907 ; T. W. Richards, E. Collins,

and G. W. Heimrod, *Zeit. phys. Chem.*, **32**. 321, 1900 ; **T. W. Richards, H. S. King, and L. P. Hall,** *Journ. Amer. Chem. Soc.*, **48**. 1530, 1926 ; H. G. Denham and A. J. Allmand, *Journ. Chem. Soc.*, **93**. 424, 1908 ; W. Esch, *Chem. Ztg.*, **27**. 297, 1903.

² N. Bohr, *Nature*, **112**. Suppl., 1923 ; W. Pauli, *Zeit. Physik*, **31**. 765, 1925; **H. Collins,** *Chem. News*, **132**. 85, 1926; J. Beckenkamp, *Zeit. anorg. Chem.*, **143**. 394, 1923.

³ F. Soddy, *Chem. News*, **107**. 97, 1913 ; *Nature*, **99**. 244, 1917 ; *Journ. Chem. Soc.*, **99**. 72, 1914 ; F. Soddy and H. Hyman, *ib.*, **105**. 1402, 1914 ; B. B. Boltwood, *Amer. Journ. Science*, **(4), 23**. 77, 1907 ; *Phil. Mag.*, (6), **9**. 599, 1905 ; E. Rutherford, *ib.*, (6), **8**. 636, 1904 ; C. S. Wright, *ib.*, (6), **17**. 295, 1909 ; J. Elster and H. Geitel, *Phys. Zeit.*, **9**. 273, 289, 1908 ; H. Geitel, *ib.*, **8**. 776, 1907 ; M. Levin and R. Ruer, *ib.*, **10**. 576, 1910 ; J. C. M⁽Lennan, *ib.*, **8**. 556, 1907 ; **9**. 440, 1908 ; K. A. Hofmann, K. L. Gonder, and V. Wölfl, *Ann. Physik*, (4), **15**. 615, 1904 ; K. A. Hofmann and V. Wölfl, *Ber.*, **35**. 692, 1902 ; **36**. 1040, 1903 ; K. A. Hofmann and E. Strauss, *ib.*, **33**. 3126, 1900 ; **34**. 8, 903, 3033, 1901 ; K. A. Hofmann, *ib.*, **35**. 1453, 1902 ; **37**. 2193, 1904 ; K. A. Hofmann, V. Wölfl, and G. Ebert, *ib.*, **40**. 2425, 1907 ; C. Winkler, *ib.*, **37**. 1657, 1904 ; F. Giesel, *ib.*, **33**. 3569, 1900 ; **35**. 105, 1902 ; A. Korn and E. Strauss, *Compt. Rend.*, **136**. 1312, 1913 ; A. Debierne, *ib.*, **139**. 281, 1904 ; A. Muguet, *ib.*, **174**. 172, 1922 ; J. Danysz, *ib.*, **143**. 232, 1906 ; H. Herchfinkel, *Le Radium*, **7**. 198, 1910 ; A. Holmes, *Proc. Roy. Soc.*, **85**. A, 248, 1914 ; *Proc. Geol. Assoc.*, **26**. 289, 1915 ; *The Age of the Earth*, London, 1913 ; *Phil. Mag.*, (7), **1**. 1055, 1926 ; *Nature*, **117**. 482, 1926 ; R. W. Lawson, *Nature*, **93**. 479, 1914 ; A. Holmes, *ib.*, **99**. 245, 1917 ; K. Fajans, *Phys. Zeit.*, **14**. 140, 1913 ; R. de M. de Ballore, *Rev. Gén. Science Pure App.*, **30**. 673, 1919 ; W. F. Hillebrand, *Amer. Journ. Science*, (3), **42**. 390, 1892 ; W. E. Hidden and J. B. Mackintosh, *ib.*, (3), **38**. 474, 1890 ; G. Kirsch, *Tschermak's Mitt.*, (2), **36**. 147, 1924.

⁴ F. Soddy, *Nature*, **107**. 41, 1921 ; *Journ. Chem. Soc.*, **99**. 72, 1914 ; F. Soddy and H. Hyman, *ib.*, **105**. 1402, 1914 ; O. Hönigschmid and S. Horovitz, *Compt. Rend.*, **158**. 1796, 1914 ; *Monatsh.*, **36**. 355, 1915 ; O. Hönigschmid and L. Birckenbach, *Ber.*, **56**. B, 1837, 1923 ; O. Hönigschmid, *Zeit. Elektrochem.*, **23**. 161, 1917 ; **25**. 91, 1919 ; T. W. Richards, *Ann. Rep. Smithsonian Inst.*, 205, 1920 ; T. W. Richards and C. Wadsworth, *Journ. Amer. Chem. Soc.*, **38**. 221, 1658, 2613, 1916 ; T. W. Richards and W. C. Schumb, *ib.*, **40**. 1403, 1918 ; T. W. Richards and L. P. Hall, *ib.*, **48**. 704, 1926 ; **T. W. Richards, H. S. King, and L. P. Hall,** *ib.*, **48**. 1530, 1926 ; T. W. Richards and M. E. Lambert, *ib.*, **36**. 1329, 1914 ; *Compt. Rend.*, **159**. 248, 1914 ; M. E. Lambert, *Ueber die Verschiedenen Atomgewichte des gewöhnlichen und des radioaktiventstandenen Bleies*, Karlsruhe, 1915; R. de Montessus de Ballore, *Rev. Gén. Science Pure Appl.*, **30**. 673, 1919 ; E. Gleditsch, M. Dorenfeldt and O. W. Berg, *Journ. Chim. Phys.*, **22**. 253, 1925 ; T. W. Richards and J. Sameshima, *Journ. Amer. Chem. Soc.*, **42**. 928, 1920 ; T. W. Richards and P. Putzeys, *ib.*, **45**. 2954, 1923 ; A. L. Davis, *Journ. Phys. Chem.*, **22**. 631, 1918 ; F. W. O. de Coninck and P. Gérard, *Compt. Rend.*, **163**. 514, 1916 ; M. Curie, *ib.*, **158**. 1676, 1914 ; *Rev. Gén. Sciences Pure App.*, **34**. 576, 1923 ; A. Piutti and D. Migliacci, *Atti Accad. Lincei*, (5), **32**. ii, 468, 1923 ; B. Perrette, *Compt. Rend.*, **180**. 1589, 1925 ; **A. Holmes,** *Nature*, **117**. 482, 1926.

⁵ B. B. Boltwood, *Amer. Journ. Science*, (4), **23**. 77, 1907 ; A. Holmes, *Proc. Roy. Soc.*, **85**. A, 248, 1911 ; A. Holmes and R. W. Lawson, *Phil. Mag.*, (6), **29**. 679, 1915 ; F. Soddy, *Chem. News*, **107**. 97, 1913 ; F. Soddy and H. Hyman, *Journ. Chem. Soc.*, **105**. 1402, 1914 ; K. Fajans, F. Richter, and F. J. Rauchenberger, *Sitzber. Heidelberg. Acad.*, 28, 1918 ; H. N. McCoy, *Phys. Rev.*, (2), **1**. 393, 401, 1913 ; F. W. Clarke, *Proc. Nat. Accad. Washington*, **4**. 181, 1918 ; *Chem. News*, **117**. 370, 1918 ; A. S. Russell, *Phil. Mag.*, (6), **48**. 365, 1924 ; *Nature*, **112**. 588, 619, 1923 ; R. F. Atkinson, *ib.*, **112**. 282, 1923 ; **113**. 495, 1924 ; J. Joly and J. H. J. Poole, *Phil. Mag.*, (6), **39**. 372, 1920 ; T. W. Richards, *Smithsonian Rep.*, 205, 1918 ; *Nature*, **103**. 74, 93, 1919 ; T. W. Richards and N. F. Hall, *Journ. Amer. Chem. Soc.*, **42**. 1550, 1920 ; T. W. Richards and P. Putzeys, *ib.*, **45**. 2954, 1923 ; T. W. Richards and W. C. Scrumb, *ib.*, **40**. 1403, 1908 ; T. W. Richards, H. S. King, and L. P. Hall, *ib.*, **48**. 1530, 1926 ; T. W. Richards and W. F. Hall, *ib.*, **39**. 531, 1907; W. D. Harkins and L. Aronberg, *ib.*, **42**. 1328, 1920 ; T. Dillon, R. Clarke, and V. M. Hinchy, *Scient. Proc. Roy. Dublin Soc.*, (2), **17**. 53, 1922 ; A. Bull, *Science*, (2), **50**. 69, 1919 ; O. Hönigschmid and M. Steinheil, *Ber.*, **56**. B, 1831, 1923 ; O. Hönigschmid and S. Horovitz, *Sitzber. Akad. Wien*, **123**. 2407, 1914 ; *Compt. Rend.*, **148**. 1797, 1914; A. Muguet, *ib.*, **174**. 172, 1922 ; C. D. and D. Cooksey, *Phys. Rev.*, (2), **16**. 327, 1920 ; M. E. Lembert, *Zeit. Elektrochem.*, **26**. 59, 1920 ; P. W. Bridgman, *Proc. Nat. Acad. Washington*, **5**. 351, 1919 ; T. R. Merton, *Proc. Roy. Soc.*, **96**. A, 388, 1920 ; **100**. A, 84, 1921 ; M. Curie, *Rev. Gén. Sciences Pure App.*, **34**. 576, 1923 ; A. Piutti and D. Magliacci, *Atti Accad. Lincei*, (5), **32**. ii, 468, 1923 ; W. Tuyn and H. K. Onnes, *Arch. Neérl.*, (3), **6**. 293, 1923 ; F. W. Clarke, *Proc. Nat. Accad. Science*, **4**. 181, 1918 ; F. W. Aston, *Phil. Mag.*, (6), **45**. 934, 1923 ; (6), **49**. 1191, 1925 ; H. Brennen, *Compt. Rend.*, **180**. 282, 1925 ; *Ann. Chim. Phys.*, (10), **4**. 127, 1925 ; J. Beckenkamp, *Zeit. anorg. Chem.*, **143**. 394, 1925 ; B. Perrette, *Compt. Rend.*, **180**. 1589, 1925; **E. S. Bieler,** *Nature*, **115**. 980, 1925; H. Collins, *Chem. News*, **132**. 85, 1926.

⁶ H. Pettersson and G. Kirsch, *Atomzertrümmerung*, Leipzig, 104, 1926.

⁷ L. Naudin, *Monit. Scient.*, (5), **10**. 121, 1920 ; W. Ramsay and F. L. Usher, *Ber.*, **42**. 2930, 1909 ; A. Smits, *Nature*, **114**. 609, 1924 ; **117**. 13, 1926 ; A. Smits and A. Karssen, *Naturwiss.*, **13**. 699, 1905.

§ 7. The Alloys of Lead with the Alkali Metals

W. Guertler[1] studied the affinity of lead for the metals generally. The alloys
of lead and *lithium* were partly examined by P. Lebeau, and W. A. Cowan mentioned
the hardening of lead by lithium. J. L. Gay Lussac and L. J. Thénard mentioned
the alloying of *sodium* with lead when the former is added to molten lead ; they
said that heat but not light is developed, and C. H. Mathewson added that with
26·4–31·6 per cent. of sodium the rise of temp. is 100°–200°. J. Percy reported the
formation of these alloys. G. D. Roos made the alloys by adding lead to sodium
melted under vaseline in a current of hydrogen. Several workers—C. T. Vautin,
F. Haber, C. E. Acker, J. Walter, L. Hulin, etc.—have noted the formation of
these alloys during the electrolysis of molten sodium hydroxide or chloride using
a cathode of molten lead ; and G. Bredig and F. Haber noted the formation of
an alloy during the cathodic spluttering of lead in an aq. soln. of sodium hydroxide.
G. S. Sérullas mentioned the formation of an alloy when lead is heated with
charred soap; W. H. Greene and W. H. Wahl, by heating a mixture of carbon,
lead, and sodium carbonate, or of lead and sodium tartrate ; A. Joannis, lead
filings and sodammonium ; and E. C. Rossiter, by stirring a mixture of sodium
hydroxide and wood charcoal in molten lead at 750°, and H. Caron, by reducing
lead chloride by sodium.

The f.p. curves of the alloys have been examined by N. S. Kurnakoff,
C. H. Mathewson, C. Calingaert and W. J. Boesch, G. Tammann, C. T. Heycock and
F. H. Neville, L. Lewin, E. Kordes, and J. Goebel. The freezing curves shown in
Fig. 31 represent results by C. H. Mathewson,
C. Calingaert and W. J. Boesch. There are four
maxima on the f.p. curve: one at 386° and 80 at.
per cent. of sodium ; one at 400° with 71·4 at. per
cent. of sodium ; one at 366° with 5 at. per cent.
of sodium ; and one at 319° with 27·4 at. per cent.
of sodium. There are four eutectics : one at 327°
and 58·8 at. per cent. of sodium ; one at 372° and
76·6 per cent. of sodium ; one at 301° with 37·3
at. per cent. of sodium ; and one at 307 with 21·1
at. per cent. of sodium. The solid soln. Na-Pb

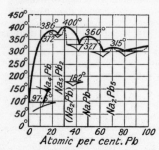

FIG. 31.—Freezing-point Curves
of the Pb–Na Alloys.

and Na$_5$Pb$_2$ are formed with 50–52 at. per cent. of
sodium ; NaPb+Na$_5$Pb$_2$ with 70·0–71·4 at. per cent.
of sodium ; and Na$_4$Pb +Na$_5$Pb$_2$ with 71·4–72·4 at.
per cent. of sodium. The hemiplumbide decomposes
at 182°, forming the dipentitaplumbide. The conditions of stability of **sodium
tetritaplumbide**, Na$_4$Pb, are indicated in Fig. 31. C. A. Kraus and H. F. Kurtz
observed the formation of this compound in the reduction of lead salts by sodium
amalgam. W. H. Greene and W. H. Wahl found that the colour is pale grey ;
and the sp. gr. 3·81 when the value calculated by the mixture rule was 3·7. The
alloy is softer than the finger-nail. N. S. Kurnakoff gave 420° for the m.p. against
C. H. Mathewson's 386°. The conditions of stability of **sodium hemiplumbide**,
Na$_2$Pb, are indicated in Fig. 31 ; the compound was made by W. H. Greene and
W. H. Wahl, A. C. Vournasos, A. Joannis, G. Calingaert and W. J. Boesch, as
well as by C. H. Mathewson. According to G. Calingaert and W. J. Boesch, the
compound which separates from alloys with between 58·8 and 76·6 at. per cent.
of sodium is **sodium dipentitaplumbide**, Na$_5$Pb$_2$, and not Na$_2$Pb. The m.p. of the
dipentitaplumbide is 400°, alloys with between 58·8 and 71·4 at. per cent. of
sodium rearrange at 182° on cooling so that Na$_5$Pb$_2$ disappears and the hemiplumbide is formed. The dipentitaplumbide forms solid soln. with both sodium
monoplumbide and tetritaplumbide. The pale blue alloy is brittle, and, according

to W. H. Greene and W. H. Wahl, the sp. gr. is 3·61 when the value calculated from the mixture rule is 3·7. The m.p. is 405°, and G. D. Roos found the latent heat of fusion to be 20·0 Cals. per gram when the molar entropy change is 7·5. C. H. Mathewson said that the compound in moist air acquires a brownish-black crust rather more slowly than does the tetritaplumbide. A. Joannis said that the hemiplumbide rapidly oxidizes in air with the evolution of much heat, and it decomposes in water with the separation of brown flocculent lead. It is soluble in liquid ammonia, and, according to C. A. Kraus, when the soln. is electrolyzed, lead separates on the anode, sodium on the cathode. The conditions of stability of **sodium plumbide**, NaPb, are indicated in Fig. 31. W. H. Greene and W. H. Wahl gave for the sp. gr. 6·91 when the value calculated from the mixture rule was 5·6. C. H. Mathewson gave 367° for the m.p. G. D. Roos found the latent heat of fusion to be 16·9 Cals. per gram when the molar change of entropy is 6·1. The conditions of stability of **sodium hemipentaplumbide**, Na_2Pb_5, are given in Fig. 31; C. H. Mathewson gave 319° for the m.p., and G. D. Roos found the latent heat of fusion to be 10·9 Cals. per gram when the molar change of entropy is 20·0. N. S. Kurnakoff reported *sodium triplumbide*, $NaPb_3$, m.p. about 316°, but this has not been confirmed. F. H. Smyth found a soln. of sodium in liquid ammonia dissolves lead, and the electrolysis of the soln. and the solubility measurements agree with the assumption that the soln. contains sodium diplumbide, and possibly also a smaller proportion of sodium triplumbide.

W. H. Greene and W. H. Wahl said that alloys with 3 to 31 per cent. of sodium are crystalline, and the brittleness is greater the larger the proportion of sodium. The alloy with 31 per cent. of sodium has a greenish tinge. C. H. Mathewson, H. Hanemann and W. Stockmeyer, and M. Wählert examined the brittleness of these alloys. J. Goebel found that the hardness of lead is increased by sodium from 4·1 when no sodium is present to 28·9 when 2 per cent. is present; as the proportion of sodium is further increased to 4 per cent., the hardness drops to 18·4. E. S. Sperry, C. O. Thieme, and C. H. Mathewson also examined the hardness of these alloys. An alloy with 1·3 per cent. of sodium is called *noheet metal*, or *tempered lead*, and has been recommended as a bearing metal, and S. K. Patteson claimed that under these conditions some sodium hydroxide is formed, which, with the lubricating oil forms a kind of soap. K. Bornemann and G. von Rauschenplat measured the electrical conductivity of the alloys. M. Sack measured the potential of a lead cathode in $3N$-NaOH against a mercury electrode; and the potential of sodium-lead alloys in a methyl alcohol soln. of lithium chloride at −80°. The curve showing the at. conc. of sodium and the potential of the alloy has breaks corresponding with *sodium diplumbide*, $NaPb_2$; the triplumbide, $NaPb_3$; and *sodium hemi-triplumbide*, Na_2Pb_3. R. Kremann and P. von Reininghaus measured the potential in pyridine soln. of sodium sulphate and iodide. They found evidence of the formation of NaPb, Na_2Pb_5, Na_2Pb, and Na_4Pb. C. H. Mathewson, and W. H. Greene and W. H. Wahl found the greater the proportion of sodium in the alloys, the more readily do they oxidize on exposure to air. According to J. L. Gay Lussac and L. J. Thénard, these alloys are decomposed by water, and L. Lewin, W. H. Greene and W. H. Wahl, and J. Goebel found the alloys are more readily attacked the higher the proportion of sodium; and L. Lewin said much lead passes into soln. According to H. Hanemann and W. Stockmeyer, alloys with 0·5 to 1 per cent. of sodium resist attack by sulphuric acid and tannic acid. They also tried the effect of an addition of magnesium or an alkaline earth metal; and J. Goebel, the effect of mercury. F. Skaupy tried the alloy as an electrode in electric lamps. G. Tammann studied the electrode potential and chemical properties of these alloys; and R. Kremann and co-workers found that on electrolysis, sodium accumulates at the cathode, lead at the anode.

J. L. Gay Lussac and L. J. Thénard [2] made alloys of lead and *potassium* by melting the two metals together; D. P. Smith heated the mixed metals to 600°. L. N. Vauquelin heated a mixture of lead oxide and potassium tartrate and obtained potassium-lead alloys. J. Percy also made these alloys. J. Walter produced the alloy by electrolyzing molten potassium chloride, using a carbon anode dipping under molten lead. G. Bredig and F. Haber obtained the alloy by the cathodic spluttering of lead in a soln. of potassium hydroxide or carbonate. The f.p. diagram of the lead-potassium alloys obtained by D. P. Smith

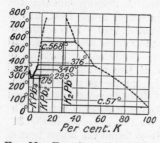

is shown in Fig. 32. The results show that the m.p. of lead is lowered to 275° by the addition of potassium; the eutectic mixture contains about 8 atoms per cent. of the latter metal. At 295°, **potassium diplumbide**, KPb_2, reacts with the fused mass to form **potassium tetraplumbide**, KPb_4; KPb_2 itself is formed by the interaction of a third compound of unknown composition and the fused mass at 337°. A fourth compound, probably **potassium hemiplumbide**, K_2Pb, melts about 568°,

FIG. 32.—Freezing-point Curves of the Pb–K Alloys.

and has a transition point at 376°. A. Joannis made what he regarded as **potassium plumbide**, KPb, or K_2Pb_2, by the action of an excess of potassioammonium on lead, or by the action of a soln. of potassium amide, KNH_2, in liquid ammonia on lead. The impure alloys obtained by J. L. Gay Lussac and L. J. Thénard, L. N. Vauquelin, and G. S. Sérullas were grey and brittle, and were decomposed by water. K. Bornemann and G. von Rauschenplat measured the electrical conductivity of the alloys; and R. Kremann and E. Pressfreund, the potential against a soln. of potassium chloride in pyridine. They found evidence of the formation of K_2Pb, and KPb_4, but not KPb_2. K. Jellinek and co-workers studied the equilibrium of the reaction between alkali metals and their molten chlorides, $Na + KCl \rightleftharpoons NaCl + K$, by the introduction of a lead phase. Mixtures of sodium and potassium chlorides were heated at 800° with lead-sodium, lead-potassium, or lead-sodium-potassium alloys, and in each experiment the percentage ratio of sodium and potassium in the lead phase was constant, no matter which of the above alloys was used. The law of mass action holds for these salts in the fused state. The chemical affinities of sodium and potassium lie much closer together at high temp. and the heat of reaction becomes very small. The alloy with about 3 per cent. of potassium was recommended by G. H. Worrall as a bearing metal. G. Tammann studied the electrode potential and chemical properties of these alloys.

REFERENCES.

[1] J. L. Gay Lussac and L. J. Thénard, *Recherches physicochimiques*, Paris, 1. 241, 1811; P. Lebeau, *Compt. Rend.*, 134. 231, 1902; H. Caron, *ib.*, 48. 440, 1859; A. Joannis, *ib.*, 114. 585, 1892; *Ann. Chim. Phys.*, (8), 7. 79, 1906; J. Percy, *The Metallurgy of Lead*, London, 90. 1870; G. D. Roos, *Zeit. anorg. Chem.*, 94. 337, 1916; C. H. Mathewson, *ib.*, 50. 173, 1906; N. S. Kurnakoff, *ib.*, 23. 457, 1900; *Journ. Russ. Phys. Chem. Soc.*, 31. 927, 1899; W. H. Greene and W. H. Wahl, *Chem. News*, 62. 314, 1890; *Journ. Franklin Inst.*, 130. 483, 1890; R. Kremann and P. von Reininghaus, *Zeit. Metallkunde*, 12. 273, 1920; R. Kremann and E. Preszfreund, *ib.*, 13. 19, 1921; R. Kremann and P. G. von Rehenburg, *ib.*, 140. 1, 1924; R. Kremann, H. Kienzl, and R. Markl, *Monatsh.*, 45. 133, 1924; M. Sack, *Ueber die Entstehung und Bedeutung von Natrium-legierungen bei der kathodischen Polarisation*, Karlsruhe, 1903; *Zeit. anorg. Chem.*, 34. 330, 1903; F. Haber and M. Sack, *Zeit. Elektrochem.*, 8. 245, 1902; F. Haber, *ib.*, 8. 541, 1902; 9. 364, 1903; J. Walter, *ib.*, 3. 387, 1897; G. Bredig and F. Haber, *Ber.*, 31. 2747, 1898; A. C. Vournasos, *ib.*, 44. 3270, 1911; C. O. Thieme, *Journ. Ind. Eng. Chem.*, 12. 446, 1920; Foreign Chemical and Electrochemical Syndicate, *German Pat.*, *D.R.P.* 74520, 1893; C. T. Vautin, *ib.*, 78001, 1894; 81710, 1894; H. Hanemann and W. Stockmeyer, *ib.*, 301721, 304224, 304405, 1916; 305611, 1917; Accumulatoren-Fabrik A.G., *ib.*, 298812, 1915; F. Skaupy, *ib.*, 308851, 1913; C. E. Acker, *ib.*, 110548, 1898; 117358, 1899; L. Hulin, *ib.*, 79935, 1894; *Zeit. angew. Chem.*, 11. 159, 1898; E. C. Rossiter, *Brit. Pat. No.* 14254, 1912; W. A. Cowan, *U.S. Pat. No.* 1360269, 1919; C. A. Kraus and H. F. Kurtz, *Journ. Amer. Chem. Soc.*, 47. 43, 1925; G. S. Sérullas, *Journ. Phys.*, 91. 123, 170, 1820; *Ann. Chim. Phys.*, (2), 21. 200, 1822; C. T. Heycock and F. H. Neville, *Journ. Chem. Soc.*, 55. 668, 1889; 57. 376, 656, 1890; 61. 888, 1892; *Chem. News*, 62. 280, 1890; L. Lewin, *München. Med. Wochschr.*,

65. 38, 1918; J. Goebel, *Zeit. Ver. deut. Ing.*, 63. 424, 1919; *Metall Erz*, 16. 280, 1919; *Zeit. Metallkunde*, 14. 388, 425, 1922; *Zeit. anorg. Chem.*, 106. 211, 1919; G. von Rauschenplat, *Die elektrische Leitfähigkeit der Metalllegierungen im flüssigen Zustande*, Aachen, 1912; K. Bornemann and G. von Rauschenplat, *Met.*, 9. 510, 1912; M. Wählert, *ib.*, 17. 232, 1920; S. K. Patteson, *Electrochem. Ind.*, 7. 21, 1909; E. S. Sperry, *Brass World*, 2. 219, 1906; *Met.*, 3. 607, 1906; G. Tammann, *Zeit. phys. Chem.*, 3. 445, 1889; *Zeit. anorg. Chem.*, 118. 92, 1921; C. A. Kraus, *Amer. Chem. Journ.*, 29. 1564, 1907; F. H. Smyth, *Journ. Amer. Chem. Soc.*, 39. 1299, 1917; C. Calingaert and W. J. Boesch, *ib.*, 45. 1901, 1923; W. Guertler, *Metall Erz*, 22. 199, 1925; E. Kordes, *Zeit. anorg. Chem.*, 154. 97, 1926.

² J. L. Gay Lussac and L. J. Thénard, *Recherches physico-chimiques*, Paris, 1. 218, 1811; J. Percy, *The Metallurgy of Lead*, London, 88, 1870; D. P. Smith, *Zeit. anorg. Chem.*, 56. 134, 1907; G. Tammann, *ib.*, 118. 92, 1921; K. Jellinek and G. Tomoff, *Zeit. phys. Chem.*, 111. 234, 1924; K. Jellinek and J. Czerwinski, *ib.*, 110. 192, 1924; *Zeit. anorg. Chem.*, 139. 233, 1924; K. Jellinek and J. Wolff, *ib.*, 146. 329, 1925; G. H. Worrall, *U.S. Pat. No.* 1360346, 1919; G. S. Sérullas, *Journ. Phys.*, 91. 123, 170, 1820; 93. 115, 1821; *Ann. Chim. Phys.*, (2), 21. 200, 1822; L. N. Vauquelin, *ib.*, (2), 7. 32, 1817; A. Joannis, *ib.*, (8), 7. 82, 1906; *Compt. Rend.*, 114. 585, 1892; J. Walter, *Zeit. Elektrochem.*, 3. 387, 1897; F. Haber, *Trans. Amer. Electrochem. Soc.*, 2. 190, 1902; G. Bredig and F. Haber, *Ber.*, 31. 2747, 1898; R. Kremann and E. Pressfreund, *Zeit. Metallkunde*, 13. 19, 1921; G. von Rauschenplat, *Die elektrische Leitfähigkeit der metalllegierungen im flüssigen Zustande*, Aachen, 1912; K. Bornemann and G. von Rauschenplat, *Met.*, 9. 511, 1912.

§ 8. The Alloys of Lead with Copper, Silver, and Gold

Alloys of lead and *copper* were described by J. F. Gmelin,[1] P. Berthier, J. H. Croockewit, etc. The so-called manilla gold, according to J. C. Welch, is an alloy consisting principally of these two metals; and, according to W. Gowland's analysis, a Japanese mirror of the seventeenth or eighteenth century is an alloy of copper and lead with about half per cent. of tin. M. Domingo recommended an alloy with 15·6 per cent. of lead as a hard solder for copper. J. Girardin found a buckle belonging to the Frankish dynasty in Gaul—it contained 72 per cent. copper; and A. Schertel reported a scaly mass with 63·31 per cent. of copper in a lead-refining furnace. At a red heat, C. T. Heycock and F. H. Neville found that copper readily dissolves in molten lead; and, according to J. Percy, the alloy obtained by melting the two metals above the m.p. of copper, when well stirred and quickly cooled in an ingot mould, gives an alloy which appears homogeneous; but if the alloy be kept for a considerable time beyond the m.p. of lead, liquation occurs, lead containing a little copper trickles away, and a more or less spongy mass of copper remains. C. J. B. Karsten found an alloy of lead with 25 per cent. copper gave lead containing from 2·0 to 2·8 per cent. copper, and copper with about 25 per cent. of lead. W. H. Creutzfeldt examined cathode deposits of the alloy from soln. of mixed silver and lead salts.

If a molten mixture of the two metals be very slowly solidified—and F. Reich found that when cupriferous lead is melted, or rather partly melted, the scum, *Abzug*, swimming on the surface contains most of the copper—the proportion of copper retained by the lead increases rapidly as the temp. rises. R. J. Nevil patented a modification of the process for liquating lead-copper alloys to recover the silver. The liquation and limited miscibility of copper-lead alloys has also been discussed by A. Streng, G. Mardus, and W. Baker. As emphasized by E. J. Ball and others, the tendency of the alloy to separate into two different liquids renders it impossible to make uniform alloys with all proportions of copper. W. Hampe said that by rapid cooling he was able to make homogeneous alloys with one per cent. of lead. H. Goldschmidt used the principle of the thermite process for making lead-copper alloys from mixtures of cupric oxide and lead; and E. Dannert obtained alloys from mixtures of copper, silica, and lead oxide. W. Spring described the preparation of the alloys by compressing an intimate mixture of the powdered elements.

The f.p. curve of these alloys has been investigated by C. T. Heycock and

F. H. Neville, K. Friedrich and A. Leroux, W. C. Roberts-Austen, M. Merle, R. H. Thurston, C. R. A. Wright, H. Gautier, K. Honda and T. Ishigaki, and F. Giolitti and M. Marantonio. The results are summarized in Fig. 33. There is no evidence of the formation of definite compounds. There is a eutectic at 949°, according to C. T. Heycock and F. H. Neville, or 969°, according to F. Giolitti and M. Marantonio, with 60 per cent. of lead ; and conjugate liquids are formed ; there is a sat. soln. of lead in copper and a sat. soln. of copper in lead ; when between 17 and 65 grm. atoms of lead are present per 100 of alloy, the f.p. remains constant at 969° (or 949°). F. C. Calvert and R. Johnson measured the heat conductivity of the copper-lead alloys ; and G. Wertheim, the elastic constants. N. A. Puschin observed no evidence of the formation of a definite compound in his study of the e.m.f. of the cell $Pb \mid N\text{-}Pb(NO_3)_2 \mid PbCu_n$, when n ranged from 15 to 95 at. per cent. G. Tammann and W. Wiederholt studied the cathodic polarization of these alloys.

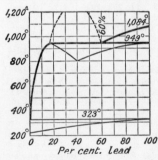

FIG. 33.—Freezing-point Curves of Lead-Copper Alloys.

A. Guettier made some observations on the effect of a small proportion of lead on the mechanical properties of copper ; and A. Matthiessen and M. Holzmann, on the electrical conductivity of these alloys. G. Lunge and E. Schmid made observations on the oxidizability of these alloys ; and J. Percy said that when the alloy is exposed for a long time to atm. air, at ordinary temp., it becomes oxidized to a considerable depth. X. Rocques found that water and salt soln. act more strongly than on lead. L. Brault and A. B. Poggiale said that if the alloy be heated with conc. sulphuric acid, the copper can be completely dissolved while the lead is scarcely attacked ; and A. Bauer, that an alloy with one per cent. of copper is slowly attacked by sulphuric acid of sp. gr. 1·843, the attack is greater at 250°, and all is dissolved at 280°. G. Mardus discussed the electro-refining of copper-lead alloys with an electrolyte containing fluoborates. F. Mylius and O. Fromm discussed the separation of the metals from dil. soln. D. Coda added an alloy of copper and lead to molten zinciferous alloys in order to concentrate the zinc in a dross from which the zinc is separated by distillation. C. J. Reed patented an alloy with 85 per cent. of lead, 10 per cent. arsenic, and (1 to) 5 per cent. of copper as an anti-friction metal ; alloys of lead, copper, and antimony were discussed by E. J. Ball, H. Schack, W. Hampe, and J. L. Lassaigne ; and alloys of lead, copper, antimony, and arsenic by W. Gowland.

A. Levol[2] said that lead and *silver* can be melted together in all proportions, but the alloys are not homogeneous, since he found that there is a strong tendency to liquefaction as is evidenced by the use of these alloys in H. L. Pattinson's process for desilvering lead ; and the tendency of the silver to concentrate towards the centre of the cast ingots—*vide* 3. 22, 4. C. R. A. Wright, however, said that homogeneous alloys of the two elements can readily be prepared. J. Joly and J. H. J. Poole could not appreciably separate the constituents of the alloy by centrifuging. N. W. Fischer said that a lead-silver alloy is produced when lead is placed in a soln. of silver nitrate. The f.p. diagram, Fig. 34, gives no support to the view that these two elements form chemical compounds. The curves were investigated by G. I. Petrenko, C. T. Heycock and F. H. Neville, R. Kremann and F. Hofmeier, C. R. A. Wright, D. H. Andrews

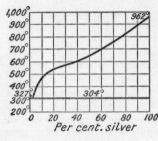

FIG. 34.—Freezing-point Curves of the Lead-Silver Alloys.

and J. Johnston, H. W. B. Roozeboom K. Honda and T. Ishigaki, E. Kordes, and K. Friedrich. The V-curves have a eutectic at 303·9° or 304° and 2·5 per cent. of silver. According to G. I. Petrenko, alloys with over 5 per cent. of lead are heterogeneous mixtures of a solid soln. with nearly 5 per cent. of silver, and lead. According to A. Levol, the alloy with Pb : Ag as 1 : 20 is white with a grey fracture; that with 1 : 12 is the colour of platinum with a fine-grained fracture; that with 1 : 10 is greyish-white with a grey fracture; and that with 1 : 4 is bluish-grey, ductile, and quickly attacked by air and hydrogen sulphide. W. C. Brögger described some crystals of an alloy with 27 per cent. of silver which he found in the bottom of a furnace. W. Campbell examined the microstructure of these alloys. A. Matthiessen gave for the sp. gr.:

Lead .	0	32·4	49·0	65·8	79·4	88·5	95·5	98·0	100 per cent.
Sp. gr.	10·468	10·800	10·925	11·054	11·144	11·196	11·285	11·334	11·367

E. von Maey represented the sp. vol., v, of alloys with p per cent. of silver by $v = 0.08791 + 0.0000760p$. W. C. Roberts-Austen, and G. Wertheim measured the elastic constants; P. Ludwik, the hardness; and W. C. Roberts-Austen, the rate of diffusion of silver in lead. H. Moissan and T. Watanabe heated an alloy with 46·24 per cent. of silver for $2\frac{1}{2}$ mins. in an electric furnace, and found the residue then contained 96·81 per cent. of silver. C. R. Groves and T. Turner also found that when heated in vacuo, the lead volatilizes faster than the silver. A. Matthiessen's values for the electrical conductivity are plotted in Fig. 35. The curve is very steep in the region where solid soln. are formed at between 97 and 100 per cent. of silver; the curve is nearly a straight line with alloys having less than 50 per cent. of silver. This is a characteristic of mechanical mixtures of two crystalline phases. N. A. Puschin found no evidence of chemical combination in his measurements of the e.m.f. of the cells $Pb \mid N\text{-}Pb(NO_3)_2 \mid PbAg_n$. A. P. Laurie, and H. le Chatelier made observations on the e.m.f. of voltaic cells. R. Kremann and O. Benda found that in the electrolysis of lead-silver alloys, the lead accumulates at the anode, the silver at the cathode; and C. G. Fink and L. C. Pan, that lead-silver anodes resisted corrosion in the electrolysis of brine better than lead-mercury alloys. T. J. Seebeck measured the thermoelectric properties. A. Bauer found that when exposed to moist air and carbon dioxide, in the presence of dil. acetic acid, the lead forms a basic carbonate leaving the silver unattacked. F. Mylius and O. Fromm discussed the separation of the metal from dil. soln.

FIG. 35.—The Electrical Conductivity of Silver-Lead Alloys.

K. Friedrich and A. Leroux, and H. Schack studied the ternary system Pb–Cu–Ag; G. Charpy, Pb–Cu–Sb; W. Guertler, Pb–Ag–Sb; and M. Goto, Pb–Bi–Ag.

C. Hatchett[3] prepared a pale yellow alloy of gold, with one-twelfth part of lead. He found it to be as brittle as glass; having a fine grained fracture; and sp. gr. 18·08. Even as little as $\frac{1}{1920}$th part of lead was found to reduce appreciably the ductility of gold. L. Nowack studied the effect of lead on gold. The f.p. curves were examined by C. T. Heycock and F. H. Neville, W. C. Roberts-Austen, R. Vogel, E. Kordes, and F. Rinne. The results by R. Vogel are plotted in Fig. 36. There are a eutectic at 215°, and breaks at 254° and 418°, making the f.p. curve consist of four branches. There are two definite compounds, gold hemiplumbide, Au_2Pb, and gold diplumbide, $AuPb_2$. At 211°, the diplumbide

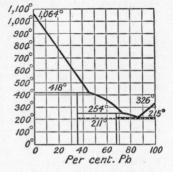

FIG. 36.—Freezing-point Curves of the Lead-Gold Alloys.

undergoes a transformation. The diplumbide forms brittle, long, white, acicular crystals with rounded contours easily distinguished from those of the hemiplumbide. H. Weiss studied the speed of formation of the gold-lead compounds. The microstructure of these alloys was examined by R. Vogel, W. C. Roberts-Austen and F. Osmond, M. Merle, F. Rinne, J. Arnold and J. Jefferson, and T. Andrews. According to A. Matthiessen, the sp. gr. at 0° is :

Gold .	0	8·7	16·0	19·2	23·9	32·3	48·9	65·4	79·2	100 per cent.
Sp. gr.	11·376	11·841	12·274	12·445	12·737	13·306	14·406	15·603	17·013	19·265

E. von Maey examined the sp. vol. of the alloys. W. C. Roberts-Austen, C. E. van Orstrand and F. P. Dewey, and S. Dushman and I. Langmuir discussed the rate of diffusion of gold in solid and molten lead ($q.v.$). W. C. Roberts-Austen and F. Osmond gave 6·57 kgrms. for the tensile strength of gold with 0·240 per cent. of lead, and an elongation of 4·9 per cent. on 76 mm. G. Wertheim measured the elastic constants, and A. Matthiessen, the electrical conductivity of these alloys. A. P. Laurie, and H. le Chatelier made observations on the e.m.f. of voltaic cells. E. Matthey examined the liquation of gold-lead alloys. According to A. Bauer, the lead alone oxidizes when the alloys are fused in air, and the lead can be completely removed from the alloys by acetic acid. G. Tammann, and R. Kremann and co-workers studied the electrode potential and the chemical properties of these alloys. F. Mylius and O. Fromm discussed the separation of the alloy from dil. soln. C. Hatchett examined some Au–Pb–Cu alloys ; and M. Goto, Au–Pb–Ag alloys.

REFERENCES.

¹ J. F. Gmelin, *Comment. Gött.*, **11**. 3, 1792 ; J. H. Croockewit, *Specimen chemicum de conjunctionibus chemicis metallorum*, Amsterdam, 1848 ; *Journ. prakt. Chem.*, (1), **63** 292, 1848 ; P. Berthier, *Ann. Mines*, (1), **9**. 63, 1824 ; W. Gowland, *Journ. Roy. Soc. Arts*, **43**. 523, 1895 ; *Bull. Soc. Enc. Nat. Ind.*, (4), **10**. 590, 1895 ; H. Gautier, *ib.*, (5), **1**. 1293, 1896 ; *Contribution à l'étude des alliages*, Paris, 93, 1901 ; M. Domingo, *Polyt. Notizbl.*, **10**. 47, 1855 ; *French Pat. No.* 4740, 1850 ; G. Wertheim, *Ann. Chim. Phys.*, (3), **12**. 581, 1848 ; J. Girardin, *Journ. Pharm. Chim.*, (3), **23**. 252, 1853 ; L. Brault and A. B. Poggiale, *ib.*, (2), **21**. 140, 1835 ; A. Schertel, *Jahrb. Sachsen*, **59**. 1900 ; J. C. Welch, *Chem. News*, **58**. 164, 1888 ; C. J. Reed. *U.S. Pat. No.* 874866, 1908 ; *Met. Chem. Engg.*, **6**. 80, 1908 ; G. Lunge and E. Schmid, *Zeit. anorg. Chem.*, **2**. 459, 1892 ; W. H. Creutzfeldt, *ib.*, **121**. 25, 1921 ; W. Spring, *Bull. Acad. Belg.*, (3), **28**. 23, 1894 ; *Zeit. phys. Chem.*, **15**. 65, 1894 ; A. Bauer, *Ber.*, **8**. 210, 1875 ; F. Mylius and O. Fromm, *ib.*, **27**. 630, 1894 ; F. Reich, *Jahrb. Berg. Hütt.*, 186, 1860 ; *Journ. prakt. Chem.*, (1), **78**. 335, 1859 ; A. Streng, *Berg. Hütt. Ztg.*, **18**. 14, 60, 67, 1859 ; W. Baker, *Chem. Gaz.*, **14**. 372, 1856 ; *Dingler's Journ.*, **142**. 281, 1856 ; A. Matthiessen and M. Holzmann, *Pogg. Ann.*, **110**. 222, 1860 ; *Phil. Trans.*, **150**. 85, 1860 ; X. Rocques, *Bull. Soc. Chim.*, (2), **33**. 499, 1880 ; D. Coda, *German Pat.*, *D.R.P.* 207019, 1907 ; E. Dannert, *ib.*, 176279, 1905 ; 186316, 1906 ; E. J. Ball, *Journ. Chem. Soc.*, **53**. 167, 1880 ; H. Goldschmidt, *Zeit. Electrochem.*, **14**. 559, 1908 ; N. A. Puschin, *Journ. Russ. Phys. Chem. Soc.*, **39**. 869, 1907 ; R. H. Thurston, *Non-ferrous Metals and Alloys*, New York, 1884 ; C. T. Heycock and F. H. Neville, *Phil. Trans.*, **189**. A, 42, 60, 1897 ; *Proc. Roy. Soc.*, **60**. 160, 1896 ; *Journ. Chem. Soc.*, **57**. 376, 656, 1890 ; **61**. 911, 1892 ; *Chem. News*, **62**. 280, 1890 ; W. Hampe, *Zeit. Berg. Hütt. Sal.*, **22**. 116, 1874 ; *Chem. Ztg.*, **12**. 893, 1888 ; W. C. Roberts-Austen, *Engg.*, **63**. 225, 1897 ; *Proc. Inst. Mech. Eng.*, **31**, 1897 ; K. Friedrich and A. Leroux, *Met.*, **4**. 200, 1907 ; A. Guettier, *Dingler's Journ.*, **114**. 280, 1849 ; *Monit. Ind.*, 1261, 1848 ; M. Merle, *Monit. Scient.*, (4), **9**. 35, 1895 ; F. Giolitti and M. Marantonio, *Gazz. Chim. Ital.*, **40**. 1, 51, 1910 ; J. Percy, *The Metallurgy of Silver and Gold*, London, **1**. 343, 1880 ; *The Metallurgy of Lead*, London, 91, 1870 ; R. J. Nevil, *Brit. Pat. No.* 9909, 1842 ; *Chem. Gaz.*, **2**. 335, 1844 ; C. J. B. Karsten, *System der Metallurgie*, Berlin, **5**. 441, 1832 ; J. L. Lassaigne, *Journ. Chim. Méd.*, **18**. 73, 1844 ; G. Mardus, *Elektrolytische Raffination von Blei aus borfluowasserstoffsaurer Lösung*, Berlin, 1908 ; F. C. Calvert and R. Johnson, *Phil. Trans.*, **148**. 349, 1858 ; C. R. A. Wright, *Journ. Soc. Chem. Ind.*, **13**. 1014, 1894 ; H. Schack, *Zeit. anorg. Chem.*, **132**. 265, 1923 ; G. Tammann and W. Wiederholt, *ib.*, **125**. 67, 1922 ; K. Honda and T. Ishigaki, *Science Rep. Tohoku Univ.*, **14**. 219, 1925.

² A. Levol, *Ann. Chim. Phys.*, (3), **39**. 163, 1853 ; G. Wertheim, *ib.*, (3), **12**. 581, 1848 ; N. W. Fischer, *Kastner's Arch.*, **13**. 224, 1828 ; K. Friedrich, *Met.*, **3**. 1, 1906 ; K. Friedrich and A. Leroux, *ib.*, **4**. 293, 1097 ; P. Ludwik, *Zeit. anorg. Chem.*, **94**. 101, 1916 ; H. Schack, *ib.*, **132**. 265, 1923 ; C. T. Heycock and F. H. Neville, *Phil. Trans.*, **189**. A, 58, 1897 ; *Chem. News*, **62** 280, 1890 ; *Proc. Roy. Soc.*. **60**. 160, 1896 ; *Journ. Chem. Soc.*, **61**. 907, 1892 ; C. R. Groves and T. Turner, *ib.*, **101**. 591, 1912 ; A. Laurie, *ib.*, **65**. 1031, 1894 ; N. A. Puschin, *Journ. Russ.*

Phys. Chem. Soc., **39**. 869, 1908; G. I. Petrenko, *Zeit. anorg. Chem.*, **50**. 138, 1906; **53**. 200, 1907; A. Bauer, *Ber.*, **4**. 453, 1871; F. Mylius and O. Fromm, *ib.*, **27**. 630, 1894; H. Moissan and T. Watanabe, *Compt. Rend.*, **144**. 16, 1907; H. L. Pattinson, *B.A. Rep.*, **50**, 1838; *Brit. Pat. No.* 6497, 1833; A. Matthiessen, *Pogg. Ann.*, **110**. 21, 212, 1860; *Phil. Trans.*, **150**. 177, 1860; *B.A. Rep.*, 37, 1863; A. Matthiessen and C. Vogt, *Pogg. Ann.*, **116**. 369, 1862; *Phil. Mag.*, (4), **23**. 171, 1862; J. Joly and J. H. J. Poole, *ib.*, (6), **39**. 376, 1920; M. Goto, *Journ. Coll. Engg. Tokyo*, **9**. 63, 1918; W. Guertler, *Forsch. Metallkunde*, 1, 1923; H. W. B. Roozeboom, *Die Heterogenen Gleichgewichte vom Standpunkte der Phasenlehre*, Braunschweig, **2**. 303, 383, 1904; C R. A. Wright, *Journ. Soc. Chem. Ind.*, **13**. 1016, 1894; R. Kremann and O. Benda, *Monatsh.*, **45**. 339, 1925; R. Kremann and F. Hofmeier, *ib.*, **32**. 570, 1911; *Monatsh.*, **44**. 401, 1923; **45**. 133, 1924; *Zeit. phys. Chem.*, **110**. 559, 1924; R. Kremann and P. G. von Rehenburg, *Zeit. anorg. Chem.*, **140**. 1, 1924; D. H. Andrews and J. Johnston, *Journ. Inst. Metals*, **32**. 385, 1924; W. C. Brögger, *Zeit. Kryst.*, **3**. 492, 1879; E. von Maey, *Zeit. phys. Chem.*, **38**. 292, 1901; G. Charpy, *Bull. Soc. Enc. Nat. Ind.*, (5), **3**. 670, 1898; *Contribution à l'étude des alliages*, Paris, 201, 1901; *Compt. Rend.*, **126**. 1645, 1898; W. Campbell, *Journ. Franklin Inst.*, **154**. 1, 131, 201, 1902; H. le Chatelier, *Bull. Soc. Enc. Nat. Ind.*, (4), **10**. 192, 1895; W. C. Roberts-Austen, *B.A. Rep.*, 402, 464, 1883; *Phil. Trans.*, **179**. A, 339, 1888; T. J. Seebeck, *Pogg. Ann.*, **10**. 203, 1827; C. G. Fink and L. C. Pan, *Trans. Amer. Electrochem. Soc.*, **46**. 126, 1924; K. Honda and T. Ishigaki, *Science Rep. Tohoku Univ.*, **14**. 219, 1925; E. Kordes, *Zeit. anorg. Chem.*, **154**. 97, 1926.

³ C. Hatchett, *Phil. Trans.*, **93**. 43, 1803; W. C. Roberts-Austen, *ib.*, **179**. A, 344, 1888; **187**. A, 383, 1896; *B.A. Rep.*, 402, 464, 1883; *Proc. Roy. Soc.*, **49**. 347, 1891; **67**. 101, 1901; *Proc. Inst. Mech. Eng.*, 543, 1891; 31, 1897; W. C. Roberts-Austen and F. Osmond, *Engg.*, **67**. 254, 1899; *Phil. Trans.*, **187**. A, 417, 1896; *Bull. Soc. Enc. Nat. Ind.*, (5), **1**. 1137, 1896; A. Matthiessen, *Pogg. Ann.*, **110**. 21, 190, 1860; *Phil. Trans.*, **150**. 161, 177, 1860; T. Andrews, *Engg.*, **66**. 441, 541, 733, 1898; J. Arnold and J. Jefferson, *ib.*, **61**. 176, 1896; F. Osmond, *ib.*, **66**. 756, 1898; G. Wertheim, *Ann. Chim. Phys.*, (3), **12**. 581, 1848; H. Weiss, *ib.*, (9), **19**. 201, 1923; (9), **20**. 131, 1923; E. von Maey, *Zeit. phys. Chem.*, **38**. 295, 1901; C. T. Heycock and F. H. Neville, *Chem. News*, **62**, 280, 1890; *Journ. Chem. Soc.*, **61**. 904, 1892; A. Laurie, *ib.*, **65**. 1031, 1894; C. E. van Orstrand and F. P. Dewey, *Prof. Paper U.S. Geol. Sur.*, 95, 1915; R. Vogel, *Zeit. anorg. Chem.*, **45**. 11, 1905; G. Tammann, *ib.*, **118**. 93, 1921; S. Dushmann and I. Langmuir, *Phys. Rev.*, (2), **20**. 113, 1922; M. Goto, *Journ. Coll. Engg. Tokyo*, **9**. 63, 1918; R. Kremann, H. Wostall, and H. Schöpfer, *Forsch. Metallkunde*, 5, 1922; A. Bauer, *Ber.*, **4**. 449, 1871; F. Mylius and O. Fromm. *ib.*, **27**. 630, 1894; E. Matthey, *Proc. Roy. Soc.*, **60**. 21, 1896; F. Rinne, *Neues Jahrb. Min.*, ii, 129, 1909; M. Merle, *Monit. Scient.*, (4), **9**. 35, 1895; H. le Chatelier, *Bull. Soc. Enc. Nat. Ind.*, (4), **10**. 192, 1895; E. Kordes, *Zeit. anorg. Chem.*, **154**. 97, 1926; L. Nowack, *ib.*, **154**. 395, 1926.

§ 9. Alloys of Lead with the Metals of the Alkaline Earths, and of the Magnesium-Zinc Family

H. Caron¹ made an alloy of *calcium* and lead by treating molten calcium chloride with the lead-sodium alloy. H. Moissan found that calcium readily alloys with molten lead, although, as B. Setlik showed, there is a great loss of calcium. L. Donsky recommended working with an atm. as free as possible from oxygen. The union of calcium with molten lead is attended by the evolution of heat and light. L. Hackspill said that the best mode of preparing calcium-lead alloys is by electrolysis of molten calcium chloride, using a molten lead cathode. W. Moldenhauer and J. Andersen added some potassium chloride to the electrolyte, and used a graphite anode. F. M. Perkin and L. Pratt heated lead chloride with calcium, and L. Hackspill used the same process in a crucible lined with magnesia. J. N. Pring, and W. Kroll heated lead oxide with calcium carbide, and N. Tarugi also recommended reducing lead salts with calcium carbide at 400°; and W. Kroll heated a salt of calcium with a lead-sodium alloy. K. Jellinek and co-workers obtained alloys of lead with the alkaline earth metals by fusing a mixture of the alkaline earth chloride and a sodium-lead alloy, and they studied the equilibrium relations in the electrolysis of the mixtures of the alkaline earth metals and sodium chloride: $M+2NaCl \rightleftharpoons MCl_2+2Na$; and $Ba+CaCl_2 \rightleftharpoons BaCl_2+Ca$ with lead electrodes. H. Moissan, and F. von Kügelgen made alloys by direct fusion of the constituent elements. E. Kordes studied the eutectic mixtures. The f.p. curves of the lead-calcium system were investigated by L. Donsky, and N. Baar.

The results are summarized in Fig. 37. There are maxima at 649° and 1105° corresponding respectively with the f.p. of calcium triplumbide, $CaPb_3$, and calcium hemiplumbide, Ca_2Pb ; another less stable compound, calcium plumbide,

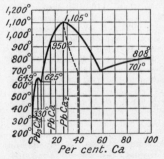

FIG. 37.—Freezing-point Curves of the Lead-Calcium Alloys.

CaPb, is formed at 950°. The eutectic point at 625° corresponds with 10 per cent. calcium, and that at 701°, with 58 per cent. of calcium. L. Hackspill claimed to have made calcium hemi-triplumbide, Ca_2Pb_3, by heating a mixture of lead-calcium alloy with 21 per cent. of calcium and twice its weight of lead at 950°–1100° in vacuo for 1½ hrs. The sp. gr. at 19° was 7·6, and the m.p. 775°. The individuality of this product has not been established. C. A. Kraus and H. F. Kurtz obtained indications of the formation of calcium hemitriplumbide, Ca_2Pb_3, in the reduction of lead salts by calcium amalgam.

B. Setlick said that the alloys are crystalline and brittle ; L. Hackspill found that they are harder than lead. L. Donsky, C. O. Thieme, A. Hart, and F. C. Frary and S. N. Temple also made observations on the hardness of these alloys. When remelted, the alloys are liable to lose some calcium. O. Ruff and H. Hartman studied the absorption of nitrogen by lead-calcium alloys. M. Wählert recommended alloys with 3 per cent. calcium as bearing metals. Alloys with less than 10 per cent. calcium can be preserved unchanged in a desiccator, but L. Donsky found that the others gradually break down into black powders in air. W. Moldenhauer and J. Andersen found the alloy with 82 per cent. of calcium acquires a black layer when kept a week under paraffin. H. Caron said the alloy with 17 per cent. of calcium does not decompose when strongly heated in a carbon crucible. L. Hackspill found that an alloy with 21 per cent. of calcium is not much altered when kept for 20 mins. in vacuo at 900°–1000° ; but if heated in air, a crust of calcium oxide and nitride is formed. E. A. Ashcroft found that moist air and water do not act so rapidly on the lead-calcium as on the lead-magnesium alloy. L. Hackspill said that cold water acts on the lead-calcium alloys slowly, while boiling water acts rapidly, forming calcium hydroxide and powdered lead. C. V. Burton said that carbon is dissolved by the alloy with one per cent. of calcium, and it can be separated, in the form of what was thought to be the diamond, by the action of steam at a red heat. G. Tammann studied the electrode potential and chemical properties of these alloys.

The alloys of lead and *strontium* have been examined only in a cursory manner. The Metallbank und Metallurgische Gesellschaft said that alloys with less than

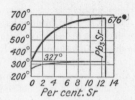

FIG. 38.—Freezing-point Curve of Mixtures of Lead and Strontium.

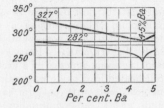

FIG. 39.—Freezing-point Curve of Some Barium-Lead Alloys.

10 per cent. of strontium are softer than those of barium, but harder than those of calcium. E. Piwowarsky found that strontium is quite insoluble in solid lead, and the two elements form one compound, strontium triplumbide, Pb_3Sr, m.p. 676°, Fig. 38 ; the eutectic containing very little strontium melts at the same temp. as

lead. W. Kroll heated mixtures of lead oxide and barium or strontium carbide. J. Czochralsky and E. Rassow made alloys of *barium* and lead by fusing a mixture of the constituent elements; H. Goldschmidt made them from the oxides by the thermite process; and the Metallbank und Metallurgische Gesellschaft, by the electrolysis of fused barium chloride using a molten lead cathode. E. Kordes studied the eutectic mixtures. J. Czochralsky and E. Rassow obtained the portion of the system of f.p. curves indicated in Fig. 39; they also reported barium triplumbide, $BaPb_3$, to be formed, but no mixed crystals. W. Mathesius gave 250° for the m.p. of the triplumbide; and W. A. Cowan and co-workers found that the microstructure of alloys with 4·5-6 per cent. of barium shows rod-like crystals of the triplumbide to be present. Alloys with about 8 per cent. of barium decompose in air, forming a grey powder. Water decomposes the alloys at ordinary temp. Acid liquids and vapours attack them superficially. E. Scheurer found that filings of the alloy with 3 per cent. barium may inflame paper. The so-called *ulco-metal* is an alloy containing 98–99 per cent. of lead plus barium or calcium, and it was used during the Great War as a substitute for antimonial lead in making shrapnel balls. One of these alloys was described by R. T. Rolfe, and W. A. Cowan and co-workers, J. Czochralsky and co-workers, E. Heyn, and W. Mathesius. Alloys of lead, calcium, and barium or strontium were investigated by W. Cowan and co-workers, W. Mathesius, and L. Filipoff.

J. Parkinson[2] made alloys of *magnesium* and lead by melting together the constituent elements in an atm. of hydrogen. They were also made directly by E. A. Ashcroft, W. Guertler, G. Tammann, N. S. Kurnakoff and N. J. Stepanoff, and G. Grube. G. Massing obtained the alloys by compressing a mixture of the finely divided constituents; C. Winkler, by the action of magnesium on lead oxide; and E. A. Ashcroft, E. Beck, and the United Lead Co., by the electrolysis of fused magnesium chloride using a molten lead cathode. The f.p. curves were investigated by C. T. Heycock and F. H. Neville, A. von Vegesack, N. S. Kurnakoff and N. J. Stepanoff, E. Kordes, and G. Grube. The results of the last-named are summarized in Fig. 40. There are two eutectics, one at 459·2° or 460° and 67 at. per cent. of lead, and the other at 246·9° or 250° corresponding with 97 at. per cent. of lead. One compound, magnesium hemiplumbide, Mg_2Pb, is formed, provided the temp. does not exceed 750°. This compound freezes at 551·3°. It is brittle, and steel-blue in colour; the sp. gr. is 5·5416 and the sp. vol. 0·1805; the compound is stable in dry air, but in moist air it quickly forms a black powder from which a hydrate, $PbO.2MgO.3H_2O$, is produced. A. J. Berry said the compound probably dissociates into its constituents when melted. A. Sacklowsky found that the X-radiogram agrees with a face centered cubic lattice, and J. B. Friauf calculated the unit cubic cell has an edge 6·78 A., and contains four molecules. The positions of the atoms correspond with the calcium fluoride arrangement.

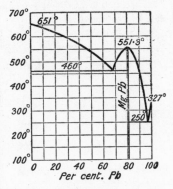

FIG. 40.—Freezing-point Curves of the Lead-Magnesium Alloys.

J. Parkinson said that the magnesium-lead alloys are crystalline, and brittle. According to P. Ludwik, magnesium hardens lead more than does bismuth, antimony, tin, cadmium, or silver. H. Hanemann and W. Stockmeyer also found that magnesium hardens and toughens lead more than does antimony; and D. Stenquist patented 0·01-0·1 per cent. of magnesium as a hardening agent for lead. I. P. Göbel also examined the hardness of these alloys. A. J. Berry found that at 680°, in vacuo, magnesium distils from these alloys carrying over only a trace of lead. N. J. Stepanoff's measurements of the electrical conductivity of these alloys are plotted in Fig. 41. The conductivity decreases rapidly with increasing proportions of lead until about 5 per cent. of lead is present. At the conc. corresponding with the hemiplumbide, the electrical conductivity passes

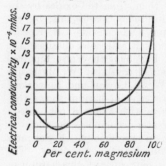

FIG. 41.—The Electrical Conductivity of Lead-Magnesium Alloys.

through a minimum. The temp. coeff. of the conductivity also indicates the existence of the same compound. W. Jenge measured the e.m.f. of the alloys in N-MgSO$_4$ against silver in a sat. soln. of silver nitrate, with N-Na$_2$SO$_4$ as intermediate electrolyte. G. Tammann, and W. Jenge studied the electrode potential and chemical properties of these alloys; and R. Kremann and J. Gmachl-Pammer found evidence of Mg$_2$Pb in the electrochemical behaviour of these alloys. H. Hanemann and W. Stockmeyer said that alloys with less than 4 per cent. of magnesium are not attacked by air and water, and only slowly by acids. I. P. Göbel said that all alloys containing the free hemiplumbide corrode rapidly. G. Grube, and E. A. Ashcroft studied the oxidation of these alloys by moist air. E. Beck found the nitride is formed when nitrogen is bubbled through the molten alloy with 46 per cent. magnesium. J. Parkinson, and G. Grube found that glass is attacked by the molten alloys. C. O. Thieme discussed the hardness of some Pb–Mg–Sb alloys.

J. F. Gmelin [3] stated that lead readily unites with zinc, thereby becoming harder, but its ductility is not impaired by any proportion of zinc. When the two elements are melted together, and the molten mixture is allowed to cool slowly, nearly complete separation occurs, the zinc solidifies first, forming the upper layer, which can be removed as a crust from the molten lead below. The f.p. curve has been studied by C. T. Heycock and F. H. Neville, P. T. Arnemann, R. Kremann and F. Hofmeier, B. E. Curry, P. Müller, G. Tammann, F. Novak, F. Mylius and co-workers, A. V. Tidblom, P. Müller, I. P. Göbel, and W. Spring and L. Romanoff; the results are summarized in Fig. 42. There is no evidence of the formation of a definite compound. Mixtures containing from 0·5 to 97 per cent. of lead separate into two conjugate liquids. The m.p. of zinc falls as lead is introduced, becoming 418° with 0·5 per cent., and then remains constant until 96·6 per cent. is present. Further additions of lead cause the m.p. to fall to 317°, which is the eutectic with 98·8 per cent. of lead. The m.p. then rises to 327° that of lead alone. Alloys with 0–98·8 per cent. of lead have zinc and eutectic, and those with more

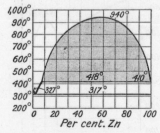

FIG. 42.—Freezing-point Curves of the Lead-Zinc Alloys.

lead show lead and eutectic. knife. The solubility of zinc W. Spring and L. Romanoff. lower layers at different temp. are:

All these alloys are soft enough to be cut with a in lead and of lead in zinc was worked out by The percentage amounts of zinc in the upper and

	334°	419°	450°	475°	514°	584°	650°	740°	800°	900°
Upper	—	98·5	—	98·0	97·0	95·0	93·0	90·0	86·0	74·5
Lower	1·2	—	8·0	9·0	11·0	14·0	17·0	21·0	25·0	41·0

The two solubility curves meet at about 940°—the critical soln. temp.—so that above that temp. the two metals are mutually soluble in all proportions. W. Heike gave for the percentage solubility of zinc in lead, 2·20 at 425°, 3·30 at 500°, and 7·38 at 600°. According to J. Fournet, when an alloy of zinc and lead is heated white-hot in a charcoal crucible, the zinc all distils away from the lead. If silver is present in the system it divides itself between the two layers, but by far the larger proportion accumulates with the lighter zinc layer, for silver at about 540° is 300 times more soluble in zinc than in lead. This subject was investigated by C. R. A. Wright and C. Thompson, C. R. A. Wright, F. Reich, D. Mazzotto, B. Bogitch, W. Alexéef, A. Guettier, and G. N. Potdar. Segregation phenomena were studied by O. Bauer and H. Arndt. The fact is at the base of A. Parkes' process for the desilveration of lead, first indicated by C. J. B. Karsten—*vide* **3.** 22, 4. W. Spring prepared the alloy by compressing an intimate mixture of the powdered elements. The structure of the alloys was examined by W. Campbell, H. Behrens, F. A. Schulze, B. E. Curry, P. T. Arnemann, and S. Konno ; and the liquation of the molten alloys by a centrifuge, by F. Hoffmann ; the sp. gr. and sp. vol., by E. von Maey—between 0° and 17°, the sp. vol. is $0·083-0·000520p$, where p denotes the percentage amount of zinc. I. P. Göbel, P. Ludwik, M. Levi-Malvano and O. Ceccarelli, and A. Guettier investigated the hardness of these alloys. G. Wertheim, R. Hoyt, P. T. Arnemann, and E. H. Schulz investigated the elastic properties ; J. Tayler, the heat of formation ; E. Matthey, the liquation of Pb–Zn–Au, Pb–Zn–Au–Ag, and Pb–Zn–Au–Ag–Cu alloys ; A. P. Laurie, N. Hesehus and N. Georgiewsky, and G. Tammann and W. Wiederholt, the electrochemical behaviour of these alloys ; S. Konno, P. Müller, and H. Rainy and R. D. Clackson, the electrical conductivity ; P. Fuchs, R. Kremann and J. Gmachl-Pammer, the electrochemical behaviour ; and W. Rollmann, and A. V. Tidblom, the thermoelectric properties. The action of acids was studied by M. Centnerswer, P. T. Arnemann, F. Novak, L. Pitkin, and F. Osmond and J. Werth. Applications of the alloys were discussed by G. T. Key, J. and T. Hall, R. Hoyt, J. S. Rae, C. Mark, Lohmann Co., G. Tammann and O. Dahl. C. R. A. Wright and C. Thompson studied the ternary system Pb–Zn–Sb. The alloys of zinc, lead, and copper—the so-called lead-brass—have been discussed by A. Arche and C. Hassack, H. Behrens, W. Flight, L. Guillet, W. N. Hartley, J. Percy, J. J. Rein, and V. A. Skinder ; and alloys of zinc, lead, copper, and antimony, by M. Beuling. The ternary system Cu–Zn–Pb was investigated by H. Niclassen, and N. Parravano and co-workers ; Ag–Zn–Pb, by C. R. A. Wright and C. Thompson, W. D. Bancroft, G. K. Williams, and R. Kremann and T. Hofmeier. G. N. Potdar studied the partition of silver between zinc and lead. R. Kremann and R. Knabl measured the electrode potentials of the Zn–Pb–Sb ternary alloys. The ternary diagram is broken up into five systems ; $Pb-Zn-Ag_2Zn_5$; $Pb-Ag_2Zn_5-Ag_2Zn_3$; $Pb-Ag_2Zn_3-AgZn$; $Pb-AgZn-Ag_3Zn_2$; and $Pb-Ag_3Zn_2-Ag$. The lead field is a very small one. Lead does not form solid soln. in any part of the system. In the zinc process for desilverizing lead, the quantity of zinc added is so small that the region of immiscible liquids is not usually entered. The removal of zinc also removes silver hemipentazincide. G. Tammann and P. Schafmeister measured the partition of copper, silver, gold, cadmium, tin, nickel, and antimony between zinc and lead ; and W. A. Naish, that of silver between zinc and lead. F. Doeblin, and G. Tammann and O. Dahl investigated the ternary system Pb–Zn–Sb. W. Heike studied the Pb–Zn–Ag and the Pb–Zn–Ag–Cu alloys.

The alloys of *cadmium* and lead are in marked contrast with those of zinc and lead, and are not what would be anticipated in view of the close analogy between zinc and cadmium. The alloys were examined by B. Wood, and C. R. A. Wright.[4] G. Tammann and W. Wiederholt measured the diffusion of cadmium in lead. The f.p. diagram was investigated by A. W. Kapp, C. T. Heycock and F. H. Neville, E. Jänecke, M. Wählert, F. Mylius and R. Funk, G. P. Luckey, I. P. Göbel, C. W. Hill, G. Tammann and W. Wiederholt, C. di Capua, W. C. Barlow, A. Matthiessen, K. Honda and T. Ishigaki, and A. Stoffel, and the results are summarized in Fig. 43. No compounds were observed, and mixed crystals within the limits indicated in the diagram are formed. A. M. Portevin studied the microstructure of the eutectic. A. Matthiessen found the sp. gr. of the alloys to be :

Lead .	0	22·8	31·8	48·2	65·0	78·8	88·2	91·7	100·0 per cent.
Sp. gr.	8·655	9·160	9·353	9·755	10·246	10·656	10·950	11·044	11·376

J. Göbel, and F. Sauerwald also measured the sp. gr.   E. von Maey represented
the sp. vol., v, of alloys of lead with p per cent. of cadmium by $v=0\cdot08791$
$+0\cdot0002673p$. A. Magnus and M. Mannheimer observed a rise of temp. occurs
when molten lead and cadmium are mixed. I. P. Göbel, F. L. Brady, and
P. Ludwik measured the hardness of these alloys.   A. Matthiessen investigated the thermal expansion; H. le Chatelier, R. Kremann and A. Langbauer,
N. W. Taylor, and A. P. Laurie, the electromotive force of cells; A. Battelli, the
thermoelectric properties; D. Mazzotti, the thermal phenomena accompanying the
formation of these alloys. The electrical conductivity determined by A. Matthiessen,
W. Guertler, G. Tammann and K. Dahl, A. Schulze, and A. Matthiessen and C. Vogt,
Fig. 44, is a linear function of the conc.   There are no critical points on the curve

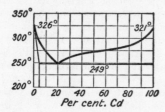

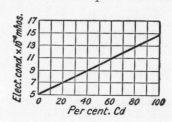

FIG. 43.—Freezing-point Curves of the
Lead-Cadmium Alloys.

FIG. 44.—Electrical Conductivity of the
Lead-Cadmium Alloys.

in the region between 95 and 100 per cent. of lead in which solid soln. are known to
be formed.   B. Beckman examined the effect of press. on the conductivity.
P. Müller, M. Herschkowitsch, and P. Fuchs measured the e.m.f. of cadmium-lead
alloys in N-CdSO$_4$ against cadmium.   R. Kremann and co-workers found that on
electrolysis, the lead accumulates at the anode, the cadmium at the cathode.
F. Mylius and O. Fromm examined the precipitation of the metal from dil. soln.
L. Pitkin, and the Accumulatoren-Fabrik examined the effects of acids on the alloys.
Some uses of the alloys were examined by W. Kaiser, G. P. Luckey, C. W. Hill, etc.
E. Becquerel measured the thermoelectric force of lead-, zinc-antimony alloys.
C. G. Fink and L. C. Pan found that in the electrolysis of brine, lead-cadmium anodes
do not resist corrosion so well as lead-silver alloys.   W. Stockmeyer and H. Hane-

FIG. 45. — Freezing-point
Curves of the Ternary
System: Cd–Pb–Bi.

mann made lead, magnesium, potassium, and lead,
magnesium, sodium alloys; W. Mathesius, lead, cadmium, and calcium alloys; the Metallbank und Metallurgische Gesellschaft made lead and magnesium alloys
with the metals of the alkaline earths; and M. Cook
studied the system Pb–Zn–Cd; and E. Becquerel,
Pb–Zn–Cd–Sb. W. E. Barlow investigated the ternary
system Cd–Pb–Bi; and the results are summarized in
Fig. 45.   There is a ternary eutectic at 91·5°, and no
compounds are formed. Observations on these alloys
were also made by B. Wood, C. von Hauer, C. P. Steinmetz, C. W. Hill, F. Novak, J. Tomes, C. S. Tomes,
A. Kirby, T. B. Hitchcock, T. Fletcher, A. Witzel,
C. R. A. Wright, and R. Kremann and A. Langsbauer;
and C. R. A. Wright, the Cd–Pb–Zn alloys; C. T. Heycock and F. H. Neville
examined the ternary alloys Pb–Cd–Ag, and Pb–Cd–Au.

The alloys of lead and *mercury* are readily obtained by triturating lead filings
with mercury, or by agitating molten lead with mercury.   They were examined
by S. Lucas,[5] W. Kettembeil, J. H. Croockewit, etc.   According to J. F. Daniell,
a bar of lead immersed for 10 days in cold mercury, though it remains ductile, is
covered at the surface with soft feathery crystals.   J. Henry found that when a
bar of lead is bent in the form of a syphon, and placed with one end in the mercury,

in due course the mercury will flow out at the other and lower end. With a bar made of non-hammered lead, the first drop of mercury appeared in 24 hrs., and when made of hammered lead, in 10 days. J. Nicklès found lead is more permeable than silver and less so than zinc. E. N. Horsford measured the rate of ascent of mercury in rods of lead; W. J. Humphreys, the diffusion of lead, and of lead-cadmium, and lead-tin alloys in mercury; and A. Gouy, the solubility of lead in mercury. J. Regnauld found the union of mercury with lead is accompanied by an absorption of heat, and D. Mazzotto found the maximum absorption occurs with 1 vol. of lead and 2 vols. of mercury. J. Schumann obtained the amalgam by stirring molten lead into heated mercury; R. Lacau, by pouring mercury into molten lead on the point of freezing, and afterwards heating the product a little to make it homogeneous. J. P. Joule dissolved the lead in mercury, forced out the excess by press., and obtained an amalgam corresponding with Pb_2Hg. R. Böttger obtained lead amalgam by immersing sodium amalgam in a soln. of lead acetate; A. C. Becquerel, by the action of mercurous chloride and water on lead-foil; J. Schumann, by the electrolysis of a soln. of lead nitrate with a mercury cathode; and G. Vortmann, by the electrolysis of a mixed soln. of lead and mercuric acetates or tartrates.

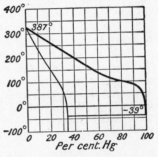

FIG. 46.—Freezing-point Curves of the Lead-Mercury Alloys.

The f.p. curves of the binary system have been investigated by H. Fay and E. North, P. T. Bach-metjeff and J. Wsharoff, K. Bornemann, G. Tam-mann, D. Mazzotto, G. W. Gressman, N. A. Puschin, E. Jänecke, and K. Honda and T. Ishigaki, and the results are summarized in Fig. 46. As empha-sized by G. McP. Smith, and N. A. Puschin, there is no sign of the formation of a chemical compound. There are two kinds of solid soln. which E. Jänecke designates α-PbHg and β-PbHg, or α-amalgam and β-amalgam.

Chemical compounds have been reported without satisfactory evidence of their individuality; thus, A. Bauer, and J. P. Joule reported *lead hemitrimercuride*, Pb_2Hg_3, a white crystalline mass of sp. gr. 12·49 at 17°; J. H. Croockewit, and J. Schumann, *lead mercuride*, PbHg; J. P. Joule, and H. Fay and E. North, *lead hemimercuride*, Pb_2Hg, in crystals isomorphous with lead, and of sp. gr. 12·11; and L. Schüz, *lead tritamercuride*, Pb_3Hg.

According to H. Fay and E. North, the amalgams of lead become more and more like a mush as the proportion of lead increases, and when the proportion has reached 65 per cent., the amalgam is quite solid. A. Battelli said that when the proportion of Hg : Pb is greater than 12 : 1, the amalgam is liquid, and solid when the proportion is less than 2 : 1. C. von Simson found that the X-radiograms corresponded with the same face-centred lattice as that of lead itself. J. Schumann, and N. A. Puschin examined the microstructure of these amalgams. H. Fay and E. North found the crystals to be like those of lead; A. C. Becquerel said that the crystals belong to the cubic system. A. Matthiessen gave for the sp. gr. of the amalgams Hg : Pb=2 : 1, 12·815 at 15·5°; 1 : 1, 12·484 at 15·7°; and 1 : 2, 11·979 at 15·9°. Observations were also made by A. T. Kupffer, J. P. Joule, C. Cattaneo, and T. W. Richards and R. N. Garrod-Thomas. E. von Maey represented the sp. vol., v, of amalgams with p per cent. of lead by $v=0.07368+0.0001422p$. G. Tammann and Q. A. Mansuri, and J. Göbel measured the hardness of these alloys. W. C. Roberts-Austen, and H. Feninger investigated the diffusion of mercury and lead. R. Lacau, and C. O. Thieme reported that lead is hardened by association with 2–5 per cent. of mercury. N. A. Puschin also noted the increased hardness imparted to lead by mercury, but the metal becomes quite brittle as the proportion of mercury approaches 20 per cent. L. Schüz found the amalgams with Hg : Pb between 1 : 1 and 2 : 7 are quite brittle. G. Meyer, and F. Schmidt measured the surface tension of dil. lead amalgams ; and E. von Schweidler found the viscosity, at different temp., of amalgams with 1 per cent. of lead ; H. Feninger also measured the viscosity.   O. Bauer and H. Arndt studied the liquation of these alloys.   N. S. Kurnakoff and S. F. Schemtschuschny measured the press. required to make the amalgam flow.   C. Cattaneo measured the thermal expansion ;   W. Ramsay measured the effect of lead on the vap. press. of mercury, and showed the results agree with the assumption that the lead is present in the amalgams in the at. state.   J. H. Hildebrand and co-workers gave for the vap. press., p. of lead amalgams at 324° : $\log (p/p_0) = \log N + 0.252/(0.31 + 0.31n)^2$, where n denotes the number of mols of mercury per mol of lead; N, the molar fraction of mercury; and p_0, the vap. press. of mercury at 324°.   L. Schüz gave 0.03458 for the sp. ht. of the 1 : 1 amalgam, and H. V. Regnault, 0.03827 between 20° and 100° ; L. Schüz found for the Hg : Pb=1 : 2 amalgam, 0.3348 ; for the 10 : 11, 0.03372 ; and for 2 : 7, 0.03050.   G. Tammann and E. Ohler measured the at. heat of soln. of lead in mercury, and found −1658 cals. at 14°, and −2172 at 97°.   The heat of soln. is the same for a gold amalgam presumably because the gold mercurides are dissociated in soln.   R. H. Gerke obtained −134 cals. for the molar free energy of lead in its mercuride.   G. Tammann and W. Jander measured the vap. press. curves of lead amalgams.   The electrical conductivity or electrical resistance of these amalgams was measured by H. Feninger, A. Lohr, A. Matthiessen and C. Vogt, G. G. Gerosa, E. von Schweidler, etc.   According to C. L. Weber, the sp. conductivities of amalgams with p parts of lead per 1000 parts of mercury, referred to the conductivity of mercury at the same temp. 15.9°–18°, are :

p .	.	0.302	1.214	2.700	6.946	10.197	13.730	17.290
Cond.	.	1.0020	1.0079	1.0171	1.0406	1.0568	1.0724	1.0773

The conductivity is increased by raising the temp. ; thus, with an amalgam having p=6.95, the conductivity at 16.8° was 1.0405, and at 80°, 1.0424 ; when p=17.29, the conductivity at 26° was 1.0876, and at 83.2°, 1.0924.   G. W. Gressman made observations at temp. down to −50°.   The effect of temp. on the conductivity was also examined by A. Larsen, C. Michaelis, R. Sabine, A. Battelli, and G. Vicentini and C. Cattaneo.   N. A. Puschin measured the e.m.f. of the cells, Pb | N-Pb(NO$_3$)$_2$ | HgPb$_n$, and found no evidence of chemical combination.   Observations on the electrode potentials of lead amalgams were made by S. Lindeck, G. Gore, J. F. Spencer, F. C. Henrici, V. Rothmund, G. Meyer, J. Roszkowsky, F. J. Mellencamp, F. Haber, J. H. Hildebrand, T. W. Richards and R. N. Garrod-Thomas, C. Hockin and H. A. Taylor, A. Oberbeck and J. Edler, etc.   R. Kremann and A. Kapaun found that on electrolysis of the lead amalgams, the lead accumulates about the cathode.   The thermoelectric properties were examined by C. L. Weber.   A. Coehn and A. Lotz found lead amalgam electropositive towards glass.

According to E. de Souza, the lead amalgams retain their mercury at 360°, but not at 440° ; and by heating the amalgams in a bath of boiling sulphur, the residue had the composition Hg : Pb=1 : 8.   V. Merz and W. Weith found that after 7 hrs. in a bath of boiling sulphur only a trace of mercury was retained, and none after 12 hrs.' heating.   According to M. N. Bannerjee, mercury cannot be completely separated from lead amalgam by distillation in vacuo, but if the amalgam be repeatedly rubbed with garlic juice, lead sulphide is formed, and in this way, mercury can be purified from lead.   The amalgams are stable in dry air, but in moist air, as P. A. von Bonsdorff, S. Lucas, and G. Vortmann showed, a black powder is formed.   G. S. Sérullas found that potassium amalgam and water separate lead from the liquid amalgam.   When lead amalgam is shaken with a violet soln. of iodine, H. Gautier and G. Charpy found that mercurous iodide is formed, and with a brown soln. of iodine, mercuric iodide.   This reaction was also examined by E. Beckmann and A. Stock.   M. G. Mellon studied the displacement of lead by copper when lead amalgam is placed in a soln. of copper nitrate ; and K. Someya, the reducing action of the amalgam on titanic sulphate, uranyl sulphate, molybdic acid, and tungstic acid. A. S. Russell and D. C. Evans studied the reducing efficiency of lead amalgam on soln. of ferric sulphate, potassium permanganate, and uranyl sulphate in dil. sulphuric acid, and interpreted the results in terms of overvoltages. J. L. Jordan prepared ternary alloys of lead, mercury, and antimony ; and H. Davy, I. P. Göbel, F. Orioli, and J. W. Döbereiner, lead, mercury, and bismuth. E. Englisch measured the electrical conductivity of alloys of lead, bismuth, and mercury. I. P. Göbel examined the lead, mercury, and sodium alloys ; and W. D. Bancroft, the zinc, lead, and mercury alloys. C. Hockin and H. A. Taylor measured the e.m.f. of the cell Pb | dil.H_2SO_4 | PbZnHg$_n$. R. B. Boulton patented a cadmium, lead, and mercury alloy; E. Jänecke studied the ternary system Pb–Hg–Cd in some detail. There were six phases—lead, cadmium, and four sets of solid soln.: α-HgPb, β-HgPb, α-HgCd, and β-HgCd. The results are summarized in Fig. 47. C. Hockin and H. A. Taylor studied the ternary alloys Pb–Hg–Cu, and Pb–Hg–Zn. R. Kremann and co-workers studied the electrical properties of the Pb–Cd–Hg alloys. G. Tammann and W. Jander measured the vap. press. curves of lead-silver, and lead-gold amalgams.

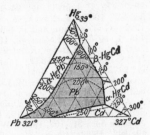

Fig. 47. — Freezing - point Curves of the Ternary System : Pb–Hg–Cd.

References.

[1] H. Moissan, *Ann. Chim. Phys.*, (7), **18**. 295, 1899 ; *Compt. Rend.*, **125**. 839, 1897 ; H. Caron, *ib.*, **48**. 440, 1859 ; L. Hackspill, *ib.*, **143**. 227, 1906 ; G. J. Kroll, *Canada. Pat. No.* 221726, 1922 ; R. T. Rolfe, *Journ. Inst. Metals*, **25**. 171, 1921 ; *Amer. Machinist*, **49**. 524, 1908 ; L. Donsky, *Zeit. anorg. Chem.*, **53**. 208, 1908 ; O. Ruff and H. Hartman, *ib.*, **126**. 167, 1922 ; N. Baar, *ib.*, **70**. 352, 1911 ; G. Tammann, *ib.*, **118**. 92, 1921 ; K. Jellinek and G. Tomoff, *Zeit. phys. Chem.*, **111**. 234, 1924 ; K. Jellinek and J. Czerwinsky, *ib.*, **110**. 192, 1924 ; *Zeit. anorg. Chem.*, **139**. 233, 1924 ; K. Jellinek and J. Wolff, *ib.*, **146**. 329, 1925 ; J. Czochralsky and A. Welter, *Lagermetalle und ihre technologische Bewertung*, Berlin, 1920 ; J. Czochralsky and E. Rassow, *Zeit. Metallkunde*, **12**. 337, 1920 ; J. Czochralsky, *ib.*, **12**. 373, 1920 ; E. Heyn, *ib.*, **12**. 399, 1920 ; W. Mathesius, *Brit. Pat. No.* 185124, 1922 ; *German Pat.*, *D.R.P.* 355429, 1920 ; *Zeit. Metallkunde*, **12**. 394, 1920 ; E. Piwowarsky, *ib.*, **14**. 300, 1920 ; Maschinenbau-Anstalt Humboldt, *German Pat.*, *D.R.P.* 297210, 1915 ; W. Kroll, *ib.*, 381577, 386602, 1916 ; Metallbank und Metallurgische Gesellschaft, *ib.*, 301380, 307672, 1917 ; 334475, 359812, 381577, 1919 ; United Lead Co., *ib.*, 323853, 323856, 1917 ; A. Hart, *Metall Technik*, **46**. 73, 1920 ; C. A. Kraus and H. F. Kurtz, *Journ. Amer. Chem. Soc.*, **47**. 43, 1925 ; W. Moldenhauer and J. Andersen, *Zeit. Electrochem.*, **19**. 446, 1913 ; F. von Kügelgen, *ib.*, **7**. 541, 557, 573, 1901 ; H. Goldschmidt, *ib.*, **4**. 497, 1898 ; *Liebig's Ann.*, **301**. 25, 1898 ; *Zeit. angew. Chem.*, **11**. 823, 1898 ; C. V. Burton, *Nature*, **72**. 397, 1905 ; F. M. Perkin and L. Pratt, *Trans. Faraday Soc.*, **3**. 179, 1908 ; E. A. Ashcroft, *ib.*, **14**. 271, 1919 ; *Chem. Met. Engg.*, **20**. 594, 1919 ; F. C. Frary and S. N. Temple, *ib.*, **19**. 523, 1918 ; L. Filipoff, *Metal Ind.*, **22**. 146, 1923 ; C. O. Thieme, *Journ. Ind. Eng. Chem.*, **12**. 446, 1920 ; J. N. Pring, *Journ. Chem. Soc.*, **87**. 1538, 1905 ; N. Tarugi, *Gazz. Chim. Ital.*, **29**. i, 512, 1899 ; M. Wählert, *Met.*, **17**. 232, 1920 ; B. Setlik, *Chem. Ztg.*, **29**. 219, 1905 ; E. Scheurer, *ib.*, **34**. 421, 1910 ; W. A. Cowan, L. D. Simpkins, and G. O. Hiers, *Trans. Amer. Electrochem. Soc.*, **40**. 27, 1921 ; *Chem. Met. Engg.*, **25**. 1182, 1921 ; E. Kordes, *Zeit. anorg. Chem.*, **154**. 97, 1926.

[2] J. Parkinson, *Journ. Chem. Soc.*, **20**. 117, 1867 ; C. T. Heycock and F. H. Neville, *ib.*, **61**. 888, 1892 ; *Chem. News*, **62**. 280, 1890 ; A. von Vegesack, *Zeit. anorg. Chem.*, **54**. 391, 1907 ; G. Grube, *ib.*, **44**. 117, 1905 ; G. Massing, *ib.*, **62**. 275, 1909 ; W. Jenge, *ib.*, **118**. 119, 1921 ; N. S. Kurnakoff and N. J. Stepanoff, *ib.*, **46**. 179, 1905 ; *Journ. Russ. Phys. Chem. Soc.*, **34**. 520, 1902 ; **37**. 668, 1905 ; N. J. Stepanoff, *ib.*, **39**. 1151, 1907 ; *Zeit. anorg. Chem.*, **60**. 209, 1908 ; P. Ludwik, *ib.*, **94**. 161, 1916 ; G. Tammann, *ib.*, **53**. 454, 1907 ; **118**. 92, 1921 ; W. Jenge, *ib.*, **118**. 105, 1921 ; C. Winkler, *Ber.*, **24**. 873, 1891 ; E. Beck, *Met.*, **5**. 509, 1908 ; H. Hanemann and W. Stockmeyer, *German Pat.*, *D.R.P.* 305087, 1915 ; United Lead Co., *ib.*, 323855, 1917 ; *U.S. Pat. No.* 1360347, 1919 ; D. Stenquist, *ib.*, 1360045, 1919 ; E. A. Ashcroft, *Trans. Faraday Soc.*, **14**. 271, 1919 ; *Chem. Met. Engg.*, **20**. 594, 1919 ; *Chem. Trade Journ.*, **65**. 224, 1919 ; *Brit. Pat. No.* 125714, 1918 ; A. J. Berry, *Proc. Cambridge Phil. Soc.*, **17**. 33, 1913 ; C. O. Thieme, *Journ. Ind. Eng. Chem.*, **12**. 446, 1920 ; R. Kremann and J. Gmachl-Pammer, *Zeit. Metallkunde*,

12. 358, 1920; I. P. Göbel, *ib.*, 14. 357, 1922; W. Guertler, *ib.*, 13. 245, 1921; P. Sustschinsky, *Zeit. Kryst.*, 38. 265, 1903; A. Sacklowsky, *Ann. Physik,* (4), 77. 241, 1926; R. B. Friauf, *Journ. Amer. Chem. Soc.*, 48. 1906, 1926; E. Kordes, *Zeit. anorg. Chem.*, 154. 97, 1926.

³ S. Konno, *Science Rep. Tohoku Univ.*, 10. 57, 1921; J. F. Gmelin, *Comment. Gött.*, 10. 28, 1790; J. Fournet, *Ann. Mines*, (3), 4. 235, 1833; C. T. Heycock and F. H. Neville, *Journ. Chem. Soc.*, 61. 888, 1892; 71. 394, 1897; *Chem. News*, 62. 280, 1890; P. T. Arnemann, *Met.* 7. 201, 1910; P. Müller, *ib.*, 7. 771, 1910; W. Spring and L. Romanoff, *Zeit. anorg. Chem.*, 13. 29, 1897; P. Ludwik, *ib.*, 94. 161, 1916; W. Reinders, *ib.*, 25. 131, 1900; G. Tammann, *ib.* 53. 453, 1907; F. Novak, *ib.*, 47. 421, 1905; G. Tammann and W. Wiederholt, *ib.*, 125. 85, 1922; G. Tammann and P. Schafmeister, *ib.*, 138. 219, 1924; G. Tammann and O. Dahl, *ib.* 144. 1, 1925; P. Fuchs, *ib.*, 109. 80, 1919; G. N. Potdar, *Journ. Coll. Science Tokyo*, 25. 9, 1907; C. J. B. Karsten, *Karsten's Arch.*, 16. 597, 1829; 26. 295, 1834; A. Parkes, *Brit. Pat. Nos* 13118, 1850; 13997, 1852; J. and T. Hall, *ib.*, 5551, 1827; G. T. Key, *ib.*, 293, 1864; J. S. Rae, *ib.*, 27730, 1910; B. Bogitch, *Compt. Rend.*, 159. 178, 1914; W. Alexéeff, *Journ. Russ. Phys. Chem. Soc.*, 17. 282, 1885; W. Campbell, *Journ. Franklin Inst.*, 154. 1, 131, 201, 1902; W. Campbell and J. Mathews, *Journ. Amer. Chem. Soc.*, 24. 253, 1902; L. Pitkin, *ib.*, 5. 228, 1883; A. Arche and C. Hassack, *Dingler's Journ.*, 253. 514, 1884; M. Beuling, *ib.*, 270. 172, 1888, *Zeit. Ver. deut. Ing.*, 31. 117, 1887; J. Percy, *Chem. Gaz.*, 8. 1, 1850; W. A. Naish, *Trans. Faraday Soc.*, 21. 102, 1925; W. Flight, *Journ. Chem. Soc.*, 41. 134, 1882; W. N. Hartley, *ib.* 69. 842, 1896; *Chem. News*, 73. 229, 1896; J. J. Rein, *Japan*, Leipzig, 2. 525, 1886; V. A. Skinder, *Bull. Acad. St. Petersburg*, (6), 2. 209, 1908; *Mitt. Kankasisch Museums*, 3. 1, 1907; L. Guillet, *Rev. Mét.*, 2. 101, 1905; H. Niclassen, *Das System Kupfer-Zink-Blei*, Berlin, 1922; *Forsch. Mettalkunde*, 7, 1922; W. D. Bancroft, *Journ. Phys. Chem.*, 3. 217, 1899; N. Parravano, C. Mazzetti, and R. Moretti, *Gazz. Chim. Ital.*, 44. ii, 475, 1914; R. Kremann and F. Hofmeier, *Monatsh.*, 32. 563, 597, 1911; H. Behrens, *Das mikroskopische Gefüger der Metalle und Legierungen*, Hamburg, 56, 1894; B. E. Curry, *Journ. Phys. Chem.*, 13. 602, 1909; E. von Maey, *Zeit. phys. Chem.*, 50. 215, 1905; M. Centnerswer, *ib.*, 92. 563, 1918; F. A. Schulze, *Zeit. Metallkunde*, 13. 178, 1921; J. Göbel, *ib.*, 14. 362, 1922; R. Kremann and J. Gmachl-Pammer, *ib.*, 12. 358, 1920; R. Kremann and R. Knabl, *Forsch. Metallkunde*, 13, 1922; M. Levi-Malvano and O. Ceccarelli, *Gazz. Chim. Ital.*, 41. ii, 317, 1911; R. Hoyt, *U.S. Pat. No.* 897953, 1908; C. W. Merril, *ib.*, 1063568, 1913; F. Hoffmann, *German Pat.*, *D.R.P.* 299724, 1919; C. Mark, *ib.*, 319734, 1915; Lohmann Co., *ib.*, 248665, 1911; Metallbank and Metallurgische Gesellschaft. *ib.*, 363125, 363126, 363127, 366189, 1918; T. Hunger, *ib.*, 309243, 1918; H. Hanemann and W. Stockmeyer, *ib.*, 339640, 1915; H. Rainy and R. D. Clackson, *Proc. Roy. Soc. Edin.*, 13. 686, 1886; O. Bauer and H. Arndt, *Stahl Eisen*, 42. 1346, 1822; N. Hesehus and N. Georgiewsky, *Journ. Russ. Phys. Chem. Soc.*, 37. 38, 1905; A. V. Tidblom, *Acta Univ. Lund.* 9. 6, 1873; 10. 3, 1874; *Termolektriska undersokningar*, Lund, 13, 1873; I. P. Göbel, *Zeit. Metallkunde*, 14. 357, 388, 425, 449, 1922; E. Matthey, *Proc. Roy. Soc.*, 60. 21, 1896; A. Guettier, *Dingler's Journ.*, 114. 128, 196, 279, 1849; A. P. Laurie, *Journ. Chem. Soc.*, 55. 677, 1889; A. Matthiessen, *B.A. Rep.*, 37, 1868; A. Matthiessen and M. von Bose, *Proc. Roy. Soc.*, 11. 430, 1862; D. Mazzotto, *Rend 1st. Lombardo*, (3), 18. 165, 1885; F. Mylius and O. Fromm, *Ber.*, 27. 630, 1894; *Zeit. anorg. Chem.*, 9. 144, 1895; F. Mylius and R. Funk, *ib.*, 13. 153, 1897; F. Reich, *Journ. prakt. Chem.*, (1), 78. 328, 1859; W. Rollmann, *Pogg. Ann.* 83. 77, 1851; 84. 275, 1851; 89. 90, 1853; W. Spring, *Bull. Acad. Belg.*, (3), 28. 23, 1894; *Zeit. phys. Chem.*, 15. 65, 1894; J. Tayler, *Phil. Mag.*, (5), 50. 37, 1900; G. Wertheim, *Ann. Chim. Phys.*, (3), 12. 581, 1844; C. R. A. Wright, *Journ. Soc. Chem. Ind.*, 13. 1014, 1894; *Proc. Roy. Soc.*, 50. 372, 1893; C. R. A. Wright and C. Thompson, *ib.*, 48. 25, 1891; F. Osmond and J. Werth, *Compt. Rend..* 104. 1802, 1887; W. Heike, *Metall Erz*, 16. 469, 1924; G. N. Potdar in J. Sakurai, *Jubilee Collection of Papers*, Tokyo, 9, 1908; F. Doeblin, *German Pat., D.R.PP* 367078, 382545, 423450, 1923; G. K. Williams, *Proc. Austral. Inst. Min. Met.*, 47, 1925.

⁴ B. Wood, *Chem. News*, 6. 135, 1862; *Journ. Franklin Inst.*, 70. 113, 1860; 73. 61, 1862; *Amer. Journ. Science*, (2), 33. 276, 1862; A. Matthiessen, *Pogg. Ann.*, 110. 190, 1860; *Phil. Trans.*, 150. 161, 1860; *B.A. Rep.*, 37, 1868; *Journ. Chem. Soc.*, 20. 201, 1867 A. Matthiessen and C. Vogt, *Pogg. Ann.*, 116. 369, 1862; *Phil. Mag.*, (4), 23. 171, 1862; A. Stoffel, *Zeit. anorg Chem.*, 53. 152, 1907; P. Fuchs, *ib.*, 109. 80, 1919; P. Ludwik, *ib.*, 94. 168, 1916; R. Kremann and P. G. von Rehenburg, *ib.*, 140. 1, 1924; R. Kremann, H. Prammer, and L. Helly, *ib.*, 127. 295, 1923; R. Kremann and A. Kapaun, *ib.*, 140. 183, 1924; W. Kremann and A. Langsbauer, *ib.*, 127. 240, 1923; G. Tammann and W. Wiederholt, *ib.*, 125. 67, 1922; G. Tammann and K. Dahl, *ib.*, 126. 117, 1923; R. Kremann, H. Kienzl, and R. Markl, *Monatsh.*, 45. 157, 1924; W. E. Barlow, *Zeit. anorg. Chem.*, 70. 183, 1911; *Journ. Amer. Chem. Soc.*, 32. 1390, 1910; C. P. Steinmetz *ib.*, 40. 100, 1918; A. W. Kapp, *Ueber vollständige Gefrierpunktskurven binärer Metallegierungen*, Königsberg, 1901; *Ann. Physik*, (4), 6. 754, 1901; M. Herschkowitsch, *Zeit. phys. Chem.*, 27. 123, 1898; E. von Maey, *ib.*, 38. 292, 1901; W. Stockmeyer and H. Hanemann, *German Pat. D.R.P.* 309758, 1916; Metallbank und Metallurgische Gesellschaft, *ib.*, 301380, 1917; United Lead Co., *ib.*, 323855, 1917; A. M. Portevin, *Journ. Inst. Metals*, 29. 239, 1923; A. Battelli, *Atti 1st. Veneto*, (6), 5. 1137, 1887; C. di Capua, *Atti Accad. Lincei*, (5), 31, i, 162, 1922; C. T. Heycock and F. H. Neville, *Chem. News*, 62. 280, 1890; *Journ. Chem. Soc.*, 57. 376, 656, 1890; 61. 888, 1892; 65. 65, 1894; A. P. Laurie, *ib.*, 55. 677, 1889; 65. 1031, 1894; H. le Chatelier, *Bull. Soc. Enc. Nat. Ind.*, (4), 10. 192, 1895; D. Mazzotti, *Rend. 1st. Lombardo* (2), 18. 165, 1885; F. Mylius and O. Fromm, *Ber.*, 27. 630, 1894; *Zeit. anorg. Chem.*, 9. 114

1895; F. Mylius and R. Funk, *ib.*, 13. 158, 1897; C. R. A. Wright, *Journ. Soc. Chem. Ind.*, 13. 1014, 1894; C. R. A. Wright and C. Thompson, *Proc. Roy. Soc.*, 48. 25, 1891; E. Becquerel, *Ann. Chim. Phys.*, (4), 8. 389, 411, 1866; N. W. Taylor, *Journ. Amer. Chem. Soc.*, 45. 2865, 1923; M. Cook, *Metal Ind.*, 24. 282, 1924; *Journ. Inst. Metals*, 31. 297, 1924; F. L. Brady, *Journ. Inst. Metals*, 28. 377, 1922; M. Wählert, *Met.*, 17. 231, 1920; W. Kaiser, *ib.*, 8. 306, 1911; P. Müller, *ib.*, 7. 769, 1910; E. Jänecke, *Zeit. phys. Chem.*, 60. 399, 1907; Accumulatoren-Fabrik, German Pat., *D.R.P.* 320096, 1917; W. Stockmeyer and H. Hanemann, *ib.*, 352471, 1916; G. P. Luckey, *U.S. Pat. No.* 1333666, 1918; W. Guertler, *Jahrb. Rad. Elektron.*, 5. 41, 1908; B. Beckman, *Ark. Mat. Astr. Fysik*, 7. 1, 1912; C. W. Hill, *Chem. Met. Engg.*, 19. 170, 1918; T. R. Merton, *Proc. Roy. Soc.*, 96. A, 388, 1920; W. Mathesius, *Brit. Pat. No.* 156552, 1921; I. P. Göbel, *Zeit. Metallkunde*, 14. 362, 1922; A. Schulze, *ib.*, 31. 321, 1924; L. Pitkin, *Journ. Amer. Chem. Soc.*, 5. 228, 1883; C. von Hauer, *Journ. prakt. Chem.*, (1), 94. 436, 1865; C. G. Fink and L. C. Pan, *Trans. Amer. Electrochem. Soc.*, 46. 129, 1924; F. Sauerwald, *Zeit. anorg. Chem.*, 153. 319. 1926; A. Magnus and M. Mannheimer, *Zeit. phys. Chem.*, 121. 267, 1926; K. Honda and T. Ishigaki, *Science Rep. Tohoku Univ.*, 14. 219, 1925.

⁵ J. Schumann, *Wied. Ann.*, 43. 113, 1891; *Untersuchungen von Amalgamen*, Erlangen, 1891; W. Kettembeil, *Studien über elektrolytische Amalgambildung und versuche zur Metalltrennung durch Amalgambildung*, Leipzig, 1903; *Zeit. anorg. Chem.*, 38. 215, 1904; J. H. Croockewit, *Specimen chemicum de conjunctionibus chemicis metallorum*, Amsterdam, 1848; *Journ. prakt. Chem.*, (1), 45. 87, 1848; R. Böttger, *ib.*, (1), 3. 283, 1834; J. L. Jordan, *ib.*, (1), 10. 439, 1837; J. C. Poggendorff, *Pogg. Ann.*, 50. 255, 1840; F. C. Henrici, *ib.*, 58. 376, 1843; D. Mazzotto, *Atti Ist. Lombardo*, (2), 18. 165, 1884; *Atti Ist. Veneto*, (7), 4. 1311, 1527, 1893; E. N. Horsford, *Amer. Journ. Science*, (2), 13. 305, 1852; A. Gouy, *Journ. Phys.*, 4. 320, 1895; J. Nicklès, *Compt. Rend.*, 36. 154, 1853; H. Gautier and G. Charpy, *ib.*, 111. 645, 1890; J. Regnauld, *ib.*, 52. 534, 1861; A. C. Becquerel, *ib.*, 56. 237, 1863; 75. 1729, 1872; *Mém. Acad.*, 38. 499, 1873; J. F. Daniell, *Journ. Roy. Inst.*, 1. 1, 1831; C. Hockin and H. A. Taylor, *Journ. Soc. Tel. Eng.*, 8. 282, 1879; W. J. Humphreys, *Journ. Chem. Soc.*, 69. 250, 1896; C. T. Heycock and F. H. Neville, *Chem. News*, 62. 280, 1890; *Journ. Chem. Soc.*, 57. 376, 1890; 61. 888, 1892; W. Ramsay, *ib.*, 55. 533, 1889; J. P. Joule, *ib.*, 16. 378, 1863; *Chem. Gaz.*, 8. 339, 1850; *B.A. Rep.*, 55, 1850; J. Henry, *Bibl. Univ. Genève*, (2), 29. 175, 1841; G. Tammann and Q. A. Mansuri, *Zeit. anorg. Chem.*, 132. 65, 1924; K. Someya, *ib.*, 145. 168, 1925; 148. 58, 1925; R. Lacau, *Éclair Élect.*, 46. 369, 1906; G. Vortmann, *Ber.*, 24. 2756, 1891; V. Merz and W. Weith, *ib.*, 14. 1441, 1881; E. de Souza, *ib.*, 9. 1050, 1876; A. Bauer, *ib.*, 4. 450, 1871; H. Fay and E. North, *Amer. Chem. Journ.*, 25. 216, 1901; A. McP. Smith, *ib.*, 36. 135, 1906; G. W. Gressman, *Phys. Rev.*, (1), 9. 20, 1899; F. J. Mellencamp, *ib.*, (1), 29. 329, 1909; H. Davy, *Elements of Chemical Philosophy*, London, 1812; F. Orioli, *Collez. di Op. Scient.*, 104, 1823; *Bull. Ferusac Math. Phys. Chim.*, 117, 1825; J. W. Döbereiner, *Kastner's Arch.*, 3. 90, 1824; *Schweigger's Journ.*, 42. 182, 1824; I. P. Göbel, *ib.*, 48. 486, 1826; W. D. Bancroft, *Journ. Phys. Chem.*, 3. 217, 1899; R. B. Boulton, *Brit. Pat. No.* 1970, 1896; F. Haber, *Zeit. phys. Chem.*, 41. 399, 1902; H. Feninger, *Die elektrische Leitfähigkeit und innere Reibung, verdünnter Amalgame*, Freiburg i. Br., 1914; A. Lohr, *Ueber Widerstandsänderungen von Amalgamen und einigen leichtschmelzbaren Legierungen mit der Temperatur und der Zeit*, Erlangen, 1914; C. Michaelis, *Ueber die elektrische Leitfähigkeit verunreinigten Quecksilbers und die Methoden zur Reinigung desselben*, Berlin, 1883; W. C. Roberts-Austen, *Phil. Trans.*, 187. A, 383, 1896; E. Jänecke, *Zeit. phys. Chem.*, 60. 400, 1907; E. Beckmann and A. Stock, *ib.*, 17. 129, 1895; J. Roszkowsky, *ib.*, 15. 307, 1894; E. von Maey, *ib.*, 38. 295, 1901; G. Tammann, *ib.*, 3. 445, 1889; T. W. Richards and R. N. Garrod-Thomas, *ib.*, 72. 174, 1910; E. von Maey, *ib.*, 38. 295, 1901; V. Rothmund, *ib.*, 15. 17, 1894; P. T. Bachmetjeff and J. Wsharoff, *Journ. Russ. Phys. Chem. Soc.*, 25. 237, 1893; N. A. Puschin, *ib.*, 32. 635, 1900; 34. 856, 1902; *Zeit. anorg. Chem.*, 36. 209, 1903; G. Tammann and W. Jander, *ib.*, 124. 105, 1922; G. Tammann and E. Ohler, *ib.*, 135. 118, 1924; M. N. Bannerjee, *ib.*, 83. 113, 1913; J. Göbel, *ib.*, 106. 209, 1909; R. Kremann, H. Prammer, and L. Helly, *ib.*, 127. 295, 1923; R. Kremann and A. Kapaun, *ib.*, 140. 183, 1924; N. S. Kurnakoff and S. T. Schemtschuschny, *Journ. Russ. Met. Soc.*, 1. 256, 1913; I. P. Goebel, *Zeit. Metallkunde*, 14. 357, 388, 425, 449, 1922; O. Bauer and H. Arndt, *ib.*, 13. 497, 1921; K. Bornemann, *Met.*, 7. 109, 1910; L. Schüz, *Wied. Ann.*, 46. 193, 1892; A. Oberbeck and J. Edler, *ib.*, 42. 209, 1891; E. Englisch, *ib.*, 45. 593, 1892; S. Lindeck, *ib.*, 35. 328, 1888; C. L. Weber, *ib.*, 23. 471, 1884; 31. 243, 1887; G. Meyer, *ib.*, 40. 244, 1890; 53. 848, 1894; 61. 225, 1897; *Zeit. phys. Chem.*, 7. 482, 1891; A. Battelli, *Mem. Accad. Lincei*, (4), 4. 206, 1887; *Atti Accad. Lincei*, (4), 3. ii, 37, 1887; G. G. Gerosa, *ib.*, (4), 2. 344, 1887; G. Vicentini and C. Cattaneo, *ib.*, (5), 1. i, 343, 1892; C. Cattaneo, *Atti Accad. Torino*, 25. 342, 492, 1890; S. Lucas, *Trommsdorff's Journ. Pharm.*, 10. 1, 1825; A. Matthiessen, *Pogg. Ann.*, 110. 21, 1860; P. A. von Bonsdorff, *ib.*, 41. 305, 1837; A. Matthiessen and C. Vogt, *ib.*, 116. 373, 1862; *Phil. Mag.*, (4), 23. 171, 1862; F. Guthrie, *ib.*, (5), 16. 321, 1883; R. Sabine, *ib.*, (4), 23. 457, 1862; E. von Schweidler, *Sitzber. Akad. Wien*, 104. 278, 1905; A. Coehn and A. Lotz, *Zeit. Physik*, 5. 242, 1921; A. T. Kupffer, *Ann. Chim. Phys.*, (2), 40. 293, 1829; G. S. Sérullas, *ib.*, (2), 34. 192, 1827; H. V. Regnault, *ib.*, (3), 1. 129, 1841; C. O. Thieme, *Journ. Ind. Eng. Chem.*, 12. 446, 1920; A. Larsen, *Ann. Physik*, (4), 1. 123, 1900; F. Schmidt, *ib.*, (4), 39. 1108, 1912; J. F. Spencer, *Zeit. Elektrochem.*, 11. 683, 1905; G. Gore, *Chem. News*, 61. 40, 1890; J. H. Hildebrand, *Journ. Amer. Chem. Soc.*, 35. 510, 1913; J. H. Hildebrand, A. H. Foster, and C. W. Beebe, *ib.*, 42. 545, 1920; G. Tammann and E. Ohler, *Zeit. anorg. Chem.*, 135. 118, 1924; G. Tammann

and Q. A. Mansuri, *ib.*, **132.** 65, 1923 ; J. Tomes, *Trans. Odontol. Soc.*, (1), **3.** 126, 1861 ;
C. S. Tomes, *ib.*, (2), **4.** 135, 1872 ; A. Kirby, *ib.*, (2), **4.** 189, 1872 ; T. B. Hitchcock, *Trans. New York Odontol. Soc.*, 26, 1874 ; T. Fletcher, *Brit. Journ. Dental Science,* **15.** 253, 1872 ; A. Witze, *Compendium der Pathologie und Therapie der Pulpakrankheiten des Zahnes,* Hagen, 195, 1886 ;
C. von Simson, *Zeit. phys. Chem.*, **109.** 183, 1924 ; R. H. Gerke, *Journ. Amer. Chem. Soc.*, **44.** 1686, 1922 ; **45.** 2507, 1923 ; M. G. Mellon, *ib.*, **44.** 2167, 1922 ; R. S. Russell and D. C. Evans, *Journ. Chem. Soc.*, **127.** 2221, **1925 ;** K. Honda **and** T. Ishigaki, *Science Rep. Tohoku Univ.* **14.** 219, 1925.

§ 10. Alloys of Lead with Aluminium, Indium, Thallium, and Tin

H. St. C. Deville [1] said that lead and *aluminium* have so small a tendency to form alloys that any small piece of lead which may have dropped into the metal may be recovered intact at the bottom of an ingot of the aluminium. A. J. Rogers made an alloy by the electrolysis of molten cryolite and sodium aluminium tetrachloride with a lead cathode ; and C. Tissier, by reducing lead oxide with aluminium —the reaction proceeds with explosive violence. These products are not alloys in the usual sense of the term, for if the two metals be melted together, or lead added to molten aluminium, alloys may exist at certain temp., but on cooling, the aluminium separates, and chilling first, floats on the surface of the molten lead. Similar observations were made by C. R. A. Wright, C. H. Hirzel, W. Campbell and J. A. Mathews, H. Schirmeister, etc. S. Mierzinsky said that this property would render it possible to use aluminium in place of zinc for desilverizing bullion, provided the cost was not too great. According to H. Pécheux, homogeneous alloys with 2–7 per cent. of lead can be obtained if they are rapidly chilled, but if more than 10 per cent. of lead be present, three layers are formed—the bottom layer consisting of lead, the top layer of aluminium, and a middle layer with 90–97 per cent. aluminium. J. W. Richards said that by cooling an ingot of the alloy slowly, he observed 94·49 per cent. lead in the lower part of the ingot, and 9·78 per cent. in the upper part. C. R. A. Wright found only 0·07 per cent. aluminium in the lower layer and 1·92 per cent. of lead in the upper layer. C. T. Heycock and F. H. Neville observed **no lowering of** the m.p. of aluminium by lead. According to A. G. C. Gwyer, the two metals are immiscible, and the cooling curves give two fixed points corresponding respectively with the m.p. of aluminium and of lead, Fig. 48. The reports of the presence of aluminium in the lead layer and of lead in the aluminium layer are due to the formation of a kind of emulsion, or to the mechanical entanglement of the one metal in the other. The dotted lines in the diagram are intended to indicate that above the m.p. of aluminium the two metals become mutually soluble in one another, and this the more the higher the temp. The presence of antimony is said to make the lead dissolve more aluminium, and alloys of lead, aluminium, and antimony have been patented by I. H. Johannes, C. B. Miller, and T. MacKellar. W. Campbell and co-workers studied the microstructure of these alloys. According to H. Pécheux, the colour of alloys with 2–7 per cent. of lead is very little different from that of aluminium ; the sp. gr. of the alloy with 2 per cent. lead is 2·600 ; with 4 per cent., 2·671 ; with 5 per cent., 2·674 ; with 6 per cent., 2·691 ; with 7 per cent., 2·745 ; and with 8 per cent., 2·765. P. Ludwik measured the hardness of these alloys, and it appears to be less than that of aluminium. H. Schirmeister found the tensile strength of aluminium falls from 10·5 kgrms. per sq. mm. to 10·0 kgrms. per sq. mm. when 4 per cent. of lead

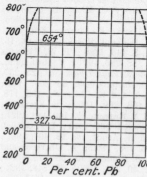

FIG. 48.—Freezing-point Curves of Lead-Aluminium Alloys.

is present. H. Pécheux measured the thermoelectric force of the alloy against copper, and found at 100° with lead alone 211·96 microvolts; with 94 per cent. aluminium, 113·55 microvolts, and with aluminium alone, 162·75 microvolts. H. Schirmeister said that alloys with 4 per cent. of lead are stable. According to H. Pécheux, each alloy is merely a mol. juxtaposition of the two metals, for on melting and drawing into rods of much smaller diameter the composition is altered, the alloy becoming richer in lead; thus, from the three alloys containing respectively 93, 95, and 98 per cent. of aluminium, three new ones were obtained containing 92, 94, and 96 per cent. of aluminium. The alloys are not acted on by moist air; hydrochloric acid dissolves the aluminium at 13°; conc. sulphuric acid dissolves both metals, liberating hydrogen at 13° and sulphur dioxide on heating; conc. nitric acid has very little action at the ordinary temp., but an energetic one on heating; the dil. acid has little or no action; conc. potassium hydroxide or aqua regia dissolves them readily in the cold; hydrogen sulphide blackens the alloys containing 92–93 per cent. of aluminium, and distilled water is without action even at 100°. The United Lead Co., and H. Hanemann and W. Stockmeyer respectively patented alloys of lead with calcium, and with magnesium. C. R. A. Wright, and W. D. Bancroft examined the ternary alloys Ag–Al–Pb; C. R. A. Wright, Al–Pb–Sb and Al–Pb–Bi alloys; and C. R. A. Wright, T. A. Bayliss, and B. G. Clark, and C. A. J. H. and H. E. R. Schroeder, Al–Zn–Pb alloys. G. Tammann and P. Schafmeister measured the partition coeff. of copper, silver, gold, magnesium, tin, and antimony between aluminium and lead.

Lead and *indium* form an ismorphous mixture in all proportions and the solid soln. crystallize in the cubic system. J. L. Haughton and G. W. Ford [2] showed that the two constituents do not crystallize in the same habit, but that the tetragonal lattice of indium differs from the face-centred cube of lead only by an elongation of 6 per cent. in the direction of one of the axes. N. S. Kurnakoff and N. A. Puschin found that the addition of 10 at. per cent. of lead to indium has very little effect on the m.p. of the latter, Fig. 49, but further additions give almost a straight line

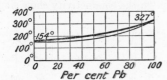

FIG. 49.—Freezing-point Curve of Mixtures of Lead and Indium.

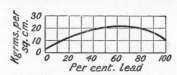

FIG. 50.—The Pressure required to produce a Flow of the Lead-Indium Alloys.

in the direction of the m.p. of lead. The press. necessary to cause these alloys to flow was measured by N. S. Kurnakoff and S. F. Schemtschuschny, and the results are shown in Fig. 50. They also measured the electrical conductivity, Fig. 51, and the temp. coeff. of alloys which form a continuous series of solid soln. G. Borelius also measured the electrical conductivity of the solid lead-indium alloys; and J. A. M. van Liempt, the X-radiograms.

The alloys of *thallium* and lead were examined by L. Rolla,[3] D. Mazzotto, L. Guillet, N. S. Kurnakoff and N. A. Puschin, W. Crookes, E. Carstanjen, and K. Lewkonja. The f.p. curve, Fig. 52, has a transition point at 309° or 309·5° corresponding with 5–5·5 at. per cent. of lead; in this region solid soln. are formed containing 0–5·5 at. per cent. of lead, and they crystallize in the same form as thallium. The f.p. curve then rises to a maximum at 374° (K. Lewkonja), or 380° (N. S. Kurnakoff and N. A. Puschin), and then falls to 327·7°, the m.p. of lead. The solid phase here deposited consists of solid soln. with 25–100 at. per cent. of lead, and crystallizes in octahedra belonging to the cubic system. P. Fuchs said that solid soln. are formed only beyond the limit 73 at. per cent. of thallium. The transformation temp. of the sat. solid soln. is 144·5°. The at.

ratio of lead to thallium corresponding with the maximum temp. varies from 1 : 1·67 to 1 : 1·83 for different preparations of lead and thallium, and this is taken by N. S. Kurnakoff and N. A. Puschin to indicate the existence of a solid indefinite compound. H. Endo also studied this diagram. K. Lewkonja interprets

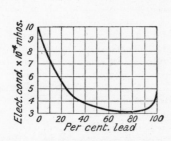

FIG. 51.—The Electrical Conductivity of Lead-Indium Alloys.

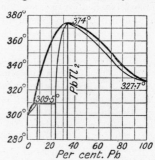

FIG. 52.—Freezing-point Curves of Lead-Thallium Alloys.

the maximum to be the f.p. of **thallium hemiplumbide**, Tl_2Pb. The existence of this compound is not definitely established. L. Rolla showed that the curves of the sp. vol., hardness, electrical conductivity, and thermoelectric power afford no evidence of a compound. C. di Capua measured the hardness of these alloys. The alloys are very soft and easily oxidized. He found that with as little as 0·5 per cent. of lead, the transition point of thallium is no longer appreciable. G. D. Roos gave 7·6 cals. per gram for the heat of formation. C. T. Heycock and F. H. Neville measured the lowering of the f.p. of lead by thallium ; and A. W. Smith, the thermal conductivity. N. S. Kurnakoff and co-worker's measurements of the resistance offered by these alloys to flow, Fig. 53, and of the electrical conductivity, Fig. 54, and of the effect of temp. on the conductivity show singular

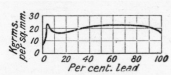

FIG. 53.—The Pressure of Flow of the Thallium-Lead Alloys.

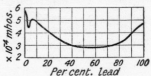

FIG. 54.—Electrical Conductivity of the Thallium-Lead Alloys.

points where the lead and thallium form isomorphous mixtures. The addition of lead to thallium causes a decrease in the electrical conductivity and in the temp. coeff. of the resistance ; this decrease is followed by an increase which extends to the conc. at which the soln. is sat. with lead. The straight line portion of the curve between 5 and 25 per cent. of lead indicates where the alloys are mechanical mixtures of two crystalline phases. W. Guertler and A. Schulze found no evidence of a compound in their study of the electrical conductivity of these alloys. G. Tammann and W. Wiederholt, W. Jenge, E. Bekier, and R. Kremann and A. Lobinger studied the electrode potential and chemical behaviour of these alloys ; and H. Endo, the magnetic susceptibility. R. Kremann and A. Lobinger found no evidence of the formation of a compound, but rather of solid soln., in their study of the electrochemical behaviour of these alloys. C. C. Fink and C. H. Eldridge studied the corrosive action of acid soln. of cupric sulphate. E. Carstanjen studied the Pb–Tl–Bi alloys ; and C. di Capua, the Pb–Tl–Cd alloys.

Lead and *tin* can be alloyed in all proportions, and are easily made by fusing the

two metals together in the desired proportions. The alloys were made and used by
the Romans. They were mentioned in the first century of our era by Pliny in his
Historia naturalis (**34**. 17, 48) ; and in the second century, G Galen, in his *De
antiodotis epitomis* (**1**. 175), drew attention to the danger attending the use of tin
adulterated with lead. The early alloys were discussed by R. Weber.[4] The tin-
lead alloys were examined by J. L. Proust, L. N. Vauquelin, A. Gummi, C. H. Pfaff,
J. W. Richards, D. Mazzotto, G. Nannes, J. Pohl, F. Rudberg, A. Matthiessen,
K. Honda, S. Konno, L. Peetz, R. C. Besley, D. Silow, R. H. Thurston, P. Bolley,
J. H. Croockewit, W. Richter, A. P. Laurie, C. R. A. Wright, C. Pack, M. L. Lissberger,
H. Stegmann, etc. C. H. Proctor, and W. Blum and H. E. Haring made the alloy
by electrodeposition from fluoborate soln. ; and W. Spring, by strongly compressing an intimate mixture of the powdered elements ; the two solids form an alloy
in a few hours at 150°–200°. The alloying of a mixture of the powdered metals by
press. was discussed by W. Hallock, and W. Rosenhain and P. A. Tucker. When lead
stannate is reduced by carbon (R. C. Besley), or when tin is heated with lead oxide,
with stannous chloride, or with an alkali plumbate (L. Peetz), the alloy is formed.
S. Bodforss and P. Frölich, and M. Kutscheroff prepared a **colloidal solution** of
the tin-lead alloy. The f.p. curves have been studied by E. Wiedemann, H. Gautier,
R. Gnehm, C. T. Heycock and F. H. Neville, F. Rudberg, E. S. Shepherd, F. C. Weld,
B. Wiesengrund, P. N. Degens, K. L. Meissner, W. Guertler, A. Stoffel,
W. C. Roberts-Austen, A. W. Kapp, L. Guillet, D. Mazzotto, C. R. A. Wright and
co-workers, W. Spring and L. Romanoff, A. P. Laurie, A. von Vegesack, F. Guthrie,
M. Plüss, M. Wählert, C. P. Steinmetz, E. Heyn and O. Bauer, K. Bornemann,
L. Losana, J. Göbel, N. S. Kurnakoff, N. Parravano and co-workers, P. Ludwik,
M. Dullo, P. Müller, K. Heine, A. Pleischl, K. Honda
and T. Ishigaki, H. Stegmann, L. Sterner-Rainer,
H. von Jüptner, D. Silow, J. Alexander, W. Rosenhain and P. A. Tucker, etc. The results are summarized in Fig. 55. There is no evidence of the
formation of a definite compound, but P. N. Degens
observed a transformation at 146° with all alloys
containing between 0 and 88 at. per cent. of lead ;
the transformation is attended by the appearance
of a constituent distributed through the lead, and
it is suggested that a compound is formed at this
temp. from the tin and lead in the solid state.
W. Rosenhain and P. A. Tucker place the temp.
at which heat is evolved with alloys containing
18–63 per cent. of tin at 149°, and rather less with
alloys containing 8–18 per cent. of tin. The
transformation is attributed to the passage of the

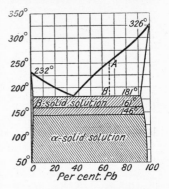

FIG. 55.—Freezing-point Curves
of Lead-Tin Alloys.

solid soln. from what is called the β-form to the α-form, and it is attended by the
rejection of part of the tin. The alloy with 8 per cent. of tin can remain in the
β-form down to the temp. of liquid air. G. H. Gulliver calculated the difference in
the relative proportions of solid (primary crystals) and liquid between the eutectic
and the liquidus curves for very slow and very rapid rates of cooling. The transformation at 161° is due to the contained tin. The f.p. curve is of the V-type with
the eutectic at 181° and 76 at. per cent. of tin ; according to W. Rosenhain and
P. A. Tucker, the eutectic is at 180° with 62·93 per cent. of tin. P. N. Degens said
that at 181° tin retains only 0·21 at. per cent. of lead in solid soln., and lead,
12 at. per cent. or more of tin. N. Parravano and A. Scortecci found for the
percentage solubility of tin in lead :

	175°	170°	162°	150°	100°	75°	50°	25°
Sn	14·5	13·5	12·5	10·0	6·5	5·0	3·0	1·5

The subject was studied by D. H. Andrews and J. Johnston. The facility with which the plumber can "wipe a joint" with solder, containing about 66 per cent. of lead, depends on the two f.p., *A*, *B*, Fig. 55, of these alloys. The "pasty" condition occurs when the freezing alloy has granules of solid lead in a liquid matrix.

The microstructure of the alloys was investigated by W. Campbell, W. Guertler, G. Charpy, A. M. Portevin, H. Behrens, K. Bux, W. Rosenhain and P. A. Tucker, J. E. Stead, J. A. Ewing and W. Rosenhain, C. H. Green, and H. von Jüptner. Figs. 56, 57, and 58 represent some results by W. Rosenhain and P. A. Tucker with

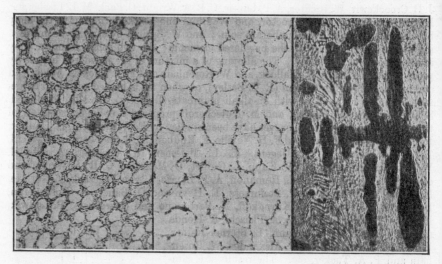

FIGS. 56, 57, 58.—Microstructure of Lead-Tin Alloys respectively with 10, 20, and 55 per cent. of Lead.

alloys containing 10, 20, and 55 per cent. of lead respectively. By means of the X-radiograms, W. C Phebus and F. C. Blake found that lead and tin form solid soln. at room temp.; with from 0 to 3·6 per cent. of tin the lead space-lattice decreases from $a=4.942$ to 4.931; and with 10–93 per cent. of tin, both tin and lead lattices are present without the tin lattice being appreciably distorted. The sp. gr. was examined by F. C. Calvert and R. Johnson, G. Pillichody, S. Grimaldi, C. Long, T. Thomson, O. Kleinstück, G. Vicentini and D. Omodei, K. Gilbert, A. T. Kupffer, P. Bolley, J. Pohl, H. Kopp, A. Riche, J. H. Croockewit, H. V. Regnault, A. Matthiessen, and B. Wiesengrund ; and C. Long gave :

Pb .	0	23·0	31·0	47·3	64·2	78·2	87·8	91·5	100 per cent.
Sp. gr.	7·924	7·927	8·188	8·779	9·460	10·080	10·590	10·815	11·376

According to E. von Maey, for alloys containing p per cent. of tin, the sp. vol. is $0.08811+0.0004900p$. The shrinkage vol. on freezing was measured by C. M. Marx, E. Wiedemann, and B. Wiesengrund ; the vol. changes during the formation of the alloy, by K. Karmarsch, D. Mazzotto, F. Wüst, K. Gilbert, J. Pohl, F. Hoffmann, H. Kopp, and B. Kosmann ; the hardness, by A. Saposhnikoff, D. Stenquist, F. L. Brady, K. Gilbert, I. P. Göbel, P. Ludwik, L. Sterner-Rainer, E. Heyn and O. Bauer, and F. C. Calvert and R. Johnson ; L. Guillet, M. Dubosc, and R. S. Dean and co-workers, the hardening of the alloys by quenching ; the diffusion of tin in lead, by W. C. Roberts-Austen ; the difficulty of thoroughly mixing the molten metals, by H. Kopp ; the viscosity and sp. gr. of the liquid alloy, by M. Plüss, and R. Arpi ; the elastic constants, by G. Wertheim, L. Sterner-Rainer, E. S. Sperry, E. Heyn and O. Bauer, I. P. Göbel, E. N. da C. Andrade, A. E. Dunstan, Z. Carrière, and J. Dewar ; the coeff. of thermal

expansion, by A. Matthiessen, and G. Vicentini and D. Omodei ; H. Moissan and
A. J. P. O'Farrelly found lead can be almost completely distilled from alloys in
the electric furnace ; J. Joly and J. H. J. Poole separated the constituents to
a small extent by centrifuging. A. Magnus and M. Mannheimer observed that a
rise of temp. occurs when molten lead and tin are mixed. The thermal con-
ductivity was measured by F. C. Calvert and R. Johnson, W. B. Brown, and
A. W. Smith ; the sp. ht., by E. van Aubel, U. Behn, H. Kopp, H. V. Regnault,
A. Saposhnikoff, W. Spring, and F. Rudberg ; the phenomenon of surfusion, by
D. Mazzotto, B. Wiesengrund and W. C. Roberts-Austen ; the heat of fusion, by
W. Spring, and D. Mazzotto ; the heat of formation, by J. Tayler ; and the electrical
conductivity, by E. Elsässer, W. H. Preece, W. Harris, S. Konno, P. W. Bridgman,
W. Guertler, A. Matthiessen and co-workers, W. C. Roberts-Austen, E. J. Cuy,
N. Parravano and A. Scortecci, C. L. Weber, P. Müller, K. Bornemann and
G. von Rauschenplat, H. Rainy and R. D. Clackson, E. F. A. Obach, and G. Vicentini
and B. Omodei. The results by W. C. Roberts-Austen are plotted in Fig. 59.
The straight line is in agreement with the fact that the alloys are heterogeneous
mixtures of the components. A. Matthiessen and C. Vogt examined the effect of
temp., and of foreign metals on the conductivity ; and H. Rainy and R. D. Clackson,
the change of conductivity at the m.p. J. Trowbridge and E. Stevens,
S. D. Muzaffar, N. A. Puschin, H. le Chatelier, A. P. Laurie, and O. Sackur measured
the electrode potential of the alloys in different soln. W. Rollmann, J. L. Haughton,
P. H. Dowling, H. Pélabon, and A. Battelli measured the thermoelectric properties,
and the results by E. Rudolfi are plotted in Fig. 60. P. H. Dowling found no change

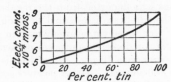

FIG. 59.—Electrical Conductivity of the
Tin-Lead Alloys.

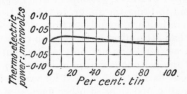

FIG. 60.—Thermoelectric Power of the
Tin-Lead Alloys.

in the e.m.f. of contact of a solid and molten lead-tin alloy with 25 per cent. lead.
R. Kremann and P. G. von Rehenburg found that on electrolyzing these alloys
the tin accumulates about the cathode, the lead at the anode. P. H. Dowling
studied the change in the contact e.m.f. of a lead-tin alloy, and Wood's metal
with a nickel surface when the alloy is solid and when fused. The magnetic
susceptibility curve, Fig. 61, by K. Honda is
nearly a straight line, but with alloys containing
0–10 per cent. of lead there is a slight curvature
corresponding with the presence of solid soln.
E. L. Dupuy also investigated this property.
M. Loutchinsky found the magnetic susceptibility of the hammered alloy less than where
it is crystallized.

J. Fordos, L. Bessnou, H. Reckleben and
J. Scheiber, A. Scala, F. Knapp, and L. Peetz
examined the influence of oxygen, air, and other
gases on the alloys. H. E. Armstrong, G. Charpy,
J. Pohl, A. Bauer and P. von Mertens, and
L. Pitkin investigated the action of acids on the

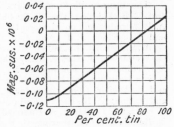

FIG. 61.—Magnetic Susceptibility
of the Tin-Lead Alloys.

lead-tin alloys ; O. Bauer, the action of sulphuric acid ; F. P. Hall, C. H. Pfaff,
J. Pohl, Z. Roussin, A. Pleischl, A. Gummi, J. L. Proust, O. Sackur, F. Knapp,
and R. Weber, the action of acetic, citric, tartaric, and lactic acids ; A. Scala, the

action of distilled water ; and F. Knapp, and C. Reichelt, the action of soln. of sodium chloride—vide the action of natural waters on lead.

The technical uses of the tin-lead alloys were discussed by A. Guettier, N. Braunschweiger, M. von Schwarz, L. Hartmann, O. and A. Neumann, W. Kaiser, etc. E. Seel and K. Hils observed that 1·27-4·44 per cent. of lead was found in some tins used for canned foods. *Solders* usually consist of tin and lead in various proportions, and when a still more fusible solder is needed, bismuth is added. According to Pliny's *Historia naturalis* (34. 17, 48), the so-called *tertiarium* of the Romans contained twice as much lead as tin, and was used as a solder. It contained very nearly the eutectic proportion. W. Gowland found that a sample dating from 300 A.D., unearthed at Silchester, contained 61·93 per cent. of lead, and 28·01 per cent. of tin. An alloy containing equal parts of tin and lead was the *argentarium* of Romans, and it is a common solder of to-day. The standard *tinman's solder* has 1 part tin and 2 parts lead, and its fusibility is indicated by the line AB, Fig. 55. The solders were discussed by G. Strahl, M. von Schwarz, F. M. Feldhaus, M. Wählert, M. L. Lissberger, J. Rothe, J. Novel, F. Singer and H. Barthel, W. Kaiser, E. Johanson, P. Yanushewsky, and A. H. Munday and co-workers. The effect of a small proportion of bismuth, antimony, arsenic, copper, silver, zinc, cadmium, aluminium, or mercury was examined by C. O. Bannister, and H. J. Tabor and H. D. Smith. *Pewter* or *latten ware*—from the French *laiton*, brass or tin-plate—is an alloy of tin and lead, 4 : 1, which came into use near the middle of the seventeenth century, and was used in making measures for wine and ale ; by a Royal decree, the pewter vessels were stamped. The Pewterers' Company, incorporated in 1474, attempted to regulate the quality of pewter by permitting enough lead to bring the sp. gr. to that of tin ; persons who departed from the regulations were liable to expulsion from the guild, but the rule was disregarded so much that it had little effect in keeping up the standard. Unalloyed tin is largely used in place of pewter being not only whiter, but also safer for domestic purposes on account of the poisonous nature of lead (*q.v.*). The pewter with 18 per cent. of lead is said to be harmless when used for vessels for wine and vinegar. Other pewters contain small proportions of other metals—*e.g.* zinc, copper, antimony, etc. Alloys of tin and lead are used for toys—*e.g.* toy soldiers—and an alloy of lead and tin in the proportions 3 : 5 is used for tinning certain articles of copper. The so-called *Fahlum brilliants*, used for stage jewellery, contain lead and tin nearly in the proportions 2 : 3 ; the molten alloy is cast in mould facetted like cut diamonds. Thin sheets of steel coated with an alloy of tin and lead (1 : 3) are used in packing dry goods and for roofing, and called *terne plates*. C. Baskerville described a cheaper substitute made by coating iron with antimony, and depositing lead thereupon. The uses of these alloys in making domestic utensils was discussed by F. Knapp.

The ternary Pb–Sn–As alloys were investigated by W. Zimmer, and H. J. Roast and C. F. Pascoe ; the Pb–Sn–Sb alloys by H. Behrens and H. Baucke, W. Hommel, A. H. Munday and co-workers, R. W. Irwin, G. Charpy, H. Kopp, O. W. Ell's, W. Campbell and F. C. Elder, J. d'Arcet, L. J. Chaudet, F. Rudberg, J. W. Döbereiner, Isaac Newton, G. A. Erman, R. Loebe, G. H. Gulliver, C. O. Thieme, A. M. Portevin, R. H. Thurston, G. Wertheim, J. Hoyle, J. Czochralsky, J. C. Work, E. Heyn and O. Bauer, C. Pack, M. Wählert, A. Halfmann, M. le Gris, J. E. Stead, M. Dreifuss, G. H. Clamer, G. von Hanffstengel, L. E. Eckelmann, R. Meyer and S. Schuster, S. Zinberg, R. W. Irwin, and R. Weber. The alloys for stereotype work have lead 72–82 per cent. ; tin, 3–10 ; and antimony, 15–19. The applications of these alloys were discussed by W. Campbell, E. Heyn and O. Bauer, A. Hague, J. Czochralsky, A. Halfmann, W. Kaiser, T. Goldschmidt, L. Revillon, H. M. Waring, C. F. Beyer, P. Yanushewsky, R. J. Shoemaker, C. Fischer, J. J. Watts and S. Harton, M. von Schwarz, F. Varrentrapp, and S. K. Patteson. M. Dubosc, R. S. Dean and co-workers, and L. Guillet, studied the hardening of the alloys by quenching. The Pb–Sn–Bi alloys were investigated by E. van Aubel, G. Charpy, M. Dullo, C. M. Marx, J. Würschmidt, K. Bux, H. Kopp, K. Gilbert, D. Mazzotto, H. Rainy and R. D. Clackson, P. T. Bachmetjeff and J. Wsharoff, C. Cattaneo, J. W. Döbereiner, C. Drewitz, G. A. Erman, G. Gore, C. C. Person, H. V. Regnault, W. C. Roberts-Austen, L. Schüz, W. Spring, C. L. Weber, G. Wiedemann, E. Heyn and O. Bauer, R. H. Thurston, G. Wertheim, M. Merle, T. J. Seebeek, H. von Iöbell, H. Stegmann, E. S. Shepherd, F. Guthrie, P. Goerens, C. P. Steinmetz,

F. Hauser, K. **Bux**, E. Wiedemann, H. Behrens, G. W. A. Kahlbaum and E. **Sturm,**
J. Faé, J. Johnston and L. H. Adams, K. Heine, C. von Hauer, J. M. Belin, L. Brennan,
F. Wüst, L. Grunmach, J. Würschmidt, J. Joly and J. H. J. Poole, C. Schaefer, F. Faktor,
etc. G. Charpy found that no compounds are formed, but there is a sharply defined
ternary eutectic at 96°, as shown in Fig. 62. F. Wüst found that the alloy with 49·88 per
cent. bismuth ; 32·47, lead ; and 17·38, tin, expands on cooling. The applications of these
alloys were discussed by C. Drewitz, M. von Schwarz, R. Clayton, R. R. Maddison,
C. W. Harrison, E. Lenssen, G. Homberg, W. Kaiser, W. F. Siemens and E. F. A. Obach,
E. von Bibra, O. Trossin, L. Brennan, R. Jobson and R. J. Ransome, C. von Hauer, D. Mazzotto, H. V. Regnault, C. C. Person, W. Spring, G. W. A. Kahlbaum and E. Sturm,
E. Jannettaz and co-workers, H. Grissel and T. Redwood, C. Cattaneo, J. Würschmidt,
and H. Behrens.

The ternary **Pb–Sn–K** alloys were examined by W. Stockmeyer and H. Hanemann ;
the **Pb–Sn–Na** alloys, by J. Göbel, and W. Stockmeyer and H. Hanemann ; the **Pb–Sn–Ca**
alloys, by C. G. Carroll and W. H. Adams ; the **Pb–Sn–Ba** alloys, by Metallbank und Metallurgische Gesellschaft ; and the **Pb–Sn–Cu** alloys, by R. E. Lee and F. B. Trace, and
R. H. Thurston ; A. French, G. Charpy, and E. J. Ball—these ternary alloys were found
by F. Giolitti and M. Marantonio to contain either Cu_4Sn or Cu_3Sn. N. Parravano studied
the **Pb–Sn–Ag** alloys ; A. von Vegesack, C. O. Thieme, and W. Stockmeyer and H. Hanemann, the **Pb–Sn–Mg** alloys ; W. Hommel, A. and L. Svanberg, C. R. A. Wright and co-
workers, F. Rudberg, J. Czochralsky, A. H. Munday and co-workers, A. Guettier, G. Wertheim, S. Fox and J. W. Slater, W. Sharman, F. Osmond and J. Werth, M. Levi-Malvano
and O. Ceccarelli, C. F. Grimm, C. Pope, H. Grissell and T. Redwood, G. Wegner, W. E. Day,
A. M. Ayala, J. R. Kinder, and A. Hanszel, the **Pb–Sn–Zn** alloys ; M. Levi-Malvano and
O. Ceccarelli obtained no compounds in the ternary system, and the ternary eutectic
occurred at 177° with an alloy containing 71 per cent. of tin, 24 of lead, and 5 of zinc.
A. K. Aster, W. J. Humphreys, A. Stoffel, E. S. Sperry, C. P. Steinmetz, M. Wählert,
W. Hommel, B. Wood, C. W. Hill, C. von Hauer, K. Heine, L. J. Gurevich and R. W. Woodward, S. W. Stratton, F. Halla and A. Hoffmann, J. Scoffern, W. Kaiser, A. Lassieur,
and P. Speier studied the **Pb–Sn–Cd** alloys. A. Stoffel observed that no compounds were
formed, and that there is a ternary eutectic at 143°, as indicated in Fig. 63. F. Weld, and

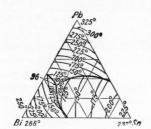

FIG. 62.—Fusion Curves of the Ternary
System : Pb–Sn–Bi.

FIG. 63.—Fusion Curves of the Ternary
System : Pb–Sn–Cd.

W. J. Humphreys studied the **Pb–Sn–Hg** alloys ; C. R. A. Wright and co-workers,
W. D. Bancroft, and J. Cayorca, the **Pb–Sn–Al** alloys ; and C. G. Fink and C. H. Eldridge,
the **Pb–Sn–Tl** alloys.

The so-called *fusible alloys*—discussed by K. Heine, N. F. Budgen, L. Losana,
E. F. Davis, G. K. Burgess and P. D. Merica, A. Lassieur, and many others—contain tin
and lead with one or more metals—bismuth, cadmium, mercury—in addition. They are
used for obtaining casts of delicate objects which would be damaged at a high temp.—
e.g. casts of portions of post-mortem specimens can be obtained by adding $\frac{1}{16}$th of its
weight of mercury to say bismuth 2, tin 1, and lead 1. The fusible alloys are used for very
soft solders. Fusible safety plugs, are used for boilers, etc. An alloy for fusible tea-
spoons is composed of bismuth 8, tin 3, lead 5, and mercury 1-2. The composition of
some well-known fusible alloys is represented in Table VIII. The so-called *G. C. Lichtenberg's*
alloy is really that given by Isaac Newton ; and that often quoted as I. Newton's alloy
(3 : 5 : 8, m.p. 94·5°) was not given by him at all.

The quaternary **Pb–Sn–Sb–P** alloys were studied by J. T. Dwyer ; the **Pb–Sn–Sb–As**
alloys, by J. E. Stead and L. J. Spencer ; the **Pb–Sn–Sb–Na** alloys, by P. S. Braucher ;
the **Pb–Sn–Al** alloys, by the Dellinger Hüttenwerke, and the Allgemeine Elektrizitäts-
Gesellschaft ; the **Pb–Sn–Bi–Sb** alloys, by S. Singley, P. Bolley, R. Clayton, W. Kaiser,
and E. Heyn and O. Bauer ; the **Pb–Sn–Bi–Na** and **Pb–Sn–Bi–K** alloys, by G. Bredig and
F. Haber ; the **Pb–Sn–Zn–P** alloys, by S. R. Bailey, and J. F. Gross ; the **Pb–Sn–Zn–Sb**
alloys, by J. U. V. de Strubing, J. Segura, B. Kohlmann, K. Küppers, S. M. Meyer and
W. James, and T. Lambert and H. C. Soper ; and the **Pb–Sn–Bi–Cd** alloys, by A. Gouy,
G. Gore, J. Faé, W. Campbell, D. Mazzotto, W. Spring, F. Guthrie, L. Losana ; E. Wiede-

TABLE VIII.—THE COMPOSITION OF SOME FUSIBLE ALLOYS.

Alloy.	Tin.	Lead.	Bismuth.	Cadmium.	Melting-point.
B. Wood's . . .	2	4	5–8	1–2	60°–72°
V. Rose's . . .	3	8	8	–	93·7°
J. d'Arcet's . .	1	1	2	–	79°
Isaac Newton's . .	3	2	5	–	91·5°
A. Lipowitz's . . .	4	8	15	3	70°

mann, H. Behrens, G. Strahl, J. H. Gladstone and W. Hibbert, C. von Hauer, J. Roszkowsky, C. L. Weber, B. Wood, E. van Aubel, C. Cattaneo, W. Hallock, H. Stegmann, G. W. A. Kahlbaum and E. Sturm, L. Grunmach, C. Friedel, C. P. Steinmetz, A. Lipowitz, M. Wählert, C. Schäfer, J. Dewar, N. Parravano and G. Sirovich found that no compounds are formed and that the most fusible alloy of the series contains 27·27 per cent. of lead, 13·13 of tin, 10·10 of cadmium, and 49·50 of bismuth. The uses of these alloys were discussed by R. Pearson, R. Threlfall, O. Troosin, etc. The Pb–Sn–Bi–Hg alloys were studied by T. J. Seebeck, A. Gory, and G. Gore; the Pb–Sn–Bi–Al alloys, by A. B. Clarke and H. H. Gregg, D. J. Millard, and W. J. Crawford and T. B. Turley; the Pb–Sn–Zn–Cu alloys, by A. Guettier, W. Broniewsky, H. F. Staley and C. P. Carr, H. Kopp, and J. Czochralsky; and the Pb–Sn–Zn–Al alloys, by A. W. King, F. Jackman and co-workers, W. R. Mitchell and J. B. Vigo, C. H. Frantz, C. C. Wells, and J. G. Kelly and co-workers. The so-called babbitt metals are quaternary Pb–Sn–Cu–Sb alloys with tin 20–80 per cent.; lead, 0–63·5; copper, 1·5–3·0; and antimony, 10–15. They are used as bearing metals, and were investigated by A. H. Mundey and co-workers, E. G. Mahin and J. F. Brocker, L. D. Staplin, J. R. Freeman, etc. W. Hommel studied the Pb–Sn–Cd–Bi alloys; and the Pb–Sn–Hg–Bi alloys, by F. C. Weld.

The quinquinary Pb–Sn–Zn–Sb–Bi alloys were studied by O. Holden, and B. D. Webster and J. Horsfall; the Pb–Sn–Zn–Sb–Al alloys, by R. L. Weatherford; the Pb–Sn–Zn–Sb–Cr alloys, by C. R. Erkens; the Pb–Sn–Cd–Sb–Bi alloys, by T. Goldschmidt; Pb–Sn–Cd–Zn–Al alloys, by O. Nicolai and F. Börner, and W. R. Mitchell and J. B. Vigo.

C. Hatchett [5] suggested that a systematic examination of all possible alloys of all the metals be made proceeding from the binary to the more complicated ternary and quaternary alloys. Supposing this were done, and that one proportion of each of thirty metals were taken, there would be 435 binary, 4060 ternary, and 27,405 quaternary alloys to be examined; and if four proportions of each of thirty metals were employed, 6655 binary, 247,660 ternary, and 1,013,985 quaternary alloys would have to be examined.

REFERENCES.

[1] H. St. C. Deville, Ann. Chim. Phys., (3), 43. 5, 1855; (3), 46. 415, 1856; De l'aluminium ses propriétés, sa fabrication, et ses applications, Paris, 41, 1859; A. J. Rogers, Chem. News, 60. 228, 237, 1889; C. Tissier, Compt. Rend., 43. 1187, 1856; H. Pécheux, ib., 138. 1042, 1904; 139. 1203, 1904; 143. 397, 1906; W. D. Bancroft, Journ. Phys. Chem., 3. 217, 1899; W. Campbell and J. A. Mathews, Journ. Amer. Chem. Soc., 24. 255, 1902; H. Schirmeister, Beiträge zur Kenntnis der binären Legierungen hinsichtlich ihrer technischen Eigenschaften, Aachen, 1914; Stahl Eisen, 35. 877, 1915; A. G. C. Gwyer, Zeit. anorg. Chem., 57. 147, 1908; United Lead Co., U.S. Pat. No. 1360272, 1919; German Pat., D.R.P. 323855, 1917; H. Hanemann and W. Stockmeyer, ib., 309758, 1916; C. T. Heycock and F. H. Neville, Journ. Chem. Soc., 61. 888, 1892; J. W. Richards, Aluminium, Philadelphia, 504, 1896; S. Mierzinsky, Die Fabrikation des Aluminiums und des Alkali metalle, Wien, 1885; I. H. Johannes, U.S. Pat. No. 443943, 1890; C. B. Miller, ib., 456898, 1891; T. MacKellar, ib., 463427, 1891; C. R. A. Wright, Journ. Soc. Chem. Ind., 11. 492, 1892; 13. 1014, 1894; Proc. Roy. Soc., 50. 372, 1891; 52. 11, 530, 1893; 55. 130, 1894; C. R. A. Wright and C. Thompson, ib., 48. 25, 1890; W. Campbell, Journ. Franklin Inst., 154. 1, 131, 201, 1902; W. Campbell and J. Mathews, Journ. Amer. Chem. Soc., 24. 253, 1902; P. Ludwik, Zeit. anorg. Chem., 94. 161, 1916; C. A. J. H. and H. E. R. Schroeder, Brit. Pat. No. 22956, 1893; T. A. Bayliss and B. G. Clark, ib., 12457, 1911; L. Guillet and J. Cournot, Compt. Rend., 174. 384, 1922; S. F. Weaver and J. M. Repplier, U.S. Pat. No. 1385223, 1920; G. Tammann and P. Schafmeister, Zeit. anorg. Chem., 138. 219, 1924; C. H. Hirzel, Zeit. Pharm., 10. 145, 177, 1858.

[2] N. S. Kurnakoff and N. A. Puschin, Zeit. anorg. Chem., 52. 44, 1907; N. S. Kurnakoff and S. F. Schemtschuschny, ib., 64. 149, 1909; J. L. Haughton and G. W. Ford, Trans. Faraday Soc., 18. 112, 1922; G. Borelius, Ann. Physik, (4), 77. 109, 1925; J. A. M. van Liempt, Rec. Trav. Chim. Pays-Bas, 45. 203, 1926.

⁵ D. Mazzotto, *Internat. Zeit. Metallog.*, **1.** 346, 1911 ; L. Guillet, *Chem. News*, **123.** 347, 1921 ; *Rev. Mét.*, **18.** 7581, 1921 ; R. Kremann and A. Lobinger, *Zeit. Metallkunde*, **12.** 246, 1920 ; E. Bekier, *Chem. Polsky*, **15.** 119, 1918 ; L. Rolla, *Gazz. Chim. Ital.*, **45.** i, 185, 1915 ; K. Lewkonja, *Zeit. anorg. Chem.*, **52.** 452, 1907 ; N. S. Kurnakoff, *ib.*, **23.** 493, 1900 ; *Journ. Russ. Phys. Chem. Soc.*, **31.** 927, 1899 ; N. S. Kurnakoff and N. A. Puschin, *ib.*, **32.** 830, 1900 ; **33.** 565, 1901 ; *Zeit. anorg. Chem.*, **30.** 86, 1902 ; **52.** 430, 1907 ; P. Fuchs, *ib.*, **107.** 308, 1919 ; G. D. Roos, *ib.*, **94.** 348, 1916 ; G. Tammann and W. Wiederholt, *ib.*, **125.** 82, 1922 ; N. S. Kurnakoff and S. F. Schemtschuschny, *Journ. Russ. Phys. Chem. Soc.*, **39.** 657, 1907 ; **40.** 724, 1908 ; **41.** 1182, 1909 ; *Zeit. anorg. Chem.*, **64.** 156, 1909 ; W. Jenge, *ib.*, **118.** 105, 1921 ; G. D. Roos, *ib.*, **94.** 329, 1916 ; E. Carstanjen, *Journ. prakt. Chem.*, (1), **102.** 65, 1867 ; W. Crookes, *On Thallium*, London, 1863 ; C. T. Heycock and F. H. Neville, *Journ. Chem. Soc.*, **61.** 888, 1892 ; **65.** 31, 1894 ; W. Guertler, *Jahrb. Rad. Elektron.*, **5.** 56, 1908 ; W. Guertler and A. Schulze, *Zeit. phys. Chem.*, **104.** 267, 1923 ; H. Endo, *Science Rep. Tohoku Univ.*, **14.** 479, 1925 ; C. C. Fink and C. H. Eldridge, *Trans. Amer. Electrochem. Soc.*, **40.** 51, 1921 ; C. di Capua, *Atti Accad. Lincei*, (5), **32.** ii, 343, 1923 ; *Gazz. Chim. Ital.*, **50.** 280, 1925 ; A. W. Smith, *Phys. Rev.*, (2), **23.** 307, 1924.

⁴ C. H. Pfaff, *Schweigger's Journ.*, **6.** 225, 1813 ; **11.** 14, 1814 ; *Ann. Chim. Phys.*, (1), **57.** 13, 1834 ; L. J. Chaudet, *ib.*, (2), **3.** 376, 1816 ; (2), **5.** 142, 1817 ; L. N. Vauquelin, *ib.*, (1), **32.** 243, 1799 ; A. T. Kupffer, *ib.*, (2), **40.** 285, 1829 ; *Kastner's Arch.*, **8.** 331, 1826 ; J. L. Proust, *Ann. Chim. Phys.*, (1), **28.** 213, 1798 ; *Journ. Phys.*, **51.** 173, 1800 ; **61.** 338, 1804 ; L. D. Staplin, *Power*, **52.** 748, 1920 ; A. Gummi, *Schweigger's Journ.*, **6.** 225, 1812 ; P. N. Degens, *Legierungen van tin en lood*, Dordrecht, 1908 ; *Zeit. anorg. Chem.*, **63.** 212, 1909 ; M. Plüss, *Zur Kenntnis der Viskosität und Dichte geschmolzener Metalle und Legierungen*, Leipzig, 1915 ; *Zeit. anorg. Chem.*, **93.** 33, 1915 ; S. D. Muzaffar, *ib.*, **126.** 254, 1923 ; A. von Vegesack, *ib.*, **54.** 391, 1907 ; A. Stoffel, *ib.*, **53.** 139, 1907 ; E. Rudolfi, *ib.*, **67.** 65, 1910 ; G. W. A. Kahlbaum and E. Sturm, *ib.*, **46.** 275, 1905 ; R. Kremann and P. G. von Rehenburg, *ib.*, **140.** 1, 1924 ; G. Tammann, *ib.*, **53.** 450, 1907 ; J. Hoyle, *Brit. Pat. No.* 2783, 1870 ; R. W. Irwin, *Journ. Chem. Met. Mining Soc., South Africa*, **23.** 171, 218, 1923 ; M. Kutscheroff, *Koll. Zeit.*, **11.** 165, 1912 ; G. Homberg, *Mém. Acad.*, **141.** 1702 ; S. Bodforss and P. Frölich, *Koll. Beihefte*, **16.** 301, 1922 ; L. Peetz, *Met.*, **1.** 294, 1904 ; F. Wüst, *ib.*, **6.** 782. 1909 ; M. Wählert, *ib.*, **17.** 231, 1920 ; W. Kaiser, *ib.*, **8.** 305, 1911 ; E. Johanson, *Russ. Pharm. Journ.*, **22.** 521, 1883 ; J. H. Croockewit, *Specimen chemicum de conjunctionibus chemicis metallorum*, Amsterdam, 1848 ; *Journ. prakt. Chem.*, (1), **45.** 87, 1848 ; C. von Hauer, *ib.*, (1), **94.** 436, 1865 ; W. Guertler, *Zeit. Elektrochem.*, **15.** 129, 953, 1909 ; *Zeit. anorg. Chem.*, **54.** 64, 430, 1906 ; *Metallurgie*, Berlin, **1.** 722, 1911 ; *Zeit. Metallkunde*, **12.** 319, 1920 ; *Jahrb. Rad. Elektron.*, **5.** 44, 1908 ; A. Lassieur, *Bull. Official Recherches Scient. Ind.*, 31, 1922 ; K. Honda, *Science Rep. Tokyo Univ.*, **2.** 11, 1913 ; W. C. Roberts-Austen, *Engg.*, **63.** 223, 1897 ; *Proc. Inst. Mech. Eng.*, 102, 1893 ; 31, 1897 ; *Phil. Mag.*, (5), **8.** 57, 1879 ; *Phil. Trans.*, **187.** A, 383, 1896 ; *Proc. Roy. Soc.*, **63.** 450, 1898 ; F. Wüst, *Met.*, **6.** 769, 1909 ; M. Wählert, *ib.*, **17.** 321, 1920 ; D. Mazzotto, *Zeit. Internat. Metallog.*, **1.** 289, 1911 ; *Nuovo Cimento*, (5), **1.** 355, 1901 ; (5), **18.** 180, 1909 ; *Mem. Acad. Modena*, (3), **10.** 2, 1912 ; *Atti Accad. Torino*, **17.** 111, 1882 ; *Rend. Ist. Lombardo*, (9), **18.** 165, 1885 ; (2), **19.** 458, 1886 ; *Mem. Ist. Lombardo*, (3), **16.** 1, 1891 ; *Journ. Phys.*, (5), **10.** 279, 1901 ; W. Rosenhain and P. A. Tucker, *Proc. Roy. Soc.*, **81.** A, 334, 1908 ; *Phil. Trans.*, **209.** A, 89, 1908 (I am much indebted to Dr. Rosenhain for the originals of Figs. 56 to 58) ; W. Harris, *ib.*, **117.** 18, 1827 ; J. A. Ewing and W. Rosenhain, *ib.*, **193.** A, 370, 1900 ; A. W. Kapp, *Ueber vollständige Gefrierpunktskurven binärer Metalllegierungen*, Königsberg, 1901 ; *Ann. Physik*, (4), **6.** 754, 1901 ; C. Drewitz, *Verh. Ver. Beförd. Gewerb.*, **81.** 325, 1902 ; *Ueber einige physikalische Eigenschaften von Legierungen*, Rostock, 33, 1902 ; F. Rudberg, *Pogg. Ann.*, **18.** 240, 1830 ; **21.** 317, 1831 ; **71.** 460, 1847 ; *Svenska Vet. Akad. Handl.*, 157, 1829 ; G. A. Erman, *Pogg. Ann.*, **9.** 557, 1827 ; **20.** 283, 1830 ; A. and L. Svanberg, *ib.*, **26.** 280, 1832 ; *Svenska Vet. Akad. Handl.*, 205, 1830 ; H. Davy, *Elements of Chemical Philosophy*, London, 1812 ; K. Heine, *Chem. Ztg.*, **30.** 1139, 1906 ; W. Hommel, *Zeit. Metallkunde*, **13.** 456, 511, 565, 1921 ; H. E. Armstrong, *Chem. News*, **53.** 211, 1886 ; E. van Aubel, *Journ. Phys.*, (3), **9.** 493, 1900 ; *Phys. Zeit.*, **1.** 452, 1900 ; J. Würschmidt, *Zeit. Physik*, **5.** 39, 1921 ; F. Hauser, *ib.*, **5.** 220, 1921 ; K. Bux, *ib.*, **14.** 316, 1923 ; A. Battelli, *Atti Accad. Torino*, (2), **36.** 487, 1814 ; A. K. Aster, *Phys. Rev.*, (2), **20.** 349, 1922 ; A. Bauer, *Ber.*, **8.** 210, 1875 ; O. Bauer, *Stahl Eisen*, **35.** 446, 1915 ; E. Heyn and O. Bauer, *Untersuchungen über Lagermetalle : Sb–Pb–Sn Legierungen*, Berlin, 1914 ; *Metal Ind.*, **25.** 1, 1919 ; W. Blum and H. E. Haring, *Trans. Amer. Electrochem. Soc.*, **40.** 287, 1921 ; *Chem. Met. Engg.*, **25.** 690, 1921 ; U. Behn, *Ann. Physik*, (4), **1.** 257, 1900 ; C. Schaefer, *ib.*, (4), **9.** 1126, 1902 ; H. F. Staley and C. P. Carr, *Trans. Amer. Inst. Min. Met. Engg.*, 2511, 1919 ; P. Bolley, *Dingler's Journ.*, **162.** 217, 1861 ; M. Crinsoz, *ib.*, **182.** 78, 1866 ; *Schweiz. Polyt. Zeit.*, **11.** 120, 1866 ; C. Long, *Phil. Trans.*, **150.** 177, 1860 ; F. C. Calvert and R. Johnson, *Phil. Trans.*, **148.** 349, 1858 ; *Phil. Mag.*, (4), **17.** 114, 1859 ; (4), **18.** 354, 1859 ; C. O. Bannister and H. J. Tabor, *Journ. Inst. Metals*, **2.** 58, 1909 ; J. H. Gladstone and W. Hibbert, *B.A. Rep.*, 347, 1888 ; G. Charpy, *Bull. Soc. Enc. Nat. Ind.*, (5), **2.** 384, 1897 ; (5), **3.** 670, 1898 ; *Contribution à l'étude des alliages*, Paris, 119, 201, 1901 ; *Compt. Rend.*, **124.** 957, 1897 ; **126.** 1569, 1645, 1898 ; A. Riche, *ib.*, **55.** 143, 1862 ; J. Novel, *ib.*, **116.** 256, 1895 ; J. Fordos, *ib.*, **79.** 678, 1874 ; L. Bessnou, *ib.*, **78.** 322, 1874 ; H. Moissan and A. J. P. O'Farrelly, *ib.*, **138.** 1659, 1904 ; P. Leroux, *ib.*, **156.** 1765, 1913 ; E. L. Dupuy, *ib.*, **158.** 794, 1914 ; M. Loutchinsky, *ib.*, **148.** 1759, 1909 ; *Rev. Mét.*, **6.** 986, 1909 ; W. Broniewsky, *ib.*, **7.**

340, 1910 ; M. le Gris, *ib.*, **8.** 621, 1911 ; M. Dullo, *Deut. Gewerbeztg.*, **30.** 167, 1865 ; *Chem. News*, **13.** 122, 1865 ; L. Sterner-Rainer, *Zeit. Metallkunde*, **13.** 373, 1921 ; H. Rainy and R. D. Clackson, *Proc. Roy. Soc. Edin.*, **13.** 686, 1886 ; E. Elsässer, *Wied. Ann.*, **8.** 455, 1879 ; L. Schüz, *ib.*, **46.** 177, 1892 ; C. L. Weber, *ib.*, **34.** 576, 1888 ; E. Wiedemann, **3.** 237, 1878 ; G. Wiedemann, *ib.*, **20.** 228, 1883 ; *Pogg. Ann.*, **89.** 498, 1853 ; R. Weber, *Dingler's Journ.*, **232.** 153, 264, 1879 ; J. Pohl, *Sitzber. Akad. Wien*, **4.** 402, 1850 ; *Dingler's Journ.*, **122.** 62, 1851 ; **189.** 428, 1868 ; H. Gautier, *Bull. Soc. Enc. Nat. Ind.*, (5), **1.** 1293, 1896 ; *Contribution à l'étude des alliages*, Paris, 93, 1901 ; E. G. Mahin and J. F. Brocker, *Proc. Indiana Acad.*, 91, 1919 ; F. C. Weld, *Amer. Chem. Journ.*, **13.** 121, 1891 ; F. P. Hall, *ib.*, **4.** 411, 1883 ; R. Gnehm, *Monit. Scient.*, (3), **4.** 424, 1874 ; M. Merle, *ib.*, (4), **9.** 35, 1895 ; L. Guillet, *Rev. Mét.*, **18.** 758, 1921 ; E. Obach, *Pogg. Ann. Ergbd.*, **7.** 280, 1876 ; W. Spring, *Journ. Chim. Phys.*, **1.** 593, 1903 ; *Bull. Acad. Belg.*, (2), **39.** 548, 1875 ; (3), **11.** 355, 1886 ; (3), **28.** 23, 1894 ; *Bull. Acad. Belg.*, (2), **39.** 561, 594, 1875 ; (3), **11.** 403, 1886 ; 1066, 1903 ; *Rec. Trav. Chim. Pays-Bas*, **23.** 1, 1904 ; *Bull. Soc. Chim.*, (2), **40.** 525, 1883 ; (2), **46.** 255, 1886 ; *Zeit. phys. Chem.*, **15.** 65, 1894 ; *Ann. Chim. Phys.*, (5), **7.** 178, 1876 ; *Ber.*, **15.** 595, 1882 ; W. Spring and L. Romanoff, *Zeit. anorg. Chem.*, **13.** 30, 1897 ; W. Hallock, *Amer. Journ. Science*, (3), **37.** 402, 1889 ; *Chem. News*, **63.** 17, 1891 ; R. H. Thurston, *The Non-ferrous Metals and Alloys*, New York, 1884 ; J. Trowbridge and E. Stevens, *Proc. Amer. Acad.*, **18.** 221, 1883 ; *Phil. Mag.*, (5), **16.** 435, 1883 ; G. Gore, *ib.*, (5), **32.** 27, 1891 ; J. Joly and J. H. J. Poole, *ib.*, (6), **39.** 376, 1920 ; A. W. Smith, *Phys. Rev.*, (2), **23.** 307, 1924 ; W. B. Brown, *ib.*, (2), **22.** 171, 1923 ; G. Vicentini and D. Omodei, *Atti Accad. Lincei*, (4), **3.** ii, 235, 294, 321, 1887 ; (4), **4.** i, 718, 805, 1888 ; (4), **4.** 19, 39, 75, 1888 ; (5), **1.** i, 419, 1892 ; A. Scala, *ib.*, (5), **22.** i, 155, 1913 ; N. Parravano, *ib.*, (5), **21.** i, 575, 1912 ; *Ann. Chim. Appl.*, **9.** 78, 1918 ; *Zeit. Internat. Metallog.*, **3.** 15, 1912 ; N. Parravano and A. Scortecci, *Gazz. Chim. Ital.*, **50.** i, 83, 1920 ; N. Parravano and G. Sirovich, *ib.*, **42.** i, 333, 577, 1912 ; L. Losana, *ib.*, **53.** 1, 393, 1923 ; **43.** i, 630, 1912 ; C. Cattaneo, *Atti Accad. Torino*, **27.** 691, 1892 ; B. Wiesengrund, *Ueber die Vorgänge bei Ausschmelzungen von Blei-Zinnlegierungen*, Rostock, 1894 ; *Wied. Ann.*, **52.** 777, 1894 ; E. Seel and K. Hils, *Pharm. Weekbl.*, **56.** 74, 1919 ; C. R. A. Wright, *Proc. Roy. Soc.*, **50.** 383, 1892 ; **52.** 16, 1893 ; *Journ. Soc. Chem. Ind.*, **13.** 1014, 1894 ; C. R. A. Wright and C. Thompson, *Proc. Roy. Soc.*, **45.** 461, 1889 ; C. R. A. Wright, C. Thompson, and J. Leon, *ib.*, **49.** 174, 1891 ; W. Gowland, *Archelogia*, **57.** 1, 1901 ; *Journ. Inst. Metals*, **2.** 68, 1909 ; H. D. Smith, *ib.*, **2.** 70, 1909 ; A. H. Mundey, C. C. Bissett, and J. Cartland, *ib.*, **28.** 159, 1922 ; O. W. Ellis, *ib.*, **19.** 151, 1918 ; J. L. Haughton, *ib.*, **23.** 499, 1920 ; A. M. Portevin, *ib.*, **29.** 239, 1923 ; F. L. Brady, *ib.*, **28.** 377, 1922 ; G. H. Gulliver, *ib.*, **9.** 120, 1913 ; **11.** 252, 1914 ; **13.** 263, 1915 ; *Proc. Roy. Soc. Edin.*, **32.** 36, 1912 ; W. Campbell, *Journ. Amer. Chem. Soc.*, **26.** 1308, 1904 ; *Journ. Franklin Inst.*, **154.** 1, 131, 201, 1902 ; *Met.*, **9.** 422, 1912 ; *Trans. Amer. Inst. Min. Eng.*, **44.** 828, 1913 ; *Bull. Amer. Inst. Min. Eng.*, 1381, 1921 ; W. Campbell and F. C. Elder, *School Mines Quart.*, **32.** 244, 1911 ; J. R. Freeman, *Proc. Amer. Soc. Testing Materials*, **22.** i, 207, 1922 ; J. Faé, *Lumière Élect.*, **25.** 630, 1887 ; T. Thomson, *Proc. Glasgow Phil. Soc.*, **1.** 77, 1844 ; E. J. Ball, *Journ. Chem. Soc.*, **53.** 167, 1888 ; W. J. Humphreys, *ib.*, **69.** 1679, 1896 ; S. Konno, *Science Rep. Tohoku Univ.*, **10.** 55, 1921 ; C. C. Person, *Compt. Rend.*, **25.** 444, 1847 ; **27.** 258, 1848 ; **29.** 300, 1849 ; *Ann. Chim. Phys.*, (3), **24.** 129, 265, 1848 ; (3), **27.** 250, 1849 ; C. H. Pfaff, *ib.*, (1), **57.** 13. 1806 ; *Schweigger's Journ.*, **6.** 225, 1812 ; **11.** 14, 1814 ; C. M. Marx, *ib.*, **58.** 468, 1830 ; J. W. Döbereiner, *ib.*, **42.** 182, 1824 ; H. Reckleben and J. Scheiber, *Chem. Ztg.*, **39.** 42, 1915 ; F. M. Fieldhaus, *ib.*, **34.** 1133, 1910 ; B. Kohlmann, *ib.*, **36.** 1506, 1912 ; C. O. Thieme, *Journ. Ind. Eng. Chem.*, **12.** 446, 1920 ; A. French, *Journ. Soc. Chem. Ind.*, **8.** 36, 1889 ; E. S. Sperry, *ib.*, **18.** 113, 1899 ; L. Pitkin, *Journ. Amer. Chem. Soc.*, **5.** 228, 1883 ; C. P. Steinmetz, *ib.*, **40.** 96, 1918 ; H. von Löbell, *Journ. prakt. Chem.*, (1), **26.** 511, 1842 ; C. Fischer, *ib.*, (1), **55.** 192, 1852 ; C. von Hauer, *ib.*, (1), **94.** 456, 1865 ; E. Lenssen, *ib.*, (1), **85.** 98, 1862 ; G. Nannes, *Œfvers. Vet. Förh. Stockholm*, **56.** 735, 1899 ; I. P. Göbel, *Zeit. anorg. Chem.*, **106.** 209, 1919 ; *Zeit. Ver. deut. Ing.*, **63.** 428, 1919 ; *Zeit. Metallkunde*, **14.** 357, 1922 ; E. Breunning, *ib.*, **14.** 303, 1922 ; B. Wood, *Amer. Journ. Science*, (2), **30.** 291, 1860 ; *Chem. News*, **6.** 135, 1862 ; *Journ. Franklin Inst.*, **73.** 61, 1862 ; G. H. Clamer, *ib.*, **156.** 49, 1903 ; Isaac Newton, *Opera quae exstant omnia*, **4.** 404, 1782 ; see also *Dingler's Journ.*, **129.** 438, 1853 ; F. Varrentrapp, *ib.*, **175.** 37, 1865 ; A. Lipowitz, *ib.*, **158.** 376, 1860 ; J. Czochralsky, *Zeit. Metallkunde*, **12.** 379, 1920 ; **13.** 171, 1921 ; *Giesserei Ztg.*, **18.** 85, 103, 1921 ; J. d'Arcet, *Journ. Phys.*, **9.** 217, 1777 ; *Journ. Méd. Chir. Pharm.*, **43.** 552, 1775 ; H. V. Regnault, *Ann. Chim. Phys.*, (3), **1.** 129, 1841 ; G. Wertheim, *ib.*, (3), **12.** 581, 1848 ; P. H. Dowling, *Phys. Rev.*, (2), **25.** 812, 1925 ; V. Rose, *Stralsundisches Mag.*, **2.** 24, 1772 ; G. C. Lichtenberg in J. C. P. Erxleben, *Anfangsgründe der Naturlehre*, Göttingen, 1806, 1791 ; M. Levi-Malvano and O. Ceccarelli, *Gazz. Chim. Ital.*, **41.** ii, 209, 314, 1911 ; F. Giolitti and M. Marantonio, *ib.*, **40.** 51, 1910 ; *Journ. Roy. Microscop. Soc.*, **526,** 1910 ; G. Bredig and F. Haber, *Ber.*, **31.** 2741, 1898 ; A. Bauer and P. von Mertens, *ib.*, **8.** 210, 1875 ; K. Foehr, *Chem. Tech. Centralanzeiger*, **4.** 803, 1886 ; *Zeit. anal. Chem.*, **26.** 396, 1887 ; K. Bux, *Zeit. Physik*, **14.** 316, 1923 ; **20.** 45, 1923 ; F. Guthrie, *Phil. Mag.*, (5), **17.** 462, 1884 ; *Chem. News*, **49.** 242, 1884 ; K. Gilbert, *Zeit. Metallkunde*, **14.** 245, 1922 ; W. Hommel, *ib.*, **13.** 459, 1921 ; A. Hanszel, *ib.*, **13.** 214, 1921 ; G. von Hanffstengel, *ib.*, **12.** 395, 1920 ; O. Sackur, *Arb. Kaiser Ges. Amt.*, **22.** 137, 1904 ; *Zeit. Elektrochem.*, **10.** 522, 1904 ; *Zeit. phys. Chem.*, **51.** 503, 1905 ; J. Roszkowsky, *ib.*, **15.** 314, 1894 ; W. Blum and H. E. Haring, *Trans. Amer. Electrochem. Soc.*, **40.** 287, 1921 ; S. Grimaldi, *Stat. Sperim. Agrar.*, **37.** 1026, 1904 ; F. Faktor, *Pharm. Post*, **38.** 219, 1905 ; O. Kleinstück, *Arch. Pharm.*, **227.** 638, 1889 ; Metallbank und Metallurgische Gesellschaft, *German Pat.*, *D.R.PP.* 307672, 1917 ; 351656, 1919 ; Dellinger Hüttenwerke, *ib.*, 315074, 1918 ; Allgemeine Elektrizitäts

Gesellschaft, *ib.*, 257868, 1911 ; F. Hoffmann, *ib.*, 299714, 1916 ; W. Stockmeyer and H. Hanemann, *ib.*, 306892, 1915 ; W. Zimmer, *ib.*, 299769, 1916 ; A. M. Ayala, *ib.*, 365124, 1917 ; G. Hassler, *ib.*, 297291, 1916 ; A. V. Tidblom, *Acta Univ. Lund.*, **9.** 6, 1873 ; **10.** 3, 1874 ; *Termoelektriska Undersökningar*, Lund, 1873 ; R. Arpi, *Fysiska Sällskop*, **11.** 10, 1913 ; *Internat. Zeit. Metallog.*, **5.** 142, 1914 ; G. von Rauschenplat, *Die elektrische Leitfähigkeit der Metalllegierungen im flüssigen Zustand*, Halle a. S., 1912 ; K. Bornemann and G. von Rauschenplat, *Met.*, **9.** 511, 1912 ; C. G. Fink and C. H. Eldridge, *Trans. Amer. Electrochem. Soc.*, **40.** 51, 1921 ; *Chem. Met. Engg.*, **25.** 685, 1921 ; Z. Roussin, *Journ. Chim. Pharm.*, (4), **3.** 103, 1866 ; J. Alexander, *Chem. Met. Engg.*, **26.** 170, 1922 ; A. Pleischl, *Deut. Ind. Ztg.*, **36.** 85, 1871 ; P. Yanushewsky, *Journ. Soc. Mech. Eng.*, **34.** 972, 1912 ; S. K. Patteson, *Elektrochem. Ind.*, **7.** 22, 1909 ; J. Rothe, *Mitt. Tech. Versuchsanst.* Berlin, **1.** 86, 1889 ; L. Grunmach, *Ver. deut. phys. Ges.*, **1.** 21, 1899 ; M. Dreifuss, *Zeit. Elektrochem.*, **28.** 100, 1922 ; P. Goerens, *ib.*, **15.** 618, 1909 ; R. Meyer and S. Schuster, *Zeit. angew. Chem.*, **27.** 121, 1914 ; S. Zinberg, *ib.*, 27. 437, 1914 ; L. E. Eckelmann, *Eng. Min. Journ.*, **106.** 794, 1918 ; E. S. Sperry, *ib.*, **87.** 1140, 1909 ; H. J. Roast and C. F. Pascoe, *Foundry*, **51.** 67, 1923 ; L. Revillon, *The Horseless Age*, **21.** 614, 1908 ; A. Guettier, *Dingler's Journ.*, **114.** 128, 196, 279, 1849 ; K. Karmarsch, *ib.*, **226.** 329, 1877 ; F. Knapp, *ib.*, **220.** 446, 1876 ; C. Reichelt, *ib.*, **172.** 155, 1864 ; G. Pillichody, *Schweiz. Polyt. Ztg.*, **6.** 120, 1861 ; T. C. Heycock and F. H. Neville, *Chem. News*, **59.** 175, 1889 ; **62.** 280, 1891 ; *Journ. Chem. Soc.*, **55.** 666, 1889 ; **57.** 376, 656, 1890 ; **61.** 888, 1892 ; A. P. Laurie, *ib.*, **55.** 677, 1889 ; P. Ludwik, *Zeit. anorg. Chem.*, **94.** 161, 1916 ; *Zeit. Ver. deut. Ing.*, **61.** 547, 1917 ; H. Behrens and H. Baucke, *Versl. Akad. Amsterdam*, **7.** 58, 1899 ; H. Behrens, *Das mikroskopische Gefüge der Metalle und Legierungen*, Hamburg, 51, 1894 ; M. von Schwarz, *Legierungen*, Stuttgart, 76, 1920 ; H. von Jüptner, *Stahl Eisen*, **19.** 23, 1899 ; E. J. Cuy, *Phil. Mag.*, (6), **49.** 758, 1925 ; P. W. Bridgman, *Phys. Rev.*, (2), **17.** 161, 1921 ; T. J. Seebeck, *Abhand. Akad. Berlin*, 265, 1823 ; H. Kopp, *Liebig's Ann.*, **40.** 184, 1841 ; **93.** 219, 1855 ; *Liebig's Ann. Suppl.*, **3.** 289, 1864 ; *Ueber die Modifikation der mittleren Eigenschaft, oder über die Eigenschaft von Mischungen in Rücksicht auf ihrer Bestandthiele*, Frankfurt a. M., 41, 1841 ; E. S. Shepherd, *Journ. Phys. Chem.*, **6.** 519, 1902 ; **7.** 15, 1903 ; W. D. Bancroft, *ib.*, **3.** 217, 1899 ; B. Kosmann, *Berg. Hütt. Ztg.*, **54.** 51, 1891 ; R. Loebe, *Met.*, **8.** 7, 33, 1911 ; K. Bornemann, *ib.*, **8.** 272, 1911 ; P. Müller, *ib.*, **7.** 756, 1910 ; J. W. Richards, *Journ. Amer. Chem. Soc.*, **16.** 541, 1894 ; J. Johnston and L. H. Adams, *ib.*, **34.** 563, 1912 ; C. Baskerville, *Journ. Ind. Eng. Chem.*, **12.** 152, 1920 ; G. K. Burgess and P. D. Merica, *ib.*, **7.** 824, 1915 ; C. P. Steinmetz, *ib.*, **40.** 100, 1918 ; H. le Chatelier, *Bull. Soc. Enc. Nat. Ind.*, (4), **10.** 192, 1895 ; *Rev. Gén. Sciences*, **6.** 529, 1895 ; *Contribution à l'étude des alliages*, Paris, 441, 1901 ; P. T. Bachmetjeff and J. Wsharoff, *Journ. Russ. Phys. Chem. Soc.*, **25.** 115, 1893 ; N. S. Kurnakoff, *ib.*, **37.** 579, 1905 ; N. A. Puschin, *ib.*, **39.** 528, 1907 ; A. Saposhnikoff, *ib.*, **40.** 92, 1908 ; **41.** 1708, 1909 ; E. von Maey, *Zeit. phys. Chem.*, **38.** 292, 1901 ; D. Silow, *ib.*, **3.** 605, 1889 ; D. Stenquist, *ib.*, **70.** 536, 1910 ; A. Matthiessen, *B.A. Rep.*, 37, 1863 ; *Journ. Chem. Soc.*, **20.** 201, 1867 ; *Pogg. Ann.*, **103.** 428, 1858 ; **110.** 190, 1860 ; **130.** 50, 1867 ; *Phil. Trans.*, **148.** 383, 1858 ; **150.** 111, 161, 1860 ; **156.** 861, 1866 ; A. Matthiessen and C. Vogt, *ib.*, **154.** 167, 1864 ; *Phil. Mag.*, (4), **23.** 171, 1862 ; *Pogg. Ann.*, **116.** 369, 1862 ; **122.** 19, 1864 ; W. Rollmann, *ib.*, **83.** 77, 1851 ; **84.** 275, 1851 ; **89.** 90, 1853 ; C. Pack, *Amer. Metal Ind.*, **18.** 410, 1920 ; C. H. Proctor, *Metal Ind.*, **16.** 74, 1918 ; C. W. Hill, *ib.*, **16.** 412, 1918 ; P. Speier, *ib.*, **16.** 127, 1907 ; M. L. Lissberger, *Chem. Met. Engg.*, **19.** 658, 1918 ; *Bull. Amer. Inst. Min. Eng.*, 1759, 1918 ; H. Stegmann, *Metall. Tech.*, **46.** 69, 1920 ; L. Hartmann, *ib.*, **46.** 52, 1920 ; R. C. Besley, *U.S. Pat. No.* 1060527, 1912 ; *Eng. Min. Journ.*, **96.** 406, 1913 ; C. G. Carroll and W. H. Adams, *U.S. Pat. No.* 906383, 1907 ; P. S. Braucher, *ib.*, 1269000, 1916 ; J. T Dwyer, *ib.*, 1059982, 1913 ; J. R. Kinder, *ib.*, 125010, 1917 ; W. E. Day, *ib.*, 1195955, 1916 ; 1239465, 1917 ; F. E. J. Litot, *ib.*, 1224941, 1917 ; C. F. Grimm, *ib.*, 1093403, 1913 ; J. C. Webster, *ib.*, 707472, 1902 ; C. H. Frantz, *ib.*, 1067016, 1913 ; C. C. Wells, *ib.*, 1239854, 1917 ; J. G. Kelly, A. L. Pringle, and H. Hall, *ib.*, 1376339, 1920 ; J. F. Gross, *ib.*, 1145307, 1915 ; J. Segura, *ib.*, 1328694, 1919 ; R. L. Weatherford, *ib.*, 1194101, 1916 ; C. R. Erkens, *ib.*, 1033565, 1912 ; L. J. Gurevich and R. W. Woodward, *ib.*, 1301688, 1919 ; J. Cayorca, *ib.*, 1161612, 1915 ; C. R. Erkens, *ib.*, 1033565, 1912 ; R. J. Shoemaker, *ib.*, 1330399, 1920 ; *Chem. Met. Engg.*, **22.** 857, 1920 ; S. W. Stratton, *ib.*, **19.** 652, 1918 ; Z. Carrière, *Sur les déformations de l'alliage eutectique plomb-étain et les métaux visqueux*, Paris, 1905 ; N. F. Bugden, *Journ. Soc. Chem. Ind.*, **43.** 200, T, 1924 ; J. Joly and J. H J. Poole, *Phil. Mag.*, (6), **39.** 376, 1920 ; E. F. Davis, *Metal Ind.*, **10.** 520, 540, 1917 ; H. Pélabon, *Compt. Rend.*, **176.** 1305, 1923 ; P. H. Dowling, *Phys. Rev.*, (2), **25.** 812, 1925 ; J. Dewar, *Chem. News*, **71.** 200, 1895 ; A. E. Dunstan, *Phil. Mag.*, (6), **17.** 192, 1909 ; E. N. da C. Andrade, *Proc. Roy. Soc.*, **84.** A, 1, 1910 ; W. H. Preece, *ib.*, **44.** 109, 1888 ; N. Braunschweiger, *Repert. Pharm.*, **9.** 72, 1860 ; F. Halla and A. Hoffmann, *Austrian Pat. No.* 139, 1911 ; G. Strahl, *Elektrochem. Zeit.*, **19.** 174, 1913 ; O. and A. Neumann, *Brit. Pat. No.* 184762, 1921 ; F. Singer and H. Barthel, *ib.*, 21162, 1892 ; T. Goldschmidt, *ib.*, 158562, 1921 ; 186058, 1922 ; J. J. Watts and S. Harton, *ib.*, **434.** 1861 ; R. Clayton, *ib.*, 4064, 1816 ; R. R. Maddison, *ib.*, 2001, 1893 ; C. W. Harrison, *ib.*, 1412, 1857 ; O. Troosin, *ib.*, 1700, 1875 ; L. Brennan, *ib.*, 8979, 1899 ; R. Jobson and R. J. Ransome, *ib.*, 2055, 1860 ; W. F. Siemens and E. F. A. Obach, *ib.*, 6565, 1893 ; 14846, 1896 ; H. Grisell and T. Redwood, *ib.*, 13442, 1851 ; W. J. Crawford and T. B. Turley, *ib.*, 18904, 1900 ; D. J. Millard, *ib.*, 2935, 1870 ; A. B. Clarke and H. H. Gregg, *ib.*, 132984, 1919 ; W. Sharman, *ib.*, 2621, 1857 ; S. Fox and J. W. Slater, *ib.*, 2240, 1857 ; G. Wegner, *ib.*, 6038, 1892 ; C. Pope, *ib.*, 4773, 1823 ; F. Jackman, J. M. Woodcock, and J. Ledgard, *ib.*, 17031, 1905 ; W. R. Mitchell and J. B. Vigo, *ib.*, 3507, 1907·

S. R. Bailey, *ib.*, 27835, 1912 ; J. U. V. de Strubing, *ib.*, 12876, 1849 ; S. M. Meyer and W. James, *ib.*, 182098, 1922 ; T. Lambert and H. C. Soper, *ib.*, 2495, 1864 ; B. D. Webster and J. Horsfall, *ib.*, 2486, 1858 ; O. Holden, *ib.*, 3785, 1875 ; J. Scoffern, *ib.*, 345, 1879 ; R. Threlfall, *ib.*, 26401, 1901 ; R. Pearson, *ib.*, 23586, 1900 ; O. Nicolai and F. Börner, *ib.*, 6969, 1902 ; C. F. Beyer, *ib.*, 22199, 1894 ; R. E. Lee and F. B. Trace, *Trans. Amer. Foundry Assoc.*, **30.** 511, 1923 ; W. C. Phebus and F. C. Blake, *Phys. Rev.*, (2), **25.** 107, 1925 ; V. de Luynes, *Bull. Soc. Enc. Nat. Ind.*, (2), **9.** 649, 1862 ; E. von Bibra, *Polyt. Centrb.*, 888, 1857 ; K. L. Meissner, *Zeit. Metallkunde*, **16.** 439, 1924 ; K. Gilbert, *ib.*, **4.** 245, 1922 ; E. Jannettaz, E. Neel, and P. Clermont, *Bull. Soc. Chim.*, (2), **40.** 53, 1883 ; C. Friedel, *ib.*, (2), **40.** 528, 1883 ; J. Tayler, *Phil. Mag.*, (5), **50.** 37, 1900 ; L. Losana, *ib.*, **53.** i, 393, 1923 ; J. N. Slater, *Chem. Gaz.*, **16.** 296, 1858 ; K. Küppers, *French Pat. No.* 330377, 1903 ; F. Osmond and J. Werth, *Compt. Rend.*, **104.** 1802, 1887 ; A. Halfmann, *Glaser's Ann.*, **81.** 1916 ; *Metal Erz.*, **17.** 11, 1920 ; A. Hague, *Engg.*, **89.** 826, 1910 ; J. E. Stead and L. J. Spencer, *ib.*, **108.** 663, 1919 ; J. E. Stead, *Journ. Soc. Chem. Ind.*, **16.** 509, 1897 ; J. C. Work, *School Mines Quart.*, **36.** 48, 1914 ; R. Schäfer, *Zeit. prakt. Maschinenbau*, **3**, 1913 ; P. H. Dowling, *Phys. Rev.*, (2), **25.** 812, 1925 ; A. Magnus and M. Mannheimer, *Zeit. phys. Chem.*, **121.** 267, 1926 ; W. Richter, *Chem. Ztg.*, **49.** 774, 1925 ; R. W. Irwin, *Journ. Chem. Met. Soc. S. Africa*, **23.** 171, 1923 ; K. Honda and T. Ishigaki, *Science Rep. Tohoku Univ.*, **14.** 219, 1925 ; C. H. Green, *Trans. Amer. Inst. Min. Met.*, **71.** 651, 1926 ; A. Lassieur, *Bull. Officiel Recherches Sciences Inventions*, 31, 1922 ; D. H. Andrews and J. Johnston, *Journ. Inst. Metals*, **32.** 385, 1924 ; M. Dubose, *Réunion de l'Assoc. Int. pour l'essai des matériaux de construction*, 1905 ; L. Guillet, *Chim. Ind.*, 5. 371, 1921 ; *Compt. Rend.*, **182.** 1362, 1926 ; R. S. Dean, L. Zickrick and F. C. Nix, *Min. Met.*, **7.** 76, 1926 ; *Trans. Amer. Inst. Min. Eng.*, 1539, 1926 ; J. Fordos, *Compt. Rend.*, **79.** 678, 1874 ; H. M. Waring, *Chem. Met. Engg.*, **19.** 657, 1918 ; S. Singley, *U.S. Pat. No.* 429249, 1890 ; A. W. King, *ib.*, 811725, 1906 ; A. Gouy, *Journ. Phys.*, (3), **4.** 320, 1895 ; J. M. Belin, *French Pat. No.* 414592, 1909.

⁵ C. Hatchett, *Phil. Trans.*, **93.** 193, 1803.

§ 11. Lead Suboxide, or Hemioxide

The grey film which is first formed when lead is heated below its m.p. in air was regarded by J. J. Berzelius [1] as **lead suboxide or hemioxide**, Pb_2O. P. Bolley also made it from spongy lead, and he stated that lead is not present in the hemioxide because the product gives up no lead to mercury ; and that when heated in a glass tube, it forms lead and ordinary lead oxide. F. J. Brislee showed that there is no break in the hyperbolic curve representing the increase in weight at different periods when lead is heated in oxygen ; but there is a definite break in the time-reduction curve with carbon monoxide—*vide infra*. F. Glaser found that lead oxide in hydrogen at 211° forms grey lead suboxide ; and P. Sabatier and L. Espil obtained a similar result at 190°, or more quickly at 240° ; red-lead passes into the hemioxide under similar conditions at 250° ; G. Bischof worked at 250°–300°, and H. G. Denham showed that lead oxide prepared in different ways requires different temp. for the reduction in hydrogen. A. Salmony saw that the product obtained by the partial reduction of lead oxide is impure. P. L. Dulong, J. B. J. D. Boussingault, and J. Pelouze obtained the hemioxide by cautiously heating lead oxalate in a retort from which air was excluded. The retort was kept at a temp. not exceeding 300° until gas ceased to be evolved. The retort and contents are cooled before the black powder is removed. L. Gutersohn made the suboxide by heating lead oxalate, or a mixture of litharge or red-lead with oxalic acid, sucrose, or starch to 250°–300° in the absence of air.

G. C. Winkelblech regarded the suboxide as a mixture of lead and lead monoxide ; and S. M. Tanatar, as a mixture of lead and lead hemioxide. R. W. E. McIvor said that as fast as the carbon monoxide is formed it should be swept from the apparatus by carbon dioxide and the temp. should not exceed 300°. J. B. J. D. Boussingault, and J. Pelouze said that the suboxide contains no metallic lead, because mercury extracts nothing from it either dry or under water ; and no lead monoxide is present because a boiling soln. of lead acetate does not extract any lead oxide from it. S. M. Tanatar recommended making the hemioxide by heating lead oxalate at as low and as uniform a temp. as possible in a current of carbon dioxide until no more gas is given off. H. G. Denham said that when carbon dioxide is used traces of a horn-like substance, possibly subcarbonate, are formed ; and that if nitrogen be used, the time must be prolonged—say a week at 300°. He recommended mixing the oxalate with four times its weight of silica, and heating the mixtures at 270°–275° while removing the gaseous products by suction at about 50 mm. press. ; and when the press. becomes very small, raising the temp. to 335°. E. Puxeddu said that lead dioxide reacts instantly and vigorously with phenylhydrazine, yielding lead and its monoxide and hemioxide ; and red-lead gives the same products when heated with phenylhydrazine. G. Shimadzu described a large-scale process for making a mixture of the suboxide with finely divided lead.

The greyish-black or greyish-brown lead hemioxide was stated by R. W. E. McIvor to be stable in dry air. L. Gutersohn found that in moist air it becomes covered with a film of hydroxide. The greyish-green product with a sp. gr. 9·973–9·979 is considered by S. M. Tanatar to be a decomposition product, for the hemioxide itself has a sp. gr. 8·3404 to 8·3475. S. M. Tanatar gave for the heat of the reaction $Pb_2O=Pb+PbO+5·452$ cals. F. Aufenast and H. Terrey found the heat of dissolution in acetic acid to be very close to the value for litharge. H. G. Denham, H. G. Denham and A. J. Allmand, and M. M. Bell cited evidence in favour of the possible existence of ions of subvalent lead in soln. A. E. van Arkel observed that the X-radiogram of lead suboxide shows that it is a mixture of tetragonal lead oxide and the metal.

H. G. Denham said that the hemioxide can be heated in vacuo at 375° without decomposition, but it is paler and does not react so readily as the hemioxide which has not been heated to so high a temp. J. B. J. D. Boussingault, and J. Pelouze said that when heated to dull redness out of contact with air, it forms a greenish-yellow mixture of lead and yellow oxide from which the lead can be extracted with mercury, and the lead oxide by a soln. of lead acetate or acetic acid ; M. Herschkowitsch said that heat is evolved when lead hemioxide decomposes into lead and lead monoxide. When heated in air, lead hemioxide ignites and oxidizes with a glimmering light. P. Sabatier and L. Espil said that dry hydrogen reduces it to the metal slowly at 250°, and rapidly at 300°. I. W. Fay and co-workers found that reduction can be detected at 202° when the suboxide is heated in ammonia or methane for 6 hrs. S. M. Tanatar said that it is insoluble in and not decomposed by water ; but if the moist suboxide be exposed to air, S. M. Tanatar, J. B. J. D. Boussingault, and J. Pelouze found that oxygen is rapidly absorbed and the ordinary hydroxide is formed, the reaction being accompanied by a rise of temp. They also stated that dil. sulphuric, nitric, hydrochloric, or acetic acid transforms the hemioxide into a salt of the acid and a little finely divided lead. A similar result is obtained with a soln. of sodium hydroxide ; and, according to J. Pelouze, with a cold soln. of lead nitrate, while with a hot soln., the whole of the suboxide is dissolved and basic lead nitrite is formed. In the method of making white-lead by G. Bischof's process, the suboxide is supposed to be first formed, and subsequently converted by direct hydration and oxidation into the ordinary hydroxide, which in turn is carbonated for white-lead. H. G. Denham showed that ethyl chloride at 311° transformed the suboxide into *lead subchloride*, PbCl ; ethyl bromide at 261° into *lead subbromide*, PbBr ; and methyl iodide at 250°–262° into *lead subiodide*, PbI. According to E. A. Ashcroft, when an alloy of magnesium with 85 per cent. of lead is exposed to moist air, oxidation of both the magnesium and lead proceeds so rapidly that a lump of the alloy swells up and falls to a black powder in a couple of hours. It is assumed that magnesium hydroxide and **lead subhydroxide, or lead monohydroxide,** PbOH, are formed, and when exposed for a still longer time, ordinary lead hydroxide is formed. The second stage of the oxidation requires more time than the first stage. The oxidation of the subhydroxide can be accelerated by adding water to the powder. Some hydrogen is evolved. By shaking the oxidized alloy with an aq. soln. of carbonic acid, white lead is produced. L. Kahlenberg and W. J. Trautmann found that lead hemioxide is but little affected when heated with

powdered silicon, even in the electric arc.   A. V. Blom used lead suboxide as a
pigment with linseed oil.

REFERENCES.

¹ J. J. Berzelius, *Gilbert's Ann.*, **40**. 166, 186, 1812 ; **46**. 131, 1814 ; *Schweigger's Journ.*, **7**.
71, 1813 ; G. Shimadzu, *Brit. Pat. No.* 218119, 1923 ; P. Bolley, *Dingler's Journ.*, **116**. 358,
1850 ; J. B. J. D. Boussingault, *Ann. Chim. Phys.*, (2), **54**. 264, 1833 ; J. Pelouze, *ib.*, (2), **79**
108, 1841 ; G. C. Winkelblech, *Liebig's Ann.*, **21**. 21, 1837 ; *Journ. prakt. Chem.*, (1), **10**. 221,
1837 ; S. M. Tanatar, *Zeit. anorg. Chem.*, **27**. 305, 1901 ; F. Glaser, *ib.*, **36**. 1, 1903 ; M. Herschkowitsch, *ib.*, **115**. 159, 1921 ; E. A. Ashcroft, *Chem. Trade Journ.*, **65**. 224, 1919 ;
F. J. Brislee, *Journ. Chem. Soc.*, **93**. 154, 1908 ; H. G. Denham, *ib.*, **93**. 41, 1908 ; **111**. 30,
1917 ; **113**. 249, 1918 ; H. G. Denham and A. J. Allmand, *ib.*, **93**. 833, 1908 ; P. Sabatier and
L. Espil, *Compt. Rend.*, **159**. 137, 1914 ; A. Salmony, *Chem. Ztg.*, **31**. 955, 1907 ; P. L. Dulong
L'Inst., **14**. 198, 1815 ; *Schweigger's Journ.*, **17**. 229, 1816 ; R. W. E. McIvor, *Chem. News*
86. 192, 1902 ; E. Puxeddu, *Gazz. Chim. Ital.*, **46**. i, 71, 1916 ; G. Bischof, *German Pat.*, *D.R.P*
107625, 1898 ; L. Gutersohn, *Chem. Ztg.*, **48**. 381, 1924 ; I. W. Fay, A. F. Seeker, F. H. Lane
and G. E. Ferguson, *Polyt. Eng.*, **10**. 72, 1910 ; L. Kahlenberg and W. J. Trautmann, *Trans*
Amer. Electrochem. Soc., **39**. 377, 1921 ; A. E. van Arkel, *Rec. Trav. Chim. Pays-Bas*, **44**. 652,
1925 ; A. V. Blom, *Farbe Lack*, 504, 1925 ; F. Aufenast and H. Terrey, *Journ. Chem. Soc.*
129. 1546, 1926 ; N. M. Bell, *Trans. Faraday Soc.*, **11**. 74, 1915.

§ 12. Lead Monoxide

Dioscorides, in his *De materia medica*, and Pliny, in his *Historia naturalis*—both
written in the first century of our era—referred to preparations of lead which were
impure litharge. The λιθάργυρος of Dioscorides was made from a plumbiferous
silver, from lead, and from a plumbiferous sand. He said that there were three
grades—the best grade, *chrystis*, had a yellow colour and came from Greece ; the
second grade, *argyritis* had a silver-white colour, and came from Spain ; while
the poorest grade, *lauritis*, was made from silver, and came from Puteoli, Campania
and Sicily. Pliny (**33**. 35) referred to the first two preparations, but called the
poorest grade *molybditis*. The *molybdœna* of both Pliny and Dioscorides was o
a somewhat shining gold colour, and free from metallic lead ; it became reddish
yellow when powdered, and was found in gold and silver (cupellation) furnaces
as well as in the native condition. The σκωρία ἀργύρον, the ἕλκυμα, or the
ἔγκαυμα of Dioscorides, and the *scoria argenti* or *spuma argenti* of Pliny ; the
σκωρία μολύβδον of Dioscorides or the *scoria plumbi* of Pliny ; and the λίθος
μολυβδοείδης of Dioscorides or the *lapis plumbaris* of Pliny were impure pre
parations of litharge. Pliny described the production of litharge during the
process of cupellation.

Lead monoxide has been reported to occur naturally in quite a number of places
but some of the reports are not considered to be well established. J. G. Wal
lerius [1] referred to the yellow oxide as *terra plumbaria citrina*, and the red oxid
—red-lead—as *terra plumbaria rubia*. J. B. L. Romé de l'Isle referred to the
yellow and red oxides as *mine de plomb terreuse ;* R. J. Haüy mentioned the sam
oxides. J. G. Lehmann showed that the yellow oxide reported from the Harz wa
considered by J. G. Lehmann to come from the remains of an old silver-works
and that reported by J. F. John from Breinig, near Stolberg, was shown by
J. J. Nöggerath to be an old furnace product.

A. G. Werner's *lead-earth* was a carbonate. L. A. Emmerling, and C. C. von Leonhar
both described the yellow oxide as a mineral. The *lead-ochre* of M. Bauer, F. Klockmann
and P. Groth was regarded as lead monoxide ; and that of E. F. Glocker, and C. Hartman
as red-lead. E. F. Glocker in 1839 applied the term *Bleiglätte* for massicot ; A. d'Achiard
used the term *massicottite*, and A. Weisbach. *chrysitine*.

J D Dana reported lead oxide from the lead slags of the Laurium, Greece ; A. Pellou
from Sardinia ; C. A. Tenne and S. y C. del Rio Calderon, in Mertola, Portugal, and Murcia
Spain ; A. Lacroix, in various departments of France—Gard, Haute-Loire, Isère, Ruy
de-Dôme, Rhône, Vosges, and Haute-Marne. J. D. Dana, F. A. Quenstedt, M. Baue

C. Koch, G. A. Kenngott, V. R. von Zepharovich, in Germany—Baden, Nassau, and Siebenbürgen; V. R. von Zepharovich, at Dubrava, Hungary; E. S. Larsen, in Austria —in crystals; A. Scott, Zarshuran, Persia—red tetragonal crystals; J. B. Dana, in Virginia; E. S. Larsen, in California—in crystals; F. von Gerolt, J. J. Nöggerath, L. W. Bailey, C. F. de Landero, E. Pugh, in various parts of Mexico—Ixtacihuatl, Popacatepetl, Chihuahua, Cohahuila, and Zomclahhuacan; I. Domeyko, in Caracoles, Bolivia; W. F. Petterd, in Dundas, Tasmania. The occurrence of lead oxide as a furnace product, etc., was mentioned by E. Mitscherlich, J. J. Nöggerath, J. D. Dana, C. M. Marx, F. Sandberger, W. J. Grailich, J. S. S. Brame, etc.

All varieties of ordinary lead oxide, *i.e.* lead monoxide, are called **litharge,** although many confine the term to the fused and crystalline oxide, and they call the oxide which has not been fused **massicot.** J. B. L. Romé de l'Isle [2] said : *a mésure que la chaux grise de plomb se combine avec l'acide igné, sa couleur change ;* the yellow oxide is called *massicot,* and the *verre de plomb* which has crystallized is called *litharge.* The so-called amorphous lead oxide is pulverulent like massicot, and is not necessarily non-crystalline. Lead oxide is formed by the direct oxidation of lead, and is therefore liable to contain the impurities originally associated with the lead. Modifications by oxidizing molten lead spray were made by W. P. Thompson,[3] and G. Shimadzu ; or finely divided lead in a tube furnace, by G. Shimadzu ; by air under press., or air mixed with steam, by L. Kühler. Many other modifications have been patented by H. M. Gabel, G. Shimadzu, etc. Commercial litharge is usually fairly pure, and is seldom adulterated. It contains a little iron, copper, silver, antimony and silica, and metallic lead. Sometimes a little sulphate and carbonate are present, and maybe a little red-lead. The purification has been described by G. Bischof, E. F. Anthon, R. H. Bradford, etc. It is difficult to make the amorphous monoxide by oxidizing lead because, as J. F. Sacher showed, if the temp. is too low, red-lead is produced, and if too high, the lead oxide fuses and crystallizes on cooling. Lead is vaporized by making an electric arc with a lead electrode, and the vapour oxidized as described by V. Kohlschütter and co-workers, and T. Goldschmidt. W. N. Hartley oxidized the vapour in the induction spark between lead electrodes. The so-called *flores plumbi* or flowers of lead, and the so-called *lead-ash* are examples the mode of preparation of which was indicated in connection with the action of oxygen on lead. Lead oxide is a by-product in the cupellation of lead. If the lead employed is impure, the litharge produced at the beginning is impure, that last formed contains silver, while the middle portion is collected in pots in a fused condition. Exfoliation occurs during solidification, forming a friable mass which is broken up, screened, and sold as *flake litharge ;* the knottings on the screen are ground in water, and the sludge collected in settling tanks is dried and sold as *levigated litharge.* Lead oxide is usually prepared by drossing lead in a small reverberatory furnace ; as the oxide is formed, it is pushed back with an iron rabble so as to expose a fresh surface of metal to the air. Pigs of lead are added as required, and the operation continued until sufficient oxide has accumulated. The product is then ground and the finely powdered product levigated in water ; or collected by pneumatic separation. Modifications of the calcination process have been suggested by H. A. Hünicke, W. Eckford, A. Salmony, G. Shimadzu, T. Goldschmidt, C. A. Hall, etc. The so-called *sublimed litharge* is obtained as a by-product in the fume from the manufacture of litharge by hearth or cupellation process. It is a very fine grained sulphur-yellow material. G. T. Lewis made lead oxide by boiling the fumes from lead smelting furnaces in a soln. of sodium hydroxide or carbonate for about an hour, then allowing to settle, washing the precipitate (carbonate and hydrated oxide of lead) to free it from sodium sulphate and roasting to form litharge or red-lead. If the fumes contain zinc the latter must first be dissolved out with sulphuric acid.

The hydroxide decomposes when heated, forming the oxide, and, according to J. B. A. Dumas, 2 or 3 per cent. of oxygen are given off at the same time. S. Glasstone made litharge by this process. J. Milbaur said the decomposition is complete at about 130° in vacuo. V. Kohlschütter and co-workers found that at 110°, red oxide is formed, and at 650°, the yellow oxide. T. Carnelley and J. Walker obtained lead oxide by heating red-lead to 520°–530°; at 521°, said W. Reinders and L. Hamburger, the decomposition is incomplete. J. E. Mackenzie, and W. Mostowitsch said that lead dioxide decomposes at 800°–820°, forming the monoxide. Formerly, lead oxide was obtained of a high degree of purity by calcining the oxalate. J. J. Berzelius obtained the oxide by heating lead nitrate; the reaction, said H. C. Cooper and co-workers, is complete at 357°. C. R. A. Wright and A. P. Luff used this process, and added that the lead nitrate should not be melted. G. Gore obtained the oxide by reducing lead carbonate with carbon monoxide; J. Riban, V. Kohlschütter and H. Röseti heated lead carbonate to 400° in air, and obtained the red oxide by heating the resulting basic carbonate in nitrogen at 450°, and the lemon-yellow oxide at 650°; W. Dominik, reduced the carbonate at 300° with steam; H. S. Reed and H. L. Purlow manufactured lead oxide by heating the basic carbonate in air at 310° in a rotating tube furnace, and afterwards at 600°–650° in the absence of air; J. Riban, by calcining the acetate; A. Leclerc, by heating the nitrato-oxalate, and V. A. Kroll, by melting electrolytic lead dioxide. According to V. Thomas, lead oxide is formed during the action of nitrogen peroxide on lead iodide. G. Kassner obtained litharge by heating powdered lead with calcium plumbate, or by stirring together molten calcium plumbate and lead. R. Kayser obtained lead oxide by heating a mixture of lead sulphate and sodium nitrate to dull redness and washing the product; M. Liebig gradually added lead to molten sodium nitrate at about 300°; and subsequently washed the sodium nitrite from the lead oxide. Lead oxide is produced during the electrolysis of soln. of sulphates (C. Pollak), oxalates (L. Lejeune), hydroxides (C. Luckow), and phosphates (F. Fischer), using lead electrodes. A. C. Becquerel obtained cubic or tabular crystals of lead oxide by fusing a mixture of lead oxide with 4–6 times its weight of potassium hydroxide in a silver crucible at a dull red heat, and washing the alkali away with water. L. Michel obtained some red-coloured lead oxide and some lead dioxide at the same time. F. C. Calvert said that if sodium hydroxide be employed the red-coloured " amorphous " oxide is produced which becomes brownish-red if heated between 300° and 400°, but if heated above 400°, the cold mass is sulphur-yellow. G. Grube, A. Geuther, and V. Kohlschütter and co-workers also obtained yellowish-green crystals by heating the hydroxide with a conc. soln. of potassium or sodium hydroxide—say $8N$- to $12N$-KOH. According to J. J. Houton-Labillardière, if a hot soln. of sodium or potassium hydroxide be sat. with lead oxide, and the soln. kept in a stoppered bottle all through the winter, small, white, rhombic dodecahedra are formed. E. Mitscherlich added that a boiling conc. soln. of potassium hydroxide sat. with lead oxide gives yellow scales of lead oxide on cooling; if the soln. be not fully sat., or if the mother-liquor from the preceding operation be allowed to stand in a cool place, red scales of lead oxide are formed. The red crystals are soluble in acetic acid showing the absence of red-lead, and when heated, they become yellow on cooling. A. G. Fell destroyed any higher oxides present in a soln. of lead oxide in alkali-lye, by allowing the liquid to stand in contact with spongy or finely divided lead for a short time. F. C. Calvert dissolved lead hydroxide in boiling soda-lye of sp. gr. 1·38–1·39, and, on cooling, obtained rose-red crystals of lead oxide which lose about 0·1 per cent. of water at 400° and turn black; at low redness, the crystals become sulphur-yellow without changing their form. A. C. Becquerel prepared greenish crystals of lead oxide by wrapping copper about a piece of lead, placed in a soln. of silica or alumina in potash- or soda-lye. E. Frémy showed that when lead hydroxide is boiled with a quantity of alkali-lye not sufficient to dissolve it all, the undissolved part is converted into the crystalline, anhydrous oxide, and the dissolved portion is obtained as crystals by evaporating the liquid. According to A. Ditte, when potash-lye is added with continual agitation to lead hydrate, $Pb(OH)_2$, suspended in water at 25°, the amount of lead oxide dissolved increases with the quantity of alkali added until the latter amounts to 300 grams per litre of water. At this point, the amount of lead oxide dissolved decreases slightly, but afterwards increases as more alkali is added, and, at the same time, the amorphous hydrate is converted into transparent, microscopic crystals. When the quantity of alkali added reaches 400 grms. per litre of water, the amount of lead oxide dissolved again suddenly diminishes, but afterwards increases as more and more alkali is added. The hydroxide, $Pb(OH)_2$, dissolves at first in the dil. potash-lye, but as the conc. of the latter increases, it is converted into the hydrate $3PbO.H_2O$, and this, in its turn, is converted into the anhydrous oxide when the conc. of the alkali passes a certain point. The same changes take place at all temp., but more readily the higher the temp. The hydrate, $3PbO.H_2O$, separates out in the form of transparent, white, flattened, hexagonal prisms (sp. gr. at $0°=7·592$), when a soln. of alkali containing 100–300 grms. per litre of water is sat. with lead hydrate at a temp. insufficient for its decomposition, and allowed to cool. The anhydrous oxide is obtained in several different forms depending on the temp. and the conc. of the potash-lye. When the hydrate is heated with a soln. of about 130 grms. of potash in a litre of water, the oxide is obtained in small plates, with a greenish-yellow tinge; sp. gr. at $0°=9·1699$. With 230 grms. potash in a litre of water, the oxide forms brilliant sulphur-yellow crystals; sp. gr. at $0°=9·2089$. With 300 grms. potash in a litre of water, the oxide separates out on cooling in small, compact, heavy, brownish-yellow needles; sp. gr. at $0°=9·8835$. If potash is added gradually to lead hydrate suspended in water at $20°$ until it amounts to 400 grms. per litre of water, the anhydrous lead oxide separates out after several days in the form of a hard, compact, greyish-green crust, composed of large, brilliant laminæ; sp. gr. at $0°=9·5605$. When a hot soln. of 185 grms. potash in a litre of water is sat. with lead oxide, the latter separates out on cooling in long, dark green, almost black needles; sp. gr. at $0°=9·4223$. All these different varieties of the oxide are formed of small, thin, transparent crystals, the colour varying with the thickness of the plates, which are rhombic, the ratio of the diagonals being about 1 : 3. All the crystals become red when heated, and sulphur-yellow on cooling; their sp. gr. increases the more they are heated.

Lead oxide is obtained by treating lead salts with aq. ammonia or soln. of alkali or alkaline earth hydroxides—assisted by light or heat. If the soln. be heated, the anhydrous oxide is precipitated, and if cold, the hydroxide. V. Zotier obtained red, microscopic crystals by slowly heating at $160°$ a mush of lead nitrate and water with twice its weight of a 50 per cent. soln. of sodium hydroxide. A. Geuther obtained the red oxide by heating to $170°$ basic lead nitrate, and shaking the product in a stoppered cylinder with a soln. of sodium hydroxide (1 : 10–20). W. Reinders and L. Hamburger boiled lead nitrate with an excess of a 40–50 per cent. soln. of sodium hydroxide. Analogous processes by using lead acetate were described by V. Kohlschütter and H. Rösti, and S. Glasstone; M. Pleissner found the precipitate obtained with baryta-water and lead nitrate always contains a trace of nitrate. A. Ditte found the hydrated oxide, $3PbO.H_2O$, is converted into the anhydrous oxide by exposure to light or heat; and the basic chloride, $Pb_3O_2Cl_2$, passes into the anhydrous oxide when treated with potash-lye. C. E. A. Wichmann obtained the yellowish-red oxide by the action of a boiling aq. soln. of sodium hydroxide, sp. gr. 1·25, on lead sulphate; with a more conc. alkaline soln., the product is redder. A. G. Fell patented a method of making lead oxide by heating the basic sulphate with alkali hydroxide. V. Kohlschütter and H. Rösti heated the sulphate, or chloride with $10N$-NaOH; and M. Lachaud and C. Lepierre, the chromate with 45 per cent. potassium hydroxide soln. A. Wohl obtained the sulphur-yellow oxide by the action of alkali-lye or lime-water on basic lead carbonate. The recovery of lead oxide from saccharate soln. has been discussed by G. Kassner, J. L. Babé and W. Witter, and A. Wohl.

J. Tünnermann exposed a soln. of lead acetate containing an excess of ammonia to sunlight for a few days, and obtained olive-green crystals of the anhydrous oxide; W. Behrens added sufficient ammonia to a soln. of lead acetate to dissolve the precipitate first formed, and exposed the filtered soln. in a stoppered vessel to sunlight for a few hours. Colourless crystals first separate out, and these become yellow and yellowish-grey in a few hours. The white powder becomes dark brown after long trituration. According to A. Payen, when 4 vols. of an aq. soln. of lead acetate, sat. at 30°, are mixed with 100 vols. of boiling water, and then with 45 vols. of aq. ammonia, the anhydrous oxide separates out, in delicate, yellowish-white, rhomboidal laminæ. These can be separated by levigation from the crystalline granules of hydroxide which form at the same time, washed with boiling water, and dried in vacuo. When ignited, the crystals give off only a trace of water with decrepitation. The crystals can be obtained without the hydroxide by boiling 100 vols. of a sat. soln. of the basic acetate, $Pb_3O(C_2H_3O_2)_2H_2O$, with 50 vols. of water, adding 50 vols. of water at 80° and 8 vols. of aq. ammonia, and heating the mixture on a water-bath. G. C. Winkelblech obtained reddish-yellow spangles by mixing boiling soln. of two mols of lead acetate and 3 mols of potassium hydroxide (1 : 10). M. Pleissner obtained an oxide of a high degree of purity by the action of 150 c.c. of a boiling soln. 4 per cent. soln. of barium hydroxide on 36 c.c. of a boiling soln. of lead acetate (1 : 6). The greyish-yellow plates of oxide were washed with boiling water. According to F. Brendcke, if a soln. of lead acetate be dropped with constant stirring into a conc. soln. of calcium hydroxide at 88°, until crystalline scales appear, and a little more be added, the scaly crystals continue separating as the liquid cools. When dry, they are yellowish-white, with a silvery lustre, and feel like talc ; when heated, they become red without loss of weight, but on cooling regain their original colour and appearance. N. Kromer agitated a mixture of powdered lead acetate, $Pb(C_2H_3O_2)_2.3H_2O$, and barium hydroxide, $Ba(OH)_2.8H_2O$—or strontium or calcium hydroxides, $Sr(OH)_2.8H_2O$, or $Ca(OH)_2.H_2O$—and yellow crystalline lead oxide was formed, which became red in about a month.

Lead oxide appears as a product in many chemical processes—*vide supra* in connection with the action of aerated water, etc., on lead. Thus, in the action of an aq. soln. of oxygen on lead, M. Pleissner showed that lead oxide is produced provided the soln. is kept sat. with oxygen; if only a limited supply of oxygen is available, the lead is converted into the hydroxide. P. Yorke obtained lead oxide by placing a piece of lead and some water inside a leaden vessel exposed to air. White flecks of hydrocarbonate are first formed, and then grey, mica-like crystals of lead oxide. These become orange when heated. T. Benfield patented a process for making lead oxide by shaking granular lead with water in presence of air or oxidizing gases. H. V. Regnault obtained lead oxide as a product of the action of steam on lead at a white heat, but, according to P. A. von Bonsdorff, not at a red heat. According to A. Bergmann and co-workers, the conversion of lead into litharge is effected by mechanically agitating the lead in a closed vessel in the presence of hot air and superheated steam, and so projecting the molten metal against a distribution plate as to reduce it to an impalpable powder. Under the action of the mixture of air and superheated steam this is immediately and quantitatively converted into litharge, which is carried forward by the current of air into deposition chambers. By suitable regulation of the temp. of the mixture of air and steam, red litharge (at 250°–300°) or yellow litharge (at 300°–400°) may be obtained. Several modifications have been suggested by the original inventors, E. Barthelmess, etc. To convert galena into lead oxide, T. Huntington and F. Heberlein recommended tl at the mineral be mixed with sufficient lime or other alkaline earth to react with the sulphur present, and that the mixture be heated to bright redness (about 700°) in a reverberatory or other furnace. It is then cooled to a dull red heat (about 500°) and transferred to a vessel in which it is exposed to a current of air, which may be preheated, and which is introduced by means of a blower. Under these conditions rapid oxidation takes place, sulphur dioxide is evolved (and may be utilized) ; much heat is generated, and the mixture fuses and gradually settles down to a mass of oxide of lead with the gangue of the ore. W. S. Kilpatrick roasted the galena in order to obtain a mixture of lead oxide and sulphate ; heated the product with an eq. proportion of a carbonate of the alkalies, alkaline earths, magnesium, or zinc ; and removed the sulphate by elutriation or by washing. T. Goldschmidt volatilized **lead** oxide **from** lead, lead sulphide, carbonate, or red-lead in a current of air.

Analyses by P. Berthier,[4] T. Thomson, J. B. Trommsdorff, J. L. Proust, J. W. Döbereiner, L. N. Vauquelin, J. Davy, J. J. Berzelius, and C. F. Bucholz established the composition of lead oxide. The brownish-yellow colour of commercial litharge, said R. Ruer, is not due to the presence of the higher oxides of lead, but to the presence of other impurities. Analyses of the purest obtainable commercial lead oxide by W. Mostowitsch showed the presence of 99·2 per cent. PbO, some silica and some iron ; E. J. Kohlmeyer reported 0·9 per cent. carbon dioxide ; J. Gaudin, some Pb_3O_4 ; J. Löwy, and L. Michel, silver, gold, and platinum ; J. S. Remington and R. F. Hartley, metallic lead, iron, copper, and carbonate ; F. C. Schlagdenhausen, some calcium sulphate ; M. Liebig, 0·006 per cent. chlorine. C. A. Klein gave the following as typical analyses of commercial samples of lead monoxide (the insoluble matter refers to acetic acid **as** solvent) :

	Pb	Cu	Bi	Sb	Fe	Insoluble
Process oxide . . .	—	<0·0070	0·0081	0·0066	0·019	0·079
Fused litharge . . .	0·4	0·0064	0·0005	0·0015	0·007	0·650

V. Kohlschütter and J. L. Tüscher obtained highly dispersed lead oxide by vaporizing the metal in the electric arc, and passing a current of air through the vapour.

REFERENCES.

[1] J. G. Wallerius, *Mineralogia*, Stockholm, 1747 ; J. B. L. Romé de l'Isle, *Cristallographie*, Paris, 3. 405, 1783 ; R. J. Haüy, *Traité de minéralogie*, Paris, 3. 455, 1801 ; 3. 384, 1822 ; J. F. John, *Schweigger's Journ.*, 4. 219, 1812 ; A. G. Werner, *Letztes Mineral-system*, Freiberg, 22, 1817 ; L. A. Emmerling, *Lehrbuch der Mineralogie*, Giessen, 2. 406, 1796 ; C. C. von Leonhard, *Handbuch der Oryktognosie*, Heidelberg, 231, 1821 ; J. G. Lehmann, *Versuche Geschichte von Flötzgebürgen*, Berlin, 213, 1756 ; M. Bauer, *Lehrbuch der Mineralogie*, Stuttgart, 508, 1904 ; F. Klockmann, *Lehrbuch der Mineralogie*, Stuttgart, 360, 1903 ; P. Groth, *Tabellarische Uebersicht der Mineralien*, Braunschweig, 46, 1898 ; C. Hartmann, *Handbuch der Mineralogie*, Weimar, 2. 489, 1843 ; A. d'Achiardi, *I metalli loro mineralie e miniere*, Milan, 1. 221, 1883 ; A. Weisbach, *Synopsis mineralogica*, Freiberg, 54, 1875 ; 66, 1897 ; E. F. Glocker, *Handbuch der Mineralogie*, Nürnberg, 387, 935, 1839 ; 564, 1851 ; C. A. Tenne and S, y C. del Rio Calderon, *Die Mineralfundstätten der iberischen Halbinsel*, Berlin, 1902 ; J. D. Dana, *A System of Mineralogy*, New York, 496, 1850 ; 209, 1892 ; 45, 1899 ; A. Lacroix, *Minéralogie de la France et de ses colonies*, Paris, 3. 312, 1901 ; C. F. de Landero, *Sinopsis mineralogica ó catalogo descriptivo de los minerales*, Mexico, 313, 1888 ; I. Domeyko, *Mineralojia*, Santiago, 317, 715, 1879 ; W. F. Petterd, *Catalogue of the Minerals of Tasmania*, Launceston, 58, 1896 ; J. J. Nöggerath, *Mag. Nat. Freunde Berlin*, 7. 53, 1815 ; *Zeit. deut. geol. Ges.*, 6. 675, 691, 1855 ; A. Pelloux, *Atti Accad. Lincei*, (5), 13. ii, 34, 1904 ; E. Mitscherlich, *Pogg. Ann.*, 49. 403, 1840 ; *Journ. prakt. Chem.*, (1), 19. 451, 1840 ; C. M. Marx, *ib.*, (1), 3. 217, 1834 ; J. S. S. Brame, *Journ. Soc. Chem. Ind.*, 37. 40, 1918 ; F. Sandberger, *Jahrb. Nassau. Ver. Nat.*, 131, 1851 ; W. T. Grailich. *Sitzber. Akad. Wien*, 28. 282, 1858 ; F. von Gerolt, *Karsten's Arch.*, 4. 564, 1832 ; L. W. Bailey, *Amer. Journ. Science*, (2), 8. 420, 1849 ; E. Pugh, *Liebig's Ann.*, 100. 128, 1856 ; *Miscellaneous Chemical Analyses*, Göttingen, 1856 ; F. A. Quenstedt, *Handbuch der Mineralogie*, Tübingen, 561, 1854 ; 810, 1877 ; G. Leonhard, *Die Mineralien Badens*, Stuttgart, 1876 ; C. Koch, *Ver. Nat. Nassau*, 12. 400, 1858 ; V. R. von Zepharovich, *Mineralogisches Lexicon für das Kaiserthum Oesterreich*, Wein, 60, 1859 ; 39, 1893 ; G. A. Kenngott, *Uebersicht der Resultate mineralogischer Forschungen*, Wien, 143, 1857 ; A. Scott, *Min. Mag.*, 17. 143, 1914 ; E. S. Larsen, *Bull. U.S. Geol. Sur.*, 679, 1921 ; *Amer. Min.*, 2. 18, 1917 ; G. Shimadzu, *Japan. Pat. No.* 41953, 1922 ; *Brit. Pat. No.* 176924, 1920.

[2] J. B. L. Romé de l'Isle, *Cristallographie*, Paris, 1. 283, 1783.

[3] A. Geuther, *Liebig's Ann.*, 219, 60, 1883 ; G. C. Winkelblech, *ib.*, 21. 21, 1837 ; *Journ. prakt. Chem.*, (1), 10. 221, 1837 ; E. Mitscherlich, *ib.*, (1), 19. 451, 1840 ; C. M. Marx, *ib.*, (1), 3. 217, 1834 ; C. A. Klein, *Journ. Oil Colour Assoc.*, 11. 8, 1919 ; P. A. von Bonsdorff, *Pogg. Ann.*, 41. 305, 1837 ; L. Lejeune, *German Pat.*, *D.R.P.* 150620, 1902 ; C. Pollak, *ib.*, 97821, 1897 ; W. Eckford, *ib.*, 265641, 1912 ; W. P. Thompson, *ib.*, 328044, 1916 ; L. Kühler, *ib.*, 351328, 355649, 1920 ; A. Wohl, *ib.*, 90307, 96544, 1895 ; R. Kayser, *ib.*, 99531, 1898 ; E. Barthelmess, *ib.*, 292695. 1913 ; J. L. Babé and W. Witter, *ib.*, 198072, 1906 ; A. Bergmann, and Simons Ges. and Lindgrens und Söhne, *ib.*, 228729, 229245, 1909 ; G. Kassner, *ib.*, 82985, 1894 ; 97481, 1896 ; *Brit. Pat. No.* 23171, 1895 ; *Dingler's Journ.*, 298. 65, 1895 ; 300. 94, 118, 1896 ;

G. T. Lewis, *ib.*, 248. 220, 1883 ; *Brit. Pat. No.* 2278, 1882 ; A. G. Fell, *ib.*, 14985, 1900 ; W. S. Kilpatrick, *ib.*, 23548, 1892 ; T. Benfield, *ib.*, 25009, 1896 ; C. V. Barton, *ib.*, 190733, 190955, 1921 ; P. Wefelscheid, *ib.*, 220548, 1924 ; T. Huntington and F. Heberlein, *ib.*, 8064, 1896 ; 3795, 1897 ; T. Goldschmidt, *ib.*, 189132, 1922 ; G. Shimadzu, *ib.*, 176924, 1920 ; 529369, 1921 ; 236368, 1924 ; H. S. Reed and H. L. Purlow, *U.S. Pat. No.* 1376581, 1920 ; H. M. Gabel, *ib.*, 1382282, 1919 ; J. Milbauer, *Chem. Ztg.*, 33. 513, 1909 ; E. J. Kohlmeyer, *ib.*, 36. 993, 1912 ; A. Salmony, *ib.*, 31. 955, 1907 ; J. F. Sacher, *ib.*, 34. 1262, 1910 ; J. Schiel, *Ber.*, 12. 507, 1879 ; H. C. Cooper, L. I. Shaw, and N. E. Loomis, *ib.*, 42. 3991, 1909 ; M. Pleissner, *Art. Kaiser Ges. Amt.*, 26. 393, 1907 ; C. Luckow, *Brit. Pat. No.* 24960, 1899 ; J. A. Thibault, *ib.*, 137288, 1919 ; C. A. Hall, *ib.*, 251449, 1925 ; J. J. Berzelius, *Gilbert's Ann.*, 40. 166, 186, 1812 ; 46. 131, 1814 ; *Schweigger's Journ.*, 7. 71, 1813 ; F. Fischer, *Zeit. Elektrochem.*, 16. 356, 1910 ; G. Grube, *ib.*, 28. 278, 1922 ; V. Kohlschütter and J. L. Tüscher, *ib.*, 27. 243, 256, 1921 ; V. Kohlschütter and H. Röseti, *Ber.*, 56. B, 285, 1923 ; H. V. Regnault, *Ann. Chim. Phys.*, (2), 62. 363, 1836 ; A. Payen, *ib.*, (3), 66. 51, 1862 ; (4), 8. 302, 1866 ; J. B. A. Dumas, *ib.*, (2), 49. 398, 1832 ; F. C. Calvert, *Compt. Rend.*, 16. 1361, 1843 ; V. Thomas, *ib.*, 126. 1349, 1898 ; A. Leclerc, *ib.*, 125. 893, 1897 ; A. C. Becquerel, *ib.*, 34. 29, 1852 ; *Ann. Chim. Phys.*, (2), 51. 510, 1832 ; A. Ditte, *ib.*, (5), 28. 127, 1883 ; *Compt. Rend.*, 94. 1311, 1882 ; J. Riban, *ib.*, 93. 1141, 1881 ; *Bull. Soc. Chim.*, (2), 38. 158, 1882 ; V. Zotier, *ib.*, (4), 21. 246, 1917 ; M. Lachaud and C. Lepierre, *ib.*, (3), 6. 231, 1891 ; H. Hélier, *ib.*, (3), 21. 43, 1899 ; W. Mostowitsch, *Met.*, 4. 648, 1907 ; H. Reinders and L. Hamburger, *Zeit. anorg. Chem.*, 89. 79, 1914 ; V. A. Kroll, *ib.*, 78. 100, 1912 ; F. M. Jäger and H. C. Germs, *ib.*, 119. 147, 1921 ; H. C. Germs, *De thermische Analyse van loodsulfaat, chromaat, molybdaat, en walframaat en van hun binaire combinaties*, Gröningen, 1917 ; J. E. Mackenzie, *Chem. News*, 99. 146, 1909 ; G. Gore, *ib.*, 48. 295, 1884 ; T. Carnelley and J. Walker, *Journ. Chem. Soc.*, 53. 59, 1888 ; C. R. A. Wright and A. P. Luff, *ib.*, 33. 527, 1878 ; S. Glasstone, *ib.*, 119. 1689, 1914, 1921 ; 121. 64, 1922 ; E. Frémy, *Journ. Pharm. Chim.*, (3), 3. 30, 1843 ; J. J. Houton-Labillardière, *ib.*, (1), 3. 335, 1817 ; W. Behrens, *ib.*, (3), 4. 18, 1843 ; P. Yorke, *Phil. Mag.*, (3), 5. 280, 1834 ; J. Joly, *ib.*, (6), 27. 1, 1914 ; L. Michel, *Bull. Soc. Min.*, 13. 86, 1890 ; J. Tünnermann, *Kastner's Arch.*, 19. 339, 1830 ; C. E. A. Wichmann, *Journ. Pharm. Chim.*, (3), 38. 236, 1860 ; F. Brendecke, *Repert. Pharm.*, 53. 155, 1835 ; 55. 318, 1836 ; E. F. Anthon, *ib.*, 58. 387, 1837 ; N. Kromer, *Russ. Pharm. Journ.*, 34. 534, 1895 ; R. H. Bradford, *Journ. Ind. Eng. Chem.*, 1. 181, 1909 ; G. Bischof, *Schweigger's Journ.*, 64. 65, 1832 ; H. A. Hünicke, *Eng. Min. Journ.*, 54. 606, 1892 ; M. Liebig, *Zeit. angew. Chem.*, 17. 1673, 1904 ; W. N. Hartley, *Proc. Roy. Soc.*, 46. 88, 1889 ; W. Dominik, *Przemist Chemiczny*, 6. 25, 1922 ; J. F. G. Hicks, *Journ. Phys. Chem.*, 25. 545, 1921 ; H. T. S. Britton, *Journ. Chem. Soc.*, 127. 2148, 1925 ; T. Goldschmidt, *Brit. Pat. No.* 228900, 1925 ; C. A. Hall, *ib.*, 248602, 1925.

⁴ P. Berthier, *Ann. Chim. Phys.*, (2), 39. 244, 1828 ; J. W. Döbereiner, *Schweigger's Journ.*, 17. 241, 1816 ; C. F. Bucholz, *Gehlen's Ann.*, 5. 253, 1805 ; L. N. Vauquelin, *Ann. Chim. Phys.*, (1), 62. 221, 1807 ; T. Thomson, *Nicholson's Journ.*, 8. 280, 1804 ; J. J. Berzelius, *Gilbert's Ann.*, 27. 252, 1811 ; *Pogg. Ann.*, 19. 314, 1830 ; J. Davy, *Edin. Phil. Journ.*, 6. 128, 1829 ; J. B. Trommsdorff, *Trommsdorff's Journ. Pharm.*, 8. 3, 1824 ; J. L. Proust, *Journ. Phys.*, 56. 206, 1802 ; 59. 324, 1804 ; W. Mostowitsch, *Met.*, 4. 648, 1907 ; E. J. Kohlmeyer, *Metall Erz.*, 10. 452, 1913 ; J. Gaudin, *Journ. Pharm. Chim.*, (6), 6. 28, 1897 ; F. C. Schlagdenhausen, *ib.*, (5), 3. 397, 1874 ; M. Liebig, *Zeit. angew. Chem.*, 17. 1674, 1904 ; J. S. Remington and R. F. Hartley, *Pharm. Journ.*, (4), 28. 670, 1909 ; R. Ruer, *Zeit. anorg. Chem.*, 50. 267, 1906 ; J. Löwy, *Chem. Ztg.*, 39. 287, 1915 ; L. Michel, *Bull. Soc. Min.*, 13. 86, 1890 ; C. A. Klein, *Journ. Oil Colour Chem. Assoc.*, 2. 1, 1919 ; V. Kohlschütter and J. L. Tüscher, *Zeit. Elektrochem.*, 27. 225, 1921.

§ 13. The Physical Properties of Lead Monoxide

As indicated in connection with the different modes of preparation, the **colour** of lead monoxide may be yellowish-white, greyish-yellow, greenish-yellow, sulphur-yellow, reddish-yellow, red, or reddish-brown. The yellow massicot form is also called *argyritis*, or *Silberglätte*, and the red form *chrysitis* or *Goldglätte*. E. Mitscherlich [1] showed that the colour of the red form is not due to the presence of red-lead because it is wholly soluble in acetic acid. F. le Blanc attributed the difference to a variation in the physical structure, and not in the chemical composition, since either form may be obtained by regulating the temp. and the rate of cooling—the red variety, which is specifically lighter than the yellow, is formed most abundantly when the cooling is slow. According to E. Mitscherlich, and F. C. Calvert, the red form passes into the yellow when heated ; and, according to N. Kromer, and R. Ruer, the yellow becomes red by long-continued action of light at ordinary temp., or, according to W. Behrens, R. Ruer, and A. Geuther, by prolonged trituration—R. Ruer did not change the yellow to the red form by a press. of 2000 atm.

A. Geuther found that below 105°, only the yellow form is produced in a boiling aq. soln. of potassium or sodium hydroxide ; and at 110°-130°, only the red form. R. Ruer, however, showed that the temp. is dependent on the conc. of the alkali-lye ; in a sealed tube with 7·10 per cent. sodium hydroxide soln., at 150°, the red oxide remains red, and the yellow oxide, yellow. A. Ditte, R. Ruer, and H. C. Germs consider that two enantiotropic forms of lead monoxide are here involved, the red form being more stable at ordinary temp., and at all temp. up to the **transition point** which has not been precisely determined. R. Ruer found that at ordinary temp. the yellow form is not stable, but is stable above 620°, so that the transition temp. is near 620° because the reddish-brown form when heated to this temp. assumes the yellow form—the red oxide required a temp. of 720° for the conversion. The reverse change was induced only by grinding or by heating with conc. alkali-lye. H. C. Germs, emphasizing the difference in the colour, sp. gr., and solubility of the two forms, concluded that the transition point is 587°. The rate of conversion at this temp. was found to be very slow, but the speed increases as the temp. rises. It was not found possible to change the yellow to the red form except by dissolving the oxide in molten alkali. S. Glasstone found that the heating curve showed no signs of a transition temp., and that no visible change was observed by keeping the red form at 540° for 4 hrs., although W. Reinders and L. Hamburger observed a slow change at this temp. S. Glasstone added that measurements of the potential $Pb \mid PbO, N\text{-}NaOH$ show no signs of a transition ; that no definite difference in sp. gr. or crystal form has been established ; and that the solubilities of lead oxide made by different methods are always the same and independent of the colour. He therefore attributed the difference to a difference in the state of aggregation of the particles. The yellow agglomerated form produces a reddish-brown powder on trituration owing to the production of smaller particles ; and it is assumed that the red particles are of an intermediate state of subdivision. He showed that the passage from the red to the yellow form on heating is not due to the intermediate formation of red-lead ; at 200°-450° the reaction is symbolized : $6PbO + O_2 = 2Pb_3O_4$; and at 600° by $2Pb_3O_4 = 6PbO + O_2$—the change occurs in an atm. of nitrogen.

On the other hand, R. Ruer said that the solubility of the two forms in water is different, the value for the yellow oxide being $1·00 \times 10^{-4}$ gram-eq. per litre, and for the red form, $0·56 \times 10^{-4}$ gram-eq. per litre. F. le Blanc, A. Geuther, and R. Ruer found the red form to be specifically lighter than the yellow form, whereas M. P. Applebey and R. D. Reid found the yellow to be specifically lighter than the red. It is assumed that S. Glasstone's preparations were mixtures of both red and yellow forms because M. P. Applebey and R. D. Reid obtained both oxides in definite crystals by the action of conc. soln. of potassium hydroxide at a temp. near the b.p.—which form is produced depends on the conc. of the alkali—highly conc. soln. produce the red variety ; soln. of moderate conc. give the yellow form ; and dil. soln. give a black or steel-grey variety with the same crystalline form as the yellow variety. For example, uniaxial and negative, square, tetragonal plates of the red form were obtained with $15N\text{-}KOH$; biaxial and positive, needle-like, rhombic bipyramids of the yellow form were obtained with $10N\text{-}KOH$; and steel-black crystals, otherwise resembling the yellow crystals, were obtained with $3N\text{-}KOH$. With conc. intermediate between 10 and $15N\text{-}KOH$, mixed red and yellow crystals were produced, and with $3\text{-}10N\text{-}KOH$, crystals of various shades of green were obtained. The differences in the properties of the two forms were very marked at 20°. Thus,

	Red oxide.	Yellow oxide.
Crystalline form	Tetragonal	Rhombic
Optical properties	Uniaxial, negative	Biaxial, positive
Sp gr.	9·27	8·70
Potential $Pb \mid PbO, N\text{-}NaOH$ . . .	0·5668	0·5594 volts
Solubility gram-eq. per litre . .	$0·90 \times 10^{-15}$	$1·80 \times 10^{-15}$
Solubility product $[Pb''][OH']^2$.	$0·47 \times 10^{-15}$	$0·91 \times 10^{-15}$
Ionization constant of acid H_2PbO_2 .	$0·33 \times 10^{-11}$	$0·39 \times 10^{-11}$

It is therefore assumed that the yellow and red forms exhibit a true case of dimorphism. J. F. G. Hicks, H. Hélier, and V. Kohlschütter and H. Rösti regarded the red and yellow forms as polymerized varieties of lead monoxide ; and V. Kohlschütter and P. Scherrer claimed that this view is supported by the difference in the X-radiograms of the two forms. A. Geuther suggested the hypothesis that the yellow form is Pb_3O_3, and the red form Pb_6O_6, this view is favoured by E. J. Wade, D. I. Mendeléef, and G. Kassner, but the evidence is valueless.

E. Mitscherlich,[2] A. E. Nordenskjöld, C. F. Rammelsberg, and W. J. Grailich described the crystals of lead oxide as belonging to the rhombic system, and C. M. Marx, and F. S. Beudant and A. C. Becquerel described them as belonging to the cubic system, but J. L. F. Hausmann showed that the latter are really aggregates of rhombic crystals. The pseudocubic form of these crystals was confirmed by P. Termier. O. Luedecke found that while the yellow form furnishes rhombic bipyramidal crystals, the red form is tetragonal. A. Scott showed the optical characters of a native red litharge from Zarshuran, Persia, to be in conformity with the tetragonal form. L. Michel found the red crystals to be optically negative ; and E. S. Larsen said that the yellow form is always biaxial and positive while the red form is uniaxial and negative. According to A. E. Nordenskjöld, the axial ratios of the yellow, rhombic crystals of lead oxide are $a : b : c = 0.6706 : 1 : 0.9764$. E. S. Larsen found the central portion of plates of native litharge to consist of the yellow rhombic modification, and the borders of the red tetragonal form. According to T. V. Barker :

The colour of the red form is extremely variable, passing from red through brown to light yellow. It crystallizes in square plates which exhibit a negative uniaxial figure in convergent light, and the system is therefore presumably tetragonal. The yellow modification, which is uniformly yellow when freshly prepared, crystallizes in elongated, strongly doubly refracting plates with straight extinction. The ray vibrating parallel to the direction of elongation has the greater refractive index, so that even if the system be tetragonal (which is in doubt) the sign of the double refraction is positive. The two forms, then, exhibit distinctly different optical properties and must be held to present a true case of dimorphism.

R. G. Dickinson and J. B. Friauf found the X-radiograms correspond with the tetragonal lattice with two PbO-mols per unit cell with the dimensions (100), 3·99 A. ; and (001), 5·01 A. The oxygen atoms are at (000) and ($\frac{1}{2}\frac{1}{2}$0), and the lead atoms at ($0\frac{1}{2}u$) and ($\frac{1}{2}0u$). G. R. Levi showed that stannous oxide and red plumbous oxide are isomorphous, and he gave for the axial ratio $a : c$ of red lead monoxide $1 : 0.900$; and for the dimensions of the tetragonal cell, $a = 5.55$ A., and $c = 5.00$ A. A. E. van Arkel gave for the base of the tetragonal cell 3·87 A., and for the height, 5·02 A. E. von Federoff studied the symmetry of the crystals, and V. Kohlschütter and H. Rösti described pseudomorphs after lead chloride. A. Sommerfeld discussed the electronic structure of the oxide. The specific gravity of lead oxide has been determined by C. J. B. Karsten,[3] who obtained 9·2092 ; W. Herapath, 9·277 at 17·5° ; E. Filhol, 9·361 ; P. F. G. Boullay. 9·500 ; L. Playfair and J. P. Joule, 9·363 at 3·9° ; and G. R. Levi, 9·51. A. Ditte found the sp. gr. depended on the mode of preparation, one sample with a sp. gr. 9·1699, after heating to 160° became lemon-yellow, and had a sp. gr. of 9·4342. S. Glasstone obtained numbers ranging from 9·20 to 9·53 according to the mode of preparation ; and he found that no definite conclusion could be drawn as to the relation between the sp. gr. and colour. The following oxides were prepared by boiling the hydroxide with potash-lye : a greenish-yellow oxide, 9·1699 ; yellow, 9·2089 ; brownish-yellow, 9·8835 ; grey, 9·5605 ; and dark green, 9·4223. A. Geuther found that the yellow oxide prepared in the wet way had a sp. gr. 9·28–9·36, at 14°–15° ; while the red oxide had a sp. gr. 8·74– 9·126, at 14°–15°. R. Ruer gave 9·52 at 20°/4° for the yellow oxide, and 9·28 at 20°/4° for the red oxide. H. C. Germs found that the yellow forms always have a higher sp. gr. than the red ; while M. P. Applebey and R. D. Reid obtained results in the opposite direction. Samples of a high degree of purity with all the occluded air removed in vacuo, had a sp. gr. 9·27 when red, and 8·70 when yellow. The oxide which had been fused and finally powdered was found by E. J. Kohlmeyer to have a sp. gr. 9·514; while A. le Royer and J. B. A. Dumas gave 8·01 for a glassy sample which had been melted in a fireclay crucible, and which must, as pointed out by J. N. von Fuchs, and E. Biewend, have contained some silica; a similar remark applies to the crystalline sample of a furnace product which W. J. Grailich found to have a sp. gr. of 8·02. According to E. Biewend, the solidification of molten lead oxide into a crystalline mass is attended by expansion. E. Pugh gave 7·83–7·98 for the sp. gr. of the native oxide from Mexico. O. W. Brown and co-workers showed that the apparent sp. gr. (*i.e.* the weight of oxide occupying a given vol.) of heavy crystalline lead oxide is diminished initially by grinding, and after reaching a minimum value, increases to a constant value— greater than the initial value. A. Balandin studied the mol. vol., 23·45. The initial decrease is not shown by the light amorphous oxide. The **hardness on** Moh's scale is 2·0. S. Motvlewsky found the drop weight of the molten oxide near the m.p. to be 161, when that of water at 0° is 100.

L. Playfair and J. P. Joule gave 0·0000795 for the coeff. of **thermal expansion** (cubic). H. V. Regnault [4] gave 0·05118 for the **specific heat** of crystalline lead monoxide between 22° and 98°, and 0·05089 for the sp. heat of the fused monoxide prepared from red lead. H. Kopp obtained 0·0553 for the sp. ht. between 19° and 50°. The first two of the following values for the sp. ht. and **molecular heat** of lead oxide are by A. Magnus, the last two are by W. Nernst and F. Schwers, and the others are by A. S. Russell:

	144°	58°	2°	−73·9°	−80·3°	−190·3°	−251·7°
Sp. ht.	0·0523	0·05078	0·0517	0·0459	0·0349	0	0
Mol. ht.	11·64	11·34	11·57	10·26	7·75	6·42	1·55

E. J. Kohlmeyer [5] found that lead oxide sinters strongly at 830°, and, according to C. M. Marx, it fuses at a red heat, and, on cooling, forms a mass of crystalline plates; but, as J. N. von Fuchs, and E. Biewend showed, if a very small proportion of silica be present, the molten oxide forms a glass as it cools. G. Tammann and Q. A. Mansuri said that lead monoxide sinters together at 410°. According to R. Ruer, the **melting point** of lead oxide is 835°; J. W. Mellor and co-workers, 877°; F. O. Döltz and W. Mostowitsch, 906°; W. Mostowitsch, 883°; F. O. Döltz and C. A. Graumann, 900°; H. C. Cooper and co-workers, 888°; **F. M. Jäger and** H. C. Germs, 875°; L. Belladen, 870°; R. Schenck and W. Rassbach, 879°; J. C. J. Cunningham, 875°; S. Hilpert and P. Weiller, 776°; and H. le Chatelier, 830°. The last-named also said that an allotropic transformation of lead monoxide occurs at 580°. R. Lorenz and W. Herz studied the relation between the transition temp. and the m.p. According to J. Fournet,[6] lead oxide volatilizes at a white heat, but less readily than **lead** itself. C. Zenghelis said that lead monoxide volatilizes at ordinary temp. because if silver-leaf be suspended over a layer of lead oxide, it begins to acquire a yellowish colour after a longer or shorter time, and may be detected in the silver. The presence of moisture, or of a reducing substance like hydrogen or alcohol vapour, favours the action; and so does the partial exhaustion of the containing vessel. T. W. Hogg cited the following experiment to show that the **volatilization** of lead monoxide occurs at a scarcely visible red heat—presumably near 530°:

If a plate of glass be written upon, using lead oxide as a pigment, and another plate, preferably of some dark blue or ruby tinted glass, be placed immediately over it but prevented from actual contact by suitable means—if these be then heated for about an hour to a temp. of scarcely visible redness, the upper glass always has its polish so altered that a distinct reverse of the writing appears upon it, more or less sharp according to the distance between the two surfaces.

F. O. Doeltz and C. A. Graumann found that lead oxide lost 0·1 per cent. in weight when heated for 1 hour at 700°; 0·2 per cent. at 800°; 2 per cent. at 900°; 5 per cent. at 950°; and 10 per cent. at 1000°. E. J. Kohlmeyer found only a small loss in weight at 1170° when the ratio of the mass to the surface exposed is large. The volatilization is reduced when the lead oxide is fixed by silica or iron oxide. For the observations of M. Störmer, O. Andersen, W. Thomason, S. Hilpert, etc., on the volatilization of lead oxide from lead silicates, *vide* lead silicates, 6. 40, 50. Alumina inhibits the volatilization. W. R. Mott gave 870° for the **boiling point** of lead oxide, but, as E. P. Dewey pointed out, the estimate is far too low.

G. H. Bailey and W. P. Hopkins said that lead monoxide seems to be reduced to a lower oxide at high temp. T. Carnelley and J. Walker found that lead oxide is stable over 815°, and A. A. Read, that it is not decomposed at 1750°. According to W. Stahl, the **dissociation pressure** of the reaction $2PbO \rightleftharpoons 2Pb + O_2$ is equal to 0·21 atm.—the partial press. of oxygen in the atm.—at 2075°; and he calculated the oxygen press., p, mm., in the system:

	500°	700°	900°	1100°	1300°	1500°
p	$3·1 \times 10^{-38}$	$2·1 \times 10^{-25}$	$3·2 \times 10^{-18}$	$1·3 \times 10^{-13}$	$2·1 \times 10^{-10}$	$4·8 \times 10^{-8}$

	1700°	1900°	2000°
	$3·2 \times 10^{-6}$	$8·9 \times 10^{5}$	$3·7 \times 10^{-4}$

S. Glasstone calculated the dissociation press. from Nernst's formula (1. 13, 11), using 100,600 cals. for the heat of formation per mol of oxygen, and obtained $1·9 \times 10^{-67}$ atm. at 25°, a result in agreement with $4·2 \times 10^{-67}$ atm. calculated from the e.m.f. of the cell $Pb \mid PbO, N\text{-}NaOH, H_2 \mid Pt$, *viz.* 0·247 volt; he also estimated that the oxide would be completely dissociated if heated to 2600° in air; and showed that if $Q = 100,600$ cals., and the ratio $PbO : Pb$ be constant, $R \log_e p = -QT^{-1} + 32$, where p denotes the partial press. of the oxygen at the absolute temp. $T°$. Hence, at 2587°, the partial press. of oxygen is 0·21 atm. On the other hand, F. Damm and F. Krafft found that at 750° lead oxide gives a metallic mirror when heated in the vacuum of the cathode light. J. Thomsen gave for the **heat of formation** of lead monoxide $Pb + O = PbO + 50·3$ Cals.; M. Berthelot gave 50·8 Cals.; W. D. Treadwell gave $Pb + \frac{1}{2}O_2 = PbO + 50·4$ Cals.; G. Chaudron, 50·2 Cals.; and S. Glasstone calculated from the e.m.f. of the cell $Pb \mid PbO_{red}, N\text{-}NaOH, H_2 \mid Pt$, 49·61 Cals. for the heat of formation of the red-coloured monoxide at 25°; and D. F. Smith and H. K. Woods, 45,050 cals. at 25° for the **free energy** of formation of lead monoxide. A. L. Marshall and B. Bruzs gave 19·41 Cals. per mol. for the heat of soln. of lead oxide in nitric acid, 50 per cent. by vol. Values approximating 15·6 Cals. were also obtained by J. Svéda, M. Herschkowitsch, S. M. Tanatar, and F. Aufenast and H. Terrey.

The **optical properties** of the crystals of lead monoxide were examined by P. Termier,[7] and L. Michel. E. S. Larsen found that the birefringence in both forms is very strong; the optical character of the biaxial rhombic form is positive, and that of the uniaxial tetragonal form is negative. The **index of refraction** given by E. S. Larsen is $\beta = 2·61$ for the yellow rhombic variety; and $\omega = 2·64$ for the red tetragonal form. According to W. W. Coblentz, the **ultra-red emission spectrum** gives a curve with a depression at $3·3\mu$, and a possible band at $5·5\mu$. G. A. Dima examined the photoelectric effect with lead monoxide (*vide* lead dioxide). J. Ewles found a whitish **cathodoluminescence** with lead oxide; and E. L. Nichols and D. T. Wilber, the feeble **luminescence** of the oxide sublimed in the electric arc.

According to M. Faraday,[8] molten lead monoxide conducts electricity; F. Beijerinck said the **electrical conductivity** of the natural oxide is smaller than that of the artificial lead oxide; and C. Fritsch made some observations on this subject. G. Tammann and H. Bredemeier studied the conductivity of thin films of the oxide. F. Horton measured the effect of temp. on the electrical resistance (ohms) and electrical conductivity (mhos) of lead monoxide melted in an atm. of oxygen and cast into a slab.

	384°	462°	600°	687°	700°	757°	787°
Ohms .	7×10^6	65×10^4	45000	4050	2870	730	330
Mhos .	$3 \cdot 86 \times 10^{-8}$	$4 \cdot 15 \times 10^{-7}$	$6 \cdot 00 \times 10^{-6}$	$6 \cdot 67 \times 10^{-5}$	$9 \cdot 39 \times 10^{-5}$	$3 \cdot 695 \times 10^{-4}$	$8 \cdot 175 \times 10^{-6}$

There was evidence of a slight electrolysis during the passage of the current. F. Streintz said that the pressed powder does not conduct electricity; and J. Rosenthal found that the conductivity of the powder pressed at 108° is too small to measure; at 228°, 0·070; at 271°, 0·229; at 357°, 5·536. After strongly heating the mixture the conductivity was increased because of *eine Molekular-umwandlung*. G. von Hevesey said that the conductivity of lead monoxide is partly electrolytic. E. Baur and co-workers found the **electromotive force** of the cell PbO,Pb | electrolyte | C, and obtained 1·0 volt at 1200°; and for the cell PbO,Pb | electrolyte | CuO,Cu₂O, 0·44 volt at 990°. W. D. Treadwell measured the potential of lead oxide against molten silver sat. with oxygen, and found for the cell Pb,PbO | electrolyte | O₂.Ag, 0·478 volt. M. P. Applebey and R. D. Reid measured the e.m.f. of the cell Hg | HgO in N-NaOH; PbO$_{red}$ in N-NaOH | Pb, and obtained 0·6808 volt, and with yellow lead oxide, 0·6734 volt. D. S. Smith and H. K. Woods measured the e.m.f. of the cell H₂ | 0·0766M—0·2242M | Ba(OH)₂ | PbO ; and G. Tammann, of litharge against the normal hydrogen electrode. S. Glasstone measured the **electrode potential** for Pb | PbO,N-NaOH with different forms of lead monoxide and obtained for the yellow form —0·5512 to —0·5514 volt at 0°, and —0·5597 to —0·5599 volt at 25°; and for the red form, —0·5536 to —0·5538 volt at 0°, and —0·5619 to —0·5621 volt at 25°. C. M. Newton gave for the e.m.f. cell ZnO | PbO in NaOH | Fe, 0·69 volt. G. Tammann also measured the electrode potential of litharge in soln. of various salts. The **dielectric constant** was found by C. B. Thwing to be 25·9, and J. Dewar and J. A. Fleming gave 78·5 at —197·4°; 90 at —184·8°; and 93 at —159·2° to —128·3°. S. Meyer gave —0·31×10⁻⁶ to —0·449×10⁻⁶ for the **magnetic susceptibility** ; and —0·024×10⁻⁶ for the mol. magnetism of the sulphur-yellow oxide.

REFERENCES.

¹ F. le Blanc, *Journ. Pharm. Chim.*, (3), **8**. 181, 1845 ; W. Behrens, *ib.*, (3), **4**. 18, 1843 ; A. Geuther, *Liebig's Ann.*, **219**. 60, 1883 ; R. Ruer, *Zeit. anorg. Chem.*, **50**. 269, 1906 ; W. Reinders and L. Hamburger, *ib.*, **89**. 79, 1914 ; W. Böttger, *Zeit. phys. Chem.*, **46**. 580, 1903 ; F. C. Calvert, *Compt. Rend.*, **16**. 361, 1843 ; A. Ditte, *ib.*, **94**. 1311, 1882 ; *Ann. Chim. Phys.*, (5), **28**. 127, 1883 ; H. C. Germs, *De thermische Analyse van loodsulfaat, chromaat, molybdaat en van walframaat en van hun binaire combinaties*, Gröningen, 1917 ; M. Jäger and H. C. Germs, *Zeit. anorg. Chem.*, **119**. 147, 1921 ; S. Glasstone, *Journ. Chem. Soc.*, **119**. 1689, 1914, 1921 ; M. P. Applebey and R. D. Reid, *ib.*, **121**. 2129, 1922 ; J. F. G. Hicks, *Journ. Phys. Chem.*, **25**. 545, 1921 ; E. Mitscherlich, *Journ. prakt. Chem.*, (1), **19**. 451, 1840 ; N. Kromer, *Russ. Pharm. Journ.*, **34**. 534, 1895 ; G. Kassner, *Arch. Pharm.*, (3), **28**. 177, 1890 ; D. I. Mendeléeff, *Principles of Chemistry*, St. Petersburg, 561, 1903 ; London, **2**. 134, 1891 ; E. J. Wade, *Secondary Batteries*, London, 220, 1902 ; V. Kohlschütter and H. Rösti, *Ber.*, **56**. 277, 1923 ; V. Kohlschütter and J. L. Tüscher, *Zeit. Elektrochem.*, **27**. 225, 1921 ; V. Kohlschütter and P. Scherrer, *Helvetica Chim. Acta*, **7**. 337, 1924 ; H. Hélier, *Bull. Soc. Chim.*, (3), **21**. 43, 1899.

² E. Mitscherlich, *Sitzber. Akad. Berlin*, 11, 1840 ; *Pogg. Ann.*, **49**. 403, 1840 ; A. E. Nordenskjöld, *ib.*, **114**. 629, 1861 ; C. F. Rammelsberg, *Handbuch der krystallographischen Chemie*, Berlin, 30, 1855 ; *Handbuch der krystallographisch-physikalischen Chemie*, Leipzig, **1**. 181, 1881 ; W. J. Grailich, *Sitzber. Akad. Wien*, **28**. 282, 1858 ; C. M. Marx, *Journ. prakt. Chem.*, (1), **3**. 217, 1834 ; F. S. Beudant and A. C. Becquerel, *Journ. Chim. Pharm.*, (3), **24**. 115, 1853 ; J. L. F. Hausmann, *Gött. Nachr.*, 40, 1855 ; G. R. Levi, *Nuovo Cimento*, (7), **1**. 335, 1924 ; A. E. van Arkel, *Rec. Trav. Chim. Pays-Bas*, **44**. 652, 1925 ; V. Kohlschütter and H. Rösti, *Ber.*, **56**. 285, 1923 ; O. Luedecke, *Zeit. Kryst.*, **8**. 82, 1884 ; E. von Federoff, *ib.*, **53**. 361, 1914 ; L. Michel, *Bull. Soc. Min.*, **13**. 86, 1890 ; P. Termier, *ib.*, **18**. 367, 1895 ; A. Scott, *Min. Mag.*, **17**. 143, 1914 ; E. S. Larsen, *Bull. U.S. Geol. Sur.*, 679, 1921 ; *Amer. Min.*, **2**. 18, 1917 ; T. V. Barker, *Journ. Chem. Soc.*, **121**. 2131, 1922 ; R. G. Dickinson and J. B. Friauf, *Journ. Amer. Chem. Soc.*, **46**. 2457, 1924 ; A. Sommerfeld, *Zeit. Physik.*, **36**. 36, 1926.

³ H. C. Germs, *De thermische Analyse van loodsulfaat, chromaat, molybdaat en walframaat en van hun binaire combinaties*, Gröningen, 1917 ; F. M. Jäger and H. C. Germs, *Zeit. anorg.*

Chem., **119**. 147, 1921 ; R. Ruer, *ib.*, **50**. 269, 1906 ; S. Motylewsky, *ib.*, **38**. 410, 1904 ; S. Glasstone, *Journ. Chem. Soc.*, **119**. 1689, 1914, 1921 ; M. P. Applebey and R. D. Reid, *ib.*, **121**. 2129, 1922 ; L. Playfair and J. P. Joule, *ib.*, **1**. 137, 1849 ; *Mem. Chem. Soc.*, **3**. 84, 1848 ; A. Geuther. *Liebig's Ann.*, **219**. 60, 1906 ; A. Ditte, *Compt. Rend.*, **94**. 1311, 1882 ; *Ann. Chim. Phys.*, (5), **28**. 127, 1883 ; P. F. G. Boullay, *ib.*, (2), **43**. 266, 1830 ; E. Filhol, *ib.*, (3), **21**. 415, 1847 ; W. J. Grailich, *Sitzber. Akad. Wien*, **28**. 282, 1858 ; O. W. Brown, S. V. Cook, and J. C. Warner. *Journ. Phys. Chem.*, **26**. 477, 1922 ; E. J. Kohlmeyer, *Metall. Erz*, **10**. 489, 1913 ; P. Niggli, *Zeit. Kryst.*, **56**. 42, 1922 ; N. N. Beketoff, *Journ. Russ. Phys. Chem. Soc.*, **19**. 57, 1887 ; V. Kohlschütter and J. L. Juscher, *Zeit. Elektrochem.*, **27**. 244, 1921 ; J. N. von Fuchs, *Edin. Phil. Journ.*, **18**. 263, 1835 ; *Schweigger's Journ.*, **67**. 429, 1833 ; C. J. B. Karsten, *ib.*, **65**. 394, 1832 ; E. Biewend, *Journ. prakt. Chem.*, (1), **23**. 253, 1841 ; W. Herapath, *Phil. Mag.*, (1), **64**. 321, 1824 ; A. le Royer and J. B. A. Dumas, *Ann. Pharm. Chim.*, **92**. 408, 1821 ; E. Pugh, *Miscellaneous Chemical Analyses*, Göttingen, 1856 ; G. R. Levi, *Nuovo Cimento*, (7), **1**. 335, 1924 ; A. Balandin, *Zeit. phys. Chem.*, **121**. 299, 1926.

[4] A. Magnus, *Phys. Zeit.*, **14**. 5, 1913 ; A. S. Russell, *ib.*, **13**. 59, 1912 ; W. Nernst and F. Schwers, *Sitzber. Akad. Berlin*, 355, 1914 ; M. Goldstein, *Wied. Ann. Biebl.*, **7**. 360, 1887 ; H. V. Regnault, *Ann. Chim. Phys.*, (3), **1**. 129, 1841 ; H. Kopp, *Liebig's Ann. Suppl.*, **3**. 289, 1865.

[5] E. J. Kohlmeyer, *Metall Erz*, **10**. 489, 1913 ; J. N. von Fuchs, *Edin. Phil. Journ.*, **18**. 263, 1835 ; *Schweigger's Journ.*, **67**. 429, 1833 ; C. J. B. Karsten, *ib.*, **65**. 394, 1832 ; E. Biewend, *Journ. prakt. Chem.*, (1), **23**. 253, 1841 ; C. M. Marx, *ib.*, (1), **3**. 217, 1834 ; J. W. Mellor, A. Latimer, and A. D. Holdcroft, *Trans. Cer. Soc.*, **9**. 217, 1910 ; H. C. Cooper, L. J. Shaw, and N. E. Loomis, *Ber.*, **42**. 3991, 1909 ; R. Schenck and W. Rassbach, *ib.*, **40**. 2185, 1907 ; S. Hilpert and P. Weiller, *ib.*, **42**. 2969, 1909 ; F. O. Döltz and W. Mostowitsch, *Met.*, **4**. 289, 1907 ; F. O. Döltz, *ib.*, **4**. 649, 1907 ; W. Mostowitsch, *ib.*, **4**. 648, 1907 ; F. O. Döltz and C. A. Graumann, *ib.*, **3**. 408, 1906 ; H. le Chatelier, *Bull. Soc. Chim.*, (3), **17**. 791, 1897 ; H. C. Germs, *De thermische Analyse van loodsulfaat, -chromaat, en wolframaat en van hun binaire Combinaties*, Gröningen, 1917 ; F. M. Jäger and H. C. Germs, *Zeit. anorg. Chem.*, **119**. 147, 1921 ; R. Lorenz and W. Herz, *ib.*, **135**. 374, 1924 ; G. Tammann and Q. A. Mansuri, *ib.*, **126**. 121, 1923 ; R. Ruer, *ib.*, **50**. 269, 1906 ; J. C. J. Cunningham, *ib.*, **89**. 49, 1914 ; L. Belladen, *Gazz. Chim. Ital.*, **52**. ii, 160, 1922.

[6] J. Fournet, *Ann. Chim. Phys.*, (2), **55**. 414, 1833 ; G. Chaudron, *ib.*, (9), **16**. 220, 1921 ; M. Berthelot, *ib.*, (4), **30**. 191, 1873 ; W. R. Mott, *Trans. Amer. Electrochem. Soc.*, **34**. 266, 1919 ; F. P. Dewey, *Trans. Amer. Inst. Min. Met. Eng.*, **64**. 601, 1920 ; *Chem. Met. Engg.*, **22**. 801, 1920 ; T. W. Hogg, *B.A. Rep.*, 534, 1889 ; *Journ. Soc. Chem. Ind.*, **8**. 684, 1889 ; W. Thomason, *ib.*, **23**. 469, 1904 ; M. Störmer, *Chem. Ztg.*, **25**. 818, 1901 ; C. Zenghelis, *Zeit. phys. Chem.*, **50**. 219, 1904 ; D. F. Smith and H. K. Woods, *Journ. Amer. Chem. Soc.*, **45**. 2632, 1923 ; T. Carnelley and J. Walker, *Journ. Chem. Soc.*, **53**. 59, 1888 ; S. Glasstone, *ib.*, **119**. 1914, 1921 ; A. A. Read, *ib.*, **65**. 313, 1894 ; W. Stahl, *Met.*, **4**. 682, 1907 ; F. O. Doeltz and W. Graumann, *ib.*, **4**. 289, 1907 ; S. Hilpert, *ib.*, **5**. 539, 1908 ; E. J. Kohlmeyer, *Metall. Erz*, **10**. 489, 1913 ; F. Damm and F. Krafft, *Ber.*, **40**. 4775, 1907 ; J. Thomsen, *Thermochemische Untersuchungen*, Leipzig, **3**. 329, 1883 ; *Journ. prakt. Chem.*, (2), **12**. 112, 1875 ; G. H. Bailey and W. P. Hopkins, *Chem. News*, **61**. 117, 1890 ; O. Andersen, *Journ. Amer. Cer. Soc.*, **2**. 784, 1919 ; W. D. Treadwell, *Zeit. Elektrochem.*, **22**. 414, 1916.

[7] P. Termier, *Bull. Soc. Min.*, **18**. 367, 1895 ; L. Michel, *ib.*, **13**. 86, 1890 ; A. Scott, *Min. Mag.*, **17**. 143, 1914 (the value given in the paper is a misprint) ; E. S. Larsen, *Bull. U.S. Geol. Sur.*, 679, 1921 ; *Amer. Min.*, **2**. 18, 1917 ; G. A. Dima, *Bul. Soc. Stiinte Cluj*, **1**. 321, 1922 ; *Compt. Rend.*, **157**. 591, 1913 ; E. L. Nichols and D. T. Wilber, *Phys. Rev.*, (2), **17**. 707, 1921 ; W. W. Coblentz, *Bull. Bur. Standards*, **5**. 176, 1908 ; *Supplementary Investigations of Infra-red Spectra*, Washington, 118, 1908 ; J. Ewles, *Phil. Mag.*, (6), **45**. 957, 1923 ; J. Svéda, *Chem. Listy*, **17**. 47, 81, 112, 1923 ; M. Herschkowitsch, *Zeit. anorg. Chem.*, **115**. 159, 1921 ; S. M. Tanatar, *ib.*, **27**. 304, 1901 ; F. Aufenart and H. Terrey, *Journ. Chem. Soc.*, **129**. 1646, 1926.

[8] M. Faraday, *Phil. Trans.*, **124**. 77, 1834 ; C. Fritsch, *Wied. Ann.*, **60**. 300, 1897 ; J. Dewar and J. A. Fleming, *Proc. Roy. Soc.*, **61**. 245, 1897 ; W. D. Treadwell, *Zeit. Elektrochem.*, **22**. 414, 1916 ; E. Baur, A. Petersen, and G. Füllen.ann, *ib.*, **22**. 409, 1916 ; C. B. Thwing, *Zeit. phys. Chem.*, **14**. 286, 1894 ; F. Beijerinck, *Neues Jahrb. Min. B.B.*, **11**. 455, 1897 ; M. P. Applebey and R. D. Reid, *Journ. Chem. Soc.*, **121**. 2129, 1922 ; S. Glasstone, *ib.*, **119**. 1689, 1914, 1921 ; F. Streintz, *Ann. Physik*, (4), **9**. 864, 1902 ; G. Tammann, *Zeit. anorg. Chem.*, **113**. 149, 1920 ; G. Tammann and H. Bredemeier, *ib.*, **144**. 64, 1925 ; G. von Hevesy, *Danske Vid. Medd.*, **3**. 12, 1921 ; J. Rosenthal, *Wied. Ann.*, **43**. 718, 1891 ; S. Meyer, *ib.*, **69**. 245, 1899 ; C. M. Newton, *Lumière élect.*, **26**. 434, 1887 ; *Brit. Pat. No.* 7030, 1887 ; F. Horton, *Phil. Mag.*, (6), **11**. 505, 1906 ; D. F. Smith and H. K. Woods, *Journ. Amer. Chem. Soc.*, **45**. 2632, 1923.

§ 14. The Chemical Properties of Lead Monoxide

A. Ditte [1] reported that in sunlight, the honey-yellow needles of lead monoxide (in contact with their own mother-liquor) gradually become greenish and finally black. The action of light, trituration, and press. has been discussed in connection with the red and yellow forms of lead monoxide. According to G. Kassner, if lead monoxide be exposed to sunlight and air for about a year, some red-lead is formed provided moisture be present; with air dried by phosphorus pentoxide, no red-lead is formed. The action of light was found by G. A. Dima to be stronger than with other oxides reduced with greater difficulty; the action increases with press. up to a maximum and then decreases. M. P. Applebey and R. D. Reid said that the yellow form is converted into the grey form when exposed to light in air or in vacuo so that the presence of oxygen is not necessary for the change. According to C. Renz, when lead oxide is exposed to light under water, a partial reduction to metallic lead occurs, whilst the oxygen set free oxidizes part of the lead oxide to dioxide, and this in turn combines with lead oxide to form plumbate. The metallic lead is reoxidized by air contained in the water. The formation of metallic lead is proved by exposing to light a mixture of lead oxide and lead chloride which had been boiled with hydrochloric acid. When the product is treated with dil. nitric acid, lead is dissolved with evolution of hydrogen and a slight residue of dioxide remains.

According to J. J. Berzelius,[2] the first stage in the reduction of heated lead monoxide by **hydrogen** is lead suboxide (q.v.). According to G. C. Winkelblech, the crystalline oxide obtained by the action of potash-lye on a hot soln. of lead acetate is reduced by hydrogen at a temp. not much above 100°. W. Müller said that the reduction to lead begins at 310°–311°; and, added S. Hilpert and P. Weiller, there is a perceptible reduction at 240°; while C. R. A. Wright and A. P. Luff said reduction begins at 190°–195°. W. Mostowitsch said that grey lead suboxide is formed between 290° and 300°, and at 410°, small beads of lead are formed. F. Glaser said the reduction to the suboxide occurs at 211°, and to the metal, above 235°. H. Hélier said that lead monoxide becomes brown in hydrogen at 350°. I. W. Fay and co-workers detected signs of reduction after heating for 6 hrs. in hydrogen at 190°; S. Hauser placed the temp. a little higher. W. Ipatjeff and W. Werchowsky said that hydrogen reduces with difficulty lead monoxide which is confined under water at a temp. in the vicinity of 200° and 180 atm. press. H. Mennicke showed that lead oxide suspended in a mixture of zinc and hydrochloric acid is quickly reduced to lead, particularly if a little platinum be present. The hydrogen developed at the cathode during electrolysis also reduces lead monoxide. F. Paneth and co-workers made *lead hydride* by passing activated hydrogen over powdered lead. A. de Hemptinne also found that in the silent electric discharge, lead monoxide is quickly reduced, but not so rapidly as is lead dioxide. G. Tammann investigated the exchange of ions on the surface of lead. H. Moissan found lead oxide to be reduced by **potassium hydride** at a gentle heat; and F. M. Perkin and L. Pratt, by **calcium hydride.** For the action of **oxygen,** *vide* the higher oxides of lead. C. W. Scheele[3] said that lead oxide dissolves in **water,** but J. Tünnermann, F. Siebold, J. E. Herberger, and F. Brendecke reported that lead oxide is insoluble in water; although the last-named said that the moist oxide turns red litmus blue. P. A. von Bonsdorff said that a litre of water can dissolve 0·13 grm. of lead oxide; and P. Yorke, 0·083 grm. of this oxide. The latter added that the aq. soln. slightly reddens turmeric, and turns red litmus blue; it becomes turbid when shaken up with air, or when boiled; when electrolyzed it deposits lead at the cathode, and lead dioxide at the anode; it gives a brownish-black precipitate with hydrogen sulphide; is rendered turbid by carbon dioxide not in excess, or by sulphuric acid or soluble sulphates; and gives a yellow precipitate with potassium iodide, and with potassium chromate. If soluble sulphates or carbonates are present in the water, L. B. G. de Morveau, R. Christison, F. Clowes, and G. Wetzlar showed that the amount of lead oxide dissolved is very much reduced; hence the reports of the insolubility of the oxide in water are probably due to the dissolution and subsequent precipitation of the oxide by the action of the carbon dioxide of the air.

From conductivity measurements, M. Pleissner calculated the solubility of lead oxide in water at 18° to be from 0.077×10^{-3} to 0.403×10^{-3} mol per litre; R. Ruer gave 0.28×10^{-4} and 0.50×10^{-4} mol per litre at 22°; S. Glasstone, 0.26×10^{-3} at 25°; A. C. Cumming gave 3.8×10^{-6} mol PbO per litre; and W. Böttger, 0.80×10^{-4} to 1.22×10^{-4} grm. eq. per litre, or $0.0128-0.026$ grm. per litre at 19.96°. H. Remy and A. Kuhlmann found that a litre of water dissolved 12.36 mgrms. of lead oxide. The results are based on conductivity determinations, and depend on the unknown degree of ionization of the lead oxide in water. A. Bineau's value 0.143 grm PbO per litre was directly determined by precipitation. He said that if the litharge has been previously fused, it does not dissolve in water ; J. Percy, however, showed that this is not the case. S. Glasstone gave 1.7×10^{-15} for the solubility product, $[Pb''][OH']^2$; while M. P. Applebey and R. D. Reid gave 0.47×10^{-15} for the red-coloured oxide, and 0.91×10^{-15} for the yellow.

C. W. G. Kastner found lead oxide to be readily dissolved by a hot aq. soln. of **potassium hydroxide,** forming a yellow, non-crystallizable liquid. A. Ditte said the amount of lead oxide dissolved increases regularly with the conc. of the alkali. According to M. P. Applebey and R. D. Reid, at 20°, a normal soln. of **sodium hydroxide** dissolves 0.0237 mol per litre of the yellow oxide, and 0.0140 mol per litre of the red—*vide infra*, plumbites. E. Berl and G. Austerwell said that the solubility of lead oxide in soln. of sodium hydroxide, **sodium carbonate,** and **potassium carbonate** corresponds with that in potassium hydroxide ; the product in dil. sodium hydroxide is said to be sodium hydroplumbite, $NaHPbO_2$, and in a conc. soln., sodium plumbite, Na_2PbO_2 (*q.v.*). P. Bechtereff found lead oxide to be readily soluble in molten sodium hydroxide.

H. Moissan [4] found that the cold **fluorine** does not attack lead oxide, but that when heated, a yellow compound is formed, probably an oxyfluoride. R. Weber found dry **chlorine** quickly converts lead oxide into lead chloride, but C. F. Cross and S. Suguira said that an oxychloride, $Pb_4O.Cl_7$, is formed, and with a mixture of air and chlorine, the composition of the product ranges from Pb_8OCl_{16} to $Pb_{12}O_4Cl_{21}$. C. Löwig found that an aq. soln. of chlorine forms lead dioxide and chloride ; A. Michael and A. Murphy also showed that the same products are formed by the action of a soln. of chlorine in carbon tetrachloride. C. F. Cross and S. Suguira found that in the presence of air, **bromine** forms the oxybromides, $Pb_4O_2Br_5$ and $Pb_7O_2Br_{11}$. C. Löwig obtained a mixture of lead dioxide and bromide by the action of an aq. soln. of bromine. C. F. Cross and S. Suguira obtained $Pb_9O_8I_2$ and $Pb_9O_6I_4$ by the action of a mixture of air and **iodine** vapour. J. B. Moyer found that lead oxide is completely converted into lead chloride at ordinary temp. by **hydrogen chloride ;** and A. E. Atkinson said that when **hydrogen bromide** is passed over heated lead oxide, it forms an **oxybro**mide. Lead monoxide readily unites with acids forming salts, and the solubility of the oxide in acids, say **hydrochloric acid,** is therefore determined by the solubility of the resulting salt in the acid (*vide* the salts). A. Jäger said that the oxide is not dissolved by conc. **hydrofluoric acid,** but is very slightly soluble in the dil. acid, and air.

According to F. Isambert, when **ammonium chloride** and lead oxide are triturated together at ordinary temp., there is a slow endothermal reaction, and an oxychloride is formed. The press. of the ammonia at different temp. is :

Press.	17°	24.2°	29.7°	36.3°	42°	48.9°
	296	377	469	599	733	926 mm.

W. O. de Coninck and L. Arzalier obtained lead bromide in a similar manner from a mixture of lead oxide and **ammonium bromide;** and lead iodide, when **ammonium iodide** is used in place of the bromide. For the action of **potassium iodide,** *vide* the lead oxyiodides. O. Schott, and H. Houben showed that lead oxide is slightly soluble in fused **sodium chloride,** and on cooling the soln., the lead oxide separates in globules. C. W. Scheele discovered that sodium chloride in aq. soln. reacts with lead oxide, forming sodium hydroxide ; and L. N. Vauquelin reported on this reaction in his *Reflexions sur la décomposition du muriate de soude par l'oxide de plomb*. In dil. soln., E. Berl and G. Austerwell found that for equilibrium at 18°, the ratio OH' : Cl' is 1·02 ; at 48°, 0·75 ; and at 74°, 0·58. The subject was also examined by W. Dominik, and J. F. G. Hicks and W. Craig. According to A. Jäger, lead oxide reacts with the **alkali halides** until equilibrium is attained with the free alkali depending on the solubility of the lead halides ; complex compounds with the lead halides appear to be formed. W. Bersch showed that lead oxide decomposes in alkali halides, forming alkali hydroxide ; if the lead halide be insoluble, and an excess of lead oxide is present, all the halogen is extracted from the soln. ; but if the lead halide be soluble, a state of equilibrium is reached. The state of equilibrium is influenced by the heat of the reaction, so that if heat be absorbed, the proportion of alkali hydroxide increases with rise of temp. and conversely ; the time required to attain equilibrium is smallest with the iodides, and diminishes as the temp. rises. The amount of decomposition is dependent only on the halogen ; the alkali metal in combination with the halogen seems to have very little influence on the result. In illustration, with $0.1N$-soln. of the alkali halides, the following percentage amounts of alkali hydroxide are formed:

	KCl	NaCl	KBr	NaBr	KI	NaI
25°	33·60	33·50	80·00	80·10	85·10	85·00
50°	36·80	36·80	79·20	79·30	84·00	83·80
79°	41·62	41·64	77·60	77·75	83·40	83·50
88·5°	56·08	56·20	76·40	76·35	82·90	82·86

E. P. Perman found that potassium iodide acts more slowly on lead oxide than on lead chloride. G. André found that lead oxide is soluble in a boiling soln. of **barium chloride**, forming an oxychloride ; similarly also with **strontium chloride** when $SrCl_2.2PbO.5H_2O$ is formed ; and with **calcium chloride,** $CaO.CaCl_2.2PbO.4H_2O$, is formed. A soln. of **magnesium chloride** readily dissolves lead oxide ; the solubility increases with the temp. and conc. of the soln. A. Voigt said that lead oxychloride, $3PbO.PbCl_2.H_2O$, is deposited as a gelatinous mass ; and H. Hof and B. Rinck showed that with a boiling soln. of magnesium chloride of sp. gr. 1·32, crystals of $Mg_2PbCl_6.13H_2O$ are deposited on cooling. O. Unger found lead oxide to be soluble in a soln. of **zinc chloride ;** and G. André showed that after a long contact of the lead oxide with the zinc chloride soln., needle-like crystals of what appears to be a compound of $3ZnO.ZnCl_2$ and $PbCl_2.PbO$ are formed. F. Roderbourg patented the use of a reaction in which molten zinc chloride reacts with lead oxide, forming lead chloride. A soln. of **manganese chloride** converts lead oxide into lead chloride. G. L. Fowler and J. Grant found that **potassium chlorate** mixed with lead oxide forms lead dioxide and potassium chloride at a temp. below its normal temp. of decomposition ; and W. R. E. Hodgkinson and F. K. S. Lowndes showed that the presence of lead oxide favours the evolution of oxygen from decomposing potassium chlorate, and results in the liberation of some chlorine.

When a mixture of lead oxide and **sulphur** is heated, lead sulphide and sulphur dioxide are formed, but, according to P. Berthier,[5] no sulphate is produced. J. B. Senderens showed that when a mixture of lead oxide, sulphur, and water is heated in a sealed tube, lead sulphide and sulphate are formed with the evolution of 15·8 Cals. of heat per mol of PbO. P. Berthier said that not the slightest trace of lead is produced when a mixture of **selenium** and lead monoxide is heated ; but the two substances react in all proportions, forming products which resemble those obtained by fusing mixtures of **lead selenide** and litharge. The lead oxide may be dissolved out by hydrochloric acid. Hence, sulphur may be separated from selenium by fusion with litharge. P. Berthier said that with **tellurium,** telluric acid is formed, and when the litharge is in excess lead tellurate is produced, but if the litharge be not in excess, most of the telluric acid is volatilized, and lead telluride remains. A. Gautier found that when heated with **carbon disulphide,** crystals of lead sulphide are formed and carbon and sulphur dioxides are evolved, but no carbonyl sulphide is produced. According to E. Priwoznik, and F. Isambert, with **ammonium hydrosulphide,** lead sulphide and ammonia are produced. P. Richter found that an intimate mixture of **calcium sulphide** and lead oxide, at ordinary temp., becomes grey owing to the formation of lead sulphide ; and when heated, in air, calcium sulphate is produced. In his memoir, *De l'action de la litharge sur différents sulfures métalliques,* P. Berthier showed that when an excess of lead monoxide is fused with an excess of a metal sulphide, some, like barium sulphide, are decomposed with the formation of a sulphate ; and some, like the sulphides of the heavy metals, give off sulphur dioxide. The metal of the sulphide either unites directly with the lead, or is converted into oxide, and fuses along with the lead oxide while lead separates out. Some lead sulphide may be produced as well as the metal. Any undecompoesd sulphide fuses, with the excess of lead oxide and the metal, forming a slag. He examined the effect of lead oxide on the **sulphides of barium, zinc, tin (stannic), manganese, arsenic, antimony, and bismuth.** With **ferrous sulphide,** and an excess of lead oxide, the products are sulphur dioxide, iron oxide, and metallic lead ; and with a smaller proportion of lead oxide, some lead sulphide is produced. A mixture of **lead sulphide** and oxide, in theoretical proportions, at a strong red heat, reacts as symbolized : $PbS+2PbO=3Pb+SO_2$; if the lead oxide be in excess, the reduced lead will be found covered with a layer of fused oxide ; and if lead sulphide be in excess, part will dissolve in the reduced lead, and part will accumulate on top of the metal. H. Rose found that with stannic sulphide, lead and stannic oxide are formed : $6PbO+SnS_2=6Pb+SnO_2$ $+2SO_2$. According to R. Schenck and co-workers, when lead monoxide is treated with **sulphur dioxide,** lead sulphide and sulphate are formed, or a basic sulphate is produced. The reaction was studied by D. L. Hammick, who showed that when the lead oxide is just below visible redness, a dull red glow passes through the mass of oxide, and lead sulphide and sulphate are produced without sulphur trioxide or sulphur : $4PbO+4SO_2=PbS+3PbSO_4$. The black powder absorbs 8–17 per cent. of sulphur dioxide, and with a more prolonged heating (3 weeks), lead sulphate and some sulphur and sulphur trioxide are produced. It is possible that the secondary reactions : $PbS+PbSO_4=2Pb+2SO_2$, and $4Pb+PbSO_4=PbS$ $+4PbO$, occur ; and that the sulphur and sulphur trioxide are due to the reaction indicated by J. Uhl : $Pb+6SO_2=PbS+4SO_3+S$. According to J. A. Wilkinson, the reaction between **sulphur trioxide** and lead oxide is attended by a white luminescence. The solubility of lead oxide in **sulphuric acid** is determined by the solubility of lead sulphate (*q.v.*) in that acid. A. Seyewetz and P. Trawitz found that **ammonium persulphate** converts lead monoxide into the dioxide.

Lead monoxide was found by E. C. Franklin [6] to be soluble in liquid **ammonia.** I. W. Fay and co-workers detected signs of reduction when the oxide is heated in ammonia gas for 6 hrs. at 299°. H. Leroux found that in an oxidizing atm., $6PbO+2Sb_2O_3+O_2\rightarrow2Pb+2(PbO)_2Sb_2O_5$; and in a closed vessel, $2PbO+Sb_2O_3$ $\rightarrow2Pb+Sb_2O_5$. The oxide is readily soluble in **nitric acid,** forming lead nitrate. E. Müller and H. Barck observed no action with **nitric oxide** occurs up to 650°. F. Ephraim found **sodium amide,** $NaNH_2$, rapidly reduces lead oxide. T. B. W. Welsh and H. J. Broderson found that, at room temp., 100 c.c. of anhydrous **hydrazine** dissolve a gram of the red variety of lead oxide ; and E. Müller and H. Barck, that **nitric oxide** is slightly decomposed at 600°. H. Braconnet attributed the low solubility of lead in conc. **nitric acid** to the formation of a protective film of lead nitrate ; and U. R. Evans saw that conc. nitric acid converts litharge into a basic nitrate which dissolves at once when the acid is diluted. According to A. Oppenheim, a soln. of **phosphorus** in benzene reacts with a soln. of lead monoxide in alkali-lye, and, on heating, a black precipitate containing 98–99 per cent. of lead is formed. The product melts when heated in hydrogen gas without forming phosphine. A. Michaelis said that **phosphorus trichloride** does not react with lead oxide at 160°, but at a higher temp., a vigorous reaction occurs : $2PCl_3+6PbO=Pb(PO_3)_2+3PbCl_2+2Pb$. When lead oxide is heated with an excess of **phosphoric acid,** T. Fleitmann found that lead tetra-metaphosphate is produced. P. Berthier found that **arsenic** is oxidized to the trioxide when it is heated with lead monoxide, some slag is formed, and if the litharge be not in excess arsenical fumes are also evolved. P. Berthier, and J. Percy reported that under similar circumstances **antimony** is similarly oxidized to the trioxide ; while with **bismuth,** part is oxidized, and unites with the lead oxide so that the latter loses its oxidizing power. According to H. Leroux, the composition of the regulus obtained when different proportions of antimony of 98·6 per cent. purity is heated with lead oxide is as follows :

Antimony .	0·4	0·8	1·6	3·2	5·2	6·4	8·74	12·8 per cent.
Regulus {Sb	—	—	—	0·51	2·24	13·02	18·43	21·62
{Pb	0·16	0·76	1·60	5·09	9·64	11·14	13·69	18·18

When litharge is heated with **arsenic trioxide,** both P. Berthier, and J. Percy reported that fusible, orange-yellow, glassy masses are produced, and the former concluded that the trioxide is not oxidized to the pentoxide since only a trace of metallic lead was formed. P. Berthier found that when heated with **arsenic pentoxide,** litharge formed very fluid liquids which solidified to crystalline enamels. He also showed that a mixture of lead oxide and **antimony trioxide** (5 : 1) is readily fusible. G. Tammann said that the reactions with arsenic and antimony trioxides begin respectively at 310° and 400°. For the action of arsenic, antimony, and bismuth sulphides, *vide supra.* Lead oxide is soluble in a boiling soln. of **copper nitrate,** with the precipitation of cupric oxide ; it is partially soluble in soln. of **cadmium nitrate,** and of **manganese nitrate** with the precipitation of the corresponding oxides. According to J. Persoz, lead oxide is not acted on by soln. of the **nitrates of silver, cerium, cobalt, nickel,** and **magnesium.** V. Kohlschütter and A. d'Almendra found that lead monoxide is coated with silver when immersed in a soln. of silver nitrate.

Lead oxide is quickly reduced to the metal when heated to dull redness with **carbon**—charcoal, coal, or coke. According to J. Percy,[7] the temp. of reduction is below that at which carbon dioxide is converted to carbon monoxide by carbon, and hence carbon dioxide is evolved during the reduction. C. R. A. Wright and A. P. Luff gave 435° for the temp. of reduction with dense sugar-carbon, and 415° with a porous form ; and F. O. Doeltz and C. A. Graumann said that no perceptible reduction occurred in 30 mins. at 500° ; at 530°, some reduction occurred in 15 mins. ; and at 600° the reduction was very marked in 30 mins. Observations were also made by F. Kügelgen, R. Lüpke, and C. G. Baert. As shown by K. Stammer, and I. L. Bell, lead monoxide is completely reduced by **carbon monoxide.** G. C. Winkelblech said that the reaction with lead oxide, made by the action of alkali-lye on a hot soln. of lead acetate, occurs not far above 100° ; C. R. A. Wright and A. P. Luff gave 160°–185° for the temp. of the reaction ; L. Peetz found the reaction very slow at 240°–300° ; F. Glaser said a temp. over 300° is necessary for the reduction of lead oxide by carbon monoxide. F. J. Brislee measured the rate of reduction of lead oxide by carbon monoxide; at 300°, and found a break in the time-reduction curve, corresponding with the formation of lead suboxide :

Time . .	0	3	6	7½	9	12	18	21	30 hrs.
Weight . .	2·000	1·957	1·936	1·919	1·917	1·913	1·901	1·896	1·861 grms.

I. W. Fay and co-workers found signs of reduction when lead oxide is heated in an atm. of carbon monoxide for 6 hrs. at 160°. The subject was studied by W. Fränkel and co-workers. The catalytic effect of lead oxide on the proportion of carbon monoxide obtained during the oxidation of carbon was discussed by E. Berger and L. Delmas. M. Dennstedt and F. Hassler, and O. L. Erdmann found that lead monoxide is not much affected by **carbon dioxide** in the cold, and at 100°, only a trace is absorbed. P. Termier found that in air both the rhombic and tetragonal forms of lead oxide absorb carbon dioxide with equal rapidity.

F. J. Brislee observed no sign of an equilibrium in the reaction : Pb_2O+CO_2 $=2PbO+CO$; and $2Pb+CO_2=Pb_2O+CO$. I. W. Fay and co-workers observed signs of reduction when lead oxide is heated in **methane** for 6 hrs. at 210°. H. N. Warren found that **calcium carbide** reduces lead oxide, and the reaction is accompanied by incandescence ; a calcium-lead alloy is formed and carbon dioxide is evolved. H. Moissan added that no alloy is produced. J. Percy said that heated lead monoxide is reduced by **cyanogen ;** and the oxide is also reduced by fusion with **potassium cyanide ;** J. von Liebig, and H. Rose showed that potassium cyanate is formed at the same time. L. Hackspill and R. Grandadam found that with fused alkali cyanides under ordinary atm. conditions, lead and alkali carbimide are formed ; but with cyanide in vacuo at 570°-575°, the sodium carbimide seems to decompose into sodium, nitrogen, carbon, and **carbon** monoxide and dioxide.

P. Sabatier and A. Mailhe [8] found that the vapours of the primary **alcohols** slowly reduce lead oxide above 260°, forming carbon dioxide and aldehyde ; the action is more rapid at 325° when some aldehyde is oxidized to acid. The acid forms a salt which is partially decomposed, forming ketone. H. Franzen and L. Hauck found that combustion occurs when lead monoxide is shaken with an aq. soln. of **formaldehyde.** V. Kohlschütter and H. Rösti found that a dil. soln. of **acetic acid,** or a $0·2N$-soln. of **tartaric acid** in amyl alcohol dissolves the yellow oxide faster than the red one. According to J. Pelouze, dry **glycerol,** or, according to E. Frémy, an aq. soln. of glycerol dissolves lead monoxide. When rubbed up with glycerol, lead monoxide forms a hard cement—say 50 grms. of lead oxide and 5 c.c. of glycerol—discussed by J. Persoz, O. Rost, T. Morawsky, C. H. Hirzel, H. E. Merwin, F. Bayer, etc. With **glycol,** also, T. Goldschmidt obtained a sticky mass which hardened to a cement ; and a similar result is obtained with **phenol.** The compound with phenol was investigated by A. Laurent, F. C. Calvert, C. Grabe, and F. F. Runge. Lead oxide forms a sparingly soluble saccharate when treated with a soln. of **sugar.** A. Wohl found that the yellow form of litharge dissolves much more rapidly than the red form ; the speed of soln. is fastest about 80° or 90°. J. Babé and W. Witter added that the solubility of the oxide in sugar soln. is much augmented if alkali or alkaline earth hydroxides be present. Lead oxide can be separated from arsenic oxide, etc., in virtue of its solubility in sugar soln. The solubility of lead oxide in sugar was examined by J. Peschier ; in **glucose,** by J. Persoz ; and in **dextrin,** by M. Lachaud, who found that lead oxide removes dextrin from its aq. soln. Lead oxide saponifies some of the **fatty esters,** forming lead soaps studied by W. Schrauth, and C. de la Harpe and W. A. van Dorp. Lead oxide is used as a drier since it hastens the setting of **linseed oil** by accelerating the absorption of oxygen ; the reaction was discussed by W. Lippert, and L. L. Steele. R. Schweitzer found lead oxide to be soluble in **volatile oils ;** W. Eidmann, insoluble in **acetone,** and L. Pincussohn, easily soluble in **pyridine** nitrate and hydrochloride. According to E. Seidl, P. I. Bean, C. O. Weber, and D. F. Twiss, lead oxide accelerates the hot vulcanization of **rubber.** Lead oxide was found by J. Aloy and C. Rabaut to inhibit the hydrolysis of benzoylated **cyanohydrins** by acetic acid. L. Kahlenberg and H. W. Hillyer found that when lead oxide is added to a boiling soln. of normal potassium tartrate, it is freely dissolved, and the soln. becomes alkaline owing to liberation of potassium hydroxide. Lead oxide is freely dissolved until the soln. contains lead oxide and potassium tartrate in mol. proportions ; beyond this point, soln. takes place with difficulty only, but by long-continued boiling with fairly conc. soln. of the tartrate, about $1·24$ mol. proportions of lead oxide can be dissolved in 1 mol. proportion of potassium tartrate. Where the ratio of oxide to tartrate is above unity, only half the potassium in the tartrate is liberated as hydroxide. From a conc. boiling soln. containing excess of lead, a precipitate is formed, on cooling, which is a basic lead tartrate of the formula $(PbO)_2C_4H_4O_6Pb$. From dil. soln., alcohol causes a precipitate which is probably a mixture of a tartrate of the proportion $Pb : K = 1 : 1$ with a more basic lead tartrate. The normal tartrates of sodium, lithium, rubidium, and ammonium act like potassium tartrate, but thallium tartrate and potassium anti-monyl tartrate do not act on lead oxide. When potassium ethyl tartrate is treated with lead oxide, it is saponified, but the resulting white lead salt goes into soln. only on adding an alkali hydroxide. Potassium hydrotartrate acts on lead oxide like ethyl potassium tartrate, only much more slowly ; the action is much accelerated by the addition of a little potassium hydroxide. Potassium malate, citrate, lactate, and glycerate take up but insignificant quantities of lead oxide, whilst potassium succinate, malonate, acetate, and propionate do not act on it. Potassium mucate and potassium saccharate act on lead oxide in a similar way to the tartrate, forming basic salts of the probable formulæ $C_6H_4O_8Pb_3$. The actions take place between two mols of lead oxide and one mol of mucate or saccharate. It is concluded that : (i) In order that its normal potassium salt may react readily with lead oxide, the organic acid must be dibasic, and must contain two, or a multiple of two, alcoholic hydroxyl groups ; (ii) The number of mols of the oxide with which one mol of salt readily reacts is equal to one-half the number of alcoholic hydroxyl groups contained in the acid. J. Béchamp found that water-free **acetic acid** unites directly with lead oxide. W. Kubel, and B. Kosmann found that soln. of **magnesium acetate** dissolve lead oxide in quantities dependent on the conc. and temp. of the soln. Conc. soln. deposit $Mg(C_2H_3O_2)_2.Pb(OH)_2$. Soln. of **lead acetate** dissolve lead oxide but no red-lead basic acetates are formed. The reaction was studied by F. Rochleder, D. Woodman, and W. Kubel. H. Rheinboldt and E. Wedekind studied the adsorption of **organic dyes** by lead oxide. A. J. Carlson and A. Woelfel found lead oxide to be soluble in **gastric juice** ; and J. Aub gave 1·1520 grms. per litre for the solubility of lead oxide in **blood serum.**

H. Moissan [9] found that **boron** reduces lead oxide when heated, and the mass becomes incandescent ; H. Moissan and P. Williams also showed that **calcium boride,** CaB_6, reduces lead oxide at a red heat. When fused with **boric oxide,** lead borate is formed (q.v.). H. N. Warren [10] said that **silicon** reduces lead oxide vigorously ; and a mixture of silicon, aluminium, and lead oxide explodes when heated. L. Kahlenberg and W. J. Trautmann found that lead oxide is rapidly reduced by powdered silicon when heated, $3PbO+Si=PbSiO_3+2Pb$; H. N. Warren's state-ment that a lead silicide is formed was not confirmed. E. Lay noted that lead oxide is reduced by **silicon hydronitride,** Si_2HN_3. For the action of lead oxide on **silica,** vide lead silicates. Quartz glass was found by F. Damm and F. Krafft to be strongly attacked by the vapour of lead oxide. J. C. J. Cunningham found that **alumina,** **asbestos,** and **porcelain** are rapidly attacked by fused lead oxide. R. Canaval opened up **silicates** for analysis by melting them with lead oxide. V. Vesely found the fusibility of **glass** is lowered by admixture with lead oxide. T. W. Hogg found that glass is attacked by lead oxide at a temp. below **visible** redness :

If a polished plate of glass be coated with oxide of lead, and then heated up to a temp. of scarcely visible redness, or even slightly below this, it will be found, after cooling and removing the surplus oxide, that the surface has been distinctly corroded, owing to the oxide having entered into combination with the constituents of the glass. The corroded parts produced by conducting the operation at this temp. possess quite a smooth surface, but if the corrosion be allowed to take place at a decided red heat the parts are rough and not unlike the effect produced by dry hydrofluoric acid. By soaking these corroded plates in a soln. of ammonium sulphide the lead may be converted into sulphide of lead, and the corrosion may be so varied under different conditions that brilliant mirror-like films may be obtained of considerable durability and of sufficient thickness to be quite opaque, or so thin that light of a brownish hue is transmitted. Using lead oxide as a pigment on a glass plate, and if another plate, preferably of some dark blue or ruby tinted glass, be placed immediately over it but prevented from actual contact by suitable means—and the two plates heated for about an hour to a temp. of scarcely visible redness, the upper glass always has its polish so altered that a distinct reverse of the writing appears upon it, more or less sharp according to the distance between the two surfaces.

An aq. soln. of lead oxide **was** found **by** M. Pleissner **to** attack glass **at**

25°–40°, so strongly that it appeared to have been etched by hydrofluoric acid. E. J. Kohlmeyer discussed the attack of firebricks by lead vapours, and he found the **spinel**, $3MgO.Al_2O_3$, resisted the attack best. P. Berthier obtained an opaque mass by fusing **titanic oxide** with eight times its weight of litharge. G. Tammann found that the reaction with silica, titania, and zirconia begins respectively at 580°, 470°, and 700°.

According to J. L. Gay Lussac and L. J. Thénard,[11] and J. von Liebig, **potassium** or **sodium**, just above its m.p., vigorously reduces lead oxide to the metal; and M. Rosenfeld found that sodium, reduced to a fine state of subdivision by trituration with a suitable solid, when mixed with lead oxide ignites spontaneously, leaving a residue of metallic lead. J. A. Wilkinson observed no luminescence during the reduction of lead oxide by sodium. F. M. Perkin found that lead oxide is readily reduced by **calcium**; C. Winkler, by **magnesium**; and T. Goldschmidt showed that the reduction by **aluminium** is explosively violent. C. E. Wait found that **silver** reacts with lead oxide, forming **lead** and silver oxide; E. J. Kohlmeyer showed that molten lead oxide can dissolve 3–6 per cent. of silver which is present as silver oxide; the f.p. is at the same time depressed—*vide* silver plumbite. K. Williams found that in assaying silver if an excessively high proportion of litharge is present in the flux, low results are obtained owing to the dissolution of silver in the slag. P. Berthier showed that litharge oxidizes many metals and metalloids. Observations on **copper, zinc, tin,** and **iron** were reported by P. Berthier, and J. Percy. Iron, **nickel,** and silver were found by J. C. J. Cunningham to be attacked by heated litharge. E. J. Kohlmeyer, and J. C. J. Cunningham noted that **platinum** is rapidly attacked by lead oxide at 1000°–1175°; and about 3 per cent. of platinum can dissolve in the molten oxide.

M. Höhnel observed that when lead oxide is stirred into a mixture of **sodium dioxide** and a little water, sodium plumbate, $Na_2PbO_3.4H_2O$, is formed. J. A. Hedvall and N. von Zweigbergk showed that a higher oxide of lead, not the dioxide, is formed when lead oxide is heated with **barium dioxide,** and at the same time, some barium orthoplumbate is formed over 500°. P. Berthier investigated quantitatively the action of heat or rather the fusibility of mixtures of litharge with **cuprous and cupric oxides, zinc oxide, iron oxides, manganese oxide,** and **stannic oxide**—*vide infra.* plumbites; and F. de Carli, on **molybdic, tungstic, vanadic,** and **chromic oxides.** G. Tammann said that the reaction with molybdic oxide begins at 460°; with tungstic oxide, at 480°; with zinc sulphate, at 490°; with magnesium sulphate, at 490°; with copper sulphate, at 495°; with silver sulphate at 425°; and with silver nitrate at 175°. The reaction with zinc sulphide was represented: $ZnS + PbO = ZnO + PbS + 12.6$ Cals.; with ferric sulphate, 15.2 Cals. are evolved at 460°; and with ferrous sulphate, 11 Cals. at 540°. The reaction with vanadium pentoxide sets in at 325°. J. Milbauer found that when litharge and **chromic hydroxide** are heated together, lead chromate is formed. J. A. Hedvall observed no sign of combination when a mixture of **cobalt oxide** and litharge is heated to 1100°–1300°. According to G. Tammann, if lead oxide be kept under a soln. of **silver nitrate** or **sulphate,** it is gradually blackened in diffuse light, the action is rapid in sunlight; and silver oxide is formed.

REFERENCES.

[1] G. Kassner, *Arch. Pharm.*, **241**. 696, 1903; **249**. 22, 1911; A. Ditte, *Compt. Rend.*, **94**. 1311, 1882; *Ann. Chim. Phys.*, (5), **28**. 127, 1883; W. Reinders and L. Hamburger, *Zeit. anorg. Chem.*, **89**. 79, 1914; R. Ruer, *ib.*, **50**. 267, 1906; O. Brunck, *ib.*, **10**. 222, 1895; F. Fischer and H. Plötze, *ib.*, **75**. 18, 1912; C. Renz, *ib.*, **116**. 62, 1921; J. Milbauer, *Chem. Ztg.*, **40**. 587, 1916; E. Warburg, *Wied. Ann.*, **54**. 727, 1895; G. A. Dima, *Bul. Soc. Stiinte din Cluj*, **1**. 321, 1922; P. Termier, *Bull. Soc. Min.*, **18**. 378, 1895; M. P. Applebey and R. D. Reid, *Journ. Chem. Soc.*, **121**. 2130, 1922.

[2] J. J. Berzelius, *Gilbert's Ann.*, **40**. 166, 186, 1812; **46**. 131, 1814; *Schweigger's Journ.*, **7**. 71, 1813; N. B. Pilling and R. E. Bedworth, *Journ. Inst. Metals*, **29**. 529, 1923; F. Paneth,

Zeit. Elektrochem., **26**. 452, 1920 ; F. Paneth, M. Mathies, and E. Schmidt-Hebbel, *Ber.*, **55**. B, 777, 1922 ; W. Ipatjeff and W. Werchowsky, *ib.*, **42**. 2088, 1909 ; *Journ. Russ. Phys. Chem. Soc.*, **41**. 484, 1909 ; C. R. A. Wright and A. P. Luff, *Journ. Chem. Soc.*, **33**. 529, 1878 ; J. W. Fay, A. F. Seeker, F. H. Lane, and G. E. Ferguson, *Polyt. Eng.*, **10**. 72, 1910 ; S. Hauser, *Ueber Reduktion einiger Metalloxyde durch Gase*, Strassburg, 1907 ; H. Hélier, *Bull. Soc. Chim.*, (3), **21**. 43, 1899 ; H. Moissan, *ib.*, (3), **27**. 1143, 1902 ; *Ann. Chim. Phys.*, (7), **27**. 354, 1902 ; F. M. Perkin and L. Pratt, *Trans. Faraday Soc.*, **3**. 179, 1908 ; G. Tammann, *Zeit. anorg. Chem.*, **113**. 149, 1920 ; W. Müller, *Pogg. Ann.*, **136**. 51, 1869 ; S. Hilpert and P. Weiller, *Ber.*, **42**. 2969, 1909 ; W. Mostowitsch, *Met.*, **4**. 654, 1907 ; H. Mennicke, *Zeit. öffent. Chem.*, **6**. 227, 1900 ; A. de Hemptinne, *Bull. Acad. Belg.*, 249, 1919 ; G. C. Winkelblech, *Liebig's Ann.*, **21**. 21, 1837 ; *Journ. prakt. Chem.*, (1), **10**. 221, 1837 ; F. Glaser, *Zeit. anorg. Chem.*, **36**. 13, 1903 ; K. Kindler and O. Giese, *Ber.*, **56**. B, 2063, 1923.

³ C. W. G. Kastner, *Schweigger's Journ.*, **5**. 575, 1812 ; G. Wetzlar, *ib.*, **54**. 324, 1828 ; J. Tünnermann, *Kastner's Arch.*, **19**. 338, 1830 ; F. Brendecke, *Repert. Pharm.*, **53**. 155, 313, 1831 ; F. Siebold, *ib.*. **53**. 174, 1835 ; J. E. Herberger, *ib.*, **55**. 55, 1831 ; M. Pleissner, *Arb. Kaiser Ges. Amt.*, **26**. 393, 1907 ; A. C. Cumming, *Trans. Faraday Soc.*, **2**. 199, 1907 ; R. Ruer, *Zeit. anorg. Chem.*, **50**. 273, 1906 ; C. Löwig, *Pogg. Ann.*, **14**. 114, 1828 ; **16**. 376, 1829 ; R. Böttger, *Journ. prakt. Chem.*, (1), **76**. 235, 1859 ; W. Böttger, *Jahrb. Elektrochem.*, **10**. 245, 1903 ; *Zeit. phys. Chem.*, **46**. 521, 1903 ; A. Bineau, *Compt. Rend.*, **41**. 509, 1855 ; G. André, *ib.*, **104**. 359, 1887 ; A. Ditte, *ib.*, **94**. 1311, 1882 ; *Ann. Chim. Phys.*, (5), **28**. 127, 1883 ; P. Bechtereff, *Zeit. Elektrochem.*, **17**. 864, 1911 ; E. Berl and G. Austerwell, *ib.*, **13**. 167, 1907 ; P. Yorke, *Mem. Chem. Soc.*, **2**. 399, 1843 ; *Phil. Mag.*, (3), **5**. 82, 1834 ; (3), **28**. 17, 1846 ; R. Christison, *ib.*, (3), **21**. 158, 1842 ; *Trans. Edin. Roy. Soc.*, **15**. 263, 1844 ; F. Clowes, *Proc. Chem. Soc.*, **18**. 46, 1902 ; P. A. von Bonsdorff, *Acad. Handl. Stockholm*, 268, 1836 ; *Pogg. Ann.*, **41**. 306, 1837 ; **42**. 325, 1837 ; *Répert. Chim.*, **3**. 44, 1838 ; L. B. G. de Morveau, *Mém. Inst.*, 267, 1809 ; *Nicholson's Journ.*, **26**. 102, 1810 ; *Ann. Chim. Phys.*, (1), **71**. 189, 1909 ; C. W. Scheele, *Crell's Neusten Entdeckung. Chem.*, 1. 30. 1784 ; S. Glasstone, *Journ. Chem. Soc.*, **119**. 1689, 1921 ; M. P. Applebey and R. D. Reid, *ib.*, **121**. 2129, 1922 ; J. Percy, *The Metallurgy of Lead*, London, 16, 1870 ; H. Remy, *Zeit. Elektrochem.*, **31**. 88, 1925 ; H. Remy and A. Kuhlmann, *Zeit. anal. Chem.*, **65**. 161, 1924.

⁴ A. Voigt, *Chem. Ztg.*, **13**. 695, 1889 ; H. Hof, *ib.*, **33**. 1077, 1909 ; H. Hof and B. Rinck, *German Pat.*, *D.R.P.* 227389, 1909 ; O. Unger, *ib.*, 171467, 1904 ; R. Weber, *Pogg. Ann.*, **112**. 619, 1861 ; C. F. Cross and S. Suguira, *Journ. Chem. Soc.*, **33**. 405, 1878 ; G. L. Fowler and J. Grant, *ib.*, **57**. 272, 1903 ; A. Michael and A. Murphy, *Amer. Chem. Journ.*, **44**. 365, 1910 ; W. O. de Coninck and L. Arzalier, *Bull. Acad. Belg.*, 713, 1907 ; F. Isambert, *Compt. Rend.*, **100**. 857, 1885 ; **102**. 1313, 1886 ; G. André, *ib.*, **104**. 359, 1887 ; **106**. 854, 1888 ; E. P. Perman, *Chem. News*, **88**. 197, 1903 ; W. R. E. Hodgkinson and F. K. S. Lowndes, *ib.*, **58**. 309, 1888 ; J. F. G. Hicks and W. Craig, *Journ. Phys. Chem.*, **26**. 563, 1922 ; C. Löwig, *Das Brom und seine chemischen Verhältnisse*, Heidelberg, 1829 ; E. Berl and G. Austerwell, *Zeit. Elektrochem.*, **13**. 165, 1907 ; C. W. Scheele, *Svenska Ved Handl.*, 1, 1779 ; W. Bersch, *Zeit. phys. Chem.*, **8**. 383, 1891 ; A. Jäger, *Zeit. anorg. Chem.*, **27**. 22, 1901 ; H. Hof, *ib.*, **81**. 40, 1913 ; H. Houben, *Met.*, **9**. 592, 1912 ; O. Schott, *Beiträge zur Kenntnis der anorganische Verbindungen*, Braunschweig, 1881 ; *Zeit. Kryst.*, **5**. 611, 1881 ; H. Moissan, *Ann. Chim. Phys.*, (6), **24**. 261, 1891 ; L. N. Vauquelin, *ib.*, (1), **31**. 3, 1799 ; *Mém. Inst.*, **5**. 171, 1804 ; *Nicholson's Journ.*, **3**. 470, 1808 ; O. Schott, *Beiträge zur Kenntniss der anorganische Schmelzverbindungen*, Braunschweig, 16, 1880 ; J. F. G. Hicks and W. A. Craig, *Journ. Phys. Chem.*, **26**. 563, 1922 ; E. A. Atkinson, *Journ. Amer. Chem. Soc.*, **20**. 800, 1898 ; J. B. Moyer, *ib.*, **18**. 1032, 1896 ; F. Roderbourg, *German Pat.*, *D.R.P.* 241483, 1910 ; W. Dominik, *Przemisl Chemiczny*, **6**. 25, 1922.

⁵ P. Berthier, *Ann. Mines*, (2), **2**. 385, 1827 ; *Ann. Chim. Phys.*, (2), **39**. 244, 1828 ; *Traité de essais par la voie sèche*, Paris, **1**. 382, 1834 ; **2**. 680, 1834 ; J. B. Senderens, *Compt. Rend.*, **104**. 58, 1887 ; F. Isambert, *ib.*, **100**. 857, 1885 ; A. Gautier, *ib.*, **107**. 911, 1888 ; **109**. 913, 1888 ; A. Seyewetz and P. Trawitz, *ib.*, **137**. 130, 1903 ; *Bull. Soc. Chem.*, (3), **29**. 868, 1903 ; H. Rose, *Pogg. Ann.*, **91**. 104, 1853 ; E. Priwoznik, *Ber.*, **6**. 1291, 1873 ; J. Uhl, *ib.*, **23**. 2151, 1890 ; R. Schenck and W. Rassbach, *ib.*, **40**. 2185, 1907 ; R. Schenck, *Physikalische Chemie der Metalle*, Halle, 179, 1909 ; London, 220, 1919 ; J. A. Wilkinson, *Journ. Phys. Chem.*, **13**. 707, 1909 ; D. L. Hammick, *Journ. Chem. Soc.*, **111**. 383, 1917 ; P. Richter, *Chem. Ztg.*, **32**. 632, 1908.

⁶ A. Oppenheim, *Ber.*, **5**. 979, 1872 ; J. Persoz, *Ann. Chim. Phys.*, (2), **63**. 273, 1836 ; T. B. W. Welsh and H. J. Broderson, *Journ. Amer. Chem. Soc.*, **37**. 816, 1915 ; I. W. Fay, A. F. Secker, F. H. Lane, and G. E. Ferguson, *Polyt. Eng.*, **10**. 72, 1910 ; V. Kohlschütter and A. d'Almendra, *Ber.*, **54**. 13, 1961, 1921 ; A. Michaelis, *Journ. prakt. Chem.*, (2), **4**. 449, 1871 ; *Jenaische Zeit.*, **7**. 110, 1871 ; F. Ephraim, *Zeit. anorg. Chem.*, **44**. 185, 1905 ; E. Müller and H. Barck, *ib.*, **129**. 314, 1923 ; T. Fleitmann, *Pogg. Ann.*, **78**. 353, 1849 ; *Traité des essais par la voie sèche*, Paris, **1**. 382, 516, 1834 ; J. Percy, *The Metallurgy of Lead*, London. 19, 1870 ; E. C. Franklin, *Amer. Chem. Journ.*, **20**. 828, 1898 ; H. Leroux, *Metall Erz*, **21**. 421, 1924 ; P. Berthier, *Traité des essais par la voie sèche*, Paris, **1**. 382, 1834 ; U. R. Evans, *Journ Soc. Chem. Ind.—Chem. Ind.*, **45**. 504, 1926 ; H. Braconnet, *Pogg. Ann.*, **29**. 174, 1833 ; G. Tammann, *Zeit. anorg. Chem.*, **149**. 35, 46, 1925 ; E. Müller and H. Barck, *ib.*, **129**. 309, 1923.

⁷ J. Percy, *The Metallurgy of Lead*, London, 15, 1870 ; C. R. A. Wright and A. P. Luff, *Journ. Chem. Soc.*, **33**. 1, 529, 1878 ; F. O. Doeltz and C. A. Graumann, *Met.*, **4**. 421, 1907 ;

L. Peetz, *ib.*, **1**. 296, 1904 ; R. Lüpke, *Zeit. phys. chem. Unterr.*, **6**. 176, 1893 ; C. G. Baert, *Chem. Weekbl.*, **5**. 985, 1908 ; G. C. Winkelblech, *Liebig's Ann.*, **21**. 21, 1837 ; *Journ. prakt. Chem.*, (1), **10**. 221, 1837 ; O. L. Erdmann, *ib.*, (1), **81**. 177, 1860 ; (1), **82**. 317, 1861 ; K. Stammer, *Pogg. Ann.*, **82**. 136, 1851 ; I. L. Bell, *Chem. News*, **23**. 258, 1871 ; H. N. Warren, *ib.*, **75**. 2, 1897 ; E. Berger and L. Delmas, *Bull. Soc. Chim.*, (4), **29**. 68, 1921 ; I. W. Fay, A. F. Seeker, F. H. Lane, and G. E. Ferguson, *Polyt. Eng.*, **10**. 72, 1910 ; L. Hackspill and R. Grandadam, *Compt. Rend.*, **180**. 930, 1925 ; F. Glaser, *Zeit. anorg. Chem.*, **36**. 13, 1903 ; M. Dennstedt and F. Hassler, *Zeit. anal. Chem.*, **42**. 417, 1903 ; H. Moissan, *Compt. Rend.*, **125**. 839, 1897 ; F. Kügelgen, *Zeit. Elektrochem.*, **7**. 541, 552, 573, 1900 ; J. von Liebig, *Liebig's Ann.*, **41**. 289, 1842 ; H. Rose, *Pogg. Ann.*, **91**. 104, 1854 ; P. Termier, *Bull. Soc. Min.*, **18**. 378, 1895 ; F. J. Brislee *Journ. Chem. Soc.*, **93** 154, 1908 ; W. Fränkel, *Festschrift zur Jahrundertfeier des physikalisel en Vereins*, Frankfurt a. M., **136**, 1924 ; W. Fränkel and W. Snipschsky, *Zeit. anorg. Chem.*, **125**. 235, 1922.

[8] H. Franzen and L. Hauck, *Journ. prakt. Chem.*, (2), **21**. 261, 1915 ; T. Morawsky, *ib.*, (2), **22**. 401, 1880 ; *Dingler's Journ.*, **235**. 213, 1880 ; W. Schrauth, *Siefensieder Ztg.*, **35**. 441, 1908 ; J. Aloy and C. Rabaut, *Bull. Soc. Chim.*, (4), **19**. 44, 1916 ; M. Lachaud, *ib.*, (3), **15**. 1105, 1896 ; J. Persoz, *Ann. Chim. Phys.*, (2), **63**. 273, 1836 ; P. Sabatier and A. Mailhe, *ib.*, (8), **20**. 322, 1910 ; R. Schweitzer, *Zeit. anal. Chem.*, **29**. 414, 1890 ; E. Frémy, *Ann. Chim. Phys.*, (2), **63**. 25, 1836 ; J. Pelouze, *ib.*, (2), **63**. 19, 1836 ; A. Laurent, *ib..* (3), **3**. 195, 1841 ; F. J. Brislee, *Journ. Chem. Soc.*, **93**. 154, 1908 ; A. Bonnet, *Compt. Rend.*, **121**. 700, 1895 ; J. Béchamp, *ib.*, **85**. 799, 1877 ; O. Rost, *Chem. Tech. Repert.*, i, 145, 1879 ; F. Rochleder, *Sitzber. Akad. Wien*, **29**. 3, 1858 ; *Journ. prakt. Chem.*, (1), **74**. 1, 1858 ; C. H. Hirzel, *Zeit. Pharm.*, **10**. 145, 177, 1858 ; W. Lippert, *Zeit. angew. Chem.*, **10**. 363, 1897 ; H. E. Merwin, *Journ. Ind. Eng. Chem.*, **9**. 390, 1917 ; D. F. Twiss, *Journ. Soc. Chem. Ind.*, **36**. 786, 1917 ; E. Seidl, *Gummi Ztg.*, **25**. 710, 748, 1911 ; C. O. Weber, *ib.*, **16**. 564, 1902 ; J. Peschier, *Journ. Pharm. Chim.*, (1), **3**. 508, 1817 ; T. Goldschmidt, *German Pat.*, *D.R.P.* 302852, 1917 ; F. Bayer and Co., *ib.*, 303805, 305174, 305175, 1917 ; J. Babé and W. Witter, *ib.*, 198072, 1906 ; A. Wohl, *ib.*, 90507, 92919, 92920, 92921, 96544, 1895 ; *Monit. Scient.*, (4), **10**. 766, 1896 ; F. C. Calvert, *Compt. Rend.*, **59**. 441, 1864 ; *Zeit. Chem.*, (2), 1. 531, 1865 ; F. F. Runge, *Pogg. Ann.*, **42**. 308, 1834 ; C. Grabe, *Ber.*, **7**. 396, 1874 ; C. de la Harpe and W. A. van Dorp, *ib.*, **8**. 1048, 1875 ; V. Kohlschütter and H. Rösti, *ib.*, **56**. B, 285, 1923 ; L. L. Steele, *Journ. Ind. Eng. Chem.*, **16**. 957, 1924 ; H. Rheinboldt and E. Wedekind, *Koll. Beihefte*, **17**. 115, 1923 ; D. Woodman, *Journ. Amer. Chem. Soc.*, **19**. 339, 1897 ; L. Kahlenberg and H. W. Hillyer, **16**. 94, 1894 ; L. Kahlenberg, *Zeit. phys. Chem.*, **17**. 574, 1895 ; W. Bersch, *ib.*, **8**. 393, 1891 ; W. Kubel, *Arch. Pharm.*, **230**. 175, 1892 ; B. Kosmann, *ib.*, **230**. 352, 1892 ; W. Eidmann, *Ein Beitrag zur Erkenntnis des Verhaltens chemischer Verbindungen in nichtwässrigen Lösungen*, Giessen, 1889 ; P. I. Bean, *India Rubber Journ.*, **64**. 1051, 1922 ; L. Pincussohn, *Zeit. anorg. Chem.*, **14**. 379, 1897 ; J. Aub, *Lead Poisoning*, Baltimore, 19, 1926 ; A. J. Carlson and A. Woelfel, *Journ. Amer. Med. Assoc.*, **61**. 181, 1913 ; *Amer. Journ. Public Health*, **3**. 755, 1913 ; *Journ. Pharmacol. Exp. Therap.*, **5**. 549, 1914 ; *Proc. Soc. Exp. Biol. Med.*, **10**. 189, 1913.

[9] H. Moissan, *Compt. Rend.*, **114**. 636, 1892 ; H. Moissan and P. Williams, *ib.*, **125**. 629, 1897 ; W. Guertler, *Zeit. anorg. Chem.*, **40**. 225, 1904 ; *Ueber wasserfreie Borate und über Entglasung*, Leipzig, 1904.

[10] H. N. Warren, *Chem. News*, **64**. 75, 1891 ; E. Lay, *Ueber Silicium-Stickstoff-Wassertoff Verbindungen*, München, 58, 1910 ; T. W. Hogg, *B.A. Rep.*, 534, 1889 ; *Journ. Soc. Chem. Ind.*, **8**. 684, 1889 ; W. Mostowitsch, *Met.*, **4**. 647, 1907 ; V. Vesely, *Arch. Phys. Chem. Glases ker. Massen*, **1**. 33, 1912 ; F. Damm and F. Krafft, *Ber.*, **40**. 4775, 1907 ; R. Canaval, *Zeit. prakt. Geol.*, **18**. 460, 1910 ; M. Pleissner, *Arb. Kaiser Ges. Amt*, **26**. 393, 1907 ; J. C. J. Cunningham, *Zeit. anorg. Chem.*, **89**. 48, 1914 ; E. J. Kohlmeyer, *Metall Erz*, **10**. 451, 1913 ; P. Berthier, *Traité des essais la voie sèche*, Paris, **1**. 513, 1834 ; F. M. Perkin, *Trans. Faraday Soc.*, **3**. 115, 1908 ; F. M. Perkin and L. Pratt, *ib.*, **3**. 182, 1908 ; L. Kahlenberg and W. J. Trautmann, *Trans. Amer. Electrochem. Soc.*, **39**. 377, 1921 ; G. Tammann, *Zeit. anorg. Chem.*, **149**. 69, 1925.

[11] J. C. J. Cunningham, *Zeit. anorg. Chem.*, **89**. 48, 1914 ; K. Williams, *Journ. Ind. Eng. Chem.*, **2**. 406, 1910 ; J. von Liebig, *Liebig's Ann.*, **41**. 289, 1842 ; T. Goldschmidt, *German Pat.*, *D.R.P.* 96317, 1895 ; M. Rosenfeld, *Ber.*, **23**. 3147, 1890 ; C. Winkler, *ib.*, **23**. 44, 120, 1890 ; **24**. 873, 1891 ; J. A. Wilkinson, *Journ. Phys. Chem.*, **13**. 708, 1909 ; E. J. Kohlmeyer, *Chem. Ztg.*, **36**. 1079, 1912 ; *Metall Erz*, **10**. 451, 1913 ; J. N. Pring, *Journ. Chem. Soc.*, **87**. 1530, 1905 ; J. L. Gay Lussac and L. J. Thénard, *Mém. Inst.*, 332, 1809 ; *Nicholson's Journ.*, **24**. 92, 1809 ; F. M. Perkin, *Trans. Faraday Soc.*, **3**. 115, 1907 ; C. E. Wait, *Journ. Amer. Chem. Soc.*, **18**. 254, 1896 ; F. Kügelgen, *Zeit. Elektrochem.*, **7**. 541, 552, 573, 1900 ; J. Percy, *The Metallurgy of Lead*, London, 18, 1870 ; P. Berthier, *Traité des essais par la voie sèche*, Paris, 1834 ; *Ann. Mines*, (1), **11**. 483, 1825 ; M. Höhnel, *Arch. Pharm.*, **232**. 223, 1894 ; J. Milbauer, *Chem. Ztg.*, **40**. 587, 1916 ; J. A. Hedvall, *Zeit. anorg. Chem.*, **93**. 316, 1915 ; J. A. Hedvall and N. von Zweigbergk, *ib.*, **108**. 127, 1919 ; G. Tammann, *ib.*, **144**. 151, 1920 ; **149**. 21, 1925 ; H. Leroux, *Metall Erz*, **21**. 421, 1924 ; F. de Carli, *Atti Accad. Lincei*, (6), **1**. 533, 1925.

§ 15. Lead Hydroxides

According to M. Pleissner,[1] normal **lead hydroxide,** $Pb(OH)_2$, separates when a soln. of lead acetate is added to one of ammonium, sodium, or barium hydroxide. This hydroxide may remain in the liquor as the solid phase, but when separated from the soln. it decomposes into **lead dioxydihydroxide,** $Pb_3O_2(OH)_2$, in the cold, and into lead monoxide, PbO, if heated. At 100°, only lead monoxide is stable in the binary system: $PbO-H_2O$. The passage of the dioxydihydroxide to the monoxide can be effected at a low temp. by light, and by saturating the liquid with oxygen. According to A. Ditte—*vide supra*—while the normal hydroxide is first precipitated at 25°, by adding an aq. soln. of potash-lye to a soln. of a lead salt, the potassium hydroxide transforms the normal hydroxide into the dioxydihydroxide. The preparation of the normal hydroxide has been reported by A. Payen, V. Kohlschütter and co-workers, and E. Müller. Besides lead dioxydihydroxide, another basic hydroxide, namely, *lead oxydihydroxide*, $2PbO.H_2O$, or $Pb_2O(OH)_2$, has been reported by L. Schaffner, A. Ogata and T. Kai'un, and C. Lüdeking.

M. Traube-Mengarini and A. Scala found that distilled water acts on lead in vacuo, and **colloidal lead hydroxide** is formed. The clear sol becomes turbid when exposed to air. V. Kohlschütter and H. Roesti made it by pouring a soln. of lead acetate into one of ammonia. N. G. Charterji and N. Dhar said that when lead hydroxide dissolves in alkali hydroxide a large proportion of colloidal lead hydroxide is formed. M. Kimura found that when lead at a red heat is poured into cold water, some colloidal hydroxide is formed. V. Kohlschütter, and A. Scala said that filter-paper adsorbs the hydroxide from the sol. B. Szilard found that lead hydroxide is peptonized by thorium nitrate, forming a colloidal sol. N. R. Dhar and S. Ghosh found that the hydroxide is peptized by alkali-lye with sugar, starch, or glycerol.

Most of the reported methods of preparing lead hydroxide, refer to the dioxydihydroxide. Thus, according to P. A. von Bonsdorff, when lead is exposed to the action of water, and of air freed from carbon dioxide, white flakes of lead hydroxide are formed. J. Tünnermann made it by dropping a soln. of lead acetate into an excess of ammonia until a permanent precipitate is formed; and drying the washed product at a gentle heat. A. Payen saw that the precipitate should be washed out of contact with air, and dried at 15°. He also obtained crystals of the anhydrous oxide and of hydroxide by mixing 4 vols. of water sat. at 30° with lead acetate, 400 vols. of boiling water, and 4 vols. of aq. ammonia. The two compounds were separated by levigation. He also mixed 100 vols. of water sat. at 25° with lead acetate, 60 vols. of cold water freed from air by boiling, and 4 vols. of aq. ammonia diluted with 60 vols. of air-free water. The mixture was kept at 30° for 24 hrs. E. Mitscherlich precipitated the soln. of a lead salt with potassium or sodium hydroxide; G. J. Mulder poured off the mother-liquor, boiled the precipitate with potash-lye for some time, and dried the washed product at 100°. G. C. Winkelblech added that if potassium hydroxide be added to lead nitrate or acetate, even in excess and aided by heat, a basic salt, not the hydroxide, is precipitated. According to W. Böttger, the hydroxide formed by the action of aq. ammonia on a soln. of lead acetate, or of baryta-water on one of lead nitrate, has a variable composition; S. Glasstone said that the product is a basic salt; and E. Euston found that lead hydroxide forms adsorption complexes with barium sulphate or carbonate, calcium or lead carbonate, and zinc dihydroxycarbonate. H. T. S. Britton showed that lead hydroxide is precipitate by alkali hydroxide when the H-ion conc. is about 10^{-8}.

R. F. Jackson studied the ternary system: lead acetate, lead oxide, and water at 25°, and found that lead hydroxide, $Pb(OH)_2$, is the only solid phase in equilibrium with soln. containing less than 4·8 per cent. of lead acetate. W. Herz found that when lead oxide is shaken with an aq. soln. of alkali halide and water, a pasty mass is formed ; but when the equilibrium is approached from the other side : $PbCl_2$ $+2KOH \rightleftharpoons 2KCl+Pb(OH)_2$, the constant $[PbCl_2][KOH]^2/[KCl]^2=0.0073$; for the corresponding reaction with aq. ammonia, 0.00082 ; and with methylamine, 0.00066. M. Pleissner obtained lead oxide by the action of baryta-water on a soln. of lead acetate ; and basic nitrate and basic chloride respectively with soln. of lead nitrate and chloride. W. B. Priest heated a suspension of lead sulphate in lime-water, until the liquid had a neutral reaction, and removed the resulting calcium sulphate by levigation. A. Ditte obtained crystals of this hydroxide by saturating with precipitated lead hydroxide a soln. containing 100–300 grms. of K_2O in a litre of water, and on raising the temp., this hydroxide was precipitated. S. Hughes obtained lead hydroxide by grinding lead fume with a soln. of sodium hydroxide. A. Ditte treated hydrated lead dioxide with a soln. of potassium iodide, and obtained lead hydroxide. R. Lorenz prepared this hydroxide by electrolyzing an aq. soln. of alkali chloride or nitrate using a platinum plate as cathode, and a plate of lead as anode. The electrolyte was continually stirred during the electrolysis. Modifications of the process were made by W. Hartmann, H. Sjögren, and T. G. Timby. Analyses by J. Tünnermann, A. Payen, E. Mitscherlich, and G. J. Mulder correspond with $3PbO.H_2O$, i.e. lead dioxyhydroxide, $Pb_3O_2(OH)_2$, or, as S. Glasstone expresses it, $Pb(HPbO_2)_2$—**lead hydroplumbite**. A. Ogata and T. Kai'un do not recommend lead nitrate for the preparation of lead hydroxide, but with lead acetate a product $2PbO.H_2O$ is formed.

M. F. Heddle described minute crystalline scales of a mineral which he named *hydroplumbite*, and which was found with cerussite and pyromorphite on galena from Leadhills. The composition was reported as $3PbO.H_2O$; but the evidence is unsatisfactory. An approximation to this product was said to be formed in rhombic crystals by allowing the precipitate, produced by adding ammonia to a soln. of lead acetate, to stand under water for a long time.

S. Glasstone found that no known method of preparation yields a substance which has definitely the composition $Pb(OH)_2$, $3PbO.H_2O$, or $2PbO.H_2O$. The products he obtained were either individuals with the composition $5PbO.2H_2O$, or $8PbO.3H_2O$, or solid soln. of two or more simple hydrates. The composition depends on the temp. and conc. of the precipitants, for these determine the amount of adsorbed water. He explains the chemical and physical properties of the so-called hydrated oxide by assuming that it is a *lead plumbite*, $Pb(HPbO_2)_2$, where the *plumboformic acid*, $H.PbO.OH$, is analogous to formic acid, $H.CO.OH$. The appearance of lead dioxydihydroxide varies with its mode of preparation. Usually, it appears as a white powder, which, under the microscope, consists of crystals which A. Payen regarded as strongly refracting octahedra, and A. Ditte, as transparent hexagonal prisms. According to R. S. Owens, crystals of lead hydroxide can be precipitated by adding a soln. of sodium hydroxide to an equal vol. of one of lead acetate at a given temp. The size of the crystals can be varied within rather wide limits by varying the temp. and conc. of the soln. Thus, at $20°$:

Conc. of soln.	N-	$\frac{1}{2}N$-	$\frac{1}{4}N$-	$\frac{1}{8}N$-	$\frac{1}{16}N$-	$\frac{1}{32}N$-
Diam. crystals, mm. $\times 10^3$	1.0	1.5	7.5	25.0	37.5	white p.p.

By varying the temp. of, say, the $\frac{1}{8}N$-soln., at $20°$ the diam. was 25 mm. ; at $33°$, 30 mm. ; at $47°$, 50 mm. long and 7.5 mm. wide ; at $66°$, 17.5 mm. for the crosses, and 12.5 mm. for the cubes. A. Ditte gave 7.592 at $0°$ for the sp. gr. of the crystals. M. Pleissner found that when confined with water in a sealed tube and exposed to sunlight, or heated for 3 hrs. at $100°$, the crystals pass into orange-yellow flakes of lead monoxide. A. Ditte also noted the change which occurs in sunlight. E. Mitscherlich thought that the compound retains its water and colour at $100°$, and A. Payen said that water begins to come off at $130°$, and is all expelled at $145°$. S. Glasstone found no loss in weight occurs in vacuo at ordinary temp. ; and he calculated the free energy of the reversible reaction, $PbO.nH_2O \rightleftharpoons PbO+nH_2O$, to be 965.4 joules per mol of lead monoxide at $20°$. He observed no appreciable vap.

press. for the partly decomposed hydrated oxide at room temp., and this is in agreement with the fact that the hydrated oxide does not lose weight in a vacuum desiccator. If the vap. press. of N-NaOH is 15 mm., and that of the hydrated oxide is p mm., then, on the assumption that the reaction is reversible, $\log p=0\cdot17241\ x+\log 15$; for Pb(OH)$_2$, $x=1$ and $p=22$ mm.; for 2PbO.H$_2$O, $x=4\frac{1}{2}$, and $p=33$ mm.; for 3PbO.H$_2$O, $x=\frac{1}{3}$, and $p=49$ mm. M. Pleissner noted that if heated with water in a sealed tube at 100°, it gives orange-red crystals of lead oxide, and, added V. Kohlschütter and H. Roesti, the crystals are pseudomorphs after 3PbO.H$_2$O. J. J. Berzelius noted that the compound reacts alkaline to litmus, and M. Pleissner, to phenolphthalein, and to iodeosin. J. Sehnal said that the compound dissolves in hot and cold water, and he gave 138·5 mgrms. Pb per litre for the solubility at 20° ; F. Kohlrausch gave 0·4 millimol per litre at 18° ; M. Pleissner, 0·45 millimol, or 100·5 mgrms. PbO, per litre at 18° when the solid phase is Pb$_3$O$_2$(OH)$_2$; W. Herz, 0·93 $\times10^{-4}$ mol per litre at 25° ; W. Böttger, 0·092 millimol, or 20·6 mgrms. per litre at 20°. The values of F. Kohlrausch, W. Herz, and W. Böttger calculated from the electrical conductivity are based on assumption as to the nature of the ionization. M. Pleissner's values for the mol. conductivity, μ, the percentage degree of ionization, a, and the ionization constant, K, are :

Pb-mgrms. per litre			93·3	106·0	111·4	124·4	131·4
μ			60·5	60·3	59·1	57·6	57·6
a	$\{$Pb(OH)$^2\rightleftharpoons$Pb(OH)$\cdot$+OH$'$		27·0	26·9	26·4	25·7	25·7
	$\{$Pb(OH)$\rightleftharpoons$Pb$\cdots$+OH$'$		12·9	12·8	12·5	12·2	12·2
K	$\{$Pb(OH)$^2\rightleftharpoons$Pb(OH)$\cdot$+OH$'$		4·50	5·07	5·10	5·35	5·62
	$\{$Pb(OH)$\rightleftharpoons$Pb$\cdots$+OH$'$		20·0	25·2	25·3	29·9	33·4

E. Berl and G. Austerweil estimated that the ionization in a soln. with 0·262 millimol of lead hydroxide per litre is complete. As previously indicated, M. P. Applebey and R. D. Reid estimated the ionization constant of H$_2$PbO$_2$ regarded as an acid— to be $0\cdot33\times10^{-11}$ to $0\cdot39\times10^{-11}$, and S. Glasstone gave $1\cdot35\times10^{-12}$ at 25° ; and for the solubility product, the latter gave $0\cdot82\times10^{-15}$, and the former $0\cdot47\times10^{-15}$ to $0\cdot91\times10^{-5}$. W. R. Cooper discussed the *lead hydroxide accumulator* in which more conc. sulphuric acid is employed as electrolyte than is the case with the ordinary lead dioxide accumulator. There is a greater output from the former cell, but the variation in voltage over the discharge is greater.

Lead hydroxide is amphoteric, behaving both as a weak acid and as a weak base. W. Biltz and F. Zimmermann said that lead hydroxide is a feebler base than magnesium hydroxide, and, according to J. K. Wood, lead hydroxide is more basic than zinc and beryllium hydroxides, since, for the weaker hydroxyl-ion, the ionization constant for beryllium hydroxide is $5\cdot2\times10^{-11}$; for zinc hydroxide, $145\cdot0\times10^{-11}$; and for lead hydroxide, $3090\cdot0\times10^{-11}$. The soln. of lead hydroxide in aq. soln. of the hydroxides of the alkalies and alkaline earths furnishes **plumbites**, M$_2$PbO$_2$, or Pb(OK)$_2$—*vide infra*. At ordinary temp., V. Kohlschütter and H. Roesti observed only a partial transformation to plumbite with 2N- to 10N-NaOH ; 10N-NaOH reddens the hydroxide ; 2N- to 12N-soln. of ammonia does not change the product. W. Herz added that the solubility of lead hydroxide in sat. soln. of the alkali hydroxides, is not altered by desiccation at 60°–70° ; and that it is completely dissolved when the soln. has 8·5–8·8 mols of hydroxyl groups for one gram-atom of lead. G. Carrara and G. B. Vespignani found that if the potash-lye be not in too great excess, Pb(OH)(OK), is formed—*vide infra*. R. C. Wells found that lead hydroxide is more soluble than the hydroxides of copper, zinc, aluminium, and iron (ic), and less soluble than those of silver, calcium, magnesium, manganese, iron (ous), and nickel.

Ordinary lead salts, in which the lead oxide acts as a base, are produced by the action of acids on lead hydroxides. A. Jäger showed that dil. hydrofluoric acid alone can dissolve a little lead hydroxide. M. Pleissner found that iodine is adsorbed, and potassium iodide decomposed, by lead hydroxide. J. Kersten found that alkali chlorides in soln. are quantitatively converted into the oxychloride, 5Pb(OH)$_2$.PbCl$_2$, and alkali hydroxide; G. André found that with chlorides of the alkaline earths, complex oxychlorides are formed. H. Böttger found that with sodium polysulphide, lead sulphide, alkali thiosulphate, as well as some free alkali hydroxide, are formed. A. Geuther considers the thiosulphate to be produced by a secondary reaction between sulphur and alkali hydroxide. D. Strömholm showed that soln. of ammonium or potassium fluoride or chlorate give no basic salts; $0.05N$-soln. of potassium chloride, bromide, or iodide produce basic salts; soln. of borax do not attack the hydroxide; and a soln. of potassium cyanide dissolves a little hydroxide. According to W. Biltz and F. Zimmermann, lead hydroxide becomes violet-brown when immersed in $\frac{1}{10}N$-AgNO$_3$ owing to the precipitation of a little silver hydroxide; with $\frac{1}{10}N$-Hg(NO$_3$)$_2$, a yellowish-red coloration is acquired owing to the formation of a little mercuric hydroxide. L. Kahlenberg found that hydroxylic organic substances—like tartaric, malic, or lactic acids, glycerol, or sugar—form complexes. The action on glycerol was investigated by T. Morawsky, and E. Fischer and V. Tafel; and the action of formaldehyde, by H. Franzen and L. Hauck. D. Strömholm found that soln. of ammonium oxalate, or potassium picrate, produce basic salts; alkali acetate, methylethyl-sulphonate, benzosulphonate and naphthosulphonate have very little action; while the alkali succinate, camphorate, and phthalate also have very little action. R. Haller showed that the hydroxide readily adsorbs dye-stuffs. M. Pleissner said that glass is strongly attacked when treated with an aq. soln. of lead hydroxide.

L. Schaffner reported the hydrated oxide, 2PbO.H$_2$O, or **lead oxydihydroxide**, Pb$_2$O(OH)$_2$, to be formed when a soln. of lead acetate is treated with potash-lye. S. Glasstone regards this compound as a basic lead plumbite, **lead hydroxhydroplumbite**, Pb(OH)HPbO$_2$. C. Lüdeking prepared it in large crystals by boiling lead oxide with a conc. soln. of potassium hydroxide, and allowing the cold soln. to absorb carbon dioxide slowly from the air. J. Löwe said the alkali should be in excess. As the potassium hydroxide becomes converted into carbonate, short, thick, well-developed, colourless, transparent, tetragonal crystals are deposited; the axial ratios are $a : b : c = 1 : 1 : 0.824$. The crystals are highly refractive. The oxydihydroxide has an alkaline reaction, and becomes opaque when exposed to the air owing to the formation of carbonate; it becomes yellow when heated, and retains its original crystalline form.

R. Weinland and F. Paul[2] referred the various basic salts of lead to those having the bivalent groups, [Pb(OH)$_2$Pb]$\cdots$; [Pb{(OH)$_2$Pb}$_2$]$\cdots$; or [PbO.Pb(OH)$_2$Pb]$\cdots$; and to the tervalent groups, [Pb$_4$(OH)$_5$]$\cdots$, and [Pb$_6$(OH)$_9$]$\cdots$.

REFERENCES.

[1] P. A. von Bonsdorff, *Pogg. Ann.*, **41**. 305, 1837; J. J. Berzelius, *ib.*, **25**. 396, 1832; J. Tünnermann, *Kastner's Arch.*, **19**. 338, 1830; A. Payen, *Compt. Rend.*, **5**. 431. 538, 1837; *Ann. Chim. Phys.*, (2), **66**. 49, 1837; *ib.*, (4), **8**. 302, 1866; A. Ditte, *ib.*, (5), **24**. 240, 1881; (5), **28**. 123, 1883; G. J. Mulder, *Bull. Sciences Phys. Neerl.*, 302, 1839; *Liebig's Ann.*, **33**. 242, 1840; *Journ. prakt. Chem.*, (1), **19**. 79, 1840; T. Morawsky, *ib.*, (2), **22**. 406. 1880; H. Franzen and L. Hauck, *ib.*, (2), **91**. 261, 1915; E. Mitscherlich, *ib.*, (1), **19**. 451, 1840; R. F. Jackson, *Journ. Amer. Chem. Soc.*, **36**. 2347, 1914; *Journ. Franklin Inst.*, **178**. 482, 1915; M. F. Heddle, *Min. Mag.*, **8**. 200, 1889; *Amer. Journ. Science*, (3), **38**. 250, 1889; M. Pleissner, *Arb. Kaiser Ges. Amt*, **26**. 398, 1907; G. C. Winkelblech, *Liebig's Ann.*, **21**. 21, 1837; L. Schaffner, *ib.*, **51**. 175, 1844; W. Herz, *Zeit. anorg. Chem.*, **28**. 474, 1901; **68**. 421, 1910; R. Lorenz, *ib.*, **12**. 436, 1896; A. Jäger, *ib.*, **27**. 22, 1901; J. Rubenbauer, *ib.*, **30**. 331, 1902; D. Strömholm, *ib.*, **38**. 432, 1904; W. Hartmann, *German Pat.*, *D.R.P.* 139078, 1903; H. Sjögren, *ib.*, 152227, 1903; J. Kersten, *ib.*, 255688, 1911; S. Hughes, *Journ. Ind. Eng. Chem.*, **4**. 262, 1912; A. Ogata and T. Kai'un, *Journ. Japan. Pharm. Soc.*, 492, 1923; W. B. Priest, *Brit. Pat. No.*, 17145, 1894; A. W. Topp, *ib.*, 200693, 1922; T. G. Timby, *U.S. Pat. No.* 1056382, 1913; *Chem. Met. Engg.*, **11**. 292, 1913; M. Traube-Mengarini and A. Scala, *Zeit. Koll.*, **6**. 240, 1910; *Atti Accad. Lincei*, (5), **19**. ii, 505, 1910; R. S. Owens, *Trans. Amer. Electrochem. Soc.*, **25**. 481, 1914; *Journ. Phys. Chem.*, **18**. 461, 1914; W. Biltz and F. Zimmermann, *Ber.*, **40**. 4979, 1907; E. Fischer and V. Tafel, *ib.*, **21**. 2635, 1888; J. K. Wood, *Journ. Chem. Soc.*, **97**. 878, 1910; S. Glasstone, *ib.*, **119**. 1689, 1914.

1921 ; **121**. 58, 1922 ; **M. P.** Applebey and R. D. Reid, *ib.*, **121**. 2129, 1922 ; **A. C. Cumming**, 95. 1772, 1909 ; F. Kohlrausch, *Sitzber. Akad. Berlin*, 90, 1897 ; J. Sehnal, *Compt. Rend.*, **148**. 1394, 1909 ; G. André, *ib.*, **104**. 359, 1887 ; W. Böttger, *Zeit. phys. Chem.*, **46**. 521, 1903 ; E. Müller, *ib.*, **114**. 129, 1925 ; H. Böttger, *Liebig's Ann.*, **223**. 342, 1884 ; A. Geuther, *ib.*, **226**. 232, 1884 ; V. Kohlschütter and E. Fischmann, *ib.*, **387**. 116, 1912 ; V. Kohlschütter and H. Roesti, *Ber.*, **56**. 277, 1923 ; W. R. Cooper, *Electrician*, **88**. 654, 1922 ; G. Carrara and G. B. Vespignani, *Gazz. Chim. Ital.*, **30**. ii, 62, 1900 ; R. C. Wells, *Bull. U.S. Geol. Sur.*, 609, 1916 ; E. Berl and G. Austerweil, *Zeit. Elektrochem.*, **13**. 169, 1907 ; L. Kahlenberg, *Zeit. phys. Chem.*, **17**. 577, 1895 ; F. Jirsa, *ib.*, **94**. 1, 1920 ; C. Lüdeking, *Amer. Chem. Journ.*, **13**. 120, 1891 ; *Chem. News*, **63**. 279, 1891 ; B. Szilard, *Journ. Chim. Phys.*, **5**. 636, 1907 ; E. Euston, *Journ. Ind. Eng. Chem.*, **6**. 383, 1914 ; R. Haller, *Koll. Zeit.*, **27**. 30, 1920 ; J. Löwe, *Journ. prakt. Chem.*, (1), **98**. 405, 1866 ; N. G. Charterji and N. Dhar, *Chem. News*, **121**. 253, 1920 ; M. Kimura, *Mem. Coll. Kyoto*, **5**. 211, 1913 ; H. T. S. Britton, *Journ. Chem. Soc.*, **127**. 2148, 1925 ; N. R. Dhar and S. Ghosh, *Zeit. anorg. Chem.*, **152** 409, 1926.

² R. Weinland and F. Paul, *Zeit. anorg. Chem.*, **129**. 243, 1923.

§ 16. The Plumbites

E. Aston[1] was unable to isolate **sodium plumbite, or potassium plumbite,** and the evidence for the existence of these salts is determined by the behaviour of soln. of lead oxide in alkali-lye. C. W. G. Karsten found that lead monoxide dissolves in a soln. of alkali hydroxide or carbonate, forming a yellow liquid, which does not crystallize. G. Grube said that freshly precipitated lead dioxydihydroxide gives with 8N- to 12N-KOH a soln. with 0·1–0·2 mol K_2PbO_2. J. Milbauer found red-lead, dissolved in alkali-lye, gives a mixed soln. of plumbite and plumbate. O. Seidel, and S. Meunier found that lead oxide likewise dissolves in molten potassium hydroxide—some alkali plumbate is formed at the same time. M. H. Klaproth found that on cooling the colourless soln. of white-lead in boiling alkali-lye, small silvery-white scales are deposited, and they acquire a grey colour on exposure to air. The mother-liquor yields a brownish-red scaly mass which redissolves in water with the exception of a few scarlet scales.

There is evidence of the existence of compounds in which lead monoxide acts as an acid anhydride, forming a series of salts called **plumbites**, M_2PbO_2, where M represents a monad radicle. In his memoir : *Sur la combinaison des oxides métalliques avec les alkalies et le chaux*, C. L. Berthollet showed that certain metal oxides exercise the functions of an alkali towards the acids, and they can act as acids with the alkalies. T. Bergman found that alkali-lye dissolves lead oxide ; and C. L. Berthollet, that lime-water dissolves lead oxide, and when the soln. is conc., it yields a crystalline solid. A. Hantzsch said that the conductivity of alkaline soln. of the metal hydroxide, and the rate at which this soln. saponifies ethyl acetate give no grounds for G. Grube's, and C. Liebenoff's assumption that PbO_2''-ions exist in soln. ; the plumbites all appear to be salts of a monobasic acid analogous with the corresponding stannites and germanites. Lead hydroxide as a base is stronger than beryllium hydroxide, and it might be anticipated that the acid would be weaker. This is not the case, and he said that this is explained by assuming that there is an internal constitutive change by which the lead becomes quadrivalent and the acid character becomes strengthened. He therefore regards the plumbites as salts of a kind of *plumboformic acid*, H.PbO.OH, analogous with formic acid H.CO.OH, and not as salts of *plumbous acid*, H_2PbO_2.

$$O=Pb{<}^H_{OH} \qquad\qquad Pb{<}^{OH}_{OH}$$

Plumboformic acid, H.PbO.OH.   Plumbous acid, H_2PbO_2.

W. Herz found that equilibrium is but slowly attained when dried lead hydroxide is employed. J. Raubenbauer found that the quantity of lead hydroxide dissolved by sodium hydroxide soln. varies with the conc., and there is a maximum value for the solubility when the at. ratio Pb : Na is 1 : 14. The existence of the maximum

is attributed to two independent factors : (i) the hydrolysis decreasing as the soln.
becomes more conc. ; and (ii) the dehydration of the hydroxide by the conc. alkali-
lye producing a less soluble monoxide. S. Glasstone obtained for conc. in mols per
litre at 25° :

Conc. NaOH	Conc. PbO.nH$_2$O	Conc. KOH	Conc. PbO.nH$_2$O	Ratio NaOH : PbO.nH$_2$O	Ratio KOH : PbO.nH$_2$O
0·9985	0·0620	0·9985	0·0631	16·1	15·8
0·1177	0·00881	0·1177	0·00892	13·4	13·2

According to E. Bert and G. Austerweil, the solubility of lead oxide, in mol per litre,
in soln. of sodium hydroxide, is :

N-NaOH .	0·0510	0·1024	0·2035	0·4794	1·0045	1·9872	4·9705
Mol PbO (18°) .	0·0041	0·0067	0·0123	0·0273	0·0560	0·1008	0·2316
Mol PbO (74°) .	0·0034	0·0067	0·0180	0·0362	0·0807	0·1430	—

They infer that in soln. containing less than a mol of NaOH per litre, the lead oxide
dissolves as **sodium hydroplumbite**, NaHPbO$_2$, and in more conc. soln. some normal
plumbite, Na$_2$PbO$_2$, is formed. They calculate the ionization constant of the
monobasic acid H$_2$PbO$_2$ to be $1·1 \times 10^{-12}$ at 18° ; S. Glasstone gave $1·3 \times 10^{-12}$ at
20° ; and M. P. Applebey and R. D. Reid gave $0·33 \times 10^{-11}$ for the red form of lead
oxide at 20°, and $0·39 \times 10^{-11}$ for the yellow form. According to J. K. Wood, with
different soln. of sodium hydroxide, the proportion of lead hydroxide dissolved
is nearly in the at. ratio Pb : Na=1 : 15 for soln. of different conc., and that the
hydrolysis constant is 0·0035, so that $0·1N$-Pb(OH)(ONa) is 17 per cent. hydrolyzed.

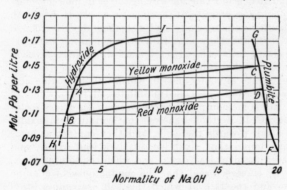

E. Müller and co-workers'
equilibrium diagram for the
system lead hydroxide and
oxide, and alkali plumbite
and hydroxide, is shown in
Fig. 64. The curves AC and
BD refer to the yellow and
red oxides and the points
of intersection of these lines
with FG, represent the transformation of the yellow and
red oxides into the alkali
plumbite. The curve HI
represents the solubility of
lead hydroxide in alkali-lye

FIG. 64.—Equilibrium Diagram for the System
PbO–H$_2$O–NaOH.

of different conc. ; and FG,
of alkali plumbite. To the
right of HI, the hydroxide passes into oxide, and to the left, the oxide passes
into hydroxide. N G. Chatterji and N. R. Dhar found that the peptization of
lead hydroxide by alkali-lye is a case of true peptization and not of chemical
combination.

A. C. Cumming measured the potential of lead against a soln. of 0·0576 mol
of lead oxide in a litre of N-NaOH and found 0·539 volt referred to the normal
hydrogen electrode, while for 0·0089 mol in a litre of $0·1N$-NaOH, he obtained
0·484 volt. He considered that the soln. contained NaPb(OH)$_2$. For S. Glasstone's,
and M. P. Applebey and R. D. Reid's observations, *vide* lead oxide. G. Carrara
and G. B. Vespignani measured the mol. conductivity, μ, of soln. with a mol of
potassium hydroxide, in v litres, and of soln. with 0·5621 grm. of lead oxide per
litre, at 25° :

v . . .	5	10	20	40	80	160	320	640	1280
μ {KOH . .	217·71	221·48	225·30	229·38	231·18	232·75	232·5	—	—
{KOH+PbO	184·07	193·42	195·38	200·12	201·88	202·40	206·40	204·16	199·68

and they inferred that the soln. probably contains **potassium hydroplumbite,** $Pb(OH)(OK)$. G. Grube found the normal potential of lead against K_2PbO_2 in $8.42N$-KOH, at $18°$, is -0.613 volt ; and in a molar soln., there is 2.05×10^{-17} gram-ion per litre. S. Glasstone found the potential of the electrode $Pb \mid PbO.nH_2O$, N-NaOH against the $Hg \mid HgO$, N-NaOH electrode to be 0.554 volt at $20°$, where the corresponding value for lead monoxide is -0.559 volt at $20°$. The nature of the oxidation product is determined by the character of the electrode material. Under the same conditions, yellow, flocculent lead sesquioxide is formed with palladium electrodes, while with nickel or iron electrodes the product is of a darker colour and is powdery. Secondary and side reactions take place with electrodes of zinc, tin, aluminium, chromium, and manganese. Oxidation does not always take place, for, according to conditions, simple reduction or alternate oxidation and reduction may occur.

G. Grube found that air passed into an alkaline soln. of a plumbite, in which was dipped a platinum plate, does not form plumbate. G. Grube electrolyzed a soln. of potassium plumbate and obtained a deposit of lead dioxide. According to F. Jirsa, the electrolysis of a N-soln. of potassium hydroxide between lead electrodes by means of an alternating current of 49 periods brings about the formation of potassium plumbite as the only product. The plumbite may be electrolytically oxidized to plumbate if electrodes of copper, silver, gold, cadmium, magnesium, mercury, nickel, iron, platinum, and palladium are used, but no oxidation occurs when lead, bismuth, cobalt, thallium, or carbon is used. V. Zotier found that when a soln. of lead oxide in sodium hydroxide is treated with hydrogen dioxide, lead dioxide is first formed, which then reacts with some hydrogen dioxide, giving rise to oxygen and some lead oxide, so that the precipitate produced usually consists of both oxides. With increasing quantities of hydrogen dioxide, the quantity of lead dioxide rises to a maximum, and then remains constant. For the quantity of hydrogen dioxide necessary to produce this maximum quantity of lead dioxide, the reaction is expressed by this equation, $10PbO + 10H_2O_2 = 10H_2O + 4PbO_2 + 6PbO + 3O_2$. The amount of lead dioxide formed diminishes with rise of temp., slightly up to $30°$, considerably from $30°$ to $60°$, and very rapidly above $60°$. At about $90°$–$95°$ lead dioxide is formed, but disappears immediately, due to the second phase of the reaction. Water has but little influence on the reaction, and considerable quantities must be introduced before differences greater than those due to experimental error are noticeable. The quantity of lead dioxide formed diminishes as the ratio $NaOH : PbO$ increases, and with sufficient sodium hydroxide the lead dioxide formed is immediately decomposed. R. F. Weinland and A. Gutmann found that sodium thiosulphate, at ordinary temp. or when heated, does not act on sodium or potassium plumbite. M. H. Klaproth found that metallic lead is precipitated from the soln. by phosphorus and zinc, but not by iron ; and N. W. Fischer showed that tin precipitates all the lead from a soln. of potassium plumbite. H. Erdmann and P. Köthner said that acetylene gives no precipitate with a soln. of potassium plumbite ; an alkaline soln. of chromic oxide was found by G. Chancel to give a precipitate ; and A. Streng obtained precipitates with similar soln. of stannous or stannic oxide, arsenious oxide, and antimonous oxide. T. hondelli found that iron and steel are superficially oxidized by a soln. of sodium plumbite. J. G. F. Druce could not obtain a *methyl plumbite* by treating potassium plumbite with methyl iodide ; only potassium and lead iodides, and methyl alcohol were formed. According to A. Bonnet, when cotton is mordanted with an alkali plumbite and then washed with a large quantity of water, dissociation takes place, and the fibre becomes charged with lead dioxide, which partially oxidizes and destroys it. A similar change takes place with plumbates, except that the fibre is not oxidized, lead monoxide being deposited.

According to C. W. G. Karsten,[2] lead oxide dissolves in aq. ammonia or ammonium carbonate, forming a dark yellow liquid which decomposes on evaporation. G. C. Wittstein said that the soln. is turbid. There is no evidence of an *ammonium plumbite* or of *lead amminoxide*, although F. C. Calver reported such.

According to C. W. G. Karsten,[3] lead oxide unites with cuprous oxide when the two compounds are fused ; and a similar product, *cuprous plumbite*, is said to be formed by fusing cupric oxide with a proportionate quantity of lead ; if the lead is in excess, some copper is also formed. A similar product is obtained by fusing copper with lead oxide. An alloy of copper and lead is formed at the same time and part of the lead remains unreduced even when the copper is in large excess. The dark-coloured, fused mass formed in the cupellation of cupriferous silver with lead is said to contain *cupric plumbite*. S. Glasstone failed to make copper plumbite. P. Berthier examined the fusibility of mixtures of lead oxide with cuprous and cupric oxides. J. C. J. Cunningham melted mixtures of lead oxide (m.p. 875°)

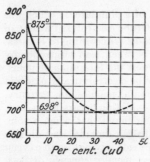

FIG. 65.—Freezing-point Curve of Mixtures of Lead and Cupric Oxides.

and cupric oxide and found a eutectic of 698° and about 30 per cent. of cupric oxide. The ascending branch on the cupric oxide side could not be determined—Fig. 65. No evidence of chemical combination appeared. F. Wöhler described a compound of silver and lead oxides with the composition of a *silver plumbite*, $Ag_2O.2PbO$, which he obtained by adding potassium hydroxide and silver nitrate to a soln. of potassium plumbite, or potassium hydroxide to a mixed soln. of silver and lead salts. The yellow precipitate is freed from free lead oxide by the solvent action of an excess of the precipitant. The product readily dissolves in nitric acid ; it blackens in light ; decomposes into lead oxide and metallic silver at a red heat, and is reduced to an alloy of silver and lead when heated in a current of hydrogen.

J. Krutwig's product, using sodium hydroxide as precipitant, has a composition $Ag_2O.PbO.2H_2O$. H. Rose, and E. Aston found the precipitate to have a variable composition ; and H. Rose also obtained a product of variable composition by the action of moist silver oxide on a soln. of lead nitrate or acetate. According to F. Bullnheimer, **silver plumbite**, $Pb(OAg)_2$, is produced by adding excess of a soln. of lead nitrate in aq. potash-lye to a soln. of silver nitrate in aq. potash-lye, with just so much ammonia that no precipitate forms at once when this soln. is mixed with the lead soln., about 2 grms. of lead nitrate being added for every gram of silver nitrate. The mixture is warmed gently on the water-bath, when a crust of small needles with the above composition is deposited. P. Groth gave for the axial ratios of the rhombic crystals $a : b : c = 0.73 : 1 : 0.79$. F. Bullnheimer found the sp. gr. to be 8·6 ; the crystals are stable towards light, but when heated to 140°–150°, they become greyish-black and only lose a little in weight at 400°. Decomposition into silver, lead oxide, and oxygen occurs on melting. The plumbite is insoluble in water, aq. ammonia, or potash-lye ; it is precipitated by potassium hydroxide as a yellow powder from its soln. in acetic acid. It is readily soluble in dil. nitric acid, conc. sulphuric, hydrofluoric, or hydriodic acid ; it is very stable towards dil. sulphuric or hydrochloric acid. When triturated, it gives an olive-green powder.

According to C. W. G. Karsten,[4] and C. L. Berthollet, lead oxide dissolves in a hot soln. of lime-water, forming a yellow liquid, which, on evaporation, furnishes small spiculæ, once thought to be *calcium plumbite*. They have a caustic taste, and are slightly soluble in water, forming a soln. which blackens wool, nails, and horn. C. W. G. Karsten also found that baryta-water forms with lead oxide a deep yellow soln. of *barium plumbite*, which decomposes into its constituent oxides on evaporation. E. Aston was not able to prepare *strontium plumbite* or the plumbites of the other alkaline earths by adding a conc. boiling soln. of the hydroxide to a lead salt. Crystalline scales of lead oxide were deposited in every case.

G. Grube obtained a mixture, $2MgO.PbO.3H_2O$, or *magnesium plumbite*, by the oxidation of magnesium hemiplumbide in the presence of moisture. P. Berthier heated mixtures of lead and zinc oxides, but no *zinc plumbite* was isolated. S. Glasstone attempted to make *mercury plumbite*, and *tin plumbite*, but without success. He considered the ordinary hydrated monoxide to be *lead plumbite—vide supra*. P. Berthier failed to make *manganese plumbite*, and *iron plumbite*; nor was J. A. Hedvall able to make *cobalt plumbite*. J. J. Berzelius added ammonia to a mixed soln. of nickel and lead salts; and excess of ammonia does not extract the nickel oxide from the precipitate which was thought to be *nickel plumbite*.

REFERENCES.

[1] C. L. Berthollet, *Ann. Chim. Phys.*, (1), 1. 52, 1789; T. Bergman, *De attractionibus electivis*, Upsala, 1775; N. G. Chatterji and N. R. Dhar, *Chem. News*, 121. 253, 1920; A. Hantzsch, *Zeit. anorg. Chem.*, 30. 289, 338, 1902; W. Herz, *ib.*, 28. 474, 1900; J. Raubenbauer, *ib.*, 30 331, 1902; H. Erdmann and P. Köthner, *ib.*, 18. 53, 1898; P. Köthner, *Ueber Ruthenium*, Halle, 1896; E. Bert and G. Austerweil, *Zeit. Elektrochem.*, 13. 165, 1907; G. Grube, *ib.*, 28. 273, 1922; C. Liebenoff, *ib.*, 2. 420, 1896; M. P. Applebey and R. D. Reid, *Journ. Chem. Soc.*, 121. 2129, 1922; S. Glasstone, *ib.*, 119. 1689, 1914, 1921; 121. 58, 1922; E. Aston, *ib.*, 59. 1093, 1891; J. K. Wood, *ib.*, 97. 887, 1910; G. Carrara and G. B. Vespignani, *Gazz. Chim. Ital.*, 30. ii, 62, 1900; N. W. Fischer, *Pogg. Ann.*, 9. 263, 1827; G. Chancel, *Compt. Rend.*, 43. 927, 1856; S. Meunier, *ib.*, 60. 1234, 1865; A. Bonnet. *ib.*, 117. 518, 1893; A. Streng, *Liebig's Ann.*, 129. 238, 1864; C. W. G. Karsten, *Scherer's Journ.*, 5. 535, 1801; M. H. Klaproth, *Gehlen's Journ.*, 2. 501, 1803; J. Milbauer, *Chem. Ztg.*, 38. 566, 1914; F. Jirsa, *Zeit. phys. Chem.*, 94. 1, 1920; E. Müller, E. Reissmann, and O. Ballin, *ib.*, 114. 129, 1924; T. Rondelli, *Brit. Pat. No.* 137436, 1919; O. Seidel, *Ueber einige Verbindungen des Bleihyperoxyds (der Bleisäure)*, Breslau, 1878; *Journ. prakt. Chem.*, (2), 20. 201, 1879; A. C. Cumming, *Trans. Faraday Soc.*, 2. 210, 1907; J. G. F. Druce, *Chem. News*, 124. 215, 1922; V. Zotier, *Bull. Soc. Chim.*, (4), 13. 61, 1913; A. Gutmann, *Ueber den Abbau der Thiosulfate und einiger Polythionate zu Sulfiten durch reducierende Salze in alkalischer Lösung und über einige Monosulfoxyarsenate*, München, 1897; R. F. Weinland and A. Gutmann, *Zeit. anorg. Chem.*, 17. 409, 1898.

[2] C. W. G. Karsten, *Scherer's Journ.*, 5. 515, 1801; G. C. Wittstein, *Repert. Pharm.*, 63. 329, 1833; F. C. Calvert, *Compt. Rend.*, 22. 480, 1846.

[3] C. W. G. Karsten, *Schweigger's Journ.*, 66. 395, 1832; H. Rose, *Pogg. Ann.*, 101. 505, 1857; F. Wöhler, *ib.*, 41. 344, 1837; P. Groth, *Chemische Krystallographie*, Leipzig, 2. 296, 1908; J. Krutwig, *Ber.*, 15. 307, 1264, 1882; F. Bullnheimer, *ib.*, 31. 1287, 1898; E. Aston, *Journ. Chem. Soc.*, 59. 1093, 1891; S. Glasstone, *ib.*, 121. 58, 1922; J. C. J. Cunningham, *Zeit. anorg. Chem.*, 89, 48, 1914; P. Berthier, *Traité des essais par la voie sèche*, Paris, 1. 513, 1834; *Ann. Mines*, (1), 11. 483, 1825.

[4] C. W. G. Karsten, *Scherer's Journ.*, 5. 515, 1801; C. L. Berthollet, *Ann. Chem. Phys.*, (1), 1. 52, 1789; E. Aston, *Journ. Chem. Soc.*, 59. 1094; 1891; S. Glasstone, *ib.*, 121. 58, 1922; G. Grube, *Zeit. anorg. Chem.*, 44. 117, 1905; J. A. Hedvall, *ib.*, 93. 316, 1915; P. Berthier, *Traité des essais par la voie sèche*, Paris, 1. 513, 1834; J. J. Berzelius, *Schweigger's Journ.*, 32. 156, 1821; J. G. F. Druce, *Chem. News*, 124. 215, 1922.

§ 17. The Higher Oxides of Lead

A number of higher oxides of lead have been reported—Pb_4O_5, Pb_3O_4, Pb_5O_6, Pb_5O_7, Pb_2O_3, Pb_5O_8, and PbO_2. For Pb_3O_4 and PbO_2, *vide infra*, but the evidence of the chemical individuality of many of the other oxides is not satisfactory. W. Reinders and L. Hamburger [1] consider that lead monoxide and lead dioxide are end-members of a series of solid soln., and that the intermediate oxides with $Pb : O = 4 : 5, 5 : 7, 2 : 3$, and $5 : 8$ are arbitrary steps in the series.

G. J. Mulder, J. Löwe, and J. J. Houton-Labillardière found that many samples of commercial red-lead approximated in composition to *lead tetritapentoxide*, Pb_4O_5; and A. P. West considered that commercial red-lead contains PbO, Pb_3O_4, and Pb_4O_5. G. Kassner went so far as to make assumptions on the constitution of this product on the assumption that it is a true compound, and not imperfectly oxidized red-lead. C. R. A. Wright and A. P. Luff [2] found that a commercial sample of red-lead had the composition Pb_5O_8, and when heated in an atm. of carbon dioxide for 4 hrs. at 200°, no carbonate was formed. It was therefore concluded that the material was a definite com pound—*lead pentitahexoxide*—because had it been a mixture of Pb_3O_4 and $2PbO$, some carbonate would have been formed. The experiment is not an adequate proof of the conclusion. R. Brauner reported *lead pentitaheptoxide*, $3PbO.2PbO_2.3H_2O$, or $Pb_5O_7.3H_2O$ or $Pb_5(OH)_6O_4$, to be formed by treating a soln. of lead nitrate with an excess of hydrogen dioxide, and after filtration treating the liquid with dil. potassium hydroxide. The same compound was reported by J. Milbauer; and F. Fischer and H. Plötze obtained a similar product by the action of oxygen at 375° and 100 atm. press. on a mixture of equal vol. of lead oxide and potassium hydroxide. The product is orange-yellow; and, according to W. Reinders and L. Hamburger, it is not stable above 440°. B. Brauner said that it is not changed by a cold soln. of potassium hydroxide, but dissolves in the hot soln. It reacts with various reagents more quickly than lead sesquioxide or red-lead.

F. Fischer and H. Plötze heated lead carbonate to 400°–450° in oxygen under a 100 atm press. The dark brown product has a composition corresponding with *lead pentitoctoxide*, Pb_5O_8. Lead hydroxide, or dioxide, can be used in place of the carbonate, but not red-lead. Alkali hydroxides, carbonates, or borates act as catalytic agents. At 500°, it forms red-lead. They regard the Pb_5O_8 oxide as *lead pyroplumbate*, $Pb_2(Pb_3O_8)$; but W. Reinders and L. Hamburger consider the product to be a chance member of a series of solid soln. G. Kassner said that lead pyroplumbate:

$$Pb\underset{O}{\overset{O}{<}}{>}Pb\underset{O}{\overset{O}{<}}{>}\mathbf{Pb}\underset{O}{\overset{O}{<}}{>}Pb\underset{O}{\overset{O}{<}}{>}Pb$$

serves to bring lead into line with silicon in the production of poly-acids. The only known poly-acid of tin is $H_2Sn_5O_{11}$. While the polysilicates are decomposed when heated with water under press., the polyplumbates are produced by the hydrothermal treatment of the orthoplumbates.

G. C. Winkelblech [3] found that sodium hypochlorite first precipitates from soln. of lead salts a reddish-yellow mixture of lead chloride and **lead sesquioxide,** or **lead hemitrioxide,** Pb_2O_3, and if the warm mixture is allowed to stand for some time it furnishes lead dioxide. To obtain the sesquioxide free from chloride, lead nitrate or acetate is treated with a sufficient excess of potassium hydroxide to redissolve the precipitate, and the soln. treated with sodium chloride. The yellow precipitate is then washed and dried. J. F. L. Hausmann employed a similar method of preparation, and he found that the product is not completely dehydrated at 140°–150°. F. Jirsa electrolyzed a soln. of 40 grms. of potassium hydroxide and 4·5 grms. of lead monoxide per litre, with palladium electrodes, using an alternating current. Yellow lead sesquioxide was deposited, and a soln. of lead metaplumbate was formed—*vide* lead plumbite. F. Fischer and H. Plötze regard this oxide as *lead metaplumbate*, $Pb(PbO_3)$.

M. Höhnel obtained the sesquioxide by the action of a soln. of lead acetate on calcium plumbate; H. Bollenbach, by the action of potassium permanganate on a soln. of sodium plumbite; V. A. Jacquelain, by pouring a soln. of red-lead in acetic acid into a dil. soln. of ammonia, washing the product with hot water and a little very dil. acetic acid, and drying at 100°; and L. Marino, by the action of 3 per cent. nitric acid on a soln. of lead pyroselenate in sodium hydroxide. H. Debray obtained it by heating lead dioxide at 350°; T. Carnelley and J. Walker worked at 280°–290°; and F. Fischer and H. Plötze by the action of oxygen at 100 atm. press., on lead monoxide at 410°–480°, but not on lead dioxide or red-lead at that temp.

According to E. Frémy, and O. Seidel, when alkaline soln. of potassium plumbate and plumbite are mixed, the precipitate, after washing and drying over sulphuric acid, has the composition of *lead trihydroxide*, $Pb_2O_3.3H_2O$, or $Pb(OH)_3$. E. Frémy regarded it as a hydrated form of red-lead. G. Grube, O. Seidel, S. Glasstone, and L. Bellucci and N. Parravano obtained this substance by a somewhat analogous process. The colour is variously described as yellowish-brown, and orange-yellow. E. Zintl and A. Raach tested the theory that the colour of compounds is due to the vibration of atoms or the oscillatory change in valency within the molecule of lead hemitrioxide by means of radioactive indicators. If such oscillations occur in a compound containing inactive quadrivalent lead and induced active bivalent lead, a regular distribution of the radioactive isotopes over all the lead atoms is to be expected. A preparation of lead hemitrioxide with incited bivalent lead yields, after treatment with nitric acid, bi- and quadri-valent lead of equal activity, but the experiment is regarded as inconclusive since atomic exchange during the production or decomposition of the hemitrioxide is not improbable. If, however, lead hemitrioxide is obtained by the precipitation of a 3N-alkaline soln. of inactive plumbate with a 3N-alkaline soln. of radioactively incited plumbite and the precipitate, after being illuminated during 3 hrs., is dissolved in 12N-alkali hydroxide, a soln. is obtained from which barium hydroxide precipitates barium plumbate of such small activity that it can be attributed only to co-precipitated barium plumbite. An oscillatory exchange in the mol., $Pb_2O_3.3H_2O$, is therefore considered not to occur under the influence of light.

According to S. Glasstone, the different methods of preparation of lead sesqui-oxide involve the oxidation of alkali plumbite to plumbate—by chlorine, bromine, iodine, hydrogen dioxide, potassium persulphate, etc.—or the reduction of alkali plumbate to plumbite—by nascent hydrogen from zinc dust or aluminium powder, or from sodium stannite or sulphite. He found the most satisfactory mode of preparing the hydrated sesquioxide to be as follows:

Sodium hydroxide soln. (250 c.c. of 12 per cent.) sat. with lead monoxide was dil. to 500 c.c., and 500 c.c. of sat. bromine water were added. The mixture was kept over-night and then washed by decantation with water containing a little acetic acid to remove the excess of hypobromite and alkali. A paste of the precipitate and water was stirred into a soln. of 60 grms. of sodium hydroxide in 300 c.c. of water, warmed at 50°. The liquid was filtered, 40 grms. of acetic acid diluted with 150 c.c. of water were slowly added to the cold filtrate with continual stirring, and the gelatinous, yellowish-brown precipitate obtained was washed by decantation and filtered by the aid of the pump. Before drying, a small portion of the precipitate was analyzed in order to determine the ratio of dioxide to monoxide. If the precipitate still contained excess of monoxide, it was redissolved in alkali and again precipitated with acid. On drying in a desiccator, the sesquioxide darkened in colour and shrunk into small lumps, which gave a brown powder by gentle grinding; with fine grinding the colour became somewhat lighter.

S. Glasstone's analysis agreed with $Pb_2O_3.3H_2O$. A. Hutchinson and W. Pollard regarded lead sesquioxide as *plumbous metaplumbate*, $Pb(PbO_3)$; or, as L. Bellucci and N. Parravano expressed it, the hydrated sesquioxide is plumbous metaplumbate, $Pb[Pb(OH)_6]$. L. Marino considered the sesquioxide to be an oxide of quadrivalent lead; and, with less probability, it can be regarded as an oxide of bivalent lead:

$$Pb{<}{{O}\atop{O}}{>}Pb{=}O \qquad O{<}{{Pb{\equiv}O}\atop{Pb{\equiv}O}} \qquad O{<}{{Pb{-}O}\atop{Pb{-}O}}$$

G. C. Winkelblech said that lead sesquioxide is a non-crystalline reddish-yellow powder which holds hygroscopic water so very tenaciously that it is removed only slowly by heating the product in vacuo. O. Seidel said that the hydrated oxide does not change perceptibly in air, and at 160°–190° it becomes brown, and loses a mol of water. L. Bellucci and N. Parravano found it lost a mol of water at 170°, and the whole of the water is given off at a higher temp. and at the same time some oxygen is lost and lead monoxide formed. As indicated above, the dehydration of the sesquioxide is probably attended by its decomposition into a mixture of monoxide and dioxide. The colour is not changed at 100°, and V. A. Jacquelain found that it darkened without giving off oxygen at 150°. T. Carnelley and J. Walker observed no loss of oxygen below 360°, but at 360°–415°, it forms red-lead; and G. C. Winkelblech observed that at a red-heat it furnishes lead monoxide and oxygen. H. Debray said that the greenish-brown sesquioxide passes slowly into red-lead at 350°, and rapidly at 440°. J. F. L. Hausmann showed that the oxide absorbs carbon dioxide from the air without changing colour; and G. C. Winkelblech showed that it is reduced to the monoxide by oxalic or formic acid; and that when heated with nitric, sulphuric, hydrofluosilicic, or acetic acid it forms a yellow liquid from which it is precipitated by alkalies; on standing a few minutes, however, the liquid decomposes—*e.g.* with hydrochloric acid into free chlorine and lead chloride. O. Seidel obtained similar results. H. Schulze found that sodium sulphite changes the sesquioxide lemon-yellow, and then white, forming a mixture of lead sulphite and sulphate. E. Müller and H. Barck said that at 200° the sesquioxide is decomposed by nitric oxide.

O. Seidel found that a boiling aq. soln. of potassium hydroxide first dissolves some lead monoxide and afterwards some lead dioxide. S. Glasstone said that the sesquioxide is soluble in the alkali-lye, but not so soluble as the monoxide, while the dioxide is almost insoluble. The boiling soln. in alkali-lye precipitates lead dioxide, and alkali plumbate remains in soln. The soln. of the sesquioxide in alkali-lye contains plumbite and plumbate, for, on boiling such a mixture, similar results are obtained. Hence, the dissolution of the sesquioxide in an alkali may be represented as a balanced reaction, $Pb_2O_3.3H_2O_{solid}+3OH'\rightleftharpoons HPbO'_2+Pb(OH)_6{}^{..}+H_2O$. Hence, $[HPbO'_2][Pb(OH)_6{}'']=K[OH']^3$, where K is constant. The solubility of the sesquioxide in alkaline soln. of varying conc., expressed in mols per litre, shows that :

NaOH	Plumbite	Plumbate	$K \times 10^6$
1·20	0·00875	0·000412	2·09
1·26	0·01212	0·000350	2·08
1·79	0·00160	0·011500	3·20
2·41	0·02000	0·001200	1·72
2·63	0·02150	0·002650	3·12

The electrode potential of mixtures of alkali plumbite and plumbate is of the order 0·30 volt, with the hydrogen electrode, at 17° ; and the potential of the electrode $Pt\,|\,Pb_2O_3.H_2O,\ PbO_2\,|\ N\text{-}NaOH$, with the hydrogen electrode, is 0·302 volt at 17°. S. Glasstone hence computed the free energy of the reaction : $2PbO_2+H_2=Pb_2O_3+H_2O$ to be $2·224 \times 96540$ joules ; and for $PbO_2+PbO \rightarrow Pb_2O_3$, $0·068 \times 96540$ joules ; for $Pb_2O_3+PbO \rightarrow Pb_3O_4$, $0·160 \times 96540$ joules ; and for $PbO_2+2PbO \rightarrow Pb_3O_4$, $0·228 \times 96540$ joules.

REFERENCES.

[1] W. Reinders and L. Hamburger, *Zeit. anorg. Chem.*, **89**. 71, 1914 ; J. Löwe, *Dingler's Journ.*, **271**. 472, 1889 ; G. J. Mulder, *Scheikund. Onderzoek.*, 5. 410, 1850 ; *Journ. prakt. Chem.*, (1), 50. 438, 1850 ; G. Kassner, *Arch. Pharm.*, **228**. 177, 1890 ; J. J. Houton-Labillardière, *Ann. Chim. Phys.*, (2), 35. 96, 1827 ; A. P. West, *Philippine Journ. Science*. 8. 429, 1913.

[2] C. R. A. Wright and A. P. Luff, *Journ. Chem. Soc.*, 33. 504, 1878 ; B. Brauner, *Ber. Böhm. Ges.*, 259, 1885 ; *Zeit. anorg. Chem.*, 7. 2, 1894 ; W. Reinders and L. Hamburger, *ib.*, 89. 95, 1914 ; F. Fischer and H. Plötze, *ib.*, 75. 21, 1912 ; J. Milbauer, *Chem. Ztg.*, 38. 566, 587, 1914 ; G. Grube. *Zeit. Elektrochem.*, 28. 285. 1922.

[3] J. F. L. Hausmann, *Liebig's Ann.*, **91**. 235, 1854 ; G. C. Winkelblech, *ib.*, 21. 21, 1837 ; *Journ. prakt. Chem.*, (1), **10**. 227, 1837 ; O. Seidel, *ib.*, (2), 20. 203, 1879 ; *Ueber einige Verbind-ungen des Bleihyperoxydes (der Bleisäure)*, Breslau, 1878 ; H. Debray, *Compt. Rend.*, 86. 513, 1878 ; V. A. Jacquelain, *ib.*, 31. 626, 1850 ; A. Hutchinson and W Pollard, *Journ. Chem. Soc.*, 69. 226, 1896 ; T. Carnelley and J. Walker, *ib.*, 53. 59, 1888 ; S. Glasstone, *ib.*, 121. 1456, 1922 ; W. Reinders and L. Hamburger, *Zeit. anorg. Chem.*, 89. 71, 1914 ; F. Fischer and H. Plötze, *ib.*, 75. 16, 1912 ; E. Müller and H. Barck, *ib.*, 129. 309, 1923 ; L. Bellucci and N. Parravano, *ib.*, 50. 112, 1906 ; *Atti Accad. Lincei*, (5), 14. i, 382, 1905 ; *Gazz. Chim Ital.*, 35. ii, 500, 1905 ; L. Marino, *ib.*, 39. i, 640, 1909 ; *Atti Accad. Lincei*, (5), 17. i, 863, 1908 ; *Zeit. anorg. Chem.*, 59. 456, 1908 ; 62. 174, 1909 ; H. Schulze, *Jena. Zeit.*, 1. 428, 1864 ; M. Höhnel, *Arch. Pharm.*, 234. 399, 1896 ; H. Bollenbach, *Zeit. anal. Chem.*, 46. 584, 1907 ; E. Frémy, *Ann. Chim. Phys.*, (3), 12. 488, 1844 ; G. Grube, *Zeit. Elektrochem.*, 28. 273, 1922 ; F. Jirsa, *Zeit. phys. Chem.*, 94. 1, 1920 ; E. Zintl and A. Raach, *Ber.*, 57. B, 1739, 1924.

§ 18. Red-lead, or Minium

The preparation of **red-lead**, Pb_3O_4, is described by Vitruvius in his *De archi-tectura* (7. 12, c. 15 B.C.). He called it *sandaraca*, and stated that it was accidentally discovered, for some jars of ceruse or white-lead, for use as a cosmetic, were con-verted into red-lead during a fire ; and it was afterwards made by roasting ceruse

—cerussa si coquatur rusescit. Dioscorides, in his *De materia medica* (**5**. 103, c. A.D. 75), also said that it is made by heating white-lead in the following manner:

> Put a new earthen vessel, preferably an Attic one, over coals ; sprinkle it with powdered ceruse, stir constantly, and when it has acquired the colour of ashes, remove and cool it for use. If you desire to burn it, place the powdered product in a hollow platter, and having set this on coals, stir with an iron rod until the product has acquired the colour of sandarach. Then remove it from the fire, and use the product.

Pliny, in his *Historia naturalis* (**34**. 54 ; **35**. 20, c. A.D. 77), repeated much of what had been said by Vitruvius and Dioscorides. He confused red-lead, or *cerussa usta*, as he called it, with many other red substances—*purpurea rubica* (iron oxide), *cinnabaris* (the resin of the *dracæna cinnabari*), *sil marmoreum crematum* (calcined ochre), *minium* (cinnabar), and *sandaraca* (red orpiment, or arsenic sulphide). Dioscorides pointed out that *minium* and *cinnabaris* can be distinguished by heating, when the former gives off a suffocating vapour from which the operator should be protected by covering his face with a bladder. Minium (mercuric sulphide), we are told, was adulterated with red-lead, and in time the adulterant alone received the name *minium*—the term minium being now applied to red-lead, and not to cinnabar, vermilion, or mercuric sulphide. Pliny said that about 320 B.C. a painter called Nicias first used red-lead as a pigment. The term *miniature* has now lost all trace of its association with red-lead used in painting. It is not known who found that red-lead could be prepared from litharge or from metallic lead ; as previously indicated, the fact is mentioned in the Latin, twelfth-century, translations of Geber's *Summa perfectionis magisterii ;* in Albertus Magnus' *Compositum de compositis ;* and in works by subsequent writers.

G. Agricola's [1] *minium nativum* was cinnabar. The occurrence of red-lead or minium in nature has been indicated in connection with litharge. [2] It has been reported from the Isle of Anglesey, Wales ; from Grassington Moor, and Weardale, England ; Leadhills, Scotland ; Bleialf, Eifel ; Badenweiler, Baden ; Brillon, Westphalia ; Zmeinogorsk, Siberia ; Zimapan, Mexico ; Wythe Co., Virginia ; Alturas Co., Idaho ; Leadville, Colorado ; etc.

Red-lead is formed when lead monoxide at a dull red heat is exposed for a considerable time to air. According to P. A. von Bonsdorff,[3] when lead-shavings in contact with water, and protected from dust, are exposed to the air for some months, the red-lead appears on those surfaces which are directly exposed to the air. Drawings made on paper with metallic lead are stated by P. A. von Bonsdorff to have acquired a red colour owing to the oxidation of the film of lead. J. J. Nöggerath, and A. Levol made confirmatory observations. According to J. Milbauer, the air of towns forms only a basic carbonate ; but sea-air oxidizes the lead further ; and the presence of ozone is particularly favourable to the production of red-lead ; and according to J. B. Huffard and P. E. Haynes, compressed oxygen accelerates the reaction. E. J. Kohlmeyer observed some red-lead to be formed on lead which had been embedded in cement. C. F. Schönbein found that lead precipitated by zinc and washed, when exposed to the vapour from aq. ammonia and air, becomes covered with a film of red-lead, and lead carbonate. O. W. Brown and A. R. Nees found that when spongy lead obtained by electrodeposition, ordinary lead, and atomized lead are oxidized in a rotating furnace at different temp. up to 500°, the finer particles are converted into red-lead, while the larger ones are merely coated with oxide ; the product was ground, the finer particles were separated by levigation, and the residue was roasted again. The product was again ground and levigated. The finer portions, reddish-brown in colour, were roasted for 3–4 hrs. at 430°–450°, when they yielded brilliant, amorphous red-lead. J. A. Wilkinson found that sodium dioxide quickly converts molten lead into red-lead.

G. Kassner showed that when lead monoxide is exposed to the action of light and moist oxygen at ordinary temp., red-lead is formed. J. Milbauer found that ozonized air converts lead hydroxide or carbonate, moistened with sodium or potassium hydroxide, first to a honey-yellow oxide and then to red-lead. According to J. B. A. Dumas, when finely divided massicot is heated for 24 hrs. or more either on the flat hearth of a reverberatory furnace, or in vessels with wide mouths projecting from the side of the furnace, and the mass frequently stirred, red-lead is formed provided the temp. does not rise above dull redness. Ordinary litharge is so dense that it oxidizes much more slowly than massicot; and massicot in turn oxidizes more slowly than the softer oxide obtained by heating white-lead. Thus, after three firings, each of 24 hrs.' duration, the red-lead from massicot contained 58 per cent. of Pb_3O_4, while that obtained under similar conditions from white-lead contained 95·3 per cent. H. Hocking worked with air under pressure. On a manufacturing scale, lead is first drossed into massicot at about 340°, and afterwards oxidized; and then heated at a higher temp.—near 500°—until a sample, on cooling, has the required tint. The red-lead is then withdrawn, sieved, and levigated. A small proportion of white-lead from the stack process, which is rejected because of stains, is worked for red-lead either alone or mixed with the ordinary materials.

V. A. Jacquelain showed that lead oxide at 450° in air is slowly converted into red-lead. M. Liebig said that the temp. should not exceed 350°. H. le Chatelier found the dissociation press. of red-lead to be 5 mm. at 455°; 60 mm. at 500°; 183 mm. at 555°; and 763 mm. at 636°. The partial press. of the oxygen in air is about 150 mm., so that red-lead cannot be formed in air above 550°, and oxidation of litharge occurs most rapidly at about 500°. When red-lead is heated, T. Carnelley and J. Walker found that it becomes redder, then violet and black, and on cooling again it resumes its scarlet-red colour; it is stable at 530°. O. W. Brown and A. R. Nees found lead monoxide is converted into red-lead rapidly and completely when heated in air at 525°–530°. J. Milbauer said that in the presence of oxygen, decomposition begins at 470°, and a state of equilibrium occurs in about 3 hrs.: $Pb_3O_4 \rightleftharpoons 3PbO + \frac{1}{2}O_2$; in vacuo, the oxide is completely decomposed at 530°; and in 2 hrs. at 550°. Red-lead cannot exist in oxygen at 600°; in air at 565°; and in carbon dioxide at 550°. No red-lead is obtained from litharge at 450°, the product is always brown; and between 450° and 550°, the product is red. The optimum temp. is 470°. Small amounts of impurities in the litharge have a marked effect on the rate of oxidation. Nitric acid and ammonia reduce the rate of oxidation one-third and one-seventh respectively; small amounts of sodium nitrate slightly accelerate the reaction; 0·1 per cent. of lead nitrate produces a fine pink colour; and 0·1 per cent. of sodium hydroxide gives an intense red. J. Milbauer also found that silver facilitates the oxidation at 300°, but has no appreciable effect at higher temp.; zinc, and antimony act unfavourably; while bismuth was said to be inert— O. Herting, on the contrary, said bismuth interferes with the reaction. He said that red-lead made from lead carbonate is reduced at 475°, but O. W. Brown and A. R. Nees could not confirm this. They found that yellow litharge oxidized more slowly than the red variety, and if litharge be treated with water, dil. tannic acid, or a dil. soln. of glue, the rate of oxidation is much decreased. J. Milbauer found that an increase of 10° in the temp. multiplied the rate of reaction by about 1·05. The slopes of the curves in Fig. 66, by O. W. Brown and A. R. Nees,

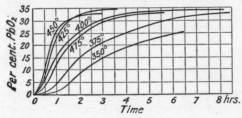

FIG. 66.—Speeds of Oxidation of Lead Monoxide (as PbO_2) at Different Temperatures.

represent the speed of the reaction, dx/dt, at the temp. named, where red-lead is regarded as a compound of PbO and PbO_2, so that the higher the proportion of lead dioxide, x, in the product, the greater the proportion of red-lead formed. The most favourable temp. is clearly 425°. W. Reinders and L. Hamburger found the dissociation press., p mm., $Pb_3O_4 \rightleftharpoons 3PbO_{yellow} + \frac{1}{2}O_2$, at different temp. to be:

	444·8°	484·4°	511·2°	537·6°	558·3°	588·1°	600·7°	607°
p · · ·	8·4	30·4	76·0	155	270	589	859	1045

The results were represented by $\log_{10} p = -7·8595 T^{-1} + 11·8976$; or $\log_{10} p = -7·0895 T^{-1} + 1·751 \log T + 0·000216 T + 2·8$. The dissociation press. curve is smooth, and gives no evidence of solid soln. or of intermediate oxides. F. A. Henglein gave for the partial press., p, of oxygen for $2Pb_3O_4 \rightarrow 6PbO + O_2$, $\log p = -1373281 T^{-1·8611} + 4·6222$ mm.

C. Zenghelis said that at ordinary temp. red-lead is more volatile than lead monoxide. The dissociation press. at 17° is $6·6 \times 10^{-19}$ atm., S. Glasstone calculated $3·3 \times 10^{-19}$ atm. from the data for the e.m.f. of cells with Pb_3O_4 electrodes. He also gave for the dissociation press. at 0·21 atm. (the partial press. of oxygen in air), 570°–573°; W. Reinders and L. Hamburger's value is 539°. C. Schubert, and W. Stahl gave 510°–640° for the temp. at which red-lead forms oxygen and lead oxide. A. Bouzat gave 300 mm. for the dissociation press. at 585°, and 700 mm. at 632°. F. Fischer and H. Plötze showed that at 530° under a press. of 100 atm. of oxygen, red-lead is not changed between 280° and 410°, and at 530°, lead monoxide is rapidly converted into red-lead. With the time constant, 2 hrs., the proportion of red-lead present at different temp. when lithge is heated in air is shown in Fig. 67, by O. W. Brown and A. R. Nees. This again shows that the most favourable temp. for the oxidation of lead monoxide is 425°.

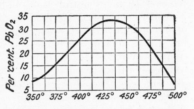

FIG. 67.—Proportion of Red-lead (as PbO_2) formed from Lead Monoxide at Different Temperatures.

O. W. Brown and A. R. Nees found that red-lead is best obtained from lead dioxyhydroxide in the vicinity of 450°. J. Milbauer, O. W. Brown and A. R. Nees, L. Michel, and G. Jansen found lead carbonates to be suitable for the preparation of red-lead at 425°–430° because of the fine state of subdivision and the flocculent nature of the resulting monoxide formed before it is converted to red-lead. M. Alsburg prepared red-lead by heating lead oxide mixed with lead nitrate; A. Levol, by heating a mixture of 4 parts of litharge (derived from white-lead), one of potassium chlorate, and 8 parts of potassium nitrate—brown lead dioxide is first produced, and by further heating to dull redness, red-lead is formed. The cold mass was well-boiled with distilled water. C. L. P. Burton used a modification of the process. A small amount of red-lead is manufactured as a by-product in the preparation of sodium nitrite by fusing sodium nitrate with lead or litharge. J. Milbauer found potassium chlorate or bromate converts litharge into red-lead at 470°, but not so potassium iodate.

W. Reinders and L. Hamburger found that the higher oxides of lead are converted into red-lead by heating them to 420°. B. Brauner found that a hot soln. of the Pb_5O_7 oxide in not too much potash-lye furnishes red-lead on cooling. The reaction was studied by W. Reinders and L. Hamburger. and J. Milbauer. The preparation of red-lead by heating mixtures of lead dioxide and monoxide, or lead dioxide alone, was studied by V. A. Jacquelain, and J. E. Mackenzie. J. Milbauer heated a mixture of 3 eq. lead monoxide, 2 eq. lead dioxide, with a soln. containing 200 grms. of potassium hydroxide per 100 c.c. of water. He also heated lead dioxide with potassium nitrate at 470°, and extracted the soluble matters with water. A. Levol boiled a soln. of potassium plumbite for 1–2 hrs. with lead dioxide, removed the excess of lead dioxide with cold oxalic acid, and the oxalic acid with alkali-lye. The process was examined by J. Milbauer, who found that oxalic acid attacks red-lead in the cold.   E. Frémy boiled a soln. of lead oxide in alkali plumbate soln., and J. Milbauer represented the reaction: $K_4PbO_4+2K_2PbO_2$ $+4H_2O=Pb_3O_4+8KOH$.   G. Grube allowed a mixture of soln. of two mols of potassium plumbite and one mol of potassium plumbate to stand in contact with $6 \cdot 9 - 12 \cdot 5N$-KOH, and after decantation, and suction, washed the precipitate with absolute alcohol, and dried it over potassium hydroxide in vacuo.   S. Glasstone allowed lead dioxide to stand in contact with spongy lead in a 15 per cent. soln. of sodium hydroxide for some months ; also a mixture of lead dioxide and monoxide in N-NaOH.

The production of the deepest and most prized shades of red-lead is considered to be a trade secret.   According to J. B. A. Dumas, commercial red-lead can be freed from the associated yellow oxide by rapidly digesting it with a soln. of lead acetate ; and J. Milbauer recommended two one-hour digestions with a 20 per cent. soln.   J. J. Berzelius, and J. Dalton recommended cold, very dil. acetic acid ; while R. Phillips said that if the acetic acid be too conc., some brown lead dioxide is produced, and J. B. A. Dumas said that the brown dioxide always appears before all the monoxide has been removed.   J. Milbauer said that dil. nitric acid is not satisfactory because of the formation of the dioxide, nor does a soln. of lead nitrate, as recommended by J. Löwe, offer any advantages over one of lead acetate. A. Levol recommended boiling the product with very dil. potash-lye, and J. Milbauer said that this process is more rapid than is the case with lead acetate, and it removes at the same time lead sulphate and carbonate, but not calcium carbonate. A 10 per cent. soln. of sodium acetate acts slowly ; while a 10 per cent. hot soln. of. ammonium oxalate decomposes red-lead.   The adulteration of red-lead with brick-dust, bole, or iron oxide, was formerly more common than it is to-day.   Most commercial red-lead is fairly pure.   There are combination red-leads on the market which have their tints brightened by an organic dye precipitated on an inert base like barytes.   The adulteration of red-lead has been discussed by W. F. Edwards, D. B. Dott, and V. Frehse.   Red-lead for use in the manufacture of vermilion is evaluated on its purity of tone, etc. ; glassmaker's red-lead should be free from metallic lead, lead sulphate, antimony, iron, and copper ; while red-lead for match-making is evaluated on its peroxide content which may vary from 28 to 33 per cent. Red-lead for accumulator plates is preferred with less than 0·005 per cent. of iron. The so-called orange-lead approximates 33 per cent. PbO_2, rather more than is the case with ordinary red-lead.   C. A. Klein gave for the composition of a good commercial red-lead : 26·5 per cent. PbO_2 ; 0·0008, Ag ; 0·006, CuO ; 0·0004, Sb_2O_4 ; 0·009, Fe_2O_3 ; 0·032, Al_2O_3 ; and 0·075, insoluble in nitric acid.   Cadmium, arsenic, and zinc were absent.   C. R. A. Wright and A. P. Luff noted that commercial red-lead gave off a little carbon-dioxide at 360°, owing to its contamination with a little organic matter.   The composition of red-lead has been discussed by M. Longchamp, J. Milbauer, J. J. Houton-Labillardière, J. Löwenthal, J. B. A. Dumas, C. L. Vlaanderen, V. A. Jacquelain, M. Liebig, W. Reinders and L. Hamburger, C. Marchese, E. Szterkhers, W. F. Edwards, D. Woodman, A. P. West, and E. E. Dunlap.   Although the composition is somewhat variable, depending on what L. N. Vauquelain called the *suroxigenation*, analyses by J. J. Berzelius, J. B. A. Dumas, and L. N. Vauquelin showed that in the limiting case, the composition is summarized by the formula Pb_3O_4.   There has been some discussion as to the constitution of the oxide.   J. B. A. Dumas regarded red-lead as *un oxide salin, un plombate de plombe, dont lequel la bas renferme la même quantité d'oxygène que l'acide, sa formule étant* $2PbO.PbO_2$.   S. Glasstone's observations on the electrochemical behaviours of the oxide agree with J. B. A. Dumas' hypotheses.   It is assumed that lead dioxide is first produced during the oxidation of litharge, and that the dioxide acts as an acid anhydride uniting with the remaining lead monoxide to form **plumbic plumbite**, $Pb(PbO_2)_2$, a salt of hydroplumbic acid, H_2PbO_2 ; or, as A. Hutchinson and W. Pollard express it, red-lead is **plumbous orthoplumbate**, Pb_2PbO_4, a salt of orthoplumbic acid,

H_4PbO_4. G. Grube had a similar opinion. G. Kassner's, A. Hutchinson and W. Pollard's, and L. Marino's formulæ are respectively :

$$Pb{<}{^O_O}{>}Pb{<}{^O_O}{>}Pb \qquad\qquad Pb{<}{^O_O}{>}Pb{<}{^O_O}{>}Pb \qquad\qquad Pb{<}{^{O-Pb{\equiv}O}_{O-Pb{\equiv}O}}$$

Plumbic plumbite, $Pb(PbO_2)_2$.   Plumbous orthoplumbate, Pb_2PbO_4.   Plumbous plumbate, $Pb(PbO_2)_2$.

F. Fischer and H. Ploetze also represented red-lead as lead orthoplumbate. D. I. Mendeléef, and A. Geuther assumed that litharge (*q.v.*) is a polymerized oxide, say, $Pb_{12}O_{12}$; and E. J. Wade, accepting this, stated that when lead monoxide is oxidized it passes successively along the stages $Pb_{12}O_{13}$, $Pb_{12}O_{14}$, $Pb_{12}O_{15}$, and when the stage $Pb_{12}O_{16}$ is reached, the product is red-lead, $(Pb_3O_4)_4$. This hypothesis is, of course, a leap in the dark. Another view of the nature of red-lead assumes that it is a mixture or solid soln. of lead monoxide and dioxide as indicated by C. A. Klein. From the effect of temp. on the speed of the reaction, J. Milbauer also considered that the oxidation of litharge is rather a physical than a chemical change, and is to be explained by the theory of solid soln. advanced by A. Horstmann ; but in their study of the dissociation press., W. Reinders and L. Hamburger observed no signs of the formation of solid soln. or of compounds other than those indicated in the equation $Pb_3O_4{\rightleftharpoons}3PbO+\frac{1}{2}O_2$. S. S. Bhatnagar, M. Prasad, and D. C. Bahl obtained **colloidal red-lead** by using soap as protective agent.

The physical properties of red-lead.—Red-lead is a scarlet-red, or brownish-red powder ; which, according to O. W. Brown and A. R. Nees,[4] is usually made up of crystals mixed with a small proportion of amorphous material, but samples can be obtained wholly amorphous or wholly crystalline. J. Milbauer observed that red-lead obtained from a hot conc. soln. of potassium hydroxide is in reddish-brown microscopic crystals ; while L. Michel found that the oxide obtained from fused alkali nitrate consists of orange-yellow prisms. When red-lead is heated the colour darkens and becomes quite black, but the original colour is restored on cooling. M. Bamberger and R. Grengg found that natural red-lead lost its colour when cooled to $-190°$. P. von Muschenbrock gave 8·94 for the sp. gr. of red-lead ; W. Herapath, 9·096 at 15° ; P. F. G. Boullay, 9·190 ; C. J. B. Karsten, 8·62. G. Hauser found the sp. gr. of red-lead and orange red-lead varied with the mode of preparation ; and O. W. Brown and A. R. Nees found the sp. gr. of 52 samples of red-lead varied between comparatively wide limits, from 8·32 to 9·16 ; they observed no relation between the crystalline form of the powder and the sp. gr. Amorphous samples have a sp. gr. from 8·66 to 8·90, and crystalline samples usually have a higher sp. gr., and as a rule the sp. gr. increases slightly with the time of heating ; and, in general, the higher the temp. at which oxidation occurs, the higher the sp. gr. The more nearly the composition of the powder approaches Pb_3O_4, the lower the sp. gr. The sp. gr. also depends on the physical nature of the starting material. O. W. Brown and co-workers found that the apparent sp. gr. or the weight of powder occupying 1 c.c. decreases by fine grinding and afterwards increases to a maximum. Thus, with finer grinding, the weight of red-lead occupying 1·484 grms. per c.c. fell to 1·226 grms. per c.c., and then rose to 1·932 grms. per c.c. F. B. Hofmann obtained a fine durable emulsion by shaking red-lead with a mixture of chloroform and water. W. Spring found that when the moist powder is compressed at 3000 atm., a little of it appeared glassy as if it had fused. The action of heat on red-lead has been previously discussed. G. Tammann noticed that mercury does not sink through powdered red-lead at temp. up to 300°.

S. Glasstone found that the $Pt\,|\,(Pb_3O_4,PbO),N\text{-}NaOH$ electrode did not behave reversibly and the values were erratic ; the electrode potential of $Pt\,|\,(Pb_3O_4),PbO_2),N\text{-}NaOH$ was 0·325 volt on the hydrogen scale at 17° ; the potential of the $Pb\,|\,Pb_3O_4,N\text{-}NaOH$ electrode was -0.610 volt at room temp. The plumbous ion concentration of red-lead in $N\text{-}NaOH$ for complete ionization : $Pb_3O_4{\rightleftharpoons}2Pb^{\cdot\cdot}+PbO_4''''$, is 2.2×10^{-17} ; the solubility of red-lead in $N\text{-}NaOH$ is 1.1×10^{-17} mol per litre at 17° ; and the solubility in water is probably of the same order of magnitude; the solubility - product of red-lead is $[Pb^{..}][PbO_4'''']=5\cdot32\times10^{-51}$. S. Glasstone found the e.m.f. of the cell $Pt\,|\,(PbO,PbO_2),N\text{-}NaOH,H_2(atm.)\,|\,Pt$ to be $1\cdot078$ volts at $17°$, and hence the free energy of the reaction $PbO_2+H_2=PbO+H_2O$ to be $2\cdot156\times96540$ joules; for the cell $Pt\,|\,(Pb_3O_4,PbO_2),N\text{-}NaOH,H_2(atm.)\,|\,Pt$ he found $1\cdot135$ volts at $17°$, and hence the free energy of the reaction : $3PbO_2+2H_2=Pb_3O_4+2H_2O$, is $4\cdot540\times96540$ joules. Consequently also for $Pb_3O_4+H_2=3PbO+H_2O$ the free energy is $1\cdot928\times96540$ joules. If the cell $Pt\,|\,(Pb_3O_4,PbO),N\text{-}NaOH,H_2(atm.)\,|\,Pt$ were reversible its e.m.f. would be $0\cdot964$ volt. S. Glasstone calculated the free energy of the reaction $3PbO+\tfrac{1}{2}O_2=Pb_3O_4$ to be 12,350 cals. or $0\cdot536\times96540$ joules at $17°$, when the total energy of the reaction is 16,750 cals. W. Schmidt found the dielectric constant to be $17\cdot8$ for $\lambda=75$ cms. S. Meyer found the magnetic susceptibility to be $-0\cdot478\times10^{-6}$, and the mol. magnetization, $-0\cdot114\times10^{-6}$.

The chemical properties of red-lead.—Red-lead is converted into lead monoxide by numerous reducing agents. H. Mennicke [5] showed that **hydrogen,** *in statu nascendi,* say from zinc and hydrochloric acid in the presence of platinum, reduces red-lead rapidly and quantitatively ; and F. Peters found that at ordinary temp., electrolytic hydrogen reduces red-lead to the metal. According to C. R. A. Wright and A. P. Luff, reduction by hydrogen begins at $230°$; I. W. Fay and co-workers found that reduction can be detected after heating red-lead in hydrogen for 6 hrs. at $170°$. P. Sabatier and L. Espil inferred that at $250°$ red-lead is reduced by hydrogen to lead hemioxide without the intermediate formation of the monoxide, and subsequently to the metal. W. Müller found that red-lead is reduced by hydrogen to the metal at $310°-315°$. For the free energy of the reaction, *vide supra.* O. Brunck found that **ozone**—*i.e.* ozonized oxygen—has very little action, and it possibly forms a little lead dioxide. C. P. van Hoek examined the hygroscopicity ; for the solubility of red-lead in **water,** and **alkali hydroxide** soln., *vide supra.* O. Seidel said that a boiling soln. of the alkali-lye first dissolves lead monoxide, and then slowly takes up the lead dioxide. P. Beck found that in the presence of nitric acid, **hydrogen dioxide** is reduced by red-lead. According to H. Moissan, **fluorine** has no action on red-lead in the cold, but when warmed, lead fluoride is formed. F. Fischer and K. Thiele found red-lead to be sparingly soluble in **hydrofluoric acid,** forming hydrofluoplumbic acid. R. Weber showed that when heated in dry **chlorine,** red-lead is readily converted into lead chloride ; A. Classen and B. Zahorsky found that liquid chlorine acts only in the presence of hydrochloric acid. C. Löwig observed that with chlorine-water, lead chloride and dioxide are formed, while **bromine** water acts in an analogous manner. A. Vogel showed that with a small proportion of **hydrochloric acid,** lead chloride, dioxide, and water are formed ; but with more acid, lead chloride, chlorine, and water are produced. L. L. de Koninck said that with conc. hydrochloric acid, lead trichloride, not tetrachloride, is formed (*q.v.*).

An aq. soln of **sulphur dioxide** was found by A. Vogel to transform red-lead into lead sulphate at ordinary temp. ; with conc. **sulphuric acid,** red-lead furnishes lead sulphate and oxygen ; and with dil. sulphuric acid, lead sulphate and lead dioxide. H. B. North and A. M. Hageman observed that with an excess of **thionyl chloride,** at $150°$, lead chloride and sulphate, sulphuryl chloride, and sulphur dioxide are formed. I. W. Fay and co-workers detected a reduction of red-lead after heating it in an atm. of **ammonia** for 6 hrs. above $300°$. T. W. B. Welsh and H. J. Broderson found that anhydrous hydrazine dissolves $0\cdot01$ grm. of red-lead per c.c. ; C. Finzi and E. Rapuzzi, an acetic acid soln. of **hydrazine** forms lead acetate with the evolution of nitrogen ; and E. Puxeddu, that **phenyl-hydrazine** has no action at ordinary temp., but when warmed, lead hemioxide is formed. E. Müller and H. Barck showed that **nitric oxide** does not react with red-lead at room-temp., but at $200°$, lead nitrite is quantitatively produced ; and J. Milbauer, that **nitrogen peroxide** forms lead nitrate ; and A. Vogel found that with **nitric acid,** lead nitrate and dioxide are formed ; with boiling acid, the red-lead gradually dissolves, and on adding water a colourless soln. of lead nitrate is formed. The complete dissolution of red-lead in dil. nitric acid, or dil. acetic acid proceeds very quickly in the presence of hydrogen dioxide; R. Fresenius recommended **cane sugar** or **oxalic acid** for this purpose; A. Partheil, **lactic acid**; A. Reinsch, J. Milbauer, E. Pieszczek, F. P. Dunnington, L. Opificius, and H. Schlossberg, **methyl alcohol, glycerol, ammonium tartrate, phenol, formaldehyde, phenylhydrazine,** and **hydroxylamine hydrochloride.** According to C. R. A. Wright and A. P. Luff, **carbon** begins to reduce the oxide at 330°; and **carbon monoxide** at 200°, for in a sealed tube containing carbon monoxide, red-lead forms lead carbonate. I. W. Fay and co-workers detected a reduction of red-lead after heating it in an atm. of **carbon monoxide** for 6 hrs. at 150°, and in an atm. of **methane** at 158°. Under similar conditions, **carbon dioxide** has no action. W. Eidmann found that red-lead is insoluble in **acetone.** J. Milbauer found that red-lead is slowly transformed by dil. **acetic acid** into lead acetate, and H. Forestier said that 10 c.c. of acetic acid and 20 c.c. of water suffice for the dissolution of a gram of red-lead in 30 mins. on a water-bath. C. Marchese, and J. J. Berzelius made some observations on this subject. L. Kahlenberg and W. J. Trautmann observed that red-lead is quickly reduced by powdered silicon when the temp. is raised. A. Colson said that about one-third of the red-lead produces lead tetracetate, $Pb(C_2H_3O_2)_4$, and the remainder the normal acetate, $Pb(C_2H_3O_2)_2$. The soln. prepared at 40° was found by V. A. Jacquelain not to be decomposed by **alcohol** or **ether**; and C. F. Schönbein noted that lead dioxide separated from the soln., slowly at ordinary temp., rapidly when heated. A. Chwala and H. Colle found that a soln. of **sodium acetate** removes a little lead dioxide from red-lead, forming sodium plumbate. D. Woodman said that, unlike lead monoxide, red-lead is insoluble in a soln. of **lead acetate**; L. Kahlenberg and H. W. Hillyer also found that, unlike lead monoxide, red-lead is insoluble in a boiling soln. of **potassium tartrate,** and F. C. Krauskopf observed no evolution of oxygen during the action. A. Levol said that red-lead does not react with oxalic acid alone. *Orange-lead* is used for the production of paints, colours, printing inks, and enamels; it resembles red-lead in composition, and usually has a high proportion of lead dioxide as indicated above. It differs from red-lead in colour, bulkiness, grain-size, and in its behaviour towards **linseed oil** or **varnish.** While a mixture of linseed oil or varnish and orange-lead remains soft on keeping, red-lead soon becomes stiff with these media, and the product cannot be thinned again. Hence, when red-lead is used as a paint, it is usual to mix it shortly before use. The poorer grades of red-lead—with their free lead monoxide—quickly stiffen linseed oil.

L. Moser showed that **titanium trichloride** is oxidized by red-lead; E. Lay also noted that with **siliconhydrotrinitride,** Si_2HN_3, red-lead is reduced with incandescence partly to lead and partly to lead monoxide. A. Vogel reported that with a soln. of **stannous chloride,** a white mixture of lead chloride and stannic oxide is formed; and C. Russo and G. Sensi found **ferrous sulphate** is quantitatively oxidized by red-lead. A. Levol observed no reaction between red-lead and a soln of **mercurous nitrate.**

REFERENCES.

[1] G. Agricola, *Interpretatio germanica vocum rei metallicæ*, Basileæ, 466, 1546.

[2] J. J. Nöggerath, *Zeit. deut. geol. Ges.*, 6. 693, 1855; E. Dittler, *Centr. Min.*, 521, 1916; J. D. Hawkins, *Amer. Journ. Science*, (3), 39. 42, 1890; J. Smithson, *Phil. Trans.*, 96. 267, 1806.

[3] P. A. von Bonsdorff, *Pogg. Ann.*, 41. 305, 1867; J. J. Nöggerath, *Jahrb. Min.*, 1, 1847; A. Levol, *Journ. Pharm. Chim.*, (3), 34. 358, 1858; *Ann. Chim. Phys.*, (2), 75. 108, 1840; (3), 42. 196, 1854; E. Frémy, *ib.*, (3), 12. 499, 1844; J. B. A. Dumas, *ib.*, (2), 49. 398, 1832; M. Longchamp, *ib.*, (2), 34. 105, 1827; J. J. Houton-Labillardière, *ib.*, (2), 35. 96, 1827; E. J. Kohlmeyer, *Chem. Ztg.*, 36. 993, 1912; J. Milbauer, *ib.*, 33. 522, 950, 1909; 34. 139, 1341, 1910; 36. 1484, 1912; 37. 97, 1913; 38. 588, 1914; 39. 858, 1915; O. Herting, *ib.*, 27. 923, 1903; W. Stahl, *ib.*, 45. 781, 1921; O. W. Brown and A. R. Nees, *Journ. Ind. Eng. Chem.*, 4. 870, 1912; J. A. Wilkinson, *Journ. Phys. Chem.*, 13. 705, 1919; C. F. Schönbein, *Journ. prakt. Chem.*, (1), 74. 323, 1858; G. Kassner, *Arch. Pharm.*, 241. 696, 1903; J. B. Huffard and P. E. Haynes,

U.S. Pat. No. 1491237, 1924 ; V. A. Jacquelain, *Compt. Rend. Trav. Chim.*, 1, 1851 ; *Compt. Rend.*, 31. 626, 1850 ; A. Bouzat, *ib.*, 136. 1396, 1903 ; W. Reinders and L. Hamburger, *Zeit. anorg. Chem.*, 89. 82, 1914 ; J. C. J. Cunningham, *ib.*, 89. 49, 1914 ; F. Fischer and H. Plötze, *ib.*, 75. 18, 1912 ; B. Brauner, *ib.*, 7. 2, 1894 ; *Ber. Böhm. Ges.*, 295, 1885 ; H. le Chatelier, *Bull. Soc. Chim.*, (3), 17. 791, 1897 ; H. Hocking, *Brit. Pat. No.* 220609, 1923 ; L. Michel, *Bull. Soc. Min.*, 13. 56, 1890 ; M. Liebig, *Zeit. angew. Chem.*, 17. 1674, 1904 ; C. L. P. Burton, *Brit. Pat. No.* 1350, 1862 ; Rheinische Maschinenfabrik, *German Pat.*, *D.R.P.* 247371, 1911 ; G. Jansen, *ib.*, 291564, 1911 ; M. Alsburg, *U.S. Pat. No.* 431026, 1890 ; J. E. MacKensie, *Chem. News*, 99. 146, 1909 ; T. Carnelley and J. Walker, *Journ. Chem. Soc.*, 53. 59, 1888 ; S. Glasstone, *ib.*, 121. 1456, 1922 ; C. R. A. Wright and A. P. Luff, *ib.*, 33. 504, 1878 ; A. Hutchinson and W. Pollard, *ib.*, 69. 212, 1896 ; J. Löwe, *Dingler's Journ.*, 271. 472, 1889 ; J. J. Berzelius, *Gilbert's Ann.*, 40. 166, 186, 1812 ; 46. 131, 1814 ; *Schweigger's Journ.*, 7. 71, 1813 ; J. Dalton, *A New System of Chemical Philosophy*, Manchester, 1. 42, 1827 ; R. Phillips, *Phil. Mag.*, 3. 125, 1828 ; C. A. Klein, *Journ. Oil Colour Chem. Assoc.*, 2. 8, 1919 ; J. Löwenthal, *Zeit. anal. Chem.*, 3. 176, 1864 ; G. Grube, *Zeit. Elektrochem.*, 28. 286, 1822 ; C. Marchese, *Gazz. Chim. Ital.*, 37. ii, 289, 1907 ; L. Marino, *ib.*, 39. i, 639, 1909 ; *Zeit. anorg. Chem.*, 62. 173, 1909 ; F. Fischer and H. Ploetze, *ib.*, 75. 15, 1912 ; E. Szterkhers, *Ann. Chim. Anal.*, 7. 214, 1902 ; V. Frehse, *ib.*, 11. 176, 1906 ; A. Reinsch, *Ber. Chem. Unters. Amt. Altona*, 1, 1906 ; D. Woodman, *Journ. Amer. Chem. Soc.*, 19. 339, 1897 ; E. E. Dunlap. *ib.*, 30. 611, 1908 ; W. F. Edwards, *Chem. Met. Engg.*, 20. 35, 1919 ; A. P. West, *Philippine Journ. Science*, 8. 429, 1913 ; D. B. Dott, *Pharm. Journ.*, (4), 27. 802, 1908 ; C. L. Vlaanderen, *Rép. Chim.*, 1. 169, 1859 ; L. N. Vauquelin, *Mém. Inst.*, 5. 184, 1804 ; D. I. Mendeléeff, *Principles of Chemistry*, St. Petersburg, 561, 1903 ; London, 2. 134, 1891 ; E. J. Wade, *Secondary Batteries*, London, 220, 1902 ; A. Horstmann, *Zeit. phys. Chem.*, 6. 1, 1890 ; E. Zenghelis, *ib.*, 50. 220, 1905 ; F. A. Henglein, *ib.*, 98. 1, 1921 ; C. Schubert, *Beiträge zur Kenntnis der Dissoziation einiger Oxyde, Karbonate, und Sulfide*, Dresden, 1910 ; A. Geuther, *Liebig's Ann.*, 219. 56, 1883 ; S. S. Bhatnagar, M. Prasad and D. C. Bahl, *Journ. Indian Chem. Soc.*, 2. 11, 1925.

[4] J. Milbauer, *Chem. Ztg.*, 38. 588, 1914 ; L. Michel, *Bull. Soc. Min.*, 13. 56, 1890 ; O. W. Brown and A. R. Nees, *Journ. Soc. Chem. Ind.*, 4. 870, 1912 ; O. W. Brown, S. V. Cook, and J. C. Warner, *Journ. Phys. Chem.*, 26. 477, 1922 ; W. Herapath, *Phil. Mag.*, (1), 64. 321, 1824 ; C. J. B. Karsten, *Schweigger's Journ.*, 65. 394, 1832 ; P. von Muschenbrock, *Phil. Trans.*, 33. 370, 1726 ; P. F. G. Boullay, *Ann. Chim. Phys.*, (2), 43. 266, 1830 ; S. Glasstone, *Journ. Chem. Soc.*, 121. 1456, 1922 ; M. Bamberger and R. Grengg, *Centr. Min.*, 65, 1921 ; W. Spring, *Zeit. phys. Chem.*, 2. 532, 1888 ; *Ann. Soc. Géol. Belg.*, 15. 156, 1888 ; S. Meyer, *Wied. Ann.*, 69. 245, 1899 ; G. Hauser, *Farben Ztg.*, 26. 2914, 1921 ; W. Schmidt, *Ann. Physik*, (4), 11. 114, 1903 ; F. B. Hofmann, *Zeit. Biol.*, 63. 386, 1914 ; G. Tammann, *Zeit. anorg. Chem.*, 135. 194, 1924.

[5] C. R. A. Wright and A. P. Luff, *Journ. Chem. Soc.*, 33. 1, 1878 ; W. Müller, *Pogg. Ann.*, 136. 51, 1869 ; R. Weber, *ib.*, 112. 619, 1861 ; T. W. B. Welsh and H. J. Broderson, *Journ. Amer. Chem. Soc.*, 37. 820, 1915 ; H. B. North and A. M. Hageman, *ib.*, 35. 543, 1913 ; F. C. Krauskopf, *ib.*, 33. 943, 1911 ; D. Woodman, *ib.*, 19. 339, 1897 ; P. Beck, *Zeit. anal. Chem.*, 47. 465, 1908 ; C. Finzi and E. Rapuzzi, *ib.*, 52. 36, 1913 ; A. Chwala and H. Colle, *ib.*, 50. 227, 1911 ; A. Vogel, *Kastner's Arch.*, 23. 84, 1832 ; L. L. de Koninck, *Bull. Assoc. Belg.*, 16. 94, 1902 ; C. P. van Hoek, *Farben Ztg.*, 19. 2017, 1914 ; L. Kahlenberg and W. J. Trautmann, *Trans. Amer. Electrochem. Soc.*, 39. 377, 1921 ; H. Mennicke, *Zeit. öffent. Chem.*, 6. 227, 1900 ; P. Sabatier and L. Espil, *Compt. Rend.*, 159. 137, 1914 ; A. Colson, *ib.*, 136. 891, 1903 ; V. A. Jacquelain, *ib.*, 31. 626, 1850 ; *Compt. Rend. Trav. Chim.*, 1, 1851 ; C. F. Schönbein, *Journ. prakt. Chem.*, (1), 74. 325, 1858 ; O. Seidel, *ib.*, (2), 20. 205, 1879 ; *Ueber einige Verbindungen des Bleihyperoxyds* (*der Bleisäure*), Breslau, 24, 1878 ; E. Lay, *Ueber Silicium-Stickstoff-Wasserstoff-Verbindungen*, München, 57, 1910 ; E. Puxeddu, *Gazz. Chim. Ital.*, 46. i, 76, 1916 ; C. Russo and G. Sensi, *ib.*, 44. i, 9, 1914 ; C. Marchesse, *ib.*, 37. ii, 289, 1907 ; O. Brunck, *Zeit. anorg. Chem.*, 10. 222, 1895 ; A. Classen and B. Zahorsky, *ib.*, 4. 102, 1893 ; F. Fischer and K. Thiele, *ib.*, 67. 302, 1910 ; E. Müller and H. Barck, *ib.*, 129. 314, 1923 ; J. Milbauer, *Chem. Ztg.*, 33. 522, 950, 1909 ; 34. 139, 1341, 1910 ; 36. 1484, 1912 ; 37. 97, 1913 ; 38. 588, 1914 ; 39. 858, 1915 ; L. Moser, *ib.*, 39. 245, 1915 ; J. F. Sacher, *ib.*, 32. 62, 1908 ; I. W. Fay, A. F. Seeker, F. H. Lane, and G. E. Ferguson, *Polyt. Eng.*, 10. 72, 1910 ; C. Löwig, *Pogg. Ann.*, 14. 114, 1828 ; 16. 376, 1829 ; *Das Brom und seine chemischen Verhältnisse*, Heidelberg, 1829 ; J. J. Berzelius, *Gilbert's Ann.*, 40. 166, 186, 1812 ; 46. 131, 1814 ; *Schweigger's Journ.*, 7. 71, 1813 ; F. Peters, *Centr. Accumul.*, 2. 293, 305, 321, 1901 ; 3. 83, 112, 140, 202, 246, 1902 ; 4. 273, 285, 1903 ; 5. 1, 13, 26, 38, 1904 ; H. Forestier, *Zeit. angew. Chem.*, 11. 176, 1898 ; L. Kahlenberg and H. W. Hillyer, *Amer. Chem. Journ.*, 16. 101, 1894 ; A. Partheil, *Arch. Pharm.*, 245. 519, 1907 ; *Chem. Ztg.*, 31. 941, 1907 ; *Ver. Ges. deut. Naturforsch. Aertze*, 159, 1907 ; E. Pieszczek, *Pharm. Ztg.*, 52. 922, 1908 ; 53. 87, 1908 ; A. Reinsch, *Centr. Chem.*, i, 993, 1907 ; W. Eidmann, *Ein Beitrag zur Erkenntnis des Verhaltens chemischer Verbindungen in nichtwässrigen Lösungen*, Giessen, 1899 ; A. Levol, *Ann. Chim. Phys.*, (2), 75. 108, 1840 ; H. Moissan, *ib.*, (6), 24. 261, 1891 ; F. P. Dunnington, *Zeit. anal. Chem.*, 28. 338, 1889 ; L. Opificius, *ib.*, 28. 345, 1889 ; H. Schlossberg, *ib.*, 41. 740, 1902 ; R. Fresenius, *Anleitung zur quantitative Analyse*, Braunschweig, 2. 484, 1903 ; J. W. Mellor, *A Treatise on Quantitative Analysis*, London, 322, 1913.

§ 19. Lead Dioxide

The oxide of lead, known as **lead dioxide**, PbO_2, *lead peroxide*, or *pure oxide of lead*, was first prepared by C. W. Scheele [1] in 1774 by the action of chlorine on red-lead, and it was described in his essay : *Om Brunsten eller Magnesia*, as a dark brown calx of lead containing little or no phlogiston, and therefore having a strong tendency to unite with it again.   Soon afterwards J. Priestley also made the same substance by the action of nitric acid on red-lead.

A. Breithaupt [2] described a mineral from Leadhills, Scotland, which he called *Schwerbleierz* or *diplasites plumbicus*—$\delta\iota\pi\lambda\acute{a}\sigma\iota\sigma$, double—because the metal is twice as strongly oxidized as is the case with litharge ; J. F. L. Hausmann called it *brown lead oxide;* and W. Haidinger proposed its name **plattnerite**—after C. F. Plattner. Specimens from Dumfriesshire, Scotland, and Mullan, Idaho, have been described or analyzed by E. Kinch, M. F. Heddle, H. A. Wheeler, J. D. and E. N. Hawkins, and W. S. Yeates and E. F. Ayres.

M. E. Chevreul [3] said that when litharge is heated in a platinum crucible it yields lead dioxide and an alloy of platinum and lead.   There is something wrong with this statement.   While red-lead is obtained by heating lead oxide in air, lead dioxide cannot be so produced.   F. Fischer and H. Plötze heated the lead oxide between 400° and 450° in oxygen under 100 atm. press. and obtained a product with the composition Pb_5O_8—*vide supra*.   The action takes place at 375° in the presence of alkali hydroxide, carbonate, or borate.   Lead monoxide can be oxidized to the dioxide, as L. N. Vauquelin showed, by treatment with chlorine water, or, as A. J. Balard showed, by treatment with bromine water, or a soln. of hypochlorous acid.   A. Ditte found that in the chlorine process, the product is always contaminated with lead chloride.   N. A. E. Millon said that chlorine water produces lead dioxide from lead chloride only when some hypochlorous acid is formed by the action of light on the chlorine water.   L. Friderich and co-workers treated with chlorine a mixture of lead sulphate and magnesia suspended in hot water. A. Sobrero and F. Selmi passed chlorine into a soln. of sodium and lead chlorides, and E. W. Wescott represented the reaction $PbCl_{2solid}+Cl_{2gas}+2H_2O \rightleftharpoons PbO_{2solid}$ $4HCl$, where the equilibrium constant, $[H']^4[Cl']^4/p$, is $2\cdot4\times10^{-5}$ on the assumption that ionization is complete ; the thermal value of the reaction is eq. to 43,500 joules. W. Kubel also made the dioxide by the action of chlorine on basic lead acetate. F. Wöhler, F. Muck, and A. Geuther also oxidized lead salts with chlorine ; A. Seyewetz and P. Trawitz oxidized an alkaline soln. of lead oxide with the same agent ; and L. E. Rivot and co-workers oxidized lead sulphide, oxide, or carbonate in a hot soln. of alkali-lye by means of chlorine.   E. Rupp obtained a 91 per cent. yield by the action of bromine on a dil. acetic acid soln. of a lead salt.   A. Chwala and H. Colle oxidized lead iodide by iodine in the presence of potassium hydroxide. J. Pelouze obtained finely divided lead dioxide by the action of hypochlorous acid on a dil. soln. of lead acetate ; and G. C. Winkelblech added sodium hypochlorite to a boiling soln. of lead acetate so long as any precipitate is formed ; the soln. was then decanted, and the lead chloride, simultaneously precipitated, was extracted by boiling dil. nitric acid.   V. Zotier used a hypobromite as the oxidizing agent. C. Puscher, and G. Iioka and K. K. S. Seisakujo, treated lead oxide with a clear soln. of bleaching powder ; C. Fahlenberg, J. Strachan, S. Glasstone, and R. Böttger also oxidized a boiling soln. of lead acetate, and A. Fehrmann, a soln. of lead chloride at 50°–60° by means of bleaching powder.   F. M. Lyte used the same oxidizing agent.   C. F. Schönbein, and F. Mailfert oxidized lead acetate with ozonized air ; or by evaporating soln. of litharge in turpentine.   V. Zotier treated a soln. of an alkaline plumbite with hydrogen dioxide.   P. Jannasch, E. Rupp and G. Schaumann used an alkaline soln. of hydrogen dioxide to oxidize soln. of lead salts to lead dioxide.   A. Seyewetz and P. Trawitz oxidized lead hydroxide suspended in water by sodium dioxide, or ammonium persulphate; G. Panopolus agitated lead oxide with a soln. of potassium persulphate: lead salts are attacked more slowly than the oxide, and much lead sulphate is formed at the same time; A. Overbeck boiled lead hydroxide with a conc. soln. of potassium ferrocyanide and hydroxide; A. Guttmann used diazobenzene perbromide as the oxidizing agent; A. Reynoso treated lead oxide with potassium permanganate in the presence of an excess of potassium hydroxide. M. E. Chevreul, and L. Michel obtained lead dioxide along with red plates of the monoxide by fusing litharge with potassium hydroxide; and W. Minor stirred some potassium nitrate in the fused mass and, after washing away the soluble matters with water, obtained lead dioxide of a high degree of purity. F. Göbel melted a mixture of lead oxide and potassium chlorate; and A. Levol, a mixture of potassium chlorate and nitrate.

N. W. Fischer found that during the electrolysis of a soln. of a lead salt, lead dioxide is deposited in crystalline scales on the anode, and he added that the deposit occurs even in soln. containing only one part of lead in 12,000 parts of liquid. W. Wernicke electrolyzed an alkaline soln. of lead tartrate. The electro-deposition of lead as dioxide has been previously discussed, and it is a well-known process in analytical chemistry. The preparation of lead dioxide by the electrolytic process was discussed by F. Wöhler, H. Bardt, W. Borchers, C. Luckow, F. Peters, S. Glasstone, H. N. Warren, M. G. Mellon and H. F. Reinhard, J. H. Mellquist, A. Rokotnitz, A. C. Becquerel, F. R. Steigelmann, W. Beetz, Konsortium für Elektrochemische Industrie, P. Ferchland, H. Blumenberg, W. Palmaer, and F. Fischer and H. Plötze. The Fabrik Griesheim-Elektron recommends the use of a diaphragm cell for the electrolysis to avoid *der Abscheidung von Blei an der Kathode*. F. Jirsa electrolyzed a soln. with 40 grms. of potassium hydroxide, and 4·5 grms. of lead monoxide per litre, using an alternating current with nickel or iron electrodes, and obtained dark brown, pulverulent lead dioxide —*vide* lead sesquioxide. W. Palmaer said the lead dioxide deposited from an acid soln. of a lead salt is free from the hydrate H_2PbO_3.

According to F. Fischer and K. Thiele, when hydrofluoplumbic acid is exposed to air, lead dioxide is formed. In a modification of C. W. Scheele's process, red-lead is treated with chlorine-water, or chlorine is passed into water in which red-lead is suspended, and the liquid frequently agitated so long as any absorption of gas occurs. Lead dioxide is precipitated, and can be readily washed free from chlorides by boiling water. In a modification of J. Priestley's process red-lead is boiled for a sufficient length of time with dil. nitric acid, when the lead monoxide is converted into the nitrate and can be washed away from the residual dioxide. J. Milbauer, and G. Grube employed this process. V. A. Jacquelain, and F. Fischer and K. Thiele treated red-lead with an excess of glacial acetic acid at 40°, and washed the resulting lead acetate away from the lead dioxide. A. C. Becquerel also extracted the lead monoxide from red-lead by fusion with potassium hydroxide; C. L. Berthollet found that no oxygen is lost in the process. G. Kassner obtained lead dioxide by digesting calcium orthoplumbate with nitric acid, or heating it under press. using an aq. soln. of an ammonium salt—*e.g.* the nitrate—which will dissolve calcium hydroxide. M. Höhnel obtained the oxide by heating sodium metaplumbate with water or with dil. nitric acid; and M. Lachaud and C. Lepierre, by the action of molten potassium hydroxide on lead chromate.

Lead dioxide can be purified by boiling it with a 10 per cent. soln. of sodium hydroxide, and then with hot dil. nitric acid. W. Reinders and L. Hamburger boiled the commercial dioxide for a long time with nitric acid, and obtained a 99–100 per cent. product by washing and drying at a temp. not exceeding 100°. Analyses reported by A. Breithaupt, T. Thomson, L. N. Vauquelin, and J. J. Berzelius correspond with PbO_2. H. Weil[4] reported that commercial lead dioxide always contains some carbon dioxide which it gives off if heated at 280°, or if treated on a water-bath with 65 per cent. nitric acid or phosphoric acid: but M. Dennstedt and F. Hassler proved that the source of the carbon dioxide is organic contamination, for neither the monoxide nor the dioxide can absorb carbon dioxide between 100° and 350°. Sometimes sulphuric acid, or chlorine is present. W. F. Edwards reported that some commercial samples had less than 50 per cent. PbO_2, some just over 60 per cent., and some had 95 per cent. PbO_2. A. Gutbier and H. O. Meyer obtained **colloidal lead dioxide** by adding dry lead tetracetate (1·5 grms.) slowly, at the ordinary temp. and with rapid stirring, to a 0·3 per cent. soln. of gum arabic (250 c.c.) to which $0·2N$-ammonia soln. (30 c.c.) has been added. The sol was filtered from small quantities of brown precipitate, and dialyzed as rapidly as possible. The pure preparation is dark brown. A white precipitate of hydrated lead dioxide separates slowly on long keeping.

J. Heyes represented lead dioxide with a quadrivalent oxygen atom : $Pb=O=O$. A. Colson showed that in the dioxide the lead is quadrivalent, $O=Pb=O$, because when an acetic acid soln. of lead acetate is treated with chlorine, lead chloride and lead tetracetate are formed. L. Marino argued that the lead is quadrivalent, and one or both the oxygen atoms quadrivalent. The unsymmetrical formula for the oxide is preferred because the lead sulphite obtained by reducing the dioxide with sulphur dioxide is unsymmetrical :

$$Pb{\lessgtr}^O_O \qquad\qquad Pb{\lessgtr}^{\cdot\cdot}_O \qquad\qquad {}^{Pb}_{SO_2}{\gtrdot}O$$

Unsymmetrical lead dioxide. Symmetrical lead dioxide. Lead sulphite.

because when boiled with dimethyl sulphate in the presence of alcohol, lead methyl sulphonate is formed whether the sulphite is produced by the action of sulphur dioxide on lead dioxide, or by double decomposition. He also assumed that lead dioxide can exist in both single and double molecules :

$$Pb{\lessgtr}^{\cdot\cdot}_O \qquad\qquad\qquad O{\lessgtr}^{Pb\equiv O}_{Pb\equiv O}{\gtrdot}O$$

because at low temp. and high conc., selenious acid reacts to form lead pyroselenate, $Pb_2Se_2O_7$, while in dil. soln., the single molecules react to form normal lead selenite, $PbSeO_3$.

The physical properties of lead dioxide.—Native lead dioxide usually occurs massive, sometimes in globular or mammillary forms, and rarely in crystals. It has a metallic lustre. The **colour** is iron-black, and when powdered chestnut-brown. The artificial dioxide is a reddish-brown or puce-coloured powder. F. Dolezalek and K. Finckh[5] said that the red-lead obtained by oxidation processes is crystalline, and that obtained by hydrolysis is amorphous, but gradually becomes crystalline on exposure to light. According to A. C. Becquerel, red-lead may be produced in brown, six-sided plates or scales with a yellow lustre in reflected light ; the crystals of plattnerite are transluscent or opaque. B. Wäser and R. Kühnel gave some photographs of the crystals of electrodeposited lead dioxide. According to W. S. Yeates and E. F. Ayres, the native **crystals** belong to the tetragonal system, and have the axial ratio $a : c = 1 : 0·6764$. The crystals were said to be isomorphous with rutile, TiO_2 ; cassiterite, SnO_2 ; and polianite, MnO_2. L. Michel obtained tetragonal prisms of the dioxide mixed with red monoxide when lead oxide is melted with potassium hydroxide. By a somewhat similar process, using lead hydroxide, A. Geuther claimed to have prepared small hexagonal plates, and these were examined by O. Luedecke. According to W. S. Yeates and E. F. Ayres, the **fracture** of plattnerite is subconchoidal and uneven ; no **cleavage** was observed. L. Michel found the **optical character** of artificial crystals to be negative. The **X-radiogram** has been studied by M. L. Huggins, W. P. Davey, and A. E. van Arkel. A. Ferrari showed that the results correspond with a tetragonal space lattice of the rutile type with $a=4·98A$, $c=3·40A$, and $a : c = 1 : 0·682$. A. Sommerfeld discussed the electronic structure.

The **specific gravity** of artificial lead dioxide, obtained by W. Herapath, is 8·902 at 16·5°; L. Playfair and J. P. Joule gave 8·756–8·897 at 3·9°; C. J. B. Karsten, 8·933; W. Wernicke, 9·045 ; P. F. G. Boullay, 9·190 ; K. Schreber, 9·3 for a visible layer deposited by electrolysis on a platinum plate ; and W. A. Palmaer, 9·360 for electro-deposited crystals. P. Niggli gave 8·56–8·90 for the sp. gr., and 27–28 for the eq. vol. A. Breithaupt gave 9·392–9·440 for plattnerite ; E. Kinch, 8·54 ; M. F. Heddle, 8·80–8·96 ; W. S. Yeates and E. F. Ayres, 8·56 ; H. A. Wheeler, 9·41 ; W. Palmaer, 9·363 at 20°/4° ; and J. D. and E. N. Hawkins, 7·25. J. Königsberger and W. J. Müller calculated the greatest diameter of the molecule to be 0·74$\mu\mu$ from the optical properties of electrodeposited films. T. von Hagen pressed the oxide into a smooth, compact mass, and W. Spring found the moist powder behaved like red-lead under compression. W. A. Palmaer gave 5–6 for the hardness of the crystals ; E. Kinch gave 5 for that of plattnerite. A. Reis and L. Zimmermann studied the relation between the mol. vol. and the hardness. W. Palmaer gave 0·057 for the linear coeff. of thermal expansion between 25° and 150°. A. S. Russell gave for the mean specific heat of a sample dried in air at 160°, 0·0398 at −134° ; 0·0570 at −38° ; and 0·0648 at 24° ; and for the molecular heat respectively 9·52, 13·65, and 15·50. W. A. Palmaer gave for the sp. ht. 0·0639 between 20° and 100°, and for the mol. ht. 15·24. C. Zenghelis found signs of a very slight volatilization at ordinary temp. According to S. Glasstone, the dissociation pressure of the dioxide at 17° is 7·1×10⁻¹² atm. ; and the oxygen dissociation press. at 0·21 atm. is 394°. W. Reinders and L. Hamburger showed that when lead dioxide is heated, a series of solid soln. with lead monoxide are formed, and their results give a much greater value for dissociation press. of lead dioxide with some monoxide in solid soln. E. Winterhalder described demonstration experiments for the dissociation of lead dioxide. I. M. Tscheltzoff gave PbO$_\text{solid}$+O$_\text{gas}$=PbO$_\text{2solid}$ +12·14 Cals. for the heat of formation at 17° ; F. Streintz gave 10·1 Cals. at 14° ; E. W. Wescott gave Pb$_\text{solid}$+O$_\text{2gas}$=PbO$_\text{2solid}$+219000 joules. K. Schreber calculated 2·2 for the index of refraction with D-light. B. A. Dima compared the photoelectric effect with the lead oxides, and observed that the effect diminishes with increasing valency of the metal, and that the photoelectric fatigue is greatest with the lower oxides. B. Aulenkamp examined the photoelectric sensitivity of lead dioxide.

F. Streintz and G. Neumann said that the electrical conductivity of lead dioxide is metallic. F. Streintz found the electrical resistance of a wire a metre long and 1 sq. mm. sectional area to be 2·3(1+0·00065θ)×10⁻⁴ ohm. W. Palmaer said the sp. resistance of the crystals at 18° is 0·000845 ohm and 0·0₄919 ohm at 20°, and the sp. electrical conductivity 10180. In the temp. range 22°–84°, the sp. resistance falls 0·06 per cent. per degree ; and therefore lead dioxide is a better conductor than mercury or bismuth. Measurements were also made by K. Bädeker, P. Ferchland, J. F. Weyde, and T. Sundorpf. According to A. C. Cumming, the electrode potential of lead dioxide in 7·45N-sulphuric acid against a calomel electrode is 1·479 volts, and with 4·82N-H₂SO₄, 1·434 volts. Measurements were also made by D. A. MacInnes and co-workers ; and J. Königsberg and W. J. Müller. J. Miesler gave −1·3 volts against sulphuric acid ; −0·97 volt against zinc sulphate ; and −0·89 volt against copper sulphate. A. von Oettingen, and S. B. Christy gave 0·160 volt in a normal soln. of potassium cyanide at 25°, and 0·110–0·118 volt with 0·1N-KCy ; −0·062 to +0·070 volt in 0·01N-KCy ; and −0·006 volt in 0·001N-KCy. A. C. Cumming gave for the potential of the Pb····/Pb″ electrode against the hydrogen electrode at 25°, 1·82 volt with electrolytic dioxide, and 1·75 volt with the chemically prepared dioxide. According to S. Glasstone, 1·75 volt is probably too high, but is yet the best representative value for the Pb····/Pb″-electrode ; but the lead dioxide electrode is unstable. He computed for the solubility product of lead dioxide [Pb][OH′]⁴=3·25×10⁻⁶⁶. The e.m.f. of the cell Pb | (PbO,PbO₂), N-NaOH,H₂ (atm.) Pt=1·078 volts at 17°. A. Hollard found that the lead dioxide deposited electrolytically on a platinized platinum anode from a slightly acid soln. of lead nitrate has more oxygen than is required for the dioxide.

S. Glasstone also showed that the electromotive behaviour of electrodeposited lead dioxide is explained by the presence of a trace of a higher acidic oxide—possibly *lead trioxide,* PbO_3—in the deposit. K. Schreber studied the effect of the conc. of the acid on the e.m.f. of lead accumulators. L. Kahlenberg and A. S. McDaniel measured the potential difference between lead dioxide and soln. of lithium chloride in various solvents, *e.g.* with water, $-1\cdot194$ volts was obtained; with acetone, $-1\cdot337$ volts; with pyridine, $-0\cdot840$ volt; and with amylamine, $-0\cdot476$ volt. By adding water to these liquids, the effect increases slowly with pyridine and amylamine, and rapidly with acetone; with sulphuric acid in place of lithium chloride, the e.m.f. for water rises from $-1\cdot194$ to $-1\cdot756$ volts. J. Cayrel studied lead chloride as a **radio-detector.** S. Meyer gave for the **magnetic susceptibility** $0\cdot302\times10^{-6}$; and for the mol. magnetism, $0\cdot245\times10^{-6}$.

Hydrated forms of lead dioxide.—In the electrolysis of alkaline soln. of lead salts, the anodic lead dioxide contains variable proportions of water, and, according to H. Nissenson and H. Danneel,[6] the water is driven off at about 180°. H. J. S. Sand also found that at 200° lead dioxide absorbs moisture very readily, but not at 230°. The adsorbed moisture is given off but slowly when heated in a dry atm. If the temp. rises above 300°, there is a risk of the decomposition of the dioxide. H. Zocher said that the water-free dioxide is alone stable, and that the so-called hydrates are really gel-forms of the colloid. Plumbic hydroxide acts as a very feeble base, but F. Hein and H. Meininger showed that if three of the hydroxyl groups are replaced by ethyl or phenyl radicles, relatively strong bases are formed.

A number of problematic hydrates has been supposed to be acids corresponding with definite salts. Thus, G. Kassner, and F. Fischer and H. Plötze speak of *pyroplumbic acid,* or *triplumbic acid,* $3PbO_2.2H_2O$, or $H_4Pb_3O_8$, corresponding with the plumbate $CaH_2Pb_3O_8$. There are also G. Kassner's *tetraplumbic acid,* $H_6Pb_4O_{11}$, corresponding with $Ca_2H_2Pb_4O_{11}$; and *diplumbic acid,* $H_4Pb_2O_6$, corresponding with $CaH_2Pb_2O_6$. The orthoplumbates are usually regarded as salts of an *orthoplumbic acid,* H_4PbO_4. G. Grube, and K. Schreber supposed orthoplumbic acid to be formed by the hydrolysis of alkali metaplumbate (*vide infra*). N. Parravano and G. Calcagni's *hexahydroxyplumbic acid,* $H_2[Pb(OH)_6]$, has not been isolated; it is represented by the salt $K_2[Pb(OH)_6]$, and $Pb[Pb(OH)_6]$. The so-called *metaplumbic acid,* H_2PbO_3, or $PbO(OH)_2$, *lead dihydroperoxide,* was obtained by J. J. Berzelius, and W. Wernicke by the electrolysis of an alkaline soln. of lead tartrate. S. Glasstone made it by the electrolysis of dil. soln. of sodium hydroxide with anodes of lead or lead dioxide; and G. Grube by the electrolysis of a soln. of lead hydroxide in $8N$- to $12N$-KOH at 50° with a platinum anode. G. Grube, and K. Schreber suggested that the composition is $PbO_2.2H_2O$, or orthoplumbic acid, $Pb(OH)_4$, or H_4PbO_4. F. Streintz and G. Naumann confirmed W. Wernicke's observations, and found that the electrode potentials of the elements $Pb \mid PbO_2$, and $Pb \mid H_2PbO_3$ in sulphuric acid against zinc were respectively $2\cdot41$ volts and $0\cdot96$ volt. W. Wernicke said that the bluish-black deposit has a sp. gr. $6\cdot267$ at 15°; and has the refractive indices $1\cdot801$ for the C-line; $1\cdot862$ for the D-line; and $1\cdot914$ for the E-line. G. Grube, and I. Bellucci and N. Parravano have described metaplumbates corresponding with the supposed metaplumbic acid. S. Glasstone showed that the anhydrous oxide is metastable with respect to the hydrated form, and the composition of the so-called metaplumbic acid is variable; he therefore inferred that the evidence for the existence of the supposed metaplumbic acid is indecisive.

Colloidal lead dioxide, or colloidal plumbic acid.—N. Parravano and G. Calcagni found that a $0\cdot012N$-soln. of potassium plumbate is completely hydrolyzed into potassium hydroxide, etc., and I. Bellucci and N. Parravano showed that cryoscopic measurements of the liquid indicate that the dissolved substances have a mol. wt. corresponding with $\frac{1}{2}KOH$. The plumbic acid does not pass through a parchment membrane, and the soln., which appears turbid in reflected light, can be filtered, diluted with water, heated to boiling, and allowed to solidify without in any way changing the plumbic acid. The soln. can be evaporated on the water-bath to a syrupy consistency without coagulating, and the residual gelatinous mass, provided it is not dried, is soluble in water, giving the hydrosol. In this case the impurity which is essential for the maintenance of the plumbic acid in the condition of hydrosol, the so-called *Solbildner,* is potassium hydroxide, the proportion of which is gradually diminished by continued dialysis until, after 104 hrs., the percentage of K_2O is 1·87, and that of PbO_2, 98·13. This proportion of K_2O is of the same order as the amounts of hydrochloric acid essential for the existence of hydrosols of aluminium, chromium, and ferric hydroxides. The coagulating actions of the anions (potassium salts) decrease according to the series : (1) iodide, ferrocyanide, tartrate, fluoride ; (2) acetate, chromate, iodate, nitrate, sulphate, thiocyanate, chloride, bromide, dichromate, permanganate, chlorate, perchlorate, ferricyanide ; (3) periodate, oxalate, carbonate, arsenate ; and those of the cations (chlorides) according to the series : (1) aluminium, ferric, calcium, strontium, barium, magnesium, cadmium, mercury, manganese, nickel, cobalt, copper ; (2) ammonium, cæsium, lithium, potassium, rubidium, and sodium. The anions and cations of series (1) produce total coagulation, and those of series (2) partial coagulation, whilst the anions of class (3) are without coagulating action. On increasing the vol. of the coagulating soln. used, it was found that the coagulating action was always increased, but not to the same extent for all electrolytes. G. Grube made deep brown colloidal soln. by the hydrolysis of sodium metaplumbate with warm water.

According to A. Gutbier, E. Sauer, and M. Wissmüller, when small quantities of ammonium chloroplumbate are added to a large vol. of water, a brown, colloidal soln. of lead dioxide is obtained. The reaction may be represented by the equation : $(NH_4)_2PbCl_6+4H_2O=Pb(OH)_4+4HCl+2NH_4Cl$. The soln. is unstable, and soon becomes colourless as a consequence of the action of the hydrochloric acid, which is liberated, on the colloid in accordance with the equation : $Pb(OH)_4+4HCl$ $=PbCl_2+Cl_2+4H_2O$. This may be prevented to a large extent if ammonia is added to the water in quantity sufficient to neutralize the acid which is subsequently set free. If, in addition, small quantities of gum arabic are dissolved in the water, it is possible to obtain fairly stable soln. of the dioxide. The best conditions are attained when 20 c.c. of $0·2N$-NH_3 are added to 250 c.c. of a 0·1 per cent. soln. of gum arabic and one gram of the chloroplumbate added gradually to the well-stirred soln. A. Gutbier and H. O. Meyer used a similar process, using lead tetracetate in place of the chloroplumbate. When freed from electrolytes by dialysis, the soln. can be kept for a considerable time without much decomposition. On evaporation of the soln. to dryness, the dioxide becomes insoluble. The colloidal particles move to the positive pole in an electrical field. When mixed with hydrochloric and nitric acid soln. the brown, colloidal soln. is gradually decolorized, the velocity of the reaction increasing with the conc. of the acid. Sodium hydroxide has a similar action, but the change takes place much less rapidly. Sodium chloride, barium chloride, and aluminium sulphate have no coagulating action, and in presence of these electrolytes the dioxide appears to be approximately as stable as in pure water.

V. Zotier found that when dil. alkali plumbite soln. are treated with hydrogen dioxide, colloidal plumbic acid is formed. He also showed that hydrogen dioxide reacts with basic lead acetates in two stages. In the first, colloidal lead dioxide is formed, and in the second, the lead dioxide reacts with the hydrogen dioxide. At the end of the reaction, the liquid always contains some lead dioxide in soln. Basic lead formates and nitrates react similarly, except for the fact that dil. soln. of these salts only give colloidal lead dioxide. The amount of residual lead dioxide is controlled by four factors. It is at its maximum when the hydrogen dioxide and the lead oxide of the basic salt are in equimol. proportions. It diminishes with increase in the basicity of the lead salt, and also with rise in temp. For different basic acetates it is at its maximum when the salts have undergone the same mol. dilution. The soln. of lead dioxide obtained is exceedingly stable, being unaltered by prolonged boiling. On warming, the lead dioxide is reduced by formaldehyde, dextrose, and sulphites, but not by alcohol. In several of its reactions, such as the liberation of iodine from iodides, it resembles hydrogen dioxide. It presents the characteristic properties of colloidal suspensions. It has a distinct absorption spectrum, showing a broad band from the violet to the blue or green, according to the conc. and thickness of the liquid. The Chemische Fabrik von

Heyden made colloidal lead dioxide by oxidizing a lead salt soln. containing gum arabic or starch. H. Zocher prepared plumbic acid sol in amyl alcohol. He showed that while stannic acid is a lyophile, plumbic acid is a lyophobe. The colloidal soln. of plumbic acid are not very stable, they are easily precipitated, and do not gelatinize.

Chemical properties of lead dioxide.—Lead dioxide is decomposed when exposed to light, forming red-lead and oxygen. According to J. E. Mackenzie,[7] at a moderate heat, it also furnishes red-lead, and if strongly heated, red-lead and oxygen are formed. The reported temp. of decomposition are very discordant. H. Debray said that lead sesquioxide is formed at 350°, and red-lead at 440°; T. Carnelley and J. Walker reported that it forms lead sesquioxide at about 280°; P. Sabatier and J. B. Senderens, V. A. Kroll, and J. Milbauer also made some observations on this subject. M. Dennstedt and F. Hassler said that lead dioxide gives off oxygen between 290° and 320°; and acquires a red colour at 450°; and W. Hempel and C. Schubert, and W. Stahl said that lead dioxide decomposes at 290°–390° into lead sesquioxide and oxygen; at 410°–450°, into red-lead and oxygen; and at 510°–640°, into lead monoxide and oxygen. According to W. Reinders and L. Hamburger, there is a perceptible dissociation at 100°; oxygen can be detected at 141°; and over 200°, dissociation is very marked. The electrolytic dioxide gives off oxygen in vacuo at 250°. S. Glasstone computed the dissociation press. to be 0·21 atm. at 394°—*vide supra*. F. Fischer and H. Plötze showed that in an atm. of oxygen at 100 atm. press. the residue at 410° corresponded with Pb_5O_8; and at 530°, Pb_2O_3. The oxygen which lead dioxide evolves at 400° was found by O. Brunck to contain some ozone. D. Balareff found that the heating curve of lead dioxide at atm. press. has two terraces, one at 360° and the other at 553°. The latter disappears when the press. is 180 mm. This agrees with the assumption that the lead dioxide first decomposes into lead monoxide, and that the latter is afterwards oxidized to red-lead. The temp. 360° is not a temp. at which the dioxide and oxygen are in equilibrium. W. Biltz studied the effect of temp. on valency in connection with lead dioxide.

According to W. Müller,[8] lead dioxide is reduced by **hydrogen** at 155°. C. R. A. Wright and A. P. Luff said that the reaction begins at 140°. I. W. Fay and co-workers detected signs of reduction after heating lead dioxide in an atm. of hydrogen for 6 hrs. at 150°. F. Glaser said that lead monoxide is formed at 194°; lead hemioxide, at 211°; and lead itself at 235°. P. Sabatier and L. Espil gave 150°–190° for the formation of lead monoxide; 190°–240°, for lead hemioxide; and 250°, lead. K. Frenzel and co-workers said that reduction at 300° is rapid; A. de Hemptinne, that the silent electrical discharge in hydrogen causes the reduction of lead dioxide. S. Glasstone gave for the energy of the reaction: $3PbO_2+2H_2 =2H_2O+Pb_3O_4$, $4·54\times96540$ joules at 17°; for $PbO_2+H_2=PbO+H_2O$, $2·156\times96540$ joules; and for $2PbO_2+H_2=Pb_2O_3+H_2O$, $2·224\times96540$ joules. H. J. S. Sand found that **water** vapour is absorbed by lead dioxide below 230°, and but incompletely expelled at 300°. The solubility of lead dioxide in water is very small. S. Glasstone said the solubility product in N-NaOH at 25° is $3·25\times10^{-66}$, and of the same order for water. J. Milbauer found that when lead dioxide is heated or triturated with **potassium hydroxide**, some potassium orthoplumbate, and maybe some red-lead, are formed. If a mixture of lead monoxides and dioxides in the molar proportions 3 : 2 be boiled with a conc. soln. of potassium hydroxide (150–200 grms. per 100 c.c.), red-lead is formed; with equimolar proportions, and 300 grms. of potassium hydroxide per 100 c.c. of water, a green unstable product is formed. V. Zotier found that 0·1 grm. of lead dioxide is decomposed by 20 c.c. of **sodium hydroxide** in 15–20 days at ordinary temp., and in less than an hour at 100°. H. Zocher said that freshly prepared lead dioxide soon dissolves in an aq. soln. of sodium dioxide, but the aged dioxide does not dissolve for a long time.

C. F. Schönbein[9] found that lead dioxide is reduced by **ozone,** ozonized turpentine, or by **hydrogen dioxide,** and lead monoxide is formed. A. Mailfert said that lead oxide is converted by ozone into lead dioxide, and in the presence of alkali hydroxide into alkali plumbate. B. Brauner found that in alkaline soln. the reduction is not complete, and the composition of the product corresponds with Pb_5O_7. E. Pieszczek, and H. Schlossberg showed that in the presence of nitric acid, lead dioxide is smoothly and completely reduced to lead monoxide, oxygen, and water. T. Gigli, and E. Schöne said that the reduction occurs only in the presence of acids—*vide* red-lead.

H. Moissan [10] found that **fluorine** attacks lead dioxide at ordinary temp., forming lead fluoride or an oxyfluoride. B. Brauner said that **hydrofluoric acid** does not dissolve lead dioxide, but if freshly precipitated, F. Fischer and K. Thiele found that some dioxide is dissolved, and hydrofluoplumbic acid is formed. M. Dennstedt and F. Hassler found that lead dioxide absorbs **chlorine** at 200°–220°, and at 260°–280° the reaction is complete; similar results were obtained with **bromine.** At 350°, chlorine forms normal lead chloride, and from 350°–450°, an oxychloride; bromine forms oxybromides. A. Classen and B. Zahorsky found that liquid chlorine attacks lead dioxide only when hydrogen chloride is present. G. Bozza and M. Bertozzi studied the action of soln. of chlorine on peroxidized lead anodes. **Hydrogen chloride or bromide** were found by M. Dennstedt and F. Hassler to be absorbed by lead dioxide as in the case of the halogens themselves, forming lead halide, water, and free halogen; thus, A. Alessi found that in a stream of hydrogen chloride, lead chloride, water, and chlorine are formed. With conc. hydrochloric acid, some lead tetrachloride is formed (*q.v.*). H. Zocher found that hydrochloric acid is adsorbed by colloidal plumbic acid so that after a soln. of **ammonium, potassium,** or **sodium chloride** has been shaken up with the colloid, the reaction is alkaline. M. Dennstedt and F. Hassler found that, unlike chlorine and bromine, **iodine** is not absorbed by lead dioxide; A. Chwala and H. Colle, that **hydriodic acid** is converted into iodic acid; and C. F. Schönbein, that **potassium iodide** is decomposed with the separation of iodine—this reaction occurs in aq. or acidic soln., but, as A. Chwala and H. Colle showed, lead dioxide is formed from lead iodide and iodine. According to A. Ditte, when hydrated lead dioxide acts on a soln. of potassium iodide out of contact with air, iodine is set free, and white brilliant needles of the oxyiodide, $(PbI_2.PbO)_2.H_2O$, are formed. In the presence of air, the potassium hydroxide set free absorbs carbon dioxide from the air; the potassium carbonate formed complicates the reaction, and slightly yellowish needles of the compound $PbI_2.PbO.K_2CO_3.2H_2O$ separate out. When heated, the crystals lose water, and melt to a brown liquid, which forms a yellow mass on cooling : the compound is decomposed by dil. acids, carbon dioxide being given off, whilst the lead dissolves, and a residue of less soluble iodide is left. The same compound may be obtained more readily by passing a few bubbles of carbon dioxide into a mixture of potassium iodide soln. and lead dioxide, or by adding a small quantity of hydrogen potassium carbonate. If too much hydrocarbonate or carbon dioxide is added, the compound $2(PbOI_2.PbO).3K_2CO_3.2H_2O$ is formed. When a current of carbon dioxide is passed into a mixture of lead dioxide and potassium iodide, the latter being in excess, iodine is set free, and soon all the dioxide is converted into brilliant needles of either $PbI_2.2KI.2H_2O$, or if the unaltered potassium iodide and the potassium carbonate formed are present in the necessary proportions, $PbI_2.2KI.K_2CO_3.3H_2O$. Both these compounds are decomposed by water. If, on the other hand, lead dioxide acts on potassium iodide in presence of an excess of potassium hydrocarbonate, iodine is set free, and a double carbonate, $2PbCO_3.K_2CO_3$, is obtained as a white, crystalline powder. All the products previously obtained were converted into this double carbonate by the action of an excess of hydrogen potassium carbonate. The product of the action of lead dioxide on potassium iodide in presence of potassium carbonate thus varies with the relative proportions of iodide and carbonate. An increase of temp. has the same effect as an increase in the proportion of carbonate present. Similar results were obtained with **sodium iodide.** A. J. Balard showed that **hypochlorous acid** transforms lead dioxide into lead chloride with the evolution of oxygen and a little chlorine ; E. Müller and O. Friedberger, that iodic acid produces a little periodic acid ; and W. R. Hodgkinson and F. K. L. Lowndes, that lead dioxide is reduced to red-lead by fused potassium chlorate.

The powerful oxidizing property of lead dioxide is illustrated by its effect on sulphur. According to L. N. Vauquelin,[11] when lead dioxide is triturated with one-sixth its weight of sulphur, the latter is inflamed, and lead sulphide is formed ; and, according to D. H. Grindel, a mixture of the dioxide with half its weight of sulphur is inflamed when touched with a drop of sulphuric acid ; and if the mixture contains phosphorus, a violent explosion ensues on trituration. L. Vanino and O. Hauser showed that when hydrogen sulphide is passed over moist or dry lead dioxide the mass became red-hot, and there is a blue flame as the dioxide burns to sulphide. The heat of the reaction is such that explosives like gun-cotton or picrates are detonated by its means. M. V. N. Swamy and V. Simhachelan, however, found that hydrogen sulphide mixed with five vols of air does not attack 98·6 per cent lead dioxide cold or warm, but the mass is reddened, and adsorption products are formed. When an aq. or alcoholic soln. of hydrogen sulphide is treated with an excess of lead dioxide, some lead sulphide is formed and the liquid is freed from the gas—vide lead disulphide. Ammonium sulphide is likewise decomposed into ammonia and sulphur, and lead sulphide is formed. In analytical work, S. Bogdan showed that a liquid may be freed from ammonium sulphide in a few minutes by digestion with lead dioxide. E. Priwoznik found that yellow ammonium sulphide transforms lead dioxide into lead sulphide. A. Vogel, E. J. Russell and N. Smith, and D. L. Hammick found that at ordinary temp. sulphur dioxide reacts with lead dioxide with incandescence, forming lead sulphate, and freshly washed and not too dry lead dioxide absorbs sulphur dioxide from gases, and if oxygen be present, only a little sulphur trioxide is formed by surface action. O. Henry, and M. Dennstedt and F. Hassler showed that lead dioxide retains sulphur dioxide as lead sulphate during the combustion of organic substances. A. Vogel found that sulphurous acid transforms lead dioxide into lead sulphate—slowly in the cold, rapidly when heated. P. Marino could detect no signs of the formation of a dithionate ; lead sulphite is first formed and the sulphurous acid is oxidized to sulphuric acid, which forms lead sulphate. F. Streintz found that lead dioxide is soluble in a mixture of sulphurous and hydrochloric acids, forming lead sulphate with the evolution of 76·7–84·4 Cals. When lead dioxide is heated with conc. sulphuric acid, oxygen and lead sulphate are formed. According to V. Zotier, the complete decomposition requires 25–30 days at ordinary temp., and 3–4 hrs. at 100°. F. Dolezalek and K. Finckh showed that 1·0 millimol of crystalline lead dioxide is dissolved by a litre of conc. sulphuric acid at 22° ; and is changed to lead disulphate ; contrary to K. Elbs and F. W. Rixon, they found lead dioxide to be slightly soluble in acid containing less than 3 mols of H_2SO_4 per mol of water. O. F. Tower attempted to measure the oxidation potential of lead dioxide in sulphuric acid. M. Traube said that 40 per cent. sulphuric acid does not attack lead dioxide ; but if the dioxide be wetted with that acid, and persulphuric acid be added, oxygen is immediately evolved and lead sulphate is formed. G. Chancel and E. Diacon found that hot soln. of pentathionic acid form water and lead tetrathionate ; W. Spring, that tetrathionic acid has no action on lead dioxide, but hyposulphurous acid attacks the oxide ; M. Liebig found that sodium thiosulphate in the presence of acetic acid is completely decomposed in the cold ; and, according to A. Chwala and H. Colle, some lead tetrathionate is formed, which is partially decomposed to lead sulphide, sulphate, and thiosulphate. E. Spelta found that sulphuryl chloride reacts with lead dioxide in the cold, forming lead sulphate and chloride, and oxygen ; in excess, with hot soln., some chlorine is produced ; H. B. North and A. M. Hageman found that in a sealed tube, at 150°, lead dioxide and thionyl chloride form lead chloride and sulphuryl chloride. P. Marino showed that a dil. soln. of selenious acid does not reduce lead dioxide even after a prolonged boiling ; a more conc. soln. forms a mixture of lead selenite with a little selenate ; and with a still more conc. soln., lead selenite and lead pyroselenate.

According to A. Smits,[12] **magnesium nitride** reacts vigorously with lead dioxide. O. Michel and E. Grandmougin showed that **ammonia** gas reacts with heated lead dioxide, forming nitrogen, lead monoxide, and ammonium nitrite and nitrate ; I. W. Fay and co-workers detected signs of reduction after lead dioxide had been heated in an atm. of ammonia for 6 hrs. at 198° ; C. A. Lobry de Bruyn, that **hydroxylamine** is decomposed with inflammation ; E. Puxeddu, that **phenyl-hydrazine** reduces lead dioxide to the hemioxide at 17°, to red-lead at 60° ; and at higher temp., some metallic lead is formed ; and E. Lay, that **silicon hydro-trinitride**, Si_2N_3H, forms lead and lead monoxide. According to H. A. Auden and G. J. Fowler, lead dioxide dissolves in **hyponitrous acid,** forming lead nitrate ; **nitrous acid** is oxidized ; and **nitric oxide** gives a basic nitrate and lead. E. Müller and H. Barck found that lead dioxide at room temp. absorbs nitric oxide completely, forming lead nitrate ; at 200°, oxygen splits from the lead dioxide and forms nitrogen peroxide. B. C. Dutt and S. N. Sen found that nitric oxide acts on lead dioxide suspended in water, forming a mixture of lead nitrite and nitrate. The reaction was also examined by P. Sabatier and J. B. Senderens. P. Sabatier and J. B. Senderens found that the reduction to a basic nitrate by **nitrogen peroxide** is complete at 315° ; while **nitrous oxide** and nitric oxide give oxygen and lead monoxide ; when lead dioxide is shaken with water and nitric oxide in the absence of air, lead nitrite is formed. E. Müller and H. Barck found that nitric oxide at room temp. is completely absorbed, forming lead nitrite ; at 200°, a gram of lead dioxide absorbs 35 c.c. of nitric oxide ; and over 200°, some nitrogen peroxide is formed. The absorption of nitrogen peroxide and the higher oxides of nitrogen was discussed by F. Pregl, C. Gränacher, and M. Dennstedt and F. Hassler. The action of **nitric acid** on lead dioxide was examined by E. Franke, and J. F. Sacher. G. Grube found that a little lead dioxide is dissolved when warmed with dil. nitric acid ; and V. Zotier found that the dioxide is perceptibly attacked when stirred for 8 days with nitric acid ; in 15 days at ordinary temp., or in 3 hrs. at 100°, 20 c.c. of acid dissolved 0·1 grm. of dioxide. A. Chwala and H. Colle found $0·5N\text{-}HNO_3$ dissolves with a prolonged boiling less dioxide than $0·2N$-acid boiled for a short time. In time, however, all the dioxide is dissolved and oxygen is evolved. Probably the tetranitrate, $Pb(NO_3)_4$, is the first product of the reaction. According to A. C. Cumming, at 25°, nitric acid dissolves the following quantities of lead dioxide :

Normality of acid .	.	.	5·30	7·50	9·20	11·5
Millimol Pb per litre	.	.	0·140	0·415	0·802	1·54

F. Foerster found that lead dioxide is deposited when the soln. of lead dioxide in **nitric acid** is electrolyzed. E. Szterkhers showed that a mixture of nitric acid and sodium nitrite converts lead dioxide into lead and sodium nitrates. When lead dioxide and red **phosphorus** are triturated, the mass inflames ; with yellow phosphorus there is an explosion. A. Wurtz found that **hypophosphorous acid** forms lead phosphate ; A. Sänger, **phosphorous acid** forms phosphoric acid ; and V. Zotier, 50 per cent. **phosphoric acid** decomposes lead dioxide in a few months. A. Michaelis found that when lead dioxide is added to warm **phosphorus trichloride**, lead chloride, lead metaphosphate, and phosphoryl chloride are formed with incandescence ; the reaction is more vigorous if phosphorus trichloride be dropped on to lead dioxide ; and the addition of lead dioxide to cold phosphorus trichloride produces a hissing noise. According to C. F. Schönbein, finely divided arsenic is oxidized when shaken in water with lead dioxide ; and arsenic trioxide is oxidized to the pentoxide. C. Reichard said that the oxidation of arsenic trioxide does not occur in water or aq. ammonia, but only in conc. alkali-lye. T. E. Thorpe and J. W. Rodger found **thiophosphoryl fluoride** is completely absorbed by lead dioxide.

According to C. R. A. Wright and A. P. Luff,[13] **carbon** reduces lead dioxide at 260°; and **carbon monoxide** at 80°—in a sealed tube at 100° some carbon dioxide was formed. I. W. Fay and co-workers observed signs of reduction after heating lead dioxide in carbon monoxide for 6 hrs. at 110°, or in **methane** at 45°. No action was observed with **carbon dioxide.** H. Weil said that a little carbon dioxide is retained by lead dioxide, but M. Dennstedt and F. Hassler observed only a trace of adsorption below 100°, and none between 100° and 350°. A. de Hemptinne observed that under the influence of a silent discharge, the carbon monoxide behaves in a manner analogous to hydrogen. L. J. Constam and A. von Hansen found that **potassium percarbonate** is reduced. Aq. **hydrocyanic acid** furnished lead cyanide, water, and cyanogen: $PbO_2+4HCy=PbCy_2+2H_2O+Cy_2$. S. Tanatar found that a mixture of eq. proportions of potassium cyanide and hydrocyanic acid dissolve a little lead dioxide. C. F. Schönbein observed that **potassium ferrocyanide** is oxidized by lead dioxide, and **potassium ferrous ferrocyanide**, $K_2Fe(FeCy_6)$, is coloured blue. P. Sabatier and A. Mailhe found that the vap. of primary **alcohols** easily reduce the dioxide at 180°, forming lead monoxide, carbon dioxide, aldehyde, and acid; above 260°, the lead monoxide becomes active. H. Geisow showed that **formaldehyde** is oxidized to formic acid, and not carbon dioxide; J. F. Sacker, **acetic acid** reduces lead dioxide; and A. Chwala and H. Colle, **sodium acetate** soln. dissolves lead dioxide, forming the alkali plumbate. R. Böttger triturated lead dioxide with an eq. weight of **oxalic acid,** and obtained without ignition, steam, carbon dioxide, and lead carbonate; in the cold, a soln. of oxalic acid was found by A. Chwala and H. Colle to yield lead oxalate slowly and completely evolving oxygen gas. R. Böttger showed that lead dioxide becomes incandescent when triturated with one-sixth its weight of **tartaric acid, gallic acid, glucose,** or **mannite,** and with one-eighth its weight of **racemic acid, tannin,** or **cane-sugar.** F. C. Krauskopf found that a N-soln. of **potassium tartrate** dissolves lead dioxide without the evolution of oxygen; and A. Vogel, that lead oxide is formed when the dioxide is heated with sugar, or **turpentine.** C. F. Schönbein noted that the colours of many organic substances are destroyed; but tincture of **guaiacum** is coloured blue (R. Dupouy); an acetate acid soln. of **diphenylamine,** blue, by one part of the dioxide in 3,000,000 (C. G. Hinrichs); **methyldiaminodiphenylmethane,** blue (A. Trillat); and a conc. hydrochloric acid soln. of **aniline hydrochloride,** purple (W. V. Morgan). Numerous other reactions with lead dioxide as an oxidizing agent for organic substances have been examined. L. Kahlenberg and W. J. Trautmann found that lead dioxide behaves like red-lead towards powdered **silicon.** G. Rauter showed that **silicon tetrachloride** furnishes lead monoxide and chloride, silica, and chlorine; E. Lay, that with **silicon hexamminotetrabromide** lead is formed; and L. Moser, that **titanium trichloride** is oxidized when boiled with lead dioxide.

C. F. Schönbein [14] noticed that when finely divided **tin or lead** is shaken in water with lead dioxide, the metal is oxidized. According to G. von Hevesy, at the surface of contact of lead dioxide with a soln. containing $0·001N$-lead nitrate, and $0·001N$-nitric acid, and sat. with lead dioxide mixed with a trace of thorium-B, the rate of exchange was smaller than is the case of lead (q.v.), and approximated to the condition of thermodynamic equilibrium. H. Moissan noted that powdered **molybdenum** or **tungsten** mixed with lead dioxide becomes incandescent when heated, and oxidation occurs. F. de Carli found that lead dioxide reacts with **barium dioxide** but not with calcium, zinc, cadmium, or magnesium oxide. E. Müller and M. Soller found that a soln. of **chromic sulphate** furnishes chromic acid; and W. Crum, that soln. of **manganese salts** when warmed with lead dioxide and dil. nitric acid, become purple owing to the formation of a permanganate. This reaction is utilized in the colorimetric determination of manganese. C. F. Schönbein added that in the presence of dil. nitric acid, and lead dioxide, manganous salts furnish manganese dioxide; and manganese dioxide, manganese heptoxide, Mn_2O_7. D. Vitali said that under these conditions manganese sulphate, $MnSO_4$, becomes manganic sulphate, $Mn_2(SO_4)_3$. The reaction was studied by E. I. Dyrmont, and N. A. Waljaschko. L. L. de Koninck showed that a boiling soln. of a manganese salt in fuming hydrochloric acid becomes greenish-black when treated with lead dioxide, owing to the formation of lead tetrachloride—red-lead does not act in the same way. According to H. N. Morse, in the presence of nitric acid, lead dioxide and **permanganic acid** both lose oxygen : $3PbO_2+2HMnO_4=H_2O+2MnO_2+3PbO+3O_2$. H. Moissan found oxygen is evolved when a mixture of carbon, and lead and manganese dioxides is heated. A. Levol said lead dioxide dissolves completely in a soln. of **mercurous nitrate,** forming mercuric nitrate and lead monoxide. A. Vogel found **stannous chloride** reacts with lead dioxide, forming lead chloride and stannic oxide. C. F. Schönbein found that **ferrous salts** are oxidized by lead dioxide, and, according to C. Russo and G. Sensi, the reaction is quantitative. The reaction was studied by L. Lucas, and C. Semper and C. Fahlberg, etc. When a mixture of lead dioxide and ferrous sulphate is heated, J. G. McIntosh obtained red ferric oxide—the so-called *Venetian red*. Lead dioxide is chiefly used in making safety matches, in the manufacture of accumulator plates, and in the dye industry.

REFERENCES.

[1] C. W. Scheele, *Svenska Vet. Handl.*, 35. 89, 177, 1774 ; J. Priestley, *Experiments and Observations on Different Kinds of Air*, Birmingham, 2. 121, 1790.

[2] A. Breithaupt, *Vollstandiges Handbuch der Mineralogie*, Dresden, 3. 825, 1847 ; *Journ. prakt. Chem.*, (1), 10. 508, 1837 ; J. F. L. Hausmann, *Handbuch der Mineralogie*, Göttingen, 202, 1847 ; W. Haidinger, *Handbuch der bestimmenden Mineralogie*, Wien, 504, 1845 ; E. Kinch, *Min. Mag.*, 7. 63, 1886 ; M. F. Heddle, *ib.*, 8. 203, 1889 ; *The Mineralogy of Scotland*, Edinburgh, 1. 103, 1901 ; H. A. Wheeler, *Amer. Journ. Science*, (3), 38. 79, 1889 ; J. D. and E. N. Hawkins, *ib.*, (3). 38. 165, 1889 ; W. S. Yeates and E. F. Ayres, *ib.*, (3), 38. 79, 1889 ; (3), 43. 407, 1892.

[3] W. Minor, *Der Techniker*, 16. 80, 1894 ; *Journ. Soc. Chem. Ind.*, 13. 940, 1894 ; L. Michel, *Bull. Soc. Min.*, 13. 86, 1890 ; F. Göbel, *Schweigger's Journ.*, 67. 77, 1833 ; C. F. Schönbein, *Verh. Nat. Ges. Basel*, 2. 20, 1858 ; L. E. Rivot, F. S. Beudant, and P. A. Daguin, *Ann. Mines*, (5), 4. 221, 1853 ; A. Overbeck, *Arch. Pharm.*, (2), 85. 6, 1856 ; M. Höhnel, *ib.*, 232. 224, 1894 ; G. Kassner, *ib.*, 228. 113, 1890 ; 255. 130, 1917 ; W. Kubel, *ib.*, 230. 180, 1892 ; C. Panopolus, *Chem. Ztg.*, 40. 340, 1916 ; J. Milbauer, *ib.*, 38. 587, 1914 ; W. Palmaer, *Medd. Vet. Nobel-Inst.*, 5. 31, 1919 ; *Zeit. Elektrochem.*, 29. 415, 1923 ; C. L. Berthollet, *Essai de statique chimique*, Paris, 2. 377, 1803 ; F. Muck, *Pharm. Vierteljahr.*, 4. 546, 1855 ; A. Seyewetz and P. Trawitz, *Bull. Soc. Chim.*, (3), 29. 456, 1903 ; V. Zotier, *ib.*, (4), 13. 61, 1913 ; (4), 15. 402, 1914 ; (4), 21. 241, 1917 ; C. Fahlenberg, *ib.*, (2), 38. 154, 1882 ; M. Lachaud and C. Lepierre, *ib.*, (3). 6. 231, 1891 ; C. Puscher, *Dingler's Journ.*, 140. 54, 1856 ; L. Friderich, E. Mallet, and P. A. Guye, *Monit. Scient.*, (4), 20. 514, 1906 ; E. W. Wescott, *Journ. Amer. Chem. Soc.*, 42. 1335, 1920 ; G. Schaumann, *Beiträge zur Iodometrie der Superoxyde*, Freiberg, 1903 ; C. W. Scheele, *Svenska Vet. Handl.*, 35. 89, 177, 1774 ; J. Priestley, *Experiments and Observations on Different Kinds of Air*, Birmingham, 2. 121, 1790 ; E. Rupp, *Zeit. anal. Chem.*, 42. 732, 1903 ; A. Chwala, and H. Colle, *ib.*, 50. 226, 1911 ; R. Böttger, *Journ. prakt. Chem.*, (1), 76. 235, 1859 ; A. Breithaupt, *ib.*, (1), 10. 508, 1837 ; F. M. Lyte, *Brit. Pat. No.* 1721, 1882 ; H. Bardt, *ib.*, 194340, 1921 ; A. Fehrmann, *Ber.*, 25. 1882, 1882 ; A. Guttmann, *ib.*, 45. 829, 1912 ; G. Iioka and K. K. S. Seisakujo, *Japan. Pat. No.* 44220, 1922 ; P. Jannasch, *Praktischer Leitfaden der Gewichtsanalyse*, Leipzig, 88, 1904 ; J. J. Berzelius, *Gilbert's Ann.*, 40. 166, 186, 1812 ; 46. 131, 1814 ; *Schweigger's Journ.*, 7. 71, 1813 ; T. Thomson, *Nicholson's Journ.*, 8. 280, 1804 ; W. Beetz, *Pogg. Ann.*, 61. 209, 1844 ; J. von Liebig and F. Wöhler, *ib.*, 24. 172, 1832 ; W. Wernicke, *ib.*, 139. 132, 1870 ; F. Wöhler, *Liebig's Ann.*, 146. 263, 375, 1868 ; A. Geuther, *ib.*, 96. 382, 1855 ; G. C. Winkelblech, *ib.*, 21. 21, 1837 ; *Journ. prakt. Chem.*, (1), 10. 227, 1837 ; F. Jirsa, *Zeit. phys. Chem.*, 94. 1, 1920 ; H. N. Warren, *Chem. News*, 74. 144, 1896 ; J. Strachan. *ib.*, 98. 103. 1908 ; C. Luckow, *German Pat., D.R.P.* 91707, 1894 ; 105143, 1895 ; H. Blumenberg, *ib.*, 109823, 1898 ; Griesheim-Elektron, *Brit. Pat. No.* 12186, 1901 ; *German Pat., D.R.PP.* 124512 1900 ; 133379, 1901 ; Konsortium für Elektrochemische Industrie, *ib.*, 195117, 1906 ; P. Ferchland, *ib.*, 140317, 1902 ; F. R. Steigelmann, *ib.*, 162107, 1903 ; H. Bardt, *Brit. Pat. No.* 194340, 1921 ; J. H. Mellquist, *ib.*, 220944, 1923 ; L. Grunbaum, *U.S. Pat. No.* 1506633, 1924 ; W. Borchers, *Zeit. Elektrochem.*, 3. 484, 1897 ; G. Grube, *ib.*, 28. 285, 1922 ; F. Peters, *Centrb. Accumul.*, 2. 293, 305, 321, 1901 ; 3. 83, 112, 140, 202, 246, 1902 ; 4. 273, 285, 1903 ; 5. 1, 13, 26, 38, 1904 ; A. Rokotnitz, *ib.*, 4. 213, 227, 237, 251, 261, 1903 ; *Studien über die elektrolytische Bildung von Bleisuperoxyd aus metallischen Blei*, Berlin, 1903 ; N. W. Fischer, *Kastner's Arch.*, 16. 219, 1829 ; F. Fischer and H. Plötze, *Zeit. anorg. Chem.*, 75. 27, 1912 ; F. Fischer and K. Thiele, *ib.*, 67. 302, 1910 ; A. Gutbier and H. O. Meyer, *ib.*, 141. 95, 1924 ; W. Reinders and L. Hamburger, *ib.*, 89. 82, 1914 ; L. N. Vauquelin, *Mém. Inst.*, 5. 184, 1804 ; *Ann. Chim. Phys.*, (1),

62. 221, 1807 ; **A. J.** Balard, *ib.*, (2), **32.** 337, 1826 ; A. Ditte, *ib.*, (5), **24.** 241, 1881 ; A. Levol, *ib.*, (2), **75.** 108, 1840 ; M. E. Chevreul, *ib.*, (1), **80.** 315, 1811 ; A. C. Becquerel, *ib.*, (2), **51.** 104, 1832 ; (3), **8.** 402, 1843 ; **A.** Sobrero and F. Selmi, *ib.*, (3), **21.** 161, 1847 ; N. A. E. Millon, *ib.*, (3), **29.** 506, 1850 ; *Compt. Rend.*, **28.** 42, 1849 ; A. Reynoso, *ib.*, **32.** 646, 1851 ; F. Mailfert, *ib.*, **94.** 860, 1186, 1882 ; V. A. Jacquelain, *ib.*, **31.** 626, 1850 ; J. Pelouze, *ib.*, **13.** 1051, 1841 ; *Ann. Chim. Phys.*, (3), **4.** 104, 1842 ; S. Glasstone, *Journ. Chem. Soc.*, **121.** 1469, 1922 ; M. G. Mellon and H. F. Reinhard, *Proc. Indiana Acad.*, 181, 1921.

⁴ A. Colson, *Compt. Rend.*, **137.** 660, 1903 ; L. Marino, *Gazz. Chim. Ital.*, **38.** i, 249, 1908 ; **39.** ii, 640, 1909 ; *Zeit. anorg. Chem.*, **56.** 233, 1907 ; **62.** 173, 1909 ; H. Weil, *Ber.*, **43.** 149, 1910 ; M. Dennstedt and F. Hassler, *ib.*, **43.** 1197, 1911 ; *Zeit. angew. Chem.*, **18.** 1562, 1905 ; W. F. Edwards, *Met. Chem. Engg.*, **20.** 36, 1919 ; A. Hutchinson and W. Pollard, *Journ. Chem. Soc.*, **69.** 226, 1896 ; J. Heyes, *Phil. Mag.*, (5), **25.** 221, 1888 ; **A.** Gutbier and H. O. Meyer, *Zeit. anorg. Chem.*, **141.** 95, 1924.

⁵ W. S. Yeates and E. F. Ayres, *Amer. Journ. Science*, (3), **38.** 79, 1889 ; (3), **43.** 407, 1892 ; H. A. Wheeler, *ib.*, (3), **38.** 79, 1889 ; J. D. and E. N. Hawkins, *ib.*, (3), **38.** 165, 1889 ; L. Michel, *Bull. Soc. Min.*, **13.** 56, 1899 ; A. Geuther, *Liebig's Ann.*, **219.** 56, 1883 ; O. Luedecke, *Zeit. Kryst.*, **8.** 82, 1884 ; P. Niggli, *ib.*, **56.** 41, 1922 ; F. Dolezalek and K. Finckh, *Zeit. anorg. Chem.*, **51.** 320, 1907 ; W. Reinders and L. Hamburger, *ib.*, **89.** 71, 1914 ; B. Wäser and R. Kühnel, *Elektrochem. Zeit.*, **18.** 151, 1912 ; A. Breithaupt, *Journ. prakt. Chem.*, (1), **10.** 508, 1837 ; R. Böttger, *ib.*, (1), **76.** 235, 1859 ; **A.** C. Becquerel, *Ann. Chim. Phys.*, (2), **51.** 104, 1832 ; (3), **8.** 405. 1843 ; P. F. G. Boullay, *ib.*, (2), **43.** 266, 1830 ; J. Königsberger and W. J. Müller, *Phys. Zeit.*, **6.** 849, 1905 ; **12.** 606, 1911 ; A. S. Russell, *ib.*, **13.** 62, 1912 ; T. Sundorpf, *Wied. Ann.*, **69.** 319, 1899 ; K. Schreber, *ib.*, **36.** 662, 1889 ; S. Meyer, *ib.*, **69.** 245, 1899 ; F. Streintz and G. Neumann, *ib.*, **41.** 97, 1890 ; F. Streintz, *ib.*, **53.** 698, 1894 ; *Ann. Physik*, (4), **9.** 861, 1902 ; *Zeit. Elektrochem.*, **10.** 414, 1904 ; P. Ferchland, *ib.*, **9.** 670, 1903 ; T. von Hagen, *ib.*, **25.** 375, 1919 ; G. Grube, *ib.*, **28.** 285, 1922 ; W. Herapath, *Phil. Mag.*, (1), **64.** 321, 1824 ; C. J. B. Karsten, *Schweigger's Journ.*, **65.** 394, 1832 ; W. Wernicke, *Pogg. Ann.*, **139.** 132, 1870 ; I. M. Tscheltzoff, *Compt. Rend.*, **100.** 1458, 1885 ; B. A. Dima, *ib.*, **157.** 591, 1913 ; A. Hollard, *ib.*, **136.** 229, 1903 ; **138.** 142, 1904 ; L. Playfair and J. P. Joule, *Mem. Chem. Soc.*, **3.** 84. 1848 ; E. W. Wescott, *Journ. Amer. Chem. Soc.*, **42.** 1335, 1920 ; W. Spring, *Ann. Soc. Géol. Belg.*, **15.** 156, 1888 ; *Zeit. phys. Chem.*, **2.** 532, 535, 1888 ; M. L. Huggins, *Phys. Rev.*, (2), **21.** 719, 1922 ; W. P. Davey, *ib.*, (2), **23.** 763, 1924 ; B. Aulenkamp, *Zeit. Physik*, **18.** 70, 1923 ; W. A. Palmaer, *Medd. Nobelinst.*, **5.** 31, 1919 ; *Zeit. Elektrochem.*, **29.** 415, 1923 ; E. Kinch, *Min. Mag.*, **7.** 63, 1887 ; M. F. Heddle, *ib.*, **8.** 203, 1889 ; *The Mineralogy of Scotland*, Edinburgh, **1.** 103, 1901 ; J. Shields, *Chem. News*, **65.** 87, 1892 ; A. Reis and L. Zimmermann, *Zeit. phys. Chem.*, **102.** 298, 1922 ; E. Winterhalder, *Zeit. phys. Chem. Unterr.*, **36.** 117, 1923 ; L. Kahlenberg and A. S. McDaniel, *Trans. Amer. Electrochem. Soc.*, **9.** 369, 1906 ; D. A. MacInnes, L. Adler, and D. B. Joubert, *ib.*, **37.** 641, 1920 ; K. Bädeker, *Ann. Physik*, (4), **22.** 749, 1917 ; *Ueber die elektrische Leitfahigkeit und die thermoelektrische Kraft einiger Schwermetallverbindungen*, Leipzig, 1906 ; J F. Weyde, *Elektrotech. Zeit.*, **13.** 315, 1892 ; C. Zenghelis, *Zeit. phys. Chem.*, **50.** 221, 1905 ; A. C. Cumming, *Trans. Faraday Soc.*, **2.** 209, 1907 ; A. von Oettingen, *Journ. South Africa Chem.*, **2.** 9, 21, 1899 ; S. B. Christy, *Amer. Chem. Journ.*, **27.** 368, 1902 ; J. Miesler, *Monatsh.*, **8.** 626, 1887 ; S. Glasstone, *Journ. Chem. Soc.*, **121.** 1469, 1922 ; J. Cayrel, *Compt. Rend.*, **81.** 1127, 1925 ; A. Ferrari, *Atti Acad. Lincei*, (6). **2.** ii, 186, 1925 ; K. Schreber, *Zeit. Elektrochem.*, **32.** 143, 1925 ; A. Sommerfeld, *Zeit. Physik*, **36.** 36, 1926 ; A. E. van Arkel, *Physica*, **5.** 162, 1926.

⁶ H. Nissenson and H. Danneel, *Zeit. Elektrochem.*, **9.** 760, 1903 ; **H.** J. S. Sand, *Chem. News*, **100.** 264, 1909 ; H. Zocher, *Zeit. anorg. Chem.*, **112.** 60, 1920 ; F. Fischer and H. Plötze, *ib.*, **75.** 21, 1912 ; I. Bellucci and N. Parravano, *ib.*, **50.** 107, 1906 ; *Atti Accad. Lincei*, (5), **14.** i, 378, 1905 ; (5), **15.** ii, 542, 631, 1906 ; *Gazz. Chim. Ital.*, **35.** ii, 500, 1905 ; **37.** i, 171, 1907 ; N. Parravano and G. Calcagni, *ib.*, **37.** ii, 264, 1907 ; G. Kassner, *Arch. Pharm.*, **232.** 386, 1894 ; **233.** 501, 1895 ; **255.** 130, 1917 ; J. J. Berzelius, *Pogg. Ann.*, **4.** 139, 1825 ; W. Wernicke, *ib.*, **139.** 172, 1870 ; **141.** 109, 1870 ; W. Zotier, *Bull. Soc. Chim.*, (4), **13.** 61, 1913 ; (4), **15.** 402, 1914 ; A. Gutbier and H. O. Meyer, *Zeit. anorg. Chem.*, **141.** 95, 1924 ; A. Gutbier and E. Sauer, *Zeit. Koll.*, **12.** 171, 1913 ; Chemische Fabrik von Heyden, *German Pat.*, *D.R.P.* 227491, 1909 ; S. Glasstone, *Journ. Chem. Soc.*, **121.** 1469, 1922 ; S. S. Bhatnagar, *ib.*, **119.** 1760, 1921 ; G. Grube, *Zeit. Elektrochem.*, **28.** 273, 1922 ; F. Streintz and G. Naumann, *Wied. Ann.*, **41.** 97, 1890 ; K. Schreber, *ib.*, **36.** 662, 1889 ; M. Wissmüller, *Zur Kenntnis des vierwertigen Bleis*, Erlangen, 39, 1916 ; **F.** Hein and H. Meininger, *Zeit. anorg. Chem.*, **145.** 95, 1925.

⁷ J. E. Mackenzie, *Chem. News*, **99.** 146, 1909 ; P. Sabatier and J. B. Senderens, *Compt. Rend.*, **114.** 1467, 1892 ; H. Debray, *ib.*, **86.** 513, 1878 ; T. Carnelley and J. Walker, *Journ. Chem. Soc.*, **63.** 59, 1888 ; S. Glasstone, *ib.*, **121.** 1480, 1922 ; J. Milbauer, *Chem. Ztg.*, **34.** 140, 1910 ; W. Stahl, *ib.*, **45.** 781, 1921 ; F. Fischer and H. Plötze, *Zeit. anorg. Chem.*, **75.** 25, 1912 ; O. Brunck, *ib.*, **10.** 244, 1895 ; V. A. Kroll, *ib.*, **78.** 100, 1912 ; W. Reinders and L. Hamburger, *ib.*, **89.** 71, 1914 ; D. Balareff, *ib.*, **134.** 75, 1924 ; W. Biltz, *ib.*, **109.** 132, 1920 ; W. Hempel and C. Schubert, *Zeit. Elektrochem.*, **18.** 729, 1912 ; C. Schubert, *Beiträge zur Kenntnis der Dissoziation einiger Oxyde, Karbonate, und Sulfide*, Dresden, 1910 ; M. Dennstedt and F. Hassler, *Zeit. anal. Chem.*, **42.** 417, 1903.

⁸ A. de Hemptinne, *Bull. Acad. Belg.*, **5.** 249, 1919 ; **7.** 146, 458, 590, 1921 ; W. Müller, *Pogg. Ann.*, **136.** 51, 1869 ; F. Glaser, *Zeit. anorg. Chem.*, **36.** 1, 1903 ; H. Zocher, *ib.*, **112.** 61, 1920 ; B. Brauner, *ib.*, **7.** i, 1894 ; *Ber. Böhm. Ges.*, 295, 1885 ; K. Frenzel, S. Fritz, and V. Meyer,

Ber., **30**. 2517, 1897 ; P. Sabatier and L. Espil, *Ber.*, **159**. 137, 1914 ; C. F. Schönbein, *Verh. Nat. Ges. Basel*, **2**. 20, 113, 1858 ; H. Schlossberg, *Zeit. Anal. Chem.*, **41**. 741, 1902 ; E. Pieszeczek, *Pharm. Ztg.*, **52**. 922, 1907 ; T. Gigli, *Boll. Chim. Pharm.*, **12**. 675, 1893 ; H. J. S. Sand, *Trans. Faraday Soc.*, **5**. 209, 1910 ; I. W. Fay, A. F. Seeker, F. H. Lane, and G. E. Ferguson, *Polyt. Eng.*, **10**. 72, 1910 ; J. Milbauer, *Chem. Ztg.*, **36**. 1484, 1912 ; V. Zotier, *Bull. Soc. Chim.*, (4), **21**. 244, 1917 ; C. R. A. Wright and A. P. Luff, *Journ. Chem. Soc.*, **33**. 532, 1878 ; S. Glasstone, *ib.*, **121**. 1459, 1922.

⁹ C. F. Schönbein, *Verh. Nat. Ges. Basel*, **2**. 20, 113, 1858 ; A. Mailfert, *Compt. Rend.*, **94**. 860, 1186, 1882 ; B. Brauner, *Ber. Böhm. Ges.*, 295, 1885 ; *Zeit. anorg. Chem.*, **7**. 2, 1894 ; E. Pieszczek, *Pharm. Ztg.*, **52**. 922, 1907 ; E. Schöne, *Liebig's Ann.*, **196**. 72, 1879 ; T. Gigli, *Boll. Chim. Pharm.*, **12**. 675, 1893 ; H. Schlossberg, *Zeit. anal. Chem.*, **41**. 741, 1902.

¹⁰ M. Dennstedt and F. Hassler, *Zeit. anorg. Chem.*, **42**. 417, 1903 ; A. Classen and B. Zahorsky, *ib.*, **4**. 102, 1893 ; H. Zocher, *ib.*, **112**. 60, 1920 ; F. Fischer and K. Thiele, *ib.*, **67**. 302, 1910 ; B. Brauner, *ib.*, **7**. 2, 1894 ; *Ber. Böhm. Ges.*, 295, 1885 ; C. F. Schönbein, *Pogg. Ann.*, **78**. 162, 1849 ; A. Chwala and H. Colle, *Zeit. anal. Chem.*, **50**. 227, 1911 ; *Gazz. Chim. Ital.*, **41**. ii, 551, 1911 ; E. Spelta, *ib.*, **34**. i, 262, 1904 ; A. Alessi, *Ber.*, **22**. 485, 1889 ; C. L. Müller and G. Kircher, *ib.*, **15**. 812, 1882 ; E. Müller and O. Friedberger, *ib.*, **35**. 2652, 1902 ; H. B. North and A. M. Hageman, *Journ. Amer. Chem. Soc.*, **35**. 543, 1913 ; A. J. Balard, *Taylor's Scientific Memoirs*, **1**. 269, 1837 ; *Ann. Chim. Phys.*, (2), **32**. 350, 1826 ; (2), **57**. 225, 1834 ; H. Moissan, *ib.*, (6), **24**. 261, 1891 ; W. R. Hodgkinson and F. K. L. Lowndes, *Chem. News*, **59**. 63, 1889 ; A. Ditte, *Compt. Rend.*, **93**. 64, 1881 ; G. Bozza and M. Bertozi, *Giorn. Chim. Ind. Appl.*, **6**. 571, 1924.

¹¹ L. N. Vauquelin, *Ann. Chim. Phys.*, (1), **62**. 221, 1807 ; A. Vogel, *Kastner's Arch.*, **4**. 434, 1825 ; M. V. N. Swamy and V. Simhachelan, *Proc. Science Assoc. Maharadjah Coll.*, **17**, 1923 ; E. J. Russell, *Journ. Chem. Soc.*, **77**. 352, 1900 ; E. J. Russell and N. Smith, *ib.*, **77**. 340, 1900 ; D. L. Hammick, *ib.*, **111**. 388, 1917 ; O. Henry, *Journ. Pharm. Chim.*, (2), **20**. 59, 1834 ; A. Chwala and H. Colle, *Zeit. anal. Chem.*, **50**. 241, 1911 ; *Gazz. Chim. Ital.*, **41**. ii, 551, 1911 ; S. Bogdan, *Bull. Soc. Chim.*, (3), **29**. 594, 1903 ; V. Zotier, *ib.*, (4), **21**. 244, 1917 ; D. H. Grindel, *Schweigger's Journ.*, **15**. 478. 1815 ; L. Vanino and O. Hauser, *Ber.*, **33**. 625, 1900 ; E. Priwoznik, *ib.*, **6**. 1291, 1873 ; M. Traube, *ib.*, **22**. 1524, 1889 ; F. Streintz, *Monatsh.*, **15**. 285, 1894 ; *Wied. Ann.*, **53**. 698, 1894 ; P. Marino, *Atti Accad. Lincei*, (5), **17**. i, 589, 1908 ; *Zeit. anorg. Chem.*, **59**. 452, 1908 ; F. Dolezalek and K. Finckh, *ib.*, **50**. 82, 1906 ; 51. 320, 1907 ; K. Elbs and F. W. Rixon, *Zeit. Elektrochem.*, **9**. 267, 1903 ; W. Spring, *Liebig's Ann.*, **201**, 377, 1880 ; O. F. Tower, *Zeit. phys. Chem.*, **18**. 20, 1895 ; M. Liebig, *Zeit. angew. Chem.*, **14**. 828, 1901 ; G. Chancel and E. Diacon, *Compt. Rend.*, **56**. 710, 1863 ; E. Spelta, *Gazz. Chim. Ital.*, **34**. i, 262, 1904 ; H. B. North and A. M. Hageman, *Journ. Amer. Chem. Soc.*, **35**. 543, 1913 ; M. Dennstedt and F. Hassler, *Zeit. anal. Chem.*, **42**. 419, 1903.

¹² E. Lay, *Ueber Silicium-Stickstoff-Wasserstoff Verbindungen*, München, 1910 ; C. A. Lobry de Bruyn, *Rec. Trav. Chim. Pays-Bas*, **11**. 18, 1892 ; A. Smits, *ib.*, **15**. 135, 1896 ; F. Pregl, *Die quantitative Mikroelementaranalyse*, Berlin, 1917 ; P. Sabatier and J. B. Senderens, *Compt. Rend.*, **114**. 1429, 1476, 1892 ; 120. 618, 1895 ; *Ann. Chim. Phys.*, (7), **7**. 348, 1896 ; O. Michel and E. Grandmougin, *Ber.*, **26**. 2565, 1893 ; I. W. Fay, A. F. Seeker, F. H. Lane, and G. E. Ferguson, *Polyt. Eng.*, **10**. 72, 1910 ; B. C. Dutt and S. N. Sen, *Proc. Asiatic Soc. Bengal*, **10**. 287, 1914 ; A. Michaelis, *Journ. prakt. Chem.*, (2), **4**. 449, 1871 ; T. E. Thorpe and J. W. Rodger, *Journ. Chem. Soc.*, **53**. 766, 1888 ; H. A. Auden and G. J. Fowler, *Chem. News*, **72**. 163, 1895 ; A. Wurtz, *Compt. Rend.*, **18**. 702, 1844 ; E. Puxeddu, *Gazz. Chim. Ital.*, **46**. i, 75, 1916 ; A. Sänger, *Liebig's Ann.*, **232**. 14, 1886 ; C. Gränacher, *Helvetica Chim. Acta*, **2**, 76, 1919 ; E. Müller and H. Barck, *Zeit. anorg. Chem.*, **129**. 314, 1923 ; C. F. Schönbein, *Pogg. Ann.*, **78**. 162, 1849 ; M. Dennstedt and F. Hassler, *Zeit. anal. Chem.*, **42**. 419, 1903 ; A. Chwala and H. Colle, *ib.*, **50**. 241, 1911 ; *Gazz. Chim. Ital.*, **41**. ii, 551, 1911 ; E. Franke, *Zeit. phys. Chem.*, **16**. 477, 1895 ; J. F. Sacher, *Chem. Ztg.*, **35**. 731, 1911 ; C. Reichard, *ib.*, **22**. 774, 1898 ; E. Szterkhers, *Ann. Chim. Anal.*, **7**. 214, 1902 ; F. Foerster, *Zeit. Elektrochem.*, **3**. 530, 1897 ; G. Grube, *ib.*, **28**. 285, 1922 ; A. C. Cumming, *ib.*, **13**. 19, 1907 ; *Trans. Faraday Soc.*, **2**. 199, 1908 ; V. Zotier, *Bull. Soc. Chim.*, (4), **21**. 244, 1917 ; E. Müller and H. Barck, *Zeit. anorg. Chem.*, **129**. 309, 1923.

¹³ C. R. A. Wright and A. P. Luff, *Journ. Chem. Soc.*, **33**. 1, 542, 1875 ; A. de Hemptinne, *Bull. Acad. Belg.*, 249, 1919 ; C. Graebe and H. Kraft, *Ber.*, **39**. 794, 1906 ; M. Dennstedt and F. Hassler, *ib.*, **43**. 1197, 1910 ; H. Weil, *ib.*, **43**. 149, 1910 ; S. Tanatar, *ib.*, **42**. 1517, 1909 ; H. Geisow, *ib.*, **37**. 517, 1904 ; J. F. Sacker, *Chem. Ztg.*, **35**. 731, 1911 ; L. Moser, *ib.*, **39**. 245, 1915 ; L. J. Constam and A. von Hansen, *Zeit. Elektrochem.*, **3**. 137, 1896 ; A. Chwala and H. Colle, *Zeit. anal. Chem.*, **50**. 241, 1911 ; *Gazz. Chim. Ital.*, **41**. ii 551, 1911 ; C. Russo and G. Sensi, *ib.*, **44**. i, 9, 1914 ; F. C. Krauskopf, *Journ. Amer. Chem. Soc.*, **33**. 943, 1911 ; C. F. Schönbein, *Pogg. Ann.*, **78**. 162, 1849 ; R. Dupouy, *Repert. Pharm.*, (3), **9**. 346, 1897 ; *Pharm. Centrh.*, **38**. 705, 1897 ; C. G. Hinrichs, *Bull. Soc. Chim.*, (3), **33**. 1002, 1905 ; A. Trillat, *Compt. Rend.*, **136**. 1205, 1903 ; G. Rauter, *Liebig's Ann.*, **270**. 236, 1892 ; R. Böttger, *Journ. prakt. Chem.*, (1), **76**. 235, 1859 ; P. Sabatier and A. Mailhe, *Ann. Chim. Phys.*, (8), **20**. 323, 1910 ; W. V. Morgan, *Journ. Ind. Eng. Chem.*, **11**. 1055, 1919 ; E. Lay, *Ueber Silicium-Stickstoff-Wasserstoff Verbindungen*, München, 1910 ; I. W. Fay, A. F. Seeker, F. H. Lane, and G. E. Ferguson, *Polyt. Eng.*, **10**. 72, 1910 ; L. Kahlenberg and W. J. Trautmann, *Trans. Amer. Electrochem. Soc.*, **39**. 477, 1921 ; A. Vogel, *Kastner's Arch.*, **23**. 84, 1832.

¹⁴ H. N. Morse, *Ber.*, **30**. 48, 1897 ; C. Semper and C. Fahlberg, *Brit. Pat. No.* 5579, 1881 ;

C. Fahlberg, *Bull. Soc. Chim.*, (2), **38**. 155, 1882 ; H. Moissan, *ib.*, (3), **13**. 969, 1895 ; *Compt. Rend.*, **97**. 196, 1883 ; **122**. 1289, 1896 ; C. F. Schönbein, *Pogg. Ann.*, **78**. 162, 1849 ; W. Crum, *Mem. Chem. Soc.*, **2**. 387, 1845 ; *Journ. prakt. Chem.*, (1), **37**. 158, 1846 ; *Liebig's Ann.*, **60**. 219, 1846 ; L. L. de Koninck, *Bull. Assoc. Belg.*, **16**. 94, 1902 ; D. Vitali, *Boll. Chim. Pharm.*, **37**. 545, 1899 ; **38**. 210, 1899 ; E. Müller and M. Soller, *Zeit. Elektrochem.*, **11**. 863, 1905 ; J. G. McIntosh, *Chem. News*, **89**. 197, 1904 ; G. Russo and G. Sensi, *Gazz. Chim. Ital.*, **44**. i, 9, 1914 ; G. von Hevesy, *Phys. Zeit.*, **16**. 52, 1915 ; A. Vogel, *Kastner's Arch.*, **23**. 84, 1833 ; L. Lucas, *German Pat.*, *D.R.P.* 154085, 1903 ; A. Levol, *Ann. Chim. Phys.*, (2), **75**. 108, 1840 ; E. I. Dyrmont, *Journ. Russ. Phys. Chem. Soc.*, **48**. 1807, 1917 ; N. A. Waljaschko, *ib.*, **48**. 1815, 1917 ; F. de Carli, *Atti Accad. Lincei*, (6), **1**. 533, 1925.

§ 20. The Plumbates

According to E. Frémy,[1] **potassium metaplumbate**, $K_2PbO_3.3H_2O$, is formed by fusing lead dioxide with an excess of potassium hydroxide in a silver crucible, dissolving the product in water, and evaporating the soln., which then furnishes definite crystals. The same product is obtained by fusing potassium hydroxide and lead monoxide. The monoxide is oxidized to dioxide during the fusion, and the reaction then proceeds as before. S. Meunier, and O. Seidel used similar processes. I. Bellucci and N. Parravano added lead dioxide to a hot soln. of 100 grms. of potassium hydroxide and 20–30 grms. of water, until no more dissolved. The cold mass was dissolved in a small proportion of water, filtered, and the soln. seeded with crystals of potassium stannate or platinate. The crystals were washed rapidly with absolute alcohol, dried first between folds of filter-paper, and afterwards over potassium hydroxide in a desiccator. The yield was said to be good. G. L. Clark used a similar process. G. Grube prepared this plumbate by the anodic soln. of a lead anode in a conc. soln. of alkali hydroxide by means of a direct current of high current density on which is superposed an alternating current. In another method, a soln. of lead monoxide in alkali-lye is submitted to anodic oxidation at a platinum electrode. In both cases, alkali plumbates crystallize from the liquid during the electrolysis. F. Jirsa electrolyzed a soln. of 40 grms. of potassium hydroxide and 4·5 grms. of lead monoxide per litre, using an alternating current, and palladium electrodes. There was a deposit of yellow sesquioxide and a soln. of lead plumbate was formed—*vide* lead dioxide, and alkali plumbates. For the oxidation of plumbite to plumbate, *vide* the plumbites.

Analyses of the products, by E. Frémy, G. Grube, and I. Bellucci and N. Parravano, agree with the formula $K_2PbO_3.3H_2O$. As G. L. Clark, and I. Bellucci and N. Parravano have shown, the water is constitutional because, when it is expelled, the compound decomposes. By analogy with the isomorphous stannate, and platinate, the formula is written $K_2Pb(OH)_6$; and this is confirmed by the formation of the sesquioxide, $Pb_2O_3.3H_2O$, or rather $Pb[Pb(OH)_6]$, when the soln. is treated with potassium plumbite, K_2PbO_2. On the other hand, G. Grube found that when the sodium salt is heated, the water can be all expelled without decomposing the salt, and hence he inferred that the 3 mols of combined water are water of crystallization, and that the compound is therefore a salt of metaplumbic acid. A. Geuther claimed to have made the anhydrous salt from the product obtained by passing oxygen into a fused soln. of lead monoxide in potassium hydroxide. The pale, yellowish-brown, dichroic plates, according to O. Lüdecke, belong to the hexagonal system. As indicated above, G. L. Clark found the trihydrate decomposes as the water is expelled.

Crystals of trihydrated potassium plumbate were described by E. Frémy as colourless, transparent rhombohedra ; by O. Seidel, as six-sided plates belonging to the tetragonal system ; by O. Lüdecke, and F. Zambonini, as colourless plates belonging to the trigonal system, which, according to the latter, have the axial ratios $a : c$ =1 : 1·9518, and $a = 70° 10·26'$, and are isomorphous with the corresponding stannate and platinate. E. Frémy said the crystals deliquesce in air, O. Seidel that they effloresce. The moist crystals were found by O. Seidel, and F. Zambonini to turn quickly yellow, and slowly to acquire a brown colour owing to the separation of lead dioxide. The original salt is regenerated when the changed material is returned to the mother-liquid. E. Frémy said that the metaplumbate gives off oxygen and water when heated ; and O. Seidel said that the expulsion of the last mol. of water is attended by the evolution of oxygen. G. L. Clark said that the salt is stable below 100° in the presence of potassium hydroxide ; at 150°, it acquires a pale yellow colour ; and at a higher temp., it decomposes into potassium hydroxide, oxygen, lead monoxide, and water. I. Bellucci and N. Parravano said that in an indifferent gas at 100°, the metaplumbate does not lose its weight during a long period of time, but if more strongly heated, the mol. is broken down, and water and oxygen are evolved, leaving a residual mixture of potassium hydroxide and lead monoxide. E. Frémy, O. Seidel, and I. Bellucci and N. Parravano observed that water decomposes the metaplumbate with the separation of lead dioxide. G. L. Clark said that the salt is hydrolyzed by water in accord with the equation : $K_2Pb(OH)_6+2H_2O \rightleftharpoons 2KOH+H_2Pb(OH)_6$, and that the latter breaks down $H_2Pb(OH)_6=H_4PbO_4+2H_2O$. If 20 per cent. of water be present, the hydrolysis proceeds so far that hydrated lead dioxide is precipitated. I. Bellucci and N. Parravano showed that if the soln. be cooled by a freezing mixture, and neutralized with acetic acid, a pale yellowish-brown, flocculent precipitate appears which gradually darkens, and after being filtered and dried forms chestnut-brown, anhydrous lead dioxide. O. Seidel found that alcohol behaves like water. According to E. Frémy, and O. Seidel, the metaplumbate dissolves without decomposition in potash-lye of moderate conc. G. Grube said that while the normal potential of lead against potassium plumbite in $8\cdot42N$-KOH at 18° is $-0\cdot613$ volt (hydrogen electrode), the potential of lead against the alkali plumbate is $-0\cdot203$ volt. A decrease in the conc. of the alkali displaces the potential towards the more negative values. From the electric conductivity and the effect on the saponification of acetic ether, N. Parravano and G. Calcagni inferred that only in conc. soln. is any undecomposed salt present ; the hydrolysis is almost complete in $0\cdot012N$-KOH soln. I. Bellucci and N. Parravano came to the same conclusion from their measurements of the f.p. of the soln. G. Grube showed that the conc. alkaline soln. contains ions of both orthoplumbic acid, PbO_4'''', and of metaplumbic acid, PbO_3'', or hexahydroxyplumbic acid, $Pb(OH)_6''$. The oxidation potential in alkaline soln. was also measured by G. Grube.

G. Grube showed that the conc. alkaline soln. of the metaplumbate is reduced to plumbite by lead ; and E. Frémy said that soln. of various oxides—e.g. lead, zinc, or aluminium oxide—in potassium hydroxide precipitate plumbates ; and O. Seidel found that calcium, barium, and magnesium oxides form insoluble plumbates when boiled with a soln. of potassium metaplumbate in alkali-lye. Lead, according to G. Grube, reduces the alkali plumbate to plumbite. When the soln. of alkali plumbate is mixed with one of alkali plumbite, E. Frémy found that yellowish-brown hydrated lead tritatetraoxide is precipitated ; and O. Seidel, and I. Bellucci and N. Parravano, with not very dil. soln., obtained the trihydrated sesquioxide. G. Grube found the composition of the precipitate depends on the conc. of the mixed alkali plumbite and plumbate soln. : if less conc. than $4\cdot9N$-KOH, the hydrated sesquioxide is deposited ; and if more conc. than $6\cdot9N$-KOH, red-lead is separated.

H. Zocher reported the formation of trihydrated lithium metaplumbate, $Li_2PbO_3.3H_2O$, or $Li_2[Pb(OH)_6]$, in microscopic, colourless, six-sided plates, by the action of a sat. soln. of lithium hydroxide on a soln. of sodium metaplumbate in one of sodium hydroxide. The birefringence of the crystals is small, and the salt was thought to be isomorphous with the sodium salt. G. Grube, E. Frémy, O. Seidel, and I. Bellucci and N. Parravano prepared trihydrated sodium metaplumba e, $Na_2PbO_3.3H_2O$, or $Na_2[Pb(OH)_6]$, by methods similar to those employed for the potassium salt. G L. Clark mixed 150 grms. of sodium hydroxide with 50 c.c.

of water at 100°, and added lead dioxide so as to form a paste, 25 c.c. of water were then added and more lead dioxide. The resulting product was considered to be **hexahydrated sodium metaplumbate,** $Na_2PbO_3.6H_2O$. H. Zocher prepared sodium plumbate by dissolving freshly precipitated lead dioxide in small quantities at a time in boiling $8N$- to $10N$-NaOH. The salt is very sparingly soluble in this menstruum, and separates in crystals supposed to be isomorphous with sodium stannate. G. Grube said that the white crystals have a yellow tinge, and when heated under the alkali-lye, between 250° and 300°, they form the anhydrous salt. G. L. Clark could not make **sodium metaplumbate,** Na_2PbO_3, by fusing together dry sodium hydroxide and lead dioxide. A. Chwala and H. Colle obtained sodium metaplumbate from a soln. of lead dioxide in an aq. soln. of sodium acetate. M. Höhnel added sodium dioxide to a mush of lead dioxide and water until the mixture became white. The product was washed with 50 per cent. alcohol, then with 95 per cent. alcohol, until the filtrate was nearly neutral, and finally dried in vacuo over sulphuric acid. The composition corresponded with **tetrahydrated sodium metaplumbate,** $Na_2PbO_3.4H_2O$. I. Bellucci and N. Parravano showed that the product is impure owing to hydrolysis; and H. Zocher obtained only the trihydrate by this process.

E. Frémy, H. Zocher, and M. Höhnel observed that if the salt be exposed to the air for a short time it acquires a bronze colour. G. L. Clark said that the decomposition in air proceeds rapidly at 100°, and that it is more rapidly hydrolyzed than the potassium salt. M. Höhnel said that the hydrolysis is rapid and complete in boiling water. A. Bonnet showed that as with the alkali plumbite (q.v.) lead hydroxide can be deposited as a mordant on cotton by soaking the fibres in alkali plumbate followed by treatment with hot water. According to W. G. Mixter, the heats of formation are $(Na_2O,PbO_2,aq.)=15.5$ Cals. ; $(Na_2,O,PbO_2)=139.7$ Cals. H. Zocher found that in the presence of a great excess of sodium hydroxide, the soln. is rich in plumbate ions and is colourless, consequently it does not contain colloidal lead dioxide ; dil. soln. become yellow and then brown owing to the formation of colloidal lead dioxide ; G. Grube also obtained a colloidal soln. of lead dioxide by heating the alkaline soln. The colloid is flocculated by nitric acid. On standing a few days, H. Zocher found that the conc. soln. deposits acicular crystals of red-lead on the walls of the vessel. M. Höhnel said that sodium plumbate is slowly hydrolyzed by alcohol. Cold dil. nitric, sulphuric, and acetic acids decompose the metaplumbate like boiling water ; conc. sulphuric acid forms lead sulphate and oxygen ; and hydrochloric acid forms lead chloride and water. According to M. Höhnel, if sodium metaplumbate is washed with water, saffron-red **sodium hydrometaplumbate,** $NaHPbO_3.3H_2O$, is formed. I. Bellucci and N. Parravano, and H. Zocher doubt the accuracy of this conclusion.

J. Milbauer reported the formation of **lead orthoplumbate,** K_4PbO_4, or $Pb(OK)_4$, by heating a very conc. aq. soln. of potassium hydroxide in a silver dish with lead dioxide ; the sat. soln. of lead dioxide is allowed to stand in another dish for some days over sulphuric acid. The crystals which separate are pressed between porous tiles. The same product was obtained by triturating lead dioxide with a cold sat. soln. of potassium hydroxide. If red-lead is used some plumbite is also formed. The existence of the orthoplumbate is not definitely established. A. Geuther heated a soln. of lead monoxide in fused potassium hydroxide for a long time in air, and obtained black crystals of what was considered to be **potassium deuterotriplumbate,** $K_4Pb_3O_8$ (vide silicates, 6. 40, 50), and the same product was said to be formed by the action of oxygen on a soln. of lead oxide in a very conc. aq. soln. of lead oxide in potassium hydroxide. The crystals were washed rapidly with cold water, dried between filter-paper over sulphuric acid. Here again there is some doubt about the identification of the product. Sodium orthoplumbate could not be prepared. K. Elbs and F. Fischer found that soln of lead sulphate in an excess of a cold 20 per cent. soln. of sodium hydroxide contains both the meta- and the ortho-plumbate. According to

A. Gutmann, if cyanogen iodide be added to a soln. of 3 grms. of lead acetate in 80 grms. of aq. sodium hydroxide, a red precipitate is formed, and after washing out the lead iodide, lead dioxide remains. G. Grube said that soln. of sodium plumbate in conc. alkali-lye contain ions of **sodium orthoplumbate**, Na_4PbO_4, but the salt cannot be isolated because, on adding more sodium hydroxide the conc. of the sodium orthoplumbate does not increase while the solubility product of $[Pb''][PbO_4'''']$ is exceeded and lead orthoplumbate—red-lead—is deposited. According to G. Kassner, when steam is passed over sodium metaplumbate, **sodium dihydrorthoplumbate**, $Na_2H_2PbO_4$, or **sodium orthodiplumbate**, $Na_4H_2Pb_2O_7$, is produced. The former gives off water, and oxygen at a temp. exceeding 300°, and furnishes sodium plumbite, Na_2PbO_2; in the presence of oxidizing agents, however, only water is given off, and sodium orthoplumbate remains. H. Zocher prepared **trihydrated lithium plumbate**, $Na_2PbO_3.3H_2O$, or $Na_2Pb(OH)_6$, isomorphous with the sodium salt.

By digesting tetrahydrated calcium metaplumbate with an excess of an aq. soln. of cupric acetate; washing the product with water; and then with dil. ammonia, M. Höhnel obtained a deep black, amorphous powder of **cupric metaplumbate**—presumably $CuPbO_3$—which loses no copper when digested with dil. ammonia. Acetic acid dissolves the copper, and leaves the lead as dioxide. B. Grützner and M. Höhnel[2] prepared **silver metaplumbate**, Ag_2PbO_3, as a grey powder consisting of microscopic cubes, by digesting calcium metaplumbate with an aq. soln. of silver nitrate. The crude product contains silver oxide which can be removed by washing with aq. ammonia.

E. Frémy[3] made the alkaline earth plumbates by heating a mixture of, say, calcium oxide and lead oxide, the required oxygen is absorbed from the air; S. Melzer heated lead sulphate with calcium oxide and water; and O. Seidel, J. Marx, and W. Crum employed a similar process. S. Meunier added lead to a soln. of barium or calcium oxide in molten alkali hydroxide. No definite formula was assigned to the products. G. Kassner reported anhydrous **calcium metaplumbate**, $CaPbO_3$, or $CaO.PbO_2$, to be formed, not by heating a mixture of equimolar proportions of lead and calcium oxides in air, but by heating the tetrahydrated orthoplumbate to 250° in the absence of the carbon dioxide of the air; the product is said to be a mixture of equimolar proportions of calcium metaplumbate and calcium hydroxide. The latter can be removed by washing with water free from carbon dioxide. The pale brown powder is said to decompose when heated, forming calcium orthoplumbate, lead oxide, and oxygen. Calcium metaplumbate is not soluble in water; but after it has stood a long time in water it is said to form **dihydrated calcium metaplumbate**, $CaPbO_2.2H_2O$, when the product is dried at a gentle heat, or over sulphuric acid. The brown dihydrate loses its water at 300°. B. Grützner and M. Höhnel prepared **barium metaplumbate**, $BaPbO_3$, by heating a mixture of barium dioxide and lead monoxide; by boiling lead dioxide with a soln. of barium hydroxide; and by the action of sodium dioxide or potassium hydroxide on barium orthoplumbate. A. Chwala and H. Colle made it by digesting, without boiling, lead dioxide or red-lead with a conc. soln. of sodium acetate; and then adding a soln. of lead nitrate. The product is washed, and then dried at 120°. O. Seidel made the same salt by boiling a soln. of potassium metaplumbate with barium oxide. D. Balareff found evidence of a slight thermal change when mixtures of barium and plumbic oxides are heated between 360° and 365°.

B. Grützner and M. Höhnel prepared **tetrahydrated calcium metaplumbate**, $CaPbO_3.4H_2O$, by digesting the orthoplumbate with sodium dioxide and water; a less pure product is obtained by substituting alkali hydroxide for the dioxide. G. Kassner used somewhat similar processes. According to B. Grützner and M. Höhnel, the white powder consists of microscopic cubes, and it has a faint yellow tinge. It loses a little water when dried in vacuo; 0·26 per cent. when heated to 60°–70°; 1·11 per cent. at 115°; and at 120° it begins to decompose, and acquires a yellow colour. It then gives off water and oxygen leaving a yellowish-brown residue. G. Kassner said that in air free from carbon dioxide the tetrahydrate loses no water at 130°; at 180°, a little water is given off and a pale brown colour appears; at 250°, about three-fourths of the water is driven off, but not all is expelled at 300°. It becomes anhydrous if heated rapidly to 350° with air excluded—some free calcium oxide is then present. B. Grützner and M. Höhnel added that the tetrahydrate is not changed by hot or cold water; a hot soln. of alkali carbonate leads to the separation of lead dioxide; nitric acid, dil. sulphuric acid, and dil. acetic acid, when boiled with calcium metaplumbate also separate lead dioxide; conc. sulphuric acid furnishes lead sulphate and oxygen; hydrochloric acid produces lead chloride and chlorine; and carbon dioxide acts slowly in the cold, and rapidly when heated, forming lead dioxide.

W. Crum prepared an orthoplumbate by heating a soln. containing milk of lime, bleaching powder, and red-lead for 5 hrs. at 71°. G. Kassner prepared anhydrous **calcium orthoplumbate**, from an intimate mixture of equal parts of calcium hydroxide and lead oxide, or of two mols of calcium carbonate and one mol of lead oxide by calcination in air at about 850°. K. Wedemeyer used a similar process. G. Kassner prepared **strontium orthoplumbate**, Sr_2PbO_4, and **barium orthoplumbate**, Ba_2PbO_4, in an analogous manner. J. A. Hedvall and co-workers heated to 500° a mixture of the required proportions of barium dioxide and lead monoxide or red-lead. Calcium orthoplumbate is a yellowish-red powder which looks very like litharge; the sp. gr. of a 97 per cent. orthoplumbate is 5·71. Oxygen is gradually evolved when the orthoplumbate is heated. On the other hand, oxygen is more quickly and completely absorbed from the air by the dioxygenated plumbate than by barium oxide. G. Kassner recommended the following process for preparing oxygen, with carbon dioxide as a by-product:

Porous calcium plumbate is moistened with steam and subjected to the action of washed furnace gases, preferably, at a temp. below 100°. The carbon dioxide of the furnace gases is rapidly absorbed, and the material, which retains its porous condition, then consists of a mixture of calcium carbonate and lead dioxide. This is transferred to a retort kept constantly at a red heat, and in this oxygen is evolved, the evolution being much helped by the introduction of a current of steam. After the evolution of the oxygen, the current of steam is continued, and the temp. raised, when carbon dioxide is liberated, and may be collected for use. The calcium plumbate is then regenerated by means of a current of air.

H. le Chatelier said the dissociation pressures, p, are about 200° lower than those for barium dioxide, being

	880°	940°	950°	1020°	1060°	1070°	1100°	1110
p	47	112	117	350	557	570	940	1040

With cold water, it furnishes the tetrahydrate; **and** with hot water, **calcium dihydroproterodiplumbate**, $CaH_2P_2O_6$. If the orthoplumbate be triturated in a mortar along with potassium hydrocarbonate, and water at 40°, the mixture begins to turn brown, and the temp. then rapidly rises to the b.p. of water. Cold dil. acids cause the separation of lead dioxide. It is decomposed by water containing carbon dioxide in soln. G. Kassner prepared **tetrahydrated calcium orthoplumbate**, $Ca_2PbO_4.4H_2O$, by stirring the anhydrous salt with a little warm water, free from carbon dioxide. In a few days the product can be dried in vacuo, or over sulphuric acid. The colourless transparent crystals lose much water at 100°, but all the water is not expelled at 145°.

According to G. Kassner, calcium orthoplumbate can be used for the preparation of oxygen; the purification of aluminium salt soln. from iron; in the match industry; in the manufacture of glass and glazes; and, according to W. Kwasnik and K. Wedemeyer, as an oxidizing agent in the analysis of ashes.

G. Kassner reported a number of **calcium polyplumbates**. He treated calcium orthoplumbate with water under press., or at 150°, and obtained a yellowish-green, voluminous powder which was regarded as a mixture of calcium hydroxide and calcium dihydroproterodiplumbate, $CaH_2Pb_2O_6$, which he represented graphically as indicated below. The calcium hydroxide is removed by washing the product with water free from carbon dioxide, or very dil. acids, and drying at 105°. The yellow or olive-green powder is slowly darkened or blackened by acids at ordinary temp., forming lead dioxide ; boiling acetic acid quickly produces the same change. It loses half its combined water at 310°, forming $Ca_2H_2Pb_4O_{11}$, and the other half at 380°, forming $Ca_2Pb_4O_{10}$. It loses oxygen at 550°, and forms a mixture of calcium orthoplumbate and lead dioxide. G. Kassner heated tetrahydrated calcium metaplumbate in a stream of air free from carbon dioxide at 250° ; and also tetrahydrated calcium orthoplumbate in a stream of air free from carbon dioxide, or in dry oxygen, at 260°–280° ; in nitrogen at 245°–255° ; or in an evacuated sealed tube at 240°–245°. The composition of the product corresponded with **calcium orthodiplumbate**, $Ca_2Pb_2O_7$, or else with *calcium proterodiplumbate*, $Ca_2Pb_2O_6$ (polymerized metaplumbate). Graphically, he employed the formulæ :

$$CaH_2Pb_2O_6 \qquad Ca_2Pb_2O_7 \qquad CaPb_2O_6$$

The reddish-brown powder of calcium orthodiplumbate is decomposed by water with the evolution of oxygen ; and the decomposition with acids—particularly nitric acid—is vigorous. Alcohol does not act on the compound.

G. Kassner treated calcium dihydroproterodiplumbate with 10 per cent. nitric acid, and obtained a greyish-brown powder resembling the original substance in general properties, and decomposing suddenly at a definite temp. into oxygen, lead dioxide, etc. The composition of the compound dried at 110°, corresponds with **calcium dihydrodeuterotriplumbate**, $CaH_2Pb_3O_8$. As previously indicated, when calcium dihydroproterodiplumbate, $CaH_2Pb_2O_6$, is heated from 300° to 320°, half the contained water is expelled, and the mol. coalesce in pairs, forming **calcium dihydrodeuterotetraplumbate**, $Ca_2H_2Pb_4O_{11}$:

$$Ca_2H_2Pb_4O_{11}$$

as a yellow powder which loses all its water at 380°–400°, forming **calcium triterotetraplumbate**, $Ca_2Pb_4O_{10}$. The grey powder loses practically no lime when treated with water free from carbon dioxide.

According to G. Kassner, when a mixture of calcium and lead oxides in the proportion CaO : PbO is heated at 450°–480° in a current of air freed from carbon dioxide, the product is not calcium metaplumbate, $CaPbO_3$, but appears to be a mixture of uncombined lime with a mixed salt, **calcium lead orthoplumbate**, $CaPb(PbO_4)$. This has a red colour ; hydrochloric acid acts on it with liberation of chlorine, whilst nitric and acetic acids cause a separation of lead dioxide ; above 550°, it appears to decompose in accord with the equation $4CaPb(PbO_4)=2Ca_2PbO_4 +6PbO+O_2$.

According to O. Seidel,[4] and C. Jones and co-workers, when a mixture of eq. proportions of lead and magnesium oxides is heated in a current of air at about 800°, **magnesium metaplumbate**, $MgPbO_3$, is formed. S. Meunier obtained it by the action of a soln. of magnesia in molten alkali hydroxide on molten lead; and O. Seidel found that when an alkaline soln. of potassium plumbate is boiled with an excess of magnesia, the same compound is formed as a brown powder which gives off oxygen at a dull red heat. E. Frémy, and O. Seidel, mixed soln. of potassium plumbate and potassium zirconate, and obtained yellow flocculent precipitates corresponding with Pb_4O_7. M. Höhnel treated finely divided tetrahydrated calcium metaplumbate with a slight excess of a sat. soln. of zinc carbonate in acetic acid, for some hours, and washed the product with water, and dil. sodium hydroxide. On drying between filter-paper, and over calcium chloride, the product corresponded with dihydrated **zinc metaplumbate**, $ZnPbO_3.2H_2O$. The reddish-brown powder consisted of microscopic cubes. Hot water does not act on the plumbate, and soda-lye does not dissolve it; with conc. sulphuric acid, oxygen is evolved, and with hydrochloric acid, chlorine; and dil. nitric acid or acetic acid furnishes lead dioxide. I. Bellucci and N. Parravano did not get a product suitable for analysis by the above method of preparation. E. W. Buskett said zinc plumbate is probably present in the so-called sublimed white lead. I. Bellucci and N. Parravano made brown trihydrated **thallous metaplumbate**, $Tl_2PbO_3.3H_2O$, or $Tl_2Pb(OH)_6$, by mixing alkaline soln. of potassium metaplumbate with thallous nitrate soln., washing, and drying over sulphuric acid. The compound loses very little water at 100°, and thallium readily volatilizes when heated to a higher temp. The compound is hydrolyzed by water.

REFERENCES.

[1] E. Frémy, *Journ. Pharm. Chim.*, (3), 3. 32, 1843; *Ann. Chim. Phys.*, (3). 12. 490, 1844; O. Seidel, *Ueber einige Verbindungen ds Bleihyperoxyds (der Bleisäure)*, Breslau, 13, 1878; *Journ. prakt. Chim.*, (2), 20. 201, 1879; A. Bonnet, *Compt. Rend.*, 117. 518, 1893; S. Meunier, *ib.*, 60. 1234, 1865; O. Lüdecke, *Zeit. Kryst.*, 8. 82. 1884; F. Zambonini, *ib.*, 41. 55, 1906; *Atti Accad. Lincei*, (5), 14. i, 457, 1905; I. Bellucci and N. Parravano, *ib.*, (5), 14. i, 378, 1905; (5), 15. ii, 542, 1906; *Zeit. anorg. Chem.*, 50. 108. 1906; *Gazz. Chim. Ital.*, 35. ii, 500, 1905; 37. i, 171, 1907; N. Parravano and G. Calcagni, *ib.*, 37 ii, 264, 1907; A. Chwala and H. Colle, *ib.*, 41. ii, 551, 1911; *Zeit. anal. Chem.*, 50. 241, 1911; G. L. Clark, *Journ. Amer. Chem. Soc.*, 41. 1479, 1919; A. Geuther, *Liebig's Ann.*, 219. 68, 1883; G. Grube, *Zeit. Elektrochem.*, 28. 235, 1922; K. Elbs and F. Fischer, *ib.*, 7. 346, 1901; J. Milbauer, *Chem. Ztg.*, 38. 566, 1914; G. Kassner, *ib.*, 37. 1211, 1913; F. Jirsa, *Zeit. phys. Chem.*, 94. 1, 1920; H. Zocher, *Zeit. anorg. Chem.*, 112. 1, 1920; A. Gutmann, *Ber.*, 42. 3626, 1909; M. Höhnel, *Arch. Pharm.*, 232. 223, 1894; 234. 399, 1896; W. G. Mixter, *Amer. Journ. Science*, (4), 27. 396, 1909.

[2] B. Grützner and M. Höhnel, *Arch. Pharm.*, 233. 512, 1895.

[3] W. Crum, *Mem. Chem. Soc.*, 2. 387, 1843; *Liebig's Ann.*, 55. 218. 1845; *Journ. prakt. Chem.*, (1), 37. 158, 1846; O. Seidel, *ib.*, (2), 20. 203, 1879; *Ueber einige Verbindungen des Bleihyperoxyds (der Bleisäure)*, Breslau. 1878; K. Wedemeyer, *Arch. Pharm.*, 230. 264, 1892; W. Kwasnik, and K. Wedemeyer, *ib.*, 278. 468, 1890; B. Grützner and M. Höhnel, *ib.*, 233. 514, 1895; G. Kassner, *ib.*, 228. 112, 1890; 232. 376, 1894; 233. 502, 1895; 237. 410, 1899; 238. 452, 1900; 241. 143, 1903; 255. 130, 1917; *Dingler's Journ.*, 274. 141, 187, 230, 275, 1889; 278. 477, 1890; *Chem. Ztg.*, 22. 225, 1898; *Chem. Ind.*, 13. 104, 392, 1890; *German Pat., D.R.PP.* 52459, 1889; 82583, 85020, 1894; S. Melzer, *ib.*, 379316, 1921; J. Marx, *ib.*, 79454. 1893; H. le Chatelier, *Compt. Rend.*, 117. 109, 1893; S. Meunier, *ib.*, 60. 1234, 1865; J. Milbauer, *Chem. Ztg.*, 38. 560, 1914; E. Frémy, *Journ. Pharm. Chim.*, (3), 3. 32, 1843; *Ann. Chim. Phys.*, (3), 12. 490, 1844; A. Chwala and H. Colle, *Zeit. anal. Chem.*, 50. 229, 1911; *Gazz. Chim. Ital.*, 41. ii, 551, 1911; J. A. Hedvall and N. von Zweigbergk, *Zeit. anorg. Chem.*, 108. 127, 1919; J. A. Hedvall and J. Heuberger, *ib.*, 135. 49, 1924; D. Balareff, *ib.*, 136. 216, 1924.

[4] C. Jones, A. Morton, and N. Terzieff, *U.S. Pat. No.* 1037261, 1891; S. Meunier, *Compt. Rend.*, 60. 1234, 1865; O. Seidel, *Ueber einige Verbindungen des Bleihyperoxyds (der Bleisäure)*, Breslau, 18, 1878; *Journ. prakt. Chem.*, (2), 20. 203, 1879; E. W. Buskett, *Eng. Min. Journ.*, 83. 760, 1907; M. Höhnel, *Arch. Pharm.*, 234. 398, 1896; I. Bellucci and N. Parravano, *Zeit. anorg. Chem.*, 50. 113. 1906; *Atti Accad. Lincei*, (5), 14. i, 382, 1905; *Gazz. Chim. Ital.*, 35. ii, 500, 1905; E. Frémy, *Journ. Pharm. Chim.*, (3), 3. 32, 1843; *Ann. Chim. Phys.*, (3), 12. 490, 1844.

§ 21. Lead Fluorides

C. W. Scheele [1] stated that lead is not dissolved by hydrofluoric acid, but the oxide dissolves in the acid, forming a sweet soln. J. L. Gay Lussac and L. J. Thénard, however, showed that the acid, heated below its b.p., attacks the metal easily; and E. Frémy, and J. J. Berzelius and H. von Helmolt obtained **lead fluoride**, PbF_2, by dissolving lead hydroxide or carbonate in an excess of hydrofluoric acid, evaporating the soln. to dryness, and igniting the product. C. W. Scheele, and E. Frémy obtained a precipitate of lead fluoride, by adding hydrofluoric acid or an alkali fluoride to a soln. of lead nitrate or acetate. A. Guntz obtained lead fluoride by the action of hydrogen fluoride on lead. H. Moissan also obtained lead fluoride by the action of fluorine on lead, or on several compounds of lead—oxides, iodide, nitrate, carbonate, etc. O. Ruff and E. Geisel electrolyzed a sat. soln. of ammonium fluoride in a U-tube of lead at 0°, and found that lead fluoride is deposited in the tube.

E. Frémy said that lead fluoride forms a white, crystalline powder. M. L. Dundon found that the crystals belong to the rhombic system, having an average refractive index of 1·83, and a hardness of 2. The sp. gr. is 8·24 ; the mol. vol. 29·7 ; and the surface energy of the solid is 900 ergs at 25°. A. Reis and L. Zimmermann gave 9·2 for the scratching hardness when that of ammonium bromide is unity. H. Schottky gave for the sp. ht., 0·07216 between 0° and 34° ; and 17·67 for the mol. ht. ; C. Sandonnini observed no transformation on the heating curve up to 300°. J. J. Berzelius said that lead fluoride melts easily, and C. Sandonnini added that it fuses without decomposition at about 824° ; N. A. Puschin and A. Baskoff gave 855° for the m.p. ; and M. Amadori, 820°. According to H. von Wartenberg and O. Bosse, the heat of vaporization of lead fluoride formed from hydrofluoric acid and water by fusion is 39·425 Cals. ; and the vap. press., p, in atm. is log $p=-39425/4·571T$ $+5·510$. There is no sign of doubled mol. at 1440°. R. Lorenz and W. Herz studied this subject. H. von Wartenberg gave 156 Cals. for the heat of formation of PbF_2 ; and A. Guntz gave 2·2 Cals. for the heat of precipitation, and 105·2 for the heat of formation when that of hydrogen fluoride is 37·5 Cals.—M. Berthelot and H. Moissan found 38·9 for the latter. W. Beetz said that lead fluoride conducts electricity electrolytically. M. le Blanc found that the electrical conductivity of the pressed powder is very small, but it increases appreciably by previously heating the mass in a current of dry air. C. Fritsch made observations on this subject. F. Kohlrausch gave for the electrical conductivity of an almost sat. soln., at 8·99°, 0·003310 ; at 18°, 0·004310 ; at 26·61°, 0·005350 ; and at $\theta°$, $0·004310\{1+0·0208(\theta-18)+0·00003(\theta-18)^2\}$. C. Tubandt found that with fused lead fluoride, the current was entirely carried by the F'-ion, so that the gain in weight in the anode compartment was exactly eq. to the cathode deposit of a silver voltameter included in the circuit. S. Meyer gave $-0·519\times10^{-6}$ for the magnetic susceptibility, and $-0·046\times10^{-6}$ for the mol. magnetism.

C. Sandonnini said that the properties of lead fluoride stand closer to those of lead monoxide than to those of the other three lead halides. E. Frémy found that at a red heat lead fluoride is reduced to the metal by **hydrogen ;** and, according to H. Moissan, by **sodium hydride.** E. Frémy said that it is not oxidized at a red heat by **oxygen,** but when heated in air or the vapour of **water,** it furnishes hydrogen fluoride, and lead oxyfluoride. It is sparingly soluble in water; at 8·99°, F. Kohlrausch found that water dissolves 598 mgrms. per litre, or $0·0_5488$ gram-eq. per c.c. ; at 18°, $0·0_5524$ gram-eq. per c.c. ; and at 26·61°, 681 mgrms. per litre, or $0·0_566$ gram-eq. per c.c. M. L. Dundon also measured the solubility from conductivity data for particles of $0·3\mu$ average diameter and found an increase of 9 per cent. above the ordinary value. E. Brunner observed that lead fluoride dissolves very slowly in a hot 2N-soln. of **sodium hydroxide.** C. J. Knox found that **chlorine** has scarcely any action on lead fluoride, and O. Unverdorben made a similar remark in connection with **iodine.** J. J. Berzelius said that lead fluoride is not more soluble in **hydrofluoric acid** than in water ; C. H. Herty said it is sparingly soluble in that acid ; and F. Fischer and K. Thiele, insoluble. J. L. Gay Lussac and L. J. Thénard said that it is more soluble in **hydrochloric acid,** and, according to J. J. Berzelius, lead fluoride is decomposed when evaporated with hydrochloric acid. H. Fonzes-Diacon said it is slightly soluble in a conc. boiling soln. of **ammonium chloride or bromide;** C. H. Herty said that the solubility in soln. of the **alkali halides** increases with the at. wt. of the halides, and, according to E. Field, the action is similar to that observed with lead chloride (q.v.). O. Unverdorben showed that when lead fluoride and **sulphur** are heated in a glass retort, lead sulphide, sulphur dioxide, and silicon fluoride are formed ; but L. Pfaundler observed no action below 140°. J. L. Gay

Lussac and L. J. Thénard, and P. Louyet found that conc. **sulphuric acid** in the cold decomposes lead fluoride, forming hydrogen fluoride, and lead sulphate. A. Ditte studied the equilibrium conditions between potassium fluoride and **lead sulphate** (*q.v.*). A. Guntz showed that **sulphur monochloride** converts heated lead fluoride into chloride. J. L. Gay Lussac and L. J. Thénard found that lead fluoride is sparingly soluble in **nitric acid ;** and J. J. Berzelius found that the aq. soln. of lead fluoride forms an oxyfluoride when treated with **ammonia.** O. Unverdorben found that **phosphorus** has scarcely any action on lead fluoride, and L. Pfaundler showed that red phosphorus acts on lead fluoride only in contact with silica. A. Guntz found that **phosphorus pentachloride,** and **phosphoryl chloride** convert lead fluoride into the chloride ; and T. E. Thorpe and J. W. Rodger, that with **phosphorus pentasulphide,** thiophosphoryl fluoride is formed. E. Frémy observed that **carbon** has no action on lead fluoride, and likewise also **carbon monoxide,** and **carbon dioxide.** F. Fischer and K. Thiele found that a soln. of **ammonium formate** dissolves a small proportion of lead fluoride ; and H. Mandal, that lead fluoride is insoluble in **aniline.** A. Guntz found that **carbon tetrachloride** converts heated lead fluoride into the chloride. L. Kahlenberg and W. J. Trautmann studied the reduction of lead fluoride when heated with powdered **silicon.** E. Berger found that with silicon, lead and silicon fluoride are formed—**calcium silicide** acts more vigorously than silicon, forming calcium and silicon fluorides ; with a mixture of **aluminium,** and **boric oxide,** aluminium and boron fluorides are formed ; with **magnesium,** only magnesium fluoride is produced. G. Sandonnini found that the f.p. curve of mixtures of lead oxide and lead fluoride shows no signs of a compound ; there is a simple eutectic at 494° with 54 molar per cent. of **lead oxide** (Fig. 68).

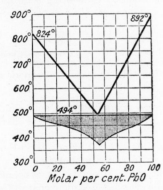

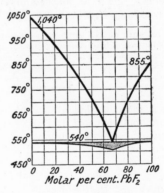

Fig. 68.—Freezing-point Curves of Mix-   Fig. 69.—Freezing-point Curves of Mixtures of Lead Monoxide and Fluoride.   tures of Sodium and Lead Fluorides.

J. J. Berzelius claimed to have made *lead oxyfluoride* by decomposing lead fluoride with aq. ammonia ; by fusing alkali fluoride with lead oxide and washing away soluble matters with water ; E. Frémy, by the action of steam on lead fluoride ; and H. Moissan, by the action of fluorine on lead monoxide or dioxide. D. Strömholm said that when lead hydroxide is shaken with a soln. of ammonium or potassium fluoride, no oxyfluoride is formed, and no lead hydroxide goes into soln. The existence of the so-called lead oxyfluoride has not been definitely established. J. J. Berzelius' product was said to have a sweet, yet astringent, taste ; and to be resolved into soluble acid salt and insoluble basic salt when boiled with water.

The soln. of lead fluoride and hydrofluoric acid is said to contain *hydrofluoplumbous acid*, H_2PbF_4, but the acid has not been isolated ; nor has an *ammonium fluoplumbite* been prepared. N. A. Puschin and A. Baskoff measured the f.p. of mixtures of lead and sodium fluorides, Fig. 69, but observed no signs of the formation of *sodium fluoplumbite ;* there is a simple eutectic at 540° and 67·5 per

cent. PbF_2. No *potassium fluoplumbite* has been definitely isolated. C. H. Herty
noticed that lead dissolves in a hot soln. of potassium fluoride, but the amount is
smaller than in the corresponding case with the chloride, bromide, or iodide.
C. Fritsch, and M. le Blanc noted the marked increase in the electrical conductivity
of slabs made from mixtures of lead and potassium fluorides than from lead fluoride
alone.   M. le Blanc obtained similar results with mixtures of lead and barium
fluorides, but no *barium fluoplumbite* has been made.

B. Brauner claimed to have made a soln. of **lead tetrafluoride**, PbF_4, by projecting powdered potassium fluoplumbate on to the surface of cold, conc. sulphuric
acid.   Hydrogen fluoride escapes, and a pale yellow soln. is obtained.   The yellow
liquid soon becomes turbid, and in about half an hour, a thick, lemon-yellow,
gelatinous emulsion is produced, which he stated (without proof) to contain a
colloidal form of lead tetrafluoride.   At 100°–110°, some hydrogen fluoride
escapes, and a heavy lemon-yellow powder is deposited which he regarded (without
proof) as a third modification of lead tetrafluoride.   The lead tetrafluoride was not
isolated because no method of separating the sulphuric acid is known without at the
same time decomposing the salt.   When the sulphuric acid soln. of the tetrafluoride
is heated on a water-bath, it furnishes a yellow crust of lead dioxide and hydrogen
fluoride is evolved : $PbF_4+2H_2O=PbO_2+4HF$.   The soln. of lead tetrafluoride
liberates iodine from potassium iodide, etc.   O. Ruff and G. Winterfeld could not prepare lead tetrafluoride by the action of sulphuric acid on potassium fluoplumbate by
B. Brauner's process ; nor could it be prepared by heating triammonium hydroctofluoplumbate in vacuo ; nor by passing dry hydrogen fluoride over lead tetracetate,
and digesting the product in chloroform or carbon tetrachloride.   W. L. Argo and
co-workers, and F. C. Mathers obtained lead tetrafluoride by heating lead dioxide
with potassium hydrofluoride :

A mixture of 219 grms. of potassium hydrofluoride (containing 2 per cent. of water)
and 164 grms. of lead dioxide (containing 93·5 per cent. PbO_2) was fused at from 250°–300°
in a copper vessel.   The heating was continued until the black colour disappeared and the
mass became grey, and semi-solid.   The product contained 37·5 per cent. of PbF_4.   The
substance was purified by leaching the finely ground material in warm hydrofluoric acid,
and allowing the soln. to crystallize.

It is assumed that a soln. of lead tetrafluoride in hydrofluoric acid contains
hydrofluoplumbic acid, H_2PbF_6.   According to A. Hutchinson and W. Pollard, a
37 per cent. soln. of hydrofluoric acid dissolves lead tetracetate readily, and gives
a colourless soln., which, in all probability, contains either PbF_4 or H_2PbF_6.   If
excess of acid is present, the soln. is stable at the ordinary temp., but, like the liquid
obtained when hydrochloric acid is used, it is entirely broken up on evaporation
even in vacuo ; the decomposition in this case, however, takes a somewhat different
course, and results in the quantitative deposition of lead dioxide in accordance with
the equation $PbF_4+2H_2O=PbO_2+4HF$.   F. C. Mathers showed that while lead
dioxide and red-lead are not acted upon by 50 per cent. hydrofluoric acid, the 96
per cent. acid readily acts on these oxides, forming soln. of lead tetrafluoride.   The
soln. is rapidly hydrolyzed by water depositing a black precipitate of hydrated lead
dioxide—the presence of a little ammonium or potassium fluoride, as noted by
A. Hutchinson and W. Pollard, hinders the hydrolysis.   F. Fischer and K. Thiele
also made soln. of lead tetrafluoride by the action of hydrofluoric acid on freshly
prepared lead dioxide.   G. L. Clark made **sodium hexafluoplumbate**, Na_2PbF_6, by
dissolving sodium plumbate in 50 per cent. hydrofluoric acid.   The short, thick,
tabular crystals are hydrolyzed at 25° by water and the percentage solubility of the
salt when sodium fluoride and hydrofluoric acid are present was found to be :

HF .	.	. 38·61	40·0	24·5	7·9	37·23 per cent.
NaF	.	. 0·368	trace	0·4	2·33	2·33 ,,
Solubility .	.	9·358	10·47	Hydrolysis	5·0	,,

B. Brauner supposed the soln. of lead tetracetate in conc. hydrofluoric acid to contain *hydroctofluoplumbic acid*, H_4PbF_8; and F. Fischer and K. Thiele removed most of the liberated acetic acid by keeping the soln. over soda-lime in a paraffined desiccator. B. Brauner said that the soln. is very unstable at ordinary temp. depositing lead dioxide, and the salts of the acid are easily decomposed. The acid was found by F. Fischer and K. Thiele to dissolve lead carbonate. The stabilizing effect of ammonium fluoride on soln. of hydrofluoplumbic acid was noted by A. Hutchinson and W. Pollard, and F. C. Mathers, and attributed to the formation of ammonium fluoplumbate. O. Ruff prepared **ammonium hydroctofluoplumbate**, $(NH_4)_3HPbF_8$, by dissolving lead tetracetate in conc. hydrofluoric acid and adding ammonium hydrogen fluoride, filtering, and evaporating. The salt may be heated at 190° under atm. press. or even under 10 mm. press. without change, but in a good vacuum decomposition takes place at 100°, nitrogen being evolved. B. Brauner reported **potassium hydroctofluoplumbate**, K_3HPbF_8, to be formed by treating freshly precipitated lead heptoxide with a mixture of potassium hydrofluoride and hydrofluoric acid; by evaporating a soln. of a mol of lead tetracetate and 3 mols of potassium hydrofluoride in conc. hydrofluoric acid; and by the action of an excess of conc. hydrofluoric acid on a fused mixture of potassium hydroxide and lead dioxide. F. C. Mathers, and G. L. Clark employed modifications of the process last described; and O. Ruff used the lead tetracetate process. The monoclinic crystals were reported by B. Brauner to have the axial ratios $a:b:c=0.62228:1:0.48177$, and $\beta=86°43'$; and to be isomorphous with the corresponding fluostannate, K_3HSnF_8. The crystals are stable in dry air, and they can be preserved in paraffined vessels without discoloration, but in glass vessels they become superficially black. They are not changed in weight by heating for 4 hrs. at 100°–110°; at 230°, they lose hydrogen fluoride, and at 250°, some fluorine. O. Ruff said that very little decomposition occurs below 250° at which temp. **potassium heptafluoplumbate**, K_3PbF_7, is formed. When heated in a platinum tube in the blast gas flame the decomposition is represented $2K_3PbF_7=K_2PbF_6 +PbF_4+4KF$. F. C. Mathers said that a small amount of fluorine is given off at 300°. The salt becomes brown in moist air, and is completely decomposed by a little water. G. L. Clark said that moisture decomposes the salt into H_2PbO_3, KHF_2, and hydrogen fluoride. The hydrolysis was studied by F. C. Mathers, and G. L. Clark. The latter found that in the presence of hydrofluoric acid and sodium fluoride at 25°, the solubility was:

HF . . .	29 1	30·0	17·0	20·0	20·0 per cent.
NaF . .	1·71	0	1·71	0	25·0 ,,
Solubility . .	11·23	12·21	Hydrolysis		1·7 ,,

With sulphuric acid, a yellow soln. of lead tetrafluoride is formed; and when triturated in an agate mortar, it becomes brown owing to a reaction with the silica of the agate: $4K_3HPbF_8+SiO_2=4PbF_4+12KF+SiF_4+H_2O$. According to O. Ruff, both the hepta- and the octofluoplumbates at 400° react with sulphur, forming what is probably sulphur fluoride; iodine produces an iodine fluoride; silicon is not inflamed; liquid silicon tetrafluoride acts only superficially; and with antimony pentafluoride, below 150°, fluorine appears to be evolved.

B. Brauner reported that when a mixture of potassium hydroxide and lead dioxide (3 : 1) is fused in a silver crucible, and the cold mass treated with hydrofluoric acid, oxygen is given off, and an insoluble crystalline mass—probably *potassium oxyfluoperplumbate*—is formed.

A. Skrabal and J. Gruber reported **rubidium hexafluoplumbate**, Rb_2PbF_6, to be formed by mixing a gram of lead tetracetate and 1·5 grms. of rubidium carbonate with cold hydrofluoric acid, and after some days, separating the crystals by suction, washing with cold acetic acid, and drying between bibulous paper. The six-sided plates belong to the rhombohedral system, and have the axial ratio $a:c=0.7884$. The crystals of the corresponding **cæsium hexafluoplumbate**, Cs_2PbF_6, have the axial ratio $a:c=0.7885$. The crystals are decomposed by moist air.

REFERENCES.

[1] C. W. Scheele, *Svenska Akad. Handl.*, **33**. 120, 1771 ; J. L. Gay Lussac and L. J. Thénard, *Mém. Soc. Arcueil*, **2**. 317, 1809 ; E. Frémy, *Ann. Chim. Phys.*, (3), **47**. 37, 1856 ; A. Ditte, *ib.*, (5). 14. 209, 1878 ; M. Berthelot and H. Moissan. *ib.*, (6), **23**. 570, 1891 ; A. Guntz, *ib.*, (6), **3**. 42, 1884 ; *Compt. Rend.*, **98**. 819, 1884 ; **103**. 58, 1886 ; E. Berger. *ib.*, **170**. 1492, 1920 ; P. Louyet, *ib.*, **23**. 960, 1846 ; 24. 434, 1847 ; O. Unverdorben, *Trommsdorff's Journ.*, **9**. 22, 1824 ; J. J. Berzelius, *Pogg. Ann.*, **1**. 34, 1824 ; H. von Helmolt, *Zeit. anorg. Chem.*, **3**. 150, 1893 ; D. Strömholm, *ib.*, **38**. 449, 1904 ; F. Fischer and K. Thiele, *ib.*, **67**. 312, 1910 ; C. Tubandt, *ib.*, **115**. 119, 1921 ; F. Fischer and K. Thiele, *ib.*, **67**. 303, 1910 ; B. Brauner, *Journ. Chem. Soc.*, **65**. 393, 1894 ; *Zeit. anorg. Chem.*, **7**. 1, 1894 ; O. Ruff, *Zeit. angew. Chem.*, **20**. 1218, 1907 ; *Zeit. anorg. Chem.*, **98**. 27, 38, 1916 ; O. Ruff and G. Winterfeld, *ib.*, **98**. 35, 1916 ; G. Winterfeld, *Versuche zur Darstellung von Blei tetrafluorid*, Berlin, 1904 ; O. Ruff and E. Geisel, *Ber.*, **36**. 2677, 1903 ; H. Schottky, *Phys. Zeit.*, **10**. 634, 1909 ; N. A. Puschin and A. Baskoff, *Journ. Russ. Phys. Chem. Soc.*, **45**. 82, 1913 ; *Zeit. anorg. Chem.*, **31**. 358, 1913 ; R. Lorenz and W. Herz, *ib.*, **143**. 336, 1925 ; M. Amadori, *Gazz. Chim. Ital.*, **49**. i, 42, 1919 ; C. Sandonnini, *ib.*, **41**. ii, 145, 1911 ; *Atti Accad. Lincei.*, (5), **23**. i, 959, 1914 ; C. Fritsch, *Wied. Ann.*, **60**. 300, 1897 ; M. le Blanc, *Zeit. Elektrochem.*, **18**. 551, 1912 ; H. von Wartenberg and O. Bosse, *ib.*, **28**. 384, 1922 ; O. Bosse, *Dampfdrucke einiger Schwermetallsalze*, Danzig, 1922 ; W. Beetz, *Pogg. Ann.*, **92**. 461, 1854 ; M. L. Dundon, *Journ. Amer. Chem. Soc.*, **45**. 2658, 1923 ; H. Mandal, *Ber.*, **54**. 704, 1921 ; H. Moissan, *Ann. Chim. Phys.*, (6), **24**. 247, 1891 ; (7), **27**. 359, 1902 ; *Bull. Soc. Chim.*, (3), **27**. 1147, 1902 ; H. Fonzes-Diacon, *ib.*, (3), **17**. 350, 1897 ; S. Meyer, *Sitzber. Akad. Wien*, **108**. 877, 1899 ; *Monatsh.*, **20**. 797, 1899 ; *Wied. Ann.*, **69**. 245, 1899 ; A. Skrabal and J. Gruber, *Monatsh.*, **38**. 22, 1917 ; F. Kohlrausch, *Zeit. phys. Chem.*, **44**. 197, 1903 ; **50**. 355, 1904 ; **64**. 168, 1908 ; A. Reis and L. Zimmermann, *ib.*, **102**. 298, 1922 ; T. W. B. Welsh and H. J. Broderson, *Journ. Amer. Chem. Soc.*, **37**. 819, 1915 ; V. Lenher, *ib.*, **23**. 681, 1901 ; F. C. Mathers, *ib.*, **42**. 1309, 1920 ; G. L. Clark, *ib.*, **41**. 1480, 1919 ; L. Pfaundler, *Sitzber. Akad. Wien*, **46**. 258, 1863 ; C. H. Herty, *Amer. Chem. Journ.*, **14**. 107, 1892 ; E. Field, *Chem. News*, **67**. 157, 1893 ; *Journ. Chem. Soc.*, **63**. 541, 1893 ; A. Hutchinson and W. Pollard, *ib.*, **69**. 220, 1896 ; T. E. Thorpe and J. W. Rodger, *ib.*, **53**. 766, 1888 ; W. L. Argo, F. C. Mathers, B. Humston, and C. O. Anderson, *Trans. Amer. Electrochem. Soc.*, **35**. 335, 1919 ; *Journ. Phys. Chem.*, **23**. 348, 1919 ; *Chem. Eng.*, **27**. 107, 1919 ; E. Brunner, *Helvetica Chim. Acta*, **3**. 818, 1920 ; C. J. Knox, *Phil. Mag.*, (3), **16**. 199, 1840 ; C. J. and T. Knox, *ib.*, (3), **9**. 107, 1836 ; *Proc. Roy. Irish Acad.*, **1**. 54, 1841 ; L. Kahlenberg and W. J. Trautmann, *Trans. Amer. Electrochem. Soc.*, **39**. 477, 1921 ; H. von Wartenberg, *Zeit. anorg. Chem.*, **151**. 326, 1926; H. von Wartenberg and O. Fitzner, *ib.*, **151**. 313, 1926.

§ 22. Lead Chlorides

H. G. Denham [1] prepared **lead monochloride, or lead subchloride,** PbCl, by passing the vap. of ethyl chloride slowly over lead hemioxide, at 311°. C. Tubandt and S. Eggert observed no sign of its formation during the electrolysis of fused lead chloride. The grey colour of the subchloride is not due to the presence of carbon, because in vacuo, at 400°, it becomes nearly white : $2PbCl = Pb + PbCl_2$, for the dark colour of the lead is masked by the whiteness of the chloride. The subchloride is fairly stable in air, and is rather more soluble in water than the corresponding sub-bromide and sub-iodide ; a litre of water dissolves 2·2 milli-eq. of PbCl per litre. The sub-chloride is readily decomposed by acids, forming the metal and lead chloride ; it rapidly decolorizes bromine water and permanganate soln. A sat. aq. soln. prepared in vacuo gives a faint precipitate with silver nitrate and with hydrogen sulphide.

About the beginning of our era, Dioscorides, in his *De materia medica*, said that a white substance is obtained by heating λιθάργυρος with common salt and water. This must have been impure lead chloride. Normal **lead chloride,** $PbCl_2$, has been known from the Middle Ages, the crystals being called *magisterium plumbi*, and the translucent horny mass obtained when the salt has been fused, *plumbum corneum,* or *horn lead.* Thus, J. R. Glauber,, in his *Explicatio miraculi rundi* (Amstelodami, 1656), described how hydrochloric acid precipitated *plumbum corneum* from a soln. of lead in nitric acid. T. Monticelli and N. Covelli [2] found *plombo muriato corneo* accompanied by sodium chloride, and copper sulphate and chloride, in the crater of Vesuvius after the 1817 and 1822 eruptions. He called it *cotunnia*—after D. Cotugno. According to F. Zambonini, F. von Kobell used the name **cotunnite**. A. Scacchi obtained some at Plunto del Mauro in 1840 ; and afterwards A. Scacchi, and G. Guiscardi found it in the lava in the Fosso de la Vetrana after the eruption of 1855. The oxychloride reported by R. Cappa from the lava of the 1868 eruption was shown by A. Scacchi to be cotunnite. The Vesuvian occurrences have also been discussed by G. vom Rath, A. Lacroix, W. P. Jervis, and F. Zambonini. I. Domeyko, and A. Frenzel found it massive in the Sierra Gorda, Chili ; A. Raimondi, in Tarapacá, Chili, and in Pallasca, Peru. A. Lacroix reported it on a lead plate which was estimated to have been submerged for 2000 years in the sea-water near Mahdia, Tunis. A. Russell found crystals of cotunnite on some metallic lead taken in 1846 from a fire-ship wrecked in Falmouth harbour in 1789. In both cases, the mineral had been formed by the action of sea-water on lead. S. Meunier observed its formation during the action of hydrochloric acid on an impure (plumbiferous) fluorite during 27 years.

Lead chloride is slowly formed when chlorine is passed over molten lead, as indicated in connection with lead. R. Weber [3] also found that lead reacts readily and quantitatively with dry chlorine, forming lead chloride. Lead reacts slowly with hydrochloric acid in the cold, but faster when heated, and hydrogen is evolved ; in place of lead, the hydroxide gives better results. J. G. A. Rhodin found that lead monoxide readily reacts with hydrochloric acid in an autoclave at 200° and 15 atm. press. A. R. Davis also made it by the action of hot dil. hydrochloric acid on lead monoxide. C. Renz obtained it by triturating and shaking lead monoxide with 19–38 per cent. hydrochloric acid. As indicated in connection with lead dioxide, chlorine, hydrogen chloride, hypochlorous acid, sulphuryl chloride, and phosphorus trichloride transform the dioxide into lead chloride. W. O. de Coninck and L. Arzalier obtained lead chloride by triturating lead monoxide and ammonium chloride ; S. C. C. Currie obtained it by the electrolysis of hydrochloric acid or neutral soln. of metallic chlorides—say zinc chloride—using a lead anode. E. Langguth, H. J. E. Hamilton, and others treated lead sulphide with chlorine, hydrochloric acid, sulphuryl chloride, or soln. of metal chlorides—e.g. sodium or zinc chloride. F. Becke, and O. Mügge obtained good crystals by the action of hydrochloric acid on galena ; and A. Lacroix synthesized cotunnite by the action of this acid on pieces of galena at 100°. A. Levallois found lead chloride is formed when lead sulphide is heated with silver chloride or mercuric chloride ; E. F. Smith treated the sulphide at 250° with sulphur dichloride.

Lead chloride is also produced when solid lead salts are treated with hydrogen chloride or chlorides, e.g. A. Conduché treated lead sulphate at 350° with the vap. of chloroform. J. W. Thomas passed dry hydrogen chloride over lead nitrate ; W. C. Ebaugh, and E. F. Smith and J. G. Hibbs passed that gas over lead arsenate ; and A. Ditte treated lead sulphate with a soln. of alkali chloride. Lead chloride is also obtained by adding hydrochloric acid or a soluble chloride to a soln. of a lead salt. K. Fajans and J. Fischler obtained lead chloride by a modification of this process. O. Lehmann studied the formation of these crystals microscopically. G. P. Baxter and co-workers recommended the following process in their work on the at. wt. of lead :

About 75 grms. of nitrate were dissolved in water and the soln. was filtered through platinum sponge into a quartz dish. Constant boiling hydrochloric acid which had been freshly distilled through a quartz condenser was then slowly added, with constant stirring, until an excess was present. Chlorine was never freed in the mother-liquor. After the precipitate had settled, it was thoroughly washed by decantation with chilled water and was drained in a platinum centrifugal apparatus. The last wash waters, when tested with diphenylamine, were found to be essentially free from nitrate. The salt was next recrystallized either from water or, because salt crystallized from water was subsequently found to be basic, from very dil. (0·006N) hydrochloric acid, in platinum vessels. The salt was heated to boiling with the solvent in a large platinum still, and, when the soln. was nearly sat., it was poured into a large platinum dish and was cooled with ice.

J. Schabus, and F. Stöber obtained very fine crystals by the slow evaporation

(6–8 mons.) of a soln. of lead chloride in hydrochloric acid. R. Lorenz and W. Eitel recommended heating the purest commercial lead chloride in a stream of equal vols. of dry chlorine and hydrogen chloride—the product is optically clear fogged crystals, containing colloidal lead, are obtained on cooling the fused salt in which some pieces of lead have been placed. F. Field obtained needle-like crystals by allowing a mixture of a lead salt soln. and aniline hydrochloride to stand in contact for some time. A. C. Becquerel obtained needle-like crystals by the slow-action (seven years) of soln. of copper sulphate and sodium chloride on pieces of lead sulphide ; and cubic crystals were formed when the pieces of lead sulphide were wrapped about with platinum wire. W. P. Dreaper found that crystals of lead chloride are slowly formed when a soln. of lead acetate in a capillary tube is dipped in hydrochloric acid.

The *rhythmic precipitation* of lead chloride in gelatine or agar-agar was studied by E. Hatschek. A. van de Veld prepared **colloidal lead chloride** by mixing two soln., one containing 379 grms. (1 mol) of sugar of lead, the other 117 grms. (2 mols) of sodium chloride per litre ; a slimy precipitate forms consisting of a mixture of amorphous lead chloride and crystals of the same substance. Excess of one or other salt does not alter the result, but the more dil. the soln. the more the crystalline predominates ; on filtering, the liquid passes through turbid, whilst that which remains on the filter becomes crystalline on washing with water. Potassium, ammonium, calcium, or barium chloride may be used instead of sodium chloride ; hydrochloric acid, however, forms only a crystalline precipitate. Basic lead acetate or lead propionate, formate, or lactate may be used instead of lead acetate ; but lead nitrate, chlorate, or perchlorate yields only fine crystals.

The physical properties of lead chloride.—Lead chloride crystallized from hot aq. soln. was found by J. Schabus [4] to furnish needles and plates ; and, according to A. Classen and B. Zahorsky, C. E. Guignet, and J. Schabus, when the salt is crystallized from solutions in hydrochloric acid it furnishes white, acicular and tabular crystals. F. Stöber showed that the **crystals** from hydrochloric acid soln. have the pseudohexagonal habit, and belong to the rhombic bipyramidal system having the axial ratios $a : b : c = 0.5952 : 1 : 1.1872$. J. Schabus gave $0.5941 : 1 : 1.1902$; and F. Zambonini, $0.5947 : 1 : 1.1855$ for cotunnite. The **cleavage** on the (001)-face is perfect. The **optic axial angle** given by F. Stöber is $2V = 67° 12'$. P. Gaubert obtained cubic **crystals** from ammonium chloride soln., and J. W. Retgers, octahedra from potassium chloride soln. E. Korreng obtained white rhombic crystals from the molten magma ; and O. Schott obtained microscopic tabular crystals, in part hemimorphic, from molten sodium chloride ; prisms from molten barium chloride ; and rods from molten potassium nitrate. O. Lehmann said that two kinds of doubly refracting crystals separate from the molten magma. K. Treis said the salt is monotropic. W. Biltz studied what he called the **lattice energy** of the crystals ; and A. Sommerfeld, the **electronic structure.**

C. J. B. Karsten gave 5·8022 for the **specific gravity** of the crystals which had not been fused, and 5·6824 for those which had been fused ; J. Schabus gave 5·802 for the sp. gr. of the crystals ; H. Schiff, 5·78 ; G. Brügelmann, 5·88 ; and F. Stolba, 5·80534 at 15° ; G. P. Baxter and C. F. Hawkins obtained 5·899 at 0°, 5·885 at 25°, and 5·872 at 50°. R. Lorenz and W. Eitel gave 5·840 for the sp. gr. at 17° ; and R. Lorenz, H. Frei and A. Jabs gave for the sp. gr., D, of the molten chloride at $\theta°$, $D = 4.907 - 0.00144(\theta - 500)$. R. Lorenz and W. Herz gave 4·910 for the sp. gr. and 56·64 for the mol. vol. at the m.p. F. Ephraim studied the vol. contraction attending the formation of lead halides ; and F. A. Henglein, the mol. vol. I. I. Saslawsky gave 0·93 for the ratio of the mol. vol. to the sum of the at. vols. of the constituent elements. According to D. M. Lichty, the sp. gr. of aq. soln. of lead chloride, sat. at $\theta°$, are :

$\theta°$.	.	0°	15°	25°	35°	45°	55°	65°	80°	95°
Sp. gr.	.	1·00665	1·00693	1·00725	1·00600	1·00423	1·00200	0·99933	0·99474	0·98941

M. Pleissner gave 1·007 for the sp. gr. of a soln. sat. at 18°. According to
V. Czepinsky, the molten liquid is yellow, transparent, and refracting at temp.
between 600° and 800°, and, according to K. Treis, at higher temp. it is dark
orange. L. Poincaré gave 5·21 for the sp. gr. of the liquid at 600°, and at temp.
$\theta°$ between 520° and 700°, R. Lorenz and co-workers gave $5·627-0·00144\theta$.
G. Tammann and Q. A. Mansuri noted evidence of the coalescence of particles of
lead chloride by recrystallization at 149°–161°. A. Reis and L. Zimmermann
found the scratching hardness to be 6·9 when that of ammonium bromide is
unity. S. Motylewsky found the drop-weight of the liquid at the m.p. to
be 165 when that of water at 0° is 100. R. Lorenz and H. T. Kalmus
gave 0·05532 for the viscosity constant at the m.p. 498°. W. Herz and
E. Martin measured the viscosity of soln. of lead chloride in pyridine. R. Lorenz
and F. Kaufler found that the mol. surface energy equation had the constant
between 0·680 and 0·915 from 500°–600°, thus showing that the mol. is complex,
for the simple molecule $PbCl_2$ would give a constant near 2·12. According to
E. Jannettaz and co-workers, the crystalline powder forms a crystalline mass
when compressed by 6000–8000 atm. press. R. Lorenz and W. Eitel found the
hardness to be the same as that of rock salt. Cotunnite is easily scratched with
the finger-nail. The vapour density at a high temp. was found by A. Scott to be
262·7—calculated 278·0; H. E. Roscoe gave 9·62 (air unity).

G. P. Baxter and C. F. Hawkins gave 0·00009 for the coeff. of thermal expansion of lead chloride between 0° and 50°. R. Lorenz and W. Herz gave 0·000294
for the coeff. of thermal expansion, a, and the product $aT_m=0·228$ is in accord
with the value obtained for related halides. The following values for the specific
heat are by G. Linder :

	0°	100°	150°	200°	250°
Sp. ht.	0·06497	0·06647	0·06779	0·06920	0·07043

while the molecular heats by F. Koref, below −160°, and above −160°, by
A. Eucken, are :

	−257·4°	−249·0°	−211·5°	−188·6°	−156·5°	−67·5°	17·5°
C_p	0·72	1·17	3·91	4·46	4·97	17·41	18·32
C_v	0·72	1·17	3·88	4·41	4·88	—	—

Values for the sp. ht. were also obtained by H. V. Regnault, F. E. Neumann,
W. Louguinine, J. N. Brönsted, and O. Ehrhardt. H. M. Goodwin and
H. T. Kalmus gave 0·0778 between 260° and 493° ; 0·121 between 493° and 580°.
The mol. ht. was determined by J. N. Brönsted, W. Nernst, and H. Schottky.
A. Magnus gave $18·52\pm0·06$ between 15° and 100° ; $18·97\pm0·04$ from 15°–250° ;
$19·26\pm06$ from 16°–300° ; and $19·58\pm0·06$ from 16°–350°. H. S. Allen calculated
the sp. ht. in terms of the vibration frequency. H. F. Fernau, and C. L. von Ende
measured the mol. lowering of the freezing point, δ, of aq. soln. of lead chloride,
and found for

	0·0012N-	0·0048N-	0·0077N-	0·0154N-	0·0192N-
δ	0·004	0·014	0·017	0·035	0·037

F. Braun gave 580° for the melting point ; L. Graetz, 520° ; O. H. Weber, 506° ;
E. Korreng, 500° (heating) and 501° (cooling) ; G. Herrmann, and K. Hachmeister,
501° (cooling) ; R. Ruer, and W. Truthe, 499° ; R. Lorenz and co-workers, G. Tam-
mann, and C. Tubandt and S. Eggert, 498° ; T. Carnelley, 498°–501° ; K. Mönkemeyer,
F. Matthes, C. Sandonnini, and E. D. Eastman and L. H. Duschak, 495° ;
M. Amadori, 494° ; R. Lorenz and W. Ruckstuhl, 493° ; and W. Ramsay and
N. Eumorfopoulos, 447°. The best representative value is 501°. M. Lembert
gave 501° for the m.p. of lead chloride made from ordinary and radio-lead.
K. Hachmeister observed no marked singularity on the cooling curve of the solid.
J. Rosenthal said that the salt is quite plastic at a temp. much below the m.p.
K. Mönkemeyer showed that under-cooling may occur through 6°. K. Hachmeister
found that when lead chloride is melted, it loses about 0·1 per cent. in weight

presumably by volatilization. J. Davy said that the salt does not volatilize at a bright red heat in the absence of air, but J. W. Döbereiner found that in the presence of air, lead oxychloride is formed. J. B. Moyer observed that lead chloride volatilizes slightly when heated to 225° in a stream of hydrogen chloride. T. Carnelley and W. C. Williams gave 861° for the boiling point ; O. H. Weber, 956° ; E. D. Eastman and L. H. Duschak, 948·5° at 754 mm. ; and C. G. Maier, 954·4° at 760 mm. Measurements of the partial press. of the chlorine at different temp. were made by K. Jellinck and R. Uloth. C. G. Maier gave for the vapour pressure:

	400°	500°	600°	700°	800°	900°
Vap. press . .	0·00174	0·141	2·82	22·4	116	433 mm. Hg.

H. von Wartenberg and O. Bosse represented the vap. press., p atm., by log p $=-28\cdot518/4\cdot571T+5\cdot085$. C. G. Maier, and R. Lorenz and W. Herz studied this subject. The molecular heat of fusion was given as 5·607 Cals. per mol by O. H. Weber ; 5·806 Cals. by F. Rudberg ; 5·81 Cals. by O. Ehrhardt ; and 5·15 Cals. by H. M. Goodwin and H. T. Kalmus. E. D. Eastman and L. H. Duschak gave 40,600 cals. for the latent heat of vaporization ; and H. von Wartenberg and O. Bosse, 28,518 cals. per mol. C. G. Maier gave for the mol. heat of vaporization 29,510 cals. at 954·4° ; 29,800 cals. at 888·0° ; 30,200 cals. at 834·9° ; 32,110 cals. at 762·7° ; and 34,010 cals. at 718·9°. W. Braunbek discussed the relations between the sp. ht., m.p., and latent heat of fusion.

For the heat of formation of lead chloride, using gaseous chlorine with solid lead, J. Thomsen [5] gave 82·77 Cals., and M. Berthelot, 83·9 Cals. F. Pollitzer considers these values to be 2·0–3·0 Cals. too small, and this was confirmed by the calculations of E. Cohen, and F. Koref and H. Braune. A. Guntz gave 85·2 Cals.; F. Koref, and H. Braune, 85·57–85·70 Cals.; and P. Günther, 85·39 Cals. C. Krahmer calculated from the e.m.f. of some cells, 85·491 Cals. ; R. Lorenz and M. Katayama, 82·6 Cals. ; M. de K. Thompson, 82·7 Cals. (and from the solubility, 74·3 Cals.) ; F. H. Getman, 84·44 Cals. ; and G. D. Roos, 296 cals. per gram. W. C. McC. Lewis calculated 77·66 Cals. from the quantum theory, and the vibration frequency. For the reaction $Pb+2AgCl=2Ag+PbCl_2$, R. Lorenz and M. Katayama gave 23·6 Cals. ; A. Magnus, 24·59 Cals. ; and W. C. McC. Lewis, 21·3 Cals. For the reaction $Pb+2HgCl=2Hg+PbCl_2$, P. Günther gave 21·8 Cals. ; W. C. McC. Lewis, 23·19 ; and F. H. Getman, 21·84 Cals. For the heat of formation of lead chloride in the molten state, R. Lorenz and M. G. Fox calculated 82·4 Cals. ; V. Czepinsky, 86·2–95·0 Cals. ; R. Lorenz gave 82·569 Cals. between 466° and 766° ; and O. H. Weber, 77·9 to 78·35 Cals. between 506° and 890°. J. Thomsen gave −3·4 Cals. for the integral heat of solution per mol at 18° ; M. Berthelot, −2·98 Cals. ; and J. N. Brönsted, −3·282 Cals. M. de K. Thompson gave 74,800 cals. for the free energy of formation of lead chloride, and 82,700 cals. for the total energy with the halogen gaseous. The entropy of the reaction $Pb+Cl_2=PbCl_2$ was discussed by K. Wohl, and A. Eucken and F. Fried.

C. Tubandt and S. Eggert [6] found that, on electrolysis, in light, solid lead chloride is rapidly coloured red and violet. This is not due to the production of a subchloride. J. A. Wilkinson observed a feeble fluorescence when lead reacts with chlorine ; and he found that lead chloride exhibits a bluish fluorescence. According to H. Rubens, the rays reflected from lead chloride have the mean wave-length of 91·0μ. A. Balandin examined the ultra-red spectrum. The energy curves show interference effects due to water vapour. B. A. Dima found that the photoelectric effect is less than with lead bromide or iodide. A. T. Waterman found that when heated lead chloride emits no Pb''-ions. Cotunnite from Vesuvius was found by F. Zambonini,[7] and P. Rossi to be strongly radioactive. G. C. Schmidt found that when lead chloride is heated it emits negatively charged particles.

M. Faraday [8] found that solid lead chloride is a very poor electrical conductor, but the fused salt conducts fairly well, and he electrolyzed it with carbon electrodes.

E. **Wartmann,** and **F.** Beijerinck classed cotunnite as a non-conductor. H. Buff said that the **electrical conductivity** of solid lead chloride is metallic ; E. Wiedemann, that it is not wholly metallic, for with rising temp. it conducts electrolytically ; and C. Tubandt and S. Eggert, arguing from the transport numbers, said that the conductivity of the solid is wholly electrolytic. G. Tammann and H. Bredmeier measured the conductivity of thin films of the chloride. J. Rosenthal found the conductivity of pieces pressed from the powder is immeasurably small at 112°, at higher temp., the conductivity of pastiles pressed from the amorphous powder is less than that made from the crystalline powder ; as the temp. approaches the softening point, the conductivity of the former approaches that of the latter. C. Tubandt and H. Reinhold, M. le Blanc and M. Kröger, and R. Ketzer measured the conductivity of the compressed powder ; and observations on the conductivity of the solid were made by L. Graetz, W. E. Ayrton, R. Ketzer, V. Czepinsky, A. Benrath, and C. Tissot. C. Tubandt and H. Reinhold measured the effect of potassium and sodium chlorides on the conductivity of the solid at 275°. T. A. Heppenstall and W. J. Shutt studied the electrolysis of the fused chloride. C. Tubandt and S. Eggert were unable to verify Faraday's law for solid lead chloride because of the short-circuiting due to a bridge of metal between anode and cathode during the electrolysis. Fine delicate threads and dendritic growths of the metal spread from electrode to electrode very rapidly. They found at 498° a conductivity of 1·44 mhos ; at 508°, 1·478 ; at 548°, 1·692 ; at 578°, 1·826 ; and at 608°, 1·941 ; while W. Biltz and W. Klemm gave for the eq. conductivity $\lambda = 40\cdot7 + 0\cdot150(\theta - 498°)$. F. Braun, V. Czepinsky, and C. Sandonnini measured the conductivity of the fused salt :

	498°	518°	538°	558°	578°	598°	608°
Mhos	1·395	1·544	1·645	1·738	1·826	1·904	1·941

L. Poincaré gave $1\cdot97\{1 + 0\cdot0020(\theta - 600)\}$, and also $1\cdot56\{1 + 0\cdot003(\theta - 508) + 0\cdot0_{7}(\theta - 508)^{2}\}$; the mol. conductivity at 600° was 0·1132. R. Lorenz and H. T. Kalmus found the product of the viscosity and conductivity to be constant. A. Bogorodsky showed that the conductivity in molten sodium nitrate, is :

PbCl$_2$		3·09	7·01	8·01 per cent.
At 350°		1·113	1·083	1·079 mhos.
At 360°		1·152	1·118	1·106 „

J. W. Frers found that the electrolytic conductivity in solid and liquid lead chloride indicates a constitutional difference in the species of ions. The mol. electrical conductivities, μ, of aq. soln. of lead chloride obtained by H. C. Jones and co-workers are as follow, where the conc. is expressed as a mol of salt in v litres of soln. :

v		64	128	512	1024	2048	4096
μ	at 0°	104·41	116·27	133·10	136·89	138·88	144·70
	at 65°	331·22	379·39	452·75	476·90	502·84	515·18

The temp. coeff. were also calculated by H. C. Jones and co-workers ; the eq. conductivity was determined by F. L. Hunt ; A. A. Noyes and K. G. Falk, S. J. Bates, E. Franke, W. Böttger, and M. Pleissner. The percentage degree of ionization, a, obtained by H. C. Jones and co-workers for the above soln., were :

v		64	128	512	1024	2048	4096
a	at 0°	72·2	80·4	92·0	94·6	96·0	100·0
	at 65°	64·29	73·64	87·88	92·57	97·60	100·0

P. Fischer measured the conductivity of mixtures of lead and cuprous chlorides A. A. Noyes, W. Böttger, and W. D. Harkins studied the **degree of ionization** of soln. of lead chloride. According to C. L. von Ende, lead chloride ionizes in aq. soln. in two stages, $PbCl_2 \rightleftharpoons PbCl + Cl'$, and $PbCl' \rightleftharpoons Pb^{\cdot\cdot} + Cl'$. At 25°, he estimated that a sat. aq. soln. contains 6·2 per cent. of non-ionized salt 50·1 per cent. Pb·· and 43·7 per cent. PbCl'. The first stage is about six times stronger than the second stage, for the ionization constant of the former is 0·0009469, and of the latter 0·00006075. S. Labendzinsky, and R. Abegg showed that the soln. also contains complex ions ; and C. L. von Ende indicated that the calculations based on simple ionization are affected by hydrolysis—*vide infra*. F. Haber and S. Tolloczko [9] found the **electromotive force,** E, of two dry Daniell's cells, $PbCl_2|AgCl$, to be 0·519 volt in agreement with theory ; O. H. Weber gave for $Pb|PbCl_2|Cl_2$, at θ' $E=1·2818-0·000584(\theta-506)$; and between 498° and 600°, R. Lorenz and M. G Fox gave $E=1·263-0·000679(\theta-498)$; and M. Katayama gave $E=1·581 -0·00065(\theta-60)$ between 60° and 155°. R. Lorenz and M. G. Fox found that with molten salts, the e.m.f. of the cell $Zn|ZnCl_2|PbCl_2|Pb$, at about 500° is approximately equal to the difference in the values for the cells $Zn|ZnCl_2|Cl_2$ and $Pb|PbCl_2|Cl_2$. G. Tammann studied the voltages of Daniell's cell with fused chlorides with lead in contact with stannic, cuprous, and silver chlorides ; and with manganese, magnesium, aluminium, thallium, and zinc in contact with lead chloride. K. Arndt and H. Probst examined the disturbance which occurs at the anode during the electrolysis of the fused chloride. V. Czepinsky found that the polarization during the electrolysis of molten lead chloride is independent of the current density. J. N. Brönsted measured the e.m.f. of the cell $PbHg_x|PbCl_2(conc. soln.)AgCl|Ag$; and R. B. Mason and J. H. Mathews, the decomposition potential in pyridine soln. J. Thiele measured the **thermo-electric force** of the molten chloride against metals.

A. Lenert [10] found the **dielectric constant** of lead chloride to be 4·20, and after melting and freezing, 17·26. L. Ebert studied the dielectric polarization of the lead salts. S. Meyer gave for the **magnetic susceptibility,** $-0·535\times10^{-6}$, and for the mol. magnetism, $-0·068\times10^{-6}$ at 15°.

The chemical properties of lead chloride.—C. Renz [11] showed that when lead chloride—moist or dry—is exposed to an intense light, it becomes covered with greyish-yellow, grey, and a greyish-black film of a photochloride ; lead chloride crystallized from hot hydrochloric acid is quickly blackened. N. R. Dhar and A. C. Chatterji found that the rhythmic rings of lead chloride formed in silica gel are not affected by light. When lead chloride is heated in air, J. W. Döbereiner found that some decomposition occurs and lead oxychloride is formed ; and J. B. A. Dumas added that water is retained very tenaciously by the chloride, and this at 205° reacts with the chlorine giving off hydrogen chloride, and forming lead oxychloride. The apparent oxidation thus occurs in an atm. of an inert gas, say carbon dioxide. A. Benrath also noticed the reaction with adsorbed water, and possibly with the silica of the glass containing vessel. If moisture be quite absent, the chloride can be volatilized without decomposition in an atm. of carbon dioxide. The formation of oxychlorides when lead chloride is heated to its m.p. and the accompanying colour changes—grey, yellowish-brown, or yellow—were noted by E. Korreng, and K. Treis. K. Hachmeister found that ammonium chloride does not hinder the reaction. R. Ketzer said that the chloride is discoloured when melted in nitrogen, or in vacuo, but not so in chlorine. There is no sign of a transition temp. on the heating curve of lead chloride H. Schulze found that when lead chloride is heated in oxygen, lead oxide is formed, and W. H. Sodeau showed that a mixture of lead chloride and chlorate gives off no chlorine at about 200°, and a mixture of lead dioxide and chlorate, none when heated to 450° in a stream of oxygen. W. Spring found that oxygen reacts at 400°–500°. A. Mailfert found lead chloride is slowly converted to the dioxide by ozone. According to M. Berthelot, hydrogen reduces lead chloride by a reversible reaction ; and A. Jouniaux found that at 600° there is very little change, while W. C. Ebaugh added that the reduction is incomplete because of the close proximity of the temp. of reduction and sublimation. K. Jellinek and R. Uloth measured the equilibrium conditions in the reaction $PbCl_2+H_2\rightleftharpoons Pb+2HCl$, and found for $\log (K_1^{-1}=p^2_{HCl}/p_{H_2})$ at 560°, 650°, and 700° respectively 0·773–3, 0·523–2, and 0·316–1. They also found the vap. press.

of the chlorine from $PbCl_2 \rightleftharpoons Pb + Cl_2$ at these temp. to be log $p_{Cl_2} = -14{\cdot}50$ atm., $-12{\cdot}61$ atm., and $-10{\cdot}69$ atm. respectively. N. Parravano and G. Malquori also studied this subject. F. de Carli studied the reaction. A. de Hemptinne found that the silent electric discharge in hydrogen produces a reduction of the contained lead chloride. The nascent hydrogen evolved from a mixture of zinc and hydrochloric acid reduces rapidly and quantitatively any lead chloride contained in the soln.; and, added A. Gawalowsky, in the presence of water, the zinc reduces lead chloride to tabular flakes; in the presence of ammonia, to a microcrystalline black powder—and in the presence of sulphuric acid, some nitric oxide is evolved and dendritic crystals of lead are produced.

Observations have been made by G. Bischof, J. C. Bell, G. André, C. L. Wagner, G. J. Mulder, C. R. A. Wright and C. Thompson, G. C. Wittstein, J. Formanek, W. D. Harkins, C. L. von Ende, A. A. Noyes, W. Böttger, M. Pleissner, G. Kernot and U. Pomilio, A. J. J. van de Velde, and K. Fajans and J. Fischler, on the **solubility** of lead chloride in water. According to D. M. Lichty, the solubility, S, expressed in grams of lead chloride, $PbCl_2$, in 100 grms. of water, is :

	0°	15°	25°	35°	45°	55°	65°	80°	95°	100°
S .	0·6728	0·9090	1·0842	1·3244	**1·5673**	1·8263	2·1265	2·6224	3·1654	3·342

The **solubility product** given by G. N. Lewis and T. B. Brighton is $2{\cdot}29 \times 10^{-5}$. J. Schürr measured the **speed of solution.** R. Flatt tried to correlate the solubility with the electronic structure. J. N. Brönsted observed no special transition point on the curve between 20° and 100°. G. von Hevesy and E. Rona measured the velocity of exchange between the mol. of lead chloride and its sat. soln. Owing to **hydrolysis,** M. Pleissner found that the aq. soln. reacts acid to litmus, and, when very dil., alkaline to iodeosin. G. P. Baxter and F. L. Grover also found that the salt is feebly hydrolyzed in aq. soln. so that the chlorine content of the salt obtained by crystallization from aq. soln., or from dil. hydrochloric acid, is short of about 0·1 per cent. chlorine. The salt melted in dry hydrogen chloride is neutral. C. L. von Ende showed that in a sat. soln. containing about 38·80 millimols per litre the hydrolysis is very small ; about 1·3 per cent. in a soln. with 21·4 millimols per litre ; and 4·4 per cent. with about 16·8 millimols per litre. C. Kullgren estimated that in a soln. with 128 eq. $PbCl_2$ per litre, there is a 0·495 per cent. hydrolysis at 85·5°, and 0·768 per cent. at 100° ; J. K. Wood found 0·2 per cent. hydrolysis in a 0·1N-soln. at 25° ; and H. Ley, 0·6 per cent. in a soln. with a 0·01 mol per litre. H. R. Fernau, and C. L. von Ende discussed the disturbing effects of hydrolysis on calculations from the lowering of the f.p., the electrical conductivity, and the e.m.f. of cells ; and O. Schärer, the effects of strong electrolytes on the solubility. H. E. Armstrong and J. V. Eyre regarded the first action in the dissolution of the salt to be a depolymerization of a complex mol., and that this is followed by hydration of the salt : $mPbCl_2 + nH_2O \rightleftharpoons (PbCl_2)_m(H_2O)_n$. R. Norris found that water-vap. at 110° decomposes lead chloride ; W. Spring found that hydrogen chloride is slowly given off at 110°, the reaction is faster at 150° ; and very rapid at the m.p. of lead chloride. F. Koref and H. Braune found that lead chloride is soluble in a soln. of **sodium hydroxide,** forming, according to A. Ditte, a series of oxychlorides when the alkali-lye is not in excess, and lead oxide, if an excess be used. W. Herz regarded the reaction with **potassium hydroxide** as a balanced reaction : $2KOH + PbCl_2 = Pb(OH)_2 + 2KCl$, where the constant $K[KCl]^2[Pb(OH)_2] = [PbCl_2][KOH]^2$, is 0·00076. A. Schott found that oxychlorides are produced when lead chloride is added to molten sodium hydroxide. V. Kohlschütter and H. Roesti found that at ordinary temp. lead chloride is converted by alkali hydroxide into red lead monoxide without change of the crystalline form; the change with 10N-NaOH is very fast; and with 5N-NaOH, it is complete in an hour. V. Zotier examined the catalytic effect of lead chloride on the decomposition of **hydrogen dioxide.**

According to W. W. Fischer, **chlorine** does not react with dry lead chloride, but with a soln. of lead chloride in one of potassium chloride or hydrochloric acid, it furnishes lead tetrachloride (*q.v.*). A. Classen and B. Zahorsky, and W. Biltz and E. Meinecke, said that liquid chlorine does not act on lead chloride provided hydrogen chloride be absent. N. A. E. Millon, and A. Ditte said that chlorine-water in sunlight oxidizes lead chloride, forming lead dioxide and evolving chlorine. A. Potilitzin found that **bromine** replaces 12·2 per cent. of the chlorine under 2 atm. press.; 20·5 per cent. at 8 atm. press.; and 33·8 per cent. at 18 atm. press. F. Ephraim did not obtain a chloro-acid by the action of dry **hydrogen chloride** on lead chloride. M. Berthelot noticed that the addition of dil. **hydrochloric acid** to a sat. soln. of lead chloride precipitates some of the salt. Hence, as noted by A. Craig, M. Pleissner, G. Bischof, J. C. Bell, etc., the solubility of the salt is depressed in the presence of dil. hydrochloric acid; on the other hand, the chloride is fairly soluble in the conc. acid as observed by G. André, A. Craig, and others. A. Ditte obtained the data indicated in Table IX. Expressing the solubility, S, of lead

TABLE IX.—THE SOLUBILITY OF LEAD CHLORIDE IN HYDROCHLORIC ACID AT DIFFERENT TEMPERATURES.

Gram HCl per 1000 grms. of water.	Grams PbCl$_2$ per 100 grms. of solution.				
	0°	20°	40°	55°	80°
0	8·0	11·8	17·0	21·0	31·0
100	2·1	1·4	3·2	5·5	12·0
150	1·5	2·0	5·0	7·5	16·0
200	3·5	5·0	8·2	11·7	21·5
250	6·5	8·0	13·0	16·2	28·5
300	10·7	12·5	17·5	22·0	35·0
400	21·5	24·0	—	—	—

chloride, and hydrogen chloride, in grams per litre, the results for dil. soln. at 0° (R. Engel), and at 25° (A. A. Noyes):

HCl .	0	0·5	1·0	2·0	3·0	6·0	10·0
$S \begin{cases} 0° \\ 25° \end{cases}$	5·83	4·5	3·6	2·2	1·6	1·4	1·2
	10·79	9·0	7·6	6·0	5·0	3·1	1·8

These results show that very little hydrochloric acid is sufficient to diminish considerably the solubility of lead chloride; that there is a minimum range through which the solubility is nearly constant; and that the solubility increases considerably when the soln. of hydrochloric acid is very conc. The explanation of the lowering of the solubility of dil. hydrochloric acid is in accord with the ionization theory (1. 15, 12), and has been discussed by H. R. Fernau, C. Immerwahr, C. L. von Ende, K. Beck, and P. Stegmüller, R. Kremann and H. Breymesser, and A. A. Noyes. H. E. Armstrong and J. V. Eyre applied the hydrone theory of association to the results. The increased solubility in conc. hydrochloric acid is explained by M. Berthelot, and A. Ditte on the assumption that a *hydrochloro-plumbous acid*, H_2PbCl_4, is formed.

The influence of the presence of various chlorides on the solubility of lead chloride has also been examined, and the results in Table X are by A. A. Noyes, and W. Herz and M. Hellebrandt. The results are all expressed in grams of salt per litre. With the exception of **mercuric chloride**, the solubility of the lead chloride in soln. of **potassium chloride**, etc., is depressed as in the case of hydrochloric acid. W. W. Randall, C. L. von Ende, N. Demassieux, and J. N. Brönsted measured the effect with *ammonium chloride—vide infra*, complex salts. M. Berthelot, C. L. von Ende, W. D. Harkins, H. Ley, A. A. Noyes, and J. N. Brönsted studied the effect with *potassium chloride;* W. Herz and M. Hellebrandt, A. Ditte, N. Demassieux, and E. Field, the effect with *sodium chloride;* W. Herz and M. Hellebrandt, with **potassium and sodium bromides** ; G. Bischof, and A. A. Noyes, with **calcium chloride** ; W. Herz and M. Hellebrandt, with calcium, **barium and strontium chlorides and bromides** ; A. A. Noyes, with **magnesium, zinc, cadmium, and manganese chlorides** ; A. A. Noyes, and J. Formanek, with mercuric chloride ;

TABLE X.—THE SOLUBILITY OF LEAD CHLORIDE IN THE PRESENCE OF OTHER CHLORIDES AT 25°.

Grams salt per litre.	Grams of PbCl₂ dissolved in aqueous solutions of						
	KCl	CaCl₂	MgCl₂	ZnCl₂	CdCl₂	HgCl₂	MnCl₂
0	10·79	10·79	10·79	10·79	10.79	10·79	10·79
1	9·3	8·7	7·7	—	10·2	11·0	9·5
2	8·2	7·6	6·5	—	9·7	11·4	8·3
3	7·2	6·7	5·7	—	9·2	11·7	7·3
4	6·5	6·0	5·2	—	8·6	12·0	6·3
6	5·3	4·8	4·4	—	7·7	12·7	5·0
8	4·5	3·9	—	—	7·0	13·3	4·1
10	3·9	3·3	—	—	6·5	14·0	3·5
14	3·1	—	—	3·0	5·4	—	2·8
20	—	—	—	—	4·7	—	—

and J. Formanek, with **ferrous and ferric chlorides.** K. Treis, and O. Schott studied the action of fused metal chlorides—*vide infra.* F. Ruyssen and E. Varenne found that the solubility **of silver chloride** in hydrochloric acid is somewhat lessened in the presence of lead chloride, but less hydrochloric acid is required to dissolve the mixed chlorides than for each taken singly. V. Thomas found that when **hydrobromic acid** is evaporated with lead chloride, lead bromide is formed ; and with **potassium bromide,** a complex salt may be produced ; likewise also H. Fonzes-Diacon obtained a complex salt by using **ammonium bromide** or **ammonium iodide** ; and E. Field, by using **potassium iodide** or ammonium iodide. V. Thomas obtained a chloroiodide by adding a soln. of potassium iodide to one of lead chloride. E. H. Perman obtained no reaction between dry lead chloride and potassium iodide ; but in a sealed tube for 7–10 days in darkness, or for 3 days at 100°, the mixture assumes a yellow colour. A soln. of **hypochlorous acid** was found by A. J. Balard to oxidize lead chloride to the dioxide.

A. Vogel found that molten **sulphur** converts lead chloride into lead sulphide ; and with **sulphammonium,** H. Moissan obtained small, yellow crystals. H. Sommerlad found that when heated with **arsenic trisulphide,** arsenic trichloride is formed by an incomplete reaction, and with **antimony trisulphide,** lead sulphantimonite is formed. H. N. Stokes found that when iron disulphide, FeS_2, and a soln. of lead chloride are heated in a sealed tube, crystals of lead sulphide are formed. According to A. Ditte, with an excess of lead chloride, **sulphuric acid** is wholly converted into lead sulphate, but with smaller proportions there is a balanced reaction : $PbCl_2+H_2SO_4 \rightleftharpoons 2HCl+PbSO_4$; F. A. H. Schreinemakers found that in an evacuated vessel, the press. of the hydrogen chloride at 27·2° is 1 atm. ; and at 43°, 2 atm. ; hence, under atm. press., hydrogen chloride liberates sulphuric acid from lead sulphate until equilibrium press. is attained ; he also found that the heat of the reaction is 8 Cals. A. Colson observed no reaction between sulphuric acid and lead chloride in an atm. of hydrogen chloride at 15°. M. Pleissner showed that a small proportion of sulphuric acid lowers the solubility of lead chloride in water. A. Ditte obtained complex salts by the action of **potassium and sodium sulphates.** According to J. Schröder, lead chloride reacts with a pyridine soln. of **silver sulphate,** forming lead sulphate. O. Ruff found that the conversion of **chlorosulphuric acid,** $HClSO_3$, into sulphuryl chloride, SO_2Cl_2, is catalytically accelerated by one per cent. of lead chloride. C. R. Wise found lead chloride is insoluble in **selenyl chloride, SeOCl₂**.   J. F. W. Herschel found that lead chloride is soluble in an aq. soln. of **sodium thiosulphate**, but less so than is the case with silver chloride, and K. A. Hofmann and V. Wölfl showed that when the soln. is exposed to a strong light, a red sulphochloride, $Pb_4S_4Cl_2$, is formed ; but in diffuse daylight, or when heated in darkness, black lead sulphide is deposited.   If a mixture of sodium thiosulphate and lead chloride be heated in a porcelain crucible, F. Faktor found that lead sulphide is formed.

E. P. Lewis observed that activated **nitrogen** had no effect on lead chloride. E. C. Franklin and C. A. Kraus said the chloride is slightly soluble in liquid **ammonia**.   H. Rose observed that lead chloride unites with ammonia gas—the chloride swells up and much heat is evolved.   W. Biltz found that the vol. increases four or five times, and very little passes into soln.—*vide infra*.   W. Biltz and W. Fischer obtained **lead octamminodichloride**, $PbCl_2.8NH_3$, by the action of liquid ammonia on lead chloride dried at 100°–120°.   The vap. press. of the ammonia at −78·5° is 1·8 mm. ; at −50·0°, 26·6 mm. ; at −36°, 100 mm. ; and at −21·2°, 338 mm.   The heat of dissociation per mol. of ammonia is 8·2 Cals. They obtained **lead tetritatridecamminodichloride**, $4PbCl_2.13NH_3$, from the octammine at −21·2°.   The vap. press. at −21·2° is 34·1 mm. ; at −13°, 100 mm. ; at −11·1°, 113·2 mm. ; and at 0°, 360 mm.   It is possibly a mixture of some of the other ammines.   The heat of formation is given as 9·4 Cals. per mol of ammonia.   F. Ephraim made **lead diamminodichloride**, $PbCl_2.2NH_3$, from lead chloride and undried ammonia ; and W. Biltz and W. Fischer, from the octammine or the tridecatetrammine at 0°.   At 20·5°, the vap. press. is 32·8 mm. ; at 30°, 100 mm. ; at 34·65°, 140·5 mm. ; at 46·1°, 346 mm. ; and at 76°, 760 mm.   The heat of dissociation is 11·0 cals. per mol of ammonia ; F. Ephraim gave 12·4 Cals. H. Rose's product indicated above had a composition very near *lead sesquiammino- dichloride*, or **lead hemitriamminodichloride**, $2PbCl_2.3NH_3$; and it was made by J. White by adding lead chloride to a soln. of ammonium acetate.   W. Biltz and W. Fischer gave for the vap. press., 16 mm. at 21·7° ; 100 mm. at 34·65° ; and 267 mm. at 46°.   The heat of formation per mol of ammonia is 11·3 Cals.   W. Biltz and W. Fischer also made **lead monamminodichloride**, $PbCl_2.NH_3$, from the octam- mine at 78·46°.   The vap. press. at 78·46° is 13·2 mm. ; at 80·14°, 18 mm. ; at 100°, 93 mm. ; and at 99·6°, 167 mm.   The heat of dissociation is 13·3 Cals. G. L. Clark studied the secondary valencies of these ammines.   J. Wood and J. L. Borden found that lead oxychlorides are formed when lead chloride is treated with an aq. soln. of ammonia.   G. André observed no reaction between ammonia and lead chloride in a sealed tube at 150° ; while W. Herz represented the equi- librium constant, K, in the reaction : $PbCl_2+2NH_4OH \rightleftharpoons 2NH_4Cl+Pb(OH)_2$, by 0·0081—*vide* the action of potash-lye.   V. Kohlschütter and H. Roesti found that with $2N$- to $4N$-NH_3, the crystals of lead chloride become greenish and opaque, but no lead monoxide is produced after prolonged contact.   T. W. B. Welsh and H. J. Broderson found that 100 c.c. of anhydrous **hydrazine** dissolve 3 grms. of lead chloride at ordinary temp. and the soln. becomes black.   V. Thomas showed that **nitrogen peroxide** does not attack the cold solid, but when melted, a little oxychloride is formed.   G. P. Baxter and F. L. Grover found that when fused lead chloride dissolves in dil. **nitric acid**, about 0·004 per cent. of black residue remains undissolved.   C. L. von Ende found that the solubility of lead chloride in nitric acid increases proportionally with the amount added and some lead nitrate is formed. $0.001N$-, $0.01N$-, and $0.051N$-soln. of nitric acid dissolve respectively 38·87, 39·71, and 42·92 millimols of lead chloride per litre.   He also found the solubility is increased in the presence of **potassium nitrate** ; and W. D. Harkins, C. L. von Ende, and H. E. Armstrong and J. V. Eyre found that the solubility increases with increasing additions of **lead nitrate**.   Expressing the results in grams of salt per litre, A. A. Noyes found :

$Pb(NO_3)_2$	.	0	1	4	8	10	20	40
$PbCl_2$	.	10·79	10·80	10·90	11·0	11·05	11·20	11·70

O. Schott found that molten potassium nitrate dissolves lead chloride which is deposited in rhombic crystals as the soln. cools. H. Rose found that with **phosphine,** hydrogen chloride, lead, and phosphorus are produced.

According to F. Göbel,[12] and A. G. Bloxam, lead chloride at a red heat reacts with **carbon monoxide.** forming carbonyl chloride and lead : but A. Benrath found that the salt can be sublimed in **carbon dioxide** without decomposition provided moisture be excluded—*vide supra.* W. Spring made observations on this subject. A boiling soln. of **sodium carbonate** was found by R. Salvadori to convert the chloride into a basic carbonate. G. Gore found that **coal-gas** reduces it with the separation of carbon ; and J. Gathy, that **water-gas** reduces it at a red heat. A. P. N. Franchimont found lead chloride to be insoluble in **benzene ;** and H. Arctowsky, insoluble in **carbon disulphide.** Lead chloride and **ethyl iodide** do not react at ordinary temp., but in sealed tubes at 150°–160° the exchange of halides is nearly complete, with alcohol (R. Brix), or without (B. Köhnlein). H. E. Armstrong and J. V. Eyre, G. C. Wittstein, H. Arnold, G. Bischof, and C. J. Fritsch showed that lead chloride is virtually insoluble in conc. **ethyl alcohol,** and only silghtly soluble in cold or hot 76 per cent. alcohol. G. Kernot and U. Pomilio found that at 25° with concentrations expressed in grams per litre of soln. :

C_2H_5OH	.	0	5·75	11·51	23·02	46·05	92·10	184·20
$PbCl_2$	.	10·75	10·16	9·36	9·14	8·25	7·12	4·76

H. E. Armstrong and J. V. Eyre found that with 15·01 and 60·06 grms. of **propyl alcohol** per 1000 grms. of water, the sat. soln. contained per 1000 grms., respectively 10·08 and 9·36 grms. of lead chloride ; with 11·01 and 33·03 grms. of **acetaldehyde** per 1000 grms. of water, 1000 grms. of sat. soln. contained respectively 10·54 and 9·82 grms. of lead chloride ; with 11·01 and 33·02 grms. of **paraldehyde** per 1000 grms. of water, 1000 grms. of a sat. soln. contained respectively 10·50 and 9·96 grms. of lead chloride ; and with 15·51 and 62·04 grms. of **glycol** per 1000 grms. of water, a sat. soln. contained respectively 10·75 and 10·90 grms. of lead chloride per 1000 grms. of soln. The solubility in **glycerol** was measured by C. H. Piesse, and H. E. Armstrong and J. V. Eyre ; the former gave

Glycerol	.	.	.	12·5	25	50	100	per cent.
$PbCl_2$	.	.	.	0·91	1·04	1·32	2·0	,,

G. Kernot and U. Pomilio found with soln. containing 0–11·38, and 91·06 grms. of **mannitol** per litre, respectively 10·75, 10·64, and 11·29 grms. of lead chloride were dissolved. A. Naumann found the salt is insoluble in **acetone ;** W. Eidmann, insoluble in **methylal ;** and A. Naumann, insoluble in **benzonitrile.** F. Fischer and K. Thiele found a soln. of **ammonium formate** dissolves a little chloride. A. Benrath, W. Herz and E. Martin, A. Colson, and A. E. Hill examined the solubility in **acetic acid ;** the last-named gave

Acetic acid	0	0·5	0·10	0·20	0·465	0·929	1·845	3·680 normal
$PbCl_2$	. 10·77	10·82	10·85	10·70	10·27	9·45	7·90	5·26 grms. per litre

L. Carius, and J. White found that the solubility of lead chloride in soln. of **lead acetate** is greater than with water alone ; E. F. Anthon noted that lead chloride is very soluble in a soln. of **sodium acetate ;** A. Naumann, that it is insoluble in **methyl acetate ;** and A. Naumann, and J. White, that it is but slightly soluble in **ethyl acetate.** F. Koref and H. Braune observed that lead chloride is soluble in an alkaline amyl alcohol soln. of **sodium tartrate ;** and F. Mohr, that **oxalic acid** dissolves but a small proportion of the lead as oxalate. As with aq. ammonia, and alkali-lye, W. Herz found the equilibrium constant with **methylamine** to be 0·0066 ; and **ethylamine** behaves similarly ; A. Werner noted that lead chloride dissolves with difficulty in **ethylenediamine monohydrate.** According to H. Röhler, lead chloride forms a complex with **formamide ;** H. Mandal noted that lead chloride is soluble in **aniline**; H. E. Armstrong and J. V. Eyre, that 10·25 grms. of lead chloride can dissolve per 1000 grms. of a soln. of 29·82 grms. of **methyl acetanilide** per 1000 grms. of water; and A. Classen and B. Zahorsky, that it has a low solubility in **pyridine** and **pyridine hydrochloride**; C. W. Heise gave for the solubility in grams per 100 grms. of pyridine when the solid phase is $PbCl_2.2C_5H_5N$:

	−20°	0°	22°	44°	65°	76°	90°	102°
$PbCl_2$	0·303	0·364	0·459	0·559	0·758	0·893	1·07	1·31

R. Fosse and L. Lesage observed that a complex is formed with naphthapyryl; G. Grüttner and E. Krause, that with **magnesium chloromethide, bromoethide, or chloropropide,** lead tetralkide is formed; W. Göbbels found **picoline hydrochloride,** and **lutidine hydrochloride** form complexes with lead chloride.

L. Kahlenberg and W. J. Trautmann [13] found that powdered **silicon** when heated with lead chloride, reacted: $2PbCl_2+Si=SiCl_4+2Pb$; and when heated in air, $2PbCl_2+3Si+3O_2=2PbSiO_3+SiCl_4$. Lead chloride is reduced by **calcium** (F. M. Perkin and L. Pratt), **calcium silicide** (E. Berger), **magnesium** (K. Seubert and A. Schmidt), and **aluminium,** or **manganese** (E. Berger). For the action of **zinc** in the presence of water or acids, *vide supra;* J. Ball noted that the presence of lead chloride accelerates the dissolution of zinc in acids; and H. le Chatelier, that a paste made of dil. hydrochloric acid and lead chloride dissolves zinc, but not copper zincide, $CuZn_2$. W. Reinders discussed the equilibrium $Zn+PbCl_2 \rightleftharpoons Pb+ZnCl_2$ in the electrolysis of the molten chloride; and R. Lorenz and co-workers, and G. Tammann, that with **cadmium,** $Cd+PbCl_2 \rightleftharpoons Pb+CdCl_2$; and R. Lorenz and co-workers, that with **tin**: $Sn+PbCl_2 \rightleftharpoons Pb+SnCl_2$. Molten lead chloride was found by C. Tubandt and S. Eggert to react with **silver,** forming silver chloride. H. Rose said that **mercuric oxide** precipitates lead oxide from soln. of lead chloride, and A. Mailhe found that a complex, $2Pb(OH)_2.HgCl_2$, is formed; A. Mailhe also obtained $Pb(OH)Cl$ by adding **cupric hydroxide** to a soln. of lead chloride. T. Carnelley and W. C. Williams found that **glass** is attacked by boiling lead chloride.

Lead tetrachloride.—When chlorine is passed into a sat. soln. of lead chloride in a conc. soln. of sodium or calcium chloride, a yellow soln. is obtained which was supposed by A. Sobrero and F. Selmi,[14] and J. Nicklès, to contain an unstable higher chloride of lead. The analysis of A. Sobrero and F. Selmi, $PbCl_4+9NaCl$; and that of J. Nicklès, $PbCl_4+16CaCl_2$, merely represented the composition of soln., not chemical individuals; and the results do no more than indicate the possible existence of lead tetrachloride. W. W. Fischer cited some inconclusive experiments to prove the existence of lead tetrachloride. O. Seidel tried unsuccessfully to isolate lead tetrachloride and its double salts with other metals, and in 1881, A. Ditte doubted the existence of lead tetrachloride. In 1885, J. Nikoljukine isolated some chloroplumbates and established their chemical individuality. L. L. de Koninck argued that the action of hydrochloric acid on red-lead furnishes not lead tetrachloride but rather *lead trichloride,* $PbCl_3$, because a boiling soln. of a manganese salt in fuming hydrochloric acid becomes dark green in the presence of lead dioxide, but not in the presence of red-lead.

According to H. Friedrich, if ammonium chloroplumbate be added in small quantities at a time to conc. sulphuric acid, cooled with ice, a vigorous reaction occurs, and hydrogen chloride is evolved, and there is a smell of hypochlorous acid. The oily liquid which separates is purified by shaking with fresh sulphuric acid, and its composition corresponds with $PbCl_4$. The same process was used by J. M. Matthews; and H. Erdmann and P. Köthner employed rubidium chloroplumbate in place of the ammonium salt. Lead tetrachloride is a translucent, yellow, highly refractive liquid which fumes in contact with moist air, with decomposition into lead dichloride and chlorine. H. Friedrich found the sp. gr. of lead tetrachloride at 0° to be 3·18, and it solidifies to a yellowish, crystalline mass at −15°. A. Voigt and W. Biltz found that the electrolytic conductivity of lead tetrachloride is very small—0.0_680 mho, at $0°$; and W. Biltz and W. Klemm gave 0.0_420 for the eq. conductivity. Lead tetrachloride forms a hydrate in the presence of a little water which, by the further addition of water, decomposes into lead peroxide and hydrogen chloride; when brought into contact with a small quantity of cooled hydrochloric acid, a crystalline derivative, probably $PbCl_4.2HCl$, is formed. W. Biltz and E. Meinecke found lead tetrachloride to be completely miscible with liquid chlorine. Lead tetrachloride may be kept under cold conc. sulphuric acid. J. M. Matthews said that the liquid decomposes in 12 hrs. According to H. Friedrich, when heated with cold soln. of sulphuric acid, it decomposes with explosion into lead dichloride and chlorine. When, however, lead tetrachloride is heated in a retort with conc. sulphuric acid, and a current of chlorine passed through, a certain quantity of the tetrachloride distils over below 105°, at about which temp. the explosion occurs. With potassium iodide, it is probable that lead tetraiodide is first formed, and this immediately decomposes into lead iodide and iodine; potassium and sodium float on lead tetrachloride and become covered with a brown protective film of lead dioxide; when heated with potassium, an explosion occurs. J. M. Matthews found that the tetrachloride is soluble in chloroform. V. Lenher and W. C. Hill found that with tellurium or tellurium dioxide, an impure tellurium tetrachloride is formed. According to J. M. Matthews, lead tetrachloride does not combine with nitrosyl chloride, nitrogen peroxide, sulphur monochloride, phosphorus chlorides, cyanogen, hydrogen cyanide, cyanogen chloride, acetonitrile, or benzonitrile, but it unites with ammonia, forming **lead diamminotetrachloride**, $PbCl_4.2NH_3$, when dry ammonia is passed into a fairly conc. soln. of lead tetrachloride in chloroform. The orange-yellow mass fumes in air, and decomposes on standing; less conc. soln. of lead chloride furnish **lead tetramminotetrachloride**, $PbCl_4.4NH_3$, which is white and stable in air. Lead tetrachloride unites with the amines—methylamine, ethylamine, propylamine, aniline, pyridine, quinoline, and β-naphthylamine. The compounds with toluidine, and diphenylamine readily decompose. There is no reaction with the acid amides of acetic and benzoic acids—*vide* silicon tetrachloride (**6**. 40, 57). H. Schiff examined the reaction of lead tetrachloride with alkaloids. H. L. Wells proposed separating cæsium from the other alkalies in virtue of the low solubility of cæsium chloroplumbate.

According to N. A. E. Millon, when lead dioxide is gradually added to well-cooled conc. hydrochloric acid, a yellow liquid is formed, which, when diluted with water, forms lead dioxide and chloride, and when treated with oxalic acid, furnishes carbon dioxide. O. Seidel said that no chlorine is evolved when the lead dioxide is added to the cold hydrochloric acid; and W. W. Fischer found that two gram-atoms of chlorine were needed to precipitate one gram-atom of lead as dioxide, and that the lead is precipitated quantitatively as dioxide when the soln. is treated with sodium acetate. Modifications of N. A. E. Millon's process of making the soln. of lead tetrachloride in hydrochloric acid were used by J. Nikoljukine, H. L. Wells, A. Seyewetz and P. Trawitz, J. Strachan, and L. E. Rivot and co-workers. If chlorine be passed into dil. hydrochloric acid in which lead chloride is suspended, W. W. Fischer, A. Fränkel, and A. Ditte showed that lead dioxide is precipitated, but with conc. hydrochloric acid, the amount of chlorine absorbed is greater than can be explained by the solubility of the gas. The soln. has a strong yellow colour, and when treated with ammonium chloride it furnishes clear, yellow, octahedral crystals, the composition of which can be represented by the formula $(NH_4)_2PbCl_6$. E. Krause found that lead tetrachloride which has been purified by distillation in a high vacuum gives intensely brownish-red soln. in benzene and its homologues; the colour is discharged by the addition of carbon tetrachloride, chloroform, dibromoethane, glacial acetic acid, or ether without conversion of the lead tetrachloride into the dichloride. Cold dil. soln. may be preserved unchanged in the dark during several hours, after which gradual decomposition occurs with the separation of lead dichloride. Conc. soln. decompose after some time with explosive violence without any apparent cause. For the action of hydrogen sulphide, *vide* lead disulphide.

When ammonium chloroplumbate is treated with sulphuric acid, lead tetrachloride is formed as a heavy, yellow, oily liquid. It is therefore inferred that the series of salts typified by $(NH_4)_2PbCl_6$ is derived from the hypothetical **hydrohexachloroplumbic acid, H_2PbCl_6**. A. Classen and B. Zahorsky obtained a soln. of this acid by mixing fuming hydrochloric acid, lead chloride, and liquid chlorine in a press. flask cooled by a mixture of ice and salt. The flask is cooled by solid carbon dioxide and ether before it is opened. J. Strachan oxidized a solid soln. of lead acetate and conc. hydrochloric acid by means of bleaching powder ; A. Hutchinson and W. Pollard treated lead tetracetate with cold conc. sulphuric acid ; A. Nathansohn and F. Leyser treated lead sulphide and hydrochloric acid at a low temp. with chlorine or hypochlorites ; and K. Elbs and F. Fischer treated lead persulphate, $Pb(SO_4)_2$, with hydrochloric acid.

F. Försted, K. Elbs and R. Nübling, E. Müller, and M. Wissmüller obtained the acid by the electrolysis of a hydrochloric acid soln. of lead chloride. Hydrochloric acid of sp. gr. 1·18 and at 10° was electrolyzed with an anode compounded of two lead plates and a carbon plate, and a soln. of lead chloride surrounded by a porous pot. The anode was so arranged that one-half of the current passed through the lead part of the anode and the other half through the carbon plate, where the current densities were 0·007 and 0·04 ampere per sq. cm. respectively. Under these circumstances, the lead chloride formed at the lead anode was converted into plumbic chloride by the chlorine produced at the carbon anode. The yield of the acid H_2PbCl_2 was 70–80 per cent. of the theoretical quantity. According to R. Kremann and H. Breymesser, the electro-oxidation of the soln. of lead chloride in hydrochloric acid may be due to the formation of lead tetrachloride on the anode which acts as a depolarizer on the carbon electrode, or to the formation of lead chloride on the anode and its subsequent reaction with the chlorine liberated from the carbon electrode. They compared the decomposition voltage of soln. of hydrochloric acid of sp. gr. 1·18, at 0° and 21°, with that of similar soln. with lead chloride. They found that two breaks occur in each of the current-voltage curves. The first break occurs at 0·83 volt at 0° and 0·87 volt at 21°, and is the same for both soln. The second occurs for hydrochloric acid alone at 0·99 volt at 0° and 0·95 volt at 21°, whilst for hydrochloric acid sat. with lead chloride the values are 1·04 volts at 0° and 1·00 volt at 21°. From these results it was inferred that the formation of lead tetrachloride is a secondary process between the lead chloride and chlorine formed respectively on the lead and carbon anodes, and differs in no way from the chemical method of formation of this substance as described by H. Friedrich. G. von Hevesy and L. Zechmeister showed that a dynamic equilibrium exists between bivalent and quadrivalent lead ions in glacial acetic acid soln., and in consequence it follows that electrons can pass of themselves, in certain circumstances, from one ion to an isomeric ion and also to an electrode. A. Voigt and W. Biltz found that the electrical conductivity of fused lead tetrachloride is of the order 8×10^{-7} mho. A. Sommerfeld discussed the electronic structure of the tetrachloride.

The formation of the chloroplumbates, R'_2PbO_6, as just indicated, led to the assumption that the orange-yellow liquid produced by the action of chlorine on a hydrochloric acid soln. of lead chloride contains hydrohexachloroplumbic acid, $PbCl_{2solid} + Cl_{2gas} + 2HCl = H_2PbCl_6$. E. W. Wescott determined the conditions of equilibrium of this reaction with acid of conc. down to the point where lead dioxide separates as a solid phase. The results showed that the complex acid in these soln. is **hydropentachloroplumbic acid, $HPbCl_5$**, because, with a given chlorine press. the quantity of this complex acid present in equilibrium with solid plumbous chloride is proportional to the first power of the chloride-ion conc. The hydrogen-ion conc., which would not be involved in the equilibrium if the ionization of the substances was complete, has a small secondary effect, probably owing to an influence on the ionization of the chloroplumbic acid. The equilibrium constant corresponding with the expression $(PbCl'_5)/(Cl')$.p_{Cl} is given by the expression $K'=0.055+0.07 p_{Cl}$, when the conc. are expressed in mols. per 100 grams of water ; the partial press. of chlorine, in atmospheres ; and the ionizations of hydrochloric acid and chloroplumbic acid are assumed equal. The equilibrium constant of the reaction $PbCl_{2solid}+Cl_{2gas}+2H_2O=PbO_{2solid}+4H\cdot+4Cl'$, is given by the expression $K=(H\cdot)^4.(Cl')^4/p_{Cl}$, is 2.4×10^{-8}, under the assumption that the ionizations of the hydrochloric acid and the chloroplumbic acid is complete. From these equilibrium constants and from other known data, the values of the decrease of free energy at 25° calculated on the assumption that the conc. of all dissolved substances are molecular, except that of chlorine, the partial press. of which is one atm., were : $PbCl_{2solid}+Cl_{2gas}+Cl'=PbCl_5'-6590$ joules, $PbCl_{2solid}+2H_2O+Cl_{2gas}=PbO_{2solid}+4H°+4Cl'-43,500$ joules, and $Pb_{solid}+O_{2gas}=PbO_{2solid}+219,000$ joules.

According to K. Elbs and R. Nübling, the orange-yellow liquid containing the acid can be preserved an indefinite time in a sealed tube, but in open vessels. chlorine is given off continuously, and lead chloride deposited. J. Strachan found the liquid is decomposed in sunlight, and by organic substances with the separation of lead chloride. O. Seidel, and A. Nathansohn and F. Leyser observed no change when the liquid stands in contact with sulphuric acid in a sealed tube. J. Nikoljukine found that the liquid is rapidly decomposed by water, forming a reddish-brown fluid. According to E. W. Wescott, the liquid is hydrolyzed to lead dioxide when less than 100 millimols of HCl is present in 100 grms. of water. W. W. Fischer found that lead dioxide is precipitated by water, alkali hydroxides, borates, carbonates, and acetates, as well as by the hydroxides of magnesium, zinc, lead, or mercury. K. Elbs and R. Nübling showed that soln. of ammonium chloride, pyridine, or quinoline in dil. hydrochloric acid precipitate the double salts in yellow crystals. E. Sakellarios,[15] and F. D. Chattaway and co-workers prepared a series of *diazonium hexachloroplumbates*, $(RN_2)_2PbCl_6$.

REFERENCES.

[1] H. G. Denham, *Journ. Chem. Soc.*, 113. 254, 1918 ; C. Tubandt and S. Eggert, *Zeit. anorg. Chem.*, 110. 230, 1920.

[2] T. Monticelli and N. Covelli, *Prodromo della mineralogia vesuviana*, Napoli, 47, 1825 ; F. Zambonini, *Mineralogia Vesuviana*, Napoli, 45, 1910 ; *Rend. Accad. Lincei*, (5), 15. 235, 1906 ; *Atti Accad. Napoli*, 13. 8, 1906 ; S. Meunier. *Compt. Rend. Géol. Soc.*, 32, 1918 ; *Rev. Géol.*, 2. 132, 1921 ; F. von Kobell, *Charakteristik der Mineralien*, Nürnberg, 2. 179, 1830 ; A. Scacchi, *Rend. Accad. Napoli*, 15, 1850 ; 45, 1870 ; *Atti Accad. Napoli*, 5. 37, 1873 ; 6. 38. 1874 ; *Contribuzioni mineralogiche per servire alla storia dell' incendio vesuviano, del mese di aprile*, 1872, Napoli, 2. 38, 1874 ; G. vom Rath, *Berh. Ver. Rheinl. Bonn.*, 152, 1877 ; G. Guiscardi, *Zeit. deut. geol. Ges.*, 9. 562, 1857 ; W. P. Jervis, *Itesori sotterranei Italia*, Turin, 2. 602, 1874 ; R. Cappa, *Ann. Osserv. Ves.*, 65, 1859 ; *Compt. Rend.*, 50. 955, 1860 ; A. Lacroix. *ib.*, 143. 727, 1906 ; 144. 1397, 1907 ; 151. 276, 1910 ; *Bull. Soc. Min.*, 30. 226, 1907 ; 31. 260, 1908 ; *Minéralogie de la France et de ses colonies*, Paris, 4. 890, 1910 ; I. Domeyko, *Elementos de mineralojia*, Santiago, 318, 705, 1879 ; A. Raimondi, *Les minéraux du Pérou*, Paris, 144, 172, 1878 ; A. Frenzel, *Tschermak's Mitt.*, (2), 11. 222, 1890 ; A. Russell, *Min. Mag.*, 19. 64, 1920.

[3] A. C. Becquerel, *Compt. Rend.*, 34. 29, 1852 ; A. Levallois, *ib.*, 96. 1666, 1883 ; A. Conduché, *ib.*, 158. 1181, 1914 ; W. P. Dreaper, *Koll. Zeit.*, 14. 163, 1914 ; E. Hatschek, *ib.*, 8. 193, 1911 ; *Journ. Soc. Chem. Ind.*, 30. 193, 1911 ; G. P. Baxter and F. L. Grover, *Journ. Amer. Chem. Soc.*, 37. 1050, 1915 ; G. P. Baxter and J. H. Wilson, *ib.*, 30. 187, 1908 ; F. Field, *Journ. Chem. Soc.*, 26. 575, 1873 ; J. W. Thomas, *ib.*, 33. 370, 1878 ; A. Lorenz and W. Eitel, *Zeit. anorg. Chem.*, 91. 47, 1915 ; C. Renz, *ib.*, 116. 62, 1921 ; K. Fajans and J. Fischler, *ib.*, 95. 290, 1916 ; E. F. Smith, *ib.*, 15. 292, 1893 ; F. F. Smith and J. G. Hibbs, *ib.*, 17. 685, 1895 ; W. C. Ebaugh, *ib.*, 24. 495, 1902 ; *Atomic Weight of Arsenic*, Philadelphia, 1901 ; J. G. Hibbs, *The Action of Hydrochloric Acid Gas upon Arsenates and Nitrates. The Atomic Weights of Nitrogen and Arsenic*, Philadelphia, 1896 ; *Journ. Amer. Chem. Soc.*, 18. 1044, 1896 ; A. Ditte, *Ann. Chim. Phys.*, (5), 14. 210, 1878 ; S. C. C. Currie, *German Pat.*, *D.R.P.* 68834, 1892 ; E. Langguth. *ib.*, 240768, 1911 ; W. P. Dreaper, *Journ. Soc. Chem. Ind.*, 32. 678, 1913 ; R. Weber, *Pogg. Ann.*, 112. 659, 1861 ; J. G. A. Rhodin, *Brit. Pat. No.* 12953, 1895 ; A. R. Davis, *ib.*, 8914, 1895 ; H. J. E. Hamilton, *ib.*, 152289, 1920 ; W. O. de Coninck and L. Arzalier, *Bull. Acad. Belg.*, 713, 1907 ; F. Stöber, *ib.*, 30. 345, 1895 ; A. Lacroix, *Bull. Soc. Min.*, 30. 226, 1907 ; O. Lehmann, *Zeit. Kryst.*, 1. 130, 483, 1877 ; 10. 340, 1885 ; J. Schabus, *Sitzber. Akad. Wien*, 4. 456, 1850 ; F. Becke,

Tschermak's Mitt., (2), **6**. 240, 270, 1885 ;   O. Mügge, *Neues Jahrb. Min. B.B.*, **16**. 362, 1903 ; A. van de Velde, *Chem. Ztg.*, **17**. 1908, 1893.

⁴ J. W. Döbereiner, *Schweigger's Journ.*, **17**. 255, 1816 ; C. J. R. Karsten, *ib.*, **65**. 394, 1832 ; F. Stolba, *Journ. prakt. Chem.*, (1), **97**. 503, 1866 ; G. Brügelmann, *Ber.*, **17**. 2359, 1884 ; H. Schiff, *Liebig's Ann.*, **108**. 21, 1858 ; C. L. Poincaré, *Ann. Chim. Phys.*, (6), **21**. 314, 1900 ; W. Louguinine, *ib.*, (5), **27**. 398, 1882 ; H. V. Regnault, *ib.*, (3), **1**. 129, 1841 ; O. Ehrhardt, *Wied. Ann.*, **24**. 215, 1885 ; S. Meyer, *ib.*, **69**. 245, 1899 ; L. Graetz, *ib.*, **29**. 314, 1886 ; **40**. 27, 1890 ; H. S. Allen, *Phil. Mag.*, (6), **35**. 404, 1918 ; W. Ramsay and N. Eumorfopoulos, *ib.*, (5), **41**. 366, 1896 ; W. E. Ayrton, *ib.*, (5), **6**. 132, 1878 ; *Chem. News*, **37**. 247, 1878 ; A. Magnus, *Ann. Physik*, (4), **31**. 606, 1910 ; W. Nernst, *ib.*, (4), **36**. 429, 1911 ; F. Zambonini, *Mineralogia Vesuviana*, Napoli, 45, 1910 ; H. M. Goodwin and H. T. Kalmus, *Phys. Rev.*, (1), **28**. 1, 1909 ; E. Wiedemann, *Pogg. Ann.*, **154**. 318, 1874 ; *Ber. Sächs. Akad.*, **26**. 112, 1874 ; C. Sandonnini, *Atti Accad. Lincei*, (5), **20**. i, 173, 1911 ; (5), **24**. i. 616, 1915 ; *Gazz. Chim. Ital.*, **41**. ii, 145, 1911 ; M. Amadori, *ib.*, **49**. i, 42, 1919 ; E. D. Eastman and L. H. Duschak, *Tech. Paper U.S. Bur. Mines*, 225, 1919 ; E. Jannettaz, E. Neel, and P. de Clermont, *Bull. Soc. Chim.*, (2), **40**. 53, 1883 ; F. Ephraim, *Helvetica Chim. Acta*, **7**. 298, 1924 ; C. E. Guignet, *Compt. Rend.*, **103**. 875, 1886 ; F. Stöber, *Bull. Acad. Belg.*, (3), **30**. 345, 1895 ; J. Schabus, *Sitzber. Akad. Wien*, **4**. 456, 1850 ; T. Carnelley, *Journ. Chem. Soc.*, **29**. 496, 1876 ; T. Carnelley and W. C. Williams, *ib.*, **33**. 278, 1878 ; P. Gaubert, *Bull. Soc. Min.*, **38**. 149, 1915 ; G. P. Baxter and C. F. Hawkins, *Journ. Amer. Chem. Soc.*, **38**. 270, 1916 ; J. B. Moyer, *ib.*, **18**. 1032, 1896 : A. Scott, *Proc. Roy. Soc. Edin.*, **14**. 410, 1887 ; H. E. Roscoe, *Proc. Roy. Soc.*, **27**. 426, 1878 ; M. Pleissner, *Arb. Kaiser Ges. Amt*, **26**. 433, 1907 ; D. M. Lichty, *Journ. Amer. Chem. Soc.*, **25**. 471, 1903 ; E. Korreng, *Kristallographische und thermische Untersuchungen von binären Systemen aus Thallochlorid und chloriden zweiwertiger Metalle*, Stuttgart, 1913 ; *Neues Jahrb. Min. B.B.*, **37**. 76, 1914 ; K. Mönkemeyer, *ib.*, **22**. 22, 1906 ; F. Matthes, *ib.*, **31**. 242, 1910 ; G. Lindner, *Die Abhängigkeit der specifischen Wärme fester Körper von der Temperatur*, Erlangen, 1903 ; *Sitzber. Akad. Erlangen*, **34**. 217, 1903 ; *Zeit. Kryst.*, **39**. 602, 1904 ; K. Treis, *Kristallographische und thermische Untersuchungen von Systemen aus Bleichlorid und Chloriden einwertiger Metalle*, Berlin, 1914 ; *Neues Jahrb. Min. B.B.*, **37**. 770, 1914 ; F. E. Neumann, *Pogg. Ann.*, **126**. 123, 1865 ; O. Schott, *Beiträge zur Kenntniss der anorganische Schmelzverbindungen*, Braunschweig, 1881 ; G. Tammann and Q. A. Mansuri, *Zeit. anorg. Chem.*, **126**. 119, 1923 ; O. Lehmann, *Zeit. Kryst.*, **1**. 130, 483, 1877 ; H. Schottky, *Phys. Zeit.*, **10**. 634, 1909 ; F. Koref, *ib.*, **13**. 185, 1912 ; A. Eucken, *ib.*, **10**. 586, 1909 ; R. Lorenz, *ib.*, **16**. 204, 1905 ; *Zeit. anorg. Chem.*, **19**. 284, 1899 ; R. Lorenz and W. Herz, *ib.*, **145**. 88, 1925 ; R. Lorenz and F. Kaufler, *Ber.*, **41**. 3727, 1908 ; R. Lorenz and H. T. Kalmus, *Zeit. phys. Chem.*, **57**. 30, 1907 ; **59**. 244, 1907 ; A. Reis and L. Zimmermann, *ib.*, **102**. 298, 1922 ; R. Lorenz and M. G. Fox, *ib.*, **63**. 117, 1908 ; R. Lorenz, H. Frei, and A. Jabs, *ib.*, **61**. 468, 1908 ; R. Lorenz and W. Eitel, *Zeit. anorg. Chem.*, **91**. 48, 1915 ; R. Lorenz and W. Ruckstuhl, *ib.*, **51**. 72, 1906 ; S. Motylewsky, *ib.*, **38**. 410, 1904 ; F. A. Henglein, *ib.*, **120**. 77, 1921 ; K. Hachmeister, *ib.*, **109**. 155, 1920 ; W. Herz and E. Martin, *ib.*, **132**. 41, 1923 ; R. Ruer, *ib.*, **49**. 369, 1906 ; W. Truthe, *ib.*, **76**. 163, 1912 ; G. Herrmann, *ib.*, **71**. 261, 1911 ; O. Menge, *ib.*, **72**. 187, 1911 ; C. Tubandt, *ib.*, **115**. 118, 1921 ; C. Tubandt and S. Eggert, *ib.*, **110**. 219, 1920 ; O. H. Weber, *ib.*, **21**. 322, 1899 ; A. Classen and B. Zahorsky, *ib.*, **4**. 110, 1893 ; F. Haber and S. Tolloczko, *ib.*, **41**. 407, 1904 ; G. Tammann and Q. A. Mansuri, *ib.*, **126**. 127, 1923 ; H. F. Fernau, *ib.*, **17**. 334, 1893 ; C. L. von Ende, *ib.*, **26**. 162, 1901 ; *Ueber das Verhalten der Bleisalze in Lösungen*, Göttingen, 1899 ; C. G. Maier, *Vapor Pressures of the Common Metallic Chlorides*, Washington, 28, 1925 ; V. Czepinsky, *Journ. Russ. Phys. Chem. Soc.*, **31**. 315, 1899 ; *Zeit. anorg. Chem.*, **19**. 245, 1899 ; R. Lorenz and W. Herz, *ib.*, **135**. 180, 1924 ; **143**. 366, 1925 ; **147**. 135, 1925 ; I. I. Saslawsky, *ib.*, **146**. 315, 1925 ; C. C. Garrard, *ib.*, **25**. 273, 1900 ; *Zeit. Elektrochem.*, **6**. 214, 1899 ; J. N. Brönsted, *ib.*, **18**. 714, 1912 ; M. le Blanc, *ib.*, **18**. 552, 1912 ; O. Bosse, *Ueber die Dampfdrucke einiger Schwermetallsalze*, Danzig, 1922 ; H. von Wartenberg and A. Bosse, *Zeit. Elektrochem.*, **28**. 384, 1922 ; W. Biltz, *ib.*, **29**. 348, 1923 ; C. Tubandt and H. Reinhold, *ib.*, **29**. 313, 1923 ; A. Benrath, *Zeit. phys. Chem.*, **64**. 694, 1908 ; M. Katayama, *ib.*, **61**. 566, 1908 ; J. W. Retgers, *ib.*, **9**. 301, 1892 ; F. Rudberg, *Pogg. Ann.*, **18**. 240, 1830 ; **21**. 317, 1831 ; **71**. 460, 1847 ; J. Davy, *Phil. Trans.*, **102**. 169, 1812 ; M. Lembert, *Zeit. Elektrochem.*, **26**. 59, 1920 ; W. Braunbek, *Zeit. Physik*, **38**. 561, 1926 ; F. Braun, *Pogg. Ann.*, **154**. 190, 1875 : J. Rosenthal, *Wied. Ann.*, **43**. 706, 1891 ; A. Sommerfeld, *Zeit. Physik*, **36**. 36, 1926 ; G. Tammann, *Zeit. anorg. Chem.*, **149**. 65, 1925 ; K. Jellinek and R. Uloth, *ib.*, **151**. 157, 1926 ; *Zeit. phys. Chem.*, **119**. 161, 1926 ; R. Uloth, *Ueber die Chlortensionen von Metallchloriden und die chemischen Konstanten des Chlors*, Leipzig, 1926.

⁵ M. Berthelot, *Thermochimie*, Paris, **2**. 169, 1897 ; *Compt. Rend.*, **81**. 1160, 1875 ; J. Thomsen, *Thermochemische Untersuchungen*, Leipzig, **3**. 337, 1883 ; F. Pollitzer, *Zeit. Elektrochem.*, **17**. 12, 1911 ; E. Cohen, *ib.*, **17**. 143, 1911 ; C. Krahmer, *ib.*, **26**. 97, 1920 ; A. Magnus, *ib.*, **16**. 273, 1910 ; P. Günther, *ib.*, **23**. 198, 1917 ; F. Koref and H. Braune, *ib.*, **18**. 820, 1912 ; *Zeit. anorg. Chem.*, **87**. 183, 1914 ; G. D. Roos, *ib.*, **94**. 356, 1916 ; O. H. Weber, *ib.*, **31**. 322, 1899 ; R. Lorenz, *ib.*, **19**. 286, 1899 ; R. Lorenz and M. Katayama, *Zeit. phys. Chem.*, **62**. 119, 1908 ; R. Lorenz and M. G. Fox, *ib.*, **63**. 121, 1908 ; J. N. Brönsted, *ib.*, **56**. 645, 1906 ; K. Wohl, *ib.*, **100**. 168, 1924 ; A. Eucken and F. Fried, *Zeit. Physik*, **29**. 36, 1924 ; M. de K. Thompson, *Journ. Amer. Chem. Soc.*, **28**. 731, 1906 ; F. H. Getman, *ib.*, **40**. 611, 1918 ; G. N. Lewis and T. B. Brighton, *ib.*, **39**. 1906, 1917 ; W. C. McC. Lewis, *Journ. Chem. Soc.*,

11. 1099, 1917; V. Czepinsky, *Journ. Russ. Phys. Chem. Soc.*, **31.** 315, 1899; *Zeit. anorg. Chem.*, **19.** 249, 1899; A. Guntz, *Ann. Chim. Phys.*, (6), **3.** 64, 1884.

6 C. Tubandt and S. Eggert, *Zeit. anorg. Chem.*, **110.** 219, 1920; J. A. Wilkinson, *Journ. Phys. Chem.*, **13.** 701, 1909; H. Rubens, *Sitzber. Akad. Berlin*, 513, 1913; A. T. Waterman, *Phil. Mag.*, (6), **33.** 225, 1917; B. A. Dima, *Compt. Rend.*, **157.** 592, 1912; A. Balandin, *Zeit. Physik*, **26.** 145, 1924.

7 F. Zambonini, *Mineralogia Vesuviana*, Napoli, 48, 1910; *Riv. Min. Crist. Ital.*, **39.** 88, 1909; *Rend. Accad. Lincei*, (5), **16.** i, 975, 1907; P. Rossi, *ib.*, (5), **16.** ii, 630, 1907; G. C. Schmidt, *Ann. Physik*, (4), **75.** 337, 1924.

8 M. Faraday, *Phil. Trans.*, **123.** 507, 1833; **124.** 77, 1834; H. Buff, *Liebig's Ann.*, **110.** 257, 1859; F. Braun, *Pogg. Ann.*, **154.** 190, 1874; E. Wiedemann, *ib.*, **154.** 318, 1874; *Ber. Sächs. Akad.*, **26.** 112, 1874; F. Beijerinck, *Neues Jahrb. Min. B.B.*, **11.** 462, 1898; C. Tissot, *Compt. Rend.*, **156.** 1523, 1913; E. Wartmann, *Mém. Sciences Genève*, **12.** 1, 1853; A. Bogorodsky, *Journ. Russ. Phys. Chem. Soc.*, **37.** 760, 1905; V. Czepinsky, *ib.*, **31.** 315, 1899; *Zeit. anorg. Chem.*, **19.** 249, 1899; G. Tammann and H. Bredmeier, *ib.*, **144.** 64, 1925; G. Tammann, *ib.*, **133.** 267, 1924; C. Tubandt and H. Reinhold, *ib.*, **29.** 313, 1923; C. Tubandt, *Zeit. anorg. Chem.*, **115.** 118, 1921; C. Tubandt and S. Eggert, *ib.*, **110.** 219, 1920; C. L. von Ende, *ib.*, **26.** 162, 1901; *Ueber das Verhalten der Bleisalze in Lösungen*, Göttingen, 1899; J. Rosenthal, *Ueber die electrische Leitfähigkeit fester Elektrolyte bei verschiedenen Temperaturen*, Erlanger, 1891; *Wied. Ann.*, **43.** 706, 1891; L. Graetz, *ib.*, **29.** 314, 1886; R. Ketzer, *Ueber die Leitfähigkeit fester Salze und Salzegemische*, Leipzig, 1919; *Zeit. Elektrochem.*, **26.** 78, 1920; M. le Blanc, *ib.*, **18.** 552, 1912; R. Abegg, *ib.*, **10.** 78, 1904; S. Labendzinsky, *Zur Kenntnis der Konstitution der gelösten Schwermetallsalze auf Grund von Potentialmessungen*, Breslau, 1904; C. Sandonnini, *Atti Accad. Lincei*, (5), **20.** i, 173, 1911; (5), **24.** i, 616, 1915; *Gazz. Chim. Ital.*, **41.** ii, 145, 1911; T. A. Heppenstall and W. J. Shutt, *Trans. Faraday Soc.*, **20.** 97, 1924; A. Benrath, *Zeit. phys. Chem.*, **64.** 694, 1908; R. Lorenz and H. T. Kalmus, *ib.*, **59.** 17, 244, 1907; E. Franke, *ib.*, **16.** 463, 1895; J. N. Brönsted, *ib.*, **56.** 645, 1906; W. Böttger, *ib.*, **46.** 521, 1903; *Löslichkeitsstudien an schwer löslichen Stoffen*, Leipzig, 1903; W. E. Ayrton, *Phil. Mag.*, (5), **6.** 132, 1878; *Chem. News*, **37.** 247, 1878; L. Poincaré, *Ann. Chim. Phys.*, (6), **21.** 314, 1900; M. Pleissner, *Arb. Kaiser Ges. Amt.*, **26.** 433, 1907; L. G. Winston and H. C. Jones, *Amer. Chem. Journ.*, **46.** 392, 1911; S. F. Howard and H. C. Jones, *ib.*, **48.** 521, 1912; A. A. Noyes, *Zeit. phys. Chem.*, **9.** 626, 1892; A. A. Noyes and K. G. Falk, *Journ. Amer. Chem. Soc.*, **34.** 461, 1912; S. J. Bates, *ib.*, **35.** 519, 1913; W. D. Harkins, *ib.*, **33.** 1818, 1911; F. L. Hunt, *ib.*, **33.** 802, 1911; J. W. Frers, *Ber.*, **57.** B, 1693, 1925; M. le Blanc and M. Kröger, *Zeit. Elektrochem.*, **30.** 253, 1924; P. Fischer, *ib.*, **32.** 136, 1926; W. Biltz and W. Klemm, *Zeit. anorg. Chem.*, **152.** 267, 1926.

9 F. Haber and S. Tolloczko, *Zeit. anorg. Chem.*, **41.** 407, 1904; O. H. Weber, *ib.*, **21.** 322, 1899; G. Tammann, *ib.*, **133.** 267, 1924; R. Lorenz, *ib.*, **19.** 284, 1899; **134.** 105, 1924; V. Czepinsky, *ib.*, **19.** 249, 1899; *Journ. Russ. Phys. Chem. Soc.*, **31.** 315, 1899; R. Lorenz and M. G. Fox, *Zeit. phys. Chem.*, **63.** 109, 1908; M. Katayama, *ib.*, **61.** 566, 1908; J. N. Brönsted, *ib.*, **56.** 645, 1906; J. Thiele, *Phys. Zeit.*, **26.** 321, 1925; K. Arndt and H. Probst, *Zeit. Electrochem.*, **29.** 323, 1923; R. B. Mason and J. H. Mathews, *Journ. Phys. Chem.*, **29.** 1379, 1925.

10 A. Lenert, *Verh. deut. phys. Ges.*, **12.** 1051, 1910; S. Meyer, *Wied. Ann.*, **69.** 245, 1899; L. Ebert, *Zeit. phys. Chem.*, **113.** 1, 1924.

11 J. Formanek, *Listy Chem.*, **11.** 87, 1887; G. Bischof, *Schweigger's Journ.*, **64.** 76, 1832; J. W. Döbereiner, *ib.*, **17.** 255, 1816; J. C. Bell, *Chem. News*, **16.** 79, 1867; *Journ. Chem. Soc.*, **21.** 355, 1868; J. K. Wood, *ib.*, **85.** 473, 1910; E. Field, *ib.*, **26.** 575, 1873; **63.** 545, 1893; *Chem. News*, **67.** 157, 1893; W. W. Fischer, *Journ. Chem. Soc.*, **35.** 282. 1879; T. Carnelley and W. C. Williams, *ib.*, **33.** 283, 1878; W. H. Sodeau, *ib.*, **77.** 723, 1900; G. André, *Ann. Chim. Phys.*, (6), **3.** 115, 1884; (6), **17.** 361, 1899; *Bull. Soc. Chim.*, (2), **40.** 18, 1883; *Compt. Rend.*, **97.** 1302, 1883; N. Demassieux, *Étude de l'equilibre entre le chlorure et l'iodure de plomb et quelques chlorures et iodures alcalins en solution aqueuse*, Paris, 1923; *Compt. Rend.*, **158.** 702, 1914; F. Ruyssen and E. Varenne, *ib.*, **92.** 525, 1881; A. Colson, *ib.*, **124.** 81, 1897; G. J. Mulder, *Bijdragen tot de geschiedenis van het scheikundig gebonder water*, Rotterdam, 1864; W. Herz and M. Hellebrandt, *Zeit. anorg. Chem.*, **130.** 188, 1923; W. Böttger, *Löslichkeitsstudien an schwer löslichen Stoffen*, Leipzig, 1903; *Zeit. phys. Chem.*, **46.** 521, 1903; A. A. Noyes, *ib.*, **9.** 623, 1892; G. von Hevesy and E. Rona, *ib.*, **89.** 294, 1915; C. Kullgren, *ib.*, **85.** 473, 1913; F. Kohlrausch, *ib.*, **64.** 129, 1908; J. N. Brönsted, *ib.*, **56.** 679, 1907; C. L. Wagner, *ib.*, **71.** 423, 1910; M. Pleissner, *Arb. Kaiser Ges. Amt*, **26.** 433, 1907; K. Beck and P. Stegmüller, *ib.*, **34.** 446, 1910; K. Beck, *Zeit. Elektrochem.*, **17.** 845, 1911; K. Arndt and H. Probst, *ib.*, **29.** 323, 1923; C. Immerwahr, *ib.*, **7.** 480, 1901; *Beiträge zur Loslichkeits bestimmung schwerlöslicher Salze des Quicksilbers, Kupfers, Bleis, Cadmiums, und Zinks*, Breslau, 1900; R. Kremann and H. Breymesser, *Monatsh.*, **38.** 113, 1917; W. W. Randall, *Amer. Chem. Journ.*, **15.** 495, 1893; E. C. Franklin and C. A. Kraus, *ib.*, **20.** 828, 1898; J. White, *ib.*, **35.** 218, 1906; H. Rose, *Pogg. Ann.*, **20.** 157, 1830; **24.** 334, 1830; O. Ruff, *Ber.*, **34.** 3509, 1901; E. H. Perman, *Proc. Roy. Soc.*, **79.** A, 310, 1907; *Chem. News*, **88.** 197, 1903; G. C. Wittstein, *Repert. Pharm.*, **63.** 329, 1838; *Zeit. anal. Chem.*, **2.** 19, 1863; G. Kernot and U. Pomilio, *Rend. Accad. Napoli*, (3), **17.** 353, 1911; A. J. J. van de Velde, *Chem. Ztg.*, **17.** 1908, 1893; D. M. Lichty, *Journ. Amer. Chem. Soc.*, **25.** 471, 1903; W. D. Harkins, *ib.*, **33.** 1816, 1911; G. N. Lewis and

T. B. Brighton, *ib.*, **39**. 1906, 1917 ; G. P. Baxter and F. L. Grover, *ib.*, **37**. 1027, 1915 ; A. E. Hill, *ib.*, **39**. 218, 1916 ; W. C. Ebaugh, *Journ. Amer. Chem. Soc.*, **24**. 495, 1902 ; J. Wood and J. L. Borden, *ib.*, **6**. 218, 1884 ; T. W. B. Welsh and H. J. Broderson, *ib.*, **37**. 819, 1915 ; H. N. Stokes, *ib.*, **29**. 313, 1907 ; C. R. Wise, *ib.*, **45**. 1233, 1923 ; C. L. von Ende, *Ueber das Verhalten der Bleisalze in Lösungen*, Göttingen, 1899 ; *Zeit. anorg. Chem.*, **26**. 162, 1901 ; K. Fajans and J. Fischler, *ib.*, **95**. 292, 1916 ; H. R. Fernau, *ib.*, **17**. 334, 1898 ; C. R. A. Wright and C. Thompson, *Phil. Mag.*, (5), **17**. 288, 1884 ; (5), **19**. 1, 1885 ; J. Schürr, *Journ. Chim. Phys.*, **2**. 245, 1904 ; A. Jouniaux, *ib.*, **1**. 609, 1903 ; *Compt. Rend.*, **136**. 1005, 1903 ; H. Ley, *Ber.*, **30**. 2192, 1897 ; K. A. Hofmann and V. Wölfl, *ib.*, **37**. 249, 1904 ; W. Spring, *ib.*, **18**. 344, 1885 ; V. Kohlschütter and H. Roesti, *ib.*, **56**. 287, 1923 ; W. Conrad, *Beiträge zum elektrochemischen Verhalten des Bleis*, Göttingen, 1903 ; H. E. Armstrong and J. V. Eyre, *Proc. Roy. Soc.*, **88**. A, 234, 1913 ; A. Craig, *Amer. Met. Ind.*, **20**. 338, 1920 ; M. Berthelot, *Compt. Rend.*, **81**. 1160, 1875 ; *Ann. Chim. Phys.*, (5), **23**. 88, 1881 ; (5). **29**. 294, 1883 ; R. Engel, *ib.*, (6), **17**. 359, 1880 ; *Bull. Soc. Chim.*, (3), **1**. 694, 1889 ; H. Fonzes-Diacon, *ib.*, (3), **17**. 350, 1897 ; H. Moissan, *ib.*, (3), **27**. 659, 1902 ; A. Potilitzin, *ib.*, (2), **38**. 258, 1882 ; *Journ. Russ. Phys. Chem. Soc.*, **14**. 82, 1882 ; E. Korreng, *Kristallographische und thermische Untersuchungen von binären Systemen aus Thallochlorid und Chloriden zwei-wertiger Metalle*, Stuttgart, 1913 ; *Neues Jahrb. Min. B.B.*, **37**. 76, 1914 ; K. Treis, *ib.*, **37**. 770, 1914 ; *Kristallographische und thermische Untersuchungen von Systemen aus Bleichlorid und Chloriden einwertiger Metalle*, Berlin, 1914 ; R. Flatt, *Helvetica Chim. Acta*, **6**. 698, 1923 ; E. P. Lewis, *Phys. Rev.*, (2), **21**. 713, 1923 ; R. Ketzer, *Ueber die Leitfähigkeit fester Salze und Salzegemische*, Leipzig, 1919 ; *Zeit. Elektrochem.*, **26**. 78, 1920 ; F. Koref and H. Braune, *ib.*, **18**. 820, 1912 ; *Zeit. anorg. Chem.*, **87**. 180, 1914 ; W. Herz, *ib.*, **68**. 421, 1910 ; W. Biltz and W. Fischer, *ib.*, **124**. 231, 1922 ; C. Renz, *ib.*, **116**. 62, 1921 ; W. Biltz and E. Meinecke, *ib.*, **131**. 1, 1923 ; W. Biltz , *ib.*, **124**. 231, 1922 ; K. Hachmeister, *ib.*, **109**. 182, 1920 ; A. Classen and B. Zahorsky, *ib.*, **4**. 102, 1893 ; H. Sommerlad, *ib.*, **18**. 420, 442, 1898 ; N. R. Dhar and A. C. Chatterji. *Journ. Phys. Chem.*, **28**. 41, 1924 ; G. L. Clark, *Amer. Journ. Science*, (5), **7**. 1, 1924 ; A. Benrath. *Zeit. phys. Chem.*, **64**. 694, 1908 ; C. L. Wagner, *ib.*, **71**. 423, 1910 ; Y. Ephraim, *ib.*, **83**. 218, 1913 ; J. B. A. Dumas, *Ann. Chim. Phys.*, (3), **55**. 129, 1859 ; A. J. Balard, *ib.*, (2), **32**. 337, 1826 ; A. Ditte, *ib.*, (5), **14**. 197, 1878 ; (5), **28**. 131, 1883 ; *Compt. Rend.*, **91**. 765, 1880 ; **92**. 718, 1881 ; A. Mailfert, *ib.*, **94**. 860, 1186, 1882 ; N. A. E. Millon, *ib.*, **28**. 42, 1849 ; V. Thomas, *ib.*, **126**. 1349, 1381, 1898 ; **128**. 1234, 1899 ; *Bull. Soc. Chim.*, (3), **15**. 1091, 1896 ; V. Zotier, *ib.*, (4), **21**. 241, 1917 ; H. Schulze, *Zeit. prakt. Chem.*, (2), **21**. 407, 1880 ; A. Gawalowsky, *Œster. Chem. Ztg.*, **19**. 150, 1916 ; A. de Hemptinne, *Bull. Acad. Belg.*, 249, 1919 ; H. Mennicke, *Zeit. öffentl. Chem.*, **6**. 227, 1900 ; R. Norris, *Liebig's Ann.*, **117**. 189, 1861 ; O. Schott, *Beiträge zur Kenntnis der anorganische Schmelzverbindungen*, Braunschweig, 17, 1890 ; A. Vogel, *Kastner's Arch.*, **23**. 84, 1832 ; F. Faktor, *Pharm. Posk.*, **38**. 527, 1905 ; O. Schärer, *Phys. Zeit.*, **25**. 145, 1924 ; F. A. H. Schreinemakers, *Chem. Weekbl.*, **1**. 81, 1903 ; J. Schröder, *Reaktionen von Metallsalzen in Pyridin*, Giessen, 1904 ; J. F. W. Herschel, *Edin. Phil. Journ.*, **1**. 8, 396, 1819 ; **2**. 154, 1820 ; F. de Carli, *Atti Accad. Lincei*, (5), **33**. ii. 94, 1924 ; F. Ephraim, *Ber.*, **58**. B, 2262, 1925 ; K. Jellinek and R. Uloth, *Zeit. phys. Chem.*, **119**. 161, 1926 ; N. Parravano and G. Malquori, *Gazz. Chim. Ital.*, **56**. i, 3, 1926.

¹² G. Bischof, *Schweigger's Journ.*, **64**. 76, 1832 ; E. F. Anthon, *Repert. Pharm.*, **76**. 229, 1836 ; G. C. Wittstein, *ib.*, **63**. 331, 1838 ; A. Benrath, *Zeit. phys. Chem.*, **64**. 694, 1908 ; *Journ. prakt. Chem.*, (2), **72**. 228, 1905 ; C. J. Fritsch, *ib.*, (1), **97**. 278, 1866 ; W. Spring, *Ber.*, **18**. 344. 1885 : G. Grüttner and E. Krause, *ib.*, **49**. 1915, 1916 ; G. Grüttner, *ib.*, **51**. 1293, 1918 ; W. Göbbels, *ib.*, **28**. 793, 1895 ; H. Mandal, *ib.*, **54**. 704, 1921 ; A. Naumann, *ib.*, **37**. 4329, 1904 ; **42**. 5790, 1909 ; **43**. 314, 1910 ; **47**. 1370, 1914 ; R. Salvadori, *Gazz. Chim. Ital.*, **34**. 1, 89, 1904 ; H. Rose, *Pogg. Ann.*, **110**. 433, 1860 ; A. Colson, *Compt. Rend.*, **136**. 891, 1903 ; R. Fosse and L. Lesage, *ib.*, **141**. 625, 1905 ; F. Göbel, *Journ. prakt. Chem.*, (1), **6**. 388, 1835 ; G. Gore, *Chem. News*, **50**. 124, 1884 ; A. G. Bloxam, *ib.*, **52**. 183, 1885 ; J. Gathy, *German Pat.*, *D.R.P.* 183530, 1905 ; H. Röhler, *Zeit. Elektrochem.*, **16**. 409, 1910 ; F. Koref and H. Braune, *ib.*, **18**. 820, 1920 ; *Zeit. anorg. Chem.*, **87**. 180, 1914 ; A. Werner, *ib.*, **15**. 6, 1897 ; W. Herz, *ib.*, **68**. 421, 1910 ; W. Herz and E. Martin, *ib.*, **140**. 339, 1924 ; F. Fischer and K. Thiele, *ib.*, **67**. 303, 1910 ; A. Classen and B. Zahorsky, *ib.*, **4**. 109, 1893 ; H. Arctowsky, *ib.*, **6**. 257, 1894 ; H. Arnold, *Zeit. anal. Chem.*, **51**. 550, 1912 ; F. Mohr, *ib.*, **12**. 147, 1873 ; A. P. N. Franchimont, *Rec. Trav. Chim. Pays-Bas*, **1**. 55, 1883 ; *Ber.*, **16**. 387, 1883 ; C. H. Piesse, *Journ. Chem. Soc.*, **27**. 505, 1874 ; A. E. Hill, *Journ. Amer. Chem. Soc.*, **39**. 218, 1917 ; J. White, *Amer. Chem. Journ.*, **34**. 4, 1904 ; **35**. 218, 1906 ; R. Brix, *Liebig's Ann.*, **225**. 161, 1884 ; B. Köhnlein, *ib.*, **225**. 174, 1884 ; L. Carius, *ib.*, **125**. 87, 1863 ; H. E. Armstrong and J. V. Eyre, *Proc. Roy. Soc.*, **88**. A, 234, 1913 ; G. Kernot and U. Pomilio, *Rend. Accad. Napoli*, (3), **17**. 353, 1912 ; G. W. Heise, *Journ. Phys. Chem.*, **16**. 373, 1912 ; W. Eidmann, *Ein Beitrag zur Erkenntnis des Verhaltens chemischer Verbindungen in nichtwässrigen Lösungen*, Giessen, 1899.

¹³ R. Lorenz, *Trans. Amer. Electrochem. Soc.*, **47**. 243, 1925 : *Naturwiss.*, **13**. 81, 1926 ; *Zeit. anorg. Chem.*, **134**. 105, 1924 ; R. Lorenz, W. Fränkel, and J. Silberstein, *ib.*, **131**. 247, 1923 ; R. Lorenz and M. Mannheimer, *ib.*, **150**. 343, 1926 ; **152**. 314, 1926 ; R. Lorenz, W. Fränkel, and M. Ganz, *ib.*, **153**. 281, 1926 ; G. Tammann, *ib.*, **133**. 267, 1923 ; C. Tubandt and S. Eggert, *ib.*, **110**. 230, 1920 ; W. Reinders, *ib.*, **25**. 126, 1900 ; F. M. Perkin and L. Pratt, *Trans. Faraday Soc.*, **3**. 185, 1908 ; E. Berger, *Compt. Rend.*, **171**. 29, 1920 ; H. le Chatelier, *ib.*, **20**. 836, 1895 ; H. Rose, *Pogg. Ann.*, **107**. 278, 1859 ; A. Mailhe, *Ann. Chim. Phys.*, (7),

27. 379, 1902 ; J. Ball, *Chem. News*, 74. 303, 1896 ; K. Seubert and A. Schmidt, *Liebig's Ann.*, 267. 218, 1892 ; T. Carnelley and W. C. Williams, *Journ. Chem. Soc.*, 33. 283, 1878 ; L. Kahlenberg and W. J. Trautmann, *Trans. Amer. Electrochem. Soc.*, 39. 377, 1921.
¹⁴ A. Sobrero and F. Selmi, *Atti Accad. Torino*, 11, 345, 1851 ; *Ann. Chim. Phys.*, (3), 29. 161, 1850 ; J. Nicklès, *ib.*, (4), 10. 323, 1867 ; A. Ditte, *ib.*, (5), 24. 241, 1881 ; *Compt. Rend.*, 91. 765, 1880 ; H. Friedrich, *Monatsh.*, 14. 512, 1893 ; *Ber.*, 26. 1434, 1893 ; H. Schiff, *ib.*, 8. 1198, 1875 ; H. Erdmann and P. Köthner, *Liebig's Ann.*, 294. 74, 1897 ; J. M. Matthews, *Journ. Amer. Chem. Soc.*, 20. 817, 1898 ; V. Lenher and W. C. Hill, *ib.*, 30. 737, 1908 ; E. W. Wescott, *ib.*, 42. 1335, 1920 ; L. L. de Koninck, *Bull. Assoc. Chim. Belg.*, 16. 94, 1902 ; H. L. Wells, *Amer. Journ. Science*, (3), 46. 180, 186, 1893 ; J. Nikoljukine, *Journ. Russ. Phys. Chem. Soc.*, 17. 307, 1485 ; W. W. Fischer, *Journ. Chem. Soc.*, 35. 282, 1879 ; A. Hutchinson and W. Pollard, *ib.*, 69. 219, 1896 ; O. Seidel, *Journ. prakt. Chem.*, (2), 20. 205, 1879 ; N. A. E. Millon, *Journ. Pharm. Chim.*, (3), 18. 299, 1850 ; A. Seyewetz and P. Trawitz, *Bull. Soc. Chim.*, (3), 29. 457, 1903 ; J. Strachan, *Chem. News*, 98. 102, 1908 ; A. Fränkel, *Mitt. Techn. Gew. Mus.*, 13. 124, 1903 ; L. E. Rivot, F. S. Beudant, and P. A. Daguin, *Ann. Mines*, (5), 4. 239, 1853 ; R. Kremann and H. Breymesser, *Monatsh.*, 38. 113, 1917 ; A. Classen and B. Zahorsky, *Zeit. anorg. Chem.*, 4. 102, 1893 ; A. Voigt and W. Biltz, *ib.*, 133. 277, 1924 ; W. Biltz and E. Meinecke, *ib.*, 131, 1, 1923 ; K. Elbs, *Zeit. Elektrochem.*, 8. 512, 1902 ; K. Elbs and R. Nübling, *ib.*, 9. 777, 1903 ; K. Elbs and F. Fischer, *ib.*, 7. 343, 1901 ; F. Försted, *ib.*, 3. 507, 1897 ; A. Nathansohn and F. Leyser, *ib.*, 28. 310, 1922 ; G. von Hevesy and L. Zechmeister, *ib.*, 26. 151, 1920 ; E. Müller, *Elektrochemisches Praktikum*, Dresden, 168, 1913 ; M. Wissmüller, *Zur Kenntnis des vierwertigen Bleis*, Erlangen, 14, 1916 ; A. Gutbier and M. Wissmüller, *Journ. prakt. Chem.*, (2), 90. 498, 1914 ; E. Krause, *Ber.*, 57. B, 318, 1924 ; A. Sommerfeld, *Zeit. Physik*, 36. 36, 1926 ; W. Biltz and W. Klemm, *Zeit. anorg. Chem.*, 152. 267, 1926.
¹⁵ E. Sakellarios, *Ber.*, 56. B, 2536, 1923 ; F. D. Chattaway, F. L. Garton, and G. D. Parkes, *Journ. Chem. Soc.*, 125. 1980, 1924.

§ 23. Complex Salts with the Lead Chlorides—Chloroplumbites

According to A. C. Becquerel,[1] if a soln. of ammonium chloride be placed above lead dioxide, and a rod of lead be immersed therein so as to touch the oxide, the rod becomes covered with needle-like crystals which were thought to be those of a double salt of lead and ammonium chlorides. L. J. Thénard also showed that a mixed soln. of the two chlorides gives no precipitate with sulphuric acid, presumably owing to the formation of a double salt. C. L. von Ende measured the solubilities of lead chloride in $0.25N$-, $0.50N$-, and N-soln. of ammonium chloride to be respectively 9·47, 7·11, and 4·35 millimols per litre. G. André reported a complex series of **ammonium chloroplumbites** in which the ratios : $PbCl_2 : NH_4Cl : H_2O$ were respectively 1 : 18 : 4, 1 : 10 : 1, 2 : 18 : 3, 1 : 6 : 1, 4 : 22 : 7, 4 : 18 : 5, and 2 : 1 : 3. No one else has succeeded in verifying a single one of these preparations ; and G. André seems to have been guided solely by the analyses of crops of crystals obtained either by cooling a soln. of the lead halide in a hot soln. of the corresponding ammonium halide, or by cooling a boiling soln. of lead oxide in one of the ammonium halide. H. L. Wells and W. R. Johnston repeated G. André's directions for the preparation of this salt, and then concluded that " not one of the salts described by G. André exists."

H. W. Foote and L. H. Levy measured the solubility of lead chloride in soln. of ammonium chloride of different conc., and found for equilibrium at 25°, evidence of the existence of the double salt $NH_4Cl.2PbCl_2$. J. N. Brönsted, working at 22°, found the solubility curves of lead chloride and ammonium chloride intersect at a conc. $0.52N$-NH_4Cl, when both solid lead chloride and the double salt $NH_4Cl.2PbCl_2$ are in equilibrium. N. Demassieux, also, found the solubility curves indicated in Fig. 70. At 17°, the two phases $PbCl_2$ and $NH_4Pb_2Cl_5$ occur with 3·48 grms. of ammonium chloride and 0·076 grm. of lead chloride in 100 c.c. of soln., and the two phases $NH_4Pb_2Cl_5$ and NH_4Cl eutectic with 26·49 grms. of ammonium chloride, and 0·64 grm. of lead chloride per 100 c.c. The compound $2(NH_4)_2PbCl_4$ is stable only above 70°. The solubility curves at 100°, Fig. 71, have the two phases $PbCl_2$ and $NH_4Pb_2Cl_5$ with 8·59 grms. of ammonium chloride and 1·76 grms. of lead chloride per 100 c.c. ; the two phases $NH_4Pb_2Cl_5$ and $(NH_4)_2PbCl_4$ with 37·62 grms. of ammonium chloride and 12·67 grms. of lead chloride per 100 c.c. ; **and the** two phases $(NH_4)_2PbCl_4$ and NH_4Cl with 41·90 grms. of ammonium chloride and 9·26 grms. of lead chloride per 100 c.c. The solubility curves show the presence

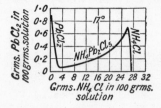
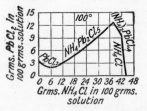

FIGS. 70 and 71.—Solubility of Lead Chloride in Solutions of Ammonium Chloride at Different Concentrations.

of no complex salts other than these two. The curves are shown in three dimensions in Fig. 72. K. Hachmeister was unable to melt mixtures of lead and ammonium chlorides.

H. L. Wells and W. R. Johnston found that **ammonium pentachlorodiplumbite,** $NH_4Pb_2Cl_5$, is produced under a wide variation of conditions from soln. containing 100–400 grms. of ammonium chloride, 20–80 grms. of lead chloride in 1000 c.c.

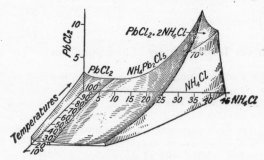

FIG. 72.—The Phases in the System $NH_4Cl–PbCl_2–$ H_2O at Different Temperatures.

of water. H. Fonzes-Diacon obtained it by cooling a soln. of lead chloride in a 30 per cent. soln. of ammonium chloride, washing the crystals with a very dil. soln. of ammonium chloride, centrifuging the product, and drying. W. W. Randall, J. N. Brönsted, J. Kendall and C. H. Sloan, and H. W. Foote and L. H. Levy obtained the salt in a similar manner. The conditions of stability are indicated by N. Demassieux in Figs. 70 and 71. H. W. Foote and L. H. Levy

found that this salt is formed on cooling a hot soln. of lead chloride in one of ammonium chloride. W. W. Randall, and H. L. Wells and W. R. Johnston regarded the crystals as rhombic pyramids ; and H. Fonzes-Diacon, and H. W. Foote and L. H. Levy said they belong to the monoclinic system. The colourless, short, transparent prisms retain their lustre when dried. J. N. Brönsted said that the sp. ht. between 0° and 19° is 0·0866, and the mol. heat, 52·78 ; and the dissociation in boiling soln. is such that 1·26 grm.-eq. per litre of free ammonium chloride are present. H. Fonzes-Diacon found that the salt is decomposed by water, and is soluble in dil. acids or dil. alkali-lye.

G. André reported a *trihydrate*, $NH_4Pb_2Cl_5.3H_2O$, in mica-like crystals from an aq. soln. of $6NH_4Cl.PbCl_2$. This hydrate has not been found by any other worker. H. L. Wells and W. R. Johnston reported *tritahydrated ammonium trichloroplumbite*, $NH_4PbCl_3.\frac{1}{3}H_2O$, to be formed by cooling a soln. of lead chloride in a hot conc. soln. of ammonium chloride. The double salt was deposited in colourless, transparent, prismatic crystals while the soln. was somewhat warm. As indicated above, the salt does not appear as a solid phase in the system, $NH_4Cl–PbCl_2–H_2O$, between 17° and 100°, and, as H. L. Wells showed later, it probably does not exist.

H. Fonzes-Diacon, and W. W. Randall obtained **ammonium tetrachloroplumbite,** $(NH_4)_2PbCl_4$, by slowly cooling a soln. of 50 grms. lead chloride in one litre of a boiling, 30 per cent. soln. of ammonium chloride. Neither F. W. Foote and

L. H. Levy nor H. L. Wells and W. R. Johnston were able to establish the existence of this compound ; but N. Demassieux showed that it is formed as a solid phase within certain limits, Fig. 71, at temp. over 70°. E. Rimbach and K. Fleck mixed molar proportions of the component salts in aq. soln., and allowed the solid phase to separate, and sat. the liquid with the same mixture, and on cooling, crystals of *ammonium hexachloroplumbite*, $(NH_4)_4PbCl_6.H_2O$, were formed. The salt does not appear on the equilibrium diagrams, Figs. 70 and 71 ; and it therefore appears likely to be a solid soln. of ammonium chloride with the pentachlorodiplumbite.

K. Treis,[2] and T. Liebisch and E. Korreng measured the f.p. of mixtures of *lithium and lead chlorides*, Fig. 74, and of *sodium and lead chlorides*, Fig. 73, but in no

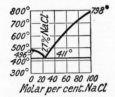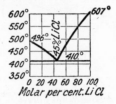

FIGS. 73 and 74.—Freezing-point Curves of Mixtures of Lead Chloride with Lithium or Sodium Chloride.

case was any evidence of the formation of a compound found. Both the mixtures furnish the simple V-eutectics shown in the diagrams. N. Demassieux measured the solubility of lead chloride in soln. of lithium or sodium chloride of different conc., and obtained no evidence of the formation of a compound. J. Kendall and C. H. Sloan, however, reported the preparation of **lithium pentachlorodiplumbite**, $LiCl.2PbCl_2$, and of **sodium pentachlorodiplumbite**, $NaCl.2PbCl_2$. The

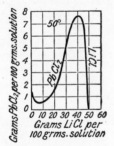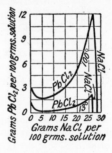

FIGS. 75 and 76.—Phases in the Systems : $LiCl-PbCl_2-H_2O$, and $NaCl-PbCl_2-H_2O$.

solubility curves are shown in Figs. 75 and 76. A. Ditte, and C. H. Herty also failed to prepare a double sodium salt, although A. C. Becquerel reported one such. C. Fritsch, R. Ketzer, and M. le Blanc measured the electrical conductivity of mixtures of the two salts.

R. Lorenz and co-workers have studied the f.p. curves of the binary system $PbCl_2-KCl$, and the results are summarized in Fig. 77. There is a flat maximum at 430° and 33·3 molar per cent. of potassium chloride corresponding with the compound $2PbCl_2,KCl$, and two breaks at 440° and 60 molar per cent. and 480° and 68 molar per cent. of potassium chloride respectively, indicating the existence of two other compounds, the compositions of which are $PbCl_2.2KCl$ and $PbCl_2.4KCl$ respectively. The latter decomposes above 480° into solid potassium chloride and a fused mass corresponding in composition with the break in the curve at 480° ; the former decomposes above 440° into solid $PbCl_2.4KCl$ and a fused mass corresponding in composition with the break in the curve at that temp. The compound $2PbCl_2,KCl$ forms two series of mixed crystals from 31·7 to 33·3 and 33·3 to 34·1 molar per cent. of potassium chloride respectively. There are two eutectic points, at 410° and 20 molar per cent. and 405° and 50 molar per cent. of potassium chloride respectively.

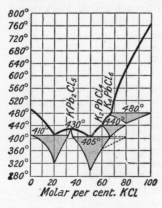

FIG. 77.—Freezing-point Curves of the Binary System: PbCl₂–KCl.

K. Treis did not verify the 440° singularity. The f.p. curves were also studied by A. Appelberg, E. Korreng, and K. Treis. The system PbCl₂–KCl–H₂O was studied by O. Lehmann, J. R. Strohecker, M. Berthelot, A. Immerwahr, C. L. von Ende, and J. N. Brönsted. The results of N. Demassieux are summarized in Figs. 78 and 79. Expressing the conc. of the soln. in grams per 100 grms. of soln., she found that there are two phases, PbCl₂ and KPb₂Cl₅, with 0·15 grm. of lead chloride and 3·79 grms. of potassium chloride; the two phases KPb₂Cl₅ and KPbCl₃.⅓H₂O with 0·12 grm. lead chloride and 16·83 grms. potassium chloride; and the two phases KPbCl₃.⅓H₂O and KCl with 0·20 grm. of lead chloride and 24·61 grms. potassium chloride. At 100°, Fig. 79, there are the two phases PbCl₂ and KPb₂Cl₅ with 0·60 grm. lead chloride and 6·50 grms. of potassium chloride; the two phases KPb₂Cl₅ and KPbCl₃.⅓H₂O with 0·94 grm. potassium chloride and 23·60 grms. of lead chloride; and the two phases KPbCl₃.⅓H₂O and KCl with 1·50 grms. of lead chloride and 31·24 grms. of potassium chloride. The curves at different temp. are embodied in the three-dimensional

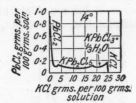

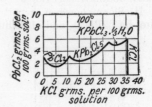

FIGS. 78 and 79.—Solubility of Lead Chloride in Solutions of Potassium Chloride at Different Concentrations.

diagram, Fig. 80. L. J. Burrage also found for the mutual solubilities of lead and potassium chlorides, at 25°, when the conc. are expressed in grams per 1000 grms. of soln. :

KCl	0	0·37	30·22	49·69	129·3	187·4	225·4	264·3	264·9	265·3
PbCl₂	10·83	10·08	2·05	2·27	1·42	2·36	3·03	3·86	1·22	0
Solid phase		PbCl₂		KPb₂Cl₅			KPbCl₃.⅓H₂O		KCl	

The sp. gr. of mixtures of the two components have been determined by R. Lorenz, H. Frei, and A. Jabs; the surface tension, by R. Lorenz and A. Liebmann; the electrical conductivity by R. Ketzer; the e.m.f. of cells Pb | KCl–PbCl₂ | Cl, by R. Lorenz and co-workers; the electrode potential of lead in mixed soln. of the two salts by A. Immerwahr; and the crystals, by O. Lehmann.

R. Lorenz and co-workers, K. Treis, and T. Liebisch and E. Korreng obtained **potassium pentachlorodiplumbite**, KPb₂Cl₅, from the molten constituents. The conditions of formation are indicated in Fig. 78. H. L. Wells, J. Kendall and C. H. Sloan, L. J. Burrage, and N. Demassieux obtained it in aq. soln., and the conditions of formation at different temp. are shown in Figs. 78 and 79. The white prismatic crystals are considered by K. Treis to belong to the rhombic system. They melt without decomposition at 430° (R. Lorenz) or 440° (K. Treis). J. N. Brönsted gave 2200 cals. for the mol. heat of formation. E. Rimbach and K. Fleck, J. Kendall and C. H. Sloan, and C. H. Herty claim to have made anhydrous **potassium trichloroplumbite**, $KPbCl_3$, from soln. of the constituents, but H. L. Wells, and N. Demassieux showed that the salt which separates from the aq. soln. is the trita-hydrate. H. L. Wells said that only 0·25 per cent. of this water is lost in 8 days over sulphuric acid. The water is rapidly given off at 200°. The salt **potassium tetra-chloroplumbite**, K_2PbCl_4, occurs in nature as the mineral *pseudocotunnite*. It was found by A. Scacchi as acicular, yellow, opaque crystals accompanying cotunnite from the eruption of Vesuvius in 1872. He called it *pseudocotunnia*, a term altered by G. vom Rath to pseudocotunnite. A. Scacchi represented the composition by $KPbCl_3$, but F. Zambonini showed that the analyses are better represented by K_2PbCl_4. Some fluorine is present in pseudocotunnite. A. Lacroix obtained the crystals by washing with hot water the cotunnite crusts of the Vesuvian fumaroles. F. Zambonini showed that the mineral named *mellonite* —after M. Melloni—by L. Palmieri, is pseudocotunnite contaminated with chlorides and sulphates of sodium, potassium, copper, and lead. Neither H. L. Wells nor N. Demassieux could obtain the salt from aq. soln.; but R. Lorenz and co-workers found that it is formed when the constituents are melted in the proportions shown in Fig. 77. According to K. Treis, the rhombic crystals melt at 490° and decompose into molten lead chloride, and crystals of potassium chloride. N. Demassieux, and L. J. Burrage obtained **potassium trichloroplumbite**, $KPbCl_3.\frac{1}{3}H_2O$, as indicated above. R. Lorenz and co-worker also obtained **potassium hexachloroplumbite**, K_4PbCl_6, from the molten constituents as illustrated in Fig. 80. It decomposes at 480°, but K. Treis could not verify this.

O. Lehmann obtained from the system NH_4Cl–KCl–$PbCl_2$–H_2O six-sided prisms of what was thought to be *ammonium potassium chloroplumbite*, but this has not been

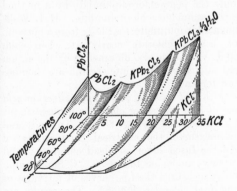

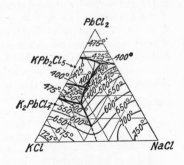

FIG. 80.—The Phases in the System KCl–$PbCl_2$–H_2O at Different Temperatures.

FIG. 81.—Fusion Curves in the Ternary System: KCl–$NaCl$–$PbCl_2$.

confirmed. K. Treis studied the ternary system KCl–$NaCl$–$PbCl_2$, and obtained the fusion curves illustrated by Fig. 81. Expressing the composition in molar percentages, there are two eutectics; the solid phases $PbCl_2.2PbCl_2.KCl$ and $NaCl$ coexist in the eutectic point at 383°, where the composition of the fused mass is $71PbCl_2,11KCl$, and $18NaCl$. The coexisting solid phases in the second eutectic point are $2PbCl_2.KCl.PbCl_2.2KCl$, and $NaCl$; the temp. is 387°, and the composition $48PbCl_2,38KCl$, and $16NaCl$.

K. Treis studied the f.p. curves of mixtures of rubidium and lead chlorides, and the results are indicated in Fig. 82. Observations on this subject were also made by T. Liebisch and E. Korreng. H. L. Wells made **rubidium pentachlorodiplumbite**, $RbPb_2Cl_5$, from hot soln. of mixtures of rubidium and lead chlorides; E. Rimbach and H. Fleck employed the process used for the corresponding potassium salt; and

K. Treis obtained it from a molten mixture of the component salts as indicated in Fig. 82. The prismatic crystals are probably rhombic and isomorphous with the corresponding potassium salt. They melt without decomposition at 423°. H. L. Wells and G. F. Campbell, and E. H. Ducloux made white tabular crystals of

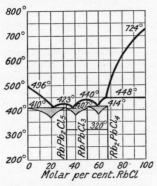

FIG. 82.—Freezing-point Curves of the Binary System: PbCl₂–RbCl.

cæsium pentachlorodiplumbite, $CsPb_2Cl_5$, by a process similar to that employed for the rubidium salt. K. Treis obtained crystals of rubidium trichloroplumbite, $RbPbCl_3$, from the molten constituents as indicated in Fig. 82. Above 310°, the crystals are cubic; below 310°, they are probably rhombic. They melt at 440° without decomposition. H. L. Wells and G. F. Campbell, and E. H. Ducloux obtained crystals of cæsium trichloroplumbite, $CsPbCl_3$, from a hot soln. of lead and cæsium chlorides. K. Treis obtained rubidium tetrachloroplumbite, Rb_2PbCl_4, from a mixture of the molten constituents at 448°; it also decomposes at that temp., Fig. 82; H. Erdmann and P. Köthner also made it by melting rubidium hexachloroplumbate. The white, acicular crystals are probably isomorphous with the rhombic crystals of the corresponding potassium salt; they melt at 448° into molten lead chloride and crystals of potassium chloride. H. L. Wells obtained the *hemihydrate* from a hot soln. of the component salts. The colourless, transparent, prismatic crystals lose about 25 per cent. of their water at 100° in 12 hrs., and all is rapidly expelled at 200°. E. H. Ducloux made cæsium tetrachloroplumbite, Cs_2PbCl_4. E. Rimbach and K. Fleck obtained only the pentachlorodiplumbite by a method analogous to that employed for making potassium hexachloroplumbite. H. L. Wells and G. F. Campbell obtained cæsium hexachloroplumbite, Cs_4PbCl_6, from a hot soln. of lead chloride in a hot soln. of cæsium chloride nearly sat. when cold. E. H. Ducloux prepared this salt; and J. Vermande also obtained it by the action of a sat. soln. of cæsium chloride on lead sulphate. The white crystals are rhombohedral, and serve as a microchemical test for lead.

No compounds have been prepared with *lead chloride, and copper, silver, or gold chloride*. K. Treis found that mixtures of lead and silver chlorides furnish simple

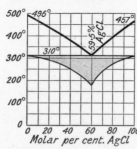

FIG. 83.—Freezing Points of Mixtures: PbCl₂–AgCl.

V-curves as illustrated in Fig. 83; C. Tubandt and co-workers measured the electrical conductivity of mixtures of the fused silver and lead chlorides; and obtained a curve analogous to Fig. 83. C. Sandonnini, and O. Menge measured the f.p. curves of mixtures of *calcium and lead chlorides*, Fig. 84. The results are summarized in Fig. 84. O. Menge observed that calcium chloride does not form solid soln. with lead chloride. R. Otto and D. Drewes claimed to have made calcium hexachloroplumbite, $Ca_2PbCl_6.nH_2O$, as a precipitate when a conc. soln. of lead chloride is added to a boiling conc. aq. soln. of calcium chloride; and J. Kendall and C. H. Sloan reported the formation of calcium tetrachloroplumbite, $CaCl_2.PbCl_2.6H_2O$; and so of strontium tetrachloroplumbite, $SrCl_2.PbCl_2$. C. Sandonnini found that *lead and strontium chlorides* form mixed crystals in all proportions, and the f.p. curves are illustrated in Fig. 85. Similar results were obtained with mixtures of *lead and barium chlorides*, Fig. 86. O. Ruff and W. Plato made solid soln. of these chlorides. R. Lorenz and co-workers measured the sp. gr. of the mixtures. A. C. Becquerel reported the formation of crystals of a double salt, but this has not been confirmed. J. Kendall and C. H. Sloan claimed to have made **barium tetrachloroplumbite,** $BaCl_2.PbCl_2$; as well as **magnesium tetrachloroplumbite,** $MgCl_2.PbCl_2.6H_2O$. O. Menge found that the f.p. curves of mixtures of *lead and magnesium chlorides,* Fig. 87, give no evidence of the

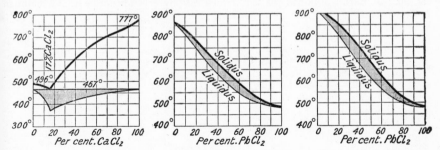

FIGS. 84 to 86.—Freezing-point Curves of Binary Mixtures of Lead Chloride with Calcium, Strontium, or Barium Chloride.

formation of a double salt. R. Otto and D. Drewes reported the formation of tridecahydrated **magnesium hexachloroplumbite,** by adding a soln. of 17 grms. dried lead chloride to a hot 32 per cent. soln. of magnesium chloride. The crystals were separated from the mother-liquor by suction; pressed between filter-paper; and dried over sulphuric acid. H. Hof and B. Rirck also obtained the same salt by dissolving lead oxide or lead sulphate in a boiling conc.

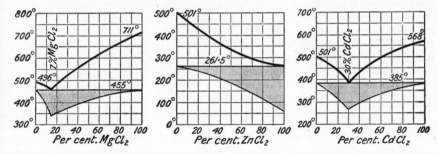

FIGS. 87 to 89.—Freezing-point Curves of Binary Mixtures of Lead Chloride with Magnesium, Zinc, or Cadmium Chloride.

soln. of magnesium chloride of sp. gr. 1·32. The crystals are either tetragonal or hexagonal plates. They deliquesce and decompose in air; they are decomposed by water and alcohol into lead and magnesium chlorides. They are not blackened by dry hydrogen sulphide, but they are blackened by the moist gas and also by the vapour of ammonium sulphide. The crystals lose their water at 200°. J. Kendall and C. H. Sloan reported the formation of **mercuric tetrachloroplumbite,** $HgCl_2.PbCl_2$. G. Hermann measured the f.p. curve of mixtures of *lead and zinc chlorides,* Fig. 88, and obtained no evidence of a double salt. Similar remarks apply to G. Herrmann's and C. Sandonnini's observations on the f.p. of mixtures of *lead and cadmium chlorides,* Fig. 89—*vide supra,* the action of cadmium on soln. of lead chloride. C. Sandonnini and G. Scarpa found no sign of a compound of *lead and manganese chlorides* on the f.p. curve of mixtures of the two chlorides. There is a simple ∨-curve with a eutectic at 408° and 70 molar per cent. of lead chloride. The beginning of the crystallization with the different molar percentages of lead chloride is as follows :

PbCl₂.	0	10	20	40	50	60	80	100
F.p.	650°	627°	600°	540°	510°	463°	29°	495°

According to E. Korreng, molten mixtures of *lead and thallous chlorides* **furnish** two compounds : **thallous pentachloroplumbite,** Tl_3PbCl_5, melting at 407°, and **thallous trichloroplumbite,** $TlPbCl_3$, melting at 435°. The f.p. curves are shown in Fig. 90. **J.** Barlot obtained the last-named salt by crystallization from a boiling

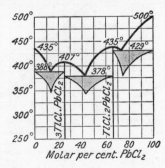

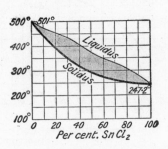

FIG. 90.—Freezing-point Curves of Mix-tures of Thallous and Lead Chlorides.

FIG. 91.—Freezing-point Curves of Mix-tures of Lead and Stannous Chlorides.

aq. soln. of eq. proportions of the constituent salts ; and F. Ephraim and P. Bar-teczko obtained it from a hydrochloric acid soln. of these salts. J. Barlot described the crystals as white, rhombic plates. A. A. Noyes obtained thallous pentachloro-plumbite by adding a half sat. soln. of lead chloride to one of thallous chloride, and recrystallizing from hot water. J. Barlot found the electrical conductivity curves of the mixed salt soln. intersect at a point corresponding with Tl_2PbCl_4, but he was unable to prepare this salt. There is a break in the curve corresponding with the trichloroplumbite. F. Ephraim and P. Barteczko obtained what were probably mixed crystals with the composition $TlCl : PbCl_2 = 4 : 3$, and $3 : 4$. J. Nicklès reported *ammonium thallic chloroplumbite* to be formed by the action of ammonium hexachlorothallate on a soln. of a lead acetate. G. Herrmann, and C. Sandonnini and G. Scarpa found no evidence of a stannous chloroplumbite on the f.p. curves, Fig. 91, of mixtures of *stannous and lead chlorides*. The two chlorides form a continuous series of solid soln. A. Benrath and H. Tesche measured the electrical conductivity of mixtures of the two salts between 100° and 480°.

C. Sandonnini [3] examined the f.p. curve of mixtures of lead fluoride and chloride

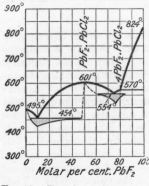

FIG. 92.—Freezing-point Curves of Mixtures of Lead Fluoride and Chloride.

(Fig. 92). Starting from the m.p. of the pure chloride, the curve descends to an eutectic point at 454°, the conc. being about 10 molar per cent. of fluoride. It then rises to a maximum at 601°, which corresponds to 50 molar per cent. of fluoride, and it afterwards descends again to another eutectic point at 554° (composition 75 molar per cent. of fluoride). When the conc. of fluoride is further raised, the curve rises slowly to 570° (composition 80 molar per cent.), where an evident pause occurs. Finally, the curve ascends rapidly to the m.p. of the pure fluoride. The existence of a **lead fluochloride,** $PbCl_2.PbF_2$, melting without decomposition is thus established, whilst the pause at 570° shows the existence of a **lead octofluodichloride,** $Pb_5Cl_2F_8$, $PbCl_2.4PbF_2$, which decomposes on fusion. J. J. Ber-zelius obtained lead fluochloride, $PbFCl$, by adding a soln. of sodium fluoride to a boiling soln. of lead chloride ; and by adding lead acetate to an aq. soln. of 2 parts of sodium fluoride and 3 parts of sodium chloride. H. Fonzes-Diacon made it by boiling for a long time a soln. of lead fluoride in a conc. soln. of ammonium chloride. The white crystals belong to the tetragonal system. C. Sandonnini said that the salt melts at 601° without decomposition. J. J. Berzelius found it to be slightly soluble in water without decomposition; G. Starck showed that 100 grms. of water at 0° dissolve 0·0211 grm. of the salt; at 18°, 0·0325 grm.; at 25°, 0·0370 grm.; at 100°, 0·1081 grm. The solubility is greater in the presence of a little hydrochloric or acetic acid; and it is practically insoluble in a dil. soln. of lead chloride. J. J. Berzelius said that it is easily soluble in nitric acid. H. Fonzes-Diacon could not obtain *ammonium fluochloroplumbite* from mixed soln. of ammonium chloride and lead fluoride.

REFERENCES.

¹ N. Demassieux, *Étude de l'équilibre entre le chlorure et l'iodure de plomb et quelques chlorures t iodures alcalins en solution aqueuse*, Paris, 1923 ; *Compt. Rend.*, 156. 894, 1913 ; G. André, *ib.*, 96. 1502, 1883 ; *Ann. Chim. Phys.*, (6), 3. 111, 1884 ; *Bull. Soc. Chim.*, (2), 40. 15, 109, 1883 ; H. Fonzes-Diacon, *ib.*, (3), 17. 347, 1897 ; K. Hachmeister, *Zeit. anorg. Chem.*, 109. 145, 1919 ; E. Rimbach and K. Fleck, *Zeit. anorg. Chem.*, 94. 154, 1916 ; K. Fleck, *Zur Kenntnis der Stanno und Plumboalkalidoppelhalogenide*, Bonn, 35, 1915 ; C. L. von Ende, *Zeit. anorg. Chem.*, 26. 162, 1901 ; *Ueber das Verhalten der Bleisalze in Lösungen*, Göttingen, 1899 ; J. N. Brönsted, *Dansk. Vid. Selsk. Forh.*, (7), 5. 451, 1910 ; *Zeit. phys. Chem.*, 77. 129, 1911 ; *Zeit. Elektrochem.*, 18. 714, 1912 ; H. W. Foote and L. H. Levy, *Amer Chem. Journ.*, 37, 120, 1907 ; W. W. Randall, *ib.*, 15. 495, 1893 ; H. L. Wells, *ib.*, 37. 119, 1907 ; H. L. Wells and W. R. Johnston, *Amer. Journ. Science*, (3), 46. 25, 1893 ; L. J. Thénard, *Ann. Chim. Phys.*, (1), 42. 210, 1802 ; A. C. Becquerel, *ib.*, (2), 41. 33, 1829 ; *Traité expérimental de l'électricité et du magnétisme*, Paris. 2. 86, 1855 ; J. Kendall and C. H. Sloan, *Journ. Amer. Chem. Soc.*, 47. 2306, 1925.
² J. N. Brönsted, *Zeit. phys. Chem.*, 80. 213, 1912 ; A. A. Noyes, *ib.*, 9. 622, 1892 ; R. Lorenz, *ib.*, 70. 230, 1910 ; R. Lorenz, H. Frei, and A. Jabs, *ib.*, 61. 473, 1908 ; G. von Hesvesy and R. Lorenz, *ib.*, 74. 443, 1910 ; R. Lorenz and A. Liebmann, *ib.*, 83. 459, 1913 ; R. Lorenz and M. G. Fox, *ib.*, 63. 109, 1908 ; A. Benrath and H. Tesche, *ib.*, 96. 474, 1920 ; C. Tubandt and H. Reinhold, *Zeit. Elektrochem.*, 29. 313, 1923 ; C. Tubandt and S. Eggert, *Zeit. anorg. Chem.*, 110. 196, 1920 ; R. Lorenz and W. Ruckstuhl, *ib.*, 51. 41, 1907 ; R. Lorenz and G. Fausti, *Zeit. Elektrochem.*, 10. 632, 1904 ; M. le Blanc, *ib.*, 18. 552, 1912 ; A. Immerwahr, *ib.*, 7. 480, 1901 ; *Beiträge zur Loslichkeitsbestimmungen schwerlöslicher Salze des Quecksilbers, Kupfers, Bleis, Cadmiums, und Zinks*, Breslau, 1900 ; R. Ketzer, *Ueber die Leitfahigkeit fester Salze und Salzgemische*, Leipzig, 1919 ; *Zeit. Elektrochem.*, 26. 78, 1920 ; T. Liebisch and E. Korreng, *Sitzber. Akad. Berlin*, 196, 1914 ; E. Korreng, *Kristallographische und thermische Untersuchungen von binären Systemen aus Thallochlorid und Chloriden zweiwertiger Metalle*, Stuttgart, 1913 ; *Neues Jahrb. B.B.*, 37. 76, 1914 ; J. Barlot, *Compt. Rend.*, 171. 794, 1920 ; K. Treis, *ib.*, 37. 770, 1914 ; *Kristallographische und thermische Untersuchungen von Systemen aus Bleichlorid und Chloriden einwerfiger Metalle*, Berlin, 1914 ; N. Demassieux, *Étude de l'équilibre entre le chlorure et l'iodure de plomb et quelques chlorures et iodures alcalins en solution aqueuse*, Paris, 1923 ; *Ann. Chim. Phys.*, (9), 20. 233, 1923 ; *Compt. Rend.*, 158. 183, 1914 ; H. Erdmann and P. Köthner, *Liebig's Ann.*, 294. 71, 1896 ; J. R. Strohecker, *Viertelj. prakt. Pharm.*, 18. 396, 1869 ; M. Berthelot, *Ann. Chim. Phys.*, (5), 29. 294, 1883 ; A. Ditte, *ib.*, (5), 14. 212, 1878 ; O. Lehmann, *Zeit. Kryst.*, 10. 340, 1885 ; J. Vermande, *Pharm. Weekbl.*, 55. 662, 1918 ; H. L. Wells, *Amer. Journ. Science*, (3), 45. 121, 1893 ; (3), 46. 34, 1893 ; H. L. Wells and G. F. Campbell, *ib.*, (3), 45. 127, 1893 ; C. L. von Ende, *Ueber das Verhalten der Bleisalze in Lösungen*, Göttingen, 1899 ; *Zeit. anorg. Chem.*, 19. 249, 1899 ; A. Appelberg, *ib.*, 36. 63, 1903 ; O. Menge, *ib.*, 72. 206, 1911 ; E. Rimbach and K. Fleck, *ib.*, 94. 155, 1916 ; K. Fleck, *Zur Kenntnis der Stanno- und Plumboalkalidoppelhalogenide*, Bonn, 1915 ; H. Hof and B. Rinck, *German Pat.*, *D.R.P.* 227389, 1909 ; H. Hof, *Chem. Ztg.*, 33. 1078, 1909 ; *Zeit. anorg. Chem.*, 81. 42, 1913 ; G. Herrmann, *ib.*, 71. 281, 1911 ; F. Ephraim and P. Barteczko, *ib.*, 61. 249, 1909 ; C. H. Herty, *Amer. Chem. Journ.*, 14. 124, 1892 ; A. C. Becquerel, *Compt. Rend.*, 34. 29, 1852 ; F. Zambonini, *Atti Accad. Napoli*, 6. 9, 1873 ; 13 8, 1906 ; A. Scacchi, *Contribuzione mineralogische per servire alla storia dell' incendio Vesuviano, del mese di Aprile 1872*, Napoli, 2. 38, 1874 ; *Mineralogia Vesuviana*, Napoli, 49, 1910 ; *Bull. Soc. Min.*, 1. 41, 1878 ; A. Lacroix, *ib.*, 30. 228, 1907 ; 31. 261, 1908 ; G. vom Rath, *Verh. Nat. Hist. Rheinl. Bonn.*, 151, 1877 ; O. Ruff and W. Plato, *Ber.*, 36. 2363, 1903 ; E. H. Ducloux, *Anal. Asoc. Quim. Argentina*, 9. 215, 1921 ; *Mikrochemie*, 2. 108, 1924 ; L. Palmieri, *Rend. Accad. Napoli*, 12. 92, 1873 ; C. Fritsch, *Wied. Ann.*, 60. 300, 1897 ; R. Otto and D. Drewes, *Arch. Pharm.*, 228. 497, 1890 ; C. Sandonnini, *Atti Accad. Lincei*, (5), 20. ii, 500, 646, 1911 ; (5), 22. ii, 21, 1913 ; C. Sandonnini and G. Scarpa, *ib.*, (5), 20. ii, 62, 1911 ; J. Nicklès, *Journ. Pharm. Chim.*, (4). 2. 219, 1865 ; J. Kendall and C. H. Sloan, *Journ. Amer. Chem. Soc.*, 47. 2306, 1925 ; L. J. Burrage, *Journ. Chem. Soc.*, 129. 1703, 1926.
³ C. Sandonnini, *Atti Accad. Lincei*, (5), 20. i, 172, 1911 ; *Gazz. Chim. Ital.*, 41. ii, 144, 1911 ; J. J. Berzelius, *Pogg. Ann.*, 1. 34, 1824 ; *Lehrbuch der Chemie*, Dresden, 4. 497, 1838 ; H. Fonzes-Diacon, *Bull. Soc. Chim.*, (3), 17. 350, 1897 ; G. Starck, *Zeit. anorg. Chem.*, 70. 173, 1911.

§ 24. Chloroplumbates

As previously indicated in connection with lead tetrachloride, impure chloroplumbates were possibly made by A. Sobrero and F. Selmi [1] in 1850, by J. Nicklès in 1867, etc. J. Nikoliukin first isolated double salts of lead tetrachloride with ammonium and potassium chlorides. He dissolved lead dioxide in conc. hydrochloric acid in a sealed tube, and added a conc. soln. of ammonium chloride to the product so obtained. The yellow crystals were washed with a conc. soln. of ammonium chloride, at 0°, and pressed between paper. The analysis approximated ammonium chloroplumbate, $(NH_4)_2PbCl_6$. A. Classen and B. Zahorsky said that the aq. soln. of ammonium chloride decomposed the salt to some extent. H. L. Wells showed that the sealed tube was unnecessary ; he added slightly dil. hydrochloric acid to an excess of lead dioxide at 0° ; filtered the soln. through asbestos ; added a cold sat. soln. of ammonium chloride until an abundant, yellow, crystalline precipitate was produced ; pressed the salt between filter-paper ; and dried the product in air. H. Friedrich passed chlorine into a soln. of lead chloride in hydrochloric acid ; and obtained ammonium chloroplumbate on adding ammonium chloride to the product. J. M. Matthews, and A. Fränkel used a somewhat similar process—vide lead tetrachloride. A. Seyewetz and A. Trawitz added ammonium persulphate to a cold soln. of lead chloride in hydrochloric acid ; K. Elbs and F. Fischer treated a soln. of lead persulphate, in cold hydrochloric acid, with ammonium chloride ; A. Hutchinson and W. Pollard added ammonium chloride to a soln. of lead tetracetate in cold, conc. hydrochloric acid ; A. Gutbier and M. Wissmüller treated a soln. of lead tetrachloride with ammonium chloride ; and K. Elbs and R. Nübling added ammonium chloride to a soln. of hydrochloroplumbic acid. According to A. Seyewetz and H. Tatu, ammonium chloroplumbate can be economically prepared by adding a slow stream of nitric acid to an agitated suspension of 1 mol. of lead chloride (or sulphate) and 2 mols. of ammonium chloride in four times the theoretical quantity of conc. hydrochloric acid. The filtered product, freed from acid with alcohol and ether, and heated at 80°, is a yellow powder, insoluble in the common organic solvents, which turns bright red at 70°–80° and loses chlorine at 140°. F. Förster electrolyzed a soln. of hydrochloric acid saturated at 0° with lead chloride, and mixed with some ammonium chloride.

The lemon-yellow, octahedral crystals are isomorphous with ammonium chloroplatinate (K. Elbs and R. Nübling), and with ammonium chlorostannate (H. Friedrich, and E. Carozzi). E. Carozzi gave 2·925 for the sp. gr. The crystals are not hygroscopic in air. M. Wissmüller said that the colour becomes orange-red at 100°, and pale yellow on cooling. K. Elbs and R. Nübling found that the crystals can be kept many hours at 115° without decomposition, and at a still higher temp. for a short time. J. Nikoliukin said that the salt decomposes at 120°, and H. L. Wells said 225°. When decomposed by heat, chlorine is first evolved, then ammonium chloride vap., and lead dichloride remains. The salt is soluble in water, but H. Friedrich, and A. Seyewetz and P. Trawitz, found an excess of water decomposes the salt, forming, according to A. Gutbier and E. Sauer, the hydrosol of lead dioxide. A. Seyewetz and H. Tatu said that in a 0·08 per cent. aq. soln. it forms colloidal lead dioxide, which slowly settles ; in this form, it may be used as an active oxidizing agent. Soln. between 4 per cent. and 22 per cent. (saturation) decompose into lead chloride and an oxygenated chlorine compound ; with concentrations between 0·08 per cent. and 4 per cent., both reactions occur. The second type of decomposition is avoided by dissolving in conc. hydrochloric acid, but can be favoured by carefully regulating the quantity and conc. of the acid. Phosphoric acid in all concentrations does not hinder the second type of decomposition. It stabilizes dil. soln. in which the first type of decomposition occurs, by retarding the flocculation of the oxide, even at concentrations slightly below that at which the formation of the oxide is hindered. Acetic acid behaves similarly to phosphoric acid, although much higher concentrations are necessary. H. Friedrich said that cold conc. hydrochloric acid does not readily dissolve the salt, and that the soln., when warmed, gives off chlorine without depositing lead dichloride ; dil. hydrochloric acid acts similarly, but lead chloride is then deposited. K. Elbs and R. Nübling said that about 0·25 grm. of the salt dissolves in 20 per cent. hydrochloric acid at room temp. H. Friedrich found that with potassium iodide, iodine eq. to two gram-atoms of chlorine per mol. separates. J. M. Matthews showed that fuming sulphuric acid of sp. gr. 1·879 furnishes lead tetrachloride ; H. Friedrich found that the salt is soluble in conc. nitric acid without decomposition, and when the soln. is warmed, nitrogen oxides are evolved and a precipitate is formed which is sparingly soluble in water. Dil. nitric and sulphuric acids act similarly. A warm soln. of sodium carbonate colours the salt pale brown, while lead and carbon dioxides are formed. A. Seyewetz and co-workers found that aromatic hydrocarbons, as well as their chlorine and nitroxyl derivatives, are chlorinated when heated in a sealed tube with the chloroplumbate. Above 120° in a non-aqueous medium, plumbic ammonium chloride yields nascent chlorine, and so may be used as a chlorinating agent.

A. Classen and B. Zahorsky considered that the salt indicated above is impure, and that the composition of the purified product is *ammonium tridecachlorodiplumbate*, $(NH_4)_5Pb_2Cl_{13}$, but H. Friedrich showed that it is probable that the salt analyzed by these investigators contained free ammonium chloride.

The soln. prepared by A. Sobrero and F. Selmi had the composition $PbCl_4$ +9NaCl, and for a time this was represented as the composition of the complex salt—e.g. D. J. Carnegie used the formula $PbCl_4.9NaCl$ in support of a theory of the double halides. H. L. Wells, however, was unable to make the double *sodium chloroplumbate*. K. Elbs and co-workers, A. Gutbier and M. Wissmüller, J. Nikoli-ukin, and H. L. Wells made **potassium chloroplumbate**, K_2PbCl_6, by a method resembling that employed for the ammonium salt. The general properties of the two salts are similar. M. Wissmüller found the potassium salt to be rather less stable in air and water than the ammonium salt. H. L. Wells said that it decomposes at about 190°. J. Nikoliukin said that it is easily soluble in a conc. soln. of potassium chloride. H. L. Wells found that hydrochloric acid, sat. with chlorine, is best used for washing the salt ; it is decomposed by boiling hydrochloric acid, while it can be preserved under conc. hydrochloric acid. H. Friedrich, A. Gutbier and M. Wissmüller, and H. L. Wells made **rubidium chloroplumbate**, Rb_2PbCl_6, by methods analogous to those employed for the ammonium salt. H. Erdmann and P. Köthner used the method employed by H. Friedrich, and obtained yellow, regular octahedral crystals. Conc. sulphuric acid acts on it, liberating hydrogen chloride, and precipitating lead tetrachloride as an oil (*q.v.*), whilst the dil. acid converts the metals into sulphates, and liberates chlorine. Rubidium chloride may be precipitated almost quantitatively from its soln. in methylic alcohol sat. with chlorine by adding a soln. of lead tetrachloride, the precipitate being washed with 80 per cent. alcohol. Potassium chloroplumbate is much less stable than the rubidium salt, and evolves chlorine when dried in air ; the same change takes place when the rubidium salt is heated, the chloroplumbite, $PbRb_2Cl_4$, being produced. The rubidium salt is also indifferent towards dil. hydrochloric acid and 96 per cent. alcohol, the potassium salt being decomposed by both agents ; the changes produced under the influence of water and ammonia are less rapid than those which the potassium salt undergoes. In spite of these differences in behaviour, the estimation of rubidium in the presence of potassium by means of lead tetrachloride is inaccurate. H. L. Wells, and A. Gutbier and M. Wissmüller made **cæsium chloroplumbate**, Cs_2PbCl_6, by similar methods. The lemon-yellow crystals are regular octahedra. They are stable in air, and decompose at 280°. One c.c. of a soln. of fuming hydrochloric acid (1 : 1) containing twice the theoretical amount of lead chloride sat. with chlorine, dissolved 0·000068 grm. of Cs_2PbCl_6 ; with rubidium chloroplatinate, the solubility was 0·003 grm. per c.c.

J. Nicklès prepared a soln. which had the composition $PbCl_4+16CaCl_2$, but no *calcium chloroplumbate* was isolated ; H. L. Wells also failed to make this compound.

REFERENCES.

[1] A. Sobrero and F. Selmi, *Atti Accad. Torino*, **11**. 345, 1851 ; *Ann. Chim. Phys.*, (3), **29**. 161, 1850 ; J. Nicklès, *ib.*, (4), **10**. 323, 1867 ; A. Gutbier and E. Sauer, *Zeit. Koll.*, **12**. 171, 1913 ; A. Gutbier and M. Wissmüller, *Journ. prakt. Chem.*, (2), **90**. 498, 1914 ; M. Wissmüller, *Zur Kenntnis des vierwertigen Bleis*, Erlangen, 24, 1916 ; A. Seyewetz and H. Tatu, *Bull. Soc. Chim.*, (4), **39**. 647, 1926 ; A. Seyewetz and P. Trawitz, *ib.*, (3), **39**. 457, 1903 ; *Compt. Rend.*, **136**. 686, 1903 ; A. Seyewetz and M. Biot, *ib.*, **135**. 1120, 1902 ; A. Hutchinson and W. Pollard, *Journ. Chem. Soc.*, **69**. 219, 1896 ; F. Förster, *Zeit. Elektrochem.*, **3**. 527, 1897 ; K. Elbs and F. Fischer, *ib.*, **7**. 345, 1901 ; K. Elbs and R. Nübling, *ib.*, **9**. 777, 1903 ; H. Friedrich, *Ber. Böhm. Ges.*, 161, 1889 ; *Chem. Listy*, **17**. 67, 1890 ; *Monatsh.*, **14**. 507, 1893 ; *Ber.*, **26**. 1434, 1893 ; J. Nikoliukin, *Journ. Russ. Phys. Chem. Soc.*, **17**. 200, 1885 ; H. L. Wells, *Amer. Journ. Science*, (3), **46**. 180, 186, 1893 ; A. Fränkel. *Mitt. Tech. Gew. Mus.*, **13**. 124, 1903 ; A. Classen and B. Zahorsky, *Zeit. anorg. Chem.*, **4**. 103, 1893 ; J. M. Matthews, *Journ. Amer. Chem. Soc.*, **20**. 818, 1898 ; D. J. Carnegie, *Amer. Chem. Journ.*, **15**. 10, 1893 ; H. Erdmann, *Arch. Pharm.*, **232**. 23. 1894 ; H. Erdmann and P. Köthner, *Liebig's Ann.*, **294**. 71, 1896 ; E. Carozzi, *Gazz. Chim. Ital.*, **54**. i, 556, 1924.

§ 25. Lead Oxychlorides

A large number of lead oxychlorides have been reported. Starting from

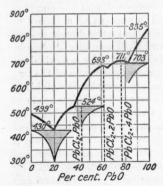

$PbO : PbCl_2 : H_2O$, 1 : 3 : 0, there are 1 : 2 : 0, 1 : 2 : 1, and 1 : 2 : 2 ; 1 : 1 : 0, 1 : 1 : 1, 1 : 1 : 1½, and 1 : 1 : 2½ ; 2 : 1 : 0 ; 3 : 1 : 0, 3 : 1 : ½, 3 : 1 : 1, 3 : 1 : 3, and 3 : 1 : 4 ; 4 : 1 : 0, and 4 : 1 : 2 ; 5 : 1 : 0, and 5 : 1 : 5 ; 6 : 1 : 0, and 6 : 1 : 2 ; and 7 : 1 : 0. C. F. Cross and S. Sugiura reported some oxychlorides with an excess of oxygen or chlorine above that required for plumbous salts—*e.g. octolead oxyhexadecachloride*, Pb_8OCl_{16}, was obtained as a grey, crystalline mass by the action of a mixture of air and chlorine on lead monoxide ; when red-lead was used, *pentalead oxyenneachloride*, Pb_5OCl_9, was formed ; and with lead dioxide, *dodecalead tetrahenicosichloride*, $Pb_{12}O_4Cl_{21}$, was formed. With lead dioxide at a red heat and chlorine, *tetralead oxyheptachloride*, Pb_4OCl_7, was formed. None of these compounds could be prepared by R. Ruer. He obtained only $PbCl_2.PbO$, *matlockite ;* $PbCl_2.2PbO$,

FIG. 93.—Freezing-point Curves of Mixtures of Lead Monoxide and Dichloride.

mendipite ; and $PbCl_2.4PbO$ on the f.p. curves. The graphic formulæ were given as :

$$\begin{matrix} Cl-Pb \\ Cl-Pb \end{matrix}\!\!>\!O \qquad\qquad \begin{matrix} Cl-Pb.O \\ Cl-Pb.O \end{matrix}\!\!>\!Pb \qquad\qquad \begin{matrix} Cl-Pb.O.Pb.O \\ Cl-Pb.O.Pb.O \end{matrix}\!\!>\!Pb$$

$PbCl_2.PbO$ $\qquad\qquad\qquad$ $PbCl_2.2PbO$ $\qquad\qquad\qquad$ $PbCl_2.4PbO$

The equilibrium conditions of the ternary system $PbO-PbCl_2-H_2O$ have not been established. Consequently the distinction between those which are truly chemical individuals, and those which are mere mixtures, has not been established. Several of these oxychlorides have been reported in nature. The binary system has been investigated—Fig. 93—by R. Ruer.[1] There are no signs of *lead oxyhexachloride*, $PbO.3PbCl_2$, reported by L. N. Vauquelin to be formed by melting a mixture of the two constituents. The curve shows two maxima at 693° and 62 per cent. and 711° and 76 per cent. by weight of lead oxide, corresponding with the composition of the compounds $PbCl_2.2PbO$ and $PbCl_2.4PbO$ respectively; three eutectic points at 438° and 20 per cent., 691° and 64 per cent., and 703° and 82 per cent. of lead oxide respectively, as well as a break in the curve at 524° and 36 per cent. of the oxide. The latter arises from the fact that the compound, $PbCl_2.2PbO$, which separates primarily from mixtures containing 47–62 per cent. by weight of lead oxide, reacts below 524° with the fused mass to form a third compound, $PbCl_2.PbO$. Between 68 and 78 per cent. of lead oxide, the compound $PbCl_2.4PbO$ forms mixed crystals with $PbCl_2.2PbO$ and PbO respectively.

There is no evidence of the formation of **lead oxytetrachloride**, $PbO.2PbCl_2$, on R. Ruer's equilibrium diagram, although A. Wächter reported it to be formed, as a yellow mass, by heating lead chlorate for a long time at a temp., according to W. H. Sodeau, at 225°. F. A. Genth reported it to have been formed in white, hexagonal prisms by the action of sea-water on the ancient slags of Laurion, Greece; he called the mineral **penfieldite**—after S. L. Penfield. S. L. Penfield gave for the axial ratio of the hexagonal crystals $a : c = 1 : 0.8967$. According to A. Lacroix and A. de Schulten, the crystals are uniaxial, and have a feebler birefringence than the other lead oxychlorides; the optical character is positive. A. Raimondi reported a specimen from Challacollo, Tarapaca, with a rather smaller proportion of chloride than $PbO.2PbCl_2$. G. vom Rath reported monoclinic crystals of a mineral in the lead slags of Laurion; he called it **fiedlerite**—after K. G. Fiedler. A. Lacroix and A. de Schulten showed that its composition corresponds with **monohydrated lead oxytetrachloride**, $PbO.2PbCl_2.H_2O$, or *lead dihydroxytetra-chloride*, $PbCl_2.2Pb(OH)Cl$. The rectangular plates were shown by G. vom Rath to be monoclinic with a rhombic habit, and to have the axial ratios $a : b : c$ $= 0.81918 : 1 : 0.89152$, and $\beta = 102°\ 40'$. G. F. H. Smith gave $0.8299 : 1 : 0.7253$, and $\beta = 77°\ 31'$; and for the refractive indices with Na-light, $\alpha = 1.816$, $\beta = 2.1023$, and $\gamma = 2.026$. A. Lacroix and A. de Schulten found the sp. gr. to be 5.88, and the hardness over 3. The mineral decrepitates when heated, and it becomes opaque and anhydrous at 150°; thereafter it melts and sublimes. It is easily attacked by cold water, and becomes opaque in about an hour; it is dissolved by cold nitric acid. G. André obtained fine, needle-like crystals of **dihydrated lead oxytetra-chloride**, $PbO.2PbCl_2.2H_2O$, by pouring the mother-liquor from the salt, $(NH_4)_6PbCl_8.H_2O$, into an excess of water, and heating the product for 5 hrs. in a sealed tube at 200°. The product dissolves in boiling soda-lye, forming a yellow soln.

The mineral **matlockite** reported by R. P. Greg to occur along with phosgenite in an old mine at Cromford, near Matlock, Derbyshire, is a **lead oxydichloride**, $PbO.PbCl_2$. A. Lacroix found matlockite about the old slag heaps of Laurion, Greece; A. Raimondi, and I. Domeyko reported it at Challacollo, Tarapaca, Chile; W. F. Petterd, at Zeehan, Tasmania; and W. P. Jervis, R. Cappa, and A. Scacchi in the sublimation product of Vesuvius. The conditions of equilibrium for lead oxydichloride are indicated in R. Ruer's diagram, Fig. 93. J. W. Döbereiner obtained a product of the same composition by heating lead chloride in air until fumes were no longer evolved; and also by fusing a mixture of lead chloride and carbonate in equimolar proportions. G. André obtained a similar product by precipitating a soln. of lead chloride with the calculated quantity of potassium hydroxide, washing with cold water, and drying at 100°; S. Ganelin, by adding water to a mixture of lead chloride with half an eq. amount of magnesia, or to a similar mixture of magnesia with lead sulphate and sodium chloride; V. Thomas, by subliming the iodine from the product by the action of nitrogen peroxide on lead chloroiodide; A. Voigt, by heating monohydrated lead trioxydichloride, $3PbO.PbCl_2.H_2O$, to redness; G. André, by pouring into cold water a sat. soln. of lead oxide in a hot soln. of ammonium chloride (1 : 2), washing the product with cold water, and drying at 100°; and R. Brandes, by heating the washed product obtained by the action of a conc. soln. of lead acetate on lead chloride. The synthesis of matlockite was also discussed by F. Fouqué and A. M. Lévy, and

C. W. G. Fuchs. Matlockite was found by A. C. Becquerel among the products obtained in the synthesis of cotunnite. Analyses were reported by R. P. Greg, R. Brandes, V. Thomas, C. F. Rammelsberg, etc. P. Groth represents its composition by the formula Cl–Pb–O–Pb–Cl. The crystals were examined by R. P. Greg and W. G. Lettsom, G. Rose, G. A. Kenngott, P. Groth, A. Lacroix, H. Buttgenbach, K. Treis, etc. R. Ruer obtained the salt in yellowish-brown needles. W. H. Miller found the tabular crystals of matlockite belong to the tetragonal system, and have the axial ratio $a : c = 1 : 1.7627$. The colour of matlockite is yellow, sometimes with a greenish tinge. The artificial salt may be greyish-white. The cleavage parallel to (001) is imperfect. Besides the uniaxial crystals, A. Lacroix observed some which consisted of four biaxial sectors ; he gave for the optic axial angle $2E = 55°$. A. des Cloizeaux found the optical character is negative. According to R. P. Greg, the sp. gr. is 7.21 ; and the hardness, 2–3. C. F. Rammelsberg's 5.3947 for the sp. gr. is too small. R. Ruer found the salt melts at 524° with decomposition. G. André gave 3.26 Cals. for the heat of formation from anhydrous lead oxide and chloride ; and the heat of soln. of the salt in a soln. of hydrochloric acid sat. with lead chloride, was 9.04 Cals. at 10°. H. Buttgenbach measured the indices of refraction. K. Keilhack found the crystals phosphoresce when exposed to the X-rays. A. Braley studied the blowpipe reactions of matlockite.

R. Köchlin found groups of colourless, clear crystals associated with phosgenite and cerussite in cavities in the lead slags at Laurion, Greece ; they appear to have been formed by the action of sea-water on the slag which has been exposed for some 2000 years. The crystals analyzed by G. vom Rath, and A. de Schulten had the composition of **monohydrated lead oxydichloride,** $PbO.PbCl_2.H_2O$, or *lead hydroxychloride,* $Pb(OH)Cl$. The mineral was called **laurionite.** The salt has been synthesized in many ways. H. L. Pattinson obtained monohydrated lead oxydichloride by adding a sat. soln. of a cubic metre of lime-water to a soln. of 1.2 krgms. of lead chloride in a cubic metre of water. The product, once used as a pigment, was called *Pattinson's white-lead.* The manufacture was described by J. Percy. H. Hof made the salt by dissolving lead oxide in a conc. soln. of magnesium chloride, and decomposing the hot soln. with water. The product was contaminated with magnesium hydroxide and chloride. M. Pleissner prepared the same product by shaking 5–10 grms. of lead chloride, 4 grms. of lead hydroxide, $3PbO.H_2O$, and 500 c.c. of water for 4 or 5 days at 18° ; washing the product with 400 c.c. of water renewed from time to time until the lead in soln. was very small ; and drying in vacuo over soda-lime. J. Wood and J. L. Borden heated 5–7 grms. of lead chloride with 140–145 c.c. of aq. ammonia until the smell of ammonia was no longer perceptible. The product was washed, and dried in air. H. L. Wells and W. R. Johnston saturated a boiling sat. soln. of ammonium chloride with lead chloride, added an equal vol. of a sat. soln. of ammonium chloride, and then an excess of ammonia. The product was washed and dried. G. André heated a double chloride of ammonium and lead with much water in a sealed tube at 200° for 5 hrs., and dried the product between **bibulous** paper ; he obtained a similar result by repeatedly boiling the double salt with much water. A. de Schulten added a hot soln. of 50 grms. of sodium chloride in 250 c.c. of water to a boiling soln. of one kgrm. of lead acetate in 2.5 litres of water ; the filtrate was heated 12–16 hrs. on a water-bath, and the crystalline precipitate washed with cold water, alcohol, and ether.

G. André reported the *hemitrihydrate,* $PbO.PbCl_2.1\frac{1}{2}H_2O$, to be formed by the action of an excess of water on the filtrate from a mixed soln. of lead and manganese chlorides. The product was washed and dried at 100°. A. Mailhé obtained the *hemipentahydrate* in white or grey rhombic or hexagonal plates by the action of brown copper oxyhydroxide, $Cu_4O_3(OH)_2$, on a conc. soln. of lead chloride ; and an amorphous mass of the same composition by using blue cupric hydroxide in place of the oxyhydroxide.

Lead hydroxychloride appears as a voluminous, white or pale yellow powder ; the mineral laurionite occurs in colourless, clear, minute, prismatic crystals flattened parallel to the (010)-face, and with feather-like striations on the (010)-faces. According to R. Köchlin, the axial ratios of the rhombic crystals are $a : b : c$ =0·7328 : 1 : 0·8315, and, according to G. F. H. Smith, 0·738̄ : 1 : 0·8346. The crystals were described by E. Repossi, G. vom Rath, V. Goldschmidt, A. Lacroix, A. de Schulten, F. Grünling, G. Cesaro, and C. A. Ktenas. W. Biltz studied the mol. vol. The salt is dimorphous—*vide infra*, paralaurionite which occurs in monoclinic crystals. The indices of refraction obtained by G. F. H. Smith were a=2·0767, β=2·1161, and γ=2·1580; and the optic axial angle $2V$=81° 32′. The birefringence is $\gamma-a$=0·098, and $\gamma-\beta$=0·040. A. de Schulten gave 6·241 for the sp. gr. at 15°. When heated, laurionite decrepitates; according to A. de Schulten, the artificial salt is not changed at 100°, but at dull redness, it loses all its water and melts. G. vom Rath said laurionite loses all its water at 142°. M. Pleissner said that the sat. aq. soln. contains 99 mgrms. of salt per litre, and the sp. conductivity is 0·0₄682. A. de Schulten said that the salt is attacked very slowly by cold water, and that it rapidly becomes opaque in boiling water. G. André found that the soln. in boiling soda-lye has a yellow colour. A. de Schulten found that artificial laurionite in the presence of water is attacked by carbon dioxide first forming phosgenite, and then cerussite. A. Braley studied the blowpipe reactions of laurionite.

M. Websky reported a colourless or greenish mineral occurring as an incrustation and in crevices in a gangue of galena, etc., from Mina Beatriz, Sierra Gorda, Atacama, about 20 miles from Caracoles, Chili. The mineral was named **caracolite**. Its composition corresponds with **sodium lead hydroxychlorosulphate**, $2Pb(OH)Cl.Na_2SO_4$, and it was analyzed by F. Sandberger, and L. Fletcher. The crystals have the form of a hexagonal pyramid with base and prism, but they are supposed to be pseudohexagonal with trillings, like aragonite. The crystals are supposed to be rhombic, and M. Websky gives for the axial ratios $a : b : c$=0·5843 : 1 : 0·4213. The sp. gr. is 4·5. Water extracts sodium sulphate, and the aq. extract of the mineral, on evaporation, yields sodium chloride, etc.

G. F. H. Smith obtained from the lead slags of Laurion, monoclinic crystals of a mineral with the same chemical composition as laurionite; and, accordingly, the mineral was called **paralaurionite**. The crystals were found to be identical with those of *ein neues Bleioxychlorid* obtained by A. Arzruni from the San Rafael mine in Sierra Gorda, Chili, and called *rafaelite*—but for which no quantitative analysis has been made. The monoclinic crystals have the axial ratios $a : b : c$ =2·7036 : 1 : 1·8019, and β=62° 47′. The crystals may be tabular or prismatic; and they usually appear pseudorhombic on account of twinning on the (100)-plane. The cleavage on the (001)-plane is perfect. The optic figure seen through the (100)-plane is complex owing to the overlapping of two plates in the twin position; in this respect, paralaurionite is easily distinguished from the dimorphous mineral laurionite which shows no such figure, and fiedlerite in which the figure is not central. Paralaurionite is white; rafaelite was coloured violet-red, and exhibited a strong pleochroism. The crystals were also examined by A. Lacroix and A. de Schulten. The sp. gr. of paralaurionite given by G. F. H. Smith is 6·05 at 15°; the refractive index for Na-light is β=2·1463; and the water is given off at 180°. According to C. A. Ktenas, a comparison of the twinning, corrosion figures, and optical properties of crystals of laurionite and paralaurionite is in agreement with the hypothesis that the rhombic crystals of laurionite are formed by submicroscopic twinning lamellæ of monoclinic paralaurionite. The two minerals have similar chemical properties.

The lead mines of the Mendip Hills, Somersetshire, are thought to have been worked from pre-Roman times, and descriptions of the lead minerals collected by J. Woodward, P. Rashleigh, and A. F. Cronstedt enabled L. J. Spencer and E. D. Mountain to identify the mineral which was later on called **mendipite**. This mineral was examined by J. J. Berzelius in 1823, and shown to be **lead dioxydichloride**, $2PbO.PbCl_2$. He called it *saltsydradt Bly*, *i.e. Salzsaures Blei*. F. S. Beudant confused it with phosgenite and called it *kerasine* or *cerasite;* A. Breithaupt called it *Chlorspath* ; W. Haidinger, *peritomous lead-baryte* ; A. Lévy, *berzelite* ; E. F. Glocker, *mendipite* ; and P. A. Dufrénoy, *churchillite.* Analyses were reported by C. F. Rammelsberg, R. Rhodius, C. Schnabel, and L. J. Spencer and E. D. Mountain, in addition to those by J. J. Berzelius. P. Groth represented the constitution Cl–Pb–O–Pb–O–Pb–Cl. The mineral has been also reported from the Kunibert Mine near Brilon, Westphalia, by R. Rhodius, and C. Schnabel ; and from the Altai Mountains, Siberia, by P. P. Pilipenko. Mendipite has been synthesized by A. Ditte, G. André, and R. Ruer. The conditions of equilibrium of lead dioxydichloride are shown in R. Ruer's diagram, Fig. 93 ; and it is also formed when the oxydichloride is heated to 524°. A. Ditte made it by gradually adding potassium hydroxide to lead chloride suspended in water, constantly agitated, until the liquid has an alkaline reaction. The product was washed with water. G. André employed an analogous process. A. Ditte also made it by shaking lead hydroxide with enough of a soln. of potassium chloride to give an alkaline reaction. The crystals of mendipite are colourless or tinged pale yellow, red, or blue. They occur in fibrous or columnar masses, often radiated. R. Ruer's preparation was in silky, yellowish-brown needles. The crystals belong to the rhombic system, and, according to W. H. Miller, they have the axial ratios $a : b : c = 0.8115 : 1 : —$; or, according to L. J. Spencer and E. D. Mountain, $0.8002 : 1 : —$. The crystals have also been examined by W. Haidinger, J. J. Berzelius, A. Lévy, L. Fletcher, E. S. Larsen, A. Breithaupt, J. F. L. Hausmann. The (110)-cleavage is perfect ; and the (100)- and (010)-cleavages, less perfect. The cleavage angle is from 77° 19' (L. Fletcher) to $77\frac{1}{2}°$ (J. J. Berzelius). E. S. Larsen found the optic axial angle $2V =$ nearly 90° ; and the indices of refraction $\alpha = 2.24$, $\beta = 2.27$, and $\gamma = 2.31$; the dispersion and birefringence are high. W. Haidinger gave 7.077 for the sp. gr. ; A. Breithaupt, 7.377–7.400 ; R. Rhodius, 7.0 ; and L. J. Spencer and E. D. Mountain, 7.240 at 16.2°/4°. R. Ruer gave 639° for the m.p. of the mineral, and this is not attended by decomposition. According to L. J. Spencer and E. D. Mountain, when heated in a bulb tube, mendipite becomes yellow, decrepitating violently, and splitting up into dark yellow fibres ; before melting, a cloud of lead chloride vapour begins to fill the bulb, and condenses on the side of the tube. The fibres then melt to a yellow liquid (lead oxide) which spreads over the surface of the bulb, and the sublimate on further heating furnishes yellow drops (lead chloride). G. André gave 4.62 Cals. for the heat of formation from anhydrous lead oxide and chloride ; and 19.98 Cals. for the heat of soln. in hydrochloric acid sat. with lead chloride. The salt acquires a reddish-brown surface coloration when exposed to light. According to A. Ditte, if potash-lye be slowly added to lead dioxydichloride, suspended in water, about 110 grms. of the salt dissolve in a litre of liquid at 19°, and the soln. acquires a yellowish colour, forming potassium chloride and lead oxide. The mineral readily dissolves in nitric acid. A. Braley studied the blowpipe reactions of mendipite.

L. Fletcher found a colourless mineral resembling mendipite sparingly associated with the anglesite at the Mina Beatriz, Sierra Gorda, Atacama ; and he named it daviesite— after T. Davies. The minute prismatic crystals are sometimes striated horizontally ; they belong to the rhombic system, and have the axial ratios $a : b : c = 0.7940 : 1 : 0.4777$. The optical character is positive. No cleavage was observed. The mineral is lead oxychloride, but analyses have not been made. Meanwhile it is thought to be a form of mendipite from which it differs in cleavage and in speed of dissolution in nitric acid. Daviesite remains unchanged after being 8 weeks in contact with cold water, and also after being a short time in hot water. It is rapidly attacked by dil. nitric and sulphuric acids. W. H. Twelvetrees reported a lead oxychloride from Zeehan, Tasmania, which he named *petterdite*—after W. F. Petterd—but C. Anderson showed that it is probably an impure mimetesite.

J. W. Döbereiner obtained a yellow substance by fusing a mixture of a mol of lead chloride with three mols of lead oxide ; and he also obtained a similar product by heating one of the hydrated forms indicated below. L. N. Vauquelin, and J. Wood and J. L. Borden also obtained it from the hydrated forms. M Pleissner, however, questioned whether the product obtained by dehydration is really a compound ; and R. Ruer observed no evidence of **lead trioxydichloride**, $3PbO.PbCl_2$, in his study of the equilibrium diagram, Fig. 93 ; and he regarded the alleged compound as a mixture of lead dioxydichloride and tetroxydichloride. G. André claimed to have made this compound by adding potassium hydroxide to a soln. containing the calculated quantity of lead chloride, and heating the washed product at 100°. He added that the heat of formation from the anhydrous oxide and chloride is 5·30 Cals., and that the heat of soln. in hydrochloric acid sat. with lead chloride is 31·60 Cals. The yellowish-green, scaly mass is sometimes called *J. Turner's yellow—vide infra.* **Tetrahydrated lead trioxydichloride**, $3PbO.PbCl_2$. $4H_2O$, was obtained by J. J. Berzelius by treating a soln. of lead chloride with alkali hydroxide ; G. André used aq. ammonia, and said that crystals are not produced when the precipitate is heated for a day with water in a sealed tube at 250°. J. J. Berzelius also made it by treating a soln. of lead acetate with sodium chloride ; and C. W. Scheele, by decomposing a soln. of sodium chloride with lead monoxide. According to L. N. Vauquelin, one part of sodium chloride requires 7 parts of powdered lead oxide. When the mixture is worked up with water into a thick pulp, it turns white and thickens by the swelling of the lead oxide ; consequently, it is necessary to add more water and work up the mixture again. After standing 4 days, the mixture is diluted with water, and the soln. filtered. The filtrate contains sodium hydroxide, and a little lead chloride, but no sodium chloride. According to E. F. Anthon, the sodium chloride is but half decomposed even when ten times its weight of lead oxide is used, and the mixture frequently agitated for 12 days. The manufacture of sodium hydroxide by this reaction has been previously discussed (2. 20, 11) ; and the reaction was examined by F. R. Curaudau, F. M. Bachet, R. C. Clapham, J. Morrison, etc. According to G. Austerweil, the reaction is reversible : $2NaCl+4PbO+H_2O \rightleftharpoons 2NaOH+3PbO.PbCl_2$, and the equilibrium constant at 18° is 0·7 for $2N$-NaCl, and 0·5 for $5N$-NaCl. L. N. Vauquelin said that when the white flocculent mass is heated, it loses 7 per cent. of water ; that acids dissolve out the lead oxide leaving behind the chloride ; and that the compound is insoluble in water, but slightly soluble in a soln. of sodium hydroxide. E. Berl and G. Austerweil showed that at 18°, a litre of water dissolves 0·059 millimol ; at 48°, 0·14 millimol ; and at 74°, 0·74 millimol. It is less soluble in a soln. of sodium chloride than is lead sulphide.

G. André said that if the precipitate obtained by adding aq. ammonia to a soln. of lead chloride be dried between bibulous paper, **trihydrated lead trioxydichloride**, $3PbO.PbCl_2.3H_2O$, is formed ; and he obtained the same hydrate by treating lead oxychloride with an excess of water and drying the washed precipitate at 100°. J. Wood and J. L. Borden reported **monohydrated lead trioxydichloride**, $3PbO.PbCl_2.H_2O$, to be formed by heating lead chloride with aq. ammonia on a water-bath for 12 hrs. ; A. Voigt, by boiling lead oxide with a conc. soln. of magnesium chloride for a long time, and drying the washed product at 100° ; and M. Pleissner, by shaking a mixture of 6·2 grms. of finely divided lead hydroxide, $3PbO.H_2O$, 2·5 grms. of lead chloride, and 500 c.c. of water, for 5 days at 18°, and drying the washed product over soda-lime. The light yellow powder was found by A. Voigt to lose water at 130°, and, according to M. Pleissner, is anhydrous at 250°, and then takes up oxygen, forming a canary-yellow mass which melts at a red heat. A. Voigt said that the monohydrate is very sparingly soluble in hot water, and M. Pleissner said that a litre of water at 18° dissolves 25 mgrms. of the salt, and that the soln. has a sp. conductivity of $0·0_419$. A. Voigt found that the salt is slightly soluble in aq. ammonia, and is readily dissolved by mineral acids, and acetic acid, particularly if heated. D. Strömholm reported a pale yellow voluminous precipitate of **hemihydrated lead trioxydichloride**, $3PbO.PbCl_2.\frac{1}{2}H_2O$, consisting of small needles, to be formed by adding conc. aq. ammonia to a soln. of lead chloride until the liquid is about $0·61N$ with respect to ammonia, and $0·18N$ with respect to chlorine.

R. Ruer obtained yellow, tabular crystals of **lead tetroxydichloride,** $4PbO.PbCl_2$, from a fused mixture of the components, Fig. 93 ; the salt melts at 711°. E. Berl and G. Austerweil prepared white coloured **dihydrated lead tetroxydichloride,** $4PbO.PbCl_2.2H_2O$, from a mixture of lead oxide, and a soln. of sodium chloride below normal conc. The reaction is reversible, and the equilibrium constant at 18° is 1 ; at 48°, 0·75 ; and at 74°, 0·6. The product is less soluble than lead sulphide in a soln. of sodium chloride, and $2N$-NaCl converts the tetroxydichloride into the trioxydichloride. Lime-water in excess converts the salt into lead monoxide. J. W. Döbereiner reported *lead pentoxydichloride,* $5PbO.PbCl_2$, to be formed by melting the constituents in the right proportions, but R. Ruer obtained no evidence of the formation of such a compound, Fig. 93. J. Kersten said that *pentahydrated lead pentoxydichloride,* $5PbO.PbCl_2.5H_2O$, is produced by the action of a boiling dil. soln. of alkali chloride on lead hydroxide, $3PbO.H_2O$, but the individuality of the product requires confirmation.

R. C. Wells and E. S. Larsen obtained honey-yellow, slabby masses of a mineral from Loretto, Tennessee, which they called **lorettoite.** Its composition corresponded with **lead hexoxydichloride,** $6PbO.PbCl_2$, or $13PbO.2PbCl_2$. There is no evidence of the formation of such a compound on the fusibility curve. The mineral has an adamantine lustre, and a bladed structure, with a perfect cleavage along the blades. The crystals are probably tetragonal—E. Rimann said rhombic. The substance is optically uniaxial and negative. The sp. gr. 7·39 is possibly low because small gas cavities are present ; these are arranged along planes at right angles, and impart a cloudiness to the material. The hardness is 3 ; and the indices of refraction with Li-light are $\omega=2·40$, and $\epsilon=2·37$. The mineral is readily soluble in acids. D. Strömholm reported **dihydrated lead hexoxydichloride,** $6PbO.PbCl_2.2H_2O$, to be slowly formed in fine microscopic needles when fresh lead hydroxide is kept in contact with $0·05N$-KCl ; or when hemihydrated lead trioxydichloride is kept in contact with $0·095N$-NaOH. The pigment called *Turner's yellow, Cassel's yellow, Veronese yellow,* or *Mineral yellow* is obtained by melting a mixture of one part of ammonium chloride with 10 parts of lead monoxide, red-lead, or white-lead. Part of the ammonium chloride is sublimed. The yellow crystalline mass has approximately the composition *lead heptoxydichloride,* $7PbO.PbCl_2$; but there is no evidence that this represents a chemical individual. P. Berthier obtained a similar yellow pigment by using the chlorides of sodium, barium, or calcium. H. Corti reported a mineral of approximately this composition from Las Coronas, Argentine. E. Rimann represented the mineral *chubutite* by $14PbO.2PbCl_2$, or $Pb_8O_7Cl_2$, *lead heptoxydichloride.* He suggested that the oxychlorides form a continuous series of mixed crystals, and that the dimorphism of lead monoxide persists in the mixed crystals of the oxychlorides, although the dimorphism has not been observed.

H. J. Brooke reported a sky-blue mineral, supposed to be from Sonora, Mexico, which was named **percylite**—after J. Percy. The composition corresponded with hydrated **lead copper hydroxychloride,** $PbCu(OH)_2Cl_2$, or $PbCl.PbO.CuCl.CuO.nH_2O$, or according to P. Groth, $Pb(OH)Cl.Cu(OH)Cl$. N. S. Maskelyne and W. Flight reported specimens from South Africa ; J. R. Gregory, and A. Raimondi, samples from Cerro de Challacollo, Tarapaca, Chili, and Mina San Rafael, Galeria al Norte, Bolivia ; and L. Fletcher, and M. Websky, samples from Mina Beatriz, Sierra Gorda, Atamaca, Chili. H. Schulze reported a sample from Challacollo, Chili, containing some silver chloride—*silver percylite—vide* boleite. The cubic or dodecahedral crystals of percylite are pseudocubic and belong to the tetragonal system ; the hardness is $2\frac{1}{2}$. C. Friedel obtained it by the action of a soln. of cupric chloride on lead hydroxide for a few weeks. G. Friedel reported dark blue crystals of a mineral accompanying boleite and pseudoboleite in the copper deposits of Boleo, Lower California, and he called it **cumengite**—after E. Cumenge. The analysis corresponded with $4PbCl_2.4CuO.5H_2O$, or **pentahydrated lead copper tetroxychloride.** The tetragonal crystals have the axial ratio $a:c=1:1·625$; A. Hadding found 1 : 1·6186 to 1·7011. According to G. Friedel, the (101)-cleavage is very good, the (110) is poor. The sp. gr. is 4·67 at 18·7° ; A. Hadding gave 4·77. G. Friedel found that the refractive indices are ω=2·026, and ϵ=1·965 ; the birefringence $\omega - \epsilon$=0·061. A. Hadding gave ω=2·041 and ϵ=1·926 for green light with λ=510$\mu\mu$. The optical character is negative. The mineral called **pseudoboleite,** found by G. Friedel in the same locality as cumengite, has a composition corresponding with **hexahydrated lead copper tetroxydecachloride,** $5PbCl_2.4CuO.6H_2O$. The tetragonal crystals are indigo blue, and have the axial ratio $a : c$=1 : 2·023. It frequently occurs as a parallel growth on boleite, or as crystalline masses on the different pseudocubic faces of boleite, leaving re-entrant angles along the cubic edges, or it may completely envelop the edges. The (001)- and (101)- cleavages are perfect. The optical character is negative ; and the birefringence is $\omega - \epsilon$ =0·032. G. Friedel also found a mineral which he called **boleite** associated with the cumengite and pseudoboleite of Boleo, Lower California. The mineral was also examined by A. Lacroix, F. E. Mallard, and C. Friedel. H. Schulze reported samples from Tarapaca and Challacollo ; and A. Liversidge, from Broken Hill, New South Wales. The composition of the Prussian-blue crystals is $PbCl_2.3AgCl.8CuO.9H_2O$, or **enneahydrated copper silver lead octoxyhenacosichloride.** The blue crystals were analyzed by G. Friedel, F. E. Mallard, E. Cumenge, and A. Liversidge. C. Friedel synthesized boleite by the prolonged action of a soln. of cupric chloride on lead hydroxide. The crystals are in cubes ; each crystal being made up of three individuals each with its c-axis parallel to a cubic axis. The individuals are tetragonal, with the axial ratio $a : c$=1 : 3·996. The (001)-cleavage is perfect, the (100)-cleavage is poor, and the (101)-cleavage is good. The optical character is negative. The sp. gr. is 5·054 at 18·78° ; the hardness is 3 ; and the birefringence 0·020. The thin sections of the crystals have an isotropic interior and a birefringent border. A. Hadding found that the outer layers are richer in lead and the interior richer in silver. He believed that the mineral is truly cubic, and that the variation in the sp. gr. of different crystals 4·802–5·155, and in the refractive indices of different parts of the same crystals, 2·081–2·087, is due to variations in composition. The X-radiogram of boleite points to the cubic system. G. Friedel said that the mineral is not attacked by water, but is soluble in nitric acid. L. J. Spencer and E. D. Mountain reported green, blade-like crystals of hydrated **copper lead trioxydichloride,** $3PbO.CuCl_2.H_2O$, stabbing the mendipite from the Mendip Hills. They called it **chloroxiphite**—from $\chi\lambda\omega\rho os$, green ; $\xi i\phi os$, a blade or sword. The colour is dull olive-green, or pistachio-green, not unlike epidote ; and the habit, degree of symmetry, cleavage, and pleochroism of the crystals is not unlike that of epidote. The cleavage parallel to (100) is poor, that parallel to (001) is perfect. The crystals and cleavage-flakes lying on the (001)-face are bright emerald-green parallel to the length, and yellowish-brown across blades. The optic axial angle is about 80°. The crystals are monoclinic with the β-angle 62$\frac{3}{4}$°. The index of refraction and birefringence are high. The sp. gr. is 6·763 at 16·2°/4° ; and the hardness 2$\frac{1}{2}$. No change occurs when the mineral is heated to 100°, but at 250°, all the water is expelled. The colour of the mineral is then black. Chloroxiphite readily dissolves in nitric acid ; and weathers into hydrocerussite. L. J. Spencer and E. D. Mountain found both a **lead copper tetrahydroxydichloride,** $2Pb(OH)_2.CuCl_2$, which they called **diaboleite**—from $\delta\iota\acute{a}$, apart ; and boleite : in sky-blue crystals embedded in the mendipite of the Mendip Hills. The axial ratio of the tetragonal crystal is $a : c$=1 : 0·95. The sp. gr. is 6·412 at 17·6°/4°, and the hardness 2$\frac{1}{2}$. The refractive index is 1·98 ; and the crystals are dichroic, ω being deep-blue, and ϵ pale-blue or colourless. The mineral is quite soluble in nitric acid. All the water is expelled at 250°. Diaboleite weathers into hydrocerussite.

According to G. André, if a conc. soln. of calcium chloride is boiled with an excess of lead oxide, care being taken to prevent evaporation, and the liquid is filtered, the filtrate deposits an abundant precipitate, which after washing with alcohol and drying corresponds with **calcium lead trioxydichloride,** $CaCl_2.CaO.2PbO.4H_2O$.

When boiled with water it becomes yellow. If the water is left out of account, this compound may be regarded as crystallized calcium oxychloride in which 2 mols. of calcium oxide have been replaced by 2 mols. of lead oxide. When the mother-liquor, which is slightly alkaline, is poured into a large excess of cold water, the compound $CaCl_2.3PbO.2H_2O$ is obtained as an amorphous white precipitate. A soln. of barium chloride when treated in a similar manner yields small slender needles which seem to be a **barium lead oxychloride**, but they are decomposed immediately by water and yield lead oxychloride. Strontium chloride yields small, distinct, brilliant crystals which when washed with alcohol and dried correspond with **strontium lead dioxydichloride**, $SrCl_2.2PbO.5H_2O$. If the mother-liquor is poured into excess of water the compound $PbCl_2.3PbO.3H_2O$ is precipitated. Lead oxide is dissolved by either a hot or a cold soln. of magnesium chloride, but the filtered liquid deposits no precipitate, and only a very slight precipitate is obtained when the soln. is poured into an excess of water.

REFERENCES.

[1] J. W. Döbereiner, *Schweigger's Journ.*, 17. 255, 1816 ; F. M. Bachet, *Brit. Pat. No.* 939, 1869 ; 2401, 1870 ; *French Pat. No.* 98983, 1870 ; S. Ganelin, *ib.*, 255903, 1896 ; *Monit. Scient.*, (4), 11. 6, 1897 ; *U.S. Pat. No.* 558942, 1896 ; E. Repossi, *Rend. Accad. Lincei*, (5), 15. i, 511, 1906 ; R. Brandes, *Liebig's Ann.*, 10. 273, 1834 ; R. Rhodius, *ib.*, 62. 373, 1847 ; R. P. Greg and W. G. Lettsom, *Manual of the Mineralogy of Great Britain and Ireland*, London, 420, 1858 ; R. P. Greg, *Phil. Mag.*, (4), 2. 120, 1851 ; H. J. Brooke, *ib.*, (3), 36. 131, 1850 ; W. H. Miller, *ib.*, (4), 2. 120, 1851 ; *Introduction to Mineralogy*, London, 620, 1852 ; H. Corti, *Zeit. angew. Chem.*, 32. 384, 1919 ; *Anal. Soc. Quim. Argentina*, 6. 65, 1918 ; A. des Cloizeaux, *Ann. Mines*, (5), 11. 306, 1857 ; K. Treis, *Kristallographische und thermische Untersuchungen von Systemen aus Bleichlorid und Chloriden einwertiger Metalle*, Berlin, 1914 ; *Neues Jahrb. Min. B.B.*, 37. 770, 1914 ; C. F. Rammelsberg, *Handbuch der Mineralchemie*, Leipzig, 2. 199, 1875 ; *Pogg. Ann.*, 71. 516, 1847 ; 85. 141, 1852 ; J. J. Berzelius, *ib.*, 1. 272, 1824 ; *Vet. Akad. Handl. Stockholm*, 184, 1823 ; *Edin. Journ. Science*, 1. 379, 1824 ; *Ann. Phil.*, 24. 154, 1824 ; *Pogg. Ann.*, 1. 272, 1824 ; C. Schnabel, *ib.*, 71. 516, 1847 ; P. P. Pilipenko, *Bull. Imp. Univ. Tomsk*, 63, 1915 ; A. Lévy, *Ann. Phil.*, 24. 243, 1824 ; *Description d'une collection de minéraux formée par H. Heuland*, Londres, 2. 448, 1837 ; J. Woodward, *An Attempt towards a Nature History of the Fossils of England in a Catalogue of the English Fossils in the Collection of J. Woodward*, London, 1729 ; P. Rashleigh, *Specimens of British Minerals*, London, 1797 ; A. F. Cronstedt, *Mineralogie*, Stockholm, 1758 ; A. Breithaupt, *Vollständige Charakteristik des Mineral-systems*, Dresden, 61, 1832 ; F. S. Beudant, *Traité élémentaire de minéralogie*, Paris, 2. 502, 1832 ; J. F. L. Hausmann, *Handbuch der Mineralogie*, Göttingen, 1467, 1847 ; E. F. Glocker, *Handbuch der Mineralogie*, Nürnberg, 604, 1839 ; W. Haidinger, *Treatise on Mineralogy*, Edinburgh, 2. 151, 1825 ; *Edin. Journ. Science*, 1. 379, 1824 ; P. A. Dufrénoy, *Traité de minéralogie*, Paris, 1856 ; E. S. Larsen, *Bull. U.S. Geol. Sur.*, 679, 1921 ; M. Websky, *Sitzber. Akad. Berlin*, 1045, 1886 ; F. Sandberger, *Neues Jahrb. Min.*, ii, 75, 1887 ; A. Hadding, *Geol. För. Förh. Stockholm*, 41. 175, 1919 ; R. C. Clapham, *Chem. News*, 21. 148, 1870 ; *Tyneside Nat. Field Club*, 4. 332, 1808 ; E. F. Anthon, *Repert. Pharm.*, 77. 105, 1837 ; N. S. Maskelyne and W. Flight, *Journ. Chem. Soc.*, 25. 1051, 1872 ; J. Morrison, *Journ. Soc. Chem. Ind.*, 9. 160, 1890 ; K. Keilhack, *Zeit. deut. geol. Ges.*, 50. 133. 1898 ; A. Voigt, *Chem. Ztg.*, 13. 695, 1889 ; H. Schulze, *ib.*, 16. 1953, 1892 ; H. L. Pattinson, *Chem. Gaz.*, 7. 366, 1849 ; *Brit. Pat. Nos.* 8020, 1839 ; 12479, 1849 ; 14104, 1852 ; R. Rhodius, *Liebig's Ann.*, 62. 373, 1847 ; J. Wood and J. L. Borden, *Journ. Amer. Chem. Soc.*, 6. 218, 1884 ; G. A. Kenngott, *Sitzber. Akad. Wien*, 12. 281, 1854 ; *Mineralogische Notizen*, Wien, 11, 1854 ; *Uebersichte der Resultate mineralogischer Forschungen*, Wien, 40, 1852 ; 49, 1854 ; *Sitzber. Akad. Wien*, 12. 295, 1854 ; G. Austerweil, *Zur Kenntnis des Scheelschen Aetznutronprozesses*, Zürich, 1906 ; E. Berl amd G. Austerweil, *Zeit. Elektrochem.*, 13. 167, 1907 ; J. Percy, *The Metallurgy of Lead*, London, 81, 1870 ; P. Berthier, *Traité des essais par la voie sèche*, Paris, 2. 685, 1834 ; R. C. Wells and E. S. Larsen, *Journ. Washington Acad.*, 6. 669, 1916 ; C. F. Cross and S. Sugiura, *Journ. Chem. Soc.*, 33. 407, 1878 ; W. H. Sodeau, *ib.*, 77. 717, 1900 ; L. N. Vauquelin, *Ann. Chir. Phys.*, (1), 32. 243, 1799 ; *Mém. L'Inst. Nat.*, 5. 171, 1799 ; R. Köchlin, *Ann. Hofmus. Wien*, 2. 185, 1887 ; A. Lacroix, *Bull. Mus. Hist. Nat.*, 39, 1895 ; *Compt. Rend.*, 123. 955, 1896 ; A. C. Becquerel, *ib.*, 34. 29, 1852 ; A. Lacroix and A. de Schulten, *ib.*, 123. 955, 1896 ; *Bull. Soc. Min.*, 31. 80, 1908 ; A. de Schulten, *ib.*, 20. 194, 1897 ; *Compt. Rend.*, 140. 315, 1905 ; V. Thomas, *ib.*, 126. 1352, 1898 ; *Bull. Soc. Chim.*, (3), 19. 493, 1898 ; C. A. Ktenas, *Bull. Soc. Min.*, 33. 173, 1910 ; G. Friedel, *ib.*, 29. 14, 1906 ; C. Friedel, *ib.*, 15. 96, 1892 ; 17. 6, 1894 ; A. A. de Gramont, *ib.*, 18. 359, 1895 ; F. E. Mallard, *ib.*, 16. 184, 1893 ; F. E. Mallard and E. Cumenge, *ib.*, 14. 283, 1891 ; *Compt. Rend.*, 113. 519, 1891 ; E. Cumenge, *ib.*, 116. 898, 1893 ; R. Ruer, *Zeit. anorg. Chem.*, 49. 365, 1906 ; D. Strömholm, *ib.*, 38. 455, 1904 ; H. Hof, *ib.*, 81. 41, 1913 ; W. Spring, *Ber.*, 18. 344, 1885 ; M. Pleissner, *Arb. Kaiser Ges. Amt.*, 26. 440, 1907 ; A. Wächter, *Journ. prakt. Chem.*, (1), 30. 321, 1843 ; *Liebig's Ann.*, 52. 233, 1844 ; J. W. Retgers, *Zeit. phys.*

Chem., **9**. 309, 1892 ; W. H. Twelvetrees, *Proc. Roy. Soc. Tasmania*, **51**, 1901 ; W. F. Petterd, *Catalogue of the Minerals of Tasmania*, Launceston, 58, 1896 ; 113, 1910 ; *Rep. Sec. Mines Tasmania*, **1**, 1900 ; 356, 1901 ; *Amer. Journ. Science*, (4), **14**. 466, 1902 ; C. Anderson, *Rec. Australasian Museum*, **6**. 137, 1906 ; A. Liversidge, *Proc. Roy. Soc. New South Wales*, **28**. 94, 1894 ; F. A. Genth, *Amer. Journ. Science*, (3), **44**. 260, 1892 ; W. E. Ford, *ib.*, (4), **43**. 493, 1917 ; (4), **47**. 446, 1919 ; H. L. Wells and W. R. Johnston, *ib.*, (3), **46**. 25, 1893 ; S. L. Penfield, *ib.*, (3), **48**. 114, 1894 ; L. Fletcher, *ib.*, (3), **38**. 250, 1889 ; *Min. Mag.*, **8**. 171, 1889 ; G. F. H. Smith, *ib.*, **12**. 107. 183, 1898 ; L. J. Spencer and E. D. Mountain, *ib.*, **20**. 67, 1923 ; J. R. Gregory, *ib.*, **2**. 251, 1878 ; *Amer. Journ. Science*, (3), **38**. 250, 1889 ; A. Raimondi, *Les Minéraux de Pérou*, Paris, 171, 1878 ; A. Braley, *Bull. Soc. Min.*, **46**. 54, 1923 ; G. vom Rath, *Ber. Niederrh. Ges. Bonn.*, 102, 149, 1887 ; *Neues Jahrb. Min.*, i, 388, 1889 ; *Zeit. Kryst.*, **17**. 105, 1890 ; A. Arzruni, C. N. Thaddéeff, and A. Danneberg, *ib.*, **31**. 229, 1899 ; **32**. 219, 1900 ; G. André, *Compt. Rend.*, **96**. 1502, 1883 ; **97**. 1302, 1883 ; **104**. 359, 1887 ; *Bull. Soc. Chim.*, (2), **40**. 16, 1883 ; *Ann. Chim. Phys.*, (6), **3**. 110, 1884 ; A. Ditte, *ib.*, (5), **28**. 131, 1883 ; *Compt. Rend.*, **94**. 1180, 1882 ; A. Mailhé, *ib.*, **134**. 233, 1902 ; *Bull. Soc. Chim.*, (3), **27**. 1902 ; *Ann. Chim. Phys.*, (7), **27**. 379, 1902 ; H. Buttgenbach, *Ann. Soc. Géol. Belg.*, **33**. ii, 1905 ; G. Cesaro, *Bull. Acad. Belg.*, 1198, 1904 ; C. Friedel, *Arch. Sciences Genève*, (3), **27**. 23, 1893 ; S. Ganelin, *Brit. Pat. No.* 8981, 1896 ; G. Lunge and C. H. M. Lyte, *ib.*, 13656, 1893 ; W. E. Blenkinsop and C. H. M. Lyte, *ib.*, 11926, 1888 ; F. W. Emerson, *ib.*, 447, 1859 ; K. G. Fiedler, *Reise durch alle Theile des Königreiches Griechenland*, Leipzig, **1**. 42, 1840 ; I. Domeyko, *Elementos de mineralojia*, Santiago, 318, 1879 ; W. P. Jervis, *Itesori sotterranei Italia*, Turin, **2**. 603, 1874 ; A. Scacchi, *Neues Jahrb. Min.*, ii, 136, 1888 ; *Atti Ist. Napoli*, (4), **1**. 5, 1888 ; F. Fouqué and A. M. Lévy, *Synthèse des minéraux des roches*, Paris, 362, 1882 ; C. W. G. Fuchs, *Die künstlich dargestellen Mineralien nach Roses System geordnet*, Haarlem, 102, 1872 ; P. Groth, *Die Mineralien Sammlung der Universität Strassburg*, Strassburg, 118, 1878 ; *Tabellarische Uebersicht der Mineralien*, Braunschweig, 54, 1898 ; G. Rose, *Das krystallochemische Mineral-system*, Leipzig, 69, 1852 ; R. Cappa, *Ann. Osserv. Ves.*, 65, 1859 ; *Compt. Rend.*, **50**. 955, 1860 ; F. Grünling, *Zeit. Kryst.*, **17**. 112, 646, 1890 ; V. Goldschmidt, *Index der Krystallformen der Mineralien*, Berlin, **2**. 292, 362, 1890 ; *Ann. Hofmus. Wien*, **2**. 83, 1887 ; E. Rimann, *Anal. Soc. Quin. Argentina*, **6**. 323, 1918 ; C. W. Scheele, *Crell's Ann.*, ii, 220, 1785 ; J. Turner, *Brit. Pat. No.* 1281, 1781 ; F. R. Curaudau, *Journ. Phys.*, **41**. 108, 1792 ; *Journ. Mines*, **1**. 44, 1794 ; C. H. le Lièvre, B. Pelletier, J. d'Arcet, and A. Giroud, *ib.*, **1**. 29, 1794 ; W. Biltz, *Zeit. anorg. Chem.*, **115**. 241, 1921 ; J. Kersten, *German Pat.*, *D.R.P.* 255688, 1911.

§ 26. Lead Bromides

H. G. Denham [1] prepared **lead subbromide,** or **lead monobromide,** PbBr, by the action of the vap. of ethyl bromide at 261° on lead hemioxide, Pb_2O. The grey product is oxidized very slowly by dry air, but more rapidly by moist air. When heated for 2 hrs. at 280° in vacuo, it forms normal lead dibromide and lead. Water at 25° dissolves 0·4 milliequivalent per litre. Bromine-water acts slowly on the subbromide at ordinary temp., more rapidly at 50°, forming the white normal bromide. Nitric acid and acetic acid decompose it at once. forming lead and lead dibromide.

Normal **lead bromide,** $PbBr_2$, is formed by the action of bromine on lead ; and, as shown by J. A. Wilkinson,[2] a feeble luminosity occurs when lead is warmed in the vapour of bromine. J. Nicklès, and T. Hjortdahl found that bromine reacts slowly with lead in the presence of alcohol, forming lead bromide. A. J. Balard prepared lead bromide by the action of hydrobromic acid on lead oxide. R. S. Norris employed this process. If bromine-water be used, lead dioxide is produced. A. J. Balard also made this salt by treating a soln. of a lead salt with one of potassium bromide ; hydrobromic acid and other soluble bromides can be used as the precipitant. This method was employed by C. L. von Ende, and G. P. Baxter and co-workers. The latter treated an aq. soln. of purified lead nitrate with an excess of hydrobromic acid, drained the product on a centrifuge, and dissolved the washed product in hot conc. hydrobromic acid. The soln. was diluted with water, and the precipitate washed by decantation with ice-cold water, and dried on a centrifuge. This treatment was repeated a number of times, and the product dried in vacuo over fused potassium hydroxide. It was then melted in a current of hydrogen or nitrogen charged with the vap. of hydrogen bromide. E. H. Büchner and J. Kalff obtained no colloidal lead bromide by dropping a soluble bromide into a soln. of a lead salt.

A. Jeltekoff treated lead oxide or lead carbonate with a mixture of methylene bromide and water at 140°–150°. J. A. Wilkinson made lead bromide by the electrolysis of a soln. of potassium bromide using a lead anode. W. F. O. de Coninck and L. Arzalier obtained it by exposing an intimate mixture of lead oxide and ammonium bromide to a high press. M. Barre passed the vapour of sulphur dibromide over lead monoxide or red-lead at about 700°. The lead oxide should be in a thin layer or the crust of lead bromide will prevent access of the sulphur bromide to the oxide below. V. Lenher showed that lead sulphide dissolves readily in conc. hydrobromic acid; hydrogen sulphide is evolved, and lead bromide is formed; M. Berthelot, that lead iodide is converted by bromine into lead bromide; and A. Ditte, that lead sulphate dissolves in a soln. of potassium bromide, forming lead bromide, and as the potassium sulphate accumulates in the liquid, the complex salt $K_2Pb(SO_4)_2$ is formed. Hydrobromic acid was also found by A. Ditte to decompose lead sulphate in the reversible reaction, $PbSO_4+2HBr \rightleftharpoons PbBr_2+H_2SO_4$. W. C. Ebaugh observed that lead arsenate, $Pb_3(AsO_4)_2$, is gradually converted into lead bromide when heated in a stream of air charged with the vapour of hydrobromic acid.

The physical properties of lead bromide.—Lead bromide occurs as a white crystalline powder. O. Lehmann [3] found that when soln. of lead nitrate and potassium bromide are mixed, globular masses are first formed, then acicular needles, and finally these pass into six-sided plates. C. Löwig found that a hot aq. soln., on cooling, furnishes needle-like **crystals**. According to T. Hjortdahl, the action of alcoholic bromine on lead furnishes rhombic, bipyramidal crystals with the axial ratios $a:b:c=0.5883:1:1.1833$. A. E. Nordenskjöld also obtained good crystals by slowly cooling hot aq. soln., and he found them to be isomorphous with those of lead chloride. The (001)-cleavage is perfect. W. Biltz studied what he called the lattice-energy of the crystals. C. J. B. Karsten found the **specific gravity** to be 6·6302; P. Kremers, 6·611 at 17·5°; F. W. Clarke, 6·572 at 19·2°; G. P. Baxter and F. L. Grover, 6·659; and G. P. Baxter and C. F. Hawkins, 6·676 at 0°; 6·669 at 25°; and 6·644 at 50°. R. Lorenz, H. Frei and A. Jabs gave for the sp. gr., D, of the molten bromide, at $\theta°$ between 600° and 800°, $D=6·175-0·00145\theta$; and R. Lorenz and W. Herz, 5·634 for the sp. gr. and 65·14 for the mol. vol. at the m.p. F. A. Henglein studied the mol. vol. D. M. Lichty gave for the sp. gr., D, of soln. of lead bromide sat. at the temp. named (*vide infra*):

	0°	15°	25°	35°	45°	55°	65°	80°	95°
D	1·00433	1·00530	1·00608	1·00598	1·00593	1·00455	1·00282	1·00003	0·99946

I. I. Saslawsky gave 0·97 for the ratio of the mol. vol. to the sum of the at. vols. of the constituent elements. S. Motylewsky found the **drop-weight** of the molten bromide to be 143° referred to that of water, 100, at 0°. R. Lorenz and H. T. Kalmus gave for the **viscosity**:

	372°	392°	412°	432°	452°	472°	492°
η	0·10190	0·08060	0·06970	0·06133	0·05384	0·04700	0·04073

G. P. Baxter and C. F. Hawkins gave for the cubical coeff. of **thermal expansion** between 0° and 25°, 0·00010; and between 25° and 50°, 0·00009. R. Lorenz and W. Herz found the coeff. of thermal expansion, a, of the liquid to be 0·000266, and $aT_m=0·172$ to be in accord with the factor obtained with related halides. H. V. Regnault found the **specific heat** between 16° and 98° to be 0·0533: and O. Erhardt, 0·0534 between 190° and 430°. O. H. Weber gave 0·0532 from 190° to 430°; 0·0709, 190° to 440°; 0·1099, 190° to 460°; and 0·2055, 190° to 480°. H. M. Goodwin and H. T. Kalmus found 0·0566 between 199° and 488°; and 0·0780 between 488° and 587°. W. M. Latimer and H. D. Hoenshel found the mol. ht. of lead bromide, per mean gram-atom, to be:

	−254·6°	−244·5°	−233·4°	−217·5°	−192·4°	−142·8°	−91·0°	1·8°	24·0°
C_p	1·22	2·12	3·15	4·33	5·05	5·70	6·00	6·33	6·34

H. Burschall gave 17·0 for the mol. ht. between —75° and —183°; and H. Schottky gave 18·97 for the mol. ht. at ordinary temp. J. Rosenthal showed that lead bromide becomes plastic below its **melting point.** A. J. Balard noted that when heated, lead bromide forms a red liquor, which, according to C. Löwig, freezes to a horn-like mass, and O. H. Weber said that the red liquid forms a pale yellow solid which finally becomes white. W. Ramsay and N. Eumorfopoulos gave 363° for the m.p.; C. Sandonnini, 366°; G. Sandonnini, 368°; R. Lorenz and M. G. Fox, 367°; K. Mönkemeyer, and F. Matthes, 370°; C. Tubandt and G. Eggert, 373°; G. Herrmann, 380°; A. Helfenstein, 480°; H. M. Goodwin and H. T. Kalmus, 488°; O. Ehrhardt, and O. H. Weber, 490°; and T. Carnelley, 499°. K. Mönkemeyer observed an undercooling of about 3°. The mol. **heat of fusion** given by H. O. Weber is 5·101 Cals.; by O. Ehrhardt, and V. Czepinsky, 4·515 Cals.; and by H. M. Goodwin and H. T. Kalmus, 3·65 Cals. T. Carnelley and W. C. Williams observed that lead bromide does not boil before the blowpipe flame; O. H. Weber gave 918°–920° for the **boiling point,** and A. Helfenstein, 921°. H. von Wartenberg and O. Bosse found the mol. **heat of vaporization** to be 28·180 Cals., and the **vapour pressure,** p, in atm., $\log p = 28180 \cdot 4\cdot571T + 5\cdot183$; and there is a slight dissociation during vaporization. R. Lorenz and W. Herz studied this subject. W. Braunbek discussed some relations between the sp. ht., m.p., and latent heat; and K. Jellinek and R. Uloth calculated values for the partial press. of the bromine at different temp. A. T. Waterman said that no lead ions are emitted when lead bromide is heated. J. Thomsen gave for the **heat of formation** from its elements—bromine liquid—64·456 Cals.; M. Berthelot gave 66·3 Cals.; M. de K. Thompson, 69·5 Cals.; H. Braune and F. Koref, 66·35 Cals.; P. Günther, 67·1 Cals.; C. Krahmer, and T. J. Webb, 65·58 Cals.; V. Czepinsky, 73·5 at 389°; 78·58 Cals. at 452°; 75·01 at 474°; and 89·5 Cals. at 700°; R. Lorenz, 76·18 Cals. between 450° and 650°; R. Lorenz and M. Katayama, 71·6 Cals. between 60° and 162°; and R. Lorenz and M. G. Fox, 71·5 Cals. between 498° and 600°. C. Krahmer gave for the heat of the reaction: $Pb + 2AgBr = 2Ag + PbBr_2 - 17\cdot962$ Cals. at 25°. O. H. Weber gave 69·5 Cals. for the **free energy** between 430° and 480°; and 68·3 Cals. between 490° and 800°; M. de K. Thompson calculated from the solubility data 62·3 Cals. at ordinary temp., and 64·7 Cals. from the e.m.f. of the cell $Pb : PbBr_2$. W. M. Latimer and H. D. Hoenshel gave 39·7 units for the **entropy** of lead bromide per mean gram-atom from —257·15° to 25°; this is in agreement with W. M. Latimer's value 39·2.

T. Hjortdahl said that the **index of refraction** of lead bromide is high. B. A. Dima found that with **ultra-violet light,** the electrical effect is higher than with lead chloride and less than with lead iodide. T. Volmer observed the emission of positively charged particles by lead bromide at relatively low press. W. Hampe showed that pulverulent and molten lead bromide are electrical conductors. C. Tubandt and G. Eggert found that the solid conducts electrolytically. J. Rosenthal showed that the **electrical conductivity** of pressed rods is, when cold, better with crystalline than with amorphous lead bromide. R. Ketzer found the sp. conductivity of pressed rods is $7\cdot4 \times 10^{-8}$ mho. G. Tammann and H. Bredmeier measured the conductivity of thin films of the bromide. G. Wiedemann, and A. Gockel observed polarization effects with these rods at 260°. C. Sandonnini gave 1·030 mhos for the sp. conductivity of the molten bromide. Observations were made by V. Czepinsky; and R. Lorenz and H. T. Kalmus found for the sp. conductivity at different temp.:

	372°	392°	412°	432°	452°	472°	492°
Sp. cond. . .	0·5397	0·6479	0·7202	0·7900	0·8570	0·9220	0·9835

W. Biltz and W. Klemm gave for the eq. conductivity $\lambda = 18\cdot9 + 0\cdot120(\theta - 373)$. L. Graetz said that the sp. resistance changes from 2700×10^8 (mercury unity) at 0 atm. press. to 327×10^8 at 4000 atm. press. C. Tubandt and G. Eggert found that during the electrolysis of the solid, the lead dendrites extend to the anode more rapidly than with lead chloride. W. Böttger found the conductivity of a soln. of lead bromide at $19.96°$ to be 0.03692, and he calculated that about 5 per cent. of non-ionized lead chloride to be present. C. L. Wagner found the sp. conductivity of $\frac{1}{256}N$-soln. to be 0.000505; of $\frac{1}{512}N$-soln., 0.000265; and of $\frac{1}{1024}N$-soln., 0.000139. L. C. von Ende calculated that a sat. aq. soln. at $25.20°$ contained 1.06 millimols per litre of $PbBr_2$ mols.; 9.19, of $PbBr'$-ions; 16.03, of $Pb\cdot\cdot$-ions, and 41.25, of Br'-ions. The ionization constant for the first stage of the ionization is 0.0003790, and for the second stage, 0.00002727. M. Katayama found the electromotive force of the cell $Pb\,|\,PbBr_2\,|\,C$ sat. with Br at $60°-162°$, to be $E=1.138+0.00065(60-\theta)$; O. H. Weber gave for the cell $Pb\,|\,PbBr_2\,|\,Br_2$ between $490°$ and $800°$, $E=1.0571-0.000500(\theta-490)$, and R. Lorenz and M. G. Fox gave between $367°$ and $460°$, $E=1.0945-0.000714(\theta-367)$; and A. Klein gave for the cell $Pb\,|\,PbCl_2\,|\,0.01N\text{-}KCl\,|\,0.01N\text{-}KBr\,|\,PbBr_2\,|\,Pb$, at $23.1°$, 0.0062 volt, and free energy 304.6 cals., and thermal value, 3560 cals. According to R. Lorenz, the e.m.f. of the cell $Zn\,|\,ZnBr_2\,|\,PbBr_2\,|\,Pb$, between $434°$ and $593°$, is equal to the difference between those of $Zn\,|\,ZnBr_2\,|\,Br_2$ and $Pb\,|\,PbBr_2\,|\,Br_2$. Observations were also made by C. C. Garrard, A. Helfenstein, and V. Czepinsky. P. Fischer measured the conductivity of mixtures of silver and lead bromides; and J. Thiele the thermoelectric force of the molten lead halides against metals. A. Lenert gave $K=4.89$ for the dielectric constant, and after melting and freezing, 18.78 owing to some decomposition. L. Grätz and O. Fromm gave 41.79 for $\lambda=100$; 42.94 for $\lambda=122.3$; 43.7 for $\lambda=130.4$; and 48.64 for $\lambda=180.0$. L. Ebert studied the dielectric polarization of the lead salts. S. Meyer gave for the magnetic susceptibility, -0.525×10^{-6}; and for the mol. magnetism, -0.095×10^{-6}.

The chemical properties of lead bromide.—According to G. P. Baxter and F. L. Grover,[4] lead bromide, after being melted in an atm. of hydrogen bromide, is neutral. R. S. Norris, H. L. Wells, and A. K. Sanyal and N. R. Dhar found that lead bromide becomes almost black when exposed to light owing to its decomposition into lead and bromine. The darkening occurs in dry oxygen or in dry hydrogen. If kept under water the lead bromide is darkened in a few days by light. F. de Carli studied the reducing action of hydrogen. A. J. Balard, A. L. Potilizin, R. Ketzer, and O. H. Weber said that when melted in air or oxygen lead bromide emits white fumes, and on cooling forms a yellow mass containing lead oxybromide; but, according to G. P. Baxter and F. L. Grover, and R. Ketzer, if melted in a neutral atm. or in bromine, decomposition does not occur. A. L. Potilizin, and W. C. Ebaugh found that lead bromide is partially reduced by hydrogen, and A. Jouniaux found the bromide to be less readily reduced than the chloride.

C. Löwig found lead bromide to be sparingly soluble in cold water, and readily soluble in hot water. C. Löwig showed that lead bromide dissolves more quickly in water containing hydrochloric, nitric, or acetic acid than in water alone. R. S. Norris said that the salt is completely soluble in water only on the addition of one or two drops of nitric acid; and G. P. Baxter and co-workers found that the salt which has been fused in an atm. of hydrogen bromide is hydrolyzed when it dissolves in water, furnishing some insoluble basic salt. G. André said that water dissolves about 5 grms. of the salt per litre at $11°$; G. P. Baxter and F. L. Grover, 9 grms. per litre at ordinary temp.; W. Böttger, 8.34 grms. per litre at $19.96°$; G. L. Wagner, 9.74 grms. per litre at $25°$; C. L. von Ende, 26.28 millimols per litre at $25.20°$. D. M. Lichty found the solubility in grams per 100 c.c. at different temp. to be:

0	15	25	35	45	55	65	80	95	100
S . 0.4554	0.7285	0.9701	1.3124	1.7259	2.1024	2.5161	3.2350	4.1767	4.5500

The solubility at $0°$ is greater than that of lead iodide at $100°$; and at $35°$, the solubility is about the same as that of lead chloride, and at $95°$, about one-third greater than that of the chloride. G. N. Lewis and T. B. Brighton computed the

solubility product to be 8.46×10^{-6}. H. Braune and F. Koref found lead bromide to be soluble in a soln. of **sodium hydroxide** ; and A. Ditte showed that lead bromide is decomposed by alkali hydroxide, forming an oxybromide. V. Zotier examined the catalytic effect of lead bromide on **hydrogen dioxide.**

V. Thomas showed that boiling **hydrochloric acid** transforms lead bromide into the chloride by a reversible reaction. G. C. Wittstein found the salt to be slowly soluble in a cold, and easily soluble in a warm soln. of **ammonium chloride ;** with 24 grms. of ammonium chloride in 500 c.c. of water, 4 grms. of lead bromide are all converted into lead chloride. W. Herz and M. Hellebrandt studied the solubility in soln. of **potassium, sodium, calcium, strontium, and barium chlorides.** G. André found that a $\frac{1}{2}N$-soln. of **hydrobromic acid** at 11° dissolves 1·25 grms. of lead bromide per litre, and when the sat. soln. is neutralized with lead oxide, 14 Cals. of heat are evolved. M. Berthelot found that a cold, sat. aq. soln. is precipitated by dil. $\frac{1}{2}N$-hydrobromic acid, but a potassium bromide soln. of the same conc. gives no precipitate. A. Ditte found that when hydrobromic acid is gradually added to a sat. aq. soln. of lead bromide at 10°, lead bromide is at first precipitated, some of the precipitate then redissolves so that 100 grms. of water, containing 72 grms. of HBr, dissolve 55·0 grms. of lead bromide per 100 grms. of solvent at 10°, and the soln. has a sp. gr. 2·06. When the conc. of the hydrobromic acid is very great, the lead bromide becomes very soluble, and by passing hydrogen bromide into a hot soln. of lead bromide in hydrobromic acid in the presence of an excess of lead bromide, the cooling soln. furnishes white, needle-like crystals of **hydrobromoplumbous acid,** $H_2Pb_5Br_{12}.10H_2O$, or $5PbBr_2.2HBr.10H_2O$. G. André, and H. Fonzes-Diacon showed that lead bromide dissolves in soln. of **ammonium bromide,** forming complex salts. C. H. Herty said that lead bromide is less soluble in a soln. of **potassium bromide** than lead iodide in one of potassium iodide ; and that lead bromide is less soluble in a dil. than in a conc. soln. of potassium bromide. The subject was studied by W. Herz and M. Hellebrandt, with **sodium bromide** as well as potassium bromide, and **calcium, strontium, and barium bromides.** C. L. von Ende said that the soln. in $\frac{1}{2}N$-KBr is perceptibly acid towards litmus. The solubility is augmented by the addition of nitric acid owing to the formation of complex nitratobromides. V. Thomas found that **hydriodic acid** rapidly transforms lead bromide into the iodide ; E. Field, that soln. of **ammonium iodide** or **potassium iodide** form complex bromoiodides ; and C. H. Herty showed that if the soln. of potassium iodide be sufficiently concentrated, $KPbI_3.2H_2O$ crystallizes from the soln.

A. J. Balard said that conc. **sulphuric acid** decomposes lead bromide with the evolution of hydrogen bromide. According to A. Ditte, a soln. of **zinc sulphate,** in contact with excess of lead bromide, gives bromide of zinc and sulphate of lead. At high temp., the amount of action is less than it is at low temp. The same effect is seen in the action of zinc bromide on lead sulphate. E. C. Franklin showed that lead bromide is moderately soluble in liquid **ammonia ;** and G. André observed no reaction when lead bromide and ammonia are heated in a sealed tube at 150°. W. Biltz found that with liquid ammonia, at $-78.5°$, **lead octamminobromide,** $PbBr_2.8NH_3$, is formed and that the heat of formation is 8·2 Cals., while the dissociation press. at $-52°$ is 27·3 mm. ; at $-29.4°$, 100 mm. ; at $-38°$, 202·3 mm. ; and at $-10.9°$, 700 mm. Between $-52°$ and 0°, the octammine furnishes **lead hemihenamminobromide,** $PbBr_2.5\frac{1}{2}NH_3$, with a heat of dissociation 9·0 Cals., and a dissociation press. of 17 mm. at $-45°$; 71·9 mm. at $-28°$; 100 mm. at $-23°$; and 432 mm. at 0°. Between 0° and $-28°$, the octammine forms **lead triammino-bromide,** $PbBr_2.3NH_3$, which has a dissociation press. of 23·3 mm. at $-28.7°$, 100 mm. at $-9°$, 188·3 mm. at 0°, and 596 mm. at 18·5°. At 34·4°, the octammine passes into **lead diamminobromide,** $PbBr_2.2NH_3$. F. Ephraim found that at ordinary temp., ammonia forms the diammine which has a vap. press. of 760 mm. at 70°, and a heat of dissociation of 12·16 Cals. W. Biltz gave 11·4 Cals., and said that the vap. press. is 57·8 mm. at 34·74°, 100 mm. at 42·5°, 235·3 mm. at 55·6°, and 311·4 mm. at 61·2°. At 110·6°, the diammine passes into **lead monammino-bromide**, $PbBr_2.NH_3$, with a heat of dissociation 15·6 Cals.; and vap. press. of 16·7 mm. at 110·6°, 76·9 mm. at 139·4°, 100 mm. at 144°, 152·7 mm. at 156·6°, and 459 mm. at 184·35°. C. L. Clark studied the secondary valencies of these ammines. V. Thomas observed very little reaction with **nitrogen peroxide** at ordinary temp., an oxybromide being very slowly formed. A. J. Balard said that **nitric acid** decomposes lead bromide with the evolution of bromine. C. L. von Ende found that $0.001N$-HNO_3 dissolves 39·11 millimols of lead bromide per litre; $0.01N$-HNO_3, 39·87 millimols; and $0.051N$-HNO_3, 42·56 millimols. G. C. Wittstein found lead bromide is slowly dissolved by a cold soln. of **ammonium nitrate**, and rapidly by a warm soln. C. L. von Ende found the solubility is greater in a $0.04N$-soln. of **potassium nitrate** containing $0.01N$-HNO_3 than in $0.051N$-HNO_3.

J. Spiller found lead bromide is not precipitated in the presence of **sodium citrate**. A. P. N. Franchimont found lead bromide to be insoluble in **benzene**; J. Nicklès, insoluble in **alcohol**, and in **ether**; A. Naumann, difficultly soluble in **acetone**; H. Lecher and A. Goebel, insoluble in **bromoform**, and also in **methyl acetate, ethyl acetate,** or **benzonitrile**; H. Mandal, soluble in **aniline**; H. Braune and F. Koref, soluble in an alkaline amyl alcohol soln. of **sodium tartrate**; and W. Goebbels, sparingly soluble in **pyridine**. G. W. Heise found the solid phase between −26° and 19° is $3C_5H_5N.PbBr_2$, and above that temp. $2C_5H_5N.PbBr_2$.

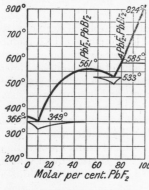

F. L. Shinn showed that with **ethylamine** an insoluble compound is formed. T. Carnelley and W. C. Williams found that **glass** is attacked when heated with lead bromide.

Mixed salts.—C. Sandonnini[5] measured the f.p. curves of mixtures of lead fluoride and bromide, and the results are summarized in Fig. 94. The system is analogous to that with lead chloride and fluoride. There is a eutectic at 349° and 7·5 molar per cent. of lead fluoride, and at about 561°, **lead bromofluoride**, PbBrF, is formed. With 75 molar per cent. of lead fluoride there is a second eutectic at 533°. There is a compound—**lead dibromocto-fluoride**, $Pb_5Br_2F_8$—formed at 585°, but it decomposes on melting. H. Fonzes-Diacon obtained the fluobromide. It is decomposed by an excess of water. F. Matthes, K. Mönkemeyer, and C. Sandonnini showed that the f.p. curve of mixtures of

Fig. 94.—Freezing-point Curves of Mixtures of Lead Fluoride and Bromide.

lead bromide and chloride is almost a straight line, Fig. 95, representing an unbroken series of mixed crystals. C. H. Herty and T. R. Boggs obtained isomorphous mixed crystals from aq. soln. The sensitiveness of the mixtures to light depends on the proportion of lead bromide present. G. Meyer found the partition law to be valid between mixed crystals and their soln. in the system $PbCl_2$-$PbBr_2$-H_2O; W. Würfel did not always find it so, owing to equilibrium not being attained. M. W. Iles found dendritic crystals of a **lead chlorobromide**, PbClBr, from the smelting furnaces at Leadville, and V. Thomas claimed to have made this compound by the action of bromine on lead chloroiodide. Boiling hydriodic acid converts it into lead iodide. V. Thomas also claimed to have made **lead trichlorobromide**, Pb_2Cl_3Br, or $3PbCl_2.PbBr_2$, from hot soln. of a gram of potassium bromide and 5 grms. of lead chloride in 250 c.c. of water, and by slowly cooling a soln. of 10 c.c. of a 10 per cent. soln. of potassium bromide and 5 grms. of lead chloride in 240 c.c. of water. The crystals are stable

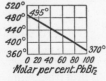

Fig. 95. — Freezing Curves of Mixtures of Lead Chloride and Bromide.

in light; decomposed by water; insoluble in cold alcohol; sparingly soluble in hot alcohol; and insoluble in chloroform. The bromine is not quantitatively displaced by nitrogen peroxide; nitrous acid attacks it vigorously at a low temp. The salt is insoluble in acetic acid; soluble in cold hydrochloric acid, and the hot soln. on cooling deposits lead chloride and the unchanged mixed salt. It is easily soluble in hydrobromic acid, forming lead bromide.

Complex salts.—G. André [6] reported a number of **ammonium bromoplumbites,** with $PbBr_2 : NH_4Br : H_2O$, as $2 : 14 : 3$, $1 : 6 : 1$, $7 : 12 : 7$, and $3 : 2 : 1$, but H. L. Wells and W. R. Johnston were unable to confirm a single one of these salts. They say that no mention is ever made of any of these products having been produced more than once, and it seems probable that whenever G. André obtained a crop of crystals or a precipitate, it was considered to be a new compound without regard to the number of different substances that it might contain. H. L. Wells and W. R. Johnston were also unable to prepare *ammonium tribromoplumbite,* NH_4PbBr_3. J. W. Retgers, and P. Gaubert studied the effect of lead bromide on the crystallization of ammonium bromide. H. Fonzes-Diacon obtained **ammonium pentabromodiplumbite,** $NH_4Pb_2Br_5$, by cooling a soln. of lead bromide in a hot 120 per cent. soln. of ammonium bromide. H. L. Wells and W. R. Johnston also obtained the same salt, using dil. soln. of the component salts. The salt forms square plates which, according to H. Fonzes-Diacon, resemble those of boric acid. The crystals darken a little on exposure to light, and do not lose their lustre when dried. H. Fonzes-Diacon reported white, acicular crystals of **ammonium tetrabromoplumbite,** $(NH_4)_2PbBr_4$, to be formed from the hot sat. soln. of lead bromide in 65 per cent. ammonium bromide. H. L. Wells and W. R. Johnston obtained **hydrated ammonium tetrabromoplumbite,** $(NH_4)_2PbBr_4.H_2O$, from a soln. of lead bromide or lead oxide in a hot conc. soln. of ammonium bromide. The radiating tufts of highly refracting, slender prisms are monohydrated. H. Fonzes-Diacon reported tetragonal plates of **ammonium chlorotetrabromodiplumbite,** $NH_4Cl.2PbBr_2$, to be formed from a sat. soln. of lead chloride in a boiling, 100 per cent. soln. of ammonium bromide. He also reported rhombic plates or prismatic crystals of **ammonium tetrachlorobromodiplumbite,** $NH_4Br.2PbCl_2$, from an aq. soln. of the two salts; and monoclinic needles of **ammonium dichlorodibromoplumbite,** $2NH_4Br.PbCl_2.4H_2O$, by cooling a soln. of lead chloride in a hot soln. of 65 per cent. ammonium bromide. The crystals are decomposed by water; and are soluble in acids and alkali-lye. No *ammonium fluobromoplumbite* could be prepared from mixed soln. of lead fluoride and ammonium bromide.

The crystallization of mixed soln. of potassium and lead bromides has been examined by O. Lehmann.[7] A. C. Becquerel observed the electrolytic formation of the complex salt from soln. of lead acetate and potassium bromide separated by a porous partition, and connected electrically by lead wires. R. Lorenz and co-workers found the sp. gr. of molten mixtures of n mol of lead bromide, and $1-n$ mol of potassium bromide, by $D=3\cdot48-0\cdot001667+(2\cdot786+0\cdot0006670)^n$. R. Ketzer found the electrical conductivity of solid lead bromide is raised when some potassium bromide is present. C. Immerwahr measured the potential of lead in soln. of lead and potassium bromides. M. Berthelot's *potassium octobromotriplumbite,* $K_2Pb_3Br_8$, is considered by H. L. Wells to be a mixture; and M. Berthelot's *potassium hexadecabromoplumbite,* $K_{14}PbBr_{16}$, is probably also a mixture.

H. L. Wells prepared quadratic plates of **potassium pentabromodiplumbite,** KPb_2Br_5, from soln. of 400 grms. of potassium bromide and 130 grms. of lead bromide made up to 1050 c.c. with water; from soln. of 400 grms. of potassium bromide and 150 grms. of lead bromide made up to 1250 c.c. with water; and 200 grms. of potassium bromide and 75 grms. of lead bromide made up to 1000 c.c. with water. The product rapidly turns pale green in daylight, and after long exposure, or rapidly in sunlight, the colour turns dirty brown. This compound was found by L. J. Burrage in his study of the ternary system:

$PbBr_2$–KBr–H_2O at 25°. Expressing conc. in grams per 1000 grms. of soln., he found for the mutual solubility of lead and potassium bromides :

KBr .	0	0·56	22·92	49·67	56·09	256·9	301·1	319·7	388·7	393·2	405·2
$PbBr_2$	9·69	9·46	2·56	3·10	2·95	14·94	31·60	36·22	72·05	49·29	0
Solid phase		$PbBr_2$			KPb_2Br_5			$KPbBr_3.\frac{1}{3}H_2O$		KBr	

H. L. Wells reported **tritahydrated potassium tribromoplumbite**, $KPbBr_3.\frac{1}{3}H_2O$, in colourless crystals, from soln. of 500 grms. of potassium bromide and 130 grms. of lead bromide in 950 c.c. or 1050 c.c. of liquid ; of 500 grms. of potassium bromide and 140 grms. of lead bromide in 900 c.c. of liquid ; and of 500 grms. of potassium bromide and 120 grms. of lead bromide in 1050 c.c. or 1125 c.c. of liquid. The crystals are stable in air ; and they lose water very slowly over sulphuric acid at 100°. C. H. Herty made **monohydrated potassium tribromo- plumbite**, $KPbBr_3.H_2O$, by dropping, with constant stirring, a sat. soln. of lead nitrate at 20° into a sat. soln. of potassium bromide at 20°, and allowing the mixture to stand for some days ; and also from a boiling soln. of 7 grms. of lead bromide, 27 grms. of potassium bromide, and 40 grms. of water. H. L. Wells obtained it from the mother-liquor from potassium pentabromodiplumbite by cooling in a freezing mixture. L. J. Burrage obtained the tritahydrate, $KPbBr_3.\frac{1}{3}H_2O$—*vide supra.* The colourless, prismatic crystals are usually stable in air, and, on drying, become opaque. Two-thirds of their water is lost over conc. sulphuric acid. C. Löwig reported **potassium tetrabromoplumbite**, K_2PbBr_4, to be formed by evaporating a filtered soln. of lead nitrate and an excess of potas- sium bromide. The octahedral crystals are dissolved without decomposition by a small proportion of water, but with an excess of water lead bromide sepa- rates out. H. L. Wells suggested that C. Löwig was mistaken in assuming that these crystals are anhydrous since **monohydrated potassium tetrabromoplumbite**, $K_2PbBr_4.H_2O$, is formed in prismatic crystals from soln. of lead bromide in sat. soln. of potassium bromide ; and of 400 grms. of potassium bromide and 70, 90, 120, or 130 grms. of lead bromide respectively made up to 700, 800, or 650 c.c. of liquid or of 500 grms. of potassium bromide and 130 grms. of lead bromide in 850 or 775 c.c. of water. C. H. Herty obtained this salt from a boiling soln. of 7 grms. of lead bromide and 27 grms. of potassium bromide in 40 c.c. of water. The prismatic crystals are stable in air, the water is slowly lost over sulphuric acid, and when heated above 110°, H. L. Wells prepared a perbromide, *potassium octobromodi- plumbite*, $K_3Pb_2Br_7.Br.4H_2O$, by allowing 400 c.c. of a cold sat. soln. of potassium and lead bromides and 20–30 c.c. of bromine, to stand over-night. The product was dried in an atm. of bromine. The dark brown, tetragonal prisms lose bromine and become white on exposure to air. They are **not** appreciably decomposed in the cold in a sealed tube. The bromine may be simply adsorbed—*vide* the corre- sponding iodide. H. L. Wells prepared quadratic plates of **rubidium penta- bromodiplumbite**, $RbPb_2Br_5$, from hot soln. of lead and rubidium bromides ; and **rubidium tetrabromoplumbite**, $Rb_2PbBr_4.\frac{1}{2}H_2O$, by the process employed for the corresponding chloride. H. L. Wells made white, tabular crystals of **cæsium pentabromodiplumbite**, $CsPb_2Br_5$, from soln. of lead bromide in one containing 50 grms. of cæsium bromide in 1250 c.c. of water. H. W. Foote obtained it from soln. of the lead bromide in a 12·83–17·24 per cent. soln. of cæsium bromide at 25°. H. L. Wells prepared pale orange, prismatic or acicular crystals of **cæsium tribromoplumbite**, $CsPbBr_3$, from hot soln. of lead bromide in soln. of cæsium bromide sat. in the cold ; and H. W. Foote found this salt to be the solid phase in soln. with 18·58–19·57 per cent. of cæsium bromide at 25°. The salt is dimorphous. H. L. Wells could not make *cæsium tetrabromoplumbite*, Cs_2PbBr_4, although the potassium salt has been made. H. L. Wells prepared white rhombohedral crystals of **cæsium hexabromoplumbite,** by the method employed for the corresponding chloride. The salt is deposited from hot soln.

of lead bromide in cold sat. soln. of cæsium bromide. H. W. Foote obtained it from soln. with 46·40–51·15 per cent. of cæsium bromide at 25°. H. L. Wells obtained a series of **cæsium chlorobromoplumbites** from hot soln. of lead bromide and cæsium chloride. The salts of the type $CsPb_2(Cl,Br)_5$ were white plates with Cl : Br=2·8—1·5 : 1 ; those of the type $CsPb(Cl,Br)_3$ were yellow prisms with Cl : Br=1·2—4·8 : 1 ; and those of the type $Cs_4Pb(Cl,Br)_6$ were rhombohedra with Cl : Br=3·8—11·2 : 1. C. H. Herty reported *sodium tribromoplumbite*, $NaPbBr_3.H_2O$, to be formed like the corresponding potassium salt ; but it exists only in soln. C. Löwig made **sodium tetrabromoplumbite**, Na_2PbBr_4, by the process used for the potassium salt. The crystals are decomposed by water. R. Ketzer found the electrical conductivity of lead bromide to be increased by admixture with sodium chloride. C. Tubandt and S. Eggert studied the electrolysis of fused mixtures of lead and silver bromides. They also found that the f.p. curves of mixtures of these two bromides, Fig. 96, show the formation of **silver pentabromoplumbite**, $2PbBr_2.AgBr$, or $AgPb_2Br_5$, and the existence of a eutectic at 276° and 46 molar per cent. of lead bromide, and a break at 295°.

R. Otto and D. Drewes prepared **magnesium hexabromoplumbite**, Mg_2PbBr_6. $16H_2O$, by dissolving magnesium carbonate in hydrobromic acid, evaporating the soln. until a skin formed on the surface, and then adding as much lead bromide as the liquid would dissolve. On cooling the filtered liquid, the salt was deposited

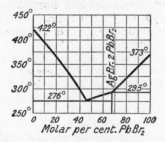

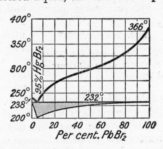

FIG. 96.—Freezing-point Curves of Mixtures of Lead and Silver Bromides.

FIG. 97.—Freezing-point Curves of Mixtures of Lead and Mercuric Bromides.

in monoclinic, hygroscopic prisms. The salt becomes anhydrous at 100°–140°, and is decomposed by water and alcohol. The solid is immediately attacked by hydrogen sulphide. The results of C. Sandonnini's examination of the f.p. of mixtures of *lead and mercuric bromides* are shown in Fig. 97. There is a simple eutectic at 232° with 5 molar per cent. of lead bromide. Solid mercuric bromide probably does not dissolve the lead bromide, nor does lead bromide dissolve mercuric bromide. J. Kendall and co-workers found evidence of **aluminium octobromoplumbite**, $2AlBr_3.PbBr_2$, m.p. 274°, on the f.p. curves of mixtures of lead and aluminium bromides. The two-liquid layers extend from 0·8 to 16·2 per cent. of $PbBr_2$ in equilibrium with the solid phase $2AlBr_3.PbBr_2$ at 210·4°. J. Barlot found that conductivity measurements and measurements of the magnetic susceptibility of mixtures of lead and thallous bromides showed the existence of the complex salts. A soln. of equimolar proportions of the component salts furnishes pale yellow acicular crystals of **thallous tribromoplumbite**, $TlPbBr_3$. The salt is decomposed by boiling with water. J. Nicklès obtained possibly *ammonium thallic bromoplumbite*, by adding ammonium tetrabromothallate to soln. of lead acetate.

The higher lead bromides.—K. Elbs and R. Nübling [8] could not make *lead tetrabromide*, $PbBr_4$, by the electrolysis of hydrobromic acid between lead electrodes, since the anode liquor decomposes, giving off bromine. A. Hutchinson and W. Pollard could not make it by the action of hydrobromic acid on lead tetracetate ; nor could H. Friedrich make it by treating lead dioxide with cold fuming hydrobromic acid, or lead bromide with hydrobromic acid and bromine. In the latter case, there was evidence that a tetrabromide is formed; but J. M. Matthews, however, did not find evidence of the existence of the tetrabromide. H. L. Wells could not prepare alkali salts of definite *hydrobromoplumbic acids*, but A. Classen and B. Zahorsky obtained the quinoline salt $2C_9H_7N.HBr.PbBr_4$.

The lead oxybromides.—G. Sandonnini [9] examined the f.p. curve of mixtures of lead bromide and oxide, and the results are shown in Fig. 98. The curve descends from 368°, the m.p. of lead bromide, to the eutectic at 349° and 13 molar per cent.

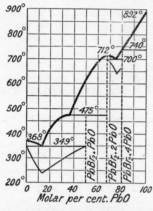

of lead oxide; it rises to 475° where there is an unstable **lead oxydibromide**, Pb_2OBr_2; it then rises to 712°, a maximum corresponding with **lead dioxydibromide**, $Pb_3O_2Br_2$, and thereafter falls to the eutectic at 700° and 75 molar per cent. of lead oxide; it then rises and shows a break at 740° corresponding with the unstable **lead tetroxybromide**, $Pb_5O_4Br_2$; and finally it rises to 892°, the m.p. of lead oxide. Lead dioxydibromide was made by G. André, and he gave 3·03 Cals. for its heat of formation from anhydrous oxide and bromide; and 24·97 Cals. for its heat of soln. in hydrobromic acid sat. with lead bromide at 10°. R. Weinland and F. Paul made **dihydrated lead dioxydibromide**, $2PbO.PbBr_2.2H_2O$, or $[Pb_3(OH)_4]Br_2$, as a yellow microcrystalline powder, by the action of potassium bromide on lead tetrahydroxydichloride.

FIG. 98.—Freezing-point Curves of Mixtures of Lead Bromide and Oxide.

A. J. Balard obtained lead oxydibromide by igniting lead bromide in air until it ceased to emit white fumes; C. Löwig, by heating lead bromocarbonate until all the carbon dioxide was expelled; R. Brandes, by leaving lead bromide for some days in contact with a soln. of lead acetate and agitating the mixture from time to time—the filtrate contained free acetic acid; and G. André, by treating a soln. of lead bromide with potassium hydroxide, washing with cold water, and drying at 100°. The yellowish-white powder when completely dried at 140° becomes yellow. When heated, it becomes lemon-yellow, then reddish-yellow, and brownish-red; on cooling, the original colour is restored. When fused, it emits dense white fumes, and on cooling, it forms a yellowish-white translucent solid. G. André gave 2·00 Cals. for the heat of formation from the anhydrous oxide and bromide, and 12·00 Cals. for the heat of solution in hydrobromic acid sat. with lead bromide at 10°. D. Strömholm reported **monohydrated lead oxydibromide**, or **lead hydroxybromide**, $PbO.PbBr_2.H_2O$, or $Pb(OH)Br$, to be formed by adding aq. ammonia to a soln. of lead bromide until the mixture has an alkaline reaction; G. André could not crystallize the precipitate by heating it with water in a sealed tube at 250°. A. de Schulten called it *bromolaurionite*, and obtained it by heating a soln. of lead acetate and sodium bromide on a water-bath for 12 hrs.; and G. André, by heating the mother-liquor from $(NH_4)_6PbBr_8.H_2O$ with an excess of water in a sealed tube at 200°. R. Weinland and F. Paul called it *diol-diplumbous bromide*, and made it by the action of sodium bromide on a boiling soln. of lead hydroxychlorate. The white needle-like crystals prepared by A. de Schulten were rhombic bipyramids with the axial ratios $a : b : c = 0.7310 : 1 : 0.8043$; the sp. gr. was 6·721 at 19°. W. Biltz examined the mol. vol. The salt melts to a red liquid which, on cooling, becomes white; the water is expelled on melting. The salt is attacked by water less readily than the corresponding chloride. G. André reported needle-like crystals of **hemitrihydrated lead oxydibromide**, $PbO.PbBr_2.1\frac{1}{2}H_2O$, by heating $(NH_4)_6PbBr_8.H_2O$ with much water in a sealed tube at 200°; before the hemitrihydrate is formed, needle-like crystals of **trihydrated lead oxydibromide**, $PbO.PbBr_2.3H_2O$, are formed. The individuality of these two hydrates has not been established.

A number of oxybromides have been reported, but their individuality has not been established. E. A. Atkinson reported lead **oxydecabromide**, $PbO.5PbBr_2$, to be formed by passing hydrogen bromide over heated lead oxide for 4 hrs. D. Strömholm reported microscopic needles of lead **trioxydibromide**, $3PbO.PbBr_2.\frac{3}{4}H_2O$, to be formed by adding sodium hydroxide to a soln. of lead bromide in the proportions $OH : Br = 0.001 : 0.070N$. It was also made by G. André, who said that the heat of formation is 4·20 Cals., and its heat of soln. 37·80 Cals. in hydrobromic acid sat. with lead bromide at 10°. D. Strömholm also reported lead **hexoxydibromide**, $6PbO.PbBr_2.2H_2O$, to be formed by the action of $0.05N$-KBr on lead hydroxide ; and by the action of $0.095N$-$NaOH$ on the trioxydibromide. The salt is a white powder consisting of microscopic needles. The salt becomes yellow when heated. C. F. Cross and S. Sugiura found that lead *dioxyhenabromide*, $Pb_7O_2Br_{11}$, is formed as a pale brown or yellow crystalline mass by the action of bromine vapour on lead monoxide or dioxide ; lead *dioxyheptabromide*, $Pb_6O_2Br_7$, as a grey powder by the action of air charged with bromine on lead monoxide ; and lead *dioxypentabromide*, $Pb_4O_2Br_5$, by the action of air charged with bromine vap. on red-lead. H. L. Wells could not make lead *dihydroxypentabromide*, $Pb_2(OH)_2Br_5$, analogous with the corresponding iodide. M. Dennstedt and F. Hassler reported an oxybromide either with plumbous lead and an excess of bromine, or with plumbic lead, by the action of bromine or hydrobromic acid on lead dioxide.

REFERENCES.

[1] H. G. Denham, *Journ. Chem. Soc.*, **113**. 249, 1918.

[2] V. Lenher, *Journ. Amer. Chem. Soc.*, **23**. 681, 1901 ; W. C. Ebaugh, *ib.*, **24**. 496, 1902 ; G. P. Baxter and F. L. Grover, *ib.*, **37**. 1034, 1915 ; G. P. Baxter and T. Thorvaldson, *ib.*, **37**. 1021, 1025, 1915 ; T. Hjortdahl, *Danske, Vod. Selsk. Forh.*, 9, 1878 ; J. Nicklès, *Compt. Rend.*, **52**. 869, 1861 ; M. Berthelot, *ib.*, **86**. 628, 1883 ; W. F. O. de Coninck and L. Arzalier, *Bull. Acad. Belg.*, 800, 1907 ; M. Barre, *Bull. Soc. Chim.*, (4), **11**. 438, 1912 ; J. A. Wilkinson, *Journ. Phys. Chem.*, **13**. 701, 1909 ; R. S. Norris, *Amer. Chem. Journ.*, **17**. 190, 1895 ; A. Jeltekoff, *Journ. Russ. Phys. Chem. Soc.*, **5**. 81, 1873 ; A. Ditte, *Ann. Chim. Phys.*, (5), **14**. 222, 1878 ; A. J. Balard, *ib.*. (2), **32**. 337, 1826 ; C. L. von Ende, *Ueber das Verhalten der Bleisalze in Lösungen*, Göttingen, 1899 ; *Zeit. anorg. Chem.*, **26**. 158, 1901 ; E. H. Büchner and J. Kalff, *Proc. Acad. Amsterdam*, **28**. 145, 1919 ; *Rec. Trav. Chim. Pays-Bas*, **39**. 135, 1920.

[3] C. Löwig, *Das Brom und seine chemischen Verhältnisse*, Heidelberg, 1829 ; C. J. B. Karsten, *Schweigger's Journ.*, **65**. 394, 1832 ; P. Kremers, *Pogg. Ann.*, **85**. 40, 1852 ; G. Wiedemann, *ib.*, **154**. 318, 1874 ; T. Hjortdahl, *Vid. Selsk. Forh. Kristiania*, 9, 1878 ; A. E. Nordenskjöld *Bihang Svenska Akad. Handl.*, **2**. 2, 1874 ; O. Lehmann, *Zeit. Kryst.*, **10**. 11, 1885 ; G. P. Baxter and F. L. Grover, *Journ. Amer. Chem. Soc.*, **37**. 1034, 1915 ; G. P. Baxter and C. F. Hawkins, *ib.*, **38**. 270, 1916 ; D. M. Lichty, *ib.*, **25**. 471, 1903 ; H. V. Regnault, *Ann. Chim. Phys.*, (3), **1**. 129, 1841 ; A. J. Balard, *ib.*, (2), **32**. 337, 1826 ; O. Ehrhardt, *Wied. Ann.*, **24**. 215, 1885 ; J. Rosenthal, *ib.*, **43**. 722, 1891 ; S. Meyer, *ib.*, **69**. 245, 1899 ; L. Graetz, *ib.*, **29**. 329, 1886 ; L. Graetz and O. Fromm, *ib.*, **54**. 636, 1895 ; H. Schottky, *Phys. Zeit.*, **10**. 634, 1909 ; M. H. Goodwin and H. T. Kalmus, *Phys. Rev.*, (1), **28**. 1, 1909 ; W. Ramsay and N. Eumorfopoulos, *Phil. Mag.*, (5), **41**. 360, 1896 ; A. T. Waterman, *ib.*, (6), **33**. 225, 1917 ; F. W. Clarke, *Amer. Chem. Journ.*, **5**. 241, 1884 ; *A Table of Specific Gravity for Solids and Liquids*, London, 32, 1888 ; R. Lorenz, H. Frei, and A. Jabs, *Zeit. phys. Chem.*, **61**. 468, 1908 ; R. Lorenz and H. T. Kalmus, *ib.*, **59**. 17, 244, 1907 ; R. Lorenz and M. G. Fox, *ib.*, **63**. 109, 1908 ; R. Lorenz and M. Katayama, *ib.*, **62**. 119, 1908 ; M. Katayama, *ib.*, **61**. 566, 1902 ; A. Klein, *ib.*, **36**. 360, 1901 ; A. Gockel, *ib.*, **34**. 544, 1900 ; R. Lorenz, *Zeit. anorg. Chem.*, **19**. 285, 1899 ; R. Lorenz and W. Herz, *ib.*, **145**. 88, 1925 ; *ib.*, **147**. 135, 1925 ; I. I. Saslawsky, *ib.*, **146**. 315, 1925 ; S. Motylewsky, *ib.*, **38**. 410, 1904 ; A. Helfenstein, *ib.*, **23**. 255, 1900 ; C. Tubandt and G. Eggert, *ib.*, **110**. 219, 1920 ; O. H. Weber, *Journ. Russ. Phys. Chem. Soc.*, **31**. 322, 1899 ; V. Czepinsky, *ib.*, **31**. 315, 1899 ; *Zeit. anorg. Chem.*, **19**. 252, 1899 ; G. Herrmann, *ib.*, **71**. 287, 1911 ; F. A. Henglein, *ib.*, **120**. 77, 1921 ; H. Braune and F. Koref, *ib.*, **87**. 183, 1914 ; K. Mönkmeyer *Neues Jahrb. Min. B.B.*, **22**. 1, 1906 ; F. Matthes, *ib.*, **31**, 342, 1915 ; C. Sandonnini, *Gazz. Chim. Ital.*, **41**. ii, 145, 1911 ; *Atti Accad. Lincei*, (5), **24**. i, 616, 1915 ; G. Sandonnini, *ib.*, (5), **23**. i, 962, 1914 ; W. Hampe, *Ber.*, **21**. 161, 1895 ; A. Lenert, *Verh. deut. phys. Ges.*, **12**. 1051, 1910 ; B. A. Dima, *Compt. Rend.*, **157**. 592, 1913 ; T. Carnelley and W. C. Williams, *Journ. Chem. Soc.*, **33**. 283, 1878 ; T. Carnelley, *ib.*, **33**. 278, 1878 ; R. Ketzer, *Leitfähigkeit fester Salze und Salzgemische*, Leipzig, 1919 ; *Zeit. Elektrochem.*, **26**. 80, 1920 ; W. Biltz, *ib.*, **29**. 248, 1923 ; P. Günther, *ib.*, **23**. 199, 1917 ; C. C. Garrard, *ib.*, **6**. 214, 1899 ; *Zeit. anorg. Chem.*, **25**. 273, 1890 ; G. Tammann and H. Bredmeier, *ib.*, **144**. 64, 1925 ; R. Lorenz and W. Herz, *ib.*, **143**. 336, 1925 ; A. K. Sanyal and N. R. Dhar, *ib.*, **128**. 212, 1923 ; L. Ebert, *Zeit. phys. Chem.*, **113**. 1, 1924 ; J. Thiele, *Phys. Zeit.*, **26**. 321, 1925 ; H. Burschall, *Zeit. Elektrochem.*, **17**. 341, 1911 ; H. von Wartenberg and O. Bosse, *ib.*, **28**. 384, 1922 ; O. Bosse, *Dampfdrucke einiger Schwermetallsalze*, Danzig, 1922 ; J. Thomsen, *Thermochemische Untersuchungen*, Leipzig, **3**. 337, 1883 ; *Journ. prakt. Chem.*, (2), **12**. 92, 1875 ; M. Berthelot, *Thermochimie*, Paris, **2**. 339, 1897 ; M. de K. Thompson, *Journ. Amer. Chem. Soc.*, **28**. 731, 1906 ; W. Böttger, *Löslichkeitsstudien an schwerlöslichen Stoffen*, Leipzig, 1903 ; *Zeit. phys. Chem.*, **46**. 521, 1903 ; C. L. Wagner, *ib.*, **71**. 423, 1910 ; F. de Carli,

Atti Accad. Lincei, (5), **33**. ii, 94, 1924; T. Volmer, *Zeit. Physik*, **26**. 285, 1924; W. M. Latimer, *Journ. Amer. Chem. Soc.*, **43**. 818, 1921; A. M. Latimer and H. D. Hoenshel, *ib.*, **48**. 19, 1926; C. Krahmer, *Zeit. Elektrochem.*, **26**. 97, 1920; T. J. Webb, *Journ. Phys. Chem.*, **29**. 816, 1925; P. Fischer, *Zeit. Elektrochem.*, **32**. 136, 1926; W. Biltz and W. Klemm, *Zeit. anorg. Chem.*, **152**. 257, 1926; K. Jellinek and R. Uloth, *ib.*, **151**. 157, 1926; *Zeit. phys. Chem.*, **119**. 161, 1926; C. L. von Ende, *Ueber das Verhalten der Bleisalze in Lösungen*, Göttingen, 1899; *Zeit. anorg. Chem.*, **26**. 158, 1901; W. Braunbek, *Zeit. Physik*, **38**. 549, 1926.

⁴ G. P. Baxter and F. L. Grover, *Journ. Amer. Chem. Soc.*, **37**. 1034, 1915; G. P. Baxter and T. Thorvaldson, *ib.*, **37**. 1021, 1025, 1915; W. C. Ebaugh, *ib.*, **24**. 496, 1902; G. N. Lewis and T. B. Brighton, *ib.*, **39**. 1906, 1917; D. M. Lichty, *ib.*, **25**. 471, 1903; R. S. Norris, *Liebig's Ann.*, **117**. 189, 1861; *Amer. Chem. Journ.*, **17**. 189, 1895; C. H. Herty, *ib.*, **14**. 126, 1892; **15**. 103, 1893; E. C. Franklin, *ib.*, **20**. 828. 1898; C. L. Clark, *Amer. Journ. Science*, (5), **7**. 1, 1924; A. L. Potilizin, *Journ. Russ. Phys. Chem. Soc.*, **4**. 137, 1872; **11**. 86, 1879; O. H. Weber, *Zeit. anorg. Chem.*, **31**. 333, 1899; H. Braune and F. Koref, *ib.*, **87**. 183, 1914; W. Biltz. *ib.*, **124**. 231. 1922; F. L. Shinn, *Journ. Phys. Chem.*, **11**. 538, 1907; G. W. Heise, *ib.*, **16**. 373, 1912; E. Field, *Chem. News.*, **67**. 157, 1893; *Journ. Chem. Soc.*, **63**. 545. 1893; T. Carnelley and W. C. Williams, *ib.*, **33**. 283, 1878; J. Spiller, *ib.*, **10**. 110, 1858; *Chem. News*, **8**. 280, 1863; **19**. 166, 1869; C. Löwig, *Das Brom und seine chemischen Verhältnisse*, Heidelberg, 1829; A. J. Balard, *Ann. Chim. Phys.*, (2), **32**. 337, 1826; M. Berthelot, *ib.*, (5), **29**. 294, 1883; A. Ditte, *ib.*, (5), **14**. 223, 1878; (5), **28**. 133, 1883; *Compt. Rend.*, **92**. 179, 720, 1881; **94**. 1182, 1882; J. Nicklès, *Compt. Rend.*, **52**. 869, 1861; G. André, *ib.*, **96**. 436, 1883; **97**. 1302, 1883; *Bull. Soc. Chim.*, (2), **40**. 18, 1883; *Ann. Chim. Phys.*, (6), **3**. 114, 1884; (6), **7**. 408, 1886; V. Thomas, *ib.*, (7), **13**. 223, 1898; *Bull. Soc. Chim.*, (3), **15**. 1091, 1896; *Compt. Rend.*, **128**. 1234, 1899; *Contribution à l'étude de quelques sels métalliques halogénés*, Paris, 1897; H. Fonzes-Diacon, *Bull. Soc. Chim.*, (3), **17**. 351, 1897; V. Zotier, *ib.*, (4), **21**. 241, 1917; R. Ketzer, *Leitfähigkeit fester Salze und Salzgemische*, Leipzig, 1919; *Zeit. Elektrochem.*, **26**. 80, 1920; C. L. von Ende, *Ueber das Verhalten der Bleisalze in Lösungen*, Göttingen, 1899; *Zeit. anorg. Chem.*, **26**. 158, 1901; W. Böttger, *Löslichkeitsstudien an schwer löslichen Stoffen*, Leipzig, 1903; *Zeit. phys. Chem.*, **46**. 521, 1903; G. L. Wagner, *ib.*, **71**. 423, 1910; F. Ephraim, *ib.*, **83**. 204, 1913; W. Goebbels, *Ber.*, **28**. 794, 1895; H. Mandal, *ib.*, **54**. 605, 1921; H. Lecher and A. Goebel, *ib.*, **54**. 2227, 1921; A. Naumann, *ib.*, **37**. 4328, 1904; **42**. 3790, 1900; **42**, 314, 1910; **47**. 1370, 1914; A. P. N. Franchimont, *Rec. Trav. Chim. Pays-Bas*, **1**. 55, 1883; H. L. Wells, *Amer. Journ. Science*, (3), **45**. 121, 1893; G. C. Wittstein, *Repert. Pharm.*, **63**. 329, 1838; A. Jouniaux, *Journ. Chim. Phys.*, **1**. 609, 1903; W. Herz and M. Hellebrandt, *Zeit. anorg. Chem.*, **130**. 188, 1923; A. K. Sanyal and N. R. Dhar, *ib.*, **128**. 212, 1923; F. D. Carli, *Atti Accad. Lincei*, (5), **33**. ii, 94, 1924.

⁵ C. Sandonnini, *Atti Accad. Lincei*, (5), **20**. i, 253, 1911; (5), **24**. i, 616, 842, 1915; *Gazz. Chim. Ital.*, **41**. ii, 149, 1911; **50**. i, 289, 1920; H. Fonzes-Diacon, *Bull. Soc. Chim.*, (3), **17**. 351, 1897; V. Thomas, *ib.*, (3), **19**. 691, 1898; (3), **21**. 533, 1899; *Compt. Rend.*, **128**. 1234, 1899; F. Matthes, *Neues Jahrb. Min. B.B.*, **31**. 342, 1915; K. Mönkemeyer, *ib.*, **22**. 1, 1908; C. H. Herty and T. R. Boggs, *Journ. Amer. Chem. Soc.*, **19**. 821, 1897; M. W. Iles, *Amer. Chem. Journ.*. **3**. 52, 1881; *Chem. News*, **43**. 216, 1881; G. Meyer, *Rec. Trav. Chim. Pays-Bas*, **42**. 301, 1923; W. Würfel. *Beiträge zur Molekulargewichtsbestimmung an Krystallisierten Substanzen*, Marburg, 1896.

⁶ G. André, *Compt. Rend.*, **96**. 1503, 1883; *Ann. Chim. Phys.*, (6), **3**. 114, 1884; *Bull. Soc. Chim.*, (2), **40**. 18, 1883; H. Fonzes-Diacon, *ib.*, (3), **17**. 354, 1897; H. L. Wells and W. R. Johnston. *Amer. Journ. Science*, (3), **46**. 25, 1893; *Zeit. anorg. Chem.*, **4**. 118, 1893; J. W. Retgers, *Zeit. phys. Chem.*, **9**. 267, 1892; P. Gaubert, *Bull. Soc. Min.*, **38**. 165, 1915.

⁷ O. Lehmann, *Zeit. Kryst.*, **10**. 339, 1885; C. Immerwahr, *Beiträge zur Löslichkeits bestimmung schwerlöslicher Salze des Quecksilbers, Kupfers, Bleis, Cadmiums, und Zinks*, Breslau, 1900; *Zeit. Elektrochem.*, **7**. 480, 1901; C. Tubandt and S. Eggert, *Zeit. anorg. Chem.*, **110**. 196, 1920; A. C. Becquerel, *Traité expérimental de l'électricité et du magnétisme*, Paris, **2**. 86, 1855; *Ann. Chim. Phys.*, (2), **41**. 33, 1829; M. Berthelot, *ib.*, (5), **29**. 294, 1883; J. Kendall, E. D. Crittenden, and H. K. Miller, *Journ. Amer. Chem. Soc.*, **45**. 963, 1923; R. Lorenz, H. Frei, and A. Jabs, *Zeit. phys. Chem.*, **61**. 468, 1908; R. Ketzer, *Leitfähigkeit fester Salze und Salzgemische*, Leipzig, 1919; *Zeit. Elektrochem.*, **26**. 80, 1920; J. Barlot, *Compt. Rend.*, **171**. 794, 1920; H. L. Wells, *Amer. Journ. Science*, (3), **45**. 121, 127, 129, 1893; (3), **46**. 190, 1893; J. Nicklès, *Journ. Pharm. Chim.*, (4), **2**. 219, 1865; C. H. Herty, *Amer. Chem. Journ.*, **14**. 124, 1892; **15**. 358, 1893; **18**. 292, 1896; W. H. Foote, *ib.*, **37**. 124, 1907; C. Löwig, *Das Brom und seine chemischen Verhältnisse*, Heidelberg, 1829; R. Otto and D. Drewes, *Arch. Pharm.*, **229**. 586, 1891; C. Sandonnini, *Atti Accad. Lincei*, (5), **21**. i, 211, 1912; *Gazz. Chim. Ital.*, **41**. ii, 144, 1911; L. J. Burrage, *Journ. Chem. Soc.*, **129**. 1703, 1926.

⁸ A. Classen and B. Zahorsky, *Zeit. anorg. Chem.*, **4**. 105, 1893; K. Elbs and R. Nübling, *Zeit. Elektrochem.*, **9**. 778, 1903; H. Friedrich, *Monatsh.*, **14**. 519, 1893; *Ber.*, **26**. 1434, 1893; J. M. Matthews, *Journ. Amer. Chem. Soc.*, **20**. 840, 1898; H. L. Wells, *Amer. Journ. Science*, (3), **46**. 190, 1893; A. Hutchinson and W. Pollard, *Journ. Chem. Soc.*, **69**. 212, 1896.

⁹ G. Sandonnini, *Atti Accad. Lincei*, (5), **23**. i, 959, 1914; E. A. Atkinson, *Journ. Amer. Chem. Soc.*, **20**. 800, 1898; G. André, *Compt. Rend.*, **96**. 1504, 1883; *Bull. Soc. Chim.*, (2), **40**. 18, 1883; *Ann. Chim. Phys.*, (6), **3**. 114, 1884; A. J. Balard, *ib.*, (2), **32**. 337, 1826; C. F. Cross and S. Sugiura, *Journ. Chem. Soc.*, **33**. 407, 1878; D. Strömholm, *Zeit. anorg. Chem.*, **38**. 437, 1904; W. Biltz, *ib.*, **115**. 241, 1921; M. Dennstedt and F. Hassler, *ib.*, **42**. 417, 1903; R. Wein-

land and F. Paul, *ib.*, **129**. 254, 1923 ; R. Brandes, *Liebig's Ann.*, **10**. 275, **1834** ; A. de Schulten, *Bull. Soc. Min.*, **20**. 188, 1897 ; C. Löwig, *Das Brom und seine chemischen Verhältnisse.* Heidelberg, 1829 ; H. L. Wells, *Amer. Journ. Science*, (4), **1**. 21, 1895.

§ 27. Lead Iodide

H. G. Denham [1] prepared **lead subiodide, or lead monoiodide,** PbI, by treating lead suboxide with the vapour of methyl iodide, free from oxygen, at 262°. The product is pale yellow, and it takes up oxygen slowly in air. In vacuo, at 300°, it decomposes into lead and normal lead iodide, and the colour darkens. Water dissolves 0·35 millieq. per litre. The subiodide is decomposed by hot sulphuric acid, hydrochloric, and acetic acids.

According to A. Frenzel,[2] **plumbous iodide, or lead iodide,** PbI_2, occurs in nature as an incrustation in the Cuatro Ties Mine, Sierra Gorda, Caracoles. As shown by H. Davy, and J. L. Gay Lussac, normal lead iodide is formed by the direct action of iodine on lead. G. Tammann observed the rate of formation of iodide films on lead confined with iodine over sulphuric acid in a desiccator. H. Braune and F. Koref introduced finely divided lead into a soln. of iodine and potassium iodide. H. St. C. Deville said that lead is attacked by hydriodic acid, forming lead iodide which dissolves in the acid. J. A. Wilkinson obtained it by the electrolysis of a soln. of potassium iodide with a lead anode ; and H. S. Taylor, by the action of lead on silver iodide : $Pb+2AgI=PbI_2+2Ag+11\cdot55$ Cals. W. F. O. de Coninck and L. Arzalier observed that lead iodide is formed when a mixture of lead oxide and ammonium iodide is strongly compressed. As J. L. Gay Lussac first showed, lead iodide is conveniently prepared by precipitation from a soln. of a lead salt by hydriodic acid, potassium iodide, or other soluble iodide. L. J. Girault used a similar process. T. Huraut used calcium iodide as the precipitant. P. Boullay treated a soln. of lead nitrate or acetate with potassium iodide ; and, added J. Inglis, and R. Brandes, if the lead acetate be in excess, some lead oxyiodide will be precipitated along with the lead iodide. O. Henry showed that if lead acetate be gradually added to a soln. of potassium iodide, the lead iodide is first precipitated as a yellow powder, and afterwards in yellow plates, and the liquid becomes acid. If a soln. of one part of potassium iodide in ten parts of water be mixed with a small proportion of acetic acid, the addition of lead acetate produces crystals of lead iodide at once, but if too much acetic acid be present, the lead iodide remains in soln., and separates only when the acid is neutralized by potassium hydroxide or ammonia. The more dil. the soln., the finer the crystals. E. Boudet said that in the use of potassium salts there is a loss owing to the formation of soluble potassium iodoplumbite. L. Hopff, and O. Lehmann recommended adding a dil. soln. of lead acetate to a soln. of one part of potassium iodide in 10 parts of water, with sufficient iodine to give the liquid a yellow colour. The lead iodide can be purified by crystallization from its soln. in boiling water. A. A. Noyes and E. H. Woodworth purified the iodide by precipitation from its potassium iodide soln. by an excess of water ; and crystallization from its hot aq. soln. The rhythmic precipitation of lead iodide, forming yellow *Liesegang's rings*, is obtained by placing a crystal of lead nitrate in agar-agar containing one per cent. of potassium iodide. This subject has been discussed by R. E. Liesegang, K. Notboom, E. Küster, and E. Hatschek. H. H. Holmes obtained them by adding an iodide to a soln. of a lead salt in gelatinous silica. V. Lehner obtained lead iodide by the action of hydriodic acid on lead sulphide ; R. Benedikt, by the action of that acid on lead sulphate ; and G. Campani, by shaking lead sulphate or phosphate with an aq. soln. of potassium iodide. A. Findlay added a mixture of sodium sulphate and iodide to a soln. of a lead salt, and found the equilibrium constant in the reaction $PbSO_4+2NaI \rightleftharpoons PbI_2+Na_2SO_4$ to be 0·25–0·30 at 25°. A. C. Becquerel obtained octahedral crystals of lead iodide by separating soln. of potassium iodide and lead nitrate by a porous plug, and electrically connecting the two soln. by a lead wire. V. Thomas found that lead bromide is rapidly converted into the iodide by hydriodic acid. Natural lead compounds are converted into lead iodide by heating a mixture of the mineral with sulphur and potassium iodide (F. von Kobell, and H. B. Cornwall), or with a mixture of silver iodide and carbon (P. Casamajor). According to P. Fischer, lead iodide is formed when a lead plate and a plate of platinum covered with iodine are dipped in a 5 per cent. soln. of potassium nitrate, and connected by a copper wire.

E. H. Büchner and J. Kalff obtained colloidal lead iodide by dropping the precipitating agent into a soln. of lead salt. W. Reinders used gelatinous soln. W. Leuze treated 5 c.c. of a 5 per cent. soln. of sodium protalbinate with 15 grms. of a 20 per cent. soln. of lead acetate, and dissolved the lead salt in sodium hydroxide, and treated it with potassium iodide. After dialysis, lead iodide sol was obtained, which was reddish-brown in transmitted light, and greenish-yellow in reflected light. The filtered liquid can be evaporated to dryness. The product furnishes a sol on treatment with water. H. Zocher examined the properties of the sol; and H. Lachs, the scintillation effects in the ultramicroscope, and found that the scintillation effect diminishes with long standing owing to the development of crystals.

The physical properties of lead iodide.—According to P. F. G. Boullay,[3] M. Denot, and J. Inglis, lead iodide appears as an orange-yellow powder, or as golden-yellow, flexible, six-sided, plates or prisms. The crystals, according to A. E. Nordenskjöld, belong to the hexagonal system having the axial ratio $a : c = 1 : 1\cdot2945$. The crystals are isomorphous with those of cadmium and mercuric iodides. A. des Cloizeaux found them to be uniaxial and negative. L. W. Fisher and F. L. Simon studied the effects of acidity and concentration of colloidal soln. on the growing crystals; and M. Volmer, growing crystals of lead iodide, in a mixed soln. of lead nitrate and potassium iodide, by means of the X-radiograms; and P. Terpstra and H. G. Westenbrink found that the unit cell of the hexagonal parallelopiped $a = 4\cdot59$ A., $c = 6\cdot78$ A.; and each cell contains one mol of PbI_2. W. Biltz studied what he called the lattice-energy of the crystals. G. F. Rodwell found the coeff. of expansion indicated that lead iodide has a transition point between 253° and 265°; but F. Matthes's, and K. Mönkemeyer's thermal observations lend no support to the view that lead iodide is dimorphous. A. Findlay said that the velocity of crystallization is greater than that of lead sulphate. The specific gravity given by P. F. G. Boullay is 6·11; by C. J. B. Karsten, 6·0212; by E. Filhol, 6·384; by R. Schiff, 6·07; by H. G. F. Schröder, 6·207; and G. F. Rodwell, 6·12, and in the molten state at 383°, 5·6247. F. A. Henglein studied the mol. vol. of lead iodide. D. M. Lichty found the sp. gr. of soln. of lead iodide :

	0°	15°	25°	35°	45°	55°	65°	80°	95°
Sp gr...	1·00056	0·99983	0·99798	0·99508	0·99153	0·98723	0·98268	0·97452	0·96709

M. L. Dundon gave 6·16 for the sp. gr. ; 74·8 for the mol. vol. ; and 130 ergs for the surface energy of the solid. S. Motylewsky found the drop weight of the molten iodide to be 106, when that of water is 100. G. F. Rodwell found the vol. of solid lead iodide at different temp. to be :

	0°	205°	253°	265°	383° (solid)	383° (liquid)
Volume .	1·000000	1·015608	1·019595	1·027248	1·048488	1·078080

The cubical coeff. of thermal expansion is $0\cdot0_47614$ between 0° and 205°; $0\cdot0_48317$ from 205° to 253°; $0\cdot0_36378$ from 253° to 265°. H. Fizeau gave $0\cdot0_433598$ for the linear coeff. of expansion. H. V. Regnault gave 0·04267 for the specific heat between 14° and 110°; O. Ehrhardt, 0·04303, between 160° and 315°. F. Koref gave 0·0407 between −190·8° and −80·8°; and W. Nernst and F. Schwers gave the following results below −177·4°, and A. Magnus the following values above that temp. :

	−250·7°	−234·8°	−210·9°	−177·4°	100°	200°	250°
Sp. ht. .	0·0153	0·0233	0·0324	0·0375	0·0427	0·0438	0·0504
Mol. ht. .	7·05	10·74	14·8	17·3	19·70	20·18	20·75

H. Schottky gave 19·49 for the mol. ht. at 18° ; and H. Burschall, 17·7 between
—75° and —183°. According to A. Heiduschka, and J. H. Kastle, when cooled
in liquid air, lead iodide becomes pale yellow; and when heated, O. Henry, and
R. Brandes noted that its colour deepens, becoming reddish-yellow, brick-red, and
finally dark reddish-brown. J. Rosenthal, and G. F. Rodwell noted that before
melting lead iodide becomes plastic. As J. L. Gay Lussac showed, lead iodide fuses
when strongly heated, and G. F. Rodwell showed that it may be fused out of contact
with air with little appreciable loss ; in air, rapid decomposition ensues, and, as indicated by V. Czepinsky, iodine is evolved, and an oxyiodide is formed. R. Brande's
also observed this decomposition, and A. Benrath said that a little iodine is given
off above the m.p. During the cooling of the molten iodide, G. F. Rodwell, and
C. Tubandt and G. Eggert noted the production of harsh crackling noises recalling
the cry of tin. The yellow cold mass, according to V. Czepinsky, may contain some
free iodine or possibly lead tetraiodide. T. Carnelley and co-workers gave 350°–383°
for the **melting point** of lead iodide ; F. Matthes, and K. Mönkemeyer, 358° ;
O. Ehrhardt, 375° ; W. Ramsay and N. Eumorfopoulos, 373° ; C. Sandonnini, 400° ;
and C. Tubandt and G. Eggert, 402°. The **heat of fusion** given by O. Ehrhardt
is 11·5 cals. per gram, or 5·28 Cals. per mol ; V. Czepinsky gave 5·278 Cals. per mol ;
and G. D. Roos, 210 cals. per at. vol. According to H. Crompton, the heat of fusion,
L, the sp. gr. D, and the absolute temp. T, are related as $LD=0.11T$. Lead iodide
volatilizes at a strong red heat ; and G. F. Rodwell, and M. Schtscherbakoff sublimed
this salt unchanged by heating it in a current of carbon dioxide. T. Carnelley and
W. C. Williams gave 861°–964° for the **boiling point.** W. Braunbek discussed
some relations between the sp. ht., m.p., and latent heat. K. Jellinek and
R. Uloth calculated values for the partial press. of the iodine in lead iodide at
different temp. C. Zengelis considered that he had proved lead iodide can
volatilize at ordinary temp. J. Thomsen gave 39·8 Cals. for the **heat of formation,**
from solid iodine, and 53·4 Cals. from the gas. M. Berthelot gave 39·6 Cals. M. de
K. Thompson gave 39·8 Cals. ; H. Braune and F. Koref, 41·85 Cals. ; P. Günther,
42·4 Cals. ; V. Czepinsky gave 53–96·4 Cals. at 405°–700° ; and G. D. Roos, 86 cals.
per gram referred to the at. vol. 1580. M. de K. Thompson gave 41·7–42·3 Cals.
for the **free energy** of formation.

The **spectrum** of lead iodide was shown by E. Wiedemann [4] to be continuous,
and J. A. Wilkinson found that it exhibits a green **fluorescence.** B. A. Dima
observed that, with ultra-violet light, the **photoelectric effect** is greater than with
the chloride or bromide. W. W. Coblentz and J. F. Eckford said that lead iodide is
the only lead halide which is photoelectrically sensitive.

M. Faraday electrolyzed molten lead iodide and noted the formation of a periodide. W. Hampe found that the fused and pulverulent iodide has a measurable
electrical conductivity, and as the temp. rises the conductivity becomes more
electrolytic and less metallic. J. Rosenthal measured the conductivity of the
pulverulent iodide pressed into rods. G. Tammann and H. Bredmeier measured the
conductivity of thin films of the iodide. C. Tubandt and S. Eggert found that
below 344° the electrical resistance is very high, and it then conducts electrolytically. According to A. Benrath, and L. Graetz, by repeated heating, the conductivity of the solid iodide is augmented. L. Graetz found that if k represents
the conductivity, mercury unity :

	290°	300°	320°	340°	360°	380°	400°
k	0·0,6	0·0,450	0·0,1000	0·0,2100	0·0,3000	0·0,4000	0·0,4600

The conductivity increases with pressure, thus, with a press. of 4000 atm., the
resistance falls from about 2000×10^8 ohms to about 200×10^8 ohms. F. Quincke,
A. Gockel, and V. Czepinsky studied the polarization of the solid and molten
iodide ; and C. C. Garard, A. Helfenstein, R. Lorenz, G. Auerbach, M. Schtscherbakoff, and V. Czepinsky, the electrolysis of the molten iodide. W. Böttger gave
0·003384 for the sp. conductivity of the aq. soln. sat. at 20·10° when the degree of

ionization was 9·7 per cent. H. G. Denham, C. L. von Ende, and G. N. Lewis and T. B. Brighton also measured the conductivity of aq. soln. C. L. von Ende said that the salt is completely ionized in water, and H. Crompton calculated the degree of ionization. A. Klein measured the e.m.f. of the cell Pb | PbCl$_2$ | 0·01N-KCl, 0·01N-KI | PbI$_2$ | Pb. J. Thiele measured the thermoelectric force of the molten lead halides against metals. A. Lenert gave 2·35 for the **dielectric constant,** and after melting and freezing, 62·47. L. Graetz and O. Fromm gave 113 for λ=101 ; 147·7 for λ=130·4 ; and 172·8 for λ=180. L. Ebert studied the dielectric polarization of the lead salts. S. Meyer found the **magnetic susceptibility** to be $-0·623 \times 10^{-6}$, and the mol. magnetism, $-0·118 \times 10^{-6}$.

The **chemical properties of lead iodide.**—Z. Roussin,[5] and W. Schmid found that light does not alter the dry iodide, but the moist iodide, particularly in air and sunlight, slowly forms lead carbonate, lead dioxide, and iodine. N. R. Dhar and A. C. Chatterji found rhythmic rings of lead iodide formed in silica gel are not affected by light. The action of **heat** has been examined by R. Brandes, A. Benrath, and M. Schtscherbakoff—*vide supra.* A. Jouniaux found that **hydrogen** does not reduce the iodide at a red heat. The reaction was studied by F. de Carli ; and the equilibrium conditions $PbI_2 + H_2 \rightleftharpoons Pb + 2HI$, by K. Jellinek and R. Uloth. The constant p_{HI}/p_{H_2} is nearly $2·6 \times 10^{-2}$.

W. D. Bancroft [6] showed that lead iodide does not take up water of crystallization as indicated by J. M. Talmadge and previously by himself ; and therefore the salt does not effloresce. No measurable rise of temp. could be detected by M. Berthelot when lead iodide was shaken with **water.** According to M. Denot, 100 c.c. of cold water dissolve 0·081 grm. of the salt, and boiling water, 0·515 grm., forming a colourless soln. J. B. Berthemot found 100 c.c. of water dissolve 0·535 grm. of the salt ; and J. L. Lassaigne, 0·17 grm. at 20° ; 0·20 at 27° ; and 0·39 at 100°. D. M. Lichty found for the solubility, S, in grams of salt per 100 grms. of water :

	0°	15°	25°	35°	45°	55°	65°	80°	95°	100°
S .	0·0442	0·0613	0·0764	0·1042	0·1453	0·1755	0·2183	0·3023	0·3960	0·4360

M. de K. Thompson gave for the solubility 0·0423 grm. ; and W. Böttger, 0·047 grm. per litre at 20·10°, and H. G. Denham said that the result is low because of the action of air on the soln. during the solubility determination. C. L. von Ende gave 1·58 milligram mols per litre at 25° ; and G. N. Lewis and T. B. Brighton, 1·64 milligram mols per litre at 25° ; and they gave for the **solubility product** $11·9 \times 10^{-9}$. M. L. Dundon found the solubility increased about 2 per cent. with particles 0·4μ diameter. J. B. Caventou found that the salt does not dissolve completely in water owing **to** the formation of a little oxyiodide, and in boiling water the smell of iodine is perceptible. P. F. G. Boullay said that the pure iodide can be obtained by crystallization from hot water, and J. White obtained no oxyiodide under these conditions, but M. Schtscherbakoff always found that some oxyiodide is formed. H. Braune and F. Koref said that lead iodide is soluble in a soln. of **sodium hydroxide,** and M. Schtscherbakoff observed no decomposition by dissolving the iodide in a 25 per cent. soln. of **potassium hydroxide.** V. Zotier examined the catalytic effect of lead iodide on **hydrogen dioxide.**

H. Moissan [7] showed that in the cold **fluorine** converts lead iodide into the fluoride. According to R. Brandes, **chlorine** transforms heated lead iodide into the chloride, and P. Hautefeuille observed that **hydrogen chloride** forms lead chloride when it acts on the heated iodide, while V. Thomas found boiling **hydrochloric acid** also produces lead chloride. P. F. G. Boullay, and R. H. Brett found lead iodide to be slightly soluble in cold and copiously soluble in hot soln. of **ammonium chloride,** forming, according to C. Völckel, H. Maisch, and V. Thomas, a complex chloroiodide. A. Mosnier, and E. Field found double salts are also formed with **potassium chloride ;** and V. Thomas showed that **a** hot soln. of **lead chloride** and iodide, on cooling, deposits crystals of the chloride, then the iodide, and then a complex salt. B. Thorp said that lead iodide is soluble in **hydrobromic acid,** and V. Thomas found the iodide is very slowly attacked so that when the boiling soln. is cooled, crystals of a bromo-iodide are deposited. A. Mosnier found that **ammonium bromide** soln. form complex bromoiodides; and A. Mosnier, and V. Thomas obtained complex bromoiodides by the solvent action of a soln. of **potassium bromide.** According to P. Fedotieff, a sat. aq. soln. of **iodine dissolves** 0·00216 mol of lead iodide per litre at 20°. V. Lenher found the salt to be very sparingly soluble in a dil. soln. of **hydriodic acid,** but readily soluble in a conc. soln. The action of hydriodic acid was also examined by F. Parmentier, and A. Ditte. E. Field, A. Mosnier, and A. Ditte showed that when treated with a soln. of **ammonium iodide,** complex salts are formed. A. Mosnier showed that **ethyl iodide** precipitates lead iodide from its aq. soln., and that lead iodide is soluble in a soln. of **triphenylammonium iodide.** According to M. Berthelot, a few drops of a soln. of a mol of hydriodic acid in 2 litres and an aq. soln. of potassium iodide precipitate lead iodide from a soln. containing 0·5 grm. per litre. J. B. Berthemot found that lead iodide is soluble in soln. of potassium, **sodium, barium, strontium, calcium, or magnesium iodide,** and A. Mosnier found that complex salts are formed with these and many other iodides. The effect of **potassium iodide** on soln. of lead iodide was studied by R. W. Balcom, A. Mosnier, A. A. Noyes and E. H. Woodworth, C. H. Herty, and A. Ditte. A. Bogo-rodsky obtained a complex salt with **lithium iodide.** F. D. Chattaway found that when lead iodide is treated with **nitrogen trihydrotriiodide,** $N_2H_3I_3$, ammonia, and lead hypoiodite are produced.

K. A. Hofmann and V. Wölfl [8] found that **ammonium sulphide** transforms lead iodide into a sulphoiodide. According to A. Michaelis and G. Koethe, **sulphur dioxide** acts on warm lead iodide, forming lead sulphite and hydrogen iodide; and with **sodium sulphite,** lead sulphite and sodium iodide are formed. G. C. Wittstein found that a soln. of **ammonium sulphate** whitens lead iodide without dissolution; A. Ditte, that a soln. of **magnesium sulphate** forms lead sulphate and magnesium iodide; and A. Naumann, that **silver sulphate** forms lead sulphate and silver iodide. C. G. Stoffella found that the exothermic reaction with **zinc sulphate :** $PbI_2 + ZnSO_4 \rightleftharpoons ZnI_2 + PbSO_4$ is complete from left to right only in dil. equimolar soln. at 100° owing to the increase in the solubility of the lead iodide with temp. The reaction is incomplete in a sat. soln. at 100°, or in very dil. soln. at 15°. F. Field showed that lead iodide is very soluble in an aq. soln. of **sodium thiosulphate.**

According to G. C. Wittstein,[9] aq. **ammonia** slowly whitens lead iodide without dissolution, forming, according to M. Labouré, a white product which can be dried in air without decomposition, but which, when heated, decomposes into ammonia and lead iodide. E. C. Franklin and C. A. Kraus found lead iodide to be readily soluble in liquid ammonia; K. Friedrichs said insoluble. C. A. Kraus and H. F. Kurtz studied the reduction of lead iodide by sodium in liquid ammonia. According to W. Biltz, lead iodide doubles its vol. under liquid ammonia at −75°, forming white **lead octamminoiodide,** $PbI_2.8NH_3$, which has a heat of formation of 7·8 Cals., and a dissociation press. of 6 mm. at −78·5°; 64·8 mm. at −56·5°; 100 mm. at −51·5°; and 423 mm. at −34°. Between −78·5° and 0°, the octammine forms pale yellow **lead pentamminoiodide,** $PbI_2.5NH_3$, with a heat of dissociation of 9·7 Cals.; and a dissociation press. of 9·8 mm. at −30·9°; 100 mm. at −3°; 122 mm. at 16·5°; 387·6 mm. at 16·5°; and 403 mm. at 17·1°. W. Biltz could not make **lead tetrammino-iodide,** $PbI_2.4NH_3$, but F. Ephraim said that it appears as a white substance when ammonia gas acts on solid lead iodide at room temp. He gave 10·69 Cals. for the heat of dissociation, and a dissociation press. of 760 mm. at 32°. C. F. Rammelsberg made **lead diamminoiodide,** $PbI_2.2NH_3$, as a result of exposing lead iodide to the action of ammonia gas. F. Ephraim obtained it from the tetrammine; and W. Biltz, from the octammine at 0°. C. F. Rammelsberg said that it loses all the combined ammonia when exposed to air; under water it remains white, but decomposes into soluble ammonium iodide and lead oxide.   F. Ephraim gave 12·75 Cals. for the heat of dissociation, and W. Biltz, 11·3 Cals.   According to the latter, the vap. press. is 13·7 mm. at 16·5° ;   100 mm. at 33° ;   111·7 mm. at 34·45° ;   and 317 mm. at 55·9° ;   while F. Ephraim gave 760 mm. at 85°.   F. Ephraim made **lead monamminoiodide**, $PbI_2.NH_3$, as a pale yellow powder, by heating the tetrammine, and W. Biltz, by heating the octammine to 60°.   The former gave 13·81 Cals. for the heat of dissociation, and the latter 13·2 Cals.   The dissociation press. found by W. Biltz were 11 mm. at 55·9° ;   71 mm. at 80·2° ;   100 mm. at 88° ;   and 302·2 mm. at 111° ;   while F. Ephraim gave 760 mm. at 112°.   W. Biltz made **lead hemiamminoiodide**, $PbI_2.\frac{1}{2}NH_3$, by heating the monammine between 80° and 115°. The heat of dissociation is 14·4 Cals. ;   and the dissociation press. at 110·6° is 48·3 mm. ;   at 114·9°, 63·9 mm. ;   at 126°, 100 mm. ;   and at 156·6°, 361·5 mm. C. L. Clark studied the secondary valencies of these ammines.

E. C. Franklin [10] found that **potassium amide** reacts with lead iodide, forming a complex product, $Pb_2N_2H_3I.PbNH$.   According to T. W. B. Welsh and H. J. Broderson, lead iodide is dissolved by anhydrous **hydrazine**, 0·02 grm. per c.c. —with decomposition.   V. Thomas found that **nitrogen peroxide** decomposes lead iodide at ordinary temp. by an endothermal reaction (−10 Cals.). forming lead oxide, and evolving iodine.   R. Benedikt and L. Gans found lead iodide to be easily soluble in dil. **nitric acid ;**   and C. L. von Ende found the solubility in $0.001N$-HNO_3 to be 38·87 millimols per litre of nitric acid at 25·2° ; in $0.01N$-HNO_3, 39·06 ;   in $0.051N$-HNO_3, 39·45 ;   and in $0.04N$-KNO_3 plus $0.01N$-HNO_3, 39·45. G. C. Wittstein found a dil. soln. of **ammonium nitrate** slowly turns lead iodide white, without dissolution.   F. W. O. de Coninck said that boiling soln. of **potassium or sodium nitrate** dissolves considerable quantities of lead iodide, and deposits it again as golden yellow plates on cooling.   P. Fedotieff found that **copper nitrate** transforms lead iodide into lead nitrate, cuprous iodide, and iodine ;   the reaction is reversible.   A. Naumann said that **silver nitrate** has no action ;   but C. Stürenberg showed that a boiling soln. of silver nitrate, incompletely saturated with lead iodide, furnishes the complex salt, $Pb(NO_3)_2.8AgNO_3.4AgI$, and with a more prolonged action, $Pb(NO_3)_2.2AgNO_3.2AgI$.   According to A. A. Noyes and E. H. Woodworth, **lead nitrate** in small proportions reduces the solubility of lead iodide in accord with the ionic hypothesis.

A. Mosnier found that phosphorous iodide reacts with lead iodide, forming **lead phosphorous enneaiodide**, $3PbI_2.PI_3.12H_2O$, in yellow needles.   It is decomposed by water and alcohol, and is dehydrated at 45°.   The heat of formation is $(3PbI_2,PI_3)=4.7$ Cals. ; $(3PbI_2,PI_3.12H_2O)=25$ Cals. for liquid water and 8 Cals. for solid water.   The heat of soln. in 40 parts of water at 15° is 2·5 Cals. for the dodecahydrate, and 27·6 Cals. for the anhydrous salt.   Lead iodide and arsenious iodide form **lead arsenious enneaiodide**, $3PbI_2.AsI_3.12H_2O$, in fine needles, and this behaves like the phosphorous compound.   The heat of formation is $(3PbI_2,AsI_3)=27.1$ Cals., and $(3PbI_2,PI_3,12H_2O)=20.7$ Cals. for liquid water and 3·6 Cals. for solid water.   The heat of soln. in 40 parts of water at 15° is −8·2 Cals. for the dodecahydrate and 12·5 Cals. for the anhydrous salt.   Similarly with **lead antimonous enneaiodide**, $3PbI_2.SbI_3.12H_2O$.   The heat of formation is $(3PbI_2,SbI_3)=21.4$ Cals., and $(3PbI_2,SbI_3,12H_2O)=29.1$ Cals. for liquid water and 12 Cals. for solid water.   The heat of soln. is −8·5 Cals. for the dodecahydrate, and 20·6 Cals. for the anhydrous salt.   Likewise with **lead bismuth enneaiodide**, $3PbI_2.BiI_3.12H_2O$, the heat of formation is $(3PbI_2,BiI_3)=13.8$ Cals., and $(3PbI_2,BiI_3,12H_2O)=33.8$ Cals. for liquid water, and 16·7 Cals. for solid water. The heat of soln. in 40 parts of water at 15° is −17·2 Cals. for the dodecahydrate, and 16·6 Cals. for the anhydrous salt.

As indicated above, lead iodide can be distilled unchanged in a current of **carbon dioxide**, but an aq. soln. of the iodide, when exposed to air, was found by H. G. Denham [11] to form lead carbonate.   J. B. Berthemot said that when boiled with water and **sodium, barium, strontium, calcium,** or magnesium carbonate, lead iodide yields lead carbonate and a soluble iodide ; the reaction is slowest with magnesium carbonate. C. F. Schlagdenhauffen studied what he called *la limite des réactions des carbonates alcalins*. A. Ditte found that potassium hydrocarbonate produces lead carbonate, and a complex salt $K_2PbI_4.4H_2O$ is formed. H. Arctowsky found that lead iodide is insoluble in carbon disulphide ; and A. P. N. Franchimont, insoluble in benzene. O. Henry said that lead iodide is sparingly soluble in alcohol ; and S. von Laszczynsky showed that amyl alcohol dissolves 0·2 grm. per litre at 133·5°. W. Eidmann, and A. Naumann said that lead iodide is insoluble in acetone, but S. von Laszczynsky found 0·2 grm. per litre is dissolved at 59°. A. Vogel found that when repeatedly boiled with ether, iodine is extracted and an oxyiodide is formed. O. Aschan reported that 100 grms. of formic acid dissolve 0·25 grm. of lead iodide at 19·8° ; and M. Denot said that, contrary to O. Henry, lead iodide is not more soluble in acetic acid than in water. D. Tommasi showed that lead iodide dissolves in a soln. of potassium acetate, forming the complex salt $KC_2H_3O_2.2PbI.C_2H_4O_2$; 100 c.c. of a conc. soln. of sodium acetate dissolve 2 grms. of lead iodide in the cold, and 4 grms. in the boiling liquid ; in the presence of 0·4 c.c. of acetic conc. acid, 12 grms. are dissolved, but greater proportions of the acid do not augment the solubility. 100 c.c. of a soln. of lithium acetate dissolve 18 grms. of lead iodide ; and 100 c.c. of ammonium acetate, 160 grms. A soln. of cupric acetate reacts by double decomposition—100 c.c. of a hot soln. of cupric acetate dissolving 12 grms. of lead iodide—some iodine escapes, and cuprous oxide is precipitated. 100 c.c. of a soln. of barium acetate dissolve 20 grms. of lead iodide ; calcium acetate, 23 grms. ; magnesium acetate, 10 grms. ; and zinc acetate, a trace. A boiling soln. of 10 grms. of mercurous acetate in 40 c.c. of water dissolves 7 grms. of lead iodide and precipitates red mercuric iodide. 100 c.c. of aluminium acetate dissolve a trace of lead iodide ; of chromium acetate, 20 grms. ; of uranium acetate, a trace ; manganese acetate, a quantity ; iron acetate, 10 grms. ; and cobalt acetate, 5 grms. J. White noted that complex acetoiodides are formed with ammonium, potassium, and sodium acetates ; with a soln. of lead acetate, the oxyiodide, $Pb(OH)I$, is formed ; with alcoholic soln. of ammonium, potassium, and sodium acetates, and also in hot alcoholic acetic acid soln., unstable complex acetoiodides are formed. A. Naumann found lead iodide is sparingly soluble in methyl acetate, and insoluble in ethyl acetate. H. Braune and F. Koref found lead iodide is soluble in an amyl alcohol soln. of sodium tartrate ; J. Spiller said that the iodide is not precipitated in the presence of sodium citrate ; and G. C. Wittstein found that ammonium succinate colours lead iodide white, without dissolution. F. L. Shinn said that lead iodide is insoluble in ethylamine, probably forming a compound. H. Mandal, and S. von Laszczynsky said that at 13°, aniline dissolves 5 grms. of lead iodide per litre at 13° ; and 11 grms. at 184°. L. Pincussohn, and G. W. Heise found that lead iodide dissolves sparingly in pyridine, and complex salts are formed ; W. Goebbels, sparingly in quinoline ; A. Naumann, sparingly in benzonitrile ; J. H. Matthews, insoluble in allyl sulphocyanide ; and J. W. Retgers, nearly insoluble in methylene iodide. According to B. Köhnlein, the iodine of lead iodide is partially replaced by chlorine when the salt is treated with isobutyl chloride ; or, according to R. Brix, with benzyl chloride. M. Wildermann found the iodine partly replaced by bromine in the presence of bromohydrocarbons containing two or more halogen atoms, and two or more carbon atoms. B. Thorp said lead iodide dissolves in thiocyanic acid without forming a complex. W. Eisner found that soln. of lead acetate and potassium iodide which give a precipitate in aq. soln. fail to do so in the presence of serum, and form a colloidal soln. Similar results are obtained with lead acetate and sodium phosphate or carbonate in the presence of bile, lecithin soln., or serum. Previously precipitated lead iodide passes into colloidal soln. in the presence of excess of serum, and lead salts of low solubility in water, when present in a colloidal soln. in serum, are not precipitated by addition of potassium iodide. The rate of dialysis of lead salts in the presence of serum is increased by addition of potassium iodide, and the latter salt, together with the chloride, inhibits the toxic action of lead on fermenting yeast. L. Kahlenberg and W. J. Trautmann studied the reduction of lead iodide when heated with powdered silicon. J. B. Berthemot found that when lead iodide is boiled with water in the presence of iron, lead and ferrous iodides are formed; the decomposition occurs more readily with zinc in place of iron.

The higher iodides of lead.—According to M. Faraday,[12] when molten lead iodide is electrolyzed with carbon or platinum electrodes, the electrochemical eq. is only about two-thirds the value which would be furnished by the iodide PbI_2. He said:

I attribute this to the formation of a periodide at the positive electrode, which, dissolving in the mass of liquid iodide, came in contact with the lead evolved at the negative electrode, and dissolved part of it, becoming itself again protiodide. Such a periodide does exist; and it is rarely that the iodide of lead formed by precipitation, and well-washed, can be fused without evolving much iodine, from the presence of this percompound; nor does crystallization from its hot aq. soln. free it from this substance. Even when a little of the protiodide and iodine are merely rubbed together in a mortar, a portion of the periodide is formed. And although it is decomposed by being fused and heated to dull redness for a few minutes, and the whole reduced to the ordinary iodide, yet that is not at all opposed to the possibility, that a little of that which is formed in great excess of iodine at the anode, should be carried by the rapid currents in the liquid into contact with the cathode.

Related observations were made by G. Auerbach, and A. Helfenstein. V. Czepinsky also assumed that lead iodide which had been melted and cooled contained lead tetraiodide, PbI_4, or plumbic iodide. K. Elbs and R. Nübling could not prepare it like the corresponding chloride by the electrolysis of hydriodic acid of sp. gr. 1·42, between lead electrodes; but when the anode liquid is treated with water, lead iodide is precipitated, and when treated with pyridine iodide, $C_5H_5N.HI$, a greyish-green precipitate approximating $(C_5H_5NH)_2PbI_6$ is formed. H. Friedrich obtained indications of the presence of lead tetraiodide in the products of the action of potassium iodide on lead tetrachloride. B. Piffard said that a dark-coloured precipitate of lead tetraiodide is produced when lead acetate is treated with a soln. of potassium iodide containing dissolved iodine, but E. Erlenmeyer said that the product is a mixture of lead dioxide and diiodide. A. Hutchinson and W. Pollard failed to make the tetraiodide by the action of hydriodic acid on lead tetracetate. C. F. Schlagdenhauffen treated a lead salt dissolved in a soln. of potassium iodide with sodium hypochlorite and obtained a blue precipitate in the presence of an excess of sodium carbonate, and a brown precipitate if an excess be not present. The product is probably an oxyiodide with adsorbed iodine. Alkali iodoplumbates have not been made. H. L. Wells reported a salt with the composition $K_3Pb_2I_8.4H_2O$, obtained by boiling a soln. of potassium iodide, lead iodide, and iodine. In arriving at this formula, H. L. Wells assumed that the material analyzed " was contaminated with 16·5 per cent. of potassium iodide, and that an excess of water was present." A. N. Meldrum prepared a similar product which was homogeneous under the microscope, and had the composition $K_9Pb_4I_{19}.10H_2O$. K. Elbs and R. Nübling obtained evidence of a pyridine lead tetraiodide, and of quinoline lead tetraiodide, $(C_9H_7NH)_2PbI_4$; and A. Classen and B. Zahorsky, of $(C_9H_7N)_2.HI.PbI_4$.

According to J. L. Lassaigne,[13] when a mixture of lead filings and hydriodic acid is exposed to air, white crystals are formed which dissolve when the acid is boiled, and are redeposited on cooling. A hot soln. of lead iodide in hydriodic acid deposits the same crystals on cooling. When the white crystals are kept in vacuo, or in dry air, hydrogen iodide is given off, and lead iodide remains; a similar result is obtained when the crystals are heated. Cold water extracts the hydriodic acid from the crystals, with only a small quantity of lead iodide; boiling water dissolves the salt completely, and on cooling deposits lead iodide, retaining the hydriodic acid in soln. The crystals are considered to be a lead hydriodide of an unknown composition. According to M. Berthelot, when lead iodide, water, and hydriodic acid are stirred together, yellow crystals of lead hydroiodide, $PbI_2.HI.5H_2O$, are formed.

They are decomposed by light, and by exposure to air ; by heat ; and by mixing with water.

Mixed salts.—H. Fonzes-Diacon,[14] and E. Field could not prepare a lead fluoiodide, but C. Sandonnini investigated the thermal diagram of mixtures of lead fluoride and iodide, and found it to be different from those obtained with the corresponding chloride and bromide. The results are shown in Fig. 99. There is a eutectic at 383° corresponding with 10 molar per cent. of fluoride ; the curve then rises to 432° and 20 molar per cent. of fluoride, corresponding with the existence of **lead fluoiodide**, PbFI, or $PbF_2.PbI_2$; thereafter the curve rises to 573° when there is a pause with 76·5 molar per cent. of fluoride, corresponding with **lead octofluodiiodide**, $PbI_2.4PbF_2$. The curve then rises to the m.p. of the fluoride.

F. Matthes [15] found that binary mixtures of lead chloride and iodide have only a limited miscibility when melted ; but solid soln. extend from 0 to 100 per cent. of lead chloride. The f.p. curve, Fig. 100, has a curved eutectic at 306° and 77 molar per cent. of the iodide. There is no sign of chemical combination ; nevertheless, V. Thomas, M. Labouré, and B. Dietzell claimed to have made **lead chloroiodide**, PbICl, by cooling a boiling soln. of lead iodide in hydrochloric acid ; V. Thomas, and E. Field, from a boiling soln. of lead iodide and ammonium chloride, or from a hot soln. of lead chloride in potassium iodide ; and A. Engelhardt, by cooling soln. of lead iodide in hot soln. of various metal chlorides—Na, Ba, Ca, Mn, Co, Ni, Zn, Sn, Al, Cr—C. H. Herty used boiling soln. of lead iodide in soln. of potassium or ammonium chloride. When this was dried at 100°, E. Field considered the product to be the *hemihydrate;* and H. Fonzes-Diacon supposed that with very slow cooling, sulphur-yellow monoclinic needles of the *dihydrate* are formed, and that when heated, the hydrates are dehydrated. The anhydrous salt furnishes sulphur-yellow prisms which are sensitive to light ; decomposed by water, attacked by nitrogen peroxide ; partially oxidized to the oxychloride, Pb_2OCl_2, with the expulsion of iodine in the cold, and all the iodine is expelled at the sublimation temp.; not attacked by boiling hydrochloric acid ; and converted by bromine into PbClBr. A. B. Poggiale regarded the yellow needles obtained by cooling a hot soln. of lead iodide and ammonium chloride, or lead chloride and sodium iodide as *lead tetrachlorodiiodide*, $2PbCl_2.PbI_2$; and V. Thomas, the pale green crystals obtained by cooling a boiling soln. of lead chloride and ammonium or potassium iodide as *lead hexachlorodiiodide*, $3PbCl_2.PbI_2$, or Pb_2Cl_3I ; on the contrary, C. H. Herty regarded

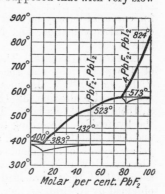

FIG. 99.—The Freezing-point Curve of Mixtures of Lead Fluoride and Iodide.

these salts as isomorphous mixtures of the component halides. S. Glasstone observed that the presence of sodium chloride increases the solubility of lead iodide; and L. J. Burrage found that when concentrations are expressed in grams per 100 c.c. of soln. :

| NaCl | . | . | . | 0 | 0·29 | 0·59 | 1·16 | 2·34 | 5·86 | 11·70 | 29·80 |
| PbI_2 | . | . | . | 0·758 | 0·778 | 0·859 | 0·951 | 1·10 | 1·41 | 1·64 | 1·79 |

at 25°, when the solid phase is lead iodide. If the conc. of the sodium chloride exceeds these limits, the solid phase contains chlorides.

F. Matthes found that binary mixtures of lead bromide and iodide have only a limited miscibility when melted ; the f.p. curve, Fig. 101, has a eutectic at 265° and 49 molar per cent. of lead iodide. C. H. Herty and T. R. Boggs consider that the products obtained by cooling aq. soln. of the component salts are only mixed crystals, and that there is no evidence of the formation of chemical individuals, in spite of reports by B. Thorp of the formation of orange-coloured crystals of *lead bromoiodide*, PbBrI, as the first crop from soln. of lead iodide in hydrobromic acid ; pale yellow crystals of *lead tr.bromoiodide*, Pb_2Br_3I, as the second crop from the same soln. ; and white crystals of *lead dodecabromodiiodide*, $Pb_7Br_{12}I_2$, as the third crop. V. Thomas also reported crystals of the tribromoiodide to be formed by cooling a soln. of lead iodide in a hot sat. soln. of lead bromide, or of lead bromide in a hot soln. of potassium iodide. E. Field also reported greenish needles of *lead tetrabromodiiodide*, $Pb_3Br_4I_2$, to be obtained by cooling a boiling soln. of lead iodide and ammonium bromide.

B. Thorp obtained silky needles of presumably mixed crystals of *lead chloride, bromide, and iodide* from a hot aq. soln. of the three salts. F. Matthes studied the

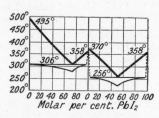

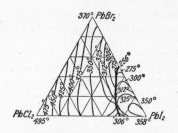

FIGS. 100 and 101.—Freezing-point Curves
of Binary Mixtures of Lead Iodide with
Lead Chloride and Bromide.

FIG. 102.—Fusion Curves of Ternary
Mixtures of Lead Chloride, Bromide,
and Iodide.

f.p. curves of ternary mixtures of these three halides, and obtained no evidence of chemical combination, Fig. 102. The eutectic rises from 256° to 325° and then falls to 306°.

The lead oxyiodides.—The lead oxyiodides have not been examined in the light of the phase rule, and the reported salts are to be considered on probation. P. B. Durand,[16] M. Jammes, and E. Filhol noted that when iodine and water act on lead hydroxide, $3PbO.H_2O$, a blue or violet substance is produced which A. Ditte likened to a lake. This makes it probable that the iodine is adsorbed by the hydroxide. According to W. Gregory, when hot dil. soln. of potassium iodide and lead acetate are mixed, and cooled, small yellowish-green needles mixed with yellow crystals of lead iodide are produced. The latter were removed by hot water. The crystals were at first thought to be those of lead iodide, but later observations showed that they were **lead oxydiiodide**, Pb_2OI_2, or $PbO.PbI_2$. The salt was obtained by R. Brandes, and M. Denot by treating a soln. of potassium iodide with a large excess of lead acetate, leaving the precipitate in contact with the mother-liquor for some time, and boiling with water to extract free lead iodide. The same product was obtained by leaving lead iodide for several days in contact with a soln. of lead acetate, and agitating the mixture every now and then. R. Brandes also treated a soln. of potassium iodide with one of basic lead acetate. J. Wood and J. L. Borden treated lead iodide with conc. ammonia on a sand-bath for 10 hrs. M. Gröger obtained it by heating the periodide, $PbO.PbI_2.I_3$, at about 200°. A. Ditte, and D. Strömholm obtained the anhydrous salt by heating one of the hydrates. H. N. Holmes obtained Liesegang's rings by leaving silica gel containing potassium iodide in contact with a soln. of lead acetate. The yellow or greenish-yellow oxydiiodide, according to M. Denot, fuses between 200° and 300°, giving off white fumes mixed with the vapour of iodine, and leaves behind a glassy mass. G. André gave 1·6 Cals. for the heat of formation from the solid iodide and oxide. According to R. Brandes, and M. Denot, the oxyiodide is insoluble in boiling water ; chlorine transforms it into lead chloride ; it is not changed by a soln. of potassium iodide ; it is soluble in hot dil. acetic acid, and on cooling, the soln. deposits crystals of lead iodide.

According to A. Ditte, when lead hydroxide is treated with a soln. of potassium iodide, protected from air, crystals of **hemihydrated lead oxydiiodide**, $PbO.PbI_2.\frac{1}{2}H_2O$, are formed. If the reaction takes place in air, the complex iodide, $2KI.PbI_2.4H_2O$, is produced. The reaction in the former case is a balanced one, but the potassium hydroxide, simultaneously formed when an excess of lead hydroxide is used, produces a pentoxydiiodide, $5PbO.PbI_2.7H_2O$. A. Ditte also obtained the hemihydrated oxydiiodide by the action of an aq. soln. of potassium iodide on lead iodide in the absence of air. The colourless, transparent crystals lose their water when heated, and become golden yellow; at a higher temp., the crystals melt and give off the vap. of iodine. Acids first dissolve lead oxide, and later the iodide. A. de Schulten made **monohydrated lead oxydiiodide**, $PbO.PbI_2.H_2O$, or **lead hydroxyiodide**, $Pb(OH)I$, or *iodolaurionite*, by adding a hot soln. of 20 grms. of potassium iodide in 100 c.c. of water, to 400 grms. of lead acetate in a litre of water and 30–40 c.c. of acetic acid. The filtered liquid was heated on a water-bath for 5–8 hrs. On cooling, yellow crystals were formed. J. White obtained the same salt by decomposing the double salt of lead acetoiodide with acetate of ammonium, potassium or sodium by means of water. O. B. Kühn treated lead oxyacetate with potassium iodide; D. Strömholm treated lead iodide with ammonia; and M. Gröger boiled lead periodide, $PbO.PbI_2.I_3$, with water. The pale yellow crystals were found by A. de Schulten to be rhombic bipyramids with the axial ratios $a : b : c = 0.7476 : 1 : 0.9081$; and to resemble the corresponding hydroxychloride and hydroxybromide. The sp. gr. is 6·827 at 15°. W. Biltz examined the mol. vol. O. B. Kühn said the water is all expelled at 100°, while A. de Schulten said the water is driven off at a red heat when the compound melts and gives off iodine vapour. It is not attacked by water. M. Gröger said that the salt is sparingly soluble in cold water and in alcohol; boiling alcohol, and a soln. of potassium iodide extracts iodine; and an alcoholic soln. of lead acetate colours it brown, probably forming iodine and another oxyiodide.

According to M. Denot, when basic lead acetate—*acetate plombique*—is treated with an excess of potassium iodide, or when lead iodide is boiled with lead carbonate in water, **lead dioxydiiodide**, $2PbO.PbI_2$, is formed. O. B. Kühn obtained it by boiling lead oxide repeatedly with fresh quantities of a sat. soln. of lead iodide. D. Strömholm reported **monohydrated lead trioxydiiodide**, $3PbO.PbI_2.H_2O$, or $2PbO.Pb(OH)_2.PbI_2$, to be formed when lead hydroxide is mixed with twice the amount of potassium iodide soln. employed in making the hexoxydiiodide—*vide infra*—and shaken for a long time; and also by mixing lead hydroxyiodide with enough $0.5N$-NaOH to make the ratio $OH : 1 = 0.006N - : 0.074N$. The pale yellow, microscopic crystals become deep yellow when heated; and they are attacked by soda-lye. O. B. Kühn made **dihydrated lead trioxydiiodide**, $3PbO.PbI_2.2H_2O$, or $PbO.2Pb(OH)_2.PbI_2$, as a white precipitate by adding an excess of aq. ammonia to a boiling soln. of lead iodide; and J. Wood and J. L. Borden, by heating lead iodide with conc. aq. ammonia for 38 hrs. on a water-bath. D. Strömholm prepared dihydrated **lead enneaoxytetraiodide**, $9PbO.2PbI_2$. $2H_2O$, or $7PbO.2Pb(OH)_2.2PbI_2$, as a bright yellow voluminous mass, by mixing lead hydroxide with a little more potassium iodide soln. than is necessary for the formation of hexoxydiiodide, and then with sufficient potassium iodide to precipitate all the lead from the soln. A. Ditte reported **heptahydrated lead pentoxydiiodide**, $5PbO.PbI_2.7H_2O$, to be formed in white needle-like crystals by treating lead iodide with a hot conc. soln. of potassium hydroxide, and cooling. When treated with acids, lead iodide remains. When heated, the water is all expelled and yellow **lead pentoxydiiodide**, $5PbO.PbI_2$, remains. D. Strömholm could not make the hydrated salt. C. Langlois prepared the anhydrous salt by heating lead dioxydiperiodate, $2PbO.Pb(IO_4)_2.2H_2O$, in a tube. J. Wood and J. L. Borden obtained a hydrated form of this oxyiodide by heating lead iodide with conc. aq. ammonia on a water-bath for 68 hrs. M. Denot said that when melted it behaves like the oxydiiodide. D. Strömholm reported **dihydrated lead hexoxydiiodide**,

$6PbO.PbI_2.2H_2O$, or $4PbO.2Pb(OH)_2.PbI_2$, to be formed as a white voluminous mass of microscopic crystals, by allowing lead hydroxide to stand in contact with $0.5N$-KI until the soln. is free from iodine. It behaves like the corresponding chloride when heated.

C. F. Cross and S. Sugiura passed iodine vapour over heated lead dioxide, and repeated the treatment on the powdered product until its composition was not changed; the orange-yellow product had the composition *lead heptoxypentaiodide*, $Pb_{11}O_7I_5$. By using lead monoxide in place of the dioxide, *lead hexoxytetraiodide*, $Pb_9O_6I_4$, was formed. By passing a mixture of air and iodine vapour over lead monoxide, *lead octoxydiiodide*, $Pb_9O_8I_2$, was produced; when lead dioxide was used, yellow *lead decoxytetraiodide*, $Pb_{13}O_{10}I_4$, of sp. gr. 7·81, was formed.

M. Gröger described a compound with a composition $PbO.PbI_2.I_3$, as an amorphous precipitate, and this was confirmed by H. L. Wells, who showed that M. Gröger overlooked the presence of water, so that the product is **monohydrated lead oxypentaiodide**, $PbO.PbI_2.I_3.H_2O$. There is no evidence that the "excess iodine" is present as lead tetraiodide. H. L. Wells obtained it in brilliant black crystals, forming octahedra belonging to the tetragonal system, and with their faces much curved and distorted. The method of preparation is as follows:

Dissolve 10 grms. iodine in 100 c.c. absolute alcohol, then 50 grms. crystallized lead acetate in 150 c.c. of water, 3 c.c. glacial acetic acid, and 300 c.c. absolute alcohol. Mix the two soln., let stand 14–16 hrs. at the temp. of the room, filter to remove the small precipitate, then dil. with 1500 c.c. of boiling water. Let the whole stand until cold, when the compound sought will have crystallized out, mixed with iodine. Pour off the liquid and wash the crystals with cold alcohol in small quantities until the iodine is removed. Dry the product upon filter-paper, and then in the air at ordinary temp.

H. L. Wells used other methods of preparation—e.g. alcoholic soln. containing lead acetate and iodine, or potassium iodide. The presence of acetate was said to be indispensable because with lead nitrate the salt is not formed. The compound cannot be recrystallized from water, alcohol, or mixtures of the two liquids; and M. Gröger suggested that it is formed by the decomposition of some complex compound by water. The crystals are stable in dry air, but when heated for a long time at 100°, or for a short time at 200°, the salt is decomposed, forming the yellow oxyiodide, $PbO.PbI_2$. The salt is scarcely acted upon by water, but it is slightly soluble in cold water; with boiling water, lead hydroxyiodide is formed. The "excess iodine" is not dissolved out by cold alcohol, but is removed by a soln. of potassium iodide; with boiling alcohol, dark yellow lead oxydiiodide is formed. Warm acetic acid decomposes it into lead acetate, lead iodide, and iodine; it forms a brown liquid with a soln. of lead acetate, and is slowly decomposed.

B. Dietzell [17] reported a lead oxychloroiodide to be formed by the action of a small excess of lead acetate on a mixture of potassium iodide and chloride. The washed precipitate was dissolved in a little dil. acetic acid and evaporated, when greenish-yellow prisms of the oxychloroiodide of variable composition were deposited before the yellow lead iodide appeared. According to I. Domeyko, M. Schwartzemberg discovered an *oxychloroiodure de plomb*, forming crusts on the galena at a mine about 15 leagues from Paposo in the desert of Atacama; it was also reported by G. F. H. Smith in samples from San Rafael mine, Bolivia; by A. Frenzel, from Sierra Gorda, Peru; etc. I. Domeyko called it *plombo oxichloroïoduro*; J. B. Dana, **schwartzembergite**; and M. Adam, *plumboiodite*. Analyses were reported by I. Domeyko, and K. T. Liebe, and they correspond with $Pb_{10}Cl_6I_2O_{12}$; or, according to G. F. H. Smith and G. T. Prior, *lead hexoxydiiodatohexachloride*, $3Pb_3O_2Cl_2.Pb(IO_3)_2$, or, according to P. Groth, **lead dioxyiodochloride**, $2PbO.Pb(I,Cl)_2$. K. T. Liebe considers everything except lead oxide and iodide to be present as an impurity. The purer samples are honey-yellow, and others vary from straw-yellow to reddish-yellow. The rhombohedral crystals were found by G. F. H. Smith and G. T. Prior to be tetragonal, with the axial ratio $a:c=1:0.430$, and not rhombohedral as stated by K. T. Liebe. E. Bertrand found the optical character negative, and uniaxial. The crystals are flat, square pyramids with rounded faces, and are optically anomalous, showing a division into sectors with the optic axial angles $2V=16°$-$28°$. K. T. Liebe gave 6·2-6·3 for sp. gr. : I. Domeyko gave 5·7-6·7, and for the hardness, $1\frac{1}{2}$-2. According to G. F. H. Smith and G. T. Prior, the refractive index is about 2·35 ; and when the mineral is heated with hydrochloric acid, chlorine is evolved ; and in the cold nitric acid soln. the iodine is present as iodate, not as iodide. A. C. Vournasos prepared *lead dibromodiiodide*. $K_2[PbI_2Br_2]$.

REFERENCES.

[1] H. G. Denham, *Journ. Chem. Soc.*, 111. 32, 1917.

[2] G. Tammann, *Gött. Nachr.*, 225, 1919 ; *Zeit. anorg. Chem.*, 111. 78, 1920 ; H. Braune and F. Koref, *ib.*, 87. 178, 1914 ; *Zeit. Elektrochem.*, 18. 819, 1912 ; F. von Kobell, *Journ. prakt. Chem.*, (2), 3. 469, 1871 ; J. L. Gay Lussac, *Ann. Chim. Phys.*, (1), 88. 311, 1813 ; (1), 91. 5, 1814 ; P. Boullay, *Journ. Pharm. Chim.*, (2), 12. 639, 1826 ; *Ann. Chim. Phys.*, (2), 34. 366, 1827 ; A. C. Becquerel, *ib.*, (2), 41. 33, 1829 ; *Traité expérimental de l'électricité et du magnétisme*, Paris, 2. 86, 1855 ; H. St. C. Deville, *Compt. Rend.*, 42. 894, 1856 ; V. Thomas, *ib.*, 128. 1234, 1889 ; J. Inglis, *Phil. Mag.*, (3), 7. 441, 1835 ; (3), 8. 12, 191, 1836 ; W. F. O. de Coninck and L. Arzalier, *Bull. Acad. Belg.*, 800, 1907 ; O. Henry, *Journ. Pharm. Chim.*, (2), 17. 267, 1831 ; L. J. Girault, *ib.*, (3), 27. 396, 1855 ; A. Frenzel, *Tschermak's Mitt.*, (2), 11. 220, 1890 ; T. Huraut, *Journ. Pharm. Chim.*, (3), 15. 34, 1849 ; E. Boudet, *ib.*, (3), 11. 274, 1847 ; H. Davy, *Phil. Trans.*, 104. 74, 1814 ; R. Brandes, *Liebig's Ann.*, 10. 266, 1834 ; R. Benedikt, *Chem. Ztg.*, 16. 43, 1892 ; L. Hopff, *Kastner's Arch.*, 22. 71, 1831 ; G. Campani, *Gazz. Chim. Ital.*, 6. 461, 1876 ; H. S. Taylor, *Journ. Amer. Chem. Soc.*, 38. 2295, 1916 ; A. A. Noyes and E. H. Woodworth, *ib.*, 20. 195, 1898 ; P. Casamajor, *ib.*, 7. 133, 1885 ; V. Lehner, *ib.*, 23. 681, 1901 ; J. A. Wilkinson, *Journ. Phys. Chem.*, 13. 695, 1909 ; E. Küster, *Koll. Zeit.*, 18. 107, 1916 ; E. Hatschek, *Proc. Roy. Soc.*, 99. A, 496, 1921 ; *Koll. Zeit.*, 10. 124, 1912 ; R. E. Liesegang, *ib.*, 12. 74, 1913 ; K. Notbohm, *ib.*, 32. 247, 1923 ; W. Reinders, *ib.*, 21. 161, 1917 ; H. H. Holmes, *Journ. Franklin Inst.*, 184. 184, 1917 ; A. Findlay, *Zeit. phys. Chem.*, 34. 409, 1900 ; H. Zocher, *ib.*, 98. 293, 1921 ; P. Fischer, *Zeit. Elektrochem.*, 31. 286, 1925 ; H. B. Cornwall, *Chem. News*, 34. 27, 1876 ; *Amer. Chemist*, 2. 324, 1872 ; W. Leuze, *Zur Kenntnis kolloider Metalle und ihrer Verbindungen*, Erlangen, 32, 1904 ; E. H. Büchner and J. Kalff, *Proc. Accad. Amsterdam*, 28. 145, 1919 ; *Rec. Trav. Chim. Pays-Bas*, 39. 135, 1920 ; O. Lehmann, *Zeit. Kryst.*, 1. 490, 1877 ; M. Volmer, *Zeit. phys. Chem.*, 102. 267, 1922 ; H. Lachs, *Journ. Phys. Rad.*, 3. 125, 1922 ; R. Benedikt, *Chem. Ztg.*, 16. 43, 1892.

[3] M. Denot, *Journ. prakt. Chem.*, (1), 1. 425, 1834 ; *Journ. Pharm. Chim.*, (2), 20. 1, 1834 ; O. Henry, *ib.*, (2), 17. 267, 1832 ; A. Magnus, *Ann. Physik*, (4), 31. 607, 1910 ; F. Koref, *ib.*, (4), 36. 61, 1911 ; W. Nernst and F. Schwers, *Sitzber. Akad. Berlin*, 369, 1914 ; H. Schottky, *Phys. Zeit.*, 10. 634, 1909 ; J. Inglis, *Phil. Mag.*, (3), 7. 441, 1835 ; (3), 8. 12, 191, 1836 ; W. Ramsay and N. Eumorfopoulos, *ib.*, (5), 41. 360, 1896 ; A. Findlay, *Zeit. phys. Chem.*, 34. 409, 1900 ; H. Burschall, *Zeit. Elektrochem.*, 17. 341, 1911 ; W. Biltz, *ib.*, 29. 248, 1923 ; P. Günther, *ib.*, 23. 199, 1917 ; H. Braune and F. Koref, *ib.*, 18. 819, 1912 ; *Zeit. anorg. Chem.*, 87. 178, 1914 ; H. Braune, *ib.*, 87. 188, 1914 ; A. E. Nordenskjöld, *Bihang Svenska Akad. Handl.*, 2. 2, 1874 ; A. des Cloizeaux, *Ann. Mines*, (5), 11. 307, 1857 ; F. Matthes, *Neues Jahrb. Min. B.B.*, 31. 342, 1915 ; K. Mönkemeyer, *ib.*, 22. i, 1906 ; C. J. B. Karsten, *Schweigger's Journ.*, 65. 394, 1832 ; H. Fizeau, *Compt. Rend.*, 64. 314, 771, 1867 ; P. F. G. Boullay, *Ann. Chim. Phys.*, (2), 43. 266, 1830 ; E. Filhol, *ib.*, (3), 21. 415, 1847 ; H. V. Regnault, *ib.*, (3), 1. 129, 1841 ; J. L. Gay Lussac, *ib.*, (1), 88. 311, 1813 ; (1), 91. 5, 1814 ; M. Schtscherbakoff, *Journ. Russ. Phys. Chem. Soc.*, 37. 682, 1905 ; G. Tschermak, *Sitzber. Akad. Wien*, 45. 605, 1862 ; R. Schiff, *Liebig's Ann.*, 108. 21, 1858 ; R. Brandes, *ib.*, 10. 266, 1834 ; G. F. Rodwell, *Phil. Trans.*, 173. 1125, 1882 ; *Proc. Roy. Soc.*, 32. 23, 1881 ; *Chem. News*, 43. 169, 1881 ; H. G. F. Schröder, *Pogg. Ann.*, 107. 113, 1859 ; S. Motylewsky, *Zeit. anorg. Chem.*, 38. 414, 1909 ; C. Tubandt and G. Eggert, *ib.*, 110. 218, 1920 ; G. D. Roos, *ib.*, 94. 356, 1916 ; V. Czepinsky, *ib.*, 19. 257, 1899 ; *Journ. Russ. Phys. Chem. Soc.*, 31. 315, 1899 ; O. Ehrhardt, *Wied. Ann.*, 24. 215, 1885 ; J. Rosenthal, *ib.*, 43. 722, 1891 ; J. H. Kastle, *Amer. Chem. Journ.*, 23. 500, 1900 ; T. Carnelley, *Journ. Chem. Soc.*, 33. 277, 1878 ; T. Carnelley and L. T. O'Shea, *ib.*, 45. 409, 1884 ; T. Carnelley and W. C. Williams, *ib.*, 37. 126, 1880 ; H. Crompton, *ib.*, 71. 924, 1897 ; M. de K. Thompson, *Journ. Amer. Chem. Soc.*, 28. 731, 1906 ; H. S. Taylor, *ib.*, 38. 2295, 1916 ; D. M. Lichty, *ib.*, 25. 472, 1903 ; M. L. Dundon, *ib.*, 45. 2658, 1923 ; J. Thomsen, *Thermochemische Untersuchungen*, Leipzig, 3. 337, 1883 ; M. Berthelot, *Thermochimie*, Paris, 2. 340, 1897 ; *Annuaire*, 395, 1877 ; C. Sandonnini, *Gazz. Chim. Ital.*, 41. ii. 145, 1911 ; A. Heiduschka, *Arch. Pharm.*, 244. 571, 1906 ; A. P. Laurie and C. I. Burton, *Proc. Roy. Soc. Edin.*, 11. 804, 1882 ; C. Zengelis, *Zeit. phys. Chem.*, 50. 219, 1904 ; F. A. Henglein, *Zeit. anorg. Chem.*, 120. 77, 1921 ; L. W. Fisher and F. L. Simon, *Amer. Min.*, 11. 124, 1926 ; P. Terpstra and H. G. Westenbrink, *Versl. Amsterdam Acad.*, 35. 75, 1926 ; K. Jellinek and R. Uloth, *Zeit. anorg. Chem.*, 151. 157, 1926 ; *Zeit. phys. Chem.*, 119. 161, 1926 ; M. Volmer, *ib.*, 102. 267, 1922 ; W. Braunbek, *Zeit. Physik*, 38. 549, 1926.

[4] M. Faraday, *Phil. Trans.*, 124. 77, 1834 ; E. Wiedemann, *Boltzmann's Festschrift*, 826, 1904 ;

Pogg. Ann., **154**. 318, 1875 ; J. Rosenthal, *Wied. Ann.*, **43**. 718, 1891 ; L. Graetz, *ib.*, **29**. 329, 1886 ; **40**. 27, 1890 ; L. Graetz and O. Fromm, *ib.*, **54**. 636, 1895 ; S. Meyer, *ib.*, **69**. 245, 1899 ; B. A. Dima, *Compt. Rend.*, **157**. 592, 1913 ; J. A. Wilkinson, *Journ. Phys. Chem.*, **13**. 695, 1909 ; C. Tubandt and S. Eggert, *Zeit. anorg. Chem.*, **110**. 219, 1920 ; F. Quincke, *ib.*, **24**. 220, 1900 ; *Zeit. Elektrochem.*, **4**. 54, 1898 ; C. C. Garrard, *ib.*, **6**. 214, 1899 ; *Zeit. anorg. Chem.*, **25** 273, 1890 ; A. Helfenstein, *ib.*, **23**. 255, 1900 ; G. Auerbach, *ib.*, **28**. 1, 1901 ; R. Lorenz, *ib.*, **23**. 99, 1900 ; **24**. 222, 1900 ; W. Hampe, *Ber.*, **21**. 161, 1888 ; A. Benrath, *Zeit. phys. Chem.*, **64**. 694, 1908 ; A. Klein, *ib.*, **36**. 360, 1901 ; A. Gockel, *ib.*, **34**. 544, 1900 ; W. Böttger, *ib.*, **46**. 521, 1903 ; *Löslich-keitsstudien an schwer löslichen Stoffen*, Leipzig, 1903 ; M. Schtscherbakoff, *Journ. Russ. Phys. Chem. Soc.*, **37**. 682, 1905 ; V. Czepinsky, *ib.*, **31**. 315, 1899 ; *Zeit. anorg. Chem.*, **19**. 257, 1899 ; A. Lenert, *Verh. deut. phys. Ges.*, **12**. 1051, 1910 ; C. L. von Ende, *Ueber das Verhalten der Bleisalze in Lösungen*, Göttingen, 1899 ; *Zeit. anorg. Chem.*, **26**. 159, 1901 ; G. Tammann and H. Bred-meier, *ib.*, **144**. 64, 1925 ; G. N. Lewis and T. B. Brighton, *Journ. Amer. Chem. Soc.*, **39**. 1906, 1917 ; H. G. Denham, *Journ. Chem. Soc.*, **111**. 39, 1917 ; H. Crompton, *ib.*, **71**. 725, 1897 ; W. W. Coblentz and J. F. Eckford, *Scient. Paper U.S. Bur. Standards*, **18**. 489, 1922 ; L. Ebert, *Zeit. phys. Chem.*, **113**. 1, 1924 ; J. Thiele, *Phys. Zeit.*, **26**. 321, 1925.

⁵ M. Schtscherbakoff, *Journ. Russ. Phys. Chem. Soc.*, **37**. 682, 1905 ; A. Benrath, *Zeit. phys. Chem.*, **64**. 694, 1908 ; R. Brandes, *Liebig's Ann.*, **10**. 266, 1834 ; W. Schmid, *Pogg. Ann.*, **127**. 493, 1866 ; A. Jouniaux, *Compt. Rend.*, **136**. 1005, 1903 ; *Journ. Chim. Phys.*, **1**. 609, 1903 ; Z. Roussin, *Ann. Chim. Phys.*, (3), **47**. 154, 1856 ; F. de Carli, *Atti Accad. Lincei*, (5), **33**. ii, 94, 1924 ; N. R. Dhar and A. C. Chatterji, *Journ. Phys. Chem.*, **28**. 41, 1924 ; K. Jellinek and R. Uloth, *Zeit. anorg. Chem.*, **151**. 157, 1926.

⁶ W. D. Bancroft, *Journ. Phys. Chem.*, **1**. 344, 786, 1897 ; J. M. Talmadge, *ib.*, **1**. 493, 1897 ; D. M. Lichty, *Journ. Amer. Chem. Soc.*, **25**. 472, 1903 ; M. de K. Thompson, *ib.*, **28**. 731, 1906 ; G. N. Lewis and T. B. Brighton, *ib.*, **39**. 1906, 1917 ; W. Böttger, *Löslichkeitsstudien an schwer löslichen Stoffen*, Leipzig, 1903 ; *Zeit. phys. Chem.*, **46**. 521, 1903 ; V. Zotier, *Bull. Soc. Chim.*, (4), **21**. 241, 1917 ; J. B. Berthemot, *Journ. Pharm. Chim.*, (2), **13**. 412, 1827 ; J. B. Caventou, *ib.*, (2), **17**. 266, 1831 ; M. Denot, *ib.*, (2), **20**. 1, 1834 ; *Journ. prakt. Chem.*, (1), **1**. 425, 1834 ; P. F. G. Boullay, *Ann. Chim. Phys.*, (2), **43**. 266, 1830 ; M. Berthelot, *ib.*, (5), **29**. 290, 1883 ; C. L. von Ende, *Ueber das Verhalten der Bleisalze in Lösungen*, Göttingen, 1899 ; *Zeit. anorg. Chem.*, **26**. 159, 1901 ; H. Braune and F. Koref, *ib.*, **87**. 178, 1914 ; *Zeit. Elektrochem.*, **18**. 820, 1912 ; J. L. Lassaigne, *Journ. Chim. Méd.*, **7**. 364, 1830 ; J. White, *Amer. Chem. Journ.*, **31**. 22, 1904 ; H. G. Denham, *Journ. Chem. Soc.*, **111**. 39, 1917 ; H. Crompton, *ib.*, **71**. 725, 1897 ; M. Schtscherbakoff, *Journ. Russ. Phys. Chem. Soc.*, **37**. 682, 1905 ; W. E. van Wijk, *Chem. Weekbl.*, **14**. 315, 1917 ; M. L. Dundon, *Journ. Amer. Chem. Soc.*, **45**. 2658, 1923.

⁷ A. Mosnier, *Ann. Chim. Phys.*, (7), **12**. 423, 1897 ; *Compt. Rend.*, **120**. 444, 1895 ; V. Thomas, *ib.*, **126**. 1350, 1898 ; **128**. 1329, 1899 ; F. Parmentier, *ib.*, **114**. 300, 802, 1892 ; A. Ditte, *ib.*, **92**. 719, 1341, 1881 ; *Ann. Chim. Phys.*, (5), **24**. 227, 252, 1881 ; P. F. G. Boullay, *ib.*, (2), **43**. 266, 1830 ; M. Berthelot, *ib.*, (5), **29**. 292, 1883 ; H. Moissan, *ib.*, (6), **24**. 258, 1891 ; P. Hautefeuille, *Bull. Soc. Chim.*, (2), **7**. 200, 1867 ; H. Maisch, *Amer. Journ. Pharm.*, **56**. 91–94, 1884 ; *Arch. Pharm.*, (3), **22**. 672, 1884 ; C. Völckel, *Liebig's Ann.*, **62**. 252, 1844 ; F. D. Chatta-way, *Chem. News*, **74**. 267, 1896 ; *Journ. Chem. Soc.*, **69**. 1572, *f*896 ; E. Field, *ib.*, **63**. 545, 1893 ; *Chem. News*, **67**. 157, 1893 ; B. Thorp, *Amer. Chem. Journ.*, **10**. 232, 1888 ; C. H. Herty, *ib.*, **14**. 126, 1892 ; V. Lenher, *Journ. Amer. Chem. Soc.*, **23**. 681, 1901 ; A. A. Noyes and E. H. Woodworth, *ib.*, **20**. 197, 1898 ; P. Fedotieff, *Zeit. anorg. Chem.*, **73**. 173, 1911 ; J. B. Berthe-mot, *Journ. Pharm. Chim.*, (2), **13**. 412, 1827 ; A. Bogorodsky, *Journ. Russ. Phys. Chem.*, **26**. 216, 1894 ; R. W. Balcom in R. Abegg, *Handbuch der anorganischen Chemie*, Leipzig, **3**. ii, 667, 1909 ; R. H. Brett, *Phil. Mag.*, (3), **10**. 95, 1837 ; R. Brandes, *Trommsdorff's Journ.*, **3**. 252, 1819.

⁸ K. A. Hofmann and V. Wölfl, *Ber.*, **37**. 250, 1904 ; A. Michaelis and G. Koethe, *ib.*, **6**. 999, 1873 ; A. Naumann, *ib.*, **37**. 4612, 1904 ; F. Field, *Journ. Chem. Soc.*, **16**. 28, 1863 ; A. Ditte, *Ann. Chim. Phys.*, (5), **14**. 227, 1878 ; G. C. Wittstein, *Repert. Pharm.*, **63**. 331, 1833 ; C. G. Stoffella, *Boll. Chim. Farm.*, **64**. 481, 1925.

⁹ C. F. Rammelsberg, *Pogg. Ann.*, **48**. 166, 1839 ; M. Labouré, *Journ. Pharm. Chim.*, (3), **4**. 328, 1843 ; F. Ephraim, *Zeit. phys. Chem.*, **83**. 204, 1913 ; E. C. Franklin, *Journ. Amer. Chem. Soc.*, **27**. 820, 1905 ; C. A. Kraus and H. F. Kurtz, *ib.*, **47**. 43, 1925 ; E. C. Franklin and C. A. Kraus, *Amer. Chem. Journ.*, **20**. 823, 1898 ; G. C. Wittstein, *Repert Pharm.*, **63**. 331, 1833 ; W. Biltz, *Zeit. anorg. Chem.*, **124**. 241, 1922 ; K. Friedrichs, *ib.*, **84**. 373, 1913 ; C. L. Clark, *Amer. Journ. Science*, (5), **7**. 1, 1924.

¹⁰ E. C. Franklin, *Journ. Amer. Chem. Soc.*, **27**. 820, 1905 ; T. W. B. Welsh and H. J. Broder-son, *ib.*, **37**. 819, 1915 ; A. A. Noyes and E. H. Woodworth, *ib.*, **20**. 197, 1898 ; R. Benedikt and L. Gans, *Chem. Ztg.*, **16**. 43, 181, 1892 ; F. W. O. de Coninck, *Bull. Acad. Belg.*, 509, 1909 ; J. B. Berthemot, *Journ. Pharm. Chim.*, (2), **13**. 412, 1827 ; G. C. Wittstein, *Repert Pharm.*, **63**. 331, 1833 ; C. Stürenberg, *Arch. Pharm.*, (2), **143**. 12, 1870 ; A. Naumann, *Ber.*, **37**. 4612, 1904 ; P. Fedotieff, *Zeit. anorg. Chem.*, **73**. 173, 1911 ; C. L. von Ende, *ib.*, **26**. 159, 1901 ; *Ueber das Verhalten der Bleisalze in Lösungen*, Göttingen, 1899 ; V. Thomas, *Contribution a l'étude de quelques sels métalliques halogénés*, Paris, 1897 ; *Bull. Soc. Chim.*, (3), **15**. 1092, 1896 ; *Compt Rend.*, **126**. 1352, 1898 ; *Ann. Chim. Phys.*, (7), **13**. 223, 1898 ; A. Mosnier, *ib.*, (7), **12**. 378, 1897 ; *Compt. Rend.*, **120**. 416, 444, 1895 ; *Sur quelques combinaisons de l'iodure de plomb avec d'autres iodures métalliques et organiques*, Paris, 1897.

[11] W. Eidmann, *Ein Beitrag zur Erkenntnis des Verhaltens chemischer Verbindungen in nichtwässrigen Lösungen*, Giessen, 1899; S. von Laszczynsky, *Ber.*, 27. 2238, 1894; H. Mandal, *ib.*, 54. 704, 1921; W. Goebbels, *ib.*, 28. 794, 1895; A. Naumann, *ib.*, 37. 4329, 1904; 42. 3790, 1909; 43. 314, 1910; 47. 1369, 1914; A. Ditte, *Compt. Rend.*, 92. 1456, 1881; *Ann. Chim. Phys.*, (5), 24. 239, 1881; D. Tommasi, *ib.*, (4), 25. 170, 1872; *Bull. Soc. Chim.*, (2), 17. 337, 1872; A. P. N. Franchimont, *Rec. Trav. Chim. Pays-Bas*, 1. 55, 1883; A. Vogel, *Journ. prakt. Chem.*, (1), 22. 148, 1841; O. Aschan, *Chem. Ztg.*, 37. 1117, 1913; W. Eisner, *Arch. Exp. Path. Pharm.*, 102. 305, 1924; H. G. Denham, *Journ. Chem. Soc.*, 111. 40, 1917; G. C. Wittstein, *Repert. Pharm.*, 63. 331, 1833; F. L. Shinn, *Journ. Phys. Chem.*, 11. 538, 1907; J. H. Matthews, *ib.*, 9. 647, 1905; G. W. Heise, *ib.*, 16. 373, 1912; W. Wildermann, *Zeit. phys. Chem.*, 9. 21, 1892; J. Spiller, *Journ. Chem. Soc.*, 10. 110, 1858; *Chem. News*, 8. 280, 1863; 19. 166, 1869; J. W. Retgers, *Zeit. anorg. Chem.*, 3. 346, 1893; H. Braune and F. Koref, *ib.*, 87. 182, 1914; *Zeit. Elektrochem.*, 18. 821, 1912; J. White, *Amer. Chem. Journ.*, 31. 5, 1904; B. Thorp, *ib.*, 10. 231, 1888; J. B. Berthemot, *Journ. Pharm. Chim.*, (2), 13. 412, 1827; O. Henry, *ib.*, (2), 17. 267, 1836; M. Denot, *ib.*, (2), 20. 1, 1834; *Journ. prakt. Chem.*, (1), 1. 425, 1834; B. Köhnlein, *Liebig's Ann.*, 225. 173, 1884; R. Brix, *ib.*, 225. 161, 1884; L. Pincussohn, *Beiträge zur Kenntnis der Pyridinverbindungen*, Berlin, 1897; *Zeit. anorg. Chem.*, 14. 385, 1897; H. Arctowsky, *ib.*, 6. 257, 1894; C. F. Schlagdenhauffen, *Journ. Pharm. d'Alsace-Lorraine*, 5. 140, 1878; L. Kahlenberg and W. J. Trautmann, *Trans. Amer. Electrochem. Soc.*, 39. 477, 1921.

[12] M. Faraday, *Phil. Trans.*, 124. 77, 1834; K. Elbs and R. Nübling, *Zeit. Elektrochem.*, 9. 779, 1903; A. Helfenstein, *Zeit. anorg. Chem.*, 23. 255, 1900; G. Auerbach, *ib.*, 28. 1, 1901; V. Czepinsky, *ib.*, 19. 257, 1899; *Journ. Russ. Phys. Chem. Soc.*, 31. 315, 1899; E. Erlenmeyer, *Zeit. Chem.*, (1), 4. 152, 1861; H. Friedrich, *Monatsh.*, 14. 514, 1893; B. Piffard, *Chem. News*, 3. 151, 1861; A. Hutchinson and W. Pollard, *Journ. Chem. Soc.*, 69. 212, 1896; A. N. Meldrum, *Proc. Chem. Soc.*, 24. 97, 1908; H. L. Wells, *Amer. Journ. Science*, (3), 46. 190, 1893; A. Classen and B. Zahorsky, *Zeit. anorg. Chem.*, 4. 105, 1893.

[13] J. L. Lassaigne, *Journ. Chim. Méd.*, (2), 2. 247, 1836; M. Berthelot, *Compt. Rend.*, 91. 1026, 1880; *Ann. Chim. Phys.*, (5), 23. 88, 1881.

[14] H. Fonzes-Diacon, *Bull. Soc. Chim.*, (3), 17. 350, 1897; E. Field, *Journ. Chem. Soc.*, 63. 545, 1893; *Chem. News*, 67. 157, 1893; C. Sandonnini, *Atti Accad. Lincei*, (5), 20. i, 253, 1911; *Gazz. Chim. Ital.*, 41. ii, 152, 1911.

[15] F. Matthes, *Neues Jahrb. Min. B.B.*, 31. 342, 1911; A. Engelhardt, *Bull. Acad. St. Petersburg*, (3), 14. 145, 1856; C. H. Herty and T. R. Boggs, *Journ. Amer. Chem. Soc.*, 19. 821, 1897; C. H. Herty, *Amer. Chem. Journ.*, 18. 293, 1896; B. Thorp, *ib.*, 10. 232, 1888; E. Field, *Journ. Chem. Soc.*, 63. 545, 1893; *Chem. News*, 67. 157, 1893; H. Fonzes-Diacon, *Bull. Soc. Chim.*, (3), 17. 350, 1897; V. Thomas, *ib.*, (3), 19. 491, 1898; (3), 21. 532, 1899; *Compt. Rend.*, 126. 1350, 1898; 128. 1329, 1899; A. B. Poggiale, *ib.*, 20. 1184, 1845; M. Labouré, *Journ. Pharm. Chim.*, (3), 4. 328, 1843; B. Dietzell, *Dingler's Journ.*, 190. 42, 1868; L. J. Burrage, *Journ. Chem. Soc.*, 129. 1896, 1926; S. Glasstone, *ib.*, 119. 1997, 1921.

[16] P. B. Durand, *Journ. Pharm. Chim.*, (3), 2. 311, 1842; M. Jammes, *ib.*, (3), 3. 356, 1843; W. Gregory, *ib.*, (2), 18. 24, 1832; M. Denot, *ib.*, (2), 20. 1, 1834; E. Filhol, *Compt. Rend.*, 19. 761, 1844; A. Ditte, *ib.*, 92. 1454, 1881; *Ann. Chim. Phys.*, (5), 24. 353, 1881; M. Berthelot, *ib.*, (5), 29. 293, 1883; G. André, *ib.*, (6), 3. 128, 1884; C. Langlois, *ib.*, (3), 34. 257, 1852; R. Brandes, *Liebig's Ann.*, 10. 269, 1834; D. Strömholm, *Zeit. anorg. Chem.*, 38. 440, 1904; M. Gröger, *Sitzber. Akad. Wien*, 101. 417, 1892; *Monatsh.*, 13. 510, 1892; H. L. Wells, *Amer. Journ. Science*, (4), 1. 21, 1895; H. N. Holmes, *Journ. Amer. Chem. Soc.*, 40. 1187, 1918; J. Wood and J. L. Borden, *ib.*, 6. 220, 1884; *Chem. News*, 52. 44, 1885; A. de Schulten, *Bull. Soc. Min.*, 20. 189, 1897; J. White, *Amer. Chem. Journ.*, 31. 21, 1904; O. B. Kühn, *Arch. Pharm.*, (2), 50. 281, 1847; C. F. Cross and S. Sugiura, *Journ. Chem. Soc.*, 33. 406, 1878; W. Biltz, *Zeit. anorg. Chem.*, 115. 241, 1921; A. C. Vournasos, *ib.*, 150. 147, 1926.

[17] I. Domeyko, *Ann. Mines*, (5), 453, 1864; *Elementos de mineralojia*, Santiago, 319, 705, 1879; *Journ. prakt. Chem.*, (1), 94. 192, 1865; G. F. H. Smith and G. T. Prior, *Min. Mag.*, 16. 79, 1911; E. Bertrand, *Bull. Soc. Min.*, 4. 87, 1881; J. B. Dana, *System of Mineralogy*, New York, 120, 1868; K. T. Liebe, *Neues Jahrb. Min.*, 162, 1867; B. Dietzell, *Dingler's Journ.*, 190. 42, 1868; P. Groth, *Tabellarische Uebersicht der Mineralien*, Braunschweig, 54, 1898; M. Adam, *Tableau minéralogique*, Paris, 67, 1869; A. Frenzel, *Tschermak's Mitt.*, (2), 11. 222, 1890; K. T. Liebe, *Neues Jahrb. Min.*, 159, 1867; A. C. Vournasos, *Zeit. anorg. Chem.*, 150. 147, 1926.

§ 28. The Complex Salts of Lead Iodide

P. F. G. Boullay [1] reported an ammonium iodoplumbite to be formed as a white precipitate when a soln. of lead nitrate is treated with an excess of ammonium iodide. The product was said to be decomposed by water. H. L. Wells and W. R. Johnston made a search for various ammonium salts, but were able to prepare only **ammonium triiodoplumbite**, $NH_4PbI_3.2H_2O$, in yellow, hair-like crystals, by dissolving 100 grms. of ammonium iodide and 10 grms. of lead iodide in sufficient hot water to make 108 c.c., and cooling. They noticed that if lead iodide was deposited from a moderately conc., hot soln. of ammonium iodide, the lead iodide disappeared on cooling, and its place was taken by a compact, silky mass of crystals. C. H. Herty said that the process employed by E. Field for the 4 : 3-salt—*vide infra*—yielded this salt. J. White obtained this salt from the mother-liquor resulting from the preparation of ammonium acetoiodoplumbite, and he said that diffused daylight colours the yellow powder brownish-red, and greyish-brown owing to the liberation of iodine. This is the only complex iodide which N. Demassieux could find in her study of the ternary system : $NH_4I-PbI_2-H_2O$. E. Field reported ammonium **decaiodotriplumbite**, $(NH_4)_4Pb_3I_{10}$, to be formed by boiling a mixture of 30 grms. of ammonium iodide, one gram of lead iodide or chloride, and 75 c.c. of water, cooling the filtered. soln., and drying the product at 100°. C. H. Herty found the 1 : 1 salt to be produced by this process. On the contrary, H. Fonzes-Diacon said that soln. of lead and ammonium iodides always furnish **hexahydrated ammonium decaiodotriplumbite**, $(NH_4)_4Pb_3I_{10}.6H_2O$, which, according to A. Mosnier, becomes anhydrous at 105°. The heat of formation for $(4NH_4I, 3PbI_2)$ is 3·75 Cals., and for the hydrated salt, 9·51 Cals. with liquid, and 0·93 Cal. with solid water. The white needle-like crystals of the hydrate have a yellow tinge, and, according to H. Fonzes-Diacon, they are monoclinic. The hydrated salt dissociates at 18°, and A. Mosnier gave for the vap. press., p mm. :

	19°	28·5°	46°	57°	72°	78°	85°	90°	98·5°
p	8	33	98	140	230	272	331	388	501

The salt is decomposed by water ; but H. Fonzes-Diacon said that if 62·7 grms. of ammonium iodide are present per litre, the complex salt is not decomposed— A. Mosnier said 168 grms. per litre at 10°, and 197 grms. per litre at 15° are needed to inhibit the decomposition. Soln. of ammonium halides were found by H. Fonzes-Diacon to replace the ammonium iodide with hot, but not with cold, soln. The solubility of the decaiodotriplumbite in soln. of ammonium iodide increases with conc. and temp. ; thus, A. Mosnier gave for the solubility, S, in grams per litre :

	10·5°	15°	16°	28°	38°
NH_4I	198	217·6	256	317·6	470·8
S	2·8	8·4	13·5	36·6	67·2

If oxy-salts are present, the decaiodotriplumbite is decomposed however much ammonium iodide be present. With ordinary or absolute ethyl alcohol, or methyl alcohol, lead iodide is precipitated as in the case of water. Expressing the solubility, S, in grams of salt per 1000 grms. of absolute alcohol :

	Methyl alcohol.			Ethyl alcohol.		
	15°	28°	38°	15°	28°	38°
NH_4I	39·16	55·8	82·9	38·8	55·4	82·14
S	0·84	1·4	2·10	0·70	1·26	1·96

The salt is not affected by pure and dried ether, but ordinary ether is coloured by the separation of lead iodide ; while ether which has been exposed to air, and therefore contains peroxides, is coloured reddish-yellow by the separation of iodine—lead oxyiodide is formed at the same time. A. Ditte claimed to have made **tetrahydrated ammonium tetraiodoplumbite**, $(NH_4)_2PbI_4.4H_2O$, by the action of a soln. of lead nitrate on one of potassium iodide, as in the case of the corresponding potassium salt. A. Mosnier prepared complex salts with tetramethylammonium, tetraethylammonium, and tetraphenylammonium iodides of the type $3PbI_2.4NH_4I$.

Both A. B. Poggiale, and C. Völckel described mixed double halides of lead and ammonium ; both products were obtained in silky needles. The former gave the composition $PbI_2.4NH_4Cl.2H_2O$, and the latter, $PbI_2.3NH_4Cl$. H. L. Wells and W. R. Johnston said that both used virtually the same mode of preparation, dissolving lead iodide in a soln. of ammonium chloride, and that both products are probably the same, being more or less contaminated with ammonium chloride. They prepared what was regarded as the true compound in a similar manner, and found that it is really **dihydrated ammonium chlorodiiodoplumbite,** $NH_4PbClI_2.2H_2O$, with only a slight variation in the composition. Possibly it would be better to write the formula $NH_4Pb(Cl,I)_3.2H_2O$, for there is a doubt if the mixed halide complex salts are variable mixtures of two isomorphous halides, as H. L. Wells and H. L. Wheeler found to be the case with cæsium chloride and lead bromide, and C. H. Herty, with potassium iodide and lead bromide. On the other hand, H. L. Wells' $Cs_2HgCl_2I_2$ shows that such mixed salts can exist as chemical individuals. H. Fonzes-Diacon obtained the chlorodiiodoplumbite from the mother-liquid left after the preparation of $PbClI.\frac{1}{3}H_2O$; and by cooling a hot aq. soln. of ammonium chloride and ammonium decaiodotriplumbite. The crystals are described as pale yellow monoclinic needles. A mol of water is lost by exposing the salt for 2 or 3 days in air, and the second mol is lost at 100°. The salt dehydrated at 100°, is rehydrated by exposure to moist air. H. Fonzes-Diacon reported **ammonium bromodiiodoplumbite,** NH_4PbBrI_2, to be formed by cooling a hot soln. of lead iodide in a 100 per cent. soln. of ammonium bromide. The yellow plates belong to the tetragonal system, and are decomposed by exposure to light, and by water ; they are soluble in potash-lye, and in the strong acids. When a 30 per cent. soln. of ammonium bromide was employed, **dihydrated ammonium bromodiiodoplumbite,** $NH_4PbBrI_2.2H_2O$, was obtained in pale yellow needles, which can be easily dehydrated, and the dehydrated salt takes up water again in moist air.

O. Lehmann [2] observed the growth of crystals of a double iodide of lead and potassium by bringing together a drop of a conc. soln. of lead nitrate and of potassium iodide on a glass slip on the stage of a microscope. A. Ditte measured the solubility of lead iodide in soln. of potassium iodide of different conc., and at different temp. He said that when lead iodide is put into a soln. of potassium iodide, it dissolves at first slowly, afterwards more rapidly, until the soln. is sat. ; after a time, the liquid becomes filled with white needles which have only the slightest yellow tinge. These crystals have the composition **tetrahydrated potassium tetraiodoplumbite,** $PbI_2.2KI.4H_2O$; they are decomposed, with re-formation of lead iodide, both by addition of water, and by raising the temp. of the soln. ; alcohol produces the same effect. He examined the effect of (1) adding water to a great excess of the double iodide, so as to decompose only a part ; and (2) adding potassium iodide by degrees to a mixture of water and lead iodide until needles of the double salt begin to form. He thus found the weight of alkali iodide which at any given temp. is necessarily present, so as to prevent the decomposition of the double salt. These quantities are, per litre of liquid :

	5°	10°	14°	20°	28°	39°	59°	67°	85°
KI	140	160	175	204	251	300	503	560	738 grms.

The decomposition of the double iodide of lead and potassium follows the general law, namely, that at all temp. a liquid, in which the double salt is capable of existing without being decomposed, must contain a definite and minimum quantity of alkaline iodide. No reaction takes place when water, lead iodide, and potassium iodide are brought together ; if the proportion of the latter is less than that already indicated, a very little lead iodide only dissolves ; if the alkaline iodide is in sufficient quantity, the two iodides will combine until there remains in the liquor just sufficient alkaline iodide to prevent the decomposition of the double salt. Similar phenomena were observed when sodium or ammonium iodide was substituted for potassium iodide. A. Ditte also obtained the same salt by passing carbon dioxide into a soln. of potassium iodide in which freshly-precipitated lead carbonate or lead dioxide was suspended ; without the carbon dioxide, the double salt is not formed. The salt furnishes white silky needles, which, when heated, lose water, and become golden yellow. At a higher temp., the salt fuses and gives off iodine. Expressing the conc. in grams per litre, the solubility, S, of the salt K_2PbI_4 in the presence of potassium iodide, is as follows :

	5°	10°	14°	20°	28°	39°	59°	67°	80°
KI	163	191	215·6	253·6	307	406·7	510	568	641
S	—	—	3·4	15·4	43·0	77·3	323	438	1276

The salt is converted into lead carbonate, etc., by the action of potassium hydrocarbonate ; and it is coloured yellow and dehydrated by absolute alcohol. According to M. Berthelot, **dihydrated potassium tetraiodoplumbite**, $K_2PbI_4.2H_2O$, is produced in warm soln. of lead iodide and potassium iodide. The heat of formation is given as 2·31 Cals. The anhydrous salt, **potassium tetraiodoplumbite**, K_2PbI_4, was obtained by A. Ditte by warming the tetrahydrate. F. P. H. Brooks made it by adding a gram of lead nitrate to 10 c.c. of a sat. soln. of potassium iodide, and after standing some time, washing the precipitate with 10 c.c. of a conc. soln. of potassium iodide in absolute alcohol. The white needles have a yellow tinge. They are decomposed by moist air and become yellow ; they are soluble in a conc. soln. of potassium iodide ; insoluble in alcohol, and sparingly soluble in chloroform. R. W. Balcom inferred from his observations of the solubility of lead iodide in soln. of potassium iodide that the complex salt K_2PbI_4, or the ion PbI''_4, is present in aq. soln. C. Immerwahr also examined the conductivity of these soln.

P. F. G. Boullay added a soln. of lead nitrate to an excess of a conc. aq. soln. of potassium iodide, and obtained pale yellow, silky needles, analyses of which agreed with *potassium heptaiodoplumbite*, $5KI.PbI_2$; when the mother-liquor was allowed to stand a few days, or mixed with alcohol, yellow prismatic crystals of what M. Berthelot considered to be *hexahydrated potassium decaiodoplumbite*, $4KI.3PbI_2.6H_2O$, were formed. C. H. Herty said they may be $K_3Pb_2I_7.4H_2O$, but more probably a mixture of potassium triiodoplumbite and iodide. J. B. Berthemot made the same salt by boiling lead iodide with a conc. soln. of potassium carbonate ; A. C. Becquerel, by separating soln. of potassium iodide and lead acetate by a porous partition and electrically connecting the soln. by a lead wire ; and E. Field boiled 60 grms. of potassium iodide, 2 grms. of lead iodide, and 150 c.c. of water, and cooled the filtered liquid—lead fluoride, chloride, or bromide can be used in place of lead iodide. A. Mosnier obtained it by a process analogous to that used for the ammonium salt. The pale yellow needles are stable in air ; they become anhydrous *potassium decaiodotriplumbite*, $K_4Pb_3I_{10}$, at 100° ; they dissolve readily in water with decomposition ; they dissolve in potash-lye, and in water acidified with nitric acid—more conc. nitric acid leads to the separation of iodine. M. Berthelot gave for the heat of formation $(4KI,3PbI_2) = -0.5$ Cal.

I. Remsen, H. L. Wells, and C. H. Herty were unable to establish the individuality of any salt other than **dihydrated potassium triiodoplumbite**, $KPbI_3.2H_2O$, when deposited from aq. soln. All the other salts which have been reported are considered to be mixtures of this salt with potassium iodide. This is the only complex iodide N. Demassieux could find in her study of the ternary system : $KI-PbI_2-H_2O$; so also with L. J. Burrage, who found that at 25° the mutual solubility of lead and potassium iodides expressed in grams per 1000 grms. of soln., at 23°, is :

KI	0	0·83	33·20	194·5	213·2	268·2	546·0	565·9	578·2	597·2
PbI_2	0·758	0·234	0·020	2·53	4·28	5·53	58·76	74·21	52·35	0
Solid phase		PbI_2			$KI.PbI_2.2H_2O$			KI		

According to C. H. Herty, *monohydrated potassium triiodoplumbite*, $KPbI_3.H_2O$, is known only in isomorphous mixture with potassium tribromoplumbite. The conditions of equilibrium were studied by F. A. H. Schreinemakers first on the assumption that the solid phase is, as first suggested by A. Ditte, $K_2PbI_4.2\frac{1}{2}H_2O$, and later with the assumption that this salt is really $KPbI_3.2H_2O$. Every one of the modes of preparation described by P. F. G. Boullay, M. Berthelot, J. B. Berthemot, W. Biltz, H. L. Wells, A. C. Becquerel, C. H. Herty, J. White, etc..

furnish this salt contaminated with more or less potassium iodide. G. Campani obtained it by the action of an excess of a soln. of potassium iodide on lead sulphate at 130°–140°. C. H. Herty made it by the following process :

A hot soln. of 15 grms. of potassium iodide in 15 c.c. of water was added to a soln. of 4 grms. of lead nitrate in 15 c.c. of water. The soln. was stirred during the mixing. When cold, crystals of the dihydrate separated out. These were separated by suction filtration, and dried by press. between bibulous paper.

The white, silky needles are stable in air, and, according to H. L. Wells, and C. H. Herty, they lose a part of their water of crystallization when standing over sulphuric acid or quicklime in a desiccator. When heated, water begins to come off at 70° and the colour becomes yellow, and the vol. of the solid decreases ; at 110°, the salt loses all its water ; and at 310°, iodine begins to be evolved. Water decomposes the salt at all temp., potassium iodide is dissolved, and lead iodide precipitated, and F. A. H. Schreinemakers concluded that the double salt $PbI_2,KI,2H_2O$ has neither a proper m.p. nor a proper solubility. It can exist only in contact with solutions in which the ratio of potassium to lead is greater than the ratio K : Pb. At elevated temp., the double salt in contact with the soln. is decomposed into another double salt—possibly $3KI.PbI_2.\frac{1}{2}H_2O$—containing only half a mol. of water, the ratio of the two iodides being unknown. There is probably no temp. of transformation for either of these double salts into their components. J. M. Talmadge showed that while the conc. at ordinary temp. of a soln. from which the double salt $KPbI_3.2H_2O$ has separated is always attended by dissolution of the double salt, at 100°, the behaviour is reversed, for there is a continuous precipitation of the double salt on evaporation. According to P. F. G. Boullay, when heated with sulphuric acid, first lead iodide and then lead sulphate are formed. C. H. Herty found that a boiling soln. of sodium carbonate produces lead carbonate. Absolute alcohol decomposes the salt like water does. Cold alcohol, said P. F. G. Boullay, has no action on the crystals, but hot alcohol leaves the lead iodide undissolved, and deposits the double salt on cooling, some potassium iodide remaining in soln. W. Biltz found that the salt is soluble in acetone, and the addition of alcohol precipitates the double salt.

H. L. Wells', and A. N. Meldrum's observations respectively on the salts $K_3Pb_2I_7.4H_2O$, and $K_9Pb_4I_{17}.10H_2O$ have been previously discussed. C. H. Herty obtained mixed crystals of the isomorphous salts $KPbBr_3.H_2O$ and $KPbI_3.H_2O$ when the attempt was made to prepare *potassium bromoiodoplumbite*, $KPb(Br,I)_3.H_2O$, by crystallization from mixed soln. of the component salts. O. Lehmann made mixed crystals by treating a soln. of potassium iodide and bromide with lead nitrate ; and H. L. Wells also obtained isomorphous mixtures of the salts $K_3Pb_2Br_7.4H_2O$ and $K_3Pb_2I_7.4H_2O$ as $K_3Pb(Br,I)_7.4H_2O$, by crystallization from a mixed soln. of the component salts.

H. L. Wells obtained **dihydrated rubidium triiodoplumbite,** $RbPbI_3,2H_2O$, as the only complex iodide obtainable from hot soln. of lead and rubidium iodides under widely varying conditions. It forms slender, hair-like, pale yellow prisms, which lose water when exposed to air—the colour first becomes orange owing to the loss of one mol of water, and then pale yellow by the loss of the other mol. Dihydrated ammonium chlorodiiodoplumbite likewise changes from yellow to orange by the loss of a mol of water on exposure to air, but a second mol is not lost under these conditions. The air-dried salt is anhydrous **rubidium triiodoplumbite,** $RbPbI_3$. A. Mosnier reported tetrahydrated **rubidium tetraiodoplumbite,** $Rb_2PbI_4.4H_2O$, to be formed in pale yellow needles from hot soln. of the component iodides. The salt becomes anhydrous at 100° ; the heat of formation $(2RbI,PbI_2)=93.17$ Cals ; $(2RbI,PbI_2,4H_2O)=107.75$ Cals. with liquid water and 102.03 Cals. with solid water and the heat of soln. of the tetrahydrate, -26.80 Cals. H. L. Wells could not obtain this salt. H. L. Wells could obtain only **cæsium triiodoplumbite,** $CsPbI_3$, from hot soln. of the component salts under a wide range of conditions. It furnishes yellow, slender, rectangular prisms which are slightly soluble in hot soln. of cæsium iodide.

A. Bogorodsky obtained **pentahydrated lithium triiodoplumbite**, $LiPbI_3.5H_2O$, by stirring lead iodide, in small portions at a time, into a soln. of lithium iodide, at 140°–150°, until yellow flakes began to separate. Water was added until the precipitate first formed was just permanent. The excess of water was evaporated, and the soln. evaporated until it became clear again. The above salt separates out in yellow needles, which should be pressed at a temp. above 72°, otherwise they may be contaminated with lithium iodide, $LiI.3H_2O$. At 95°, a mol of water is lost and the *tetrahydrate* is formed. The salt becomes anhydrous **lithium triiodoplumbite**, $LiPbI_3$, by long drying at 100°. The dried salt takes up a mol of water on exposure to air, and turns red ; the crystals thus formed become yellow at 88°. A. Mosnier reported yellow crystals of tetrahydrated **lithium tetraiodoplumbite**, $Li_2PbI_4.4H_2O$, to be formed by cooling boiling soln. of lead and lithium iodides. The salt is dehydrated by heat, and in moist air absorbs water and is decomposed. Water, alcohol, and ether act as on the corresponding sodium salt. The heats of formation are $(2LiI,PbI_2)=39.22$ Cals. ; $(2LiI,PbI_2,4H_2O)=74.74$ Cals. with liquid water and 69.02 Cals. with solid water ; the heat of soln. of the tetrahydrate is -14.02 Cals. in 40 parts of water at 15° ; and the heat of soln. of the anhydrous salt is 60.72 Cals.

A. C. Becquerel reported the formation of sodium iodoplumbite by the process which he employed for the potassium salt ; and P. F. G. Boullay, obtained evidence of the formation of a complex sodium salt analogous to the potassium salt. A. B. Poggiale, and C. H. Herty prepared **sodium triiodoplumbite**, $NaPbI_3$, by cooling a hot soln. of lead iodide in a sat. soln. of sodium iodide. The pale yellow needles (C. H. Herty), or plates (A. B. Poggiale) resemble the potassium salt ; they are deliquescent, and are decomposed by heat or by water with the separation of lead iodide. A. Mosnier considered A. B. Poggiale's product to have been Na_4PbI_6. A. Ditte reported **tetrahydrated sodium tetraiodoplumbite**, $Na_2PbI_4.4H_2O$, to be formed by cooling a soln. of lead iodide in an excess of a conc. soln. of sodium iodide ; A. Mosnier used a similar mode of preparation. C. H. Herty said that the product is contaminated with much sodium iodide. The crystals have a strong negative birefringence, and are probably triclinic. The surface of the crystals gradually becomes green on exposure to light. At 100°, the salt becomes anhydrous **sodium tetraiodoplumbite**, Na_2PbI_4, and in moist air, water is gradually absorbed, and finally passes into **hexahydrated sodium tetraiodoplumbite**, $Na_2PbI_4.6H_2O$, which is also obtained by cooling the mother-liquor from the tetrahydrate. The salts are decomposed by water and behave like ammonium and potassium iodoplumbites towards soln. of alkali iodide. Thus, expressing conc. in grams per 1000 grms. of water, the solubility, S, of the salt Na_2PbI_4 in the presence of sodium iodide is :

	8·5°	10·4°	15°	23°	28°	38°
NaI .	210·10	226·88	273·55	410·29	459	535·47
S .	5·94	20·64	34·15	55·11	66	92·73

The solubility in methyl and ethyl alcohols in grams per 1000 grms. of alcohol is :

	Methyl alcohol.			Ethyl alcohol.		
	15°	28°	38°	15°	28°	38°
NaI .	15·77	22·71	36·5	15·01	22·45	36
S .	0·58	0·99	1·81	0·49	0·90	1·48

Ether acts slowly on the salt. The heat of formation is $(2NaI,PbI_2)=76.35$ Cals. ; $(2NaI,PbI_2.4H_2O)=103.88$ Cals. with liquid water and 98.16 Cals. with solid water ; and $(2NaI,PbI_2,6H_2O)=106.63$ Cals. with liquid water, and 98.23 Cals. with solid water. The heat of soln. of the anhydrous salt is 78.95 Cals. ; of the tetrahydrate, -24.93 Cals. in 40 parts of water at 15° ; and of the hexahydrate, - 27.68 Cals.

O. Ruff and E. Geisel prepared a white compound, **silver pentamminotetraiodo-plumbite**, $Ag_2PbI_4.5NH_3$, by mixing soln. of lead and silver iodides in liquid ammonia. On exposure to air, it forms yellow **silver tetraiodoplumbite**, Ag_2PbI_4. A kind of alloy of silver and lead iodides corresponding, in composition, with **silver triiodoplumbite**, $AgPbI_3$, was obtained by G. F. Rodwell by fusing mixtures of the two salts. He found the vol. of the solid "alloy" at different temp. :

Vol. .	0°	118°	128°	130°	131°	139°	150°	300°
	1·000000	1·003610	1·002314	0·999716	0·994517	0·98412	0·984810	1·006500

The vol. of the solid alloy at 350° was 1·01370, and of the liquid "alloy" at 350°, 1·024370. The coeff. of cubical expansion, β, is :

	0°–118°	124°–128°	128°–130°	130°–131°	131°–133°	133°–139°	144°–350°
β .	+0·0₄306	−0·0₃3240	−0·0012990	−0·0017330	−0·003900	−0·0₃4329	+0·0₃1159

where the + refers to the results obtained on heating and − to those on cooling. T. Carnelley and L. T. O'Shea gave 350° for the m.p. M. Bellati and R. Romanese measured the sp. ht. G. F. Rodwell also made a number of other alloys. C. Tubandt and S. Eggert examined the conductivity of fused mixtures of lead and silver iodides, and also found the f.p. curves,
Fig. 103. Crystallization occurs at 395° correspond-
ing with silver hexaiodoplumbite, $4AgI.PbI_2$, or Ag_4PbI_6, and this compound forms mixed crystals with lead iodide with a minimum at 344°. Transition temp. occur at 144·6° and at 115°.

A. Mosnier obtained the iodides of the alkaline earths by cooling a soln. of lead iodide in a boiling soln. of the given iodide. In a few days, yellow, octahedral crystals of **calcium hexaiododiplumbite**, $CaPb_2I_6.7H_2O$, appear ; they belong to the cubic system, and become anhydrous at 100°. If exposed to light for some days under the mother-liquor, they appear brownish-red owing to the formation of calcium iodide, CaI_215H_2O. The salt is decomposed by water, and alcohol. Pure and dry ether has no action, but ordinary ether, or ether which has been exposed

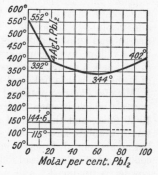

FIG. 103. — Freezing - point Curves of Mixtures of Lead and Silver Iodides.

to air, decomposes the salt. The heat of formation is $(CaI_2,2PbI_2)=-10·99$ Cals. ; and $(CaI_2,2PbI_2,7H_2O)=11·3$ Cals. with liquid water and 1·3 Cals. with solid water. The heat of soln. of the anhydrous salt in 40 parts of water at 15° is 16·61 Cals., and of the heptahydrate, 5·3 Cals. **Strontium hexaiododiplumbite**, $SrPb_2I_6.7H_2O$, was obtained in a similar manner, and its properties were similar ; it also yields the anhydrous salt when warmed. The heat of formation is $(SrI_2,2PbI_2)=3·35$ Cals. ; and $(SrI_2,2PbI_2,7H_2O)=12·85$ Cals. with liquid water and 2·84 Cals. with solid water. The heat of soln. of the anhydrous salt in 40 parts of water at 15° is 17·55 Cals., and of the heptahydrate, 4·70 Cals. Likewise also with **barium hexa-iododiplumbite**, $BaPb_2I_6.7H_2O$, which becomes anhydrous at 100°. The heat of formation is $(2PbI_2,BaI_2)=-16·70$ Cals. ; $(2PbI_2.BaI_2,7H_2O)=16·59$ Cals. with liquid water and 6·58 Cals. with solid water. The heat of soln. is 8·29 Cals. for one part of the heptahydrate in 40 parts of water at 15°, and 8·30 Cals. for the anhydrous salt. The actions of water, alcohol, and ether are like the case with the calcium salt. The solubility, S, of the barium salt in grams per 1000 grms. of solvent is as follows :

	Water.			Methyl alcohol.			Ethyl alcohol.		
	15°	28°	38°	15°	28°	38°	15°	28°	38°
BaI_2 .	68·9	94·5	141·2	35·6	48·8	73·4	33·9	56·8	72·6
S . .	5·04	21	44·8	2·8	11·2	24·3	2·5	11·2	22·4

A. Mosnier found that a soln. of lead iodide in a boiling soln. of beryllium carbonate in conc. hydriodic acid furnishes yellow needles of **beryllium tetraiodo-plumbite**, $BePbI_4.3\frac{1}{3}H_2O$, which are decomposed by water. A. Mosnier found that a boiling conc. soln. of magnesium iodide sat. with lead iodide, and allowed to evaporate 4 days in vacuo over sulphuric acid, and a mixture of quicklime and potassium hydroxide furnished topaz-yellow crystals of **magnesium hexaiodo-plumbite**, Mg_2PbI_6. The heat of formation is $(2MgI_2,PbI_2)=8·52$ Cals., and the heat of soln. in 40 parts of water at 15° is 110·52 Cals. The colour of the crystals does not change at 100°. The salt is decomposed by water and alcohol with the separation of lead iodide. Ether containing a peroxide decomposes the salt with the separation of iodine. R. Otto and D. Drewes prepared **hexadecahydrated magnesium hexaiodoplumbite**, $Mg_2PbI_6.16H_2O$. Magnesium carbonate was dissolved in aq. hydriodic acid and the soln. evaporated until a skin formed on the surface ; then as much dry lead iodide was added as the liquid would take up. On filtering hot and allowing the filtrate to remain until cold, a copious deposit of rhombohedral crystals of the given salt was obtained. The honey-yellow salt loses its water of crystallization at 140° and becomes citron-yellow. Above 150°, it decomposes with separation of iodine. Like the corresponding chloride, it is exceedingly hygroscopic. In the air it quickly becomes a magnesium iodide lye, containing lead iodide in suspension. Water decomposes it into soluble magnesium iodide and insoluble lead iodide. Exposed to hydrogen sulphide, it immediately gives rise to lead sulphoiodide, which afterwards passes into lead sulphide. A. Mosnier made yellow, hygroscopic crystals of **zinc hexaiodoplumbite**, Zn_2PbI_6, by cooling in darkness a soln. of lead iodide in a boiling conc. soln. of zinc iodide. The heat of formation is 0·74 Cal., and the heat of soln. in 40 parts of water at 15°, 23·50 Cals. A. Mosnier likewise prepared **cadmium hexaiodoplumbite**, Cd_2PbI_6, in small white crystals which become brown when exposed to light. The heat of formation is 10·30 Cals., and the heat of soln. in 40 parts of water at 15°, is 8·30 Cals. Cold water, absolute alcohol, and ordinary ether colour these salts yellow ; dried ether has no action. J. Preuss reported that *mercuric iodoplumbite* does not separate on cooling a hot soln. of lead iodide and mercuric nitrate, but on evaporation a white powder is produced ; and A. Mosnier said that mercuric iodide does not form a soluble salt with lead iodide.

A. Mosnier prepared crystals of **decahydrated aluminium dodecaiodotriplumbite**, $Al_2Pb_3I_{12}.10H_2O$, by evaporating in vacuo a soln. of lead iodide in a hot conc. soln. of aluminium iodide. The salt becomes anhydrous at 100°. Its heat of formation $(2AlI_3,3PbI_2)=42$ Cals., $(2AlI_3,3PbI_2,10H_2O)=205$ Cals. with liquid water and 190·7 Cals. with solid water. The heat of soln. of the anhydrous salt in 40 parts of water at 15° is 220 Cals., and of the decahydrate, 15 Cals. The salt is decomposed by water. J. Barlot found that the electrical conductivity measurements of mixed soln. of lead and thallous iodides indicated the existence of **thallous triiodoplumbite**, $TlPbI_3$, which was prepared by crystallization from a boiling soln. of equimolar parts of the constituent salts. The yellow, hair-like crystals are decomposed by water into lead and thallous iodides. A. Mosnier prepared needle-like crystals of **stannous tetraiodoplumbite**, $SnPbI_2.8H_2O$, by cooling a filtered soln. of lead iodide in a boiling soln. of stannous iodide in fuming hydriodic acid. This salt becomes anhydrous at 100°. The heat of formation is $(SnI_2,PbI_2)=12·1$ Cals., and $(SnI_2,PbI_2,8H_2O)=8·8$ Cals. ; the heat of soln. of the anhydrous salt in 40 parts of water at 15° is 12·7 Cals., and of the octohydrate, $-7·5$ Cals. The salt is decomposed by water. A. Mosnier obtained greenish-yellow needles of **chromous hexa-iodoplumbite**, $Cr_2PbI_6.3H_2O$, from a sat. soln. of lead iodide in a boiling conc. soln. of chromous chloride, and evaporating the liquid to a syrup. It forms the anhydrous salt at 100°. The salt is very hygroscopic and is decomposed by water. The heat of formation is $(2CrI_2,PbI_2)=9$ Cals., and $(2CrI_2,PbI_2,3H_2O)=22·7$ Cals. with liquid water and 18·4 Cals. with solid water ; the heat of soln. of the anhydrous salt in 40 parts of water at 15° is 20·4 Cals., and of the trihydrate, 2·3 Cals. By working in an analogous manner, A. Mosnier made brownish-red crystals of

LEAD 779

manganous hexaiodoplumbite, $Mn_2PbI_6.3H_2O$. The salt is decomposed by water and alcohol, and it becomes anhydrous at 100°. The heat of formation is $(2MnI_2,PbI_2)=1.5$ Cals. ; and $(2MnI_2,PbI_2,3H_2O)=48.1$ Cals. The heat of soln. of the anhydrous salt in 40 parts of water at 15° is 43.9 Cals., and of the trihydrate, −8.5 Cals. By the same mode of preparation, A. Mosnier obtained crystals of ferrous hexaiodoplumbite, $Fe_2PbI_6.3H_2O$. The salt becomes anhydrous at 100°. The heat of formation is $(PbI_2,2FeI_2)=0.3$ Cal. ; and $(PbI_2,2FeI_2.3H_2O)=57.7$ Cals. with liquid water, and 52.8 Cals. with solid water. The heat of soln. of one part of salt in 40 parts of water at 15° is −10.2 Cals. for the trihydrate, and 46.9 Cals. for the anhydrous salt. He also obtained cobaltous hexaiodoplumbite, $Co_2PbI_6.3H_2O$, in greenish needles which are decomposed by water. The salt becomes anhydrous at 100°. The heat of formation is $(2CoI_2,PbI_2)=3.9$ Cals., and $(PbI_2,2CoI_2,3H_2O)=52.1$ Cals. with liquid water and 47.8 Cals. with solid water. The heat of soln. was −10.6 Cals. for one part of the trihydrate in 40 parts of water at 15° ; and 41.5 Cals. for the anhydrous salt. Likewise also with nickelous hexaiodoplumbite, $Ni_2PbI_6.3H_2O$, which furnishes greenish needles which are decomposed by water, and becomes yellow and anhydrous at 100°. The heat of formation is $(2NiI_2,PbI_2)=1.4$ Cals. ; $(2NiI_2,PbI_2,3H_2O)=51.3$ Cals. with liquid water and 47 Cals. with solid water. The heat of soln. of the anhydrous salt in 40 parts of water at 15° is 40.2 Cals., and of the trihydrate, −11.1 Cals.

REFERENCES.

[1] P. F. G. Boullay, *Journ. Pharm. Chim.*, (2), **12**. 639, 1826 ; *Ann. Chim. Phys.*, (2), **34**. 366, 1827 ; A. Mosnier, *ib.*, (7), **12**. 378, 1897 ; *Compt. Rend.*, **120**. 444, 1895 ; A. B. Poggiale, *ib.*, **20**. 1184, 1845 ; N. Demassieux, *Ann. Chim. Phys.*, (9), **20**. 233, 1923 ; *Compt. Rend.*, **177**. 51, 1923 ; A. Ditte, *ib.*, **92**. 134, 1881 ; *Ann. Chim. Phys.*, (5), **24**. 230, 1881 ; H. Fonzes-Diacon, *Bull. Soc. Chim.*, (3), **17**. 349, 1897 ; H. L. Wells and W. R. Johnston, *Amer. Journ. Science*, (3), **46**. 25, 1893 ; H. L. Wells, *ib.*, (3), **44**. 232, 1892 ; H. L. Wells and H. L. Wheeler, *ib.*, (3), **45**. 121, 1893 ; J. White, *Amer. Chem. Journ.*, **31**. 17, 1904 ; B. Thorp, *ib.*, **10**. 232, 1888 ; C. H. Herty, *ib.*, **15**. 81, 1893 ; **18**. 293, 1896 ; C. H. Herty and T. R. Boggs, *Journ. Amer. Chem. Soc.*, **19**. 821, 1897 ; E. Field, *Journ. Chem. Soc.*, **63**. 541, 1893 ; *Chem. News*, **67**. 157, 1893 ; C. Völckel, *Liebig's Ann.*, **62**. 252, 1884.

[2] J. B. Berthemot, *Journ. Pharm. Chim.*, (2), **13**. 311, 1827 ; P. F. G. Boullay, *ib.*, (2), **12**. 639, 1826 ; *Ann. Chim. Phys.*, (2), **34**. 366, 1827 ; A. C. Becquerel, *ib.*, (2), **41**. 33, 1829 ; *Traité expérimental de l'électricté et du magnétisme*, Paris, **2**. 86, 1855 ; C. Immerwahr, *Beiträge zur Löslichkeitsbestimmung schwerlöslicher Salze des Quecksilbers, Kupfers, Bleis, Cadmiums, und Zinks*, Breslau, 1900 ; *Zeit. Elektrochem.*, **7**. 480, 1901 ; A. Bogorodsky, *Journ. Russ. Phys. Chem. Soc.*, **26**. 216, 1894 ; O. Lehmann, *Zeit. Kryst.*, **10**. 239, 1885 ; F. A. H. Schreinemakers, *Zeit. phys. Chem.*, **9**. 67, 1892 ; **10**. 476, 1892 ; W. Meyerhoffer, *ib.*, **9**. 646, 1892 ; H. L. Wells, *Amer. Journ. Science*, (3), **45**. 121, 1893 ; C. H. Herty, *Amer. Chem. Journ.*, **14**. 126, 1892 ; **15**. 97, 1893 ; **18**. 292, 1896 ; J. White, *ib.*, **31**. 15, 1904 ; I. Remsen, *ib.*, **14**. 85, 1892 ; F. P. H. Brooks, *Chem. News*, **77**. 191, 1898 ; E. Field, *ib.*, **67**. 157, 1893 ; *Journ. Chem. Soc.*, **63**. 541, 1893 ; T. Carnelley and L. T. O'Shea, *ib.*, **45**. 409, 1884 ; A. N. Meldrum, *Proc. Chem. Soc.*, **24**. 97, 1908 ; A. Ditte, *Compt. Rend.*, **92**. 1341, 1881 ; **93**. 65, 1881 ; *Ann. Chim. Phys.*, (5), **24**. 227, 1881 ; M. Berthelot, *ib.*, (5), **29**. 289, 1883 ; *Compt. Rend.*, **95**. 952, 1882 ; A. B. Poggiale, *ib.*, **20**. 1183, 1845 ; J. Barlot, *ib.*, **171**. 794, 1920 ; A. Mosnier, *ib.*, **120**. 416, 444, 1895 ; *Ann. Chim. Phys.*, (7), **12**. 378, 1897 ; *Sur quelques combinaisons de l'iodure de plomb avec d'autres iodures métalliques et organiques*, Paris, 1897 ; W. Biltz, *Ber.*, **40**. 2182, 1907 ; O. Ruff and E. Geisel, *ib.*, **38**. 2663, 1905 ; J. M. Talmadge, *Journ. Phys. Chem.*, **1**. 493, 1897 ; W. D. Bancroft, *ib.*, **1**. 344, 786, 1897 ; C. Tubandt and S. Eggert, *Zeit. anorg. Chem.*, **110**. 196, 1920 ; G. Campani, *Gazz. Chim. Ital.*, **6**. 462, 1876 ; R. W. Balcom in R. Abegg, *Handbuch der anorganischen Chemie*, Leipzig, **3**. ii, 667, 1909 ; M. Bellati and R. Romanese, *Proc. Roy. Soc.*, **34**. 104, 1882 ; G. F. Rodwell, *ib.*, **32**. 23, 540, 1881 ; *Chem. News*, **43**. 169, 1881 ; *Phil. Trans.*, **173**. 1125, 1882 ; R. Otto and D. Drewes, *Arch. Pharm.*, **228**. 498, 1890 ; **229**. 586, 1891 ; J. Preuss, *Liebig's Ann.*, **29**. 328, 1839 ; N. Demassieux, *Compt. Rend.*, **177**. 51, 1923 ; A. C. Vournasos, *Zeit. anorg. Chem.*, **150**. 147, 1926 ; L. J. Burrage, *Journ. Chem. Soc.*, **129**. 1703, 1926.

§ 29. Lead Sulphide

K. Jellinek and J. Zakowsky [1] made estimates of the affinity of sulphur and lead. It was assumed by H. V. Collet-Descotils, and others, that lead subsulphides are capable of existence because B. G. Bredberg obtained what appeared to be homogeneous products by fusing a mixture of galena and lead in the proportions required for *lead tetritasulphide*, or *lead quadrantosulphide*, Pb_4S ; and also for *lead hemisulphide*, or *lead subsulphide*, Pb_2S. J. Fournet also reported a similar product. P. Berthier claimed to have obtained the hemisulphide by igniting lead sulphate in a carbon crucible, and G. F. Rodwell, by heating the sulphate in a current of ammonia. A. Brand found steel-blue octahedral crystals in the Mechnernich lead furnaces containing lead sulphide said to be in isomorphous mixture with cuprous and ferrous sulphides, and he assumed that the lead is present as PbS, not as subsulphide. J. Percy could not verify J. Fournet's, P. Berthier's, and B. G. Bredberg's conclusions ; he said :

Lead and lead sulphide may be melted together in all proportions, and in external characters the products approximate to lead or lead sulphide according as one or other predominates. If, after fusion, cooling be rapidly effected, the mass may seem to be homogeneous throughout ; but if, on the contrary, cooling takes place slowly, the mass will be found to consist of soft, malleable, and comparatively pure lead at the bottom, and hard crystalline lead sulphide at the top. No distinct line of separation will be visible, and the passage from soft lead to hard sulphide is more or less gradual. . . . Experiments made on a small scale, in crucibles, are apt to lead to erroneous conclusions, as it is difficult to recognize the effect of liquation in a little button of metal.

A. Mourlot obtained no evidence of the existence of a subsulphide in his observations of the effect of the high temp. of the electric arc furnace on lead sulphide. K. Friedrich and A. Leroux measured the f.p. of mixtures of lead and galena. The precipitated sulphide did not give a homogeneous product when fused and examined microscopically. The curve fell from 1103°, the m.p. of galena, continuously without a break, Fig. 104. The eutectic horizontal is at 327°, and extends continuously throughout. The lead branch of the curve is so very short that it could not be explored. Micrographic examination showed the presence of only two constituents—the glistening white crystals of lead sulphide, and the duller crystals of lead. W. Guertler found a gap in the curve for the mixed crystals of lead and lead sulphide with between 5 and 10 per cent. of sulphur. The individuality of the alleged subsulphides therefore remains not proven.

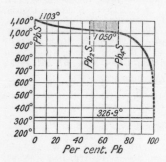

FIG. 104.—Freezing Curve of Binary Mixtures of Lead and Lead Sulphide.

Native lead sulphide, PbS, is the well-known mineral galena, or the *galenite* of F. von Kobell.[2] According to X. Fischer, galena was used by the women of ancient Egypt for painting the eyes. In ancient times, oxidized ores found near the surface of the ground were largely worked for lead, and at the beginning of our era, Pliny, in his *Historia naturalis* (**33**. 31 ; **34**. 47), used the term " galena " for these oxidized products ; with the sulphide as an inferior variety. The term *molybdœna* was used about 350 B.C. by Aristotle, in his *De generatione animalium* (**2**. 2). Dioscorides, in his *De materia medica* (**5**. 50), about 400 years later, and a century later by Gahlen, in his *De succedaneis ;* and the terms *molybdœna* and *plumbago* were also used by Pliny for these oxidized lead products. The derivation of Pliny's word " galena " is not known. Some writers in the Middle Ages—*e.g.* G. Agricola, and C. Gesner—believed it to be of Spanish origin because Pliny obtained much of his information on this subject from Spain. G. Agricola, and C. Entzelt condemned the derivation of *galena* from Galicia in Spain. The derivation of the word from γαλήνη, a calm, or from γελέω or γελάω, I laugh or shine, is considered by J. W. Evans to be improbable, and he suggested that the term may be derived from an allied Aryan idiom akin to the English *cloam* and the Slavonic *glina,* meaning any yellowish earthy material.

C. Entzelt (1551) suggested that the term *molybdœna* should be used for lead ore free from silver, and *galena* for lead ore containing that metal. J. Mathesius (1571) used the terms *Glantz* and *galena* for argentiferous galena ; *Bleischweiff* and *plumbago* for an ore of sulphur and lead ; and *molybdena*, for litharge. J. C. Boulenger (1627) used the term *galena* for a graphite. O. Worm (1655) identified galena, *plumbago*, and *molybdœna* with lead sulphide ; J. Webster (1671), like C. Entzelt, used *galena* for the ore containing a sensible quantity of silver, and *plumbago* for the ore without that metal. During the seventeenth century, *lapis plumbarius*, *plumbago*, *galena*, and *molybdœna* were used in the sense of *graphite* as well as for the ores of lead, and soon afterwards the Swedish mineralogists restricted the term *galena* to the mineral which now bears that name. G. Agricola (1546) said that the term *Glantz* was applied by the miners to galena, and suggested that they had converted a foreign word into one with a similar sound already familiar to them. J. G. Wallerius (1747) applied the term *Blyglants* (Bleiglanz), *galena*, *plumbum sulphure et argento mineralisatum* to the mineral sulphide. J. B. L. Romé de l'Isle (1783), and A. G. Werner (1817) regarded *Bleischweiff* as a dense or compact variety of *Bleiglanz ;* the early writers like C. Berward (1684) understood it to be a granular or fibrous galena. Coarse-grained galena is sometimes called *potter's ore*, because it is used in glazing some varieties of pottery, and was mentioned by Falloppius in that connection in 1606. The antimoniferous galena from Argentiera, Tuscany, was called *targionite* by E. Bechi ; and the arsenical and antimoniferous galena from Pribram, *steinmannite*, by F. H. M. Zippe.

In his posthumous *Vollständiges Laboratorium Chymicum* (Hamburg, 1716), J. Kunckel denied the existence of sulphur in galena. The sample examined may or may not be what is now understood by that mineral. In 1778, R. Watson said that the Derbyshire smelters were not aware that the ore contained sulphur, but he proved that the ore contained both lead and sulphur. Early analyses were made by J. J. Berzelius,[3] T. Thomsen, L. A. Emmerling, R. Kirwan, J. F. Westrumb, J. L. Proust, L. N. Vauquelin, and J. Davy. Innumerable other analyses have since been made for industrial purposes. Reports have been made by F. Sandberger, C. F. Rammelsberg, J. R. Blum, C. von Hauer, J. U. Lerch, H. A. Miers, G. C. Hoffmann, J. Thiel, T. Landmann, O. Schilling, A. Brunlechner, E. Bechi, L. F. Navarro, H. Sjögren, L. H. Borgström, I. Domeyko, D. Forbes, L. Pflücker y Ryco, A. Raimondi, C. Rimatori, B. Kerl, O. Luedecke, F. E. Reuss, V. R. von Zepharovich, E. Manasse, E. Metzger, etc. Galena contains silver and occasionally selenium, vanadium, tellurium, copper, zinc, cadmium, arsenic, bismuth, and iron sulphides, sometimes native gold and silver, and platinum has even been reported by M. d'Argy in the galena from the Dépt. Charente, France.

Galena is the most important lead ore, and it is one of the most widely distributed metal sulphides. C. Hintze has reported the different occurrences of the mineral in some detail. It occurs in beds and veins in crystalline and non-crystalline rocks, It occurs associated with pyrite, marcasite, zinc-blende, chalcopyrite, sphalerite, etc. ; it occurs in quartz, calcite, barytes, fluorspar, etc. ; and it is common to find it with gold, and in veins of silver ore. It may also be associated with cerussite, anglesite, etc., which are usually the result of the alteration of the galena. It is generally assumed that galena has been formed from soln. J. S. Curtis assumed that the lead ores of Eureka, Nevada, were formed from soln. ascending by solfataric action, and A. Lacroix, F. Zambonini, O. de Fiore, and U. Paniche have discussed the occurrence of galena among the sublimates from Vesuvius, where it is supposed to have been formed by the action of hydrogen sulphide, derived from steam and sulphur, upon the vapour of lead chloride. According to S. F. Emmons, the deposits at Leadville, Colorado, were produced by descending soln. which had dissolved their minerals from neighbouring eruptive rocks. F. Posepny described stalactitic formations of galena called *Röhrenerze*, occurring near Raibl. Galena occurs as a pseudomorph after pyromorphite at Bernkastel on the Mosel, etc., and this was discussed by W. Haidinger, J. R. Blum, and A. Breithaupt. The latter called it *sexangulites plumbeus*, or *plumbeine*. G. F. Becker and W. H. Melville described spring deposits formed by the pseudomorphous replacement of other minerals. W. Lindgren mentioned the replacement of calcite, dolomite, quartz, orthoclase, and rhodonite. The so-called *Tigererz*, described by A. Sigmund, is an argentiferous galena occurring in grains in the limestone near Türnitz, Austria. W. H. Hobbs has described secondary galena as a surface film on cerussite, which is supposed to have been formed by the action of hydrogen sulphide. The formation of lead in nature has also been discussed by P. Niggli, E. Dittler, W. Stelzner and A. Bergeat, F. Bernauer, K. A. Redlich, and G. Bischof.

In the first century of our era, Dioscorides, in his *De materia medica* (5. 48), described the preparation of lead sulphide, which he called μόλυβδος κεκαυμένος, which is rendered into Latin *plumbum ustum*. He said :

Strips of lead, beaten out as thin as possible, are placed in a new dish, and sprinkled over with sulphur ; more lead and sulphur are added, and again more until the dish is full. The mixture is then kindled, and stirred with a rod until it is completely reduced to ashes which are like lead well done.

Some modifications of this process are also described. Pliny, in his *Historia naturalis* (**34**. 50), written about the same time, described a similar process for making *plumbum ustum*. G. C. Winkelblech [4] described a similar process. He said that strips of lead, even tolerably thick, take fire in sulphur vapour, and burn with a vivid glow, depositing half-fused globules of lead sulphide. When sulphur is mixed with molten lead, the whole mass becomes red hot. When a mixture of equiatomic parts of sulphur and finely divided lead is placed in a glass tube and heated at one end, only so far as to induce combination, it does not continue to burn unless the tube and contents have been previously heated in boiling water. W. Heike described the preparation of the sulphide by this method. According to C. W. G. Fuchs, the product obtained by melting together lead and sulphur is a grey crystalline mass. A. Mourlot found that when amorphous lead sulphide is heated for a short time in the electric arc furnace, good crystals are produced. F. Stolba, and P. Tschirwinsky crystallized amorphous lead sulphide by heating it with chalk at a red heat ; W. Truthe, by fusing it with lead chloride ; and G. F. Rodwell, by heating it to 100° in a stream of hydrogen, carbon monoxide, or carbon dioxide. According to F. Rössler, lead sulphide crystallizes from lead in beautiful cubes, sometimes arranged in steps or needles. He melted 50 grms. of lead and one gram of sulphur under borax. The crystals were best separated from the matrix by electrolysis using a soln. of lead acetate, sodium acetate, and acetic acid in water, and a current density of 0·2–0·3 ampère. F. de Marigny obtained crystals of lead sulphide by fusing a mixture of lead or litharge, iron pyrites, and starch under borax. According to W. Spring, lead unites with sulphur at ordinary temp. under a press. of 6500 atm., and the yield of sulphide is greater, the more frequently the compression is repeated. The subject has been discussed by E. Jannettaz, C. Friedel, etc.—*vide* 1. 13, 18. L. Franck found that by rubbing flowers of sulphur on a clean lead surface, the blackening which occurs shows that lead sulphide is formed. H. C. Jenkins and E. A. Smith obtained lead sulphide by heating lead in contact with sulphur dioxide at about 300°—between 327° and 400° lead oxide and sulphate are formed. D. L. Hammick obtained lead sulphide by adding lead sulphate to molten lead ; and O. Boudouard, by reducing lead sulphate with carbon ; J. B. Senderens, by heating lead oxide with sulphur ; M. Berthelot, from lead oxide and hydrogen sulphide ; F. Fouqué and A. Michel-Lévy, from lead oxide, a lead salt, or amorphous lead sulphide at a red heat ; and L. Moser and E. Neusser, from lead oxide, hydroxide, sulphate, chloride, or carbonate at 300°–550°. E. Weinschenk obtained good crystals by heating a mixture of lead oxide, ammonium chloride, and sulphur ; R. Schneider, by melting together an intimate mixture of lead sulphide, potassium carbonate, and sulphur at a red heat, and extracting the cold mass with water ; and J. E. Reynolds, by melting lead oxide mixed with an excess of potassium thiocyanate. T. Sidot obtained good crystals of lead sulphide by heating lead silicate in sulphur vapour, and E. Grieshammer observed the formation of the sulphide in lead-glasses, and P. Berthier in slags, containing sulphides. F. Schlagdenhauffen heated lead oxide in the vapour of carbon disulphide; and J. Durocher heated lead chloride in a stream of hydrogen sulphide at a red heat—this reaction is supposed to imitate the natural process at Vesuvius—*vide supra*. K. Jellinek and J. Zabowsky studied the reaction at 500°–1100°. P. Richter found that when lead oxide is triturated with calcium sulphide, lead sulphide is formed slowly at ordinary temp., rapidly when warmed.

The occurrence of lead sulphide crystals in the masonry and flues of lead-smelting furnaces, and in furnace slags, has been observed by F. Sandberger, J. F. L. Hausmann, C. W. G. Fuchs, A. Lacroix, R. Grund, A. Himmelbauer, H. A. Wheeler, E. Metzger, F. Ulrich, C. C. von Leonard, A. Sadebeck, B. von Cotta, F. O. Doeltz and C. A. Graumann, W. Heike, A. Brand, etc. M. Mayençon noted lead sulphide as a sublimate from a burning coal mine; F. Gonnard found crystals in the flue of a flint-glass works near Lyon; and A. Lacroix, in the products of a fire about the lead chambers of a sulphuric acid works. P. Spence observed a lead pipe, used for conveying ammoniacal-water from a gas-works, wholly converted into galena.

Lead sulphide has also been produced by numerous wet processes. The precipitation of lead sulphide from soln. of lead salts by hydrogen sulphide has been discussed in connection with the analytical reactions of the metal. O. Ruff and B. Hirsch studied the fractional precipitation of lead as sulphide in the presence of salts of other metals—manganese, nickel, iron (ic and ous), chromium, aluminium, copper, silver, zinc, and cadmium. According to G. F. Rodwell, that precipitated from soln. of lead acetate is contaminated with a part of this salt; and, according to F. M. Jäger and H. S. van Klooster, the precipitate from acetic acid soln. always contains less lead than is needed for the normal sulphide. O. Ruff and B. Hirsch studied the joint precipitation of lead and nickel sulphides. F. Muck said that the sulphide obtained from acetic acid soln. by hydrogen sulphide is always amorphous, while if the soln. contains sufficient nitric acid, the lead sulphide is deposited in microscopic cubes. F. Faktor precipitated lead sulphide from hot soln. of lead nitrate, mixed with ammonium chloride, by means of a hot conc. soln. of sodium thiosulphate; and O. Hauser and E. Biesalsky precipitated the sulphide as a mirror on glass from soln. of lead salts by a mixture of thiourea and an aq. or alcoholic soln. of alkali hydroxide. J. E. Reynolds also precipitated the sulphide from lead salts by organic sulphur compounds—*e.g.* from hot soln. of lead tartrate in soda-lye by thiocarbamide. E. Weinschenk heated either a mixture of acetic acid and lead thiocyanate in a closed iron tube for 4–6 hrs. at 230°–250°, or a mixture of ammonium thiocyanate and lead nitrate in a sealed tube at 180°. Small tubes were used because violent explosions were liable to occur. J. B. Senderens obtained the sulphide by boiling a mixture of water, sulphur, and lead oxide, hydroxide, dioxide, carbonate, or acetate; F. Muck, by allowing a stick of sulphur to stand for a long time in contact with a soln. of lead oxide in potash-lye; and H. de Sénarmont, by heating in a sealed tube a mixture of amorphous lead sulphide and water sat. with hydrogen sulphide. C. Doelter allowed a mixture of lead chloride, sodium hydrocarbonate, and an aq. soln. of hydrogen sulphide to stand in a sealed tube at ordinary room temp. for five months, and obtained crystals of lead sulphide. H. N. Stokes found that when a mixture of pyrite or marcasite and an aq. soln. of lead chloride is heated in a sealed tube at 180°, crystals of lead sulphide are formed. A. Daubrée noticed that galena, mixed with anglesite and phosgenite, is formed by the action of the thermal water of Bourbonne-les-Bains on metallic lead. A. Breithaupt noted the blackening of white plumbiferous minerals near to specimens of sulphides developing hydrogen sulphide by weathering in the Freiberg museum. A. Gages suspended a bag of lead sulphate in water sat. with carbon dioxide and containing some decomposing organic matter, and found that a crust of lead sulphide crystals was formed by the reduction of the sulphate. A. Russell found that the cavernous masses of lead mixed with charcoal taken up in 1846 from beneath the partly fused lead pump of a fire-ship wrecked in Falmouth harbour in 1780, contained small crystals of galena—as well as cotunnite, anglesite, and leadhillite—formed by the action of sea-water on the lead. A. C. Becquerel immersed mercuric sulphide in a soln. of magnesium chloride contained in a glass tube, and he left a lead-plate standing in the tube, which was kept closed, for six weeks. He found that crystals of lead sulphide were deposited on the sides of the tube. The lower part of the lead plate was brittle from the absorption of mercury; and the liquor gave off sulphur dioxide when treated with a strong acid. R. Lorenz obtained lead sulphide by the electrolysis of a soln. of potassium nitrate using a cathode of cupric sulphide, and a lead anode; and F. Peters, by the electrolysis of a soln. of sodium thiosulphate using a lead anode. P. P. Lebedeff could not prepare the sulphide by the electrolysis of a soln. of sodium hydrosulphide using an alternating current and lead electrodes.

According to M. Lucas,[5] if lead sulphide be slowly precipitated from dil. soln., free from other than the soluble lead salts, and also free from alkalies, a brown or grey soln. of **colloidal lead sulphide** is produced; and, as T. Ewan pointed out, the colour of the sol obtained by adding sodium sulphide to an alkaline soln. of a lead salt depends on the nature and conc. of the other constituents. C. Winssinger prepared the soln. in which the sulphide was formed so dil. that it could be dialyzed before the sulphide became insoluble. R. Meneguzzi added hydrogen sulphide to a soln. of lead acetate containing as protective colloids peptone, white-of-egg, starch-paste, or sugar syrup; J. Lefort and P. Thibault used gum arabic, and W. Leuze, sodium protalbinate; E. W. Lewis and H. Waumsley prepared a deep brown opalescent soln. by leaving lead in contact with a soln. of caoutchouc in 90 per cent. carbon disulphide and benzene. The caoutchouc acts as a protective colloid; and a soln. of nitrocellulose in acetone acts similarly. F. V. von Hahn prepared the colloidal sulphide by the cathodic disintegration of galena.

The physical properties of lead sulphide.—The lead sulphide precipitated by hydrogen sulphide is a brownish-black powder; that prepared by fusing the elements is lead-grey with a crystalline granular fracture; and native galena is also lead-grey with a bright metallic lustre. T. Ewan[6] noted that the depth of the colour of the precipitate is influenced by the nature and conc. of the soln. A. Lallemand said that in thin layers, the powder is bluish-grey. In very thin sections, L. Henry found the colour of galena to be brownish-yellow. In 1565, C. Gesner referred to the cubic form of the **crystals** of *Glantz;* they belong to the cubic system. Galena commonly occurs in cubes or cubo-octahedra—less frequently in octahedra. It also occurs in skeleton crystals, reticulated and tabular. Massive galena (*Bleischweif*) may be cleavable or coarsely or finely granular, or even impalpably fine. It is occasionally fibrous or plumose. J. B. L. Romé de l'Isle said that *toutes les variétés qu'on y rencontre m'ont paru dériver du cube ou de l'octaèdre alumineforme.* The crystals were fully described by A. Sadebeck, in his memoir: *Krystallisation des Bleiglanzes;* and observations were reported by R. J. Haüy, C. F. Naumann, E. Weiss, M. Bauer, A. Schrauff, P. W. Jeremejeff, P. Groth, A. Lacroix, G. Greim, O. Mügge, W. Cross, G. Cesaro, J. Mélon, H. Seifert, etc. J. W. Retgers studied its relations with other isomorphous sulphides, selenides, and tellurides; H. G. Grimm, with sodium bromide; L. Royer, the growth of alkali and silver halides on the cleavage faces; and M. Volmer and A. Weber, the growth of nuclei in supersaturated soln. The **twinning** plane (111) has contact and penetration twins sometimes repeated; the twinned crystals are sometimes tabular, parallel to (111). A. Sadebeck, V. von Zepharovich, and W. Cross showed that the twinning planes (441), (311), and (331) in polysynthetic twinned lamellæ sometimes give rise to striations on a cleavage surface; while A. Schrauf and

E. S. Dana showed that in some cases, the striations are secondary, probably being due to press. since M. Bauer showed that gliding planes can be artificially produced in these directions by squeezing a crystal of the mineral. This subject was investigated by A. Johnsen, and O. Mügge. R. Brauns doubted the explanation. The cubic **cleavage** of galena is often perfect. In a few rare cases—e.g. galena from Habach, Monte Blanc, Wermland, and Nil-St.-Vincent—galena exhibits not the cubic cleavage, but a perfect octahedral cleavage. This phenomenon has been studied by H. Sjögren, V. von Zepharovich, G. Cesaro, and J. P. Cooke. The crystals exhibiting octahedral cleavage contain 1–2 per cent. of bismuth sulphide ; and they give a cubic cleavage after being heated without change in sp. gr. The change occurs without decrepitation ; this is not what would have been anticipated, because ordinary galena decrepitates when heated ; and sudden changes in crystalline structure are often attended by decrepitation. E. Weiss, E. Bauer, and W. Cross found the **percussion figures** on galena correspond with its holosymmetry. F. Becke, and G. Tammann and W. Krings studied the **corrosion figures** obtained with hydrochloric acid, and found them to be in harmony with the holosymmetry. H. Schneiderhöhn etched the crystals with nitric acid, and examined the structure of polished sections. F. N. Guild also worked on this subject, and R. Granigg examined thin sections of the mineral. J. E. Pogue described overgrowths of cubic galena with cubic crystals of pyrite from Alaska. According to W. H. and W. L. Bragg, the **X-radiogram** of the crystal of galena shows that it has the sodium chloride arrangement with the unit cube with $a=5\cdot80$ A. P. F. Kerr, and K. S. Ramsdell studied the subject. W. P. Davey discussed the arrangement of the electrons in the atoms to fit the simple cubic lattice of galena ; and estimated the size of the contained lead atoms.

In 1690, R. Boyle [7] gave 7·14 for the **specific gravity** of " tin-ore," presumably galena ; and in 1788, R. Watson found for galena 7·115–7·636. F. E. Neumann gave 7·658 ; A. Schrauf and E. S. Dana, 7·428–7·575 ; C. J. B. Karsten, 7·25–7·70 ; H. le Chatelier and F. Bogitsch, 7·590 ; J. U. Lerch, 7·252–7·324 ; F. Katzer, 7·562 ; P. Niggli, 5·57 ; G. Tschermak, 7·51 ; A. Breithaupt, 7·539 ; J. B. Hannay, 7·766 ; and P. Pilipenko, 7·226–7·502 at 14·3°. For artificial lead sulphide, R. Schneider gave 6·77 ; L. Playfair and J. P. Joule, 6·9238 at 4° ; C. J. B. Karsten, 7·5052 for precipitated and fused lead sulphide ; and A. Mourlot, 7·48 for the sulphide prepared in the electric arc furnace. F. A. Henglein studied the mol. vol. ; and A. Reis and L. Zimmermann, the relation between the **hardness** and the mol. vol. The hardness is about $2\frac{1}{2}$ and always under 3. The cleavage was found by G. Tammann and K. Dahl to disappear at $700° \pm 40°$, so that galena can then be deformed without cracking. E. Bauer studied the **plasticity** of the crystals. W. Reinders found that when powdered galena is shaken with two liquids like water and carbon tetrachloride, benzene, or ether—the powder collects at the **boundary surface** ; but with water and paraffin oil or amyl alcohol, only a part of the powder collects at the boundary surface. P. Walden studied the diffusion of potassium chloride through a membrane of lead sulphide. E. Madelung and R. Fuchs gave $1\cdot81\times10^{-12}$ to $1\cdot89\times10^{-12}$ dynes per sq. cm. or $1\cdot92\times10^{-6}$ kgrm. per sq. cm. for the coeff. of cubical **compressibility** ; and P. A. Bridgman, $0\cdot80\times10^{-6}$ kgrm. per sq. cm., or for the volume compressibility $\delta V/V_0 = 18\cdot37\times10^{-7}p - 6\cdot33\times10^{-12}p^2$ at 30°, and $18\cdot93\times10^{-7}p - 7\cdot14\times10^{-12}p^2$ at 75° ; and for the linear compressibility, $\delta l/l_0 = 6\cdot122\times10^{-7}p - 2\cdot48\times10^{-12}p^2$ at 30°, and $4\cdot126\times10^{-7}p - 2\cdot78\times10^{-12}p^2$ at 75°.

J. P. Joule and L. Playfair [8] gave 0·000032 for the cubical coeff. of **thermal expansion** of powdered lead sulphide between 44° and 398°. H. Kopp gave 0·000068 for galena between 14° and 48° ; F. Pfaff, 0·000055782 between 0° and 100°, and for the linear coeff. he gave 0·000018594 between 0° and 100° ; while H. Fizeau found 0·00002014 at 40°. F. Streintz said that the **thermal conductivity** of the amorphous sulphide is low and that of the fused sulphide higher. H. V. Regnault [9] measured the **specific heat** of galena and found 0·05086 between 13° and 99°; H. Kopp, 0·0490 between 16° and 51°; J. Joly, 0·0492–0·0522; G. Linder gave 0·04658 at 100°; 0·04720 at 200°; 0·04784 at 300°; and 0·04811 at 350°. K. Bornemann and O. Hengstenberg gave 0·0500 from 0° to 100°, and 0·0540 from 0° to 600°. E. van Aubel said that Neumann's law is not applicable. E. D. Eastman and W. H. Rodebush gave for the **molecular heat**, C_p:

	$-209·2°$	$-191·3°$	$-173°$	$-148·8°$	$-118°$	$-93°$	$-76·3°$	$-36°$	$90·7°$
C_p	7·71	8·80	9·59	10·10	10·90	11·13	11·50	11·86	12·16

L. Rolla found that between 0° and 100°, the sp. ht. of crystalline and fused lead sulphide are approximately the same. F. Streintz gave 0·0529 for the fused sulphide between 15° and 100°, 0·0557 for a large crystal; 0·061–0·0699 for crystalline powder; for the pressed powder, 0·0600–0·065; and for the amorphous precipitate, 0·117. The increase of the sp. ht. corresponds with a decrease in the electrical conductivity, and irregularities between 100° and 110° indicate a possible transition point.

Galena usually decrepitates when heated, but, as indicated above, some varieties can be heated without decrepitation. K. Friedrich [10] found that at about 90° some gas may be evolved which reddens litmus. G. Tammann and K. Dahl found that 400° below the **melting point,** there are signs of softening, and the material becomes quite plastic, under press., at 700°±40°. G. F. Rodwell, and J. Percy noted that lead sulphide at a red heat melts to a thin liquid which rapidly filters through the ordinary kind of fireclay crucibles without corroding their substance. A. Brun gave 830° for the m.p. of galena; A. Lodin, between 930° and 940°; R. Cusack, 727°; and W. Biltz, 1112°±2°. K. Friedrich gave 1120° for the m.p. of the pure sulphide; D. Iitsuka, 1051°; H. Freeman, 1130°; W. Truthe, 1106°; J. Guinchant, 1015°; and W. Heike, 1106°. C. F. Rammelsberg showed that the composition of lead sulphide is not changed by melting. P. Berthier, in 1830, found that much of the flue-dust in lead furnaces contained lead sulphate produced by the oxidation of the readily volatile sulphide. According to J. Percy, the molten sulphide volatilizes sensibly, and this the more the higher the temp. The vap., if protected from oxidation, condenses in a crystalline form. W. Biltz said that artificially prepared lead sulphide sublimes at 950°. A. Lodin said that galena volatilizes without melting at 860°. The **volatilization** is promoted by currents of gas such as those proceeding from the combustion of fuel in metallurgical furnaces where it sometimes occurs as a sublimate—*vide supra*. C. Zengelis obtained evidence of the volatilization of lead sulphide at ordinary temp. P. Berthier found that when heated for an hour in a covered brasqued crucible, the sulphide lost 40 per cent. of its weight at 1060°, and 75 per cent. at 1450°. F. O. Doeltz and C. A. Graumann said that volatilization occurs at 860°, for the sulphide in a current of nitrogen lost 18 per cent. in weight at this temp. in an hour, and it volatilizes more readily than the oxide. H. C. Jenkins noted that lead sulphide near its m.p. readily evaporates in vacuo, and F. Damm and F. Krafft said that a sublimate is rapidly formed at 600°. L. Merz noted a thin film of sublimate in a cathode-vacuo at 565°, and a thick one at 620°. W. C. Roberts-Austen found that lead sulphide can be rapidly distilled in vacuo at 1200°; and R. Schenck and A. Albers found the **vapour pressure:**

	850°	917°	940°	975°	980°	995°
Vap. press. .	2·0	4·0	6·0	11·9	13·0	17·0

Galena was found by H. E. Armstrong to volatilize rapidly in a current of air; and H. C. Jenkins found that it volatilizes more rapidly in a stream of sulphur dioxide than in vacuo, and still more rapidly in a current of nitrogen; J. B. Hannay, however, said that it volatilizes far more rapidly in a current of sulphur dioxide or water vapour than in nitrogen. W. C. Roberts-Austen found no more rapid volatilization in sulphur dioxide than in other gases. He showed that 9 grms. of galena in 20 secs. at 1357° lost 38·2 per cent. in sulphur dioxide and 37·7 per cent. in nitrogen, while at 1434°, 50·2 per cent. was lost in sulphur dioxide, and 72·3 per cent. in nitrogen. F. O. Doeltz said that galena volatilizes unchanged in a current of carbon dioxide at 850°. According to H. V. Collet-Descotils, lead sulphide in volatilizing changes to a supersulphide which escapes, and a subsulphide which remains; but this statement does not agree with the observations of E. Metzger, C. C. von Leonhard, and others, who found that the composition of the sublimed furnace product is ordinary sulphide and not a super-sulphide. A. Mourlot noted a partial dissociation of the lead sulphide in the electric arc-furnace. J. Guinchant gave 1085° for the **boiling point** of artificial lead sulphide. J. Joly gave 470° for the temp. of sublimation.

The **heat of formation** of lead sulphide was found by J. Thomsen [11] to be 20·4 to 18·42 Cals.; M. Berthelot, 20·3 Cals.; P. A. Favre and J. T. Silbermann, 22·35 Cals.; and P. Gunther, 20·9 Cals. The free energy of the reaction was given by L. Rolla as 1610·66 cals. per gram eq. M. Berthelot gave for the thermal value of the reaction $Pb(C_2H_3O_2)_{2solid} + NH_4HS$, 19·2 Cals.; J. Thomsen, for $Pb(NO_3)_{2aq.} + H_2S_{aq.}$, 11·43 Cals.; and $(PbO, H_2S, Aq.) = 29·2$ Cals.; M. Berthelot, 26·6 Cals.; and P. A. Favre and J. T. Silbermann, 22·36 Cals. W. Reinders gave $PbS + PbSO_4 = 2Pb + 2SO_2 - 99·543$ Cals.

P. Drude [12] found the **index of refraction** for Na-light to be 4·300 when determined by reflection from a cleavage surface; 2·96 when a polished surface is used; and when the surface is thoroughly cleaned, 3·313. The corresponding values for the **absorption index** were respectively 0·400, 0·629, and 0·520. The **reflecting power** was measured by E. P. T. Tyndall, and J. Königsberger; and the **spark spectrum** by A. de Gramont. The **reflecting power** of galena was found by W. W. Coblentz to be slightly greater in the visible than in the ultra-red, where it is constant at 31 per cent. to 14μ. B. Aulenkamp, and W. W. Coblentz and H. Kohler examined the **photoelectric sensitivity** of lead sulphide; and G. Mie, the optical resonance with X-rays.

J. W. Hittorff,[13] F. Braun, C. Doelter, T. du Moncel, O. Weigel, J. Bernfeld, F. Beijerinck, and H. Buff found the **electrical resistance** decreases with rise of temp., and the decrease is more marked at low temp. than at higher ones. The **electrical conductivity** has been examined by F. Streintz and co-workers, M. J. Huizinga, K. Bädeker, W. Mönch, G. Cesaro, A. Wesely, P. Collet, M. Padoa, etc. According to J. Guinchant, the electrical resistance, R, at $\theta°$ between $-25°$ and 920° is $R = 0·000298(1 + 0·00501\theta - 0·0_51230^2)$; and for lead sulphide which had been melted $0·0_3298$ ohms at 19°. E. van Aubel measured the resistance at the temp. of liquid air and found a minimum in the curve at $-189°$. O. Reichenheim gave 0·00243 ohm at 0°. F. Streintz measured the resistance of rods made by compressing the powdered sulphide. J. Konigsberger and co-workers, G. von Hevesy, and C. Doelter showed that the conductivity is probably electronic. A. C. James found the electrical conductivity of lead sulphide changes abruptly at about 160°, corresponding with the passage from α-lead sulphide to β-lead sulphide. The results are illustrated by Fig. 105, where the dotted line indicates that the temp. is decreasing while the continuous line is taken on a rising temp. F. Streintz found that the conductivity of a crystal which has been heated and cooled is higher than its original value. This is due to the presence of some of the metastable β-form. The presence of 10 per cent. silver sulphide lowered the transition temp. to 133°. The passage of a direct current through galena is accompanied by the electrolytic formation of metallic threads; this is increased by the presence of silver sulphide, and decreased by stannous sulphide. In 1906, H. H. C. Dunwoody discovered that some crystals

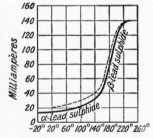

Fig. 105.—Electrical Conductivity of Galena Crystals.

will rectify an alternating current, and, in the case of carborundum, attributed unilateral conductivity to the small area of contact permitting the passage of electrons more readily in one direction than another. Other hypotheses were proposed by W. H. Eccles, G. W. Pierce, C. Florisson, and J. Strachan; and A. C. James suggested that unilateral conductivity and rectification depend on the structure of the crystals and by the fact that in solid electrolytes, the current is carried entirely by one set of ions while the other forms a fixed framework. In rectification by galena crystals, the metal ions oscillate to and fro through fixed channels of sulphur ions giving alternately metallic and non-metallic contacts. The variation of rectifying properties at different points on the crystal surface is attributed to the possible movement of metal ions without collision in some planes of the crystal, but not in others. C. W. Heaps found that the resistance of galena increases with the strength of the magnetic field, and transversely more than longitudinally as with the metals. P. Collet employed galena as a detector for long-wave radiations. G. Gehlhoff and F. Neumier measured the relation of the thermal and electrical conductivities. H. S. Roberts and L. H. Adams, and E. T. Wherry studied the **rectifying action** of galena as a radio-detector. J. Stefan found the **thermoelectric force** of galena against copper to be positive; and A. Shrauf and E. S. Dana found some crystals positive, others negative. Observations were also made by F. Streintz, K. Bädeker, J. Stefan, and G. Gehlhoff and F. Neumier. W. Skey found that galena is negative towards iron pyrites when both are immersed in sea-water. R. C. Wells found the **electrode potential** of galena towards N-KCl to be 0·28–0·38 volt; N-H_2SO_4, 0·32 volt; N-NaOH, 0·11; N-Na_2S, —0·19 volt. G. Tammann measured the potential of galena against a normal hydrogen electrode. R. C. Wells showed that a cathode of galena is attacked by a soln. of sodium carbonate. G. Trümpler also measured the potential of the Pb | PbS electrode in soln. of sodium sulphide. He found that the **passivity** of galena is due to the hydrolysis of the surface and the deposition of a film of sulphur; this is removed in a few minutes by $2N$-Na_2S. S. B. Christy found the potential towards N-KCy to be —0·28 volt when the normal electrode is —0·56 volt; with 0·1N-KCy, —0·48 volt; and with 0·01N-KCy, —0·52 volt. K. Fischbeck studied the **electrochemical reduction** of galena. P. Gaubert [14] found the octahedral faces of galena to be good **radio-detectors,** and the cubic faces poor ones; F. Trey studied the rectifying action of lead sulphide; and H. F. Vieweg, the frictional electricity. C. B. Thwing found the **dielectric constant** to be 17·92. F. Stutzer and co-workers found the **magnetic susceptibility** to be very small.

The chemical properties of lead sulphide.—According to D. S. Price,[15] when a thin layer of freshly prepared lead sulphide is exposed to **light,** oxidation occurs, and the colour becomes white; blue-light acts most quickly, yellow-light is weaker, violet-light is still weaker, and red-light does not act at all. J. F. Sacher showed that the presence of moisture favours the action because a film hermetically sealed and exposed to light for 3 years did not show the slightest bleaching action. The action of **heat** is indicated above.

According to H. V. Collet-Descotils,[16] and J. A. Arfvedson, **hydrogen** reduces lead sulphide at a bright red heat, forming lead and hydrogen sulphide; at a lower temp., reduction does not occur. According to J. E. Reynolds, reduction can be completed. In a rapid current of gas, some sulphide is volatilized and deposited on the cooler part of the tube. J. Percy said that hydrogen sulphide continues to be evolved at low redness. G. F. Rodwell showed that the amorphous sulphide becomes crystalline when heated to 100° in a current of hydrogen. The action of **air** or **oxygen** has been discussed in connection with the roasting of galena for the extraction of the metal. The cubic or (100)-faces of the crystals of galena are sometimes bluish while the octahedral or (111)-faces are brown; L. Leo said that this is because the (111)-faces are more rapidly attacked than the (100)-faces. P. B. Ganguly and N. R. Dhar [17] found colloidal lead sulphide is oxidized by air on exposure to sunlight, forming colloidal sulphur. J. B. Hannay's idea that *lead* *oxysulphide*, PbS.PbO, can be obtained lacks confirmation. C. Lückow, and F. R. Steigelmann found that electrolytic oxygen converts lead sulphide into the dioxide; and C. F. Schonbein, and A. Lamy found that ozone converts the sulphide into sulphate (1. 14, 6); and A. Mailfert said that with the prolonged action of ozone, lead dioxide is formed, and sulphuric acid set free. V. Zotier examined the catalytic action of lead sulphide on hydrogen dioxide.

G. A. Kenngott [18] reported that powdered galena from Neudorf, Harz, gives a very faint alkaline reaction when moistened with water. C. Doelter said galena is slightly soluble in water, and O. Weigel showed that at 18°, a litre of water dissolves $3 \cdot 6 \times 10^{-6}$ mol of the precipitated sulphide; $1 \cdot 21 \times 10^{-6}$ mol of Freiberg galena, and $1 \cdot 21 \times 10^{-6}$ mol of artificial galena; G. von Hevesy and F. Paneth gave 3×10^{-4} grm. of lead sulphide at 25°; W. Biltz, $5 \cdot 5 \times 10^{-6}$ mol at 16°-18°; and J. Knox, $5 \cdot 1 \times 10^{-8}$ mol at 25° on the assumption that ionization is complete. Owing to other probable reactions than those assumed in measuring the solubility by conductivity methods, L. Bruner and J. Zawadsky consider that the results are unreliable. R. Flatt tried to connect the solubility with the electronic structure. K. Jellinek and J. Czerwinsky gave 3×10^{-13} for the solubility product; and they showed that a more soluble form of lead sulphide may exist. According to J. Percy, when molten galena is poured into cold water, the odour of hydrogen sulphide is perceptible, the granulated product is remarkably fusible, and a sensible quantity of black powder floats on the surface of the water; even when heated to low redness, and plunged into cold water, galena becomes exceedingly friable. According to H. V. Collet-Descotils, when galena is heated in a current of steam, part volatilizes without decomposition, and part decomposes, giving off hydrogen and sulphur dioxide, and forming a residue of lead sulphide mixed with the oxide, and metallic lead. H. V. Regnault said that galena heated in a current of steam gives off hydrogen sulphide, and becomes covered with a film of lead. It is assumed that the first products of the reaction are hydrogen sulphide and lead oxide; and that the latter reacts with the remaining sulphide, forming lead and sulphur dioxide, by which again a portion of the hydrogen sulphide is decomposed. H. L. Pattinson obtained a fused residue and a large quantity of hydrogen sulphide by this reaction. J. Böhm found that in a sealed tube with air-free water at 150°-200°, hydrogen sulphide is formed; the liquid becomes alkaline, and in some cases a red powder—possibly red-lead—is formed. H. L. Pattinson, W. J. Jordan, and J. Percy also reported experiments on the action of steam on galena. A. Gautier said that at a bright red heat, galena is decomposed into its elements by water vapour, $3PbS + 2H_2O = 3Pb + 2H_2S + SO_2$, followed by $2H_2S + SO_2 = 2H_2O + 3S$. A small quantity of sulphur dioxide is evolved, and free sulphur mixed with a little lead sulphate collects in the cool part of the tube. The sulphate is probably formed by the reaction: $PbS + 2SO_2 = PbSO_4 + 2S$. J. B. Hannay's statement that *hydrated lead sulphide*, PbS.H₂O, is formed when galena is heated in water vapour has not been confirmed. J. Lemberg observed but a slight change when galena is boiled with a soln. of potassium hydroxide. For the action of the fused alkali hydroxides, *vide infra*, alkali carbonates. J. Lemberg made observations on the action of soln. of bromine in alkali-lye, of alcoholic soln. of hydriodic acid, and of soln. of silver salts.

L. E. Rivot [19] and co-workers showed that chlorine in the presence of water or alkali-lye furnishes lead dioxide. According to H. Rose, chlorine does not decompose galena at ordinary temp., but when heated, lead chloride and volatile sulphur chloride are formed—the yield of lead chloride, according to L. R. von Fellenberg, being 94·68 per cent. E. Schäfer found that the yield is quantitative and rapid at the m.p. of lead chloride, and more rapid and complete than the corresponding reaction with bromine. J. Lemberg said that bromine in alkaline soln. forms a yellowish-brown mixture of lead dioxide and oxybromide which is converted by alcoholic hydriodic acid into yellow lead iodide. According to E. Filhol and J. Mellin, iodine reacts vigorously on dry, powdered, artificial lead sulphide; the decomposition is also rapid in the presence of water or other solvents for iodine ; the reaction is slow in the cold, rapid when heated ; lead sulphate was not produced. V. Lenher found that galena is insoluble in **hydrofluoric acid** ; A. Lacroix that a mixture of **hydrogen chloride** and steam transforms it into lead chloride. Galena is decomposed slowly by conc. **hydrochloric acid,** when hydrogen sulphide is evolved, and lead chloride is formed. F. Becke studied the corrosion figures made by this acid. **Aqua regia** readily forms lead sulphate and chloride. W. C. Moore said that it oxidizes more rapidly than does nitric acid—lead chloride being less ionized than the nitrate. E. A. Atkinson found that **hydrogen bromide** does not remove lead from galena at 100°, but antimony is carried off. V. Lenher found galena to be readily soluble in **hydrobromic acid,** and also in **hydriodic acid.** W. Hampe, and R. Benedikt found that hydriodic acid of sp. gr. 1·7 quickly decomposes galena, a more dil. acid requires warming. R. H. Brett said that galena is insoluble in a soln. of **ammonium chloride.** J. Percy heated a mixture of ammonium chloride and galena in a crucible until fusion occurred ; some lead chloride was formed. H. Houben found that galena dissolves with difficulty in molten **sodium chloride,** even at a high temp. J. Percy found that when a mixture of sodium chloride and galena is roasted in air, sodium sulphate, lead chloride, sulphate, and oxide are formed ; if the temp. is too high, some sulphur dioxide may be given off. C. P. Townsend reduced lead sulphide by bringing the sulphide in contact with a cathode in a fused electrolyte of sodium chloride in which the lead sulphide is almost insoluble ; the alkaline earth chlorides can be similarly employed. According to A. Levallois, the **chlorides of silver, gold, magnesium, zinc, mercury** (ic), **aluminium, tin** (ous and ic), **antimony** (ous), **iron** (ous), **and platinum** act by double decomposition on galena in the presence of water in a sealed tube at 160°. If the zinc chloride is in great excess, a sulphochloride is formed, and similarly with iron, tin, antimony, etc. Mercuric chloride also gives a colourless sulphochloride which is blackened by light. At a higher temp., silver and mercuric chlorides form lead chloride and silver or mercuric sulphide. G. Viard passed a current of carbon dioxide carrying the vapour of zinc or cadmium chloride over galena, and found that a balanced reaction occurs, e.g. $ZnCl_2+PbS \rightleftharpoons ZnS+PbCl_2$. In the wet way, also, a balanced reaction may occur, and E. F. Anthon showed that finely divided galena will precipitate silver or copper sulphide from soln. of the respective salts. According to F. Raschig, when a soln. of cuprous chloride in sodium chloride is boiled with galena, cuprous sulphide and lead chloride are formed. When boiled with a dil. soln. of cupric chloride, cupric sulphide and lead chloride are produced. E. Schürmann found that a soln. of ferrous chloride does not act on galena, but a soln. of stannous chloride decomposes it completely. W. Skey noted that platinic chloride soln. is slowly reduced by galena, and gold is precipitated from a soln. of auric chloride. H. Eckenroth found that **an aq. soln. of lead chloride** dissolves galena. L. E. Rivot and co-workers showed that **alkali hypochlorites,** *in statu nascendi,* oxidized galena to lead dioxide. **According** to R. S. Dean, when galena is treated with **iodic acid,** in the presence of hydrochloric acid, the lead furnishes lead chloride, one-third of the sulphur forms sulphuric acid, and two-thirds separate as sulphur.

According to H. de Sénarmont,[20] galena is somewhat soluble in an aq. soln. of **hydrogen sulphide** when heated in a sealed tube. L. Bruner and J. Zawadsky gave for the solubility product, $[Pb^{..}][S''] = 3\cdot4 \times 10^{-28}$; J. Knox, $2\cdot6 \times 10^{-15}$; L. Rolla, $6\cdot7 \times 10^{-30}$; and G. Trümpler, 5×10^{-29}. The latter found that at 25°, a litre dissolves $5\cdot1 \times 10^{-8}$ gram-ion ; and L. Bruner and J. Zawadsky, $3\cdot1 \times 10^{-5}$ gram-ion. G. von Hevesy and F. Paneth found that a litre of a sat. aq. soln. of hydrogen sulphide dissolves $1\cdot5 \times 10^{-4}$ gram of lead sulphide. C. Doelter noted that galena is soluble in soln. of **sodium sulphide,** and I. Bernfeld reported that a litre of N-NaSH dissolves $2\cdot9 \times 10^{-5}$ gram-ion at 25°—this value was not accepted by G. Bodländer, and L. Bruner and J. Zawadsky because of the abnormal behaviour of the electrode of lead sulphide. P. P. Lebedeff said that a litre of N-NaSH sat. with both lead and hydrogen sulphides contains at atm. press. and room temp., 2.58×10^{-21} gram-ion. V. Stanek showed that no change occurs with **ammonium sulphide** in 8 hrs. at 200°. E. F. Smith found that galena at 250° is decomposed by **sulphur monochloride,** S_2Cl_2, vapour ; H. Feigel, by a soln. of sulphur monochloride in benzene ; and H. B. North and C. B. Conover, that galena in a sealed tube with **thionyl chloride** at 150°–175° furnishes lead chloride, sulphur dioxide and monochloride. According to A. Guerot, **sulphur dioxide** reacts with heated galena, forming a little lead thiosulphate, much lead sulphate, and sulphur, and hydrogen sulphide is evolved. H. Reinsch said that sulphur dioxide does not attack galena unless air be present, when lead sulphate is formed. J. B. Hannay's statement that *lead sulphitosulphide*, $PbS.SO_2$, is formed when galena is heated in a current of sulphur dioxide lacks confirmation. Galena is not decomposed by **sulphurous acid.** M. Berthelot showed that lead sulphide is decomposed by conc. **sulphuric acid,** hydrogen sulphide and sulphur dioxide being successively evolved ; with 60 per cent. acid, no sulphur dioxide was detected. F. Rosenkränzer measured the rate of soln. of galena in dil. sulphuric acid—0·0125–1·25 per cent.—and it was found to be proportional to the conc. of the acid, and the surface-area of the particles. The effect of temp. is independent of the size of the particles. The fact that rapid shaking is without effect on the velocity, shows that the velocity of the dissolution is not merely a diffusion velocity, and that a chemical process—possibly a gradual hydrolysis of the sulphide—precedes the dissolution. E. Jannettaz found that when **potassium hydrosulphate** and galena are triturated together, hydrogen sulphide is evolved. J. Percy heated a mixture of galena and **sodium sulphate,** and found a partial reduction to the metal, sulphur dioxide was evolved, and sodium sulphide formed. E. G. Zies and co-workers found that a 1·25 per cent. soln. of **copper sulphate** forms with galena, cupric sulphide, and with an excess of copper sulphate soln., cuprous sulphide. S. Meunier found that after galena has stood some years in contact with a soln. of copper sulphate, lead sulphate and brochantite are formed. J. Lemberg found that when galena is treated with an acidic soln. of **silver sulphate** at 60°, it acquires a dark steel-blue film of silver ; a similar deposit is formed at ordinary temp.—*vide supra* for the action of powdered galena. A. D. Carmichael said that galena reacts with **calcium sulphate** at 400°, forming lead sulphate and calcium sulphide ; on the other hand, F. O. Doeltz found that between 400° and 1100° in a current of carbon dioxide or nitrogen, there is very little action ; if a current of air be employed, the effect is analogous to that produced by roasting galena. J. Hanus, and S. H. Emmens found that when galena is boiled with a soln. of **ferric sulphate,** it is slowly converted into lead sulphate with the separation of sulphur and the formation of ferrous sulphate ; according to E. Jannettaz, acid soln. of **ferrous sulphate** also attack galena. E. Waller showed that galena is soluble in a soln. of **sodium thiosulphate ;** and T. Rosenbladt, insoluble in a soln. of **potassium thiocarbonate.**.

E. C. Franklin [21] said that galena is insoluble in liquid **ammonia.** Cold dil. **nitric acid** decomposes galena, forming lead nitrate, nitric oxide, and sulphur ; fuming nitric acid oxidizes both elements, forming lead sulphate with the evolution of nitrous fumes. R. H. Brett said that galena is insoluble in a soln. of **ammonium nitrate.** C. A. M. Balling showed that freshly precipitated lead sulphide reacts with a soln. of **silver nitrate,** forming silver sulphide ; for the action of powdered galena, *vide supra.* J. Fournet [22] found that when **arsenic sulphide,** or realgar, is fused with lead, arsenic is volatilized and lead sulphide is formed : $2Pb + AsS_2 = 2PbS + As$; and J. Percy added : " It is therefore reasonable to conclude that when lead sulphide is heated with **arsenic,** it will not suffer the least reduction." P. Berthier stated that when galena is heated with **antimony,** lead antimoniosulphides are formed ; J. Fournet found after fusion, one part resembled galena, the other part antimony, and there was no line of demarcation between the two. J. Percy concluded that lead sulphide is not reduced by antimony. E. Schurmann found that soln. of **thallous nitrate** and of **cobalt nitrate** do not act on galena ; and that, in general, lead sulphide is more stable towards salt soln. than the sulphides of zinc, nickel, cobalt, iron, arsenic, thallium, and manganese, and less stable than many other sulphides.

J. Fournet said that when galena is heated white-hot in a **carbon** crucible, carbon disulphide and lead subsulphides (*q.v.*) are formed. On the other hand, J. Percy described what he called a simple and pretty experiment to show the sublimation of galena :

> Put some galena at the bottom of a plumbago crucible, fill up with fragments of charcoal, and lute on the cover. Heat the crucible strongly, and leave it to cool gradually in the furnace. Beautiful crystals of lead sulphide will be found deposited on the charcoal. Care must be taken not to heat the crucible to too high temp. or too long, in which case no sulphide may remain.

This means that carbon, at these temp., is without action on galena. H. C. Geelmuyden found that **calcium carbide** readily reduces galena, forming calcium sulphide, and lead. L. R. von Fellenberg said that **carbon monoxide** has only *une action très faible*, forming a little carbon disulphide. G. F. Rodwell also observed very little action when carbon monoxide or **carbon dioxide** is passed over heated galena. H. Reinsch also observed no effect with carbon dioxide, but A. Lodin said the oxidation of galena by this gas begins at about 800°. J. Lemberg found that a sat. soln. of **potassium cyanide** and potassium hydroxide dissolves galena. A soln. of cadmium acetate decomposes galena when heated under press. in a sealed tube. According to J. Percy, fused potassium cyanide reduces much of the galena, forming potassium thiocyanate and lead ; and H. Rose observed that with several remeltings with cyanide the whole of the lead may be obtained in the metallic state. A. Levol reduced 84–84·5 per cent. of the lead in galena by heating a mixture of **potassium ferrocyanide** and that mineral. J. Percy made a number of experiments on this subject. H. C. Bolton showed that a conc. soln. of **citric acid** decomposes galena in the cold, and if potassium iodide be present, crystals of lead iodide are formed. J. Johnston, and E. Jordis and E. Schweizer observed that **carbon disulphide** dissolves sulphur from some samples of galena. L. Rosenthaler found that **mannite, glucose,** and **tartaric acid** are not adsorbed by precipitated lead sulphide, but appreciable quantities of **caffeine, amygdaline, codeine,** and **salicine** are adsorbed. A. J. Carlson and A. Woelfel found that lead sulphide is not very soluble in **gastric juice.** L. Oliver said that no miner of galena has died of plumbism in England for many years, and J. Rambousek and C. Biondi added that plumbism is practically unknown among the miners of galena ore in Bohemia, but cases have been observed among the galena miners of Sardinia.

According to P. Berthier, when galena is heated with **sodium carbonate,** there is only a partial reduction of the sulphide, and a grey fusible slag is formed containing sodium sulphate and sulphide, and lead sulphide. He showed that when galena with half its weight of sodium carbonate is heated in a retort, about 53 per cent. of lead is obtained, and he inferred that in vacuo, only 49 per cent. of lead would be reduced. He assumed that some air left in the retort contributed to the reduction, and that the reaction in the absence of air can be symbolized : $4PbS + 4Na_2CO_3 = Na_2SO_4 + 3Na_2S + 4Pb + 4CO_2$. If air has access during the operation, even the whole of the lead may be reduced, but the actual results vary with the mode of operation. The sodium sulphide is at the same time oxidized to sulphate. If potassium nitrate be added to the mixture, the result is the same as when the oxygen of the air has access. Similar results were obtained with **potassium carbonate,** or with **sodium or potassium hydroxide** used as flux. The reducing action was promoted by the presence of carbon which acts by preventing the formation of alkali sulphate so that less alkali carbonate is available for the reduction than is indicated in the given equation. H. Becquerel found that a soln. of **sodium hydrocarbonate** transforms galena into crystalline lead carbonate. P. Berthier showed that when galena mixed with **calcium oxide** is heated in a brasqued crucible, reduced lead and a slag are formed ; the slag consists of calcium and lead sulphides, and an excess of galena. W. J. Jordan [23] found that galena embedded in calcium hydroxide, in a luted crucible at the temp. of molten pig-iron, yields not a trace of reduced lead, nor was there any sign of the formation of calcium sulphide. If a small proportion of carbon is present, a small proportion of the galena is reduced to lead. W. Menzel also made observations on this subject. L. E. Rivot found that an intimate mixture of galena and lime at a red heat, with free access of air, furnishes calcium sulphate. P. Berthier found that **barium oxide,** with and without carbon, furnishes results analogous to those obtained with calcium oxide. W. Biltz also studied the desulphurization of lead sulphide with barium oxide; and with **cadmium oxide** the reaction : $PbS + CdO = PbO + CdS$ begins at 440°. P. Berthier found that when galena is heated with **manganese dioxide,** sulphur dioxide is evolved, and lead, and manganese sulphide are formed : $PbS_2 + MnO_2 = Pb + MnS + SO_2$; he also stated that galena reduces **ferric oxide** to a lower degree of oxidation and that sulphur dioxide is evolved, but the lead appears to be reoxidized by another portion of the ferric oxide. W. J. Jordan did not get the least trace of lead by heating a mixture of hæmatite and galena, but in the presence of carbon, the galena reacts by reducing the iron oxide and the iron reacts by reducing the galena to metallic lead. The peculiar actions of **lead oxide,** and of **lead sulphate** on galena have been previously discussed ; according to H. C. Jenkins, there are no grounds to justify the assumption that a complex *lead sulphatosulphide* has been formed. L. Kahlenberg and W. J. Trautmann studied the reduction of lead sulphide when heated with powdered **silicon.** J. Percy represented the reaction between **ferrous silicate** and galena by the equation : $2Fe_3SiO_5 + 5PbS = 2Fe_2SiO_4 + 2PbFeS_2 + SO_2 + 3Pb$. J. Percy found that **lead silicates** are partially decomposed by galena. E. Grieshammer showed that molten **glass** readily dissolves galena from which, on cooling, it separates in cubic crystals. E. Dittler showed that a colloidal soln. of **molybdic acid** is coagulated by a trace of lead sulphide ; soln. of molybdic acid attack galena very slowly.

Galena is reduced by **iron,** forming lead and iron sulphide. Iron is used as a reducing agent in assaying galena, and in the smelting of lead. Cast-iron is considered to be better than wrought-iron. Observations on this subject were reported by B. Kerl, J. Fournet, and J. Percy. The reaction was represented : $3PbS + 3Fe = 2Pb + PbS.Fe_2S.FeS$. J. Fournet found that when galena and **tin** are fused in a crucible, the mixture separates into two layers—the lower layer being an alloy of lead and tin, and the upper layer, a double sulphide of tin and lead. J. Percy also reported experiments on this subject. P. Berthier, and C. J. B. Karsten found that galena is reduced when heated with **copper.** J. Percy, and W. Guertler reported that the regulus which is formed is a double sulphide of copper and lead. J. Fournet reported that galena does not react with **zinc** at a red heat. J. Percy showed that galena is reduced by zinc furnishing " a hard, dull, black, porous mass in which lead sulphide and globules of lead are entangled." N. Parravano and P. Agostini found that **aluminium** readily reduces galena. According to F. M. Perkin, when a mixture of galena and **calcium** is inflamed lead and a complex calcium lead sulphide are formed. F. M. Perkin and L. Pratt showed that a mixture of galena and **calcium hydride** gives a similar product. H. G. Grimm studied the mixed crystals of lead sulphide and **sodium bromide.** J. L. Smith examined the action of alkali salts on lead sulphate. G. Tammann studied the reaction between **cadmium oxide** and lead sulphide.

The higher sulphides of lead.—L. Playfair and J. P. Joule [24] referred to a *lead sesquisulphide*, Pb_2S_3, of sp. gr. 6·335, but the existence of this compound has not been confirmed. The mineral was named by W. Haidinger *johnstonite*—after J. F. W. Johnston who studied the *supersulphuretted lead* obtained by W. Phillips from Dufton, Westmoreland. The mineral resembles galena, but it contains a higher proportion of sulphur than the Pb : S of galena. In some cases 14 per cent. excess has been reported. Examples have been reported by W. Haidinger, A. Raimondi,

F. Roemer, and A. Förster. C. F. Rammelsberg, R. P. Greg and W. G. Lettsom, and others are of the opinion that the so-called johnstonite is a mixture of galena and sulphur produced by the decomposition of a portion of the mass. A. Hutchinson and W. Pollard tried in vain to prepare *lead disulphide*, PbS_2, by the action of hydrogen sulphide on solid or dissolved lead tetracetate ; but H. Reinsch, and K. A. Hofmann and V. Wölfl consider that the sulphohalides which they prepared contained the group PbS_2 in combination with the lead halide. J. J. Berzelius also supposed that a polysulphide, probably **lead pentasulphide,** PbS_5, could exist as a reddish-brown precipitate when potassium pentasulphide is added to a soln. of a lead salt, but it breaks down very quickly into a brown mixture of lead sulphide and sulphur. F. Bodroux prepared the pentasulphide by adding a soln. of calcium polysulphide to an excess of a dil. soln. of lead nitrate cooled to $0°$, washing the precipitate successively with water, alcohol, and carbon disulphide ; and drying at a low temp. over sulphuric acid. The purple-red product is stable only below $10°$, above that temp. it decomposes into the monosulphide and sulphur. It is insoluble in soln. of the alkali sulphides ; cold nitric acid decomposes it rapidly with the separation of sulphur, and the formation of lead nitrate.

The lead sulphohalides.—V. Lenher's attempts [25] to make *lead sulphofluoride* analogous to the sulphochloride were not successful, because of the low solubility of lead fluoride in water, in soln. of the alkali fluorides, and in hydrofluoric acid. W. Truthe observed no sign of the formation of a compound in the f.p. curve of mixtures of lead sulphide and chloride, Fig. 106. The simple V-curve has a eutectic

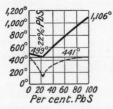

at $441°$ with 22 per cent. of lead sulphide. L. Hünefeld noticed that when hydrogen sulphide water is added to an aq. soln. of lead chloride, the precipitate first produced is yellowish-red, and then red when it contains about $3PbS.2PbCl_2$. The addition of an excess of hydrogen sulphide changes the precipitate into black lead sulphide, and the same change occurs when the red precipitate is boiled with water which extracts lead chloride. H. Reinsch added that when hydrogen sulphide is passed into a soln. containing 0.5 part of lead acetate in 100 parts of water mixed with 10 parts of hydrochloric acid of sp. gr. 1.168, a carmine-red precipitate of lead sulphochloride is formed ; and if the soln. contains 1 part of lead acetate, 112 parts of water, and 14 parts of hydrochloric acid, a yellow precipitate is formed. When boiled with water these precipitates furnish a soln. of lead chloride and a precipitate of black lead monosulphide. If instead of using 14 parts of hydrochloric acid, 14 parts of a mixture of hydrochloric and nitric acids be used in the proportion of $2 : 1$, prepared two days previously, there is first produced a yellowish-red and then a vermilion-red granular precipitate. If the hydrogen sulphide treatment be continued, the red precipitate becomes brown and finally black. When the vermilion-red precipitate is boiled with water, it gives a soln. of lead chloride, and a brownish-red flocculent powder which, when heated in a glass tube, gives off sulphur, and hydrogen sulphide, and fuses to dark brown lead sulphide. Hence it was assumed that the vermilion-red precipitate is a compound of lead chloride and polysulphide. V. Lenher obtained the red sulphochloride (i) by digesting the freshly precipitated lead sulphide with a soln. of lead chloride, and (ii) by treating galena with conc. hydrochloric acid until hydrogen sulphide is steadily evolved, and then adding water. White lead chloride is first precipitated, then the red sulphochloride, which is converted by an excess of water into black lead sulphide.

F. Parmentier said that the red precipitate obtained by passing hydrogen sulphide into a soln. of lead chloride in dil. hydrochloric acid is **lead sulphodichloride,** Pb_2SCl_2. This is decomposed by water, acids, and alkali-lye. The alkali-lye first blackens the red sulphochloride, and afterwards changes it to a white, flocculent mass. N. Tarugi claimed to have made **lead trisulphodichloride,** $3PbS.PbCl_2$, by

FIG. 106. — Freezing-point Curve of Mixtures of Lead Sulphide and Chloride.

the action of thioacetic acid on a very dil. soln. of lead chloride. The red precipitate becomes brown lead sulphide when treated with hot water. K. A. Hofmann and V. Wölfl found that by treating an excess of a cold soln. of lead chloride with very dil. ammonium polysulphide, red-coloured **lead hexasulphodichloride**, $Pb_4S_6Cl_2$, is produced ; and it is assumed that the compound is not to be regarded as $4PbS.S_2Cl_2$, but rather as $3PbS_2.PbCl_2$, that is, $Cl.Pb.S.S.Pb.S.S.Pb.S.S.Pb.Cl$. The same compound was made by mixing one part of a cold sat. soln. of lead chloride (1 : 100) and 1·5 parts of a soln. of 4 grms. of sodium thiosulphate in 100 c.c. of water in a vessel cooled with ice, and exposed to sunlight. In a few hours, the red precipitate is separated by filtration, washed with ice-cold water, then with alcohol, and finally with ether, and dried in vacuo over sulphuric acid. If the experiment be made in darkness, or in diffused daylight, black lead sulphide is formed. The red sulpho-chloride decomposes above 0°, and in darkness into black lead sulphide.

F. Parmentier reported **lead sulphodibromide**, Pb_2SBr_2, to be formed by the action of hydrogen sulphide on a dil. soln. of lead bromide in conc. hydrobromic acid, as in the case of the corresponding chloride. V. Lenher also made it by digesting galena with conc. hydrobromic acid until hydrogen sulphide is being steadily evolved, and treating the product with a large proportion of water. The brick-red product resembles the sulphodichloride, but is rather more stable. V. Lenher tried to make lead sulphoiodides, analogous to the sulphochloride, but on account of the low solubility of lead iodide in dil. hydriodic acid, the results were fruitless. Lead iodide dissolves readily in conc. hydriodic acid, but the action of hydrogen sulphide on this soln., furnishes neither the sulphide nor the iodosulphide. If, however, an aq. soln. of hydrogen sulphide be added to the hydriodic acid soln. of lead iodide, yellow lead iodide is first deposited, and with a further addition of more hydrogen sulphide, the yellow iodide changes into brick-red **lead sulphocto-iodide**, $PbS.4PbI_2$, or Pb_5SI_8. This is separated by suction, washed sucessively with a conc. soln. of potassium iodide, cold water, carbon disulphide, and absolute alcohol, and then dried by a current of cold air. The same compound is produced when an aq. soln. of hydrogen sulphide acts on a soln. of lead iodide and potassium iodide. The same compound was produced by treating freshly precipitated lead sulphide with conc. hydriodic acid, and diluting the soln. with much water as in the case of the sulphobromide. He then assumed that " whatever the method of pre-paration, the red sulphoiodide has always the same composition." This brick-red sulphide is yellower than either the sulphochloride or the sulphobromide. It is slowly decomposed by the prolonged action of light ; and rapidly by heat, acids, or alkali-lye. An excess of hydrogen sulphide water changes it to brown and finally black lead sulphide. A soln. of sodium carbonate furnishes lead sulphide and carbonate, and sodium iodide. F. Parmentier said that he made *lead sulphodi-iodide*, Pb_2SI_2, by the action of hydrogen sulphide on a soln. of lead iodide in hydriodic acid ; the product was stated to be impure because of the low solubility of lead iodide in the acid, and the difficulty in completely removing free iodine. K. A. Hofmann and V. Wölfl employed methods analogous to those used for lead hexasulphodichloride, and obtained **lead tetrasulphodiiodide**, $Pb_3S_4I_2$, or $2PbS_2.PbI_2$, that is $I.Pb.S.S.Pb.S.S.Pb.I$, the copper-red, microcrystalline powder consisting of dendrites and plates. It is said to be more stable than the hexasulphodichloride. At 100°, it forms a black mass of minute, prismatic crystals. When strongly heated, lead iodide and sulphur sublime, leaving behind scaly crystals of lead sulphide resembling graphite.

J. Sterba-Böhm and M. Auerspergrova [26] were not successful in their attempt to make **lead disulphide**, PbS_2, by the action of hydrogen sulphide on lead dioxide. With the gaseous sulphide a product was obtained containing some combined and some free sulphur. It was thought that the following reactions occur : (i) $PbO_2 +H_2S=PbO+S+H_2O$; and (ii) $PbO_2+2H_2S=PbS+S+2H_2O$. The first pre-dominates where liquid hydrogen sulphide is used at ordinary atm. press. ; and the second predominates at 100°—*vide* the action of hydrogen sulphide on lead dioxide. An aq. soln. of potassium sulphide reacts very slowly on lead dioxide, forming lead sulphide. Gaseous hydrogen sulphide gives lead sulphide with a soln of lead tetrachloride in methyl alcohol.

Complex salts with lead sulphide.—P. Niggli and K. Faesy [27] studied the complex lead sulphide minerals. According to P. Berthier, when a mixture of lead and sodium sulphates is heated to whiteness in a charcoal crucible, there are formed lead, and an impure *sodium lead sulphide* approximating $2Na_2S.3PbS$, or $Na_2S.PbS$—*sodium thioplumbite*. The shining, lead-grey, brittle mass has a close fracture, and when digested with water furnishes a soln. of sodium sulphide and lead sulphide probably mixed with excess lead. H. Freeman gave 650° for the m.p. of $Na_2S.PbS$. C. Immerwahr measured the potential of lead towards a 0·05N-soln. of sodium hydrosulphide with lead sulphide in suspension. A number of complex **cuprous lead sulphides** have been reported occurring either as minerals, or in furnace products. K. Friedrich measured the f.p. curves of mixtures of cuprous and lead sulphides, and found no evidence of the existence of any compound. The curve is of the V-type with a eutectic at 541°, and 51 per cent. of cuprous sulphide. W. Guertler and K. L. Meissner studied portions of the ternary systems Cu–Pb–S; Pb–Cu–Cu$_2$S; Pb–Cu$_2$S–PbS; and Cu$_2$S–PbS–S. A fused mixture of $9Cu_2S.2PbS$ was found by J. Fournet to have the same texture as galena; and a mixture, $3Cu_2S.2PbS$, gave, after fusion, a black radiated mass resembling cuprous sulphide. C. J. B. Karsten also reported that when copper is fused with an excess of galena, an alloy of copper and lead, and a compound of lead and copper sulphide, are formed. A. Breithaupt applied the term **cuproplumbite,** and M. Adam, *plumbocuprite*, to a massive mineral approximating $Cu_2S.2PbS$; and F. P. Dunnington applied the term to a mineral approximating $5Cu_2S PbS$. J. A. Antipoff reported minerals with the same composition. F. Field applied the term *alisonite*—after R. E. Alison—to a deep blue mineral approximating $3Cu_2S.PbS$. F. Ulrich, and A. Schertel described similar minerals. F. A. Genth found a furnace product from Argo, Colorado, with the 3:1 composition. W. H. Newhouse observed the formation of a similar mineral by the action on galena of the weathered products of some copper ores. A. Lodin, and P. Groth described a related mineral with the composition $2Cu_2S.PbS$. A. Brand obtained mixed crystals $Cu_2S.PbS$ along with some ferrous sulphide as a furnace product; and B. von Cotta, one with the composition $9Cu_2O.5PbS$. J. Fournet heated to whiteness a mixture of lead and silver sulphides in a carbon crucible, and obtained besides metallic silver, a product resembling galena—probably not *silver lead sulphide*. W. Guertler and E. Lüder studied the ternary system Pb–Ag–S, and the quaternary system Pb–Cu–Ag–S. K. Friedrich found no evidence of any compound on the f.p. curve. The curve is the simple V-type, with a eutectic at about 630° and 77 per cent. of silver sulphide, Fig. 108. The transformation of silver sulphide

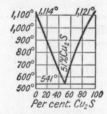

FIG. 107.—Freezing-point Curve of Mixtures of Lead and Cuprous Sulphides.

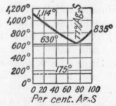

FIG. 108.—Freezing-point Curves of Mixtures of Lead and Silver Sulphides.

occurs at about 175°. J. S. Maclaurin passed sulphur vapour into a molten alloy of silver and gold to saturation, but it is not clear if a complex *gold lead sulphide* was formed—probably not.

P. Berthier heated to whiteness a mixture of lead sulphide and barium sulphate in a carbon crucible, and obtained what he regarded as a *barium lead sulphide*. Much lead sulphide volatilized during the operation. The crystalline product is decomposed by water, forming a soln. of barium sulphide, and a mass of lead sulphide. J. Fournet also fused mixtures of lead and barium sulphide without definite results. According to W. Menzel, and O. W. Brown, it is possible that a *calcium lead sulphide* is formed as a furnace product when galena is heated with calcium oxide and carbon ; or when mixtures of the two sulphides are heated. F. M. Perkin and L. Pratt said it is produced as a slag when galena and calcium or calcium hydride are heated. Several analyses show the existence of zinciferous galena—*e.g.* according to A. Liversidge,[28] a mineral at Broken Hill has 15 per cent. of zinc ; and H. A. Miers and co-workers found one corresponding with ZnS.4PbS in octahedral crystals from Bingham, Utah. K. Friedrich made an incomplete study of the system with lead and zinc sulphides. There is no evidence of the formation of *zinc lead sulphides* as chemical individuals, Fig. 109. I. Domeyko referred to a *galena blendosa* from Ingahaas, Huasco, which was called by J. D. Dana, *huascolite*. It is a bluish-grey massive mineral, and was analyzed by D. Forbes. Its composition approximates $Zn_3Pb_2S_4$. A. Raimondi, and C. F. Rammelsberg represented a sample from Dos de Mayo, Peru, called *pavonado blanco* or *chumbe blanco*, by Zn_7PbS_8 ; L. Pflücker y Ryco, the steel-grey crystals from Tuctu, Peru, by ZnS.PbS ; I. Domeyko, a sample from Morochocha, Peru, by (Zn,Fe)S.PbS ; and C. R. C. Tichborne regarded a sample from Kilmacoo, Wicklow, Ireland, which was called *kilmacooite*, as an argentiferous galenic blende. G. A. Kenngott regarded huascolite, etc., as intimate mixtures of galena and blende—*vide* the sulphostannates.

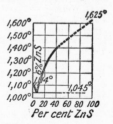

FIG. 109.—Freezing-point Curves of Mixtures of Lead and Zinc Sulphides.

J. B. Hannay called a mineral from Ballarat, Victoria, *youngite*—after J. Young. Its composition approximated 24ZnS.5MnS.5PbS.2FeS. Its homogeneity is doubtful.

G. Canneri and L. Fernandes [29] measured the f.p. curves of the binary system *lead and thallous sulphides*. They found that thallous sulphide and lead sulphide, completely miscible in the liquid state, are only partly so in the solid state, conjugate solid soln. containing respectively 3 and 75 per cent. of lead sulphide separating at 290°. This system possesses a eutectic mixture, containing 40 per cent. of lead sulphide, m.p. 290°, Fig. 110. Lead sulphide precipitated from slightly acid soln. containing thallium contains up to 4 per cent. of thallous sulphide. The results indicate the probable occurrence of thallium in arsenic minerals as thiosalts in solid soln. in the corresponding lead salts, whilst in galena the thallium occurs as sulphide in isomorphous mixture with lead sulphide.

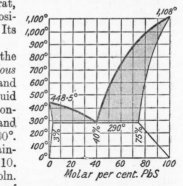

FIG. 110.—Equilibrium Diagram of Thallium and Lead Sulphides.

REFERENCES.

[1] K. Friedrich and A. Leroux, *Met.*, **2**. 536, 1906 ; A. Mourlot, *Compt. Rend.*, **123**. 54, 1896 ; *Recherches sur les sulfures métalliques*, Paris, 1899 ; K. Jellinek and J. Zakowsky, *Zeit. anorg. Chem.*, **142**. 1, 1925 ; J. Zakowsky, *Ueber die Affinität der Metalle zum Schwefel*, Danzig, 1924 ; W. Guertler, *Metall Erz*, **18**. 145, 1921 ; **92**. 199, 1925 ; B. G. Bredberg, *Pogg. Ann.*, **17**. 274, 1829 ; A. Brand, *Zeit. Kryst.*, **17**. 264, 1889 ; J. Percy, *The Metallurgy of Lead*, London, **39**, 1870 ; G. F. Rodwell, *Chem. News*, **15**. 137, 1867 ; P. Berthier, *Ann. Chim. Phys.*, (2), **22**. 240, 1823 ; H. V. Collet-Descotils, *ib.*, (2), **55**. 441, 1833 ; *Journ. Mines*, **27**. 469, 1810 ; J. Fournet, *Ann. Mines*, (3), **4**. 229, 1833.

² G. Agricola, *Bermannus sive de re metallica*, Basilæ, 1530 ; *De natura fossilium*, Basilæ, 1546 ; *Rerum metallicarum interpretatio*, Basilæ, 1546 ; C. Gesner, *De omni rerum fossilium genere*, Zürich, 1565 ; J. W. Evans, *Trans. Philog. Soc.*, 133, 1908 ; *The Meanings and Synonyms of Plumbago*, Hertford, 1908 ; C. Entzelt, *De re metallica*, Frankfurt, 1551 ; J. C. Boulenger, *De pictura plastice statuaria*, Leyden, 1627 ; J. F. Henckel, *Pyritologie*, Leipzig, 1725 ; O. Worm, *Museum Wormianum*, Leyden, 1655 ; X. Fischer, *Arch. Pharm.*, 230. 9, 1892 ; J. Webster, *Metallographia*, London, 1671 ; J. G. Wallerius, *Mineralogia*, Stockholm, 292, 1747 ; J. Mathesius, *Sarapta*, Nuremberg, 1571 ; F. von Kobell, *Die Mineralnamen*, München, 105, 1853 ; A. G. Werner, *Letztes Mineralsystem*, Freiberg, 22, 1817 ; J. B. L. Romé de l'Isle, *Cristallographie*, Paris, 3. 378, 521, 1783 ; G. Fallopius, *De metallis seu fossilibus*, Venetiæ, 327, 1606 ; E. Bechi, *Amer. Journ. Science*, (2), 14. 60, 1852 ; F. H. M. Zippe, *Ver. Ges. Mus. Böhmen*, 39, 1833 ; C. Berward, *Interpres phraseologiæ metallurgicæ*, Franckfurt am Mayn, 1684 ; R. Watson, *Phil. Trans.*, 68. 863, 1778 ; *Chemical Essays*, London, 3. 207, 1787.

³ J. J. Berzelius, *Gilbert's Ann.*, 37. 252, 1811 ; J. L. Proust, *Journ. Phys.*, 59, 260, 1804 ; L. N. Vauquelin, *Journ. Mines*, 2. 4, 1795 ; J. Davy, *Edin. Phil. Journ.*, 6. 128, 1829 ; A. Robertson, *ib.*, 7. 256, 1829 ; O. Schilling, *Berg. Hütt. Ztg.*, 20. 281, 1861 ; E. Metzger, *ib.*, 12. 238, 253, 1853 ; A. Breithaupt, *ib.*, 21. 98, 1862 ; P. Kroeber, *ib.*, 23. 30, 1864 ; B. Kerl, *ib.*, 20. 391, 1861 ; *Die oberharzer Hüttenprocesse*, Clausthal, 17, 1860 ; T. Thomson, *Outlines of Chemistry, Geology, and Mineral Analysis*, 1. 552, 1836 ; G. C. Hoffmann, *Ann. Rep. Canada Geol. Sur.*, 7. 11, 1896 ; A. Hofmann, *Œsterr. Zeit. Berg. Hütt.*, 54. 10, 1906 ; H. A. Miers, *Min. Mag.*, 12. 112, 1899 ; W. I. Macadam, *ib.*, 8. 136, 1889 ; I. Domeyko, *Elementos de mineralojia*, Santiago, 326, 1879 ; A. Raimondi, *Minéraux de Pérou*, Paris, 202, 1878 ; P. Kröber, *Berg. Hütt. Ztg.*, 23. 131, 1864 ; H. Sjögren, *Geol. För. Förh. Stockholm*, 7. 124, 1886 ; L. H. Borgström, *ib.*, 32. 1525, 1911 ; J. F. W. Johnston, *B.A. Rep.*, 577, 1832 ; *Neues Jahrb. Min.*, 55, 1834 ; P. Seidel, *ib.*, 555, 1864 ; F. Sandberger, *ib.*, 222, 1864 ; E. Bechi, *Amer. Journ. Science*, (2), 14. 60, 1852 ; V. R. von Zepharovich, *Zeit. Kryst.*, 1. 156, 1877 ; J. Thiel, *ib.*, 23. 295, 1894 ; *Sitzber. Akad. Erlangen*, 24. 57, 1892 ; C. von Hauer, *Jahrb. Geol. Reichsanst. Wien*, 13. 595, 1863 ; 15. 396, 1865 ; C. F. Eichleiter and O. Hackl, *ib.*, 65. 4, 1915 ; F. Posepny, *ib.*, 23. 84, 1873 ; T. Landmann, *Journ. prakt. Chem.*, (1), 62. 91, 1854 ; F. Sandmann, *Liebig's Ann.*, 89. 364, 1854 ; C. F. Rammelsberg, *Handbuch der Mineralchemie*, Leipzig, 24, 1849 ; *Ber.*, 7. 544, 1874 ; F. H. M. Zippe, *Verh. Ges. Mus. Böhmen*, 39, 1833 ; J. U. Lerch, *Liebig's Ann.*, 45. 325, 1843 ; F. A. Reuss, *Sitzber. Akad. Wien*, 25. 561, 1857 ; J. R. Blum, *Die Pseudomorphosen des Mineralreichs*, Stuttgart, 1. 178, 1843 ; 3. 174, 1863 ; O. Luedecke, *Die Minerale des Harzes*, Berlin, 27, 1896 ; A. Brunlechner, *Die Minerale des Herzogthums Karnten*, Klagenfurt, 40, 1884 ; M. d'Argy, *L'Inst.*, 1. 217, 1833 ; M. Villain, *ib.*, 1. 226, 241, 1833 ; P. Berthier, *ib.*, 2. 103, 1834 ; A. C. Becquerel, *ib.*, 2. 103, 1834 ; O. de Fiore, *Zeit. Vulkanologie*, 2. 12, 1915 ; A. E. Nissen and S. L. Hoyt, *Econ. Geol.*, 10. 172, 1916 ; U. Paniche, *Mem. Soc. Ital. Scienze*, 19. 3, 1916 ; F. Mohr, *Zeit. anal. Chem.*, 12. 142, 1873 ; A. Lacroix, *Bull. Soc. Min.*, 30. 229, 1907 ; F. M. Lyte, *Chem. News*, 30. 293, 1874 ; M. Tarugi and A. Calamai, *Gazz. Chim. Ital.*, 36. i, 366, 1906 ; U. Antony and O. Lucchesi, *ib.*, 19. 545, 1889 ; A. de Gramont, *Compt. Rend.*, 145. 231, 1907 ; A. Lacroix, *ib.*, 143. 727, 1906 ; E. Murmann, *Œster. Chem. Ztg.*, 6. 433, 1903 ; P. Pilipenko, *Bull. Tomsk. Univ.*, 1, 1906 ; *Neues Jahrb. Min.*, ii, 368, 1909 ; i, 390, 1912 ; *Bull. Acad. St. Petersburg*, (6), 3. 1113, 1909 ; C. Rimatori, *Atti Accad. Lincei*, (5), 12. i. 263, 1903 ; E. Manasse, *Atti Soc. Toscana*, 28. 118, 1912 ; R. Kraemer, *Mitt. Geol. Landesanst. Elsass-Lothr.*, 8. 449, 1915 ; W. R. Schoeller, *Journ. Soc. Chem. Ind.*, 32. 517, 1913 ; L. A. Emmerling, *Lehrbuch der Mineralogie*, Giessen, 2. 374, 1796 ; R. Kirwan, *Elements of Mineralogy*, London, 338, 1784 ; J. F. Westrumb, *Kleine physikalisch-chemische Abhandlungen*, Leipzig, 3. 405, 1788 ; C. Hintze, *Handbuch der Mineralogie*, Leipzig, 1. i, 467, 1904 ; J. S. Curtis, *Monograph U.S. Geol. Sur.*, 7. 80, 1884 ; S. F. Emmons, *ib.*, 12. 378, 1886 ; G. F. Becker and W. H. Melville, *ib.*, 13. 344, 1888 ; W. Haidinger, *Pogg. Ann.*, 11. 371, 1827 ; D. Forbes, *Phil. Mag.*, (4), 25. 110, 1863 ; L. Pflücker y Ryco, *Ann. Esc. Minas Peru*, 3. 60, 1883 ; L. F. Navarro, *Act. Soc. Esp. Hist. Nat.*, 4. 17, 1895 ; E. Dittler, *Zeit. Kryst.*, 53. 168, 1913 ; W. Stelzner and A. Bergeat, *Die Erzlagerstätten*, Leipzig, 426, 1904 ; P. Niggli, *Lehrbuch der Mineralogie*, Berlin, 533, 1920 ; F. Bernauer, *Die Kolloidchemie als Hilfswissenschaft der Mineralogie und Lagerstättenlehre und ihre Anwendung auf die metasomatischen Blei-Zink-Lagerstätten*, Berlin, 1924 ; G. Bischof, *Lehrbuch der chemischen und physikalischen Geologie*, Bonn, 3. 742, 1866 ; K. A. Redlich, *Zeit. prakt. Geol.*, 20. 197, 1912 ; W. H. Hobbs, *Amer. Journ. Science*, (3), 50. 121, 1895 ; W. Lindgren, *Trans. Amer. Inst. Min. Eng.*, 30. 578, 1900 ; F. Zambonini, *Compt. Rend.*, 143. 921, 1906 ; *Mineralogia Vesuviana*, Napoli, 1910 ; *Atti Accad. Lincei*, (5), 15. ii, 235, 1906 ; A. Sigmund, *Tschermak's Mitt.*, (2), 23. 87, 1904

⁴ G. C. Winkelblech, *Liebig's Ann.*, 20. 37, 1836 ; E. A. Geitner, *ib.*, 129. 350, 1864 ; W. Spring, *Zeit. phys. Chem.*, 18. 557, 1895 ; *Ann. Chim. Phys.*, (5), 22. 170, 1881 ; *Bull. Acad. Belg.*, (3), 5. 492, 1883 ; *Ber.*, 16. 1001, 1883 ; 17. 1218, 1884 ; *Bull. Soc. Chim.*, (2), 39. 644, 1883 ; (2), 41. 492, 1884 ; E. Jannettaz, *ib.*, (2), 40. 50, 1883 ; C. Friedel, *ib.*, (2), 40. 527, 1883 ; L. Franck, *ib.*, (3), 17. 506, 1897 ; O. Boudouard, *ib.*, (3), 25. 284, 1901 ; J. B. Senderens, *ib.*, (3), 6. 802, 1891 ; *Compt. Rend.*, 104. 58, 1887 ; C. C. von Leonhard, *Hüttenerzeugnisse und andere künstliche Mineralien als Stützpunkte geologischer Hypothesen*, Stuttgart, 346, 1858 ; G. F. Rodwell, *Journ. Chem. Soc.*, 16. 42, 1863 ; D. L. Hammick, *ib.*, 111. 384, 1917 ; H. C. Jenkins and E. A. Smith, *ib.*, 71. 674, 1897 ; J. E. Reynolds, *ib.*, 45. 162, 1884 ; R. Lorenz, *Zeit. anorg. Chem.*, 12. 442, 1896 ; F. M. Jäger and H. S. van Klooster, *ib.*, 78. 259, 1912 ;

K. Jellinek and J. Zabowsky, *ib.*, **142**. 1, 1925 ; F. Rössler, *Synthese einiger Erzmineralien und analoger Metallverbindungen durch Auflösen und Kristallisverenlassen derselben in geschmolzenen Metallen*, Berlin, 17, 1895 ; *Zeit. anorg. Chem.*, **9**. 31, 1895 ; W. Truthe, *ib.*, **76**. 161, 1912 ; F. Peters, *Centr. Accumul.*, **4**. 285, 1903 ; P. P. Lebedeff, *Zeit. Elektrochem.*, **18**. 896, 1912 ; A. Sadebeck, *Zeit. deut. geol. Ges.*, **26**. 653, 1874 ; P. Richter, *Chem. Ztg.*, **32**. 632, 1908 ; O. Hauser and E. Biesalsky, *ib.*, **34**. 1074, 1910 ; L. Moser and E. Neusser, *ib.*, **47**. 541, 1923 ; M. Berthelot, *Compt. Rend.*, **78**. 1175. 1874 ; F. de Marigny, *ib.*, **58**. 967, 1864 ; A. Mourlot, *ib.*, **123**. 54, 1896 ; T. Sidot, *ib.*, **62**. 999, 1866 ; J. Durocher, *ib.*, **32**. 823, 1851 ; M. Mayençon, *ib.*, **86**. 491, 1878 ; A. Gautier, *ib.*, **107**. 911, 1888 ; F. Isambert, *ib.*, **100**. 857, 1885 ; J. B. Senderens, *ib.*, **104**. 58, 1887 ; A. C. Becquerel, *ib.*, **32**. 409, 1851 ; **44**. 968, 1857 ; *Ann. Chim. Phys.*, (2), **53**. 106, 1833 ; P. Berthier, *ib.*, (2), **39**. 244, 1828 ; H. de Sénarmont, *ib.*, (3), **32**. 129, 1851 ; *Compt. Rend.*, **32**. 409, 1851 ; E. Priwoznik, *Ber.*, **6**. 1291, 1888 ; L. Dede and P. Bonin, *ib.*, **55**. 2327, 1922 ; E. Grieshammer, *Sprech.*, **43**. 153, 165, 1910 ; S. Meunier, *Les méthodes de synthèse en minéralogie*, Paris, 71, 1891 ; A. Gages, *B.A. Rep.*, 206, 1863 ; A. Himmelbauer, *Tschermak's Mitt.*, (2), **29**. 370, 1910 ; R. Grund, *ib.*, (2), **29**. 261, 1910 ; A. Gages, *B.A. Rep.*, 206, 1863 ; R. C. Wells, *Bull. U.S. Geol. Sur.*, 609, 1916 ; *Chem. News*, **113**. 149, 1916 ; P. Tschirwinsky, *Bull. Kieff. Univ.*, 1, 1906 ; I. M. Kolthoff, *Pharm. Weekbl.*, **53**. 1739, 1916 ; F. Stolba, *Journ. prakt. Chem.*, (1), **89**. 122, 1863 ; R. Schneider, *Pogg. Ann.*, **153**. 588, 1874 ; *Journ. prakt. Chem.*, (2), **2**. 91, 1870 ; H. N. Stokes, *Econ. Geol.*, **2**. 22, 1907 ; *Journ. Amer. Chem. Soc.*, **29**. 313, 1907 ; A. Daubrée, *Études synthétiques de géologie expérimentale*, Paris, 84, 1879 ; *Compt. Rend.*, **80**. 182, 1875 ; C. W. C. Fuchs, *Die künstlich dargestellten Mineralien nach Roses System geordnet*, Haarlem, 40, 1872 ; F. Fouqué and A. Michel-Lévy, *Synthèse des minéraux et des roches*, Paris, 311, 1882 ; L. Bourgeois, *Reproduction artificielle des minéraux*, Paris, 30, 1884 ; A. Breithaupt, *Mineralogische Studien*, Leipzig, 109, 1866 ; A. Lacroix, *Minéralogie de la France et de ses colonies*, Paris, **2**. 508, 1897 ; *Bull. Soc. Min.*, **30**. 229, 1907 ; F. Sandberger, *Jahrb. Ver. Herzogthum Nassau*, **7**, 1851 ; *Amer. Journ. Science*, (2), **17**. 128, 1854 ; F. Gonnard, *Bull. Soc. Min.*, **2**. 186, 1879 ; E. Metzger, *Berg. Hütt. Ztg.*, **12**. 238, 1853 ; F. Ulrich, *ib.*, **18**. 245, 1859 ; *Contributions to the Mineralogy of Victoria*, Melbourne, 48, 1866 ; A. Russell, *Min. Mag.*, **19**. 64, 1920 ; F. O. Doeltz and G. A. Graumann, *Met.*, **3**. 442, 1906 ; W. Heike, *ib.*, **9**. 313, 1912 ; J. F. L. Hausmann, *Abhand. Ges. Gött.*, **4**. 221, 1850 ; **5**. 71, 1850 ; *Nachr. Gött.*, 169, 1850 ; 177, 1852 ; *Beiträge zur metallurgischen Krystallkunde*, Göttingen, 1850–2 ; P. Spence, *Proc. Manchester Lit. Phil. Soc.*, **15**. 17, 1876 ; B. von Cotta, *Neues Jahrb. Min.*, 432, 1850 ; *Gangstudien oder Beiträge zur Kenntniss der Erzgänge*, Freiberg, **2**. 12, 1851 ; H. A. Wheeler, *Trans. Amer. Inst. Min. Met.*, **63**. 311, 1920 ; F. Schlagdenhauffen, *Journ. Pharm. Chim.*, (3), **34**. 175, 1858 ; F. Faktor, *Zeit. anal. Chem.*, **39**. 352, 1900 ; F. Muck, *Zeit. Chem.*, (2), **4**. 241, 1868 ; *Ber. Niederrh. Ges. Bonn.*, 37, 1868 ; E. Weinschenk, *Zeit. Kryst.*, **17**. 489, 1890 ; C. Doelter, *ib.*, **11**. 41, 1886 ; A. Brand, *ib.*, **17**. 264, 1889 ; O. Ruff and B. Hirsch, *Zeit. anorg. Chem.*, **146**. 388, 1925 ; **151**. 81, 1926.

⁵ M. Lucas, *Bull. Soc. Chim.*, (3), **15**. 40, 1909 ; R. Meneguzzi, *Arch. Farmacol.*, **20**. 67, 1915 ; J. Lefort and P. Thibault, *Journ. Pharm. Chim.*, (5), **6**. 169, 1882 ; *Arch. Pharm.*, **221**. 63, 1883 ; T. Ewan, *Journ. Soc. Chem. Ind.*, **10**. 10, 1909 ; E. W. Lewis and H. Waumsley, *ib.*, **31**. 518, 1912 ; *Zeit. Koll.*, **11**. 39, 1912 ; C. Winssinger, *Bull. Acad. Belg.*, (3), **25**. 390, 1888 ; W. Leuze, *Zur Kenntnis kolloidaler Metalle und ihrer Verbindungen*, Erlangen, 29, 1904 ; F. V. von Hahn, *Koll. Zeit.*, **36**. 277, 1925.

⁶ C. Gesner, *De omni rerum fossilium genere*, Zürich, 74, 1565 ; J. B. L. Romé de l'Isle, *Cristallographie*, Paris, **3**. 378, 521, 1783 ; R. J. Haüy, *Traité de minéralogie*, Paris, **3**. 458, 1801 ; C. F. Naumann, *Pogg. Ann.*, **16**. 487, 1829 ; L. Henry, *Ber.*, **3**. 353, 1870 ; W. Cross, *Proc. Colorado Scient. Soc.*, **2**. 171, 1890 ; A. Sadebeck, *Zeit. deut. geol. Ges.*, **26**. 213, 640, 1874 ; E. Weiss, *ib.*, **29**. 208, 1877 ; A. Scacchi, *ib.*, **15**. 26, 1863 ; A. Schrauf, *Atlas der Krystallformen des Mineralreiches*, Wien, **1**. 34, 1873 ; *Neues Jahrb. Min.*, 390, 1861 ; 545, 1863 ; C. Klein, *ib.*, 311, 1870 ; H. Traube, *ib.*, ii, 253, 1888 ; E. Bauer, *ib.*, i, 138, 1882 ; R. Brauns, *ib.*, i, 113, 1889 ; O. Mügge, *ib.*, i, 123, 1898 ; i, 54, 1920 ; P. W. Jeremejeff, *Zeit. Kryst.*, **17**. 625, 1890 ; V. von Zepharovich, *ib.*, **1**. 155, 1877 ; V. Dürrfeld, *ib.*, **47**. 375, 1910 ; *Mitt. Geol. Landesanst. Elsass-Lothringen*, **7**. 3, 1910 ; *Neues Jahrb. Min.*, ii, 35, 1911 ; L. Dürr, *ib.*, i, 27, 1909 ; A. Bernard, *ib.*, ii, 366, 1909 ; A. Reis and L. Zimmermann, *Zeit. phys. Chem.*, **102**. 298, 1922 ; J. Stefan, *Pogg. Ann.*, **124**. 632, 1865 ; *Sitzber. Akad. Wien*, **51**. 260, 1865 ; A. Schrauf and E. S. Dana, *ib.*, **69**. 155, 1874 ; *Amer. Journ. Science*, (3), **8**. 264, 1874 ; A. F. Rogers, *ib.*, (4), **12**. 42, 1901 ; J. P. Cooke, *ib.*, (2), **35**. 126, 1863 ; H. Sjögren, *Geol. För. Förh. Stockholm*, **7**. 124, 1884 ; J. E. Pogue, *Zeit. Kryst.*, **49**. 225, 1911 ; A. Koch, *ib.*, **10**. 95, 1885 ; A. Franzenau, *ib.*, **27**. 95, 1897 ; F. F. Graeff, *ib.*, **15**. 384, 1889 ; A. Lallemand, *Ann. Chim. Phys.*, (5), **8**. 13, 1876 ; L. Colomba, *Atti Accad. Lincei*, (5), **15**. ii, 636, 1906 ; *Atti Accad. Torino*, **45**. 617, 1910 ; F. Kretschmer, *Zeit. prakt. Geol.*, **25**. 117, 1917 ; T. Ewan, *Journ. Soc. Chem. Ind.*, **28**. 10, 1909 ; R. Granigg, *Metall Erz*, **13**. 169, 1916 ; J. W. Retgers, *Zeit. phys. Chem.*, **14**. 1, 1894 ; S. Thomson, *Min. Mag.*, **10**. 143, 1893 ; A. Brun, *Bull. Soc. Min.*, **4**. 260, 1881 ; H. Schneiderhöhn, *Anleitung zur mikroskopischen Bestimmung und Untersuchung von Erzen und Aufbreitungsprodukten*, Berlin, 200, 1922 ; L. Royer, *Compt. Rend.*, **180**. 2050, 1925 ; P. F. Kerr, *Econ. Geol.*, **19**. 1, 1924 ; F. N. Guild, *ib.*, **12**. 297, 1917 ; A. Johnsen, *Forts. Min. Krist. Petrog*, **3**. 93, 1913 ; F. L. Navarro, *Act. Soc. Espan. Hist. Nat.*, **4**. 5, 1895 ; A. Frenzel, *Tschermak's Mitt.*, (2), **3**. 507, 1881 ; F. Becke, *ib.*, (2), **6**. 237, 1885 ; (2), **9**. 16, 1888 ; P. Groth, *Die Mineralsammlung*

der Universität Strassburg, Strassburg, 49, 1878 ; A. d'Achiardi, *Mineralogia della Toscana*,
Pisa, 2. 263, 1872 ; W. Haidinger, *Treatise on Mineralogy*, Edinburgh, 3. 13, 1825 ; G. Cesaro,
Ann. Soc. Géol. Belg., 24. 39, 1897 ; G. Greim, *Die Mineralien des Grossherzogiums Hessen*,
Giessen, 6, 1895 ; A. Lacroix, *Minéralogie de la France et de ses colonies*, Paris, 2. 502, 1897 ;
Bull. Soc. Min., 30. 229, 1907 ; W. P. Davey, *Phys. Rev.*, (2), 17. 402, 1921 ; (2), 19. 248, 1922 ;
W. H. and W. L. Bragg, *X-Rays and Crystal Structure*, London, 173, 1915 ; 164, 1924 ;
H. G. Grimm, *Zeit. Elektrochem.*, 30. 467, 1924 ; G. Tammann and W. Krings, *Zeit. anorg. Chem.*,
146. 420, 1925 ; J. Mélon, *Ann. Soc. Géol. Belg.*, 45. 151, 1922 ; H. Seifert, *Zeit. Kryst.*, 63. 156,
1926 ; L. S. Ramsdell, *Amer. Min.*, 10. 282, 1925 ; M. Volmer and A. Weber, *Zeit. phys. Chem.*,
119. 277, 1926.
    [7] R. Boyle, *Hydrostatic Balance*, London, 1690 ; R. Watson, *Chemical Essays*, London, 3.
212, 1787 ; *Phil. Trans.*, 68. 863, 1778 ; C. J. B. Karsten, *Schweigger's Journ.*, 65. 394, 1832 ;
A. Breithaupt, *Journ. prakt. Chem.*, (1), 11. 151, 1837 ; R. Schneider, *ib.*, (2), 2. 91, 1870 ;
Pogg. Ann., 153. 588, 1874 ; F. E. Neumann, *ib.*, 23. 1, 1831 ; L. Playfair and J. P. Joule,
Journ. Chem. Soc., 1. 137, 1848 ; G. Tschermak, *Sitzber. Akad. Wien*, 45. 603, 1862 ;
J. B. Hannay, *Chem. News*, 67. 291, 1893 ; J. U. Lerch, *Liebig's Ann.*, 45. 325, 1843 ; P. Pili-
penko, *Bull. Acad. St. Petersburg*, (6), 3. 1113, 1909 ; A. Mourlot, *Compt. Rend.*, 123. 54, 1896 ;
H. le Chatelier and F. Bogitsch, *ib.*, 163. 459, 1916 ; W. Reinders, *Chem. Weekbl.*, 10. 700,
1913 ; F. Katzer, *Tschermak's Mitt.*, (2), 14. 483, 1895 ; G. Tammann and K. Dahl, *Zeit. anorg.
Chem.*, 126. 106, 1923 ; P. Walden, *Zeit. phys. Chem.*, 10. 714, 1892 ; P. Niggli, *Zeit. Kryst.*,
56. 42, 1922 ; A. Schrauf and E. S. Dana, *Sitzber. Akad. Wien*, 69. 155, 1874 ; E. Madlung and
R. Fuchs, *Ann. Physik*, (4), 65. 289, 1921 ; F. A. Henglein, *Zeit. Elektrochem.*, 30. 5, 1924 ;
Zeit. anorg. Chem., 120. 77, 1921 ; P. W. Bridgman, *Amer. Journ. Science*, (5), 10. 483, 1925 ;
A. Reis and L. Zimmerman, *Zeit. phys. Chem.*, 102. 298, 1922 ; E. Bauer, *Neues Jahrb. Min.*,
i, 138, 1882.
    [8] J. P. Joule and L. Playfair, *Journ. Chem. Soc.*, 1. 121, 1849 ; H. Kopp, *Liebig's Ann.*,
81. 1, 1852 ; *Pogg. Ann.*, 86. 156, 1852 ; F. Pfaff, *ib.*, 107. 148, 1859 ; H. Fizeau, *Compt. Rend.*,
66. 1005, 1072, 1868 ; F. Streintz, *Boltzmann's Festschrift*, 196, 1904.
    [9] H. V. Regnault, *Ann. Chim. Phys.*, (3), 1. 129, 1841 ; H. Kopp, *Liebig's Ann. Suppl.*,
3. 289, 1865 ; J. Joly, *Proc. Roy. Soc.*, 41. 250, 1887 ; G. Linder, *Die Abhängigkeit der specifischen
Wärme fester Körper von der Temperatur*, Erlangen, 1903 ; *Sitzber. Akad. Erlangen*, 34. 217,
1903 ; E. van Aubel, *Phys. Zeit.*, 5. 636, 1904 ; K. Bornemann and O. Hengstenberg, *Metall
Erz*, 17. 313, 339, 1920 ; L. Rolla, *Gazz. Chim. Ital.*, 43. ii, 545, 1913 ; F. Streintz, *Boltzmann's
Festschrift*, 196, 1904 ; E. D. Eastman and W. H. Rodebush, *Journ. Amer. Chem. Soc.*, 40. 489,
1918.
    [10] K. Friedrich and A. Leroux, *Mitt. Met. Inst. Freiberg*, 17, 1910 ; K. Friedrich, *Met.*,
4. 479, 1907 ; 5. 52, 1908 ; 6. 179, 1909 ; W. Heike, *ib.*, 9. 316, 1912 ; F. O. Doeltz, *ib.*, 2. 461.
1905 ; F. O. Doeltz and C. A. Graumann, *ib.*, 3. 441, 1906 ; G. Tammann and K. Dahl, *Zeit.
anorg. Chem.*, 126. 104, 1923 ; W. Truthe, *ib.*, 76. 163, 1902 ; R. Schenck and A. Albers, *ib.*,
105. 145, 1919 ; F. Rössler, *ib.*, 9. 31, 1895 ; W. Biltz, *ib.*, 59. 273, 1908 ; A. Brun, *Arch.
Sciences Genève*, (4), 13. 352, 1902 ; R. Cusack, *Proc. Irish Acad.*, 13. 309, 1898 ; F. Damm and
F. Krafft, *Ber.*, 40. 4777, 1907 ; J. Joly, *Phil. Mag.*, (6), 25. 301, 856, 1913 ; (6), 27. 1, 1914 ;
A. Lodin, *Compt. Rend.*, 120. 1164, 1895 ; J. Guinchant, *ib.*, 134. 1224, 1902 ; A. Mourlot,
ib., 123. 54, 1896 ; P. Berthier, *Ann. Chim. Phys.*, (2), 43. 285, 1830 ; H. C. Jenkins, *Chem.
News*, 70. 44, 1894 ; W. C. Roberts-Austen, *ib.*, 70. 43, 1894 ; H. E. Armstrong, *ib.*, 70. 44,
1894 ; J. B. Hannay, *ib.*, 69. 270, 1894 ; *Proc. Chem. Soc.*, 10. 113, 1894 ; G. F. Rodwell, *Journ.
Chem. Soc.*, 16. 42, 1863 ; J. Percy, *The Metallurgy of Lead*, London, 37, 1870 ; E. Metzger,
Berg. Hütt. Ztg., 12. 238, 1853 ; C. C. von Leonhard, *Hüttenerzeugnisse und andere künstliche
Mineralien als Stützpunkte geologischer Hypothesen*, Stuttgart, 351, 1858 ; C. F. Rammelsberg,
Lehrbuch der chemischen Metallurgie, Berlin, 221, 1850 ; H. V. Collet-Descotils, *Journ. Mines*,
27. 466, 1810 ; P. Berthier, *Traité de essais par la voie sèche*, Paris, 2. 670, 1834 ; L. Merz, *Ueber
das Verhalten der Elemente und Verbindungen der Schwefelgruppe in Vakuum*, Heidelberg, 1905 ;
C. Zengelis, *Zeit. phys. Chem.*, 50. 219, 1904 ; D. Iitsuka, *Mem. Coll. Science Kyoto*, 4. 61, 1919 ;
H. Freeman, *Eng. Min. Journ.*, 120. 973, 1925.
    [11] J. Thomsen, *Thermochemische Untersuchungen*, Leipzig, 3. 337, 1883 ; *Termokemiske
Undersögelser*, Kjöbenhavn, 312, 1905 ; *Journ. prakt. Chem.*, (2), 19. 1, 1879 ; P. A. Favre and
J. T. Silbermann, *Ann. Chim. Phys.*, (3), 37. 471, 1853 ; M. Berthelot, *Thermochimie*, Paris, 2.
341, 1897 ; *Compt. Rend.*, 78. 1175, 1874 ; P. Gunther, *Zeit. Elektrochem.*, 23. 199, 1917 ;
L. Rolla, *Gazz. Chim. Ital.*, 43. ii, 545, 1913 ; W. Reinders, *Proc. Acad. Amsterdam*, 17. 703,
1914.
    [12] P. Drude, *Ges. Wiss. Gött.*, 283, 1888 ; *Wied. Ann.*, 36. 548, 1889 ; J. Königsberger, *Centr.
Min.*, 565, 597, 1908 ; *Ann. Physik*, (4), 43. 1205, 1914 ; A. de Gramont, *Compt. Rend.*, 119.
68, 1894 ; 145. 231, 1907 ; *Chem. News*, 90. 140, 1904 ; *Bull. Soc. Min.*, 18. 233, 1895 ; W. W. Coblentz, *Investigations of Infra-red Spectra*, Washington, 4. 93, 1906 ; B. Aulenkamp, *Zeit. Physik*,
18. 70, 1923 ; G. Mie, *ib.*, 15. 56, 1923 ; 18. 105, 1923 ; E. P. T. Tyndall, *Phys. Rev.*, (2), 21.
162, 1923 ; W. W. Coblentz and H. Kohler, *Bull. Bur. Standards*, 15. 231, 1919.
    [13] F. Beijerinck, *Neues Jahrb. Min. B.B.*, 11. 439, 1897 ; O. Weigel, *ib.*, 21. 325, 1905 ;
H. Buff, *Liebig's Ann.*, 102. 883, 1857 ; W. Mönch, *Neues Jahrb. Min. B.B.*, 20. 365, 1905 ;
Ueber die elektrische Leitfahigkeit von Kupfer-sulfür, Silber-, Blei-, und schwarzem Quecksilbersulfid,
Göttingen, 1905 ; J. W. Hittorff, *Pogg. Ann.*, 84. 1, 1851 ; F. Braun, *ib.*, 153. 556, 1874 ; *Wied.*

Ann., **1**. 95, 1877 ; **4**. 476, 1878 ; W. Skey, *Chem. News*, **23**. 255, 1871 ; F. Streintz, *Ann. Physik*, (4), **9**. 867, 1902 ; *Boltzmann's Festschrift*, 196, 1904 ; *Phys. Zeit.*, **4**. 106, 1903 ; **13**. 673, 1912 ; **21**. 367, 1920 ; F. Streintz and A. Wesely, *ib.*, **21**. 42, 1920 ; F. Streintz and A. Wellik, *ib.*, **12**. 845, 1911 ; A. Wesely, *ib.*, **14**. 76, 1913 ; H. S. Roberts and L. H. Adams, *Amer. Min.*, **7**. 131, 1922 ; E. T. Wherry, *ib.*, **10**. 28, 1925 ; P. Collet, *Ann. Physique*, (9). **15**. 265, 1921 ; *Compt. Rend.*, **158**. 1994, 1914 ; **163**. 90, 1916 ; **170**. 1489, 1920 ; J. Guinchant, *ib.*, **134**. 1224, 1902 ; E. van Aubel, *ib.*, **135**. 734, 1902 ; C. Florisson, *ib.*, **171**. 106, 1920 ; C. W. Heaps, *Phil. Mag.*, (6), **24**. 813, 1912 ; J. Königsberger and K. Schilling, *Ann. Physik*, (4), **32**. 179, 1910 ; J. Königsberger, *Zeit. Elektrochem.*, **15**. 103, 1909 ; R. C. Wells, *Trans. Amer. Electrochem. Soc.*, **22**. 314, 1912 ; G. Cesaro, *Bull. Acad. Belg.*, 115, 1904 ; G. Tammann, *Zeit. anorg. Chem.*, **113**. 149, 1920 ; C. Doelter, *ib.*, **67**. 395, 1910 ; *Monatsh.*, **31**. 493, 1910 ; *Sitzber. Akad. Wien*, **109**. 49, 1910 ; J. Stefan, *ib.*, **51**. 260, 1865 ; *Pogg. Ann.*, **124**. 632, 1865 ; T. du Moncel, *Ann. Chim. Phys.*, (5), **10**. 194, 459, 1877 ; M. J. Huizinga, *Proc. Acad. Amsterdam*, **27**. 733, 1919 ; G. Trümpler, *Zeit. phys. Chem.*, **99**. 9, 1921 ; G. von Hevesy, *Danske Vid. Medd.*, **3**. 12, 1921 ; P. Vaillant, *Journ. Phys.*, (6), **3**. 87, 1922 ; G. Gehlhoff and F. Neumier, *Verh. deut. phys. Ges.*, **15**. 1069, 1913 ; S. B. Christy, *Amer. Chem. Journ.*, **27**. 362, 1902 ; O. Reichenheim, *Ueber die Elektrizitätsleitung einiger naturlichkristallisierter Oxyde und Sulfide und des Graphits*, Freiburg, 5, 1906 ; J. Stefan, *Pogg. Ann.*, **124**. 632, 1865 ; *Sitzber. Akad. Wien*, **51**. 260, 1865 ; A. Schrauf and E. S. Dana, *ib.*, **69**. 155, 1874 ; *Amer. Journ. Science*, (3), **8**. 264, 1874 ; H. H. C. Dunwoody, *U.S. Pat. No.* 837616, 1906 ; *Brit. Pat. No.* 5332, 1907 ; A. C. James, *Phil. Mag.*, (6), **49**. 681, 1925 ; W. H. Eccles, *Proc. Phys. Soc.*, **22**. 282, 360, 1910 ; **25**. 273, 1913 ; G. W. Pierce, *Phys. Rev.*, (1), **25**. 31, 1907 ; J. Strachan, *Wireless World*, **14**. 245, 1924 ; K. Bädeker, *Ueber die elektrische Leitfähigkeit und die thermoelektrische Kraft einiger Schwermetallverbindungen*, Leipzig, 1906 ; J. Bernfeld, *Zeit. phys. Chem.*, **25**. 46, 1898 ; H. Fischbeck, *Zeit. anorg. Chem.*, **148**. 97, 1925 ; M. Padoa, *Gazz. Chim. Ital.*, **55**. ii, 975, 1925 ; F. Trey, *Phys. Zeit.*, **26**. 849, 1925.

    ¹⁴ C. B. Thwing, *Zeit. phys. Chem.*, **14**. 286, 1894 ; F. Stutzer, W. Cross, and K. Bornemann, *Metall Erz*, **15**. 7, 1918 ; P. Gaubert, *Compt. Rend.*, **182**. 143, 1920 ; H. F. Viewig, *Journ. Phys. Chem.*, **30**. 865, 1926.

    ¹⁵ J. F. Sacher, *Chem. Ztg.*, **34**. 647, 1910 ; D. S. Price, *Journ. Chem. Soc.*, **18**. 246, 1865.

    ¹⁶ H. V. Collet-Descotils, *Journ. Mines*, **27**. 469, 1810 ; *Ann. Chim. Phys.*, (2), **55**. 441, 1833 ; J. Percy, *The Metallurgy of Lead*, London, 52, 1870 ; G. F. Rodwell, *Journ. Chem. Soc.*, **16**. 42, 1863 ; J. E. Reynolds, *ib.*, **45**. 167, 1884 ; L. Leo, *Die Anlauffarben*, Dresden, 17, 1911 ; J. Lemberg, *Zeit. deut. geol. Ges.*, **46**. 793, 1894 ; J. A. Arfvedson, *Pogg. Ann.*, **1**. 49, 1924.

    ¹⁷ P. B. Ganguly and N. R. Dhar, *Koll. Zeit.*, **31**. 16, 1922 ; C. Lückow, *Brit. Pat. No.* 14801, 1895 ; F. R. Steigelmann, *German Pat.*, *D.R.P.* 162107, 1903 ; C. F. Schönbein, *Pogg. Ann.*, **72**. 450, 1847 ; A. Mailfert, *Compt. Rend.*, **94**. 1186, 1882 ; A. Lamy, *Bull. Soc. Chim.*, (2), **11**. 210, 1869 ; J. B. Hannay, *Chem. News*, **70**. 43, 1894 ; *Proc. Chem. Soc.*, **10**. 151, 1894 ; *Trans. Amer. Inst. Min. Met. Eng.*, **3**. 183, 1894 ; V. Zotier, *Bull. Soc. Chim.*, (4), **21**. 241, 1917.

    ¹⁸ J. Percy, *The Metallurgy of Lead*, London, 37, 1870 ; H. V. Collet-Descotils, *Journ. Mines*, **27**. 469, 1810 ; *Ann. Chim. Phys.*, (2), **55**. 441, 1833 ; H. V. Regnault, *ib.*, (2), **62**. 381, 1836 ; *Ann. Mines*, (3), **11**. 47, 1837 ; J. Percy, *The Metallurgy of Lead*, London, 50, 1870 ; H. L. Pattinson, *Phil. Mag.*, **5**. 172, 1829 ; G. A. Kenngott, *Neues Jahrb. Min.*, 437, 1867 ; L. Bruner and J. Zawadsky, *Bull. Acad. Cracow*, 267, 1909 ; J. B. Hannay, *Chem. News*, **67**. 291, 1893 ; **69**. 270, 1894 ; *Zeit. anorg. Chem.*, **65**. 145, 1910 ; **67**. 454, 1910 ; G. von Hevesy and F. Paneth, *ib.*, **82**. 323, 1913 ; J. Böhm, *Sitzber. Akad. Wien*, **85**. 554, 1882 ; W. Biltz, *Zeit. phys. Chem.*, **58**. 288, 1907 ; O. Weigel, *ib.*, **58**. 293, 1907 ; *Nachr. Gött.*, 525, 1906 ; *Sitzber. Ges. Nat. Marburg*, 35, 1921 ; A. Gautier, *Compt. Rend.*, **142**. 1645, 1906 ; W. J. Jordan, *Journ. tech. ökon. Chem.*, **11**. 348, 1831 ; C. Doelter, *Tschermak's Mitt.*, (2), **11**. 319, 1890 ; J. Lemberg, *Zeit. deut. geol. Ges.*, **52**. 480, 1900 ; R. Flatt, *Helvetica Chim. Acta*, **6**. 698, 1923 ; K. Jellinek and J. Czerwinsky, *Zeit. phys. Chem.*, **102**. 438, 1922.

    ¹⁹ R. H. Brett, *Phil. Mag.*, (3), **10**. 95, 1837 ; L. E. Rivot, F. S. Beudant, and P. A. Daguin, *Ann. Mines*, (5), **4**. 221, 1853 ; *Compt. Rend.*, **37**. 126, 1853 ; A. Levallois, *ib.*, **96**. 1666, 1883 ; L. R. von Fellenberg, *Pogg. Ann.*, **50**. 73, 1840 ; H. Rose, *ib.*, **42**. 540, 1837 ; W. C. Moore, *Journ. Amer. Chem. Soc.*, **33**. 1095, 1911 ; V. Lenher, *ib.*, **23**. 681, 1901 ; R. S. Dean, *ib.*, **37**. 1134, 1915 ; E. A. Atkinson, *ib.*, **20**. 809, 1898 ; H. Houben, *Met.*, **9**. 592, 1912 ; J. Percy, *The Metallurgy of Lead*, London, 67, 1870 ; R. Benedikt, *Chem. Ztg.*, **16**. 43, 1892 ; W. Hampe, *ib.*, **18**. 190, 1894 ; G. Viard, *Bull. Soc. Chim.*, (3). **29**. 455, 1903 ; E. Filhol and J. Mellin, *Ann. Chim. Phys.*, (4), **22**. 58, 1871 ; E. F. Anthon, *Repert. Pharm.*, **59**. 250, 1832 ; E. Schäfer, *Zeit. anal. Chem.*, **45**. 158, 171, 1906 ; E. Schürmann, *Liebig's Ann.*, **249**. 326, 1888 ; W. Skey, *Chem. News*, **23**. 232, 1871 ; F. Raschig, *Ber.*, **17**. 697, 1884 ; H. Eckenroth, *Pharm. Ztg.*, **40**. 528, 1895 ; C. P. Townsend, *U.S. Pat. No.* 815881, 1906 ; *Brit. Pat. No.* 6569, 1906 ; F. Becke, *Tschermak's Mitt.*, (2), **6**. 237, 1885 ; (2), **9**. 16, 1888 ; J. Lemberg, *Zeit. deut. geol. Ges.*, **46**. 788, 1894 ; A. Lacroix, *Bull. Soc. Min.*, **30**. 230, 1907.

    ²⁰ H. de Sénarmont, *Ann. Chim. Phys.*, (3), **32**. 168, 1851 ; M. Berthelot, *ib.*, (7), **14**. 176, 1898 ; C. Doelter, *Tschermak's Mitt.*, (2), **11**. 319, 1890 ; E. Jannettaz, *Bull. Soc. Géol.*, (3), **3**. 310, 1875 ; E. Waller, *Journ. Anal. Appl. Chem.*, **5**. 646, 1891 ; J. Knox, *Trans. Faraday Soc.*, **4**. 48, 1908 ; T. Rosenbladt, *Zeit. anal. Chem.*, **26**. 15, 1887 ; E. F. Smith, *Journ. Amer. Chem. Soc.*, **20**. 289, 1898 ; P. Berthier, *Traité des essais par la voie sèche*, Paris, **2**. 672, 1834 ; J. Percy, *The Metallurgy of Lead*, London, 54, 1870 ; J. B. Hannay, *Chem. News*, **67**. 291, 1893 ; **69**. 270, 1894 ; L. Bruner and J. Zawadsky, *Bull. Acad. Cracow*, 267, 1909 ; *Zeit. anorg. Chem.*, **65**. 145,

1910 ; **67**. 454, 1910 ; G. von Hevesy and F. Paneth, *ib.*, **82**. 323, 1913 ; V. Stanek, *ib.*, **17**. 114, 1898 ; F. Rosenkränzer, *ib.*, **87**. 319, 1914 ; **88**. 452, 1914 ; J. Hanus, *ib.*, **17**. 11, 1898 ; E. G. Zies, E. T. Allen, and H. E. Merwin, *Econ. Geol.*, **11**. 407, 1916 ; I. Bernfeld, *Zeit. phys. Chem.*, **25**. 46, 1898 ; G. Bodländer, *ib.*, **27**. 64, 1898 ; G. Trümpler, *ib.*, **99**. 9, 1921 ; H. B. North and C. B. Conover, *Amer. Journ. Science*, (4), **40**. 640, 1915 ; P. P. Lebedeff, *Zeit. Elektrochem.*, **18**. 395, 1912 ; H. Reinsch, *Journ. prakt. Chem.*, (1), **13**. 130, 1838 ; *Repert. Pharm.*, **56**. 183, 1837 ; L. Rolla, *Gazz. Chim. Ital.*, **43**. ii, 545, 1913 ; S. H. Emmens, *Monit. Scient.*, (4), **7**. ii, 406, 1893 ; F. O. Doeltz, *Met.*, **2**. 461, 1905 ; A. D. Carmichael, *Brit. Pat. No.* 17580, 1902 ; E. Jannettaz, *Compt. Rend.*, **77**. 838, 1873 ; **78**. 852, 1874 ; A. Guerot, *ib.*, **75**. 1276, 1872 ; S. Meunier, *ib.*, **86**. 686, 1878 ; H. Feigel, *Verhalten von Schwermetallverbindungen gegen Polysulfide und chlorschwefel*, Erlangen, 36, 1905 ; J. Lemberg, *Zeit. deut. geol. Ges.*, **46**. 793, 1894.
    [21] E. C. Franklin, *Amer. Chem. Journ.*, **20**. 828, 1898 ; R. H. Brett, *Phil. Mag.*, (3), **10**. 95, 1837 ; C. A. M. Balling, *Chem. Ztg.*, **5**. 80, 1881 ; P. Berthier, *Traité des essais par la voie sèche*, Paris, **2**. 672, 1834 ; E. Schürmann, *Liebig's Ann.*, **249**. 326, 1888.
    [22] A. Levol, *Ann. Chim. Phys.*, (3), **46**. 472, 1856 ; H. Rose, *Traité complet de chimie analytique*, Paris, **2**. 226, 1861 ; E. Schurmann, *Liebig's Ann.*, **249**. 326, 1888 ; J. Fournet, *Ann. Mines*, (3), **4**. 229, 1833 ; J. Percy, *The Metallurgy of Lead*, London, **37**, 61, 1870 ; G. F. Rodwell, *Journ. Chem. Soc.*, **16**. 42, 1863 ; A. Lodin, *Compt. Rend.*, **120**. 1164, 1895 ; H. Becquerel, *ib.*, **63**. 1, 1866 ; H. C. Geelmuyden, *ib.*, **130**. 1026, 1900 ; A. Mourlot, *ib.*, **123**. 54, 1896 ; P. Berthier, *Ann. Chim. Phys.*, (2), **33**. 156, 1826 ; *Traité des essais par la voie sèche, Paris*, **1**. 670, 1834 ; **2**. 670, 1834 ; J. Lemberg, *Zeit. deut. geol. Ges.*, **52**. 488, 1900 ; L. R. von Fellenberg, *Pogg. Ann.*, **50**. 73, 1840 ; H. Reinsch, *Journ. prakt. Chem.*, (1), **13**. 130, 1838 ; H. C. Bolton, *Chem. News*, **38**. 168, 1878 ; *Ber.*, **13**. 729, 1880 ; L. Rosenthaler, *Arch. Pharm.*, **245**. 259, 1907 ; E. Jordis and E. Schweizer, *Zeit. angew. Chem.*, **23**. 577, 1910 ; J. Johnston, *B.A. Rep.*, 572, 1833 ; A. J. Carlson and A. Woelfel, *Journ. Amer. Med. Assoc.*, **61**. 181, 1913 ; *Proc. Soc. Exp. Biol. Med.*, **10**. 189, 1913 ; *Amer. Journ. Public Health*, **3**. 755, 1913 ; *Journ. Pharmacol. Exp. Therap.*, **5**. 549, 1914 ; T. Oliver, *Dangerous Trades*, London, 1902 ; J. Rambousek and C. Biondi, *A proposito della atossicita de solfuro di plombo e del saturnismo nei minatori della galena*, Firenze, **1**. 472, 1907.
    [23] W. J. Jordan, *Journ. tech. ökon. Chem.*, **11**. 333, 1831 ; J. Percy, *The Metallurgy of Lead*, London, 1870 ; L. E. Rivot, *Principes généraux du traitement des minérais métalliques*, Paris, **2**. 38, 1872 ; P. Berthier, *Traité des essais par la voie sèche*, Paris, **2**. 670, 1834 ; *Ann. Chim. Phys.*, (2), **33**. 156, 1826 ; J. L. Smith, *Amer. Journ. Science*, (1), **47**. 81, 1844 ; N. Parravano and P. Agostini, *Gazz. Chim. Ital.*, **49**. i, 113, 1919 ; J. Fournet, *Ann. Mines*, (3), **4**. 15, 1833 ; B. Kerl, *Die Oberharzer Hüttenprocesse*, Clausthal, 200, 1860 ; F. M. Perkin, *Trans. Faraday Soc.*, **3**. 115, 1908 ; F. M. Perkin and L. Pratt, *ib.*, **3**. 183, 1908 ; W. Menzel, *Metall Erz*, **10**. 193, 1913 ; W. Guertler, *ib.*, **17**. 193, 1920 ; E. Grieshammer, *Sprech.*, **43**. 165, 1910 ; C. J. B. Karsten, *Schweigger's Journ.*, **66**. 400, 1832 ; H. Becquerel, *Compt. Rend.*, **63**. 1, 1866 ; E. Dittler, *Zeit. Kryst.*, **53**. 166, 1914 ; **54**. 340, 1915 ; H. C. Jenkins, *Chem. News*, **70**. 43, 1894 ; H. G. Grimm, *Zeit. Elektrochem.*, **30**. 467, 1924 ; L. Kahlenberg and W. J. Trautmann, *Trans. Amer. Electrochem. Soc.*, **39**. 477, 1921 ; W. Biltz, *Zeit. anorg. Chem.*, **150**. 1, 1925 ; G. Tammann, *ib.*, **149**. 28, 1925.
    [24] W. Haidinger, *Handbuch der bestimmenden Mineralogie*, Wien, 566, 1845 ; *Jahrb. geol. Reichsanst. Wien*, **5**. 889, 1854 ; W. Phillips, *Elementary Introduction to Mineralogy*, London, 251, 1819 ; 335, 1823 ; J. F. W. Johnston, *B.A. Rep.*, 577, 1832 ; L. Playfair and J. P. Joule, *Mem. Chem. Soc.*, **3**. 89, 1848 ; R. P. Greg and W. G. Lettsom, *Manual of the Mineralogy of Great Britain and Ireland*, London, 448, 1858 ; C. F. Rammelsberg, *Handbuch der Mineralchemie*, Leipzig, 105, 1841 ; A. Raimondi, *Minéraux de Pérou*, Paris, 202, 1878 ; F. Roemer, *Schles. Ges. Vaterl. Cultur*, **43**. 39, 1865 ; A. Förster, *Berg. Hütt. Ztg.*, **24**. 107, 1865 ; K. A. Hofmann and V. Wölfl, *Ber.*, **37**. 249, 1904 ; A. Hutchinson and W. Pollard, *Journ. Chem. Soc.*, **69**. 220, 1896 ; F. Bodroux, *Compt. Rend.*, **130**. 1397, 1900 ; *Bull. Soc. Chim.*, (3), **23**. 501, 1900 ; J. J. Berzelius, *Ann. Chim. Phys.*, (2), **20**. 49, 1822 ; H. Reinsch, *Repert. Pharm.*, **56**. 183, 1837 ; *Journ. prakt. Chem.*, (1), **13**. 130, 1838.
    [25] V. Lenher, *Journ. Amer. Chem. Soc.*, **17**. 511, 1895 ; **23**. 680, 1901 ; L. Hünefeld, *Journ. prakt. Chem.*, (1), **7**. 27, 1836 ; H. Reinsch, *ib.*, (1), **13**. 130, 1838 ; *Repert. Pharm.*, **56**. 183, 1837 ; F. Parmentier, *Compt. Rend.*, **114**. 299, 802, 1892 ; K. A. Hofmann and V. Wölfl, *Ber.*, **37**. 249, 1904 ; W. Truthe, *Zeit. anorg. Chem.*, **76**. 162, 1912 ; N. Tarugi, *Gazz. Chim. Ital.*, **25**. i, 352, 1895 ; *L'Orosi*, **18**. 198, 1895.
    [26] J. Sterba-Böhm and M. Auerspergrova, *Rec. Trav. chim. Pays-Bas*, **44**. 390, 1925.
    [27] C. Immerwahr, *Zeit. Elektrochem.*, **7**. 480, 1901 ; *Beiträge zur Löslichkeitsbestimmung schwerlöslicher Salze des Quecksilbers, Kupfers, Bleis, Cadmiums und Zinks*, Breslau, 1900 ; P. Berthier, *Traité des essais par la voie sèche*, Paris, **2**. 670, 676, 1834 ; *Ann. Chim. Phys.*, (2), **22**. 245, 1823 ; (2), **33**. 156, 1826 ; K. Friedrich, *Met.*, **4**. 483, 672, 1907 ; F. P. Dunnington, *Amer. Chem. Journ.*, **14**. 620, 1892 ; F. A. Genth, *Proc. Amer. Phil. Soc.*, **20**. 404, 1882 ; A. Brand, *Zeit. Kryst.*, **17**. 264, 1890 ; P. Niggli and K. Faesy, *ib.*, **60**. 477, 1924 ; P. Groth, *ib.*, **10**. 635, 1885 ; A. Lodin, *Bull. Soc. Min.*, **6**. 179, 1883 ; F. Field, *Amer. Journ. Science*, (2), **27**. 287, 1859 ; *Journ. Chem. Soc.*, **14**. 160, 1860 ; J. S. Maclaurin, *ib.*, **69**. 1269, 1896 ; J. A. Antipoff, *Proc. Russ. Min. Soc.*, **28**. 527, 1891 ; A. Schertel, *Jahrb. Ges. Sachsen*, ii, 10, 1887 ; *Dingler's Journ.*, **271**. 20, 1889 ; F. Ulrich, *Berg. Hütt. Ztg.*, **18**. 245, 1859 ; *Contributions to the Mineralogy of Victoria*, Melbourne, 48, 1866 ; A. Breithaupt, *Pogg. Ann.*, **61**. 671, 1844 ; B. von Cotta, *Gangstudien oder Beiträge zur Kenntniss der Ergänge*, Freiberg, **2**. 82, 1851 ; *Neues Jahrb. Min.*, 432, 1850 ; J. Fournet, *Ann*

Mines, (3), **4**. 15, 1833 ; I. Domeyko, *Elementos de mineralojia*, Santiago, 168, 1860 ; M. Adam, *Tableau minéralogique*, Paris, 56, 1869 ; C. J. B. Karsten, *Schweigger's Journ.*, **66**. 400, 1832 ; O. W. Brown, *Trans. Amer. Electrochem. Soc.*, **9**. 113, 1906 ; W. Menzel, *Metall Erz*, **10**. 193, 1913 ; W. Guertler and K. L. Meissner, *ib.*, **18**. 145, 1921 ; W. Guertler and E. Lüder, *ib.*, **21**. 133, 355, 1924 ; W. Guertler, *Forsch. Metallkunde*, **1**, 1923 ; F. M. Perkin, *Trans. Faraday Soc.*, **3**. 115, 1908 ; F. M. Perkin and L. Pratt, *ib.*, **3**. 183, 1908 ; W. H. Newhouse, *Amer. Min.*, **7**. 108, 1922 ; H. Freeman, *Eng. Min. Journ.*, **120**. 973, 1925.
   [28] A. Liversidge, *Proc. Roy. Soc. New South Wales*, **29**. 316, 1885 ; *Chem. News*, **74**. 113, 1896 ; K. Friedrich, *Met.*, **5**. 1, 1908 ; G. A. Kenngott, *Mineralogische Untersuchungen*, Breslau, 304, 1865 ; H. A. Miers, E. G. T. Hartley, and A. Dick, *Min. Mag.*, **12**. 111, 1899 ; J. B. Hannay, *ib.*, **2**. 88, 1878 ; C. F. Rammelsberg, *Handbuch der Mineralchemie*, Leipzig, 110, 1863 ; 135, 1886 ; A. Raimondi, *Minéraux du Pérou*, Paris, 202, 1878 ; D. Forbes, *Phil. Mag.*, (4), **25**. 110, 1863 ; I. Domeyko, *Elementos de mineralojia*, Santiago, 168, 1860 ; 324, 1879 ; C. R. C. Tichborne, *Proc. Roy. Soc. Dublin*, **4**. 300, 1885 ; J. D. Dana, *A System of Mineralogy*, New York, **42**, 1868 ; L. Pflücker y Ryco, *Anal. Esc. Minos Per.*, **3**. 60, 1883.
   [29] G. Canneri and L. Fernandes, *Atti Accad. Lincei*, (5), **1**. i, 671, 1925.

§ 30. Lead Sulphates

H. G. Denham [1] prepared **lead subsulphate**, Pb_2SO_4, by passing the vapour of methyl sulphate over lead hemioxide, at 280° ; and C. Féry said that this substance is produced at the cathode during the normal discharge of a lead accumulator. The dark iron-grey powder, said C. Féry, is a feeble conductor of electricity, and is readily oxidized to the normal sulphate. H. G. Denham found that when heated to 120° above the m.p. of lead it does not alter its appearance, and no lead is separated ; this is not likely to be the case if the alleged subsulphate were a mixture of finely divided lead and normal lead sulphate. The subsulphate is more soluble in alcohol than the normal sulphate ; it is decomposed by water ; and by acids, forming lead and normal lead sulphate.

Normal **lead sulphate**, $PbSO_4$, was first reported in 1779 by A. G. Monnet [2] as a mineral product of the decomposition of galena ; he called it *vitriol de plomb ;* and T. Bergman, in 1782, described it as *plumbum acido vitriolico mineralisatum.* W. Withering noted that an " immense quantity " of " lead mineralized by vitriolic acid " exists in the Island of Anglesey, and F. S. Beudant applied to it the name **anglesite**—A. Breithaupt, *sardinian ;* and G. S. O. Lasius, *Bleiglas.* J. L. Proust made observations on *vitriol de plomb* from Andalusia. Analyses of anglesite or of lead sulphate have been reported by M. H. Klaproth, J. J. Berzelius, P. Berthier, C. F. Bucholz, J. S. Stas, E. A. Smith, S. T. Tyson and G. J. Brush, W. J. Jordan, F. Stromeyer, etc.

The mineral commonly occurs in cavities in galena, or on the surface of that ore. The mineral has been found at Leadhills and Wanlockhead, in Scotland ; Cumberland, Derbyshire, and Cornwall, in England ; the Harz, Silesia, in Germany ; Felsöbanya, in Hungary ; Nerchinsk, in Siberia ; Schwarzenbach and Mies, in Carinthia ; Monteponi, in Sardinia ; Linares, in Spain ; Sierra Mojada, in Mexico ; Phenixville, Pennsylvania ; Missouri lead mines ; Castle Dome district, Arizona ; Rossie, New York ; Southampton, Massachusetts ; Walton gold mine, Virginia, etc. Large quantities have been imported in England from Australia. In some cases, fine, transparent, prismatic crystals are found, *e.g.* at the mines on Parys, Island of Anglesey ; and, added J. Percy :

At those interesting and picturesque copper mines and quarries, decomposition of copper and iron pyrites by weathering action is perpetually in operation on a large scale ; and as galena, chiefly in admixture with blende, is found there, the formation of anglesite as a secondary product is easily conceivable.

In confirmation, J. Hanus, and S. H. Emmons found galena is attacked by soln. of ferric sulphate ; and E. Jannettaz, by acid soln. of ferrous sulphate such as are generated by the oxidation of pyrite or marcasite. The association of galena with pyrites is thereiore favourable to the formation of anglesite. In some cases, the native sulphate formed from galena is still cleavable in the direction of the cubic faces of the parent crystals. According to A. Lacroix and co-workers, anglesite occurs as a recent formation in the lead slags of Laurion, Greece ; and in the lead tubes of the Roman thermal springs of Bourbonne-les-Bains. A. Russell found anglesite on the cavernous masses of lead mixed with charcoal, taken up in 1846 below the partly fused lead pump of a fireship sunk in Falmouth Harbour in 1780. A. Scacchi, and F. Zambonini observed anglesite in the ejecta of Vesuvius. J. F. L. Hausmann found anglesite as a furnace product, but F. O. Doeltz and C. A. Graumann observed non-crystalline lead sulphate in the flues of lead furnaces. L. Michel detected anglesite in cavities in some old lead slags of Poullasuen, Finistère. F. Kuhlmann observed the formation of anglesite in the lead chamber of a sulphuric acid works.

According to H. C. Jenkins and E. A. Smith,[3] lead sulphate is produced when sulphur dioxide is passed over molten lead. If the temp. is near that of molten lead, a considerable proportion of sulphur trioxide is present in the effluent gases, but by working well above the m.p. of lead, but below 400°, the proportion of sulphur trioxide is small. Lead sulphide is formed at the same time. They suggest that the reactions involved are : (i) $Pb+3SO_2=PbS+2SO_3$, followed by $Pb+2SO_3=PbSO_4+SO_2$. Lead sulphate is formed when sulphuric acid and lead are heated together. P. A. Mackay said that lead is rapidly dissolved at 150° by the fuming acid ; and when once the reaction has begun, complete conversion into lead sulphate occurs without further application of heat, or at least a temp. not exceeding 100°. If the lead be first coated with an electronegative metal—e.g. mercury or copper—or if such metals be added to the acid during the operation, the working temp. is reduced to 50°–100° with a violent exothermal reaction. The lead sulphate is precipitated by diluting the soln. O. Schott showed that the amorphous sulphate can be crystallized by fusion with sodium, calcium, or lead chloride ; and F. Guthrie, by fusion with potassium nitrate. P. Gaubert obtained the lead sulphate in crystals by evaporating to dryness a soln. of the amorphous sulphate in boiling sulphuric acid. L. Bourgeois heated the amorphous sulphate with dil. hydrochloric acid (1 : 2) in a sealed tube at 150° ; or for a short time at 100° with conc. sulphuric acid. A. H. Eyles and co-workers made the sulphate by passing the dust of molten lead mixed with an oxidizing agent into dil. sulphuric acid. According to J. A. Wilkinson, when molten lead is treated with conc. sulphuric acid, persulphuric acid, or ammonium persulphate, a bluish-white luminescence appears as the mass is solidifying. This can best be seen by stirring the mass with a glass rod, and as it solidifies, a bluish-white streak will follow the rod. Lead sulphate is slowly formed when lead is placed in contact with dil. sulphuric acid exposed to air, and lead is also attacked with the formation of lead sulphate by aq. soln. of other sulphates (vide lead). If sulphuric acid be left in contact with lead oxide or its salts, or with one of the higher oxides of lead, lead sulphate is formed. H. Rose said that at ordinary temp. lead oxide does not absorb the vap. of anhydrous sulphuric acid. J. B. Senderens made the sulphate by boiling lead oxide, hydroxide, dioxide, carbonate, or acetate, or red-lead, with sulphur and water ; D. L. Hammick passed sulphur dioxide over lead oxide ; and F. O. Doeltz and C. A. Graumann treated lead oxide with sulphur trioxide at 900°. Red-lead, or lead dioxide reacts with sulphur dioxide at ordinary temp., forming lead sulphate ; sulphurous acid, or hot conc. sulphuric acid, may also be employed. H. B. North and A. M. Hagemann noted its formation when lead dioxide and thionyl chloride are heated in a sealed tube at 150°.

Lead sulphate is formed during the roasting of lead sulphide, and hence the presence of the sulphate in the flue-dust of smelting furnaces. This subject was investigated by F. Dempwolff—vide supra. C. von Ernst found that the presence of calcium oxide favoured the formation of the sulphate. J. Gitsham and H. R. Evershed oxidized the vapour of lead sulphide volatilized in an electric arc furnace. E. Jannettaz noted that lead sulphate is formed by the trituration of a mixture of galena and potassium hydrosulphate. A. C. Becquerel obtained crystals of lead sulphate by allowing a mixed soln. of copper sulphate and sodium chloride to stand in contact with galena for a few years. G. Piolti, by the prolonged immersion of galena in a soln. of potassium nitrate, and also by the immersion of iron pyrites in a soln. of lead nitrate for $16\frac{1}{2}$ years, obtained slender needles of anglesite on the pyrites. Lead sulphate is precipitated as an amorphous powder when dil. sulphuric acid, or an aq. soln. of a soluble sulphate, is added to an aq. soln. of a salt of lead—*e.g.* nitrate or acetate. A. Findlay said the precipitation is slower than is the case with lead iodide. L. L. de Koninck ignited the precipitate after washing it with a 0·7 per cent. soln. of ammonium sulphate. J. W. Mellor has discussed the contamination of the precipitated sulphate with adsorbed salts. J. A. Wilkinson observed no luminescence when a sat. soln. of lead sulphate is treated with conc. sulphuric acid, or a boiling sat. soln. of sodium sulphate. C. Winkler, and K. A. Hofmann heated lead nitrate with sulphuric acid to 400°–420°, and found some free acid still remained. J. Milbauer and K. Kohn dropped sulphuric acid into a boiling nitric acid soln. of lead diammoniate, and obtained rhombic crystals of lead sulphate. A. Drevermann found lead sulphate crystals are produced in the preparation of lead chromate if the potassium chromate used for the precipitation contains some sulphate. F. Auerbach and H. Pick treated a suspension of lead carbonate in a soln. of sodium sulphate with carbon dioxide, best under press., and obtained lead sulphate. A. Macé obtained crystallized lead sulphate by adding a soln. of ferrous sulphate very slowly to one of lead nitrate ; and an analogous process was used by C. E. Guignet, A. de Schulten, E Frémy, and E. Masing, where a soluble sulphate was allowed to diffuse very slowly into one of a lead salt. N. S. Manross obtained crystals of anglesite by fusing lead chloride with sodium sulphate ; and also by hanging a strip of lead in a soln. of potassium sulphate. F. Zambonini made crystals of the sulphate by the action of vapours of lead chloride and sulphur trioxide. J. Gitsham and H. R. Evershed passed the powdered sulphide through the arc of an electric furnace. C. G. Schlüderberg obtained the amorphous sulphate by the electrolysis of sulphuric acid with a lead anode—with an alternating current an electrodic luminescence occurred, but not with a direct current. The phenomenon was also studied by J. A. Wilkinson.

J. Hausmann observed that rhythmic precipitation of lead sulphate is produced by diffusion in gelatine. E. Hatschek found that the spaces between the strata consist of aggregates—partly sheaf-like bundles, and partly spherical aggregates, while the strata themselves consist almost exclusively of individual crystals. W. P. Dreaper found that when lead sulphate is formed by diffusion of a 5 per cent. soln. of potassium sulphate and a 2 per cent. soln. of lead acetate in a capillary tube, the stratification occurs. In about 2 months, the colloidal precipitate begins to crystallize. E. H. Büchner and J. Kalff obtained **colloidal lead sulphate** by dropping a dil. soln. of a lead salt into one of a soluble sulphate, but they could not obtain a clear gel. H. Schiff treated an alcoholic soln. of lead acetate with sulphuric acid, and obtained a starch-like mass of sulphate. P. P. von Weimarn also studied the precipitation of colloidal lead sulphate. W. Leuse treated a mixed soln. of sodium protalbinate, lead acetate, and sodium hydroxide with a soln. of sodium sulphate. The lead sulphate is not precipitated. When dialyzed in water, a brown sol is obtained which becomes opalescent and milky in about 12 hrs.

The physical properties of lead sulphate.—Lead sulphate prepared by precipitation is a white powder ; and it can be obtained in colourless or white crystals. Anglesite was found by Z. Toborffy [4] in colourless crystals ; it may also occur in white crystals tinged more or less grey, blue, violet, yellow, or green. J. G. Bornemann said that the green colour is due to the presence of a copper salt ; F. Millosevich, ferrous sulphate. The crystals of anglesite are sometimes tabular but more often prismatic ; or pyramidal of various types. The mineral also occurs massive, granular or compact ; sometimes stalactitic ; and sometimes nodular, enclosing a nucleus of galena with a concentric structure made up of layers of a different colour. The crystals were described by R. J. Haüy, N. von Kokscharoff, N. S. Manross, E. V. Shannon, L. Bourgeois, A. Pelloux, V. von Zepharovich, A. Schrauf, Q. Sella, V. Goldschmidt, R. Helmhacker, A. F. Rogers, E. H. Kraus and A. B. Peck, F. Hessenberg, F. Millosevich, H. Dauber, A. de Schulten, A. Franzenau, E. Repossi, Z. Toborffy, O. C. Farrington and E. W. Tillotson, P. Hermann, J. Milbauer and K. Kohn, A. Drevermann, etc. A. Breithaupt's sardinian was said to be monoclinic; but F. M. Jäger and H. C. Germs regard this as doubtful. Artificially prepared, and natural crystals of anglesite are rhombic bipyramids which, according to V. von Lang, have the axial ratios $a : b : c = 0.7852 : 1 : 1.2894$. R. Kolb measured the change in the crystal angles with variations of temp. The crystals of anglesite are isomorphous with those of barytes, celestine, and aragonite. A. Fock observed mixed crystals were formed with barium sulphate. P. Gaubert made observations on this subject. T. V. Barker obtained growths of crystals of potassium perchlorate and permanganate on crystals of anglesite. As indicated above, pseudomorphs after galena are not uncommon; R. S. Dale reported pseudomorphs after cubic alum. The (001) and (110) **cleavages** of anglesite are distinct. The faces (110) and (100) are often striated vertically; and the (102)-face, horizontally. The **optical character** is positive. A. des Cloizeaux found the **optic axial angles** $2H = 89° 44'$ to $90° 59'$; $2V = 66° 45'$ to $66° 47'$—with the red ray, $2V = 66° 40'$, and with the yellow ray, $2V = 60° 50'$. W. Ramsay made observations on this subject. A. Arzruni gave for the D-ray, $2V = 75° 24'$ at $20°$; $77° 40'$ at $50°$; $82° 44'$ at $100°$; and $89° 17'$ at $200°$. F. M. Jäger and H. Haga, R. W. James and W. A. Wood, and H. Mark discussed the **X-radiograms** of these crystals. O. Lehmann studied the growth of the crystals under the microscope. According to G. Tammann and Q. A. Mansuri, the crystallization of the powder begins at $310°–316°$. R. Schenck and W. Rassbach found that there is an enantiomorphous **transition point** at $850°$, showing that the crystals are dimorphous. The crystals of α-anglesite are rhombic, and those of β-anglesite (above the transition temp.), monoclinic. J. B. J. D. Boussingault gave $856°$ for the transition temp.; A. Hare, $866°$; and H. C. Germs, and F. M. Jäger and H. C. Germs, $864° \pm 1°$. The last-named say that the heat of the transformation is considerable.

The **specific gravity** of lead sulphate was given by C. J. B. Karsten [5] as 6·1691; E. Filhol gave 6·30; A. Gorgeu, 6·16; O. Pettersson, 5·97 at 16·8°, and 5·96 at 17·1°; H. G. F. Schröder, 6·329 for the native sulphate, and 6·212 for precipitated; J. L. Smith, 6·35; F. Field, 6·20; E. H. Kraus and A. B. Peck, 6·35; A. de Schulten, 6·393 at 15°; R. Popper, 6·380; and P. Niggli, 6·393, and for the eq. vol., 47·4. F. A. Henglein, and A. Balandin studied the mol. vol. G. Tammann and Q. A. Mansuri observed evidence of the coalescence of particles by crystallization at $310°–316°$. The **hardness** is 2·75–3·0. F. Paneth made observations on the surface area of granules of lead sulphate. E. Madelung and R. Fuchs gave for the **compressibility** coeff. of anglesite, $1·87 \times 10^{-12}$ dynes per sq. cm. H. V. Regnault [6] gave 0·08723 for the **specific heat** of artificial and calcined lead sulphate between 18° and 99°; H. Kopp gave 0·0827 for anglesite between 19° and 49°, and F. E. Neumann, 0·0827 between room-temp. and 100°.

J. Percy showed that lead sulphate is permanent at a low red-heat, provided reducing agents are absent. F. Guthrie said that the compound melts at a white heat. P. Berthier, and J. B. J. D. Boussingault stated that at a white heat the sulphate softens and becomes enamel-like with the evolution of a little sulphur dioxide. J. Percy showed that at bright redness in a fireclay crucible, a crystalline basic sulphate is formed; the reaction with the silica of the crucible interferes with the result. P. Berthier, indeed, showed that all the sulphur trioxide can be expelled by calcining the sulphate with silica or clay. O. L. Erdmann also found that the sulphate becomes coloured and loses in weight if calcined in an open or in a loosely covered crucible;

J. L. Gay Lussac made analogous observations; and J. B. J. D. Boussingault added that all the sulphur trioxide can be removed at a white heat in an open crucible. W. Grahmann, F. M. Jäger and H. C. Germs, and F. O. Doeltz and C. A. Graumann showed that the sulphate decomposes between 900° and 1000°; H. C. Hofman and W. Wanjukoff showed that in an open tube, in dry air, decomposition begins at 637°, and is marked at 705° when the residue has the composition $5PbO.5SO_3$; at 952°–962°, $2PbO.SO_3$. M. Bodenstein and W. Pohl said that the decomposition is marked at 700°; and with the purified sulphate, W. Mostowitch observed no change at 800° in a current of dry air, but decomposition begins above 800° and a mixture of lead oxide and sulphate is formed. The mixture $PbO.PbSO_4$ melts between 900° and 1000°. F. M. Jäger and H. C. Germs said that an accurate determination of the **melting point** is not possible because the salt begins to dissociate near this temp. By extrapolation, they obtained 1170° for the m.p. W. Ramsay and N. Eumorfopoulos gave 937° for the m.p., but this is too low; W. Grahmann gave 1080°; G. Calcagni and D. Marotta, 1000°–1010°; and R. Schenck and W. Rassbach, over 1100°. R. Lorenz and W. Herz estimate the m.p. to be 1170°. W. Grahmann said that the **heat of crystallization** is small; and F. M. Jäger and H. C. Germs, the **heat of fusion** is small. M. Berthelot [7] gave for the **heat of formation,** $(Pb,S,2O_2)=214$ Cals.; while J. Thomsen gave 216·2 Cals.; and for $(Pb,O,H_2SO_4)=75·55$ Cals.; and $(Pb,O_2,SO_2)=145·1$ Cals. P. Günther calculated $(Pb,S,2O_2)=218·8$ Cals. M. Berthelot gave $(PbO,SO_3)=605$ Cals., and for the **heat of neutralization** of PbO by H_2SO_4, 19·9 Cals.; and for lead hydroxide, A. Guntz gave 21·4 Cals. The heat of formation by the substitution of lead for magnesium in magnesium sulphate is, according to J. Thomsen, 6·17562 Cals.; and W. E. Henderson and G. Stegeman gave for the replacement of the mercury in mercurous sulphate by lead, 41·785 Cals.; and for the free energy of the reaction, 41·2 Cals. A. Hare gave 4·06 Cals. per mol. for the heat of transformation.

A. des Cloizeaux [8] gave for the **indices of refraction** of anglesite with the red ray, $a=1·8740$, $\beta=1·8795$, and $\gamma=1·8924$; and for the yellow ray, $a=1·8770$, $\beta=1·8830$, and $\gamma=1·8970$. A. Arzruni found:

	C-ray (20°)	F-ray (20°)	20°	50°	100°	200°
				D-ray		
a	1·86981	1·89549	1·87709	1·87636	1·87529	1·87260
β	1·87502	1·90097	1·88226	1·88166	1·88080	1·89134
γ	1·88630	1·91263	1·89365	1·87260	1·87833	1·88754

H. C. Sorby gave 1·882 for the mean refractive index of anglesite. For temp. ranging from 16·1° to 19·3°, A. Ehringhaus and H. Rose obtained the following values for the indices of refraction and the birefringence with light of different wavelengths:

λ	690·7	623·9	589·3	546·1	491·6	404·7
a	1·86719	1·87346	1·87739	1·88383	1·89480	1·92434
β	1·87228	1·87862	1·88266	1·88914	1·90020	1·93001
γ	1·88351	1·88998	1·89435	1·90078	1·91202	1·94252
$\beta-a$	0·00509	0·00516	0·00527	0·00531	0·00540	0·00567
$\gamma-\beta$	0·01123	0·01136	0·01169	0·01164	0·01182	0·01251
$\gamma-a$	0·01632	0·01652	0·01696	0·01695	0·01722	0·01818

The **birefringence** is positive. At ordinary temp., $\gamma-a$ and $\gamma-\beta$ decrease with increasing wave-length, while $\beta-a$ is not affected; and with rise of temp., $\gamma-a$ and $\gamma-\beta$ decrease, while $\beta-a$ increases. The **dispersion** $G-B$ was found by R. Kolb to increase with rise of temp. The **reflecting power** was measured by T. Liebisch and H. Rubens; and C. Schaefer and M. Schubert gave for the percentage reflecting power for rays of wave-length λ:

λ	22	33	39	52	63	83	94	310μ
a	8·84	5·87	5·20	53·0	74·5	69·5	70·1	54·5
β	9·54	6·12	3·00	32·2	58·0	53·5	82·6	56·8

W. W. Coblentz found that there is a large band in the **ultra-red reflection spectrum** of anglesite at intervals 4.55μ and 9.1μ, and this is characteristic of the SO_4-radicle ; the **ultra-red transmission spectrum** has complex bands at 4.55μ and 6.4μ, and deeper ones at 5μ and 6.7μ. There are slight bands at 1.9μ and 3.2μ. J. A. Wilkinson found that lead sulphate exhibits a blue **fluorescence** in cathode rays, and the colour becomes greyish-brown owing to decomposition.

G. Cesaro [9] found that anglesite has but a small **electrical conductivity**. F. Kohlrausch measured the sp. electrical conductivity of the sat. aq. soln. and found :

	$-0.26°$	$1°$	$3.48°$	$17.01°$	$17.08°$	$33.23°$
Sp. Cond.	0.0_41629	0.0_41717	0.0_41957	0.0_43181	0.0_43188	0.0_4485

W. Böttger, and M. Pleissner also made observations on this subject. H. G. Denham found that the resistance of a sat. aq. soln. at 25° is 3030 ohms when that of water is 27,000 ohms. M. Pleissner estimated that the **degree of ionization** of the aq. soln. is 80 per cent. at 18°, and that a millimol of the salt per litre has 0.027 millimol $PbSO_4$; $0.099SO_4''$-ions ; $0.062Pb$-ions ; $0.037PbOH'$-ions ; and $0.037H'$-ions. The presence of sulphuric acid lowers the hydrolysis, and increases the ionization. W. Böttger estimated a 92 per cent. ionization at 25°. A. Klein found the **electromotive force** of the cell $Pb\,|\,PbCl_2\,|\,0.01N$-$KCl\,|\,0.01N$-$K_2SO_4\,|\,PbSO_4\,|\,Pb$ to be 0.0529 volt at 23.1°, while the free energy is 2418.7 cals. and the thermal value -2480 cals. ; if the chlorides be replaced by the bromides, these values are changed to 0.0465 volt, 2095.6 and -6040 cals. respectively ; and with iodides in place of chlorides 0.0084 volt, 281.6 and -11810 cals. C. B. Thwing gave 15.80 for the **dielectric constant** ; and W. Schmidt, 28 for $\lambda = 25$ cms. H. Joachim found the dielectric constants for $\lambda = 300\mu$ to be for a, 44, and for β, 50. B. N. Chuckubutti obtained Nobili's rings with a brass plate as cathode with a soln. of lead sulphate. The rings consist of granular particles of lead or oxide—$500\mu\mu$ in diameter near the centre, and $275\mu\mu$ near the periphery. The colours are due to the diffraction of light by these granules. L. Ebert studied the dielectric polarization of lead salts.

The **chemical properties of lead sulphate.**—J. A. Arfvedson [10] showed that when lead sulphate is heated in a stream of **hydrogen**, water, sulphur dioxide, and, lastly, hydrogen sulphide are evolved, while lead and lead sulphide remain. According to G. F. Rodwell, the complete reaction at a red heat can be represented : $2PbSO_4 + 7H_2 = 2Pb + SO_2 + H_2S + 6H_2O$. H. Mennicke found that the sulphate is easily reduced to spongy lead by cathodic hydrogen or by hydrogen from zinc and dil. hydrochloric acid. P. A. Bolley fixed a thick layer of lead sulphate between two zinc plates and left the combination immersed in a soln. of sodium chloride for 9–10 days. A mass of spongy lead was formed. C. Luckow found that anodic **oxygen** from the electrolysis of soln. of sodium or magnesium sulphate transforms lead sulphate into lead dioxide.

According to M. Willenz,[11] the lead sulphate prepared in a dry way is insoluble in **water** ; according to P. Kremers, water dissolves 0.077 grm. of lead sulphate per litre at ordinary temp. ; C. R. Fresenius found 0.043 grm. at 11° ; and G. F. Rodwell, 0.031 grm. at 15°. According to H. C. Dibbits, M. Pleissner, W. Böttger, K. Beck and P. Stegmüller, and F. Kohlrausch, the solubility, S, of lead sulphate in water in grams per litre is :

	$0°$	$5°$	$10°$	$15°$	$20°$	$25°$	$30°$	$35°$	$40°$
S	0.028	0.031	0.035	0.038	0.041	0.045	0.049	0.052	0.056

J. Sehnal, M. Barre, and L. L. de Koninck also made measurements of the solubility of lead sulphate in water ; the former found 0.082 grm. per litre at 18°, and claimed that the same result is obtained at 100°. S. Mitchell gave 0.032 grm. for 1000 c.c. of water. W. A. Roth measured the speed of soln. R. Flatt tried to connect the solubility with the electronic structure. W. A. Köhler and J. H. Mathews found the **heat of wetting** lead sulphate with water sat. with the same salt is less than 0·09 cal. per 529,000 sq. cms. J. Sehnal showed that the salt in aq. soln. suffers **hydrolysis,** forming lead hydroxide and free sulphuric acid ; the presence of sulphuric acid hinders the hydrolysis and lowers the solubility. G. Carrara and G. P. Vespignani also noted the hydrolysis of lead sulphate. F. Dolezalek estimated that the aq. soln. is from 5 to 15 per cent. hydrolyzed ; M. Pleissner estimated 17 per cent. hydrolysis at 0°, and about 30 per cent. at 18°. H. Rose said that lead sulphate is soluble in aq. soln. of **potassium or sodium hydroxide,** especially if the soln. be warm. V. Kohlschütter and H. Rösti found that, at ordinary temp., 10N-NaOH dissolves lead sulphate with the separation of yellow rhombic crystals of lead monoxide, but with 2N- to 5N-soln. no separation occurs. M. C. Boswell and J. V. Dickson said that with the molten alkali hydroxide, hydrogen is developed. F. Rolle, and M. Tipp found that lead sulphate is decomposed by a soln. of **calcium hydroxide.** V. Zotier examined the catalytic effect of lead sulphate on **hydrogen dioxide.**

According to A. Ditte,[12] **hydrofluoric acid,** containing 27-54 grms. per litre, does not decompose lead sulphate after 24 hrs.' action between 15° and 100° ; it is sparingly soluble in an aq. soln. of potassium fluoride ; there is a balanced reaction : $PbSO_4 + 2KF \rightleftharpoons PbF_2 + K_2SO_4$, which is complicated by the formation of the complex salt $K_2Pb(SO_4)_2$. C. Hensgen found that dry **hydrogen chloride** attacks lead sulphate between 250° and 300°, liberating sulphuric acid ; and A. Colson said that two solid phases are present when the press. of the hydrogen chloride is 180 mm. at 0° ; 281 mm. at 10° ; and 354 mm. at 14·5°. F. Ephraim prepared lead chlorosulphate, $PbSO_4.2HCl$, with a dissociation press. of 713 mm. at 32°. H. V. Collet-Descotils said that lead sulphate is slightly soluble in hot **hydrochloric acid,** and on cooling, the soln. deposits a little lead chloride, leaving an eq. amount of sulphuric acid in soln. If the hydrochloric acid soln. is evaporated, but not boiled, A. Hayes said that the lead chloride is decomposed. C. R. Fresenius found lead sulphate to be soluble in hot acid. A. L. Young and G. F. Dixon found that a gram of lead sulphate with 4·035 grms. of hydrochloric acid, containing 1·251 grms. HCl, furnishes, on evaporation, 0·8 per cent. of lead chloride. G. F. Rodwell found that 100 grms. of an acid of sp. gr. 1·0515 dissolved 0·14665 grm. of lead sulphate ; sp. gr. 1·080, 0·35495 grm. ; 1·107, 0·946525 grm. ; 1·135, 2·113800 grms.; and 1·157, 2·854000 grms. of salt. The decimals are all out of perspective and give a distorted idea of the accuracy of the conclusions. A. Ditte studied the equilibrium conditions of the reaction. He said that when less than 7 grms. of HCl are present per litre, the acid dissolves only a trace of lead sulphate at ordinary temp. ; with a more conc. acid, some lead chloride goes into soln., and this the more the higher the temp. The system attains equilibrium in less than 24 hrs. If a denotes the initial percentage conc. of the HCl, and y the final percentage conc. of the sulphuric acid, then, for equilibrium, the free hydrochloric acid, x per cent., will be $x = 0.912ay$. K. Beck and P. Stegmüller gave for the solubility in mgrm. Pb per 100 c.c. of hydrochloric acid of different conc.

	H_2O	0·1N-HCl	0·2N-HCl	0·3N-HCl	0·4N-HCl
At 18°	2·60	19·00	35·70	55·37	75·27
At 25°	3·00	22·18	42·88	65·15	84·04
At 37°	3·80	28·04	54·50	84·04	111·90

According to A. Vogel, lead sulphate is slightly decomposed by a cold soln. of **ammonium chloride,** and to a greater extent on boiling, and completely when rapidly boiled with fresh quantities of the salt—the products are ammonium sulphate which remains in soln. and lead chloride which is precipitated on cooling. G. C. Wittstein noted the solubility of lead sulphate in ammonium chloride soln. R. H. Brett said that the cold soln. of lead sulphate in ammonium chloride gives a precipitate with a large excess of ammonia. A. Ditte showed that the reaction is a balanced one, so that if a sufficient excess of ammonium chloride be present, the decomposition of the sulphate is complete. The reaction is complicated by the formation of a complex salt, $(NH_4)_2Pb(SO_4)_2$. A. Ditte showed that the behaviour of a soln. of **potassium chloride** resembles that of ammonium chloride. L. F. Bley found that lead sulphate is slightly decomposed by a soln. of **sodium chloride**; but M. Mayer and A. Fehlmann found that hot conc. soln. readily decompose the sulphate. A. C. Becquerel said that 0·66 grm. of lead sulphate is contained in a litre of sat. soln. at room temp. F. N. Flynn also made observations on this subject. F. Matthey reported that about half the quantity of lead sulphate is decomposed by an eq. amount of sodium chloride, and after repeated treatment more and more sulphate is decomposed. F. Field showed that when lead sulphate is digested with a cold sat. soln. of sodium chloride, lead chloride is deposited after a few hours. A. Ditte found that a soln. of sodium chloride acts less energetically than hydrochloric acid ; and that the equilibrium conditions are simpler than with potassium chloride since there is no complex salt formed. A soln. with 300 grms. of sodium chloride per litre at 15° has for equilibrium, 266·66 grms. of NaCl, and 40·91 grms. Na_2SO_4 ; at 48°, respectively 282·40 and 21·49 grms. ; and at 100°, 289·60 and 12·75 grms. respectively. K. Beck and P. Stegmüller found that at 18°, the solubility, in mgrm. Pb per 100 c.c. of the soln. of sodium chloride is, at 18° :

	H_2O	0·1N-NaCl	0·2N-NaCl	0·3N-NaCl	0·4N-NaCl
Pb	2·60	11·19	18·73	26·51	33·76

P. Berthier showed that when a mixture of lead sulphate and sodium or potassium chloride is fused, vapours of lead chloride are disengaged, and a compact, grey, translucent mass with a scaly fracture is obtained. F. Marguéritte obtained a similar result and noted the formation of alkali sulphate; and showed that a soln. of lead chloride in water in the presence of calcium sulphate is converted into lead sulphate ; and if the lead sulphate be heated with an alkali chloride, alkali sulphate and lead chloride are produced. This was suggested as a means of producing alkali sulphate from gypsum without the use of sulphuric acid— J. Nicklès showed that the reactions are incomplete. O. Schott found that lead sulphate is soluble in molten sodium chloride, and, on cooling, crystallizes out in acicular six-sided crystals ; the salt dissolves more readily in molten **calcium chloride** from which both lead chloride and sulphate crystallize on cooling. F. N. Flynn noted that lead sulphate is soluble in an aq. soln. of calcium chloride. According to P. Berthier, when lead sulphate is fused with **barium chloride,** lead chloride is evaporated and a white mass with a granular fracture is formed. F. N. Flynn found that lead sulphate dissolves in a conc. soln. of **magnesium chloride,** and H. Hof and co-workers added that on cooling the boiling sat. soln., the complex salt, Mg_2PbCl_6, and magnesium sulphate are formed. M. de Jong said that an acid soln. of **stannous chloride** freely dissolves lead sulphate, converting it into the chloride, but A. van Raalte claimed that the effect is due solely to the hydrochloric acid present. A. Ditte said that lead sulphate is not perceptibly soluble in a boiling soln. of **lead chloride.** P. Berthier found that a mixture of lead sulphate and chloride readily fuses with effervescence, forming when cold, a transparent enamel. O. Schott obtained microscopic, rhombic crystals, of lead sulphate from a soln. of that salt in molten lead chloride. C. R. Fresenius found lead sulphate to be soluble in a soln. of **ferric chloride.** A. Ditte found that lead sulphate behaves towards soln. of **potassium chlorate** similarly to what it does towards a soln. of potassium chloride. The reaction is a balanced one, and for equilibrium, a soln. of 312 grms. of the chlorate in a litre of water in contact with an excess of lead sulphate, holds 1·34 grms. of potassium sulphate at 15° ; and 2·39 grms. at 100° ; while a soln. of 100 or 200 grms. of the chlorate per litre furnishes very little potassium sulphate or lead chlorate.

A. Ditte noted the solvent action of **hydrobromic acid** on lead sulphate, and the result resembles that with hydrochloric acid ; a soln. of **potassium bromide** also behaved like one of potassium chloride. A soln. of 300 grms. of the bromide per litre in contact with an excess of lead sulphate furnishes, when in equilibrium, 1·53 grms. of potassium sulphate at 13°, and 2·16 grms. at 100°. He also noticed that with **zinc bromide** there is a balanced reaction : $ZnBr_2 + PbSO_4 \rightleftharpoons PbBr_2 + ZnSO_4$, which progresses from left to right with rise of temp. A. Ditte also noted that the action of hydriodic acid on lead sulphate is similar to that of hydrochloric acid ; and that a soln. of potassium iodide behaves like a soln. of potassium chloride. A 5 per cent. soln. of potassium iodide in contact with an excess of lead sulphate furnishes 1·531 grms. of potassium sulphate at 13° ; and a 15 per cent. soln., 1·64 grms. of potassium sulphate at 15°, and 1·01 grms. at 100°. G. Campani found that with an excess of potassium iodide, either lead iodide or the complex salt, $K_2Pb(SO_4)_2$, is formed. A. Ditte also investigated the action of **magnesium iodide** : $PbSO_4 + MgI_2 \rightleftharpoons PbI_2 + MgSO_4$.

E. Filhol and J. B. Senderens [13] showed that when boiled with **sulphur** and water, lead sulphate is slowly decomposed ; the supernatant liquor is not acid, probably owing to the formation of lead hydrosulphate. According to F. Utz, lead sulphate is coloured yellow and brown much more slowly by **hydrogen sulphide** than is white-lead. J. F. Sacher found that when dry hydrogen sulphide is passed into absolute alcohol holding lead sulphate in suspension, and water is dropped slowly into the liquid, the white sulphate becomes yellow, brown, and finally black. F. O. Doeltz showed that when lead sulphate is triturated with **sodium or calcium sulphide**, the mass becomes dark grey ; and, according to F. O. Doeltz, when the mixture is heated, black lead sulphide appears. The work of J. Percy, A. Lodin, W. Reinders and co-workers, H. C. Jenkins and E. A. Smith, and R. Schenck and co-workers on the action of **lead sulphide** on lead sulphate has been previously discussed. H. Schulze showed that at ordinary temp. dry lead sulphate absorbs **sulphur trioxide**, forming what might be lead pyrosulphate, $Pb_2S_2O_7$; and, according to H. Ditz and F. Kanhäuser, the same complex may be present in a soln. of lead sulphate in fuming sulphuric acid. The solubility of lead sulphate in dil. **sulphuric acid** was found by C. R. Fresenius to be 0·0025 part per 100 parts of acid, but it is more soluble in conc. sulphuric acid from which it is partly precipitated by the addition of water, and completely by the addition of alcohol. He said that lead sulphate is more soluble in water than barium sulphate, and less soluble than strontium sulphate. C. Schultz said 100 parts of conc. sulphuric acid dissolve 6 parts of lead sulphate, while H. Struve said 0·13 part ; A. C. Cumming, that $7·4N$-H_2SO_4 at 25° dissolves approximately 6×10^{-5} mol per litre ; and T. Garside, that 100 parts of the boiling acid dissolve 1·5 parts of lead sulphate, and on cooling a few crystals are deposited, while 1·15 parts are retained in soln. ; J. H. Gladstone and W. Hibbert, that 29 per cent. sulphuric acid, sp. gr. 1·22, dissolves 0·012 grm. of lead sulphate per litre ; and J. Kolb, that at ordinary temp. 100 grms. of an acid of sp. gr. 1·841 dissolves 0·039 grm. lead sulphate ; sp. gr. 1·793, 0·011 grm. ; and sp. gr. 1·540, 0·003 grm. A. Marshall added that the value for the acid of sp. gr. 1·841 is too low because 98 per cent. H_2SO_4 dissolves 0·09 per cent. $PbSO_4$, and the 94 per cent. acid, 0·06 per cent. $PbSO_4$. A. E. Dawkins gave 0·71–1·05 mgrm. of sulphate per 100 c.c. of 0·1–20 per cent. sulphuric acid at 30°. The presence of sulphur dioxide or of nitrous oxides was found by J. Kolb to increase the solvent action of sulphuric acid, while it is increased by nitric acid. A trace of sulphuric acid has a marked effect in reducing the solubility of lead sulphate in water ; thus, expressing the conc. in grams per litre at 18°, M. Pleissner gave :

H_2SO_4	.	.	0	0·0049	0·0098	0·0245	0·0490	0·4904
$PbSO_4$	.	.	0·0382	0·0333	0·0306	0·0194	0·0130	0·0052

and J. Sehnal, at 20°, gave rather different values—

H_2SO_4	.	.	0	0·0098	0·0196	0·0980	0·4900	0·9800
$PbSO_4$	.	.	0·082	0·051	0·025	0·013	0·006	0·000

A. Hayes said that lead sulphate is more soluble in commercial sulphuric acid than in a more conc. acid.   H. Struve found that 100 grms. of fuming sulphuric acid dissolve 4·19 grms. of lead sulphate, and H. Ditz and F. Kanhäuser gave for 100 grms. of the conc. and fuming acids, at 17°–18·5° :

H₂SO₄ per cent.	98·11	98·94	100·01	101·13 (5 per cent. SO₃)	105·05 (15 per cent. SO₃)
PbSO₄ grams .	0·54	1·34	4·21	3·54	8·23

The resulting curve resembles that obtained for the electrical resistance of sulphuric acid.   As indicated above, it was assumed that the soln. contained a complex— possibly PbS_2O_7.   C. Schultz obtained **lead hydrosulphate,** $Pb(HSO_4)_2.H_2O$, by passing moist air over the crystals of lead sulphate obtained by cooling a boiling, sat. soln. of lead sulphate in conc. sulphuric acid.   A. D. Donk studied the ternary system, $PbSO_4-H_2SO_4-H_2O$, between 0° and 200°, but obtained no evidence of a solid phase $PbSO_4-H_2SO_4$—*vide* $Ba(HSO_4)_2.2H_2O$.   Expressing concentrations in grams of salt per 100 grms. of sat. soln., A. D. Donk found at 0° the results indicated in Table XI, and plotted in Fig. 111.   At temp. between 50° and 200°, the only solid

TABLE XI.—SOLUBILITY OF LEAD SULPHATE IN SULPHURIC ACID AT 0°.

Solution.		Residue.		Solid phases
H₂SO₄	PbSO₄	H₂SO₄	PbSO₄	
97·2	0·3	81·1	15·6	PbSO₄+H₂SO₄ (*f*)
97·0	0·0	—	—	H₂SO₄ (*c*)
95·8	0·0	39·6	59·1	PbSO₄
89·4	0·0	29·1	67·3	PbSO₄
89·0	0·0	—	—	PbSO₄+H₂SO₄.H₂O (*e*)
89·0	0·0	86·9	—	H₂SO₄.H₂O (*b*)
79·6	0·0	—	—	PbSO₄+H₂SO₄ (*d*)
79·7	0·0	—	—	H₂SO₄.H₂O (*a*)
76·8	0·0	38·7	50·6	PbSO₄
51·2	0·0	18·2	63·7	PbSO₄

phase present was lead sulphate.   This subject was discussed by J. Kendall and A. W. Davidson.   A. Hayes found that the cold soln. of lead sulphate in conc.

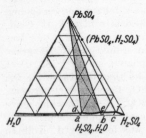

FIG. 111.—Equilibrium in the Ternary System: $PbSO_4-H_2SO_4-H_2O$ at 0°.

sulphuric acid is rendered turbid and precipitated by hydrochloric acid, but the precipitate re-dissolves on heating ; and A. du Pasquier showed that hydrogen sulphide does not precipitate lead sulphide from a soln. of the sulphate in conc. sulphuric acid, but, when the acid is diluted with water, lead sulphate is precipitated and the soln. then exhibits the usual reaction with hydrogen sulphide.   J. Löwenthal, and P. A. Bolley made some observations on this subject. H. Rose found lead sulphate to be soluble in a soln. of **ammonium sulphate.**   P. Berthier showed that mixtures of lead sulphate and **alkali sulphates** are very fusible.   J. N. Brönsted, A. Ditte, and G. Calcagni and D. Marotta, found that lead sulphate forms double salts with ammonium sulphate and **potassium sulphate,** but not with **sodium sulphate** (*q.v.*).   P. Berthier said that lead sulphate does not yield fusible products with **calcium, strontium, or barium sulphate.**   F. Zambonini found lead sulphate and **didymium sulphate,** $Di_2(SO_4)_3$, are immiscible when crystallized from warm conc. sulphuric acid.   J. Löwe showed that an aq. soln. of **sodium thiosulphate** dissolves lead sulphate owing to the formation of a double salt ; when the soln. is exposed to air, lead sulphide is produced in small quantity, but on boiling a large quantity is precipitated ; and when acids are added, lead sulphate and free sulphur are formed. This was confirmed by J. Percy; but K. Fischer and K. Thiele said the conc. of the lead in the soln. of sodium thiosulphate is so small that the electrolysis of the soln. does not give a coherent precipitate. S. E. Goldschmidt also found lead sulphate to be soluble in a soln. of calcium thiosulphate.

According to E. C. Franklin and C. A. Kraus,[14] lead sulphate is insoluble in liquid ammonia. G. F. Rodwell's observations on the action of the dry gas at a red heat agreed with the assumption that the reaction can be represented by the (probably wrong) equation : $7PbSO_4 + 20NH_3 \rightarrow 3PbS + 2Pb_2S + 22H_2O + 8N_2 + 2(NH_4)_2SO_4$; W. R. Hodgkinson and C. C. Trench found that the decomposition is not complete at a red heat, and only a little lead sulphide is formed. G. C. Wittstein showed that lead sulphate dissolves completely in warm aq. ammonia, and, on cooling, a basic salt is deposited. A. Vogel made some observations on this subject. According to A. Ditte, when conc. aq. ammonia is added to lead sulphate, there is a brisk reaction, and the mixture solidifies, all smell of ammonia disappearing if sufficient lead sulphate be present. With dil. soln., the ammonia forms ammonium sulphate and lead oxide, the latter combining with the excess of lead sulphate to form a basic sulphate, $PbO.PbSO_4$; and the complex salt, ammonium sulphatoplumbite, is formed. V. Kohlschütter and H. Rösti showed that, at ordinary temp., $2N$- to $12N$-soln. of ammonia do not attack lead sulphate. Lead sulphate dissolves in **nitric acid,** and this the more, in proportion as the temp. or the conc. of the acid is augmented. According to G. Bischof, 100 grms. of nitric acid of sp. gr. 1·144 at 12·5° dissolve 0·58 grm. of lead sulphate ; water does not render the soln. turbid, but the salt is precipitated by sulphuric acid or ammonium carbonate. H. W. F. Wackenroder, however, showed that the sulphate dissolves slowly in dil. nitric acid, and added that the salt is not precipitated by hydrochloric or phosphoric acid, not at all or very slightly by alkali sulphates ; and it is precipitated by tartaric acid or dil. sulphuric acid—the more conc. the nitric acid, the greater the proportion of sulphuric acid required for the precipitation ; the precipitate forms only slowly, and if the quantity of nitric acid be not too great, it may be complete. When the nitric acid soln. is evaporated, F. von Kobell found that needle-like crystals of the sulphate, and octahedral crystals of the nitrate, are formed. According to G. F. Rodwell, nitric acid with 60 per cent. N_2O_5 transforms lead sulphate almost completely into lead nitrate in 3 or 4 days ; but A. Ditte said that in no case of the action of nitric acid on lead sulphate was he able to verify this result. A. Ditte said that the solubility of the sulphate varies with the temp. and conc. of the acid. With an acid containing 445 grms. of N_2O_5 per litre, the quantity of lead sulphate dissolved increases with temp., but with more conc. soln., the action of heat is reversed, for the quantity of lead sulphate dissolved decreases with rise of temp. ; with fuming nitric acid, containing 800 grms. N_2O_5 per litre, not a trace of lead sulphate was dissolved at 50°. G. F. Rodwell showed that the solubility, S per 100 grms. of the acid, is for an acid of sp. gr. 1·079, 0·33 grm. ; 1·123, 0·58 grm. ; 1·250, 0·78 grm. ; 1·420, 1·01 grms. K. Beck and P. Stegmüller found the solubility, S, in mgrm. of Pb per 100 c.c. of soln. at 18° :

	H_2O	$0·1N$-HNO_3	$0·2N$-HNO_3	$0·3N$-HNO_3	$0·4N$-HNO_3
S . . .	2·60	10·48	17·48	23·41	29·84

According to J. Kolb, the presence of nitric acid increases the solvent action of sulphuric acid for 0·044 grm. of lead sulphate is dissolved by a mixture of 100 grms. of sulphuric acid, sp. gr. 1·841, and 5 grms. of nitric acid, sp. gr. 1·352 ; 0·014 grm. lead sulphate by 100 grms. sulphuric acid, sp. gr. 1·749, and 5 grms. of nitric acid, sp. gr. 1·352 ; and only a trace of lead sulphate by 100 grms. of sulphuric acid, sp. gr. 1·512, and 5 grms. of nitric acid, sp. gr. 1·352. He added that the presence of nitrogen oxides does not increase the solvent action of sulphuric acid. According to G. Bischof, 100 grms. of a soln. of **ammonium nitrate** of sp. gr. 1·29 dissolve 0·103 grm. of lead sulphate ; the soln. is rendered turbid by potassium sulphate, but not by sulphuric acid. C. Marie reported that in the presence of nitric acid, 15 grms. of ammonium nitrate are necessary for the soln. of 0·3 grm. of lead sulphate. A. Ditte reported that very little lead sulphate is dissolved by cold or hot soln. of **sodium or potassium nitrate,** and no chemical action was observed. F. Guthrie found that lead sulphate dissolves in molten potassium nitrate, and the soln., on cooling, deposits crystals of lead sulphate. L. J. Thénard said that a nitric acid soln. of **barium nitrate** produces lead nitrate. M. G. Mellon found lead sulphate to be somewhat soluble in a soln. of **copper nitrate.**

P. Berthier [15] made some observations on the action of **carbon** on lead sulphate, and J. L. Gay Lussac ascertained that if an excess of carbon is present, the lead sulphate is reduced to sulphide at *rouge sombre,* and the gas evolved is free from sulphur dioxide : $PbSO_4 + 2C = 2CO_2 + PbS$; but if less carbon than is needed for this reaction is employed, a mixture of lead sulphide and unconverted sulphate will be produced. In either case, if the temp. be raised to *cérise clair,* metallic lead, $PbS + PbSO_4 = 2Pb + 2SO_2$, or lead oxide, $PbS + 3PbSO_4 = 4PbO + 4SO_2$, will be formed according to the proportion of carbon present—*vide supra,* the action of calcium fluoride. The reduction of lead sulphate by carbon was found by W. Mostowitch to begin at 550° ; the reduction is energetic at 630°. The reactions are symbolized : $PbSO_4 + 4C = PbS + 4CO$; and $PbS + PbSO_4 = 2Pb + 2SO_2$— *vide infra.* According to G. F. Rodwell, if **carbon monoxide** be passed over heated lead sulphate, lead is produced, and carbon and sulphur dioxides are evolved ; he assumed that the first action can be symbolized : $2PbSO_4 + 6CO = Pb + PbS + SO_2 + 6CO_2$. W. Mostowitch found that the reduction begins at about 600°, and is energetic at 630° when the carbon monoxide is more active than carbon alone. At 630°, 74·4 per cent. of lead sulphate is reduced by carbon monoxide, and 36·98 per cent. by carbon : $PbSO_4 + 4CO = PbS + 4CO_2$; the lead sulphide and sulphate react : $PbSO_4 + PbS = 2Pb + 2SO_2$, and $3PbSO_4 + PbS = 4PbO + 4SO_2$; and the lead oxide is reduced by the carbon monoxide : $PbO + CO = CO_2 + Pb$. The products of the decomposition thus contain lead, and lead sulphide and sulphate in quantities varying with the temp. and time of reduction. A. Ditte showed that an aq. soln. of **carbon dioxide** under atm. press. does not attack lead sulphate cold or hot ; but L. Michel, G. Seligmann, P. von Jeremejeff, and others have noted the transformation of anglesite into cerussite under natural conditions. G. C. Wittstein found that an aq. soln. of normal **ammonium carbonate** converts lead sulphate into lead carbonate ; and A. Ditte reported that with an excess of lead sulphate, the carbonate disappears entirely from the soln. and with twice the theoretical quantity of lead sulphate, only a part forms the complex salt, $(NH_4)_2Pb(SO_4)_2$, and a part forms lead-hillite, $PbSO_4.3PbCO_3$. J. Lemberg noted that a soln. of commercial ammonium carbonate also transforms the sulphate to carbonate. J. Percy, and O. Schott reported that when lead sulphate is decomposed by **sodium or potassium carbonate,** at a red-heat, the alkali sulphate and lead monoxide are formed. According to A. Ditte, an aq. soln. of potassium carbonate acts like one of ammonium carbonate ; and a soln. of sodium carbonate produces only lead carbonate and sodium sulphate, not the double salt of sodium and lead sulphates. The **alkali hydrocarbonates** act similarly. F. Auerbach and H. Pick found that lead sulphate in contact with $0·1N\text{-}Na_2CO_3$ forms white-lead, and sodium hydrocarbonate and sulphate are produced in the molar ratio 1 : 3 ; with an excess of lead sulphate, a basic lead carbonate is precipitated until the soda-content of the soln. begins to increase, when normal lead carbonate is produced and the complex salt dissolved. There is a balanced reaction : $PbSO_4 + 2NaHCO_3 \rightleftharpoons PbCO_3 + Na_2SO_4 + CO_2 + H_2O$.

Much attention has been devoted to the action of soln. of the acetates on lead sulphate. G. Bischof found that 100 grms. of a soln. **of ammonium acetate,** sp. gr. 1·36, dissolve 2·13 grms. of lead sulphate, forming a soln. which gives a precipitate with sulphuric acid or potassium sulphate. J. Mercer also noted the solubility of lead sulphate in soln. of **ammonium acetate.** Expressing conc. in grams per litre, J. W. Marden found at 25° :

$CH_3.COONH_4$	.	.	.	0	7·96	15·91	31·70	53·4	106·8	213·7
$PbSO_4$	.	.	.	0·041	0·636	1·37	3·04	5·6	16·8	38·9

J. C. Long found at 100° :

$CH_3.COONH_4$	.	.	.	280	300	320	350	370	400	450
$PbSO_4$	.	.	.	71·2	83·6	98·8	102·6	105·8	107·8	111·0

and A. A. Noyes and W. H. Whitcomb, at 25°, for soln. with 0, 7·98, 15·96, and 31·92 grms. of ammonium acetate per litre, respectively 0·041, 0·636, 1·38, and 3·02 grms. of lead sulphate per litre. They attribute the increase in the solubility with increasing conc. of the ammonium acetate to the formation, by metathesis, of non-ionized mols. of lead acetate, $(CH_3.COO)_2Pb$. J. J. Fox found that the equilibrium $PbSO_4 + 2NH_4C_2H_3O_2 \rightleftharpoons (NH_4)_2SO_4 + Pb(C_2H_3O_2)_2$ is complicated by the formation of the complex salt, $(NH_4)_2Pb(SO_4)_2$. C. Blomberg's observations on the f.p., and electrical conductivity of the soln., led him to conclude that the increased solubility is due to the formation of either complex or basic salts. J. J. Fox made some observations on this subject. F. H. Storer found that a conc. aq. soln. of ammonium acetate mixed with alcohol exerted no solvent action on lead sulphate ; a similar result was obtained in the presence of sulphuric acid ; but with ammonium sulphate in place of sulphuric acid, much lead sulphate is dissolved. J. J. Fox examined the equilibrium : $PbSO_4 + 2KC_2H_3O_2 \rightleftharpoons K_2SO_4 + Pb(C_2H_3O_2)_2$, and found that soln. of lead sulphate in those of **potassium acetate** contain lead and potassium acetates only. The results are plotted in Fig. 112. The solid phase consists of lead potassium sulphate, which is practically insoluble as such in the acetate, no lead acetate being present in the solid phase. The formation of the salt $PbK_2(SO_4)_2$ on mixing soln. of lead acetate and potassium sulphate may be accounted for by the preliminary formation of complex acetates, such as $PbK_2(C_2H_3O_2)_4$. This would then react with more potassium sulphate to give insoluble $PbK_2(SO_4)_2$. J. Mercer noted the solubility of lead sulphate in soln. of this salt as well as in **sodium acetate.** H. C. Dibbits showed that a soln. containing 100 grms. of water, a few drops of acetic acid, and 2·05 grms. of anhydrous sodium acetate dissolved 0·054 grm. of lead sulphate ; with 8·2 grms. of the acetate, 0·90 grm. lead sulphate ; and with 41·0 grms. of the acetate 11·20 grms. of lead sulphate. The temp. had very little

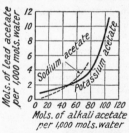

FIG. 112.—The Solubility of Lead Sulphate in Soln. of Potassium and Sodium Acetates.

effect on the result, and the soln. gave a precipitate with sulphuric acid, and other reagents ordinarily employed to precipitate lead salts from aq. soln. J. J. Fox found that the equilibrium : $PbSO_4 + 2NaC_2H_3O_2 \rightleftharpoons Na_2SO_4 + Pb(C_2H_3O_2)_2$, is not disturbed by the formation of a double salt ; and his results for the solubility of lead sulphate in soln. of sodium acetate are plotted in Fig. 112. F. H. Storer said that a dil. alcoholic soln. of sodium acetate, mixed with normal sulphuric acid, with ammonium sulphate or with lead acetate seemed to have no solvent action on lead sulphate. L. Krafft, and H. C. Dibbits studied the solvent action of soln. of **barium acetate** on lead sulphate ; J. Mercer, W. Städel, and H. C. Dibbits found that 100 grms. of a dil. soln. of **calcium acetate** dissolve 45·45 grms. of lead sulphate. J. Mercer noted the solubility of lead sulphate in soln. of **magnesium acetate.** H. C. Dibbits found lead sulphate to be soluble in a soln. of **copper acetate,** but not in one of **silver acetate ;** soluble in soln. of **zinc, manganese, and nickel acetates,** but not in a soln. of **mercury acetate ;** and E. Lenssen, J. Mercer, and

J. L. Mayer showed lead sulphate is soluble in soln. of **aluminium acetate** but not if an excess of alkali or aluminium sulphate is present. J. L. Smith, and K. Stammer found lead sulphate to be insoluble in soln. of normal **lead acetate,** but the latter found it to be soluble in basic lead acetate. F. H. Storer said that lead sulphate is not soluble in dil. alcoholic soln. of **ammonium or sodium oxalate** in the presence of sulphuric acid or ammonium sulphate. F. Wöhler, and G. C. Wittstein said that lead sulphate is soluble in an aq. soln. of **ammonium succinate,** but F. H. Storer added not in a dil. alcoholic soln. in the presence of sulphuric acid, or ammonium sulphate. J. L. Smith said that lead sulphate is soluble in a soln. of **ammonium tartrate ;** C. Reichard added that lead sulphate is insoluble in **potassium and sodium tartrates,** but is soluble in their double tartrates with ammonium. Ammonia itself does not dissolve the compound, but if added to a soln. of sodium tartrate containing lead sulphate in suspension soln. takes place. The soln. of lead sulphate in neutral **ammonium tartrate** seems to contain part of the lead as a basic salt, for on adding a small quantity of potassium dichromate, the precipitate formed at first consists of the orange-red basic lead chromate. F. H. Storer added that a dil. alcoholic soln. of potassium tartrate containing a little sulphuric acid does not dissolve lead sulphate. According to H. C. Bolton, a cold conc. soln. of **citric acid** dissolves anglesite ; J. L. Smith said the sulphate is soluble in an aq. soln. of **ammonium citrate,** but, added F. H. Storer, not if alcohol and sulphuric acid or ammonium citrate be present. A soln. of **ammonium dicitrate,** or of **potassium tricitrate,** dissolves lead sulphate in the presence of alcohol and sulphuric acid. H. W. F. Wackenroder said that the best solvents among the ammonium salts are the nitrate, citrate, and tartrate ; the two latter should be made alkaline with ammonia. H. G. Denham found the resistance of a sat. soln. of lead sulphate in **alcohol** to be 93,000 ohms at 25°. F. H. Storer found that 59 per cent. alcohol alone, or mixed with **ethylsulphuric acid,** or with **sugar,** does not dissolve lead sulphate after three months' action. A. Naumann found lead sulphate to be insoluble in **acetone,** in **methyl acetate,** and in **ethyl acetate ;** and H. Mandal, sparingly soluble in **aniline.** A. Conduché said that **chloroform** at 350° forms lead chloride. J. Percy, and H. Rose showed that when lead sulphate is fused with about five times its weight of **potassium cyanide,** the whole of the lead is reduced to the metallic state, and the process can be used for quantitative analysis. A. Ditte found that when lead sulphate is added to a soln. of potassium cyanide, lead cyanide is formed, and as the potassium sulphate accumulates in the system, the double sulphate is formed. J. Aub said that a litre of blood **serum** at 25° dissolves 0·0437 grm. of lead sulphate. J. Marc studied the **adsorption** of organic colouring agents of lead sulphate.

A. Ditte [16] showed that aq. soln. of **boric acid** and of **potassium or sodium borate** have no action on lead sulphate either in the cold or at boiling heat. J. Percy found that a mixture of borax and lead sulphate can be readily fused ; and if clay crucibles are used, some of the sulphate may be decomposed with the evolution of sulphur dioxide. E. Vigouroux observed lead sulphate is reduced by **silicon,** and L. Kahlenberg and W. J. Trautmann represented the reaction with powdered silicon at an elevated temp. by $PbSO_4 + 2Si = PbS + 2SiO_2$; $2PbS + 3O_2 = 2PbO + 2SO_2$; $PbO + SiO_2 = PbSiO_3$; and $3PbO + Si = 2Pb + PbSiO_3$. P. Berthier found that lead sulphate is decomposed by **silica** at a red heat, forming lead silicate. The time required for the reaction is no longer than with mixtures of lead oxide and silica. W. Mostowitch said that silica does not alter the temp. or progress of decomposition below 950° ; silica begins to act on lead sulphate at 975°. The progress of the decomposition depends on the nature of the silicate formed—di- and tri-silicates retard the decomposition by surrounding the sulphate with a viscous silicate. P. Berthier also found that **clay** acts similarly, and suggested that lead sulphate might be used in place of galena, or other lead compounds, in the glazing of pottery, or in place of red-lead in making flint-glass. S. Hilpert said that the reaction begins at about 720°, and progresses rapidly above 750°, as indicated in

Fig. 113. J. Percy, and M. Tipp showed that when lead sulphate is mixed with **calcium oxide,** and heated to redness, calcium sulphate and lead oxide are formed. G. Tammann studied the action of the oxides of the alkaline earths, lead oxide, and of the **alkali carbonates** on lead sulphate. W. Reinders found that the attack with **magnesium oxide** begins at about 800°. P. Berthier noted that a mixture of lead sulphate with 10 per cent. of **lead oxide** at a white heat becomes *aussi liquid que de la litharge,* and *sous-sulfates* are formed—*vide infra,* oxysulphates. O. Proske found that **ferrous oxide** at 800° favours the decomposition of lead sulphate; **ferric oxide** at 900° has not a marked influence, but the action is vigorous at 1200°. S. Hilpert compared the behaviour of ferric oxide with that of silica. J. Milbauer and K. Kohn found that, when heated, **potassium chromate** quickly transforms lead sulphate into the chromate, and they also studied the reverse reaction.

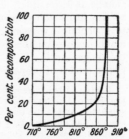

FIG. 113.—Speed of the Reaction between Lead Sulphate and Silica.

J. A. Wilkinson observed that in the reduction of lead sulphate by **sodium** no luminescence occurs. P. Berthier, and J. Percy represented the reaction which occurs when **lead** is heated with its sulphate by $PbSO_4 + Pb = 2PbO + SO_2$. The reaction has been further studied by H. C. Jenkins and E. A. Smith, W. Reinders, A. Lodin, J. B. Hannay, etc.—*vide supra,* the extraction of lead. J. Percy found that when a mixture of lead sulphate and **iron** is heated, lead and scoriaceous slag are formed. G. Tammann also studied the action of iron on the sulphate. B. N. Chuckubutti obtained Nobili's rings with a brass cathode in a lead sulphate soln.

P. Louyet [17] obtained an indefinite product, possibly *lead fluosulphate,* by the action of conc. sulphuric acid on lead fluoride. F. Matthey reported that when lead sulphate is repeatedly treated with a soln. of sodium chloride, there remains a mixture of undecomposed lead sulphate and *lead chlorosulphate.* S. Zinno treated the product of the action of iodine on an aq. soln. of sulphur dioxide and sodium sulphite—$Na_2SO_3.I_2,$ with lead acetate and obtained a white precipitate supposed to be *lead iodosulphate,* $PbSO_4.I_2.$ A. Michaelis and G. Köthe said the white precipitate is a mixture of lead sulphite and iodine which with more iodine furnishes yellow lead iodide.

The basic lead sulphates—lead oxysulphates.—As indicated above, P. Berthier [18] fused mixtures of lead oxide and sulphate and obtained what were regarded as basic lead sulphates. The fusion curve of mixtures of lead oxide and sulphate was investigated by R. Schenck and W. Rassbach, W. Reinders, F. M. Jäger and H. C. Germs, etc. The results of R. Schenck and W. Rassbach are summarized in Fig. 114. Owing to the decomposition of lead sulphate, the curve with the higher proportions of lead sulphate was not explored above 950°. The remainder of the curve shows two distinct maxima, one at 966°, corresponding with $PbO.PbSO_4$; and one at 951°, corresponding with $2PbO.PbSO_4.$ A third compound, $3PbO.PbSO_4,$ does not show a maximum because it decomposes before this can be reached, and, above 880°, furnishes the compound $2PbO.PbSO_4$ and melt. There is a eutectic at 820°, and 87 per cent. PbO between PbO and $3PbO.PbSO_4$; one at 940° and 55·3 per cent. PbO between $2PbO.PbSO_4$ and

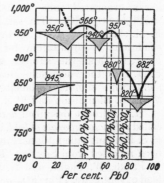

FIG. 114.—Freezing-point Curves of Mixtures of Lead Oxide and Sulphate.

$PbO.PbSO_4$; and one at 950° and 30 per cent. PbO between $PbO.PbSO_4$ and $PbSO_4.$ There is a horizontal at 845° corresponding with the transition point of lead sulphate (q.v.), and a second one at 450° between 42 and 85 per cent. of PbO, not shown in the diagram, corresponding with a rearrangement of the compound 2PbO.PbSO$_4$. The break is shown on a rising and a falling temp. so that the change is reversible. The nature of this change is not known ; it may be due to the formation of a different modification of 2PbO.PbSO$_4$, or it may be due to a chemical reaction : 2(2PbO.PbSO$_4$)⇌PbO.PbSO$_4$+3PbO.PbSO$_4$. S. Ganelin made basic sulphates by grinding lead sulphate and magnesia with water ; and G. Lunge and C. H. M. Lyte, from lead nitrate, sodium sulphate, and hydroxide. Other modes of preparation are indicated below.

The so-called *sublimed white-lead* is a mixture containing lead sulphate 75–80 per cent. ; lead oxide, 14–20 per cent. ; and zinc oxide, 5–6 per cent. It may be a mixture of basic sulphates, and is used as a painter's pigment, largely in the manufacture of mixed paints. Its use was developed by G. T. Lewis and E. O. Bartlett, and it was made by a process resembling that used for making zinc oxide, namely, by subliming the ore in an oxidizing fire, and collecting the condensed product in cloth filters or bags. The composition is naturally dependent on the character of the galena or lead ore employed as raw material ; on the amount of air which comes in contact with the ore ; on the temp. of the furnace ; etc. The process of manufacture has been the subject of numerous patents. The manufacture of this and other varieties, and the properties have been described by C. D. Holley, H. O. Hofman, C. Schnabel, F. C. Breyer and co-workers, J. A. Schaeffer, E. E. Banes, J. B. Hannay and co-workers, W. J. M. Jackson, W. Bell and co-workers, S. B. Wilson, E. C. C. Baly, A. Macdonald, L. F. Hughes, P. F. Nursey, B. S. White, etc. The so-called *non-poisonous white-lead* which has been on the market is a basic sulphate—72·74 per cent. PbO ; 24·90, SO$_3$; and 2·36, CO$_2$. It was shown by H. Kionka, and K. B. Lehmann to be just as poisonous as other varieties.

The conditions of equilibrium of **lead trioxysulphate**, 4PbO.SO$_3$, or 3PbO.PbSO$_4$, or Pb$_4$O$_3$SO$_4$, have been indicated in connection with Fig. 114. The salt was prepared by R. Schenck and W. Rassbach, E. Jänecke, F. M. Jäger and H. C. Germs, and W. Reinders. It decomposes above 880°.before its m.p. is attained. D. Strömholm reported **hydrated lead trioxysulphate**, 3PbO.PbSO$_4$.H$_2$O, or *lead hydroxydioxy-sulphate*, 2PbO.Pb(OH)$_2$.PbSO$_4$, to be formed when lead hydroxide is mixed with a soln. of ammonium sulphate—potassium sulphate does not do so well. M. Pleissner made it by shaking an intimate mixture of lead hydroxide, PbO.$\frac{1}{3}$H$_2$O, lead sulphate, and water at 18° for three days. The white mass of small crystals has a solubility of 26·2 mgrms. per litre at 18° ; the sp. conductivity of the soln. being 9·3×10^{-6} mho. The conditions of equilibrium of **lead dioxysulphate**, 3PbO.SO$_3$, or 2PbO.PbSO$_4$, or Pb$_3$O$_2$SO$_4$, by R. Schenck and W. Rassbach, are indicated in Fig. 114. The subject was also studied by E. Jänecke. W. Reinders made the dioxysulphate by heating a mixture of finely divided lead and lead oxysulphate in an evacuated tube at 700° ; the reaction was symbolized 4Pb$_2$OSO$_4$+Pb =3Pb$_3$O$_2$SO$_4$+SO$_2$. The salt melts at 951°, and has a transition point at 450°. F. M. Jäger and H. C. Germs made the salt, and gave 961° for the m.p. The conditions of equilibrium for **lead oxysulphate**, PbO.PbSO$_4$, are indicated in Fig. 114 ; and the subject was also studied by E. Jänecke. According to F. M. Lyte the basic sulphates can be converted into other basic salts by treatment with soluble carbonates, phosphates, or chlorides ; and, according to W. E. B. Blenkinsop and F. M. Lyte, with soluble borates, silicates, or oxalates.

H. J. Brooke described a rare mineral from Leadhills, Lanarkshire, which he called *sulphatocarbonate of lead*, and it was represented by the formula PbSO$_4$.PbCO$_3$. F. S. Beudant called it **lanarkite**, and A. Breithaupt, *dioxylite*. Specimens have also been reported from Siberia ; Tanne, Harz ; and Biberweier, Tyrol. Analyses by F. Pisani, W. Flight, and N. Collie show that its composition corresponds with **lead oxysulphate**, 2PbO.SO$_3$, or PbO.PbSO$_4$, or Pb$_2$OSO$_4$, and not with Pb$_2$(SO$_4$)CO$_3$. Analyses of the artificial product were made by D. Strömholm, A. de Schulten, C. T. Barfoed, and W. Reinders. The conditions of equilibrium, in its preparation by fusing mixtures of lead oxide and sulphate, worked out by R. Schenck and W. Rassbach, are indicated in Fig. 113. F. M. Jäger and H. C. Germs made it in a similar way. H. C. Jenkins and E. A. Smith made it by heating in a crucible at a dull red heat, a mixture of equimolar parts of lead and lead sulphate. W. Reinders represented the reaction: $4Pb+5PbSO_4=4Pb_2OSO_4+PbS$. O. B. Kuhn, W. Reinders, and D. Strömholm obtained it by digesting lead sulphate with aq. ammonia; M. Pleissner, by shaking a mixture of a mol of lead sulphate and one-third of a mol of lead hydroxide, $PbO.\frac{1}{2}H_2O$, and water, or by shaking lead sulphate with freshly precipitated lead hydroxide and water; C. T. Barfoed, by treating basic lead formate with an excess of sodium sulphate soln.; and A. de Schulten, by the action of a soln. of sodium sulphate on basic lead acetate.

Lanarkite occurs in crystals, and also massive with a greenish-white, pale yellow, or grey colour. The artificial salt is white or colourless. The crystals are monoclinic prisms, with axial ratios $a:b:c=0.8681:1:1.3836$, and $\beta=91°$ 49'. A. de Schulten's crystals were acicular with the same crystallographic constants as the natural crystals. The cleavage (001) is perfect; and the (100) and (103) cleavages in traces. The lustre of the cleavage faces is pearly; elsewhere, the lustre is adamantine or resinous. F. Pisani gave for the optic axial angles with red-light, $2H=65°$ 3'; the optical character is negative. The birefringence is strong. The sp. gr. given by H. J. Brooke is 6.3–6.4; F. Pisani gave 6.8 for lanarkite; and for the artificial salt, A. de Schulten gave 6.923 at 15°. The hardness is 2–2½. R. Schenck and W. Rassbach gave 966° for the m.p., and F. M. Jäger and H. C. Germs, 977°. Hence, as C. T. Barfoed said, it melts more easily than lead sulphate. The molten liquid is yellow, but it becomes white on cooling; and, according to A. de Schulten, furnishes a felted mass of long prisms. C. T. Barfoed said the salt is very sparingly soluble in water, and, according to M. Pleissner, a litre of water at 18° dissolves 13.4 mgrms. of the salt, the sp. conductivity being 8.8×10^{-6} mho. According to W. Reinders, the oxysulphate reacts with lead sulphide: $2Pb_2OSO_4+3PbS \rightleftharpoons 7Pb+5SO_2$, and the press. of the gas is 27.5 mm. at 712°; 78 mm. at 750°; and 233 mm. at 790°.

E. Toelle, and J. Kronen claimed to have made hydrated lead oxysulphate, $PbO.PbSO_4$. H_2O, or lead dihydroxysulphate, $Pb(OH)_2SO_4$, by the gradual addition of sulphuric acid to lead oxide, or by grinding lead sulphate with water to a paste, and gradually adding lead oxide. Other oxysulphates have been reported, but the evidence is not sufficient to establish their individuality. Thus, D. A. MacInnes believed that lead tetroxysulphate, $4PbO.PbSO_4$, is formed during the discharge of a lead accumulator. E. Toelle, and J. Kronen reported lead hexahydroxydisulphate, $3Pb(OH)_2.2PbSO_4$, to be formed when sulphuric acid is gradually added to lead oxide; or lead oxide gradually added to a paste made of lead sulphate and water; lead dihydroxydisulphate, $Pb(OH)_2.2PbSO_4$, was also said to have been produced in the same way. According to L. F. Hughes, sublimed white-lead has nearly the composition of lead oxydisulphate, $PbO.2PbSO_4$. E. Frankland reported lead dioxytrisulphate, $2PbO.3PbSO_4$, to be produced in the discharge of lead accumulators. H. O. Hofman and W. Wanjukow supposed lead pentoxysulphate, $5PbO.PbSO_4$, to be formed when lead sulphate is roasted to 705°.

L. Brugnatelli [19] said that some basic lead copper sulphates are produced in nature by the weathering of cupriferous galena. The bluish-green, or sky-blue mineral from Leadhills, Lanarkshire, was regarded by H. J. Brooke as cuprous lead sulphatocarbonate, and called by F. S. Beudant, caledonite—W. Flight, and N. Collie showed that the carbonate was due to the presence of admixed cerussite; and that about 10 per cent. of cupric oxide was present. The results correspond with $2(Pb,Cu)O.SO_3.H_2O$, or $(Pb,Cu)(OH)_2.(Pb,Cu)SO_4$. Analyses of samples from Monte Challacollo, Atacama, by G. Berg correspond with copper lead hexahydroxytetrasulphate, $3Pb(OH)_2.4PbSO_4$, or $3PbO.4PbSO_4.3H_2O$. A. Pelloux examined samples from Sardinia. According to H. J. Brooke, the prismatic crystals are rhombic with the axial ratios $a:b:c=0.9163:1:1.4032$; but A. Schrauf, and P. von Jeremejeff regarded them as monoclinic twins with numerous twin lamellæ; the former gave for crystals from Rezbanya, Hungary, $a:b:c$ $=1.09134:1:1.57850$, and $\beta=89°$ 18', while the latter gave for the crystals from Berezoff, Urals, $a:b:c=1.08956:1:1.57725$, and $\beta=88°$ 22'. Observations on the crystals were made by R. P. Greg and W. G. Lettsom, W. H. Miller, C. F. Peters,

F. Hessenberg, G. vom Rath, C. Busz, O. C. Farrington, A. F. Rogers, N. von Kokscharoff, H. L. Ungemach, F. N. Guild, etc. The optic axial angles given by A. des Cloizeaux are $2H_a=112°\ 27'$, $2H_0=142°\ 5·5'$, and $2V=82°\ 37'$ for the red-ray, and $2H_a=113°\ 27·5'$, $2H_0=141°\ 32'$, and $2V=83°\ 3'$ for the blue-ray. The index of refraction is $\beta=1·846$ for the red-ray, and $1·864$ for the blue-ray. The (001)-cleavage is perfect, and the (100) less so. The sp. gr. is 6·4, and the hardness 2·5–3·0.

H. J. Brooke [20] reported a *cuprous sulphate of lead* found at Leadhills, Lanarkshire. W. Phillips named it *linarite*—after Linares, Spain, where it was formerly supposed to occur. F. Sandberger, T. Liweh, and others have reported samples occurring in Germany, Siberia, Urals, etc. Analyses were reported by H. J. Brooke, T. Thomson, F. von Kobell, F. Sandberger, A. Frenzel, and N. Collie from which the mineral appears to be a *lead copper hydroxysulphate*, $(Pb,Cu)SO_4.(Pb,Cu)(OH)_2$, or $PbO.CuO.SO_3.H_2O$. P. Dudgeon reported crystals from the slag of an old lead smelting hearth of Roman origin, in Troqueer, Scotland; and L. Michel also found linarite in the slag of a lead furnace. The colour of the mineral is deep azure-blue, and the prismatic or tabular crystals, according to N. von Kokscharoff, belong to the monoclinic system and have the axial ratios $a:b:c$ $=1·71613:1:0·82963$, and $\beta=77°\ 22'\ 40''$. Twinning is common. The (100)-cleavage is perfect, and the (001) less so. The crystals were discussed by P. von Jeremejeff, H. Höfer, W. H. Miller, R. P. Greg and W. G. Lettsom, A. Schrauf, G. vom Rath, V. von Zepharovich, A. Stelzner, and F. Hessenberg. The sp. gr. is 5·3–5·45; A. Frenzel gave 5·06 at 17°. The hardness is $2\frac{1}{2}$. The optical properties were examined by L. Brugnatelli.

Complex salts with lead sulphate.—W. Grahmann [21] examined the f.p. curves of mixtures of lead and potassium sulphates, and found the results summarized in Fig. 115. Solid soln. are formed with up to 27 molar per cent. of lead sulphate. Two compounds were prepared. One, **potassium disulphatodiplumbite**,

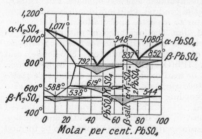

$K_2SO_4.2PbSO_4$, shows as a maximum m.p. at 948°. It is dimorphous; the transition temp. is 544°; above that temp. what was called α-$K_2Pb_2(SO_4)_3$ is stable, and below that temp. β-$K_2Pb_2(SO_4)_3$ is stable. G. Calcagni and D. Marotta also examined the system and found the same complex salt. The other compound, **potassium disulphatoplumbite**, $K_2Pb(SO_4)_2$, is formed at 619° by a reaction in the solid state. The transition from α- to β-lead sulphate occurs at 852°. The transition from α- to β-potassium sulphate, at 588°, and the effect of lead sulphate on this transition is indicated

FIG. 115.—Freezing-point Curves of Lead and Potassium Sulphates.

in the diagram. This salt has also been obtained in the wet way. In 1825, J. B. Trommsdorff treated sugar of lead with a soln. of potassium sulphate and obtained a salt which "appeared to contain equimolar parts of lead and potassium sulphates." J. J. Fox obtained this salt by shaking an excess of a soln. of lead acetate with potassium sulphate, washing the solid phase with a soln. of potassium acetate, then with alcohol, and drying in air. F. G. Belton mixed slowly 20 c.c. of a sat. soln. of potassium sulphate at 75° with 10 c.c. of a 10 per cent. soln. of lead nitrate, washed the solid by suction with a soln. of potassium sulphate. A. Ditte, M. Barre, and J. N. Brönsted digested lead sulphate with a soln. of potassium sulphate, and dried the solid product by press. between bibulous paper. A. Ditte also used other potassium salts—e.g. the chloride, bromide, iodide, cyanide, chlorate, etc. Potassium disulphatoplumbite is a white amorphous solid, or a white mass of microscopic crystals, which, according to W. Grahmann, are optically uniaxial, and show a strong birefringence. F. G. Belton said that the salt is not

attacked by a cold or hot sat. aq. soln. of potassium sulphate ; and, added
J. N. Brönsted, at 22°, it is in equilibrium with $0.0227N\text{-}K_2SO_4$, and at 0°, with
a $0.0112N$-soln. A. Ditte said that if the double salt is not to be decomposed, the
conc. of the soln. should be at least 0.35 per cent. at 10° ; 0.49 per cent. at 15° ;
and 1.45 per cent. at 100°. M. Barre said that for stability, the soln. should
have the following proportion of potassium sulphate for 100 grms. of soln . :

	7°	17°	50°	75°	100°
K_2SO_4 . .	0.562	0.620	1.095	1.373	1.695

J. J. Fox found that the salt is almost insoluble in a soln. of potassium acetate at
25°, and sparingly soluble in a soln. of potassium acetoplumbite at 25°. G. Calcagni
and D. Marotta examined the f.p. diagram of mixtures of lead and lithium sulphates, Fig. 116, but obtained no evidence of the formation of *lithium sulphatoplumbite*. Similar results were obtained with mixtures of lead and sodium sulphates,
Fig. 117, no *sodium sulphatoplumbite* was formed, but solid soln. with up to 65 per
cent. of sodium sulphate were obtained. The eutectic is at 735° with 35 per cent.
of sodium sulphate. P. Berthier made some observations on fused mixtures of the
two salts—*vide supra*—and H. le Chatelier said that the fusion curve corresponds
with the formation of *sodium disulphatoplumbite*, $Na_2Pb(SO_4)_2$; but this lacks confirmation. A. Ditte said that lead sulphate is but very slightly soluble in a boiling

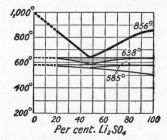

FIG. 116.—Freezing-point Curves of Mixtures of Lithium and Lead Sulphates.

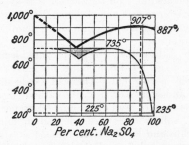

FIG. 117.—Freezing-point Curves of Mixtures of Sodium and Lead Sulphates.

soln. of sodium sulphate ; and neither A. Ditte nor M. Barre could make the salt
by the processes employed for the potassium salt ; and J. J. Fox was likewise unsuccessful. A. Lacroix discovered a mineral corresponding with $K_4Na_2Pb_4(SO_4)_7$,
or $3(K,Na)_2SO_4.4PbSO_4$, *sodium potassium heptasulphatotetraplumbite*, which he
called **palmierite**—after L. Palmieri. It was found in the fumerole deposits of
Vesuvius in microscopic micaceous plates, often hexagonal in outline. The
mineral is decomposed by water, and dissolved by nitric acid. The sp. gr. is near
3.33 ; F. Zambonini gave 4.5, and found the mineral to be uniaxial with $\omega=1.712$
for the *D*-line. He synthesized it by fusing at 1000° for an hour a mixture of
potassium, sodium, and lead sulphates (5 : 9 : 7.5 parts by weight), and cooling the
mass gradually. The tabular crystals were isolated by treating the fused mass
with a 2 per cent. soln. of potassium sulphate.

The mineral *röblingite* is a complex of $(Ca,Pb)SO_4$ with CaH_2SiO_4—*vide* silicates.
E. Mallard and E. Cumenge [22] observed a mineral from Boleo, Mexico, which they
regarded as anglesite, but it was shown by F. A. Genth to be a *calcium sulphatopium-
bite*. H. le Chatelier obtained crystals of **barium sulphatoplumbite** by fusing lead and
barium sulphates in sodium sulphate, and extracting the excess of sodium sulphate
with water. R. Ohashi reported a mineral deposited from a hot spring at Hokuto,
Formosa, and hence named *hokutolite*. The composition and optical characters
show that it is an isomorphous mixture of anglesite and barytes. The mineral is
radioactive, and self-luminescent. G. H. Bailey reported that regular octahedral
crystals of **aluminium pentasulphatodiplumbite**, $Al_2Pb_2(SO_4)_5.20H_2O$, were formed

by exposing a mixed soln. of alum and lead nitrate and acetate to a winter's cold. F. Zambonini observed no evidence of the formation of mixed crystals of *lead and didymium sulphates*. E. S. Larsen described a mineral from Beaver County, Utah, which he called *beaverite*. Its composition approximated that of a **copper lead aluminosulphate**, $CuSO_4.PbSO_4.(Fe,Al)_2O_3.4H_2O$. The optical character of the hexagonal plates was negative ; the index of refraction 1·83–1·87 ; and the bire-fringence was strong. According to R. F. Weinland and H. Kühl, **stannic sulphato-plumbite**, $SnPb(SO_4)_3.3H_2O$, is formed by mixing soln. of stannic acid in sulphuric acid with an equal proportion of a soln. of lead sulphate in hot conc. sulphuric acid. The cubic crystals are decomposed by water. They are insoluble in hydrochloric acid.

Sulphates with quadrivalent lead.—The formation of **lead disulphate**, or **plumbic sulphate**, $Pb(SO_4)_2$—lead quadrivalent—has been reported by a few investigators. B. Brauner [23] found that the yellow soln. of lead tetrafluoride in an excess of sul-phuric acid is clear at ordinary temp., but, when warmed to 100° from time to time during a period of more than two months, it furnishes an orange-yellow crust. This product, said B. Brauner, *kann nur Bleidisulfat, $Pb(SO_4)_2$, sein*. K. Elbs and F. Fischer said that the result is not satisfactory, and that if red-lead or lead dioxide be treated with sulphuric acid, an impure lead disulphate is formed. A. Hutchinson and W. Pollard found that if lead disulphate is formed by the action of conc. sul-phuric acid on lead tetracetate it is extremely unstable, and a satisfactory proof of its existence was not obtained. G. Panopolus said that unstable lead disulphate is present when a soln. of an alkali plumbite is treated with lead dioxide or potassium persulphate.

K. Elbs and F. Fischer prepared lead disulphate by the electrolysis of sulphuric acid, sp. gr. 1·7–1·8, at temp. not exceeding 30°, using a current density of 0·02–0·06 ampère per sq. cm. The lead anode should be immersed in a considerable vol. of acid and separated from the cathode by a porous pot. The salt is partly deposited in the form of mud containing 60–85 per cent. of plumbic sulphate ; an 85 to 99 per cent. salt is afterwards deposited in indistinct crystals from the anode liquid. K. Elbs and F. W. Rixon found the salt in the mud, and in the sulphuric acid of a lead accumulator. F. Dolezalek and K. Finckh could not obtain the salt free from acid. K. Elbs and F. Fischer added that the rapid disintegration of the positive plates of an accumulator with too high currents is due to the formation of lead disulphate.

K. Elbs and F. Fischer found that lead disulphate has a faint greenish colour, and is stable under sulphuric acid, sp. gr. 1·7, in darkness at room temp. ; and F. Dolezalek and K. Finckh recommended keeping it under very conc. sulphuric acid. The compound is isomeric with lead persulphate—*vide* sulphuric acid. K. Elbs and F. Fischer said that the disulphate is sparingly soluble in sulphuric acid and pyrosulphuric acid, forming greenish-yellow soln.—100 c.c. of the conc. acid dissolves about 0·345 grm. of the salt at 30°. A. C. Cumming gave for the solubility in $7.45N$-H_2SO_4, 0·0003 mol per litre at 25° ; and F. Dolezalek and K. Finckh said that the solubility increases with increasing conc. of sulphuric acid ; thus, expressing conc. in grams per litre at 22°, they found :

H_2SO_4	.	948	1014	1130	1217	1352	1470	1532	1631	1703
$Pb(SO_4)_2$	.	0	1·719	2·115	9·303	16·17	9·30	9·46	19·80	35·22
Solid Phase			$PbOSO_4,H_2O$						$Pb(SO_4)_2$	

K. Elbs said that at 100°, the soln. is decomposed with the evolution of oxygen. Lead disulphate is decomposed by water into lead dioxide and sulphuric acid. According to F. Dolezalek and K. Finckh, it is hydrolyzed by dil. sulphuric acid. The hydrolysis takes place in two stages : $Pb(SO_4)_2+2H_2O \rightleftharpoons PbOSO_4.H_2O +H_2SO_4$; and $PbOSO_4.H_2O=PbO_2+H_2SO_4$, the oxysulphate and dioxide being in equilibrium with different conc. of acid as indicated by measurements of the e.m.f plotted in Fig. 119. The maximum work of hydrolysis is represented by 0·36 volt, and the calculated value 0·367 volt. The conditions of equilibrium solubility of the **plumbic monoxysulphate**, $PbOSO_4$, are indicated in Fig. 119. E. Frankland reported a *plumbic hexoxydisulphate*, $3PbO_2.2SO_3$, to be produced during the discharge of a lead accumulator ; and H. O. Hofmann and W. Wanjukow, *plumbic tetroxysulphate*, $2PbO_2.SO_3$, to be formed by roasting lead hexoxypentasulphate, $6PbO.5SO_3$, at 952°–962°. There is no evidence establishing the chemical individuality of the two compounds last-named. K. Elbs and F. Fischer found that lead disulphate is soluble in an excess of a 20 per cent. soln. of sodium hydroxide, and it is doubtful whether $PbO(ONa)_2$ or $Pb(ONa)_4$ is formed. The disulphate is soluble in cold conc. hydrochloric acid, and the soln. has a yellow colour owing to the formation of lead tetrachloride, or hydrochloroplumbic acid. The salt also dissolves freely in glacial acetic acid, forming lead tetracetate. Like lead dioxide, lead disulphate is a strong oxidizing agent, but it acts rather more vigorously ; thus, at room temp., ferrous salts are oxidized to the ferric state ; alcohol forms aldehyde ; oxalic acid gives carbon dioxide ; the halide acids give the free halogen ; and iodine forms iodic acid. R. Kempf studied the oxidation of some organic compounds through the agency of the disulphate. F. Dolezalek and K. Finckh found the oxidizing potential with different conc. of sulphuric acid against a

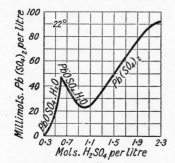

FIG. 118.—Solubility of Lead Disulphate in Sulphuric Acid at 22°.

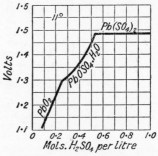

FIG. 119.—Electromotive Force of Solutions of $Pb(SO_4)_2$ in Sulphuric Acid at 11°.

hydrogen electrode at 11·5° attains a maximum of 1·9 volts when the conc. of the acid is that required for the maximum solubility of the disulphate—*i.e.* nearly 0·57 mol H_2SO_4 per litre. The conc. of acid which gives the most powerful oxidizing effect, ν, at $\theta°$ is $\nu=0·55+0·0019\theta$ mol per litre.

F. Dolezalek and K. Finckh, and W. Esch suggested that the soln. of lead disulphate in conc. sulphuric acid, or the greenish-yellow soln. obtained by the electrolysis of sulphuric acid between lead electrodes, contains **hydrotrisulphatoplumbic acid**, *hydrosulphatoplumbic acid*, or *metasulphatoplumbic acid*, $H_2Pb(SO_4)_3$, because the soln. furnishes corresponding ammonium and potassium salts. The same acid is supposed to be produced by dissolving freshly precipitated lead dioxide in sulphuric acid. Water hydrolyzes the acid soln. by a reversible reaction as indicated above. K. Elbs and F. Fischer prepared **ammonium trisulphatoplumbate**, $(NH_4)_2Pb(SO_4)_3$, as a yellow crystalline powder, by treating the acid soln. of lead disulphate with ammonium sulphate or carbonate. It is more stable than lead disulphate ; is almost insoluble in cold sulphuric acid, sp. gr. 1·7, and sparingly soluble in the warm acid ; it is more soluble in the monohydrate, $H_2SO_4.H_2O$, and still more soluble in the fuming acid. The salt reacts with water, sodium hydroxide, hydrochloric acid, acetic acid, etc., very like lead diplumbate—but more slowly. They also prepared **potassium trisulphatoplumbate**, $K_2Pb(SO_4)_3$, as in the case of the ammonium salt. It is rather more stable, but behaves similarly towards various reagents. Working in the same manner, K. Elbs and F. Fischer prepared the related salts **rubidium trisulphatoplumbate,** $Rb_2Pb(SO_4)_3$, and **cæsium trisulphatoplumbate,** $Cs_2Pb(SO_4)_3$. The lithium and sodium salts were not obtained.

REFERENCES.

[1] C. Féry, *Bull. Chim. Soc.*, (4), 25. 223, 1919; H. G. Denham, *Journ. Chem. Soc.*, 115. 111, 1919.

[2] A. G. Monnet, *Nouvelle système de minéralogie*, Paris, 371, 1779; T. Bergman, *Sciagraphia regni mineralis*, Lipsæ, 116, 1782; W. Withering, *Outlines of Mineralogy*, London, 87, 1783; A. Breithaupt, *Berg. Hütt. Ztg.*, 24. 320, 1865; 25. 194, 1866; F. S. Beudant, *Traité élémentaire de minéralogie*, Paris, 2. 459, 1832; G. S. O. Lasius, *Beobachtungen über die Harzgebirge als Baytrag zur mineralogischen Naturkunde*, Hannover, 2. 355, 1789; J. L. Proust, *Journ. Phys.*, 30. 394, 1787; J. Percy, *The Metallurgy of Lead*, London, 99, 1870; E. Jannettaz, *Bull. Soc. Géol.*, (3), 3. 310, 1875; J. Hanus, *Zeit. anorg. Chem.*, 17. 11, 1898; S. H. Emmons, *Monit. Scient.*, (4), 7. 406, 1893; A. Lacroix, *Compt. Rend.*, 123. 955, 1896; *Bull. Soc. Min.*, 30. 237, 1907; A. Lacroix and A. de Schulten, *ib.*, 31. 89, 1908; A. Russell, *Min. Mag.*, 19. 64, 1920; F. Zambonini, *Atti Accad. Napoli*, (2), 13. 8, 1906; J. F. L. Hausmann, *Nachr. Gött.*, 169, 1850; 177, 1852; *Abhand. Ges. Gött.*, 4. 221, 1850; 5. 71, 1852; *Beiträge zur metallurgischen Krystall-kunde*, Göttingen, 1850–2; L. Michel, *Bull. Soc. Min.* 31. 275, 1909; F. Kuhlmann, *Liebig's Ann.*, 38. 366, 1841; F. O. Doeltz and C. A. Graumann, *Met.*, 3. 442, 1906; P. Berthier, *Ann. Chim. Phys.*, (2), 20. 275, 1822; E. A. Smith, *Amer. Journ. Science*, (2), 20. 244, 1855; S. T. Tyson and G. J. Brush, *ib.*, (3), 5. 421, 1873; M. H. Klaproth, *Beiträge zur chemischen Kenntniss der Mineralkorper*, Berlin, 3. 162, 1802; J. J. Berzelius, *Gilbert's Ann.*, 37. 252, 1811; C. F. Bucholz, *Gehlen's Journ.*, 6. 147, 1808; A. Scacchi, *Atti Accad. Napoli*, 5 37, 1873; *Rend. Accad. Napoli*, 11. 203, 1872; W. J. Jordan, *Schweigger's Journ.*, 8. 49, 1813; F. Stromeyer, *Gilbert's Ann.*, 44. 209, 1813; 47. 93, 1814; J. S. Stas, *Bull. Acad. Belg.*, (2), 10. 308, 1860.

[3] P. A. Mackay, *Brit. Pat. No.* 155945, 1919; J. Gitsham and H. R. Evershed, *ib.*, 189160, 1921; H. C. Jenkins and E. A. Smith, *Journ. Chem. Soc.*, 71. 666, 1897; D. L. Hammick, *ib.*, 111. 383, 1917; L. Bourgeois, *Compt. Rend.*, 105. 1073, 1887; *Bull. Soc. Min.*, 10. 325, 1887; P. Gaubert, *ib.*, 32. 41, 1909; A. de Schulten, *ib.*, 26. 106, 1903; *Bull. Soc. Chim.*, (3), 29. 726, 1903; J. B. Senderens, (3), 6. 802, 1891; G. Piolti, *Atti Accad. Torino*, 45. 373, 1910; 46. 783, 1911; F. Zambonini, *Atti Accad. Napoli*, (2), 13. 8, 1906; C. E. Guignet, *Compt. Rend.*, 103. 875, 1886; A. C. Becquerel, *ib.*, 34. 29, 1852; E. Jannettaz, *ib.*, 77. 138, 1873; 78. 852, 1874; A. Macé, *ib.*, 36. 825, 1853; E. Frémy, *ib.*, 63. 714, 1866; C. G. Schlüderberg, *Journ. Phys. Chem.*, 12. 623, 1908; J. A. Wilkinson, *ib.*, 13. 695, 1909; F. O. Doeltz and C. A. Graumann, *Met.*, 3. 441, 1906; H. B. North and A. M. Hagemann, *Journ. Amer. Chem. Soc.*, 35. 543, 1913; W. Leuse, *Zur Kenntnis kolloidaler Metalle und ihrer Verbindungen*, Erlangen, 21, 1904; H. Schiff, *Chem. Ztg.*, 17. 1000, 1891; A. H. Eyles, H. S. Rapelye, and A. Applegate, *German Pat.*, *D.R.P.* 127460, 1897; E. H. Büchner and J. Kalff, *Proc. Acad. Amsterdam*, 28. 145, 1919; H. Rose, *Pogg. Ann.*, 32. 94, 1834; C. von Ernst, *Œster. Zeit. Berg. Hütt.*, 47. 619, 1899; F. Dempwolff, *Metall. Erz*, 11. 619, 1914; N. S. Manross, *Liebig's Ann.*, 82. 348, 1852; A. Drevermann, *ib.*, 89. 39, 1854; F. Auerbach and H. Pick, *Arb. Kaiser Ges. Amt.*, 45. 113, 1913; *Zeit. Elektrochem.*, 19. 830, 1913; P. P. von Weimarn, *Zeit. Koll.*, 2. 78, 1907; E. Hatschek, *ib.*, 8. 193, 1911; *Journ. Soc. Chem. Ind.*, 30. 256, 1911; W. P. Dreaper, *ib.*, 32. 678, 1913; A. Findlay, *Zeit. phys. Chem.*, 34. 409, 1900; L. L. de Koninck, *Bull. Soc. Chim. Belg.*, 21. 141, 1907; J. Hausmann, *Zeit. anorg. Chem.*, 40. 110, 1904; A. Ditte, *Ann. Chim. Phys.*, (5), 14. 236, 1878; J. Milbauer and K. Kohn, *Chem. Ztg.*, 46. 1147, 1922; C. Winkler, *Ber.*, 37. 1657, 1904; K. A. Hofmann, *ib.*, 37. 2198, 1904; E. Masing, *Journ. Russ. Pharm.*, 28. 753, 1889; F. Guthrie, *Phil. Mag.*, (5), 17. 478, 1884; O. Schott, *Beiträge zur Kenntnis der anorganische Schmelzverbindungen*, Braunschweig, 27, 1880; J. W. Mellor, *A Treatise on Quantitative Inorganic Analysis*, London, 610, 1913.

[4] R. J. Haüy, *Traité de minéralogie*, Paris, 3. 503, 1801; N. von Kokscharoff, *Materialen zur Mineralogie Russlands*, St. Petersburg, 1. 34, 1854; R. Kolb, *Zeit. Kryst.*, 49. 14, 1911; A. Arzruni, *ib.*, 1. 182, 1877; W. Ramsay, *ib.*, 12. 217, 1886; O. Lehmann, *ib.*, 1. 453, 1877; Z. Toborffy, *ib.*, 44. 61, 1908; P. Hermann, *ib.*, 39. 463, 1904; A. Fock, *ib.*, 28. 365, 1897; C. Maier, *ib.*, 58. 75, 1923; A. Pelloux, *Atti Accad. Lincei*, (5), 13. ii, 34, 1904; F. Millosevich, *ib.*, (5), 7. 248, 1898; (5), 9. 153, 1900; *Riv. Min. Crist. Ital.*, 30. 28, 1903; E. Repossi, *Atti Accad. Milano*, 43. 422, 1904; O. C. Farrington and E. W. Tillotson, *Field Pub. Columbian Museum*, 129, 1910; A. F. Rogers, *School Mines Quart.*, 23. 133, 1902; E. H. Kraus and A. B. Peck, *Neues Jahrb. Min.*, ii, 17, 1916; A. Franzenau, *Magyar Tud. Akad. Erlesitöje*, 13. 10, 1879; E. V. Shannon, *Proc. U.S. Nat. Museum*, 47. 287, 1919; 58. 437, 1921; *Amer. Journ. Science*, (4), 47. 287, 1919; V. von Lang, *Sitzber. Akad. Wien*, 36. 241, 1859; A. Schrauf, *ib.*, 39. 913, 1860; V. von Zepharovich, *ib.*, 50. 369, 1804; R. Helmhacker, *Denks. Akad. Wien*, 32. 1, 1872; Q. Sella, *Mem. Accad. Lincei*, (4), 2. 199, 1885; *Atti Accad. Lincei*, (3), 3. 150, 1879; C. Calcagni and D. Marotta, *ib.*, (5), 21. ii, 240, 1912; J. B. J D. Boussingault, *Ann. Chim. Phys.*, (4), 12. 426, 1867; V. Goldschmidt, *Index der Krystallformen der Mineralien*, 1. 205, 1886; A. des Cloizeaux, *Nouvelles recherches sur les propriétés optiques des*

cristaux, Paris, 30, 204, 1867 ; T. V. Barker, *Journ. Chem. Soc.*, **89**. 1139, 1906 ; H. C. Germs. *De thermische Analyse van Loodsulfaat-chromaat, -molybdaat, en -wolframaat en van hun binaire combinaties*, Groningen, 1917 ; F. M. Jäger and H. C. Germs, *Zeit. anorg. Chem.*, **119**. 150, 1921 ; G. Tammann and Q. A. Mansuri, *ib.*, **126**. 127, 1923 ; W. Grahmann, *ib.*, **81**. 264, 1913 ; F. M. Jäger and H. Haga, *Versl. Akad. Amsterdam*, 24. 1410, 1916 ; A. Hare, *Phil. Mag.*, (6), **48**. 412, 1924 ; F. Hessenberg, *Mineralogische Notizen*, 5. 31, 1863 ; P. Gaubert, *Compt. Rend.*, **143**. 776, 1906 : *Bull. Soc. Min.*, **32**. 41, 1909 ; A. de Schulten, *ib.*, **26**. 106, 1903 ; *Bull. Soc. Chim.*, (3), **29**. 726. 1903 ; R. Schenck and W. Rassbach, *Ber.*, **41**. 2917, 1908 ; J. G. Bornemann, *Assoc. Min. Sardinia*, 3. 6, 1898 ; F. Zambonini, *Atti Accad. Napoli*, (2), **13**. 8, 1906 ; *Riv. Min. Crist. Ital.*, 45. 1, 1915 ; *Bull. Soc. Min.*, **38**. 210, 1915 ; J. Milbauer and K. Kohn, *Chem. Ztg.*, **46**. 1147, 1922 ; A. Drevermann, *Liebig's Ann.*, **89**. 39, 1854 ; N. S. Manross, *ib.*, **82**. 348, 1852 ; H. Dauber, *Pogg. Ann.*, **108**. 444, 1859 ; A. Breithaupt, *Berg. Hütt. Ztg.*, **24**. 320, 1865 ; **25**. 194, 1866 ; L. Bourgeois, *Bull. Soc. Min.*, **10**. 187, 1887 ; C. Anderson, *Records Australasian Museum*, **13**. 201, 1922 ; G. Cesaro, *Mém. Soc. Géol. Belg.*, **39**. 239, 1912 ; G. Cesaro and A. Abraham, *ib.*, **39**. 269, 1912 ; H. Buttgenbach, *Bull. Soc. Min.*, **43**. 24, 1920 ; R. Köchlin, *Tschermak's Mitt.*, (2), **35**. 1, 1922 ; R. S. Dale, *Proc. Manchester Lit. Phil. Soc.*, **15**. 89, 1876 ; H. Mark, *Zeit. Elektrochem.*, **31**. 523, 1925 ; R. W. James and W. A. Wood, *Proc. Manchester Lit. Phil. Soc.*, **69**. 39, 1924 ; *Proc. Roy. Soc.*, **109**. A, 598, 1925.

[5] C. J. B. Karsten, *Schweigger's Journ.*, **65**. 394, 1832 ; E. Filhol, *Ann. Chim. Phys.*, (3), 21 415, 1847 ; A. Gorgeu, *ib.*, (6), **4**. 515, 1885 ; F. A. Henglein, *Zeit. Elektrochem.*, **30**. 5, 1924 ; *Zeit. anorg. Chem.*, **120**. 77, 1921 ; E. Madelung and R. Fuchs, *Ann. Physik*, (4), **65**. 289, 1921 ; H. G. F. Schröder, *Pogg. Ann. Ergbd.*, **6**. 622, 1879 ; O. Pettersson, *Nova Acta Upsala*, 9, 1875 ; J. L. Smith, *Amer. Journ. Science*, (1), **47**. 81, 1844 ; (1), **48**. 97, 1845 ; (2), **20**. 244, 1855 ; F. Field, *Journ. Chem. Soc.*, **14**. 156, 1862 ; **26**. 575, 1873 ; R. Popper, *Zeit. anal. Chem.*, 18. 25, 1879 ; E. H. Kraus and A. B. Peck, *Neues Jahrb. Min.*, ii, 17, 1916 ; A. de Schulten, *Bull. Soc. Chim.*, (3), **29**. 726, 1903 ; *Bull. Soc. Min.*, **26**. 106, 1903 ; G. Tammann and Q. A. Mansuri *Zeit. anorg. Chem.*, **126**. 119, 1923 ; P. Niggli, *Zeit. Kryst.*, **56**. 42 1922 ; F. Paneth, *Zeit. Elektrochem.*, **28**. 113, 1922 ; R. Kolb, *Zeit. Kryst.*, **49**. 14, 1911 ; A. Balandin, *Zeit. phys. Chem.*, **121**. 299, 1926.

[6] H. V. Regnault, *Ann. Chim. Phys.*, (3), **1**. 129, 1841 ; H. Kopp, *Liebig's Ann. Suppl.*, 3. 289, 1865 ; W. Mostowitch, *Journ. Russ. Met. Soc.*, 1. 303, 1915 ; F. E. Neumann, *Pogg. Ann.*, 23. 1, 1831 ; R. Lorenz and W. Herz, *Zeit. anorg. Chem.*, **135**. 374, 1924 ; F. Guthrie, *Phil. Mag.*, (5), **17**. 478, 1884 ; *Traité des essais par la voie sèche*, Paris, 2. 676, 1834 ; J. B. J. D. Boussingault, *Ann. Chim. Phys.*, (4), **12**. 426, 1867 ; P. Berthier, *ib.*, (2), **20**. 275, 1822 ; F. O. Doeltz and C. A. Graumann, *Met.*, 3. **441**, 1906 ; H. C. Hofman and W. Wanjukoff, *Bull. Amer. Inst. Min. Eng.*, 889, 1912 ; O. L. Erdmann, *Journ. prakt. Chem.*, (1), **62**. 381, 1854 ; W. Grahmann, *Zeit. anorg. Chem.*, **81**. 257, 1913 ; F. M. Jäger and H. C. Germs, *ib.*, **119**. 150, 1921 ; H. C. Germs, *De thermische Analyse van Loodsulfaat, -chromaat, -molybdaat, en -wolframaat en van hun binaire combinaties*, Groningen, 1917 ; M. Bodenstein and W. Pohl, *Zeit. Elektrochem.*, **11**. 373, 1905 ; J. L. Gay Lussac, *Journ. Mines*, 22. 325, 1807 ; *Nicholson's Journ.*, **33**. 44, 1812 ; J. Percy, *The Metallurgy of Lead*, London, 41, 1870 ; W. Ramsay and N. Eumorfopoulos, *Phil. Mag.*, (5), **41**. 366, 1896 ; G. Calcagni and D. Marotta, *Atti Accad. Lincei*, (5), **21**. ii, 240, 1912 ; R. Schenck and W. Rassbach, *Ber.*, **41**. 2917, 1908 ; J. B. J. D. Boussingault, *Ann. Chim. Phys.*, (4), **12**. 419, 1867 ; G. Marchal, *Journ. Chim. Phys.*, **22**. 325, 1925.

[7] M. Berthelot, *Compt. Rend.*, **77**. 24, 1873 ; **84**. 676, 1877 ; *Thermochimie*, Paris, 2. 342, 1897 ; *Ann. Chim. Phys.*, (5), **29**. 204, 1883 ; (6), **21**. 356, 1890 ; A. Guntz, *ib.*, (6), 3. 64, 1884 ; J. Thomsen, *Thermochemische Untersuchungen*, Paris, 3. 337, 1883 ; *Ber.*, 5. 170, 1872 ; 7. 452, 1874 ; *Journ. prakt. Chem.*, (2), 5. 248, 1872 ; (2), **12**. 96, 1875 ; P. Günther, *Zeit. Elektrochem.*, 23. 199, 1917 ; W. E. Henderson and G. Stegeman, *Journ. Amer. Chem. Soc.*, **40**. 84, 1918 ; A. Hare, *Phil. Mag.*, (6), **48**. 412, 1924.

[8] A. des Cloizeaux, *Nouvelles recherches sur les propriétés optiques des cristaux*, Paris, 30, 204, 1867 ; R. Kolb, *Zeit. Kryst*, **49**. 14, 1911 ; A. Ehringhaus and H. Rose, *ib.*, **58**. 461, 1923 ; A. Arzruni, *ib.*, 1. 182, 1877 ; W. W. Coblentz, *Investigations of Infra-red Spectra*, Washington, 3. 54, 1906 ; *Bull. Bur. Standards*, 2. 477, 1906 ; J. A. Wilkinson, *Journ. Phys. Chem.*, **13**. 691, 1909 ; T. Liebisch and H. Rubens, *Sitzber. Akad. Berlin*, 198, 1919 ; H. C. Sorby, *Min. Mag.*, 2. 1, 1878 ; C. Schaefer and M. Schubert, *Ann. Physik*, (4), **50**. 283, 1916.

[9] G. Cesaro, *Bull. Acad. Belg.*, 115, 1904 ; W. Schmidt, *Ann. Physik*, (4), **11**. 114, 1903 ; C. B. Thwing, *Zeit. phys. Chem.*, **14**. 286, 1894 ; A. Klein, *ib.*, **36**. 360, 1901 ; F. Kohlrausch, *ib.*, 44. 231, 1903 ; W. Böttger, *ib.*, **46**. 521, 1903 ; *Löslichkeitsstudien an schwer löslichen Stoffen*, Leipzig, 1903 ; H. G. Denham, *Journ. Chem. Soc.*, **115**. 112, 1919 ; M. Pleissner, *Arb. Kaiser Ges. Amt.*, 26. 419, 1907 ; L. Ebert, *Zeit. phys. Chem.*, **13**. 1, 1924 ; H. Joachim, *Ann. Physik*, (4), **60**. 570, 1919 ; B. N. Chuckubutti, *Proc. Indian Assoc. Cult. Science*, **9**. 83, 1924.

[10] J. A. Arfvedson, *Pogg. Ann.*, 1. 73, 1824 ; G. F. Rodwell, *Journ. Chem. Soc.*, **16**. 42, 1863 ; H. Mennicke, *Zeit. öffent. Chem.*, **6**. 190, 1900 ; P. A. Bolley, *Jahrb. prakt. Pharm.*, **18**. 380, 1849 ; C. Luckow, *German Pat.*, *D.R.P.* 105143, 1895.

[11] W. Böttger, *Löslichkeitsstudien an schwer löslichen Stoffen*, Leipzig, 1903 ; *Zeit. phys. Chem.*, **46**. 521, 1903 ; F. Kohlrausch and F. Rose, *ib.*, 12. 241, 1893 ; F. Kohlrausch, *ib.*, **44**. 231, 1903 ; 50. 356, 1904 ; 64. 157, 1908 ; R. Flatt, *Helvetica Chim. Acta*, 6. 698, 1923 ; V. Zotier, *Bull. Soc. Chim.*, (4), **21**. 241, 1917 ; W. A. Köhler and J. H. Mathews, *Journ. Amer. Chem. Soc.*, **46**. 1158, 1924 ; H. C. Dibbits, *Zeit. anal. Chem.*, **13**. 139, 1874 ; *Journ. prakt. Chem.*, (2), **10**.

417, 1874 ; *Maandbled Naturwet.*, **3**. 127, 1873 : M. Willenz, *Bull. Assoc. Belg.*, **15**. 230, 1901 ;
L. L. de Koninck, *Bull. Soc. Chim. Belg.*, **21**. 141, 1907 ; G. F. Rodwell, *Chem. News*, **11**. 50,
1865 ; C. R. Fresenius, *Liebig's Ann.*, **59**. 125, 1846 ; F. Dolezalek, *Theorie des Bleiakkumulators*,
Halle, 1901 ; *Zeit. Elektrochem.*, **5**. 335, 1899 ; **6**. 557, 1900 ; V. Kohlschütter and H. Rösti,
Ber., **56**. 287, 1923 ; M. C. Boswell and J. V. Dickson, *Journ. Amer. Chem. Soc.*, **40**. 1773, 1918 ;
J. Sehnal, *Compt. Rend.*, **148**. 1394, 1909 ; M. Barre, *Ann. Chim. Phys.*, (8), **24**. 190, 1911 ;
M. Pleissner, *Arb. Kaiser Ges. Amt.*, **26**. 419, 1907 ; K. Beck and P. Stegmüller, *ib.*, **34**. 446,
1910 ; *Zeit. Elektrochem.*, **17**. 844, 1911 ; W. A. Roth, *ib.*, **16**. 714, 1910 ; G. Carrara and
G. P. Vespignani, *Gazz. Chim. Ital.*, **30**. ii, 35, 1900 ; H. G. Denham, *Journ. Chem. Soc.*, **115**.
112, 1919 ; S. Mitchell, *ib.*, **129**. 1333, 1926 ; H. Rose, *Pogg. Ann.*, **95**. 426, 1855 ; P. Kremers,
ib., **85**. 247, 1852 ; F. Rolle, *Dingler's Journ.*, **127**. 446, 1853 ; M. Tipp. *Pharm. Vertelj.*, 3. 36,
1853.
    [12] H. V. Collet-Descotils, *Gehlen's Journ.*, (2), **2**. 175, 1806 ; *Bull. Soc. Philomath*, **3**. 283,
1805 ; *Ann. Chim. Phys.*, (1), **53**. 268, 1805 ; (1), **55**. 441, 1833 ; A. Ditte, *ib.*, (5), **14**. 228, 1878 ;
A. L. Young and G. F. Dixon, *Chem. News*, **36**. 179, 1877 ; G. F. Rodwell, *ib.*, **5**. 52, 1862 ;
Journ. Chem. Soc., **15**. 59, 1862 ; F. Field, *ib.*, **26**. 575, 1873 ; C. Hensgen, *Rec. Trav. Chim. Pays-
Bas*, **2**. 124, 1883 ; A. Colson, *Compt. Rend.*, **124**. 81, 1897 ; A. C. Becquerel, *ib.*, **34**. 29, 1852 ;
K. Beck and P. Stegmüller, *Arb. Kaiser Ges. Amt.*, **34**. 446, 1910 ; L. F. Bley, *Tromsdorff's Journ.
Pharm.*, **26**. 292, 1833 ; M. Mayer and A. Fehlmann, *Journ. Gasbeleucht.*, **53**. 553, 1910 ; O. Schott,
Beiträge zur Kenntnis der anorganischen Schmelzverbindungen, Braunschweig, 27, 1880 ;
F. Matthey, *Arch. Pharm.*, (3), **13**. 233, 1878 ; A. Vogel, *Journ. prakt. Chem.*, (1), **2**. 196, 1834 ;
G. Campani, *Gazz. Chim. Ital.*, **6**. 461, 1876 ; H. Hof and B. Rinck, *German Pat.*, *D.R.P.* 227389,
1909 ; H. Hof, *Chem. Ztg.*, **33**. 1078, 1909 ; R. Benedikt, *ib.*, **16**. 44, 1892 ; M. de Jong, *Zeit.
anal. Chem.*, **41**. 600, 1902 ; A. van Raalte, *ib.*, **43**. 36, 1904 ; R. H. Brett, *Phil. Mag.*, (3), **10**.
95, 1837 ; A. Hayes, *Amer. Journ. Science*, (1), **17**. 96, 1830 ; C. R. Fresenius, *Liebig's Ann.*,
59. 125, 1846 ; *Zeit. anal. Chem.*, **19**. 419, 1880 ; F. N. Flynn, *Eng. Min. Journ.*, **109**. 487, 1920 ;
P. Berthier, *Traité des essais par la voie sèche*, Paris, 1. 486, 1834 ; 2. 678, 1834 ; H. G. E. Schneder-
mann, *Polyt. Centr.*, **8**, 1850 ; F. Marguéritte, *Compt. Rend.*, **50**. 760, 1860 ; J. Nicklès, *Journ.
Pharm. Chim.*, (3), **38**. 118, 1860 ; F. Ephraim, *Ber.*, **58**. B, 2262, 1925 ; G. C. Wittstein,
Repert. Pharm., **63**. 331, 1833.
    [13] W. Reinders and F. Goudriaan, *Zeit. anorg. Chem.*, **93**. 213, 1915 ; W. Reinders, *ib.*,
109. 56, 1920 ; H. Ditz and F. Kanhäuser, *ib.*, **98**. 128, 1916 ; K. Fischer and K. Thiele, *ib.*,
67. 303, 1910 ; R. Schenck and A. Albers, *ib.*, **105**. 145, 1919 ; R. Schenck and W. Rassbach,
Ber., **41**. 2917, 1908 ; H. Schulze, *ib.*, **17**. 2707, 1884 ; C. Schultz, *Pogg. Ann.*, **133**. 137, 1868 ;
H. Rose, *ib.*, **95**. 426, 1855 ; C. S. Sellack, *ib.*, **133**. 138, 1868 ; *Zeit. anal. Chem.*, **9**. 464, 1870 ;
H. Struve, *ib.*, **9**. 38, 1870 ; *Zeit. Chem.*, (2), **6**. 444, 1870 ; A. C. Cumming, *Trans. Faraday
Soc.*, **2**. 209, 1907 ; T. Garside, *Chem. News*, **31**. 245, 1875 ; A. E. Dawkins and P. R. Weldon,
Proc. Soc. Chem. Ind. Victoria, **22**. 940, 1922 ; F. Zambonini, *Zeit. Kryst.*, **58**. 226, 1923 ;
J. F. Sacher, *Chem. Ztg.*, **34**. 647, 1910 ; A. D. Donk, *Chem. Weekbl.*, **13**. 92, 1916 ; F. Utz,
Farben Ztg., **19**. 1743, 1914 ; J. Percy, *The Metallurgy of Lead*, London, **46**, 1870 ; F. O. Doeltz,
Met., **2**. 461, 1905 ; A. Marshall, *Journ. Soc. Chem. Ind.*, **21**. 1505, 1902 ; H. C. Jenkins and
E. A. Smith, *Journ. Chem. Soc.*, **71**. 670, 1897 ; J. Sehnal, *Compt. Rend.*, **148**. 1394, 1909 ;
A. Lodin, *ib.*, **120**. 1164, 1895 ; E. Filhol and J. B. Senderens, *ib.*, **93**. 154, 1881 ; A. Hayes,
Amer. Journ. Science, (1), **17**. 196, 1830 ; C. Schultz, *Pogg. Ann.*, **133**. 137, 1868 ; *Liebig's
Ann.*, **135**. 249, 1868 ; P. A. Bolley, *ib.*, **91**. 113, 1854 ; C. R. Fresenius, *ib.*, **59**. 125, 1846 ;
J. Kolb, *Dingler's Journ.*, **209**. 268, 1873 ; J. H. Gladstone and W. Hibbert, *Phil. Mag.*, (5),
31. 42, 1891 ; A. du Pasquier, *Journ. Pharm. Chim.*, (3), **4**. 103, 1843 ; *Journ. prakt. Chem.*,
(1), **31**. 417, 1844 ; J. Löwenthal, *ib.*, (1), **60**. 267, 1853 ; J. Löwe, *ib.*, (1), **74**. 345, 348, 1858 ;
Jahrb. Phys. Ver., 73, 1857 ; S. E. Goldschmidt, *German Pat.*, *D.R.P.* 251846, 1911 ; M. Pleissner,
Arb. Kaiser Ges. Amt., **26**. 419, 1907 ; P. Berthier, *Traité des essai par la voie sèche*, Paris, 2.
678, 1834 ; *Ann. Chim. Phys.*, (2), **38**. 256, 1828 ; A. Ditte, *ib.*, (5), **14**. 221, 1878 ; J. Percy,
The Metallurgy of Lead, London, 42, 1870 ; G. Calcagni and D. Marotta, *Atti Accad. Lincei*,
(5), **21**. ii, 240, 1912 ; J. Kendall and A. W. Davidson, *Journ. Amer. Chem. Soc.*, **43**. 979, 1921 ;
J. N. Brönsted, *Zeit. phys. Chem.*, **77**. 315, 1911.
    [14] W. R. Hodgkinson and C. C. Trench, *Chem. News*, **66**. 223, 1893 ; G. C. Wittstein, *Repert.
Pharm.*, **63**. 331, 1833 ; G. F. Rodwell, *Journ. Chem. Soc.*, **15**. 59, 1862 ; **16**. 42, 1863 ; *Chem.
News*, **15**. 137, 1867 ; A. Vogel, *Journ. prakt. Chem.*, (1), **2**. 196, 1834 ; A. Ditte, *Ann. Chim.
Phys.*, (5), **14**. 232, 1878 ; G. Bischof, *Schweigger's Journ.*, **51**. 228, 1827 ; H. W. F. Wacken-
roder, *Liebig's Ann.*, **41**. 319, 1842 ; F. von Kobell, *Kastner's Arch.*, **5**. 931, 1825 ; L. J. Thénard,
Ann. Chim. Phys., (1), **42**. 210, 1802 ; *Traité de chimie élémentaire théoretique et pratique*, Paris,
2. 469, 588, 1814 ; K. Beck and P. Stegmüller, *Arb. Kaiser Ges. Amt.*, **34**. 446, 1910 ; C. Marie,
Compt. Rend., **130**. 1032, 1900 ; E. C. Franklin and C. A. Kraus, *Amer. Chem. Journ.*, **20**. 823,
1898 ; V. Kohlschütter and H. Rösti, *Ber.*, **56**. 287, 1923 ; F. Guthrie, *Phil. Mag.*, (5), **17**. 478,
1884 ; J. Kolb, *Dingler's Journ.*, **209**. 268, 1873 ; M. G. Mellon, *Journ. Amer. Chem. Soc.*, **44**.
2167, 1922.
    [15] J. Percy, *The Metallurgy of Lead*, London, 42, 1870 ; P. Berthier, *Traité des essais par la
voie sèche*, Paris ; *Ann. Chim. Phys.*, (2), **20**. 275, 1892 ; J. L. Gay Lussac, *ib.*, (2), **63**. 454, 1836 ;
A. Ditte, *ib.*, (5), **14**. 231, 1878 ; G. C. Wittstein, *Repert. Pharm.*, **63**. 331, 1833 ; G. F. Rodwell,
Journ. Chem. Soc., **16**. 42, 1863 ; H. G. Denham, *ib.*, **115**. 112, 1919 ; J. J. Fox, *ib.*, **95**. 878,
1909 ; *Proc Chem. Soc.*, **23**. 199, 1907 ; F. H. Storer, *Chem. News*, **21**. 17, 1870 ; J. L. Smith,

Amer. Journ. Science, (1), **47**. 81, 1844 ; (1), **48**. 97, 1845 ; K. Stammer, *Chem. Ztg.*, **6**. 63, 1884 ; F. Auerbach and H. Pick, *Arb. Kaiser Ges. Amt.*, **45**. 113, 1913 ; *Zeit. Elektrochem.*, **19**. 829, 1913 ; J. Lemberg, *Zeit. deut. geol. Ges.*, **52**. 488, 1901 ; O. Schott, *Beiträge zur Kenntnis der anorganischen Schmelzverbindungen*, Braunschweig, 1880 ; A. A. Noyes and W. H. Whitcomb, *Journ. Amer. Chem. Soc.*, **27**. 747, 1905 ; J. W. Marden, *ib.*, **38**. 310, 1916 ; H. W. F. Wackenroder, *Liebig's Ann.*, **41**. 319, 1842 ; F. Wöhler, *ib.*, **34**. 235, 1840 ; J. C. Long, *Amer. Chem. Journ.*, **22**. 217, 1899 ; G. Bischof. *Schweigger's Journ.*, **51**. 228, 1827 ; C. Blomberg, *Chem. Weekbl.*, **11**. 1030, 1914 ; H. C. Dibbits, *Maanblad Naturwet.*, **3**. 127, 1873 ; *Journ. prakt. Chem.*, (2), **10**. 417, 1874 ; *Zeit. anal. Chem.*, **13**. 137, 1874 ; W. Städel, *ib.*, **2**. 180, 1863 ; E. Lenssen, *Journ. prakt. Chem.*, (1), **85**. 89, 1862 ; H. Rose, *Pogg. Ann.*, **95**. 426, 1855 ; *Traité de chimie analytique*, Paris, **2**. 226, 1838 ; L. Krafft, *Répert. Chim. Appl.*, **1**. 324, 1855 ; C. Reichard, *Chem. Ztg.*, **27**. 924, 943, 1903 ; H. C. Bolton, *Ber.*, **13**. 732, 1880 ; H. Mandal, *ib.*, **54**. 704, 1921 ; A. Naumann, *ib.*, **37**. 4329, 1904 ; **42**. 3790, 1909 ; **43**. 314, 1910 ; R. Marc, *Zeit. phys. Chem.*, **75**. 710, 1911 ; A. Conduché, *Compt. Rend.*, **158**. 1181, 1914 ; J. L. Mayer, *Journ. Amer. Pharm. Assoc.*, **11**. 514, 1922 ; L. Michel, *Bull. Soc. Min.*, **13**. 212, 1890 ; G. Seligmann, *Verh. Ver. Rheinl. Bonn*, **33**. 253, 1876 ; P. von Jeremejeff, *Proc. Russ. Min. Soc.*, **18**. 108, 1883 ; *Zeit. Kryst.*, **7**. 637, 1883 ; J. Mercer, *B.A. Rep.*, 32, 1844 ; W. Mostowitch, *Journ. Russ. Met. Soc.*, **1**. 303, 1915 ; J. Aub, *Lead Poisoning*, Baltimore, 19, 1926 ; G. F. Rodwell, *Journ. Chem. Soc.*, **15**. 59, 1862 ; **16**. 42, 1863 ; *Chem. News*, **15**. 137, 1867.

[16] P. Berthier, *Traité des essais par la voie sèche*, Paris, 2. 676, 1834 ; *Ann. Chim. Phys.*, (2), **20**. 275, 1822 ; A. Ditte, *ib.*, (5), **14**. 232, 1878 ; W. Reinders, *Zeit. anorg. Chem.*, **93**. 226, 1915 ; S. Hilpert, *Met.*, **5**. 537, 1908 ; O. Proske, *Metall Erz*, **10**. 415, 1913 ; J. Milbauer and K. Kohn, *Zeit. phys. Chem.*, **91**. 410, 1916 ; H. C. Jenkins and E. A. Smith, *Journ. Chem. Soc.*, **71**. 671, 1897 ; A. Lodin, *Compt. Rend.*, **120**. 1164, 1895 ; E. Vigouroux, *ib.*, **120**. 367, 1895 ; W. Mostowitch, *Journ. Russ. Met. Soc.*, **1**. 303, 1915 ; M. Tipp, *Viertelj. prakt. Pharm.*, **3**. 26, 1853 ; J. B. Hannay, *Chem. News*, **67**. 291, 1893 ; **70**. 43, 1894 ; J. Percy, *The Metallurgy of Lead*, London, 42, 1870 ; L. Kahlenberg and W. J. Trautmann, *Trans. Amer. Electrochem. Soc.*, **39**. 447, 1921 ; B. N. Chuckubutti, *Proc. Indian Assoc.*, **9**. 83, 1924 ; G. Tammann, *Zeit. anorg. Chem.*, **149**. 21, 1925 ; J. A. Wilkinson, *Journ. Phys. Chem.*, **13**. 708, 1909.

[17] P. Louyet, *Compt. Rend.*, **23**. 960, 1846 ; **24**. 434, 1847 ; F. Matthey, *Arch. Pharm.*. (3), **13**. 233, 1878 ; S. Zinno, *Repert. Pharm.*, **20**. 449, 1871 ; A. Michaelis and G. Köthe, *Rev.*, **6**. 999, 1873.

[18] P. Berthier, *Traité des essais par la voie sèche*, Paris, **1**. 480, 1834 ; *Ann. Chim. Phys.*, (2), **43**. 287, 1830 ; W. Reinders, *Zeit. anorg. Chem.*, **93**. 225, 1915 ; D. Strömholm, *ib.*, **38**. 442, 1904 ; F. M. Jäger and H. C. Germs, *ib.*, **119**. 145, 1921 ; H. C. Germs, *De thermische Analyse van Loodsulfaat, -chromaat, -molybdaat, en -wolframaat en van hun binaire combinaties*, Groningen, 1917 ; D. A. MacInnes, L. Adler, and D. B. Joubert, *Trans. Amer. Electrochem. Soc.*, **37**. 641, 1920 ; *Met. Chem. Engg.*, **22**. 727, 1920 ; M. Pleissner, *Arb. Kaiser Ges. Amt.*, **26**. 428, 1907 ; H. C. Jenkins and E. A. Smith, *Journ. Chem. Soc.*, **71**. 671, 1897 ; N. S. Maskelyne and W. Flight, *ib.*, **27**. 103, 1874 ; N. Collie, *ib.*, **55**. 93, 1889 ; A. Schrauf, *Zeit. Kryst.*, **1**. 31, 1877 ; A. de Schulten, *Bull. Soc. Min.*, **21**. 142, 1898 ; F. Pisani, *Compt. Rend.*, **76**. 114, 1873 ; C. T. Barfoed, *Danske Vid. Selsk. Forh.*, 122, 1869 ; *Journ. prakt. Chem.*, (1), **108**. 1, 1869 ; O. B. Kühn, *Arch. Pharm.*, (2), **50**. 281, 1847 ; H. O. Hofman and W. Wanjukow, *Bull. Amer. Inst. Min. Eng.*, 889, 1912 ; R. Schenck and W. Borkenstein, *Zeit. anorg. Chem.*, **142**. 143, 1925 ; R. Schenck and W. Rassbach, *Ber.*, **41**. 2917, 1908 ; R. Schenck, *Physikalische Chemie der Metalle*, Halle a. S., 178, 1909 ; London, 220, 1919 ; K. B. Lehmann, *Hyg. Rund.*, 973, 1895 ; E. C. C. Baly, *Journ. Soc. Chem. Ind.*, **31**. 515, 1912 ; L. F. Hughes, *ib.*, **28**. 405, 1905 ; H. Kionka, *Deut. Med. Wochschr.*, **22**. 281, 1896 ; J. A. Schaeffer, *Journ. Ind. Eng. Chem.*, **4**. 836, 1912 ; **5**. 144, 1913 ; **6**. 200, 1914 ; E. Toelle, *Brit. Pat. No.* 19718, 1906 ; *German Pat.*, *D.R.PP.* 186972, 187946, 1905 ; E. E. Banes, *ib.*, 251481, 1911 ; *French Pat. No.* 431280, 1911 ; J. B. Hannay, *ib.*, 155106, 1901 ; 264526, 1912 ; J. B. Hannay and S. B. Wilson, *ib.*, 245361, 1909 ; S. B. Wilson, *Brit. Pat. No.* 133367, 1918 ; J. Kronen, *ib.*, 19732, 1906 ; F. C. Breyer, J. A. Singmaster, and A. E. Hall, *ib.*, 149925, 1919 ; S. Ganelin, *ib.*, 8981, 1896 ; G. Lunge and C. H. M. Lyte, *ib.*, 13656, 1893 ; W. J. M. Jackson, *ib.*, 233188, 1924 ; F. M. Lyte, *ib.*, 10298, 11889, 1886 ; 2920, 1888 ; W. E. B. Blenkinsop and F. M. Lyte, *ib.*, 11926, 1888 ; G. T. Lewis, *ib.*, 3938, 1879 ; 730, 1880 ; 14017, 1888 ; G. T. Lewis and E. O. Bartlett, *ib.*, 4918, 1879 ; W. Bell, T. M. and A. G. Fell, *ib.*, 1703, 1866 ; 3133, 1866 ; A. Macdonald, *ib.*, 2883, 11972, 1893 ; 25133, 1896 ; C. Schnabel, *Handbuch der Metallhüttenkunde*, Berlin, **1**. 600, 1901 ; London, **1**. 600, 1921 ; C. D. Holley, *The Lead and Zinc Pigments*, New York, 108, 1909 ; H. O. Hofman, *The Metallurgy of Lead*, New York, 138, 1908 ; J. Percy, *The Metallurgy of Lead*, London, 43, 1870 ; E. Frankland, *Proc. Roy. Soc.*, **16**. 304, 1890 ; *Chem. News*, 60, 1889 ; P. F. Nursey, *Journ. Soc. Arts*, **42**. 445, 1893 ; G. Berg, *Tschermak's Mitt.*, (2), **20**. 390, 1901 ; H. J. Brooke, *Edin. Phil. Journ.*, **3**. 117, 1820 ; F. S. Beudant, *Traité élémentaire de mineralogie*, Paris, **2**. 366, 1832 ; A. Breithaupt, *Vollständige Charakteristik der Mineralsystems*, Dresden, 1832 ; C. S. Larsen, *Bull. U.S. Geol. Sur.*, 679, 1921 ; B. S. White, *U.S. Pat. No.* 1555538, 1925 ; E. Jänecke, *Zeit. anorg. Chem.*, **155**. 291, 1926.

[19] H. J. Brooke, *Edin. Phil. Journ.*, **3**. 117, 1820 ; *Ann. Phil.*, (2), **4**. 117, 1822 ; W. H. Miller, *Elementary Introduction to Mineralogy*, London, 561, 1852 ; R. P. Greg and W. G. Lettsom, *Manual of the Mineralogy of Great Britain and Ireland*, London, 403, 1858 ; F. S. Beudant, *Traité élémentaire de minéralogie*, Paris, **2**. 367, 1832 ; N. von Kokscharoff, *Materialen zur*

Mineralogie Russlands, St. Petersburg, 9. 40, 1884 ; F. Hessenberg, *Mineralogische Notizen*, 9. 48, 1870 ; P. von Jeremejeff, *Mem. Acad. St. Petersburg*, (7), 31. 16, 1883 ; G. vom Rath, *Sitzber. Niederrh. Ges. Bonn*, 34, 1886 ; C. F. Peters, *Sitzber. Akad. Wien*, 44. 170, 1861 ; A. Schrauf, *ib.*, 64. 179, 1871 ; W. Flight, *Journ. Chem. Soc.*, 27. 101, 1874 ; N. Collie, *ib.*, 55. 92, 1889 ; A. des Cloizeaux, *Nouvelles recherches sur les propriétés optiques des cristaux*, Paris, 205, 1867 ; C. Busz, *Neues Jahrb. Min.*, i, 111, 1895 ; O. C. Farrington, *Bull. Field. Coll. Museum*, 1. 224, 1900 ; A. F. Rogers, *Amer. Journ. Science*, (4), 12. 47, 1901 ; G. Berg, *Tschermak's Mitt.*, (2), 20. 390, 1901 ; A. Pelloux, *Atti Accad. Lincei*, (5), 13. ii, 34, 1904 ; F. N. Guild, *Zeit. Kryst.*, 49. 321, 1911 ; H. L. Ungemach, *Bull. Soc. Min.*, 35. 553, 1912 ; L. Brugnatelli, *Rend. Ist. Lombardo*, (2), 30. 392, 1897 ; *Zeit. anorg. Chem.*, 17. 162, 1898.

²⁰ H. J. Brooke, *Ann. Phil.*, (2), 4. 117, 1822 ; W. Phillips, *Treatise on Mineralogy*, Boston, 552, 1844 ; F. Hessenberg, *Mineralogische Notizen*, 6. 31, 1864 ; N. von Kokscharoff, *Materialen zur Mineralogie Russlands*, St. Petersburg, 4. 139, 1866 ; 5. 206, 1869 ; *Bull. Acad. St. Petersburg*, (4), 13. 472, 1869 ; P. von Jeremejeff, *Proc. Russ. Min. Soc.*, 19. 15, 1884 ; T. Liweh, *Zeit. Kryst.*, 9. 522, 1884 ; P. Dudgeon, *ib.*, 7. 202, 1883 ; *Min. Mag.*, 5. 33, 1884 ; F. Sandberger, *Untersuchungen über Erzgänge*, Wiesbaden, 125, 1882 ; A. Frenzel, *Neues Jahrb. Min.*, 675, 1875 ; H. Höfer, *ib.*, 59, 1871 ; F. von Kobell, *Journ. prakt. Chem.*, (1), 83. 454, 1861 ; N. Collie, *Journ. Chem. Soc.*, 55. 93, 1889 ; W. H. Miller, *Introduction to Mineralogy*, London, 554, 1852 ; R. P. Greg and W. G. Lettsom, *Manual of the Mineralogy of Great Britain and Ireland*, London, 395, 1858 ; A. Schrauf, *Sitzber. Akad. Wien*, 64. 172, 1871 ; 65. 241, 1872 ; C. F. Peters, *ib.*, 44. 168, 1862 ; G. vom Rath, *Ber. Niederrh. Ges. Bonn*, 79, 1878 ; V. von Zepharovich, *Verh. geol. Reichsanst.*, 75, 1875 ; A. Stelzner, *Tschermak's Mitt.*, (1), 3. 249, 1873 ; L. Michel, *Bull. Soc. Min.*, 31. 274, 1908 ; L. Brugnatelli, *Rend. Ist. Lombardo*, (2), 30. 392, 1897 ; *Zeit. anorg. Chem.*, 17. 162, 1898 ; T. Thomson, *Phil. Mag.*, (3), 17. 402, 1840.

²¹ J. B. Trommsdorff, *Trommsdorff's Taschenbuch*, 46. 1, 1825 ; J. J. Fox, *Journ. Chem. Soc.*, 95. 187, 884, 1909 ; J. N. Brönsted, *Zeit. phys. Chem.*, 77. 315, 1911 ; M. Barre, *Compt. Rend.*, 149. 294, 1909 ; *Ann. Chim. Phys.*, (8), 24. 190, 1911 ; A. Ditte, *ib.*, (5), 14. 212, 1878 ; P. Berthier, *ib.*, (2), 38. 256, 1828 ; G. Calcagni and D. Marotta, *Atti Accad. Lincei*, (5), 21. ii, 240, 284, 1912 ; W. Grahmann, *Zeit. anorg. Chem.*, 81. 257, 1913 ; F. G. Belton, *Chem. News*, 91. 191, 1905 ; A. Lacroix, *Bull. Soc. Min.*, 30. 234, 1907 ; 31. 261, 1908 ; *Compt. Rend.*, 144. 1397, 1907 ; H. le Chatelier, *ib.*, 123. 749, 1896 ; *Zeit. phys. Chem.*, 22. 252, 1897 ; *Ann. Mines*, (9), 11. 209, 1897 ; F. Zambonini, *Compt. Rend.*, 172. 1419, 1921.

²² E. Mallard and E. Cumenge, *Compt. Rend.*, 113. 519, 1891 ; *Bull. Soc. Min.*, 14. 283, 1891 ; F. A. Genth, *Amer. Journ. Science*, (3), 45. 32, 1893 ; R. F. Weinland and H. Kühl, *Ber.*, 39. 2953, 1906 ; *Zeit. anorg. Chem.*, 54. 245, 1907 ; F. Zambonini, *Zeit. Kryst.*, 58. 226, 1923 ; E. S. Larsen, *Bull. U.S. Geol. Sur.*, 679, 1921 ; R. Ohashi, *Min. Mag.*, 19. 73, 1920 ; H. le Chatelier, *Compt. Rend.*, 123. 746, 1896 ; *Zeit. phys. Chem.*, 22. 250, 1897 ; G. H. Bailey, *Journ. Soc. Chem. Ind.*, 6. 415, 1887.

²³ K. Elbs, *Zeit. Elektrochem.*, 6. 47, 1900 ; K. Elbs and F. Fischer, *ib.*, 7. 343, 1901 ; K. Elbs and F. W. Rixon, *ib.*, 9. 267, 1903 ; F. Dolezalek and K. Finckh, *Zeit. anorg. Chem.*, 50. 82, 1906 ; 51. 321, 1906 ; B. Brauner, *ib.*, 7. 11, 1894 ; H. O. Hofman and W. Wanjukow, *Trans. Amer. Inst. Min. Eng.*, 43. 523, 1912 ; *Bull. Amer. Inst. Min. Eng.*, 889, 1912 ; E. Frankland, *Proc. Roy. Soc.*, 35. 67, 1883 ; G. Panopolus, *Chem. Ztg.*, 40. 340, 1916 ; W. Esch, *ib.*, 27. 297, 1903 ; A. C. Cumming, *Trans. Faraday Soc.*, 2. 209, 1907 ; A. Hutchinson and W. Pollard, *Journ. Chem. Soc.*, 69. 221, 1896 ; R. Kempf, *Journ. prakt. Chem.*, (2), 83. 329, 1911.

§ 31. Lead Carbonates

Lead forms normal lead carbonate and a number of oxycarbonates. Acid carbonates have been reported. Over three hundred years before our era, the preparation of a basic carbonate, white-lead, was described by Theophrastus in his Περὶ Λίθων ; and there are frequent allusions to this substance in the ancient writings where it was named ψιμύθιον by the Greeks, and *cerussa* by the Romans. This preparation was used in making plasters, as an eye-salve, and as a hair-wash. It is doubtful if the Romans used white-lead for painting pictures because H. Davy [1] could detect no lead in his examination of the materials found in ancient baths, or in scrapings from pictures. Pliny, however, alluded to the painting of ships by means of white-lead, and he stated that they were previously painted with a native cerussa from Smyrna. Perhaps the earliest allusion to white-lead occurs in the Οἰκονομικός (10. 7) of Xenophon, probably written about 400 B.C., where Ischomachus said that he discouraged his wife using white-lead and other cosmetics because he did not like the practice, and because the artifice was so easily discovered among those who lived in intimacy. Plautus, in his *Mostellaria*

—c. 200 B.C.; Ovid, in his *Medicaminia faciei*—c. 10 B.C.; and Martial, in his *Epigrammata*—c. A.D. 100—made allusion to the whiteness of cerussa.

Theophrastus gave the following directions for preparing white-lead :

> Lead is placed in earthen vessels over sharp vinegar, and after it has acquired some thickness by a kind of rust, which it commonly does in about ten days, the vessels are opened, as it were, in a kind of foulness, and the rust scraped off; the lead is then placed over vinegar again, repeating over and over the same method of scraping it until the lead is wholly dissolved. The scrapings are then beaten to powder, and boiled for a long time; and what at last subsides to the bottom of the vessel is cerusse. Verdigris is made from copper in a somewhat similar way.

In the first century of our era, Pliny, in his *Historia naturalis* (**34**. 54), repeated the description by Theophrastus, and he added (**34**. 50) that white-lead is also made by grinding water in a lead mortar with a lead pestle ; or by grinding lead-filings with rain-water in a stone mortar—sometimes with the addition of vinegar, wine, fat, or rose-leaves. During the operation, the water darkens and becomes muddy, but, after a time, it whitens and resembles white-lead. The supernatant water is removed by straining through a linen-sieve, or by absorption with a sponge. The dried residue was made into pastilles. In both cases, the product must have been a basic carbonate. The white-lead made at Rhodes was considered to be the best, and that process of manufacture was described by Vitruvius in his *De architectura* (**7**. 12), written about the beginning of our era. He said :

> The Rhodians placed a layer of vine-twigs at the bottom of a large jar. Vinegar was poured over the twigs, and in these were placed masses of lead. The vessels were covered to prevent evaporation ; and after a certain time they were opened when the lead was changed into *cerussa*.

Pliny said the thinnest lead shavings were employed ; and Dioscorides, in his $\Pi\epsilon\rho\grave{\iota}$ $\Upsilon\lambda\eta s$ $\Im\alpha\tau\rho\iota\kappa\acute{\eta}s$ (**5**. 53), contemporaneous with Pliny, emphasized the importance of not allowing the lead to come in contact with the vinegar, and with this object placed the lead on a mat suspended by a stick in the middle of the jar. These writers did not recognize the part played by warmth and carbon dioxide in the process. The use of dung was mentioned about the second century by Galen, in his *De simplicium medicamentorum temperamentis ;* about the end of the eleventh century by Theophilus,[2] in his *De diversis artibus*, and by C. Eraclius. Theophilus described a method of preparation which resembles that employed to-day. In the twelfth-century Latinized *Summa perfectionis magisterii* of Geber, it is said that when lead is placed over acetous vapours, it becomes cerussa. The Venetian process was described by P. Vernatti in 1678 ; and the Dutch process, said to have been introduced in 1622, was described by G. Jars. In 1622, C. Eland obtained a patent for " makinge white and redd-leade, as is now made for painters," but this patent probably referred to a monopoly for the sale of these products, and not to a mode of manufactuing these products. A. Barba, in 1669, described the use of perforated lead plates. Observations on the history of white-lead were made by S. J. Cook, C. A. Klein, H. Faure, W. H. Pulsifer, R. Hitchcock, P. Beck, R. W. Atkinson, and W. H. Adolph. A list of patents from 1622 to 1890 has been compiled.

Normal lead carbonate, $PbCO_3$, occurs in nature. C. Gesner,[3] and A. Cronstedt spoke of *cerussa nativa ;* J. G. Wallerius of the *minera plumbi spathacea*, and A. Cronstedt, of *spatum plumbi* or *Blyspat*—hence the German *Bleispath*, the English *lead-spar*, and the French *plomb spathique*. The mineral has also been called white-lead ore. T. Bergman called it *plumbum acido aereo mineralisatum*, so that when his *aerial acid* came to be called *carbonic acid*, the lead salt was called *lead carbonate*. F. S. Beudant called the mineral *céruse*, and W. Haidinger, cerussite. A zinciferous variety analyzed by C. M. Kersten was called *iglésiasite* by J. J. N. Huot ; the same mineral was also analyzed by H. Traube.

Cerussite is a fairly common mineral, and it occurs in conjunction with other lead minerals, being formed by the action of carbonated waters on galena, or its oxidation products. Thus, R. B. Brinsmade[4] attributed the large deposit of cerussite in the Terrible Mine, Ilse, Colorado, to the action of descending waters. Pseudomorphs after galena, anglesite, leadhillite, linarite, etc., have been noted. G. von Blöde found replacements in limestones and fossils which in some cases were transformed completely into cerussite. H. von Decken observed a thick coating of cerussite on the walls of an old mine ; it seemed to have been deposited like sinter from soln. J. D. Whitney found some stalactites from Brighen's diggings, Wisconsin, to contain about 94 per cent. of lead carbonate. A. Lacroix found crystals of cerussite in the encrustation of Roman coins of the period A. Severus, 205–234 A.D. ; F. Rathgen, on lead medals ; W. G. Brown, on some old leaden bullets among the *débris* of a battle-field at Morris Island ; A. de Schulten, on the old lead slags at Laurion, Greece ; and L. Michel, in some old lead slags at Poullaouen, Finistère. A. F. Rogers found some cerussite on some Chinese coins dating from the seventh century—he added that the coins contained no lead, and that all the constituents have come from outside sources.

The preparation of lead carbonate.—A. C. Becquerel [5] claimed to have made crystals of cerussite by allowing a conc. soln. of sodium and calcium carbonates to act for seven years on a lead plate wrapped about with platinum wire. C. F. Carrier also said that the salt is formed when a soln. of sodium acetate and sulphite or sodium chlorate and carbonate is electrolyzed with lead electrodes —the acetate, in the former case, furnishes the required carbon dioxide. F. Auerbach and H. Pick obtained the normal carbonate by repeatedly digesting basic lead carbonate, the chromate or basic chromate, or the sulphate with a soln. of sodium carbonate ; or lead sulphate with a soln. of sodium hydrocarbonate : $2NaHCO_3 + PbSO_4 \rightleftharpoons PbCO_3 + CO_2 + H_2O + Na_2SO_4$. W. Herz also made the carbonate by digesting lead bromide, chloride, or sulphate with an excess of a soln. of sodium carbonate. For equilibrium, he found the ratio of the conc. : $[Na_2CO_3]/[NaBr]^2 = 3 \cdot 1 \times 10^{-4}$; $[Na_2CO_3]/[NaCl]^2 = 1 \cdot 1 \times 10^{-4}$; and $[Na_2CO_3]/[Na_2SO_4] = 1 \cdot 1 \times 10^{-2}$, respectively. H. Becquerel also transformed lead sulphide into the carbonate by the action of a soln. of sodium hydrocarbonate ; and E. Dittler, by the action of boiling water on galena in an extraction apparatus through which a current of carbon dioxide was passing. R. Böttger obtained lead carbonate by triturating lead dioxide with oxalic acid. C. R. A. Wright and A. P. Luff said that when red-lead, or lead monoxide, is heated to 200° in a current of carbon monoxide, part of the lead is reduced, forming carbon dioxide, which reacts with some of the unreduced oxide, forming lead carbonate ; but neither carbon dioxide nor carbon monoxide has any action on lead dioxide at 100°. A. de Schulten passed a slow current of carbon dioxide over a soln. of 20 grms. of normal lead acetate and 2 grms. of sodium chloride in a litre of water. Bright crystals of laurionite first appear on the sides of the flask and at the surface of the liquid ; then crystals of phosgenite appear ; and finally cerussite is produced at the expense of the laurionite. When artificial laurionite or phosgenite is treated with carbon dioxide and water, the laurionite is converted into phosgenite ; and the phosgenite, in turn, into cerussite.

J. J. Berzelius obtained lead carbonate by treating a soln. of lead nitrate with ammonium carbonate. O. Ruff and B. Hirsch studied the fractional precipitation of lead as carbonate in the presence of salts of manganese, zinc, cadmium, copper, silver, iron (ic and ous), chromium, and aluminium. J. A. Phillips added a boiling soln. of lead nitrate to an excess of a soln. of sodium carbonate. D. Strömholm mixed a cold soln. of lead nitrate with one of sodium carbonate containing 0·2 eq. of carbon dioxide per litre, and allowed the mixture to stand for some time. J. J. Berzelius said that if sodium carbonate be employed as precipitant, and the precipitate be boiled with the liquid, much sodium carbonate is adsorbed. G. J. Mulder used potassium carbonate as precipitant ; J. Löwe, sodium hydrocarbonate ; and A. Bette, and K. Feist added the ammonium carbonate to a soln. of lead acetate. M. Pleissner recommended mixing 100 c.c. of a 15 per cent. soln. of lead acetate, and 100 c.c. of a 5 per cent. soln. of ammonium carbonate, sat.

with carbon dioxide, washing the product with water sat. with carbon dioxide and free from ammonia, and drying in vacuo over sulphuric acid ; F. Auerbach and H. Pick used a similar process, drying the product at 100°—*cf.* Figs. 120 and 121. J. Lefort added that if the soln. of the lead salt be hot, the alkali carbonates precipitate basic lead carbonates ; normal lead carbonate is obtained only with cold soln. R. Salvadori made a similar observation with respect to the soln. of lead nitrate treated with ammonium carbonate. He also observed that if a mixed soln. of sodium sulphate and carbonate is added to a mixture of lead sulphate and carbonate, the whole of the sodium carbonate is converted into sulphate when the latter is present in large excess, and lead carbonate is formed. Similarly, if a lead nitrate soln. be added to a mixed soln. of sodium sulphate and carbonate, lead carbonate alone is precipitated. Unlike the cases of partition observed by A. Findlay, the whole of the sodium carbonate is utilized before any lead sulphate is formed. J. S. Stas recommended the following process for lead carbonate of a high degree of purity :

He digested a soln. of a commercial lead acetate at 40°–50° in a leaden vessel containing some strips of lead foil. This precipitated copper and silver. The filtered soln. was then poured into dil. sulphuric acid, and the washed precipitate digested with a mixture of ammonia and ammonium carbonate ; and the resulting lead carbonate washed with water. One part of the carbonate was heated in a platinum crucible to convert it into lead oxide, and the other part was dissolved in dil. nitric acid. The lead oxide was gradually added to the boiling soln. of nitrate so as to precipitate any iron present. The filtered soln. was poured into an excess of a sat. soln. of ammonium carbonate ; and the precipitate washed, and dried.

A. Drevermann, and E. Frémy obtained crystals of cerussite by the slow diffusion of very dil. soln. of potassium carbonate and lead nitrate separated by a porous membrane. H. Rose obtained lead carbonate by passing carbon dioxide into a soln. of lead acetate, and A. Altmann added that with soln. ranging from 0·02N- to 2N-lead acetate, and at temp. between 0° and 100°, the proportion of normal lead carbonate formed decreases with rise of temp. and increased conc. of acetate. With soln. heated for some time at 100° in a reflux apparatus, normal carbonate is precipitated, but if the acetic acid set free by hydrolysis can escape, the precipitate obtained with carbon dioxide and dil. soln. is a basic carbonate, $2PbCO_3.Pb(OH)_2$; but with conc. soln., a mixture of this basic salt and normal carbonate is precipitated. L. Falk passed carbon dioxide into a soln. of the basic acetate ; and A. Wultze, and L. Falk showed that the carbon dioxide is more effective if under an increased press. L. Bourgeois obtained a mixture of crystals of cerussite and hydrocerussite by heating a mixture of ammonium carbonate, water, and lead nitrate in a sealed tube at 140° ; urea can be substituted for the ammonium carbonate since it is converted into the carbonate during the operation. J. Riban obtained good crystals of cerussite by heating 10 c.c. of a 5 per cent. aq. soln. of lead formate in a sealed tube at 175° for 75 hrs. J. W. Morris and co-workers prepared lead carbonate by the action of ammonium carbonate on a soln. of lead formate ; and G. C. Smith, by treating the sulphate first with aq. ammonia and then with carbon dioxide.

W. Leuze [6] found that **colloidal lead carbonate** is produced by treating a 10 per cent. soln. of sodium protalbinate with a dil. soln. of lead acetate, dissolving the precipitate in a 10 per cent. soln. of sodium hydroxide assisted by warming on a water-bath, and passing carbon dioxide into the liquid for 15 minutes. No precipitation of lead carbonate occurs. The sol is stable only for a short time, for when allowed to stand, it becomes turbid.

Analyses of the normal salt were reported by M. E. Chevreul,[7] J. J. Berzelius, A. Bette, G. J. Mulder, D. Strömholm, J. Riban, J. A. Phillips, M. Pleissner, A. Altmann, K. Feist, J. F. Sacher, and analyses of the mineral cerussite by M. H. Klaproth, C. W. Bergmann, W. B. Hobbs, W. F. Petterd, F. Sandberger, P. von Jeremejeff, C. F. Rammelsberg, J. L. Smith, J. F. John, A. des Cloizeaux,

R. B. Green, C. H. Warren. The results agree with the empirical formula $PbCO_3$, and L. Falk regarded it as a derivative of metacarbonic acid; while the many basic salts were referred to orthocarbonic acid, $C(OH)_4$. He also suggested that the crystalline form is a ring compound $(PbCO_3)_2$, or

$$Pb<^{CO_3}_{CO_3}>Pb$$

The physical properties of lead carbonate.—Lead carbonate occurs in simple tabular, prismatic, or pyramidal rhombic or pseudohexagonal **crystals**; and in groups or aggregates of crystals; it rarely occurs fibrous, but is often granular, massive, or compact, and, maybe, earthy—*e.g. Bleierde*. The colour may be white, or the mineral may be more or less tinged grey so as to appear almost black. The so-called *Bleischwärze* is coloured black by carbonaceous matters. In some cases the crystals are tinted blue with copper. N. von Kokscharoff[8] gave for the axial ratios of the rhombic crystals $a:b:c=0.609968:1:0.723002$; M. L. Huggins gave $0.6102:1:0.7232$. The crystals have been the subject of many observations. They are isomorphous with aragonite, witherite, strontianite, and potassium nitrate. F. Becke gave the following constants for the series:

	Mol. wt.	Sp. gr.	Eq. vol.	x	ψ	ω
$CaCO_3$.	100·0	2·94	34·01	2·64	4·23	5·05
$SrCO_3$.	147·5	3·7	39·87	2·73	4·49	3·25
$BaCO_3$.	197·0	4·3	45·82	2·84	4·70	3·44
$PbCO_3$.	266·9	6·6	40·44	2·75	4·51	3·26

For mixed crystals with aragonite, *vide infra*, plumboaragonite. The **twinning** of the crystals is common. There may be contact and penetration twins often repeated, forming six-rayed, stellate groups. Some of the faces are often striated. The (110) and (021) cleavages are distinct; and the (010) and (012) **cleavages** are indistinct. The **optical character** is negative. The **optic axial angles** found by A. Schrauf are $2V=8°\ 22'$ for the B-line, $8°\ 14'$ for the D-line, and $7°\ 35'$ for the E-line; while $2V=17°\ 16\frac{1}{2}'$ for the B-line, $17°\ 8'$ for the D-line, and $15°\ 55'$ for the E-line. A. des Cloizeaux gave, with red-light, $2E=18°\ 22'$ at $12°$; $20°\ 21'$ at $71·5°$; and $22°\ 2'$ at $95·5°$. C. Gaudefroy found the ratio of the birefringence to the wave-length is a maximum for $\lambda=620\mu\mu$ for cerussite from Tsumeb, S.W. Africa. The crystals of Hungarian specimens of cerussite were studied by L. Tokody. F. M. Jäger and H. Haga examined the **X-radiogram**; and M. L. Huggins found that cerussite has the aragonite structure with unit cell of vol. 134·1 cubic Angström units. J. F. John[9] gave 6·5 for the **specific gravity** of cerussite; C. J. B. Karsten, for precipitated carbonate gave 6·4277; J. L. Smith gave for cerussite 6·60; M. L. Huggins, 6·574; and H. G. F. Schröder, 6·510–6·517. F. Becke, and P. Niggli gave 6·6 for the sp. gr., and 40·5 for the eq. vol. F. A. Henglein studied the mol. vol., and I. I. Saslawsky gave 0·76 for the ratio of the mol. vol. to the sum of the at. vols. of the constituent elements. The **hardness** of cerussite is $3–3\frac{1}{2}$ on Mohs' scale; it is therefore harder than calcite; and F. Pfaff said that it is 8·4–8·6 times as hard as steatite. A. Reiss and L. Zimmermann studied the relation between the hardness and the mol. vol. E. Madelung and R. Fuchs gave $1·57\times10^{-12}$ dynes per sq. cm. for the coeff. of **compressibility**.

F. E. Neumann[10] found the **specific heat** of cerussite to be 0·0814, and the **molecular heat,** 21·7; H. Kopp gave 0·0791 and 21·1 respectively, each taken between 16° and 47°. G. Linder found 0·08176 between 0° and 350°, and 0·06392 between 0° and 300°. The great difference is attributed by G. Linder to chemical change.

H. Debray[11] showed that, unlike the thermal dissociation of calcium carbonate, that of lead carbonate is not reversible; apparently a change which occurs in the lead oxide prevents it absorbing the gas reversibly. A. Colson said that the action is reversible when the gas is moist. He also found that lead carbonate decomposes when heated in vacuo at 285°—silver carbonate breaks down at 220°. Traces of moisture accelerate the decomposition, thus, the **dissociation pressures,** p mm., when the system is undried, are :

		184°	210°	233°	280°
Dried	. .	10	32·5	102	548 mm.
Moist	. .	12	33	104	— ,,

The atm. press., by extrapolation, is attained at 302° ; or, according to O. Brill, at 337°. O. Brill also represented the relation between the press. and temp. by the equation : log $p=-22580/4\cdot571T+1\cdot75$ log $T+3\cdot2$—*vide* basic lead carbonate. G. Mazzetti observed no sign of the formation of basic carbonate on the curve showing the loss of weight with temp., the temp. of decomposition was 346 ; W. Eitel, and L. Joulin made some observations on this subject. K. Friedrich said that the decomposition begins at 315° when in air, and the maximum thermal change occurs at 315°—the basic carbonate simultaneously formed requires a higher temp. for decomposition—the corresponding values being 430° and 460°. In air, L. Michel said that red-lead begins to appear at about 300°. The molar **heat of formation** of lead carbonate from its elements, given by J. Thomsen, is 169·8 Cals.; M. Berthelot gave 166·7 Cals. ; P. Günther, 169·5 Cals. ; and A. Colson, 166·6 Cals. J. Thomsen gave for the heat of the reaction a soln. of a mol of sodium carbonate in 400 mols of water: $Pb(NO_3)_2+Na_2CO_3=2NaNO_3+PbCO_3+6\cdot11$ Cals. ; for (PbO,CO_2), 22·6 Cals. ; and for (PbO,O_2,CO), 139·69 Cals. A. L. Marshall and B. Bruzs gave $(PbO,CO_2)=21\cdot1$ Cals. ; and $(PbO,PbCO_3)=0\cdot34$ Cal. ; and for the heat of soln. of $PbCO_3$ in nitric acid, and 50 per cent. by vol., 1·99 Cals., and for $PbO.PbCO_3$, 8·54 Cals.

H. C. Sorby [12] gave 1·977 for the mean **index of refraction** of cerussite, and 0·441 for the refractive power. A. Schrauf gave for the indices of refraction, $a=1\cdot7915$, $\beta=2\cdot0595$, and $\gamma=2\cdot0613$ for the B-line ; and 1·8037, 2·0763, and 2·0780 respectively for the D-line ; and 1·8164, 2·0919, and 2·0934 respectively for the E-line. G. R. Negri gave for the D-line, $a=1\cdot8036, \beta=2\cdot0765$, and $\gamma=2\cdot0786$. P. Sève made photograms of the interference figures, and found that the exterior angle varies with the wave-length of the monochromatic light until it becomes uniaxial in ultra-violet light at ordinary temp. C. Gaudefroy gave for the birefringence $\gamma-\beta=0\cdot00205$ for rays of wave-length $\lambda=700\mu\mu$ to 0·00073 for $450\mu\mu$. T. Liebisch and H. Rubens found the **reflecting power** for the ultra-red rays to be very high. C. Doelter found lead carbonate to be almost opaque to the **X-rays.** A. Pochettino found that the **luminescence** produced by the cathode rays is the same colour as the fluorescence and shows no signs of polarization. W. Heintze found the **photoelectric effect** for cerussite is a maximum for light of wave-length $\lambda=280\mu\mu$.

The **dielectric constant** given by C. B. Thwing [13] is 18·58 ; and by W. Schmidt, $a=25\cdot4$, $\beta=23\cdot2$, $\gamma=19\cdot2$. L. Ebert studied the dielectric polarization of lead salts. W. G. Hankel observed the **pyroelectrical properties** of the crystals. G. Cesaro said that the **electrical conductivity** of cerussite is very small. F. Kohlrausch, and W. Böttger measured the sp. electrical conductivity of aq. soln. of lead carbonate ; and for sat. soln., the former gave $0\cdot0_52$ at 18° with soln. not quite free from carbon dioxide, the latter gave $0\cdot0_5102$ to $0\cdot0_5161$ at 19·96° ; and M. Pleissner gave $0\cdot0_516$, and for the degree of **ionization** of a soln of 0·0085 millimol $PbCO_3$ at 18°, but the true value is thought to be higher. M. Pleissner found the sp. conductivity of soln. containing, in milligrams per litre, at 18°, to be :

CO₂	. .	0	2·8	5·4	14·4	26·0	43·5	105·5
Pb	. .	1·7	4·8	5·8	8·1	9·8	11·8	15·7
Sp. cond.	.	$0\cdot0_527$	$0\cdot0_553$	$0\cdot0_568$	$0\cdot0_586$	$0\cdot0_599$	$0\cdot0_4122$	$0\cdot0_4160$

The chemical properties of lead carbonate.—H. Hélier [14] found that **hydrogen** reduces the salt completely at 325°, while the reduction of lead monoxide at 350°

is incomplete. H. Mennicke also found that nascent hydrogen—zinc and hydrochloric acid act more rapidly in the presence of platinum—reduces it rapidly and completely at ordinary temp. According to R. Fresenius, a litre of water dissolves 0·0198 grm. of lead carbonate at ordinary temp. ; A. Drevermann gave 0·02 grm. F. Kohlrausch and F. Rose calculated values from the electrical conductivity of the aq. soln., and found 3 mgrms. of normal lead carbonate are dissolved per litre at 10° ; W. Böttger gave 0·0015 grm. at 20° ; and M. Pleissner, 0·05 mgrm. at 16°. The last-named showed that the values previously deduced from the electrical conductivity are too high.   He gave for the solubility product, 0·33×10⁻¹³, whilst F. Auerbach and H. Pick showed that the true value is nearer 1·0×10⁻¹³ to 1·5 ×10⁻¹³. M. Pleissner said that the hydrolysis at ordinary temp. is not perceptible ; at 70°, the aq. soln. has an alkaline reaction which disappears on cooling.   He said that if boiled in water, while a current of air is passing, a basic carbonate, $2PbCO_3.2Pb(OH)_2$, is formed.   J. F. Sacher said that water at 18° slowly converts the normal salt into a basic carbonate, and that the change is rapid in hot water. R. Salvadori found that the basic carbonate is not formed at 30°, but is rapidly formed at 70° ; and E. Dittler, that a 0·1N-soln. of potassium hydroxide dissolves cerussite with decomposition.   H. Rose, and M. H. Klaproth noted the solubility of lead carbonate in soln. of potassium or sodium hydroxide.   J. H. Walton and D. W. O. Jones found that hydrogen dioxide, in aq. amyl alcohol, amyl acetate, isobutyl alcohol, and quinoline soln., is catalytically decomposed by lead carbonate. V. Zotier studied the reaction.

H. Moissan found the salt becomes incandescent in fluorine, carbon dioxide is evolved, and lead fluoride is formed. Lead carbonate is readily soluble in hydrochloric acid.   A. Voigt found it to be less soluble in a soln. of magnesium chloride than is lead oxide ; and H. Hof observed that cold soln. of sp. gr. 1·3 dissolve it without decomposition, but near 80°, gas is evolved and a basic salt deposited.   Unlike $2PbCO_3.Pb(OH)_2$, the soln. of normal lead carbonate in magnesium chloride of sp. gr. 1·16, when diluted with water, does not have an alkaline reaction. R. H. Brett, F. Weppen, and H. Rose said that lead carbonate is readily dissolved by a soln. of ammonium chloride ; and P. L. Dulong, that it is partially decomposed by boiling with sodium fluoride.   A. Ditte observed no reaction between freshly precipitated lead carbonate and a conc. soln. of potassium iodide.

According to J. B. Senderens, lead carbonate is decomposed more readily than the oxide when boiled with sulphur and water. L. Falk showed that when lead carbonate is suspended in water or alcohol, and treated with hydrogen sulphide, it is converted into lead sulphide.   H. N. Stokes obtained crystalline lead sulphide by heating the carbonate under press. in hydrogen sulphide.   L. Falk said that hydrogen sulphide reacts slowly with crystalline lead carbonate, and rapidly with the amorphous salt.   J. F. Sacher showed that no carbon dioxide is evolved during the blackening of white-lead by hydrogen sulphide.   P. L. Dulong said that a boiling soln. of potassium or sodium sulphite partially decomposes lead carbonate, while ammonium sulphite decomposes it completely.   Lead carbonate is converted into sulphate by sulphuric acid.   It is not dissolved by a mixture of one part sulphuric acid and six parts of absolute alcohol. P. L. Dulong found that a boiling soln. of ammonium sulphate decomposes lead carbonate completely.   H. Rose, and F. J. Malaguti said that aq. soln. of potassium sulphate do not decompose lead carbonate ; J. Persoz said that there is a slight decomposition.   If lead carbonate be suspended in a soln. of sodium sulphate, F. Auerbach and H. Pick observed very little decomposition when carbon dioxide is passed at atm. press., but at higher press., more is decomposed ; P. L. Dulong, that there is a partial decomposition by boiling soln. of potassium, sodium, calcium, or magnesium sulphate.   According to C. A. Stetefeldt, lead carbonate is insoluble in an aq. soln. of sodium thiosulphate, but when the two salts are triturated together, P. Jochum observed a slight decomposition.

According to E. C. Franklin, lead carbonate is insoluble in liquid ammonia.

J. J. Berzelius said that the carbonate is insoluble in aq. ammonia. F. Rössler found that when heated in a stream of ammonia, lead cyanamide, $PbCN_2$, is formed, which furnishes cyanamide when treated with hydrogen sulphide. Lead carbonate is easily soluble in dil. nitric acid, but conc. nitric acid forms a protective, insoluble crust of lead nitrate. W. Spring said that the rate of dissolution of cerussite in 10 per cent. nitric acid is 0·757 times that of calcite. F. W. O. de Coninck said that aq. soln. of sodium nitrate decomposed lead carbonate perceptibly. J. J. Berzelius said that the carbonate is decomposed by a boiling soln. of calcium nitrate. P. L. Dulong said that a boiling soln. of sodium hydrophosphite, sodium hydrophosphate, sodium ammonium hydrophosphate, or potassium or sodium arsenate partially decomposes lead carbonate. Similar remarks apply to a soln. of potassium chromate. This reaction was also studied by H. Goldblum and G. Stoffella. According to E. Dittler, a soln. of ammonium molybdate at 150° converts precipitated lead carbonate partially into lead molybdate ; with cerussite at 100°, an olive-green mixture of molybdenum dioxide and trioxide is formed.

J. F. John was mistaken in saying that lead carbonate is insoluble in an aq. soln. of carbon dioxide. J. Tünnermann found the salt to be slightly soluble in carbonic acid, but added that the soln. is prevented by traces of various salts. G. Wetzlar said that an aq. soln. of lead oxide is rendered turbid by a small quantity of carbon dioxide, but regains its transparency on the addition of a larger quantity. The liquid reddens litmus, and becomes turbid when heated, or mixed with a soln. of sodium carbonate. Lead covered with an aq. soln. of carbon dioxide and exposed to air was found by J. Tünnermann to tarnish after the second day, and the clear soln. contains lead carbonate in soln., and gives a precipitate when boiled. The precipitated carbonate obtained by adding carbonic acid to lead acetate soln., was found by P. Yorke to contain between 0·167 and 0·200 grm. of lead oxide per litre. The soln. gives a precipitate with potassium carbonate or hydrocarbonate. J. L. Lassaigne found that 1000 grms. of a sat. aq. soln. of carbon dioxide dissolve 0·14 grm. of lead carbonate ; and R. Wagner added that if the carbon dioxide be under 4 to 6 atm. press., 0·5 grm. of the carbonate may be dissolved. O. Hähnel found that when the partial press. of the carbon dioxide is one atm., the solubility is 0·014 per cent. ; and when the partial press. is 50 atm., 0·015 per cent. C. A. Seyler, and T. Paul and co-workers showed that in a sat. soln. the conc. of the lead ions is directly proportional to the conc. of the free carbon dioxide, and inversely as the square of the conc. of the HCO'_3-ions. Expressing conc. in milligrams per litre, M. Pleissner found the solubility to be, at 18° :

| CO_2 | . | . | 0 | 2·8 | 5·4 | 14·4 | 26 | 43·5 | 106 |
| $PbCO_3$ | . | . | 1·75 | 6·0 | 7·0 | 8·2 | 9·9 | 10·9 | 15·4 |

It is assumed that in all these cases, the liquid contains unstable lead hydrocarbonate, $Pb(HCO_3)_2$. A. Ditte said that with potassium iodide, potassium tetraiodoplumbite is formed, but with an excess of lead hydrocarbonate, lead iodide is formed. F. Auerbach and H. Pick said that sodium chromate forms basic lead chromate by a reversible reaction, and E. Dittler, that calcium molybdate forms lead molybdate. J. B. J. D. Boussingault said that when a soln. of lead nitrate or acetate is mixed with sodium sesquicarbonate, a white precipitate is formed, which, when dried in air, has a composition corresponding with the formula $4PbO.5CO_2$, or $4PbCO_3.CO_2$. This statement wants reconsideration.

According to R. Fresenius, the solubility of lead carbonate in water is nearly doubled if a little ammonium carbonate and acetate, and free ammonia be present ; and is still further increased if some ammonium nitrate and carbonate, and free ammonia be present. A. Altmann made some observations on the solubility of lead carbonate in water containing carbonic and acetic acids. F. Auerbach and H. Pick showed that with sodium carbonate a complex salt is formed (q.v.). H. Rose said that the carbonate is not absolutely insoluble, at ordinary temp., in an excess of a soln. of sodium or potassium carbonate, but is insoluble in soln. of ammonium carbonate, and in soln. of **potassium** or **sodium hydrocarbonate**. F. J. Malaguti showed that when a mol of lead carbonate is boiled with a soln. of a mol of potassium carbonate, 93·28 per cent. of the lead salt is decomposed. J. S. Stas showed that **potassium cyanide** reduces it to the metal. H. C. Bolton found that **formic acid** slowly dissolves cerussite; **acetic, oxalic, and tartaric acids** act similarly. J. Mercer showed that the carbonate is soluble in soln. of acetates; and F. Weppen, in soln. of **ammonium acetate**. A. Naumann said that lead carbonate is insoluble in **methyl acetate**. L. Falk, J. F. Sacher, and E. Euston studied the action of soln. of **lead acetate** or basic lead acetate on lead carbonate. According to L. Falk, when lead carbonate is shaken with a soln. of basic lead acetate, three parts of carbonate withdraw two parts of oxide from soln., as shown by titration, but the washed precipitate always contains too much carbonate for the formula. If boiled with the basic lead acetate soln., the ordinary basic carbonate, $2PbCO_3.Pb(OH)_2$, is obtained. Crystalline and amorphous lead carbonates differ in their chemical behaviour. Thus, whilst the amorphous compound reacts readily with lead oxide in presence of lead acetate, the crystalline modification only reacts very slowly. The formulae

$$CO<^O_O>Pb \qquad\qquad Pb<^O_O>C<^O_O>C<^O_O>Pb$$

Amorphous lead carbonate.   Crystalline lead carbonate.

are proposed for the two modifications, and a similar polymerization is assumed in the case of white-lead. Structural formulæ for the basic carbonates are proposed. P. L. Dulong said that the carbonate is partly decomposed by boiling with soln. of **potassium or sodium oxalate**. F. J. Malaguti added that when a mol of lead carbonate is boiled with a soln. of a mol of potassium oxalate, 15 per cent. of lead salt is decomposed. H. C. Bolton found that a cold conc. soln. of **citric acid** freely dissolves cerussite. J. Aub said that a litre of **serum** at 25° dissolves 0·0333 grm. of lead carbonate. R. Marc, and W. Suida noted the adsorption of **organic dyes** by lead carbonate. L. Kahlenberg and W. J. Trautmann studied the reduction of lead carbonate when heated with powdered **silicon**. R. Canaval found that **silicates** are broken down by heating to fusion with lead carbonate. P. L. Dulong noted that a boiling soln. of **sodium diborate** partially decomposes lead carbonate.

The basic lead carbonates.—Quite a large number of basic lead carbonates have been reported, and some occur as minerals in nature. M. Cszentnerszwer and co-workers [15] found that the partial press. of the carbon dioxide for lead carbonate is $\log p=-(19\cdot816/4\cdot571T)+1\cdot75 \log T+3\cdot2$; and when lead carbonate is heated under 760 mm., the normal carbonate passes to **lead trioxypentacarbonate**, $3PbO.5PbCO_3$, at 274°; into **lead oxycarbonate**, $PbO.PbCO_3$, at 285°, for which the partial press. of the carbon dioxide is $\log p=-(23\cdot047/4\cdot571T)+1\cdot75T+3\cdot2$; into **lead dioxycarbonate**, $2PbO.PbCO_3$, at 360°, for which the partial press. of the carbon dioxide is $\log p=-(25\cdot036/4\cdot571T)+1\cdot75 \log T+3\cdot2$; and into

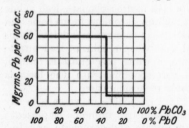

FIG. 120.—Composition-Temperature Diagram of the Basic Lead Carbonates.

lead monoxide at 4·2°. The composition-temperature diagram is shown in Fig. 120. R. Salvadori found that **lead dihydroxydicarbonate**, $2PbCO_3.Pb(OH)_2$, is formed when lead carbonate is boiled with water, or when lead sulphate or chloride is boiled with an aq. soln. of sodium carbonate. This agrees with the assumption that a chemical individual is formed; or else this substance is the end-term of a series of solid soln. On the other hand, A. Isenburg showed that when made electrolytically, the product usually has a variable composition. L. F. Hawley found that the solubilities of lead carbonate and hydroxide in water are too small to permit of the application of water as solvent, but if a soln. of sodium acetate be employed as solvent, and the conc. be kept constant, this soln. can be regarded as solvent, and the system treated as one with three components $Pb(OH)_2$-$PbCO_3$-solvent. Working at ordinary temp., and plotting the amounts of lead in the soln., expressed in milligrams per 100 c.c. of soln., as ordinates, and the molar proportions of lead hydroxide and lead carbonate in the solid phase or phases as abscissæ, the result shown in Fig. 121 was obtained. There are no solid soln., only one definite complex is formed, namely, $2PbCO_3.Pb(OH)_2$. When mixtures of lead oxide and carbonate are employed, the amount of oxide changed to hydroxide is eq. to half the lead carbonate present. It is therefore inferred that only three solid phases are possible when mixtures of lead oxide and carbonate are treated with water, viz. PbO, $Pb_3(OH)_2(CO_3)$, and $PbCO_3$.

Lead dihydroxydicarbonate is represented by the commercial product white-lead, which is probably a mixture of this compound with more or less lead hydroxide and carbonate. Indeed, E. Euston, for reasons stated below, regards this product as an adsorption compound of these two components, the basic lead carbonate occurring as a coating on native lead at Langban, Wermland, Sweden; and along with leadhillite and susannite at Leadhills, Scotland.

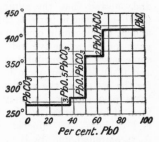

FIG. 121.—Equilibrium in the System PbO-$PbCO_3$-H_2O at Ordinary Temperatures.

P. P. Philipenko found it at Ridderovsky, Altai Mts., Siberia; and L. J. Spencer and E. D. Mountain, on the Mendip Hills, Somersetshire. Analyses reported by M. F. Heddle, P. P. Philipenko, L. Bourgeois, and L. J. Spencer and E. D. Mountain are in agreement with this formula, $2PbCO_3.Pb(OH)_2$. The mineral was called **hydrocerussite** by A. E. Nordenskjöld, and *plumbonacrite*, by M. F. Heddle. A. Lacroix reported it in the lead slags at Laurion, Greece, and also in cavities in galena at Wanlockhead, Scotland. J. S. S. Brame, and F. Southerden found products of the same composition resulting from the corrosion of lead roofing.

C. Hochstetter said that this salt is obtained when carbon dioxide is passed into a soln. of basic lead acetate—*vide infra*, white-lead. L. Bourgeois employed a boiling soln. of the basic acetate and obtained crystals of hydrocerussite. A. Altmann boiled a soln. of $0.2N$-lead acetate so as to evaporate the free acetic acid; dry carbon dioxide was passed through the soln., which was then filtered rapidly, washed, and dried at 100°. R. Salvadori, and M. Pleissner boiled normal lead carbonate with water for a long time and obtained this basic carbonate. The latter also obtained it by warming 4 grms. of the normal salt with 4 drops of a 30 per cent. soln., and the former, by boiling the normal carbonate with a soln. of sodium sulphate or chloride. M. Pleissner also obtained it by treating a soln. of lead hydroxide with carbon dioxide; by the action of oxygenated water on lead in the presence of air; and by shaking mixtures of freshly precipitated lead hydroxide and carbonate. L. Bourgeois obtained crystals of hydrocerussite by treating lead carbonate with a soln. of ammonium nitrate; and also by treating a boiling soln. of a mol of lead acetate with one and a half mols of litharge and, when cold, adding a mol of urea. The filtered liquid, when heated for some hours at 130°, furnishes nacreous spangles of hydrocerussite. C. Hochstetter, and H. Rose obtained this basic salt by adding sodium carbonate to a soln. of a lead salt; D. Strömholm recommended a soln. of sodium carbonate with 0.15 eq. CO_2 per litre. C. A. Stevens said that with strongly alkaline soln. no basic carbonate is precipitated by sodium carbonate. L. Bourgeois obtained crystals of hydrocerussite by the action of carbon dioxide on a dil. soln. of sodium plumbite. R. Salvadori obtained the basic salt by boiling lead sulphate or chloride with a $0.1N$-soln. of sodium carbonate. F. Auerbach showed that the complex salt $NaPb_2(OH)(CO_3)_2$ may be formed, and finally normal lead carbonate. L. Falk, and J. F. Sacher employed variations of this process. E. Dittler said that this basic carbonate is formed by the weathering of galena in air, and that the crystals are formed by boiling lead molybdate with soln. of sodium carbonate, and by allowing a soln. of lead molybdate, $2PbO.5MoO_3$, in one of sodium carbonate to stand in air.

A. E. Nordenskjöld, and H. Sjogren said that hydrocerussite furnishes white or colourless hexagonal plates, which, according to A. Lacroix, and E. Bertrand, are uniaxial. G. Flink said that the crystals belong to the hexagonal system, and have the axial ratios $a : c = 1 : 1.4187$. L. J. Spencer and E. D. Mountain gave $a : c = 1 : 0.61$, and showed that the symmetry is rather rhombohedral than hexagonal. The (0001)-cleavage is perfect, the birefringence is feeble and negative. L. J. Spencer and E. D. Mountain could not develop satisfactory corrosion-figures. E. S. Larsen gave for the refractive indices of the artificial crystals $\omega = 2.09$, and $\epsilon = 1.94$. In some cases the precipitated salt is an amorphous white powder. L. J. Spencer and E. D. Mountain gave for the sp. gr. 6.80 at 25°/4°. L. Bourgeois gave 6.14 for the sp. gr. of the artificial crystals, and he showed that when heated to 400°, these pass into lead monoxide tinted a rose colour, and preserve the crystalline form of hydrocerussite. L. J. Spencer and E. D. Mountain said that all the water is lost from the mineral at 250°, and all the carbon dioxide on ignition. A. L. Marshall and B. Bruzs gave for the heat of formation $(PbO,PbCO_3) = 0.34$ Cals., and for the heat of soln. in nitric acid, 50 per cent. by vol., 8.54 Cals. According to M. Pleissner, the solubility at 18° is less than 0.05 mgrm. of the salt per litre; and F. Auerbach and H. Pick gave for the solubility product at the same temp., $[OH']^2[CO_3'']^2[Pb^{..}]^3 = 3.5 \times 10^{-46}$. L. Falk found that hydrogen sulphide acts very little on the crystals suspended in water or in alcohol because they are protected by a thin superficial layer of lead sulphide; the amorphous salt is decomposed in a short time. Hydrocerussite was found by L. J. Spencer and E. D. Mountain to change to cerussite, and pseudomorphs of cerussite after hydrocerussite were found. L. Bourgeois said that hydrocerussite is soluble in nitric and acetic acid. For F. Auerbach and H. Pick's observations on the behaviour of basic lead carbonate towards soln. of alkali carbonates and hydrocarbonates, *vide infra*, complex lead carbonates. T. Thunberg found that when basic lead carbonate is boiled with a soln. of hydrogen dioxide in the presence of boric acid, some formaldehyde is produced. The reaction was studied by F. Weigert.

M. F. Heddle's *plumbonacrite* was represented as having the composition $4PbO.CO_2.H_2O$, or $2PbO.Pb(OH)_2.PbCO_3$; but A. E. Nordenskjöld showed that it was probably hydrocerussite. According to M. Delaville, A. C. Becquerel, P. Yorke, and P. A. von Bonsdorff, hydrated *lead dihydroxycarbonate*, $Pb(OH)_2.PbCO_3$, or $2PbO.CO_2.H_2O$, is formed when lead immersed in water is exposed for a long time in open air. A. Vogel, J. N. Gannal, M. Versepuy, and C. Stalmann allowed lead to stand immersed in water made alkaline with potassium hydroxide or carbonate for a long time exposed to air, and obtained a basic carbonate. E. Euston believed this compound to be formed when carbon dioxide is allowed to act slowly on the basic acetate $2PbO.Pb(C_2H_3O_2)_2$. C. A. Klein said that this basic carbonate is probably the dihydroxydicarbonate. D. Strömholm obtained a white powder which he regarded as $7PbO.4CO_2.2H_2O$, or $PbO.2Pb(OH)_2.4PbCO_3$, by digesting freshly precipitated lead hydroxide with a 0.05N-soln. of sodium carbonate. L. Falk claimed to have made the basic carbonate $5PbO.3CO_2.H_2O$, by shaking normal lead carbonate with a soln. of the basic acetate $2PbO.Pb(C_2H_3O_2)_2$; and D. Strömholm, $5PbO.3CO_2.2H_2O$, or $2Pb(OH)_2.3PbCO_3$, by the action of sodium carbonate on a soln. of sodium carbonate. J. F. Sacher, L. Falk, M. Kerstmann, and H. Tomann claimed to have made the basic carbonate $8PbO.5CO_2.2H_2O$, or $PbO.2Pb(OH)_2.5PbCO_3$, by digesting a mixture of lead carbonate and oxide with a cold soln. of lead acetate; etc. G. J. Mulder obtained a Dutch white-lead with the composition $7PbO.5CO_2.H_2O$; F. Clowes obtained a substance with the composition $4PbO.3CO_2.H_2O$ by the action of distilled water on lead; H. Rose, from soln. of sodium carbonate and lead nitrate at 200°. G. J. Mulder obtained a Dutch white-lead with the composition $5PbO.4CO_2.H_2O$, and H. Rose said that it is formed by the action of soln. of lead nitrate and sodium carbonate at 150°. J. A. Phillips obtained white-lead of the composition $6PbO.5CO_2.H_2O$, and K. Feist prepared it by washing with water the product obtained by triturating a mixture of lead acetate and sodium carbonate. R. Krzizan reported the basic carbonate, $7PbO.6CO_2.2H_2O$, or $Pb(OH)_2.6PbCO_3.H_2O$, to occur in some limestones; and H. Rose obtained it by the action of cold soln. of equimolar parts of lead nitrate and sodium carbonate. J. A. Phillips claimed to have made

$8PbO.7CO_2.nH_2O$ by the action of boiling soln. of sodium carbonate with a large excess of lead nitrate soln. There is nothing other than the analyses to justify the view that these products are chemical individuals.

REFERENCES.

[1] H. Davy, *Phil. Trans.*, 105. 97, 1815 ; Pliny, *Historia naturalis*, 34. 43 ; 35. 19, c. 77 A.D.
[2] Theophilus, also called Rugerus, *An Essay on the Various Arts* (R. Hendrie's trans.), London, 49, 1847 ; C. Eraclius, *De coloribus et artibus Romanorum*, Frankfurt, 1551 ; P. Vernatti, *Phil. Trans.*, 12. 935, 1678 ; G. Jars, *Voyages métallurgiques*, Lyons, 1774 ; A. Barba, *Arte de los metales*, Madrid, 1640 ; S. J. Cook, *Journ. Soc. Chem. Ind.*, 38. 137, 1919 ; R. W. Atkinson, *ib.*, 5. 312, 1886 ; W. H. Adolph, *Scient. Monthly*, 14. 441, 1922 ; *Met. Chem. Engg.*, 26. 914, 1922 ; C. A. Klein, *Oil and Colour Trade's Journ.*, 44. 1973, 2066, 1913 ; W. H. Pulsifer, *Notes for a History of Lead, and the Manufacture of White-lead and Lead Oxides*, New York, 1888 ; H. Faure, *Histoire de la céruse suivie d'un essai sur l'histoire du plomb*, Lille, 1889 ; P. Beck. *Chem. Ind.*, 30. 277, 1907 ; R. Hitchcock, *Eng. Min. Journ.*, 70. 668, 1900 ; C. Eland, *Brit. Pat. No.* 22, 1622.
[3] C. Gesner, *De omni rerum fossilium genere*, Tiguri, 85, 1565 ; A. Cronstedt, *Mineralogie*, Stockholm, 295, 1758 ; T. Bergman, *De acido aëro*, Upsala, 1774 ; A. Sigmund, *Mitt. Nat. Ver. Steiermark*, 53. 245, 1917 ; W. Haidinger, *Handbuch der bestimmenden Mineralogie*, Wien, 503, 1845 ; F. S. Beudant, *Traité élémentaire de minéralogie*, Paris, 2. 363, 1832 ; J. J. N. Huot, *Manuel de minéralogie*, Paris, 618, 1841 ; J. G. Wallerius, *Mineralogia*, Stockholm, 295, 1747 ; C. M. Kersten, *Schweigger's Journ.*, 65. 365, 1832 ; H. Traube, *Zeit. deut. geol. Ges.*, 46. 50, 1894 ; F. Ranfaldi, *Rend. Accad. Lincei*, (5), 31. 430, 468, 506, 1922.
[4] R. B. Brinsmade, *Eng. Min. Journ.*, 83. 844, 1907 ; F. Rathgen, *Chem. Ztg.*, 27. 825, 1903 ; W. G. Brown, *Amer. Journ. Science*, (3), 32. 377, 1886 ; L. Michel, *Bull. Soc. Min.*, 31. 275, 1908 ; A. Lacroix, *ib.*, 6. 175, 1883 ; A. de Schulten, *ib.*, 20. 194, 1897 ; F. Gonnard, *Compt. Rend.*, 106. 77, 1888 ; J. D. Whitney, *Rep. Upper Mississippi*, 291, 1862 ; H. von Decken, *Neues Jahrb. Min.*, 216, 1858 ; G. von Blöde, *ib.*, 638, 1834 ; A. F. Rogers, *Amer. Geol.*, 31. 43, 1903.
[5] C. F. Carrier, *Trans. Amer. Electrochem. Soc.*, 5. 231, 1904 ; A. C. Becquerel, *Compt. Rend.*, 34. 29, 1852 ; 63. 1, 1866 ; L. Bourgeois, *ib.*, 103. 1090, 1886 ; *Bull. Soc. Chim.*, (2), 47. 82, 1887 ; J. Riban, *ib.*, (2), 38. 110, 1882 ; *Compt. Rend.*, 93. 1024, 1881 ; F. Gonnard, *ib.*, 106. 77, 1888 ; E. Frémy, *ib.*, 63. 714, 1866 ; C. R. A. Wright and A. P. Luff, *Journ. Chem. Soc.*, 33. 542, 1878 ; J. A. Phillips, *ib.*, 4. 165, 1852 ; E. Dittler, *Zeit. Kryst.*, 54. 355, 1915 ; A. Findlay, *Zeit. phys. Chem.*, 34. 409, 1900 ; W. Herz, *Zeit. anorg. Chem.*, 72. 106, 1911 ; D. Strömholm, *Ark. Kem. Min.*, 2. 16, 1906 ; *Zeit. anorg. Chem.*, 38. 446, 1904 ; A. Altmann, *ib.*, 52. 225, 1907 ; F. Auerbach and H. Pick, *Umsetzungen schwerlöslicher Bleisalze mit wasserigen Lösungen kohlensauer Alkalien*, Berlin, 1913 ; *Zeit. Elektrochem.*, 19. 830, 1913 ; *Arb. Kaiser Ges. Amt.*, 45. 149, 1913 ; M. Pleissner, *ib.*, 26. 403, 1907 ; A. de Schulten, *Bull. Soc. Min.*, 20. 194, 1897 ; J. J. Berzelius, *Pogg. Ann.*, 47. 199, 1839 ; H. Rose, *ib.*, 84. 59, 1851 ; *Journ. prakt. Chem.*, (1), 54. 24, 1854 ; R. Böttger, *ib.*, (1), 76. 235, 1859 ; R. Salvadori, *Gazz. Chim. Ital.*, 34. i, 87, 1904 ; J. S. Stas, *Bull. Acad. Belg.*, (2), 10. 295, 1850 ; *Chem. News, 4* 307, 1861 ; A. Drevermann, *Liebig's Ann.*, 87. 122, 1853 ; 89. 39, 1854 ; J. Lefort, *Journ. Pharm. Chim.*, (3), 15. 26, 1849 ; A. Wultze, *German Pat., D.R.P.* 174024, 1904 ; J. Löwe, 42307, 1887 ; L. Falk, *ib.*, 241005, 1909 ; *Chem. Ztg.*, 34. 568, 1910 ; K. Feist, *Arch. Pharm.*, 247. 444, 1909 ; G. J. Mulder, *Miquel's Bull.*, 302, 1839 ; *Journ. prakt. Chem.*, (1), 19. 70, 1840 ; *Liebig's Ann.*, 33. 242, 1840 ; A. Bette, *ib.*, 33. 251, 1840 ; O. Ruff and B. Hirsch, *Zeit. anorg. Chem.*, 146. 388, 1925 ; J. W. Morris, J. R. Raine, J. Kerr, and C. McLachlan, *Brit. Pat. No.* 24865, 1907 ; S. C. Smith, *ib.*, 239257, 1924.
[6] W. Leuze, *Zur Kenntnis Kolloider Metalle und ihrer Verbindungen*, Erlangen, 28, 1904.
[7] M. E. Chevreul, *Ann. Chim. Phys.*, (1), 83. 91, 1812 ; C. W. Bergmann, *Chemische Untersuchungen der Mineralien des Bleibergs*, Bonn, 167, 175, 1830 ; F. Sandberger, *Untersuchungen über Erzgänge*, Wiesbaden, 1882 ; C. F. Rammelsberg, *Handbuch der Mineralchemie*, Leipzig, 2. 222, 1875 ; P. von Jeremejeff, *Proc. Russ. Min. Soc.*, (2), 18. 104, 1883 ; (2), 36. 12, 1899 ; W. F. Petterd, *Proc. Roy. Soc. Tasmania*, 18, 1902 ; W. B. Hobbs, *Amer. Journ. Science*, (3), 50. 121, 1895 ; C. H. Warren, *ib.*, (4), 16. 337, 1903 ; J. L. Smith, *ib.*, (2), 20. 245, 1855 ; M. H. Klaproth, *Beiträge zur Chemischen Kenntniss der Mineralkörper*, Berlin, 3. 167, 1802 ; J. J. Berzelius, *Pogg. Ann.*, 47. 199, 1839 ; M. Pleissner, *Arb. Kaiser Ges. Amt.*, 26. 414, 1907 ; F. Auerbach and H. Pick, *ib.*, 45. 149, 1913 ; *Umsetzungen schwerlöslicher Bleisalze mit wasserigen Lösungen kohlensauerer Alkalien*, Berlin, 1913 ; *Zeit. Elektrochem.*, 19. 830, 1913 ; A. Altmann, *Zeit. anorg. Chem.*, 52. 225, 1907 ; D. Strömholm, *ib.*, 38. 446, 1904 ; *Ark. Kem. Min.*, 2. 16, 1906 ; K. Feist, *Arch. Pharm.*, 247. 439, 1909 ; F. Sacher, *Chem. Ztg.*, 34. 1263, 1910 ; 35. 326, 1911 ; L. Falk, *ib.*, 34. 567, 938, 1910 ; G. J. Mulder, *Journ. prakt. Chem.*, (1), 18. 127, 1839 ; (1), 19. 70, 1840 ; *Liebig's Ann.*, 33. 242, 1840 ; A. Bette, *ib.*, 33. 251, 1840 ; J. Riban, *Compt. Rend.*, 93. 124, 1881 ; *Bull. Soc. Chim.*, (2), 38. 110, 1882 ; R. B. Green, *Zeit. Kryst.*, 25. 267, 1896 ; A. des Cloizeaux, *Manuel de minéralogie*, Paris, 2. 156, 1875 ; J. A. Phillips, *Journ. Chem. Soc.*, 4. 175, 1852 ; J. F. John, *Schweigger's Journ.*, 4. 227, 1812 ; 32. 114, 1821 ; *Chemische Untersuchungen*, Berlin, 2. 230, 1811.
[8] R. S. Owens, *Trans. Amer. Electrochem. Soc.*, 25. 479, 1914 ; *Journ. phys. Chem.*, 18. 461, 1914 ; G. R. Negri, *Atti Ist. Veneto*, (4), 7. 24, 1889 ; *Riv. Min. Crist. Ital.*, 4. 41, 1889 ; L. Jecker, *Compt. Rend.*, 140. 1410, 1905 ; J. Ribau, *ib.*, 93. 1024, 1881 ; *Bull. Soc. Chim.*, (2), 38. 110, 1882 ;

L. Bourgeois, *ib.*, (2), **47. 82,** 1887 ; *Compt. Rend.*, **103.** 1090, 1886 ; L. V. Pirsson, *Amer. Journ. Science*, (3), **42.** 405, 1891 ; J. H. Pratt, *ib.*, (3), **48.** 212, 1894 ; W. F. Hunt and F. R. van Horn, *ib.*, (4), **32.** 47, 1911 ; C. H. Warren, *ib.*, (4), **16.** 337, 1903 ; G. H. Williams, *Johns Hopkins Univ. Soc.*, **10.** 87, 1892 ; A. F. Rogers, *School Mines Quart.*, **23.** 133, 1902 ; L. J. Spencer, *Min. Mag.*, **17.** 49, 1894 ; J. F. Sacher, *Chem. Ztg.*, **34.** 1263, 1910 ; H. Buttgenbach, *Mém. Soc. Science Liége*, (3), **12.** 3, 1924 ; J. Scott, *Chem. Trade Journ.*, **65.** 327, 1919 ; A. Altmann, *Zeit. anorg. Chem.*, **52.** 225, 1907 ; J. A. Phillips, *Journ. Chem. Soc.*, **4.** 165, 1852 ; E. Repossi, *Atti Accad. Milano*, **43.** 422, 1904 ; H. A. Miers, *Min. Mag.*, **11.** 263, 1897 ; *Zeit. Kryst.*, **6.** 598, 1882 ; A. des Cloizeaux, *Manuel de minéralogie*, Paris, **2.** 153, 1874 ; *Nouvelles recherches sur les propriétés optiques des cristaux*, Paris, 49, 1867 ; W. H. Miller, *Introduction to Mineralogy*, London, 565, 1852 ; A. Schrauf, *Atlas der Krystallformen der Mineralreiches*, Wien, 41, 42, 1877 ; *Tschermak's Mitt.*, (1), **3.** 203, 1873 ; V. Goldschmidt, *Index der Krystallformen der Mineralien*, Berlin, **1.** 401, 1886 ; F. Becke, *Anz. Akad. Wien*, **30.** 206, 1893 ; F. M. Jäger and H. Haga, *Versl. Akad. Amsterdam*, **24.** 1410, 1916 ; L. Colomba, *Bol. Soc. Geol. Ital.*, **23.** 393, 1904 ; *Atti Accad. Lincei*, (5), **15.** 636, 1905 ; F. Millosevich, *ib.*, (5), **9.** 153, 1900 ; C. Riva, *ib.*, (5), **6.** 421, 1897 ; E. Tacconi, *ib.*, (5), **9.** 72, 1900 ; A. Pelloux, *ib.*, (5), **13.** ii, 34, 1904 ; G. d'Achiardi, *Proc. Verb. Soc. Toscana*, **10.** 210, 1897 ; E. Artini, *Atti Soc. Ital. Sci. Nat.*, **35.** 223, 1896 ; *Mem. Accad. Lincei*, (4), **5.** 605, 1888 ; A. Sigmund, *Mitt. Nat. Ver. Steiermark*, **53.** 245, 1919 ; *Neues Jahrb. Min.*, ii, 32, 1919 ; G. Seligmann, *Verh. Ver. Rheinl. Bonn*, **33.** 244, 1876 ; *Neues Jahrb. Min.*, i, 129, 1880 ; O. Mügge, *ib.*, ii, 18, 1882 ; ii, 79, 1897 ; J. L. Barvir, *ib.*, i, 173, 1902 ; ii, 23, 1903 ; A. Dannenberg, *Zeit. Kryst.*, **18.** 64, 1890 ; A. Maier, *ib.*, **58.** 75, 1923 ; E. Kaiser, *ib.*, **31.** 36, 1899 ; A. Schmidt, *ib.*, **6.** 546, 1882 ; A. Osann, *ib.*, **23.** 264, 1894 ; C. A. F. Molengraaff, *ib.*, **22.** 150, 1894 ; P. F. Hubrecht, *ib.*, **40.** 147, 1905 ; Z. von Toborffy, *ib.*, **52.** 225, 1913 ; T. Liweh, *ib.*, **9.** 512, 1884 ; M. L. Huggins, *Phys. Rev.*, (2), **19.** 354, 1922 ; N. von Kokscharoff, *Materialen zur Mineralogie Russlands*, St. Petersburg, **6.** 100, 1870 ; J. Gerstendörfer, *Sitzber. Akad. Wien*, **99.** 422, 1890 ; V. von Zepharovich, *ib.*, **62.** 439, 1870 ; *Lotos*, 1874, 1878 ; K. Zimanyi, *Földt. Közl.*, **22.** 267, 1892 ; J. Samojloff, *Materialen zur Geologie Russlands*, St. Petersburg, **23.** 1, 1906 ; *Proc. Russ. Min. Soc.*, (2), **38.** 313, 1900 ; V. von Lang, *ib.*, (2), **9.** 152, 1874 ; P. von Jeremejeff, *ib.*, (2), **18.** 104, 1883 ; (2), **36.** 12, 1899 ; L. Stibing, *Trav. Soc. Nat. St. Petersburg*, **34.** 41, 1903 ; H. Johannsson, *Geol. För. Förh. Stockholm*, **14.** 49, 1892 ; H. Buttgenbach, *Ann. Soc. Géol. Belg.*, **24.** 57, 1899 ; **25.** 49, 1900 ; **29.** 103, 1902 ; F. Gonnard, *Compt. Rend.*, **106.** 77, 1888 ; *Bull. Soc. Min.*, **15.** 35, 41, 1892 ; **17.** 49, 1894 ; J. Barthoux, *ib.*, **47.** 36, 1924 ; A. Lacroix, *ib.*, **31.** 257, 1908 ; *Compt. Rend.*, **123.** 955, 1896 ; A. Lacroix and A. de Schulten, *Bull. Soc. Min.*, **31.** 89, 1908 ; C. Gaudefroy, *ib.*, **46.** 34, 1923 ; L. Tokody, *Zeit. Kryst.*, **63.** 385, 1926.

⁹ C. J. B. Karsten, *Schweigger's Journ.*, **65.** 394, 1832 ; J. F. John, *ib.*, **4.** 227, 1812 ; **32.** 114, 1821 ; *Chemisch Untersuchungen*, Berlin, **2.** 230, 1811 ; J. L. Smith, *Amer. Journ. Science*, (2), **20.** 245, 1855 ; H. G. F. Schröder, *Pogg. Ann. Ergbd.*, **6.** 622, 1879 ; F. Pfaff, *Sitzber. Akad. Bayr.*, **255,** 1884 ; P. Niggli, *Zeit. Kryst.*, **56.** 42, 1922 ; F. Becke, *Arz. Akad. Wien*, **30.** 206, 1893 ; M. L. Huggins, *Phys. Rev.*, (2), **19.** 354, 1922 ; I. I. Saslawsky, *Zeit. anorg. Chem.*, **146.** 315, 1925 ; E. Madelung and R. Fuchs, *Ann. Physik*, (4), **65.** 289, 1921 ; F. A. Henglein, *Zeit. Elektrochem.*, **30.** 5, 1924 ; *Zeit. anorg. Chem.*, **120.** 77, 1921 ; A. Reiss and L. Zimmermann, *Zeit. phys. Chem.*, **102.** 298, 1922.

¹⁰ F. E. Neumann, *Pogg. Ann.*, **26.** 1, 1831 ; H. Kopp, *Liebig's Ann.*, **3.** 103, 295, 1865 ; G. Linder, *Sitzber. Soc. Erlangen*, **34.** 217, 1902 ; *Die Abhängigkeit der specifischen Wärme fester Körper von der Temperatur*, Erlangen, 1903.

¹¹ A. Colson, *Compt. Rend.*, **140.** 865, 1905 ; **148.** 837, 1909 ; H. Debray, *ib.*, **86.** 513, 1878 ; L. Joulin, *ib.*, **76.** 1588, 1873 ; *Bull. Soc. Chim.*, (2), **19.** 345, 1873 ; *Ann. Chim. Phys.*, (4), **30.** 276, 1873 ; M. Berthelot, *ib.*, (5), **4.** 176, 1875 ; P. Günther, *Zeit. Elektrochem.*, **23.** 199, 1917 ; G. Mazzetti, *Atti Accad. Lincei*, (5), **33.** ii, 46, 1924 ; W. Eitel, *Forts. Min. Kryst.*, **8.** 7, 1923 ; K. Friedrich, *Met.*, **9.** 409, 1912 ; *Centr. Min.*, **616,** 651, 684, 1912 ; O. Brill, *Zeit. phys. Chem.*, **57.** 736, 1907 ; L. Michel, *Bull. Soc. Min.*, **13.** 56, 1890 ; J. Thomsen, *Journ. prakt. Chem.*, (2), **21.** 44, 1880 ; *Ber.*, **12.** 2031, 1879 ; A. L. Marshall and B. Bruzs, *Journ. Phys. Chem.*, **29.** 1184, 1925 ; B. Bruzs, *ib.*, **30.** 680, 1926.

¹² A. Schrauf, *Sitzber. Akad. Wien*, **43.** 120, 1860 ; C. Gaudefroy, *Bull. Soc. Min.*, **46.** 34, 1923 ; H. C. Sorby, *Min. Mag.*, **2.** 1, 1878 ; A. Pochettino, *Atti Accad. Lincei*, (5), **13.** i, 301, 1904 ; C. Doelter, *Neues Jahrb. Min.*, ii, 931, 1896 ; T. Liebisch and H. Rubens, *Sitzber. Akad. Berlin*, 198, 1919 ; P. Sève, *Journ. Phys.*, (6), i. 161, 1920 ; G. R. Negri, *Atti Ist. Veneto*, (4), **7.** 24, 1889 ; *Riv. Min. Crist. Ital.*, **4.** 41, 1889 ; W. Heintze, *Zeit. Physik*, **15.** 339, 1923.

¹³ M. Pleissner, *Arb. Kaiser Ges. Amt.*, **26.** 405, 1907 ; W. Schmidt, *Ann. Physik*, (4), **9.** 919, 1902 ; C. B. Thwing, *Zeit. phys. Chem.*, **14.** 286, 1894 ; F. Kohlrausch, *ib.*, **44.** 238, 1903 ; W. Böttger, *ib.*, **46.** 586, 1903 ; G. Cesaro, *Bull. Acad. Belg.*, **115,** 1904 ; W. G. Hankel, *Wied. Ann.*, **18.** 426, 1883 ; L. Ebert, *Zeit. phys. Chem.*, **113.** 1, 1924.

¹⁴ W. Böttger, *Löslichkeitsstudien an schwer löslichen Stoffen*, Leipzig, 1903 ; *Zeit. phys. Chem.*, **46.** 521, 602, 1903 ; F. Kohlrausch, *ib.*, **44.** 238, 1903 ; **50.** 356, 1904 ; F. Kohlrausch and F. Rose, *ib.*, **12.** 241, 1893 ; T. Paul, W. Ohlmüller, R. Heise, and F. Auerbach, *Arb. Kaiser Ges. Amt.*, **23.** 303, 1906 ; M. Pleissner, *ib.*, **26.** 405, 1907 ; F. Auerbach and H. Pick, *ib.*, **45.** 149, 1913 ; *Zeit. Elektrochem.*, **19.** 830, 1913 ; *Umsetzungen schwerslöslicher Bleisalze mit wasserigen Löslungen kohlensauerer Alkalien*, Berlin, 1913 ; M. Pleissner and F. Auerbach *Ueber die Löslichkeit einiger Bleiverbindungen*, Berlin, 1907 ; J. F. Sacher, *Chem. Ztg.*, **34.** 647, 1910 ; C. A. Seyler, *Analyst*, **33.** 454, 1908 ; R. Fresenius, *Liebig's Ann.*, **59.** 124, 1846 ; J. F. John, *ib.*, **28.** 117.

1838 ; A. Drevermann, *ib.*, **87**. 120, 1853 ; R. Salvadori, *Gazz. Chim. Ital.*, **34**. i, 87, 1904 ; A. Altmann, *Zeit. anorg. Chem.*, **52**. 222, 1907 ; H. Hélier, *Bull. Soc. Chim.*, (3), **21**. 43, 1899 ; J. B. Senderens, *ib.*, (3), **6**. 804, 1891 ; W. Spring, *ib.*, (3), **3**. 176, 1890 ; E. Dittler, *Zeit. Kryst.*, **54**. 338, 1915 ; H. Rose, *Pogg. Ann.*, **95**. 284, 1855 ; J. H. Walton and D. W. O. Jones, *Journ. Amer. Chem. Soc.*, **38**. 1956, 1916 ; H. N. Stokes, *ib.*, **29**. 313, 1907 ; F. W. O. de Coninck, *Bull. Acad. Belg.*, **31**, 1910 ; J. S. Stas, (2), **10**. 295, 1860 ; *Chem. News*, **4**. 207, 1861 ; H. Mennicke, *Zeit. öffent. Chem.*, **6**. 227, 1900 ; J. F. Sacher, *Chem. Ztg.*, **34**. 647, 1910 ; **35**. 326, 1911 ; H. Hof, *ib.*, **33**. 1078, 1909 ; **34**. 785, 1910 ; A. Voigt, *ib.*, **13**. 695, 1885 ; L. Falk, *ib.*, **34**. 588, 1910 ; C. A. Stetefeldt, *ib.*, **9**. 233, 1885 ; A. Ditte, *Compt. Rend.*, **92**. 1455, 1881 ; *Ann. Chim. Phys.*, (5), **24**. 235, 1881 ; J. B. J. D. Boussingault, (2), **29**. 286, 1825 ; H. Moissan, *ib.*, (6), **24**. 266, 1891 ; P. L. Dulong, *ib.*, (1), **82**. 290, 1812 ; H. Goldblum and G. Stoffella, *Journ. Chim. Phys.*, **8**. 135, 1910 ; R. Canaval, *Zeit. prakt. Geol.*, **18**. 460, 1910 ; H. C. Bolton, *Ber.*, **13**. 728, 1880 ; F. Rössler, *German Pat., D.R.P.* 139456, 1901 ; E. Euston, *Journ. Ind. Eng. Chem.*, **6**. 203, 382, 1914 ; **12**. 974, 1920 ; V. Zotier, *Bull. Soc. Chim.*, (4), **21**. 241, 1917 ; O. Hähnel, *Journ. prakt. Chem.*, (2), **108**. 187, 1924 ; L. Kahlenberg and W. J. Trautmann, *Trans. Amer. Electrochem. Soc.*, **39**. 477, 1921 ; P. Jochum, *Ueber die Einwirkung des unterschwefligsauren Natrons auf Metallsalze*, Berlin, 25, 1885 ; P. Yorke, *Phil. Mag.*, (3), **5**. 82, 1834 ; R. H. Brett, *ib.*, (3), **10**. 95, 1837 ; G. Wetzlar, *Schweigger's Journ.*, **54**. 324, 1828 ; J. Tünnermann, *Kastner's Arch.*, **19**. 338, 1830 ; R. Wagner, *Zeit. anal. Chem.*, **6**. 170, 1867 ; J. Spiller, *Journ. Chem. Soc.*, **10**. 110, 1858 ; *Chem. News*, **8**. 280, 1863 ; **19**. 166, 1869 ; A. Naumann, *Ber.*, **42**. 3790, 1909 ; E. C. Franklin, *Amer. Chem. Journ.*, **20**. 828, 1898 ; J. Mercer, *B.A. Rep.*, **32**, 1844 ; F. J. Malaguti, *Compt. Rend.*, **35**, 945, 1852 ; *Ann. Chim. Phys.*, (3), **37**. 198, 1853 ; J. Persoz, *ib.*, (2), **63**. 273, 1836 ; F. Weppen, *Arch. Pharm.*, (2), **9**. 236, 1837 ; J. L. Lassaigne, *Journ. Chim. Méd.*, (2), **4**. 312, 1848 ; W. Suida, *Tschermak's Mitt.*, (2), **23**. 451, 1904 ; *Sitzber. Akad. Wien*, **113**. 725, 1904 ; R. Marc, *Zeit. phys. Chem.*, **75**. 710, 1910 ; J. F. Sacher, *Chem. Ztg.*, **34**. 647, 1910 ; J. Aub, *Lead Poisoning*, Baltimore, 19, 1926 : M. H. Klaproth, *Beiträge zur chemischen Kenntniss der Mineralkörper*, Berlin, 3. 167, 1802.

¹⁵ R. Salvadori, *Gazz. Chim. Ital.*, **24**. i, 87, 1904 ; M. Cszentnerszwer, G. Falka, and A. Awerbuch, *Zeit. phys. Chem.*, **115**. 29, 1925 ; L. F. Hawley, *Journ. Phys. Chem.*, **10**. 654, 1906 ; A. Isenburg, *Zeit. Elektrochem.*, **9**. 275, 1903 ; E. Euston, *Journ. Ind. Eng. Chem.*, **6**. 202, 382, 1914 ; **12**. 974, 1920 ; A. E. Nordenskjöld, *Geol. För. Förh. Stockholm*, **3**. 381, 1877 ; M. F. Heddle, *Mineralogy of Scotland*, Edinburgh, **1**. 147, 1901 ; *Min. Mag.*, **8**. 200, 1889 ; L. J. Spencer and E. D. Mountain, *ib.*, **20**. 67, 1923 ; A. Lacroix, *Compt. Rend.*, **123**. 761, 955, 1896 ; *Bull. Soc. Min.*, **8**. 35, 1885 ; A. Lacroix and A. de Schulten, *ib.*, **31**. 79, 1908 ; E. Bertrand, *ib.*, **4**. 87, 1881 ; L. Bourgeois, *ib.*, **11**. 222, 1888 ; *Bull. Soc. Chim.*, (2), **47**. 82, 1887 ; (2), **50**. 83, 1888 ; *Compt. Rend.*, **103**. 1089, 1886 ; J. N. Gannal, *ib.*, **16**. 1128, 1843 ; M. Versepuy, *ib.*, **16**. 1327, 1843 ; J. S. S. Brame, *Journ. Soc. Chem. Ind.*, **37**. 39, T, 1918 ; F. Southerden, *ib.*, **37**. 85, T, 1918 ; G. Flink, *Bull. Geol. Inst. Upsala*, **5**. 94, 1901 ; *Ark. Kem. Min.*, **3**. 35, 1910 ; *Zeit. Kryst.*, **36**. 198, 1902 ; E. Dittler, *ib.*, **53**. 166, 1914 ; P. A. von Bonsdorff, *Pogg. Ann.*, **40**. 207, 1837 ; H. Rose, *ib.*, **84**. 59, 1851 ; *Journ. prakt. Chem.*, (1), **54**. 24, 1854 ; C. Hochstetter, *ib.*, (1), **26**. 338, 1842 ; J. J. Prechtl, *ib.*, (1), **2**. 164, 1834 ; A. Altmann, *Zeit. anorg. Chem.*, **52**. 225, 1907 ; D. Strömholm, *ib.*, **38**. 446, 1904 ; *Ark. Kem. Min.*, **2**. 16, 1906 ; M. Pleissner, *Arb. Kaiser Ges. Amt.*, **26**. 403, 1907 ; F. Auerbach and H. Pick, *ib.*, **26**. 413, 1907 ; **45**. 117, 1913 ; *Umsetzung schwerlöslicher Bleisalze mit wassengen Lösungen Kohlensauerer Alkalien*, Berlin, 1913 ; *Zeit. Elektrochem.*, **19**. 830, 1913 ; C. A. Stevens, *Brit. Pat. No.* 16098, 1891 ; L. Falk, *German Pat., D.R.PP.* 241005, 1909 ; 265901, 1912 ; *Chem. Ztg.*, **34**. 567, 937, 1910 ; J. F. Sacher, *ib.*, **34**. 737, 833, 1910 ; **35**. 326, 1911 ; M. Kerstmann, *ib.*, **34**. 1322, 1910 ; E. S. Larsen, *Bull. U.S. Geol. Sur.*, 679, 1921 ; R. Krzizan, *Œster. Chem. Ztg.*, **8**. 173, 1905 ; K. Feist, *Arch. Pharm.*, **247**. 443, 1909 ; A. C. Becquerel, *Ann. Chim. Phys.*, (2), **54**. 146, 1833 ; M. Delaville, *ib.*, (1), **58**. 92, 1806 ; P. Yorke, *Phil. Mag.*, (3), **5**. 82, 1834 ; P. P. Philipenko, *Bull. Univ. Tomsk*, 63, 1915 ; T. Thunberg, *Zeit. phys. Chem.*, **106**. 305, 1923 ; F. Weigert, *ib.*, **106**. 313, 1923 ; C. Stalmann, *Dingler's Journ.*, **180**. 366, 1866 ; C. A. Klein, *Journ. Oil Colour Chem. Assoc.*, **2**. 8, 1919 ; A. Vogel, *Kastner's Arch.*, **23**. 84, 1832 ; H. Tomann, *Farben. Ztg.*, 279, 1904 ; G. J. Mulder, *Miquel's Bull.*, 302, 1839 ; *Liebig's Ann.*, **33**. 242, 1840 ; *Journ. prakt. Chem.*, (1), **18**. 127, 1839 ; (1), **19**. 70, 1840 ; J. A. Phillips, *Journ. Chem. Soc.*, **4**. 165, 1852 ; F. Clowes, *Proc. Chem. Soc.*, **18**. 46, 1902 ; F. Bosshardt, *Jahrb. Phil. Univ. Bern*, **4**. 63, 1924 ; A. L. Marshall and B. Bruzs, *Journ. Phys. Chem.*, **20**. 1184, 1925 ; H. Sjögren, *Geol. For. Förh. Stockholm*, **48**. 44, 1926.

§ 32. White-Lead

The manufacture of white-lead from metallic lead involves oxidation, hydration, and carbonation. In the most common method of manufacturing white-lead, the carbonation is made possible by the intermediate formation of an acetate or basic acetate. The Venetian process, clearly described by P. Vernatti [1] in 1678, is an elaboration of the methods practised about the beginning of the present era, and the process, as conducted in England, and in Holland, was described about a century later by G. Jars, J. H. G. von Justi, J. A. C. de Chaptal, J. H. M. von Poppe, S. F. Hermbstät, K. P. Funke, and J. F. Demachy. This modification is commonly called the **Dutch process,** or the **stack process.** It is possible to obtain a product of a similar composition by other processes more economical in time and labour ; but the working properties of white-lead as a pigment depend on many factors other than composition—*e.g.* fineness and uniformity of grain, covering or hiding power, etc. The pigment made by the stack process is held in greater esteem than when made by other processes, although in some cases it is almost impossible to distinguish stack white-lead from, say, chamber white-lead.

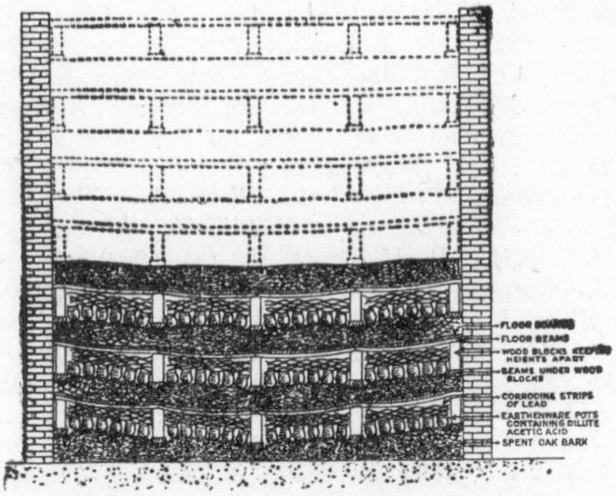

FIG. 122.—Diagrammatic Arrangements in the Stack Process.

In some stack processes, corrugated straps of lead, Fig. 122, are laid over rows of pots, containing acetic acid and water and resting on spent oak-bark. The straps of lead are covered with boards resting on beams and wooden blocks. Another layer of spent oak-bark is laid on the boards, this is followed by layers of pots, straps of lead, and boards as before. This is repeated until the chamber is filled. The stack is left for about 3 months when it is taken down. The white, opaque, corroded lead preserves the form of the original straps, but is much more bulky. Fig. 123 gives the appearance of a stack partly taken down. Trays of corroded lead are immersed in a stream of water, and passed between corrugated rollers to separate most of the " blue-lead " which has escaped corrosion from the white-lead. The white-lead is then crushed between rollers ; and after churning in water containing a little sodium carbonate to pre-cipitate the lead present as soluble lead acetate, and levigation, a white slurry is obtained. The white-lead gradually settles, and much of the water is syphoned off. The remaining " pulp " is gradually dried in shallow dishes or in other ways. A chamber 12 ft. × 20 ft. in area holds, say, 12 sets—totalling about 12,000 parts, 36 tons of lead, and 2400 gallons of dil. acetic acid. From 40 to 80 per cent. of the lead is corroded. According to C. A. Klein, the world's output of white-lead is about 250,000 tons, and of this about 180,000 tons is made by the stack process; 45,000 tons by the chamber pro-cess; and 50,000 tons by other processes.

FIG. 123.—Photograph of Stack Chamber partly taken Down.

C. Hochstetter showed that if lead is exposed to the vap. of acetic acid in air free from carbon dioxide, lead acetate alone is formed; this is taken to show that the carbon dioxide of white-lead is not derived from the decomposition of the acetic acid, and it must be obtained from some other source. If lead moist-ened with acetic acid be exposed for 24 hrs. to carbon dioxide free from air, between 30° and 40°, no change occurs, but if air be admitted, the metal becomes coated with white-lead in 6 hrs. This shows that the oxygen of the air is necessary for the oxidation of the lead. This conclusion was also made pre-viously by E. Reichardt. White-lead is formed when various basic salts of lead are treated with carbon dioxide, and since the ratio $PbCO_3 : PbO$ or $Pb(OH)_2$ in white-lead varies with the mode and conditions under which it is produced, it follows that the composition of the white lead is independent of the degree of basicity of the salt employed. It is therefore inferred that during the formation of white-lead in the stack process (i) lead is oxidized by atm. oxygen in the presence of water, forming lead hydroxide; (ii) this product is converted into normal lead acetate by the acetic acid, and the normal salt is converted into the basic acetate by the dissolution of more lead hydroxide; and (iii) the basic acetate reacts with carbon dioxide, forming basic lead carbonate, and regenerates the normal lead acetate which acts as a solvent for more lead hydroxide. The acetic acid thus plays the part of a catalytic agent in a cycle of reactions involving the production of a soln. of lead hydroxide, the conversion of the hydroxide into basic acetate, and its precipitation as white-lead by carbon dioxide. The reaction can be symbolized in various ways dependent on what composition be postulated for the basic acetate. C. Hochstetter assumed

$$3\{Pb(C_2H_3O_2)_2.2Pb(OH)_2\} + 4CO_2 = 2\{2PbCO_3.Pb(OH)_2\} + 3Pb(C_2H_3O_2)_2 + 4H_2O.$$

Since the solvent action of a soln. of lead acetate on lead hydroxide increases to a maximum as the conc. of the soln. decreases, it is highly probable that many other basic acetates are concerned in the process, or else the function of the lead acetate is merely that of a solvent, so that the essential process is the direct conversion of lead hydroxide into the basic carbonate: $3Pb(OH)_2 + 2CO_2 = 2PbCO_3.Pb(OH)_2 + 2H_2O$. J. Pelouze showed that formic acid cannot be employed in place of acetic acid because it does not form a basic formate which can be decomposed by carbon dioxide. He also showed that when a lead plate is suspended within a vessel filled with oxygen and carbon dioxide, and having a layer of acetic acid at the bottom, the production of white-lead is accompanied by the disappearance of an equivalent quantity of carbon dioxide and oxygen, while the acetic acid " suffers scarcely any diminution." The unwashed white-lead contained some normal acetate—C. Hochstetter said 2–12 per cent. Of course there is a complicated by-play of reactions; there is a steady flow of hydroxide into the reacting system ; the basic acetates and carbonates are open to attack by acetic acid ; there is a reaction between normal lead acetate and carbonate and carbon dioxide, forming in each case normal lead carbonate. If the oxidizing reactions predominate, then the carbon dioxide content of the product is low. As soon as the lead has been all converted into basic carbonate, the supply of lead hydroxide ceases, and normal lead carbonate begins to accumulate in the system. The corrosion product, as lifted from the stack, Fig. 124, is heterogeneous; and in the grinding and washing, soluble lead acetate and free acetic acid are removed, along with adventitious impurities like tan-bark, etc. The soluble acetate is converted into carbonate by the addition of sodium carbonate, and, at the same time, any lead hydroxide also present is carbonated. Some blue-lead is oxidized and carbonated.

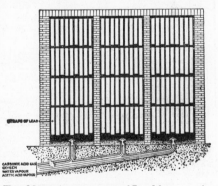

FIG. 124.—Arrangement of Lead for corrosion in the Chamber Process.

The process has been discussed by G. Lunge, J. G. Gentele, F. Bosshardt, J. A. Smythe, etc.; and numerous modifications of the details of the process have been patented.

In the original Dutch process, and Venetian process, horse-dung was employed as the source of heat and carbon dioxide ; and wet hay has also been employed. R. Fishwick in 1781 proposed to employ " used tanner's bark," and T. Grace

" spent grapes," or " spent hops." The use of tan-bark has been generally approved because there is less risk of decolorizing the white-lead by hydrogen sulphide, but the fermentation or the bacterial process of decay is slower, and the conversion of the blue-lead to white-lead is slower. The temp. may rise as high as 80° during the fermentation, but 50°–60° is about the average. Although the stack process is essentially the same as that which has been in operation for hundreds of years, the manufacturer has by numberless trials and failures found the conditions which enable him to ensure successful results—subject of course to the general perversity of inanimate objects. In order to obtain more control of the operations—temperature, proportions of air, moisture, carbon dioxide, and acetic acid vapour—the so-called *chamber process* is employed. Here the stable litter or tan-bark as a source of heat and carbon dioxide is eliminated. The product, as a pigment, can be made to rival that obtained by the stack process. This mode of manufacturing white-lead is sometimes called the *German process*, or the *Klangenfurth process*, having been extensively employed in Carinthia since the eighteenth century for the corrosion of the virgin lead of Bleiberg. This process has been discussed by T. Richardson,[2] and many others. These plates or straps of lead are suspended in brick chambers as illustrated in Fig. 124. The mixture of gases—air, carbon dioxide, water vap., and acetic acid vap.—in the desired proportions is brought into the chambers through pipes in the floor. Openings in the top and sides of the chamber enable the ventilation and the admission of air to be regulated. A chamber temp. of 55°–70° is obtained by the hot gases supplemented by the heat of the chemical action. The time occupied for the corrosion is from 42 to 60 days. The appearance of a chamber ready for " stripping " is illustrated by Fig. 125. The product is treated as indicated in connection with stack lead. According to J. A. Smythe, normal stack white-lead is usually rather more carbonated than the chamber product since the ratio $PbCO_3 : Pb(OH)_2$ in the former case is from 2·22 to 2·72, and in the latter case from 1·88 to 2·56.

Numerous modifications have been described and patented. The object is usually to increase the speed of the reactions by the comminution of the metal, as suggested by J. B. J. D. Boussingault.[3] Thus, the Union Lead and Oil Co. proposed to use fibrous lead in place of the lead strips, but without success. In the so-called *L. Carter's process*, described by J. S. Staudt, and C. D. Holley, lead is sprayed by blowing a jet of steam against molten lead; and directed into revolving wooden drums. A mixture of acetic acid and water is then sprayed into

FIG. 125.—Photograph showing the Corroded Lead in Chamber Process.

the drums, and the product carbonated. The treatment is frequently repeated during 12 days. The plant at Chicago. Ill., is said to have an annual capacity of 20,000 tons, and that at Omaha, Neb., 10,000 tons. E. Bailey and co-workers volatilized the lead between carbon electrodes, and treated the vap. with the necessary gases.

In the stack and chamber processes, the basic acetates of lead are exposed to the action of carbon dioxide, the acetate or acetic acid serving as a catalytic agent. There is a series of patents in which it is proposed to make white-lead by the action of moist air and carbon dioxide or soln. of alkali carbonates on lead vapour, molten lead, spongy lead, etc.[4] Lead monoxide is not easily hydrated, and J. Pelouze[5] showed that the direct carbonization of lead monoxide is difficult, although in the presence of a soln. of lead acetate, it is readily hydrated and carbonated ; or, as R. W. E. MacIvor showed, in the presence of ammonium acetate. On the other hand, the so-called lead suboxide is readily oxidized, hydrated, or carbonated. In the so-called *mild process*, or the *W. H. Rowley's process* for making white-lead, metallic lead, air, water, and carbon dioxide are the only substances required. In the processes of J. Welch and J. Evans, of 1814, and of S. Gardner, of 1840, lead was oxidized in rotating barrels so arranged that the metal was subjected to continual attrition, and afterwards carbonated. W. H. Rowley extended the principle and atomized the lead with superheated steam so as to form oxides, suboxides, or basic hydroxides as a sludge. This is floated into wooden cylinders and carbonated. C. D. Holley said that the composition of the finished product approximates $3PbO.2CO_2.H_2O$, *i.e.* $Pb(OH)_2.2PbCO_3$. Only one-third of the total hydration, which the lead undergoes in its conversion to white-lead, is accomplished during the hydration stage ; the remainder occurs during carbonation when there is a considerable increase in the bulk of the material. In the so-called *G. Bischof's process*, carried on in a more or less modified form by the Brimsdown Lead Co., finely ground litharge is partly reduced by water-gas at 250°–300° so as to produce the so-called suboxide. The suboxide is agitated in water while exposed to air. This converts it into hydrated oxide which is then carbonated for about 24 hrs. so as to produce white-lead. The addition of a little lead acetate to the part of hydrated oxide is said to facilitate the carbonation.

P. Bronner[6] obtained a basic sulphate by the action of soda-lye on precipitated lead sulphate at 70°, and converted this into white-lead by digestion with a soln. of sodium carbonate. Several modifications have been patented. The Earl of Dundonald[7] exposed a moist mixture of lead oxide and alkali chloride to the air, and obtained basic lead carbonate. The original observation is due to C. W. Scheele. J. G. Dale and E. Milner passed carbon dioxide into the mixture until the mixture was neutral. The sodium carbonate which was formed reacted with the basic chloride to produce white-lead. H. Hof carbonated the mixture of basic chlorides of lead and magnesium obtained by dissolving lead oxide in an aq. soln. of magnesium chloride. Several variations of these processes have been proposed. In another series of processes,[8] mixtures of normal lead carbonate and lead hydroxide or oxide are treated with carbon dioxide, maybe with a little lead acetate as catalytic agent. R. Palmer, and I. Baggs treated basic lead acetate with sodium carbonate or hydro-carbonate, and dried the washed product.

Precipitation processes.—In another series of reactions, basic lead acetate—prepared from lead splashes or litharge—is treated with carbon dioxide. For instance, the process of L. J. Thénard,[9] designed in 1801, was employed in a works at Clichy, and hence is sometimes called the *French process*. A soln. of basic lead acetate was made by digesting a soln. of the normal acetate, or pyroligneous spirit with litharge ; the liquid was treated with carbon dioxide until it was neutral or only faintly acid ; the liquor now containing normal lead acetate was again treated with litharge, etc., and the precipitate was washed and dried. The process was patented in England by W. Gossage and E. W. Benson in 1836, but given up about 1880 owing to the difficulty of preventing the formation of an undue amount of normal lead carbonate. C. Hochstetter found that when carbon dioxide is passed through five separate portions of basic lead acetate soln. until the liquids are neutral, each of the five precipitates has the composition $2PbCO_3.Pb(OH)_2$.

A modification of the French process was suggested by F. H. Sharpe. The so-called *W. L. Matheson's process*, described by C. D. Holley, is a modification of that proposed by E. W. Dahl ; there, the lead is "feathered" by running the molten metal into water. The spongy lead thus formed is put in tubs or tanks with dil. acetic acid, and converted into the basic acetate by a current of air and steam. The mixture is then treated with carbon dioxide, and the white-lead so produced is washed and dried. Some of these processes occupy only a few days, and the products are referred to as *quick process white-leads*. Instead of treating the soln. of basic acetate with carbon dioxide, H. J. B. Condy, R. Haack, J. H. Noad and Z. de Ferranti, Z. Peska, T. R. Sewell, E. Waller, and C. White and J. W. Patterson used ammonium or alkali carbonates as precipitating agents; J. Löwe, lead carbonate. R. Matthews and co-workers, J. O. Handy, and J. Frölich recommended precipitating the basic lead carbonates in the presence of colloids—gelatin, gum, etc. In another set of processes, various soln. of lead salts are treated with carbon dioxide, alkali or ammonium carbonates, magnesia or magnesium carbonate, etc. O. Eyckens used soln. of lead nitrite; P. Brown and B. Young, C. Button and H. G. Dyar, C. Delafield, J. Hemming, E. Lampe and L. Preuss, V. P. Lagrange, G. Lunge and C. H. M. Lyte, H. L. Pattinson, O. J. Steinhart and J. L. F. Vogel, and H. Wilcox, soln. of lead nitrate; W. Gossage, H. L. Pattinson, and G. Robinson, soln. of lead chloride; E. R. Blundstone, F. J. Corbett, H. Franzen, and J. S. MacArthur, soln. of lead tartrate ; and S. O. Cowper-Coles, and P. Spence, soln. of alkali plumbites.

Electrolytic processes.—Several proposals have been made to electrolyze acid soln., or salt soln. with anodes of lead or a lead compound; and convert the soluble lead salt or lead hydroxide so produced into white-lead either in the cell itself, or outside. Electrolytic processes have been discussed by C. F. Carrier,[10] L. Falk, W. Hartmann, R. G. Bowman, P. Beck, D. M. Kyte, E. H. C. Monckton, T. Okuno, M. Nicolaieff; as electrolyte, C. A. Stevens used dil. *nitric, hydrochloric, sulphuric, acetic, oxalic, tartaric, or citric acid ;* T. D. Bottome, A. B. Browne, E. D. Chaplin, S. O. Cowper-Coles, M. Manent, M. Nicolaieff, R. S. Owens, A. M. Söderlund, J. B. Tibbits, H. Weyer, R. P. Williams, and H. C. Woltereck, soln. of *ammonium or alkali nitrates ;* W. Borchers, C. F. Carrier, E. D. Chaplin, B. Huick, A. Isenburg, C. Luckow, J. Meyrueis, J. Oettli, R. S. Owens, A. J. Riban, E. Ronco, O. C. and H. H. Strecker, H. C. Woltereck, and A. Zucker, soln. of *sodium chloride ;* E. D. Chaplin, soln. of *sodium chlorate ;* J. W. Richards and C. W. Roepper, and C. F. Carrier, soln. of *sodium sulphite ;* T. D. Bottome, soln. of *sodium thiosulphate ;* F. W. Morris and co-workers, soln. of *alkali formates ;* and C. F. Carrier, Z. de Ferranti and J. H. Noad, E. A. Sperry, and C. P. Townsend, soln. of *sodium acetate.* W. G. France and D. McBurney studied the effect of gelatin on the electrodeposition of basic lead carbonate. G. Bredig and F. Haber suggested bubbling carbon dioxide and air through a soln. of sodium carbonate in which colloidal lead has been dispersed by an electrical discharge with platinum anode and lead cathode. They claimed that the product is good but the consumption of electrical energy is high.

The composition of white-lead.—In the twelfth-century Latin version of Geber's *De investigatione magisterii*, it is said that white-lead is not changed when dissolved in acetic acid and evaporated, but is purified only. This shows that Geber regarded white-lead as a compound of lead and acetic acid. A similar assumption was made in the seventeenth and eighteenth centuries by A. Libavius,[11] N. Lemery, and P. J. Macquer, but in 1774, T. Bergman showed that it contains a carbonate—*calx plumbi aerata*—because, when treated with an acid, it effervesces, giving off carbon dioxide. Analyses made between 1828 and 1874 by C. Hochstetter, C. Link, G. Bischof, A. Bette, G. J. Mulder, G. C. Wittstein, C. H. Pfaff, J. A. Phillips, F. Hofmann, etc., led to the view that white-lead is a basic carbonate, symbolized in the ideal case $Pb(OH)_2.2PbCO_3$, or $3PbO.2CO_2.H_2O$. This view is favoured by the known tendency of lead to form basic salts. If the action of the carbon dioxide in the precipitation of white-lead be long continued, the normal carbonate is formed, so that white-lead may be mixed with more or less normal carbonate. The composition of different varieties of white-lead on the market varies, and C. A. Klein said that the carbon dioxide then generally has between 11·8 and 12·5 per cent., but specimens are found with much lower and higher proportions of that gas. C. D. Holley quotes a specification in which the permissible variation in composition is $PbCO_3$, 67–80 per cent., and $Pb(OH)_2$, 20–32 per cent. G. W. Wigner and R. H. Harland regarded white-lead as a mixture of lead hydroxide and lead carbonate in the molar proportion 1 : 3. Analyses have been reported by C. F. Carrier, P. Beck, E. Euston, J. F. Sacher, P. Hamberger, R. K. Meade, C. von Weise, W. A. Davis and C. A. Klein, etc. White-lead is therefore a mixture of one or more basic carbonates with lead carbonate, and more or less lead hydroxide or hydrated lead oxide and water ; and, as shown by E. Lenoble, and J. F. Sacher, in many cases, its composition approximates to $2PbCO_3.Pb(OH)_2$. Certain impurities may be present. Some may be deliberately added. Chalk, for instance, has been used for fraudulent adulteration. On this account, the anonymous Basil Valentine recommended chemists to make their own white-lead. E. Norgate also warned artists against adulterated white-lead ; and near the middle of the eighteenth century, G. Jars said that white-lead containing chalk was called ceruse, and that the pure white-lead was called *blanc de plomb*. P. Hamberger reported a sample of white-lead with 22·8 per cent. of chalk. G. J. Mulder found traces of lead sulphate and chloride ; C. Hochstetter, and E. Euston found a little lead acetate ; and G. C. Wittstein, silica, ferric oxide, and lead sulphate. F. Weil and F. Jean showed that if free lead oxide be present, the product mixed with oil of cloves becomes yellow in 24 hrs. Sometimes the cream-colour of white-lead is masked by the addition of a little blue pigment. Mixtures of white-lead with barium sulphate,[12] silica, zinc oxide, whiting, magnesia, soapstone, china clay, or gypsum, furnish the so-called *composite white-lead*.[13]

The properties of white-lead.—White-lead is normally considered to be a white, non-crystalline powder. According to C. Hochstetter,[14] white-lead is a dense, earthy mass which when diffused through water and examined under the microscope, consists of non-crystalline, transparent, round or oval globules having an average diameter of 0·000025 cm. and rarely attaining 0·00010 cm. The particles obtained with the quicker processes are usually larger and more transparent than those furnished by the stack process. W. Stein, R. S. Owens, and J. L. Breton made some observations on this subject. From data quoted by C. D. Holley, the extreme sizes of the particles of stack process white-lead are 0·00005 cm. and 0·00065 cm.—average, 0·000175 cm. ; and for quick process white-lead 0·00005 cm. and 0·00045 cm.—average, 0·0003 cm. According to W. G. France and D. McBurney, the average size of basic lead carbonate particles, electrolytically precipitated at 20° is reduced to approximately one-third by the presence of 0·013 per cent. of gelatin. The decrease after the first addition is not so large, being approximately proportional to the conc. of the gelatin added. The particles are of more uniform size when gelatin is present. The grain-size depends on the method of preparation and grinding. The granules of white-leads made by the quick processes are more uniform in size than those made by the stack process. This, according to G. W. Thompson, enables the particles of white-lead made by the stack process to be more closely packed, and to contain the smallest volume of voids. According to C. D. Holley, it is rare to find crystalline carbonate in white-lead which has less carbon dioxide than the theoretical amount required for $2PbCO_3.Pb(OH)_2$. According to L. Bourgeois, however, under high magnification, white-lead made by the stack process contains numerous crystals, too small to measure crystallographically ; but that precipitated by sodium carbonate from a soln. of lead acetate consists of small prisms or double pyramids ; and that obtained by the French process, consists for the most part of hexagonal plates of the basic carbonate, $3PbO.CO_2.H_2O$, and the remainder of strongly doubly refracting needles of normal carbonate. He said that white-lead consists of a mixture of cerussite and hydrocerussite. L. Falk said that the white-lead prepared by the hot chamber process is a mixture of crystalline and amorphous $3PbO.2CO_2.H_2O$; and that obtained by the cold chamber process is mostly amorphous ; J. F. Sacher said that both kinds are amorphous. According to E. Euston, the hardness of the " porcelain-like " crusts which form on the crusts of white-lead, as it comes from the corroding chamber, is due to the cementing effect of the colloidal basic acetate present during the formation of the crust.

According to C. D. Holley, an experienced painter can detect the difference between aged and unaged white-leads both in the dry state and in oil. The cause of the ageing is not known. G. Hauser found the sp. gr. of white-lead to vary with the mode of preparation from 6·4 to 6·5 ; H. A. Gardner gave 6·81.

L. Meister said that in darkness, white-lead may acquire a yellow tinge which disappears on exposure to light. J. A. Phillips found that white-lead made by the stack process is stable at 105°, all its water is expelled at 155°, and the carbon dioxide begins to come off at 183° ; W. A. Davis and C. A. Klein observed no effect at 110°, decomposition began at 120°, but it required a temp. of 212° to drive off the water. The carbon dioxide began to come off at 171°. K. Friedrich said that basic lead carbonate begins decomposing at 430° and that the maximum thermal effect is at 460°. At higher temp. red-lead is formed (q.v.). J. L. Breton said that white-lead paint is inferior to the zinc oxide paints in resisting heat, and sudden variations of temp. When used as a paint, in exposed places, white-lead has a tendency to become granular ; the disease is called *chalking* or *flouring*. The cause of the phenomenon has not been established. C. D. Holley said that it may be produced by the presence of fatty acids in the oils ; over-heating during the grinding of the white-lead ; and the presence of an abnormal quantity of lead acetate—in the white-lead. C. P. van Hoeck studied the hygroscopicity of white-lead. R. Salvadori said that ordinary basic lead carbonate is fully as stable as the normal carbonate, if not more so ; and that the latter is readily converted into the former by boiling with water, or by heating it under water for several hours.

J. L. Breton said that white-lead paint resists the action of certain acids better than zinc oxide paints, but this is not the case with hydrofluoric acid. According to W. Thomason, the solubility of white-lead in 0·15–0·25 per cent. hydrochloric acid is proportional to the conc., and in food-stuffs inversely proportional to the conc. of the proteins. E. Euston found that a soln. of ammonium chloride removes the lead hydroxide from white-lead. As indicated above, H. Hof reported that white-lead is completely dissolved in the cold without decomposition by a soln. of magnesium chloride of sp. gr. 1·16, forming $2PbCO_3.PbCl_2$; with a boiling soln., lead chloride is produced. J. L. Breton said that white-lead paints resist attack by strong oxidizing agents, like sodium hypochlorite, less readily than do the zinc oxide paints. White-lead is discoloured by hydrogen sulphide owing to the formation of dark brown lead sulphide. J. L. Breton said that white-lead paint resists attack by hydrogen sulphide less readily than zinc oxide paints. E. Täuber said that the darkening of the white-lead paint vanishes on exposure to light. When white-lead suspended in water is treated with hydrogen sulphide, J. F. Sacher said that only the lead hydroxide is attacked because no carbon dioxide is given off. At ordinary temp., the attack is incomplete, forming **lead hydroxysulpho-carbonate**, $Pb(OH)_2.PbS.4PbCO_3$, but at 90° the attack is complete. E. Beckmann and P. Waentig found that in liquid hydrogen sulphide, white-lead is immediately blackened. F. W. O. de Coninck said that five hours' boiling with a soln. of sodium or potassium nitrate does not decompose white-lead. J. L. Breton found that white-lead paint resists penetration by efflorescences of saltpetre better than does zinc oxide paint.

According to J. F. Sacher, carbon dioxide in the presence of water gradually transforms white-lead into the normal carbonate ; and, according to F. Auerbach and H. Pick, with alkali carbonate, there is a balanced reaction : $3PbCO_3+K_2CO_3+2H_2O \rightleftharpoons Pb_3(OH)_2(CO_3)_2+2KHCO_3$. E. Euston found that when various samples of white-lead or lead carbonate are stirred or agitated with a soln. of basic lead acetate at room temp. lead hydroxide is invariably drawn from the soln., and there is a gain in weight ; at the same time, the carbon dioxide content was found to fall from 12·0 to 16·3 per cent. as low as 10·1 to 10·3 in extreme cases. The extent of the action depends on the basicity of the lead acetate soln., on the time, and on the relative proportion of the solid and soln. The reaction is completed only when an excess of the basic acetate soln. is present. With a sample containing both normal and basic lead carbonate, the equilibrium can be disturbed in either direction by the addition of more basic lead acetate soln. or of normal lead acetate soln. According to J. L. Breton, alcohol, benzene, toluene, or carbon disulphide does not act on white-lead paint, but ether does react therewith. E. Euston found that the lead hydroxide is not dissolved from white-lead by a soln. of sugar. J. L. Breton stated that freshly applied white-lead paint gives an emanation containing lead which can be detected by the tetramethyl diaminodiphenyl-methane test; and, added M. Herman, the exhalation only occurs during the first two days. R. S. Owens showed that specimens of white-lead with small granules take up less oil than specimens with larger granules, and the colour is better. L. Meister said that linseed oil unites intimately with white-lead, and the lead hydroxide neutralizes the free fatty acids. There has been some discussion as to whether hydrolysis or saponification occurs with normal white-lead. If free lead hydroxide were present the saponification would occur. G. J. Mulder, and M. von Pettenkofer showed that no saponification occurs with dry white-lead, but slow oxidation of the oil occurs. J. B. Hannay and A. E. Leighton questioned if saponification occurs when white-lead is ground with linseed oil, giving rise to peculiar working properties which other pigments do not have. They showed that a very small trace of lead oleate in the oil will cause serious blackening under the influence of a small proportion of hydrogen sulphide in the air, and under conditions where good white-lead would hold its colour. Hence saponification would be deleterious. They concluded that no such reaction occurs between the lead and the oil, and that dry white-lead produces a slow oxidation of the oil. J. B. Hannay and A. E. Leighton's conclusion with lead oleate, however, does not necessarily apply to lead linoleate. W. A. Davis and C. A. Klein showed that lead soaps are really produced when white-lead is mixed with linseed oil, and that some of them are soluble, others insoluble, in ether. The reaction is ascribed to the free fatty acids present in the oil; if these were absent, the evidence is against saponification.

REFERENCES.

[1] C. Hochstetter, *Journ. prakt. Chem.*, (1), **26**. 338, 1842; C. H. Pfaff, *Schweigger's Journ.*, **53**. 119, 1828; J. Richards, *Journ. Franklin Inst.*, **28**. 8, 1839; *U.S. Pat. No.* 95, 1836; J. Pelouze, *Ann. Chim. Phys.*, (3), **4**. 104, 1842; *Compt. Rend.*, **13**. 1051, 1841; J. G. Gentele, *Dingler's Journ.*, **63**. 196, 1837; J. G. Martin, *German Pat.*, *D.R.P.* 7051, 1879; *Dingler's Journ.*, **237**. 246, 1880; G. Lunge, *ib.*, **180**. 46, 1866; M. Neuerburg, *German Pat.*, *D.R.P.* 658, 1877; *Dingler's Journ.*, **229**. 33, 1878; F. Fischer, *ib.*, **224**. 293, 1877; R. Horn, *ib.*, **247**. 81, 1883; *Chem. Ztg.*, **6**. 1267, 1882; **10**. 53, 1886; H. Stegmann, *Gewerbeblatt Grossherzogthum Hessen*, **40**. 245, 1877; *Deut. Ind. Ztg.*, 337, 1877; N. Chercheffsky, *Chim. Ind.*, **11**. 45, 1921; W. R. Waelty, *Chem. Met. Engg.*, **32**. 491, 1925; G. W. Thompson, *Journ. Soc. Chem. Ind.*, **28**. 406, 1909; J. A. Smythe, *Lead*, London, 248, 1923; W. Baker, *Brit. Pat. No.* 1288, 1860; J. Brierly, *ib.*, 3190, 1809; J. Ham, *ib.*, 5377, 1826; H. Hannen, B. F. Pine, and T. Woods, *ib.*, 2998, 1868; C. D. Ismay, *ib.*, 23969, 1895; A. J. Meier, *ib.*, 26624, 1908; J. V. Walton, *ib.*, 2116, 1893; R. Fishwick, *ib.*, 1581, 1787; T. Grace, *ib.*, 2461, 1800; H. Kirberg, *Chem. Ind.*, **7**. 397, 1884; H. Endemann, *Amer. Chemist*, **7**. 457, 1876; P. Vernatti, *Phil. Trans.*, **12**. 935, 1678; G. Jars, *Voyages métallurgiques*, Paris, **2**. 530, 1780; C. A. Klein, *Oil and Colour Trades Journ.*, **2**. 8, 1919; J. H. G. von Justi, *Vollständige Abhandlung von denen Manufakturen und Fabriken*, Kopenhagen, 1758; J. H. M. von Poppe, *Geschichte der Technologie*, Göttingen, **3**. 212, 1811; S. F. Hermbstädt, *Grundriss der experimentallen Kameralchemie*, Berlin, 1808; K. P. Funke, *Naturgeschichte und Technologie*, Wien, **3**. 451, 1812; J. A. C. de Chaptal, *Chimie appliquée aux arts*, Paris, **4**. 301, 1807; J. F. Demachy, *Der Laborant im Grossen*, Leipzig, **2**. 187, 1801. I am indebted to Messrs. Cookson, Newcastle-on Tyne, for Figs. 122 to 125. F. Bosshardt, *Jahrb. Phil. Univ. Bern*, **4**. 63, 1924; E. Reichardt, *Grundlagen der Beurteilung des Trinkwassers*, Halle a. S., 107, 1880.

[2] M. Liebig, *Zeit. angew. Chem.*, **17**. 1672, 1904; O. Herting, *Chem. Ztg.*, **27**. 923, 1903; P. Beck, *Chem. Ind.*, **30**. 272, 1907; J. A. Smythe, *Lead*, London, 261, 1923; K. von Weiss, *Monatss. Gew. Ver. Köln*, 300, 1872; *Dingler's Journ.*, **208**. 434, 1873; F. W. Shaw, *Chem. Met. Engg.*, **30**. 51, 1924; W. R. Waelty, *ib.*, **32**. 491, 1925; E. Lenoble, *Chim. Ind.*, **10**. 836, 1923; S. J. Cook, *Canadian Chem. Journ.*, **3**. 145, 1919; T. Richardson, *Phil. Mag.*, (3), **34**. 116, 1849; W. Baker, *Brit. Pat. No.* 1474, 1874; J. Creed, *ib.*, 651, 1749; C. R. Lothman, *ib.*, 11521, 1847;

E. M. Noble, *ib.*, 3099, 1808; J. S. Saxelbye, *ib.*, 2758, 1804; E. V. Gardner, *ib.*, 731, 1882 ; 3839, 1885 ; 12414, 1890.
³ E. Bailey, W. T. Hey, and C. R. Cox, *Brit. Pat. No.* 7877, 1898 ; G. W. Burton, *ib.*, 260, 1858 ; L. Brumleu, *ib.*, 1437, 1875 ; W. Cross, *ib.*, 633, 1883 ; E. W. Dahl, *ib.*, 160395, 1920 ; E. V. Gardner, *ib.*, 731, 1882 ; 3839, 1885 ; 12414, 1890 ; W. Gossage and E. W. Benson, *ib.*, 7046, 1836 ; G. F. Hagner, *ib.*, 4211, 1818 ; F. M. Lyte, *ib.*, 633, 1871 ; 4491, 1877 ; J. C. Martin, *ib.*, 1300, 1877 ; 1054, 1879 ; 864, 1883 ; J. Major, W. Wright, and G. H. Jones, *ib.*, 1260, 1869 ; N. K. Morris, *ib.*, 15903, 1890 ; T. Richardson, *ib.*, 12246, 1848 ; A. A. de Rostaing, *ib.*, 937, 1858 ; A. J. Smith, *ib.*, 4405, 1882 ; 14656, 1892 ; Union Lead and Oil Co., *ib.*, 19979, 19981, 1902 ; W. P. Thompson, *ib.*, 20226, 1914 ; H. Woodward, *ib.*, 4273, 1882 ; J. B. J. D. Boussingault, *Ann. Chim. Phys.*, (2), 54. 264, 1833 ; *Journ. prakt. Chem.*, (1), 2. 162, 1834 ; Acme White Lead and Colour Works, *German Pat.*, *D.R.P.* 230543, 1910 ; J. A. de la Fontaine, *ib.*, 117038, 1899 ; E. van der Hoff, *ib.*, 81590, 1894 ; A. Munsche, *ib.*, 151514, 1903 ; J. Walter, *Zeit. anorg. Chem.*, 3. 449, 1897 ; F. Winteler, *Zeit. angew. Chem.*, 18. 1179, 1905 ; E. L. Schubarth, *Journ. prakt. Chem.*, (1), 24. 328, 1841 ; *Verh. Ver. Beförd. Gewerb. Preussen*, 20. 138, 1841 ; J. S. Staudt, *Journ. Ind. Eng. Chem.*, 1. 758, 1909 ; C. D. Holley, *The Lead and Zinc Pigments*, New York, 74, 1909.
⁴ W. Adrop and F. H. Parker, *Brit. Pat. No.* 684, 1891 ; T. T. Benfield, *ib.*, 25009, 1895 ; L. Brumleu, *ib.*, 10551, 1883 ; W. E. S. Burn and E. J. Case, *ib.*, 25130, 1899 ; A. C. J. Charlier, *ib.*, 552, 1899 ; T. H. Cobley, *ib.*, 18709, 1891 ; A. H. Eyles, H. St. Rapelye, and A. Applegate, *ib.*, 30242, 1897 ; F. M. Lyte, *ib.*, 4491, 1877 ; E. Montebruno, *ib.*, 6520, 1833 ; H. Robertson, *ib.*, 603, 1866 ; A. W. Southard, G. Cook, and A. H. Clark, *ib.*, 1658, 1899 ; G. Wildes, *ib.*, 9064, 1848 ; J. Woolrich, *ib.*, 7830, 1838 ; J. E. and A. R. Seeley, *U.S. Pat. No.* 1325960, 1917 ; A. Chenot, *Compt. Rend.*, 36. 550, 1853 ; M. Versepuy, *ib.*, 16. 1128, 1843 ; A. Girard, *Bull. Soc. Chim.*, (2), 8. 456, 1867 ; J. B. Torassa, P. I. Muston, and H. W. Wood, *Brit. Pat. No.* 6520, 1833 ; *Dingler's Journ.*, 54. 127, 1834 ; J. N. Gannal, *ib.*, 106. 273, 1847 ; *Compt. Rend.*, 16. 1327, 1843 ; E. A. Ashcroft, *Chem. Trade Journ.*, 65. 224, 1919 ; A. R. White, *Wisconsin Eng.*, 15. 133, 1910 ; C. D. Holley, *Journ. Soc. Chem. Ind.*, 28. 403, 1909 ; W. H. Rowley, *U.S. Pat. Nos.* 713155, 1902 ; 785023, 1905.
⁵ P. Beck, *Chem. Ind.*, 30. 277, 1907 ; K. Peters, *German Pat.*, *D.R.P.* 133316, 1901 ; G. Bischof, *ib.*, 56517, 1890 ; 107625, 1898 ; *Schweigger's Journ.*, 51. 228, 1827 ; *Brit. Pat. No.* 11602, 1890 ; J. G. Dale and E. Millner, *ib.*, 2443, 1869 ; E. Heard, *ib.*, 7756, 1838 ; J. W. H. James, *ib.*, 5287, 1891 ; R. W. E. McIvor, *ib.*, 10426, 1888 ; R. W. E. MacIvor, F. A. Darlington, G. Paul, and J. Allan, *ib.*, 6815, 1889 ; J. C. Martin, *ib.*, 223, 1876 ; W. Maugham, *ib.*, 7326, 1837 ; A. Orr, *ib.*, 15406, 1887 ; F. H. Sharpe, *ib.*, 21292, 1911 ; C. W. and T. R. Tebbutt, *ib.*, 7531, 1838 ; W. V. Wilson, *ib.*, 4275, 1882 ; C. D. Holley, *Journ. Soc. Chem. Ind.*, 28. 403, 1909 ; *The Lead and Zinc Pigments*, New York, 85, 1909 ; W. H. Rowley, *U.S. Pat. Nos.* 713155, 1902 ; 785023, 1905 ; S. Gardner, *ib.*, 1744, 1840 ; J. Welch and J. Evans, Aug. 14, 1814 ; J. Pelouze, *Ann. Chim. Phys.*, (3), 4. 104, 1842 ; A. Salmony, *Chem. Ztg.*, 31. 955, 978, 1907.
⁶ W. Bell and T. M. and A. G. Fell, *Brit. Pat. No.* 1703, 1866 ; W. E. B. Blenkinsop and F. M. Lyte, *ib.*, 11926, 1888 ; P. Bronner, *ib.*, 16706, 1889 ; 16184, 1892 ; S. Cooper, *ib.*, 819, 1859 ; T. M. and A. G. Fell, *ib.*, 1464, 1867 ; A. Honman and V. Vulliez, *ib.*, 8022, 1891 ; F. M. Lyte, *ib.*, 2920, 1888 ; W. B. Priest, *ib.*, 17145, 1894 ; E. Lampe and L. Preuss, *German Pat.*, *D.R.P.* 140489, 1902 ; J. N. Zeitler, *ib.*, 61237, 1890.
⁷ J. G. Dale and E. Milner, *Brit. Pat. No.* 1117, 1868 ; Earl of Dundonald, *ib.*, 2189, 1797 ; T. M. and A. G. Fell, *ib.*, 1465, 1867 ; J. M. Fourmentin, *ib.*, 11710, 1847 ; J. Keir, *ib.*, 2927, 1806 ; W. Maugham, *ib.*, 7326, 1837 ; E. Mianer, *ib.*, 1881, 1872 ; 4053, 1875 ; B. C. Molloy and D. G. Fitzgerald, *ib.*, 266, 1874 ; J. Wilkinson, *ib.*, 2321, 1799 ; J. Wright and T. Cobley, 325, 1867 ; C. W. Scheele, *Crell's Ann.*, ii, 220, 1785 ; H. Hof, *Chem. Ztg.*, 33. 1077, 1909 ; 34. 266, 1910 ; 35. 521, 1911 ; *Zeit. anorg. Chem.*, 81. 43, 1913 ; H. Hof and B. Rinck, *German Pat.*, *D.R.P.* 226245, 1910.
⁸ W. D. Bancroft, *Trans. Amer. Electrochem. Soc.*, 14. 150, 1908 ; R. S. Owens, *ib.*, 25. 482, 1914 ; *Journ. Phys. Chem.*, 18. 461, 1914 ; J. F. Sacher, *Chem. Ztg.*, 34. 737, 832, 1262, 1911 ; 35. 326, 1911 ; L. Falk, *ib.*, 34. 567, 937, 1910 ; C. Watt and T. R. Tebbutt, *Brit. Pat. No.* 7531, 1838 ; *Dingler's Journ.*, 70. 67, 1838 ; E. Toelle, *German Pat.*, *D.R.P.* 186972, 1905 ; I. Baggs, *Brit. Pat. No.* 1111, 1870 ; R. G. Hatfield, *ib.*, 1728, 1867 ; J. Kronen, *ib.*, 19732, 1900 ; J. Leigh, *ib.*, 7985, 1839 ; R. Palmer, *ib.*, 63, 1876.
⁹ L. J. Thénard, *Traité de chimie élémentaire théoretique et prâtique*, Paris, 3. 158, 1836 ; L. C. A. Barreswil, *Bull. Soc. Chim.*, (2), 4. 129, 1865 ; C. Hochstetter, *Journ. prakt. Chem.*, (1), 26. 338, 1842 ; F. Kalkow, *Zeit. angew Chem.*, 23. 2253, 1910 ; 24. 209, 400, 782, 1020, 1911 ; M. Liebig, *ib.*, 17. 1674, 1904 ; E. R. Blundstone, *Brit. Pat. No.* 8820, 1900 ; P. Brown and B. Young, *ib.*, 1411, 1858 ; C. Button and H. G. Dyar, *ib.*, 7521, 1837 ; J. Chisholm and M. H. Bellimois, *ib.*, 7895, 1838 ; H. J. B. Condy, *ib.*, 1095, 1881 ; 1693, 1884 ; N. C. Cookson, *ib.*, 708, 1876 ; F. J. Corbett, *ib.*, 10370, 1900 ; 11337, 1901 ; S. O. Cowper-Cowles, *ib.*, 14137, 1898 ; E. W. Dahl, *ib.*, 8161, 1891 ; C. Delafield, *ib.*, 301, 1866 ; C. Flude, *ib.*, 8166, 1893 ; W. Gossage, *ib.*, 1963, 1855 ; W. Gossage and E. W. Benson, *ib.*, 7046, 1836 ; E. W. Benson, *B.A. Rep.*, 60, 1839 ; A. Honman and V. Vulliez, *ib.*, 8022, 1891 ; O. Hamilton, *ib.*, 22460, 1895 ; J. Hemming, *ib.*, 7207, 1836 ; L. Labois, *ib.*, 9526, 1891 ; V. P. Lagrange, *ib.*, 2142, 1865 ; G. Lunge and C. H. M. Lyte, *ib.*, 13656, 1893 ; J. S. MacArthur, *ib.*, 9655, 1894 ; 9775, 1897 ;

R. W. E. MacIvor, *ib.*, 10426, 1888 ; R. W. E. MacIvor, F. A. Darlington, G. Paul, and J. Allen, *ib.*, 6815, 1889 ; R. W. E. MacIvor and W. Smith, *ib.*, 16093, 1890 ; W. Marriot, *ib.*, 3322, 1872 ; J. C. Martin, *ib.*, 1300, 1877 ; R. W. Matthews, *ib.*, 7129, 1894 ; M. Rasher and R. Plauelin, *ib.*, 203340, 1923 ; G. F. Lloyd, F. B. Clapp, and F. H. Campbell, *ib.*, 203301, 1923 ; R. Matthews and J. Noad, *ib.*, 20891, 1892 ; J. Mullins, *ib.*, 49501, 1842 ; J. H. Noad and S. Z. de Ferranti, *ib.*, 20239, 1893 ; G. H. Ozouff, *ib.*, 1748, 1860 ; 1498, 1864 ; H. L. Pattinson, *ib.*, 8627, 1840 ; 9102, 1841 ; J. A. Phillips, *ib.*, 642, 1861 ; J. Sadler, *ib.*, 4524, 1821 ; T. R. Sanderson, *ib.*, 6324, 1897 ; T. R. Sewell, *ib.*, 7736, 1838 ; F. H. Sharpe, *ib.*, 21292, 1911 ; W. Smith and W. Elmore, *ib.*, 19323, 19784, 1890 ; 5501, 1891 ; P. Spence, *ib.*, 2427, 1865 ; O. J. Steinhart and J. L. F. Vogel, *ib.*, 6655, 1896 ; E. Waller, *ib.*, 22294, 1893 ; E. Waller and C. A. Sniffin, *ib.*, 7631, 1892 ; H. Wilcox, *ib.*, 13202, 1894 ; B. J. White, *ib.*, 6683, 1891 ; G. Robinson, *ib.*, 88, 1860 ; C. White and J. W. Patterson, *ib.*, 9638, 1912 ; J. O. Handy, *Journ. Soc. Chem. Ind.*, 18. 232, 1899 ; W. Kubel, *Arch. Pharm.*, 230. 176, 1892 ; P. Pfund, *Dingler's Journ.*, 216. 336, 1875 ; A. Wultze, *Farben Ztg.*, 16. 1214, 1331, 1911 ; *German Pat., D.R.P.* 173105, 1904 ; R. Haack, *ib.*, 133425, 1902 ; Z. Peska, *ib.*, 158309, 1903 ; J. Frölich, *ib.*, 178983, 1905 ; J. Löwe, *ib.*, 42307, 1887 ; 45259, 1888 ; O. Eyckens, *ib.*, 39755, 1886 ; E. Lampe and L. Preuss, *ib.*, 140489, 1902 ; H. Franzen, *ib.*, 244509, 1911 ; R. Hitchcock, *Eng. Min. Journ.*, 70. 668, 1900 ; C. D. Holley, *The Lead and Zinc Pigments*, New York, 101, 1909.

¹⁰ R. P. Williams, *Journ. Amer. Chem. Soc.*, 17. 835, 1895 ; *Eng. Min. Journ.*, 61. 471, 1896 ; G. Bredig and F. Haber, *Ber.*, 31. 2743, 1898 ; C. F. Carrier, *Trans. Amer. Electrochem.*, 5. 231, 1904 ; R. S. Owens, *ib.*, 25. 482, 1914 ; *Journ. Phys. Chem.*, 18. 461, 1914 ; P. Beck, *Chem. Ind.*, 30. 276, 1907 ; L. Falk, *Chem. Ztg.*, 34. 588, 1910 ; A. B. Browne, *Brit. Pat. Nos.* 8345, 1893 ; 14988, 1896 ; *U.S. Pat. No.* 496109, 1893 ; E. D. Chaplin, *ib.*, 836177, 1907 ; 906102, 906104, 1908 ; A. B. Browne and E. D. Chaplin, *ib.*, 551361, 1895 ; 555232, 1896 ; E. D. Chaplin and H. G. Hallopan, *ib.*, 675555, 1901 ; D. M. Kyte, *ib.*, 459946, 1891 ; T. Okuno, *Journ. Japan. Chem. Ind.*, 24. 464, 1921 ; J. Meyrueis, *French Pat. No.* 227540, 1893 ; *U.S. Pat. No.* 506518, 1896 ; J. W. Richards and C. W. Roepper, *ib.*, 644779, 1898 ; E. A. Sperry, *ib.*, 1308948, 1919 ; *Met. Chem. Engg.*, 21. 255, 1919 ; A. M. Söderlund, *Swedish Pat. No.* 8626, 1897 ; T. D. Bottome, *Brit. Pat. No.* 400, 1891 ; S. O. Cowper-Coles, *ib.*, 22023, 1906 ; Z. de Ferranti and J. H. Noad, *ib.*, 6009, 23572, 1892 ; 20239, 1893 ; J. H. Noad, *ib.*, 3832, 1891 ; C. Hoepfner, *ib.*, 17745, 1895 ; E. H. C. Monckton, *ib.*, 3509, 1874 ; F. W. Morris, J. R. Raine, J. Kerr, and C. McLachlan, *ib.*, 24865, 1907 ; J. Oettli, *ib.*, 12713, 1903 ; C. A. Stevens, *ib.*, 16098, 1891 ; O. C. and H. H. Strecker, *ib.*, 26919, 26921, 26923, 1897 ; J. B. Tibbits, *ib.*, 18074, 1889 ; 2060, 1894 ; C. P. Townsend, *ib.*, 21502, 1904 ; H. C. Woltereck, *ib.*, 19179, 1897 ; 2382, 1899 ; M. Nicolaieff, *Monit. Scient.*, (4), 7. 91, 1893 ; *French. Pat. No.* 222215, 1892 ; M. Manent, *ib.*, 211073, 1891 ; W. Hartmann, *German Pat., D.R.P.* 139068, 1900 ; B. Huick, *ib.*, 230826, 1909 ; C. Luckow, *ib.*, 99121, 1894 ; 105143, 1895 ; A. J. Riban, *Journ. Pharm. Chim.*, (6), 7. 484, 1898 ; A. Isenburg, *Zeit. Elektrochem.*, 9. 275, 1903 ; W. Borchers, *ib.*, 3. 484, 1897 ; A. Zucker, *Pharm. Zeit.*, 44. 22, 1900 ; E. Ronco, *Ind. Electrochem.*, 2. 38, 1898 ; W. G. France and D. McBurney, *Journ. Amer. Chem. Soc.*, 46. 541, 1924 ; H. Weyer, *Elektrochem. Zeit.*, 2. 259, 1896 ; R. G. Bowman, *Trans. Amer. Inst. Min. Met. Eng.*, 1504, 1925.

¹¹ A. Libavius, *Alchimia*, Francofurti, 1595 ; N. Lemery, *Cours de chimie*, Paris, 1675 ; P. J. Macquer, *Élémens de chymie théorique*, Paris, 1778 ; T. Bergman, *De acido aëreo*, Upsala, 1774 ; C. Hochstetter, *Journ. prakt. Chem.*, (1), 26. 338, 1842 ; C. Link, *Liebig's Ann.*, 46. 232, 1843 ; A. Bette, *ib.*, 33. 251, 1840 ; G. J. Mulder, *ib.*, 33. 242, 1840 ; *Journ. prakt. Chem.*, (1), 18. 174, 1839 ; (1), 19. 70, 1840 ; *Miquel's Bull.*, 302, 1839 ; C. H. Pfaff, *ib.*, (1), 7. 172, 1836 ; *Schweigger's Journ.*, 53. 119, 1828 ; *Quart. Journ. Science*, 2. 438, 1828 ; F. Hofmann, *Zeit. Pharm.*, 3. 187, 1853 ; P. Hamberger, *ib.*, 43. 806, 1898 ; G. C. Wittstein, *Dingler's Journ.*, 212. 223, 1874 ; G. W. Wigner and R. H. Harland, *ib.*, 226. 83, 1877 ; K. von Weiss, *ib.*, 208. 434, 1873 ; *Monatss. Gew. Ver. Köln*, 300, 1872 ; E. Euston, *Journ. Ind. Eng. Chem.*, 6. 203, 382, 1919 ; 12. 974, 1920 ; Basil Valentine, *Letztes Testament*, Strassburg, 1651 ; (*Cf.* 1. 1, 12) ; J. F. Sacher, *Faebe Lack*, 245, 1921 ; *Chem. Ztg.*, 34. 647, 832, 1263, 1910 ; 35. 326, 1911 ; L. Falk, *ib.*, 34. 567, 937, 1910 ; H. Hof, *ib.*, 37. 784, 1910 ; *Zeit. anorg. Chem.*, 81. 40, 1913 ; P. Beck, *Chem. Ind.*, 30. 277, 1907 ; J. Scott, *Chem. Trade Journ.*, 65. 327, 1919 ; C. F. Carrier, *Trans. Amer. Electrochem. Soc.*, 5. 231, 1904 ; J. A. Phillips, *Journ. Chem. Soc.*, 4. 165, 1852 ; E. Norgate, *Miniatura or the Art of Limning*, London, 1650 ; G. Jars, *Voyages metallurgiques*, Paris, 2. 530, 1780 ; F. Weil and F. Jean, *Bull. Soc. Chim.*, (2), 28. 5, 1877 ; E. Lenoble, *Ann. Chim. Anal.*, 4. 118, 1899 ; L. Bourgeois, *Bull. Soc. Min.*, 11. 223, 1888 ; C. A. Klein, *Journ. Oil Colour Chem. Assoc.*, 2. 1, 1919 ; C. D. Holley, *Journ. Soc. Chem. Ind.*, 28. 403, 1909 ; *The Lead and Zinc Pigments*, New York, 1909 ; R. K. Meade, *Chem. Eng.*, 9. 44, 1909 ; C. von Weise, *Bull. Soc. Chim.*, (2), 20. 421, 1873 ; *Chem. News*, 28. 325, 1873 ; *Monats. Gewerbe Ver. Cöln*, 300, 1872 ; W. A. Davis and C. A. Klein, *Journ. Soc. Chem. Ind.*, 26. 848, 1907 ; G. Bischof, *Journ. prakt. Chem.*, (1), 7. 172, 1836.

¹² G. von Rockenthien, *German Pat., D.R.P.* 171460, 1904.

¹³ W. G. Scott, *White Paints and Painting Materials*, Chicago, 353, 1910.

¹⁴ L. Bourgeois, *Bull. Soc. Min.*, 11. 223, 1888 ; E. Euston, *Journ. Ind. Eng. Chem.*, 6. 202, 382, 1914 ; 12. 974, 1920 ; H. A. Gardner, *Papers on Paint and Varnish*, London, 257, 1920 ; *Journ. Franklin Inst.*, 173. 73, 1912 ; W. G. France and D. McBurney, *Journ. Amer. Chem. Soc.*, 46. 540, 1924 ; G. W. Thompson, *Journ. Soc. Chem. Ind.*, 28. 406, 1909 ;

W. A. Davis and C. A. Klein, *ib.*, **26**. 848, 1907; P. P. Bedson, *ib.*, **13**. 610, 1894; W. Thomason, *Trans. Cer. Soc.*, **9**. 198, 209, 1910; J. F. Sacher, *Chem. Ztg.*, **34**. 647, 1910; **35**. 326, 1911; L. Falk, *ib.*, **34**. 567, 937, 1910; H. Hof, *ib.*, **33**. 1078, 1909; **34**. 785, 1910; *Zeit. anorg. Chem.*, **81**. 45, 1913; E. Beckmann and P. Waentig, *ib.*, **67**. 58, 1910; C. D. Holley, *The Lead and Zinc Pigments*, London, 133, 1909; J. A. Phillips, *Journ. Chem. Soc.*, **4**. 165, 1852; K. Friedrich, *Met.*, **9**. 409, 1912; *Centr. Min.*, 616, 651, 684, 1912; L. Meister, *Farben Ztg.*, **16**. 711, 1911; C. P. van Hoeck, *ib.*, **19**. 2017, 1914; G. Hauser, *ib.*, **26**. 2914, 1921; J. L. Breton, *Compt. Rend.*, **136**. 1446, 1903; *Ann. Chim. Phys.*, (7), **30**. 554, 1903; R. S. Owens, *Trans. Amer. Electrochem. Soc.*, **25**. 482, 1914; *Journ. Phys. Chem.*, **18**. 461, 1914; J. B. Hannay and A. E. Leighton, *Proc. Chem. Soc.*, **9**. 122, 1893; F. W. O. de Coninck, *Bull. Acad. Belg.*, 508, 1909; E. Täuber, *Tech. Mitt. Malerei*, **21**. 306, 1906; *Chem. Ztg.*, **34**. 1126, 1910; R. Salvadori, *Gazz. Chim. Ital.*, **34**. i, 87, 1904; W. Hartmann, *German Pat.*, *D.R.P.* 141883, 1900; C. Hochstetter, *Journ. prakt. Chem.*, (1), **26**. 338, 1842; G. J. Mulder, *ib.*, (1), **18**. 127, 1839; W. Stein, *ib.*, (2), **4**. 276, 1871; *Dingler's Journ.*, **137**. 128, 1855; M. Herman, *Journ. Pharm. Chim.*, (7), **19**. 453, 1919; *Bull. Acad. Méd. Belg.*, (4), **28**. 489, 1914; F. Auerbach and H. Pick, *Zeit. Elektrochem.*, **19**. 827, 1913; M. von Pettenkofer, *Ueber Oelfarbe und Conservirung der Gemälde-Gallerien durch das Regenerations-Verfahren*, Braunschweig, 1870.

§ 33. Complex Salts of Lead Carbonates

D. L. G. Karsten [1] described a rare lead chlorocarbonate as *horn-lead—Hornblei;* M. H. Klaproth, *salzsaures Bleierze;* R. Jameson, *corneous lead;* A. Breithaupt, *phosgene-spar*, and **phosgenite**; F. S. Beudant, as *kerasine;* E. F. Glocker, as *galenoceratite;* and R. P. Greg and W. G. Lettsom, as *cromfordite*. Analyses, reported by M. H. Klaproth, C. F. Rammelsberg, K. von Nidda, J. Smith, and F. Philipenko, correspond with **lead chlorocarbonate**, $PbCl_2.PbCO_3$, or $(PbCl)_2CO_3$. It has been found at Cromford, Derbyshire; in Cornwall; near Elgin, Scotland; at Gibbas. Monte Poni, and Montevecchio, Sardinia; Bobrek, Silesia; and Syzjanoff, Altai. R. Köchlin, and A. Lacroix reported it together with laurionite, and cerussite, in cavities in the lead slags at Laurion, Greece, as a result of the action of sea-water to which the slags have been exposed for 2000 years. A. Daubrée found it to have been produced by the action of the thermal water of Bourbonneaux-Bains on some lead tubes.

J. W. Döbereiner made this salt by boiling lead chloride, lead carbonate, and water; C. Friedel and E. Sarasin worked with the mixture in a sealed tube at 180°. A. de Schulten made it by the action of carbon dioxide on lead hydroxychloride, $Pb(OH)Cl$; and he also allowed a filtered soln. of lead chloride to stand in a large flask while a current of carbon dioxide was passed over the liquid. Crystals were formed in about 24 hrs. These were rapidly washed by water, alcohol, and ether. W. A. Hamor and H. E. Gill made the salt by heating a mixture of lead hydroxide and carbonyl chloride in a sealed tube at 175°. M. Amadori did not succeed in getting molten lead chloride to unite with lead carbonate.

The salt may be amorphous, or crystalline, and coloured white, grey, or yellow. The crystals are prismatic or tabular, and, according to N. von Kokscharoff, belong to the tetragonal system having the axial ratio $a : c = 1 : 1.0876$. The cleavages (100), (110), and (001) are distinct. G. vom Rath, A. Lacroix and A. de Schulten, W. H. Miller, and V. Hansel made observations on the crystals. F. Rinne and W. Anders studied the corrosion figures and the X-radiograms. The sp. gr. given by D. Lovisato is 6·0–6·9; C. F. Rammelsberg gave 6·305; W. A. Waldschmidt, 6·08; and A. de Schulten gave 6·134 for the artificial crystals at 15°; the hardness is 2·75–3·0. The natural and artificial crystals were found by A. de Schulten to melt very easily, and at a higher temp. the carbon dioxide is expelled, and the oxychloride, Pb_2OCl_2, remains. H. C. Sorby gave 2·120 for the mean refractive index, and 0·572 for the refractory power; N. von Kokscharoff reported for the refractive indices $\omega = 2.114$, and $\epsilon = 2.140$. H. Baumhauer made observations on this subject. The optical character is positive. L. Sohncke, J. Schincaglia, and

K. Keilhack made observations on the luminescence and fluorescence of this mineral ; and A. Pochettino said that the luminescence produced by the cathode rays has the same colour as the fluorescence. A. de Schulten said that water soon makes the salt turbid, for, added C. F. Rammelsberg, cold water decomposes the mineral extracting the lead chloride. The salt is soluble in dil. nitric acid. A. de Schulten found that in the presence of moisture, carbon dioxide transforms the salt into the normal carbonate.

G. Lunge and C. H. M. Lyte reported a basic chlorocarbonate to be formed from a mixture of lead nitrate, and sodium chloride, carbonate, and hydroxide ; and S. Ganelin, from a mixture of lead sulphate and sodium chloride, carbonate, and hydroxide ; or from lead oxydichloride and alkali carbonate or hydrocarbonate. The composition is represented by the formula $Pb(OH)_2.PbCl_2.PbCO_3$, or $Pb(OH)_2PbCl_2.2PbCO_3$—*lead hydroxychlorocarbonate*—but there is no evidence of chemical individuality.

C. Löwig [2] reported **lead bromocarbonate,** $Pb_2Br_2CO_3$, to be formed by boiling a soln. of lead bromide with an equimolar part of lead carbonate. A. de Schulten prepared the salt by the action of carbon dioxide on a cold soln. of lead bromide as in the case of the corresponding chlorocarbonate. The colourless, transparent, tetragonal crystals are stated by A. de Schulten to resemble the chlorocarbonate, and to have a sp. gr. of 6·550 at 15°. The salt melts easily, giving off carbon dioxide. It is attacked by water more slowly than is the chlorocarbonate. A. B. Poggiale reported **lead iodocarbonate,** $Pb_2I_2CO_3$, to be formed by boiling lead carbonate with a soln. of lead iodide ; and A. Ditte, by the action of a soln. of potassium iodide and hydrocarbonate on lead hydrocarbonate. The yellow product is said to be insoluble in water. A. de Schulten could not make it by the method analogous to that employed for the chlorocarbonate.

J. F. Sacher [3] reported *lead hydroxysulphocarbonate,* $Pb(OH)_2.PbS.4PbCO_3$, to be formed by the action of hydrogen sulphide on white-lead suspended in alcohol ; if water is used in place of alcohol, the salt is hydrolyzed.

J. L. de Bournon [4] described a mineral which he called *plomb carbonaté rhomboidal* and which is considered to be the *lead sulphatotricarbonate* of H. J. Brooke ; the *psimythite* of E. F. Glocker, and the **leadhillite** of F. S. Beudant. Analyses were made by N. Collie, F. Stromeyer, H. Laspeyres, C. Hintze, E. Bertrand, P. von Jeremejeff, L. V. Pirsson and H. L. Wells, etc. There is not a general agreement as to the best representative formula. H. Laspeyres regards it as a complex of equimolar proportions of hydrocerussite and anglesite, **lead dihydroxysulphatodicarbonate,** $PbSO_4.Pb(OH)_2.2PbCO_3$; and he applied the term *maxite*— after Max Braun—to a variety from the Mala-Culzetta mine, Iglesias, Sardinia, but E. Bertrand, and afterwards H. Laspeyres, concluded that maxite is really a more or less altered leadhillite. The mineral *susannite,* from the Susanna mine, Leadhills, was regarded as lead sulphatotricarbonate, and named by W. Haidinger. It was at first regarded as rhombohedral and dimorphous with leadhillite ; but later observations have shown that it is only a modification of that mineral. L. J. Spencer found susannite to be optically uniaxial. Leadhillite occurs at Leadhills, Scotland ; at Red Gill, Cumberland ; Taunton, Somersetshire ; Matlock, Derbyshire ; Grenada, Central America ; Seriphos, Grecian Archipelago ; and Susannite, at Leadhills, Scotland ; Moldawa, Hungary ; Nerchinsk, Siberia ; and W. Granby, Missouri. W. M. Foote found pseudomorph after calcite and galena. A. Russell found leadhillite crystals along with galena, anglesite, and cotunnite in cavernous masses of metallic lead mixed with charcoal taken up in 1846 from beneath the partly fused lead pump of a fire-ship wrecked in Falmouth Harbour in 1780. These minerals are supposed to have been formed by the action of sea-water on lead. L. J. Spencer found leadhillite among the old lead slags from the Mendip Hills, Somersetshire. A. Ditte claimed to have obtained amorphous **lead sulphatotricarbonate,** $PbSO_4.3PbCO_3$, by the action of a soln. of potassium carbonate on lead sulphate. It is not altered by potassium sulphate soln. C. Friedel and

E. Sarasin also heated lead carbonate and sulphuric acid in a sealed tube at 200°–240°, and obtained crystals of this compound. The mineral *lanarkite* was formerly considered to be a sulphatocarbonate, but it was afterwards shown to be lead oxysulphate (*q.v.*). Leadhillite occurs in crystals which are commonly tabular, or in short prisms—R. Köchlin found crystals from Ljubija, Bosnia, almost octahedral. The crystals are transparent, white with a yellow, green, or grey tinge. The monoclinic crystals were found by H. Laspeyres to have the axial ratios $a:b:c=1\cdot74764:1:2\cdot21545$, and $\beta=89°\,47'\,38''$. The crystals are often twinned on the (110)-plane, like aragonite. A. des Cloizeaux found that the optic axial angle diminishes with rise of temp., and finally, a section becomes uniaxial and negative; thus, for red-light, $2E=20°\,32'$ at 15°; 20° 28' at 21·5°; 6° 46' at 47°; and zero at 121°. For blue-light, $2E=22°\,22'$ at 15°; in a second case, $2E=20°\,54'$ at 12°, and 0° at 146·5°; and in a third case, $2E=23°\,16'$ at 12°; 10° 22' at 47°; and 8° 26' at 175·8°. C. Hintze found the mineral to be uniaxial at 125°; and O. Mügge at 300° when the previous twin lamellæ had completely disappeared. E. Bertrand found for yellow-light, $2E=72°$ at ordinary temp., and 66° at 250°; L. J. Spencer gave $2E=72\frac{3}{4}°$ at ordinary temp., and $70\frac{1}{2}°$ at 97°. The cleavage (001) is perfect, and (100) in traces. The optical character is negative. The crystals were also examined by C. Palache and co-workers, A. F. Rogers, and W. M. Foote. The sp. gr. of maxite given by C. Hintze is 6·547 at 18·9°; and by H. Laspeyres, 6·874 at 19°. For leadhillite, H. Laspeyres gave 6·874 at 17°; E. Bertrand, 6·60; and L. V. Pirsson and H. L. Wells, 6·54. The hardness is $2\frac{1}{2}$. H. Steinmetz found that there is a transformation at 115°, when the monoclinic crystals become rhombic. The change is attended by a considerable expansion. C. Hintze found that there is no loss in weight at 100°, but about 0·1 per cent. is lost at 200°; and with 1–20 hrs.' heating, 0·45–1·74 per cent.

According to A. Ditte,[5] the salt **potassium tricarbonatodiplumbite,** $K_2Pb_2(CO_3)_3$, is formed when carbon dioxide is passed into a soln. containing potassium iodide, and an excess of potassium hydrocarbonate in contact with hydrated lead dioxide; it is also formed, as a yellowish-white powder, by the action of potassium hydrocarbonate on potassium iodocarbonatoplumbite. C. Immerwahr measured the electrical properties of the soln. A. Ditte obtained **potassium tetraiodocarbonatoplumbite,** $K_2CO_3.K_2PbI_4.3H_2O$, in white needles, by the action of carbon dioxide on hydrated lead dioxide suspended in a large excess of a soln. of potassium iodide; and by the action of a mixed soln. of potassium iodide and hydrocarbonate on hydrated lead dioxide. When the salt is heated, it loses its water and becomes yellow. When heated in its own mother-liquor, carbon dioxide is evolved; and potassium tricarbonatoplumbite is formed. It is decomposed by water; with dil. acids, carbon dioxide, lead iodide, etc., are formed. When the salt is fused and cooled, **potassium oxydiiodocarbonatoplumbite,** $K_2CO_3.Pb_2OI_2$, is formed. The *dihydrate* was produced by the action of a soln. of potassium iodide on hydrated lead dioxide and exposing the product to air for a few days, or treating it with a little carbon dioxide, or potassium carbonate or hydrocarbonate. The white or pale yellow needles give off water when heated; and carbon dioxide when treated with acids. A. Ditte also obtained **potassium dioxytetraiodotricarbonatotetraplumbite,** $3K_2CO_3.2Pb_2OI_2.2H_2O$, by using more carbon dioxide or potassium hydrocarbonate than is used for the preceding salt. The yellow crystals lose water when heated. A. Ditte also made **sodium tetraiodocarbonatoplumbite,** $Na_2CO_3.Na_2PbI_4.3H_2O$, in a manner analogous to that employed for the potassium salt. Likewise also for **sodium oxydiiodocarbonatoplumbite,** $Na_2CO_3.Pb_2OI_2.2H_2O$, and **sodium dioxytetraiodotricarbonatotetraplumbite,** $3Na_2CO_3.2Pb_2OI_2.2H_2O$.

E. Auerbach and H. Pick studied the conditions of stability of lead carbonate in the presence of soln. of potassium or sodium carbonate at 18° and 37°. The results with potassium carbonate show that the reaction is $3PbCO_3+K_2CO_3+2H_2O$ $\rightleftharpoons 2PbCO_3.Pb(OH)_2+2KHCO_3$, with soln. of all the conc. tried, Fig. 126. With sodium carbonate, however, when the conc. of the soln. exceeds one-tenth normal, a complex salt, **sodium lead dihydroxytetracarbonate**, $3PbCO_3.Pb(OH)_2.NaCO_3$, or $NaPb_2(OH)(CO_3)_2$, is formed as a greenish-yellow powder—Fig. 127. Water decomposes it into basic carbonate and sodium carbonate.

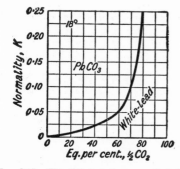

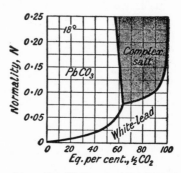

FIG. 126.—Equilibrium between Solutions of Potassium Carbonate and Lead Carbonate.

FIG. 127.—Equilibrium between Solutions of Sodium Carbonate and Lead Carbonate.

E. Euston obtained an adsorption product approximating $3BaCO_3.2Pb(OH)_2$. H. Vater prepared isomorphous mixtures of lead and barium carbonates. C. H. Warren obtained an isomorphous mixture of cerussite with 4·48 per cent. of strontium carbonate from the Terrible Mine, Colorado. E. Euston also obtained an adsorption product approximating $2CaCO_3.Pb(OH)_2$. The so-called *plumbocalcite* is an isomorphous mixture of lead and calcium carbonates, *i.e.* of cerussite and calcite. The mineral was mentioned by A. Breithaupt,[6] P. A. Dufrénoy, T. Böttger, A. des Cloizeaux, A. Lacroix, N. Collie, C. von Hauer, J. F. W. Johnston, C. F. Rammelsberg, J. S. Thomson, H. Hoefer, etc. N. Collie, and J. S. Thomson also described *plumboaragonite* from Leadhills, Scotland, containing 1·3 per cent. of lead carbonate ; and F. P. Dunnington, one from Wythe Co., Virginia, with 7·29 per cent. of lead carbonate. A. Breithaupt, W. Haidinger, M. Websky, and H. Traube called the combination *tarnowitzite* or *tarnovicite* from Tarnowitz, Silesia. E. Euston obtained an adsorption product with zinc carbonate approximating $Zn_2(OH)_2CO_3.3Pb(OH)_2$. C. M. Kersten reported a mineral from Iglesias, Sardinia, which he called *iglesiasite*, which, according to C. F. Rammelsberg, is an isomorphous mixture containing 7·02 per cent. of zinc carbonate, and the remainder cerussite. H. Traube, and F. von Kobell have also described specimens. W. F. Petterd[7] described a mineral from Dundas, Tasmania, which he called *dundasite*. He first assumed that it was a carbonatophosphate, but it was later shown to approximate $2Al(OH)_3.Pb(HCO_3)_2$. G. P. Prior found a sample near Trefriw, Wales. It forms white tufts or aggregates of radiating needles of sp. gr. 3·25, and hardness 3·25. The extinction is parallel and positive. G. T. Prior said that its physical properties resemble those of dawsonite, $Al(OH)_2(NaCO_3)$.

REFERENCES.

[1] R. Köchlin, *Ann. Hofmus*, **2**. 185, 1887 ; *Neues Jahrb. Min.*, i, 387, 1889 ; F. Philipenko, *ib.*, ii, 368, 1909 ; D. L. G. Karsten, *Mineralogische Tabellen*, Berlin, 78, 1800 ; M. H. Klaproth, *Beiträge zur chemischen Kenntniss der Mineralkörper*, Berlin, **3**. 141, 1802 ; R. Jameson, *A System of Mineralogy*, Edinburgh, 1804 ; E. F. Glocker, *Generum et specierum mineralium secundum ordines naturales digestorum synopsis*, Halle, 248, 1847 ; F. S. Beudant, *Traité élémentaire de minéralogie*, Paris, **2**. 502, 1832 ; R. P. Greg and W. G. Lettsom, *Manual of the Mineralogy of Great Britain and Ireland*, London, 421, 1858 ; A. Breithaupt, *Vollständiges Handbuch der Mineralogie*, Dresden, **2**. 183, 1841 ; *Vollständige Charakteristik der Mineralsystems*, Dresden, **61**, 1832 ; J. Smith, *Phil. Mag.*, (4), **2**. 121, 1851 ; A. Daubrée, *Compt. Rend.*, **81**. 133, 1875 ; A. Lacroix, *ib.*, **151**. 276, 1910 ; A. Lacroix and A. de Schulten, *Bull. Soc. Min.*, **31**. 86, 1908 ; A. de Schulten, *ib.*, **20**. 191, 1897 ; C. Friedel and E. Sarasin, *ib.*, **4**. 175, 1881 ; C. F. Rammelsberg, *Handbuch der Mineralchemie*, Leipzig, 750, 1875 ; *Pogg. Ann.*, **85**. 142, 1852 ; H. C. Sorby,

Min. Mag., **2.** 1, 1878 ; W. H. Miller, *Introduction to Mineralogy*, London, 622, 1852 ; K. von Nidda, *Zeit. deut. geol. Ges.*, **3.** 128, 1850 ; K. Keilhack, *ib.*, **50.** 131, 1898 ; A. Pochettino, *Atti Accad. Lincei*, (5), **13.** i, 301, 1904 ; (5), **14.** ii, 220, 1905 ; M. Amadori, *ib.*, (5), **22.** ii, 366, 1913 ; D. Lovisato, *ib.*, (4), **2.** 254, 1886 ; J. Schincaglia, *Nuovo Cimento*, (4), **10.** 212, 1899 : (4), **11.** 299, 1900 ; L. Sohncke, *Sitzber. Akad. Bayr.*, **26.** 75, 1896 ; *Wied. Ann.*, **58.** 47, 1896 ; V. Hansel, *Zeit. Kryst.*, **2.** 291, 1878 ; H. Baumhauer, *ib.*, **47.** 9, 1909 ; F. Rinne and W. Anders, *Ber. Sächs. Akad.*, **73.** 117, 1921 ; W. A. Hamor and H. E. Gill, *Amer. Journ. Science*, (4), **47.** 430, 1919 ; J. W. Döbereiner, *Schweigger's Journ.*, **17.** 256, 1816 ; G. vom Rath, *Sitzber. Niederrh. Ges. Bonn*, 130, 1887 ; N. von Kokscharoff, *Materialen zur Mineralogie Russlands*, St. Petersburg, **8.** 118, 1881 ; S. Ganelin, *Brit. Pat. No.* 8981, 1896 ; G. Lunge and C. H. M. Lyte, *ib.*, 13656, 1893 ; W. A. Waldschmidt, *Amer. Min.*, **8.** 31, 1923.

² C. Löwig, *Das Brom und seine chemischen Verhältnisse*, Heidelberg, 1829 ; A. de Schulten, *Bull. Soc. Min.*, **20.** 193, 1897 ; A. B. Poggiale, *Compt. Rend.*, **20.** 1185, 1845 ; A. Ditte, *ib.*, **92.** 1456, 1881 ; *Ann. Chim. Phys.*, (5), **24.** 239, 1881.

³ J. F. Sacher, *Chem. Ztg.*, **34.** 647, 1910.

⁴ J. L. de Bournon, *Catalogue de la collection minéralogique particulière du roi*, Paris, 343, 1817 ; H. J. Brooke, *Edin. Phil. Journ.*, **3.** 117, 138, 1820 ; F. S. Beudant, *Traité élémentaire de minéralogie*, Paris, **2.** 366, 1832 ; E. F. Glocker, *Generum et specierum mineralium secundum ordines naturales digestorum synopsis*, Halle, 256, 1847 ; H. Laspeyres, *Neues Jahrb. Min.*, 407, 508, 1872 ; 292, 1873 ; O. Mügge, *ib.*, i, 63, 204, 1884 ; E. Bertrand, *Bull. Soc. Chim.*, (2), **19.** 67, 1873 ; *Compt. Rend.*, **86.** 348, 1878 ; N. Collie, *Journ. Chem. Soc.*, **55.** 91, 1889 ; F. Stromeyer, *Gott. Anz.*, 113, 1825 ; L. V. Pirsson and H. L. Wells, *Amer. Journ. Science*, (3), **48.** 219, 1894 ; A. F. Rogers, *ib.*, (4), **12.** 42, 1901 ; W. M. Foote, *ib.*, (3), **50.** 99, 1895 ; A. Ditte, *Ann. Chim. Phys.*, (5), **14.** 230, 1878 ; C. Hintze, *Pogg. Ann.*, **152.** 256, 1872 ; H. Steinmetz, *Zeit. phys. Chem.*, **52.** 466, 1905 ; R. Köchlin, *Tschermak's Mitt.*, (2), **35.** 1, 1921 ; A. Russell, *Min. Mag.*, **19.** 64, 1920 ; L. J. Spencer, *B.A. Rep.*, 375, 1898 ; C. Palache, *Zeit. Kryst.*, **48.** 134, 1911 ; C. Palache and L. la Forge, *ib.*, **48.** 129, 1911 ; C. Palache and V. Goldschmidt, *ib.*, **48.** 140, 1911 ; W. Haidinger, *Handbuch der bestimmenden Mineralogie*, Wien, 505, 1845 ; *Trans. Roy. Soc. Edin.*, **10.** 217, 1826 ; E. Artini, *Giorn. Min.*, **1.** 1, 1890 ; W. H. Miller, *Introduction to Mineralogy*, London, 563, 1852 ; A. des Cloizeaux, *Ann. Mines*, (5), **11.** 261, 1857 ; (5), **14.** 339, 1858 ; *Nouvelles recherches sur les propriétés optiques des cristaux*, Paris, 72, 1867 ; P. von Jeremejeff, *Proc. Russ. Min. Soc.*, **36.** 12, 1899 ; C. Friedel and E. Sarasin, *Arch. Sciences Genève*, (3), **27.** 22, 1892.

⁵ C. Immerwahr, *Beiträge zur Löslichkeitsbestimmung schwerlöslicher Salze des Quecksilbers, Kupfers, Bleis, Cadmiums und Zinks*, Breslau, 1900 ; *Zeit. Elektrochem.*, **7.** 480, 1901 ; F. Auerbach and H. Pick, *ib.*, **19.** 830, 1913 ; *Arb. Kaiser Ges. Amt.*, **45.** 126, 150, 1913 ; *Umsetzungen schwerlöslicher Bleisalze mit wasserigen Lösungen kohlensauerer Alkalien*, Berlin, 1913 ; A. Ditte, *Compt. Rend.*, **92.** 1454, 1881 ; **93.** 65, 1881 ; *Ann. Chim. Phys.*, (5), **24.** 247, 1881 ; E. Euston, *Journ. Ind. Eng. Chem.*, **6.** 202, 382, 1914 ; **12.** 974, 1920 ; C. H. Warren, *Amer. Journ. Science*, (4), **16.** 337, 1903 ; H. Vater, *Zeit. Kryst.*, **21.** 462, 1893.

⁶ H. Hoefer, *Die Mineralien Kärntens*, Klagenfurt, 44, 1870 ; *Neues Jahrb. Min.*, 80, 1871 ; H. Traube, *ib.*, ii, 278, 1887 ; *Zeit. Kryst.*, **15.** 412, 1889 ; *Zeit. deut. geol. Ges.*, **46.** 50, 1894 ; M. Websky, *ib.*, **9.** 737, 1857 ; A. Lacroix, *Bull. Soc. Min.*, **8.** 35, 1885 ; J. S. Thomson, *Min. Mag.*, **7.** 143, 1887 ; C. F. Rammelsberg, *Handbuch der Mineralchemie*, Leipzig, **2.** 92, 223, 1895 ; N. Collie, *Journ. Chem. Soc.*, **55.** 91, 1889 ; J. F. W. Johnston, *Edin. Journ. Science*, (2), **6.** 79, 1832 ; C. von Hauer, *Sitzber. Akad. Wien*, **12.** 701, 1854 ; A. des Cloizeaux, *Manuel de minéralogie*, Paris, **2.** 114, 1874 ; *Bull. Soc. Géol.*, **4.** 769, 1847 ; T. Böttger, *Pogg. Ann.*, **47.** 497, 1839 ; A. Breithaupt, *Vollständiges Handbuch der Mineralogie*, Dresden, **2.** 252, 313, 1841 ; W. Haidinger, *Handbuch der bestimmenden Mineralogie*, Wien, 1845 ; F. P. Dunnington, *Proc. Amer. Chem. Soc.*, **2.** 14, 1878 ; P. A. Dufrénoy, *Traité de minéralogie*, Paris, **2.** 284, 1856 ; E. Euston, *Journ. Ind. Eng. Chem.*, **6.** 383, 1914 ; F. von Kobell, *Journ. prakt. Chem.*, (1), **28.** 480, 1843 ; C. M. Kersten, *Schweigger's Journ.*, **65.** 365, 1832.

⁷ W. F. Petterd, *Catalogue of the Minerals of Tasmania*, Launceston, 26, 1893 ; *Proc. Roy. Soc. Tasmania*, 18, 1902 ; G. T. Prior, *Min. Mag.*, **14.** 167, 1904.

§ 34. Lead Nitrates

A. Libavius, in his *Alchemia* (Francofurti, 1595), described the preparation of crystals of plumbous nitrate, or lead nitrate, $Pb(NO_3)_2$, or, as he called it, *calx plumbi dulcis*, by cooling a soln. of comminuted lead in nitric acid. The action of nitric acid on lead has been previously discussed. The reaction is accompanied by the evolution of nitrous fumes which W. Shapleigh proposed to utilize by reconverting them into nitric acid by blowing air through the liquid while dissolving the lead. The crystallization of soln. of the oxide, hydroxide, or carbonate in dil. nitric acid, and of lead chloride in nitric acid or nitrates, furnishes the anhydrous salt. The dissolution of red-lead is much facilitated by the addition of a small proportion of hydrogen dioxide. J. S. Stas [1] recommended the preparation of lead nitrate by the use of most conc. acid capable of dissolving the purified metal ; the action is slow, but the acid dissolves only a trace of lead nitrate, so that the salt, as it is formed, is precipitated as a crystalline powder. The object is to get the salt in a state where desiccation is easy, owing to the ease with which lead nitrate is decomposed when heated. If the salt is deposited by the evaporation of a soln. of the nitrate, the desiccation is much more difficult than when prepared by the conc. acid as just described. The temp. should be kept below 155°. The salt is best dried in a current of air, at 140°–155°, until its weight is constant—this requires 8–12 hrs. There is even then " a legitimate doubt as to the possibility of absolutely drying large masses of salt when they cannot be raised to a high temp. without decomposition." A. Gutbier and J. Lohmann said that lead nitrate cannot be completely dried without decomposition. According to A. Knop, the slow evaporation of a cold soln. furnishes transparent crystals, but the crystals deposited by cooling hot soln., or by evaporating hot soln., are opaque ; but C. von Hauer, and J. W. Retgers said that neutral aq. soln. always give opaque crystals, and the slow cooling of hot conc. soln., containing free nitric acid, yields large water-clear crystals. P. Gaubert added that small, transparent octohedra are precipitated when alcohol, or nitric acid is added to the aq. soln., while the slow evaporation of the soln. gives cubic crystals. Observations on this subject were also made by J. Morel. L. Wolff said that the clear crystals may include as much as 0·3 per cent. of water ; the opaque crystals include a little less. The salt obtained from aq. soln. was found by W. K. Lewis to be slightly basic owing to the slight hydrolysis of the salt. The preparation of lead nitrate of a very high degree of purity was discussed by K. Fajans and co-workers, and by G. P. Baxter and F. L. Grover. W. Mills obtained lead nitrate by treating lead fluosilicate with a soln. of sodium nitrate, and filtering off the sodium fluosilicate. E. Bonjean observed the formation of lead nitrate in leaden tubes used for conveying ozonized air for sterilization purposes.

When lead dioxide is treated with nitric acid, A. Chwala and H. Colle believe that *plumbic nitrate*, $Pb(NO_3)_4$, or *lead tetranitrate*, is first formed, but is rapidly decomposed by water.

The physical properties of lead nitrate.—The crystals of lead nitrate are alleged to be dimorphous—since the salt crystallizes in the cubic and monoclinic systems. The latter statement is by no means well-founded. When prepared by rapid evaporation, or the cooling of hot soln., L. Wolff [2] found that the crystals belong to the cubic system ; from dil. soln., the crystals are tetrahedra and pentagonal dodecahedra. A. Scacchi obtained the latter form by crystallization from soln. containing sodium nitrate ; J. Morel, nitric acid ; and L. Wolff, zinc nitrate. L. Wolff also obtained good crystals by the diffusion of aq. soln. of lead nitrate in alcohol, or nitric acid. P. Gaubert said that cubes are produced instead of octohedra by crystallization from a sat. soln. of methylene blue. The various habits of the crystals obtained with different soln. were also studied by W. G. Hankel, E. Giebe and A. Scheibe, P. Gaubert, J. Morel, W. Haidinger, and R. Wackernagel. The crystals are isomorphous with those of barium nitrate. Cubic crystals which act on polarized light were obtained by J. Morel by the slow evaporation at −4° to 18° of soln. containing free nitric acid, or feebly acid soln. containing about one per cent. of ammonium, potassium, or sodium nitrate, ferric, cupric, or lead sulphate, or the isomorphous barium or strontium nitrate. J. Morel found that the cooling of soln. containing fuming nitric acid, between 0° and 40° furnished monoclinic prisms with the axial ratios $a:b:c=0.7858:1:2.7185$, $\beta=70°\ 22'$; these crystals are geometrically isomorphous with those of potassium chlorate. The **corrosion figures** of the cubic crystals were studied by L. Wolff. P. Gaubert studied the adsorption of methylene blue by the growing crystals. T. V. Barker obtained no **overgrowths** of lead nitrate on the cubic crystals of zinc blende or fluorspar. According to

S. Nishikawa and K. Hudinuki, and L. Vegard, the **X-radiograms** of the nitrates of lead and the alkaline earth metals show that four chemical molecules are associated with each unit cube. The lead atoms form a face-centred lattice with eight cubes which have each three oxygen atoms and one nitrogen atom. The length of the sides of the unit cube for lead nitrate is 7.84×10^{-8} cm.

A. Breithaupt[3] gave 4·769 for the **specific gravity** of solid lead nitrate ; J. H. Hassenfratz, 4·068 ; C. J. B. Karsten, 4·3998 ; L. Playfair and J. P. Joule, 4·472 at 3·9° ; S. Holker, 4·41 at 15·5° ; H. J. Buignet, 4·235 ; H. G. F. Schröder, 4·423–4·509 ; E. Filhol, 4·581 ; J. Behr, 4·545 ; J. W. Retgers, 4·531 at 24° ; M. le Blanc and P. Rohland, 4·520 at 20°/20° : H. Töpsöe and C. Christiansen, 4·521 ; and P. Niggli, 4·545 for the sp. gr., and 72·9 for the eq. vol. P. Gaubert gave 4·40 for sp. gr. of the opaque crystals, and 4·45 for that of the transparent crystals. L. Vegard calculated values for the mol. vol. from the radiographic data. F. A. Heglein studied this subject. G. T. Gerlach gave 4·40 for the **sp. gr. of aq. soln. at 17·5°** :

$Pb(NO_3)_2$.	5	10	15	20	25	30	35 per cent.
Sp. gr. .	1·044	1·092	1·144	1·200	1·263	1·333	1·409

H. Schiff, working at the same temp., gave for soln. containing 2, 4, and 6 per cent. of lead nitrate, the respective sp. gr. 1·016, 1·033, and 1·050. Observations were made by J. Wagner, J. H. Long, P. Kremers, K. Bindel, J. Thomsen, F. Kohlrausch, I. Traube, etc. H. Euler said that the sp. gr. of a soln. sat. at 17° is 1·405, and E. F. Anthon, 1·372 for a soln. sat. at 8°. K. Fajans and M. Lembert gave 1.444499 ± 0.000013 at 25·45°/4° for the sp. gr. of a soln. of ordinary lead nitrate sat. at 25·45° ; 1.443587 ± 0.000016 for the sp. gr. of a sat. soln. of nitrate made from carnotite-lead, and 1.443586 ± 0.000015 for that of a soln. of nitrate made from pitchblende-lead. K. Bindel obtained the following results :

$Pb(NO_3)_2$.				8·4	37·9	42·3	47·8 per cent.
Sp. gr. (18°) .				1·0771	1·4854	1·6045	1·6663
Contraction .				1·0072	1·0498	1·0796	1·0501
Mol. vol. .				3650	586	487	415

R. Broom found that when a soln. containing 48·3 parts of salt in 100 parts of water is mixed with an equal vol. of water, there is a 0·228 per cent. contraction. M. L. Jesersky said that the thermal change during the dissolution of the salt represents a rise of temp. smaller than corresponds with the coeff. of contraction. H. Gilbault gave 0·29 for the mol. contraction at 20° ; I. I. Saslawsky gave 0·70 for the ratio of the mol. vol. to the sum of the at. vols. of the constituent elements. J. N. Rakshit studied the contraction which occurs when lead nitrate is dissolved in water, and in alcohol. A. Heydweiller studied the changes in the sp. gr. and ionization with the dilution of the soln. J. A. Groshans compared the sp. gr. of soln. of lead nitrate with those of other salts. A. Taffel studied the effect of lead nitrate on the temp. of maximum density of water.

C. A. Valson[4] found the **capillary rise** in a tube of 0·5 mm. diameter to be 54·1 units for a soln. of sp. gr. 1·133 at 15°. H. Sentis gave 76·20 dynes per cm. for the **surface tension** of a 27·30 per cent. soln. of lead nitrate, at 12·8°, when that of water at $\theta°$ is $76.09 - 0.15400\theta$; the corresponding **cohesion constant**, a^2, is 11·98 per sq. mm. J. Wagner found the **viscosity** of a N-soln. to be 1·1010 (water unity) ; that of a 0·5N-soln., 1·0418 ; of a 0·25N-soln., 1·0174 ; and of a 0·125N-soln., 1·0066 at 25°. If x denotes the number of gram-eq. of salt per litre, the viscosity$= 1.0897x$. J. B. R. Scheffer found the **diffusion** coeff. in days for a soln. of a mol of lead nitrate in 136 mols of water to be 0·66 ; and in 514 mols of water, 0·71. J. C. G. de Marignac, and J. J. Coleman made some observations on this subject. The **compressibility** of the aq. soln. was measured by H. Gilbault, and P. W. Bridgman observed no evidence of a transition point when lead nitrate crystals are compressed from 1 to 12,000 krgms. per sq. cm., at 20° or 200°.

S. de Lannoy [5] represented the **thermal expansion** of soln. of lead nitrate by the expression $v = v_0(1 + a\theta + b\theta^2)$, where the values of the constants a and b vary with the conc. and temp. of the soln.

Per cent.	40°–70°		0°–40°	
$Pb(NO_3)_2$	a	b	a	b
4	$0 \cdot 0_4 963$	$0 \cdot 0_5 349$	$0 \cdot 0_4 200$	$0 \cdot 0_5 515$
10 . . .	$0 \cdot 0_3 141$	$0 \cdot 0_5 328$	$0 \cdot 0_3 103$	$0 \cdot 0_5 410$
15 . . .	$0 \cdot 0_3 175$	$0 \cdot 0_5 310$	$0 \cdot 0_3 127$	$0 \cdot 0_5 130$
20 . . .	$0 \cdot 0_3 2438$	$0 \cdot 0_5 267$	$0 \cdot 0_3 2438$	$0 \cdot 0_5 267$

J. Morel said that when heated to 110°, the monoclinic form suffers no loss in weight, and, according to J. S. Stas, the ordinary salt does not decompose if dried in air at 200°, but acid vapours are given off at a higher temp. By extrapolation from the f.p. of ammonium trinitratoplumbite, B. Bogitsch estimated the **melting point** of lead nitrate to be 450°–470° ; the decomposition of the salt prevents a comparison with fact. E. Maumené said that the salt can be melted without decomposition only under alkali nitrates ; and O. Lehmann found that the m.p. is lowered when the salt is in contact with other nitrates. A. Colson found lead nitrate to be less stable than silver nitrate. H. Hess said that the salt decomposes in vacuo at 283° ; and if heated in a silver crucible until a metallic film appears, and the cold mass boiled with water, the filtered liquid deposits the basic nitrate, $Pb(OH)_2.Pb(NO_3)_2$, while lead nitrate remains in soln. According to L. Baekeland, decomposition begins at 205°, it is very slow between 205° and 223°, and vigorous at 357°. In vacuo, between 205° and 223°, nitrous gases are given off copiously. The reaction $Pb(NO_3)_2 \rightleftharpoons PbO + 2NO_2 + O$ is reversible. The **dissociation pressure,** p mm., in **vacuo**, is as follows :

	223°	230°	250°	274°	297°	357°	448°
p . . .	6·2	6·9	11·8	32·6	78·4	514·0	1180

An excess of oxygen or nitrogen peroxide lowers the dissociation press. Basic lead nitrate which has been heated in open vessels at 357° for 10 days shows the same dissociation press., so that it is probable that the first products of the dissociation are the basic nitrate, $PbO.2Pb(NO_3)_2$, together with oxygen, and nitrogen peroxide. If the products of the dissociation at 357° are removed from time to time, the dissociation press. falls from 514 to 260 mm., apparently owing to the decomposition of $PbO.2Pb(NO_3)_2$ to $2PbO.Pb(NO_3)_2$; and at a red-heat, this is converted into lead monoxide. L. R. Morgan showed that if p denotes the partial press. of the oxygen, p_2, that of nitrogen peroxide, the mass-action law $k = p_1{}^{\frac{1}{2}} p_2{}^2$ is valid ; at 357°, the constant $k = 0 \cdot 062$.

The **freezing point** of aq. soln. was measured by L. C. de Coppet,[6] F. M. Raoult, M. le Blanc and A. A. Noyes, A. A. Noyes and K. G. Falk, M. Randall and A. P. Vanselow, F. Rüdorff, F. Guthrie, C. L. von Ende, A. Ponsot, K. Drucker, etc. According to H. Hausrath, if C denotes the number of grams of lead nitrate in 100 grms. of water ; C', the number of millimols of the nitrate per litre ; $\varDelta$, the lowering of the f.p. of water ; and n, J. H. van't Hoff's constant (l. 15, 10) :

C	0·01198	0·03985	0·09285	0·1844	0·5749
C'	0·362	1·204	2·805	5·570	17·37
$\varDelta$	0·00199	0·00638	0·01449	0·02770	0·815
n	2·98	2·87	2·79	2·68	2·54

M. Randall and A. P. Vanselow calculated the activity coeff. from the f.p. data. J. H. Walton and A. Brann attributed the lowering of the velocity of the crystallization of ice from under-cooled soln. to the formation of *hydrates of lead nitrate* in soln. P. Kremers [7] found that the **boiling point** of a sat. aq. soln. of lead nitrate is 103·5° in an enamelled-iron vessel, and 104·1° in a glass vessel. T. Griffiths said that a soln. containing 140 parts of the salt in 100 parts of water boils at 102·2°. G. T. Gerlach gave for soln. containing in 100 grms. of water :

$Pb(NO_3)_2$.	.	.	11	26	44	65	87	111	137 grms.
Boiling point	.	.	100·5°	101·0°	101·5°	102·0°	102·5°	103·0°	103·5°

A. Smits measured the raising of the b.p., b; and the mol. raising of the b.p., B, for sols. with w mol of the salt in 1000 grms. of water, and found for J. H. van't Hoff's constant n, 1. 15, 10 :

w	.	.	.	0·0474	0·0869	0·4174	0·8793
b	.	.	.	0·070°	0·0900°	0·418°	0·824°
B	.	.	.	14·76	10·35	10·01	9·37
n	.	.	.	2·84	1·99	1·93	1·80

F. M. Raoult, and G. Tammann measured the lowering of the **vapour pressure of** aq. soln. of lead nitrate, and the latter gave 12·3 mm. for the lowering of the vap. press., Δ, with soln. containing 0·5 grm. of salt in 100 grms. of water ; 23·5 mm. with 1 grm. ; 45·0 mm. with 2 grms. ; and 63·0 mm. with 3 grms.

H. Kopp [8] found the **specific heat** of the crystals dried at 100° to be 0·110 between 16° and 48° ; and the corresponding **molecular heat** is 36·4. J. Moser said that the aq. soln. of lead nitrate is cooled by dilution ; and J. H. Pollok said that when a soln., sat. at 9°, is diluted with an equal vol. of water, the temp. falls —0·35°. J. Thomsen said that the **heat of dilution** of a soln. of a mol of lead nitrate in 40 mols of water at 18°, by 60 mols of water, is —1·23 Cals. ; by 160 mols of water, —1·98 Cals. ; and by 360 mols of water, —2·50 Cals. He also gave —7·61 Cals. for the **heat of solution** of a mol of lead nitrate in 400 mols of water. M. Berthelot gave —8·22 Cals. with a mol of the salt dissolved in 930–1860 mols of water. K. Jauch gave 0·9621 for the sp. ht. at 18° of 0·5M-soln. ; 0·9179 for that of M-soln. ; 0·8559 for that of 2M-soln. ; 0·8045 for 3M-soln. ; and 0·7566 for 4M-soln. N. de Kolossowsky made some observations on this subject. K. Jauch also gave for the heats of dilution and soln., and for the sp. ht. and the mol. ht. of soln. of different conc. :

$Pb(NO_3)_2$ per cent.	.	.	8·4	37·9	42·3	47·8
Heat of solution	.	.	—7104	—4504	—4246	—4086 cals.
Heat of dilution	.	.	—7104	—2600	—2858	—3018 cals.
Specific heat	.	.	0·919	0·646	0·603	0·569
Molecular heat	.	.	3612	562	471	393

J. C. G. de Marignac gave for the sp. ht. of soln. with 50, 100, and 200 eq. of the salt respectively 0·7507, 0·8510, and 0·9162 between 21° and 26°, and 0·7500, 0·8507, and 0·9173 between 18° and 51° ; and —0·25 Cal. for the heat of dilution of an eq. of the salt in 2 litres of water, diluted with 2 litres of water at 16°. J. Thomsen gave for the **heat of formation** from its elements, 105·5 Cals. ; M. Berthelot, 105·6 Cals. ; P. Gunther, 108·1 Cals. ; and A. Colson, 105·4 Cals. J. Thomsen gave $(Pb,O_2,N_2O_4)=$109·51 Cals. ; and M. Berthelot, $(PbO,N_2O_5)=$40·2 Cals. The latter also gave $(PbO,2HNO_3,Aq.)=$15·4 Cals. ; and J. Thomsen, 17·7 Cals. without and 25·38 Cals. with precipitation ; M. Berthelot gave 19·7 Cals. for the solid salt.

H. Töpsöe and C. Christiansen [9] measured the **index of refraction** and for C-light obtained 1·7730 ; for D-light, 1·7820 ; and for F-light, 1·8065 ; M. le Blanc and H. Rohland gave 1·7820 for Na-light at 20°, and the corresponding **equivalent refraction** in soln. 28·57—A. Heydweiller gave 15·72. F. Fouqué, and J. H. Gladstone and W. Hibbert made observations on this subject. T. W. Richards and W. C. Schumb gave 1·7815 for the index of refraction with Na-light ; and J. Behr, 1·7733 for Li-light, 1·7843 for Na-light, and 1·7933 for Ti-light. H. Marbach, G. Wulff, and F. Klocke studied the **optical anomaly**, or the abnormal **birefringence** of lead nitrate. P. Barbier and L. Roux found the **dispersion** of soln. increases with the conc. ; and the mean sp. dispersion, 0·351, is about the same as that of other salts. C. Schäfer and M. Schubert found the **reflecting power** shows maxima in the ultra-red at 7·5μ, 12·5μ, and 15μ ; and T. Liebisch and H. Rubens found a maximum at 79μ.

in the **ultra-red reflection spectrum.** C. Schäfer, and W. N. Hartley made observations on the **ultra-violet absorption spectrum** of soln. of lead nitrate; and W. N. Hartley, on the **absorption spectrum** of soln. of different conc. T. E. Aurén measured the absorption coeff. of the salt for **X-rays.** H. Greinacher made the unexplained observation that its temp. in a Dewar's flask remains one or more hundredths of a degree below the temp. of its surroundings.

Numerous observations have been made on the **electrical conductivity** of aq. soln. of lead nitrate; for instance, by S. J. Bates,[10] E. Bouty, W. Conrad, J. H. Long, K. Jauch, G. Jäger, H. C. Jones and C. A. Jacobson, R. Salvadori, W. D. Harkins and F. L. Hunt, A. Heydweiller, F. Kohlrausch and E. Grüneisen, H. Fernau, E. Franke, A. Rosenheim and V. J. Meyer, A. A. Noyes and co-workers, and K. G. Falk. According to E. J. Shaeffer and H. C. Jones, the molecular electrical conductivity, μ, and the percentage **degree of ionization, a,** at 35° and 65° are:

	v	.	2	8	16	32	128	512	1024	2048
35°	μ	.	111·5	170·2	196·6	220·4	261·0	291·0	300·0	309·6
	a	.	36·0	54·9	63·5	71·2	84·3	93·9	96·9	100·0
65°	μ	.	175·9	267·8	309·4	347·8	410·2	455·0	477·7	491·8
	a	.	35·8	54·5	62·9	70·7	83·4	92·5	97·2	100·0

K. Jauch found the eq. conductivity at infinite dilution to be 122·7. A. Thiel and L. Stoll questioned if a $0.5M$-soln. is 80 per cent. ionized, as stated by R. Abegg. For conc. soln., A. Ferguson and I. Vogel gave for the eq. conductivity, $\lambda = 123.44 - 164.50 C^{0.452}$, where C denotes the concentration. The temp. coeff. has been measured by H. C. Jones and co-workers and by F. Kohlrausch. The **ionization constant** was found by C. Kullgren to be 40×10^{-8} at 100°. K. Beck and P. Stegmüller showed that the ionization occurs in two stages, $Pb(NO_3)_2 \rightleftharpoons PbNO_3{}' + NO_3{}' \rightleftharpoons Pb^{\cdot\cdot} + 2NO_3{}'$. The ionization was investigated by C. L. von Ende, A. A. Noyes and K. G. Falk, W. D. Harkins and F. L. Hunt, W. K. Lewis, K. Fajans and M. Lembert, K. Drucker, H. C. Jones and C. A. Jacobson, W. Conrad, and H. Fernau. The tendency of the ions to form complexes is, according to S. Labendzinsky, and R. Abegg, very great. F. Kohlrausch and E. Grüneisen investigated the mobility of the ions. The **transport number** given by A. A. Noyes and K. G. Falk for $Pb^{\cdot\cdot}$ at 25° is 0·487 in $0.1N$-soln., and 0·03 in N-soln. M. Randall and A. P. Vanselow measured the activity coeff. of lead nitrate. J. Walker and E. Aston, and J. H. Long calculated the **hydrolysis** from the electrical conductivity; and C. Kullgren gave:

$Pb(NO_3)_2$.	.	.	2	8	32	128 gram-eq. per litre	
Hydrolysis $\begin{cases} 85.5° \\ 100° \end{cases}$		.	0·082 0·103	0·141 0·220	0·253 0·400	0·482 0·742	„ „ „ „

C. Immerwahr found that the **electrode potential** between lead and a N-soln. of the nitrate is 0·443 volt; and W. K. Lewis gave for $0.01N$-soln., 0·469 volt; $0.05N$-soln., 0·455 volt; $0.25N$-soln., 0·445 volt; $0.4N$-soln., 0·443 volt; and N-soln., 0·439 volt. H. Jahn, J. Moser, and J. Miesler studied this subject. A. C. Cumming measured the e.m.f. of cells: lead | lead nitrate soln. | soln. of the nitrate of ammonium, potassium, or sodium | and the calomel electrode. S. Lussana found that the current in a **concentration cell** goes from the more dil. to the more conc. soln.; and that the e.m.f. increases more rapidly than corresponds with proportionality. The polarization phenomena have been previously discussed. O. Lehmann studied the electrolysis of mixed soln. of lead and barium nitrates. A. Günther-Schulze studied the electrolysis of soln. of lead nitrate by using the vapour above the soln. as cathode, and as anode, a lead wire. W. G. Hankel [11] studied the **pyroelectricity** of the crystals; and M. von Laue, and E. Giebe and A. Schiebe, the **piezoelectricity.** W. Schmidt gave 16 for $\lambda = 75$ cms. for the **dielectric constant** of lead nitrate. A. Heydweiller calculated values for this constant. L. Ebert studied the dielectric polarization of lead salts.

The chemical properties of lead nitrate.—According to W. Ipatjeff and W. Werchowsky,[12] hydrogen under a press. of 150–219 atm. and at 209° during 48 hrs., precipitated a basic nitrate, but no metal, from aq. soln. of lead nitrate. H. Rose reported that the salt is stable in air, and dissolves in water with a marked cooling effect. J. Obermiller measured the hygroscopicity of lead nitrate. A. Mailfert found that lead nitrate is slowly converted by ozone into the dioxide. A number of isolated observations on the solubility of lead nitrate in water have been made by E. Mitscherlich, C. J. B. Karsten, H. Kopp, T. Griffiths, G. C. Wittstein, C. von Hauer, A. Michel and L. Krafft, W. K. Lewis, A. C. Cumming, W. D. Treadwell, C. Cheneveau, G. J. Mulder, H. Euler, T. W. Richards and W. C. Schumb, A. Ditte, M. le Blanc and A. A. Noyes, F. Mylius, and P. Kremers. The following results, expressed in S grms. of lead nitrate per 100 grms. of water, are averaged mainly from those of G. J. Mulder, and P. Kremers:

	0°	10°	20°	25°	30°	40°	50°	60°	80°	100°
S . .	37·6	46·3	54·4	58·5	63·6	72·2	81·8	92·5	111·3	132·9

According to K. Fajans and co-workers, the solubility of lead nitrate from carnotite-lead is the same as that from ordinary lead. J. Morel added that monoclinic lead nitrate is sparingly soluble in hot water, but more soluble in water acidified with nitric acid. According to W. D. Harkins, purified lead nitrate, recrystallized from water containing a slight amount of nitric acid, was heated to 100° for 6 hrs., and at 130° for 12 hrs. in a current of dry air. The soln. of the salt in water was acidic to rosolic acid, and alkaline to litmus. H. W. Fischer said that when heated in a sealed tube to 200°, aq. soln. of lead nitrate furnish crystals of basic nitrate ; J. H. Weibel also examined the effect of temp. and press. on the hydrolysis of aq. soln. of lead nitrate. For the hydrolysis of lead nitrate, and also the basic nitrates, *vide supra.* A. Geuther found that sodium hydroxide furnishes a basic nitrate, lead hydroxide, or lead oxide, according to the conc. of the soln. V. Zotier studied the catalytic effect of the nitrate on hydrogen dioxide.

J. W. Thomas [13] said that solid lead nitrate takes up moist hydrogen chloride rapidly with the copious evolution of red fumes. J. J. Berzelius observed that when other salts of lead are precipitated from a soln. of an excess of lead nitrate, there is a tendency for the lead nitrate to be absorbed by the precipitate. H. Moissan found fluorine does not act on lead nitrate in the cold, but at a dull red heat, lead fluoride is slowly produced. F. Fischer and K. Thiele could not prepare a *lead fluonitrate.* There is a possibility that a *lead chloronitrate* is present in mixed soln. of lead chloride and nitrate—*vide* lead chloride. P. Fedoteéff studied the reversible reaction with cuprous iodide and iodine, $Pb(NO_3)_2 + CuI + I \rightleftharpoons PbI_2 + Cu(NO_3)_2$. Lead nitrate detonates slightly when triturated with sulphur. J. Thomsen gave 11·43 Cals. for the decomposition of a mol of lead nitrate in aq. soln. by hydrogen sulphide. According to E. Schürmann, stannous and bismuth sulphides are not attacked by soln. of lead nitrate ; while zinc, thallous, cobalt, and nickel sulphides are transformed into nitrates and lead sulphide ; arsenic trisulphide is transformed when heated with a soln. of lead nitrate under press. in a sealed tube. J. Lemberg found that calcium sulphate, $CaSO_4.2H_2O$, acquires a crust of lead sulphate when immersed in a cold conc. soln. of lead nitrate ; and copper hydroxysulphate—brochantite—from lead sulphate when treated with a soln. of copper nitrate almost sat. with nitric acid. According to K. Elbs, persulphuric acid gives a white precipitate with neutral or almost neutral soln. of lead nitrate which rapidly forms brown lead dioxide.

E. C. Franklin and C. A. Kraus found lead nitrate to be readily soluble in liquid ammonia, and F. M. G. Johnson and N. T. M. Wilsmore measured the electrode potential of lead against a soln. of lead nitrate in liquid ammonia, and R. Bossuet and L. Hackspill found that lead phosphide is precipitated from a soln. of lead nitrate in liquid ammonia by a soln. of rubidium phosphide in the same solvent. K. Friedrichs said lead nitrate is readily soluble in liquid ammonia and the soln. separates into two liquid phases at 45°. H. P. Cady studied the electrical conductivity, etc., of the soln. D. Strömholm, and N. Athanasescu studied the formation of basic nitrates by the action of aq. ammonia on soln. of lead nitrate. C. A. Lobry de Bruyn found lead nitrate is soluble in **hydrazine,** and sparingly soluble in **hydrazine hydrate.** T. W. B. Welsh and H. J. Broderson showed that anhydrous hydrazine dissolves 0·52 grm. of lead nitrate per c.c., but the soln. decomposes. The soln. is an electrical conductor. E. Divers said that **nitric oxide** has no action on lead nitrate. H. Braconnot found that **nitric acid** precipitates lead nitrate from a conc. aq. soln., and the crystallization of the salt from nitric acid soln. has been recommended by A. Ditte, and others for its purification. J. Morel found that soln. of the monoclinic variety in nitric acid furnishes octahedral crystals. A. Ditte said that the conc. acid dissolves only a trace of lead nitrate in the cold, while the boiling, conc. acid dissolves 0·7 grm. per litre. According to A. C. Cumming, the solubility of lead nitrate in nitric acid of different conc., at 25°, is:

HNO_3			2·02N-	4·64N-	8·77N-	14·35N-
$Pb(NO_3)_2$			178	61·0	13·9	0·536 grm. per litre

He added that it is very unlikely that a complex hydronitratoplumbous acid is formed. For the solubility of lead nitrate in soln. of ammonium, potassium, sodium, copper, silver, barium, and strontium nitrates ; or the mutual action of the fused salts, *vide infra,* the complex salts. F. Peters found that when treated with **potassium nitrite,** it forms a complex potassium lead nitritonitrate, and basic lead nitritonitrates. W. C. Williams found that **phosphoryl chloride** reacts with lead nitrate with the copious evolution of red fumes.

The older chemists knew that lead nitrate detonates with brilliant sparks when projected on red-hot **carbon ;** and that the inflammability of tinder, blotting-paper, etc., is greatly increased when they have been soaked in a soln. of this salt, and dried. W. D. Bancroft and H. B. Weiser [14] found that a flame fed with lead nitrate deposits a metallic mirror on a cold surface. According to H. Arctowsky, lead nitrate is insoluble in cold and very slightly soluble in hot **carbon disulphide.** C. A. Lobry de Bruyn found that 100 grms. of absolute **methyl alcohol** dissolve 1·37 grms. of lead nitrate at 20·5°; and absolute **ethyl alcohol,** 0·04 grm. According to A. Gérardin, 100 grms. of ethyl alcohol of sp. gr. 0·9282, dissolve at 4°, 4·96 grms. of lead nitrate ; and 5·82 grms. at 8° ; 8·77 grms. at 22° ; 12·8 grms. at 40° ; and 14·9 grms. at 50°. W. H. Krug and K. P. McElroy, and A. Naumann said that lead nitrate is very sparingly soluble in dried **acetone.** A. Naumann found lead nitrate to be insoluble in **methyl acetate,** and in **ethyl acetate ;** H. Röhler said that **formamide** furnishes a complex precipitate with solid lead nitrate at ordinary temp., but at 200°, in vacuo, lead rapidly separates; F. L. Shinn, insoluble in dried **ethylamine ;** H. Mandal, insoluble in **aniline ;** and A. Naumann, insoluble in **benzonitrile.** B. Lachowicz, said that compounds are probably formed with the **amines** of the fatty acids, aniline, **toluidine, pyridine, quinoline, piperidine, and mono- and diethylamine.** If an aq. soln. of lead nitrate be mixed with an equal vol. of alcohol, and then treated with aniline or *o*-toluidine, basic lead nitrate is deposited. The soln. of lead nitrate in pyridine was investigated by A. Werner, J. H. Walton and R. C. Judd, A. W. Speransky and E. G. Goldberg, A. T. Lincoln, and J. H. Mathews and A. J. Johnson. R. Müller found that 100 c.c. of pyridine dissolved 4·39 grms. of lead nitrate at 0°, and 5·46 grms. at 25°. B. Lachowicz said that with the **chlorides of the organic acids,** the anhydrides and lead chloride are produced. According to A. Smolka, a complex salt is formed when a mixed soln. of lead nitrate and **mannite** is boiled. J. H. Long studied the inversion of **cane-sugar** by a soln. of lead nitrate. M. Lilienfeld studied the action of lead nitrate on **plants ;** and H. Bechhold on **bacteria.** C. W. Correns studied the adsorption of lead from dil. soln. of the nitrate by **sand, china-clay,** and **chalk.** L. Kahlenberg and W. J. Trautmann [15] studied the reduction of lead nitrate when heated with powdered **silicon.** J. L. Proust in 1802, and J. C. Bromeis in

1849 showed that the action of **lead** in soln. of lead nitrate is very complex. According to J. B. Senderens, a strip of lead, one side of which is polished and the other roughly crystalline, decomposes lead nitrate much more quickly than a strip polished entirely, the characteristic yellow colour of the nitrosonitrate appearing almost at once, whilst metallic lead and subsequently basic lead nitrate are precipitated. Since acetic acid is not capable of reduction under these conditions, the action does not take place in a soln. of lead acetate. K. Peters also observed that a complex series of basic nitrates and basic nitritonitrates are formed. J. B. Senderens found that **tin** has no action on a soln. of lead nitrate ; and likewise also with **antimony,** and **bismuth.** The precipitation by zinc was noted in the eighteenth century by T. Bergman, in his *De præcipitatis metallicis.* J. B. Senderens found that when a dil. or conc. soln. of lead nitrate is treated with **zinc,** lead is deposited, and zinc nitrate and hydroxide, and ammonia and ammonium nitrate are formed ; the lead reacts with the soln. as indicated above ; similar results were obtained with **cadmium.** Dil. soln. of lead nitrate, protected from air, do not act on **aluminium,** and conc. soln. only feebly, because a basic lead nitritonitrate is deposited as a protective film on the aluminium. N. W. Fisher said that **iron** has but a slight action on soln. of lead nitrate, but J. B. Senderens could find no evidence of the separation of lead from dil. or conc., cold or hot, acid or neutral soln. of lead nitrate. J. B. Senderens observed no action by **nickel** on neutral soln. protected from air at 10°–16° ; and with **cobalt** under similar conditions, the soln. becomes pink, and there is deposited a black film of lead which gradually forms a basic nitritonitrate. A. Ogata and T. Kai'un studied the action of **sodium hydroxide** soln. on lead nitrate and found that when the latter is in large excess, a dil. soln. of the alkali-lye gives a white precipitate : $Pb(NO_3)_2$ $+NaOH=Pb(OH)(NO_3)+NaNO_3$; if enough alkali be now added to make the filtrate alkaline, the reaction $3Pb(OH)NO_3+2NaOH=(PbO)_2Pb(OH)NO_3+2NaNO_3$ $+2H_2O$ takes place. A considerable time is required for the completion of the reaction. If a large proportion of alkali-lye is added to the lead nitrate soln., $Pb(NO_3)_2+4NaOH=Pb(ONa)_2+2NaNO_3+2H_2O$. W. Spring and M. Lucion found that when **barium dioxide** is triturated with lead nitrate, lead oxide, oxygen, and barium nitrate are produced. A. Mailhe obtained a basic lead nitrate by treating a soln. of lead nitrate with **copper hydroxide.**

Complex salts with lead nitrate.—According to B. Bogitch,[16] molten ammonium nitrate slowly dissolves lead nitrate. There is a eutectic with 33 per cent. lead nitrate, at about 131°, Fig. 128. There was no evidence of the formation of *ammonium nitratoplumbite* with mixtures containing up to 55 per cent. of lead nitrate. C. J. B. Karsten found that a sat. aq. soln. of one of the component salts dissolves some of the other ; and A. Kanitz, that the viscosity of mixed soln. of the component nitrates was greater than that deduced from the mixture rule. O. Pulvermacher discussed these experiments. A. C. Cumming measured the electrode potential of mixed soln. of the two nitrates. E. Maumené found a mixture of equal weights of sodium and lead nitrates fused at 282° when the calculated value is 374°, on the assumption that the m.p. of lead nitrate is 450°.

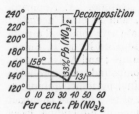

FIG. 128. — Freezing-point Curve of Lead and Ammonium Nitrates.

F. Guthrie gave 268° for the eutectic temp. obtained with mixtures containing 42·84 per cent. of lead nitrate. C. J. B. Karsten found that 100 parts of water at 18·75° dissolved 87·8 parts of lead nitrate and 34·1 parts of sodium nitrate. W. W. J. Nicol found that sodium nitrate lowers the solubility of lead nitrate in water ; and F. Isaac obtained the results indicated in Table XII, where the conc. are expressed in grams of salt per 100 grms. of sat. soln. He also studied the soln. in the metastable and labile states—1. 9, 6. M. le Blanc and A. A. Noyes found that the f.p. of the soln. agree with the assumption that a *sodium nitrato-*

TABLE XII.—MUTUAL SOLUBILITIES OF LEAD AND SODIUM NITRATES.

Lead nitrate as solid phase.			Sodium nitrate as solid phase.		
Temp. of saturation.	NaNO₃.	Pb(NO₃)₂.	Temp. of saturation.	NaNO₃.	Pb(NO₃)₂.
32° . . .	34·43	19·69	21° . .	40·97	13·62
35·5° . .	34·15	20·33	31° . .	43·18	12·88
44° . . .	33·35	22·19	41° . .	45·11	12·94
55° . . .	32·60	23·93	51° . .	47·28	12·50
65° . . .	32·19	24·89	64° . .	49·92	11·56

plumbite is formed. The observations of S. Glasstone and H. N. Saunders on the lowering of the solubility; of A. C. Cumming, and W. K. Lewis on electrode potentials of lead in the mixed soln.; and of A. Kanitz on the viscosities of mixed soln., also agree with the assumption that a complex salt is formed. On the other hand, S. Glasstone and H. N. Saunders' study of the ternary system : $NaNO_3–Pb(NO_3)_2–H_2O$ at 0°, 25°, 50°, and 100°, summarized in Fig. 129, shows

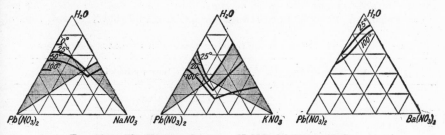

FIG. 129.—The Ternary System : $NaNO_3–Pb(NO_3)_2–H_2O$.
FIG. 130.—The Ternary System : $KNO_3–Pb(NO_3)_2–H_2O$.
FIG. 131.—The Ternary System : $Ba(NO_3)_2–Pb(NO_3)_2–H_2O$.

that no complex salt is formed under these conditions. F. Guthrie gave for the temp. of the beginning of the freezing of molten mixtures of lead and potassium nitrates :

$Pb(NO_3)_2$.	0	10	20	30	40	46·86	50	60	70 per cent.
F.p. . .	320°	300°	285°	268°	246°	207°	210°	238°	(335°)

Above 320° the decomposition interferes with the results. The eutectic temp. is therefore 207°. C. J. B. Karsten found that 100 parts of water at 18·75° dissolve 84·1 parts of lead nitrate and 29·9 parts of potassium nitrate; F. Rüdorff, that 100 parts of water at 21·2° dissolve 119·6 parts of lead nitrate and 67·1 parts of potassium nitrate; and M. le Blanc and A. A. Noyes, 100 parts of water at 20° dissolve 95·39 parts of lead nitrate and 61·05 parts of potassium nitrate. W. W. J. Nicol found that the solubility of lead nitrate is increased by the addition of potassium nitrate; and the solubility results of A. Fock, and the above-mentioned observations, are considered to be in harmony with the assumption that a *potassium nitratoplumbite* is formed. This conclusion is in agreement with the measurements of the electrode potentials by R. Abegg, S. Labendzinsky, W. K. Lewis, and A. C. Cumming working with the mixed soln. of the two salts; of A. Kanitz on the viscosity of fused mixtures; and of S. Glasstone and H. N. Saunders on the raising of the solubility of lead nitrate in water by potassium nitrate. On the other hand, S. Glasstone and H. N. Saunders' study of the ternary system : $KNO_3–Pb(NO_3)_2–H_2O$ at 25°, 50°, and 100°, summarized in Fig. 130, shows that no complex salt is formed under these conditions. For complex potassium tetranitratoplumbite, $K_2Pb(NO_3)_4$, *vide infra*. E. Maumené found the fusibility of a mixture of equal weights of lead, sodium, and potassium nitrates to be 259°, and he found that lead nitrate raised the transformation temp. of potassium nitrate. H. L. Wells and H. P. Beardsley inferred the existence of *cæsium nitratoplumbite* in soln. because of the high mutual solubilities of the component salts. They were not able to obtain the salt in crystals owing to its high solubility.

P. Fedoteéff measured the solubility of aq. soln. of copper and lead nitrates at 20°, and, expressing conc. in grams of salt per 100 grms. of water, found :

| $Cu(NO_3)_2$ | . | . | 0 | 7·7 | 15·04 | 24·63 | 37·96 | 60·32 | 83·11 | 100·29 | 127·70 |
| $Pb(NO_3)_2$ | . | . | 55·11 | 39·34 | 27·80 | 19·05 | 13·08 | 8·19 | 5·37 | 3·53 | 2·33 |

when the solid phase in contact with the soln. was a mixture of $Pb(NO_3)_2$ and $Cu(NO_3)_2.6H_2O$. There is here, no evidence of a *copper nitratoplumbite*. A. Colson said that molten silver nitrate, at 250°, dissolves about 20 per cent. whereby heat is absorbed. The 25 per cent. soln. decomposes in vacuo at 350°, and under ordinary press. at 380°–385°. According to C. Stürenberg, if a boiling conc. soln. of lead and silver nitrates be cooled in vacuo, hexagonal crystals of **silver nitratoplumbite**, $Pb(NO_3)_2.2AgNO_3$, are formed. According to C. von Hauer, W. Herz, H. Ambronn and M. le Blanc, and A. Fock, strontium and lead nitrates furnish isomorphous mixed crystals ; but no *strontium nitratoplumbite* has been formed. A. Fock obtained the results indicated in Table XIII with soln. of

TABLE XIII.—MUTUAL SOLUBILITIES OF LEAD AND STRONTIUM NITRATES.

Grams per 100 c.c.		Molar per cent. in solid phase.	
$Pb(NO_3)_2$.	$Sr(NO_3)_2$.	$Pb(NO_3)_2$.	$Sr(NO_3)_2$.
46·3	0	100	0
50·47	4·56	99·05	0·95
53·92	8·14	98·11	1·89
45·34	17·81	97·02	2·98
44·48	18·74	96·06	3·94
25·23	35·54	83·84	16·16
19·13	71·04	32·88	67·12
0		0	100

the mixed nitrates at 25°. G. Tammann found the salt decomposes too readily to form mixed crystals of the fused nitrates. According to E. Maumené, mixtures of lead and barium nitrates can be fused without decomposition if in the presence of fused sodium and potassium nitrates. The solubility of lead nitrate in water was found by F. W. Küster to be depressed by barium nitrate. H. Euler, W. Herz, G. Bödlander, and A. Fock have made observations on the mutual solubilities of the two salts. No *barium nitratoplumbite* has been isolated, but mixed crystals have been obtained and investigated by R. Brauns, C. von Hauer, P. Gaubert, J. W. Retgers, G. Tammann, H. Ambronn and M. le Blanc, and F. W. Küster. The velocity of cooling sat. soln. was found by D. Strömholm and T. Svedberg to influence the composition of the mixed crystals. S. Glasstone and E. J. Riggs studied the ternary system : $Ba(NO_3)_2$–$Pb(NO_3)_2$–H_2O at 25° and 100°, and the results are summarized in Fig. 131. The double salt could not be isolated, but in the quaternary system : KNO_3–$Ba(NO_3)_2$–$Pb(NO_3)_2$–K_2O, when the complex salt $2KNO_3.Ba(NO_3)_2$ is formed, there is also produced potassium tetranitratoplumbite. $2KNO_3.Pb(NO_3)_2$, which forms mixed crystals with the complex barium salt. G. Tammann and W. Krings said that the anomalous double refraction of mixed crystals of lead and barium nitrates is not connected with the heats of soln. because the latter are not altered at 340°, but the optical anomaly disappears at 340°, and does not reappear on cooling.

The basic lead nitrates.—The hydrolysis of lead nitrate in aq. soln. has been previously discussed. As is so often the case in reviewing the older reports on this and cognate subjects, a relatively large number of the alleged compounds are probably not chemical individuals but are mixtures whose chemical analyses have been represented by chemical formulæ. They are usually obtained by the action of alkali or ammonium or other hydroxides on a soln. of lead nitrate. For example, M. Pleissner [17] reported a white, caseous basic nitrate with 84·4 per cent. of lead to be precipitated from a cold soln. of lead nitrate ; with a hot soln., the orange-red precipitate has 89·5 per cent. of lead. R. Weinland and F. Paul said that potassium ferricyanide gives a complex salt with different basic lead nitrates. F. Herles discussed the use of the basic lead nitrate for clarifying sugar-soln. in the refinery.

J. J. Berzelius treated a soln. of lead nitrate and ammonia, and digested the washed precipitate for 12 hrs. with the precipitant, while D. Strömholm left the precipitate to stand in contact with the mother-liquid. The analysis corresponded with lead **pentoxydinitrate**, $6PbO.N_2O_5.H_2O$, or $5PbO.Pb(NO_3)_2H_2O$, or $4PbO.Pb(OH)_2.Pb(NO_3)_2$. A. Ogata and T. Kai'un represented the constitution $NO_3.Pb.O.Pb.O.Pb.OH$; and F. Meissner regarded it as a salt of orthonitric acid, $N(OH)_5$, namely :

$$Pb{<}^O_O{>}N{<}^O_O{>}Pb$$
$$O.Pb.OH$$

D. Strömholm said that intermediate stages in the hydrolysis are represented by $2PbO.N_2O_5.H_2O$, and $10PbO.3N_2O_5.H_2O$. Modifications of the process were described by A. Geuther, J. Löwe, and N. Athanasescu. A. Ditte employed potassium hydroxide as precipitant ; and M. Pleissner, barium hydroxide. D. Strömholm treated a soln. of lead acetate with sodium hydroxide free from carbon dioxide ; and also excluded this gas from the water used for washing, and from the air in contact with the hydroxide. The product was shaken with $0·05N$-ammonium nitrate, and washed as before. The washed precipitate was dried first on porous tiles, and then over sulphuric acid and soda-lime. A. Ogata and T. Kai'un recommended treating the lead nitrate soln. with just enough alkali hydroxide to make the filtrate alkaline towards phenolphthalein. The white powder has an astringent taste. According to N. Athanasescu, and D. Strömholm, the grains are microcrystalline. J. J. Berzelius, and N. Athanasescu said that the salt is insoluble in and not decomposed by water ; it is readily soluble in acids ; and, according to A. Geuther, when shaken with a soln. of sodium hydroxide (1 : 10 or 1 : 20), it forms yellow lead oxide, whereas the dehydrated salt gives yellow lead oxide under similar conditions. J. J. Berzelius said that when moderately heated, it gives off water and assumes a yellow colour, but becomes white on cooling. A. Geuther said that it becomes anhydrous lead **pentoxydinitrate**, $5PbO.Pb(NO_3)_2$, at 170° (N. Athanasescu said 180°), and loses a little nitrogen oxide at 200°. When ignited, it furnishes lead oxide. F. C. Calvert reported lead *tetroxydinitrate*, $5PbO.N_2O_5$, or $4PbO.Pb(NO_3)_2$, to be formed by the action of aq. ammonia on a soln. of lead nitrate ; but this has not been confirmed.

A. Smolka reported lead **oxyhexahydroxydinitrate**, $3Pb(OH)_2.Pb(NO_3)_2$, or $4PbO.N_2O_5.nH_2O$, to be formed when mannitol lead nitrate, $Pb(NO_3)_2.C_6H_8O_6$, is boiled with an excess of water for 4 days. N. Athanasescu made it as a white crystalline powder by digesting 50 grms. of powdered lead nitrate and 200 c.c. of aq. ammonia in a flask for 2 weeks, shaking daily. The solid product was washed with cold water and dried. It is insoluble in and not affected by water. It begins to give off water at 200°, and to give off nitrous fumes at about 300°. H. T. S. Britton found a critical point in the electrometric titration of lead nitrate soln. with sodium hydroxide, corresponding with $Pb(NO_3)_2.5Pb(OH)_2.nH_2O$. The salt $10PbO.3N_2O_5.4$(or 5)H_2O, or $3PbO.4Pb(OH)_2.3Pb(NO_3)_2$, **lead trioxyocto-hydroxyhexanitrate**, was prepared by T. Morawsky by adding ammonia eq. to two-thirds the N_2O_5 of a hot soln. of lead nitrate; the precipitate was washed, recrystallized three times, and dried at 100°. He also made it by digesting lead glyceronitrate with much water. D. Strömholm obtained it by the action of much ammonia on a soln. of lead nitrate; and J. Löwe, by treating lead dioxydiacetate with a soln. of potassium nitrate, and recrystallizing the product from its aq. soln. A. J. Wakeman and H. L. Wells say that lead hydroxynitrate is formed under these conditions. Some other basic nitrates give this salt when recrystallized from water—e.g. $3PbO.N_2O_5.H_2O$. A. J. Wakeman and H. L. Wells said that the salt furnishes flat, tabular, triclinic crystals with an extinction angle of 35°. It suffers no change when digested with boiling water or recrystallized from its aq. soln. T. Morawsky said that the salt is dehydrated at 170°. J. H. Kastle suggested that the compound $10PbO.3N_2O_5.5H_2O$ can be regarded as an acid salt, $Pb_{10}H_{10}N_6O_{30}$, of the complex acid $(H_5NO_5)_6$. A. Vogel reported that when lead acetate is treated with potassium nitrate in dil. soln. a crystalline precipitate—**lead trioxydinitrate**, $PbO.Pb(OH)_2.Pb(NO_3)_2$, or $3PbO.N_2O_5.H_2O$—is formed; with conc. soln., the precipitate is glutinous. J. Löwe also obtained it by the action of potassium nitrate on lead dioxydiacetate. The salt was also prepared by A. Smolka. J. Löwe said that the white prismatic crystals are soluble in an excess of acetic acid, and that alcohol precipitates the crystals from the aq. soln. The soln. is rendered turbid by carbon dioxide. The crystals lose their water at 150°–160°, or, according to A. Smolka, at 115°, forming **lead dioxydinitrate**, $2PbO.Pb(NO_3)_2$. The anhydrous salt was obtained by L. Baekeland by heating lead nitrate to 357° under reduced press. for 10 days; at a red heat, it forms lead monoxide. J. J. Berzelius reported a higher hydrate, $3PbO.N_2O_5.3H_2O$, **lead oxyhexahydroxytetranitrate**, $PbO.3Pb(OH)_2.2Pb(NO_3)_2$, to be formed by precipitating a soln. of lead nitrate with a slight excess of ammonia, digesting the mixture in a closed vessel, dropping in a little more lead nitrate soln., again digesting, and repeating the treatment until too small an excess of ammonia is present to be detected by its odour, and only recognizable by the fumes it gives with hydrochloric acid. The washed precipitate is dried out of contact with air. When warmed it becomes yellow, but the white colour is restored on cooling; if heated to a higher temp., lemon-yellow lead oxide is formed. J. J. Berzelius said that the salt is slightly soluble in water, but not if various salts are present which do not decompose the basic nitrate.

Many observers have described the preparation of **lead hydroxynitrate**, $Pb(OH)NO_3$, or $2PbO.N_2O_5.H_2O$. J. J. Berzelius, and M. E. Chevreul supposed it to be free from water; but J. F. Persoz, J. Pelouze, and J. Löwe demonstrated that it is hydrated. N. von Lorenz, and F. Peters obtained this salt by the action of lead on warm water; and N. Athanasescu, by heating a conc. soln. of lead nitrate (1 : 1) in a sealed tube at 310°–320° for 4–5 hrs., washing the product with the smallest possible quantity of water, and drying. J. J. Berzelius obtained it by treating a hot soln. of lead nitrate with insufficient ammonia to precipitate the whole of the lead hydroxide and cooling the filtrate—D. Strömholm recommended half the theoretical proportion of ammonia; and A. Ogata and T. Kai'un recommended adding enough alkali hydroxide to furnish a filtrate which is just alkaline to phenolphthalein. Modifications of the process were used by T. Morawsky, N. Athanasescu, and A. Ditte. E. Borsbach, and B. Lachowicz used quinoline in place of ammonia; B. Lachowicz, aniline, toluidines, methylaniline, dimethylaniline, and xylidine. M. E. Chevreul boiled equimolar parts of lead oxide and nitrate with water, and allowed the hot filtered soln. to crystallize—N. Athanasescu said that half an hour's boiling is sufficient. T. Morawsky added 15 grms. of lead oxide to a boiling soln. of 20 grms. of lead nitrate, 20 grms. of glycerol, and 200 c.c. of water. The hot filtered soln. was cooled for crystallization. J. Pelouze used white-lead in place of lead oxide, and found that an excess is no disadvantage since the hydroxynitrate cannot decompose white-lead. J. F. Persoz boiled the lead nitrate soln. with zinc oxide ; H. Klinger, cadmium oxide or hydroxide ; and A. Mailhe, copper hydroxide. J. Löwe treated a cold aq. soln. of lead nitrate with a slight excess of basic lead acetate ; and also digested a soln. of potassium nitrate with a slight excess of basic lead acetate—the slow cooling of the soln. gives prismatic crystals, and if lead nitrate is also present, tabular crystals. J. Ville obtained it by the action of ammonium nitrate on lead oxide. F. Peters treated a boiling soln. of 50 grms. of lead nitrate in 500 c.c. of water with 100 c.c. of a soln. of potassium nitrate (1 c.c.$=0.0574$ grm. N_2O_5) ; the white precipitate first formed disappears on boiling the mixture. On evaporating the soln. to about 100 c.c. and cooling, white crystals are formed. These are pressed between bibulous paper, and dried in air. E. Guignet made some observations on this subject ; so also have A. Ogata and T. Kai'un—*vide supra*, action of alkali-lye on lead nitrate.

J. J. Berzelius said that as the hot aq. soln. cools, the salt separates in white crystals which have different habits—needles, scales, prisms—dependent on the mode of preparation. N. von Lorenz said that they belong to the rhombic system. A. J. Wakeman and H. L. Wells said the crystals are either monoclinic or triclinic with a strong double refraction. J. J. Berzelius said that the salt has a sweet, slightly astringent taste, and when ignited furnishes red-lead or lead monoxide acccording to the temp. employed. J. Pelouze said that when heated for a long time at $100°$, the crystals lose a perceptible amount of water ; and they slowly become anhydrous at $160°$–$190°$; at $200°$, the salt becomes coloured and gives off fumes. B. Lachowicz observed no loss of weight at $100°$; J. Löwe said that the crystals become anhydrous at $150°$–$155°$ in vacuo. N. Athanasescu said that the water is all given off at $250°$, and decomposition occurs above $300°$. T. Morawsky said that the salt fuses before decomposition is complete. J. Thomsen gave for the heat of formation $(PbO,HNO_3)=24.25$ Cals. ; (Pb,H,O_2,NO_2) $=118.16$ Cals. ; and $(PbO,HNO_3,Aq.)=16.77$ Cals. J. J. Berzelius, and J. Pelouze said that the salt is sparingly soluble in cold water, and much more soluble in boiling water. J. J. Pohl found that at $19.2°$, 100 grms. of water dissolve 19.4 grms. of the salt. N. Athanasescu found that the powdered salt reacts distinctly alkaline towards litmus when moistened with water ; when allowed to stand in contact with water for a long time, lead hydroxide is formed. The salt is easily soluble in acids. A. Geuther said that when digested with a soln. of sodium hydroxide (1 : 10 or 1 : 20) in slight excess, yellow crystals of lead oxide are formed with intermediate formation of $6PbO.N_2O_5.H_2O$. M. E. Chevreul said that carbon dioxide reacts with half the contained lead.

According to J. B. Senderens, when a strip of lead is placed in a soln. of lead nitrate, **tetritahydrated lead hydroxynitrate,** $2PbO.N_2O_5.2\frac{1}{2}H_2O$, or $Pb(OH)NO_3.\frac{1}{4}H_2O$, is formed. It crystallizes from a soln. in hot water in monoclinic needles. It loses one-third its contained water at $100°$, and the remainder at $190°$; decomposition begins at $200°$. The salt is stable in air. 100 grms. of boiling water dissolve 6.7 grms. of salt most of which separates out on cooling.

L. Baekeland obtained **lead oxytetranitrate,** $3PbO.2N_2O_5$, or $Pb_3O(NO_3)_4$, or $PbO.2Pb(NO_3)_2$, by heating lead nitrate for 10 days in an open vessel at $397°$; and L. R. Morgan, by the dissociation of lead nitrate in the presence of much oxygen. It is more stable than lead nitrate ; its dissociation press. is 260 mm. when that of lead nitrate is 514 mm. G. Städeler [18] mixed conc. soln. of lead and mercurous nitrates and obtained white octahedral or cubic crystals of the basic salt, $2PbO.2Hg_2O.3N_2O_5$, **lead mercurous oxyhexanitrate,** $PbO.Pb(NO_3)_2.Hg4NO_3$.

Lead nitrosonitrates, or nitritonitrates.—As indicated above, when a soln. of lead nitrate is boiled with lead, a number of basic salts are formed ; and part of the lead nitrate is reduced to the nitrite. The salts are considered to be basic nitrosonitrates or nitritonitrates ; but the evidence as to their individuality is by no means satisfactory. According to J. J. Berzelius,[19] if a soln. of the basic

salt, $Pb_2(OH)_2(NO_2)(NO_3).nH_2O$, be treated with enough sulphuric acid to precipitate half the lead as sulphate ; or, according to M. E. Chevreul, if
carbon dioxide be passed through the soln. so long as lead carbonate is precipitated, the filtrate, on evaporation in vacuo, furnishes lemon-yellow octahedra
which were regarded as **lead hexanitritodinitrate**, $3Pb(NO_2)_2.Pb(NO_3)_2.4H_2O$, or
$Pb_2(NO_2)_3(NO_3).2H_2O$. C. F. Gerhardt, A. Gomès, and J. Nicklès regarded this
product as the normal nitritonitrate ; but E. M. Péligot and A. Chilesotti considered it to be a mixture of lead nitrite and nitrate.

The oldest of the basic nitritonitrates was obtained by J. L. Proust in 1812, who
considered it to be lead subnitrate, whilst J. J. Berzelius called it lead subnitrite.
The actual composition, according to the analyses of J. J. Berzelius, E. M. Péligot,
and J. C. Bromeis corresponds with **lead tetrahydroxydinitritodinitrate**,
$2Pb(OH)_2.Pb(NO_2)_2.Pb(NO_3)_2$, or $Pb_2(OH)_2(NO_2)(NO_3)$. A. Chilesotti regarded
this as a chemical individual. J. J. Berzelius heated an aq. soln. of 100 grms.
of lead nitrate and 78 grms. of lead-foil for some hours at $70°-75°$. The liquid
acquired a yellow colour, and, on cooling, deposited yellow scales of this salt. The
action begins between $50°-55°$, but is quicker between $70°-75°$; J. C. Bromeis
found that above $80°$, a portion of the salt is decomposed, and nitric oxide is
evolved. At the beginning of the reaction some basic lead nitrate is deposited.
E. M. Péligot used a similar process, and added that if from the presence of too
much lead, or boiling the liquid for too long a time, the crystals are contaminated
with orange scales of $7PbO.N_2O_3.N_2O_5.3H_2O$, the required salt can be extracted
with hot water and the soln. allowed to crystallize. According to J. J. Berzelius,
the above mixture yields only the yellow salt when the lead is all dissolved, and no
red or orange salt is formed. J. B. Senderens obtained a soln. of this salt by the
action of lead on soln. of copper or silver nitrates.

N. von Lorenz reported the hydrate $2Pb(OH)_2.Pb(NO_2)_2.Pb(NO_3)_2.1\frac{1}{3}H_2O$ to be
formed in lemon-yellow, six-sided plates by crystallization from water at $70°-80°$—if a
higher temp. is used, lead hydroxide may be formed ; and F. Peters, the hydrate
$2Pb(OH)_2.Pb(NO_2)_2.Pb(NO_3)_2.2H_2O$, in pale yellow rhombic plates, by the action of a
soln. of 50 grms. of lead nitrate in $1\frac{1}{2}$ litres of water on $27.4-3.13$ grms. of lead, and also
by adding a boiling soln. of 150 c.c. of potassium nitrate (1 c.c.$=0.0574$ grm. N_2O_3) to a
soln. of $37.5-56.26$ grms. of lead nitrate in half a litre of water. J. Fritzsche found that
if the vapours evolved when fuming nitric acid is heated are passed into water with finely
divided lead oxide in suspension, the oxide becomes white, and then dissolves, forming a
yellow liquid. The evaporation of the liquid furnishes silky scales of a lead nitrite or
basic nitritonitrate, and some lead nitrate.

J. J. Berzelius described the crystals of lead tetrahydroxydinitritodinitrate as
yellow shining laminæ, or long flat needles which, according to J. F. W. Herschel,
exhibit two axes of double refraction. J. C. Bromeis described the crystals as
rectangular prisms, with rhombic pyramids. J. J. Berzelius said that the moist
salt reddens blue litmus. M. E. Chevreul found the taste to be slightly sweet
and astringent. E. M. Péligot observed no evolution of water below $100°$, but
M. E. Chevreul reported that some acid is lost at $100°$, and the salt at a higher
temp. becomes pasty, and darker in colour. J. J. Berzelius added that at a still
higher temp., before fusion occurs, water and acid vapours are evolved.
M. E. Chevreul said that 100 parts of water dissolve 1.25 parts of salt at $25°$
(J. C. Bromeis said 1.18 parts at ordinary temp.), and 9.4 parts of salt at the boiling
point. The yellow aq. soln. is rendered turbid by carbon dioxide. J. C. Bromeis
found that the salt is not decomposed by long boiling with water, but it is decomposed if lead be present. J. J. Berzelius, and M. E. Chevreul noted that red fumes
are evolved when the salt is treated with strong acids ; and E. M. Péligot added
that cold, conc. acetic acid furnishes a yellow soln. without decomposition provided
the acid be added slowly to avoid a rise of temp. 100 parts of the salt in acetic
acid soln. dissolve 44 parts of lead dioxide, forming lead nitrate and acetate.
A. Chilesotti pointed out that the soln. in 4 mols of acetic acid contains 2 mols of

lead acetate, and a mol each of lead nitrite and nitrate. Baryta-water forms barium nitrite and nitrate; and, according to C. F. Gerhardt, silver nitrate gives a precipitate of silver nitrite.

The following twenty-six basic nitritonitrates have been reported, but probably a large proportion are mixtures. Commencing with the most basic, J. C. Bromeis boiled a soln. of lead tetrahydroxydinitritodinitrate with lead, and E. M. Péligot, with lead oxide, and obtained yellow, rhombic prisms with the composition, $7PbO.N_2O_3.N_2O_5.3H_2O$; E. M. Péligot obtained the same salt by the action of a soln. of lead nitrate on lead. J. C. Bromeis reported $14PbO.3N_2O_3.N_2O_5.6H_2O$ to be formed in orange-red crystals in the same manner as the $7:1:1:3$ salt. He also obtained rhombic prisms of $14PbO.N_2O_3.3N_2O_5.6H_2O$ by the action of a soln. of lead nitrate on an excess of lead. F. Peters obtained orange plates of $10PbO.2N_2O_3.N_2O_5.4H_2O$ by the action of a boiling soln. of 50 grms. of lead nitrate in $1\frac{1}{2}$ litres of water on 54·7 grms. of lead for $8\frac{1}{2}$ hrs.; and of a soln. of 25 grms. of lead nitrate in 500 c.c. of water on 23·4 grms. of lead for $7\frac{1}{2}$ hrs. He also obtained $16PbO.3N_2O_3.2N_2O_5.5H_2O$, in orange needles by boiling for $6\frac{1}{2}$ hrs., 50 grms. of lead nitrate, 2 litres of water, and 62·5 grms. of lead; orange-coloured, rhombic scales of $6PbO.N_2O_3.N_2O_5.2H_2O$, by boiling for 4 hrs. a mixture of 50 grms. of lead nitrate, $1\frac{1}{2}$ litres of water, and 46·9 grms. of lead; or 25 grms. of lead nitrate, 500 c.c. of water, and 19·5 grms. of lead; dark yellow plates of $9PbO.N_2O_3.2N_2O_5.4H_2O$, by boiling for 7 hrs. a mixture of 25 grms. of lead nitrate, 15·3 grms. of potassium (or sodium) nitrate, $1\frac{1}{2}$ litres of water, and 31·3 grms. of lead; yellow crystals of $23PbO.6N_2O_3.3N_2O_5.12H_2O$, by boiling for $7\frac{1}{2}$ hrs. a mixture of 25 grms. of lead nitrate, 500 c.c. of water, 50 c.c. of a soln. of potassium nitrite (1 c.c. $=0·0574$ grm. N_2O_3), and lead so that $Pb(NO_3)_2:KNO_2:Pb=2:2:3$; orange-yellow crystals $10PbO.3N_2O_3.N_2O_5.16H_2O$; by boiling for $4\frac{1}{2}$ hrs. 50 grms. of lead nitrate, 2 litres of water, and 39·1 grms. of lead; and yellow plates of $20PbO.6N_2O_3.3N_2O_5.17H_2O$, by boiling for 6 hrs. a soln. of 25 grms. of lead nitrate, 500 c.c. of water, 50 c.c. of a soln. of potassium nitrite (1 c.c. $=0·0574$ grm. N_2O_3), and 15·6 grms. of lead. H. von Lorenz reported $12PbO.5N_2O_3.N_2O_5.6H_2O$ to be formed by heating a soln. of 50 grms. of lead nitrate and 54·7 grms. of lead; and F. Peters, yellow rhombic prisms of $12PbO.5N_2O_3.N_2O_5.10H_2O$, by boiling for 30 minutes a soln. of 25 grms. of lead nitrate, 500 c.c. of water, 15·6 grms. of lead with so much potassium nitrite to give the ratio $Pb(NO_3)_2:KNO_2:Pb=1:3:1$. N. von Lorenz prepared yellow, rhombic plates of $10PbO.4N_2O_3.N_2O_5.5H_2O$, by boiling an aq. soln. of lead nitrate with an equal weight of lead; and F. Peters, by crystallization from the mother-liquid from $10PbO.2N_2O_3.N_2O_5.4H_2O$. F. Peters reported citron-yellow prisms of $8PbO.3N_2O_3.N_2O_5.4H_2O$, by crystallization from the mother-liquid of $6PbO.N_2O_5.N_2O_3.2H_2O$; N. von Lorenz obtained $8PbO.3N_2O_3.N_2O_5.4\frac{3}{4}H_2O$, in yellow plates, from a soln. containing 50 grms. of lead nitrate and 46·9 grms. of lead; and F. Peters, $8PbO.3N_2O_3.N_2O_5.6H_2O$ in yellow rhombic prisms, by boiling for 5 hrs. a soln. of 25 grms. lead nitrate, 500 c.c. water, with lead and potassium nitrite so that the ratio, $Pb(NO_3)_2:KNO_2:Pb$ is nearly $1:2:1$. F. Peters obtained orange-yellow scales of $6PbO.2N_2O_5.N_2O_3.3H_2O$ from the mother-liquid of $10PbO.3N_2O_3.N_2O_5.16H_2O$; and N. von Lorenz, yellow six-sided plates of $6PbO.2N_2O_3.N_2O_5.5H_2O$, from a soln. of 50 grms. of lead nitrate and 42 grms. of lead; and by using a mol of lead nitrate and $1\frac{1}{4}$ gram-atoms of lead he obtained $16PbO.3N_2O_3.5N_2O_5.10H_2O$. J. C. Bromeis so obtained $10PbO.3N_2O_3.2N_2O_5.7H_2O$ by the process employed for lead tetrahydroxydinitritodinitrate, but at a higher temp. F. Peters reported rhombic plates of $14PbO.4N_2O_3.3N_2O_5.12H_2O$ to be formed by boiling for 45 minutes a soln. of 25 grms. lead nitrate, 500 c.c. water; 150 c.c. of a soln. of potassium nitrite (1 c.c. $=0·0574$ grm. N_2O_3). N. von Lorenz obtained $26PbO.7N_2O_3.6N_2O_5.21H_2O$ by heating to 60°–100° for 7 hrs. a soln. of 50 grms. of lead nitrate and 31·27 grms. of lead. F. Peters obtained sulphur-yellow rhombic plates of $10PbO.2N_2O_3.3N_2O_5.9H_2O$ by heating for $2\frac{1}{2}$ hrs. a soln. of 50 grms. of lead nitrate in $1\frac{1}{2}$ litres of water and 23·5 grms. of lead; and sulphur-yellow rhombic plates of $16PbO.3N_2O_3.5N_2O_5.14H_2O$, by boiling for $6\frac{1}{2}$ hrs. a soln. of 50 grms. of lead nitrate in $1\frac{1}{2}$ litres of water with 19·6 grms. of lead; N. von Lorenz obtained sulphur-yellow rhombic plates of $6PbO.N_2O_3.2N_2O_5.3\frac{3}{4}H_2O$, by the action of a soln. of 50 grms. of lead nitrate and 31·27 grms. of lead at 60°–100°; and F. Peters, $6PbO.N_2O_3.2N_2O_5.5H_2O$, in pale yellow plates by the action of 50 grms. of lead nitrate, $1\frac{1}{2}$ litres water, and 15·6 grms. of lead at 65°–70°, and cooling to 35°.

Metallic lead was found by A. N. Meldrum to be more readily attacked by a mixed soln. of lead and potassium nitrates than it is by a soln. of lead nitrate alone. The reaction between potassium nitrite and lead acetate, nitrate, chloride, bromide, or iodide results in the production of complex compounds which, in addition to potassium, lead, nitrosyl, and water, may contain one or more eq. of the negative ion originally associated with the lead. The products vary in colour from yellow to orange, and as a rule contain potassium and lead in the at. **ratio** 3 : 2. S. D. Hayes passed nitric oxide and air into a soln. of lead nitrate containing an excess of potassium hydroxide, and obtained **potassium lead dinitritodinitrate**, $2KNO_3.Pb(NO_2)_2.H_2O$; in yellow prisms. A. N. Meldrum's analysis corresponds more nearly with $K_2Pb(NO_2)_3NO_3.H_2O$, *i.e.* $2KNO_2.Pb(NO_2)(NO_3).H_2O$. The salt becomes anhydrous at 100°. The salt is not changed by boiling water ; it gives red fumes with acids, and lead sulphate and potassium cobaltinitrite when treated with cobalt sulphate. J. Lang reported **potassium lead octonitritotetranitrate**, $K_6Pb_3(NO_2)_8(NO_3)_4.3H_2O$, from a soln. of lead nitrate and not too great an excess of potassium nitrite. The orange-yellow prisms are less soluble than potassium lead tetranitrite ; with an excess of potassium nitrite, potassium lead tetranitrite and potassium nitrate are formed, and with potassium carbonate, potassium nitrate is produced.

REFERENCES.

[1] J. S. Stas, *Bull. Acad. Belg.*, (2), **10**. 299, 1860 ; *Chem. News*, **4**. 308, 1861 ; E. Bonjean, *Compt. Rend.*, **148**. 1765, 1909 ; G. P. Baxter and F. L. Grover, *Journ. Amer. Chem. Soc.*, **37**. 1032, 1915 ; P. Gaubert, *Bull. Soc. Min.*, **25**. 228, 1902 ; J. Morel, *ib.*, **11**. 231, 1888 ; W. K. Lewis, *Die Komplexbildung zwischen Bleinitrat und Kaliumnitrat*, Breslau, 1908 ; *Zeit. phys. Chem.*, **63**. 171, 1908 ; J. W. Retgers, *ib.*, **9**. 267, 1892 ; C. von Hauer, *Sitzber. Akad. Wien*, **39**. 439, 1860 ; L. Wolff, *Zeit. Kryst.*, **4**. 147, 1880 ; K. Fajans and M. Lembert, *Zeit. anorg. Chem.*, **95**. 309, 1916 ; K. Fajans and J. Fischer, *ib.*, **95**. 290, 1916 ; A. Gutbier and J. Lohmann, *Journ. prakt. Chem.*, (2), **71**. 182, 1905 ; W. Mills, *Brit. Pat. No.* 6143, 1904 ; W. Shapleigh, *ib.*, 16213, 1889 ; A. Knop, *Chem. Centr.*, (1), **24**. 17, 1853 ; A. Chwala and H. Colle, *Zeit. anal. Chem.*, **50**. 241, 1911.

[2] L. Wolff, *Zeit. Kryst.*, **4**. 139, 1880 ; C. von Hauer, *ib.*, **6**. 528, 1882 ; S. Nishikawa and K. Hudinuki, *Proc. Math. Phys. Soc. Tokyo*, (2), **9**. 197, 1917 ; W. Haidinger, *Edin. Journ. Science*, **1**. 102, 1824 ; L. Vegard, *Skrift. Vid. Naturw. Kristiania*, 3, 1922 ; *Zeit. Physik*, **9**. 395, 1922 ; R. Wackernagel, *Kastner's Arch.*, **5**. 295, 1825 ; W. G. Hankel, *Abh. Sächs. Ges.*, **24**. 469, 1899 ; A. Scacchi, *Nuovo Cimento*, (1), **1**. 169, 1855 ; *Pogg. Ann.*, **109**. 366, 1860 ; T. V. Barker, *Journ. Chem. Soc.*, **89**. 1151, 1906 ; J. Morel, *Ann. Lyon. Soc. Agric.*, **5**. 137, 1888 ; *Bull. Soc. Min.*, **9**. 294, 1886 ; **11**. 231, 1888 ; **13**. 337, 1890 ; P. Gaubert, *ib.*, **17**. 107, 123, 1894 ; **18**. 141, 1895 ; **19**. 431, 1896 ; **23**. 211, 1900 ; **25**. 223, 1902 ; *Compt. Rend.*, **180**. 378, 1925 ; E. Giebe and A. Scheibe, *Zeit. Physik*, **33**. 760, 1925.

[3] J. H. Hassenfratz, *Liebig's Ann.*, **28**. 3, 1838 ; H. Schiff, *ib.*, **110**. 67, 1859 ; A. Breithaupt, *Schweigger's Journ.*, **68**. 291, 1833 ; C. J. B. Karsten, *Philosophie der Chemie*, Berlin, 86, 1843 ; P. Niggli, *Zeit. Kryst.*, **56**. 42, 1922 ; J. N. Rakshit, *Zeit. Elektrochem.*, **31**. 97, 1925 ; A. Taffel, *Trans. Faraday Soc.*, **19**. 99, 1923 ; L. Playfair and J. P. Joule, *Mem. Chem. Soc.*, **2**. 401, 1845 ; *Journ. Chem. Soc.*, **1**. 137, 1849 ; M. L. Jesersky, *Journ. Russ. Phys. Chem. Soc.*, **47**. 177, 1915 ; E. Filhol, *Ann. Chim. Phys.*, (3), **21**. 415, 1847 ; S. Holker, *Phil. Mag.*, (3), **27**. 214, 1845 ; H. J. Buignet, *Journ. Pharm. Chim.*, (3), **40**. 161, 337, 1860 ; H. G. F. Schröder, *Pogg. Ann.*, **106**. 226, 1859 ; P. Kremers, *ib.*, **96**. 39, 1855 ; A. Ditte, *Compt. Rend.*, **94**. 1180, 1310, 1882 ; *Ann. Chim. Phys.*, (5), **28**. 122, 1883 ; H. Gilbault, *Compt. Rend.*, **114**. 209, 1892 ; J. W. Retgers, *Zeit. phys. Chem.*, **4**. 201, 1889 ; M. le Blanc and P. Rohland, *ib.*, **19**. 277, 1896 ; J. Wagner, *Wied. Ann.*, **18**. 267, 1883 ; *Zeit. phys. Chem.*, **5**. 36, 1890 ; H. Töpsöe and C. Christiansen, *Danske Vid. Selsk. Skr.*, **9**. 645, 1873 ; *Pogg. Ann. Ergbd.*, **6**. 499, 1873 ; J. Behr, *Neues Jahrb. Min.*, i, 135, 1903 ; P. Gaubert, *Bull. Soc. Min.*, **11**. 231, 1888 ; J. H. Long, *Wied. Ann.*, **11**. 39, 1880 ; K. Bindel, *ib.*, **40**. 383, 1890 ; F. Kohlrausch, *ib.*, **6**. 1, 145, 1879 ; G. T. Gerlach, *Zeit. anal. Chem.*, **27**. 283, 1888 ; J. A. Groshans, *Rec. Trav. Chim. Pays-Bas*, **4**. 1, 1885 ; *Wied. Ann.*, **20**. 498, 1883 ; J. Thomsen, *Journ. prakt. Chem.*, (2), **17**. 165, 1878 ; *Ber.*, **6**. 710, 1873 ; **11**. 1021, 1878 ; E. F. Anthon, *Repert. Pharm.*, (2), **9**. 346, 1837 ; I. Traube, *Zeit. anorg. Chem.*, **8**. 26, 1895 ; K. Fajans and M. Lembert, *ib.*, **95**. 309, 1916 ; I. I. Saslawsky, *ib.*, **146**. 315, 1925 ; H. Euler, *Ark. Kem. Min.*, **1**. 156, 1904 ; R. Broom, *Proc. Roy. Soc. Edin.*, **13**. 172, 1885 ; A. Heydweiller, *Ann. Physik*, (4), **30**. 887, 1909 ; F. A. Henglein, *Zeit. Elektrochem.*, **30**. 5, 1924.

[4] C. A. Valson, *Compt. Rend.*, **74**. 103, 1872 ; J. Wagner, *Wied. Ann.*, **18**. 267, 1883 ; *Zeit. phys. Chem.*, **5**. 36, 1890 ; J. B. R. Scheffer, *ib.*, **2**. 400, 1888 ; H. Gilbault, *Compt. Rend.*, **114**. 209, 1892 ; J. J. Coleman, *Phil. Mag.*, (5), **23**. 1, 1887 ; J. C. G. de Marignac, *Arch. Sciences Genève*, (2), **50**. 89, 1874 ; *Ann. Chim. Phys.*, (5), **2**. 546, 1874 ; *Compt. Rend.*, **78**. 1523, 1874 ; H. Sentis, *Ann. Univ. Grenoble*, **9**. 1, 1897 ; *Journ. Phys.*, (3), **6**. 183, 1897 ; P. W. Bridgman, *Proc. Amer. Acad.*, **51**. 581, 1916.

[5] S. de Lannoy, *Zeit. phys. Chem.*, **18**. 443, 1895 ; O. Lehmann, *Wied. Ann.*, **24**. 1, 1885 ; J. Morel, *Bull. Soc. Min.*, **13**. 337, 1890 ; H. Hess, *Pogg. Ann.*, **12**. 262, 1828 ; L. Baekeland, *Journ. Amer. Chem. Soc.*, **26**. 391, 1904 ; L. R. Morgan, *Journ. Phys. Chem.*, **8**. 416, 1904 ; A. Colson, *Compt. Rend.*, **148**. 837, 1909 ; E. Maumené, *ib.*, **97**. 1216, 1883 ; B. Bogitsch, *ib.*, **161**. 790, 1915 ; J. S. Stas, *Bull. Acad. Belg.*, (2), **10**. 299, 1860 ; *Chem. News*, **4**. 308, 1861.

⁶ L. C. de Coppet, *Bull. Soc. Vaudoise*, (2), **11.** 1, 1871 ; *Zeit. phys. Chem.*, **22.** 240, 1897 ;
Ann. Chim. Phys., (4), **25.** 548, 1872 ; A. Ponsot, *ib.*, (7), **10.** 79, 1897 ; F. M. Raoult, *Compt.
Rend.*, **87.** 167, 1878 ; **98.** 1047, 1884 ; F. Rüdorff, *Pogg. Ann.*, **145.** 607, 1872 ; H. Hausrath,
Ann. Physik, (4), **9.** 543, 1902 ; J. H. Walton and A. Brann, *Journ. Amer. Chem. Soc.*, **38.** 1161,
1916 ; A. A. Noyes and K. G. Falk, *ib.*, **32.** 1025, 1910 ; M. le Blanc and A. A. Noyes, *Zeit. phys.
Chem.*, **6.** 386, 1890 ; F. Guthrie, *Phil. Mag.*, (5), **2.** 214, 1876 ; K. Drucker, *Zeit. Elektrochem.*,
11. 214, 1905 ; C. L. von Ende, *Ueber das Verhalten der Bleisalze in Lösungen*, Göttingen, 1899 ;
Zeit. anorg. Chem., **26.** 138, 1901 ; M. Randall and A. P. Vanselow, *Journ. Amer. Chem. Soc.*,
46. 2418, 1924.

⁷ P. Kremers, *Pogg. Ann.*, **92.** 497, 1854 ; G. T. Gerlach, *Zeit anal. Chem.*, **26.** 449, 1887 ;
T. Griffiths, *Quart. Journ. Science*, **18.** 89, 1825 ; A. Smits, *Zeit. phys. Chem.*, **39.** 418, 1901 ;
G. Tammann, *ib.*, **2.** 46, 1888 ; *Mém. Acad. St. Petersburg*, (7), **35.** 1, 1887 ; F. M. Raoult, *Compt.
Rend.*, **87.** 167, 1878 ; **98.** 1047, 1884.

⁸ J. C. G. de Marignac, *Arch. Sciences Genève*, (2), **55.** 113, 1876 ; *Bull. Soc. Chim.*, (2), **33.**
509, 1880 ; *Ann. pour. l'an*, 395, 1877 ; *Ann. Chim. Phys.*, (5), **8.** 410, 1876 ; M. Berthelot, *ib.*,
(5), **4.** 101, 1875 ; (6), **21.** 356, 1890 ; *Compt. Rend.*, **77.** 64, 1873 ; **78.** 1177, 1874 ; **81.** 1161,
1895 ; **90.** 779, 1880 ; A. Colson, *ib.*, **148.** 837, 1909 ; J. Moser, *Monatsh.*, **6.** 634, 1885 ; *Sitzber.
Akad. Wien*, **92.** 652, 1885 ; J. H. Pollok, *Proc. Chem. Soc.*, **15.** 8, 1899 ; *Chem. News*, **79.** 56,
1899 ; J. Thomsen, *Thermochemische Untersuchungen*, Leipzig, **1.** 387, 1882 ; **3.** 337, 1883 ;
Ber., **6.** 710, 1873 ; **11.** 1021, 1878 ; **12.** 2062, 1879 ; *Journ. prakt. Chem.*, (2), **17.** 165, 1878 ;
K. Jauch, *Zeit. Physik*, **4.** 442, 1921 ; P. Gunther, *Zeit. Elektrochem.*, **23.** 199, 1917 ; K. Bindel,
Wied. Ann., **40.** 383, 1890 ; H. Kopp, *Liebig's Ann. Suppl.*, **3.** 100, 298, 1865 ; N. de Kolossowsky,
Journ. Chim. Phys., **22.** 225, 1925.

⁹ H. Töpsöe and C. Christiansen, *Danske Vid. Selsk. Skr.*, (5), **9.** 645, 1873 ; *Pogg. Ann.
Ergbd.*, **6.** 499, 1873 ; *Ann. Chim. Phys.*, (4), **31.** 1, 1873 ; P. Barbier and L. Roux, *Compt. Rend.*,
110. 458, 1890 ; *Bull. Soc. Chim.*, (3), **3.** 420, 1890 ; (3), **4.** 9, 1890 ; H. Marbach, *Pogg. Ann.*,
94. 417, 1855 ; G. Wulff, *Zeit. Kryst.*, **31.** 511, 1899 ; F. Klocke, *Neues Jahrb. Min.*, i, 76, 1880 ;
ii, 268, 1881 ; J. Behr, *ib.*, i, 135, 1903 ; M. le Blanc and H. Rohland, *Zeit. phys. Chem.*, **19.**
277, 1896 ; T. W. Richards and W. C. Schumb, *Journ. Amer. Chem. Soc.*, **40.** 1903, 1918 ;
F. Fouqué, *Ann. Obs.*, **9.** 186, 1868 ; C. Schäfer, *Zeit. wiss. Photochem.*, **8.** 212, 1910 ; **17.** 193,
1918 ; C. Schäfer and M. Schubert, *Ann. Physik*, (4), **55.** 577, 1918 ; H. Greinacher, *ib.*, (4),
24. 79, 1907 ; A. Heydweiller, *ib.*, (4), **41.** 520, 1913 ; *Zeit. Physik*, **4.** 442, 1921 ; *Zeit. anorg.
Chem.*, **116.** 42, 1921 ; T. Liebisch and H. Rubens, *Sitzber. Akad. Berlin*, 876, 1919 ; W. N. Hartley, *Journ. Chem. Soc.*, **83.** 227, 1903 ; J. H. Gladstone and W. Hibbert, *ib.*, **67.** 831, 1895 ;
T. E. Aurén, *Phil. Mag.*, (6), **33.** 471, 1917.

¹⁰ E. J. Shaeffer and H. C. Jones, *Amer. Chem. Journ.*, **49.** 237, 1913 ; H. C. Jones and
C. A. Jacobson, *Amer. Chem. Journ.*, **40.** 394, 1908 ; M. Randall and A. P. Vanselow, *ib.*,
46. 2418, 1924 ; A. A. Noyes and E. H. Woodworth, *ib.*, **20.** 198, 1898 ; A. A. Noyes and
K. G. Falk, *ib.*, **33.** 1436, 1911 ; **34.** 462, 1912 ; K. G. Falk, *ib.*, **32.** 1565, 1910 ; W. D. Harkins
and F. L. Hunt, *ib.*, **33.** 1806, 1819, 1911 ; S. J. Bates, *ib.*, **35.** 519, 1913 ; J. H. Long, *ib.*, **18.**
717, 1896 ; *Wied. Ann.*, **11.** 39, 1880 ; *Zeit. phys. Chem.*, **22.** 140, 1897 ; O. Lehmann, *ib.*, **4.**
525, 1889 ; C. Kullgren, *ib.*, **85.** 473, 1913 ; E. Franke, *ib.*, **16.** 471, 1895 ; W. K. Lewis, *ib.*, **63.**
171, 1908 ; *Die Komplexbildung zwischen Bleinitrat und Kaliumnitrat*, Breslau, 34, 1908 ; H. Fernau, *Zeit. anorg. Chem.*, **17.** 327, 1898 ; A. Thiel and L. Stoll, *ib.*, **139.** 317, 1924 ; A. Rosenheim
and V. J. Meyer, *ib.*, **49.** 13, 1906 ; K. Fajans and M. Lembert, *ib.*, **95.** 309, 1916 ; C. L. von Ende,
ib., 26, 1901 ; *Ueber das Verhalten der Bleisalze in Lösungen*, Göttingen, 1899 ; W. Conrad,
Beiträge zur elektrochemischen Verhalten des Bleis, Göttingen, 1903 ; R. Salvadori, *Gazz. Chim.
Ital.*, **30.** ii, 547, 1900 ; K. Jauch, *Zeit. Physik*, **4.** 442, 1921 ; K. Beck and P. Stegmüller, *Arb.
Kaiser Ges. Amt.*, **34.** 446, 1910 ; *Zeit. Elektrochem.*, **17.** 844, 1911 ; K. Drucker, *ib.*, **11.** 214, 1905 ;
R. Abegg, *ib.*, **10.** 78, 1904 ; A. Günther-Schulze, *ib.*, **31.** 187, 1925 ; C. Immerwahr, *ib.*, **7.** 489,
1901 ; *Beiträge zur Löslichkeitsbestimmung schwerlöslicher Salze des Quecksilbers, Kupfers, Bleis,
Cadmiums, und Zinks*, Breslau, 1900 ; S. Labendzinsky, *Zur Kenntnis der Konstitution von
Salzlösungen*, Breslau, 1904 ; S. Lussana, *Atti Ist. Veneto*, (1), **3.** 1111, 1892 ; J. Walker and
E. Aston, *Journ. Chem. Soc.*, **67.** 576, 1895 ; A. C. Cumming, *Trans. Faraday Soc.*, **2.** 208, 1907 ;
F. Kohlrausch, *Sitzber. Akad. Berlin*, 1026, 1901 ; F. Kohlrausch and E. Grüneisen, *ib.*, 1215,
1904 ; H. Jahn, *Wied. Ann.*, **28.** 498, 1886 ; E. Bouty, *Compt. Rend.*, **98.** 140, 1884 ; **102.** 1372,
1886 ; **103.** 39, 1886 ; *Ann. Chim. Phys.*, (6), **3.** 433, 1884 ; G. Jäger, *Monatsh.*, **8.** 721, 1887 ;
J. Moser, *ib.*, **7.** 273, 1886 ; J. Miesler, *ib.*, **8.** 193, 1887 ; A. Ferguson and I Vogel, *Phil. Mag.*,
(6), **50.** 971, 1925 ; M. von Laue, *Zeit. Kryst.*, **63.** 312, 1926 ; A. Heydweiller, *Ann. Physik*, (4),
41. 514, 1913 ; (4), **37.** 750, 1912 ; *Zeit. Physik*, **3.** 310, 1920.

¹¹ W. Schmidt, *Ann. Physik*, (4), **11.** 114, 1903 ; A. Heydweiller, *Zeit. Physik*, **3.** 310, 1920 ;
E. Giebe and A. Scheibe, *ib.*, **33.** 760, 1925 ; W. G. Hankel, *Abh. Ges. Wiss. Leipzig*, **24.** 482,
1899 ; L. Ebert, *Zeit. phys. Chem.*, **113.** 1, 1924

¹² W. Ipatjeff and W. Werchowsky, *Journ. Russ. Phys. Chem. Soc.*, **41.** 769, 1909 ; *Ber.*,
42. 2081, 1909 ; H. Kopp. *Liebig's Ann.*, **34.** 260, 1840 ; A. Geuther, *ib.*, **219.** 65, 1883 ;
C. J. B. Karsten, *Schweigger's Journ.*, **65.** 394, 1832 ; J. J Berzelius, *Gilbert's Ann.*, **40.** 194,
1812 ; **46.** 156, 1814 ; V. Zotier, *Bull. Soc. Chim.*, (4), **21.** 241, 1917 ; E. Mitscherlich, *Journ.
prakt. Chem.*, (1), **19.** 451, 1840 ; H. Schiff, *Liebig's Ann.*, **109.** 326, 1859 ; T. Griffiths, *Quart.
Journ. Science*, **18.** 89, 1825 ; G. C. Wittstein, *Repert. Pharm.*, **63.** 329, 1839 ; H. Rose, *Sitzber.
Akad. Berlin*, 167, 459, 598, 793, 1851 ; C. von Hauer, *Sitzber. Akad. Wien*, **53.** 221, 1866 ;

P. Kremers, *Pogg. Ann.*, **92**. 497, 1854 ; T. Rüdorff, *ib.*, **148**. 456, 1873 ; A. Michel and L. Krafft, *Ann. Chim. Phys.*, (3), **41**. 471, 1854 ; A. Ditte, *ib.*, (5), **18**. 320, 1879 ; G. J. Mulder, *Bijdragen tot de Geschiedenis van het scheikundig gebonden Water*, Rotterdam, 1864 ; T. W. Richards and W. C. Schumb, *Journ. Amer. Chem. Soc.*, **40**. 1903, 1918 ; W. D. Harkins, *ib.*. **33**. 1809, 1911 ; K. Fajans and M. Lemberg, *Zeit. anorg. Chem.*, **95**. 323, 1916 ; K. Fajans and J. Fischler, *ib.*, **95**. 292, 1916 ; P. Fedotéeff, *ib.*, **73**. 173, 1911 ; F. Mylius, *ib.*, **74**. 411, 1912 ; D. Strömholm, *ib.*, **38**. 444, 1904 ; H. Euler, *Ark. Kem. Min.*, **1**. 156, 1904 ; J. Morel, *Bull. Soc. Min.*, **13**. 337, 1890 ; W. K. Lewis, *Die Komplexbildung zwischen Bleinitrat und Kaliumnitrat*, Breslau, 24, 1908 ; *Zeit. phys. Chem.*, **63**. 171, 1908 ; M. le Blanc and A. A. Noyes, *ib.*, **19**. 277, 1896 ; A. A. Noyes, *Journ. Amer. Chem. Soc.*, **46**. 1098, 1924 ; A. C. Cumming, *Trans. Faraday Soc.*, **2**. 208, 1907 ; W. D. Treadwell, *Helvetica Chim. Acta*, **4**. 990, 1921 ; H. W. Fischer, *Untersuchungen über Metallhydroxyde*, Breslau, 1907 ; N. Athanasescu, *Bull. Soc. Chim.*, (3), **13**. 180, 1895 ; J. H. Weibel, *Reaktionen einiger Metallsalzlösungen unter erhöhten Temperaturen und Drucken*, Zürich, 1923 ; C. Cheneveau, *Compt. Rend.*, **174**. 1019, 1922 ; J. Obermiller, *Zeit. phys. Chem.*, **109**. 145, 1924 ; A. Mailfert, *Compt. Rend.*, **94**. 860, 1186, 1882.

    [13] J. W. Thomas, *Journ. Chem. Soc.*, **33**. 367, 1878 ; *Chem. News*, **37**. 246, 1878 ; E. Divers, *ib.*, **78**. 314, 1898 ; *Journ. Chem. Soc.*, **75**. 83, 1899 ; W. C. Williams, *ib.*, **49**. 222, 1878 ; J. J. Berzelius, *Gilbert's Ann.*, **40**. 194, 1812 ; **46**. 156, 1814 ; K. Elbs, *Zeit. Elektrochem.*, **2**. 162, 1895 ; H. Braconnot, *Ann. Chim. Phys.*, (2), **52**. 288, 1833 ; A. Ditte, *ib.*, (5), **18**. 320, 1879 ; H. Moissan, *ib.*, (6), **24**. 264, 1891 ; E. Schürmann, *Liebig's Ann.*, **249**. 326, 1888 ; J. Morel, *Bull. Soc. Min.*, **13**. 337, 1890 ; E. C. Franklin and C. A. Kraus, *Amer. Chem. Journ.*, **20**. 828, 1898 ; F. M. G. Johnson and N. T. M. Wilsmore, *Trans. Faraday Soc.*, **3**. 77, 1907 ; *Zeit. Elektrochem.*, **14**. 227, 1908 ; R. Bossuet and L. Hackspill, *Compt. Rend.*, **157**. 720, 1913 ; H. P. Cady, *Journ. Phys. Chem.*, **1**. 707, 1897 ; **9**. 477, 1905 ; C. A. Lobry de Bruyn, *Rec. Trav. Chim. Pays-Bas*, **14**. 85, 1895 ; **15**. 174, 1896 ; T. W. B. Welsh and H. J. Broderson, *Journ. Amer. Chem. Soc.*, **37**. 819, 1915 ; W. D. Harkins, *ib.*, **33**. 1818, 1911 ; N. Athanasescu, *Bull. Soc. Chim.*, (3), **13**. 180, 1895 ; D. Strömholm, *Zeit. anorg. Chem.*, **38**. 444, 1904 ; P. Fedotéeff, *ib.*, **73**. 173, 1911 ; K. Friedrichs, *ib.*, **84**. 273, 1913 ; F. Fischer and K. Thiele, *ib.*, **67**. 312, 1910 ; A. C. Cumming, *Trans. Faraday Soc.*, **2**. 208, 1907 ; R. Salvadori, *Gazz. Chim. Ital.*, **30**. ii, 547, 1900 ; J. Lemberg, *Zeit. deut. geol. Ges.*, **52**. 488, 1908 ; F. Peters, *Einige Produkte die durch Einwirkung von Blei und von Kaliumnitrat auf Bleinitrat entstehen*, Berlin, 1893 ; J. Thomsen, *Journ. prakt. Chem.*, (2), **19**. 15, 1879.

    [14] A. Naumann, *Ber.*, **37**. 4328, 1904 ; **42**. 3790, 1909 ; **43**. 314, 1910 ; **47**. 1370, 1914 ; H. Mandal, *ib.*, **54**. 703, 1921 ; W. H. Krug and K. P. McElroy, *Journ. Anal. Chem.*, **6**. 184, 1892 ; C. A. Lobry de Bruyn, *Zeit. phys. Chem.*, **10**. 783, 1892 ; H. Bechhold, *ib.*, **48**. 385, 1904 ; A. Werner, *Zeit. anorg. Chem.*, **15**. 21, 1897 ; H. Arctowsky, *ib.*, **6**. 257, 1894 ; R. Müller, *ib.*, **142**. 130, 1925 ; C. W. Correns, *Koll. Zeit.*, **34**. 341, 1924 ; J. H. Walton and R. C. Judd, *Journ. Amer. Chem. Soc.*, **33**. 1036, 1911 ; J. H. Long, *ib.*, **18**. 120, 693, 1896 ; A. Gérardin, *Ann. Chim. Phys.*, (4), **5**. 129, 1865 ; B. Lachowicz, *Monatsh.*, **10**. 884, 1889 ; *Journ. prakt. Chem.*, (2), **39**. 99, 1889 ; *Ber.*, **17**. 1281, 1884 ; F. L. Shinn, *Journ. Phys. Chem.*, **11**. 538, 1907 ; A. T. Lincoln, *ib.*, **3**. 457, 1899 ; J. H. Mathews and A. J. Johnson, *ib.*, **21**. 294, 1917 ; A. W. Speransky and E. G. Goldberg, *Journ. Russ. Phys. Chem. Soc.*, **32**. 797, 1901 ; A. Smolka, *Sitzber. Akad. Wien*, **91**. 579, 1885 ; H. Röhler, *Zeit. Elektrochem.*, **16**. 433, 1910 ; M. Lilienfeld, *Ber. deut. bot. Ges.*, **23**. 91, 1905 ; W. D. Bancroft and H. B. Weiser, *Journ. Phys. Chem.*, **18**. 213, 1914.

    [15] J. B. Senderens, *Bull. Soc. Chim.*, (3), **11**. 424, 1894 ; (3), **15**. 217, 1896 ; W. Spring and M. Lucion, *ib.*, (3), **3**. 4, 1890 ; K. Peters, *Einige Produkte die durch Einwirkung von Blei und von Kaliumnitrite auf Bleinitrat entstehen*, Berlin, 1893 ; J. C. Bromeis, *Liebig's Ann.*, **72**. 38, 1849 ; E. Müller and O. Dienfonthäler, *Ber.*, **43**. 2321, 1910 ; A. Mailhe, *Compt. Rend.*, **134**. 233, 1902 ; N. W. Fischer, *Gilbert's Ann.*, **72**. 289, 1822 ; *Pogg. Ann.*, **9**. 262, 1827 ; **10**. 603, 1827 ; *Das Verhältniss der chemischen Verwandtschaft zur galvanischen Electrizität in Versuchen dargestellt*, Berlin, 1830 ; J. L. Proust, *Journ. Phys.*, **56**. 206, 1902 ; A. Ogata and T. Kai'un, *Journ. Japan. Pharm. Soc.*, 75, 1923 ; L. Kahlenberg and W. J. Trautmann, *Trans. Amer. Electrochem. Soc.*, **39**. 477, 1921.

    [16] B. Bogitch, *Compt. Rend.*, **161**. 790, 1915 ; E. Maumené, *ib.*, **97**. 1215, 1883 ; A. Colson, *ib.*, **148**. 837, 1909 ; P. Gaubert, *ib.*, **143**. 776, 1906 ; *Bull. Soc. Min.*, **39**. 141, 1909 ; A. Kanitz, *Zeit. phys. Chem.*, **22**. 347, 1897 ; M. le Blanc and A. A. Noyes, *ib.*, **6**. 387, 1890 ; F. W. Küster, *ib.*, **16**. 525, 1895 ; J. W. Retgers, *ib.*, **9**. 397, 1892 ; **16**. 525, 1895 ; H. Ambronn and M. le Blanc, *ib.*, **22**. 124, 1897 ; *Sitzber. Sächs. Akad.*, 173, 1894 ; A. C. Cumming, *Trans. Faraday Soc.*, **2**. 208, 1907 ; C. J. B. Karsten, *Philosophie der Chemie*, Berlin, 89, 95, 1843 ; F. Isaac, *Journ. Chem. Soc.*, **93**. 384, 1908 ; S. Glasstone and H. N. Saunders, *ib.*, **123**. 2134, 1923 ; S. Glasstone and E. J. Riggs, *ib.*, **127**. 2846, 1925 ; W. W. J. Nicol, *Phil. Mag.*, (5), **17**. 550, 1884 ; F. Guthrie, *ib.*, (5), **17**. 473, 1884 ; W. K. Lewis, *Die Komplexbildung zwischen Bleinitrat und Kaliumnitrat*, Breslau, 1908 ; *Zeit. phys. Chem.*, **63**. 171, 1908 ; R. Brauns, *Neues Jahrb. Min.*, ii, 102, 1883 ; F. Rüdorff, *Pogg. Ann.*, **148**. 456, 1873 ; *Ber.*, **6**. 484, 1873 ; A. Fock, *Zeit. Kryst.*, **28**. 337, 1897 ; R. Abegg, *Zeit. Elektrochem.*, **10**. 80, 1904 ; S. Labendzinsky, *Zur Kenntnis der Konstitution von Salzlösungen*, Breslau, 1904 ; P. Fedotéeff, *Zeit. anorg. Chem.*, **73**. 173, 1912 ; G. Tammann, *ib.*, **107**. 204, 1919 ; G. Tammann and W. Krings, *ib.*, **130**. 229, 1923 ; O. Pulvermacher. *ib.*, **113**. 142, 1920 ; D. Strömholm and T. Svenberg, *ib.*, **61**. 339, 1909 ; G. Bodländer, *Neues Jahrb. Min.*, i, 98, 1895 ; C. Stürenberg, *Arch. Pharm.*, (2), **143**. 12, 1870 ; C. von Hauer, *Journ. prakt. Chem.*, (1), **98**. 143, 1866 ; W. Herz, *Zur Kenntnis der Löslichkeit von Mischkristalle*, Berlin, 15,

1895; H. Euler, *Ark. Kem. Min.*, **1.** 143, 1904; M. Bellatti and J. Lussana, *Zeit. phys. Chem.*, **9.** 378, 1892; H. L. Wells and H. P. Beardsley, *Amer. Chem. Journ.*, **26.** 276, 1901.
[17] M. Pleissner, *Arb. Kaiser Ges. Amt.*, **26.** 394, 1907; B. Lachowicz, *Journ. prakt. Chem.*, (4), **39.** 99, 1889; *Ber.*, **17.** 1281, 1884; *Monatsh.*, **10.** 884, 1889; A. Smolka, *ib.*, **6.** 195, 1885; *Sitzber. Akad. Wien*, **91.** 579, 1885; J. J. Pohl, *ib.*, **6.** 597, 1851; N. von Lorenz, *ib.*, **84.** 1156, 1881; A. Geuther, *Liebig's Ann.*, **219.** 64, 1883; A. Vogel, *ib.*, **94.** 97, 1855; A. Ditte, *Compt. Rend.*, **94.** 1182, 1882; *Ann. Chim. Phys.*, (5), **28.** 125, 1883; M. E. Chevreul, *ib.*, (1), **83.** 70, 1812; J. Pelouze, *ib.*, (3), **4.** 107, 1842; J. F. Persoz, *ib.*, (2), **58.** 191, 1835; N. Athanasescu, *Bull. Soc. Chim.*, (3), **13.** 179, 1895; (3), **15.** 1079, 1896; J. B. Senderens, *ib.*, (3), **11.** 426, 1165, 1894; (3), **15.** 214, 1896; A. Mailhe, *ib.*, (3), **27.** 178, 1902; *Ann. Chim. Phys.*, (7), **27.** 284, 1902; *Compt. Rend.*, **134.** 233, 1902; E. Guignet, *ib.*, **56.** 358, 1863; F. C. Calvert, *ib.*, **22.** 480, 1846; J. Ville, *ib.*, **100.** 639, 1885; J. J. Berzelius, *Gilbert's Ann.*, **40.** 194, 200, 1812; **46.** 156, 1814; *Schweigger's Journ.*, **7.** 71, 1813; *Pogg. Ann.*, **19.** 312, 1830; H. Hess, *ib.*, **12.** 262, 1828; D. Strömholm, *Zeit. anorg. Chem.*, **38.** 444, 1904; R. Weinland and F. Paul, *ib.*, **129.** 257, 1923; F. Peters, *ib.*, **11.** 152, 1896; *Einige Produkte die durch Einwirkung von Blei und von Kaliumnitrit auf Bleinitrat entstehen*, Berlin, 1893; H. Klinger, *Ber.*, **16.** 997, 1883; E. Borsbach, *ib.*, **23.** 439, 1890; A. Ogata and T. Kai'un, *Journ. Japan. Pharm. Soc.*, 75, 1923; J. Löwe, *Zeit. anal. Chem.*, **4.** 358, 1865; *Journ. prakt. Chem.*, (1), **98.** 390, 1866; J. Thomsen, *Thermochemische Untersuchungen*, Leipzig, **3.** 337, 1883; F. Herles, *Zeit. Ver. Zuckerind.*, 782, 1909; T. Morawsky, *Journ. prakt. Chem.*, (2), **22.** 413, 1880; F. Meissner, *Jena Zeit. Med. Naturwiss.*, **10.** 26, 1877; A. J. Wakeman and H. L. Wells, *Amer. Chem. Journ.*, **9.** 301, 1887; J. H. Kastle, *ib.*, **20.** 818, 1898; L. Baekeland, *Journ. Amer. Chem. Soc.*, **26.** 398, 1904; L. R. Morgan, *Journ. Phys. Chem.*, **8.** 416, 1904; H. T. S. Britton, *Journ. Chem Soc.*, **127.** 2148, 1925.
[18] G. Städeler, *Liebig's Ann.*, **87.** 129, 1853.
[19] E. M. Péligot, *Ann. Chim. Phys.*, (3), **2.** 87, 1841; M. E. Chevreul, *ib.*, (1), **83.** 70, 1812; J. L. Proust, *Journ. Phys.*, **56.** 206, 1802; J. J. Berzelius, *Gilbert's Ann.*, **40.** 194, 200, 1812; **46.** 156, 1814; *Schweigger's Journ.*, **7.** 71, 1813; *Pogg. Ann.*, **19.** 312, 1830; J. C. Bromeis, *Liebig's Ann.*, **72.** 38, 1849; C. F. Gerhardt, *Compt. Rend. Trav. Chim.*, **6.** 166. 1849; J. Nicklès, *Compt. Rend.*, **27.** 244, 1848; A. Gomès. *ib.*, **34.** 187, 1852; J. Fritzsche, *Journ. prakt. Chem.*, (1), **19.** 179, 1840; J. Lang, *ib.*, (1), **86.** 300, 1862; *Svenska Vet. Akad. Handl.*, **3.** 14, 1860; *Pogg. Ann.*, **118.** 282, 1863; A. Chilesotti, *Atti Accad. Lincei*, (5), **17.** i, 1908; (5), **17.** ii, 295, 1908; F. Peters, *Einige Produkte die durch Einwirkung von Blei und von Kaliumnitrit auf Bleinitrat entstehen*, Berlin, 1893; *Zeit. anorg. Chem.*, **11.** 152, 1896; N. von Lorenz, *Sitzber. Akad. Wien*, **84.** 1156, 1881; J. B. Senderens, *Bull. Soc. Chim.*, (4), **15.** 211, 1896; *Compt. Rend.*, **104.** 504, 1887; S. D. Hayes, *Amer. Journ. Science*, (2), **31.** 226, 1861; *Journ. Chem. Soc.*, **13.** 337, 1861; A. N. Meldrum, *Proc. Chem. Soc.*, **24.** 97, 1908; J. F. W. Herschel, *Edin. Phil. Journ.*, **2.** 184, 1820.

§ 35. Lead Phosphates

V. A. Kroll[1] determined the cooling curves of fused mixtures of lead and phosphoric oxides. The lag was found to be considerable, and the undercooling in the case of compounds and eutectics was very marked. The mixtures with a high proportion of phosphorus pentoxide are glassy, and freezing points could not be determined by thermal methods. Crystallization begins near the temp. at which the pyrophosphate first appears, and from this point onwards, the curve shows five distinct maxima corresponding respectively with the pyrophosphate, $2PbO.P_2O_5$; the anorthophosphate, or diphosphate, $5PbO.2P_2O_5$; the normal or orthophosphate, $3PbO.P_2O_5$; *lead oxyorthophosphate*, $4PbO.P_2O_5$; and the *lead pentoxyorthophosphate*, $8PbO.P_2O_5$. The temp. in Fig. 192 are expressed in terms of the pyrometer readings. To scale the diagram, the m.p. of lead monoxide can be taken as 877°, and that of the

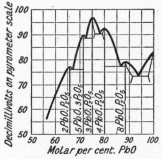

Fig. 132.—Fusion Curves of Mixtures of Lead Oxide and Phosphorus Pentoxide.

normal phosphate, $Pb_3(PO_4)_2$, as 1015°—*vide* Fig. 132. Many of the mixtures were found to expand after solidification, showing the other compounds are probably being formed at the lower temp. By measuring the temp. at which threads of the glasses are ruptured by a definite weight, A. V. Kroll found evidence that the phosphates $PbO.3P_2O_5$ and $2PbO.3P_2O_5$ are capable of existence.

J. J. Berzelius, and H. Alders and A. Stähler obtained normal *plumbous orthophosphate*, or **lead orthophosphate**, $Pb_3(PO_4)_2$, by digesting lead hydrophosphate with aq. ammonia ; and by treating a soln. of lead acetate with sodium hydrophosphate ; W. Heintz used a similar process ; and E. Mitscherlich, and H. Alders and A. Stähler worked with boiling soln. C. F. Gerhardt used a soln. of lead nitrate. The precipitate is washed by hot water and suction, but dried over sulphuric acid in vacuo. W. Heintz, and C. F. Gerhardt showed that if a soln. of lead chloride be employed, the precipitate is always contaminated with chloride. D. Strömholm digested lead hydroxide with an excess of $0.05N\text{-}Na_2HPO_4$ and obtained the normal phosphate. K. Haushofer found that when kept in a molten state for a long time, pyromorphite breaks down into lead orthophosphate and chloride. A. Stähler and W. Scharfenberg discussed the precipitation of lead as orthophosphate as an analytical process. J. H. Fischer said that if an excess of lead acetate be added to an acetic acid soln. of sodium hydrophosphate, the air-dried product is *tri- or tetrahydrated lead orthophosphate*.

The white powder is amorphous. H. Alders and A. Stähler observed no signs of crystals under the microscope. If fused, and slowly cooled, F. Zambonini found the mass consisted of hexagonal prisms which were uniaxial without showing optical anomalies. The optical character is negative, the birefringence is strong ; the indices of refraction for the B-, D-, and F-rays are respectively $\omega = 1.9549$, 1.9702, and 1.9994, and $\epsilon = 1.9232$, 1.9364, and 1.9618. The dispersion for ω is stronger than for ϵ. H. V. Regnault gave 0.0798 for the sp. ht., and 64.7 for the mol. ht. F. Zambonini gave $1015°$ for the m.p., and $1014°$ for the f.p. ; M. Amadori found $1006°$ for the m.p. of a sample contaminated with a slight trace of lead oxide. F. Zambonini observed no transition point at $782°$, although M. Amadori claimed that such a point does occur. S. Motylewsky said the drop-weight of molten lead orthophosphate at the m.p. is 275 units when that of water at $0°$ is 100 units. E. Bäcklin studied the K-series of the X-ray spectrum. According to W. Böttger, water at $19.95°$ dissolves 0.00135 grm. of lead orthophosphate per litre ; the soln. has the sp. conductivity 0.0_414, and about 98 per cent. is ionized. C. Immerwahr studied the potential of salts with a soln. of lead phosphate in alkali phosphate.

A. Mailfert found lead phosphate is slowly converted by ozone into the dioxide. R. M. Caven and A. Hill said that cold water does not hydrolyze the salt, but hot water attacks it very slowly. V. Zotier studied the catalytic action of the phosphate on hydrogen dioxide. G. Campani found that an excess of potassium iodide converts it into lead iodide or potassium lead tetraiodide. The lead orthophosphate is soluble in aq. ammonia, and more freely in potash-lye. The salt dissolves in nitric acid. H. Alders and A. Stähler said that it is precipitated therefrom by ammonia unchanged. E. Duvillier found that conc. nitric acid liberates orthophosphoric acid ; and dil. nitric acid converts it into the hydrophosphate. R. M. Caven and A. Hill found that lead phosphate is not soluble in a soln. of lead nitrate. A soln. of phosphoric acid—0.0469 per cent. H_3PO_4—begins to convert the orthophosphate into the hydrophosphate. A. Bertrand noted that 100 grms. of 38.94 per cent. acetic acid dissolve 0.128 grm. of lead orthophosphate. H. Mandal said that the salt is very sparingly soluble in aniline ; A. Naumann, insoluble in methyl and ethyl acetates.

L. Ouvrard obtained acicular crystals of **potassium lead orthophosphate**, $KPbPO_4$, from soln. of lead oxide in molten potassium hydrophosphate or pyrophosphate. He also prepared prismatic crystals of **sodium lead orthophosphate**, $NaPbPO_4$, in a similar manner. The crystals are readily soluble in dil. acids. J. A. Hedvall and co-workers found that lead orthophosphate begins to react with barium oxide at $335°$, with strontium oxide at $453°$, and with calcium oxide at $524°$. T. H. Lee and L. F. de Moraes obtained an impure **barium lead ortho-**

phosphate, $(Pb,Ba)_3(PO_4)_2.8H_2O$, as a yellowish-white mineral of sp. gr. 3·0–3·3. It was called *ferrazite*—after J. B. de A. Ferraz. G. Saring obtained the complex $Ca_3(PO_4)_2(CaO)_2(K_2O)_2.PbO_2$. Mixed crystals of *lead and cerous orthophosphates* were discussed by F. Zambonini, and G. Carobbi.

F. M. Lyte and co-workers mentioned the formation of basic lead phosphate by the action of a soln. of a phosphate on basic lead sulphate, or basic lead chloride. A. V. Kroll obtained evidence of the formation of $8PbO.P_2O_5$, or $5PbO.Pb_3(PO_4)_2$, **lead pentoxyorthophosphate,** and of $4PbO.P_2O_5$, or $PbO.Pb_3(PO_4)_2$, **lead oxyorthophosphate,** on the f.p. curve, Fig. 128. The last-named salt was obtained by C. F. Gerhardt, by calcining lead dinitratorthophosphate $Pb(NO_3)_2.Pb_3(PO_4)_2$. There was no sign of D. Strömholm's $3PbO.Pb_3(PO_4)_2$, or $6PbO.P_2O_5$, *lead trioxyorthophosphate,* on the f.p. curve. D. Strömholm obtained this product by the action of $0·05N$-Na_2HPO_4 on freshly precipitated lead hydroxide. The oxy- and pentoxy-orthophosphates were also obtained by M. Amadori in his study of the f.p. curves of the system PbO–$Pb_3(PO_4)_2$, summarized in Fig. 132.

K. Busz found an emerald-green basic lead copper phosphate as a mineral occurring in tabular crystals in Tsumeb, Otavi, South Africa; and he called it **tsumebite**; immediately afterwards V. Rosicky described a similar mineral from Frejka, and called it *preslite*—after J. S. Presl. K. Busz described it as monoclinic, but V. Rosicky showed that it is rhombic with the axial ratios $a : b : c$ $=0·977 : 1 : 0·879$. Twinning is common. The sp. gr. is 6·09–6·13, and the hardness, 3·5. It is readily soluble in hydrochloric acid. K. Busz represented the composition as a **copper lead oxyphosphate**, $5(Pb,Cu)O.P_2O_5.8H_2O$, with $Pb : Cu = 2 : 1$; it may be $Pb_3\{(Cu,Pb)(OH)_2\}_2PO_4.6H_2O$, or an isomorphous mixture of $Pb_3\{Pb(OH)_2\}_2(PO_4)_2.6H_2O$ and $Cu_3\{Cu(OH)_2\}_2(PO_4)_2.6H_2O$.

J. Démeste, and J. B. L. Romé de l'Isle referred to a *plomb rouge en stalactites ou en globules;* G. de Laumont, to *sel acide phosphorique martial* and to *plombegomme.* A similar term was used by F. S. Beudant, and J. J. Berzelius. C. U. Shepard called it **plumbogummite**; A. Breithaupt, *Gummispath;* J. D. Dana, *plumboresinate;* and R. J. Häuy, *plomb hydroalumineux.* The mineral occurs at Huelgoet, Brittany; Nussière, Dept. Rhône; Roughten Gill, Cumberland; Mine la Motte, Missouri; and Canton Mine, Georgia. The mineral usually looks like drops of gum, or coatings of gum, and at times like chalcedony or allophane. Unlike pyromorphite or sphalerite the globules are not fibrous. The **hitchcockite** of C. U. Shepard is a related mineral occurring in botryoidal crusts, and thin coatings, sometimes concentric in structure. Analyses of plumbogummite by J. J. Berzelius made it a hydrated lead aluminate, but A. Damour showed that the phosphoric acid was probably precipitated with and reported with the alumina. J. Smithson also regarded it as a native lead aluminate. Analyses by A. Damour, and E. G. J. Hartley showed that it is probably a hydrated **lead aluminophosphate,** $2PbO.3Al_2O_3.2P_2O_5.7H_2O$; and, according to G. T. Prior, it is one member of the trigonal family of minerals:

						$a : c$
Hamlinite	.	.	$2SrO.3Al_2O_3.2P_2O_5.7H_2O$	.	.	$1 : 1·1353$
Svanbergite	.	.	$2SrO.3Al_2O_3.P_2O_5.2SO_3.6H_2O$	.	.	$1 : 1·2063$
Hinsdalite	.	.	$2PbO.3Al_2O_3.P_2O_5.2SO_3.6H_2O$	.	.	$1 : 1·2667$
Corkite	.	.	$2PbO.3Fe_2O_3.P_2O_5.2SO_3.6H_2O$	.	.	$1 : 1·1842$
Beudantite	.	.	$2PbO.3Fe_2O_3.As_2O_5.2SO_3.6H_2O$	.	.	$1 : 1·1842$
Florencite	.	.	$Ce_2O_3.3Al_2O_3.2P_2O_5.6H_2O$	.	.	$1 : 1·1588$

studied by G. Wyrouboff, A. Cossa, etc. Hitchcockite was analyzed by F. A. Genth, and E. G. J. Hartley. The latter represented it by $5PbO.9Al_2O_3.4P_2O_5.2CO_2.24H_2O$, or $2PbCO_3.Pb_3(PO_4)_2.6\{AlPO_4.2Al(OH)_3.H_2O\}$. According to E. Bertrand, the mineral is uniaxial, and belongs to the hexagonal system. The sp. gr. is 4·014–4·88. A. Breithaupt probably erred in giving 6·42. E. Hussak's *lead phosphate-fava,* from Diamantina, is a kind of plumbogummite with the composition $2(Pb,Ca)O$ $2P_2O_5.3Al_2O_3.10H_2O$. The hardness is between 4 and 5. The mineral is soluble in nitric acid. E. S. Larsen and W. T. Schaller described a mineral from Hinsdale Co., Colorado, which he called **hinsdalite**. Its idealized composition corresponds with $2PbO.3Al_2O_3.P_2O_5.2SO_3.6H_2O$. The crystals are colourless but for a greenish tinge. The cube-like rhombohedra or six-sided plates are trigonal with the axial ratio $a:c=1:1\cdot12677$. The optical character is negative. The indices of refraction are $a=1\cdot670$, $\beta=1\cdot671$, and $\gamma=1\cdot689$. The crystals are zoned and exhibit optical anomalies, for a uniaxial centre may be surrounded by sectors with the optic axial angle $2E=32°$. The hardness is 4·5, the sp. gr. 3·65. The **rosierèsite** of A. Lacroix was found in greenish-yellow, yellow, or light brown stalactites, in an abandoned copper mine at Rosières, Tarn. An analysis by P. Berthier corresponds with that of a hydrated **lead copper aluminophosphate**. Its sp. gr. is 2·2 ; the refractive index about 1·5 ; and it is inactive to polarized light. It is soluble in nitric and hydrochloric acids.

L. T. Fairhall studied the ternary system, $PbO-P_2O_5-H_2O$, at 25°, and his results are summarized in Fig. 133. The area ACE represents a region where no solid phase is present. B represents lead hydrophosphate. The area ABC represents a solid phase in contact with various soln. The amount of lead oxide in soln. is a maximum at C, and this represents a univariant system where two solid phases are present: AC, lead hydrophosphate ; CE, lead dihydrophosphate.

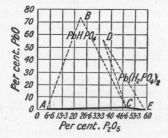

FIG. 133.—Equilibrium Conditions in the Ternary System : $PbO-P_2O_5-H_2O$, at 25°.

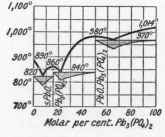

FIG. 134.—Fusion Curves of Mixtures of Lead Oxide and Orthophosphate.

These two curves therefore represent the solubilities of the respective phosphates in soln. of phosphoric acid. For equilibrium, normal lead phosphate cannot exist in the presence of even a small amount of phosphoric acid. The product of the reaction between sodium hydrophosphate and a lead salt at room temp. is normal lead phosphate. This slowly forms lead hydrophosphate which is the equilibrium product. W. Heintz reported **lead hydrophosphate**, $PbHPO_4$, to be formed by adding an aq. soln. of phosphoric acid to a boiling soln. of lead nitrate. A modification of the process was used by H. Alders and A. Stähler. J. J. Berzelius mixed sodium hydrophosphate with a hot aq. soln. of lead chloride ; and E. Mitscherlich said that the former should be added drop by drop to the lead salt so that the latter may always be in excess, or else the normal orthophosphate will also be precipitated. W. Heintz, and C. F. Gerhardt said that the precipitate obtained when the lead chloride is used is always contaminated with chloride. A. de Schulten recommended warming on a water-bath, for 7 days, a soln. of 15 grms. of lead nitrate and 10 c.c. of nitric acid of sp. gr. 1·2 in $1\frac{1}{2}$ litres of water, mixed with a soln. of 16 grms. of sodium hydrophosphate in 2 litres of water. H. Alders and A. Stähler treated at room temp. sodium hydrophosphate with an excess of a feebly acid soln. of lead acetate. H. Debray obtained needle-like crystals of the salt by the action of water on lead pyrophosphate in a sealed tube at 250°. According to H. Alders and A. Stähler, the salt forms rhombic plates and prisms ; A. de Schulten said that the crystals belong to the monoclinic system, and have the axial ratios $a:b:c=0\cdot7096:1:0\cdot8715$, and $\beta=97°\,40'$. The sp. gr. is 5·661 at 15°. When the salt is heated, it loses water, forming the pyrophosphate.

W. Heintz said that the salt can be melted before the blow-pipe, and when fused on charcoal, H. Rose said that it is not reduced to the metal. J. N. von Fuchs said that the solidification of the fused salt is attended by vivid incandescence. V. Ipatieff found that hydrogen reduces it to phosphite, phosphorus and lead oxide. When mixed with carbon and heated to a high temp., lead is formed and phosphorus volatilized. P. H. Bayrac found it to be insoluble in water and in acetic acid. F. Weppen said that it is more soluble in a soln. of ammonium acetate at 18·8°–25° than it is in water. The salt is soluble in nitric acid, and in a soln. of potassium or sodium hydroxide. E. Becquerel said that it is less soluble in a sat. soln. of sodium chloride than lead sulphate; and R. H. Brett found that it is soluble in a cold soln. of ammonium chloride and is completely precipitated therefrom by an excess of ammonia. H. Alders and A. Stähler found that ammonia precipitates the normal phosphate from the nitric acid soln. of the hydrophosphate. J. Spiller found that the salt is soluble in a soln. of sodium citrate. H. Alders and A. Stähler said that lead hydrophosphate can be recrystallized from dil. phosphoric acid—below 15 per cent. soln. If the conc. of the phosphoric acid is over 70 per cent., the dihydrophosphate is formed. The solubility in phosphoric acid is:

H_3PO_4	1	5	10	20	50	65	70	75	85	90 per cent.
PbO .	73·19	73·49	73·14	73·23	72·18	72·16	58·51	55·71	55·87	55·97 ,,

The compound can be regarded as **lead deuterotetraphosphate**, being derived from orthotetraphosphoric acid, $H_{14}P_4O_{17}$, or $(HO)_4P.O.P(OH)_3.O.P(OH)_3O.P(OH)_4$, by the loss of two mols of water so as to furnish deuterotetraphosphoric acid, $H_{10}P_4O_{15}$, or

$$(HO)_3\equiv P<^O_O>P(OH)_2.O.P(OH)_2<^O_O>P\equiv(OH)_3$$

—*vide* the polyphosphoric acids. L. T. Fairhall and C. P. Shaw found that lead hydrophosphate is soluble in water to the extent of 0·0129 grm. per litre, at 25°; its solubility in lactic acid soln. is always less than that of the lead phosphate. The amount of lead adsorbed from lead chloride soln. by bony material increases with the time of contact and with the p_H value of the soln.; with decalcified bone and kelp-charcoal true adsorption takes place, but with crushed and with ignited bone, there is a displacement of calcium which is not eq. to the amount of lead adsorbed. The chloride ion is unaffected.

J. J. Berzelius prepared impure **lead dihydrophosphate**, $Pb(H_2PO_4)_2$, by dissolving lead orthophosphate or hydrophosphate in phosphoric acid, and evaporating for crystallization. Lead dissolves slowly in aq. phosphoric acid when exposed to air and the soln. furnishes this salt on crystallization. H. Alders and A. Stähler said that this salt is best obtained by heating either of the other phosphates with 90 per cent. phosphoric acid. The salt crystallizes from conc. phosphoric acid in slender needles which, after washing with ether, are stable in air. When heated to dull redness, water is given off and lead metaphosphate is formed. The salt is decomposed by water. It also passes into one of the other salts if in contact with dil. phosphoric acid, say, below 70 per cent. conc. The salt is soluble in soln. of potassium or sodium hydroxide; when digested with aq. ammonia, the normal salt is formed. It is readily soluble in dil. nitric acid, and it is decomposed by conc. nitric acid with the separation, according to E. Duvillier, of lead nitrate. H. Alders and A. Stähler said that ammonia precipitates the normal salt from a nitric acid soln. of the dihydrophosphate. The salt is converted into lead sulphide by hydrogen sulphide and alkali sulphides. Hot conc. hydrochloric acid dissolves it completely, and lead chlorophosphate is precipitated as the soln. cools. The salt is insoluble in 50 per cent. acetic acid.

A. V. Kroll[2] reported what he called *lead anorthophosphate*, $5PbO.2P_2O_5$, intermediate between lead orthophosphate and pyrophosphate, $Pb_2P_2O_7.Pb_3(PO_4)_2$, to be formed when lead oxide and phosphoric oxide are fused together. The region of stability is indicated in Fig. 132. J. J. Berzelius, and P. Berthier found that if lead hydrophosphate be calcined, **lead pyrophosphate**, $Pb_2P_2O_7$, is formed; and, according to F. Stromeyer, A. Schwarzenberg, F. W. Winckler, and C. N. Pahl, if a soln. of a lead salt be treated with normal sodium pyrophosphate, a precipitate is formed when lead dissolves in an excess of the reagent. The washed precipitate is dried by press., etc. C. F. Gerhardt added that the precipitate which is formed by mixing an alkali pyrophosphate with an excess of lead nitrate is lead pyrophosphate, but if the alkali pyrophosphate be in excess, the precipitate is redissolved on the application of heat, and it contains a variable proportion of alkali. J. Müller obtained the pyrophosphate by stirring insoluble sodium or potassium metaphosphate with a conc. soln. of lead nitrate for 5 days at 50°–60°. L. Ouvrard dissolved lead oxide in molten potassium or sodium metaphosphate at a bright red heat, and extracted the cold mass with boiling water. If the temp. of fusion is not high enough, a complex sodium phosphate is produced; alkali pyrophosphate under similar conditions gives an alkali lead phosphate. The rhombic prisms of this salt are isomorphous with the barium and strontium salts. The sp. gr. is 5·8 at 20°. H. V. Regnault found the sp. ht. to be 0·0821, and the mol. ht. 48·3. T. Carnelley gave 799°–815° for the m.p., but remarked that there is a change to the metaphosphate on heating. L. Ouvrard said that lead pyrophosphate is easily soluble in dil. acids; A. Schwarzenberg, soluble in nitric acid and potash-lye, insoluble in aq. ammonia, acetic acid, and sulphurous acid; F. Stromeyer, soluble in a soln. of sodium pyrophosphate, and a boiling soln. of sodium hydrophosphate decomposes it into lead phosphate and sodium pyrophosphate. When heated with water in a sealed tube at 280°–300°, A. Reynoso found that it decomposes into normal lead orthophosphate, and an acid salt which in turn decomposes into the normal phosphate and phosphoric acid. A. Naumann found lead pyrophosphate to be insoluble in acetone. J. A. Hedvall and J. Heuberger observed that lead pyrophosphate begins to react with barium oxide at 364°, with strontium oxide at 461°, and with calcium oxide at about 528°.

C. N. Pahl prepared **lead dihydroxytripyrophosphate**, $Pb(OH)_2.3Pb_2P_2O_7.H_2O$, by the addition of sodium pyrophosphate to a soln. of lead acetate, and drying at 100°. The salt is easily fused, and the cold mass is crystalline. N. Menschutkin prepared *lead acetylpyrophosphate*, $Pb_3\{(C_2H_3O)P_2O_7\}_2$. C. N. Pahl mixed soln. of sodium pyrophosphate with a mixed soln. of lead and ammonium nitrates, but did not obtain a definite *ammonium lead pyrophosphate*. He added lead nitrate to a soln. of sodium pyrophosphate and a potassium salt, and found microscopic needles of a complex **potassium lead heptapyrophosphate**, $K_6Pb_{11}(P_2O_7)_7.8H_2O$, were precipitated. The crystals were washed, pressed, and dried at 100°. The salt becomes anhydrous when ignited. When the salt is boiled with water, another salt is formed, namely, $K_2Pb_{13}(P_2O_7)_7.3H_2O$. This, when calcined, is dehydrated. A. Rosenheim obtained **potassium lead pyrophosphate**, $K_2[PbP_2O_7].5H_2O$. C. F. Gerhardt reported that if lead pyrophosphate be boiled with an excess of sodium pyrophosphate in aq. soln., the resulting **sodium lead pyrophosphate** has the composition $Na_2PbP_2O_7$. A. Rosenheim also obtained this salt. G. Tammann also obtained it in columnar crystals by melting an equimolar part of lead nitrate and ammonium sodium hydrophosphate. The salt is readily dissolved by hot hydrochloric and nitric acids. C. N. Pahl mixed soln. of sodium pyrophosphate and lead nitrate or acetate and allowed the mixture to stand for some hours. The washed precipitate, consisting of microscopic needles, was dried at 100°. Its composition corresponded with **sodium lead pentapyrophosphate**, $Na_6Pb_7(P_2O_7)_5.5H_2O$. When calcined, the salt becomes anhydrous. If boiled for some time with a soln. of ammonium nitrate, four-sided plates of the composition $Na_2Pb_{13}(P_2O_7)_7.2H_2O$, are formed, and this salt becomes anhydrous when calcined.

J. Persoz [3] said that when a soln. of lead nitrate is mixed with metaphosphoric acid, and then with ammonia, a precipitate is produced which is insoluble in an excess of ammonia. A. Michaelis said that a **lead metaphosphate** is formed by the action of phosphorous chloride on lead oxide. F. Warschauer added that when lead oxide is dissolved in fused orthophosphoric acid below 400°, the tetrametaphosphate is formed, and above that temp., the hexametaphosphate. A. Glatzel said that **lead dimetaphosphate,** $Pb(PO_3)_2$, is not formed by strongly heating lead acetate and phosphoric acid, but T. Fleitmann prepared it by mixing a very dil. soln. of sodium dimetaphosphate with an excess of lead nitrate. The crystals are contaminated with a little lead nitrate. If ammonium dimetaphosphate is employed as precipitant, the precipitate is amorphous. The salt readily fuses without bubbling, and congeals to a transparent glass. T. Carnelley gave 800° for the m.p. of lead dimetaphosphate—a result which seems much too high. S. Motylewsky said that the drop-weight, at the m.p., is 256 units when that of water at 0° is 100. A. Glatzel found that dil. soln. of sodium dimetaphosphate gives a crystalline precipitate with lead acetate. The composition corresponds with the *hemitrihydrate,* $Pb(PO_3)_2.1\frac{1}{2}H_2O$. The salt is dehydrated at 150°, and melts at 350°, furnishing, when cooled slowly, the tetrametaphosphate. The salt is almost insoluble in water, and is readily decomposed by boiling sulphuric acid. A. Glatzel obtained only lead dimetaphosphate from a mixture of equimolar parts of lead dimetaphosphate and ammonium chloride; but T. Fleitmann obtained crystals of **ammonium lead dimetaphosphate,** $(NH_4)_2Pb(PO_3)_4$, from a mixed soln. of lead and ammonium dimetaphosphates. There was no loss in weight at 150°, but at a higher temp., ammonia was given off. The salt is sparingly soluble in water; and acids attack it with difficulty. A. Glatzel could not prepare *potassium lead dimetaphosphate* from mixed soln. of lead dimetaphosphate and potassium chloride.

T. Fleitmann and W. Henneberg made a conc. soln. of sodium trimetaphosphate with an eq. quantity of lead nitrate; the filtered liquid, on standing, furnishes oblique prismatic crystals of **lead trimetaphosphate,** $Pb_3\{(PO_3)_3\}_2.3H_2O$. G. von Knorre, and C. G. Lindbom employed modifications of this process. T. Fleitmann and W. Henneberg found that the water is expelled with intumescence when the salt is heated; and C. G. Lindbom added that at a higher temp. the salt fuses to a colourless glass which is insoluble in water, and freely soluble in nitric acid. Lead trimetaphosphate is the least soluble of all the trimetaphosphates. M. Stange reported a basic salt, **lead dioxytrimetaphosphate,** $2PbO.Pb_3\{(PO_3)_3\}_2$, obtained as a caseous precipitate when sodium triphosphate, $Na_5P_3O_{10}$, is added to an excess of lead nitrate or acetate. The precipitate is contaminated with soda, and rapidly changes into lead pyrophosphate.

T. Fleitmann prepared **lead tetrametaphosphate,** $Pb_2(PO_3)_4$, by fusing a mixture of lead oxide and orthophosphoric acid—according to F. Warschauer, the temp. should not exceed 400°. A. Glatzel, and F. Warschauer employed modifications of this process. The product consists of columnar or acicular crystals, which melt when heated and, on cooling, yield a glassy mass. The precipitate was stated by T. Fleitmann, and A. Glatzel to be insoluble in water, and by F. Warschauer to be *nachweisbar löslich.* When boiled with acids it decomposes more easily than the other tetrametaphosphates—*e.g.* those of barium, aluminium, and copper. Alkali hydrosulphides decompose it in the cold. The salt is decomposed by molten sodium chromate. A. Glatzel reported an *octohydrate* to be formed when a soln. of sodium tetrametaphosphate is treated with an excess of lead acetate. The white crystals become anhydrous when heated, and melt at a red heat. The cold mass is partly crystalline. The octohydrate is soluble in dil. acids, and is easily decomposed by hot, conc. sulphuric acid. A. V. Kroll prepared a basic salt, **lead oxytetrametaphosphate,** $PbO.Pb_2(PO_3)_4$, by passing the strongly heated vapour of phosphorus pentoxide mixed with a little oxygen, over lead contained in a combustion tube. The molten mass solidified to a mass partly crystals, partly glass. F. Schwarz added sodium triphosphate in slight excess to a soln. of lead nitrate, and heated the hydrated product in a platinum crucible. M. Stange could not prepare it by this process.   H. Lüdert said that boiling water converts the crystalline salt into lead pyrophosphate.

F. Warschauer found that **lead hexametaphosphate,** $Pb_3(PO_3)_6$, is formed when a mixture of lead oxide and phosphoric acid is heated above $400°$ to a clear liquid, and gradually cooled.   The mass of radiating crystals so obtained is decomposed by a soln. of sodium sulphide.   H. Lüdert obtained a *hydrate* by mixing slowly, with constant stirring, a soln. of lead nitrate and sodium hexametaphosphate.   The flocculent mass was washed with cold water, and dried at $60°$.   The white amorphous powder melts, forming a colourless glass.   It is almost insoluble in water; soluble in acids; and when treated with hydrogen sulphide, liberates metaphosphoric acid.

A. V. Kroll called the lead phosphates containing higher proportions of phosphoric oxide, **lead ultraphosphates**—*vide* polyphosphoric acids.   They can also be called *lead phosphatophosphates.*   When heated, they form glasses, whose f.p. cannot be investigated in the usual manner.   He therefore prepared threads of the glassy phosphate by dipping a platinum needle into the molten mixture and drawing it into threads.   Threads of constant sectional diameter were selected by drawing them through dies.   The threads were loaded with a definite weight, and heated until rupture occurred.   The curve showing the composition and temp. of rupture has distinct breaks corresponding with the two ultraphosphates—**lead hexaphosphate,** $PbO.3P_2O_5$, and **lead hemihexaphosphate,** $2PbO.3P_2O_5$.   The metaphosphate caused no discontinuity, while the phosphate $5PbO.3P_2O_5$ gave a distinct break; and there is also a discontinuity on the curve corresponding with lead hexaphospate, $4PbO.3P_2O_5$.   The tendency to devitrify corresponded with the mechanical properties.   Devitrification occurred with these glasses at a temp. much below the m.p. A. V. Kroll therefore suggested that glasses are not undercooled liquids, but colloidal solids, *i.e.* a soln. of one amorphous solid in another, for which he proposed the term *cryosol.*

M. Stange [4] reported what is possibly *sodium lead triphosphate,* $Na_4Pb_5P_3O_{27}.10H_2O$, to be formed when a soln. of sodium triphosphate is poured into one of acid-free lead nitrate.

Mixed salts.—M. Amadori [5] examined the f.p. curves of mixtures of lead ortho-phosphate and fluoride, and the results are summarized in Fig. 135.   There is a eutectic at $698°$ and 5 molar per cent. of phos-phate; and a maximum at $1098°$ and 75 molar per cent. of phosphate corresponding with **lead fluotriorthophosphate,** or *fluopyromorphite,* $PbF_2.3Pb_3(PO_4)_2$, a compound analogous with apatite. There is a eutectic at $1004°$ with 95 molar per cent. of lead phosphate.   There is a transforma-tion point at $782°$ in lead orthophosphate, and one with fluotriorthophosphate at $696°$, and probably also a third transition.   The α-forms of the ortho-phosphate and the fluophosphate are completely miscible; and an extensive solubility in the solid state between the fluoride and the α-fluotri-orthophosphate.   There is probably also complete miscibility between β-orthophosphate and β-fluotri-orthophosphate, and the latter compound and the fluoride probably also form a series of mixed crystals.   The γ-fluotriorthophosphate is probably not miscible, or miscible only to a very limited extent with β-orthophosphate, and is not miscible with the fluoride. F. Fischer and K. Thiele were unable to prepare either the fluophosphate, or the hydrofluophosphoric acid in the wet way.   J. G. Wallerius [6] described a *grön blyspat,* or *minera plumbi viridis,* and C. F. Schulze, a *Grünbleierz* which was shown by

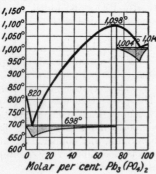

FIG. 135.—Fr ezing-point Curve of Mixtures of Lead Ortho-phosphate and Fluoride.

Molar per cent. $Pb_3(PO_4)_2$

M. H. Klaproth to contain phosphoric acid.   J. F. L. Hausmann called it *polychrom*, and also **pyromorphite**—from πῦρ, fire ; and μορφή, form—in allusion to the crystalline form a molten globule assumes on cooling.   A. Breithaupt alluded to a calcareous form as *polysphœrite*, and to a brown variety from Mies, Bohemia, as *miesite*.   G. Barruel called an impure variety from Nussière, Beaujeu, *nussierite*; and C. U. Shepard, a milk-white or pink variety from Cherokee Co., Georgia, *cherokine*.   Analyses by P. Berthier,[7] C. M. Kersten, G. Barruel, F. Sandberger, L. E. Rivot, E. Jannettaz and L. Michel, M. Amadori, A. Hilger, C. Hidegh, M. F. Heddle, N. Collie, J. Eyermann, T. Haege, F. Wöhler, C. F. Rammelsberg, C. Baerwald, etc., show that the composition of the idealized mineral is $PbCl_2.3Pb_3(PO_4)_2$.   A. Werner represented it by the formula $[Pb\{(PbPO_3.O)_2Pb\}_3]Cl_2$.   Many pyromorphites contain much lime, and it is thought that part of the lead chloride is replaceable by calcium chloride, or lead phosphate by calcium phosphate.   C. W. C. Fuchs, A. F. Rogers, F. Sandberger, E. Jannettaz and L. Michel, H. Ungemach, G. Barruel, T. Petersen, O. Bowles, and F. Gonnard also showed that some calcareous pyromorphites can be regarded as mixtures of apatite and pyromorphite.   The replacement of lead phosphate by lead arsenate or mimetite in arsenious pyromorphites has been considered by E. Bertrand, H. Struve, C. F. Rammelsberg, F. Wöhler, E. Jannettaz and L. Michel, F. Sandberger, T. Petersen, O. Bowles, G. Barruel, and H. Ungemach.   The analyses by C. Baerwald were taken to represent mixtures of $(Pb,Ca)_3Al_2O_6$, $Pb_3(PO_4)_2$, and $(Pb,Zn)_3(VO_4)_2$ in the proportion 1 : 2 : 4·2.   A. F. Rogers regarded a sample of pyromorphite as having the chlorine partly replaced by the carbonate radicle. According to J. Danne, the pyromorphite of Issy-l'Éveque contains radium in variable quantity ; B. B. Boltwood found no uranium in pyromorphite.   M. Bamberger and C. Weissenberger found 9.66×10^{-2} to 1.30×10^{-9} grm. of radium per gram of pyromorphite from Johanngeorgenstadt, and 8.20×10^{-5} to 9.88×10^{-5} grm. of thorium ; they also found 3.04×10^{-13} to 8.44×10^{-13} grm. of radium and 1.32×10^{-5} to 4.78×10^{-5} grm. of thorium per gram of pyromorphite from Ems.

W. Heintz [8] obtained anhydrous lead chlorotriorthophosphate by heating **hydrated lead chlorotriorthophosphate**, $PbCl_2.3Pb_3(PO_4)_2.H_2O$, which he obtained by pouring an excess of sodium hydrophosphate soln. into a boiling soln. of lead chloride, boiling the mixture for some time, and washing with boiling water.   When this compound is ignited, lead chloride and water are volatilized.   The hydrate was said to be insoluble in water ; and easily soluble in dil. nitric acid.   Conc. pitric acid transforms it into sparingly soluble lead nitratophosphate. M. Amadori's observations on the f.p. of mixtures of lead chloride and lead orthophosphate are summarized in Fig. 136.   Only one compound is formed, namely, lead chlorotriorthophosphate. The two eutectics are at 480° with 4·44 molar per cent. of phosphate, and 996° with 95·75 molar per cent. of phosphate.   The anhydrous salt was prepared by N. S. Manross by fusing lead chloride and normal sodium phosphate ; H. St. C. Deville and H. Caron fused a mixture of lead phosphate, lead chloride, and sodium chloride.   L. Michel omitted the sodium chloride. E. Weinschenk heated a mixture of lead chloride, ammonium hydrophosphate, and an excess of ammonium chloride for several hours in a sealed tube at 150°–180°.   L. Ouvrard melted a mixture of lead oxide, sodium pyrophosphate, and an excess of sodium chloride.   J. H. Debray heated a mixture of lead chloride, lead pyrophosphate, and water in a sealed tube at 250°.   A mixture of lead chloride soln. and calcium hydrophosphate furnished

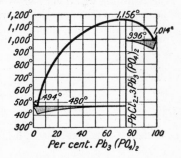

Fig. 136.—Fusion Curves of Mixtures of Lead Chloride and Orthophosphate.

a mixture of pyromorphite and apatite. The synthesis of pyromorphite was also discussed by G. Lechartier, A. Ditte, A. Daubrée, A. de Schulten, G. Forchhammer, F. Briegleb, F. K. Cameron and W. J. McCaughey, F. Zambonini, C. C. McDonnell and C. M. Smith, W. Eissner, and M. Amadori. F. Gonnard referred to the formation of pyromorphite in Pontgibaud by the action of a soln. of apatite in carbonetted water upon galena. G. Bischof, and E. Dittler pointed out the deriva ion of pyromorphite from galena with the intermediate formation of cerussite. J. J. Nöggerath found crystals of pyromorphite in furnace slags.

Pyromorphite occurs in prismatic crystals with the (10Ī0)-face striated vertically ; in branching groups of acicular crystals, and in moss-like forms ; in barrel-shaped crystals ; in globular, reniform, botryoidal, or verruciform groups or masses of crystals with an angular surface ; in fibrous or granular masses ; and in earthy incrustations. The colour may be green, yellow, various shades of brown, greyish-white, and cream colour. O. Clerc [9] has reported blue and black pyromorphites. When pure, the salt is colourless. M. Bamberger and R. Grengg found a green pyromorphite was colourless at −190°. P. Groth showed that many green and yellow pyromorphites contain chromium either mechanically mixed, or in solid soln. N. Collie found no chromium in an orange-coloured sample he analyzed, and no ferrous iron in a green sample. According to R. Brauns, the crystals are hexagonal bipyramids with the axial ratio between $a : c = 1 : 0.72926$ and $1 : 0.73544$; W. Haidinger gave $1 : 0.7362$. R. Brauns emphasized the close analogy between the crystals of pyromorphite and those of apatite and mimetesite. Thus, the axial ratio $a : c$ are $1 : 0.7330$ for apatite, $1 : 0.72926$ for pyromorphite, 1.73544 for a calcareous pyromorphite, and $1 : 0.7282$ for mimetesite. M. Amadori and E. Viterbi obtained mixed crystals of pyromorphite with mimetesite, and vanadinite. G. Carobbi and S. Restaino found that cerium, lanthanum, didymium, and samarium can replace the lead isomorphously in pyromorphite. The crystals of pyromorphite were also studied by E. Tacconi, E. V. Shannon, R. J. Haüy A. Lévy, C. F. Naumann, W. H. Miller, G. Seligmann, V. Goldschmidt, J. D. Dana G. Cesaro, V. Dürrfeld, A. Breithaupt, O. Bowles, A. Lacroix, J. Gerstendörfer, K. Zimanyi, G. Rose, J. Schabus, G. A. Kenngott, A. Karpinsky, G. R. Traverso, E. Weinschenck, L. Michel, J. H. Debray, N. S. Manross, H. Rose, J. Schabus, P. von Jeremejeff, and L. J. Spencer. The corrosion figures were found by H. Baumhauer to be conformable with the pyramidal hemihedrism of the crystals. The (10Ī1) and (10Ī0) cleavages are imperfect. The optical character is negative. The twinning was described by C. Klein, and V. Goldschmidt. W. Eissner found the change of the crystal angles with temp. between −160° and 650° exhibits certain abrupt changes ; an example with the angle $(1121) : (\bar{1}2\bar{1}1)$ is illustrated by Fig. 137.

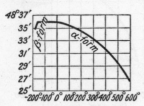

FIG. 137.—The Effect of Temperature on the Crystal Angle of Pyromorphite.

This is taken to mean that pyromorphite is dimorphous, so that β-pyromorphite begins to change into α-pyromorphite as the temp. rises from −160° to about −140°.

N. S. Manross [10] gave 7·008 for the specific gravity of artificial pyromorphite ; G. Rose, 7·054–7·208 for that of the mineral ; C. W. C. Fuchs, 7·36 ; H. Struve, 6·715, and for a sample mixed with mimetesite, 5·537 ; O. Bowles, 7·013 for a yellow sample with apatite, and 7·051 for a green one with apatite and mimetesite ; and T. Petersen, 6·461 also for a sample with both impurities. The hardness is 3·5–4. W. Eissner found no transition point on the heating curve of natural or artificial pyromorphite. M. Amadori gave 1156° for the melting point of pyromorphite free from lead oxide ; and for the m.p. of mixtures of fluomorphite with 20 per cent. of chloropyromorphite, 1108° ; with 50 per cent., 1126° ; and with 80 per cent., 1144°. E. Jannettaz found for the ratio of the thermal conductivity in the direction of the base to that in the direction of the chief axis. H. L. Bowman gave for the indices of refraction respectively for red-, yellow-, and blue-light, $\epsilon = 2\cdot042$, $2\cdot0494$, and $2\cdot0832$; and $\omega = 2\cdot0504$, $2\cdot0614$, and $2\cdot0964$. Hence the **birefringence** for yellow-light, $\omega - \epsilon = 0\cdot0120$. E. Jannettaz and L. Michel said that the crystals are uniaxial unless they consist of groups of small prisms. Observations were also made by M. Kirpatic. Samples from various localities were reported by J. Danne, P. Gaubert, E. Jannettaz, L. Francesconi and co-workers, M. Bamberger and G. Weissenberger, and E. Puxeddu and A. Marini to be **radioactive**. The luminescence of pyromorphite when exposed to the **X-rays**, or to the **cathode rays** has been studied by K. Keilhack, and C. Doelter. The latter also investigated the action of **radium rays**, and W. G. Hankel, the pyroelectricity of the crystals. W. Schmidt gave 26·0 for the **dielectric constant** perpendicular to the extraordinary ray, and 150, parallel thereto; and 47·5 for $\lambda = 75$ cms. A. Coehn and A. Lotz studied this subject.

G. Bischof [11] found that 1000 grms. of water sat. with carbon dioxide dissolve 0·047 grm. of pyromorphite; the mineral also freely dissolves in nitric acid, and the non-calcareous varieties also dissolve in alkali-lye. H. C. Bolton found citric acid feebly attacks pyromorphite when cold. J. Barlot and E. Chauvenet showed that pyromorphite is attacked by carbonyl chloride at 350°; and at 500°, the lead is all transformed into chloride. The mineral occurs in nature altered to galena, cerussite, calamine, calcite, and limonite. This subject was investigated by G. Bischof, J. R. Blum, and G. Sillem.

W. Heintz [12] reported **lead chlorodiorthophosphate**, $PbCl_2.2Pb_3(PO_4)_2$, to be formed by pouring into a soln. of lead chloride insufficient sodium hydrophosphate soln. for complete precipitation. The product was boiled with water. C. F. Gerhardt obtained crystals of **lead chlorobishydrophosphate**, $PbCl_2.2PbHPO_4$, by the process employed by W. Heintz. The crystals are slowly dehydrated at 100°. L. Ouvrard mentioned the formation of a *sodium lead chlorophosphate* by melting a mixture of lead oxide and sodium pyrophosphate with an excess of sodium chloride. A. Ditte reported **lead bromotriorthophosphate**, $PbBr_2.3Pb_3(PO_4)_2$, or *bromopyromorphite*, by fusing a mixture of 12 parts of lead orthophosphate and 5 parts of lead bromide together with a great excess of sodium bromide. The yellowish-white crystalline powder consists of hexagonal prisms or plates, soluble in dil. nitric acid. A. Werner regarded it as being constituted like pyromorphite. A. Ditte also made small golden yellow prisms of **lead iodotriorthophosphate**, $PbI_2.3Pb_3(PO_4)_2$, by fusing a mixture of two parts of lead orthophosphate and one of lead iodide, together with a great excess of sodium iodide.

According to J. J. Berzelius, [13] when phosphoric acid is poured into an aq. soln. of lead nitrate, or a soln. of lead phosphate in nitric acid is evaporated, crystalline grains of **lead nitratobisdihydrophosphate**, $Pb(NO_3)_2.2Pb(H_2PO_4)_2$, are formed. F. Dujardin said that a soln. of lead phosphate in warm nitric acid deposits crystals of lead nitrate on cooling. The octahedral crystals are elongated into four-sided prisms. When the salt is heated, lead orthophosphate is formed. C. F. Gerhardt poured a soln. of sodium hydrophosphate into excess of a soln. of lead nitrate and obtained **lead nitratorthophosphate**, $Pb(NO_3)_2.Pb_3(PO_4)_2.2H_2O$, as a crystalline precipitate. The soln. in hot conc. nitric acid deposits monoclinic crystals on cooling. When calcined, a white basic phosphate remains. The salt is soluble in cold water, and is decomposed by boiling water into lead nitrate and orthophosphate.

The plumbic phosphates.—C. F. Schönbein [14] noted that when red-lead is shaken with conc. phosphoric acid, a strongly oxidizing liquid is obtained which in the cold loses oxygen slowly and rapidly if heated. B. Brauner said that when lead tetracetate is treated with a phosphate an unstable plumbic phosphate is precipitated. F. Fischer electrolyzed dil. phosphoric acid, sp. gr. 1·02, using a lead anode and a current density of 0·05 ampère per sq. dm. for 24 hrs., and obtained a golden-yellow or wine-red soln. from which acids or salt soln. precipitate a lemon-yellow or orange-yellow voluminous compound. The precipitate dissolves in phosphoric acid ; it is hydrolyzed by water, forming hydrated lead dioxide ; with hydrogen dioxide, oxygen is evolved, and lead phosphate is formed. Aq. ammonia and alkali hydroxides when added to the phosphoric acid soln. give a precipitate which readily decomposes. With hydrochloric acid, chlorine is liberated ; with potassium iodide, iodine is liberated and lead iodide is formed ; and ferrous sulphate is converted into ferric sulphate with the precipitation of a plumbous salt. All this agrees with the assumption that a plumbic phosphate has been formed. K. Elbs and R. Nübling electrolyzed orthophosphoric acid of sp. gr. 1·75 at 10° with an anode compounded of two lead plates and a carbon plate, and a lead cathode surrounded by a porous pot. Half the current is arranged to pass through the lead part of the anode, and the other half through the carbon plate where the current densities are respectively 0·007 and 0·04 ampère per sq. cm. In the anode compartment a brown liquid is formed which deposits most of the lead as a mud. When the mud is drained on a porous plate and dried at 70°, its composition corresponds closely with **plumbic dihydrophosphate**, $Pb(H_2PO_4)_4$. This salt is fairly stable, and its properties agree with F. Fischer's preparation just indicated. It is suggested that the brown anode liquid contains *hydrophosphatoplumbic acid*. According to A. Hutchinson and W. Pollard, when a 50 per cent. aq. soln. of orthophosphoric acid is allowed to act on lead tetracetate, a pale yellow gelatinous mass is formed, which readily turns brown when treated with an excess of water, and evolves chlorine in contact with hydrochloric acid. Analyses show that an impure **plumbic bishydrophosphate**, $Pb(HPO_4)_2$, is formed. G. Saring reported **potassium calcium phosphatoplumbate**, $Ca_3(PO_4)_2(CaO)_2(K_2O)_2PbO_2$, analogous with the corresponding phosphatosilicate.

REFERENCES.

[1] A. V. Kroll, *Zeit. anorg. Chem.*, **76**. 387, 1912 ; **77**. 1, 1912 ; **78**. 95, 1912 ; D. Strömholm, *ib.*, **38**. 445, 1904 ; J. B. Trommsdorff, *Trommsdorff's Journ.*, **11**. 10, 1803 ; J. J. Berzelius, *Ann. Chim. Phys.*, (2), **2**. 161, 1816 ; E. Mitscherlich, *ib.*, (2), **19**. 359, 1821 ; H. V. Regnault, *ib.*, (3), **1**. 129, 1841 ; H. Debray, *ib.*, (3), **61**. 444, 1861 ; C. F. Gerhardt, *ib.*, (3), **22**. 505, 1848 ; *Compt. Rend. Trav. Chim.*, **6**. 234, 1849 ; H. Alders and A. Stähler, *Ber.*, **42**. 2263, 1909 ; A. Stähler and W. Scharfenberg, *ib.*, **38**. 3869, 1905 ; H. Mandal, *ib.*, **54**. 704, 1921 ; A. Naumann, *ib.*, **42**. 3790, 1909 ; **43**. 314, 1910 ; K. Haushofer, *Zeit. Kryst.*, **7**. 264, 1883 ; P. Niggli, *ib.*, **56**. 42, 1922 ; V. Rosicky, *ib.*, **51**. 521, 1912 ; W. Heintz, *Pogg. Ann.*, **73**. 119, 1848 ; H. Rose, *ib.*, **9**. 42, 221, 1827 ; K. Busz, *Festschr. Med. Nat. Ges. Munster*, 1, 1912 ; *Zeit. Kryst.*, **51**. 526, 1912 ; M. Amadori, *Atti Arcad. Lincei*, (5), **21**. ii, 768, 1912 ; (5), **27**. i, 143, 1918 ; *Atti 1st. Veneto*, **76**. 419, 1917 ; *Gazz. Chim. Ital.*, **49**. i, 55, 1919 ; G. Campani, *ib.*, **6**. 461, 1876 ; R. M. Caven and A. Hill, *Journ. Soc. Chem. Ind.*, **16**. 29, 1877 ; F. M. Lyte, *Brit. Pat. Nos.* 2920, 1888 ; 11926, 1888 ; J. Spiller, *Journ. Chem. Soc.*, **10**. 110, 1858 ; *Chem. News*, **8**. 280, 1863 ; **19**. 166, 1869 ; S. Motylewsky, *Zeit. anorg. Chem.*, **38**. 410, 1904 ; F. Weppen, *Arch. Pharm.*, (2), **9**. 236, 1837 ; W. Böttger, *Löslichkeitsstudien an schwer löslichen Stoffen*, Leipzig, 1903 ; *Zeit. phys. Chem.*, **46**. 521, 1903 ; L. T. Fairhall, *Journ. Amer. Chem. Soc.*, **46**. 1593, 1924 ; A. Bertrand, *Monit. Scient.*, (3), **10**. 477, 1880 ; J. H. Fischer, *Pharm. Viertelj.*, **15**. 179, 1866 ; E. Duvillier, *Compt. Rend.*, **81**. 1251, 1875 ; L. Ouvrard, *ib.*, **110**. 1335, 1890 ; E. Becquerel, *ib.*, **20**. 1524, 1845 ; F. Zambonini, *Rev. Min. Crist. Ital.*, **45** .1, 1915 ; *Zeit. Kryst.*, **58**. 226, 1923 ; *Bull. Soc. Min.*, **38**. 237, 1915 ; A. de Schulten, *ib.*, **27**. 111, 1904 ; P. H. Bayrac, *Journ. Pharm. Chim.*, (5), **28**. 500, 1893 ; J. N. von Fuchs, *Schweigger's Journ.*, **18**. 292, 1816 ; R. H. Brett, *Phil. Mag.*, (3), **10**. 95, 1837 ; C. Immerwahr, *Beiträge zur Löslichkeitsbestimmung schwerlöslicher Salze des Quecksilber, Kupfers, Bleis, Cadmiums, und Zinks*, Breslau, 1900 ; *Zeit. Elektrochem.*, **7**. 480, 1901 ; J. Smithson, *Ann. Phil.*, (1), **14**. 31, 1819 ; G. de Laumont, *Journ. Phys.*, **28**. 385, 1786 ; J. J. Berzelius, *Schweigger's Journ.*, **27**. 65, 1819 ; *Nouveau système de minéralogie*, Paris, 283, 1819 ; R. J. Häuy, *Traité de minéralogie*, Paris, 3. 410, 1822 ; C. U. Shepard, *A Treatise on Mineralogy*, New Haven, 2. 113, 1835 ; J. D. Dana, *A System of Mineralogy*, New York, 230, 1837 ; E. Bäcklin, *Zeit. Physik*, **33**. 547, 1925 ; E. S. Larsen and W. T. Schaller, *Amer. Journ. Science*, (4), **32**. 251, 1911 ; L. T. Fairhall and C. P. Shaw, *Journ. Ind. Hyg.*, **6**. 159, 1924 ; V. Zotier, *Bull. Soc. Chim.*, (4), **21**. 241, 1917 ; F. Zambonini, *Zeit. Kryst.*, **58**. 226, 1923 ; F. S. Beudant, *Traité élémentaire de minéralogie*, Paris, 2. 549, 594, 1832 ; J. B. L. Romé de l'Isle, *Cristallographie*, Paris, 3. 399, 1783 ; J. Démeste, *Lettres sur la minéralogie*, Paris, 2. 399, 1779 ; A. Breithaupt, *Vollständige Charakteristik der mineralsystems*, Dresden, 56, 1832 ; E. Bertrand, *Bull. Soc. Min.*, **4**. 37, 1881 ; G. Wyrouboff, *ib.*, **19**. 281, 1896 ; E. G. J. Hartley, *Min. Mag.*, **12**. 223, 1900 ; G. T. Prior, *ib.*, **12**. 249, 1900 ; H. A. Miers, *ib.*, **12**. 239, 1900 ; F. A. Genth, *Amer. Journ. Science*, (2), **23**. 424, 1857 ; T. H. Lee and L. F. de Moraes, *ib.*, (4),

48. 353, 1919; A. Dumour, *Ann. Mines*, (8), **17.** 191, 1890; P. Berthier, *ib.*, (3), **19.** 669, 1841; A. Cossa, *Compt. Rend.*, **98.** 990, 1884; A. Mailfert, *ib.*. **94.** 860, 1186, 1882; A. Lacroix, *Minéralogie de la France et de ses Colonies*, Paris, **4.** 532, 1910; E. Hussak, *Tschermak's Mitt.*, (2), **25.** 341, 1906; J. A. Hedvall and J. Heuberger, *Zeit. anorg. Chem.*, **135.** 49, 1924; J. A. Hedvall and E. Nordström, *ib.*, **154.** 1, 1926; G. Saring, *Versuche über den Ausschluss von Phosphaten durch Kieselsäure be hohen Temperaturen*, Dresden, 1906; G. Carobbi, *Atti Accad. Napoli*, (3), **31.** 83, 1925; M. Busz, *Festschr. Med. Nat. Ges.*, Münster, 84, 1912; V. Rosicky, *Zeit. Kryst.*, **51.** 521, 1913; V. Ipatieff, *Ber.*, **59.** B, 1412, 1926.

² J. Müller, *Beiträge zur Kenntnis der Metaphosphate*, Berlin, 1906; F. W. Winckler, *Jahrb. prakt. Pharm.*, **5.** 304, 1842; A. Schwarzenberg, *Liebig's Ann.*, **65.** 133, 1848; *Untersuchungen über die pyrophosphorsauren Salze*, Göttingen, 1847; L. Ouvrard, *Compt. Rend.*, **110.** 334, 1890; A. Reynoso, *ib.*, **34.** 795, 1852; **36.** 511, 1853; N. Menschutkin, *ib.*, **60.** 533, 1865; C. N. Pahl, *Ark. Kem. Min.*, **2.** 6, 1905; A. Naumann, *Ber.*, **37.** 4329, 1904; C. F. Gerhardt, *Ann. Chim. Phys.*, (3), **22.** 505, 1848; H. V. Regnault. *ib.*, (3), **1.** 129, 1841; T. Carnelley, *Journ. Chem. Soc.*, **33.** 280, 1878; P. Berthier, *Traité des essais par la voie sèche*, Paris, **2.** 681, 1834; J. J. Berzelius, *Ann. Chim. Phys.*, (2), **2.** 161, 1816; F. Stromeyer, *Schweigger's Journ.*, **58.** 132, 1830; A. V. Kroll, *Zeit. anorg. Chem.*, **76.** 387, 1912; **77.** 1, 1912; **78.** 95, 1912; J. A. Hedvall and J. Heuberger, *ib.*, **135.** 49, 1924; A. Rosenheim, *ib.*, **153.** 126, 1926; G. Tammann, *Journ. prakt. Chem.*, (2). **45.** 471, 1892.

³ F. Warschauer, *Beiträge zur Kenntnis der Metaphosphate*, Berlin, 63, 1903; *Zeit. anorg. Chem.*, **36.** 137, 1903; S Motylewsky, *ib.*, **38.** 410, 1904; A. V. Kroll, *ib.*, **76.** 387, 1912; **77.** 1. 1912; **78.** 95, 1912; H. Lüdert, *ib.*, **5.** 31, 1894; G. von Knorre, *ib.*, **24.** 380, 1900; A. Glatzel, *Ueber dimetaphosphorsäure und tetrametaphosdäure Salze*, Würzburg, 39, 1880; M. Stange, *Ueber einige Metallverbindungen der Triphosphorsäure*, Rostock, 29, 1896; *Zeit. anorg. Chem.*, **12.** 460, 1896: F. Schwarz, *ib.*, **9.** 263, 1896; *Ueber eine neue Polyphosphorsäure, $H_5P_3O_{10}$, und einige Verbindungen derselben*, Rostock, 31, 1895; T. Fleitmann, *Pogg. Ann.*, **78.** 253, 343, 1849; T. Fleitmann and W. Henneberg, *Liebig's Ann.*, **65.** 304, 1848; C. G. Lindbom, *Acta Univ. Lund.*, **10.** 7, 1873; *Magra undersökningar öfver Trimetafosforsgran*, Lund, 12, 1873; A. Michaelis, *Journ. prakt. Chem.*, (2), **4.** 449, 1871; J. Persoz, *Ann. Chim. Phys.*, (2), **58.** 191, 1835; T. Carnelley, *Journ. Chem. Soc.*, **33.** 280, 1878.

⁴ M. Stange, *Ueber einige Metallverbindungen der Triphosphorsäure*, Rostock, 28, 1896; *Zeit. anorg. Chem.* **12.** 459, 1896.

⁵ M. Amadori, *Atti Accad. Lincei*, (5), **21.** ii, 768, 1912; (5), **27.** i, 143, 1918; *Gazz. Chim. rtal.*, **49.** i, 38, 69, 1919; F. Fischer and K. Thiele, *Zeit. anorg. Chem.*, **67.** 313, 1910.

⁶ J. G. Wallerius, *Mineralogia*, Stockholm, 296, 1747; A. Breithaupt, *Vollständige Charakteristik der Mineralsystems*, Dresden, 54, 1832; *Vollständiges Handbuch der Mineralogie*, Dresden, 285, 1841; J. F. L. Hausmann, *Handbuch der Mineralogie*, Göttingen, 1089, 1813; C. U. Shepard, *Treatise on Mineralogy*, New Haven, 407, 1857; *Amer. Journ. Science*, (2), **24.** 38, 1857; C. F. Schulze, *Dresd. Mag.*, **2.** 70, 1761; **2.** 467, 1765; M. H. Klaproth, *Crell's Ann.*, i, 394, 1784; G. Barruel, *Ann. Chim. Phys.*, (2), **62.** 217, 1837.

⁷ C. M. Kersten, *Schweigger's Journ.*, **62.** 1, 1831; *Pogg. Ann.*, **26.** 489, 1832; F. Wöhler, *ib.*, **4.** 161, 1825; F. Sandberger, *Untersuchungen über Erzgänge*, Wiesbaden, 1, 1882; *Journ. prakt. Chem.*, (1), **47.** 462, 1849; *Neues Jahrb. Min.*, 222, 1864; 449, 1867; T. Petersen, *ib.*, 393, 1871; A. Hilger, *ib.*, 129, 1879; C. W. C. Fuchs, *ib.*, 824, 1867; J. J. Nöggerath, *ib.*, i, 1847; E. Jannettaz and L. Michel, *Bull. Soc. Min.*, **4.** 196, 1881; H. Ungemach, *ib.*, 33. 401, 1910; F. Gonnard, *ib.*, **5.** 44, 1882; E. Bertrand, *ib.*, **4.** 35, 1881; J. Eyermann, *The Minerals of Pennsylvania*, Easton, 1911; *Zeit. Kryst.*, **54.** 96, 1915; M. Amadori, *Gazz. Chim. Ital.*, **49.** i, 87, 1919; P. Berthier, *Ann. Mines*, (1), **7.** 152, 1822; T. Haege, *Die Mineralien des Siegerlandes*, Siegen, 1912; N. Collie, *Journ. Chem. Soc.*, **55.** 93, 1889; C. Hidegh, *Zeit. Kryst.*, **8.** 535, 1883; C. Baerwald, *ib.*, **7.** 172, 1883; M. F. Heddle, *Min. Mag.*, **5.** 21, 1882; H. L. Bowman, *ib.*, **13.** 324, 1903; G. Barruel, *Ann. Chim. Phys.*, (2), **62.** 217, 1837; O. Bowles, *Amer. Journ. Science*, (4), **28.** 40, 1909; A. F. Rogers, *ib.*, (4), **33.** 475, 1912; J. C. H. Mingaye, H. P. White, and W. A. Greig, *Rec. Geol. Sur. New South Wales*, **8.** 182, 1906; J. C. H. Mingaye, *ib.*, **6.** 116, 1896; R. Brauns, *Centr. Min.*, 257, 1909; L. E. Rivot, *Ann. Mines*, (4), **19.** 463, 1851; C. F. Rammelsberg, *Handbuch der Mineralchemie*, Leipzig, **2.** 299, 1875; **2.** 141, 1895; A. Schmidt, *Zeit. prakt. Geol.*, **27.** 157, 1919; H. Struve, *Proc. Russ. Min. Soc.*, 1, 1857; A. Werner, *Ber.*, **40.** 4448, 1907; A. Schmidt, *Zeit. prakt. Geol.*, **27.** 157, 1919; J. Danne, *Compt. Rend.*, **140.** 241. 1905; B. B. Boltwood, *Amer. Journ. Science*, (4), **18.** 97, 1904; M. Bamberger and C. Weissenberger, *Sitzber. Akad. Wien*, **123.** 2065, 1914.

⁸ W. Heintz, *Pogg. Ann.*, **73.** 119, 1847; J. H. Debray, *Compt. Rend.*, **52.** 44, 1861; *Ann. Chim. Phys.*, (3), **61.** 419, 1861; H. St. C. Deville and H. Caron, *ib.*, (3), **67.** 451, 1863; *Compt. Rend.*. **47.** 985, 1858; L. Ouvrard, *ib.*, **110.** 1334, 1890; G. Lechartier, *ib.*, **65.** 172, 1867; A. Ditte, *ib.*, **94.** 1592, 1882; **96.** 575, 846, 1226, 1883; A. Daubrée, *ib.*, **39.** 135, 1854; F. Gonnard, *ib.*, **106.** 77, 1888; N. S. Manross, *Liebig's Ann.*, **82.** 348, 1852; G. Forchhammer, *ib.*, **90.** 77, 1854; F. Briegleb, *ib.*, **97.** 95, 1856; G. Bischof, *Lehrbuch der chemischen und physikalischen Geologie*, Bonn, **3.** 742, 1871; E. Weinschenk, *Zeit. Kryst.*, **17.** 490, 1890; E. Dittler, *ib.*, **53.** 168, 1913; L. Michel, *Bull. Soc. Min.*, **10.** 134, 1887; A. de Schulten, *ib.*, **23.** 7, 1900; *Bull. Soc. Chim.*, (3), **1.** 472, 1889; M. Amadori, *Atti Accad. Lincei*, (5), **27.** i, 143, 1918; *Gazz. Chim. Ital.*, **49.** i, 55, 1919; G. Cesaro, *Bull. Acad. Belg.*, 327, 1905; F. K. Cameron and W. J. McCaughey, *Journ. Phys. Chem.*, **15.** 463, 1911; F. Zambonini, *Riv. Min. Crist. Ital.*, **45.** 100, 1915;

C. C. McDonnell and C. M. Smith, *Amer. Journ. Science*, (4), **42**. 139, 1916; W. Eissner, *Neues Jahrb. Min.*, i, 205, 1914; *Die Aenderung der Winkel des Apatits, Vanadinits, Pyromorphits, und Mimetesits, sowie der optischen Verhältnisse des Apatits im Temperaturbereich von* −160° *bis* +650°, *und der Dimorphismus der Apatitgruppe*, Weida i. Th., 1913; J. Nöggerath, *Neues Jahrb. Min.*, i, 1847.

⁹ H. Debray, *Ann. Chim. Phys.*, (3), **61**. 419, 1861; E. Weinschenk, *Zeit. Kryst.*, **17**. 490. 1890; L. Michel, *Bull. Soc. Min.*, **10**. 134, 1887; A. Lacroix, *ib.*, **17**. 120, 1894; **31**. 256, 1908; O. Bowles, *Amer. Journ. Science*, (4), **28**. 40, 1909; E. Tacconi, *Atti Accad. Lincei*, (5), **9**. 72, 1900; R. Brauns, *Centr. Min.*, 263, 1909; N. S. Manross, *Liebig's Ann.*, **82**. 348, 1852; M. Amadori, *Atti Accad. Lincei*, (5), **21**. ii, 768, 1912; (5), **27**. i, 143, 1918; *Gazz. Chim. Ital.*, **49**. i, 55, 1919; *Atti 1st. Veneto*, **76**. ii, 419, 1917; *Rend. 1st. Lombardo*, **49**. 137, 1916; M. Amadori and E. Viterbi, *Mem. Accad. Lincei*, (5), **10**. 386, 1914; W. Haidinger, *Pogg. Ann.*, **11**. 371, 1827; *Treatise on Mineralogy*, Edinburgh, 2. 134, 1825; H. Baumhauer, *Neues Jahrb. Min.*, 411, 1876; H. Rose, *Pogg. Ann.*, **9**. 209, 1827; G. Rose, *ib.*, **85**. 294, 1852; J. Schabus, *ib.*, **100**. 300, 1857; P. von Jeremejeff, *Proc. Russ. Min. Soc.*, **22**. 179, 1886; *Zeit. Kryst.*, **13**. 191, 1887; K. Zimanyi, *ib.*, **36**. 252, 1902; P. Groth, *ib.*, **6**. 310, 1882; O. Clerc, *Proc. Russ. Min. Soc.*, **41**. 28, 1903; A. Karpinsky, *ib.*, **42**. 20, 1904; J. Gerstendörfer, *Sitzber. Akad. Wien*, **99**. 422, 1890; L. J. Spencer, *Min. Mag.*, **15**. 1, 1908; G. R. Traverso, *Sarsabas e suoi minerali*, Alba, 1898; N. Collie, *Journ. Chem. Soc.*, **55**. 91, 1889; G. A. Kenngott, *Sitzber. Akad. Wien*, **10**. 180, 1853; W. Eissner, *Die Aenderung der Winkel des Apatits, Vanadinits, Pyromorphits, und Mimetesits, sowie der optischen Verhältnisse des Apatits im Temperaturbereich von* −160° *bis* +650°, *und der Dimorphismus der Apatitgruppe*, Weida i. Th., 1913; P. Groth, *Die Mineraliensammlung der Universitat Strassburg*, Strassburg, 179, 1878; V. Goldschmidt, *Krystallographische Winkeltabellen*, Berlin, 280, 1897; *Zeit. Kryst.*, **51**. 362, 1913; J. D. Dana, *A System of Mineralogy*, New York, 770, 1892; W H. Miller, *Introduction to Mineralogy*, London, 483, 1852; A. Lévy, *Description d'une collection de minéraux ormée par M. Henri Heuland*, London, 2. 410, 1837; C. F. Naumann, *Elemente der Mineralogie*, Leipzig, 76, 1828; G. Seligmann, *Verh. Nat. Ver. Bonn*, **33**. 257, 1876; G. Cesaro, *Mém. Acad. Belg.*, **53**. 13, 1897; V. Dürrfeld, *Zeit. Kryst.*, **50**. 589, 1912; R. J. Haüy, *Traité de minéralogie*, Paris, 3. 385, 1822; A. Breithaupt, *Berg. Hütt. Ztg.*, **21**. 99, 1862; **22**. 36, 1863; M. Bamberger and R. Grengg, *Centr. Min.*, 72, 1921; C. Klein, *ib.*, 748, 1902; E. V. Shannon, *Amer. Journ. Science*, (4), **43**. 325, 1919; G. Carobbi and S. Restaino, *Gazz. Chim. Ital.*, **56**. i, 59, 1926.

¹⁰ C. W. C. Fuchs, *Neues Jahrb. Min.*, 824, 1867; T. Petersen, *ib.*, 393, 1871; N. S. Manross, *Liebig's Ann.*, **82**. 348, 1852; H. Struve, *Proc. Russ. Min. Soc.*, 1, 1857; O. Bowles, *Amer. Journ. Science*, (4), **28**. 40, 1909; M. Amadori, *Atti Accad. Lincei*, (5), **27**. i, 143, 1918; *Gazz. Chim. Ital.*, **49**. i, 55, 1919; L. Francesconi, L. Granata, A. Nieddu, and G. Angelino, *ib.*, **48**. i, 112, 1918; H. L. Bowman, *Min. Mag.*, **13**. 324, 1903; W. Schmidt, *Ann. Physik*, (4), **9**. 919, 1902; (4), **11**. 114, 1903; K. Keilhack, *Zeit. deut. geol. Ges.*, **50**. 131, 1898; C. Doelter, *Das Radium und die Farben*, Dresden, 46, 1910; J. Danne, *Compt. Rend.*, **140**. 241, 1905; E. Jannettaz, *ib.*, **114**. 1352, 1892; *Bull. Soc. Min.*, **15**. 133, 1892; E. Jannettaz and L. Michel, *ib.*, **4**. 198, 1881; P. Gaubert, *ib.*, **29**. 56, 1906; W. G. Hankel, *Abh. Sächs. Akad.*, **12**. 551, 1882; *Wied. Ann.*, **18**. 423, 1883; G. Rose, *Pogg. Ann.*, **85**. 294, 1852; W. Eissner, *Die Aenderung der Winkel des Apatits, Vanadinits, Pyromorphits, und Mimetesits, sowie der optischen Verhältnisse des Apatits im Temperaturbereich von* −160° *bis* +650°, *und der Dimorphismus der Apatitgruppe*, Weida i. Th., 1913; M. Bamberger and G. Weissenberger, *Monatsh.*, **35**. 169, 1915; E. Puxeddu and A. Marini, *Ann. Chimica Appl.*, **13**. 34, 1923; A. Coehn and, A. Lotz, *Zeit. Physik*, 5. 246, 1921; M. Kirpatic, *Tschermak's Mitt.*, (2), 28. 297, 1909.

¹¹ J. Barlot and E. Chauvenet, *Compt. Rend.*, 157. 1153, 1913; H. C. Bolton, *Ber.*, **13**. 732, 1880; G. Bischof, *Lehrbuch der chemischen und physikalischen Geologie*, Bonn, 3. 891, 1871; G. Sillem, *Neues Jahrb. Min.*, 388, 1848; J. R. Blum, *Die Pseudomorphosen des Mineralreichs*, Stuttgart, 178, 1843; 1. 93, 1847; 3. 172. 1863.

¹² W. Heintz, *Pogg. Ann.*, **73**. 119, 1848; C. F. Gerhardt, *Ann. Chim. Phys.*, (3), **22**. 505, 1848; A. Ditte, *ib.*, (6), **8**. 521, 1886; *Compt. Rend.*, **96**. 846, 1883; L. Ouvrard, *ib.*, **110**. 1335, 1890; A. Werner, *Ber.*, **40**. 4448, 1907.

¹³ J. J. Berzelius, *Ann. Chim. Phys.*, (2), **2**. 161, 1816; C. F. Gerhardt, *Compt. Rend. Trav. Chim.*, **6**. 234, 1849; F. Dujardin, *L'Inst.*, **6**. 18, 1838; *Journ. prakt. Chem.*, (1), **15**. 309, 1838.

¹⁴ F. Fischer, *Zeit. Elektrochem.*, **8**. 398, 1902; K. Elbs and R. Nübling, *ib.*, **9**. 781, 1903; A. Hutchinson and W. Pollard, *Journ. Chem. Soc.*, **69**. 221, 1896; B. Brauner, *Zeit. anorg. Chem.*, **7**. 2, 1894; C. F. Schönbein, *Verh. Naturforsch. Ges. Basel*, 1. 487, 496, 1857; G. Saring, *Versuche über den Aufschluss durch Kieselsäure bei hohen Temperaturen*, Dresden, 1906.

CHAPTER XLVIII

INERT GASES

§ 1. The History of the Inert Gases

THE **inert gases** represent a family of elements including (1) *helium*, (2) *neon*, (3) *argon*, (4) *krypton*, (5) *xenon*, (6) *thoron* or *thorium emanation*, (7) *niton* or *radon* or *radium emanation*, and (8) *actinon* or *actinium emanation*. The three last-named are not well known, and they are considered in connection with thorium, radium, and actinium respectively. The nomenclature has been discussed by W. Ramsay and J. N. Collie,[1] J. Perrin, C. Schmidt, N. R. Campbell, E. Q. Adams, J. A. Gray and W. Ramsay, S. Meyer, etc. F. O. Giesel obtained indications of yet another inert gas as an emanation from actinium.

While investigating the density of nitrogen, Lord Rayleigh[2] compared the values obtained with atm. nitrogen, and nitrogen derived from ammonia. The former weighed about one-thousandth part than the gas of chemical origin. Actually, the mean value for the relative density of chemical nitrogen was found to be 2·2990 and that of atm. nitrogen, 2·3102.

It was shown that chemical nitrogen does not contain a gas specifically lighter than nitrogen ; that chemical nitrogen is not partly dissociated into atomic nitrogen ; and that atm. nitrogen does not contain mols. consisting of more than two atoms. There remained the possibility that atm. nitrogen contains an unknown gas specifically heavier than nitrogen. Lord Rayleigh and W. Ramsay tested this hypothesis, and found that when the nitrogen was removed by heating it in contact with magnesium, the one per cent. residuum contained a new gas which was named **argon**—from the Greek privative and ἔργον, work, in allusion to the chemical inertness of the gas. The first announcement of this discovery was made August 13, 1894.

Over a century previously, H. Cavendish seems to have obscurely anticipated this discovery, for he laboriously eliminated all the known constituents of atm. air, and obtained a remnant which could not be removed. This must have been impure argon. H. Cavendish asked if there are not many different substances in atm. air confounded together under the name phlogisticated air (nitrogen). He therefore passed electric sparks through a mixture of air and oxygen (dephlogisticated air) and absorbed

FIG. 1.—H. Cavendish's Experiment.

the resulting nitrous acid with soap-lees. The illustration, Fig. 1, gives an idea of the apparatus employed. The experiment was continued until the addition of more oxygen and sparking gave no more products soluble in the soap-lees. H. Cavendish said :

Having by these means condensed as much as I could of the phlogisticated air, I let up some soln. of liver of sulphur to absorb the dephlogisticated air ; after which, only a small bubble of air remained unabsorbed, which certainly was not more than $\frac{1}{120}$th of the bulk of the phlogisticated air let up into the tube ; so that if there is any part of the phlogisticated air of our atm. which differs from the rest, and cannot be reduced to nitrous acid, we may safely conclude that it is not more than $\frac{1}{120}$th part of the whole.

The spectrum of argon was first seen by H. F. Newall, for he observed seventeen unfamiliar bright lines which frequently flashed out when an electric discharge was passed through tubes containing highly rarefied air. W. Crookes showed that these lines had a place amongst the 200 lines which he mapped in the spectrum of argon.

W. Ramsay and M. W. Travers liquefied argon, and obtained a solid, whose spectrum, when gasified, was different from that of argon. They named this substance *metargon*. J. Dewar questioned the validity of this discovery ; and A. Schuster, and later W. Ramsay and M. W. Travers, showed that the spectrum was that of a mixture of argon with a hydrocarbon derived from the phosphorus used in the absorption of the oxygen from the air. Soon after the discovery of argon, J. Dewar,[3] and others discussed the possibility that argon is not a new element, but rather an allotropic modification of nitrogen—possibly N_3. This hypothesis, however, was soon definitely disproved.

On August 18, 1868, J. N. Lockyer[4] observed a bright orange-yellow ray in the spectrum of the sun's photosphere taken during an eclipse of the sun. At first, the yellow ray was confounded with the D-line of sodium. P. J. C. Janssen, and E. Frankland and J. N. Lockyer established the separate identity of this line, which, forming a trio with the two D-lines of sodium, came to be known as the D_3-line. At first, J. N. Lockyer regarded the substance emitting the D_3-line as a form of hydrogen, or as a product of the dissociation of hydrogen ; but A. Secchi, and later J. N. Lockyer, showed that the D_3-line is not produced by hydrogen, and the existence of a new element was postulated to which the name **helium** was applied —from ἥλιος, the sun. In 1881, L. Palmieri recognized the D_3-line in the spectra of the gaseous ejecta of Vesuvius. After the discovery of argon, W. Ramsay and co-workers recalled an observation of W. F. Hillebrand that uraninite and cleveite evolved nitrogen when treated with sulphuric acid, or fused with alkali carbonate. In 1895, W. Ramsay extracted some of the supposed nitrogen, and W. Crookes found that the spectrum gave the vivid-yellow D_3-line as its distinctive feature ; A. Bélopolsky showed that the D_3-line is double ; and the observations of C. Runge and F. Paschen, W. Huggins, G. E. Hale, and H. Deslandres showed that the spectrum of terrestrial helium is the same as that furnished by the helium in the solar chromosphere. At first, C. Runge and F. Paschen found that the spectrum extending from the ultra-red to the ultra-violet furnished three rhythmically arranged series of doublets, and many more solitary lines ; true helium was supposed to give rise to the first doublet ; the second was attributed to an admixed gas which was provisionally called co-helium. J. N. Lockyer named the components helium and *asterium*. E. A. Hill believed that the spectrum of helium by W. Crookes indicated the existence of 15 new elements ! The divided ownership of the spectrum has not been confirmed. W. Ramsay and J. N. Collie, however, by atmolysis, were able to separate helium into two portions with the relative densities 1·874 and 2·133, and refractive index 0·1350 (air unity) and 0·1524 respectively. Both fractions gave identical spectra. It was therefore assumed that atmolysis had separated helium into light and heavy mols. of one elemental form of matter. W. Ramsay, and M. W. Travers obtained no evidence of the separation of helium into two different elements by atmolysis. The later experiments of C. Runge and F. Paschen, and of M. W. Travers, showed that the complexity of the spectrum is no proof that the element is heterogeneous, for oxygen can be made to give similar evidence of complexity. J. S. Ames and W. H. Humphrey also showed that the so-called light and heavy constituents of helium give the same spectra. Hence, helium is an elemental gas.

W. Ramsay and J. N. Collie tested the homogeneity of argon by atmolysis, and obtained fractions of sp. gr. 19·93 and 20·01 respectively. This difference was considered to be within the limits of experimental error. W. Ramsay and

M. W. Travers [5] fractionally distilled liquid argon, and obtained a first fraction consisting of a gas which they called neon—from νέος, new. It had a characteristic spectrum and a relative density 14·67 (O=16). They also obtained a gas with a characteristic spectrum, and relative density 22·51 (oxygen 16), which they called krypton—from κρυπτός, hidden ; and yet another gas, xenon—from ξένος, the stranger—with a characteristic spectrum, and relative density 65 (oxygen 16).

J. J. Thomson, and R. B. Moore, could find no evidence of a gas *heavier than xenon* in atm. air ; while W. Ramsay said that if such a gas be present, air must contain less than one vol. in 2,560,000,000 vols. of air. Later, J. J. Thomson reported constituents with mol. wts. 163 and 260, but F. W. Aston could not verify the existence of new elements to the extent of more than one vol. in 10^{15} or 2×10^{16} vols. of air. G. D. Liveing and J. Dewar, E. C. C. Baly, and R. Schmidt discussed the spectroscopic properties of the higher boiling constituents of air from this point of view ; and F. W. Aston likewise examined these constituents by positive ray analysis. R. Nasini and co-workers, G. D. Liveing and J. Dewar, and J. E. Coates, reported unknown spectral lines in the lighter constituents of the atm., but H. E. Watson, and F. Bordas and F. Touplain found no spectroscopic or other evidence of the existence of a constituent *lighter than helium*. C. Borel and A. Jaquerod sought for any hitherto unrecognized gas in atm. air, by diffusion through quartz, but with negative results.

W. Ramsay found helium in liquid argon. Hence, crude argon obtained by removing the oxygen and nitrogen from atm. air contains five elements— helium, neon, argon, krypton, and xenon. There is approximately one vol. of helium in 1800 vols. of crude argon. Otherwise expressed, the crude argon has the percentage composition :

Helium.	Neon.	Argon.	Krypton.	Xenon.
0·055	0·16	99·785	0·0005	0·00006 per cent.

The following memoirs, etc., treat the subject in a general manner : Lord Rayleigh, *Proc. Roy. Inst.*, **14**. 524, 1895 ; *Collected Scientific Papers*, Cambridge, **4**. 188, 1903 ; J. N. Lockyer, *Nature*, **51**. 386, 1895 ; **52**. 8, 55, 214, 327, 1895 ; **53**. 319, 342, 1896 ; W. Ramsay, *The Gases of the Atmosphere*, London, 1905 ; *Ann. Chim. Phys.*, (7), **13**. 433, 1898 ; *Arch. Sciences Genève*, (4), **25**. 329, 1908 ; (4), **26**. 237, 1909 ; *Zeit. angew. Chem.*, **21**. 1304, 1908 ; *Revue Scientifique*, (5), **10**. 353, 1908 ; *Die edlen und die radioaktiven Gase*, Leipzig, 1908 ; H. F. Kellas, *Journ. Franklin Inst.*, **153**. 419, 1902 ; **154**. 47, 1902 ; H. Happel, *Phys. Zeit.*, **10**. 484, 1909 ; A. Debierne, *Journ. Amer. Chem. Soc.*, **33**. 1388, 1911 ; C. le Roy Parker, *ib.*, **19**. 124, 1897 ; M. W. Travers, *The Experimental Study of Gases*, London, 1901 ; M. Mugdan, *Argon und Helium, zwei neue gas förmige Elemente*, Stuttgart, 1896 ; Lord Rayleigh and W. Ramsay, *Argon, a New Constituent of the Atmosphere*, Washington, 1896 ; W. Ramsay and G. Rudorf, *Die Edelgase*, Leipzig, 1918 ; J. J. van Laar, *L'hydrogène et les gas nobles*, Layde, 1923 ; R. B. Moore, *Journ. Franklin Inst.*, **191**. 145, 1921. E. R. Weaver has compiled a bibliography of the literature on helium—*Journ. Ind. Eng. Chem.*, **11**. 682, 1919.

REFERENCES.

[1] W. Ramsay and J. N. Collie, *Proc. Roy. Soc.*, **73**. A, 476, 1904 ; J. A. Gray and W. Ramsay, *ib.*, **84**. A, 536, 1911 ; *Compt. Rend.*, **151**. 126, 1910 ; *Ann. Chim. Phys.*, (8), **21**. 145, 1911 ; *Jahrb. Rad. Elektron.*, **8**. 5, 1911 ; S. Meyer, *ib.*, **19**. 344, 1922 ; E. Q. Adams, *Journ. Amer. Chem. Soc.*, **42**. 2205, 1920 ; C. Schmidt, *Zeit. anorg. Chem.*, **103**. 114, 1918 ; J. Perrin, *Ann. Chim. Phys.*, (9), **11**. 5, 1919 ; N. R. Campbell, *Nature*, **84**. 203, 1910 ; *Radium*, **7**. 224, 1910 ; F. O. Giesel, *Ber.*, **40**. 3011, 1907.

[2] Lord Rayleigh, *Chem. News*, **67**. 183, 198, 211, 1893 ; **69**. 231, 1894 ; **71**. 51, 1895 ; *Proc. Roy. Soc.*, **53**. 134, 1893 ; **55**. 340, 1894 ; **57**. 266, 1895 ; H. F. Newall, *ib.*, **57**. 346, 1895 ; Lord Rayleigh and W. Ramsay, *B.A. Rep.*, 614, 1894 ; *Proc. Roy. Soc.*, **57**. 265, 1895 ; *Argon, A New Constituent of the Atmosphere*, Washington, 1896 ; *Chem. News*, **70**. 87, 1894 ; **71**. 51, 1895 ; *Phil. Trans.*, **186**. A, 187, 1895 ; H. Cavendish, *ib.*, **75**. 372, 1785 ; W. Crookes, *ib.*, **186**. A, 243, 1895 ; *Nature*, **51**. 354, 1895 ; W. Ramsay and M. W. Travers, *Compt. Rend.*, **126**. 1610, 1762, 1898 ; *Chem. News*, **78**. 154, 1898 ; *Proc. Roy. Soc.*, **63**. 437, 1898 ; **67**. 329, 1900 ; *Phil. Trans.*, **197**. 47, 1900 ; A. Schuster, *Nature*, **58**. 151, 199, 269, 1899 ; J. Dewar, *Chem. News*, **70**. 87, 88, 109, 1894 ; **78**. 70, 1898 ; M. Mugden, *Argon und Helium, zwei neue gasförmige Elemente*, Stuttgart, 1896 ; C. le Roy Parker, *Journ. Amer. Chem. Soc.*, **19**. 124, 1897.

[3] J. Dewar, *Chem. News*, **70.** 87, 109, 1894; B. Brauner, *ib.*, **71.** 79, 271, 1895; **74.** 223, 1896; G. J. Stoney, *ib.*, **71.** 67, 1895; T. L. Phipson, *ib.*, **71.** 91, 1895; **81.** 230, 1900; Lord Rayleigh, *ib.*, **74.** 260, 1896; L. de Boisbaudran, *Compt. Rend.*, **120.** 361, 1895; H. Wilde, *ib.*, **125.** 649, 1897; A. Peratoner and G. Odds, *Gazz. Chim. Ital.*, **25.** ii, 13, 1895; J. Sperber, *Naturwiss. Wochschr.*, **13.** 5, 1897; G. Martin, *Proc. Chem. Soc.*, **17.** 259, 1902; H. Schild, *Chem. Ztg.*, **19.** 554, 1895; M. Dennstedt, *ib.*, **19.** 2164, 1895; C. Jakobi, *ib.*, **22.** 20, 1898.

[4] P. J. C. Janssen, *Compt. Rend.*, **68.** 93, 181, 312, 367, 1869; W. F. Hillebrand, *Bull. U.S. Geol. Sur.*, 78, 1891; *Amer. Journ. Science*, (3), **38.** 329, 1889; (3), **40.** 384, 1890; (3), **42.** 390, 1892; A. Bélopolsky, *Mem. Soc. Spett. Ital.*, **23.** 89, 1895; L. Palmieri, *Rend. Accad. Napoli*, **20.** 233, 1882; G. E. Hale, *Astrophys. Journ.*, **2.** 165, 1895; J. N. Lockyer, *Phil. Mag.*, (4), **37.** 143, 1869; *Compt. Rend.*, **120.** 1103, 1895; *Chem. News*, **72.** 283, 1895; *Proc. Roy. Soc.*, **17.** 131, 350, 415, 1869; **18.** 74, 1869; **58.** 67, 113, 116, 192, 193, 1895; **59.** 4, 342, 1896; **61.** 148, 1897; **62.** 52, 1897; *Nature*, **51.** 586, 1895; **52.** 8, 55, 214, 327, 1895; *Phil. Trans.*, **159.** 425, 1869; E. Frankland and J. N. Lockyer, *Proc. Roy. Soc.*, **17.** 288, 1869; G. D. Liveing and J. Dewar, *ib.*, **68.** 389, 1901; E. C. C. Baly, *ib.*, **72.** 84, 1903; *Phil. Trans.*, **202.** A, 183, 1903; A. Secchi, *Compt. Rend.*, **67.** 1123, 1868; **68.** 237, 1869; **72.** 362, 1871; H. Deslandres, *ib.*, **120.** 1112, 1331, 1895; R. Schmidt, *Verh. deut. phys. Ges.*, **8.** 277, 1906; R. B. Moore, *Journ. Chem. Soc.*, **93.** 2181, 1908; W. Ramsay, *Nature*, **51.** 512, 543, 1895; **52.** 7, 1895; *Chem. News*, **71.** 151, 211, 1895; *Journ. Chem. Soc.*, **67.** 1107, 1895; *Compt. Rend.*, **52.** 224, 1895; *Proc. Roy. Soc.*, **58.** 65, 1895; **81.** 178, 1908; *Ann. Chim. Phys.*, (7), **13.** 433, 1898; M. W. Travers, *ib.*, **60.** 449, 1897; W. Ramsay, J. N. Collie, and M. W. Travers, *ib.*, **58.** 81, 1895; *Journ. Chem. Soc.*, **67.** 684, 1895; *Nature*, **52.** 7, 306, 331, 1895; W. Ramsay and J. N. Collie, *Proc. Roy. Soc.*, **60.** 206, 1896; *Compt. Rend.*, **123.** 214, 1896; W. Huggins, *Chem. News*, **71.** 283, 1895; **72.** 27, 1895; W. Crookes, *ib.*, **71.** 151, 1895; **72.** 87, 1895; *Nature*, **51.** 543, 1895; C. Runge and F. Paschen, *Chem. Ztg.*, **19.** 997, 1895; *Phil. Mag.*, (5), **40.** 297, 1895; *B.A. Rep.*, 610, 1895; *Chem. News*, **72.** 181, 1895; *Nature*, **52.** 520, 544, 1895; **53.** 245, 1896; *Sitzber. Akad. Berlin*, 639, 759, 1895; *Astrophys. Journ.*, **3.** 4, 1896; **8.** 97, 1898; J. J. Thomson, *Nature*, **91.** 333, 1913: *Proc. Cambridge Phil. Soc.*, **17.** 201. 1913; E. A. Hill, *Amer. Journ. Science*, (3), **50.** 359, 1895; J. S. Ames and W. H. Humphreys, *Astrophys. Journ.*, **5.** 97, 1897; W. J. S. Lockyer, *Nature*, **105.** 300, 1920.

[5] W. Ramsay and M. W. Travers, *Compt. Rend.*, **126.** 1762, 1898; *B.A. Rep.*, 828, 1898; *Proc. Roy. Soc.*, **63.** 405, 437, 1898; W. Ramsay, *Gases of the Atmosphere*, London, 245, 1905; H. E. Watson, *Proc. Roy. Soc.*, **81.** A, 181, 1908; J. E. Coates, *ib.*, **78.** A, 479, 1906; F. W. Aston, *ib.*, **103.** A, 462, 1923; G. D. Liveing and J. Dewar, *ib.*, **67.** 467, 1900; **68.** 389, 1901; E. C. C. Baly, *ib.*, **72.** A, 84, 1903; *Phil. Trans.*, **202.** A, 183, 1903; R. Nasini, F. Anderlini, and R. Salvadori, *Mem. Accad. Lincei*, (5), **2.** 375, 1895; R. Schmidt, *Verh. deut. phys. Ges.*, **8.** 277, 1906; R. B. Moore, *Journ. Chem. Soc.*, **93.** 2181, 1908; J. J. Thomson, *Nature*, **91.** 333, 1913; *Proc. Cambridge Phil. Soc.*, **17.** 201. 1913; *Proc. Roy. Soc.*, **101.** A, 290, 1922; F. W. Aston, *ib.*, **103.** A, 462, 1923; F. Bordas and F. Touplain, *Compt. Rend.*, **147.** 591, 1908; C. Borel and A. Jaquerod, *Arch. Sciences Genève*, (5), **2.** 265, 1920.

§ 2. The Occurrence of the Inert Gases

Air contains about one per cent. of argon. This small proportion, however, represents an enormous total. It follows, therefore, that about 800,000,000 lbs. of argon must be supported by each square mile of the surface of the globe. The total argon content of the earth's atm. is prodigious. The seas and oceans must also contain a proportionate share, since this gas is appreciably soluble in water. T. Schlösing[1] showed that atm. nitrogen contains an average of 1·182 per cent. of argon, and A. Kellas, 1·186 per cent. With the former value, it follows that air contains 0·934 per cent. of argon; and taking a litre of nitrogen to weigh 1·2511 grms., and a litre of argon, 1·7809 grms., a litre of atm. nitrogen should weigh 1·2573 grms.—Lord Rayleigh found 1·2572 grms. H. Cavendish's estimate would agree with the presence of about 0·83 per cent. of argon in air; Lord Rayleigh and W. Ramsay estimated between 0·986 and 1·11 per cent. C. Moureu estimated 1·29 by weight and 0·9323 by vol. in 100 parts of air. H. Moissan obtained 0·9492 per cent. of argon in air over the Atlantic Ocean, and for air of

Mer de Glace	.	0·9335 per cent.	London	.	0·9325 per cent.
Mt. Blanc	.	0·9339 „	Berlin	.	0·9323 „
Mt. Pelée	.	0·9366 „	St. Petersburg	.	0·9329 „
Paris	.	0·9337 „	Moscow	.	0·9323 „

T. Schlösing gave for air from the ground in a pine forest at a depth of 0·20 metre, 1·170 per cent. of argon ; for air from the soil, 0·40 metre deep, 1·155–1·169 per cent. ; and for air from the soil of a garden, 0·40 metre deep, 1·118 per cent. G. W. Morey found 2·8 per cent. of argon in commercial liquid air. Estimates of the composition of air in the higher regions of the atm. have been made by J. Hahn, G. D. Hinrichs, W. J. Humphreys, J. H. Jeans, and A. Wegener—*vide* air. Results by A. Wegener are given in Table I—*vide* atmospheric air.

A. Voller and B. Walter found the natural gas of Neuengamme contained 0·05 per cent. of argon. T. Schlösing, and C. Moureu and A. Lepape found 1–3 per cent. of argon in some mine gases in Alsace-Lorraine. R. Nasini and co-workers found argon in the gases and vapours from the boric acid soffioni, as well as in volcanic gases. R. J. Strutt, and H. Grossman proved the presence of argon in lavas and pumice-stone. H. Moissan detected 0·68–0·71 per cent. of argon in the gases from the fumaroles of Mt. Pelée, Guadeloupe, etc.

TABLE I.—ESTIMATED PERCENTAGE COMPOSITION OF THE ATMOSPHERE AT DIFFERENT ELEVATIONS.

Height (km.)	Pressure (mm. Hg)	H_2	He	N_2	O_2	A
0	760	0·0033	0·0005	78·1	20·9	0·937
20	41·7	0	0	85	15	0
40	1·92	1	0	88	10	—
60	0·106	12	1	77	6	—
80	0·0192	55	4	21	1	—
100	0·0128	67	4	1	0	—
120	0·0106	65	3	0	—	—
140	0·0090	62	2	—	—	—
200	0·00581	50	1	—	—	—
300	0·00329	29	—	—	—	—
400	0·00220	15	—	—	—	—
500	0·00162	7	—	—	—	—

Lord Rayleigh and W. Ramsay found the ratio of argon to nitrogen in rain-water to be greater than it is in air. This is due to the greater solubility of the argon. L. Troost and L. Ouvrard, and J. Dewar found argon in river-water and sea-water. Lord Rayleigh and W. Ramsay found 1·36 per cent. of argon in the gases from the spring-water of Bath ; and W. Ramsay obtained 0·964 per cent. of inert gases of which 0·7363 per cent. was argon. Numerous other observations on the occurrence of argon in the gases from various springs have been made by Lord Rayleigh, E. Czako and co-workers, A. Kellas and W. Ramsay, F. Heinrich and co-workers, F. Prytz and T. Thorkelsson, W. Ramsay and M. W. Travers, R. Nasini and co-workers, M. Bamberger and A. Landsiedl, C. Bouchard, H. Moissan, G. Massol, F. Pesendorfer, P. Ewers, F. Heinrich and G. Prell, C. Moureu and co-workers, B. Walter, F. Diaz de Rada, etc. (*vide* Table I). C. Moureu found argon in the gases of 49 thermal springs—Alsace-Lorraine, Madagascar, Réunion, etc.—and in 39 cases the argon was accompanied by helium. P. P. Bedson and S. Shaw found it mixed with nitrogen effervescing from rock-salt springs near Middlesbrough, where it must have been immured for ages. This evidence shows that argon formed part of what has been called the " geological " atmosphere of antediluvian periods.

H. F. Newall, W. N. Hartley, and O. Neovius found argon lines in the spectrum of air ; but not in the spectrum of the sun and stars ; nor did W. Ramsay and M. W. Travers observe any signs of argon in the spectra of light from extraterrestrial sources. This does not necessarily mean that argon is absent from those regions. A mixture of argon with 3–4 per cent. of nitrogen gives only the nitrogen spectrum ; the main bulk of gas in the tube is not revealed because the electric discharge preferentially selects as its vehicle the insignificant quantity of nitrogen, and passes by the argon. W. Ramsay found argon in extraterrestrial minerals, in the meteoric iron which fell in Augusta County, Virginia ; but R. J. Strutt considers this statement doubtful.

W. Ramsay and M. W. Travers, R. Thomas, A. Eggert, and C. Runge and F. Paschen found small quantities of argon occluded with helium in some minerals— e.g. cleveite, malacone, etc. P. T. Cleve found no argon in cleveite ; R. J. Strutt found only helium in Norwegian malacone; while E. S. Kitchen and W. G. Winterson found that the gas from 100 grms. of malacone contained

	Carbon dioxide.	Hydrogen.	Nitrogen.	Argon.	Helium.
C.c. . .	33·24	0·57	0·34	2·82	0·94
Grm. . .	0·06530	0·00005	0·00042	0·00504	0·00017

C. F. Hogley found that the helium from malacone contained one per cent. argon. A. von Antropoff found argon in a Brazilian zirconiferous mineral ; R. E. Hodgkinson, in minerals of the euxenite and samarskite family; H. Moissan and H. Deslandres. and G. Tschernik, in some cerium minerals ; A. Gautier, in garnet ; R. J. Strutt, in quartz, basalt, phonolite, diorite, granite, and garnierite ; E. Hochheim, in bröggerite ; and J. Schniederjost, in monazite. In the opinion of R. J. Strutt, the argon associated with the helium occluded in these different minerals is not produced by an internal change, as suggested by B. B. Boltwood, but was extracted from the atm. by the mineral at the time of its formation.

A. Kellas and G. W. Macdonald could detect no trace of argon in the nitrogen obtained from peas, or from mice ; J. Zalesky, none in the colouring matter of blood ; but C. Regnard and T. Schlösing found 0·419 c.c. of argon per litre in the blood of a horse ; and T. Schlösing and J. Richard, 1·18 per cent. of the gas in the air-bladder of the whale (physalia) ; 1·85 per cent., in the air-bladder of the muræna helena; and 1·94 per cent., in the air-bladder of the synapobranchus pinnatus. The argon in these cases is doubtless derived from the air. A. Kellas showed that the proportion of argon to nitrogen in atmospheric air is not altered by the respiration of animals even when the composition has been greatly altered. Argon, like free nitrogen, plays no important part in the animal economy, save as a diluent. G. Tolomei showed that the argon in the roots of legumes is only mechanically absorbed, and not chemically combined.

H. Kayser [2] first demonstrated the presence of helium in atmospheric air. He showed that the spectrum of crude argon contained some helium lines ; and S. Friedlander demonstrated that some of the lines at first attributed to argon were really due to helium. G. J. Stoney explained the air-less condition of the moon's atm. by assuming that solid globes possess an atm. in virtue of their gravity ; and the strength of the gravity determines the composition of the atm. Unless the velocity of the particles of a gaseous atm. be checked by gravitation, they would fly off into space to return no more. Neglecting the impeding effect of air, a particle shot from the surface of the earth at the rate of seven miles a second, would finally escape. The average velocity of a hydrogen mol. is about 70 miles a minute ; but the range of deviation on either side of this average is very wide. Hence, the critical rate seven miles a second would from time to time be attained by individual mols., which would then pass away from the earth into outer space. Similar remarks apply to helium mols. which have a velocity related to that of hydrogen as about seven to ten. The problem has been further discussed by E. Rogowsky, J. E. Jones, S. R. Cook, E. A. Milne, G. H. Bryan, and J. W. Evans. According to F. W. Aston, the rarity of the inert gases in the earth's atm., etc., is not solely due to the tendency of a gravitating planet to collect heavier molecules in certain circumstances and to lose lighter ones ; but it is also an effect of their chemical inertness. In the collisions of bodies resulting in the formation of a solar system, the atoms unconstrained by chemical combination would collide and rebound indefinitely, gravitating towards the larger masses—e.g. the sun. As pointed out by H. Jeffreys, if the light elements can form stable compounds with other heavier elements, they will not so readily escape.

Lord Rayleigh found argon to be more soluble in water than helium, and therefore the dissolved gas has a higher ratio—argon: helium, than the original gas. W. Ramsay and co-workers, and E. C. C. Baly showed that the spectral lines obtained by H. Kayser, and S. Friedlander were probably due to krypton, not helium. Argon must have 25 per cent. of helium before the latter can be so detected by spectral analysis; and, according to O. W. Richardson and R. C. Ditto, the green not the yellow line appears first. The presence of helium in atm. air was proved by E. C. C. Baly, F. Bordas and F. Touplain, J. N. Coates, W. Crookes, W. Ramsay and M. W. Travers, G. D. Liveing and J. Dewar, J. Dewar, S. Valentiner and R. Schmidt, L. T. de Bort, A. Piutti, H. and E. Erdmann, and H. E. Watson. W. Ramsay found one part of helium in 245,300 vols. of air, or 0·0004 per cent. by vol. ; and one part of helium in 1,800,000 parts of air, or 0·000056 per cent. by weight. C. Moureu estimated 0·00007 per cent. by wt., and 0·0005 per cent. by vol. G. Claude, and H. E. Watson also estimated that there is one vol. of helium per 185,000 vols. of air—*vide* Table I.

A. Voller and B. Walter [3] found about 0·01 to 0·02 per cent. of helium in the natural gas at Neuengamme ; and H. Sieveking and L. Lautenschläger, 0·025 per cent. The latter also reported 0·007 per cent. of helium in the natural gas at Siebenbürgen. C. Moureu and A. Lepape found less than 0·05 per cent. of helium in the gas at Liévin, Anzin, Lens, Mons, and Frankenholz ; and 0·0006 to 1·68 per cent. in mines, borings, and mineral springs in Alsace-Lorraine. H. P. Cady and D. F. McFarland found that the natural-gas bore at Dexter, Kansas, contained a trace up to 1·84 per cent. of helium. G. S. Rogers also found an average of 0·5 per cent. of helium in the natural gas in the zone extending from Texas through Oklahoma, South-East Kansas, South Illinois, up through Ohio into Pennsylvania and New York. The heliferous gas is also found in Indiana, Kentucky, and West Virginia, but the richest gas is found in Texas, Oklahoma, and Kansas. J. C. McLennan and co-workers reported on the helium content of the natural gas of Canada and New Zealand. The percentage of helium in the former case ranges from 0·017 to 0·052 ; and the latter case from 0·001 to 0·077. It is estimated that the natural gas at Calgary, Canada, with about 0·3 vol. per cent. of helium could furnish 10^6 c. ft. of that gas per annum. A. G. G. Leonard and A. M. Richardson found 0·074 per cent. in the gas from St. Edmundsbury's well in Lucan. Y. Kano and B. Yamaguti found helium in many natural gases of Japan; and J. E. G. Harris in natural gas from Hurghoda, Egypt. E. Erdmann found helium in the gas from the carnallite deposits of Leopoldshall ; E. Czako, in the gases from Kissarmas, Pechelbronn, Zeche Gneisenau, Wels, Neuengamme, and Elsass ; L. Palmieri, R. Nasini and co-workers, and R. J. Strutt detected helium occluded in the lava of Vesuvius ; and C. Porlezza and G. Norzi, and R. Nasini and co-workers in the boric acid soffioni of Larderello. W. Ramsay and M. W. Travers found no helium in the lava of Iceland. H. Grossmann detected helium in the pumice-stone of Mt. Pelée, while R. J. Strutt found pumice-stone free from helium.

Helium is present in air, and is soluble in water, hence, as might have been anticipated, J. Dewar [4] proved that helium is present in rain-, river-, and sea-water. Argon and helium occur together in the gases dissolved in many spring-waters. For example, H. Kayser, and E. Czako and co-workers, found helium in the waters of Wildbad, Schwarzwald ; and H. Sieveking and L. Lautenschläger found 0·71 per cent. of helium in the gases from the Wildbad spring ; 0·85 per cent. in the gas from Baden-Baden ; 0·38 per cent. in the gas from Elsass spring ; 0·009 per cent. in the spring-water of Baden-Baden. C. Bouchard, W. Ramsay, and M. W. Travers found helium in the spring-water at Cauterets, Pyrenees ; Lord Rayleigh, and W. Ramsay, in the spring-water at Bath—0·0297 to 0·12 per cent. ; Lord Rayleigh, at Buxton ; F. Pesendorfer and A. Herrmann, Carlsbad ; P. Ewers, Gasteiner

Thermen; F. Henrich and G. Bugge, Wiesbaden; F. Prytz and T. Thorkelsson, Iceland; G. Massol, Uriage, Isère; C. Moureu, and C. Moureu and R. Biquerd, in the gases from the waters at Plombieres, Bains-les-Bains, Luxeuil, Maizières, Bourbon-Lancy, Aix, and Eaux-Bonnes, in amounts ranging from 0·097 to 5·34 per cent.; A. Gautier and C. Moureu, 1·6 per cent. in the waters at Lanternier, Nancy, and 0·0194 c.c. of helium per litre of the artesian water at Ostend; R. Nasini and co-workers, Uliveto; and C. Moureu and co-workers, in the springs at Santenay, Alsace-Lorraine, Madagascar, and Réunion. No relationship has been observed between the helium content and the radioactivity of spring-water.

Helium has been detected in a large number of minerals. The occluded gas can be obtained by heating the powdered mineral in a hard glass tube, A, Fig. 2, with or without conc. sulphuric acid, or sodium pyrosulphate. The tube is fitted as shown in the diagram, and exhausted by means of an air pump—say Toepler's mercury pump. The mineral is heated under reduced press., and the gases are collected in D, the receiver of the pump —vide infra. The gases on their way to the pump travel through a flask, B, containing sticks of solid potassium hydroxide to absorb water and sulphur compounds. The gas collected in the gas-holder D can then be analyzed, or freed from hydrogen and hydrocarbons by passage over hot copper oxide (or molten phosphorus); from oxygen by passage over hot copper; from carbon dioxide by soda-lime, or potassium hydroxide; from nitrogen by hot magnesium; and from moisture by phosphorus pentoxide. The residue can be examined by the spectroscope for helium, etc. The helium occluded in monazite sand can be readily obtained by this process. The following minerals have been examined:

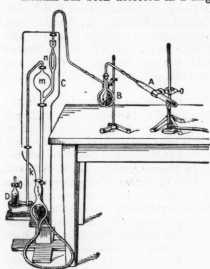

FIG. 2.—Removal of Occluded Gases from Minerals.

Æschynite, 0·0043–0·17 per cent.—W. Ramsay and M. W. Travers,[5] and R. J. Strutt; bröggerite, 0·18 per cent.—W. Ramsay and E. Gleditsch; carnotite, 0·0002 per cent.— R. J. Strutt, and E. Gleditsch (E. P. Adams found only argon); cerite, $0·0_518–0·0_523$ per cent.—W. Ramsay and co-workers, and R. J. Strutt; cleveite, 0·014–0·146 per cent.— W. Ramsay, M. W. Travers, R. Thomas, P. Ewers, E. Gleditsch, A. Sieverts and E. Bergner; columbite, 0·023 per cent.—W. Ramsay; cuprouranite, 0·0018 per cent.—R. J. Strutt; cyrtolite, 0·02 per cent.—R. J. Strutt; euxenite, 0·013 per cent.—R. J. Strutt; fergusonite, 0·19–0·32 per cent.—W. Ramsay and M. W. Travers, and M. W. Travers; fluorspar, 0·00048 per cent.—J. Thomsen; gadolinite, 0·043 per cent.—R. J. Strutt; malacone—W. Ramsay and M. W. Travers, and E. S. Kitchen and W. G. Winterson; microlite, 0·0009 per cent.— R. J. Strutt; monazite, 0·014–0·043 per cent.—W. Ramsay and M. W. Travers, and R. J. Strutt; orangeite, 0·0019 per cent.—R. J. Strutt; pitchblende, 0·0002–0·0048 per cent. —W. Ramsay and co-workers, and R. J. Strutt; pyromorphite, 0·0004 per cent.— R. J. Strutt; samarskite, 0·005–0·027 per cent.—W. Ramsay and co-workers, R. J. Strutt, and V. Kohlschütter; sipilite, 0·011 per cent.—R. J. Strutt; thorianite, 0·15–0·19 per cent.—W. R. Dunstan and G. S. Blake, E. H. Büchner, and R. J. Strutt; zirconiferous mineral, 0·0016 per cent.—A. von Antropoff.

R. J. Strutt found helium in albite (A. Piutti), antimony-glance, apatite, argyrodite, astrakanite, autunite (W. Marckwald and A. S. Russell, and E. Gleditsch), barytes, basalt, beryl (R. J. Strutt, and A. Piutti), beryllonite, bornite, cadmium blende, calcite, carnallite, cassiterite, castor (A. Piutti), chromite, chrysoberyl, clausthalite, cœlestine, columbite, corandite, corundum, cryolite (A. J. Halland), cuprite, diorite, embolite, eudialite, galena, galliferous zinc blende, garnierite, granite, hæmatite, indiferous zinc blende, ilmenite, iodyrite, kainite, keilhauite, kieserite, krugite, kunzite (A. Piutti), langbeinite, lepidolite,

(A. Piutti), mellephanite, molybdænite, orthite, orthoclase, phenacite, phonolite, plumbo-columbite (W. Marckwald and A. S. Russell), polyhalite, quartz, rhodonite, rock-salt (R. J. Strutt, and S. Valentiner), rutherfordite (W. Marckwald and A. S. Russell), schönite, smaltite, spodumene, sylvine, tachyhydrite, tin pyrites, topaz, tourmaline (A. Piutti), triphyllen, tuffa (C. Porlezza and G. Norzi), wolframite, zinc blende, zircon.

Helium was found by R. J. Strutt in cinnabar, pollux, and vanadinite; by R. C. Wells, in brannerite; A. A. C. Swinton found none in the diamond; F. Soddy found the gas occluded in some, but not in all, gold nuggets; he also found it to be present in all the samples of platinum he examined, but W. Ramsay and co-workers found none in two specimens of that metal. F. Bordas found helium in bismuth from Saxony but not in Cornish bismuth; R. J. Strutt detected helium in silver (Broken Hill), iron (Greenland), iron meteorite (Virginia), bismuth (Australia), tellurium (Transylvania), and graphite (Cumberland). J. J. Thomson found that most substances give off helium when exposed to the cathode rays—e.g. lead, iron, nickel oxide; zinc, copper, platinum and mica. The relation between the helium content, and the radium or uranium contents of minerals has been studied by A. S. Eve, W. Marckwald and A. S. Russell, H. N. McCoy, A. Piutti, E. Rutherford and B. B. Boltwood, A. S. Russell, R. J. Strutt, etc., and genetic relations have been established. B. B. Boltwood gave $Ra/U = 3 \cdot 4 \times 10^{-7}$; F. Heimann and W. Marckwald, $3 \cdot 328 \times 10^{-7}$; and E. Gleditsch, and F. Soddy and R. Pirret, $3 \cdot 15 \times 10^{-7}$. There are deviations which in some cases may be due to the leaching of the radium salts from the mineral by water. The ratio He/U_3O_8 has been examined by R. J. Strutt, and, expressing the results in c.c. of helium per gram of uranium oxide,

	Samarskite.	Hæmatite.	Galena.	Quartz.
Ratio He/U_3O_3 . .	14	9	17	10

The low values of the ratio were explained by W. Marckwald and A. S. Russell as a result of the escape of the occluded helium; but the high values for sylvine and carnallite were attributed by R. J. Strutt to the radioactivity of the contained potassium.

As indicated in connection with radium and thorium, the helium in minerals is produced by radioactive changes, and was not occluded at the time the mineral was formed. On the assumptions that a gram of radium produces 0·11 c.c. of helium per annum; a gram of uranium oxide, U_3O_8, produces $9 \cdot 13 \times 10^{-8}$ c.c. of helium per annum; and a gram of thorium oxide is eq. to 0·203 grm. of uranium oxide, attempts to estimate the geological age of some minerals have been made by R. J. Strutt, E. Rutherford and B. B. Boltwood, W. Ramsay and F. Soddy, H. N. McCoy, J. A. Gray, A. Piutti, F. Gleditsch, F. Soddy and R. Pirret, A. Holmes, F. Zambonini, and J. Joly. In illustration, R. J. Strutt gave:

	Sphærosiderite (Oligocene).	Hæmatite (Eocene).	Hæmatite (Carboniferous).	Sphene (Archaic).
Age . . .	84×10^5	31×10^6	150×10^6	710×10^6 years

E. Rutherford and B. B. Boltwood estimated 400×10^6 years for the age of fergusonite and thorianite. These periods are minimal values because of the unknown allowance for the leakage of helium, and R. J. Strutt showed that helium is not always present in larger quantity in geologically older minerals than in more recent minerals of equal radioactivity. W. A. Tilden expressed the view that the helium in these minerals is occluded, and not chemically combined; and found that when the gas was removed from cleveite, some gas could be re-absorbed; but W. Ramsay and co-workers, and V. Kohlschütter could not confirm this. A. Piutti, however, observed that some salts could absorb helium, and give it off again when heated. V. Kohlschütter and K. Vogdt suggested that the amount of occluded helium is related to the water-content of the mineral, but R. J. Strutt showed that this is not correct. W. Ramsay and M. W. Travers found that heat is developed during the evolution of helium from heated fergusonite, etc. This agreed with the assumption that the helium is united with the mineral as a helide, a view supported by J. Thomsen, and V. Kohlschütter. M. W. Travers, however, showed that some minerals containing no helium suffer an exothermal change when heated, so that the helide argument is not valid. The amount of helium given off by the mineral is very small, at temp. below 300°. D. O. Wood found that with monazite the following percentage amounts of helium escaped at the temp. named :

	280°	350°	450°	720°	900°	1200°
Loss of helium . .	0·7	2·1	12·7	68·6	88·5	98·3 per cent.

and with thorianite :

	300°	500°	750°	1000°
Loss of helium . . .	0·7	8·5	62·3	100 per cent.

F. Bordas obtained somewhat analogous results with thorianite ; and A. Sieverts and E. Bergner, with cleveite. These results do not agree with the assumption that an endothermal helide is present in the mineral because the decomposition of such a compound at any temp. once begun, should continue to the end. R. J. Moss suggested that the helium is contained in fine pores because he found about 1·17 per cent. of the total helium in pitchblende was given off during the grinding of the mineral. M. W. Travers attributed this to the heat developed by friction during the grinding. R. J. Strutt showed that helium is given off from powdered monazite and thorianite at a rate which far exceeds the rate of production of that gas by radioactive change. Thus, with monazite the leakage in c.c. per day per gram amounted to

Time exposed .	0·031	0·59	1·6	2·6	4·6	10·6	33·0
Leakage . .	0·261	0·0766	0·0171	0·0123	0·0097	0·00438	0·00114

This shows that the accumulation of the gas must be due to the conditions of existence of the minerals in nature which are much more favourable to the retention of the helium. J. A. Gray found that with thorianite, the leakage of helium began when the grain-size is less than 0·01 mm. and more helium then escapes the smaller the grain-size ; when the particles were less than 0·003 mm., 28 per cent. of the helium was given off.

W. Ramsay [6] found 0·00123 per cent. by vol. or 0·00086 per cent. by wt. of neon to be present in atm. air : or one vol. of neon is present in 80,790 vols. of air, or one gram in 116,000 grms. of air. C. Moureu estimated 0·0012 per cent. by wt., and 0·0018 per cent. by vol. G. Claude gave 1·5 vols. in 100,000 vols. of air. H. E. Watson gave rather a higher value—one part by vol. of neon in 55,000 vols. of air ; G. Gehlhoff also reported on this subject. W. Ramsay, W. Crookes, and G. D. Liveing and J. Dewar found neon in the gases from the springs at Bath ; C. Moureu and co-workers in the gases from the French thermal springs, Alsace-Lorraine, Madagascar, and Réunion ; and R. Nasini and co-workers, in the waters of Uliveto. E. Erdmann found neon in the gases from the carnallite deposits of Leopoldshall. The occurrence of neon in minerals is doubtful. R. J. Strutt found traces of neon occluded in zircon, cyrtolite, syenite, and pumice from Lipari Island, but the amount was so small that it may have been derived from contamination with atm. air. J. Schneiderjost denied H. Schultze's report that neon is present in the helium derived from monazite. J. J. Thomson obtained neon as well as helium (q.v.) from many substances bombarded by the cathode rays.

W. Ramsay [7] found that one vol. of krypton is present in 20,000,000 vols. of air ; or one gram of krypton in 7,000,000 grms. of air. C. Moureu estimated 0·0003 per cent. by wt., and 0·0001 per cent. by vol. ; while E. Rabinowitsch gave 0·0001 per cent. by vol. C. Moureu and co-workers found krypton in the ratio Kr/A = 1·1 to 1·8 among the gases from 26 thermal springs ; and also in the gas from Vesuvius (vide Table I); while C. Moureu and co-workers found it in the gas from the thermal springs of Madagascar, and Réunion. W. Ramsay detected krypton in the helium obtained from cleveite ; and C. F. Hogley reported but 0·1 c.c. of krypton in 140 grms. of fergusonite. According to W. Ramsay, one vol. of **xenon** occurs in 170,000,000 vols. of air, or one gram of xenon in 40,000,000 grms. of air ; C. Moureu estimated 0·00004 per cent. by wt., and 0·0001 per cent. by vol. ; and E. Rabino-witsch, 0·00001 per cent. per vol. C. Moureu and A. Lepape found xenon in the gases from 26 springs ; and also in the gas from Vesuvius (*vide* Table II) ; while C. Moureu and co-workers found it in gas from the thermal springs of Madagascar, and Réunion.

TABLE II.—OCCURRENCE OF ARGON, KRYPTON, AND XENON IN THE GASES FROM THERMAL SPRINGS, ETC.

Origin.	A/N × 10²	Kr/A	X/A
Aix-les-Bains	1·245	1·2	1·6
Bagnères-de-Bigorre . . .	1·38	1·1	1·6
Bagnères-de-Luchon . . .	1·28–1·42	1·1–1·2	1·2–1·9
Bourbon-l'Archambault . . .	0·92	1·5	1·6
Cauterets	1·29–1·40	1·2–1·3	1·2–2·2
La Bourboule	1·87	1·8	1·9
Longwy	1·39	1·2	1·6
Luxeuil	1·32–1·35	1·4	1·9
Nancy	1·35	1·5	1·9
Plombières	1·34–1·62	1·2–1·4	1·2–1·6
Saint Honoré	1·2	1·3	1·9
Vichy	1·66–3·37	1·4–1·5	1·2–2·5
Vesuvius	—	1·1	1·0

S. C. Lind [8] said that the inert gases cannot have been produced or retained in the earth's crust by chemical action. In the case of helium, its origin may be either primordial or due to radioactive decomposition. The gas will have been migrating slowly to the surface, be swept along at times by other gases, and be retained where a bed of shale, capped by clay, forms a favourable geological struc-ture. It is generally, but not always, found in hydrocarbon gases, but in some cases with nitrogen which may possibly have been produced by the action of α-particles on nitrogenous organic matter or nitrides ; it is almost universally associated with some nitrogen.

REFERENCES.

[1] Lord Rayleigh and W. Ramsay, *Proc. Roy. Soc.*, **57**. 265, 1895 ; *Chem. News*, **71**. 51, 1895 ; *Argon—A New Constituent of the Atmosphere*, Washington, 1896 ; *Phil. Trans.*, **186**. A, 187, 1895 ; H. Cavendish, *ib.*, **75**. 372, 1785 ; H. F. Newall, *Proc. Roy. Soc.*, **57**. 346, 1895 ; Lord Rayleigh, *ib.*, **59**. 198, 1896 ; A. Kellas, *ib.*, **59**. 66, 1896 ; *Chem. News*, **72**. 308, 1905 ; L. Troost and L. Ouvrard, *ib.*, **72**. 153, 309, 1895 ; *Compt. Rend.*, **121**. 394, 798, 1895 ; G. Massol, *ib.*, **151**. 1154, 1910 ; G. W. Morey, *Journ. Amer. Chem. Soc.*, **34**. 491, 1912 ; O. Neovius, *Wied. Ann.*, **66**. 162, 1898 ; W. N. Hartley, *Proc. Roy. Soc.*, **57**. 295, 1895 ; R. J. Strutt, *ib.*, **79**. 436, 1907 ; **80**. 572, 1908 ; T. Schlösing, *Compt. Rend.*, **121**. 525, 604, 615, 1895 ; **123**. 233, 302, 1896 ; H. Moissan, *ib.*, **137**. 600, 1903 ; *Bull. Soc. Chim.*, (3), **31**. 729, 1904 ; (3), **29**. 434, 437, 1903 ; *Compt. Rend.*, **135**. 1085, 1278, 1902 ; **137**. 600, 1903 ; **138**. 936, 1904 ; H. Moissan and H. Deslandres, *ib.*, **126**. 1689, 1898 ; A. Voller and B. Walter, *Ueber den Helium- und Argongehalt des Erdgases von Neuengamme*, Halle, 1907 ; *Phys. Zeit.*, **9**. 235, 1908 ; E. Czako, *Zeit. anorg. Chem.*, **82**. 249, 1913 ; E. Czako and L Lautenschläger, *Chem. News*, **108**. 16, 1913 ; *Chim. Ztg.*, **37**. 936, 1913 ; H. Grossmann, *Compt. Rend.*, **148**. 991, 1909 ; W. Ramsay, *ib.*, **120**. 1049, 1895 ; *Nature*, **52**. 224, 1895 ; *Chem. News*, **105**. 133, 1912 ; A. Kellas and W. Ramsay, *ib.*, **72**. 295, 1895 ; *Proc. Roy. Soc.*, **59**. 68, 1895 ; W. Ramsay and M. W. Travers, *ib.*, **60**. 442, 1897 ; **62**. 225, 316, 1898 ; L. Palmieri, *Rend. Accad. Napoli*, **20**. 233, 1882 ; R. Nasini, F. Anderlini, and R. Salvadori, *Atti Accad. Lincei*, (5), **2**. 375, 1895 ; (5), **5**. 25, 1904 ; *Gazz. Chim. Ital.*, **30**. i, 189, 1900 ; **36**. i, 429, 1906 ; *Nature*, **58**. 269, 1898 ; R. Nasini, L. Marino, F. Ageno, and C. Porlezza, *Gazz. Chim. Ital.*, **43**. i, 3²1, 1913 ; K. Prytz and T. Thorkelson, *Danske Vid. Selsk. Forh.*, 317, 1905 ; F. Diaz de Rada, *Chem. Ztg.*, **36**. 688, 1912 ; C. Bouchard and L. Troost, *Chem. News*, **72**. 152, 1895 ; *Compt. Rend.*, **121**. 392, 1895 ; M. Bamberger, *Monatsh.*, **17**. 604, 1896 ; M. Bamberger and A. Landsiedl, *ib.*, **19**. 114, 1898 ; P. P. Bedson

and S. Shaw, *Proc. Chem. Soc.*, **11.** 143, 1895 ; *Chem. News*, **72.** 48, 1895 ; W. R. E. Hodgkinson, *ib.*, **71.** 248, 1895 ; J. H. Jeans, *The Dynamical Theory of Gases*, Cambridge, 315, 1904 ; A. Wegener, *Phys. Zeit.*, **12.** 170, 214, 1910 ; *Zeit. anorg. Chem.*, **75.** 107, 1912 ; G. D. Hinrichs, *Compt. Rend.*, **131.** 442, 1900 ; J. Hahn, *Meteor. Zeit.*, **20.** 122, 1903 ; W. J. Humphreys, *Physics of the Air*, Philadelphia, 68, 1920 ; *Journ. Franklin Inst.*, **175.** 207, 1913 ; C. F. Hogley, *Phil. Mag.*, (6), **18.** 672, 1909 ; A. Gautier and C. Moureu, *Journ. Chim. Pharm.*, (7), **3.** 391, 1911 ; *Compt. Rend.*, **152.** 546, 1911 ; C. Moureu, *Journ. Chem. Soc.*, **123.** 1905, 1923 ; *Compt. Rend.*, **142.** 1155, 1906 ; C. Moureu and R. Biquard, *ib.*, **143.** 180, 795, 1906 ; A. Gautier, *ib.*, **132.** 58, 932, 1901 ; P. T. Cleve, *ib.*, **120.** 834, 1895 ; L. Troost and L. Ouvrard, *ib.*, **121.** 798, 1895 ; C. Moureu and A. Lepape, *ib.*, **152.** 691, 934, 1533, 1911 ; **153.** 740, 847, 1043, 1911 ; **171.** 941, 1920 ; C. Moureu, A. Lepape, H. Moureu, and M. Geslin, *ib.*, **182.** 602, 1926 ; C. Moureu, *Journ. Chem. Soc.*, **123.** 1905, 1923 ; A. Gautier, *Compt. Rend.*, **132.** 58, 932, 1901 ; C. Regnard and T. Schlösing, *ib.*, **124.** 302, 1897 ; T. Schlösing and J. Richard, *ib.*, **122.** 615, 1896 ; B. Walter, *Zeit. Elektrochem.*, **12.** 178, 1911 ; **14.** 695, 1908 ; A. von Antropoff, *ib.*, **14.** 585, 1908 ; *Proc. Roy. Soc.*, **83.** 474, 1910 ; C. Runge and F. Paschen, *Nature*, **53.** 245, 1896 ; E. S. Kitchen and W. G. Winterson, *Journ. Chem. Soc.*, **89.** 1568, 1906 ; R. Thomas, *Bestimmung des specifischen Wärme von Helium und die Atomwärme von Argon und Helium*, Marburg, 1908 ; A. Eggert, *Bestimmung des specifischen Wärme des Heliums bei verschieden Temperaturen und Untersuchung ihrer Beziehung zur kinetischen Theorie einatomiger Gase*, Marburg, 1910 ; E. Hochheim, *Bestimmung der Dielektrizitätskonstante von Helium*, Marburg, 1909 ; *Verh. deut. phys. Ges.*, **10.** 446, 1908 ; J. Schneiderjost, *Beiträge zur Kenntnis der Spektra von H_2, He, Luft, N_2, und O_2 im Ultraviolet*, Halle, 1904 ; *Zeit. wiss. Photochem.*, **2.** 265, 1904 ; A. Kellas and G. W. MacDonald, *Proc. Roy. Soc.*, **57.** 490, 1895 ; *Chem. News*, **71.** 169, 1895 ; J. Zalesky, *Ber.*, **30.** 965, 1897 ; G. Tolomei, *Riv. Scient. Ind.*, **29.** 17, 1897 ; *Giorn. Farm. Chim.*, **46.** 145, 1897 ; G. Tschernik, *Journ. Russ. Phys. Chem. Soc.*, **29.** 291, 1899 ; H. Kayser, *Chem. News*, **72.** 89, 1895 ; *Chem. Ztg.*, **19.** 1549, 1895 ; P. Ewers, *Phys. Zeit.*, **7.** 224, 1906 ; F. Prytz and T. Thorkelsson, *Danske Vid. Selsk. Forh.*, 317, 1905 ; T. Thorkelsson, *Mem. Acad. Danemark*, (7), **8.** 182, 1910 ; B. B. Boltwood, *Amer. Journ. Science*, (4), **20.** 253, 1905 ; F. Heinrich, *Ber.*, **53.** B, 1940, 1920 ; F. Heinrich and G. Prell, *ib.*, **55.** B, 3021, 3026, 1922 ; J. Dewar, *Proc. Roy. Soc.*, **64.** 231, 1899 ; **74.** 127, 1904 ; *Proc. Roy. Inst.*, **18.** 127, 1905 ; *Chem. News*, **94.** 173, 185, 1906 ; F. Pesendorfer, *Chem. Ztg.*, **29.** 359, 1905 ; C. Bouchard, *Chem. News*, **72.** 152, 1895 ; *Compt. Rend.*, **121.** 392, 1895.

² H. Kayser, *Chem. Ztg.*, **19.** 1549, 1895 ; *Chem. News*, **72.** 89, 99, 1895 ; *Sitzber. Akad. Berlin*, 551, 1896 ; *Astrophys. Journ.*, **4.** 1, 1896 ; S. Friedlander, *Zeit. phys. Chem.*, **19.** 657, 1896 ; *Chem. News*, **74.** 179, 1896 ; F. W. Aston, *Nature*, **114.** 786, 1924 ; G. J. Stoney, *Of Atmospheres on Planets and Satellites*, Dublin, 1897 ; *Scient. Trans. Dublin Soc.*, (2), **6.** 305, 1897 ; *Chem. News*, **71.** 67, 1895 ; *Trans. Roy. Soc. Dublin*, **6.** 305, 1898 ; *Astrophys. Journ.*, **7.** 25, 1898 ; **11.** 251, 325, 356, 1900 ; **12.** 201, 1900 ; **20.** 69, 1904 ; *Phil. Mag.*, (6), **7.** 690, 1903 ; O. W. Richardson and R. C. Ditto, *ib.*, (6), **22.** 704, 1911 ; H. and E. Erdmann, *Ergebnisse Arb. Preuss. Aeronaut. Obs.*, **6.** 227, 1911 ; *Chem. Centr.*, (4), **24.** i, 522, 1912 ; Lord Rayleigh, *Phil. Mag.*, (6), **1.** 100, 1905 ; *Proc. Roy. Soc.*, **59.** 198, 1896 ; W. Ramsay, *ib.*, **76.** 111, 1905 ; **80.** 599, 1908 ; W. Ramsay and J. N. Collie, *ib.*, **80.** 206, 1896 ; *Compt. Rend.*, **123.** 214, 1896 ; W. Ramsay and M. W. Travers, *ib.*, **126.** 2610, 1898 ; *Proc. Roy. Soc.*, **63.** 405, 1898 ; **67.** 329, 1900 ; *Phil. Trans.*, **197.** A, 47, 1901 ; *Zeit. Phys. Chem.*, **38.** 641, 1901 ; E. C. C. Baly, *Phys. Zeit.*, **4.** 799, 1903 ; *Phil. Trans.*, **202.** A, 183, 1903 ; *Nature*, **58.** 545, 1898 ; *Proc. Roy. Soc.*, **72.** 84, 1903 ; E. A. Milne, *Trans. Cambridge Phil. Soc.*, **22.** 483, 1924 ; J. E. Jones, *ib.*, **22.** 535, 1924 ; W. Crookes, *Phil. Trans.*, **166.** 243, 1895 ; *Chem. News*, **78.** 98, 1898 ; *Nature*, **58.** 570, 1898 ; G. D. Liveing and J. Dewar, *Proc. Roy. Soc.*, **67.** 467, 1900 ; J. Dewar, *ib.*, **64.** 231, 1899 ; **74.** 127, 1904 ; *Proc. Roy. Inst.*, **18.** 127, 1905 ; *Chem. News*, **94.** 173, 185, 1906 ; *Ann. Chim. Phys.*, (7), **17.** 12, 1899 ; (8), **3.** 12, 1904 ; *Amer. Journ. Science*, (4), **18.** 290, 1904 ; J. N. Coates, *Proc. Roy. Soc.*, **78.** 479, 1906 ; F. Bordas and F. Touplain, *Compt. Rend.*, **147.** 591, 1908 ; G. Claude, *ib.*, **147.** 624, 1908 ; **148.** 1454, 1909 ; L. T. de Bort, *ib.*, **147.** 219, 1908 ; S. Valentiner and R. Schmidt, *Sitzber. Akad. Berlin*, 816, 1905 ; *Ann. Physik*, (4), **18.** 187, 1905 ; H. E. Watson, *Proc. Roy. Soc.*, **81.** 181, 1908 ; *Journ. Chem. Soc.*, **97.** 810, 1910 ; A. Piutti, *Le Radium*, **7.** 142, 1910 ; *Gazz. Chim. Ital.*, **40.** i, 435, 1910 ; E. Rogowsky, *Astrophys. Journ.*, **14.** 234, 1901 ; S. R. Cook, *ib.*, **11.** 36, 1900 ; G. H. Bryan, *Proc. Roy. Soc.*, **66.** 335, 1900 ; *Phil. Trans.*, **196.** A, 1, 1901 ; *Nature*, **66.** 54, 1902 ; J. W. Evans, *ib.*, **77.** 535, 1908 ; H. Jeffreys, *ib.*, **114.** 934, 1924 ; C. Moureu and A. Lepape, *Compt. Rend.*, **171.** 941, 1920 ; C. Moureu, *Journ. Chem. Soc.*, **123.** 1905, 1923.

³ A. Voller and B. Walter, *Ueber den Helium- und Argongehalt des Erdgases von Neuengamme*, Hamburg, 1911 ; H. Sieveking and L. Lautenschläger, *Phys. Zeit.*, **13.** 1043, 1912 ; *Verh. deut. phys. Ges.*, **14.** 910, 1912 ; C. Moureu and A. Lepape, *Compt. Rend.*, **153.** 847, 1043, 1911 ; **171.** 941, 1920 ; H. Grossmann, *ib.*, **148.** 991, 1909 ; H. P. Cady and D. F. McFarland, *Journ. Amer. Chem. Soc.*, **29.** 1533, 1907 ; G. S. Rogers, *Prof. Paper, U.S. Geol. Sur.*, 121, 1921 ; R. C. Moore, *Nature*, **111.** 89, 1923 ; L. Palmieri, *Rend. Accad. Napoli*, **20.** 233, 1882 ; C. Porlezza and G. Norzi, *Atti Accad. Lincei*, (5), **20.** ii, 338, 1911 ; R. Nasini, F. Anderlini, and R. Salvadori, (5), **5.** i, 25, 1904 ; (5), **14.** ii, 70, 1905 ; *Mem. Accad. Lincei*, (5), **2.** 375, 1895 ; *Rend. Accad. Lincei*, (5), **7.** ii, 73, 269, 1898 ; *Nature*, **58.** 269, 1898 ; *Gazz. Chim. Ital.*, **36.** i, 429, 1906 ; **37.** i, 218, 1906 ; R. Nasini and F. Anderlini, *ib.*, **36.** ii, 557, 570, 1906 ; *Atti Accad. Lincei*, (5), **13.** i, 217, 368, 535, 1904 ; R. Nasini, *ib.*, (5), **13.** i, 217, 367, 1904 ; J. C. McLennan and Associates, *Report on Some Sources*

of Helium in the British Empire, Ottawa, 1920 ; R. J. Strutt, *Proc. Roy. Soc.*, **79**. 436, 1907 ;
W. Ramsay and M. W. Travers, *ib.*, **60**. 442, 1897 ; E. Erdmann, *Ber.*, **43**. 777, 1910 ; E. Czako,
Zeit. anorg. Chem., **82**. 249, 1913 ; E. Czako and L. Lautenschläger, *Chem. News*, **108**. 16, 1913 ;
Chem. Ztg., **37**. 936, 1913 ; A. G. G. Leonard and A. M. Richardson, *Proc. Roy. Dublin Soc.*, **17**.
89, 1922 ; Y. Kano and B. Yamaguti, *Rep. Aeronautical Research Tokyo*, **1**. 347, 1926 ;
J. E. G. Harris, *Journ. Inst. Petrol. Tech.*, **7**. 14, 1921.

⁴ J. Dewar, *Chem. News*, **90**. 141, 1904 ; *Compt. Rend.*, **139**. 421, 1904 ; C. Bouchard, *ib.*, **121**.
392, 1895 ; *Chem. News*, **72**. 152, 1895 ; H. Kayser, *Chem. Ztg.*, **19**. 1549, 1895 ; *Chem. News*,
72. 89, 99, 1895 ; N. J. Lockyer, *ib.*, **72**. 283, 1895 ; *Compt. Rend.*, **120**. 1103, 1895 ; P. T. Cleve,
ib., **120**. 834, 1895 ; *Chem. News*, **71**. 201, 1895 ; W. Ramsay, J. N. Collie, and M. W. Travers,
Journ. Chem. Soc., **67**. 684, 1895 ; *Proc. Roy. Soc.*, **60**. 442, 1897 ; Lord Rayleigh, *ib.*, **59**. 198,
1896 ; **60**. 56, 1896 ; *Chem. News*, **72**. 223, 1895 ; **73**. 247, 1896 ; W. Ramsay, *ib.*, **105**. 133, 1912 ;
Ann. Chim. Phys., (7), **13**. 433, 1898 ; M. W. Travers, *Nature*, **71**. 248, 1906 ; E. Czako, *Zeit.
anorg. Chem.*, **82**. 249, 1913 ; E. Czako and L. Lautenschläger, *Chem. News*, **108**. 16, 1913 ; *Chem.
Ztg.*, **37**. 936, 1913 ; F. Pesendorfer and A. Herrmann, *Phys. Zeit.*, **6**. 70, 1895 ; F. Pesendorfer,
Chem. Ztg., **29**. 359, 1905 ; F. Prytz and T. Thorkelsson, *Danske Vid. Selsk. Forh.*, 317, 1905 ;
F. Henrich, *Ber.*, **41**. 4196, 1908 ; F. Henrich and G. Bugge, *Monatsh.*, **27**. 1259, 1906 ; *Zeit.
angew. Chem.*, **20**. 49, 277, 1907 ; *Phys. Zeit.*, **8**. 112, 1907 ; P. Ewers, *ib.*, **7**. 224, 1906 ; B. Walter,
ib., **12**. 178, 1911 ; H. Sieveking and L. Lautenschläger, *ib.*, **13**. 1043, 1912 ; *Verh. deut. phys.
Ges.*, **14**. 910, 1912 ; C. Moureu, *Compt. Rend.*, **121**. 819, 1895 ; **135**. 1335, 1902 ; **139**. 852, 1904 ;
142. 1155, 1906 ; *Bull. Soc. Chim.*, (3), **29**. 204, 1903 ; C. Moureu and R. Biquard, *Compt. Rend.*,
143. 180, 795, 1906 ; **146**. 435, 1908 ; C. Moureu and A. Lepape, *ib.*, **155**. 197, 1912 ; **171**. 941,
1920 ; C. Moureu and L. Troost, *ib.*, **121**. 392, 1895 ; G. Massol, *ib.*, **151**. 1124, 1910 ; L. Troost
and L. Ouvrard, *ib.*, **121**. 798, 1895 ; H. Moissan and H. Deslandres, *ib.*, **126**. 1688, 1898 ;
A. Gautier and C. Moureu, *ib.*, **152**. 546, 1911 : *Journ. Pharm. Chim.*, (7), **3**. 391, 1911 ;
R. J Moss, *Trans. Roy. Soc. Dublin*, (2), **8**. 153, 1906 ; E. P. Adams, *Amer. Journ. Science*, (4),
19. 321, 1905 ; H. Wilde, *Phil. Mag.*, (5), **40**. 466, 1895 ; G. Tschernik, *Journ. Russ. Phys.
Chem. Soc.*, **29**. 291, 1899 ; J. Thomsen, *Zeit. phys. Chem.*, **25**. 112, 1898 ; V. Kohlschütter and
K. Vogdt, *Ber.*, **38**. 1419, 1905 ; V. Kohlschütter, *Liebig's Ann.*, **317**. 158, 1901 ; R. Nasini,
L. Marino, F. Ageno, and C. Porlezza, *Gazz. Chim. Ital.*, **43**. i, 321, 1913 ; C. Moureu, A. Lepape,
H. Moureu, and M. Geslin, *Compt. Rend.*, **182**. 602, 1926 ; Y. Kano and B. Yamaguti, *Rep.
Aeronautical Research, Tokyo*, **1**. 347, 1926.

⁵ W. Ramsay, *Proc. Roy. Soc.*, **59**. 325, 1896 ; W. Ramsay and M. W. Travers, *ib.*, **60**. 442,
1897 ; **61**. 267, 1897 ; **62**. 225, 316, 325, 1898 ; M. W. Travers, *ib.*, **60**. 449, 1897 ; **64**. 130, 1898 ;
Nature, **71**. 248, 1905 ; *Zeit. phys. Chem.*, **61**. 241, 1907 ; W. Ramsay, J. N. Collie, and
M. W. Travers, *Journ. Chem. Soc.*, **67**. 684, 1895 ; E. S. Kitchen and W. G. Winterson, *ib.*, **89**.
1568, 1906 ; R. Thomas, *Bestimmung der specifischen Wärme von Helium und die Atomwärme von
Argon und Helium*, Marburg, 1905 ; A. Sieverts and E. Bergner, *Ber.*, **45**. 2576, 1912 ; H. N. Mc-
Coy, *ib.*, **37**. 2641, 1904 ; V. Kohlschütter and K. Vogdt, *ib.*, **38**. 1419, 2992, 1905 ; V. Kohl-
schütter, *Liebig's Ann.*, **317**. 158, 1901 ; A. Holmes, *Proc. Roy. Soc.*, **85**. 248, 1911 ; R. J. Strutt,
ib., **76**. 88, 1905 ; **80**. 572, 1908 ; **81**. 278, 1908 ; **82**. 166, 1909 ; W. R. Dunstan and G. S. Blake,
ib., **76**. 253, 1905 ; A. von Antropoff, *ib.*, **83**. 474, 1910 ; *Zeit. Elektrochem.*, **14**. 585, 1905 ;
J. Thomsen, *Danske Vid. Forh.*, **2**. 53, 1904 ; *Zeit. Phys. Chem.*, **25**. 112, 1898 ; E. H. Büchner,
Jabrb. Rad. Elektron., **3**. 372, 1906 ; *Proc. Roy. Soc.*, **78**. 385, 1906 ; J. A. Gray, *ib.*, **82**. 301, 1908 ;
Phil. Mag., (6), **18**. 816, 937, 1909 ; J. Joly, *ib.*, (6), **22**. 375, 1911 ; B. B. Boltwood, *ib.*, (6), **9**.
599, 1905 ; *Amer. Journ. Science*, (4), **18**. 97, 1904 ; *ib.*, (4), **25**. 269, 1908 ; A. S. Eve, *ib.*, (4),
22. 4, 1906 ; E. Rutherford and B. B. Boltwood, *ib.*, (4), **20**. 55, 1905 ; (4), **22**. i, 1906 ;
E. P. Adams, *ib.*, (4), **19**. 321, 1905 ; E. Gleditsch, *Compt. Rend.*, **148**. 1451, 1908 ; **149**. 267,
1908 ; *Le Radium*, **8**. 269, 1911 ; F. Soddy and R. Pirret, *Phil. Mag.*, (6), **20**. 345, 1910 ; F. Soddy,
Proc. Roy. Soc., **78**. 429, 1907 ; *Chem. News*, **95**. 15, 28, 42, 51, 1907 ; *Nature*, **73**. 151, 1905 ;
84. 296, 1910 ; W. Ramsay and F. Soddy, *Proc. Roy. Soc.*, **72**. 204, 1903 ; **73**. 346, 1904 ; *Chem.
News*, **88**. 100, 1903 ; **89**. 245, 266, 1904 ; A. S. Russell, *Nature*, **84**. 238, 1910 ; W. Marckwald
and A. S. Russell, *Chem. News*, **103**. 277, 1911 ; *Gahrb. Rad. Elektron.*, **8**. 457, 1911 ; A. Piutti,
Le Radium, **7**. 142, 146, 178, 1910 ; **8**. 13, 204, 1911 ; *Gazz. Chim. Ital.*, **40**. 435, 476, 1910 ; *Rend.
Accad. Lincei*, (5), **8**. 457, 1911 ; A. J. Halland, *Journ. Ind. Eng. Chem.*, **3**. 63, 1911 ; W. A. Tilden,
Proc. Roy. Soc., **59**. 218, 1896 ; J. A. Gray, *ib.*, **82**. 301, 1909 ; D. O. Wood, *ib.*, **84**. 70, 1910 ;
R. J. Moss, *Trans. Dublin Roy. Soc.*, (2), **8**. 153, 1906 ; A. Sieverts and E. Bergner, *Ber.*, **45**.
2576, 1912 ; F. Bordas, *Compt. Rend.*, **146**. 628, 896, 1908 ; A. Gautier, *ib.*, **132**. 58, 932, 1901 ;
B. Brauner, *Chem. News*, **71**. 116, 271, 1895 ; A. C. C. Swinton, *ib.*, **99**. 131, 1909 ; *Proc. Roy.
Soc.*, **82**. 176, 1909 ; P. Ewers, *Phys. Zeit.*, **7**. 224, 1906 ; *Ann. Physik*, (4), **17**. 781, 1905 ; F. Zambonini, *Rend. Accad. Lincei*, (5), **20**. ii, 131, 1911 ; C. Porlezza and G. Norzi, *Gazz. Chim. Ital.*,
43. i, 504, 1913 ; S. Valentiner, *Kali.*, **6**. 1, 1912 ; J. J. Thomson, *Nature*, **90**. 645, 1913 ; **91**.
333, 1913 ; F. Heimann and W. Marckwald, *Jahrb. Rad. Elektron.*, **10**. 299, 1913 ; *Phys. Zeit.*,
14. 303, 1913 ; R. C. Wells, *Journ. Franklin Inst.*, **189**. 779, 1920 ; *Chem. News*, **121**. 22, 1920.

⁶ W. Ramsay, *Chem. News*, **105**. 133, 1912 ; *Proc. Roy. Soc.*, **76**. 111, 1905 ; **80**. 599, 1908 ;
G. D. Liveing and J. Dewar, *ib.*, **67**. 467, 1900 ; J. Dewar, *ib.*, **74**. 127, 1904 ; *Ann. Chim. Phys.*,
(8), **3**. 12, 1904 ; G. Claude, *Compt. Rend.*, **147**. 624, 1908 ; **148**. 1454, 1909 ; C. Moureu and
A. Lepape, *ib.*, **171**. 941, 1920 ; C. Moureu, A. Lepape, H. Moureu, and M. Geslin, *ib.*, **182**. 602,
1926 ; C. Moureu, *Journ. Chem. Soc.*, **123**. 1905, 1923 ; C. Moureu and R. Biquard, *ib.*, **143**. 180,
1906 ; H. E. Watson, *Journ. Chem. Soc.*, **97**. 810, 1910 ; E. Erdmann, *Ber.*, **43**. 777, 1910 ;

R. J. Strutt, *Nature*, **75**. 102, 271, 1907; J. J. Thomson, *ib.*, **90**. 645, 1913; **91**. 333, 1913; W. Crookes, *ib.*, **58**. 570, 1898; *Chem. News*, **78**. 98, 1898; A. Gautier and C. Moureu, *Compt. Rend.*, **152**. 546, 1911; *Journ. Pharm. Chim.*, (7), **3**. 391, 1911; H. Schultze, *Ann. Physik*, (4), **6**. 302, 1901; J. Schneiderjost, *Zeit. wiss. Photochem.*, **2**. 265, 1904; *Beiträge zur Kenntnis der Spektra von H₂, He, Luft, N₂, und O₂ im Ultraviolet*, Halle, 1904; G. Gehlhoff, *Phys. Zeit.*, **14**. 833, 1913; R. Nasini, L. Marino, E. Ageno, and C. Porlezza, *Gazz. Chim. Ital.*, **43**. i. 321, 1913.
  ⁷ W. Ramsay, *Proc. Roy. Soc.*, **71**. 421, 1903; *Chem. News*, **87**. 159, 1903; *Bull. Soc. Chim.*, (3). 28. 214, 1902; *Zeit. phys. Chem.*, **38**. 641, 1901; C. Moureu and A. Lepape, *Compt. Rend.*, **149**. 1171, 1909; **152**. 691, 934, 1911; **153**. 847, 1043, 1911; **171**. 941, 1920; C. Moureu, A. Lepape, H. Moureu, and M. Geslin, *ib.*, **182**. 602, 1926; C. Moureu, *Journ. Chem. Soc.*, **123**. 1905, 1923; E. Rabinowitsch, *Zeit. angew. Chem.*, **39**. 737, 1926; M. W. Travers and A. Jaquerod, *Proc Roy. Soc.*, **70**. 484, 1903; C. F. Hogley, *Phil. Mag.*, (6), **18**. 672, 1909; A. Ladenburg and C. Krügel, *Sitzber. Akad. Berlin*, 727, 1900.
  ⁸ S. C. Lind, *Proc. Nat. Acad.*, **11**. 772, 1926.

§ 3. The Preparation of the Rare Gases

Helium is formed, along with hydrogen and oxygen, from an aq. soln. of radium bromide—*vide* **4**. 26, 7. The relation between helium and the α-particles emitted in radioactive changes was discussed by E. Rutherford [1] and co-workers, P. Ewers, J. Dewar, E. Regener, etc. W. Ramsay and F. Soddy found that 50 mgrms. of radium bromide in 60 days produced about 30 c.c. of gas consisting of 19·5 c.c. of hydrogen, 10·1 c.c. of oxygen—the remainder was air. A trace of helium was present, and it was estimated that a gram of radium bromide gives 0·0022 mgrm. of helium per annum. The reaction has been also observed by J. Dewar and P. Curie, E. Rutherford, E. Rutherford and H. Geiger, H. Kauffmann, F. Himstedt and G. Meyer, R. Schenck, F. N. Indrikson, W. Crookes, A. Debierne, F. Giesel, and J. Danysz and W. Duane. W. Ramsay and F. Soddy, W. Ramsay and A. T. Cameron, E. Rutherford and B. B. Boltwood studied the formation of helium from radium emanation; K. A. Hofmann and V. Wölfl, and E. Rutherford and B. B. Boltwood, from radium-D; K. A. Hofmann and V. Wölfl, H. Greinacher, H. Greinacher and M. Kernbaum, F. Giesel, and E. Rutherford and B. B. Boltwood, from radium-F or polonium; A. Debierne, and F. Giesel, from actinium salts; F. Soddy, from uranium salts; W. Ramsay and F. Soddy, from thorium salts; and B. B. Boltwood, from ionium.

As previously indicated—**4**. 26, 14—W. Ramsay, J. N. Collie and H. S. Patterson, and I. Masson reported the conversion of hydrogen into neon by the action of the cathode rays; but J. J. Thomson, R. J. Strutt, T. R. Merton, A. C. G. Egerton, and A. Piutti and E. Cardoso were unable to verify this. R. W. Riding and E. C. C. Baly found that by the bombardment of a hollow anticathode coated with the nitride of magnesium or of aluminium and placed in the focus of a concave cathode in a tube containing oxygen, the nitrogen atoms are disintegrated, helium, hydrogen, and neon being found as products. Previous failures are attributed to the strong occlusion of the rare gases in the electrode splash. By heating the powdered discharge tubes, after 60 hours' discharge, at 800° in vacuo, a considerable amount of helium was obtained. With a single induction coil giving a 6-inch spark, the rare gases were always obtained, only minor variations in their amounts being observed when the hammer break was replaced by a mercury break and when a condensed discharge was used. Negative results were obtained when a larger coil was used. R. C. Tolman discussed the thermodynamics of the transmutation of hydrogen into helium.

The extraction of helium from minerals.—Helium is conveniently obtained from a number of minerals—cleveite, monazite, thorianite, etc. W. J. Hillebrand obtained the gas by boiling the pulverized mineral with sulphuric acid. The yield is good, but the reaction is slow. The air should be removed from the apparatus by suction or by a stream of carbon dioxide. N. A. Langlet, and P. T. Cleve heated a mixture of the mineral with potassium pyrosulphate in a current of carbon dioxide. In this process it is difficult to remove all the gas ; the mixture is liable to foam ; and the glass tube may crack. Fused alkali hydrosulphate, carbonate, or dichromate may be used. The gas is also extracted from the mineral by heating it in vacuo at a high temp. D. O. Wood, H. Wilde, F. Himstedt and G. Meyer, etc., used this process—*vide* Fig. 2. The extraction of helium was also described by A. Eggert, P. Ewers, E. Hochheim, N. A. Langlet, W. Ramsay, J. F. Schierloh, K. Schmitt, H. Schultze, J. Stark and co-workers, K. Peters, and R. Thomas. The purification of the crude gas has been previously described. The last purification can be effected by cooling the gas with liquid hydrogen as recommended by M. W. Travers and A. Jaquerod ; by treating the gas with red-hot calcium as recommended by F. Soddy ; with molten potassium, as recommended by G. Gehlhoff, and K. Mey ; with a mixture of magnesium and lime, as recommended by L. Maquenne ; or by treatment with cocoanut charcoal at the temp. of liquid air, as recommended by J. Dewar. The last-named process removes all but neon and hydrogen from the helium. Hydrogen is easily removed, and neon does not usually accompany the helium extracted from minerals. W. Ramsay and M. W. Travers purified helium by fractional diffusion ; and A. Jaquerod and F. L. Perrot, by diffusion through a heated vessel of quartz glass.

The extraction of helium from natural gas.—J. Dewar extracted helium, contaminated with neon, from the gases emitted by the thermal springs of Bath. J. C. McLennan and co-workers, A. H. Graham, J. A. Rafferty and H. E. Thompson, R. L. Bottoms, G. A. Burrell, R. J. Lang, P. E. Haynes, M. A. Worobéeff, M. Bridel, P. Damm, F. G. Cottrell, J. W. Davis, W. S. Lesniansky, M. Gohlke, C. Porlezza, and R. B. Moore have studied the extraction of helium from natural gas with the idea of using it in place of hydrogen for dirigibles for war purposes since helium has 92 per cent. of the lifting power of hydrogen, and is not inflammable. The gas was first liquefied by a modified air-liquefying machine (1. 13, 26) and the helium recovered by fractionation of the liquid. The product finally purified with charcoal approaches 100 per cent. purity.

The extraction of helium from air.—W. Ramsay and M. W. Travers extracted helium from atm. air. When a large amount of liquid air is allowed to evaporate quietly, the residue, after the removal of oxygen and nitrogen, consists of argon mixed with a small proportion of krypton and xenon. Argon being the more volatile is separated by alternate liquefaction and evaporation ; and at the temp. of boiling liquid air, krypton has a marked volatility while xenon has an inappreciable vap. press. To obtain the neon and helium from liquid air, the gas— mainly nitrogen—escaping from the liquefier is condensed to a liquid and a current of air blown through. The first portion of the liquid to evaporate contains most of the neon and helium, along with nitrogen, oxygen, and argon. The oxygen and nitrogen are removed in the usual way, and the neon and helium separated from the argon by fractional distillation. Neon may be freed from helium by a few fractionations at the temp. of boiling hydrogen ; neon is liquefied or solidified at this temp., while the helium remains gaseous. J. Dewar took advantage of the selective adsorption of wood charcoal to separate rare gases from atm. air. All the gases excepting helium and neon are adsorbed by wood charcoal at the temp. of liquid air. E. Edwards and R. T. Elworthy, W. Heuse, T. S. Taylor, G. Gehlhoff, H. E. Watson, and A. von Antropoff used this process. In place of charcoal, G. P. Baxter and H. W. Starkweather used chabazite which had been dehydrated at 550°. M. W. Travers removed argon from helium by taking advantage of the fact that the former is alone adsorbed by platinum.

The extraction of neon from air.—As just indicated, W. Ramsay and M. W. Travers obtained neon by allowing liquid air to evaporate quietly. G. Claude devised an apparatus for producing considerable quantities of the lighter constituents of atm. air. W. Ramsay and M. W. Travers separated the neon from helium by fractionation from the mixture cooled by liquid hydrogen. H. E. Watson found that the diffusion of helium through a quartz glass tube at 1200° gave a poor separation. Since, as indicated above, all gases other than helium, neon, and hydrogen were found to have no appreciable vap. press. when in contact with charcoal at the temp. of liquid air, it is easy to separate these three gases from all other gases provided sufficient time for diffusion and absorption is allowed. If the dead space in the charcoal vessel is small, one hour is sufficient. H. E. Watson found that the helium and neon can be separated by a fractionation of the mixture from charcoal at liquid air temp. The preparation of neon has been also described by J. Dewar, S. Valentiner and R. Schmidt, A. von Antropoff, H. E. Watson, J. E. Coates, G. Claude, P. Siedler, R. Mewes, G. P. Jaubert, F. Pollitzer, F. Schröter, and C. A. Crommelin. C. A. Crommelin purified neon by solidification with liquid hydrogen, evaporating so as to collect the first portion, and repeated the treatment. The oxygen was separated by leading the neon at a low press. through a worm-condenser cooled to —253°.

The extraction of argon from air.—The separation of argon rests on the chemical indifference of the gas. The oxygen, nitrogen, and other constituents are removed by absorption; the product contains helium and neon which are more volatile than argon, and krypton and xenon which are less volatile. Hence, W. Ramsay and M. W. Travers [2] were able to separate argon from its companions by the fractional evaporation of liquid air. G. R. Fonda and co-workers studied the concentration of argon by the liquefaction of air, and found that if 5 per cent. of a given vol. of air is liquefied, the liquid will contain 40 per cent. of oxygen and 2·35 per cent. of argon; and at the other end of the series, an 80 per cent. liquefaction gives a gas with 1·6 per cent. of argon. Hence, the most favourable condition for obtaining argon from air lies in condensing only a small fraction of the air. The purification of crude argon has been also discussed by Lord Rayleigh, A. Ladenburg and C. Krügel, W. P. Jorissen, G. D. Liveing and J. Dewar, J. F. Schierloh, J. Dewar, S. Valentiner and R. Schmidt, E. Barbet, R. Mewes, G. Claude, F. Pollitzer, J. Stark, G. W. Money, O. Ruff and F. Förster, C. A. Crommelin, F. Soddy, G. Gehlhoff, L. Holborn and H. Schultze, F. Fischer and G. Iliovici, H. Dember, P. Mey, F. Fischer and V. Froboese, etc., from different points of view. B. Brauner suggested separating argon from air by atmolysis, but this is impracticable. In one process for isolating crude argon, the nitrogen is removed by sparking the air mixed with an excess of oxygen in the presence of alkali-lye which absorbs the nitrogen oxides which are formed. The best conditions for this were studied by A. Becker, F. Henrich, W. Crookes, H. Schultze, Lord Rayleigh and W. Ramsay. The oxygen was then removed by passing the product over heated copper. In another process, the carbon dioxide is removed by alkali-lye; the oxygen and hydrogen by hot copper; and the nitrogen by hot magnesium. H. N. Warren, and A. Guntz used heated lithium for absorbing the nitrogen; C. Limb, a mixture of sodium and barium fluorides; L. Maquenne, W. Hempel, H. Sieveking and L. Lautenschläger, and H. Moissan and A. Rigaut, a mixture of magnesium and lime; H. Moissan, A. Guntz and H. Bassett, F. Soddy, C. A. Crommelin, R. Brandt, O. Ruff, and F. Fischer and O. Hähnel, calcium. H. Moissan and A. Rigaut, F. Soddy, and G. Gehlhoff, potassium. J. Stark heated mercury; A. Rossel, calcium carbide and magnesium (or aluminium, zinc, iron, or copper); and G. Vater, and F. Fischer and O. Ringe, calcium carbide. The magnesium-lime and the calcium carbide processes are considered to be the best. O. Ruff and H. Hartmann said that calcium alloys with 5 per cent. of nitride furnish argon from atm. nitrogen in a few minutes. J. Stark found that commercial oxygen in cylinders contained 6 per cent. of nitrogen and 4 per cent. of argon; and when the gas was passed through heated tubes filled with mercury, the oxygen and nitrogen combine with mercury, leaving the argon alone. M. Bodenstein and L. Wachenheim found that commercial oxygen prepared from air contained as much as 3 per cent. of argon, and recommended that as the source of argon. K. Prytz, F. Fischer and O. Ringe, A. Becker, and C. A. Crommelin discussed the efficiency of the different modes of isolating argon. The Osram G.m.B.H. described the preparation of argon from mixtures of nitrogenous gases.

The extraction of krypton from air.—The mixture remaining after the separation of most of the argon and the lighter constituents of liquefied crude argon contains some argon, krypton, and xenon. By repeatedly condensing and slowly evaporating the product, the argon can be removed. The mixture of krypton and xenon at the temp. of liquid air loses most of the krypton. By repeated liquefaction and slow evaporation it is possible to separate the xenon and krypton. This method was employed by W. Ramsay and M. W. Travers, R. B. Moore, A. Ladenburg and C. Krügel, and the Soc. Anon. d'Eclairage. The selective adsorption by charcoal —*vide supra*—was employed by J. Dewar, and S. Valentiner and R. Schmidt.

The extraction of xenon from air.—It is easier to prepare pure xenon than pure krypton since xenon is more readily freed from argon than is the case with krypton. The isolation of xenon by the processes outlined above was effected by W. Ramsay and M. W. Travers, A. Ladenburg and C. Krügel, R. B. Moore, and the Soc. Anon. d'Eclairage.

REFERENCES.

¹ W. J. Hillebrand, *Bull U.S. Geol. Sur.*, 78, 1891 ; *Amer. Journ. Science*, (3), **38**. 329, 1889 ; (3), **40**. 384, 1890 ; (3), **42**. 390, 1892 ; N. A. Langlet, *Zeit. anorg. Chem.*, **10**. 287, 1895 ; A. von Antropoff, *Ber.*, **56**. B, 2135, 1923 ; H. Schultze, *Ann. Physik*, (4), **6**. 302, 1901 ; F. Himstedt and G. Meyer, *ib.*, (4), **15**. 184, 1904 ; (4), **17**. 1005, 1905 ; J. Stark, A. Fischer, and H. Kirschbaum, *ib.*, (4), **40**. 499, 1913 ; J. F. Schierloh, *Ueber die Koeffizienten der inneren Reibung von reinem Argon und reinem Helium*, Halle, 1908 ; K. Schmitt, *Die innere Reibung von Luft und Helium bei tiefen Temperaturen*, Halle, 1909 ; *Ann. Physik*, (4), **30**. 393, 1909 ; R. Thomas, *Bestimmung der specifischen Wärme von Helium und die Atomwärme von Argon und Helium*, Marburg, 1905 ; E. Hochheim, *Bestimmung der Dielektrizitätskonstante von Helium*, Marburg, 1909 ; *Verh. deut. phys. Ges.*, **10**. 446, 1908 ; G. Gehlhoff, *ib.*, **13**. 271, 1911 ; *Phys. Zeit.*, **14**. 838, 1913 ; K. Mey, *ib.*, **5**. 72, 1903 ; R. C. Tolman, *Amer. Chem. Soc.*, **44**. 1902, 1922 ; A. Eggert, *Bestimmung der specifischen Wärme des Heliums bei verschiedenen Temperaturen und Untersuchung ihrer Beziehung zur kinetischen Theorie einatomiger Gase*, Marburg, 1910 ; P. Ewers, *Phys. Zeit.*, **7**. 224, 1906 ; *Ann. Physik*, (4), **17**. 781, 1905 ; W. Ramsay, *Chem. News*, **105**. 133, 1912 ; *Proc. Roy. Soc.*, **59**. 325, 1896 ; *Ann. Chim. Phys.*, (7), **13**. 449, 1898 ; W. Ramsay and F. Soddy, *Proc. Roy. Soc.*, **72**. 204, 1903 ; **73**. 346, 1904 ; W. Ramsay and M. W. Travers, *Proc. Roy. Soc.*, **62**. 316, 1898 ; **67**. 329, 1900 ; M. W. Travers and A. Jaquerod, *ib.*, **70**. 484, 1903 ; F. Soddy, *ib.*, **78**. 429, 1907 ; *Phil. Mag.*, (6), **16**. 513, 1908 ; *Chem. News*, **95**. 15, 28, 42, 51, 1907 ; H. Greinacher, *Natur. Rund.*. **21**. 51, 671, 683, 1906 ; **22**. 481, 1907 ; H. Greinacher and M. Kernbaum, *Phys. Zeit.*, **8**. 339, 1907 ; F. Giesel, *Ber.*, **38**. 2299, 1905 ; **39**. 2244, 1906 ; **40**. 3011, 1907 ; **41**. 1059, 1908 ; E. Regener, *Verh. deut. phys. Ges.*, **10**. 78, 1908 ; P. Ewers, *Phys. Zeit.*, **7**. 224, 1906 ; *Ann. Physik*, (4), **17**. 781, 1905 ; M. W. Travers, *Phil. Trans.*, **197**. A, 47, 1901 ; *Proc. Roy. Soc.*, **60**. 449, 1896 ; D. O. Wood, *ib.*, **84**. 70, 1910 ; J. Dewar, *ib.*, **74**. 127, 1904 ; **81**. 280, 1908 ; *Chem. News*, **84**. 293, 1901 ; *Brit. Pat. No.* 13638, 1904 ; 7808, 1905 ; *Proc. Roy. Inst.*, **19**. 730, 1908 ; *Le Radium*, **3**. 332, 1908 ; J. Dewar and P. Curie, *Compt. Rend.*, **138**. 190, 1904 ; *Chem. News*, **89**. 85, 1904 ; G. Claude, *ib.*, **147**. 624, 1908 ; *Brit. Pat. No.* 22316, 1909 ; *French Pat. No.* 403777, 1908 ; H. Wilde, *Phil. Mag.*, (5), **40**. 466, 1895 ; E. Rutherford, *ib.*, (6), **10**. 290, 1905 ; (6), **12**. 348, 1906 ; *Arch. Sciences Genève*, (5), **19**. 31, 125, 1905 ; *Radioactivity*, Cambridge, 1904 ; *Radioactive Substances and their Radiations*, Cambridge, 1913 ; *Nature*, **68**. 366, 1903 ; E. Rutherford and O. Hahn, *ib.*, (6), **12**. 371, 1906 ; E. Rutherford and T. Royds, *ib.*, (6), **16**. 313, 812, 1908 ; (6), **17**. 281, 1909 ; E. Rutherford and H. Geiger, *ib.*, (6), **22**. 621, 1911 ; E. Rutherford and B. B. Boltwood, *Amer. Journ. Science*, (4), **20**. 55, 1905 ; (4), **22**. 1, 1906 ; B. B. Boltwood, *Proc. Roy. Soc.*, **85**. A, 77, 1911 ; *Le Radium*, **8**. 104, 1911 ; J. Danysz and W. Duane, *ib.*, **9**. 417, 1912 ; *Compt. Rend.*, **155**. 500, 1912 ; *Amer. Journ. Science*, (4), **35**. 295, 1913 ; W. Ramsay and A. T. Cameron, *ib.*, **4**. 394, 1907 ; *Journ. Chem. Soc.*, **91**. 1266, 1907 ; K. A. Hofmann and V. Wölfl, *Ber.*, **40**. 2425, 1907 ; P. E. Haynes, *Canada Pat. No.* 245587, 1924 ; J. A. Rafferty and H. E. Thompson, *ib.*, 245588, 1924 ; *U.S. Pat. No.* 1529625, 1925 ; A. Debierne, *Compt. Rend.*, **141**. 383, 1905 ; **148**. 1264, 1909 ; *Chem. News*, **99**. 301, 1909 ; C. A. Crommelin, *Rec. Trav. Chim. Pays-Bas*, **42**. 814, 1923 ; *Comm. Univ. Leiden*, 162, 1924 ; *Phys. Ber.*, **5**. 1376, 1924 ; F. N. Indrikson, *Phys. Zeit.*, **5**. 214, 1904 ; W. Crookes, *Chem. News*, **94**. 144, 1906 ; H. E. Watson, *Journ. Chem. Soc.*, **97**. 810, 1910 ; **144**. 135, 1907 ; P. T. Cleve, *ib.*, **120**. 834, 1895 ; A. Jaquerod and F. L. Perrot, *ib.*, **144**. 135, 1907 ; *Arch. Sciences Genève*, (4), **20**. 454, 1905 ; F. Giesel, *Ber.*, **38**. 2299, 1905 ; A. Sieverts and E. Bergner, *ib.*, **45**. 2576, 1912 ; S. Valentiner and R. Schmidt, *Sitzber. Akad. Berlin*, 816, 1915 ; *Ann. Physik*, (4), **18**. 187, 1905 ; H. Kauffmann, *Zeit. angew. Chem.*, **17**. 1393, 1904 ; R. Schenck, *Sitzber. Akad. Berlin*, 37, 1904 ; R. B. Moore, *Nature*, **111**. 88, 1923 ; *Trans. Amer. Inst. Min. Met.*, **69**. 110, 1923 ; *Journ. Franklin Inst.*, **191**. 145, 1921 ; J. C. McLennan, *Brit. Journ. Rad. Röntgen Soc.*, **20**. 171, 1924 ; J. C. McLennan

and Associates, *Report on Some Sources of Helium in the British Empire*, Ottawa, 1920 ; *Trans, Roy. Soc. Canada*, (3), **13**. 53, 1919 ; *Journ. Chem. Soc.*, **117**. 923, 1920 ; *Chem. Trade Journ.*, **66**. 827, 1920 ; G. A. Burrell, *Chem. Met. Engg.*, **29**. 1013, 1923 ; F. G. Cottrell, *ib.*, **20**. 104, 1919 ; *Engg.*, **107**. 574, 1919 ; R. J. Lang. *Trans. Roy. Soc. Canada*, (3), **17**. 181, 1923 ; R. L. Bottoms, *Oil and Gas Journ.*, **23**. 20, 76, 1924 ; A. H. Graham, *U.S. Pat. No.* 1530461, 1925 ; P. Damm, *Zeit. angew. Chem.*, **35**. 121, 1922 ; M. A. Worobéeff, *Neftjanoe i slancevoe Chozjajstro*, **4**. 668, 1923 ; W. S. Lesniansky, *Przemysl Chem.*, **3**. 53, 1920 ; M. Gohlke, *Umschau*, **23**. 487, 1919 ; M. Bridel, *Journ. Pharm. Chim.*, (7), **22**. 428, 1920 ; J. W. Davis, *Eng. Min. Journ.*, **109**. 84, 1920 ; W. Ramsay, *Compt. Rend.*, **153**. 373, 1911 ; *Journ. Chem. Soc.*, **91**. 931, 1907 ; J. N. Collie and H. S. Patterson, *ib.*, **103**. 419, 1913 ; I. Masson, *Proc. Chem. Soc.*, **29**. 233, 1913 ; J. J. Thomson, *ib.*, **90**. 645, 1913 ; *Rev. Scient.*, (5), **57**. 129, 1919 ; *Rays of Positive Electricity*, London, 122, 1913 ; R. J. Strutt, *Proc. Roy. Soc.*, **89**. A, 499, 1914 ; T. R. Merton, *ib.*, **90**. A, 549, 1914 ; A. C. G. Egerton, *ib.*, **91**. A, 180, 1915 ; A. Piutti and E. Cardoso, *Journ. Chim. Phys.*, **18**. 81, 1920 ; R. W. Riding and E. C. C. Baly, *Proc. Roy. Soc.*, **109**. A, 186, 1925 ; K. Peters, *Naturwiss.*, **13**. 746, 1925 ; L. Maquenne, *Compt. Rend.*, **121**. 1147, 1895 ; C. Porlezza, *Giorn. Chim. Ind. Appl.*, **2**. 638, 687, 1920 ; G. P. Baxter and H. W. Starkweather, *Proc. Nat. Acad.*, **11**. 231, 1925 ; W. Heuse, *Verh. deut. phys. Ges.*, **15**. 520, 1913 ; T. S. Taylor, *Phys. Rev.*, (2), **10**. 653, 1917 ; G. Gehlhoff, *Phys. Zeit.*, **14**. 838, 1913 ; J. E. Coates, *Proc. Roy. Soc.*, **78**. A, 479, 1906 ; G. P. Jaubert, *German Pat.*, *D.R.P.* 262728, 1911 ; F. Pollitzer, *Zeit. kompr. flüss Gase*, **22**. 72, 1922 ; R. Mewes, *Zeit. Sauerstoff Ind.*, **10**. 2, 9, 1918 ; F. Schröter, *ib.*, **12**. 42, 52, 1920 ; P. Siedler, *Umschau*, **24**. 466, 1920 ; E. Edwards and R. T. Elworthy, *Trans. Roy. Soc. Canada*, (3), **13**. 47, 1919.

² W. Ramsay and M. W. Travers, *Phil. Trans.*, **197**. 47, 1901 ; *Proc. Roy. Soc.*, **64**. 183, 1899 ; **67**. 329, 1900 ; Lord Rayleigh, *ib.*, (6). 5. 677, 1903 ; *Journ. Chem. Soc.*, **71**. 181, 1897 ; R. B. Moore, *ib.*, **93**. 2181. 1908 ; Lord Rayleigh and W. Ramsay, *Proc. Roy. Soc.*, **57**. 265, 1895 ; **70**. 87, 1894 ; **71**. 51, 1895 ; *Phil. Trans.*, **186**. 187, 1895 ; *Journ. Chem. Soc.*, **70**. 99, 1895 ; *Chem. News*, **70**. 87, 1894 ; **71**. 51, 1895 ; W. Crookes, *ib.*, **65**. 301, 1892 ; H. N. Warren, *ib.*, **74**. 6, 1896 ; B. Brauner, *ib.*, **71**. 116, 1895 ; W. P. Jorissen, *Chem. Weekbl.*, **14**. 1151, 1917 ; G. D. Liveing and J. Dewar, *Proc. Roy. Soc.*, **68**. 389, 1901 ; J. Dewar, *Proc. Roy. Inst.*, **18**. 433, 1906 ; *Chem. News*, **97**. 4, 16, 1908 ; *Proc. Roy. Soc.*, **74**. 127, 1904 ; F. Soddy, *ib.*, **78**. 429, 1907 ; *Chem. News*, **95**. 15, 28, 42, 51, 1907 ; A. Becker, *Ann. Physik*, (4), **17**. 381, 1905 ; *Zeit. Elektrochem.*, **9**. 600, 1903 ; F. Henrich, *Ber.*, **41**. 4196, 1909 ; *Zeit. Elektrochem.*, **15**. 749, 1909 ; F. Fischer, *ib.*, **13**. 107, 1907 ; *Ber.*, **44**. 92, 1911 ; F. Fischer and O. Ringe, *ib.*, **41**. 2017, 1908 ; F. Fischer and O. Hähnel, *ib.*, **42**. 1435, 1909 ; F. Fischer and G. Iliovici, *ib.*, **42**. 527, 1909 ; F. Fischer and V. Froboese, *ib.*, **44**. 92, 1911 ; V. Froboese, *Versuche über die fraktionierte Kristallisation von Argon*, Berlin, 1911 ; G. W. Morey, *Journ. Amer. Chem. Soc.*, **34**. 491, 1912 ; H. Schultze, *Ann. Physik*, (4), **5**. 156, 1901 ; L. Holborn and H. Schultze, *ib.*, (4), **47**, 1103, 1915 ; P. Mey, *ib.*, (4), **11**. 127, 1903 ; R. Schmidt, *ib.*, (4), **18**. 390, 1901 ; H. Dember, *ib.*, (4), **20**. 379, 1906 ; H. Sieveking and L. Lautenschläger, *Phys. Zeit.*, **13**. 1043, 1912 ; W. Hempel, *Zeit. anorg. Chem.*, **21**. 19, 1899 ; O. Ruff, *ib.*, **121**. 167, 1922 ; O. Ruff and F. Förster, *ib.*, **131**. 327, 1923 ; R. Brandt, *German Pat.*, *D.R.P.* 314907, 1916 ; *Ueber das metallische Calcium und seine Anwendung in der Gasanalyse*, Weida, 1915 ; G. Bredig, *Zeit. Elektrochem.*, **13**. 69, 1907 ; R. Mewes, *Zeit. Sauerstoff Ind.*, **10**. 9, 1918 ; **11**. 37, 1919 ; G. Vater, *Studien über die Absorption von Gasen durch Kohle und einige andere poröse Körper*, Dresden, 1910 ; C. Limb, *Compt. Rend.*, **121**. 887, 1903 ; A. Guntz, *ib.*, **120**. 777, 1895 ; **123**. 995, 1896 ; A. Rossel, *ib.*, **121**. 941, 1895 ; H. Deslandres, *ib.*, **121**. 886, 1895 ; L. Maquenne, *ib.*, **121**. 1147, 1895 ; H. Moissan, *ib.*, **137**. 600, 1903 ; H. Moissan and A. Rigaut, *ib.*, **137**. 773, 1903 ; *Bull. Soc. Chim.*, (3), **31**. 735, 1904 ; A. Guntz and H. Bassett, *ib.*, (3), **35**. 404, 1906 ; A. Ladenburg and C. Krügel, *Sitzber. Akad. Berlin*, 212, 727, 1900 ; S. Valentiner and R. Schmidt, *ib.*, 816, 1905 ; *Ann. Physik*, (4), **18**. 187, 1905 ; M. Bodenstein and L. Wachenheim, *Ber.*, **51**. 265, 1918 ; *German Pat.*, *D.R.P.* 295572, 1913 ; J. F. Schierloh, *Ueber den Koeffizienten der inneren Reibung von reinem Argon und reinem Helium*, Halle, 1908 ; J. Stark, *Phys. Zeit.*, **14**. 497, 1913 ; G. Gehlhoff, *Verh. deut. phys. Ges.*, **12**. 963, 1910 ; **13**. 271, 1911 ; G. Gehlhoff and K. Rottgardt, *ib.*, **12**. 492, 1910 ; K. Rottgardt, *Ann. Physik*, (4), **33**. 1161, 1910 ; K. Prytz, *ib.*, **5**. 206, 1903 ; C. A. Crommelin, *Metingen betreffende de toetstandsverglijking von Argon*, Leiden, 1910 ; G. Claude, *Compt. Rend.*, **151**. 752, 1910 ; **166**. 492, 1918 ; *Brit. Pat. No.* 184454, 1922 ; E. Barbet, *ib.*, 129989, 131321, 1919 ; Soc. Anon. d'Eclairage, *ib.*, 218266, 226783, 1924 ; R. Wucherer and F. Pollitzer, *U.S. Pat. No.* 1420802, 1922 ; *Zeit. kompr. flüss. Gase*, **22**. 71, 1922 ; Osram G.m.B.H., *German Pat.*, *D.R.P.* 340987, 1918 ; M. Zack, *Brit. Pat. No.* 179947, 1922 ; O. Ruff and H. Hartmann, *Zeit. anorg. Chem.*, **121**. 167, 1922 ; G. R. Fonda, F. W. Reynolds, and S. Robinson, *Journ. Ind. Eng. Chem.*, **17**. 676, 1925.

§ 4. The Physical Properties of the Inert Gases

The five gases—helium, neon, argon, krypton, and xenon—are colourless, and without odour. They are chemically indifferent and are hence called the *inert gases* or the *rare gases*, or the *noble gases* of the atm. For the **vapour density** of helium W. Ramsay, J. N. Collie, and M. W. Travers,[1] found 2·152–2·187 for helium from bröggerite when that of oxygen is 16 ; and 2·205 for helium from cleveite ; and W. Ramsay gave 2·181 for helium from bröggerite ; 2·121–2·122 for helium from samarskite ; and 2·134–2·147 for helium from fergusonite. W. Ramsay and J. N. Collie, and A. Hagenbach separated helium of density, say 2·315, into fractions with the densities 2·032 and 2·576 respectively. The gas was probably contaminated with some argon and krypton. N. A. Langlet gave 2·00 for the density of the gas from cleveite, but M. W. Travers suggested that the gas was probably contaminated with hydrogen since raw helium obtained from that mineral has a higher density. W. Ramsay and M. W. Travers gave 1·98 as the best representative value for purified helium ; K. Olschewsky gave 1·995 ; A. Lonius, 1·979 ; H. K. Onnes, 1·99–2·04 ; J. F. Schierloh, 1·9815 ; R. Schmidt, and W. Schwarze, 2·083 ; K. Schmitt, 1·979 ; H. Schultze, 2·084 : P. Tänzler, 1·979 ; and H. E. Watson, 1·995. T. S. Taylor gave 1·17850 (oxygen 1·4290). A. Leduc also measured the density of neon. H. E. Watson gave for the weight of a normal litre of helium from thorianite, 0·1782 grm., hence, helium at 0° and 760 mm., weighs 0·0001782 grm. per c.c. ; W. Heuse found 0·0001756 ± 0·00008 grm. ; and G. P. Baxter and H. W. Starkweather, 0·0001784·6. The best representative values are :

	He	Ne	A	Kr	X	Nt
D_{gas} .	0·0001782	0·0009002	0·0017826	0·003709	0·005842	0·00995

F. W. Aston found the vap. density of purified neon to be 10·096 when that of oxygen is 16. W. Ramsay and M. W. Travers, and G. Rudorf gave for neon at 792·05° K. and 306·5 mm., 0·01100 grm. per 32·697 c.c. ; or, at 292·2° K. and 313·8 mm., 0·01120 grm. per 32·697 c.c. This makes 0·890 grm. for the weight of a normal litre. H. E. Watson obtained 0·9002 grm. for neon of a high degree of purity. Hence, neon, at 0° and 760 mm., weighs 0·0009002 grm. per c.c. The first vap. density determinations of Lord Rayleigh, and W. Ramsay for argon gave 19·086 when that of oxygen is 16 ; later determinations gave 19·88–19·94. F. Fischer and co-workers gave 19·945 ; O. Mehliss, 19·96 ; O. Niemeyer, 19·94 ; R. Schmidt, 19·948 ; H. Schultze, 19·91 ; W. Schwarze, 19·948 ; and P. Tänzler, 19·946. A. Leduc also measured the density of argon. W. Ramsay found that while the vap. density of crude argon is 19·94, that of purified argon is 19·953 ; W. Ramsay and M. W. Travers gave 19·957 for purified argon ; A. Lonius, 19·969 ; and J. F. Schierloh, 19·964. The last value corresponds closely with the assumption that crude argon contains 99·785 per cent. of argon, 0·16 per cent. of neon, and 0·055 per cent. of helium. These values agree with 0·17809 grm. per litre of raw argon, and 0·17826 for purified argon. Hence, at 0° and 760 mm., raw argon weighs 0·00017809 grm. per c.c., and purified argon 0·0001786 grm. per c.c. W. Ramsay and M. W. Travers gave 0·003648 grm. per c.c. for the weight of krypton at 0° and 760 mm. ; and R. B. Moore, 0·0037085 grm. Hence, a normal litre of krypton weighs 3·709 grms. W. Ramsay and M. W. Travers found that one c.c. of xenon at 0° and 760 mm. weighs 0·00567 grm. ; and R. B. Moore, 0·005842 grm. Hence, a normal litre of xenon weighs 5·842 grms.

H. K. Onnes found the **specific gravity** of liquid helium to be 0·1452 at −271·53° ; 0·1459 at −270·60° ; 0·1393 at −269·74° ; 0·1275 at −269·02°; 0·1208 at −268·67°. J. Dewar gave 0·17 at −258°. H. K. Onnes, and E. Mathias and co-workers found the sp. gr. of liquid and vapour follow the law of rectilinear diameters such that $\frac{1}{2}(D_l + D_g) = 0·0831 – 0·00342T$. E. Mathias and co-workers found the sp. gr. of neon to be 1·23824 and 0·00534 respectively for liquid and sat. vapour, at 25·170 K. ; at 33·09° K., 1·08832 and 0·03831; and at 43·02° K., 0·74866 and 0·23935. It is concluded that neon obeys the law of rectilinear diameters having for the equation of the line $y = −1·154406 – 0·0071б1460θ$, at $θ°$. K. Olschewsky gave 1·5 for the sp. gr. of liquid argon ; and W. Ramsay and M. W. Travers, 1·212 at −185°. E. C. C. Baly and F. G. Donnan gave for the **atomic volume,** 28·4 ; and they also found 1·4233 for the sp. gr. at −189°; 1·4169 at −188°; 1·4104 at −187°; 1·4039 at −186°; 1·3975 at −185°; 1·3910 at −184°; 1·3845 at −183°; or at $T°$ K., sp. gr.$=1·42333-0·006467(T-84)$. E. Mathias and co-workers found that neon obeys the law of rectilinear diameters between its critical temp., −228·71°, and its normal b.p., −245·92°. The coeff. of the diameter is −0·00716146. C. A. Crommelin gave 1·0268 for the sp. gr. of liquid argon at −140·80°; 0·9339 at −134·72°; 0·8581 at −129·83°; and 0·7557 at −125·49°. E. H. Mathias and co-workers found

	−183·15°	−175·39°	−161·23°	−150·76°	−140·20°	−135·51°	−131·54°	−125·17°
Sp. gr. .	1·37396	1·32482	1·22414	1·13851	1·03456	0·97385	0·91499	0·77289

which are higher than those obtained by C. A. Crommelin. The law of rectilinear diameters for liquid and vapour is $\frac{1}{2}(D_v + D_l)=0·70956-0·0026235\theta$. H. K. Onnes and C. A. Crommelin, H. K. Onnes and J. D. A. Boks, C. A. Crommelin, E. H. Mathias, W. A. Goldhammer, J. J. van Laar, U. Karpen, and H. von Jüptner made observations on this subject. C. A. Crommelin found that at the m.p., solid argon is specifically heavier than the liquid. J. de Smedt and W. H. Keesom gave 1·68 for the sp. gr. of solid argon at −250°; and F. Simon and C. von Simson, 1·62. The best representative values for the sp. gr. of the liquid, D_l, and the at. vols. are :

	He	Ne	A	Kr	X	Nt
D_e . . .	0·1215	—	1·4039	c. 2·4	3·063	c. 5·53
At. vol. . .	32·9	—	28·4	34·6	42·6	40·4

H. Happel calculated values for the specific volume from the latent heat of vaporization, λ, when $\lambda=RT+a/v_l$, where a is constant, and $\lambda=RT^2(dp/d\theta)/p$, and obtained for the sp. vol., v_l, of the liquid, 0·707—in agreement with E. C. C. Baly and F. G. Donnan's value. H. Happel calculated values for the $dp/d\theta$ from $T=74·988$ $+1·645p+0·0213p^2-0·0034p^3$; and G. Rudorf used J. H. van der Waals' vap. press. equation log p_c—log $p=f(T_c/T-1)$, and obtained at −189°, 0·6829, and at −183°, 0·6890 when the observed values were respectively 0·7026 and 0·7223 ; he also calculated values from A. Keindorff's equation log $(p+19)=6·9788-f(T-)8^{-1}$, where log $f=2·5901$. C. A. Crommelin also calculated values from W. H. Keesom's equation $D_1=D\{1+0·9758(1-T/T_c)+1·999(1-T/T_c)^{0·3795}\}$.

W. Ramsay and M. W. Travers found the sp. gr. of liquid krypton to be 2·155 at −127°; and G. Rudorf calculated 2·155 at the b.p. −121·33° from E. H. Mathias' equation $D_c=\frac{1}{2}(D_g-D_l)/(2-T/T_c)$. At the b.p., R. W. Gray obtained 2·47, and for the at. vol. 33·6. For liquid xenon at −102°, W. Ramsay and M. W. Travers obtained sp. gr. 3·52; G. Rudorf calculated 2·68; and H. S. Patterson and co-workers found

	−66·8°	−42·9°	−20·25°	−5°	0°	5°	10°	16°
D_l . .	2·763	2·605	2·297	2·074	1·987	1·879	1·750	1·468
D_g . .	0·059	0·103	0·235	0·363	0·421	0·501	0·602	0·844

The mean densities lie very closely on the straight line $\frac{1}{2}(D_l+D_g)=1·205-0·003055\theta$, in accord with the law of rectilinear diameters. J. J. van Laar studied this subject. The sp. gr. of the liquid at its b.p., −106·9°, is 3·063, and the at. vol. 42·7. The ratios of the sp. gr. of liquid and gas are :

	He	Ne	A	Kr	X	Nt
D_l/D_g . .	682·3	—	787·7	c. 646	524·3	c. 555

C. del Fresno studied the at. vol. of the inert gases. H. K. Onnes measured the vapour pressure, p mm., of liquid helium :

	−268·71°	−269·03°	−269·74°	−270·66°	−271·53°
p . .	760	565	197	51	3
f . .	1·581	1·499	1·339	1·227	1·073

and when the results are applied to J. H. van der Waals' vap. press. equation

$\log p_c$ $\log p = f(T_c/T-1)$, for $T_c = 5.25°$ K., and $p_c = 1718$ mm., the values of f are not constant. W. Ramsay and M. W. Travers found the vap. press. of liquid argon to be:

	$-195.7°$	$-190°$	$-187.5°$	$-185.2°$	$-150.9°$	$-136.2°$	$-117.4°$
p . . .	215.0	485.8	633.4	821.6	10313	20700	40200

K. Olschewsky obtained rather lower values. W. Ramsay and S. Young compared the results with those for benzene, ethyl alcohol, and oxygen. H. Happel applied the above data to J. H. van der Waals' vap. press. formula ; and to A. Keindorff's equation $\log (p+19) = 6.9787958 - f(8+T)^{-1}$, where $\log f = 2.5901094$. H. von Jüptner, V. Dolezalek, J. J. van Laar, and H. K. Onnes and C. A. Crommelin also studied the observed data. C. A. Crommelin and co-workers measured the isotherms for neon between 20° and $-217°$. F. Born gave for the vap. press. of argon :

			Solid.		Liquid.		
$T°$ K. .	65.49	70.49	79.06	83.93	87.31	87.88	90.35
p . .	21.97	59.26	255.6	512.17	746.1	792.3	1026.0

and he represented the values for the solid by $\log p = -366.87T^{-1} + 1.75 \log T -0.0028293T + 1.0698$ between 65° K and 83.93° K. ; and for the liquid, by $\log p = -339.3T^{-1} + 1.75 \log T - 0.006737T + 1.0698$, between 83.93° K. and 91° K. P. G. Cath and H. K. Onnes obtained for liquid neon, $\log p = -65.061T^{-1} + 0.01118T +2.8191$ (p in atm.) ; and E. Mathias and co-workers gave for neon $\log p =-84.3796T^{-1} + 2.81911 + 0.1118T$. A. C. Egerton discussed this subject.

W. Nernst gave 0.6 for the **chemical constant** of helium, and F. Pollitzer, 0.64 ; F. Born gave 0.79 ± 0.04 for that of argon. F. Simon, E. Brody, O. Stern, and M. Planck calculated the chemical constants of the inert gases. O. Sackur represented the chemical constants, C, by $C = -1.617 + 1.5 \log M$, and also $C = -2.051 + 1.5 \log M$, where M is the mol. wt. ; A. Eucken gave $C = -1.587 +1.5 \log M$; and F. Pollitzer, $C = 1.33 \log T_b - 0.00098T_b$, where T_b denotes the b.p. on the absolute scale of temp.

E. Mathias and co-workers found the vap. press. of neon can be represented by $\log p = 2.81911 - 84.3796T^{-1} + 0.1118T$. J. K. H. Inglis studied the isothermal distillation of mixtures of argon and oxygen at 82.09°, and found the results indicated in Table III. The vap. press. of solid argon at 82.09 is 411 mm. C. A. Crommelin found the vap. press. of liquid argon could be represented by $\log p = 4.85033$

TABLE III.—VAPOUR PRESSURE OF MIXTURES OF LIQUID OXYGEN AND ARGON.

Molar per cent. argon.		Partial pressure mm.	
Liquid.	Vapour.	Oxygen.	Argon.
0	**0**	300.0	0.0
3.30	**5.76**	290.5	17.0
5.6	**9.15**	283.5	28.5
10.2	**16.0**	269.8	37.4
13.6	**20.6**	260.0	67.5
92.7	**97.8**	9.0	411.0

$-634.391T + 30769.09T^2 - 107646T^3$ atm. ; and E. Mathias and co-workers gave for argon $\log p = 4.8033 - 634.391T^{-1} - 30769.09T^{-2} - 1076464T^{-3}$. C. A. Crommelin observed :

Liquid $\{p$ . .	$-150.57°$	$-161.28°$	$-183.01°$	$-185.90°$	$-189.30°$
	1041.0	564.53	103.53	79.371	51.565 mm.

Solid $\{p$ . .	$-139.30°$	$-191.36°$	$-194.58°$	$-197.62°$	$-206.04°$
	51.565	39.429	25.101	16.348	(6.717)

The number in brackets is doubtful. For the triple point, $(\delta p/\delta T)_l=0.08162$; and $(\delta p/\delta T)_s=0.08623$; so that the vap. press. curve at the m.p. suffers only a small change of direction. F. Dolezalek measured the vap. press. of liquid mixtures of argon and nitrogen. W. Ramsay and M. W. Travers obtained for krypton

	$-188.6°$	$-184.4°$	$-160.3°$	$-102.1°$	$-75.1°$	$-72°$	$-66.6°$	$-22.5°$
p . .	9.0	17.4	386.6	11970	28808	30837	37006	41245

H. Happel applied J. D. van der Waals' vap. press. formula; and A. Keindorff's formula becomes log $(p+12)=7.0384730-f(39+T)^{-1}$, where log $f=2.7157442$. At lower temp., W. Ramsay found

	$-205°$	$-200°$	$-195°$	$-190°$	$188.8°$	$-182.4°$
p	0.27	0.97	2.8	7.5	9.0	17.4 mm.

Solid krypton thus exerts an appreciable vap. press. W. Ramsay and M. W. Travers gave for the vap. press. of xenon :

	$-189.8°$	$-41.6°$	$-31.8°$	$-20.4°$	$-15.6°$	$0.5°$
p . .	2020	11134	14696	19984	22310	31501 mm.

and H. Happel applied J. D. van der Waals' vap. press. formula; and A. Keindorff's formula becomes log $(p+12)=7.0385481-f(8+T)^{-1}$, where log $f=2.8531501$. H. von Jüptner also made observations on this subject. W. Ramsay found at

	$-205°$	$-200°$	$-195°$	$-190°$	$-188.8°$	$-182.4°$
p . . .	0.0005	0.007	0.02	0.04	0.11	0.17 mm.

and H. S. Patterson and co-workers gave at $-20°$, 19056 mm.; at 0°, 31360 mm.; and at $-16.6°$, 44270 mm.

Isothermal pv-curves were determined by W. Ramsay and M. W. Travers,[2] L. Holborn and J. Otto, and H. K. Onnes. J. J. van Laar discussed the deviations from Boyle's law for helium, neon, and argon; and A. Leduc found 0.0_585 for the coeff. of deviation from Boyle's law for argon. Values for the constants a, b, c in the equation $pv=a+bv^{-1}+cv^{-2}$, were calculated by H. K. Onnes. The results for helium, with p expressed in atm., and v in normal vols., are as follow :

						a	b	c
100.35°	$\begin{cases}p\\pv\end{cases}$	.	42.574	54.459	66.590	1.36667	0.0_3673	0.0_616
		.	1.38725	1.39314	1.39929			
20.00°	$\begin{cases}p\\pv\end{cases}$	.	27.539	36.303	53.708	1.07273	0.0_3534	0.0_613
		.	1.08664	1.09028	1.09918			
0°	$\begin{cases}p\\pv\end{cases}$	.	26.632	38.565	50.240	0.99970	0.0_3512	0.0_612
		.	1.01392	1.01851	1.02521			
$-103.57°$	$\begin{cases}p\\pv\end{cases}$	.	20.580	29.185	33.383	0.62036	0.0_3337	0.8_77
		.	0.63135	0.63597	0.63845			
$-182.75°$	$\begin{cases}p\\pv\end{cases}$	.	13.751	16.019	18.189	0.33066	0.0_3176	0.0_74
		.	0.33787	0.33898	0.34025			
$-216.56°$	$\begin{cases}p\\pv\end{cases}$	.	9.564	10.502	11.448	0.20693	0.0_496	0.0_72
		.	0.21132	0.21171	0.21219			
$-252.72°$	$\begin{cases}p\\pv\end{cases}$	.	53.948	60.716	65.997	—	—	—
		.	0.09120	0.09533	0.09867			
$-258.82°$	$\begin{cases}p\\pv\end{cases}$	.	40.012	53.326	59.797	—	—	—
		.	0.06150	0.07063	0.07531			

Isotherms for helium at $-205°$ to $-258°$ were obtained by F. M. Penning and H. K. Onnes; and F. M. Penning measured isochores for helium over the same temp. range. F. P. Burt obtained the values for pv at 0° shown in Table IV. L. Holborn and J. Otto gave for helium $pv=0.99930+0.0_369543p$ at 0°; $pv=1.18223+0.0_368887p$ at 50°; and $pv=1.36518+0.0_366804p$ at 100°. They also compiled a table of values between $-183°$ and 400°. E. H. Amagat calculated values for the coeff. $dp/d\theta$, and found it to be almost independent of the temp. W. Ramsay

TABLE IV.—pv-CURVES FOR HELIUM AND NEON AT 0°.

Helium.			Neon.		
p mm.	v c.c.	pv	p mm.	v c.c.	pv
837·63	67·547	56580·5	860·44	68·502	58942
732·17	77·278		740·87	79·547	58934
613·09	92·279	56567·0	618·65	95·250	58926
462·54	122·320		533·95	110·342	58918
409·38	138·217	56582·5	397·92	148·036	589 7
269·81	209·724		288·69	204·015	58897
237·84	237·895	56585·0	200·50	293·762	58899
147·16	384·539		144·42	407·848	58900

and M. W. Travers obtained isothermal pv-curves for neon when p is expressed in metres of mercury, and v in c.c. per mol. (Table V). G. Rudorf found that the

TABLE V.—ISOTHERMAL pv-CURVES FOR NEON.

142°			237·3°		
p	v	pv	p	v	pv
29·870	590·5	17638	33·810	925·9	31304
38·370	458·4	17588	41·530	751·1	31193
48·876	359·4	17564	57·381	541·0	31036
59·980	294·2	17643	64·582	483·0	31190
71·458	248·8	17777	71·840	433·2	31124

data are too irregular to permit the calculation of the constants for the gas equation. F. P. Burt obtained the results shown in Table IV for neon at 0°. L. Holborn and J. Otto compiled a table of values for neon between −183° and 400°.

W. Ramsay, and W. Ramsay and M. W. Travers investigated the isothermal pv-curves of argon; and H. Happel calculated for $T_c/P_c(dp/dT)_c$, 5·17–5·42; G. Rudorf, 4; G. van Rij, 6·19; and C. A. Crommelin, 5·712. H. Happel obtained for $(dp/dT)_c$, 1337–1400: and G. van Rij, 1477. H. K. Onnes and C. A. Crommelin obtained the following results for the isothermal curves when p is measured in atm., and v is expressed in normal vols.:

20·39°	p	.	21·783	27·320	34·487	37·248	49·604	61·741
	v	.	0·048783	0·038821	0·030684	0·028305	0·021134	0·016878
	pv	.	1·0627	1·0606	1·0582	1·0543	1·0483	1·0420
0°	p	.	20·576	26·070	31·572	36·743	49·871	62·230
	v	.	0·047900	0·037621	0·030958	0·026468	0·019290	0·015308
	pv	.	0·98560	0·98077	0·097740	0·097250	0·096201	0·095261
−57·72°	p	.	17·872	21·488	25·288	35·127	46·209	62·079
	v	.	0·042537	0·034996	0·029592	0·020783	0·015397	0·011026
	pv	.	0·76023	0·75200	0·74654	0·73004	0·71148	0·68448
−102·51°	p	.	14·864	19·790	32·394	40·976	51·398	62·239
	v	.	0·039107	0·028509	0·016067	0·011904	0·086296	0·063286
	pv	.	0·58130	0·56420	0·52047	0·48780	0·44354	0·39388
−149·60°	p	.	11·150	12·788	—	—	—	—
	v	.	0·034266	0·028863	—	—	—	—
	pv	.	0·38205	0·36910	—	—	—	—

The results were used in testing the relation $pv=a+bv^{-1}+cv^{-2}+dv^{-4}+ev^{-6}+fv^{-8}$ H. Happel applied the equation $p=RT/v\{1+1\cdot2v^{-1}+\ \cdot625(1\cdot2v^{-1})^2+0\cdot2869(1\cdot2v^{-1})^3+...\}-10\times10^8v^{-2}$, where $R=2\cdot083\times10^6$; and G. Rudorf, $pv=RTv(v-30\cdot18)^{-1}-9\cdot886\times10^5v^{-1}$, where $R=62\cdot372$. L. Holborn and J. Otto compiled a table of values for argon between $-183°$ and $400°$. E. H. Amagat calculated values for $dp/d\theta$ at different temp.; and H. K. Onnes and C. A. Crommelin, values for $T(d^2p/dT^2)_v$; $T(dp/dT)_v-p$; $T(dp/dT)_v-p$; $(dp/dT)_v$, which did not give constant values; and $(d^2p/dT^2)_v$, which was not zero. W. Ramsay and M. W. Travers obtained the following values for the pv-curves of krypton, p being expressed in metres, and v in c.c. per mol:

11·2°	p	19·669	29·359	37·682	47·933	66·420	77·329
	v	879·2	562·8	422·8	318·8	214·8	180·1
	pv	17166	16523	15934	15280	14264	13924
237·3°	p	38·707	45·113	49·448	54·109	68·044	79·108
	v	824·8	704·5	644·0	583·7	462·5	402·4
	pv	31924	31783	31680	31583	31473	31830

H. Happel, and G. van Rij applied the equation $p=1·014\times10^6Tv^{-1}\{1+0·764v^{-1}+0·625(0··764v^{-1})^2+0·2869(0·740v^{-1})^3+ . . .\}-424\times10^6v^{-2}$; and G. Rudorf, $pv=62·372Tv(v-39·79)^{-1}-17·63\times10^5v^{-1}$. H. Happel gave $T_c/p_c(dp/dT_c)=5·17$, and 5·42; G. van Rij, 6·19; and H. Happel, $(dp/dT)_c$, 1085, and 1030. W. Ramsay and M. W. Travers obtained the following values for the pv-curves of xenon— p being expressed in metres, and v in c.c. per mol.:

11·2°	p	19·492	22·851	26·270	30·923	35·125	40·430
	v	771·6	632·6	525·5	417·0	339·4	234·3
	pv	15042	14456	13805	12894	11917	9240
237·3°	p	40·681	48·042	52·915	58·927	66·997	77·935
	v	736·4	618·5	560·4	947·4	436·2	375·8
	pv	30114	29714	29655	29313	29223	29288

H. Happel, and G. van Rij applied the equation $p=RTv\{1+0·633v^{-1}+0·625(0·633v^{-1})^2+0·2869(0·633v^{-1})^3+. . .\}-307\times10^6v^{-2}$; and G. Rudorf, $pv=RTv(v-51·57)^{-1}-312·4v^{-1}$. H. Happel obtained $T_c/p_c(dp/dT)_c=5·17$ and 5·40; H. S. Patterson and co-workers, 5·87; and G. van Rij, 6·19. H. Happel gave $(dp/dT)_c=796$. The best representative values are:

$\dfrac{T_c}{p_c}\left(\dfrac{dT}{dp}\right)_e$	A	Kr	X
	5·23	5·48	5·40

P. W. Bridgman found for the press., p, in kgrms. per sq. cm.; the vol., v c.c. per grm. of helium, at $65°$; and the product pv, where the v represents the vol. of helium which under 1 kgrm. press. per c.c. at $0°$, occupies 1 c.c.

p	3000	5000	7000	9000	11000	13000	15000
v	5·54	4·31	3·77	3·44	3·21	3·06	2·94
p	2·31	2·99	3·66	4·29	4·89	5·52	6·11

P. W. Bridgman found for the press., p in kgrms. per sq. cm.; and the change in vol. δv in c.c. per gram of argon at $55°$:

p	2000	3000	5000	7000	9000	11000	13000	15000
δv	0·083	0·000	0·085	0·134	0·167	0·190	0·209	0·224

J. H. Perry found the inversion temp. in the **Joule-Thomson effect** occurs at about $100°$ K. W. Meissner found that when compressed helium, at $15°$ K., is allowed to expand, the proportion liquefied is 0·19 of the whole. This is greater than is computed from the theory of corresponding states. F. P. G. A. J. van Agt and H. K. Onnes compared the hydrogen and helium thermometers; and W. Heuse studied helium, and neon thermometers. The subject was discussed by H. K. Onnes and co-workers, F. Henning, G. K. Burgess, J. Dewar, K. Olschewsky, J. P. Kuenen and W. W. Randall, M. W. Travers and co-workers, F. Dorn, F. Cario, etc.

J. P. Kuenen and W. W. Randall obtained for the **pressure coefficient** of argon, $\beta=0·003665$; M. W. Travers and co-workers, 0·00366255, the same as for hydrogen; H. K. Onnes gave 0·0036613–0·0036616. J. P. Kuenen and W. W. Randall found for argon, $a=0.003668$.   L. Holborn and F. Henning found for helium between $0°$ and $100°$, $a=0.0036618$; and L. Holborn and J. Otto gave for helium $\beta=0.003661$ at $p=0$, and 0.0036518 at $p=60$ m. ; and the mean coeff. of thermal expansion 0.0036605, for $p=0$, and 0.0034552 for $p=80$ m. press.   The constants in J. D. van der Waals' equation of state were studied by W. Ramsay and G. Rudorf, P. A. Guye and L. Friderich, and H. Happel.   The results show that when p is expressed in atm., v is unity at $0°$ and 1 atm. press., and $R=1/273.09$:

	He	Ne	A	Kr	X	Nt
a . . .	0.0_46898	—	0.002671	0.004633	0.008149	0.01291
b . . .	0.001063	—	0.001435	0.001778	0.002277	0.002768

and when p is expressed in dynes per sq. cm., and v in c.c. per gram :

	He	Ne	A	Kr	X	Nt
9×10^{-6} . .	2204	—	833.3	342.2	243.5	83.16
b . .	5.969	—	0.8060	0.4798	0.3910	0.2209

F. G. Keyes gave for the equation of state of argon $p=2.0578(v-1.278)^{-1}T$ $-995.7(v-0.247)^{-2}$; but P. W. Bridgman found that the compressibility at high press. does not fall off so rapidly as is indicated by this equation.   M. F. Carroll replaced the constants a and b of J. D. van der Waals' equation by $a=a'(1-0.293a)$, and $b=b'(1-0.369a)$, where for helium, $a=0.269$, $a' \times 10^{-6}=0.0282$, and $b'=22.80$; for argon, $a=0.380$, $a' \times 10^{-6}=1.074$, and $b'=29.13$; and for xenon, $a=0.522$, $a' \times 10^{-6}=3.268$, and $b'=46.77$.   W. J. Walker studied the equation of state of helium.   F. Zwicky calculated an equation of state for helium and argon from the electronic structure.   J. E. Jones discussed the equations of state for these gases ; and J. J. van Laar, the constants of the equations of state.

I. Masson and L. G. F. Dolley found that for mixtures of argon and ethylene, the total press. is greater than the sum of those of the constituents taken separately; while with argon-oxygen mixtures, the deviations from the additive mixture rule are less.   Analogous deviations occur in the measurement of the volumes of the mixed gases.   Assuming that internal pressure or cohesion in a gas of moderate density is due partly to the formation of mol. aggregates of varying complexity, it is concluded that at the ordinary temp. these complexes are in reversible equilibrium with their original constituents.   Regarded from the point of view of the electronic theory of mol. structure, it would appear that mol. cohesion between any two gases would be that of the gas or gases of the argon group, the electronic configurations of which the gases simulate.   J. P. Dalton calculated the sp. attraction coeff. of argon to be 4.963 when that of oxygen is 5.689, and that of hydrogen, 6.863.   The effect of mol. attractions on the pressure of helium, etc., was investigated by O. Maass and D. M. Morrison.

A. Jaquerod and O. Scheuer found that, like hydrogen and neon, the compressibility of helium, corrected for argon, is positive, and it amounts to $+0.0006$; and later they obtained 0.001 when the value for hydrogen is $+0.00055$.   F. P. Burt obtained a zero or negative value.   P. A. Guye obtained 0.001009 from the equation $A=-a+b+0.0_4623T_c/22.412$, where $a=6.898 \times 10^{-5}$, $b=106.3 \times 10^{-5}$, and T_c $=5.25°$; the corresponding value for hydrogen is 0.000569.   F. P. Burt obtained for the compressibility of neon between 0 and 1 atm. press. $+0.00105$; and P. A. Guye calculated $+0.00038$.   Lord Rayleigh found -0.00076 at $11.2°$ and -0.00094 at $0°$, for the compressibility of argon between 0.5 and 1 atm.   P. A. Guye gave -0.000841; and H. E. Watson, -0.00103.   With the formula $C_p-C_v=Tva^2/\beta$, A. Eucken calculated the compressibility of liquid argon to be $\beta=2.45 \times 10^{-4}$ kgrm. per sq. cm.   For krypton gas P. A. Guye obtained -0.00227 and -0.002103 ; H. E. Watson, -0.00228 and -0.00210.   For xenon, P. A. Guye obtained -0.005924, and H. E. Watson, -0.00690 and -0.00798.   The best representative value is -0.00592. F. P. G. A. J. van Agt and H. K. Onnes measured the compressibility of helium between $-259°$ and $-180°$.   S. F. Pickering compiled some data on this subject. P. W. Bridgman found for the change in vol. of argon, c.c. per gram at $55°$, -0.083

at 2000 kgrms. per sq. cm. press. : zero, 3000 ; 0·112 at 6000 ; 0·201 at 12,000 ; and 0·224 at 15,000. The best representative values for the compressibilities of the inert gases are :

	He	Ne	A	Kr	X	Nt
Compressibility	+0·001	+0·00105	−0·000841	−0·00218	−0·00592	−0·01816

Lord Rayleigh[3] measured the **viscosity** of helium and found 0·96 with air unity; H. Schultze obtained $\eta=0.0_31969$ at 15·3° ; 0·0$_3$2348 at 99·6° ; and 0·0$_3$2699 at 184·6°. J. F. Schierloh gave 0·0$_3$1980 at 18·7° ; 0·0$_3$2337 at 99·8° ; and 0·0$_3$2681 at 183·7° ; M. N. States, 0·0$_3$19623 at 23° ; and K. Schmitt, 0·0$_3$1967 at 17·6° ; 0·0$_3$1587 at −609° ; 0·0$_3$1506 at −78·5° ; and 0·0$_4$8947 at −193·2°. H. K. Onnes and S. Weber found for the viscosity at low temp :

	21·5°	−22·7°	−69·9°	−102·5°	−183·25°	−198·3°	−252·83°	−258°
$\eta \times 10^7$	1994	1788	1564	1392	918·6	813·2	349·8	294·6

H. Vogel found 0·0$_3$1876 for helium at 0·1° ; 0·0$_3$1496 at −78·4° ; 0·0$_4$875 at −191·4° ; and 0·0$_4$348 at −252°. W. J. Walker made some observations on the viscosity of helium. Lord Rayleigh gave $c=72.2$ for Sutherland's constant (1. 13, 3); H. Schultze, 80·3 ; J. F. Schierloh, 78·2 ; R. A. Millikan, 113; H. K. Onnes and S. Weber, 78·2 ; A. O. Rankine, 70. P. Tänzler measured the viscosity of mixtures of helium and argon ; and calculated the results, using the formulæ of J. Puluj, and M. Thiesen. Y. Ishida gave 1·087 for the ratio of the viscosity of helium to that of air ; and 1·212 for argon and air. Observations on this subject were made by S. Chapman, and P. Günther. The viscosity of neon, found by A. O. Rankine, is 1·721 for air unity at 10·1° ; and in absolute units, $\eta=0.0003036$, and at 0°, 0·0002981. Sutherland's constant is 56. Lord Rayleigh obtained 1·21, air unity, for the viscosity of impure argon. H. Schultze gave for purified argon, 0·0$_3$1811 at 15° ; 0·0$_3$2208 at 99·7° ; and 0·0$_3$2571 at 182·9°. P. Tänzler gave 0·0$_3$2202 at 11·9° ; 0·0$_3$2197 at 12·1° ; 0·0$_3$2746 at 99·6° ; and 0·0$_3$3231 at 183°. W. Kopsch obtained 0·0$_3$2207 at 13·17° ; 0·0$_3$21156 at −0·21° ; 0·0$_3$19866 at −20·25° ; 0·0$_3$18535 at −40·17° ; 0·0$_3$16966 at −60·16° ; 0·0$_3$15746 at −78·82° ; 0·0$_3$13797 at −104·40° ; 0·0$_3$11061 at −132·30° ; and 0·0$_4$7356 at −183·17°. He also compared the results obtained with M. Knudsen's formula. S. Chapman and W. Hainsworth, J. F. Schierloh, A. O. Rankine, H. Markowsky, J. E. Jones, and K. Schmitt made observations on this subject. For Sutherland's constant for argon, Lord Rayleigh gave 150·2 ; H. Schultze, 169·9 ; W. Kopsch, 174·6 ; A. O. Rankine, 142. The viscosity of krypton, air unity, was found by A. O. Rankine to be 1·361 at 10·6°, and $\eta=0.0_32405$; and at 0°, 0·0$_3$2334 ; K. Schmitt gave $\eta=0.0_31736$ at 0°. A. O. Rankine's value for Sutherland's constant is 188 for krypton, and 252 for xenon. He also gave for the viscosity of xenon, air unity, 1·234 at 10·9° or $\eta=0.0_32180$; and at 0°, $\eta=0.0_32107$; while K. Schmitt gave 0·0$_3$2121 at 0°. M. Reinganum, W. J. Fisher. and A. O. Rankine studied the subject generally ; and H. Sirk, and E. Lohr, the relation between the viscosity coeff. and the index of refraction. The best representative values for the viscosity η, and at 0°, and for Sutherland's constant C, are :

	He	Ne	A	Kr	X
δ	0·0$_3$1879	0·0$_3$2981	0·0$_3$2102	0·0$_3$2334	0·0$_3$2107
	70	56	142	188	252

F. Schuster gave 860 atm. for the **internal pressure** of argon, and 1234 atm. for krypton. M. N. States, and E. Blanckenstein measured the **coefficient of slip** of helium and oxygen. W. Ramsay and J. N. Collie[4] found that the **diffusion** of helium through pipe-clay proceeds more rapidly than corresponds with Graham's law. A similar observation was made by W. Ramsay and M. W. Travers. who also found that at about 950°, platinum, palladium, and iron are impermeable to helium. A. Jaquerod and F. L. Perrot found that while platinum is impermeable to helium at 1000°, the gas passes readily through quartz. The diffusion through fused quartz is rapid even at 520°, and perceptible at 220°. The gas also diffuses through porcelain so that vessels of fused quartz or porcelain are not suitable containers for helium at an elevated temp.—*vide* quartz and glass. E. Dorn found that a vessel of platinum-iridium alloy is impermeable at 1420°. A. Sieverts and E. Bergner, H. E. Watson, and A. Jaquerod studied the diffusion of helium through quartz and porcelain. O. W. Richardson and R. C. Ditto found that neon also diffuses through quartz glass at 1000°, but not so fast as helium. W. Ramsay and J. N. Collie showed that the rate of diffusion of argon through pipe-clay is in accord with Graham's law. D. Tsakalotos measured the diffusion of hydrogen mixed with argon through palladium at 280°—*vide infra*. Lord Rayleigh found that argon diffuses through indiarubber more quickly than nitrogen. J. Dewar found the rate of diffusion of argon through rubber 0·01 mm. thick to be 2·56 c.c. per sq. cm. per day at 15° and atm. press.; for helium, the rate was 3·5; and for nitrogen, 1·38. J. C. McLennan and W. W. Shaver, and R. T. Elworthy and V. F. Murray also measured the diffusion of helium through rubber fabrics; and J. C. McLennan and W. W. Shaver, through soap films. R. Schmidt investigated the interdiffusion of helium and argon and obtained $k=0.25405$ at 15° for the coeff. of diffusion. He also represented the effect of temp. by the expression $k=k_0\{(273+\theta)273\}^{1.75}$. F. W. Aston, and A. Lonius also made observations on this subject. T. L. Ibbs studied the thermal diffusion of hydrogen and argon, and helium and argon; G. A. Elliott and I. Masson, helium and carbon dioxide mixtures; G. Jaumann, the separation of hydrogen and helium by a diffusion process; and S. Chapman and W. Hainsworth, the kinetic theory of the diffusion of argon and helium.

F. G. Donnan measured the rate of **effusion** or the efflux of helium through a small hole in a thin-walled partition. The efflux is faster than the speed calculated from the density even when a relatively large viscosity factor is introduced. It is concluded that the Joule-Thomson effect is negative because it can be shown that a gas will effuse more slowly or more rapidly than an ideal gas according as the Joule-Thomson effect is negative or positive. F. G. Donnan also measured the effusion of argon, and found it is in qualitative but not quantitative agreement with Graham's law.

The observations on the **surface tension** of argon by E. C. C. Baly and F. G. Donnan,[5] re-calculated by G. Rudorf, are as follow :

	−189°	−188°	−187°	−186°	−185°	−184°	−183°
σ	13·45	13·19	12·93	12·68	12·42	12·17	11·91
$\sigma(Mv)^{\frac{2}{3}}$	124·12	122·10	120·08	118·06	116·04	114·02	112·00
a^2	1·925	1·90	1·87	1·84	1·81	1·78	1·755

The molecular **surface energy** is represented by (Mv), and the effect of temp. by $(Mv)=2.02(145.44-T)$; and J. D. van der Waals' equation assumes the form $=23.20(1-T/Tc)^{0.8102}$. The values for the **specific cohesion**, a^2, are indicated above. P. Walden represented the relation between the mol. wt., M, and the sp. cohesion by $M=0.435T/a^2$. P. Walden and R. Swinne represented the temp. coeff. of the surface energy by $d\{\sigma(Mv^{\frac{2}{3}})\}/d\theta=-\{1.90+0.011(E\sqrt{A})\}$; and of the mol. cohesion, by $d(Ma^2)/d\theta=-\{0.0027(E\sqrt{A})+0.0103\}$, where $\sqrt{A}$ for argon is 6·32. A. T. van Urk and co-workers found for liquid helium the mol. surface tensions :

	−268·80°	−269·00°	−269·500°	−270·00°	−270·50°	−271·00°	−272·50°
$M\sigma$	0·98	1·19	1·68	2·19	2·69	3·08	3·22

The **molecular constants** of the rare gases have been discussed in connection with the kinetic theory of gases by O. E. Meyer,[6] R. Gans, J. H. Jeans, G. Rudorf, H. Sirk, W. Hillers, M. Reinganum, W. Sutherland, etc. The **mean velocity** of mol. motion, V, and the velocity of mean square, U, of helium calculated by G. Rudorf, are respectively 13.06×10^4 and 12.035×10^4 cm. per sec.; the mean velocity, by O. E. Meyer, is 11.62×10^4, and by R. Schmidt, 12.077×10^4 cm. per sec.; while the velocity of mean square, by J. H. Jeans, is $13 \cdot 11 \times 10^4$ cm. per sec. G. Rudorf found for neon $V = 5 \cdot 385 \times 10^4$ and $U = 5 \cdot 845 \times 10^4$ cm. per sec.; and for argon, respectively $3 \cdot 806 \times 10^4$ and $4 \cdot 13 \times 10^4$ cm. per sec. H. Schultze gave for argon, $U = 4 \cdot 148 \times 10^4 - 4 \cdot 135 \times 10^4$; J. H. Jeans, $4 \cdot 13 \times 10^4$ cm. per sec.; and P. Tänzler, $4 \cdot 13 \times 10^4$ cm. per sec.; and for the mean velocity, V, O. E. Meyer gave $3 \cdot 81 \times 10^4$ cm. per sec.; R. Schmidt, $3 \cdot 806 \times 10^4$ cm. per sec., $U = 2 \cdot 86 \times 10^4$ cm. per sec., and $V = 2 \cdot 64 \times 10^4$ cm. per sec., and for xenon, respectively $2 \cdot 28 \times 10^4$ and $2 \cdot 10 \times 10^4$ cm. per sec. The **mean free path,** L, of the mols. of helium calculated by Lord Rayleigh is $2 \cdot 40 \times 10^{-5}$ to $2 \cdot 6 \times 10^{-5}$ cm.; H. Schultze, $2 \cdot 857 \times 10^{-5}$ cm.; J. F. Schierloh, $2 \cdot 85 \times 10^{-5}$; and by A. O. Rankine, $2 \cdot 421 \times 10^{-5}$ cm. The last-named gave for neon, $1 \cdot 709 \times 10^{-5}$ cm. For argon, Lord Rayleigh gave $0 \cdot 99 \times 10^{-5}$ cm.; H. Schultze, $1 \cdot 002 \times 10^{-5}$ to $1 \cdot 012 \times 10^{-5}$ cm.; P. Tänzler, $1 \cdot 004 \times 10^{-5}$ cm.; and J. F. Schierloh, $1 \cdot 006 \times 10^{-5}$ cm. For krypton, G. Rudorf gave $0 \cdot 659 \times 10^{-5}$ cm. and $0 \cdot 77 \times 10^{-5}$ cm.; and for xenon, $0 \cdot 474 \times 10^{-5}$ cm. and $0 \cdot 554 \times 10^{-5}$ cm. The **molecular diameter,** D, of the rare gases calculated by A. O. Rankine, M. Reinganum, O. E. Meyer, J. H. Jeans, H. Sirk, J. Robinson, W. H. Westphal, G. Rudorf, C. C. Darwin, W. Sutherland, range from $0 \cdot 4745 \times 10^{-8}$ to $2 \cdot 130 \times 10^{-8}$ cm. for helium; $0 \cdot 6440 \times 10^{-8}$ to $2 \cdot 532 \times 10^{-8}$ cm. for neon; $1 \cdot 342 \times 10^{-8}$ to $3 \cdot 580 \times 10^{-8}$ cm. for argon; $1 \cdot 561 \times 10^{-8}$ to $4 \cdot 08 \times 10^{-8}$ cm. for krypton; and $1 \cdot 824 \times 10^{-8}$ cm. for xenon. S. Chapman calculated for argon $2 \cdot 84 \times 10^{-8}$ cm.; P. W. Bridgman gave $1 \cdot 98 \times 10^{-8}$ to $2 \cdot 20 \times 10^{-8}$ cm.; and W. L. Bragg calculated $1 \cdot 30$ A. for the diameter of the atoms of neon; $2 \cdot 05$ A., for those of argon; $2 \cdot 35$ A., for those of krypton; and $2 \cdot 70$ A., for those of xenon. A. O. Rankine calculated values from viscosity determinations. R. G. Lunnon, H. G. Grimm, W. Schütz, and H. G. Grimm and H. Wolff made some calculations on this subject. S. Mokruschin calculated for the mol. diameter of argon at the b.p., $1 \cdot 212 \times 10^{-8}$ cm., and for helium, $0 \cdot 122 \times 10^{-8}$ cm. M. N. Saha calculated from the ionization potential for helium $0 \cdot 28 \times 10^{-8}$ cm.; and neon, $0 \cdot 33 \times 10^{-8}$; and H. Schmidt calculated from the viscosity, helium, $0 \cdot 795 \times 10^{-8}$ cm.; neon, $0 \cdot 946 \times 10^{-8}$ cm.; argon, $1 \cdot 336 \times 10^{-8}$ cm.; krypton, $1 \cdot 553 \times 10^{-8}$ cm.; and xenon, $1 \cdot 794 \times 10^{-8}$ cm. C. Ramsauer discussed the collision area of the mols. of the inert gases; and W. P. Davey, the packing radii of the atoms of the inert gases. The best representative values for the mol. constants may be taken as

	He	Ne	A	Kr	X	Nt
$U \times 10^{-4}$	$13 \cdot 06$	$5 \cdot 182$	$4 \cdot 13$	$2 \cdot 86$	$2 \cdot 28$	$1 \cdot 75$
$V \times 10^{-4}$	$12 \cdot 035$	$5 \cdot 355$	$3 \cdot 806$	$2 \cdot 64$	$2 \cdot 10$	$1 \cdot 61$
$L \times 10^5$	$2 \cdot 421$	$1 \cdot 709$	$0 \cdot 857$	$2 \cdot 659$	$0 \cdot 474$	—
$D \times 10^8$	$1 \cdot 89$	$2 \cdot 35$	$2 \cdot 87$	$3 \cdot 19$	$3 \cdot 51$	—

The at. radii calculated by M. Pierucci are roughly proportional to the numbers 3, 4, 6, 7, 8. B. Cabrera obtained values about half those computed from the kinetic theory when he calculated the values from Bohr's electronic struction, and from the magnetic susceptibility. J. E. L. Jones calculated the attractive and repulsive forces between the atoms of the inert gases. J. J. van Laar computed values for Avogadro's number; and V. Kiréef, values for the intermolecular attraction of helium, neon, and argon.

K. Olschewsky,[7] J. Dewar, and M. W. Travers and A. Jaquerod tried without success to liquefy helium. No **liquefaction** occurred, even by suddenly relieving the press. at 180 atm. at the temp. of solid hydrogen. H. K. Onnes reported having solidified the gas by cooling it in liquid hydrogen, and A. W. Porter accordingly suggested that helium passes directly from the gaseous to the solid state. The helium employed was probably contaminated with hydrogen, but by using the purified gas cooled to $-258°$, liquefaction occurred during the free expansion of the compressed gas.

According to H. K. Onnes, with a mixture of an ideal gas and an incompressible liquid without vap. press., in which the gas does not dissolve, under the action of gravity, the gas will gather above the liquid if the press. is sufficiently low, whereas the compressed gas will sink in the liquid if the press. is made high enough. With a mixture of one part of helium and 6 parts of hydrogen, cooled by liquid hydrogen, at press. up to 49 atm., the liquid hydrogen is separated from the supernatant gaseous helium by a distinct hollow meniscus ; at 49 atm., the gas, mainly helium, sinks in the liquid just as water goes through oil, and remains at the bottom like a large drop. By increasing the compression up to 60 atm., and decreasing the press. to 32 atm., the vol. of the bubble seems to follow the change of press. as that of a gas ; at 32 atm. press., the bubble rises in the liquid. By changing the press., the bubble can be made to rise or sink in the liquid at pleasure.

J. C. McLennan and G. M. Schrum, and W. Meissner described an apparatus for the liquefaction of helium.

J. Dewar estimated the **boiling point** of helium to be about 5° K., while the determinations of H. K. Onnes showed the b.p. is 4·25° K. ; W. H. Keesom gave —268·87°. G. Rudorf estimated the b.p. of neon to be 47° K.–51° K., but the basis of the estimate—Ramsay and Young's rule—is not reliable. W. Ramsay and M. W. Travers liquefied neon at the temp. of liquid hydrogen, but it is not liquefied at —205° and 100 atm. press. **M. W.** Travers and A. Jaquerod estimated the b.p. of neon to be between —244·5° and —239°. W. H. Keesom gave —245·92° for the b.p. of neon. The b.p. of argon given by K. Olschewsky was —187° at 740·5 mm. ; W. H. Keesom, —185·84° ; and W. Ramsay and M. W. Travers gave —185·8°. The last-named also gave —101·67° for the b.p. of krypton, and —106·9° for xenon. W. Ramsay and M. W. Travers estimated the **melting point** of helium to be less than 1° K. H. Erdmann estimated 1° K., and H. K. Onnes, 0·9° K. H. Erdmann gave —253° for the m.p. of neon, and H. K. Onnes and C. A. Crommelin, —248·6°. K. Olschewsky gave —189·6° for the m.p. of argon, and W. Ramsay and M. W. Travers, —187·9°. The latter gave .—169° for the m.p. of krypton, and —140° for that of xenon. The m.p. and b.p. of argon are only 1·8° apart. E. H. Mathias gave 4·99° K. for helium ; 44·74° K. for neon ; 150·65° K. for argon ; and 289·7° K. for xenon. W. H. Keesom gave —267·84° for helium, —228·35° for neon and —122·44° for argon. J. Narbut gave for the latent heat of fusion L Cals. per gram-atom at the m.p. :

	Helium.	Neon.	Argon.	Krypton.	Xenon.	Niton.
L	<0·004	0·08	0·268	0·33	0·43	0·65
m.p.	<—273·85°	—249°	—189°	—169°	—140°	—71°

K. Olschewsky said that the **crystals** of argon are white and transparent ; and W. Wahl showed that the crystals are isotropic belonging to the cubic system. The crystals grow rapidly, and usually furnish dendritic forms with many branches. F. Simon and C. von Simson observed that the **X-radiograms** of solid argon correspond with a face-centred cubic lattice with the closest spherical packing. At —233°, the edge of the cube is 5·42 A., and sp. gr. 1·62 ; J. de Smedt and W. H. Keesom gave 5·4 OA., and sp. gr. 1·63 at 20° K. J. E. Jones calculated the interatomic distances and the potential energy in the crystals of argon.

Estimates of the **critical temperature** of helium by J. Dewar, M. W. Travers and A. Jaquerod, K. Olschewsky, and W. M. Tate varied from 2° K. to 13° K. A direct determination by H. K. Onnes gave 5·25°K for the critical temp. of helium. E. Mathias and co-workers gave —267·90°. The ratio of the critical temp. to the b.p., $T_c/T_b = 1·235$, has a value lower than is the case with the other inert gases. W. Ramsay and M. W. Travers said that the critical temp. of neon must be below —205° and above —250° ; M. W. Travers and A. Jaquerod said that the critical temp. lies between —213° and —223° ; A. O. Rankine estimated —211·9° to —210·3° ; E. Mathias, H. K. Onnes and C. A. Crommelin gave —228·62° ; and C. Cuthbertson, —227°. Working with neon of a high degree of purity, C. A. Crommelin found —228·71°. K. Olschewsky gave —121° for the critical temp. of argon ; W. Ramsay and M. W. Travers, —117·4° ; and C. A. Crommelin, —122·44° ; and E. Mathias and co-workers, —122·35°. W. Ramsay and M. W. Travers gave —62·5° for the critical temp. of krypton ; and 14·75° for that of xenon.

H. S. Patterson and co-workers gave 16·6° for the critical temp. of xenon. For the **triple point**, W. H. Keesom gave —248·67°, and 323·5 mm. press. for neon; and —189·30° and 515·64 mm. for argon. H. K. Onnes and C. A. Crommelin gave for neon —248·6° and 323·5 mm. of mercury; E. Mathias and C. A. Crommelin gave what they thought to be the best representative values for the critical constants :

	Helium.	Neon.	Argon.	Krypton.	Xenon.
Critical temp. . .	—267·90°	—228·71°	—122·44°	—	16·6°
Critical press. . .	2·26	26·86	47·996	—	58·218 atm.
Critical density .	0·066	0·4835	0·53078	—	1·154
Triple point { temp. .	—272·2°	—248·67°	—189·19°	—	—140°
Triple point { press. .	0·002	32·35	51·217	—	— atm.

H. K. Onnes, and W. H. Keesom found 2·26 atm. for the **critical pressure** of helium, and later, 2·75 atm. The ratio $T_c/p_c = 2·32$ is lower than for the other inert gases. He found the critical press. of neon is about 29 atm. W. H. Keesom gave 26·86 atm. K. Olschewsky gave 50·6 atm. for the critical press. of argon; W. Ramsay and M. W. Travers, 40,200 mm. or 52 atm.; W. H. Keesom, 47·996 atm.; and C. A. Crommelin, 47·996 atm. W. Ramsay and M. W. Travers gave 41,245 mm. or 54·3 atm. for the critical press. of krypton, and 43·500 mm. or 57·2 atm. for that of xenon. W. R. Fielding discussed the relations between the critical constants of xenon and nitrogen; W. Herz, the critical constants of argon, helium, etc.; and H. Carlson, some relation between the m.p. and the b.p. of the inorganic halides and hydrides. H. K. Onnes found the **critical density** of helium to be 0·065, while values calculated from a number of other formulæ are lower. E. Mathias and co-workers gave 0·06930. D. Berthelot obtained 0·434 for the critical density of argon; H. Happel, 0·432–0·505; G. Rudorf, 0·488; P. Walden, 0·525; R. O. Herzog, 0·672; W. A. Goldhammer, 0·5149; C. A. Crommelin and co-workers, 0·509–0·53078. E. H. Mathias gave the values for the critical densities indicated in Table VI; C. A. Crommelin gave for neon, 0·483; A. Predwoditeleff, 0·4835; W. H. Keesom, 0·066 for helium, and 0·53078 for argon, and E. C. C. Baly and F. G. Donnan, 0·4841–0·5106. P. G. Rudorf calculated 0·775 for the critical density of krypton; and W. A. Goldhammer, 0·694–0·927. For the critical density of xenon, G. Rudorf gave 1·26; H. S. Patterson and co-workers, 1·155; H. Happel, 0·889; R. O. Herzog, 1·475; P. Walden, 1·147; and W. A. Goldhammer, 1·142–1·151. Best representative values for the critical constants are given in Table VI. J. A. Muller's values for the degree of polymerization, n, of some of these gases in the critical state are included.

TABLE VI.—SOME PHYSICAL CONSTANTS FOR THE INERT GASES (°K.).

	Helium.	Neon.	Argon.	Krypton.	Xenon.	Niton.
M.p. . .	c. 1°	24·4°	c. 85°	104°	133°	202°
B.p., T_b	4·25°	27·08°	87·2°	121·33°	166·1°	211°
T_c. .	4·99°	44·74°	150·65°	210·5°	289·7°	377·5°
p_c (atm.)	2·26	26·86	47·996	54·3	58·2	62·3
T_c/T_b .	1·235	1·652	1·725	1·735	1·740	1·790
T_c/p_c .	2·32	1·66	3·14	3·88	4·97	6·07
T_c/T_b .	1°	—	63·36°	86·17°	123·4°	166·5°
D_c . .	0·065	0·525	0·5308	c. 0·6	0·7661	—
n . . .	0·923	—	1·285	—	—	1·358

The **heat conductivity** of helium was found by W. Schwarze [8] to be 0·0003386 at 0°, and the temp. coeff. between 0° and 100° to be 0·00318. S. Chapman and W. Hainsworth studied the kinetic theory of conductivity. Observations were made by M. Smoluchowsky, E. Schreiner, and A. Eucken ; the last-named found that the conductivity, k, varies with temp. as follows :

	$-192 \cdot 7°$	$-78 \cdot 4°$	$0°$	$100°$
$k \times 10^7$	$33 \cdot 40 \times 0 \cdot 436$	$3340 \times 0 \cdot 788$	3340	$3340 \times 1 \cdot 193$
K	$2 \cdot 184$	$2 \cdot 363$	$2 \cdot 373$	$2 \cdot 280$

hence, the temp. coeff. increases rapidly as the temp. falls. $k = K/\eta c_v$, where k denotes the thermal conductivity ; c_v, the sp. ht. per gram ; K, a constant ; and η, the viscosity. S. Weber found for neon at $105 \cdot 81°$, $\eta = 0 \cdot 0_31344$; $0 \cdot 0_31087$ at $0°$; $0 \cdot 0_4879$ at $-74 \cdot 37°$; and $0 \cdot 0_4499$ at $-181 \cdot 43°$. J. Wachsmuth, and S. Chapman studied the thermal conductivity of mixtures of argon and helium. M. Smoluchowsky, and F. Soddy and A. J. Berry investigated the thermal conductivity of gases at low press. If $Q = \frac{1}{6}(n/N)C_v V$, where n denotes the number of mols. in 1 c.c. of gas at $0 \cdot 01$ mm. press., and $\theta°$; N, the number of mols. per mol of gas at $0°$ and 760 mm. press. ; C_v, the mol. ht. at constant vol. ; and V, the mean mol. velocity at $\theta°$, then, F. Soddy and A. J. Berry obtained for helium, neon, and argon at $22°$, $k \times 10^5 = 1 \cdot 99$, $1 \cdot 78$, and $1 \cdot 32$ respectively ; $Q \times 10^5$, $3 \cdot 75$, $1 \cdot 68$, and $1 \cdot 18$ respectively ; and K/Q, $0 \cdot 53$, $1 \cdot 06$, and $1 \cdot 12$ respectively. E. Schreiner also measured the mol. ht. of argon. O. Mehliss obtained for argon at $5 \cdot 75°$, $k = 0 \cdot 0_43852$, and at $0°$, $0 \cdot 0_43796$ with a temp. coeff. of $0 \cdot 0026$. H. Schwarze gave at $0°$, $0 \cdot 0_43894$; and A. Eucken,

	$-182 \cdot 6°$	$-78 \cdot 4°$	$0°$	$100°$
$k \times 10^7$	$388 \times 0 \cdot 366$	$388 \times 0 \cdot 750$	388	$388 \times 1 \cdot 311$
K	$2 \cdot 555$	$2 \cdot 485$	$2 \cdot 460$	$2 \cdot 469$

R. Thomas [9] measured the **specific heat** of helium at constant press. and found $c_p = 1 \cdot 2504 \pm 0 \cdot 0222$. A. Eggert obtained

	$-15°$ to $8°$	$15°$ to $50°$	$15°$ to $100°$	$15°$ to $150°$
c_p	$1 \cdot 26449$	$1 \cdot 26485$	$1 \cdot 26962$	$1 \cdot 26298$

These results are taken to mean that the sp. ht. of helium, between $-15°$ and $150°$, does not change, and that the best representative value is $1 \cdot 2662 \pm 0 \cdot 0011$. This result is about $1\frac{1}{4}$ per cent. higher than that of R. Thomas. The value calculated from the sp. ht. ratio $c_p/c_v = \frac{5}{3}$ is $1 \cdot 246$. If $c_p = 1 \cdot 2662$, then $c_v = 0 \cdot 7681$; and if $c_p = 1 \cdot 246$, $c_v = 0 \cdot 7477$. K. Scheel and W. Heuse gave $c_p = 1 \cdot 245$ at $-180°$, and $1 \cdot 260$ at $18°$; or the mol. ht. $C_p = 4 \cdot 97$ at $-180°$ and $5 \cdot 03$ at $18°$. A. Eucken found that the at. ht. of helium containing $9 \cdot 30$ mols per litre at $18°$ K. is $3 \cdot 02$; and at $26°$ K., $2 \cdot 99$; and with the gas having $34 \cdot 1$ mols per litre, $2 \cdot 95$ at $18°$ K., and $3 \cdot 20$ at $30°$ K. Liquid argon was found to have the mol. sp. ht. $C_p = 10 \cdot 5$, and $C_v = 5 \cdot 54$; and for the solid, $C_p = 7 \cdot 8$, and $C_v = 5 \cdot 66$. F. Richarz calculated from W. Ramsay's value for c_p/c_v, the sp. ht. c_p of neon is $0 \cdot 247$, and $c_v = 0 \cdot 149$. For argon between $20°$ and $90°$, W. Dittenberger obtained $c_p = 0 \cdot 1212 \pm 0 \cdot 0019$; and when corrected by comparison with air, $c_p = 0 \cdot 1252$. The value calculated from the sp. ht. ratio is $c_p = 0 \cdot 1243$. M. Pier obtained $c_p = 0 \cdot 1252$, and $c_v = 0 \cdot 0746$. The at. ht. at constant press. was measured by M. Pier, and the results were re-calculated by N. Bjerrum. E. Mathias and co-workers discussed this subject. W. Nernst's results are as follow :

	$0°$	$100°$	$200°$	$500°$	$1200°$	$2000°$
Ac_p	$2 \cdot 98$	$2 \cdot 98$	$2 \cdot 98$	$2 \cdot 98$	$3 \cdot 0$	$3 \cdot 0$

A. Eucken found that the at. ht. of solid argon is $C_p = 2 \cdot 44$, and $C_v = 2 \cdot 39$ at $17 \cdot 8°$ K. ; and $C_p = 7 \cdot 80$ and $C_v = 5 \cdot 61$ at $78 \cdot 3°$ K. The value of C_p was calculated from that of C_v from $C_p - C_v = ATC_p^2$, where the constant A is $4 \cdot 5 \times 10^{-4}$. For liquid argon, $C_p = 10 \cdot 50$ at $87 \cdot 9°$ K., and $10 \cdot 62$ at $93 \cdot 9°$ K. ; $C_v = 5 \cdot 60$ at $87 \cdot 9°$ K., and $5 \cdot 44$ at $92 \cdot 8°$ K. W. Ramsay and M. W. Travers obtained for krypton, $c_v = 0 \cdot 0362$, and $c_p = 0 \cdot 0603$; and W. Ramsay obtained for xenon, $c_v = 0 \cdot 023$, and $c_p = 0 \cdot 0384$. L. I. Dana and H. K. Onnes gave $0 \cdot 222$ for the sp. ht. of liquid helium at $2 \cdot 5°$ K.

W. Ramsay's value for the ratio of the two sp. hts. of helium, $\gamma = c_p/c_v$, was too high; but, working with purified helium of vap. density 2·133, W. Ramsay and co-workers obtained $\gamma = 1·652$. N. A. Langlet found for helium from cleveite, $\gamma = 1·667$; U. Behn and H. Geiger, $\gamma = 1·63$; and K. Scheel and W. Heuse, 1·668. For neon, W. Ramsay obtained $\gamma = 1·642$; and for argon, 1·648. O. Niemeyer found that for argon at 0°, $\gamma = 1·6671$; at 12·86, 1·66715; and at 99·84°, 1·6673. Hence, the value of γ between 0° and 100° does not change, and $\gamma = 1·6628$. J. Kapp measured the ratio of the sp. hts. of mixtures of argon with nitrogen and with carbon dioxide. W. Ramsay and M. W. Travers found for krypton $\gamma = 1·666$; and W. Ramsay gave for xenon, $\gamma = 1·666$. The best representative values are (when $R = 1·9875$ cals.):

	He	Ne	A	Kr	X	Nt
c_p	1·2662	0·247	0·1252	0·0603	0·0384	0·0225
c_v	0·7681	0·149	0·0746	0·0362	0·023	0·0135
γ	1·63	1·642	1·667	1·689	1·666	1·667
$(C_p-C_v)R$	1·9875	1·989	1·989	2·016	2·056	2·129

According to A. Eucken,[10] the **heat of fusion** of argon is 267·9 cals. per mol. The **heat of vaporization**, λ, of helium calculated from W. Nernst's equation is $\lambda = 6·37$ Cals., and $M\lambda = 25·42$ Cals. O. Sackur gave for neon at absolute zero, 223 Cals. per mol. For the latent heat, L, of vaporization of neon, E. Mathias and co-workers gave $L^2 = 43·56922(T_c-T) - 1·744347(T_c-T)^2 + 0·0371203(T_c-T)^3$ Cals. per gram. For argon, A. Eucken gave 1501 cals. per mol; W. Nernst, $\lambda = 38·95$ Cals. per gram; G. Rudorf, $\lambda = 42·8-44·4$ Cals.; C. A. Crommelin, 69·4 Cals. at $-185·5°$; D. L. Hammick, 38·7 cals.; H. Happel, $\lambda = 38·1-38·8$ Cals.; and E. Mathias and co-workers, 38·10 Cals. per gram, or $L^2 = 41·59246(T_c-T)$ $-0·448963(T_c-T)^2 + 0·0026163(T_c-T)^3$ Cals. per gram. For krypton, G. Rudorf gave $\lambda = 25·5-27·7$ Cals.; and for xenon, 22·49 –25·36 Cals. R. de Forcrand gave for the latent heats of vaporization:

	He	Ne	A	Kr	X	Nt
λ	5·13	—	37·86	27·04	24·62	19·11
L	<0·004	0·08	0·268	0·33	0·43	0·65

The last line shows J. Narbut's values of the latent heat of fusion: L Cals. per gram-atom at the m.p. A. Henglein calculated values for krypton, and xenon; and F. S. Mortimer calculated for helium. L. I. Dana and H. K. Onnes obtained a maximum of 6 cals. at about 3·5° K. in the curve of the variation of the latent heat of vaporization of liquid helium with temp. The **entropy** of the inert gases was studied by K. Bennewitz and F. Simon. G. N. Lewis and co-workers calculated for 25° and one atm. press., the at. entropies: He, 29·83; Ne, 34·66; A, 36·70; Kr, 38·88; Xe, 40·23; and Nt, 41·81.

Lord Rayleigh [11] found a sample of helium from clevite had a **refractive index** of 0·146 (air unity) with white light; W. Ramsay and J. N. Collie obtained 0·135 with a purified sample; and W. Ramsay and M. W. Travers, 0·1238 for a sample of a high degree of purity. The last-named obtained for D-light a refractive index $\mu = 0·0000361$. W. Burton, and C. Cuthbertson and co-workers obtained values about 3 per cent. lower. W. Burton gave $\mu = 0·0_43510$ for light of wave-length $\lambda = 486·1\mu\mu$; $\mu = 0·0_43500$ for $\lambda = 587·6\mu\mu$; and $\mu = 0·0_43506$ for $\lambda = 656·3\mu\mu$. W. Burton represented his results by the formula $\mu - 1 = 0·0_43478(1 + 2·2 \times 10^{-11}\lambda^{-2})$, while C. Cuthbertson and E. P. Metcalfe gave $0·0_4347(1 + 2·4 \times 10^{-11}\lambda^{-2})$, and M. Cuthbertson gave $\mu - 1 = 2·42476 \times 10^{27}/(34991·7 \times 10^{27} - n^2)$, where $n = V/\lambda$, v denoting the velocity of light. C. Herrmann gave $\mu = 0·0_4353$ for $\lambda = 453·9\mu\mu$; and $0·0_43405$ for $\lambda = 643·8\mu\mu$. J. Koch obtained for ultra-violet light, $\mu = 0·0_436254$ for $\lambda = 237·9\mu\mu$; $0·0_435598$ for $\lambda = 334·2\mu\mu$; and $0·0_435138$ for $\lambda = 410·9\mu\mu$. C. Herrmann, and H. Erfle studied the dispersion of helium. K. F. Herzfeld and K. L. Wolff studied various dispersion formulæ for the inert gases. W. Ramsay and M. W. Travers measured the index of refraction of mixtures of helium and hydrogen, and the results were about 3 per cent. higher than corresponded with the mixture rule ; a similar result was obtained with a mixture of hydrogen and carbon dioxide. W. Ramsay and M. W. Travers found that the index of refraction for neon with white light was 0·2345 (air unity), or $\mu=0\cdot0_4685$. C. and M. Cuthbertson gave for 0° and 760 mm. :

$$2(\mu-1)\times10^6\begin{cases}\lambda\ .\ .\ .\ \ 479\cdot9 \quad 508\cdot6 \quad 520\cdot9 \quad 546\cdot0 \quad 576\cdot9 \quad 579\cdot0 \quad 643\cdot8 \quad 670\cdot8\mu\mu\\ \text{Neon}\ .\ \ 134\cdot62 \quad 134\cdot46 \quad 134\cdot42 \quad 134\cdot32 \quad 134\cdot21 \quad 134\cdot21 \quad 134\cdot03 \quad —\\ \text{Krypton}\ \ 863\cdot61 \quad 860\cdot68 \quad 859\cdot55 \quad 855\cdot48 \quad 855\cdot29 \quad 855\cdot22 \quad 851\cdot60 \quad 850\cdot66\\ \text{Xenon}\ .\ \ 142\cdot57 \quad 141\cdot85 \quad 141\cdot58 \quad 141\cdot09 \quad 140\cdot58 \quad 140\cdot55 \quad 139\cdot78 \quad 139\cdot46\end{cases}$$

They represented the results by $\mu-1=0\cdot0_4666(1+2\cdot38\times10^{-11}\lambda^{-2})$ or by $\mu-1=2\cdot5936\times10^{27}/(38916\times10^{27}-n^2)$, when $n=V/\lambda$, V denoting the velocity of light. Lord Rayleigh gave for argon, with white light, 0·961 when air is unity ; and for D-light, $\mu=0\cdot0_32828$. W. Burton represented his results by $\mu-1=0\cdot0002792(1+5\cdot6\times10^{-11}\lambda^{-2})$, and C. and M. Cuthbertson, $\mu-1=9\cdot124\times10^{27}/(16335\times10^{27}-n^2)$, where $n=V/\lambda$ as indicated above. F. Ahrberg gave $\mu=0\cdot0002851$ for $\lambda=435\cdot9\mu\mu$; 0·0002802 for $\lambda=576\cdot95$; C. and M. Cuthbertson, $\mu=0\cdot0002838$ for $\lambda=479\cdot9\mu\mu$; and $\mu=0\cdot0002808$ for $\lambda=643\cdot8\mu\mu$; and W. Burton, $\mu=0\cdot0002860$ for $\lambda=486\cdot1\mu\mu$; and $\mu=0\cdot0002829$ for $\lambda=656\cdot3\mu\mu$. W. Ramsay and M. W. Travers studied binary mixtures of argon with air, oxygen, and nitrogen ; and for krypton, with white light, they gave 0·450 (air unity), or $\mu=0\cdot000423$. C. and M. Cuthbertson's results are indicated above, and they represented their results by $\mu-1=0\cdot0004189(1+697\times10^{-11}\lambda^{-2})$, and by $\mu-1=5\cdot3446\times10^{27}/(12767\cdot9\times10^{27}-n^2)$, where n has the value indicated above. W. Ramsay and M. W. Travers gave 1·364 for the refractive index of xenon in white light, air unity ; or $\mu=0\cdot000292$. The results of C. and M. Cuthbertson are indicated above, and they employed the formula $\mu-1=0\cdot0006823(1+10\cdot14\times10^{-11}\lambda^{-2})$, or $\mu-1=6\cdot1209\times10^{27}/(8977\cdot87^{27}-n^2)$, where n has the value indicated above ; and for krypton $\mu=1+10\cdot945\times10^{27}/(13039\times10^{27}-n^2)$, or $1+12\cdot47\times10^{27}/(9140\times10^{27}-n^2)$. J. A. Wasastjerna calculated values for the atomic refraction equivalents of the inert gases and obtained for neon, 1·01 ; for argon, 4·23 ; for krypton, 6·42 ; and for xenon, 10·56. J. E. Calthrop made estimates of the refractivity and the size of the atoms. M. Czerny and G. Hettner studied the radiometer phenomena in argon and helium ; Lord Rayleigh, and J. Cabannes, the scattering of light by argon and helium ; W. H. McCurdy and A. Bramley, the effect of the glow discharge on the refractive index ; and C. P. Smyth discussed the relation between the refractivity and the mol. structure. W. H. Keesom and J. de Smedt studied the diffraction of X-rays in liquid argon ; and J. Cabannes and A. Lepape, the scattering of light by argon. The indices of refraction, and the **atomic refraction**, C. and M. Cuthbertson calculated, are :

	He	Ne	A	Kr	X
μ . . .	$0\cdot0_43465$	$0\cdot0_46663$	$0\cdot0_327729$	$0\cdot0_341860$	$0\cdot0_368180$
At. refraction .	0·519	0·995	4·13	6·22	10·1

The **spark spectra** of the inert gases, with the exception of helium, are very rich in lines. Those of helium, neon, and niton are only slightly changed by the introduction of a Leyden jar into the circuit, those of argon, krypton, and xenon give different coloured spectra with and without the condenser. The general

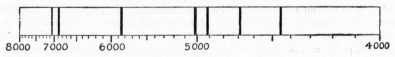

8000 7000 6000 5000 4000

FIG. 3.—Line Spectrum of Helium.

colour with helium is greenish-white ; with neon, orange-red ; and with niton, bluish-green. Argon, krypton, and xenon without the Leyden jar are respectively red, greenish-lilac, and dark violet ; and with the condensed discharge, respectively blue, blue, and sky-blue. The blue spectra of argon, krypton, and xenon are mixtures of three spark spectra of successive orders. The line spectra of helium, neon, argon (red and blue), krypton, and xenon are shown in Figs. 3–7.

The spectrum of helium in sun and stars was discussed by H. Faye,[12] G. Rayet, J. N. Lockyer, E. Frankland and J. N. Lockyer, A. Secchi, H. L. d'Arrest, A. Cornu, H. A. Rowland, W. Huggins, G. E. Hale, C. A. Young, A. de Forest Palmer, R. Ricco, etc. The different spectra of helium are relatively simple and complete ; and the series arrangements are clear and definite, although the allocation of the sequence types is not yet definitely settled. Four spectral systems have been observed with helium : (i) The ordinary spectrum ; (ii) a spectrum corresponding with the enhanced type requiring a highly condensed discharge, and generally referred to ionized helium ; (iii) a spectrum far in the ultra-violet ; and (iv) a spectrum of the band type. The spectrum of helium has been examined by W. Ramsay and J. N. Collie, C. B. Bazzoni and J. T. Lay, J. F. Mohler and L. E. Jewell, W. Heuse, J. H. van Vleck, H. C. Offerhaus, A. L. Hughes and P. Lowe, Lord Rayleigh, P. Kunze, W. Ritz, C. V. Raman, J. Schniederjost, A. Hagenbach and H. Konen, E. Gehrcke and O. von Baeyer, H. M. Hansen and S. Werner, etc. ; the ultra-red spectrum, by F. Paschen ; the intensity relations of the arc spectrum lines with voltage, by C. B. Bazzoni and J. T. Lay ; and the spectrum excited by electronic bombardment, by A. Udden and J. C. Jacobsen ; the effect of the inert gases on the spectrum of nitrogen, by W. Steubing and M. Toussaint ; the effect of press., by L. W. Taylor, and R. T. Dufford and L. Thompson. The ordinary spark spectrum of helium was first measured by W. Crookes, and he gave for the yellow line, $\lambda=5874 \cdot 5A$, and P. T. Cleve gave $\lambda=5875 \cdot 9A$. The helium lines were accurately measured by C. Runge and F. Paschen between 7281 and 2644A, and by P. W. Merrill. The ultra-red spectrum was measured by F. Paschen. It was found by C. Runge and F. Paschen that all the lines could be arranged in two systems, one consisting of series of single lines, and the other of doublets with the weaker constituent on the red-side—usually the stronger constituent is on the blue-side. At first it was assumed that the two complete series systems represented two different elements. The one producing the doublet system was called helium, and the other producing the singlet system, *parhelium*. In connection with his work on stellar spectra, J. N. Lockyer called the latter *asterium*. The doublet and singlet systems are sometimes distinguished as He-I and He-II respectively. R. W. Merrill gave for the singlet series $\lambda=27175 \cdot 17-109723 \cdot 2(m+0 \cdot 862157-0 \cdot 010908m^{-1})^2$; and for the doublet system, $\lambda=29223 \cdot 88-109723 \cdot 2(m+0 \cdot 996982+0 \cdot 001698m^{-1})^2$. All the observed lines are included either in the main series of singlets or doublets, or accounted for as combinations. This subject was discussed by A. Fowler, J. S. Forster, W. E. Curtis, W. M. Hicks, A. Kratzer, Y. Takahashi, and L. S. Ornstein and H. C. Burger.

The two separate systems of spectral series produced by helium are said to belong to two forms of helium—*viz.* normal helium and **parhelium.** J. Hanck and F. Reiche said that the electronic orbits of the former are co-planar, and in the case of parhelium, they are supposed to be inclined at an angle as described by A. Landé. Parhelium is the less stable form and the ordinary ionizing potential is really that of parhelium. F. M. Kannenstine found that helium has an abnormal post-arc conductivity which persists for 0·007 second after the extinction of the arc, and the phenomenon was attributed to the formation of the so-called **metastable helium.** The valency electron of an atom in such a state is supposed to move in an orbit whose energy is greater than that of the normal orbit. This energy cannot escape from the atom without the co-operation of some external agent, most likely another atom, and a process involving two atoms is much less probable, other things being equal, than one involving a single atom. The phenomenon was studied by J. Franck and F. Reiche, T. B. Dorgelo, J. S. Forster, H. Nyquist, T. Takamine and H. Kokubu, A. Unsöld, A. J. Dempster, and M. Marshall. It is estimated that the life of metastable helium is of the order 10^{-2} to 10^{-3} seconds. C. Eckart said that the phenomenon is not due to metastable helium at all but is produced by positive ions and their accompanying electrons. For the supposed isotope of helium—*isohelium, vide* **4.** 26, 14.

W. H. Pickering observed in the spectrum of the star ζ-Puppis a set of lines which were ascribed to hydrogen ; J. R. Rydberg made a study of these lines, and showed that the lines could be represented by $n=N\{2^{-2}-(m+0.5)^{-2}\}$; and A. Fowler showed that the whole of the lines formed two series, one of which corresponded with W. H. Pickering's set. According to N. Bohr's theory of atomic structure, helium should exhibit a set of lines analogous to those of hydrogen, but involving the constant $4N$ in place of N (*cf.* **4.** 27, 3). When the theory was modified with $n/(1+m/M)$ in place of N, where m denotes the mass of the electron, and M that of the nucleus, the series corresponded with those under observation. The work of A. Fowler, E. J. Evans, J. Stark, H. Rau, and J. S. Plaskett showed that W. H. Pickering's lines were probably due to the helium series $\nu=4\times109723.22(4^{-2}-m^{-2})$; and A. Fowler represented another series corresponding with $\nu=4\times109723.23(3^{-2}-m^{-2})$. These lines were further discussed by T. Lyman, H. A. Kramers and co-workers, and W. M. Hicks. N. Bohr's theory was later modified to allow for the increased effective inertia due to the moving field of the electron, and applied by A. Sommerfeld to the structure of these lines. The series spectrum of helium was discussed by L. S. Ornstein and H. C. Burger, R. A. Millikan and I. S. Bowen, M. Deslandres, R. Brunetti, S. Werner, E. O. Hulburt, L. B. Ham, L. Silberstein, N. Bohr, W. M. Hicks, S. Goudsmit and G. E. Uhlenbeck, R. S. Mulliken, F. Hund, F. Paschen, W. H. McCurdy, H. Bell, A. Landé, J. J. Hopfield and S. W. Leifson, C. V. Raman and A. S. Ganesan, A. Kratzer, and A. E. Ruark and co-workers. J. C. Slater emphasized the relations between the spectra of helium, hydrogen, the alkali metals, and the alkaline earth metals. F. Skaupy said that the spectrum of helium has a greater resemblance to the spectra of the alkali metals than to any other spectrum, and this is attributed to the presence of a negative helium ion. L. Janicki and E. Lau studied the effect of metallic surfaces on the spectrum of helium. The enhanced lines of the helium spectrum produced in strong electric fields were studied by T. R. Merton, W. Tschulanowsky, J. S. Foster, J. Stark, G. Liebert, and F. Paschen. The system of lines produced by the action of strong discharges on helium are assumed to be produced by the ionized gas He^+. The lines observed by T. Lyman far in the ultra-violet are represented by $\nu=4\times109723.22(2^{-2}-m^{-2})$, where m denotes 3, 4, 5, and 6. W. Grotrian, R. A. Millikan and I. S. Bowen, H. Fricke and T. Lyman, J. J. Hopfield and S. W. Liefson, J. C. McLennan and P. A. Petrie, H. B. Dorgelo and J. H. Arbink, T. Lyman, and L. Silberstein and A. C. Davies discussed the ultraviolet spectrum of helium. K. T. Compton and co-workers found that the ordinary and the parhelium lines are excited whenever the arc strikes, but the line $\lambda=4686$ was never observed below 55 volts and was stronger above 80 volts. C. Déjardin found the band spectrum cannot be observed unless the press. exceeds 3 mm. ; and the minimum voltage for its excitation is approximately 20·4 volts. At 3 mm. press., the lines 4686, 13203, and 2733 appear strongly at 80 volts, and they can be seen at 51 volts when the press. is 4–8 mm. ; but they do not appear at 10 mm. press., presumably because the number of electrons which can acquire the minimum velocity required for double ionization at the higher press. is too small. F. J. von Wisniewsky computed the energy levels of the spectral lines of helium and neon. C. B. Bazzoni and J. T. Lay measured the voltages necessary to stimulate the different spectral lines of helium—*vide infra,* ionizing potentials.

A **band spectrum** of helium was observed about the same time by A. Fowler, A. W. Curtis, and E. Goldstein. The spectrum is said to include some conspicuous bands with single heads, others with double heads, and a number of complex regions in which no heads are recognizable at sight., The double-headed bands follow closely the series law, corresponding lines in each band being represented with rough accuracy by ordinary series formulæ. W. M. Hicks added that it may be suspected that the supposed bands are only apparent and that the observed lines are analogous to the very large number of satellites which are conspicuous in the blue spectra of the inert gases from argon onwards; and that they may be representatives of the triplet series. The band spectrum was studied by T. R. Merton and J. G. Pilley, and W. E. Curtis. W. E. Curtis and R. G. Long, W. A. McNair and W. H. McCurdy, and D. Burger examined the doublet bands of helium.

T. R. Merton and J. W. Nicholson, and C. B. Bazzoni and J. T. Lay, discussed the relative intensities of the spectral lines of helium; L. W. Taylor, and T. Takamine, the effect of press.; and B. Curry, the effect of current intensity. A. Udden and J. C. Jacobsen studied the excitation of the spectrum by electronic bombardment. A. A. Michelson, G. Berndt, A. Gray and co-workers, J. E. Purvis, H. Nagaoka, N. A. Kent and R. M. Frye, F. Paschen and E. Back, W. E. Curtis and W. Jones, P. Tartakowsky, H. P. Waran, A. Landé, and W. Lohmann investigated the **Zeeman effect** with helium lines; and H. Nyquist, U. Yoshida, A. Sommerfeld, J. S. Foster, and T. Takamine and N. Kokubu, the effect of an electric field, or the **Stark effect.** The broadening of the spectral lines analogous to the **Doppler effect** was examined by D. Fabry and H. Buisson, G. F. Hull, H. Rau, H. C. Urey, J. Stark and co-workers, E. Dorn, H. Gerdien and R. Holm, and H. M. Hansen and J. C. Jacobson. According to R. W. Lawson, a high frequency discharge has very little influence on the spectrum of helium. J. Stark, W. Tschulanowsky, J. S. Foster, and E. Böttcher and F. Fuczek studied the influence of an electric field on the spectrum; R. Seeliger and F. Pommering, the emission of light from the cathodic dark space; F. W. Aston and T. Kikuchi, the striations in the discharge tube; R. C. Johnson, the effect of argon and helium on the spectrum of hydrogen, etc.; K. W. Meissner, the effect of neon on the spectrum of helium; D. A. Keys, and M. S. Home, the effect of hydrogen and of nitrogen on the spectrum of helium; and J. C. McLennan and co-workers, the effects of helium on the spectra of various elements; J. Stark and G. von Wendt, and W. Wein, the spectrum of the positive rays; and F. J. von Wisniewsky, the K-series of the helium **X-ray spectrum.** H. B. Lemon found that helium plays only a secondary role in the spectra of comets' tails. J. C. McLennan obtained the auroral green line, $5577 \cdot 35 \pm 0 \cdot 15A$, in the spectrum of air mixed with an excess of helium—*vide* nitrogen.

W. Ramsay and M. W. Travers [13] found a yellow line $\lambda = 5849 \cdot 6$ to be characteristic of neon. The values of λ for the corresponding lines of sodium, helium, neon, and krypton are :

Na	He	Ne	Kr
λ . . 5896·16	5876·209	5852·65	5871·12
λ . . 5890·19	5875·870		

The spectrum of neon is marked by the sharpness and homogeneity of its lines. There is a large number of lines in the red region, and a number of strong individual monochromatic lines. The lines were measured by G. D. Liveing and J. Dewar, E. C. C. Baly, H. E. Watson, L. St. C. Broughall, A. Pérard, H. Buisson and

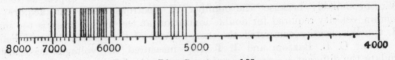

8000 7000 6000 5000 4000

FIG. 4.—Line Spectrum of Neon.

C. Jausseran, L. and E. Block and G. Déjardin, W. H. J. Childs, T. Lyman and F. A. Sanders, I. G. Priest, W. F. Meggers, G. S. Monk, K. Burns, W. H. J. Childs, K. Burns and P. W. Merrill, G. Wentzel, K. W. Meissner, F. Hand, P. Jordan, and F. Paschen. The more important lines of neon are shown in Fig. 4. K. W. Meissner examined the ultra-red spectrum of neon, and also the absorption spectrum; and T. Lyman and F. A. Saunders, and H. B. Dorgelo and J. H. Arbink, the ultra-violet spectrum. H. E. Watson found that many of the strong lines of neon could be arranged in quadruplets or triplets. Fifteen such groups were found. R. Rossi found two doublet series. The great achievement with this element, added W. M. Hicks, is the allocation of the whole of the 840 measured lines, with the exception of about 50, to definite series. These have been discussed by A. Fowler, W. M. Hicks, F. Paschen, K. W. Meissner, H. Deslandres, S. Goudsmit, A. Sommerfeld, J. S. Foster, L. B. Ham, W. Grotrian, A. Landé and co-workers, G. Wentzel, etc. T. R. Merton found a second spectrum of neon is developed under the condensed discharge. M. R. and R. C. Johnson studied the variations in the intensities of the spectral lines of neon. The Zeeman effect was examined by W. Lohmann, E. Back, H. P. Waran, J. E. Purvis, H. Nagaoka, H. Nagaoka and T. Takamine; and the Stark effect, by H. Nyquist. The broadening of the spectral lines analogous to the Doppler effect was examined by C. Fabry and H. Buisson, and E. Dorn. K. W. Meissner studied the effect of helium on the spectrum of neon; F. W. Aston and T. Kikuchi, the striations in the discharge tube; H. B. Dorgelo, the distribution of energy over the lines in the series spectra; F. Holweck, the K-series in the X-ray spectrum; and G. Hertz and J. C. S. de Visser the excitation of spectral lines by electronic impact. L. Vegard and co-workers studied the spectrum of the light produced when mixtures of nitrogen and neon are bombarded with high velocity cathode rays at the temp. of liquid helium; and W. H. B. Cameron, the effect of neon on the spectra of carbon, oxygen, and nitrogen.

In their memoir on the discovery of argon, Lord Rayleigh and W. Ramsay [14] reported some measurements of the spectral lines. They regarded the red lines with $\lambda=7056\cdot4$ and $6965\cdot5$ as being characteristic. The spectrum of argon was examined by H. F. Newall, W. N. Hartley, M. Berthelot, E. Dorn and H. Erdmann, H. Kayser, J. Trowbridge and T. W. Richards, J. R. Rydberg, G. Stead, A. Ladenburg and C. Krügel, A. Hagenbach and H. Konen, E. Warburg, J. E. Lilienfeld, A. S. King, F. Fischer and G. Iliovici, W. W. Shaver, K. W. Meissner, and G. Déjardin and co-workers. W. Crookes showed that argon furnishes two spectra: the one rich in red lines—called the *red spectrum*—is obtained without a condenser; and the other rich in blue and ultra-violet lines—called the *blue spectrum*—is obtained with a condenser. Many of the strong lines in the red spectrum appear in the blue spectrum with diminished intensity, or appear to be replaced by a number of weak lines in the immediate vicinity. W. Crookes measured 80 lines in the red spectrum and 119 lines in the blue. Twenty-six lines were common to both spectra. Other observations were made by J. M. Eder and E. Valenta, H. Kayser, H. Deslandres, P. Lowe and D. C. Rose, S. Friedländer, E. Paulson, A. Ladenburg and C. Krügel, C. Runge, W. F. Meggers, C. Runge and F. Paschen, F. Paschen, R. Nasini and co-workers, E. C. C. Baly, W. Stahl, J. Frommel, E. Gehrcke and O. von Baeyer, P. Lowe and D. C. Rose, K. W. Meissner, A. E. Ruark and

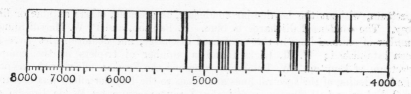

FIG. 5.—Red and Blue Line Spectra of Argon.

R. L. Chenault, and W. W. Shaver. The more important lines respectively in the red and blue spectra of argon are shown in Fig. 5. Many of the lines in the red spectrum were arranged by J. R. Rydberg, K. A. Nissen, and E. Paulson in quadruplets, some of which were incomplete; but neither F. R. Rydberg nor

H. Kayser, and C. Runge could trace typical series spectra. W. M. Hicks says that the spectrum shows definite systems of triplets, but the analysis is yet incomplete. E. Paulson, and K. A. Nissen also found some groups of lines in the blue spectrum. G. Berndt, A. A. Michelson, W. Lohmann, A. Dufour, J. J. Hopfield and G. H. Dieke, and O. Lüttig investigated the Zeeman effect with argon. The effect of an electric field, and the Doppler effect were examined by E. Dorn, W. Steubing, K. Friedersdorff, and E. Böttcher and F. Tuczek; the ultra-red spectrum, by R. Nasini, W. Meissner and co-workers, C. Runge, T. Lyman, T. Lyman and F. A. Saunders, F. A. Saunders, and J. J. Hopfield and S. W. Leifson ; the X-ray spectrum, by L. A. Turner; D. Coster and J. H. van der Tuuk, the K-series in the X-ray spectrum ; the spectrum of the electrodeless discharge, by H. Donaldson; the cathode spectrum, by P. G. Nutting; E. Böttcher and F. Tuczek and T. Takamine and N. Kokubu, the effect of an electric field, or the Stark effect, and the effect of current density and capacity, by C. Sheard. The spectrum of the high frequency discharge was examined by R. W. Lawson; J. M. Eder and E. Valenta found in addition to the blue and red spectra of argon, a *white spectrum* obtained by the application of a very large condenser. Under press. of 2–10 mm. the third spectrum is distinguished by the fact that many of the lines peculiar to the blue argon spectrum appear more distinct, and others weaker, and that entirely fresh lines become visible. The red spectrum of argon disappears completely in low press. tubes, but appears again partially when the press. is increased. At 20 mm. press. many of the lines completely coincide with those of the red and blue spectra, but whole groups of lines show a displacement towards the red end of the spectrum, although the connection between these and corresponding lines of the blue spectrum is apparent. P. Zeeman and H. W. J. Dijk compared the spectra of ionized argon and potassium ; and T. L. de Bruin and P. Zeeman found the relation is closer with the blue argon spectrum than with the red one. R. C. Johnson and co-workers, and A. G. Worthing and R. Rudy examined the effect of nitrogen on the spectrum of argon.

W. Ramsay and M. W. Travers,[15] the discoverers of krypton, made approximate measurements of 14 spectral lines. Other measurements were made by E. C. C. Baly, G. D. Liveing and J. Dewar, C. Runge, R. Schmidt, A. Ladenburg and C. Krügel, W. Ramsay, W. F. Meggers, L. and E. Block and G. Déjardin, J. N. Collie, O. Otsuka, and P. W. Merrill. The more important lines in the spectrum of krypton are shown in Fig. 6. Some describe the ordinary spark

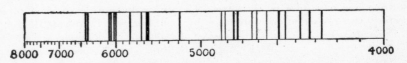

FIG. 6.—The Line Spectrum of Krypton.

spectrum, without the Leyden-jar condenser, as greenish, others as lilac or lilac-grey. The condensed discharge is blue. E. Paulson, and P. W. Merrill found a number of pairs of lines in the condensed discharge, but definite series have not been established ; W. M. Hicks found a number of triplets in the complex spectrum of krypton. W. Lohmann examined the Zeeman effect with krypton. The broadening of the spectral lines analogous to the Döppler effect was examined by C. Fabry and H. Buisson ; and the X-ray spectrum by M. de Broglie and A. Lepape.

Measurements of the spectrum of xenon were made by E. C. C. Baly,[16] W. F. Meggers, P. W. Merrill, L. and E. Block and G. Déjardin, C. Runge, J. N. Collie, and G. D. Liveing and J. Dewar. The more important lines in the spectrum of xenon are shown in Fig. 7. Like argon, and krypton, xenon furnishes two spectra. The one, without a Leyden jar in the circuit, is blue, and relatively poor in lines ;.

and the other, with a Leyden jar in circuit, is greenish or greenish-violet, and rich
in lines. E. Paulson, and W. M. Hicks found some triplets in these lines ; but no
typical series have yet been recognized. L. A. Sommer has, however, arranged

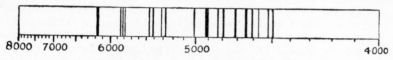

FIG. 7.—The Line Spectrum of Xenon.

148 lines in pairs and groups. W. Lohmann examined the Zeeman effect with
xenon ; B. B. Ray, A. Lepape and A. Dauvillier, and M. de Broglie and A. Lepape,
the X-ray spectrum.

K. Fredenhagen [17] examined the effect of helium on the light absorption of
sodium vapour ; R. W. Wood and J. Franck, the effect of helium on the resonance
spectrum of iodine, and on the resulting fluorescence spectrum ; R. W. Wood also
examined the effect of neon, argon, krypton, and xenon on the resonance spectrum
of iodine. W. Ramsay and F. Soddy found that the inert gases are not radioactive. P. G. Nutting, N. Schoorl, K. von Auwers, C. C. Paterson, E. Liebenthal,
F. W. Aston, A. Boltzmann and A. Basch, R. A. Brockbank and L. E. Ryall,
A. Palme, and E. Karrer and A. Poritsky showed that the yellowish-white light
emitted by helium in a discharge tube is well suited for photometric work. He
studied variations in the **luminosity** of the gas with current, potential gradient,
gas density, frequency of alternation of current, orientations of tube and diameter
of capillary. J. Taylor and W. Stephenson, J. C. McLennan and G. M. Shrum,
P. G. Nutting and O. Tugman examined the luminosity of tubes containing argon,
helium, and hydrogen. L. Vegard found solid argon to be luminous when bombarded by cathode rays below 237·5°. S. O. Pearson and H. S. G. Anson found
that the resistance of the neon tube increases as the current decreases. There is a
critical voltage below which the lamp does not glow. No current passes when the
lamp is not glowing. If the voltage is just above its critical value the lamp will
glow even though only a fraction of a microampère is passing. The intensity of
the glow decreases with the current. H. E. Watson found that the current passing through the lamp is intermittent when the anode is in the dark space, and the
current density is low. J. W. Ryde, and B. N. Ghose showed that the whole of the
light from these tubes comes from the negative glow, the electrodes being so
close together that the positive column is absent. He also studied the variation
in the resistance of the tube with current ; and the relation between the intensity
of the lamp with current. A. L. Foley examined the effect of the exposure of the
five inert gases to ultra-violet light and to X-rays, on the spectra ; M. N. Saha,
the temp. radiation of helium, etc. ; H. E. Watson, the physiological effect of the
light from the helium tube. The inert gases have been advantageously employed
in the filling of bulbs, etc., for illuminating and other purposes. This, said
F. Schröter,[18] is because of their high luminosity during the passage of an electric
current, their high electrical conductivity, and their small heat conductivity in
comparison with other gases. This subject has been discussed by O. von Auwers,
G. Claude, W. R. Cooper and P. C. Hewitt, H. Danzer, F. Dorn, J. Elster and
H. Geitel, H. Greinacher, A. Gunther-Schulze, T. Hamburger, P. Hardegen,
H. Harting, K. Hellmuth, L. K. Hirshberg, G. Holst and E. Oosterhuis, J. C. McLen-
nan, R. B. Moore, J. Nienhold, P. G. Nutting, U. A. Oschwald and A. G. Tarrant,
J. Pintsch, M. Pirini and A. R. Meyer, W. Ramsay and G. Rudorf, I. Rosenthal,
O. Schaller, N. Schoorl, B. E. Shackelford, F. Skaupy, H. C. Snook, E. Urbain,
C. Scal and W. Feige, H. E. Watson, L. Zehnder.

H. Dember [19] examined the relation between the **photochemical effect** and the
cathode fall of potential with an alkali electrode in various gases. The cathode
fall was larger in helium than in hydrogen, or in argon. J. Elster and H. Geitel

constructed a photoelectric cell with potassium and helium or argon; and J. Rosenthal, a rubidium-helium cell. K. Bergwitz, and P. P. Koch also made a study of these cells. V. L. Chrisler examined the photoelectric effect with a number of metals—Al, Sb, Bi, Cd, Fe, Pb, Ni, Pt, Ag, Sn, Zn—in helium and found it to be much less than in hydrogen. He inferred that if the metals were quite free from hydrogen no effect would occur in an atm. of helium. J. S. Townsend and S. P. McCallum studied photoelectric currents in helium; and U. A. Oschwald and A. G. Farrow, in neon. P. Auger obtained evidence of the emission of photo-electrons by means of the photographic cloud method, with a beam of X-rays in argon, krypton, and xenon. F. L. Mohler studied the photoionization of neon and argon.

J. N. Collie and W. Ramsay [20] measured the distance through which electric sparks from an induction coil strike in helium and argon. The distance with argon is greater than with air, oxygen, or hydrogen; while with helium the spark can pass very large distances. Thus:

	O_2	Air	H_2	A	He
Sparking distances . .	23·0	33·0	39·0	45·0	250–300 mm.
Change to ribbon . . .	81	73–74	42–43	—	1270 mm.

The press. at which the spark discharge changes to a ribbon discharge is also indicated. Helium, unlike other gases, exhibits the phenomena of a vacuum tube discharge at ordinary atm. press. R. J. Strutt found the minimum sparking potential in helium to be about 230 volts., and noticed that for a definite spark length, the press. in helium is about five times greater than in air. The presence of impurities in the gas has a great influence on the results. J. S. Townsend and H. E. Hurst found a relation between the conductivity and sparking potential with the gap between the electrodes. Measurements were also made by H. E. Watson. E. W. B. Gill and F. B. Pidduck tested the relation, and measured the minimum voltage required to produce a spark in argon or helium, and the conductivity at various press. Argon is more readily ionized than air by both positive and negative ions. Helium is much more readily ionized than hydrogen. It was found that after the passage of one spark a higher potential was required to pass another immediately afterwards; the passage of a spark in the reverse direction facilitated recovery. E. R. Stockle measured the sparking potential of argon under reduced press. F. Ritter found that the ratio of the sparking potentials of helium and air diminishes as the sparking distance and press. increase. The curves obtained by plotting sparking potential against sparking distance are concave to the horizontal axes for all gases excepting helium when the curve is a straight line. S. P. McCallum and C. M. Focken studied the current-voltage relation with neon; J. S. Townsend and S. P. McCallum, with helium; and R. Rudy, the transition to the arc stage in discharges through argon. F. Soddy and T. D. Mackenzie found that non-conductance equivalent to that represented by an inch gap in air at atm. press. was attained at the following press.:

	He	A	Ne	H_2	N_2	CO_2
Press. in mm. . .	0·35	0·04	0·07	0·03–0·04	0·035	0·02

Mercury vapour resembles helium in the high press. at which it ceases to be conducting. The difference between helium and other gases is one of degree only; the monatomic gases being inert chemically and electrically.

K. T. Compton and co-workers found the arcing voltage of helium under various conditions of gas press. and voltage. The arc could be made to strike at the minimum voltage of 20 volts, but the arc could be maintained under favourable conditions at 8 volts with a gas press. of 5 mm. and a current of about one ampère. F. M. Kannenstine, and F. A. Thees examined the effect with an alternating current. E. Warburg, T. E. Foulke and co-workers, A. Moskvin, and J. P. Ewers investigated the discharge in helium and argon; K. Przibram, the brush and oscillating discharge ; T. E. Foulke, the exponential rise of discharge currents in neon ; F. M. Penning, and H. Geffcken, the intermittent discharge in neon ; B. Davis, and J. Wachsmuth and B. Winawer, the electrodeless discharge in helium, neon, and argon ; H. Fischer, the colour of the Tesla discharge in argon ; K. T. Compton and C. Eckart, the diffusion of electrons in the non-oscillatory arc; R. J. Strutt, R. Bär and co-workers, W. Heuse, R. Defregger, K. Mey, H. Dember, P. G. Nutting and O. Tugman, and G. Claude the normal cathode fall in helium ; R. J. Strutt, and K. Rottgardt, that in argon ; and A. Günther-Schulze in neon ; H. E. Watson and G. R. Paranjpe, and A. Günther-Schulze, the cathode fall in helium, argon, neon, krypton, and xenon ; R. Bär and co-workers, and W. H. McCurdy and P. Dalton, the low-voltage luminous discharge in helium ; G. Gehlhoff, the effect of ultra-violet light on the cathode fall in argon ; G. Holst and E. Oösterhuis, the low-voltage arc in argon and neon ; R. Whiddington, fatigue effect at the cathode of a discharge tube ; E. Bouty, the dielectric cohesion of helium, neon, argon, and J. N. Collie, and H. K. Onnes, that of neon ; L. Zehnder, and E. Dorn, the detection of electric waves by the helium tube ; G. Gehlhoff, the effect of helium on the discharge in alkali vapour ; J. Stark and J. Giesel, the luminosity produced by the α-rays of polonium ; E. Gehrcke and O. Reichenheim, V. Königsberger and J. Kutschewsky, and J. J. Thomson, the positive rays in helium and argon ; A. Perot, F. W. Aston and T. Kikuchi, and T. Kikuchi, the motion of luminous striations in the discharge tube with helium ; G. Gehlhoff, and G. Gehrcke and P. Seeliger, the luminosity in the discharge tube ; R. J. Pierrot, and A. Rüttenauer, press. differences in the positive columns ; G. W. C. Kaye, the spluttering of aluminium electrodes in helium ; O. Reichenheim, the anomalous anode fall in helium ; W. de Groot, the anode temp. of the tungsten arc in neon and argon ; J. Franck and G. Hertz, the collision of electrons and helium atoms ; W. Clarkson, the flashing of argon-nitrogen discharge tubes ; and F. W. Aston and H. E. Watson, the relation between the current, voltage, gas press., and length of dark space with helium, neon, argon, krypton, and xenon. C. A. Skinner found that however carefully helium was purified, the hydrogen lines persistently appeared in the spectrum of the cathode glow with helium, and argon. There was, simultaneously, a continuous increase in the gas press. with time of discharge. The hydrogen came from the cathode, and the quantity of hydrogen evolved by a fresh cathode obeys Faraday's law for electrolytes. and a fresh anode absorbs hydrogen according to the same law. F. Fischer and G. Iliovici studied the arc and spark discharge in liquid argon using cadmium electrodes ; G. Holst and E. Oösterhuis, the conduction of electricity in neon. Cadmium nitride was formed from traces of nitrogen in the argon, and the argon was absorbed by the nitride. E. O. Hulbert examined the potential required to set up luminosity in argon, etc. ; A. Duvallier, the intensity of the radiations from helium, neon, and argon when a discharge is passed through the gases ; A. J. Dempster, the energy from a radiating atom of helium ; and K. W. Meissner, and P. Jordan, the absorption of light by neon excited by the passage of an electric current. R. G. Lunnon observed no change in the viscosity of argon while being subjected to an electric discharge.

The ionization of helium by α-rays and the effect of the canal rays were discussed by E. P. Metcalfe,[21] T. S. Taylor, F. Paschen, R. W. Gurney, H. Gerdien and R. Holm, C. F. Hull, H. Rau, J. Stark, P. M. S. Blacket, P. Auger and F. Perrin, E. P. Adams, J. Franck and R. Pohl, and J. J. Thomson ; the ionization of helium by the absorption of slow electrons, by J. F. Lehmann and T. H. Osgood ; H. F. Meyer, and W. P. Jesse, the ionization of helium, neon, and argon by slow electrons ; ionization by collision in argon, by E. W. B. Gill and F. B. Pidduck ; the tracks of the α-particles in helium, by D. M. Bose and S. K. Ghosh ; the range of the α-particles in the rare gases, by L. F. Bates, and R. W. Gurney ; ionization of helium by collision, by J. S. Townsend ; and ionization by electrons, by J. Franck, H. A. Barton, G. A. Anslow, K. T. Compton and C. C. van Voorhis, I. Langmuir and H. A. Jones; T. L. R. Ayres discussed the ionization of argon by collision; and F. Horton, the effect of impurities on the velocity of the ionization of helium. V. L. Chrisler concluded from observations on the absorption of helium in discharge tube that the negative helium ions exist; F. Skaupy, from spectroscopic observations. L. Hamburger inferred that the negative ion may contain a number of atoms. The ionization press. in helium, neon, and argon was measured by R. T. Beatty, J. Franck, and G. Hertz; the absorption of α-rays, by N. Bohr; the scattering of α-rays, by E. Rutherford and J. M. Nuttall; the range of the α-particles in the five inert gases, by L. B. Loeb and E. Condon, R. H. Fowler, G. H. Henderson. S. Rosseland, and L. F. Bates; the production of δ-rays by α-particles, by J. Chadwick and K. G. Emeléus; and the β-rays associated with scattered X-rays in argon, by J. M. Nuttall and E. J. Williams. The secondary cathodic radiation in helium was examined by W. Kossel; the absorption coeff. for electrons in helium, and argon, by A. Becker, R. B. Brode, and J. Robinson; the mobilities of the positive ions in helium, by H. B. Wahlin; the diffusion in neon, by T. E. Foulke and W. H. McCurdy; and in argon, by H. A. Erickson; the velocity of cathode rays in helium, and argon, by P. Lenard; the effect of helium and neon on cathode and anode rays, by R. Rudy; the influence of press. on the passage of X-rays, by C. L. and F. A. Lindemann; and ionization by photoelectrons, by J. T. Tykociner and J. Kunz. According to P. Auger, when X-rays are passed into pure argon only secondary β-rays are produced, but, if the argon is diluted with hydrogen, tertiary β-rays of a few millimetres range are also formed. In krypton diluted with hydrogen, the tertiary rays have a range comparable with that of the secondary rays, and there are traces of quaternary β-rays. The tertiary rays start from the same origin as the secondary and are distinguished from the latter in that they are not affected by changes in the tension of the exciting X-rays.

According to F. Horton and A. C. Davies, radiation occurs when electrons impressed by a velocity of about 20·5 volts—resonance potential—collide with helium atoms, but this is not accompanied by any ionization of the gas. The ionization occurs—ionization potential—when the velocity is raised to 25·7 volts. The positive ions from a glowing filament do not ionize helium when they collide with helium atoms up to 200 volts, but they liberate electrons from a negatively charged platinum surface when they bombard it with velocities greater than 20 volts. J. Franck and P. Knipping gave 20·5 ± 0·25 volts and 25·3 ± 0·25 volts respectively for the resonance and ionization potentials of helium. W. de Groot studied the resonance of neon. According to W. M. Hicks, for helium the preliminary potential required to raise one electron to the radiating state is 20·8 volts; and to raise the second electron to this state after the ejection of the first, 45·7 volts. The true radiation potentials are therefore 1·14 and 7·4 volts, and the observed radiating potentials are 21·9 and 73·9 volts; while the true ionizing potentials are 4·75 and 13·5 volts, and the observed volumes are 25·6 and 80 volts. W. H. McCurdy studied the resonance potential of helium. For neon, its radiating potentials are 11·8 and 17·8 volts; and the ionizing potentials 16·7, 20·0, and 22·8 volts; for argon, the radiating and ionizing potentials are respectively 11·5 and 15·1 volts. W. P. Jesse said the maximum ionization occurs at 140 volts with helium; 220 volts with neon; and 100 volts with argon. The ionizing potentials of argon, etc., were investigated by J. C. McLennan, F. Horton and co workers, E. G. Dymond, G. Déjardin, F. Holweck, G. Hertz, A. L. Hughes and A. A. Dixon. A. L. Hughes and E. Klein, K. T. Compton and co-workers, H. D. Smyth and H. A. Barton, H. A. Barton, L. A. Turner, C. G. Found, H. C. Rentschler, G. Stead and B. S. Gossling, C. A. Mackay, J. Franck and P. Knipping, F. S. Goucher, F. L. Mohler, L. S. Palmer, F. Strewe, E. R. Stoekle, R. Seeliger and E. Schramm, C. B. Bazzoni, and J. Franck; the critical electron velocities, by F. Holweck, and F. Horton and A. C. Davies; the ionizing potential of helium was discussed by A. C. Davies, L. Silberstein, F. M. Kannenstine, E. G. Dymond, G. Glockler,

G. Déjardin ; that of neon by G. Hertz F. L. Mohler, F. Holweck, and G. K. Rollefson ; that of krypton by G. Déjardin ; and G. Glockler found 10 volts for niton. G. Hertz and co-workers gave :

	He	Ne	A	Kr	X
Resonance potentials	$\begin{cases} 19\cdot77 \\ 20\cdot55 \\ - \\ - \end{cases}$	16·6 18·5 — —	11·5 13·0 13·9 —	9·9 10·5 11·5 12·1	8·3 9·9 11·0 —
Ionizing potentials	24·5	21·5	15·4	13·3	11·5

The motion of electrons in helium and the other inert gases was discussed by F. Horton, H. Compton, L. St. C. Broughall, H. A. Erikson, L. B. Loeb, H. B. Wahlin, H. R. Hassé, H. Sponer, R. Minkowsky and H. Sponer, V. A. Bailey, J. C. McLennan and E. Evans, and J. S. Townsend and V. A. Bailey ; and G. P. Thomson, the free path of protons in helium. C. G. Found and S. Dushman investigated the relation between the ionization current and the number of electrons per molecule of neon and helium ; and W. W. Merrymon, the effect of press. on the residual ionization of helium. The active cross-sections of mols. of the inert gases for the absorption of slow electrons were shown by C. Ramsauer to exhibit a maximum with increasing electron velocity which for neon, argon, krypton, and xenon is 13, 82, 98, 141 sq. cm. per c.c. at 0° and 1 mm. press. respectively. The active cross-sections for electrons of 1 volt. press. were for hydrogen 1260×10^{-18} cm., and for argon and helium respectively 75×10^{-18} and 550×10^{-18}. A. J. Dempster, C. Ramsauer, and R. B. Brode estimated the mean free path of electrons in argon, and helium. The energetic relations in collisions between electrons and gas molecules show that, in general, the process is essentially non-mechanical. The slow electrons in rare gases possess free-paths longer than would be anticipated from the kinetic theory. I. Langmuir, E. G. Dymond, and W. Elsasser studied the angles of scattering after collision. H. F. Mayer, F. M. Kannenstine, and A. J. Dempster discussed the life of metastable, partially ionized helium—vide supra. L. St. C. Broughall calculated the frequency of the electrons in the neon atom ; and W. Kossel found the luminosity of the discharge depends on electronic movements. S. P. McCallum and C. M. Focken measured the rate of increase of current due to ionization when the electrons are produced by a heated filament, and by ultra-violet light ; and they compared the effects of ionization by collision with that due to radiation. J. J. Thomson examined the radiation produced by the passage of cathode and anode rays through argon.

T. Alty [22] studied the cataphoresis of bubbles of helium in water. E. Hochheim found the dielectric constant of helium at 15° and 735 mm. to be 1·000068 ; and at 0° and 760 mm., 1·000074. C. and M. Cuthbertson gave 1·0000693 ; and M. Wolfke and H. K. Onnes, 1·048 for liquid helium at −268·8° and 765 mm. G. L. Addenbrooke studied the relation between the dielectric constant and the optical properties of helium—liquid and gas. E. Lehrer observed no change in the dielectric constant of argon with variations of press. ; and B. B. Weatherby and A. Wolf no change with helium in a magnetic field. G. Jung discussed the orientation of the molecules in the five inert gases considered as dielectrics. P. Tänzler found helium to be feebly diamagnetic, and gave $-0\cdot00175 \times 10^{-3}$ for the magnetic susceptibility ; A. P. Wills and L. G. Hector gave $-0\cdot80 \times 10^{-10}$ for the vol. susceptibility of helium ; L. G. Hector gave $-0\cdot780 \times 10^{-10}$ for helium ; $2\cdot77 \times 10^{-10}$ for neon ; and $-7\cdot52 \times 10^{-10}$ for argon at 20° and 760 mm. T. Soné gave $-5\cdot86 \times 10^{-6}$ for the sp. susceptibility of argon at 20°, and $0\cdot0104 \times 10^{-6}$ for the vol. susceptibility. L. Crow gave $-31\cdot5 \times 10^{-6}$ and $-32\cdot8 \times 10^{-10}$ for the respective mass and vol. susceptibilities of krypton at 20° and 760 mm. ; and respectively $-38\cdot2 \times 10^{-6}$ and $-16\cdot2 \times 10^{-10}$ for xenon. G. Joos and W. Pauli studied the atomic structure to account for the diamagnetism of the rare gases.

REFERENCES.

[1] W. Ramsay and M. W. Travers, *Proc. Roy. Soc.*, **62**. 316, 1898 ; **64**. 183, 1898 ; **67**. 329, 1900 ; *Phil. Trans.*, **197**. A, 47, 1901 ; W. Ramsay and S. Young, *ib.*, **186**. A, 257, 1895 ; W. Ramsay, *Chem. News*, **87**. 189, 1903 ; *Proc. Roy. Soc.*, **59**. 325, 1896 ; **71**. 421, 1903 ; W. Ramsay and J. N. Collie, *ib.*, **60**. 53, 206, 1896 ; W. Ramsay, J. N. Collie, and M. W. Travers, *Journ. Chem. Soc.*, **67**. 684, 1895 ; M. W. Travers, *Proc. Roy. Soc.*, **60**. 449, 1897 ; **64**. 130, 1898 ; *Nature*, **71**. 248, 1905 ; *Zeit. Phys. Chem.*, **61**. 241, 1907 ; R. W. Gray, in W. Ramsay and G. Rudorf, *Die Edelgase*, Leipzig, 1918 ; G. P. Baxter and H. W. Starkweather, *Proc. Nat. Acad. Science*, **11**. 231, 1925 ; **12**. 20, 1926 ; F. W. Aston, *Proc. Roy. Soc.*, **89**. 439, 1913 ; Lord Rayleigh, *ib.*, **59**. 198, 1896 ; H. S. Patterson, R. S. Cripps, and R. W. Gray, *ib.*, **86**. 579, 1912 ; O. Niemeyer, *Das Verhaltnis der specifischen Wärme von Argon und seine Aenderung mit der Temperatur*, Hulle, 1902 ; O. Mehliss, *Die Wärmeleitung des Argons bestimmt nach der Methode von Stefan-Winkelmann*, Halle, 1902 ; F. Fischer and O. Hähnel, *Ber.*, **42**. 1435, 1909 ; F. Fischer and O. Ringe, *ib.*, **41**. 2017, 1908 ; J. Dewar, *Proc. Roy. Inst.*, **18**. 433, 1906 ; A. Keindorff, *Die Zustandsgleichung der Dämpfe, Flüssigkeiten und Gase*, Leipzig, 1906 ; E. H. Amagat, *Compt. Rend.*, **156**. 272, 1913 ; *Le point critique des corps purs*, Paris, 164, 1904 ; H. von Jüptner, *Zeit. phys. Chem.*, **85**. 1, 1913 ; W. A. Goldhammer, *ib.*, **71**. 577, 1910 ; J. H. van der Waals, *Arch. Néerl.*, (2), **9**. 1, 1904 ; G. Rudorf, *Phil. Mag.*, (6), **17**. 795, 1909 ; *Ann. Physik*, (4), **29**. 751, 1909 ; (4), **31**. 416, 1910 ; W. Heuse, *Verh. deut. phys. Ges.*, **15**. 518, 1913 ; J. K. H. Inglis, *Phil. Mag.*, (6), **11**. 640, 1906 ; A. Hagenbach, *Wied. Ann.*, **60**. 124, 1897 ; N. A. Langlet, *Zeit. anorg. Chem.*, **10**. 287, 1895 ; A. Lonius, *Der Diffusionskoeffizient von Argon-Helium und seine Abhangigkeit von Mischungsverhältnis*, Halle, 1909 ; *Ann. Physik*, (4), **29**. 664, 1909 ; H. Happel, *ib.*, (4), **13**. 340, 1904 ; (4), **21**. 342, 1907 ; (4), **30**. 175, 1909 ; (4), **31**. 841, 1910 ; (4), **32**. 868, 1910 ; *Phys. Zeit.*, **10**. 1026, 1909 ; V. Dolezalek, *Zeit. phys. Chem.*, **93**. 585, 1919 ; F. Simon, *ib.*, **110**. 572, 1924 ; H. Schultze, *Die innere Reibung von Argon und ihre Aenderung mit der Temperatur*, Halle, 1901 ; *Ann. Physik*, (4), **5**. 140, 1901 ; (4), **6**. 302, 1901 ; W. Schwarze, *ib.*, (4), **11**. 303, 1903 ; *Phys. Zeit.*, **4**. 229, 1903 ; *Bestimmung der Wärmeleitung von Argon nach der Methode von Schleiermacher*, Halle, 1902 ; R. Schmidt, *Ueber die Diffusion von Argon und Helium*, Halle, 1904 ; *Ann. Physik*, (4), **14**. 801, 1904 ; F. Born, *ib.*, (4), **69**. 473, 1922 ; K. Schmitt, *ib.*, (4), **30**. 393, 1909 ; *Die innere Reibung von Luft und Helium bei tiefer Temperaturen*, Halle, 1909 ; J. F. Schierloh, *Ueber den Koeffizienten der inneren Reibung von reinem Argon und reinem Helium*, Halle, 1908 ; P. Tänzler, *Ueber die Koeffizienten der inneren Reibung für Gemische Zwischen Argon und Helium*, Halle, 1906 ; *Verh. deut. phys. Ges.*, **8**. 222, 1906 ; J. Wachsmuth, *Phys. Zeit.*, **9**. 235, 1908 ; *Ueber die Wärmeleitung von Gemischen zwischen Argon und Helium*, Halle, 1907 ; K. Olschewsky, *Ann. Physik*, (4), **17**. 997, 1905 ; *Ann. Chim. Phys.*, (8), **8**. 139, 1906 ; *Proc. Roy. Soc.*, **57**. 290, 1895 ; *Phil. Trans.*, **186**. A, 253, 1895 ; *Chem. News*, **71**. 59, 1895 ; C. A. Crommelin, J. P. Martinez, and H. K. Onnes, *Versl. Akad. Amsterdam*, **27**. 1316, 1919 ; P. G. Cath and H. K. Onnes, *Proc. Akad. Amsterdam*, **20**. 1160, 1918 ; H. K. Onnes, *Comm. Phys. Lab. Leiden*, 108, 1908 ; 119, 1911 ; 124, b, 1911 ; H. K. Onnes and J. D. A. Boks, *ib.*, 170, b, 1924 ; *Internat. Cong. Refrigeration*, **4**. i, 189, 1924 ; C. A. Crommelin, *ib.*, **4**. 61, 1924 ; *Comm. Phys. Lab. Leiden*, 118, 1910 ; 138, C, 1913 ; W. H. Keesom, *ib.*, 96, c, 1907 ; Suppl., 18, 1907 ; H. K. Onnes and C. A. Crommelin, *ib.*, 120, 1911 ; 138, c, 1913 ; 140, a, 1915 ; E. Mathias, H. K. Onnes, and C. A. Crommelin, *ib.*, 131, 1912 ; *Ann. Physik*, (4), **17**. 442, 1922 ; *Compt. Rend.*, **156**. 129, 1913 ; **174**. 1395, 1922 ; **175**. 933, 1922 ; E. Mathias, C. A. Crommelin, H. K. Onnes, and J. C. Swallow, *ib.*, **180**. 1005, 1925 ; *Ann. Physique*, (10), **5**. 359, 1926 ; H. E. Watson, *Journ. Chem. Soc.*, **97**. 810, 833, 1910 ; E. C. C. Baly and F. G. Donnan, *ib.*, **81**. 907, 1902 ; R. B. Moore, *ib.*, **93**. 2181, 1908 ; *Proc. Roy. Soc.*, **81**. 195, 1908 ; A. Leduc, *Compt. Rend.*, **158**. 864, 1914 ; **167**. 70, 1919 ; E. Brody, *Zeit. Physik*, **6**. 79, 1921 ; M. Planck, *Sitzber. Akad. Berlin*, 653, 1916 ; O. Stern, *Zeit. Elektrochem.*, **25**. 66, 1919 ; J. J. van Laar, *Zeit. anorg. Chem.*, **140**. 53, 1924 ; A. C. Egerton, *Phil. Mag.*, (6), **48**. 1048, 1924 ; V. Karpen, *Bull. Acad. Roumaine*, **8**. 175, 1923 ; F. Simon and C. von Simson, *Zeit. Physik*, **21**. 168, 1924 ; J. de Smedt and W. H. Keesom, *Physica*, **5**. 344, 1926 ; A. del Fresno, *Zeit. anorg. Chem.*, **152**. 25, 1926 ; S. Mokruschin, *ib.*, **153**. 273, 1926 ; O. Sackur, *Nernst's Festschrift*, 405, 1921 ; *Ann. Physik*, (4), **40**. 67, 1913 ; A. Eucken, *Grundriss der physikalische Chemie*, Leipzig, 152, 1924 ; F. Pollitzer, *Die Berechnung chemischer Affinitäten nach dem Nernstschen Wärmetheorem*, Stuttgart, 122, 1912 ; W. Nernst, *Die theoretischen und experimentellen Grundlagen des neuen Warmesatzes*, Halle (Saale), 112, 1918 ; T. S. Taylor, *Phys. Rev.*, (2), **10**. 653, 1917.

[2] W. Ramsay, *Phil. Trans.*, **186**. A, 237, 1895 ; W. Ramsay and M. W. Travers, *ib.*, **197**. A, 47, 1901 ; *Proc. Roy. Soc.*, **64**. 183, 1898 ; **67**. 329, 1900 ; M. W. Travers and A. Jaquerod, *ib.*, **70**. 484, 1903 ; M. W. Travers, G. Senter, and A. Jaquerod, *ib.*, **70**. 488, 1903 ; J. E. Jones, *ib.*, **106**. A, 441, 463, 1924 ; H. S. Patterson, R. S. Cripps, and R. W. Gray, *ib.*, **86**. A, 579, 1912 ; J. P. Kuenen and W. W. Randall, *ib.*, **59**. 60, 1895 ; W. Ramsay and G. Rudorf, *Die Edelgase*, Leipzig, 79, 1918 ; F. M. Penning and H. K. Onnes, *Arch. Néerl.*, (3), **7**. 166, 1924 ; F. M. Penning, *ib.*, (3), **7**. 172, 1924 ; P. G. Cath and H. K. Onnes, *ib.*, (3), **6**. 1, 1922 ; H. K. Onnes, *Proc. Acad. Amsterdam*, **10**. 589, 1908 ; *Versl. Akad. Amsterdam*, **19**. 1187, 1911 ; *Comm. Phys. Lab. Leiden*, 102, a, b, c, 1907 ; 156, a, 1922 ; H. K. Onnes and C. A. Crommelin, *ib.*, 118, b, 1910 ; 120, a, 1911 ; 131, c, 1912 ; C. A. Crommelin, *ib.*, 115, 1910 ; H. K. Onnes and J. D. A. Boks, *ib.*, 170, b, 1924 ; *Internat. Congress Refrigeration*, **4**. i, 81, 189, 1924 ; C. A. Commelin, *ib.*, **4**,

t, 61, 1924 ; F. P. G. A. J. van Agt and H. K. Onnes, *Versl. Akad. Amsterdam,* **34**. 638, 644, 1925 ;
H. K. Onnes and G. Holst, *ib.,* **23**. 175, 1915 ; H. K. Onnes and F. Burger, *Proc. Acad. Amsterdam,*
20. 1163, 1918 ; E. H. Amagat, *Compt. Rend.,* **154**. 909, 1912 ; E. Mathias, C. A. Crommelin,
and H. K. Onnes, *ib.,* **174**. 1395, 1922 ; **176**. 939, 1923 ; A. Jaquerod and O. Scheuer, *ib.,* **140**.
1384, 1905 ; *Mém. Sciences Genève,* **35**. 659, 1908 ; J. J. van Laar, *Journ. Chim. Phys.,* **17**.
266, 1919 ; *Die Zustandsgleichung von Gasen und Flussigkeiten,* Leipzig, 1924 ; *Proc. Acad.
Amsterdam,* **18**. 1220, 1915 ; **19**. 2, 1916 ; P. W. Bridgman, *Proc. Amer. Acad.,* **59**. 173, 1924 ;
J. P. Dalton, *Trans. Roy. Soc. South Africa,* **11**. 209, 1924 ; J. H. Perry, *Journ. Phys. Chem.,*
28. 1108, 1924 ; O. Maass and D. M. Morrison, *Trans. Roy. Soc. Canada,* (3), **18**. 49, 1924 ;
L. Holborn and J. Otto, *Zeit. Physik,* **10**. 367, 1922 ; **30**. 320, 1924 ; **33**. 1, 1925 ; **38**. 359, 1926 ;
F. P. Burt, *Trans. Faraday Soc.,* **6**. 19, 1910 ; A. Eucken, *Ber. deut. phys. Ges.,* **18**. 4, 1916 ;
G. Rudorf, *Ann. Physik,* (4), **29**. 751. 1909 ; L. Holborn and F. Henning, *ib.,* (4), **35**. 761, 1911 ;
F. Henning and W. Heuse, *Zeit. Physik,* **5**. 284, 1921 ; P. A. Guye and L. Friderich, *Arch. Sciences
Genève,* (4), **13**. 559, 1902 ; P. A. Guye, *Journ. Phys. Chim.,* **3**. 321, 1905 ; *Compt. Rend.,* **140**.
1241, 1905 ; **144**. 976, 1360, 1907 ; **145**. 1164, 1330. 1907 ; A. Leduc, *ib.,* **164**. 1003, 1917 ; **167**.
70, 1918 : D. Berthelot, *ib.,* **144**. 76, 194, 269, 1907 ; **145**. 65, 180, 317, 1907 ; Lord Rayleigh, *Phil.
Trans.,* **198**. A, 417, 1902 ; *Proc. Roy. Soc.,* **73**. 153, 1904 ; **75**. 446, 1905 ; H. E. Watson,
Journ. Chem. Soc., **97**. 833, 1910 ; I. Masson and L. G. F. Dolley, *Proc. Roy. Soc.,* **103**. A,
524, 1923 ; G. van Rij, *Schijnassociatie tes verklaring van de verschillen tusschen de vit komsten
van het experiment en de toestandsvergelijking van de Waals,* Amsterdam, 1908 ; H. Happel,
Phys. Zeit., **10**. 1026, 1909 ; *Ann. Physik,* (4), **21**. 342, 1907 ; F. Zwicky, *Phys. Zeit.,* **22**. 449,
1921 ; S. F. Pickering, *Misc. Publ. Bur. Standards,* 71, 1925 ; W. Meissner, *Zeit. Physik,* **36**.
325, 1926 ; W. Heuse, *ib.,* **37**. 157, 1926 ; P. W. Bridgman, *Proc. Amer. Acad.,* **59**. 173, 1924 ;
F. G. Keyes, *ib.,* **59**. 208, 1924 ; M. F. Carroll, *Phil. Mag.,* (7), **2**. 385, 1926 ; W. J. Walker,
ib., (6), **50**. 1244, 1925 ; F. Cario, *Ueber das Verhalten von Helium in Platen iridium gefässen
bei hohen Temperaturen,* Halle a. S., 1907 ; F. Dorn, *Phys. Zeit.,* **7**. 312, 1906 ; G. K. Burgess,
ib., **14**. 153, 1913 ; *Journ. Chim. Phys.,* **11**. 531, 1913 ; F. Henning, *Zeit. Electrochem.,* **18**. 823,
1912 ; **19**. 185, 1913 ; **21**. 506, 1915 ; K. Obschewsky, *Wied. Ann.,* **59**. 184, 1896 ; J. Dewar,
Amer. Journ. Science, (4), **11**. 291, 1901.
  ³ Lord Rayleigh, *Proc. Roy. Soc.,* **59**. 198, 1896 ; J. E. Jones, *ib.,* **106**. A, 441, 463, 1924 ;
T. L. Ibbs, *ib.,* **107**. A, 479, 1925 ; G. A. Elliott and I. Massow, *ib.,* **108**. A, 378, 1925 ; H. Schultze,
Die innere Reibung von Argon und ihre Aenderung mit der Temperatur, Halle, 1901 ; *Ann. Physik,*
(4), **5**. 140, 1901 ; (4), **6**. 302, 1901 ; K. Schmitt, *ib.,* (4), **30**. 393, 1909 ; *Die innere Reibung von
Luft und Helium bei tiefen Temperaturen,* Halle, 1909 ; J. F. Schierloh, *Ueber den Koeffizienten
der inneren Reibung von reinem Argon und reinem Helium,* Halle, 1908 ; S. Chapman and W. Hainsworth, *Phil. Mag.,* (6), **48**. 593, 1924 ; A. O. Rankine, *Proc. Roy. Soc.,* **83**. 516, 1910 ; **84**. 181,
1910 ; *Phil. Mag.,* (6), **21**. 45, 1911 ; *Phys. Zeit.,* **11**. 745, 1910 ; M. Reinganum, *ib.,* **12**. 779,
1911 ; P. Tänzler, *Ueber die Koeffizienten der inneren Reibung für Gemische zwischen Argon und
Helium,* Halle, 1906 ; *Verh. deut. phys. Ges.,* **8**. 222, 1906 ; M. Thiesen, *ib.,* **4**. 348, 1902 ; **8**. 336,
1906 ; J. Puluj, *Sitzber. Akad. Wien,* **79**. 97, 745, 1879 ; E. Lohr, *ib.,* **146**. 1281, 1907 ; H. Sirk, *ib.,*
117. 1159, 1908 ; **119**. 655, 1910 ; G. Jaumann, *ib.,* **130**. 189. 1921 ; M. Knudsen, *Ann. Physik,* (4),
29. 73, 1909 ; H. Markowsky, *ib.,* (4), **14**. 742, 1904 ; R. A. Millikan, (4), **41**. 759, 1913 ; P. Günther,
Zeit. phys. Chem., **110**. 626, 1924 ; F. Schuster, *Zeit. anorg. Chem.,* **146**. 299, 1925 ; W. Kopsch,
Ueber den Koeffizienten der inneren Reibung von Wasserstoff und Argon bei neideren Temperaturen,
Halle, 1909 ; H. K. Onnes and S. Weber, *Comm. Phys. Lab. Leiden,* 134, b, 1913 ; S. Chapman,
Phil. Trans., **211**. A, 433, 1912 ; H. Vogel, *Ueber die Viskosität einiger Gase und ihre Tempera-
turabhängigkeit bei tiefen Temperaturen,* Berlin, 1914 ; W. J. Fisher, *Phys. Rev.,* (1), **24**. 237,
1907 ; M. N. States, *ib.,* (2), **21**. 662, 1923 ; Y. Ishida, *ib.,* (2), **21**. 550, 1923 ; E. Blankenstein,
ib., (2), **21**. 703, 1923 ; (2), **22**. 582, 1923 ; F. W. Aston, *Engg.,* **96**, 423, 1916 ; W. J. Walker,
Phil. Mag., (6), **50**. 1244, 1925.
  ⁴ W. Ramsay and M. W. Travers, *Proc. Roy. Soc.,* **61**. 267, 1897 ; **62**. 316, 1897 ; W. Ramsay
and J. N. Collie, *ib.,* **60**. 206, 1896 ; *Compt. Rend.,* **123**. 214, 1896 ; A. Jaquerod and F. L. Perrot,
ib., **139**. 789, 1904 ; **140**. 1542, 1905 ; *Arch. Sciences Genève,* (4), **18**. 613, 1904 ; (4), **20**. 128,
454, 1905 ; A. Jaquerod, *ib.,* (4), **34**. 255, 1912 ; E. Dorn, *Phys. Zeit.,* **7**. 312, 1896 ; A. Sieverts
and E. Bergner, *Ber.,* **45**. 2576, 1912 ; R. Schmidt, *Ueber die Diffusion von Argon und Helium,*
Halle, 1904 ; *Ann. Physik,* (4), **14**. 801, 1904 ; A. Lonius, *ib.,* (4), **29**. 664, 1909 ; *Die Diffusions-
koeffizient von Argon-Helium und seine Abhängigkeit vom Mischungsverhältnis,* Halle, 1909 ;
D. Tsakalotos, *Proc. Chem. Soc.,* **24**. 208, 1908 ; Lord Rayleigh, *Phil. Mag.,* (5), **49**. 220, 1901 ;
W. Ramsay, *ib.,* (5), **38**. 206, 1894 ; F. G. Donnan, *ib.,* (5), **49**. 423, 1900 ; O. W. Richardson and
R. C. Ditto, *ib.,* (6), **22**. 704, 1911 ; H. E. Watson, *Journ. Chem. Soc.,* **97**. 810, 1910 ;
F. W. Aston, *Engg.,* **96**. 423, 1916 ; T. L. Ibbs, *Proc. Roy. Soc.,* **107**. A, 479, 1925 ; G. A. Elliott and
I. Masson, *ib.,* **108**. A, 378, 1925 ; G. Jaumann, *Sitzber. Akad. Wien,* **130**. 189, 1921 ; S. Chapman
and W. Hainsworth, *Phil. Mag.,* (6), **48**. 593, 1924 ; J. Dewar, *Proc. Roy. Inst.,* **21**. 813, 1918 ;
C. C. van Voorhis, *Phys. Rev.,* (2), **23**. 557, 1925 ; J. C. McLennan and W. W. Shaver, *Phil. Mag.,*
(6), **40**. 272, 1920 ; R. T. Elworthy and V. F. Murray, *Proc. Roy. Soc. Canada,* (3), **13**. 37, 1919.
  ⁵ E. C. C. Baly and F. G. Donnan, *Journ. Chem. Soc.,* **81**. 907, 1902 ; P. Walden, *Zeit. phys.
Chem.,* **65**. 129, 1908 ; P. Walden and R. Swinne, *ib.,* **82**. 305, 1913 ; G. Rudorf, *Ann. Physik,*
(4), **29**. 751, 1909 ; A. T. van Urk, W. H. Keesom, and H. K. Onnes, *Proc. Amsterdam Acad.,*
28. 958, 1925.
  ⁶ W. Hillers, *Phys. Zeit.,* **11**. 133, 1910 ; M. Reinganum, *ib.,* **2**. 241, 1900 ; **11**. 347, 1910 ;

12. 779, 1911; *Ann. Physik*, (4), **28**. 142, 1909; H. Sirk, *Phil. Mag.*, (6), **49**. 708, 1925; *Ann. Physik*, (4), **25**. 894, 1908; R. Schmidt, *ib.*, (4), **14**. 801, 1904; *Ueber die Diffusion von Argon und Helium*, Halle, 1904; G. Rudorf, *Phil. Mag.*, (6), **17**. 795, 1909; (6), **39**. 238, 1920; W. Sutherland, *ib.*, (5), **36**. 507, 1893; (4), **17**. 320, 1909; C. C. Darwin, *ib.*, (6), **23**. 901, 1912; O. E. Meyer, *Die kinetische Theorie der Gase*, Breslau, 1899; J. H. Jeans, *The Dynamical Theory of Gases*, Cambridge, 1904; J. J. Thomson, *Conduction of Electricity through Gases*, Cambridge, 450, 1903; H. Schultze, *Die innere Reibung von Argon und ihre Aenderung mit der Temperatur*, Halle, 1901; *Ann. Physik*, (4), **5**. 140, 1901; P. Tänzler, *Ueber die Koeffizienten der inneren Reibung für Gemische zwischen Argon und Helium*, Halle, 1906; *Verh. deut. phys. Ges.*, **8**. 222, 1906; P. W. Bridgman, *Proc. Amer. Acad.*, **59**. 173, 1924; H. Sirk, *Naturwiss.*, **12**. 920, 1924; J. F. Schierloh, *Ueber den Koeffizienten der inneren Reibung von reinem Argon und reinem Helium*, Halle, 1908; J. Robinson, *Ann. Physik*, (4), **31**. 769, 1910; F. Mayer, *ib.*, (4), **41**. 931, 1913; J. E. L. Jones, *Proc. Roy. Soc.*, **106**. A, 441, 463, 1924; **109**. A, 584, 1925; W. H. Westphal, *Zeit. Physik*, **4**. 254, 1920; A. O. Rankine, *ib.*, **83**. 265, 516, 1910; **84**. 181, 1910; **86**. 162, 1912; *Phys. Zeit.*, **11**. 745, 1910; *Phil. Mag.*, (6), **21**. 45, 1911; C. Ramsauer, *Jahrb. Rad. Elektron.*, **19**. 345, 1923; S. Chapman, *Phil. Trans.*, **211**. A, 433, 1912; Lord Rayleigh, *Proc. Roy. Soc.*, **59**. 198, 1896; M. Reinganum, *Phys. Zeit.*, **2**. 241, 1900; R. Gans, *Ann. Physik*, (4), **65**. 95, 1921; W. P. Davey, *Phys. Rev.*, (2), **22**. 211, 1923; M. Pierucci, *Nuovo Cimento*, (6), **22**. 189, 1921; H. G. Grimm, *Zeit. Elektrochem.*, **28**. 75, 1922; B. Cabrera, *Anal. Fis. Quim.*, **23**. 172, 1925; *Journ. Phys. Rad.*, (6), **6**. 241, 1925; J. J. van Laar, *Journ. Chim. Phys.*, **17**. 266, 1919; *Chem. Weekbl.*, **16**. 1243, 1919; W. L. Bragg, *Phil. Mag.*, (6), **40**. 169, 1920; A. O. Rankine, *ib.*, (6), **40**. 516, 1920; *Proc. Roy. Soc.*, **98**. A, 360, 1921; H. G. Grimm, *Zeit. phys. Chem.*, **122**. 177, 1926; H. G. Grimm and H. Wolff, *ib.*, **119**. 254, 1926; V. Kiréeff, *Zeit. anorg. Chem.*, **155**. 121, 1926; R. G. Lunnon, *Proc. Phys. Soc.*, **38**. 93, 1926: H. Schmidt, *Zeit. Electrochem.*, **28**. 50, 1922; M. N. Saha, *Nature*, **107**. 682, 1921; *Phil. Mag.*, (6), **40**. 619, 1920; W. Schütz, *Zeit. Physik*, **38**. 864, 1926.

⁷ A. W. Porter, *Nature*, **77**. 437, 1908; K. Olschewsky, *Wied. Ann.*, **59**. 184, 1896; *Ann. Chim. Phys.*, (8), **8**. 139, 1906; *Ann. Physik*, (4), **17**. 997, 1905; *Phil. Trans.*, **186**. A, 253, 1895; *Chem. News*, **71**. 59, 1895; *Proc. Roy. Soc.*, **57**. 290, 1895; M. W. Travers and A. Jaquerod, *ib.*, **70**. 484, 1903; J. Dewar, *ib.*, **63**. 256, 1898; *Ann. Chim. Phys.*, (7), **14**. 145, 1898; *Compt. Rend.*, **139**. 421, 1904; *Chem. News*, **84**. 49, 1901; **90**. 141, 1904; E. Mathias, C. A. Crommelin, H. K. Onnes and J. C. Swallow, *Compt. Rend.*, **180**. 1005, 1925; H. K. Onnes, *Chem. Ztg.*, **32**. 901, 1908; *Comm. Phys. Lab. Leiden*, **102**, a, 1907; **105**, 1908; **108**, 1908; **112**, 1909; **124**, b, 1911; H. K. Onnes and M. H. Keesom, *ib.*, **96**, b, 1906; Suppl., **15**, 1907; **16**, 1907; H. K. Onnes and C. A. Crommelin, *ib.*, **121**, e, 1910; C. A. Crommelin, *ib.*, **115**, 1910; **118**, a, 1910; E. H. Mathias, H. K. Onnes, and C. A. Crommelin, *ib.*, **131**, a, 1912; *Proc. Acad. Amsterdam*, **15**. 961, 1913; *Ann. Physik*, (4), **17**. 442, 1922; *Compt. Rend.*, **174**. 1375, 1922; **176**. 939, 1923; *Onnes' Festschrift*, 197, 1922; E. H. Mathias, *ib.*, 165, 1922; *Phys. Ber.*, **4**. 701, 1923; W. H. Keesom, *ib.*, **4**. 613, 1923; *Onnes' Festschrift*, 89, 1922; C. A. Crommelin, *Comm. Phys. Lab. Leiden*, 162, 1924; *Phys. Ber.*, **5**. 1376, 1924; E. Mathias and C. A. Crommelin, *Internat. Congress Refrigeration*, **4**. i. 89, 1924; W. Ramsay and M. W. Travers, *Phil. Trans.*, **197**. A, 47, 1901; *Proc. Roy. Soc.*, **67**. 329, 1900; W. Wahl, *ib.*, **87**. A, 371, 1912; J. C. McLennan, *Chem. News*, **126**. 369, 1923; *Trans. Roy. Soc. Canada*, **14**. iii, 31, 1921; J. C. McLennan and G. M. Schrum, *ib.*, **16**. iii, 181, 1922; W. M. Tate, *Medd. Nobelinst.*, **1**. 1, 1906; G. Rudorf, *Ann. Physik*, (4). **29**. 751, 1909; *Zeit. Elektrochem.*, **15**. 746, 748, 1909; F. Simon and C. von Simson, *Zeit. Physik*, **21**. 168, 1924; J. A. Muller, *Compt. Rend.*, **175**. 760, 1922; W. Herz, *Zeit. anorg. Chem.*, **143**. 40, 1925; **145**. 378, 1925; **150**. 326, 1926; C. Cuthbertson, *Phil. Mag.*, (6). **21**. 69, 1911; A. O. Rankine, *ib.*, (6), **21**. 45, 1911; *Proc. Roy. Soc.*, **86**. A, 162, 1912; H. S. Patterson, R. S. Cripps, and R. W. Gray, *ib.*, **86**. A, 579, 1912; J. E. Jones, *ib.*, **106**. A, 441, 463, 709, 1924; E. C. C. Baly and F. G. Donnan, *Journ. Chem. Soc.*, **81**. 907, 1902; D. Berthelot, *Journ. Phys.*, (3), **10**. 611, 1901; H. Happel, *Phys. Zeit.*, **8**. 204, 1907; *Ann. Physik*, (4), **21**. 342, 1907; W. A. Goldhammer, *Zeit. phys. Chem.*, **71**. 577, 1910; P. Walden, *ib.*, **65**. 129, 257, 1908; **66**. 385, 1909; R. O. Herzog, *Zeit. Elektrochem.*, **15**. 345, 1909; W. R. Fielding, *Chem. News*, **117**. 379, 1918; W. Meissner, *Phys. Zeit.*, **26**. 689, 1925; J. de Smedt and W. H. Keesom, *Physica*, **5**. 344, 1925; H. Carlsohn, *Ber.*, **58**. B, 1747, 1925; A. Predwoditeleff, *Zeit. Physik*, **36**. 557, 1926; H. Erdmann, *Chem. Ztg.*, **31**. 1075, 1907; J. Narbut, *Phys. Zeit.*, **22**. 52, 1921.

⁸ W. Schwarze, *Bestimmung der Wärmeleitung von Argon nach der Methode von Schleiermacher*, Halle, 1902; *Ann. Physik*, (4), **11**. 303, 1903; *Phys. Zeit.*, **4**. 229, 1903; M. Smoluchowsky, *Sitzber. Akad. Wien*, **107**. 304, 1898; *Phil. Mag.*, (6), **21**. 11, 1911; *Ann. Physik*, (4), **35**. 983, 1911; A. Eucken, *Phys. Zeit.*, **12**. 1101, 1911; A. Wassilijewa, *ib.*, **5**. 737, 1904; S. Chapman and W. Hainsworth, *Phil. Mag.*, (6), **48**. 593, 1924; J. Wachsmuth, *Ueber die Wärmeleitung von Gemischen zwischen Argon und Helium*, Halle, 1907; *Phys. Zeit.*, **9**. 235, 1908; F. Soddy and A. J. Berry, *Proc. Roy. Soc.*, **83**. 254, 1910; **84**. 576, 1911; O. Mehliss, *Die Wärmeleitung des Argons bestimmt nach der Methode von Stefan-Winkelmann*, Halle, 1902; S. Chapman, *Phil. Trans.*, **211** A, 433, 1912; S. Weber, *Versl. Akad. Amsterdam*, **26**. 1338, 1918; E. Schreiner, *Zeit. phys. Chem.*, **112**. 1, 1924.

⁹ R. Thomas, *Bestimmung der specifischen Wärme von Helium und die Atomwärme von Argon und Helium*, Marburg, 1905; A. Eggert, *Bestimmung der specifischen Wärme des Heliums bei verschiedenen Temperaturen und Untersuchung ihrer Beziehung zur kinetischen Theorie einatomiger Gase*, Marburg, 1910; W. Ramsay, *Phil. Trans.*, **186**. A, 237, 1895; *Proc. Roy. Soc.*, **58**. 81,

1895 ; **86.** A, 100, 1912 ; W. Ramsay, J. N. Collie, and M. W. Travers, *Journ. Chem. Soc.*, **67.** 684, 1895 ; W. Ramsay and M. W. Travers, *Proc. Roy. Soc.*, **63.** 405, 1898 ; *Compt. Rend.*, **126.** 2610, 1898 ; N. A. Langlet, *Zeit. anorg. Chem.*, **10.** 287, 1895 ; V. Behn and H. Geiger, *Verh. deut. phys. Ges.*, **9.** 657, 1907 ; W. Dittenberger, *Ueber die specifische Wärme des Argon*, Halle, 1897 ; O. Niemeyer, *Das Verhältnis der specifischen Wärme von Argon und seine Aenderung mit der Temperatur*, Halle, 1902 ; H. W. Moody, *Phys. Zeit.*, **13.** 383, 1912 ; W. Nernst, *ib.*, **13.** 1064, 1912 ; M. Pier, *Zeit. Elektrochem.*, **15.** 536, 1909 ; N. Bjerrum, *ib.*, **18** 101, 1912; J. Kapp, *Versuche über das Verhältnis Kappa der specifischen Wärmen eines Gasgemisches*, Marburg, 1907 ; W. Kotowitsch. *Journ. Russ. Phys. Chem. Soc.*, **40.** 16, 1908 ; F. Richarz, *Ann. Physik*, (4), **19.** 639, 1906 ; K. Scheel and W. Heuse, *ib.*, (4), **40.** 473, 1913 ; W. Heuse, *ib.*, (4), **59.** 86, 1919 ; A. Eucken, *Ber. deut. phys. Ges.*, **18.** 4, 18, 1916 ; E. Schreiner, *Zeit. phys. Chem.*, **112.** 1, 1924 ; E. Mathias, C. A. Crommelin, and H. K. Onnes, *Compt. Rend.*, **174.** 1395, 1922 ; L. I. Dana and H. K. Onnes, *Versl. Akad. Amsterdam*, **34.** 1340, 1925.

[10] A. Eucken, *Ber. deut. phys. Ges.*, **18.** 4, 1916 ; W. Nernst, *Gött. Nachr.*, 1, 1906 : *Phys. Zeit.*, **13.** 1064, 1911 ; K. Bennewitz and F. Simon, *Zeit. Physik*, **16.** 198, 1923 ; W. Ramsay and M. W. Travers, *Proc. Roy. Soc.*, **67.** 329, 1900 ; *Phil. Trans.*, **197.** A, 47, 1901 ; D. L. Hammick, *Phil. Mag.*, (6), **44.** 590, 1922 ; P. Walden, *Zeit. phys. Chem.*, **65.** 257, 1908 ; G. Rudorf, *Phil. Mag.*, (6), **39.** 238, 1920 ; *Ann. Physik*, (4), **29.** 751, 1909 ; (4), **31.** 416, 1910 ; H. Happel, *ib.*, (4), **21.** 342, 1907 ; (4), **30.** 175, 1909 ; (4), **31.** 841, 1910 ; O. Sackur, *ib.*, (4), **36.** 958, 1911 ; *Nernst's Festschrift*, 405, 1912 ; R. de Forcrand, *Compt. Rend.*, **156.** 1439, 1809, 1913 ; E. Mathias, C. A. Crommelin, and H. K. Onnes, *Compt. Rend.*, **174.** 1395, 1922 ; **176.** 939, 1923 ; C. A. Crommelin, *Zeit. Sauerstoff Stickstoff Ind.*, **11.** 81, 1919 ; G. N. Lewis, G. E. Gibson, and W. M. Latimer, *Journ. Amer. Chem. Soc.*, **44.** 1008, 1922 ; F. S. Mortimer, *ib.*, **44.** 1429, 1922 ; L. I. Dana and H. K. Onnes, *Versl. Akad. Amsterdam*, **34.** 1335, 1925 ; F. A. Henglein, *Zeit. Elektrochem.*, **26.** 431, 1920 ; J. Narbut, *Phys. Zeit.*, **22.** 52, 1921.

[11] W. Ramsay and M. W. Travers, *Phil. Trans.*, **197.** A, 47, 1901 ; *Proc. Roy. Soc.*, **62.** A, 225, 316, 345, 1898 ; **67.** A, 330, 1900 ; Lord Rayleigh, *ib.*, **59.** 198, 1896 ; **83.** A, 149, 1909 ; W. Burton, *ib.*, **80.** A, 404, 1908 ; C. and M. Cuthbertson, *ib.*, **84.** A, 13, 1910 ; C. Cuthbertson and E. P. Metcalfe, *ib.*, **80.** A, 418, 1908 ; **83.** A, 149, 1909 ; W. Ramsay and J. N. Collie, *ib.*, **60.** 53, 1896 ; *Compt. Rend.*, **123.** 214, 1896 ; J. Cabannes and A. Lepape, *Compt. Rend.*, **179.** 325, 1924 ; J. Cabannes, *Ann. Physique*, **15.** 5, 1921 ; M. Czerny and G. Hettner, *Zeit. Physik*, **30.** 258, 1924 ; K. F. Herzfeld and K. L. Wolff, *Ann. Physik*, (4), **76.** 71, 1925 ; C. P. Smyth, *Phil. Mag.*, (6), **50.** 361, 1925 ; K. Scheel and R. Sehmidt, *Verh. deut. phys. Ges.*, **10.** 207, 1908 ; H. Erfle, *ib.*, **10.** 331, 1908 ; C. Herrmann, *ib.*, **10.** 211, 478, 1908 ; *Die Brechung und Dispersion des Heliums*, Halle, 1908 ; J. Koch, *Arkiv. Mat. Astr. Fysik*, **8.** 20, 1912 ; **9.** 6, 1913 ; F. Ahrberg, *Die Brechung und Dispersion von Argon und Sauerstoff*, Halle, 1909 ; A. Wasastjerna, *Comm. Soc. Scient. Fennica*, **1.** 37, 1923 ; W. H. Keesom and J. de Smedt, *On the Diffraction of Röntgen-rays in Liquids*, Amsterdam, 1923 ; W. H. Keesom, *Physica*, **2.** 118, 1922 ; J. E. Calthrop, *Phil. Mag.*, (6), **47.** 772, 1924 ; W H. McCurdy and A. Bramley, *Phys. Rev.*, (2), **27.** 314, 1926 ; Lord Rayleigh, *Proc. Roy. Soc.*, **98.** A, 57, 1920 ; *Compt. Rend.*, **171.** 1002, 1920 ; A. Cabannes, *ib.*, **171.** 852, 1920.

[12] J. N. Lockyer, *Nature*, **51.** 586, 1895 ; **52.** 8, 55, 56, 214, 327, 547, 1895 ; **53.** 319, 342, 1896 ; *Chem. News*, **72.** 283, 1895 ; *Compt. Rend.*, **69.** 121, 1869 ; **120.** 1103, 1895 ; *Phil. Trans.*, **159.** 425. 1869 ; *Phil. Mag.*, (4), **37.** 143, 1869 ; *Proc. Roy. Soc.*, **17.** 91, 131, 350, 415, 1869 ; **18.** 74, 354, 1869 ; **58.** 67, 113, 116, 192, 193, 1895 ; **59.** 1, 4, 342, 1896 ; **60.** 133, 1896 ; J. N. Lockyer and F. E. Baxandall, *ib.*, **74.** A, 546, 1905 ; W. E. Curtis and R. G. Long, *ib.*, **108.** A, 513, 1925 ; J. C. McLennan, *Nature*, **115.** 382, 607, 1925 ; *Proc. Roy. Soc.*, **98.** A, 114, 1920 ; J. C. McLennan and G. M. Schrum, *ib.*, **108.** A, 501, 1925 ; J. C. McLennan and A. C. Lewis, *ib.*, **98.** 109, 1920 ; J. C. McLennan, J. F. T. Young, and H. J. C. Ireton, *ib.*, **98.** A, 95, 1920 ; J. C. McLennan and P. A. Petrie, *Trans. Roy. Soc. Canada*, (3), **15.** 15, 1921 ; E. Frankland and J. N. Lockyer, *ib.*, **17.** 288, 1869 ; *Phil. Mag.*, (4), **38.** 66, 1869 ; H. A. Rowland, *ib.*, (5), **36.** 49, 1893 ; *Astrom. Astrophys.*, **12.** 321, 1893 ; A. Secchi, *Compt. Rend.*, **67.** 1123, 1868 ; **68.** 237, 358, 1869 ; **72.** 362, 1871 ; H. Faye, *ib.*, **68.** 112, 1869 ; G. Rayet, *ib.*, **68.** 320, 1869 ; A. Ricco, *ib.*, **102.** 851, 1886 ; *Mem. Soc. Spettr. Ital.*, **15.** 41, 1886 ; *Astrophys. Journ.*, **2.** 236, 1895 ; G. F. Hull, *ib.*, **25.** 1, 1907 ; W. H. Pickering, *ib.*, **4.** 369, 1896 ; **5.** 92, 1897 ; C. V. Raman and A. S. Ganesan, *ib.*, **59.** 45, 1924 ; L. Silberstein, *ib.*, **57.** 248, 1925 ; *Nature*, **110.** 247, 1922 ; **111.** 46. 1923 ; *Astrophys. Journ.*, **57.** 248, 1923 ; *Phys. Rev.*, (2), **19.** 399, 1922 ; (2), **21.** 389, 721, 1923 ; J. S. Foster, *ib.*, (2), **20.** 100, 1922 ; H. B. Lemon, *Proc. Nat. Acad. Science*, **11.** 41, 1925 ; J. J. Hopfield and S. W. Leifson, *Astrophys. Journ.*, **58.** 59, 1923 ; J. S. Plaskett, *Nature*, **108.** 209, 1921 ; C. V. Raman, *ib.*, **110.** 800, 1922 ; T. Lyman, *ib.*, **104.** 314, 565, 1919 ; **110.** 278, 1922 ; *Phys. Rev.*, (2), **21.** 202, 1923 ; *Science*, (2), **50.** 484, 1919 ; (2), **59.** 422, 1924 ; *Nature*, **104.** 314, 1919 ; *Astrophys. Journ.*, **60.** 1, 1924 ; H. Fricke and T. Lyman, *Phil. Mag.*, (6), **41.** 814, 1921 ; H. L. d'Arrest, *Astron. Nachr.*, **79.** 1, 1872 ; L. Palmieri, *Rend. Accad. Napoli*, **20.** 233, 1882 ; H. C. Offerhaus, *Arch. Néerl.*, (3), **7.** 60, 1923 ; A. Cornu, *Journ. l'École Polyt.*, **53.** 175, 1883 ; W. Ramsay, *Compt. Rend.*, **120.** 1049, 1895 ; *Nature*, **51.** 512, 543, 1895 ; **52.** 7, 224, 1895 ; *Chem. News*, **71.** 151, 211, 1895 ; *Proc. Roy. Soc.*, **58.** 65, 1895 ; **59.** 325, 1896 ; **76.** A, 111, 1905 ; *Journ. Chem. Soc.*, **67.** 1107, 1895 ; W. Ramsay, J. N. Collie, and M. W. Travers, *ib.*, **67.** 684, 1895 ; *Nature*, **52.** 55, 306, 331, 1895 ; *Proc. Roy. Soc.*, **58.** 81, 1895 ; W. Ramsay and J. N. Collie, *ib.*, **59.** 257, 1896 ; **60.** 53, 206, 1896 ; *Compt. Rend.*, **123.** 214. 1896 ; M. W. Travers, *Proc. Roy. Soc.*, **60.** 449, 1897 ; W. Ramsay and M. W. Travers, *ib.*, **60.** 442,

1897 ; W. Ramsay and F. Soddy, *ib.*, **73**. 346, 1904 ; *Nature*, **69**. 246, 1903 ; E. J. Evans, *ib.*, **92**. 5, 1913 ; *Phil. Mag.*, (6), **29**. 284, 1915 ; T. R. Merton, *Proc. Roy. Soc.*, **95**. A, 30, 1918 ; A. Fowler, *ib.*, **91**. A, 208, 1915 ; *Report on Series in Line Spectra*, London, 1922 ; *Month. Notices Roy. Astron. Soc.*, **73**. 62, 1912 ; W. Crookes, *Nature*, **51**. 543, 1895 ; **58**. 570, 1898 ; *Astrophys. Journ.*, **2**. 227, 1895 ; *Chem. News*, **71**. 151, 1895 ; **72**. 87, 256, 1895 ; **78**. 98, 1898 ; **94**. 144, 1906 ; P. T. Cleve, *ib.*, **71**. 212, 1895 ; *Compt. Rend.*, **120**. 834, 1895 ; H. Deslandres, *ib.*, **120**. 1112, 1331, 1895 ; **179**. 5, 1924 ; C. Bouchard, *ib.*, **121**. 392, 1895 ; L. Troost and L. Ouvrard, *ib.*, **121**. 394, 1895 ; C. Moureu, *ib.*, **121**. 819, 1895 ; **142**. 1155, 1906 ; M. Berthelot, *ib.*, **124**. 113, 1897 ; *Ann. Chim. Phys.*, (7), **11**. 15, 1897 ; J. Dewar, *ib.*, (7), **17**. 12, 1899 ; *Proc. Roy. Soc.*, **64**. 231, 1899 ; J. Dewar and E. Curie, *Compt. Rend.*, **138**. 190, 1904 ; *Journ. Phys.*, (4), **3**. 193, 1904 ; C. A. Young, *Nature*, **52**. 458, 1895 ; C. Runge, *ib.*, **52**. 128, 1895 ; **53**. 245, 1896 ; C. Runge and F. Paschen, *ib.*, **52**. 520, 1895 ; *Chem. News*, **72**. 181, 1895 ; *Chem. Ztg.*, **19**. 997, 1895 ; *Sitzber. Akad. Berlin*, 639, 759, 1895 ; *B.A. Rep.*, 610, 1895 ; *Astrophys. Journ.*, **3**. 4, 1896 ; G. E. Hale, *ib.*, **2**. 165, 384, 1895 ; J. F. Mohler and L. E. Jewell, *ib.*, **3**. 351, 1896 ; J. R. Rydberg, *ib.*, **4**. 91, 1896 ; **7**. 233, 1899 ; *Wied. Ann.*, **58**. 674, 1896 ; A. Hagenbach, *ib.*, **60**. 124, 1887 ; A. Hagenbach and H. Konen, *Atlas der Emissionsspectra*, Jena, 1905 ; W. Huggins, *Chem. News*, **71**. 283, 1895 ; **72**. 27, 1895 ; H. Kayser, *ib.*, **72**. 89, 1895 ; J. H. van Vleck, *Phys. Rev.*, (2), **21**. 372, 1923 ; R. T. Dufford and L. Thompson, *ib.*, (2), **21**. 212, 1923 ; C. B. Bazzoni and J. T. Lay, *ib.*, (2), **25**. 885, 1925 ; J. S. Foster, *ib.*, (2), **23**. 667, 765, 1924 ; A. Udden and J. C. Jacobsen, *ib.*, (2), **23**. 322, 1924 ; C. B. Bazzoni and J. T. Lay, *ib.*, (2), **23**. 327, 769, 1924 ; K. T. Compton, E. G. Lilly, and P. S. Olmstead, *ib.*, (2), **16**. 282, 1920 ; K. T. Compton, *Phil. Mag.*, (6), **40**. 553, 1920 ; E. A. Hill, *Amer. Journ. Science*, (3), **50**. 359, 1895 ; H. Wilde, *Phil. Mag.*, (5), **40**. 466, 1895 ; G. Trowbridge and T. W. Richards, *ib.*, (5), **43**. 77, 135, 1897 ; A. de Forest Palmer, *ib.*, (5), **40**. 547, 1895 ; *Amer. Journ. Science*, (3), **50**. 357, 1895 ; A. C. Davies, *ib.*, (6), **45**. 786, 1923 ; R. Nasini, J. Anderlini, and R. Salvadvri, *Mem. Accad. Lincei*, (5), **2**. 375, 1895 ; A. E. Ruark, P. D. Foote, and F. L. Mohler, *Journ. Amer. Opt. Soc.*, **8**. 17, 1924 ; J. S. Ames and W. J. Humphreys, *Astrophys. Journ.*, **5**. 97, 1897 ; A. A. Michelson, *ib.*, **7**. 131, 1898 ; *Nature*, **59**. 440, 1899 ; *Phil. Mag.*, (5), **45**. 348, 1898 ; A. Schuster, *ib.*, **57**. 320, 1898 ; H. M. Hansen and S. Werner, *ib.*, **112**. 618, 1923 ; S. Werner, *ib.*, **115**. 191, 1925 ; E. C. C. Baly, *ib.*, **58**. 545, 1898 ; A. Gray and W. Stewart, *ib.*, **65**. 54, 1901 ; H. Nagaoka, *ib.*, **81**. 188, 1909 ; P. G. Nutting and O. Tugman, *ib.*, **81**. 189, 1900 ; *Bull. Bur. Standards*, **7**. 49, 1911 ; P. G. Nutting, *ib.*, **8**. 487, 1912 ; *Nature*, **92**. 401, 1913 ; P. W. Merrill, *Astrophys. Journ.*, **46**. 357, 1917 ; N. A. Kent and R. M. Frye, *ib.*, **37**. 183, 1913 ; L. W. Taylor, *ib.*, **56**. 16, 1922 ; J. Thomsen, *Zeit. phys. Chem.*, **25**. 112, 1898 ; W. Heuse, *Verh. deut. phys. Ges.*, **2**. 16, 1900 ; F. Gehrcke and O. Reichenheim, *ib.*, **10**. 217, 1908 ; E. Goldstein, *ib.*, **15**. 402, 1913 ; Lord Rayleigh, *Phil. Mag.*, (6), **1**. 100, 1901 ; (6), **11**. 685, 1906 ; (6), **15**. 548, 1908 ; G. Berndt, *Ann. Physik*, (4), **8**. 625, 1902 ; L. Janicki and E. Lau, *ib.*, (4), **71**. 562, 1923 ; F. Himstedt and G. Meyer, *ib.*, (4), **17**. 1005, 1905 ; F. Gehrcke and O. von Baeyer, *ib.*, (4), **20**. 269, 1906 ; F. Paschen and E. Back, *ib.*, (4), **39**. 897, 1912 ; F. Paschen, *ib.*, (4), **27**. 537, 1908 ; (4), **29**. 628, 1909 ; (4), **50**. 901, 1916 ; R. Seeliger and F. Pommering, *ib.*, (4), **59**. 589, 1919 ; H. Gerdien and R. Holm, *ib.*, (4), **27**. 844, 1908 ; J. Koch, *ib.*, (4), **48**. 98, 1915 ; J. Stark, *Phys. Zeit.*, **8**. 397, 1907 ; *Verh. deut. phys. Ges.*, **16**. 468, 1914 ; *Astrophys. Journ.*, **74**. 129, 687, 1910 ; *Ann. Physik*, (4), **56**. 577, 1918 ; G. Liebert, *ib.*, (4), **56**. 600, 1918 ; A. Sommerfeld, *ib.*, (4), **51**. 1, 1916 ; *Ann. Physik*, (4), **65**. 36, 1921 ; J. Schniederjost, *Beiträge zur Kenntnis der Spectra von Wasserstoff, Helium, Luft, Stickstoff, und Sauerstoff im Ultraviolet*, Halle, 1904 ; *Zeit. wiss. Photochem.*, **2**. 265, 1904 ; W. Lohmann, *Zeit. wiss. Photochem.*, **6**. 25, 1908 ; *Beiträge zur Kenntnis des Zeeman-Phänomens*, Halle, 1906 ; *Phys. Zeit.*, **7**. 809, 1906 ; T. Indrikson, *ib.*, **5**. 214, 1904 ; H. Rau, *Ann. Physik*, (4), **73**. 266, 1924 ; *Phys. Zeit.*, **7**. 421, 1907 ; **8**. 360, 1907 ; J. Stark and F. Giesel, *ib.*, **8**. 580, 1907 ; J. Stark, A. Fischer, and H. Kirschbaum, *Ann. Physik*, (4), **40**. 499, 1913 ; W. Wein, *ib.*, (4), **73**. 483, 1924 ; J. Stark, *Sitzber. Akad. Berlin*, 932, 1913 ; J. Stark and G. von Wendt, *Ann. Physik*, (4), **38**. 669, 690, 1912 ; J. Stark and H. Kirschbaum, *Phys. Zeit.*, **11**. 433, 1913 ; E. Dorn, *ib.*, **8**. 589, 1907 ; F. J. von Wisniewsky, *ib.*, **26**. 255, 1925 ; W. Ritz, *ib.*, **9**. 521, 1908 ; F. Giesel, *Ber.*, **38**. 2299, 1905 ; **39**. 2244, 1906 ; A. A. C. Swinton, *Proc. Roy. Soc.*, **79**. A, 134, 1907 ; W. E. Curtis, *ib.*, **89**. A, 146, 1913 ; **101**. A, 38, 1922 ; **103**. A, 315, 1923 ; F. W. Aston and T. Kikuchi, *ib.*, **98**. A, 50, 1920 ; A. L. Hughes and P. Lowe, *ib.*, **104**. A, 480, 1923 ; *Phys. Rev.*, (2), **21**. 714, 1921 ; F. Bordas, *Compt. Rend.*, **146**. 628, 896, 1908 ; **147**. 591, 1908 ; G. Claude, *ib.*, **148**. 1454, 1909 ; J. E. Purvis, *Proc. Cambridge Phil. Soc.*, **25**. 45, 1908 ; Y. Takahashi, *Proc. Phys. Math. Soc. Japan*, **4**. 187, 1922 ; W. M. Hicks, *A Treatise on the Analysis of Spectra*, Cambridge, 1922 ; *Nature*, **104**. 393, 1919 ; **110**. 309, 1923 ; **111**. 146, 1923 ; N. Bohr, *ib.*, **92**. 231, 1923 ; *Phil. Mag.*, (6), **26**. 1, 476, 1913 ; *Danske Selsk. Skrif.*, (8), **4**. 101, 1922 ; R. W. Lawson, *Phil. Mag.*, (6), **26**. 966, 1913 ; A. Gray, W. Stewart, R. A. Honstoun, and D. B. McQuistan, *Proc. Roy. Soc.*, **72**. 16, 1903 ; R. C. Johnson, *ib.*, **106**. A, 195, 1924 ; A. Gray and W. Stewart, *Nature*, **65**. 54, 1901 ; H. Nagaoka, *ib.*, **81**. 188, 1909 ; C. Fabry and H. Buisson, *Journ. Phys.*, (5), **2**. 442, 1912 ; *Observatory*, **36**. 217, 1913 ; *Compt. Rend.*, **154**. 1224, 1912 ; W. Grotrian, *Naturwiss.*, **11**. 321, 1923 ; H. A. Kramers, *Zeit. Physik*, **13**. 343, 351, 1923 ; W. Steubing and M. Toussaint, *ib.*, **21**. 128, 1924 ; W. Tschulanowsky, *ib.*, **16**. 300, 1923 ; H. C. Urey, *ib.*, **29**. 86, 1924 ; G. Déjardin, *Journ. Phys. Rad.*, **4**. 121, 1923 ; *Ann. Physique*, (10), **2**. 241, 1924 ; A. Kratzer, *Zeit. Physik*, **13**. 82, 1923 ; **16**. 353, 1923 ; W. Tschulanowsky, *ib.*, **16**. 300, 1923 ; L. S. Ornstein and H. C. Burger, *ib.*, **26**. 57, 1924 ; B. Curry, *Phys. Rev.*, (2), **21**. 203, 1923 ;

R. A. Millikan and I. S. Bowen, *ib.*, (2), **23.** 1, 1924; L. B. Ham, *ib.*, (2), **23.** 104, 1924; A. Udden and J. C. Jacobsen, *ib.*, (2), **23.** 322, 1924; J. S. Forster, *ib.*, (2), **23.** 293, 1924; E. O. Hulburt, *ib.*, (2), **23.** 107, 1924; H. M. Hansen and J. C. Jacobson, *Medd. Kopenhagen*, **3.** 11, 1923; *Phys. Ber.*, **5.** 50, 1924; L. S. Ornstein and H. C. Burger, *Zeit. Physik*, **26.** 57, 1924; E. J. von Wisniewsky, *Phys. Zeit.*, **25.** 297, 1924; D. Brunetti, *Atti Accad. Lincei*, (5), **33.** ii, 413, 1924; K. W. Meissner, *Phys. Zeit.*, **26.** 687, 1925; W. E. Curtis and W. Jevons, *Nature*, **116.** 746, 1925; T. Takamine, *Chem. News*, **133.** 167, 1926; T. Takamine and N. Kokubu, *Mem. Coll. Science Kyoto*, **3.** 271, 275, 1919; F. M. Kannenstine, *Phys. Rev.*, (2), **22.** 115, 1922; (2), **23.** 107, 1924; *Astrophys. Journ.*, **59.** 135, 1924; M. Marshall, *ib.*, **60.** 142, 1924; J. P. Dempster, *ib.*, **59.** 142, 1924; J. S. Foster, *ib.*, **63.** 191, 1926; *Nature*, **116.** 135, 1926; *Phys. Rev.*, (2), **23.** 765, 1924; J. Franck and F. Reiche, *Zeit.*, *Physik*, **1.** 154, 1920; A. Tandé, *Kerh. deut. phys. Ges.*, **21.** 585, 1919; C. Eckart, *Phys. Rev.*, (2), **26.** 454, 1925; D. A. Keys and H. S. Home, *ib.*, (2), **27.** 709, 1926; L. W. Taylor, *ib.*, (2), **19.** 255, 1923; H. B. Dorgelo, *Zeit. Physik*, **34.** 766, 1925; H. Nyquist, *Proc. Nat. Acad. Science*, **3.** 399, 1917; J. C. Slater, *ib.*, **11.** 732, 1925; R. S. Mulliken, *ib.*, **12.** 158, 1926; W. A. McNair and W. H. McCurdy, *Nature*, **117.** 159, 1926; W. H. McCurdy, *Phil. Mag.*, (7), **2.** 529, 1926; H. Bell, *ib.*, (6), **40.** 489, 1920; P. Tartakowsky, *Zeit. Physik*, **34.** 216, 1925; S. Goudsmit and G. E. Uhlenbeck, *Physica*, **5.** 266, 1925; T. A. Merton and J. G. Pilley, *Proc. Roy. Soc.*, **109.** A, 267, 1926; F. Hund, *Zeit. Physik*, **33.** 345, 1925; H. B. Dorgelo and J. H. Arbink, *ib.*, **37.** 667, 1926; D. Burger, *ib.*, **38.** 437, 1926; A. Unsöld, *ib.*, **36.** 92, 1926; P. Kunze, *Ann. Physik*, (4), **79.** 610, 1926; F. Paschen, *Sitzber. Akad. Berlin*, **135**, 1926; H. P. Waran, *Cambridge Phil. Soc.*, **20.** 45, 1920; U. Yoshida, *Mem. Coll. Science Kyoto*, **4.** 187, 1920; K. Skaupy, *Zeit. Physik*, **3.** 175, 1920; A. Landé, *Phys. Zeit.*, **20.** 228, 1919.

[13] G. D. Liveing and J. Dewar, *Proc. Roy. Soc.*, **67.** A, 467, 1900; H. E. Watson, *ib.*, **81.** A, 181, 1908; *Proc. Cambridge Phil. Soc.*, **16.** 130, 1911; *Astrophys, Journ.*, **33.** 399, 1911; E. C. C. Baly, *Proc. Roy. Soc.*, **72.** A, 84, 1913; *Phil. Trans.*, **202.** A, 183, 1903; W. M. Hicks, *ib.*, **220.** A, 335, 1920; *A Treatise on the Analysis of Spectra*, Cambridge, 1922; I. G. Priest, *Bull. Bur. Standards*, **8.** 2, 1912; W. F. Meggers, *ib.*, **12.** 198, 1915; K. Burns, W. F. Meggers, and P. W. Merrill, *Measurements of Wave-lengths in the Spectrum of Neon*, Washington, 1918; H. Nagaoka, *Proc. Phys. Soc.*, **33.** 83, 1921; K. W. Meissner, *Ann. Physik*, (4), **51.** 115, 1916; (4), **58.** 333, 1919; *Phys. Zeit.*, **17.** 549, 1916; G. Wentzel, *ib.*, **24.** 104, 1923; F. Paschen, *Ann. Physik*, (4), **60.** 405, 1919; (4), **63.** 201, 1920; (4), **76**, 124, 1925; A. Sommerfeld, *ib.*, (4), **63.** 221, 1920; E. Back, *ib.*, (4), **76.** 317, 1925; W. Grotrian, *Phys. Zeit.*, **21.** 638, 1920; *Zeit. Physik*, **8.** 116, 1921; P. Jordan, *ib.*, **31.** 377, 1925; A. Landé, *ib.*, **5.** 231, 1921; **7.** 398, 1921; **11.** 353, 1922; **17.** 292, 1923; *Phys. Zeit.*, **22.** 417, 1921; A. Landé and W. Heisenberg, *Zeit. Physik*, **25.** 279, 1924; R. Rossi, *Phil. Mag.*, (6), **26.** 981, 1913; L. St. C. Broughall, *ib.*, (6), **43.** 339, 1922; (6), **44.** 204, 1929; T. R. Merton, *Proc. Roy. Soc.*, **89.** A, 447, 1914; W. Ramsay and M. W. Travers, *ib.*, **63.** 437, 1898; F. W. Aston and T. Kikuchi, *ib.*, **98.** A, 50, 1920; A. Fowler, *Report on Series in Line Spectra*, London, 1922; W. Lohmann, *Zeit. wiss. Photochem.*, **6.** 25, 1908; *Beiträge zur Kenntnis des Zeeman-Phenomens*, Halle, 1906; *Phys. Zeit.*, **7.** 809, 1906; **9.** 145, 1908; E. Dorn, *ib.*, **8.** 589, 1907; J. E. Purvis, *Proc. Cambridge Phil. Soc.*, **15.** 45, 1909; S. Goudsmit, *Zeit. Physik*, **32.** 111, 1925; H. Nagaoka and T. Takamine, *Proc. Tokyo Univ.*, (2), **5.** 278, 1910; C. Fabry and H. Buisson, *Observatory*, **36.** 217, 1913: *Journ. Phys.*, (5), **2.** 442, 1912; G. Wentzel, *Phys. Zeit.*, **24.** 104, 1923; H. Deslandres, *Compt. Rend.*, **179.** 5, 1924; A. Pérard, *Compt. Rend.*, **176.** 375, 1923; H. Buisson and C. Jausseran, *ib.*, **180.** 505, 1924; G. Déjardin, *ib.*, **182.** 452, 1926; L. and E. Block and G. Déjardin, *ib.*, **180.** 731, 1925; **182.** 451, 1926; *Journ. Phys. Rad.*, **7.** 129, 1926; L. Vegard, H. K. Onnes, and W. H. Keesom, *Compt. Rend.*, **180.** 1084, 1925; W. H. J. Childs, *Nature*, **115.** 572, 1925; G. Hertz and J. C. S. de Visser, *Zeit. Physik*, **31.** 470, 1925; G. Hertz, *Naturwiss.*, **13.** 489, 1925; T. Lyman and F. A. Saunders, *Phys. Rev.*, (2), **25.** 886, 1925; *Nature*, **116.** 358, 1925; H. P. Waran, *Proc. Cambridge Phil. Soc.*, **20.** 45, 1920; O. Otsuka, *Zeit. Physik*, **36.** 786, 1926; H. B. Dorgelo and J. H. Arbink, *ib.*, **37.** 667, 1926; W. H. J. Childs, *Nature*, **115.** 572, 1925; K. Burns, *Journ. Amer. Opt. Soc.*, **11.** 301, 1925; J. S. Foster, *Phys. Rev.*, (2), **23.** 293, 1925; L. B. Ham, *ib.*, (2), **23.** 107, 1925; W. H. B. Cameron, *Phil. Mag.*, (7), **1.** 405, 1926; M. R. and R. C. Johnson, *ib.*, (7), **2.** 593, 1926; G. S. Monk, *Astrophys. Journ.*, **62.** 375, 1925; H. Nyquist, *Proc. Nat. Acad. Science*, **3.** 399, 1917; K. W. Meissner, *Phys. Zeit.*, **26.** 687, 1925; H. B. Dorgelo, *Physica*, **5.** 90, 1925; F. Hund, *Zeit. Physik*, **34.** 296, 1925; F. Holweck, *Compt. Rend.*, **182.** 53, 1925.

[14] Lord Rayleigh and W. Ramsay, *Proc. Roy. Soc.*, **57.** 265, 1895; **60.** 56, 1896; *Phil. Trans.*, **186.** A, 187, 1895; E. C. C. Baly, *ib.*, **202.** A, 183, 1903; Lord Rayleigh, *Proc. Roy. Inst.*, **14.** 524, 1895; *Nature*, **52.** 159, 1895; W. Ramsay, *ib.*, **52.** 224, 1895; *Chem. News*, **72.** 51, 1895; *Compt. Rend.*, **120.** 1049, 1895; W. Ramsay, J. N. Collie, and M. W. Travers, *Proc. Roy. Soc.*, **58.** 81, 1895; A. Kellas and W. Ramsay, *ib.*, **59.** 66, 68, 1895; W. Ramsay and J. N. Collie, *ib.*, **59.** 257, 1896; **60.** 53, 206, 1896; *Compt. Rend.*, **123.** 214, 1896; H. Deslandres, *ib.*, **179.** 5, 1924; M. Berthelot, *ib.*, **120.** 581, 662, 797, 1386, 1895; **124.** 113, 1897; *Ann. Chim. Phys.*, (7), **7.** 5, 1896; (7), **11.** 15, 1897; W. W. Shaver, *Trans. Roy. Soc. Canada*, **16.** iii, 135, 1922; C. Bouchard, *Compt. Rend.*, **121.** 392, 1895; L. Troost and L. Ouvrard, *ib.*, **121.** 394, 1895; C. Moureu, *ib.*, **121.** 819, 1895; **142.** 1155, 1906; C. Déjardin, *ib.*, **172.** 1347, 1921; **173.** 1782, 1921; L. and E. Block and C. Déjardin, *ib.*, **178.** 766, 1924; *Ann. Physique*, (10), **2.** 461, 1925; A. A. Michelson, *Nature*, **59.** 440, 1899; W. Crookes, *ib.*, **51.** 354, 1895; *Phil. Trans.*, **166.** A, 243, 1895; *Chem. News*, **72.** 99, 1895; H. E. Armstrong, *ib.*, **71.** 115, 1895;

W. R. E. Hodgkinson, *ib.*, **71**. 248, 1895 ; H. Kayser, *ib.*, **72**. 89, 99, 1895 ; *Sitzber. Akad. Berlin,* 551, 1896 ; *Chem. News,* **72**. 89, 99, 1895 ; *Chem. Ztg.,* **19**. 1549, 1895 ; *Astrophys. Journ.,* **4**. 1, 1896 ; P. G. Nutting, *ib.*, **19**. 239, 1904 ; C. Runge, *ib.*, **9**. 281, 1899 ; C. Runge and F. Paschen, *ib.*, **8**. 97, 1898 ; J. R. Rydburg, *ib.*, **6**. 338, 1897 ; H. F. Newall, *Proc. Roy. Soc.,* **57**. 346, 1895 ; W. N. Hartley, *ib.*, **57**. 293, 1895 ; *Chem. News,* **74**. 209, 1896 ; H. A. Barton, *Nature,* **114**. 826, 1924 ; E. Dorn and H. Erdmann, *Liebig's Ann.,* **287**. 230, 1892 ; E. Dorn, *Phys. Zeit.,* **8**. 589, 1907 ; E. Paulson, *ib.*, **15**. 831, 1914 ; *Astrophys. Journ.,* **41**. 75, 1915 ; *Beiträge zur Kenntnis der Linienspektren,* Lund, 1914 ; J. M. Eder and E. Valenta, *Anz. Akad. Wien,* **32**. 218, 1895 ; *Sitzber. Akad. Wien,* **114**. 1171, 1895 ; *Denks. Akad. Wien,* **63**. 189, 1896 ; *Monatsh.,* **16**. 893, 1895 ; **17**. 50, 1896 ; P. G. Nutting and O. Tugman, *Bull. Bur. Standards,* **7**. 49, 1911 ; P. G. Nutting, *ib.*, **4**. 511, 1908 ; W. F. Meggers, *ib.*, **17**. 193, 1921 ; *Phys. Rev.,* (2), **18**. 160, 1921 ; B. Hodgson and L. S. Palmer, *Radio Rev.,* **1**. 525, 1920 ; E. A. Hill, *Amer. Journ. Science,* (3), **50**. 359, 1895 ; J. Trowbridge and T. W. Richards, *ib.*, (4), **3**. 15, 117, 1897 ; *Phil. Mag.,* (5), **43**. 77, 135, 1897 ; H. Donaldson, *ib.*, (6), **22**. 720, 1911 ; R. W. Lawson, *ib.*, (6), **26**. 966, 1913 ; R. C. Johnson and W. H. B. Cameron, *Proc. Roy. Soc.,* **106**. A, 195, 1924 ; R. C. Johnson, *Phil. Mag.,* (6), **48**. 1069, 1924 ; G. Stead and B. S. Gossling, *ib.*, (6), **40**. 413, 1920 ; W. M. H˙cks, *ib.*, (6), **45**. 480, 1923 ; *A Treatise on the Analysis of Spectra,* Cambridge, 1922 ; R. Nasini, E. Anderlini, and R. Salvadvri, *Nature,* **58**. 269, 1898 ; *Mem. Accad. Lincei,* (5), **2**. 375, 1895 ; *Rend. Accad. Lincei,* (5), **7**. ii, 73, 269, 1898 ; *Atti Accad. Lincei,* (5), **5**. 25, 1904 ; S. Friedländer, *Zeit. phys. Chem.,* **19**. 657, 1896 ; M. Bamberger, *Monatsh.,* **17**. 604, 1896 ; G. B. Rizzo, *Atti Accad. Torino,* **32**. 830, 1897 ; O. Neovius, *Wied. Ann.,* **66**. 162, 1898 ; C. Sheard, *Phys. Rev.,* (1), **27**. 258, 1908 ; L. A. Turner, *ib.*, (2), **26**. 143, 1925 ; J. C. McLennan, *ib.*, (2), **10**. 84, 1917 ; H. C. Tentschler, *ib.*, (2), **13**. 297, 1919 ; C. G. Found, *ib.*, (2), **16**. 41, 1920 ; H. Fricke, *ib.*, (2), **16**. 202, 1920 ; P. Lowe and D. C. Rose, *Trans. Roy. Soc. Canada,* (3), **18**. 313, 1924 ; A. Ladenburg and C. Krügel, *Sitzber. Akad. Berlin,* 211, 1900 ; E. Warburg, *ib.*, 1196, 1904 ; G. Berndt, *Ann. Physik,* (4), **8**. 625, 1902 ; P. Zeeman and H. W. J. Dik, *ib.*, (4), **71**. 199, 1923 ; E. Gehrcke and O. von Baeyer, *ib.*, (4), **20**. 269, 1906 ; F. Paschen, *ib.*, (4), **27**. 537, 1908 ; J. E. Lilienfeld, *ib.*, (4), **16**. 931, 1905 ; K. W. Meissner, *ib.*, (4), **50**. 713, 1916 ; (4), **51**. 95, 1916 ; *Phys. Zeit.,* **17**. 549, 1916 ; *Untersuchungen und Wellenlängenbestimmungen im roten und infraroten Spektralbezirk,* Tübingen, 1916 ; A. Hagenbach and H. Konen, *Atlas der Emissions spectra,* Jena, 1905 ; A. S. King, *Astrophys. Journ.,* **21**. 344, 1905 ; T. Lyman, *ib.*, **33**. 98, 1911 ; N. A. Kent and R. M. Frye, *ib.*, **37**. 183, 1913 ; J. J. Hopfield and S. W. Leifson, *ib.*, **58**. 59, 1923 ; C. V. Raman and A. S. Ganesan, *ib.*, **57**. 243, 1923 ; L. Silberstein, *ib.*, **57**. 248, 1923 ; F. Fischer and G. Iliovici, *Ber.,* **41**. 4449, 1908 ; W. Lohmann, *Beiträge zur Kenntnis des Zeeman-Phänomens,* Halle, 1906 ; L. Hamburger, *Over Licht-emissie door gassen en mengsels van gassen bij electrische ontladingen,* Amsterdam, 1917 ; *Zeit. wiss. Photochem.,* **18**. 1, 1918 ; W. Stahl, *ib.*, **9**. 302, 1911 ; *Untersuchungen über die Spektrum des Argons,* Bonn, 1911 ; O. Lüttig, *Das Zeeman-Phänomen im sichtbasen Spektrum von Mangan und Argon,* Halle, 1911 ; *Ann. Physik,* (4), **38**. 43, 1912 ; J. Stark, G. Wendt, H. Kirschbaum, and R. Künzer, *ib.*, (4), **42**. 241, 1913 ; K. Friedersdorff, *ib.*, (4), **47**. 737, 1915 ; E. Böttcher and F. Tuczek, *ib.*, (4), **61**. 107, 1919 ; R. Seeliger and E. Pommering, *ib.*, (4), **59**. 589, 1919 ; R. Seeliger and G. Mierdel, *Zeit. Physik,* **5**. 182, 1921 ; R. Seeliger and E. Schramm, *ib.*, **7**. 93, 1921 ; R. Seeliger, *ib.*, **5**. 182, 1921 ; **7**. 93, 1921 ; A. Dufour, *Le Raàium,* **8**. 97, 1911 ; A. Fowler, *Report on Series in Line Spectra,* London, 1922 ; G. Stead, *Proc. Cambridge Phil. Soc.,* **16**. 607, 1912 ; J. Franck and G. Hertz, *Phys. Zeit.,* **20**. 132, 1919 ; J. Franck, *ib.*, **22**. 466, 1921 ; K. A. Nissen, *ib.*, **21**. 25, 1920 ; W. Steubing, *ib.*, **23**. 427, 1922 ; F. Horton and A. Davies, *Nature,* **104**. 406, 1919 ; *Phys. Rev.,* (2), **15**. 498, 1920 ; *Proc. Roy. Soc.,* **97**. A, 1, 1920 ; **102**. A, 131, 1922 ; J. Frommel, *Die Ergebnisse der Serienforschung,* Tübingen, 1920 ; E. Böttcher, *Der Effekt des elektrischen Feldes im Spektrum des Argons und Sauerstoff,* Greisswald, 1919 ; E. Schramm, *Die Anregung der Lichtemission durch den Stoss schneller Elektronen,* Greisswald, 1921 ; P. Zeeman and H. W. J. Dijk, *Proc. Acad. Amsterdam,* **25**. 67, 1922 ; *Ann. Physik,* (4), **71**. 199, 1923 ; T. L. de Bruin and P. Zeeman, *Nature,* **114**. 352, 1924 ; P. Lowe and D. C. Rose, *Phys. Rev.,* (2), **23**. 770, 1924 ; F. A. Saunders, *ib.*, (2), **27**. 799, 1926 ; T. Lyman and F. A. Saunders, *ib.*, (2), **25**. 886, 1925 ; *Nature,* **116**. 358, 1925 ; D. Coster and J. H. van der Tuuk, *ib.*, **117**. 586, 1926 ; *Zeit. Physik,* **37**. 347, 1926 ; K. W. Meissner, *ib.*, **37**. 238, 1926 ; W. Schütz, *ib.*, **38**. 864, 1926 ; W. F. Meggers, *Scient. Papers Bur. Standards,* **17**. 193, 1921 ; A. G. Worthing and R. Rudy, *Phys. Rev.,* (2), **23**. 767, 1924 ; J. J. Hopfield and G. H. Dieke, *ib.*, (2), **27**. 638, 1926 ; T. Takamine and N. Kokubu, *Mem. Coll. Science Kyoto,* **3**. 281, 1919 ; A. E. Ruark and R. L. Chenault, *Phil. Mag.,* (6), **50**. 937, 1925 ; E. Böttcher and F. Tuczek, *Ann. Physik,* (4), **61**. 107, 1920.

¹⁵ W. Ramsay and M. W. Travers, *Compt. Rend.,* **126**. 1610, 1898 ; *Nature,* **58**. 127, 1898 ; *Zeit. Phys. Chem.,* **26**. 362, 1898 ; **38**. 641, 1901 ; *Proc. Roy. Soc.,* **63**. 405, 1898 ; G. D. Liveing and J. Dewar, *ib.*, **68**. 389, 1901 ; W. Ramsay, *Nature,* **59**. 53, 1898 ; C. Runge, *ib.*, **59**. 29, 1890 ; *Astrophys. Journ.,* **10**. 73, 1899 ; *Nature,* **59**. 29, 1898 ; E. C. C. Baly, *Phil. Trans.,* **202**. A, 183, 1903 ; *Proc. Roy. Soc.,* **72**. 84, 1904 ; W. Lohmann, *Phys. Zeit.,* **7**. 809, 1906 ; **9**. 145, 1908 ; *Zeit. wiss. Photochem.,* **6**. 25, 1908 ; *Beiträge zur Kenntnis des Zeeman-Phänomens,* Halle, 1906 ; R. Schmidt, *Verh. deut. phys. Ges.,* **8**. 277, 1906 ; A. Ladenburg and C. Krügel, *Sitzber. Akad. Berlin,* 211, 1900 ; P. W. Merrill, *Measurements of the Wave-lengths in the Spectrum of Neon,* Washington, 1919 ; E. Paulson, *Ann. Physik,* (4), **45**. 428, 1914 ; W. F. Meggers, *Scient. Papers Bur. Standards,* **17**. 193, 1921 ; W. M. Hicks, *Phil. Trans.,* **220**. A, 335, 1920 ; *A Treatise*

on the Analysis of Spectra, Cambridge, 199, 1922; A. Fowler, Report on Series in Line Spectra, London, 179, 1922; C. Fabry and H. Buisson, Observatory, 36. 217, 1913; Journ. Phys., (5), 2. 442, 1912; Compt. Rend., 154. 1224, 1912; L. and E. Block and G. Déjardin, Ann. Physique, (10), 2. 461, 1924; Compt. Rend., 178. 766, 1924; G. Déjardin, Ann. Physique, (14), 2. 241, 1924; M. de Broglie and A. Lepape, ib., 176. 1611, 1923; J. N. Collie, Proc. Roy. Soc., 97. A, 349, 1920; O. Otsuka, Zeit. Physik, 36. 786, 1926.

[16] E. Paulson, Astrophys. Journ., 40. 307, 1914; C. Runge, ib., 10. 73, 1899; E. C. C. Baly, Proc. Roy. Soc., 72. 84, 1904; Phil. Trans., 202. A, 183, 1904; W. M. Hicks, ib., 220. A, 335, 1920; A Treatise on the Analysis of Spectra, Cambridge, 199, 1922; W. Ramsay and M. W. Travers, B.A. Rep., 828, 1898; Phil. Trans., 179. A, 47, 1901; Proc. Roy. Soc., 67. 329, 1900; A. T. Cameron and W. Ramsay, ib., 81. A, 210, 1908; A. Fowler, Report on Series in Line Spectra, London, 179, 1922; G. D. Liveing and J. Dewar, Proc. Roy. Soc., 68. 389, 1901; B. B. Ray, Phil. Mag., (6), 48. 707, 1924; W. F. Meggers, Scient. Papers Bur. Standards, 17. 193, 1921; P. W. Merrill, Measurements of the Wave-lengths in its Spectrum of Neon, Washington, 1918; W. Lohmann, Zeit. wiss. Photochem., 6. 25, 1908; Beiträge zur Kenntnis des Zeeman-Phänomens, Halle, 1906; Phys. Zeit., 7. 809, 1906; 9. 145, 1908; L. and E. Block and G. Déjardin, Ann. Physique, (10), 2. 461, 1924; Compt. Rend., 178. 766, 1924; A. Broglie and A. Lepape, ib., 176. 1611, 1923; A. Lepape and A. Dauvillier, ib., 177. 34, 1923; L. A. Sommer, Phys. Zeit., 13. 85, 1923; J. N. Collie, Proc. Roy. Soc., 97. A, 349, 1920.

[17] R. W. Wood, Phil. Mag., (6), 22. 469, 1911; (6), 24. 673, 1912; Phys. Zeit., 12. 1204, 1911; K. Fredenhagen, ib., 12. 909, 1911; 14. 1047, 1913; R. W. Wood and J. Franck, ib., 12. 81, 1911; Phil. Mag., (6), 22. 469, 1911; H. E. Watson, Proc. Cambridge Phil. Soc., 17. 90, 1913; W. Ramsay and F. Soddy, Proc. Roy. Soc., 73. 346, 1904; Chem. News, 89. 245. 266, 1904; J. C. McLennan and G. M. Shrum, Proc. Roy. Soc., 106. A, 138, 1924; P. G. Nutting, Bull. Bur. Standards, 4. 511, 1908; 8. 487, 1912; P. G. Nutting and O. Tugman, ib., 7. 49, 1911; Astrophys. Journ., 81. 189, 1909; E. Liebenthal, Zeit. Instrkunde, 15. 157, 1895; 43. 209, 1923; C. C. Paterson, Journ. Inst. Elect. Eng., 38. 271, 1906; A. Boltzmann and A. Basch, Sitzber. Akad. Wien, 131. 1, 1922; N. Schoorl, Ber., 56. B, 1047, 1923; K. von Auwers, ib., 49. 827, 1916; S. O. Pearson and H. S. G. Anson, Proc. Phys. Soc., 34. 175, 204, 1922; L. Vegard, Compt. Rend., 179. 151, 1924; B. N. Ghose, Phys. Rev., (2), 25. 66, 1925; J. W. Ryde, Nature, 112. 944, 1923; R. A. Brockbank and L. E. Ryall, Electrician, 90. 2, 1923; J. Taylor and W. Stephenson, ib., 94. 145, 1925; A. Palme, Elect. World, 81. 216, 1923; E. Karrer and A. Poritsky, Phys. Rev., (2), 23. 110, 1924; F. W. Aston, Proc. Cambridge Phil. Soc., 19. 300, 1919; R. Seeliger and G. Mierdel, Zeit. Physik, 5. 182, 1921; G. Déjardin, Ann. Physique, (10), 2. 241, 1924; A. L. Foley, Proc. Indiana Acad., 34. 185, 1925; M. N. Saha, Phil. Mag., (6), 41. 267, 1921.

[18] F. Schröter, Zeit. Sauerstoff Ind., 12. 43, 1920; Naturwiss., 8. 631, 1920; Technik Ind., 333, 1911; Zeit. Elektrotech., 35. 943, 1914; Zeit. Elektrochem., 24. 132, 1918; O. Schaller, ib., 24. 131, 1918; W. R. Cooper and P. C. Hewitt, U.S. Pat. Nos. 682690, 1901; 814695, 1906; L. Zehnder, Phys. Zeit., 13. 446, 1912; G. Claude, Compt. Rend., 151. 1122, 1910; 157. 432, 1913; 158. 479, 692, 1914; 180. 890, 1925; H. E. Watson, Proc. Cambridge Phil. Soc., 17. 90, 1913; U. A. Oschwald and A. G. Tarrant, Proc. Phys. Soc., 36. 262, 1924; T. Hamburger, Zeit. wiss. Photochem., 18. 1, 1917; F. Skaupy, Zeit. tech. Phys., 1. 189, 1920; German Pat., D.R.PP. 286753, 1913; 341871, 1915; J. Pintsch, ib., 336571, 1918; 355288, 355855, 1917; H. Danzer, ib., 299540, 1917; J. Nienhold, ib., 310751, 1916; E. Urbain, C. Scal, and W. Feige, ib., 235152, 1910; Compt. Rend., 150. 548, 1910; J. C. McLennan, Journ. Chem. Soc., 117. 938, 1920; R. B. Moore, Trans. Amer. Electrochem. Soc., 44. 175, 1923; H. Greinacher, Elektrotech. Zeit., 35. 259, 1914; M. Pirani and A. R. Meyer, ib., 36. 496, 507, 1915; K. Hellmuth, ib., 45. 579, 1924; P. Hardegen, ib., 43. 921, 1922; P. G. Nutting, Bull. Bur. Standards, 4. 511, 1908; 8. 487, 1912; Journ. Washington Acad., 1. 221, 1911; L. K. Hirshberg, Journ. Gas Lighting, 118. 720, 1912; G. Holst and E. Oösterhuis, Versl. Akad. Amsterdam, 29. 849, 1920; I. Rosenthal, Verh. deut. phys. Ges., 10. 828, 1908; H. C. Snook, Brit. Pat. No. 12256, 1913; Journ. Franklin Inst., 175. 9, 1913; R. Rudy, ib., 202. 374, 1926; F. Dorn, Ann. Physik, (4), 16. 784, 1905; (4), 20. 127, 1906; B. E. Shackelford, Chem. Met. Engg., 26. 703, 1922; H. Harting, Arch. Optik, 1. 97, 1907; Zeit. Instrkunde, 28. 273, 1908; O. von Auwers, Ber., 49. 828, 1916; N. Schoorl, ib., 56. A, 1047, 1923; J. Elster and H. Geitel, Phys. Zeit., 12. 609, 758, 1911; W. Ramsay and G. Rudorf, Die Edelgase, Leipzig, 318, 1918.

[19] J. Rosenthal, Verh. deut. phys. Ges., 10. 828, 1908; Phys. Zeit., 9. 803, 1908; J. Elster and H. Geitel, ib., 11. 257, 1910; 12. 609, 614, 758, 1911; 13. 468, 739, 852, 1912; K. Bergwitz, ib., 8. 373, 1907; U. A. Oschwald and A. G. Farrow, Proc. Phys. Soc., 36. 214, 1924; V. L. Chrisler, Phys. Rev., (1), 27. 269, 1908; H. Dember, Ann. Physik, (4), 20. 379, 1906; P. P. Koch, ib., (4), 39. 705, 1912; (4), 40. 797, 1913; (4), 41. 115, 1913; J. S. Townsend and S. P. McCallum, Phil. Mag., (6), 47. 737, 1924; P. Auger, Journ. Phys. Rad., 6. 205, 1925; F. L. Mohler, Phys. Rev., (2), 28. 46, 1926.

[20] J. N. Collie and W. Ramsay, Proc. Roy. Soc., 59. 257, 1896; F. Soddy and T. D. Mackenzie, ib., 80. 92, 1908; F. Soddy, ib., 78. 429, 1907; Chem. News, 95. 15, 28, 42, 51, 1907; R. J. Strutt, Phil. Trans., 193. A, 377, 1900; Phil. Mag., (5), 49. 293, 1901; H. Donaldson, ib., (6), 22. 720, 1911; N. Bohr, ib., (6), 25. 10, 1913; R. T. Beatty, ib., (6), 26. 183, 1913; Phys. Zeit., 14. 622, 1913; F. Ritter, Ann. Physik, (4), 14. 118, 1904; H. Erfle, ib., (4), 23. 594, 1907; Verh. deut. phys. Ges., 10. 331, 1908; W. Heuse, ib., 2. 16, 1900; Ann. Physik, (4), 5. 678, 1901;

J. P. Ewers, *ib.*, (4), **17**. 781, 1905; H. Dember, *ib.*, (4), **20**. 379, 1906; E. W. B. Gill and F. B. Pidduck, *Phil. Mag.*, (6), **16**. 280, 1908; (6). **23**. 837, 1912; J. S. Townsend and H. E. Hurst, *ib.*, (6), **8**. 738, 1904; J. J. Thomson, *ib.*, (6), **13**. 561, 1907; (6), **16**. 657, 1908; (6), **20**. 752, 1910; (6), **21**. 225, 1911; (6), **24**. 668, 1912; *Proc. Roy. Inst.*, **19**. 171, 1908; *Nature*, **79**. 52, 1908; **91**. 333, 1913; E. Warburg, *Ann. Physik*, (4), **3**. 295, 1900; W. Kossel, *ib.*, (4), **37**. 393, 1912; J. Wachsmuth and B. Winawer, *ib.*, (4), **42**. 585, 1913; E. Dorn, *ib.*, (4), **16**. 784, 1905; (4), **20**. 127, 1906; K. Rottgardt, *ib.*, (4), **33**. 1161, 1910; J. Stark, A. Fischer, and H. Kirschbaum, *ib.*, (4), **40**. 499, 1913; J. Stark and H. Kirschbaum, *Phys. Zeit.*, **14**. 433, 1913; K. Przibram, *Sitzber. Akad. Wien*, **116**. 557, 1907; A. Perot, *Compt. Rend.*, **156**. 1679, 1913; G. Glaude, *ib.*, **155**. 968, 1912; **157**. 432, 1913; B. Davis, *Phys. Rev.*, (1), **20**. 129, 1905; E. R. Stockle, *ib.*, (2), **19**. 258, 1922; K. T. Compton and C. Eckast, *ib.*, (2), **25**. 139, 1925; R. T. Piersol, *ib.*, (2), **23**. 296, 1924; C. A. Skinner, *ib.*, (1), **21**. 1, 169, 1905; *Phil. Mag.*, (6), **12**. 481, 1906; *Phys. Zeit.*, **6**. 610, 1905; E. Gehrcke and O. Reichenheim. *ib.*, **11**. 732, 1910; *Verh. deut. phys. Ges.*, **10**. 217, 1908; **12**. 414, 1910; E. Gehrcke and R. Holm, *Ann. Physik*, (4), **27**. 844, 1908; R. Holm. *Phys. Zeit.*, **9**. 558, 1909; **10**. 158, 1910; J. Stark and J. Giesel, *ib.*, **8**. 580, 1907; L. Zehnder, *ib.*, **13**. 446, 1912; K. Mey, *Verh. deut. phys. Ges.*, **5**. 72, 1903; G. Gehlhoff, *ib.*, **13**. 182, 266, 1911; **14**. 960, 1912; G. Gehrcke and P. Seeliger, *ib.*, **14**. 335, 1023, 1912; O. Reichenheim, *ib.*, **15**. 658, 1913; R. Defregger, *Ann. Physik*, (4), **12**. 662, 1903; K. W. Meissner, *ib.*, (4), **76**. 124, 1925; J. Königsberger and J. Kutschewsky, *ib.*, (4), **37**. 161, 1912; R. Whiddington, *Proc. Cambridge Phil. Soc.*, **15**. 183, 1909; H. E. Watson, *ib.*, **17**. 90, 1903; F. W. Aston and H. E. Watson, *Proc. Roy. Soc.*, **86**. A, 168, 1912; J. N. Collie, *ib.*, **82**. A, 378, 1909; F. Horton and A. C. Davies, *ib.*, **95**. A, 408, 1919; E. Bouty, *Compt. Rend.*, **138**. 616, 1691, 1904; **145**. 225, 1907; **150**. 149, 1386, 1643, 1910; *Journ. Phys.*, (4), **3**. 489, 1904; (4), **4**. 317, 1905; *Ann. Chim. Phys.*, (8), **23**, 5. 1911; J. Franck, *Jahrb. Rad. Elektron.*, **9**. 235, 1912; *Verh. deut. phys. Ges.*, **12**. 291, 1910; G. Gehlhoff, *ib.*, **12**. 411, 1910; **13**. 182, 266, 271, 1911; J. Franck and G. Hertz, *ib.*, **15**. 34, 373, 613, 929, 1913; *Phys. Zeit.*, **14**. 1115, 1913; H. K. Onnes, *Comm. Phys. Lab. Leiden*, 112, 1909; P. G. Nutting and O. Tugman, *Bull. Bur. Standards*, **7**. 50, 1911; F. Fischer and G. Iliovici, *Ber.*, **41**. 3802, 1908; T. S. Taylor, *Phil. Mag.*, (6), **26**. 402, 1913; E. Rutherford and J. M. Nuttall, *ib.*, (6), **26**. 702, 1913; G. W. C. Kaye, *Proc. Phys. Soc.*, **25**. 198, 1913; K. T. Compton, E. G. Lilly, and P. S. Olmstead, *Phys. Rev.*, (2), **16**. 282, 1920; E. O. Hulbert, *ib.*, (2), **20**. 104, 127, 1922; K. T. Compton, *Phil. Mag.*, (6), **40**. 553, 1920; K. T. Compton and C. Eckart, *Phys. Rev.*, (2), **25**. 139, 1925; F. M. Kannenstine, *ib.*, (2), **19**. 540, 1923; R. Bär, M. von Laue, and E. Meyer, *Zeit. Physik*, **20**. 83, 1923; R. Bär, *ib.*, **31**. 430, 1925; P. Jordan, *ib.*, **31**. 877, 1925; A. Ruttenauer, *ib.*, **10**. 269, 1922; A. Günther-Schulze, *ib.*, **22**. 70, 97, 1924; **28**. 129, 1924; **33**. 810, 1925; **34**. 549, 1925; *Zeit. Elektrochem.*, **30**. 386, 1924; G. Holst and E. Oösterhuis, *Physica*, **4**. 42, 1924; W. de Groot, *ib.*, **5**. 234, 1925; H. Fischer, *Zeit. phys. Chem.*, **104**. 74, 1923; H. E. Watson and G. R. Paranjpe, *Journ. Indian Inst.*, **2**. 143, 166, 1918; W. Kossel, *Jahrb. Rad. Elektron.*, **18**. 326, 1921; R. Rudy, *Journ. Franklin Inst.*, **201**. 802, 1926; S. P. McCallum and C. M. Focken, *Phil. Mag.*, (6), **49**. 1309, 1925; J. S. Townsend and S. P. McCallum, *ib.*, (6), **47**. 737, 1924; R. G. Lunnon, *ib.*, (7), **1**. 482, 1926; W. H. McCurdy and P. Dalton, *Phys. Rev.*, (2), **27**. 163, 1926; T. E. Foulke, *ib.*, (2), **23**. 776, 1924; A. J. Dempster, *ib.*, (2), **27**. 804, 1926; F. A. Thees, *Journ. Electricity*, **56**. 225, 1926; A. Moskvin, *Russ. Electrichestoo*, **8**. 464, 1925; G. Holst and G. Oösterhuis, *Physica*, **1**. 78, 1921; F. M. Penning, *Phys. Zeit.*, **27**. 187, 1926; H. Geffcken, *ib.*, **26**. 241, 1925; T. Kikuchi, *Proc. Roy. Soc.*, **99**. A, 257, 1921: F. W. Aston and T. Kikuchi, *ib.*, **98**. A, 50, 1920; A. Duvallier, *Compt. Rend.*, **182**. 575, 1926; W. Clarkson, *Proc. Phys. Soc.*, **37**. 130, 1924; **38**. 10, 1925.

[21] E. P. Metcalfe, *Phil. Mag.*, (6), **18**. 878, 1909; L. B. Loeb, *ib.*, (6), **46**. 517, 1923; C. A. Mackay, *Phys. Rev.*, (2), **21**. 717, 1923; (2), **23**. 553, 1924; *Phil. Mag.*, (6), **46**. 828, 1923; J. S. Townsend, *ib.*, (6), **45**. 1071, 1923; (6), **46**. 657, 1923; F. Horton, *ib.*, (6), **39**. 592, 1920; L. St. C. Broughall, *ib.*, (6), **43**. 339, 1922; E. W. B. Gill and F. B. Pidduck, *ib.*, (6), **16**. 280, 1908; (6), **23**. 837, 1912; T. S. Taylor, *ib.*, (6), **26**. 402, 1913; E. P. Adams, *ib.*, (6), **6**. 563, 1903; N. Bohr, *ib.*, **25**. 10, 1913; R. T. Beatty, *ib.*, (6), **26**. 183, 1913; E. Rutherford and J. M. Nuttall, *ib.*, (6), **26**. 702, 1913; A. C. Davies, *ib.*, (6), **45**. 786, 1923; T. L. R. Ayres, *ib.*, (6), **45**. 353, 1923; J. Franck and R. Pohl, *Verh. deut. phys. Ges.*, **9**. 194, 1907; J. Franck, *Jahrb. Rad. Elektron.*, **9**. 235, 1912; W. Kossel, *ib.*, **18**. 326, 1921; *Ann. Physik*, (4), **37**. 393, 1912; H. B. Wahlin, *Proc. Nat. Acad. Science*, **10**. 475, 1924; *Phys. Rev.*, (2), **27**. 588, 1926; P. Auger, *Compt. Rend.*, **180**. 65, 266, 1925; S. P. McCallum and C. M. Focken, *Phil. Mag.*, (6), **49**. 1309, 1925; J. J. Thomson, *The Conduction of Electricity through Gases*, Cambridge, 50, 1906; A. Becker, *Zeit. Elektrochem.*, **9**. 600, 1903; *Ann. Physik*, (4), **17**. 381, 1905; C. Ramsauer, *ib.*, (4), **72**. 345, 1923; P. Lenard, *ib.*, (4), **12**. 714, 1903; H. Gerdien and R. Holm, *ib.*, (4), **27**. 844, 1908; F. Paschen, *ib.*, (4), **29**. 625, 1909; J. Robinson, *ib.*, (4), **31**. 769, 1910; *Phys. Zeit.*, **11**. 11, 1910; C. L. and F. A. Lindemann, *ib.*, **13**. 104, 1912; J. Franck and G. Hertz, *ib*, **14**. 1115, 1913; *Verh. deut. phys. Ges.*, **15**. 34, 373, 613, 929, 1913; C. F. Hull, *Astrophys. Journ.*, **25**. 1, 1907; A. J. Dempster, *ib.*, **59**. 142, 1924; *Proc. Nat. Acad.*, **12**. 96, 1926; I. Langmuir and H. A. Jones, *Science*, (2), **59**. 380, 1924; *Phys. Rev.*, (2), **27**. 806, 1926; H. Rau, *Phys. Zeit.*, **7**. 421, 1906; **8**. 360, 1907; J. Stark, *ib.*, **8**. 397, 1907; E. Dorn, *ib.*, **8**. 589, 1907; J. C. McLennan, *Phys. Rev.*, (2), **10**. 84, 1917; C. G. Found, *ib.*, (2), **16**. 41, 1920; K. T. Compton, *Phil. Mag.*, (6), **40**. 553, 1920; *Phys. Rev.*, (2), **22**. 432, 1923; H. C. Rentschler, *ib.*, (2), **13**. 297, 1919; (2), **14**. 503, 1920; G. K. Rollefson, *ib.*, (2), **25**. 740, 1925; L. Silberstein, *ib.*, (2), **21**. 721, 1923; A. L. Hughes and A. A. Dixon, *ib.*, (2), **10**. 495, 1917; A. L. Hughes and E. Klein, *ib.*, (2),

23. 111, 1924 ; A. L. Hughes and F. E. Poindexter, *ib.*, (2), **23.** 769, 1924 ; L. B. Loeb, *ib.*, (2), **23.** 157, 1924 ; C. G. Found and S. Dushman, *ib.*, (2), **23.** 734, 1924 ; J. T. Tykociner and J. Kunz, *ib.*, (2), **25.** 245, 1925 ; K. T. Compton and C. G. Lilly, *Astrophys. Journ.*, **52.** 1, 1920 ; K. T. Compton, E. G. Lilly and P. S. Olmstead, *ib.*, (2), **16.** 282, 1920 ; K. T. Compton and C. C. van Voorhis, *ib.*, (2), **25.** 245, 1925 ; (2), **26.** 436, 1925 ; (2), **27.** 724, 1926 ; H. D. Smyth and H. A. Barton, *ib.*, (2), **25.** 245, 1925 ; F. Horton and A. C. Davies, *ib.*, (2), **15.** 498, 1920 ; *Nature*, **104.** 406, 1919 ; *Proc. Roy. Soc.*, **97.** A, 1, 1920 ; **100.** A, 399, 1921 ; F. Horton and A. C. Davies, *ib.*, **95.** A, 333, 408, 1919 ; **102.** A, 131, 1922 ; P. M. S. Blacket, *ib.*, **102.** A, 294, 1922 ; G. Stead and B. S. Gossling, *Phil. Mag.*, (6), **40.** 413, 1920 ; L. A. Turner, *ib.*, (6), **48.** 1010, 1924 ; J. Franck, *Phys. Zeit.*, **22.** 466, 1921 ; J. Franck and P. Knipping, *ib.*, **20.** 481, 1919 ; G. Hertz, *Proc. Acad. Amsterdam*, **25.** 90, 179, 442, 1923 ; **27.** 179, 1922 ; **28.** 767, 1925 ; *Zeit. Physik*, **18.** 307, 1923 ; **32.** 933, 1925 ; G. Hertz and R. K. Kloppers, *Physica*, **4.** 367, 1924 ; *Zeit. Physik*, **31.** 463, 1925 ; G. Hertz and J. C. S. de Visser, *ib.*, **31.** 470, 1925 ; H. A. Erikson, *Phys. Rev.*, (2), **25.** 890, 1925 ; (2), **26.** 465, 1925 ; H. A. Barton, *ib.*, (2), **25.** 469, 1925 ; G. A. Anslow, *ib.*, (2), **25.** 484, 1925 ; R. B. Brode, *ib.*, (2), **23.** 664, 1924 ; (2), **25.** 636, 1925 ; C. B. Bazzoni, *Journ. Franklin Inst.*, **196.** 627, 1923 ; C. B. Bazzoni and J. T. Lay, *Phys. Rev.*, (2), **23.** 554, 1924 ; (1), **25.** 885, 1925 ; G. Déjardin, *Ann. Physique*, (10), **2.** 241, 1924 ; *Journ. Phys. Rad.*, **4.** 121, 1923 ; *Compt. Rend.*, **176.** 894, 1923 ; **178.** 1069, 1924 ; F. Holweck, *Journ. Chim. Phys.*, **22.** 311, 1925 ; *Compt. Rend.*, **173.** 709, 1925 ; **180.** 266, 1925 ; **182.** 53, 1215, 1926 ; P. Auger and F. Perrin, *ib.*, **175.** 340, 1922 ; J. S. Townsend, *Journ. Franklin Inst.*, **200.** 563, 1925 ; J. S. Townsend and V. A. Bailey, *Phil. Mag.*, (6), **42.** 875, 1921 ; (6), **43.** 5936, 1127, 1922 ; (6), **44.** 1033, 1922 ; (6), **46.** 657, 1923 ; V. A. Bailey, *ib.*, (6), **47.** 319, 1924 ; F. Horton and D. Bailey, *ib.*, (6), **40.** 400, 1920 ; F. Horton and A. C. Davies, *ib.*, (6), **41.** 921, 1921 ; F. Horton, *ib.*, (6), **40.** 440, 1920 ; W. M. Hicks, *ib.*, (6), **45.** 480, 1923 ; C. Ramsauer, *Ann. Physik*, (4), **64.** 513, 1921 ; (4), **66.** 546, 1921 ; (4), **72.** 345, 1923 ; H. Sponer, *Zeit. Physik*, **18.** 249, 1923 ; R. Minkowsky and H. Sponer, *ib.*, **15.** 399, 1923 ; J. Franck, *ib.*, **11.** 155, 1922 ; J. Franck and P. Knipping, *Phys. Zeit.*, **20.** 481, 1919 ; *Zeit. Physik*, **1.** 320, 1920 ; F. M. Kannenstine, *Astrophys. Journ.*, **55.** 345, 1923 ; *Phys. Rev.*, (2), **22.** 115, 1922 ; (2), **23.** 107, 1924 ; W. P. Jesse, *ib.*, (2), **26.** 208, 1925 ; R. B. Brode, *ib.*, (2), **23.** 664, 1924 ; (2), **25.** 636, 1925 ; E. G. Dymond, *Proc. Cambridge Phil. Soc.*, **22.** 405, 1924 ; *Nature*, **115.** 910, 1925 ; H. A. Barton, *ib.*, **114.** 826, 1924 ; D. M. Bose and S. K. Ghosh, *ib.*, **111.** 463, 1923 ; L. Silberstein, *ib.*, **111.** 567, 1923 ; L. F. Bates, *Proc. Roy. Soc.*, **106.** A, 622, 1924 ; E. G. Dymond, *ib.*, **107.** A, 291, 1925 ; R. W. Gurney, *ib.*, **107.** A, 332, 340, 1925 ; J. F. Lehmann and I. H. Osgood, *Nature*, **116.** 242, 1925 ; G. P. Thomson, *ib.*, **117.** 235, 1926 ; G. Glocker, *Phil. Mag.*, (6), **50.** 997, 1925 ; *Nature*, **115.** 909, 1925 ; *Phys. Rev.*, (2), **27.** 423, 1926 ; W. W. Merrymon, *ib.*, (2), **27.** 659, 1926 ; R. Rudy, *ib.*, (2), **27.** 807, 1926 ; E. R. Stoekle, *ib.*, **19.** 258, 1922 ; T. E. Foulke and W. H. McCurdy, *ib.*, (2), **23.** 776, 1924 ; F. L. Mohler, *Science*, (2), **63.** 405, 1926 ; W. H. McCurdy, *Proc. Nat. Acad. Science*, **12.** 231, 1926 ; *Phil. Mag.*, (7), **2.** 529, 1926 ; J. Chadwick and K. G. Emeléus, *Phil. Mag.*, (7), **1.** 1, 1926 ; J. M. Nuttall and E. J. Williams, *ib.*, (7), **1.** 1217, 1926 ; W. de Groot, *Naturwiss.*, **14.** 104, 1926 ; *Physica*, **6.** 53, 1926 ; H. F. Mayer, *Ann. Physik*, (4), **64.** 469, 1921 ; L. B. Loeb and E. Condon, *Journ. Franklin Inst.*, **200.** 595, 1926 ; R. H. Fowler, *Proc. Cambridge Phil. Soc.*, **21.** 521, 531, 1923 ; G. H. Henderson, *Phil. Mag.*, (6), **44.** 680, 1922 ; S. Rosseland, *ib.*, (6), **45.** 65, 1923 ; H. R. Hassé, *ib.*, (7), **1.** 139, 1926 ; J. J. Thomson, *ib.*, (7), **2.** 674, 1926 ; L. F. Bates, *Proc. Roy. Soc.*, **106.** A, 622, 1924 ; F. Strewe, *Zeit. Physik*, **36.** 410, 1926 ; F. Skaupy, *ib.*, **2.** 213, 1920 ; **3.** 175, 1920 ; *Verh. deut. phys. Ges.*, **19.** 264, 1917 ; E. G. Dymond, *Nature*, **118.** 336, 1926 ; I. Langmuir, *Phys. Rev.*, (2), **27.** 806, 1926 ; W. Elsasser, *Naturwiss.*, **13.** 711, 1925 ; J. C. McLennan and E. Evans, *Trans. Roy. Soc. Canada*, (3), **14.** 19, 1921 ; V. L. Chrisler, *Phys. Zeit.*, **10.** 745, 1909 ; L. Hamburger, *Zeit. wiss. Photochem.*, **18.** 1, 1919 ; F. S. Goucher, *Proc. Phys. Soc.*, **33.** 13, 1920 ; R. Seeliger and E. Schramm, *Zeit. Physik*, **7.** 93, 1921 ; L. S. Palmer, *Radio Rev.*, **2.** 113, 1921.

²² C. and M. Cuthbertson, *Proc. Roy. Soc.*, **84.** A, 13, 1910 ; T. Alty, *ib.*, **106.** A, 315, 1924 ; **110.** A, 178, 1926 ; E. Hochheim, *Bestimmung der Dielektrizitätskonstante von Helium*, Marburg, 1919 ; *Verh. deut. phys. Ges.*, **10.** 446, 1908 ; G. Joos, *Zeit. Physik*, **19.** 347, 1923 ; P. Tänzler, *Ann. Physik*, (4), **24.** 931, 1908 ; A. P. Wills and L. G. Hector, *Phys. Rev.*, (2), **21.** 475, 1923 ; (2), **23.** 209, 1924 ; L. G. Hector, *ib.*, (2), **24.** 418, 1924 ; M. Wolfke and H. K. Onnes, *Proc. Acad. Amsterdam*, **27.** 621, 1924 ; T. Soné, *Phil. Mag.*, (6), **39.** 305, 1920 ; *Science Rep. Univ. Tohoku*, **8.** 115, 1919 ; G. L. Addenbrooke, *Phil. Mag.*, (7), **1.** 225, 1926 ; L. Crow, *Trans. Roy. Soc. Canada*, (3), **19.** 63, 1925 ; G. Jung, *Zeit. phys. Chem.*, **123.** 281, 1926 ; E. Lehrer, *Zeit. Physik*, **37.** 155, 1926 ; W. Pauli, *ib.*, **2.** 201, 1920 ; B. B. Weatherby and A. Wolf, *Phys. Rev.*, (2), **27.** 252, 1926.

§ 5. The Chemical Properties of the Inert Gases

The term inert gases is applied to this family of elements because of their chemical indifference towards other elements. The small density of helium and its chemical inactivity—*e.g.* its non-inflammability—make it better suited than hydrogen for filling air-ships. The subject was discussed by H. Erdmann, J. C. McLennan,

G. S. Rogers, C. Porlessa, C. Loeser, G. Gallo, W. S. Andrews, etc.   The inflammability of mixtures of hydrogen and helium was studied by P. G. Ledig,[1] and J. Satterly and E. F. Burton.   A mixture of helium with 15 per cent. of hydrogen is non-inflammable and non-explosive.   The supplies of helium associated with natural gas are a convenient source of helium in Canada, and the United States. Other applications of the inert gases have been previously indicated—e.g. in place of hydrogen in thermometry; helium with a b.p. of 4·21° K. has been used as a cryoscopic agent in the study of the properties of matter in the vicinity of absolute zero; and neon, etc., have been used in bulbs for electrical discharge to be employed for illuminating and other purposes.   The use of an artificial atmosphere, with inert gases in place of nitrogen, is indicated below.

W. Ramsay[2] gave 0·0073 for the coeff. of absorption of helium in water at 18·2°; and 0·0394 for argon at 12°, and 0·0405 at 13·9°.   Lord Rayleigh found 100 c.c. of water dissolve 4·05 c.c. of argon at 13·9°.   T. Estreicher determined the solubility of helium and argon in water, and obtained the results indicated in Table VII, expressed in S, the weight of gas taken up by 100 grms. of solvent

TABLE VII.—THE SOLUBILITIES OF HELIUM AND ARGON IN WATER.

	Helium.				Argon.		
		Absorption coefficient.				Absorption coefficient.	
Temp.	S	Minus vap. press. water.	Including vap. press. water.	Temp.	S	Minus vap. press. water.	Including vap. press. water.
0°	0·000270	—	0·0150	0°	0·0102	—	0·0578
0·5°	—	0·0149	0·0149	1°	0·0099	0·0561	0·0561
5°	0·000260	0·0144	0·0146	5°	0·0090	0·0507	0·0508
10°	0·000255	0·0142	0·0144	10°	0·0079	0·0450	0·0453
15°	0·000246	0·0137	0·0140	15°	0·0072	0·0404	0·0410
20°	0·000242	0·0135	0·0139	20°	0·0066	0·0369	0·0379
25°	0·000238	0·0133	0·0137	25°	0·0060	0·0339	0·0347
30°	0·000238	0·0133	0·0138	30°	0·0056	0·0312	0·0326
35°	0·000234	0·0131	0·0138	35°	0·0052	0·0288	0·0305
40°	0·000232	0·0129	0·0139	40°	0·0048	0·0265	0·0286
45°	0·000229	0·0127	0·0140	45°	0·0045	0·0246	0·0273
50°	0·000223	0·0124	0·0140	50°	0·0041	0·0241	0·0257

at a press. of 760 mm. which includes the partial press. of the gas plus that of water; β, the absorption coeff. representing the vol. of gas at 0° and 760 mm. absorbed by one vol. of the liquid.   The data were also examined by C. J. J. Fox, and A. von Antropoff.   H. P. Cady and co-workers measured the solubility of helium and found no minimum on the curve.   A. von Antropoff obtained the solubilities of neon, krypton, and xenon, and the results are indicated in Table VIII.   Excepting

TABLE VIII.—SOLUBILITIES OF THE INERT GASES IN WATER.

Temp.	He	Ne	A	Kr	X
0°	0·0134	0·0114	0·0561	0·1207	0·2189
10°	0·0100	0·0118	0·0438	0·0921	0·1500
20°	0·0138	0·0147	0·0379	0·0729	0·1109
30°	0·0161	0·0158	0·0348	0·0679	0·0900
40°	0·0191	0·0203	0·0338	0·0650	0·0812
50°	0·0226	0·0317	0·0343	0·0716	0·0878

neon, the solubilities increase with increasing at. wt.   The data for neon and krypton are less accurate than those of the others. Minima occur at 10° for helium, 0° for neon, 40° for argon, 35° for krypton, and 40° for xenon. T. Estreicher gave 25° for the minimum with argon. The solubilities of helium and argon were discussed by L. W. Winkler, W. M. Tate, and T. E. Thorpe and J. W. Rodger. P. Villard considered that an *argon hydrate* existed with a dissociation press. of 150 atm. at 0°, and 210 atm. at 8°; R. de Forcrand calculated A.5·14–5·50H$_2$O for the formula at 8°; vap. press., 98·5 atm. at 0°–0·4°, and 210 atm. at 8°; and heat of formation, 14·855 Cals. He also reported *krypton hydrate*, Kr. 5·08H$_2$O; vap. press. 14·5 atm. at 0°, 23·5 atm. at 4·8°, 38·7 atm. at 10·3°, and 47·5 atm. at 12·5°; heat of formation, 14·712 Cals. between 0° and 12°; and the critical point of decomposition, 12·5°–13·0°. The dissociation press. of *xenon hydrate* is 1·15 atm. at 0°. The heat of formation from liquid water is 18·266 cals. No *neon hydrate* was formed at 260 atm. press. at 0°. The dissociation pressures of the hydrates Kr.5H$_2$O, and of A.5(or 6)H$_2$O, were discussed by G. Tammann and G. J. R. Krige.

W. Ramsay found that liquid oxygen at —205° dissolves one part of helium in 80 parts, and a small amount of argon in the *oxygen* raises the solubility. Neon is less soluble than argon in liquid oxygen. He also found that helium is insoluble in *benzene* and in *alcohol*. M. Berthelot said that argon is not absorbed by members of the fatty series of organic compounds, but with members of the aromatic series, absorption varied from 8 per cent. by volume for benzene, and one per cent. for *aniline*. A. von Antropoff measured the solubility of krypton and xenon in *pentane*, and of krypton in *acetic acid*, and aniline. P. Régnard and T. Schlösing found that a litre of *blood* absorbs 25·3 c.c. of argon; G. Gaertner said that nitrogen at high press. is the cause of diving sickness, whilst pure oxygen at press. above 2·5 atm. acts on the lungs as a rapid poison. Helium is innocuous and suitable for the dilution of the oxygen. The subject was discussed by R. R. Sayers and co-workers. J. D. Edwards and S. F. Pickering found that if the permeability of *rubber* to hydrogen be unity, the value for argon is 0·26, and helium 0·65—*vide supra*, diffusion. F. Garelli observed no definite depression of the f.p. when helium is dissolved in several organic solvents.

The **occlusion** of helium by glass electrical discharge tubes was discussed by A. A. C. Swinton,[3] B. Hodgson, N. R. Campbell and J. W. H. Ryde, R. Pohl, and F. Soddy and T. D. Mackenzie. J. Plücker noted that when a discharge tube has been running some time, the gas press. becomes progressively lower with the continuation of the discharge. S. Brodetsky and B. Hodgson favour the view of older workers that the phenomenon is due to the absorption of gas by the metal of the cathode, but add that the disintegrated part is the effective absorber. S. E. Hill found that the phenomenon occurs even with electrodeless tubes, and hence the glass wall of the tube is the absorber. A. A. C. Swinton concluded that the gas is driven into the glass by the discharge so that when the glass is subsequently melted, the gas collects as small bubbles as previously observed by L. G. Gouy, and by P. Villard. The depth of the absorption layer did not exceed 0·015 mm. S. E. Hill, and R. S. Willows attribute the effect to chemical action between the glass and the gas. W. Ramsay found helium, a trace of neon, and hydrogen in the glass of an old X-ray bulb; and A. N. Goldsmith found that high speed molecules of helium and hydrogen can penetrate a mica sheet 0·001–0·006 mm. thick under conditions where air, argon, or carbon dioxide cannot penetrate. G. Claude noted the occlusion of neon by the metal spluttered from the metal cathode of a discharge tube. With a mixture of helium and argon, M. W. Travers found that the latter is more readily absorbed than the former gas. The absorption of argon by magnesium, aluminium, or platinum under similar conditions was discussed by L. Troost and L. Ouvrard, J. M. Eder and E. Valenta, S. Friedländer, B. Brauner, and V. Kohlschütter and co-workers. The occlusion of helium, and argon by solid and liquid metals—Cu, Au, Ni, Fe, Pd, U, Ta—by A. Sieverts and E. Bergner, R. W. Lawson, and A. Jaquerod and F. L. Perrot, and Lord Rayleigh and W. Ramsay found argon is not absorbed by platinum black; and W. Ramsay and

J. N. Collie, and A. F. Benton found that helium is not absorbed by that substance. The occlusion of helium by glass, porcelain, or quartz was studied by A. T. Cameron and W. Ramsay, A. Jaquerod and F. L. Perrot, B. Iliin, and A. Sieverts and E. Bergner—*vide* glass and quartz glass. A. Lo Surdo found hydrogen, helium, and neon are able to pass through hot glass, and G. A. Williams and J. B. Ferguson, E. Cardoso, H. M. Elsey, and C. C. van Voorhis, have discussed this subject. A. Piutti and E. Boggio-Lera found that at 480°, helium cannot traverse thin sheets of mica or thin sections of quartz cut either parallel or perpendicular to the optic axes, though it is able to pass through both ordinary and silica glasses—these glasses are liquids of high viscosity. The occlusion by charcoal has been investigated by J. Dewar, and J. F. Homfray—*vide* carbon ; the occlusion of neon, etc., by J. Dewar, W. Ramsay, H. E. Watson, and S. Valentiner and R. Schmidt ; of argon, by J. Dewar, and J. F. Homfray.

It is not certain that any chemical compound of the inert gases has been yet prepared. W. Ramsay and J. N. Collie [4] said that if combination occurs, the reaction will be endothermal. No method known for the preparation of endothermal compounds has given any result. It is, therefore, assumed that argon and helium cannot form chemical compounds, and that their valency is zero. This view was supported by J. Thomsen, and M. Berthelot—*vide infra*. The chemical affinity of the rare gases is not necessarily zero under all conditions, even though they appear to be so under ordinary conditions. In discussing the architecture of the atom—4. 27, 3—it was shown that atoms like the inert gases, supposed to possess two or eight external electrons, are particularly stable, and null-valent. Helium has two electrons belonging to the external or K-ring or K-shell—Fig. 7, 4. 27, 3—and when bombarded by cathode rays one of these might be knocked off. When a new electron darts back, it may not get into the K-ring at once, but be less firmly bound in some metastable position farther out. Under these conditions the atom of helium might appear to act like an atom of hydrogen. Thus, J. J. Thomson observed particles of mass 5 in the gas which had been in contact with radium chloride for 13 years ; and F. W. Aston observed particles of mass 5 in his examination of helium. It was supposed that these particles are molecules of helium hydride, HeH.

Lord Rayleigh and W. Ramsay found that no combination occurs when argon is subject to the electrical discharge in the presence of oxygen, water, and dry or moist chlorine. At a red heat sulphur, phosphorus, tellurium, and sodium have no action on the gas ; soda-lime, sodium peroxide, molten sodium hydroxide or nitrate are without action. Liquid oxidizing agents—bromine-water, a mixture of potassium permanganate and hydrochloric acid, and aqua regia are without action. Copper, copper oxide, and magnesium at a red heat have no action. T. Schlösing said that heated magnesium absorbs argon ; but R. Nasini and F. Anderlini, and H. von Wartenberg observed no evidence of this at 1500°–2000°. T. Schlösing found cupric oxide, porcelain, asbestos, copper, and steel have no action on argon. H. Moissan detected no sign of combination between argon and titanium, boron, uranium, or lithium; and C. Matignon, none with thorium, cerium, lanthanum, praseodymium, neodymium, or samarium. W. Ramsay thought that carbon and argon could enter into combination. In 1896, M. Berthelot reported that when argon or helium is submitted to the silent electric discharge in the presence of benzene or carbon disulphide, the gas is absorbed, and a solid substance is deposited on the walls of the containing vessel. When this solid is heated, the gas is given off again. This was taken to prove that helium and argon can form chemical compounds. R. J. Strutt showed that the solid product with carbon disulphide is a decomposition product of that compound, and that very little helium is absorbed mechanically or chemically. This was confirmed by W. Crookes, W. Ramsay and J. N. Collie, H. Deslandres, and E. Dorn and H. Erdmann. According to R. J. Strutt, the little absorption which takes place may be likened to the absorption of helium by the aluminium scattered from the cathode of a vacuum discharge tube observed by F. Soddy and T. D. Mackenzie. There is no ground for assuming that helium is chemically absorbed by carbon disulphide under the influence of an electric discharge. Helium is slightly absorbed by phosphorus under electric discharge, but in much less quantity than is hydrogen or nitrogen.

W. Ramsay found that helium is not absorbed by heated cupric oxide, or magnesium ; and no change occurs when a mixture of helium and oxygen is sparked in the presence of potassium hydroxide. W. Ramsay and co-workers demonstrated that red-hot uranium absorbs no helium, and W. Ramsay and J. N. Collie found that at a red-heat sodium, sulphur, selenium, silicon, zinc, cadmium, thallium, tin, lead, phosphorus, arsenic, antimony, bismuth, or cobalt ; or a mixture of magnesium dust and the oxide of beryllium, boron, yttrium, titanium, thorium, or uranium has no action on helium. The silent electric discharge produces no result with a mixture of helium and chlorine. Helium at a red-heat has no action on a mixture of soda-lime with nitre or sulphur. Benzene vapour does not react with helium.

F. Fischer and co-workers tried if sparking between metal cathodes under liquid argon would produce a chemical compound, but in no case was such formed. The metals tried were—Li, Na, K, Rb, Cs, Cu, Ag, Au, Be, Mg, Ca, Sr, Ba, Zn, Cd, Hg, B, Al, In, Tl, C, Si, Ti, Zr, Ce, Th, Sn, Pb, V, Cb, Ta, As, Sb, Bi, Cr, Mo, W, U, Te, Mn, Fe, Co, Ni, Pd, Ir, and Pt. The spluttering of metal cathodes in the inert gases was studied by E. C. C. Baly, W. Crookes, S. Valentiner and R. Schmidt, and V. Kohlschütter and co-workers. The relative degrees of spluttering of different metals in argon, helium, etc., reported by V. Kohlschütter and co-workers are as follow :

	Al	Fe	Cu	Pt	Ag	Au
Hydrogen	0	0	0·23	0·23	0·27	0·5
Helium	0	1	0·1	0·1	0·4	0·25
Nitrogen	0	0	0	0·3	0·4	1·1
Oxygen	0	0·1	0·35	1·2	2·05	3·3
Argon	0·15	0	0·4	1·9	4·1	9

The spluttering was considered to be due to a chemical process. The subject was also discussed by F. Fischer and co-workers, J. Stark, and B. Walter, without any definite conclusion being evident. According to W. T. Cooke, the vapour density of zinc in argon being 12 per cent. higher than in nitrogen, it may be concluded that zinc and argon have a distinct tendency to form a compound. This tendency is found to exist also in the case of cadmium and helium, mercury and argon, mercury and helium, selenium and argon (slight), selenium and helium (slight). H. von Wartenburg considered that there is no evidence of combination ; the results with bismuth, lead, and zinc are normal within the limits of experimental error. J. J. Manley reported that in presence of an electric glow discharge mercury and helium can be made to combine, forming *mercury decahelide*, $HgHe_{10}$, as a stable substance, which decomposes at a bright red-heat. J. J. Manley added that the formation of the helide is accompanied by a decrease in the press. of the helium. The maximum decrease in press. during any synthesis was never greater than 3·3 per cent. of the initial press. of 6 mm. As the synthesis progressed, the refractive index of the mixture became somewhat greater than that of the helium alone. At ordinary temp. the helide possesses stability ; but on passing the gas over a red-hot platinum spiral it is completely resolved into its components ; and as a result of the decomposition the helium is restored to its original vol. and press. The compound is neither liquefied nor absorbed by charcoal at the temp. of liquid air. The helide is most readily formed when the press. of the helium approximates 6 mm. of mercury. J. J. Manley prepared a second helide, *mercury monohelide*, HgHe. This is a gas of density 1·150 (helium unity). It is gaseous at the temp. of liquid air, it is not absorbed by charcoal ; and it is decomposed by passage over a red-hot platinum spiral. E. H. Boomer examined mixtures of helium with mercury, iodine, sulphur, and phosphorus vapours under the influence of electron bombardment and in the presence of surfaces cooled by liquid air. The helium disappears more quickly than under the ordinary conditions in a discharge tube. Solid substances, believed to be compounds of helium, were obtained which suddenly liberate the original amount of helium when warmed to —70° in the cases of *mercury* and *sulphur*, and —125° in the case of *phosphorus*. The vap. press. at —185° are of the order of 0·0005 mm. E. H. Boomer also found that when helium is subjected to an intense electronic bombardment (1000 volts, 5 to 10 milliamp.) at low press. in the presence of a heated tungsten filament, both helium and tungsten disappear and a black deposit is formed. In general, the atomic ratio between the loss in weight of the filament and the loss of helium was 1 : 2, but the proportion of tungsten was increased when a large amount of mercury was present in the discharge tube. In nitric acid or potassium hydroxide, the black deposit was decomposed with the evolution of helium, and the formation of tungstic oxide or a clear soln. If the ratio of tungsten to helium which had disappeared was greater than 1 : 2, only the amount of tungsten necessary to form **tungsten helide**, WHe_2, was dissolved from the black deposit in potassium hydroxide, the tungsten in excess of this ratio remaining in the metallic state. The rate of disappearance of helium was greatest in the press. range 0·1 to 0·45 mm., reaching a value 4 to 5 c.cm. helium at n.p. θ per minute. The velocity of the reaction decreased as the discharge voltage was decreased, and was markedly affected by the material composing the leads, or by the presence of mercury vapour. A. Günther-Schulze inferred from his observations on the cathode fall of potential with mixtures of oxygen with argon and with helium, that reactions do occur though the products cannot be isolated. S. C. Lind and D. C. Bardell could get no evidence of the combination of mercury and helium bombarded by radium rays ; but they found that helium, neon, and argon act catalytically in accelerating the polymerization of acetylene, cyanogen, and hydrogen cyanide, and the synthesis of water.

REFERENCES.

[1] Anon., *Mining Met.*, **6**. 458, 1926 ; P. E. Barbour, *ib.*, **6**. 56, 1926 ; H. Erdman, *Chem. Ztg.*, **43**. 767, 1919 ; G. Gallo, *Rend. 1st. Sper. Aeronaut.*, (2), **9**. 37, 1921 ; W. S. Andrews, *Gen. Elect. Rev.*, **23**. 227, 1920 ; C. Porlessa, *Giorn. Chim. Ind. Appl.*, **2**. 638, 687, 1920 ; C. Loeser, *Umschau*, **26**. 690, 1922 ; J. C. McLennan, *Chem. News*, **126**. 369, 1923 ; *Journ. Chem. Soc.*, **117**. 923, 1920 ; G. S. Rogers, *Chem. News*, **123**. 304, 1921.

[2] T. Estreicher, *Zeit. phys. Chem.*, **31**. 176, 1899 ; L. W. Winkler, *ib.*, **55**. 344, 1906 ; G. Tammann and G. J. R. Krige, *Zeit. anorg. Chem.*, **146**. 179, 1925 ; C. J. J. Fox, *Trans. Faraday Soc.*, **5**. 68, 1909 ; A. von Antropoff, *Zeit. Elektrochem.*, **14**. 585, 1905 ; **25**. 269, 1919 ; *Proc. Roy. Soc.*, **83**. A, 474, 1910 ; P. Régnard and T. Schlösing, *Compt. Rend.*, **124**. 303, 1897 ; M. Berthelot, *ib.*, **129**. 71, 1899 ; Lord Rayleigh, *Chem. News*, **71**. 51, 299, 1895 ; W. Ramsay, *Phil. Trans.*, **186**. A, 225, 1895 ; *Zeit. phys. Chem.*, **55**. 347, 1906 ; *Journ. Chem. Soc.*, **67**. 684, 1895 ; *Ber.*, **31**. 3118, 1898 ; W. M. Tate, *Meddel. Nobelinst.*, **1**. 1, 1906 ; T. E. Thorpe and J. W. Rodger, *Journ. Chem. Soc.*, **65**. 782, 1894 ; P. Villard, *Compt. Rend.*, **123**. 377, 1896 ; R. de Forcrand, *ib.*, **135**. 959, 1902 ; **176**. 355, 1923 ; **181**. 15, 1925 ; J. D. Edwards and S. F. Pickering, *Permeability of Rubber to Gases*, Washington, 1920 ; H. P. Cady, H. M. Elsey, and E. V. Berger, *Journ. Amer. Chem. Soc.*, **44**. 1456, 1922 ; A. Piutti and E. Boggio-Lera, *Atti Accad. Lincei*, (5), **33**. 532 ; 1924 ; *Rend. Accad. Napoli*, (3), **29**. 111, 1923 ; F. Garelli, *Atti Accad. Lincei*, (6), **2**. i, 120, 1925 ; G. Gaertner, *Umschau*, **30**. 50, 1926 ; R. R. Sayers, W. P. Yant, and J. H. Hildebrand, *Journ. Franklin Inst.*, **199**. 560, 1925 ; P. G. Ledig, *Journ. Ind. Eng. Chem.* **12**. 1098, 1920 ; J. Satterly and E. F. Burton, *Trans. Roy. Soc. Canada*, (3), **13**. 211, 1919.

[3] J. Plücker, *Pogg. Ann.*, **104**. 113, 1858 ; **105**. 67, 1858 ; A. A. C. Swinton, *Proc. Roy. Soc.*, **79**. A, 134, 1907 ; **81**. A, 453, 1908 ; **82**. A, 176, 1909 ; *Chem. News*, **95**. 134, 1907 ; **99**. 131, 1909 ; R. Pohl, *Verh. deut. phys. Ges.*, **9**. 306, 1907 ; **11**. 135, 1909 ; F. Soddy and T. D. Mackenzie, *Proc. Roy. Soc.*, **80**. A, 92, 1908 ; W. Ramsay and J. N. Collie, *ib.*, **69**. 53, 206, 1896 ; M. W. Travers, *ib.*, **60**. 449, 1897 ; W. Ramsay, *ib.*, **76**. A, 111, 1905 ; *Journ. Chem. Soc.*, **103**. 264, 1913 ; Lord Rayleigh and W. Ramsay, *Proc. Roy. Soc.*, **57**. 265, 1895 ; *Phil. Trans.*, **186**. A, 187, 1895 ; *Chem. News*, **70**. 87, 1894 ; **71**. 51, 1895 ; W. M. Watts, *ib.*, **97**. 95, 1908 ; *Monthly Weather Rev.*, **35**. 402, 1908 ; R. W. Lawson, *Phys. Zeit.*, **14**. 938, 1913 ; B. Hodgson, *ib.*, **13**. 595, 1912 ; A. T. Cameron and W. Ramsay, *Journ. Chem. Soc.*, **91**. 1266, 1907 ; S. E. Hill, *Proc. Phys. Soc.*, **25**. 35, 1912 ; R. S. Willows, *Phil. Mag.*, (6), **1**. 503, 1901 ; A. Jaquerod and F. L. Perrot, *Compt. Rend.*, **140**. 1542, 1905 ; G. Claude, *ib.*, **153**. 713, 1911 ; **156**. 1317, 1913 ; L. Troost and L. Ouvrard, *ib.*, **121**. 394, 1895 ; *Chem. News*, **72**. 153, 1895 ; L. G. Gouy, *ib.*, **122**. 775,

1197, 1896; **123**. 43, 1896; P. Villard, *ib.*, **123**. 377, 1897; J. **Dewar,** *Ann. Chim. Phys.*, (8), **3**. 5, 1904; *Compt. Rend.*, **139**. 261, 1904; **145**. 110, 1907; *Chem. News*, **94**. 173, 185, 1906; *Proc. Roy. Soc.*, **74**. 122, 1904; **79**. 529, 1907; *Proc. Roy. Inst.*, **18**. 127, 1905; S. Brodetsky and B. Hodgson, *Phil. Mag.*, (6), **31**. 478, 1916; (6), **32**. 239, 1916; N. R. Campbell and J. W. H. Ryde, *ib.*, (6), **40**. 585, 1920; R. J. Strutt, *Proc. Roy. Soc.*, **87**. A, 381, 1912; J. F. Homfray, *ib.*, **84**. A, 99, 1910; *Zeit. phys. Chem.*, **74**. 129, 687, 1910; S. Friedländer, *ib.*, **19**. 657, 1896; *Chem. News*, **74**. 179, 1896; B. Brauner, *ib.*, **71**. 116, 1895; A. Sieverts and E. Bergner, *Ber.*, **45**. 2576, 1912; H. E. Watson, *Journ. Chem. Soc.*, **97**. 810, 1910; A. N. Goldsmith, *Phys. Rev.*, (2), **2**. 16, 1913; S. Valentiner and R. Schmidt, *Sitzber. Akad. Berlin*, 816, 1905; *Ann. Physik*, (4), **18**. 187, 1905; J. M. Eder and E. Valenta, *Monatsh.*, **16**. 893, 1895; **17**. 50, 1896; V. Kohlschütter, *Zeit. Elektrochem.*, **12**. 869, 1906; V. Kohlschütter and T. Goldschmidt, *ib.*, **14**. 221, 1908; V. Kohlschütter and R. Müller, *ib.*, **12**. 365, 1906; A. Lo Surdo, *Atti Accad. Lincei*, (5), **30**. i, 85. 1921; E. Cardoso, *ib.*, (5), **31**. i, 28, 1922; G. A. Williams and J. B. Ferguson, *Journ. Amer. Chem. Soc.*, **44**. 2160, 1922; A. Piutti and E. Boggio-Lera, *Rend. Accad. Napoli*, (3), **29**. 111, 1923; C. C. van Voorhis, *Phys. Rev.*, (2), **23**. 557, 1924; H. M. Elsey, *Journ. Amer. Chem. Soc.*, **48**. 1600, 1926; B. Iliin, *Phil. Mag.*, (6), **50**. 1144, 1925; N. R. Campbell, *ib.*, (6), **41**. 685, 1921; A. F. Benton, *Journ. Amer. Chem. Soc.*, **48**. 1850, 1926.

⁴ F. Fischer and O. Hähnel, *Zeit. Elektrochem.*, **14**. 366, 433, 677, 1908; F. Fischer and G. Iliovici, *Ber.*, **41**. 3802, 4449, 1908; **42**. 527, 1909; F. Fischer and F. Schröter, *ib.*, **43**. 1452, 1454, 1910; V. Kohlschütter, *Liebig's Ann.*, **317**. 158, 1901; *Zeit. Elektrochem.*, **12**. 869, 1906; **14**. 417, 437, 681, 1908; **15**. 316, 930, 1909; **17**. 393, 1911; V. Kohlschütter and T. Goldschmidt, *ib.*, **14**. 221, 1908; V. Kohlschütter and R. Müller, *ib.*, **12**. 365. 1906; V. Kohlschütter and A. Noll, *ib.*, **18**. 419, 1912; A. Günther-Schulze, *ib.*, **30**. 386, 1924; B. Walter, *ib.*, **14**. 695, 1908; J. Stark, *ib.*, **14**. 754, 1908; **15**. 509, 1909; W. Ramsay, *Proc. Roy. Soc.*, **58**. 81, 1895; **59**. 325, 1896; *Chem. News*, **72**. 51, 1895; W. Ramsay, J. N. Collie, and M. W. Travers, *Journ. Chem. Soc.*, **67**. 684, 1895; Lord Rayleigh and W. Ramsay, *Chem. News*, **70**. 87, 1894; **71**. 51, 1895; *Phil. Trans.*, **186**. A, 187, 1895; *Proc. Roy. Soc.*, **57**. 265, 1895; W. Ramsay and J. N. Collie, *ib.*, **60**. 53, 206, 1896; *Compt. Rend.*, **123**. 214, 1896; T. Schlösing, *ib.*, **121**. 525, 604, 1895; **123**. 233, 302, 1896; H. Deslandres, *ib.* **120**. 1112, 1331, 1895; C. Matignon, *ib.*, **131**. 837, 1900; M. Berthelot, *ib.*, **120**. 238, 521, 581, 662, 797, 1386, 1895; **124**. 113, 1897; *Traité prâtique de l'analyse des gaz*, Paris, 1906; *Ann. Chim. Phys.*, (7), **7**. 5, 1896; (7), **11**. 15, 1897; H. Moissan, *Bull. Soc. Chim.*, (3), **13**. 973, 1895; *Chem. News*, **71**. 297, 1895; *Proc. Roy. Soc.*, **58**. 120, 1895; W. T. Cooke, *Zeit. phys. Chem.*, **55**. 537, 1906; *Proc. Roy. Soc.*, **77**. A, 148, 1906; R. J. Strutt, *ib.*, **87**. A, 381, 1912; F. Soddy and T. D. Mackenzie, *ib.*, **80**. A, 92, 1907; E. Dorn and H. Erdmann, *Liebig's Ann.*, **287**. 230, 1895; W. Crookes, *Chem. News*, **72**. 99, 1895; H. von Wartenberg, *Zeit. anorg. Chem.*, **56**. 320, 1907; R. Nasini and F. Anderlini, *Gazz. Chim. Ital.*, **36**. ii, 557, 570, 1906; *Atti Accad Lincei*, (5), **13**. i, 368, 535, 1904; J. Thomsen, *Zeit. phys. Chem.*, **25**. 112, 1898; S. Valentiner and R. Schmidt, *Sitzber. Akad. Berlin*, 816, 1905; *Ann. Physik*, (4), **18** 187, 1905; E. C. C. Baly, *Proc. Roy. Soc.*, **72**. A, 84, 1903; *Phil. Trans.*, **202**. A, 183, 1903; J. J. Manley, *Nature*, **114**. 861, 1924; **115**. 947, 1925; **117**. 587, 1926; E. H. Boomer, *ib.*, **115**. 16, 1925; *Proc. Roy. Soc.*, **109**. A, 198, 1925; S. C. Lind and D. C. Bardwell, *Science*, (2), **61**. 344, 1925; (2), **62**. 593, 1925; *Journ. Amer. Chem. Soc.*, **48**. 1575, 1926; F. W. Aston, *Isotopes*, London, 118, 1924; J. J. Thomson, *Proc. Roy. Soc.*, **101**. A, 290, 1922.

§ 6. The Atomic and Molecular Weights of the Inert Gases

The **molecular weight** of helium obtained by H. E. Watson [1] from the relative density is 3·99; or, calculated from the limiting density, 3·998. W. Heuse gave 4·002; G. P. Baxter and H. W. Starkweather, 4·000; and J. J. van Laar, 3·9998; H. E. Watson found that the mol. wt. of neon is 20·20; and F. W. Aston, 20·19. M. C. Neuberger calculated 3·00113 for the at. wt. of iso-helium. The relative density of argon likewise furnished H. E. Watson, 39·881; J. J. van Laar, 39·95; and P. A. Guye, 39·866. H. E. Watson gave 82·955 for the mol. wt. of krypton, and R. B. Moore, 130·82 for that of xenon, or 130·71 calculated from the compressibility. From the ratio of the sp. hts. of helium it follows that the **atomic weight** and mol. wt. are probably the same; *i.e.* the mol. is monatomic. W. Ramsay obtained a similar conclusion with respect to neon. Lord Rayleigh and W. Ramsay likewise showed the at. wt. of argon is the same as the mol. wt. The experiments of W. Ramsay and co-workers, E. A. Hill, W. Crookes, W. N. Hartley, S. Friedlander, E. C. C. Baly, and F. Fischer and V. Froböse show that there is no reason to regard argon as anything but a simple element. E. W. Wetherell discussed the at. wt. of argon. W. Ramsay, and W. Ramsay and W. M. Travers found the ratio of the sp. hts. of krypton agreed with the at. wt. 83 in accord with the observed mol.

wt. W. Ramsay also found xenon has monatomic molecules with an at. wt. 130·17–130·82. The best representative values are :

	Helium.	Neon.	Argon.	Krypton.	Xenon.
At. wt.	4·00	20·2	39·88	82·92	130·2

The isothermal curves of press. and vol. show no evidence of a polymerization of the mols. of the inert gases on passing into the liquid state. E. C. C. Baly and F. G. Donnan, and G. Rudorf showed that the mol. wt. of argon deduced from the cohesion corresponds with 39·9 ; and S. Chapman obtained values for the viscosity and sp. ht. in harmony with the assumption that the inert gases have monatomic mols. in both the liquid and gaseous states. J. J. Thomson reported the possible existence of xenon and krypton as diatomic mols. because the positive ray analysis of the higher boiling constituents of air showed masses with mol. wts. 163 and 260. F. W. Aston attributed the results to multiple charged xenon, and mercury complexes.

The positive ray analysis of helium by F. W. Aston showed that it is a simple element with no **isotopes**. J. J. Thomson, and F. W. Aston showed that neon possesses two isotopic forms with at. wts. respectively 20 and 22, with a faint possibility of a third isotope of mass 21. F. W. Aston likewise found that argon has two isotopic forms of masses 36 and 40 ; krypton, six isotopes of masses 78, 80, 82, 83, 84, and 86 ; and xenon, seven isotopes of masses 124, 129, 130, 131, 132, 134, and 136 with two other possibles 126 and 128. E. Rutherford and J. Chadwick obtained evidence of **atomic disintegration** where neon, and argon are bombarded by α-rays ; but not with helium, krypton, and xenon. E. Briner observed no evidence of any transmutation when a mixture of helium and hydrogen is exposed to the electric arc.

The alleged synthesis of helium or neon by the action of cathode rays on hydrogen by W. Ramsay,[2] J. N. Collie and H. S. Patterson, and I. Masson was considered by J. J. Thomson to be a *mal*-inference because of the possible evolution of the gas condensed in the occluded state in the electrodes—**4.** 27, 14. A. Lo Surdo thought the foreign gas passed through the heated glass from outside ; but E. Cardoso showed this explanation will not do. No confirmation of the alleged synthesis could be obtained by E. Cardoso, R. J. Strutt, R. T. Merton, A. C. G. Egerton, and A. Piutti and E. Cardoso. S. K. Allison and W. D. Harkins found no helium in the gases left after the passage of electrical discharges between fine wires in vacuo ; through hydrogen ; or through mercury vapour. G. Kirsch and H. Pettersson, and L. F. Bates and J. S. Rogers, discussed the formation of helium as a product of atomic disintegration—*vide* **4.** 26, 7.

The nugatory attempts to prepare compounds of the inert gases with other elements are in harmony with the assumption of L. Errera[3] that these elements are **null-valent**. The possibility of the existence of such elements was indicated by J. Thomsen, F. Flawitzky, and G. J. Stoney. G. Woodiwiss suggested, on unreliable grounds, that the valency of these elements is one-half ; and A. P. Mathews, that the valency has a fractional value. After the discovery of argon, Lord Rayleigh and W. Ramsay suggested that argon should be allocated between chlorine and potassium in the **periodic tables** ; after the discovery of helium, W. Ramsay favoured placing argon and helium between the alkali metals and the halogens ; and after the discovery of neon, krypton, and xenon, W. Ramsay and M. W. Travers proposed arranging the five elements in a special series between the halogens and the alkali metals. It was afterwards suggested by B. Brauner, R. Abegg, A. Werner, and G. Rudorf that the inert gases be placed either as a special group before the alkalies, or else in the eight group. The former suggestion has been adopted. This subject has been discussed by M. Berthelot, L. de Boisbaudran, H. Wilde, C. J. Reed, W. Sedgwick, W. Crookes, A. Piccini, A. von Antropoff, J. L. Howe, P. J. F. Rang, W. W. Andrews, R. Nasini, W. Preyer, R. M. Deeley, J. H. Gladstone, K. Skraupy, and E. A. Hill. Mathematical formulæ for representing the at. wts. of these elements were suggested by A. L. Bernoulli, and J. W. Nicholson.

The **electronic structures** of the atoms of the inert gases are assumed by N. Bohr [4] to be :

Helium (2)	. .	(2)				
Neon (10)	. .	(2)	**(4,4)**			
Argon (18)	. .	(2)	(4,4)	**(4,4)**		
Krypton (36)	. .	(2)	(4,4)	(6,6,6)	**(4,4)**	
Xenon (54)	. .	(2)	(4,4)	(6,6,6)	(6,6,6)	**(4,4)**
Niton (86)	. .	(2)	(4,4)	(6,6,6)	(8,8,8,8)	(6,6,6)	**(4,4)**

and the occurrence of isotopes is explained on the assumption that the nuclear protons in, say, the atoms of neon have 20 or 22 positive charges and respectively 10 or 12 electrons, leaving in both cases the same number of orbital electrons.

E. Rutherford thus described the probable structure of the atoms : The nuclei of the atoms are supposed to be exceedingly minute, and in them is concentrated almost all the mass of the atoms. They carry a positive charge, and are surrounded at appropriate distances (very large in comparison with their own dimensions) by a number of electrons sufficient to render the normal atom neutral. This number is the atomic number of the element. It is 1 in the case of hydrogen, 2 in the case of helium, and so on up to uranium, which has 92 electrons around its nucleus. The hydrogen atom has but one electron, and is the simplest ; the helium atom has 2. It is not quite certain how these two electrons move, but it is generally believed that they move in crossed orbits. The atomic number of lithium is 3, and it has three electrons external to the nucleus. Of these, 2 are arranged in the same way as the 2 of helium, but the third moves in a very much larger orbit. In all the elements, save hydrogen, the two innermost electrons are arranged on the helium model, and are known as the K-electrons. As we pass in order from element to element, the atomic number increases, and when we come to neon there are 10 electrons, of which the two innermost are arranged as in helium, and the remaining 8 form an outer shell. The electrons in this shell belong to what is known as the L-group. The next element after neon is sodium, which has 11 electrons, of which 2 belong, as stated, to the K-group and 8 to the L-group ; whilst with the eleventh a third or M-shell, of much greater radius than the L-shell, commences. After sodium comes magnesium, which has two electrons in the M-shell. This is followed by aluminium, which has in all 13 of these electrons, of which 3 are in the M-shell. Proceeding in this way up the list of the chemical elements, the number in the M-shell increases until it contains 8. The total number is then 18, which is the atomic number of the inert gas argon. After argon comes potassium with 19 electrons, with one of which a new shell known as the N-shell is commenced. In all cases the inert gases mark stepping stones in the list of the chemical elements, and in their outermost shell these inert gases always contain eight electrons. These are not, in all cases, moving in exactly the same way, but in some sense it is evident that they must be very symmetrically arranged, and they, more or less, mark out a space, outside of which there is very little stray force. It is owing to this that the atoms of these gases have very little attraction, either for each other or for those of other elements. All the elements immediately preceding an inert gas have similar properties, and this is also true of those immediately following an inert gas.

W. Kossel, W. Pauli, and E. C. Stoner have suggested other systems ; and the subject has been discussed by H. G. Grimm, J. H. van Vleck, J. H. Jones, H. A. Kramers, M. S. Vallarta, H. Deslandres, R. del Kronig, F. J. von Wisniewsky, I. Woodward, Y. Takahashi, A. Landé, H. S. Allen, H. O. Newboult, C. P. Smyth, H. Collins, O. Halpern, I. Langmuir, W. Kossel, M. Born and W. Heisenberg, A. Sommerfeld, T. M. Lowry, R. T. Birge, R. Reinicke, E. Brummer, V. Trkal, F. R. Bichowsky and H. C. Urey, J. Kudar, P. Tartakowsky, R. S. Mulliken, K. K. Darrow, and A. O. Rankine. The electronic orbits of the atoms of the rare gases were studied by G. E. Gibson, L. St. C. Groughall, J. H. Jones, R. A. Milliken, E. Rutherford, E. Gehrcke, W. Lenz, A. Smekal, W. D. Harkins, T. W. Nicholson, A. C. Crehore, J. Beckenkamp, J. Franck and P. Knipping, J. Franck and F. Reiche, F. C. Kemble, K. F. Herzfeld and K. L. Wolf, etc.

The **atomic numbers** are : helium, 2 ; neon, 10 ; argon, 18 ; krypton, 36 ; xenon, 54 ; and niton, 86. J. C. Thompson found that at. numbers form a simple arithmetical series. L. A. Turner found that a linear relation subsists between the at. number and the quantum defect $n-x$, where n is the quantum number of the electronic orbit ; and x, the effective quantum number defined by $\gamma = R/x^2$, where R is Rydberg's constant, and γ is the value of a spectroscopic term. The life of metastable helium was discussed by A. P. Dempster, and F. M. Kannenstine—*vide supra;* and the general subject, by L. Brüninghaus. G. E. M. Jauncey and A. L. Hughes investigated the radiation which occurs when helium is obtained by the disruption of hydrogen. A. S. Eve discussed this subject.

Owing to the formation of helium as a product of so many radioactive changes —4. 26, 7—it has been suggested that helium—as just indicated, a proton with two electrons—is a structural unit in the architecture of the atoms. This subject has been discussed by A. van den Brock,[5] K. Fajans, E. Gehrcke, W. D. Harkins, E. Kohlweiller, W. Kossel, L. Meitner, S. Miall, M. C. Neuburger, J. W. Nicholson, E. Rutherford and co-workers, J. J. Thomson, F. P. Valeras, H. Wilde, and H. T. Wolff. Attempts to measure the mass of the helium nucleus were made by F. W. Aston,[6] D. M. Rose and S. K. Ghosh, A. Einstein, W. D. Harkins and E. D. Wilson, M. C. Neuburger, F. Paneth, E. Rutherford and co-workers, A. Smekal, A. Sommerfeld, and L. A. Turner; and attempts to measure the dimensions of the helium nucleus were made by C. G. Darwin, M. C. Neuburger, E. Rutherford, L. Silberstein, and A. Smekal.

REFERENCES.

[1] H. E. Watson, *Journ. Chem. Soc.*, 97. 810, 833, 1910; R. B. Moore, *ib.*, 93. 2181, 1908; P. A. Guye, *Compt. Rend.*, 140. 1241, 1905; *Journ. Chim. Phys.*, 3. 321, 1905; Lord Rayleigh and W. Ramsay, *Chem. News*, 70. 87, 1894; 71. 51, 1895; *Proc. Roy. Soc.*, 57. 265, 1895; *Phil· Trans.*, 186. A, 187, 1895; S. Chapman, *ib.*, 211. A, 433, 1912; W. Ramsay, *ib.*, 186. A, 237, 1895; *Proc. Roy. Soc.*, 86. A, 100, 1912; W. Ramsay and M. W. Travers, *ib.*, 63. 405, 1898; 64. 183, 1898; W. Ramsay and J. N. Collie, *ib.*, 60. 206, 1896; F. W. Aston, *ib.*, 89. A, 439, 1913; *Phil. Mag.*, (6). 39. 449, 611, 1920; (6), 45. 935, 1923; (6), 39. 449, 1920; (6), 42. 140, 1921; (6), 49. 1191, 1925; *Nature*, 104. 334, 1919; 111. 739, 1923; *Proc. Roy. Soc.*, 103. A, 462, 1923; *Isotopes*, London, 114, 1922; G. B. Rizzo, *Atti Accad. Torino*, 32. 830, 1897; E. A. Hill, *Amer. Journ. Science*, (3), 50. 359, 1895; S. Friedlander, *Zeit. phys. Chem.*, 19. 657, 1896; *Chem. News*, 74. 179, 1896; W. N. Hartley, *ib.*, 74. 209, 1896; W. Crookes, *Phil. Trans.*, 166. 243, 1895; E. C. C. Baly, *ib.*, 202. A, 183, 1903; *Proc. Roy. Soc.*, 72. 84, 1903; F. Fischer and V. Fröböse, *Ber.*, 44. 92, 1911; W. Heuse, *Verh. deut. phys. Ges.*, 15. 518, 1913; J. J. Thomson, *Rays of Positive Electricity*, London, 1913; *Proc. Roy. Soc.*, 101. A, 290, 1922; E. C. C. Baly and F. G. Donnan, *Journ. Chem. Soc.*, 81. 907, 1902; G. Rudorf, *Ann. Physik*, (4), 29. 751, 1909; E. W. Wetherell, *Chem. News*, 90. 260, 1904; E. Rutherford and J. Chadwick, *Nature*, 113. 457, 1924; G. P. Baxter and H. Starkweather, *Proc. Nat. Acad.*, 11. 231, 1925; 12. 20, 1926; J. J. van Laar, *Chem. Weekbl.*, 16. 1243, 1919; *Journ. Chim. Phys.*, 17. 266, 1919; E. Briner, *ib.*, 19. 9, 1921; M. C. Neuburger, *Phys. Zeit.*, 23. 145, 1922.

[2] R. J. Strutt, *Proc. Roy. Soc.*, 89. A, 499, 1914; R. T. Merton, *ib.*, 90. A, 549, 1914; A. C. G. Egerton, *ib.*, 91. A, 180, 1915; J. N. Collie, *ib.*, 90. A, 554, 1914; 91. A, 30, 1914; J. N. Collie and H. S. Patterson, *Journ. Chem. Soc.*, 103. 419, 1913; W. Ramsay, *ib.*, 91. 931, 1907; A. T. Cameron and W. Ramsay, *ib.*, 91. 1593, 1907; 93. 992, 1908; W. Ramsay and F. L. Usher, *ib.*, 95. 624, 1909; I. Masson, *Proc. Chem. Soc.*, 29. 233, 1913; A. Piutti, *Zeit. Elektrochem.*, 28. 452, 1922; A. Piutti and E. Cardoso, *Journ. Chim. Phys.*, 18. 81, 1920; *Gazz. Chim. Ital.*, 50. i, 5, 1920; A. Piutti and E. Boggio-Lera, *Mem. Accad. Lincei*, (5), 13. 687, 1921; E. Cardoso, *Atti Accad. Lincei*, (5), 31. i, 28, 1922; A. Lo Surdo, *ib.*, (5), 30. i, 85, 1921; S. K. Allison and W. D. Harkins, *Journ. Amer. Chem. Soc.*, 46. 814, 1924; G. Kirsch and H. Pettersson, *Naturwiss.*, 12. 646, 1924; L. F. Bates and J. S. Rogers, *Nature*, 112. 435. 938, 1923; *Proc. Roy. Soc.*, 105. A, 97, 1924; J. J. Thomson, *Nature*, 90. 645, 1913; *Rays of Positive Electricity*, London, 122, 1913.

[3] L. Errera, *Bull. Acad. Belg.*, 152, 1900; Lord Rayleigh and W. Ramsay, *Chem. News*, 71. 51, 1895; *Phil. Trans.*, 186. A, 187, 1895; *Proc. Roy. Soc.*, 57. 265, 1895; W. Ramsay, *Chem. News*, 73, 283, 1896; *Proc. Roy. Soc.*, 58. 81, 1895; W. Ramsay and J. N. Collie, *ib.*, 60. 206, 1896; W. Ramsay and M. W. Travers, *ib.*, 62. 316, 1898; 67. 329, 1900; *Phil. Trans.*, 197. A, 47, 1901; R. Abegg, *Zeit. anorg. Chem.*, 39. 330, 1904; J. Thomsen, *ib.*, 9. 283, 1895; F. Flawitzky, *Ber.*, 11. 264, 1887; A. Werner, *ib.*, 38. 914, 2022, 1905; G. Rudorf, *Das periodische System*, Leipzig, 113, 1904; A. von Antropoff, *Zeit. angew. Chem.*, 37. 217, 1924; G. J. Stoney, *Proc. Roy. Soc.*, 43. 115, 1888; *Phil. Mag.*, (6), 4. 411, 504, 1902; J. W. Nicholson, *ib.*, (6), 22. 864, 1911; A. L. Bernoulli, *Zeit. phys. Chem.*, 65. 391, 1909; G. Woodiwiss, *Chem. News*, 97. 265, 1908; A. P. Mathews, *Journ. Phys. Chem.*, 17. 337, 1913; M. Berthelot, *Compt. Rend.*, 120. 235, 1895; L. de Boisbaudran, *ib.*, 120. 361, 1895; H. Wilde, *ib.*, 134. 770, 1902; *Chem. News*, 72. 291, 1895; C. J. Reed, *ib.*, 71. 213, 1895; W. Sedgwick, *ib.*, 71. 139, 1895; 78. 293, 1898; J. L. Howe, *ib.*, 80. 74, 1899; R. M. Deeley, *ib.*, 71. 75, 1895; 72. 297, 1895; 73. 13, 1895; P. J. F. Rang, *ib.*, 72. 200, 1895; W. W. Andrews, *ib.*, 71. 235, 1895; J. H. Gladstone,

ib., **72**. 223, 1895 ; E. A. Hill, *Amer. Journ. Science*, (3), **49**. 407, 1895 ; R. Nasini, *Gazz. Chim. Ital.*, **25**. ii, 37, 1895 ; W. Preyer, *Ber.*, **29**. 1040, 1896 ; B. Brauner, *ib.*, **32**. 708, 1899 ; A. Piccini, *L'Orosi*, **21**. 361, 1898 ; W. Crookes, *Proc. Roy. Soc.*, **63**. 408, 1898 ; *Zeit. anorg. Chem.*, **18**. 72, 1898 ; N. Bohr, *Nature*, **112**. Suppl., 1923 ; K. Skaupy, *Ann. Physik*, (4), **3**. 408, 1920.

⁴ N. Bohr, *Nature*, **112**. Suppl., 1923 ; *Zeit. Phys.*, **9**. 1, 30, 1922 ; *Phil. Mag.*, (6), **26**. 488, 1913 ; *Danske Selsk. Skr.*, (8), **4**. 101, 1922 ; *Naturwiss.*, **11**. 619, 1923 ; N. Bohr and D. Coster, *Zeit. Physik*, **12**. 342, 1923 ; E. C. Stoner, *Phil. Mag.*, (6), **48**. 719, 1924 ; W. Kossel, *Verh. deut. phys. Ges.*, **16** 953, 1914 : *Naturwiss.*, **7**. 339, 350, 1919 ; W. Pauli, *Zeit. Physik*, **31**. 765, 1925 ; J. E. Jones, *Proc. Roy. Soc.*, **107**. A, 157, 1925 ; H. A. Kramers, *Zeit. Physik*, **13**. 292, 312, 1923 ; O. Halpern, *ib.*, **18**. 344, 1923 ; M. Born and W. Heisenberg, *ib.*, **16**. 229, 1923 ; **25**. 175, 1924 ; L. Silberstein, *Astrophys. Journ.*, **57**. 257, 1923 ; *Nature*, **111**. 567, 1923 ; **112**. 53, 1923 ; H. S. Allen, *Proc. Roy. Soc. Edin.*, **44**. 116. 1924 ; Y. Takashashi, *Proc. Phys. Math. Soc. Japan*, **5**. 137, 1924 ; H. Collins, *Chem. News*, **128**. 81, 1924 ; M. S. Vallarta, *Journ. Math. Phys. Mass. Inst. Tech.*, **4**. 65, 1925 ; F. J. von Wisniewsky, *Phys. Zeit.*, **25**. 135, 1924 ; A. Landé, *ib.*, **20**. 228, 1919 ; **21**. 114, 1920 ; *Naturwiss.*, **13**. 604, 1925 ; J. H. Jones, *Proc. Roy. Soc.*, **105**. A, 650, 1924 ; H. Deslandres, *Compt. Rend.*, **179**. 1006, 1924 ; A. Sommerfeld, *Journ. Amer. Opt. Soc.*, **7**. 509, 1923 ; H. O. Newboult, *Phil. Mag.*, (6), **45**. 1085, 1923 ; C. P. Smyth, *ib.*, (6), **50**. 361, 1923 ; J. H. van Vleck, *Phys. Rev.*, (2), **19**. 419, 1922 ; *Phil. Mag.*, (6), **44**. 842, 1922 ; L. St. C. Broughall, *ib.*, (6), **43**. 339, 1922 ; I. Woodward, *ib.*, (6), **47**. 992, 1924 ; G. E. Gibson, *Phys. Rev.*, (2), **22**. 203, 1923 ; T. M. Lowry, *Trans. Faraday Soc.*, **18**. 285, 1922 ; A. O. Rankine, *ib.*, **17**. 1, 1922 ; H. G. Grimm, *Zeit. Elecktrochem.*, **28**. 75, 1922 ; *Zeit. phys. Chem.*, **101**. 410, 1922 ; R. del Kronig, *Science*, (2), **58**. 537, 1923 ; K. F. Herzfeld and K. L. Wolf, *Ann. Physik*, (4), **76**. 71, 1925 ; G. Glockler, *Nature*, **115**. 909, 1925 ; E. G. Dymond, *ib.*, **115**. 910, 1925 ; *Proc. Roy. Soc.*, **107**. A, 291, 1925 ; C. Eckert, *Science*, (2), **61**. 517, 1925 ; I. Langmuir, *ib.*, (2), **51**. 605, 1920 ; *Phys. Rev.*, (2), **17**. 339, 401, 1921 : F. R. Bichowsky and H. C. Wrey, *Proc. Nat. Acad.*, **12**. 80, 1926 ; R. S. Mulliken, *ib.*, **12**. 158, 1926 ; J. Kudar, *Phys. Zeit.*, **27**. 59, 1926 ; P. Tartakowsky, *Zeit. Physik*, **34**. 216, 1925 ; V. Trkal, *ib.*, **36**. 194, 1926 ; R. Reinicke, *ib.*, **37**. 210, 1926 ; J. Franck and P. Knipping, *ib.*, **1**. 320, 1920 ; J. Franck and F. Reiche, *ib.*, **1**. 154, 1920 ; K. K. Darrow, *Bell Tech. Journ.*, **4**. 642, 1925 ; E. Brummer, *Zeit. Elektrochem.*, **32**. 7, 1926 ; R. T. Birge, *Phys. Rev.*, (2), **27**. 255, 1926 ; G. E. M. Jauncey and A. L. Hughes, *ib.*, (2), **27**. 509, 1926 ; A. S. Eve, *ib.*, (2), **27**. 517, 1926 ; R. A. Millikan, *ib.*, (2), **18**. 456, 1921 ; W. M. Thornton, *Phil. Mag.*, (7), **1**. 13, 1926 ; F. C. Kemble, *ib.*, (6), **42**. 123, 1921 ; *Science*, (2), **52**. 581, 1920 ; E. Rutherford and J. Chadwick, *Proc. Phys. Soc.*, **36**. 417, 1924 ; *Nature*, **113**. 457, 1924 ; E. Rutherford, *Engg.*, **121**. 353, 388, 438, 458, 1926 ; *Phil. Mag.*, (6), **27**. 488, 1914 ; (6), **37**. 560, 1919 ; (6), **42**. 809, 1921 ; L. A. Turner, *ib.*, (6), **48**. 1010, 1924 ; J. W. Nicholson, *ib.*, (6), **22**. 864, 1911 ; A. C. Crehore, *ib.*, (6), **43**. 886, 1922 ; J. P. Dempster, *Astrophys. Journ.*, **59**. 142, 1924 ; F. M. Kannenstine, *ib.*, **59**. 135, 1924 ; *Phys. Rev.*, (2), **22**. 115, 1922 ; (2), **23**. 107, 1924 ; L. Brüninghaus, *Rev. Gen. Élect.*, **12**. 466, 1922 ; J. C. Thompson, *Chem. News*, **129**. 123, 1924 ; W. D. Harkins, *Journ. Amer. Chem. Soc.*, **39**. 856, 1916 ; E. Gehrcke, *Verh. deut. phys. Ges.*, (2), **21**. 779, 1919 ; A. Smekal, *ib.*, (3), **1**. 56, 1920 ; *Sitzber. Akad. Wien*, **129**. 464, 1920 ; W. Lenz, *Sitzber. Akad. Bayr.*, 355, 1918 ; J. Beckenkamp, *Sitzber. Phys. Med. Ges. Würzburg*, **45**. 135, 1918.

⁵ E. Rutherford, *Proc. Roy. Soc.*, **97**. A, 374, 1920 ; *Rep. Smithsonian Inst.*, 167, 1915 ; E. Rutherford and J. Chadwick, *Nature*, **107**. 41, 1921 ; *Phil. Mag.*, (6), **42**. 809, 1921 ; H. Wilde, *ib.*, (6), **26**. 732, 1913 ; *Chem. News*, **108**. 52, 1913 ; K. Fajans, *Ber.*, **46**. 433, 1913 ; *Verh. deut. phys. Ges.*, **15**. 250, 1913 ; E. Gehrcke, *ib.*, **21**. 779, 1919 ; *Sitzber. Akad. Heidelburg*, 19, 1919 ; J. J. Thomson, *Engg.*, **105**. 317, 1918 ; J. W. Nicholson, *Phil. Mag.*, (6), **45**. 801, 1923 ; W. D. Harkins, *Journ. Amer. Chem. Soc.*, **39**. 856, 1917 ; **42**. 1956, 1920 ; S. Miall, *Nature*, **105**. 294, 1920 ; L. Meitner, *Naturwiss.*, **9**. 423, 1921 ; *Phys. Zeit.*, **4**. 146, 1921 ; **23**, 305, 1922 ; E. Kohlweiller, *ib.*, **21**. 203, 311, 1920 ; F. P. Valeras, *ib.*, **23**. 304, 1922 ; W. Kossel, *ib.*, **20**. 265, 1919 ; M. C. Neuberger, *ib.*, **23**. 305, 389, 1922 ; *Zeit. anorg. Chem.*, **120**. 150, 1922 ; *Zeit. phys. Chem.*, **99**. 161, 321, 454, 1921 ; H. T. Wolff, *Ann. Physik*, (4), **60**. 685, 1919 ; A. van den Brock, *Elster and Geitel's Festschrift*, 428, 1915.

⁶ F. W. Aston, *Phil. Mag.*, (6), **39**. 611, 1920 ; (6), **40**. 629, 1920 ; *Isotopes*, London, 69, 1924 ; *Nature*, **105**. 8, 1920 ; D. M. Bose and S. K. Ghosh, *ib.*, **111**. 463, 1923 ; E. Rutherford, *Rep. Smithsonian Inst.*, 167, 1915 ; *Proc. Roy. Soc.*, **97**. A, 374, 1920 ; *Phil. Mag.*, (6), **27**. 488, 1914 ; (6), **37**. 560, 1910 ; E. Rutherford and J. M. Nuttall, *ib.*, (6), **26**. 702, 1913 ; L. A. Turner, *ib.*, (6), **48**. 1010, 1924 ; F. Paneth, *Zeit. angew. Chem.*, **38**. 758, 1925 ; A. Einstein, *Jahrb. Rad. Elektron.*, **4**. 442, 1907 ; W. D. Harkins and E. D. Wilson, *Journ. Amer. Chem. Soc.*, **37**. 1367, 1383, 1396, 1915 ; *Phil. Mag.*, (6), **30**. 723, 1915 ; C. G. Darwin, *ib.*, (6), **27**. 506, 1914 ; A. Smekal, *Naturwiss.*, **9**. 77, 1921 ; *Sitzber. Akad. Wien*, **129**. 464, 1920 ; *Verh. deut. phys. Ges.*, (3), **1**. 56, 1920 ; M. C. Neuburger, *Ann. Physik*, (4), **68**. 574, 1922 ; (4), **70**. 139, 1923 ; *Phys. Zeit.*, **23**. 133, 145, 1922 ; L. Silberstein, *Phys. Rev.*, (2), **19**. 399, 1922 ; A. Sommerfeld, *Atombau und Spektrallinien*, Braunschweig, 1919.

INDEX

A

Acceptor, 565
Accumulators, 542
—— lead, 542
Actinium emanation, 889
Actinon, 889
Adelpholite, 100
Ægirite, 100
Ænigmatite, 3
Ærugo nobilis, 357
 Æs candidum, 279
Æschynite, 3, 185, 896
Aikinite, 491
Ainalite, 394
Alamosite, 491
Alaskaite, 491
Albite, 896
Algiers metal, 332
Alisonite, 491, 796
Alkali iodoplumbate, 764
Alkyl stannous iodides, 459
Alshedite, 3
Altaite, 491
Aluminium, 20
—— bromostannate, 456
—— chlorostannate, 449
—— dodecaiodotriplumbite, 778
—— hemitristannide, 383
—— hemizirconide, 116
—— octobromoplumbite, 753
— · — octobromostannite, 454
—·— octochlorostannite, 434
—— pentabromostannite, 454
—— pentachloride, 434
—— pentachlorostannate, 434
—— pentasulphatodiplumbite, 821
—— stannide, 383
—— tetritastannide, 383
—— titanate, 56
—— (ditrita) titanide, 20
—— (tetrita) titanide, 21
—— (trita) titanide, 21
—— tritetritazirconide, 117
—— zirconium, 116
Alvite, 100, 167
Amalgams, dental, 370
Ammonium bromodiiodoplumbite, 773
—— —— dihydrate, 773
—— bromoiodostannate, 463
—— bromoplumbite, 751
—— bromostannates, 456
—— bromotitanate, 88
—— carbonatostannite, 480
—— chlorobromostannate, 456
—— chlorodiiodoplumbite, 773
—— chloroplumbate, 734
—— chloroplumbites, 725

Ammonium chlorostannate, 447
—— chlorotetrabromodiplumbite, 751
—— chlorotitanate, 85
—— copper fluotitanate, 72
—— cupric, α·stannate, 418
—— decaiodotriplumbite, 772
—— —— hexahydrate, 772
—— dibromodichlorostannite, 454
—— dichlorodibromoplumbite, 751
—— fluobromoplumbite, 751
—— fluochloroplumbite, 733
—— fluoplumbite, 703
—— fluostannate, 422
—— fluostannite, 422
—— fluotitanate, 70, 670
—— fluozirconate, 139
—— heptafluohafniate, 171
—— heptafluotitanate, 70
—— heptafluozirconate, 139
—— heptasulphotristannate, 474
—— hexabromostannite, 453–454
—— hexachloroplumbite, 727
—— hexachlorostannite, 432
—— hexafluohafniate, 171
—— hexafluotitanite, 66
—— hydrodofluoplumbate, 705
—— iodostannate, 463
—— iodostannite, 460
—— lead dimetaphosphate, 881
—— —— pyrophosphate, 880
—— mesodistannate (α-), 417
—— nitratoplumbite, 864
—— nitratostannate, 481
—— oxyfluopertitanate, 68
—— pentabromodiplumbite, 751
—— pentachlorodiplumbite, 726
—— —— trihydrate, 726
—— pentafluotitanite, 66
—— peroxypertitanate, 65
—— plumbite, 668
—— potassium chloroplumbite, 729
—— stannate (β-), 417
—— stannyl chloride, 442
—— sulphatopertitanate, 95
—— sulphatotitanite, 92
—— sulphostannate, 474
—— —— heptahydrated, 474
—— —— trihydrated, 474
—— sulphostannite, 478
—— tetrabromoplumbite, 751
—— —— monohydrate, 751
—— tetrabromostannite, 453
—— tetrachlorobromodiplumbite, 751
—— tetrachloroplumbite, 726
—— tetrachlorostannite, 432
—— tetraiodoplumbite, 772
—— —— dihydrate, 774
—— —— tetrahydrate, 773

Ammonium tetraoctofluostannate, 423
—— thallic bromoplumbite, 753
—— —— chloroplumbite, 732
—— thorium carbonate, 249
—— —— dodecachloride, 234
—— —— fluoride, 227
—— —— hexachloride, 234
—— —— hexanitrate, 251
—— —— hexasulphate, 247
—— —— hydronitrate, 251
—— —— pentachloride, 235
—— —— pentanitrate, 250
—— —— —— dihydrate, 251
—— —— —— pentahydrate, 250
—— —— pentasulphate, 246
—— —— tetrasulphate, 245
—— —— trisulphate, 245
—— titanate, 50
—— titanium carbonate, 96
—— —— oxysulphate, 95
—— titanous alum, 92
—— —— sulphate, 92
—— titanyl sulphate, 95
—— tribromoplumbite, 751
—— tribromostannite, 453
—— trichloroplumbite, 726
—— trichlorostannite, 432
—— triiodoplumbite, 771
—— trisulphatoplumbate, 823
—— zirconium carbonate, 161
—— —— octohydroxyhexasulphate, 159
—— —— tetrasulphate, 159
—— zirconyl tetrasulphate, 159
—— —— (tri) tetrasulphate, 159
—— —— trisulphate, 159
Anak, 277
Anatase, 2, 30
Ancylite, 185
Anderberjite, 100
Anglesite, 491, 803
Annerödite, 100
Antifriction metals, 362
Antimonious lead enneaiodide, 762
Antimony-glance, 896
Aonia, 277
Apatite, 896
Aræoxene, 491
Arbor jovis, 298, 338
—— saturni, 516
Arfvedsonite, 100
Argentarium, 630
Argentine, 298
Argento-titanium, 20
Argon, 889
—— atomic disruption, 948
—— —— weight, 947
—— electronic structure, 949
—— history, 889
—— hydrate, 943
—— isotopes, 948
—— occurrence, 892
—— preparation, 902
—— properties, chemical, 941
—— —— physical, 906
Argyritis, 638, 644
Argyrodite, 254, 275, 896
Arizonite, 2, 60
Arkansite, 2, 31
Arrhenite, 100
Arsenious lead enneaiodide, 762

Arsenomelan, 491
Art bronzes, 348
Aspidelite, 3
Asterium, 890
Astrakanite, 896
Astrophyllite, 3
Auer, 218
Auerbachite, 100
Auerlite, 100, 185
Aurum mosaicum, 469
—— musioum, 469
Autoxidation, 565
Autunite, 896
Azorite, 100

B

Babbit metal, 362
Baddeleyite, 100, 123
Barium chlorostannate, 449
—— fluoplumbite, 704
—— fluostannate, 423
—— —— trihydrate, 423
—— fluotitanate, 72
—— —— hemihydrated, 72
—— fluozirconate, 141
—— hexaiododiplumbite, 777
—— iodostannite, 460
—— isopropylstannonate, 410
—— lead orthophosphate, 876
—— —— oxychloride, 744
—— —— sulphide, 797
—— mesotrititanate, 54
—— metaplumbate, 698
—— metatitanate, 54
—— metazirconate, 136
—— nitratoplumbite, 866
—— orthoplumbate, 699
—— oxyfluopertitanate, 69
—— peroxypertitanate, 65
—— plumbite, 668
—— silicotitanate, 54
—— sodium silicotitanate, 54
—— stannate (a-), 419
—— —— heptahydrate, 419
—— —— trihydrate, 419
—— sulphatoplumbite, 821
—— sulphatostannate, 499
—— sulphometastannate, 476
—— tetrachloroplumbite, 731
—— tetrachlorostannite, 434
—— tetradecafluozirconate, 141
—— thorium orthophosphate, 259
—— titanic sulphate, 94
—— triplumbide, 615
Barysilite, 491
Barytes, 896
Basalt, 896
Basanomelane, 57
Base-bullion, 277
Baumhauerite, 491
Bayldonite, 491
Bearing metals, 362
Beaverite, 822
Beccarite, 100
Bedil, 276, 484
Beegerite, 491
Bell-metal ore, 283, 475
Bell metals, 348

Benitoite, 3, 54
Beresovite, 491
Beresowite, 491
Beryl, 896
Beryllium chlorostannate, 449
—— tetraiodoplumbite, 778
Beryllonite, 896
Berzelite, 740
Berzelium, 174, 209
Beudantite, 491, 877
Bindheimite, 491
Bismuth hydroxysulphatostannate, 479
Bismuthoplagionite, 491
Bismuthplagionite, 491
Bjelkite, 491
Blanc de plomb, 847
Bleierde, 832
Bleierze salzsaures, 852
Bleiglanz, 781
Bleiglas, 803
Bleiglätte, 638
Bleinière, 491
Bleischwärze, 832
Bleischweiff, 781
Bleispath, 829
Blomstrandine, 3
Blomstrandite, 3
Blyglants, 781
Blyspat, 829
—— grön, 882
Boleite, 491, 743
Bornite, 896
Borotitanates, 3
Boulangerite, 491
Bournonite, 491
Brackebushite, 491
Brasses, machine, 347
Brazilite, 123
Britannia metal, 332
Bröggerite, 185, 896
Bromolaurionite, 754
Bromoplumbites, 751
Bromopyromorphite, 885
Bromostannates, 456
Bromostannites, 453
Bromozirconates, 149
Brongniardtite, 255, 491
Bronze, 347
—— complex, 347
—— phosphor, 347
—— siliceux, 356
—— silicon, 348
—— zinc, 347
Brookite, 30
Bullion base, 503, 504
—— lead, 503, 504
Butter of tin, 424, 437

C

Cadmium and stannous chlorides, 434
—— blende, 896
—— chloroplumbite, 731
—— chlorostannate, 449
—— decafluozirconate, 142
—— fluostannate, 424
—— fluotitanate, 73
—— —— hexhydrated, 73
—— gold distannide, 384

Cadmium (di) gold stannide, 384
—— hexaiodoplumbite, 778
—— octofluozirconate, 142
—— tetrastannide, 376
Cælestine, 896
Cæsium bromostannate, 456
—— chlorobromoplumbite, 753
—— chloroplumbate, 735
—— chlorostannate, 449
—— chlorotitanite, 77
—— fluogermanate, 269
—— fluostannate, 423
—— fluotitanate, 72
—— fluozirconate, 141
—— hexabromoplumbite, 752
—— hexachloroplumbite, 730
—— hexafluoplumbate, 705
—— iodostannate, 463
—— nitratoplumbite, 866
—— octofluotitanate, 72
—— pentachlorodiplumbite, 730, 752
—— pentafluozirconate, 140
—— pentaiodostannite, 460
—— tetrabromoplumbite, 752
—— tetrachloroplumbite, 730
—— tetradecafluotrizirconate, 141
—— thorium fluoride, 228
—— —— hexachloride, 235
—— —— —— dodecahydrate, 236
—— —— —— henahydrate, 235
—— —— —— octohydrate, 255
—— —— hexanitrate, 251
—— —— octochloride, 235
—— —— trisulphate, 247
—— titanous alum, 93
—— —— pentachloride, 77
—— tribromoplumbite, 752
—— trichloroplumbite, 730
—— trichlorostannite, 433
—— triiodoplumbite, 775
—— triiodostannite, 460
—— trisulphatoplumbate, 824
—— zirconium trioxydisulphate, 158
Calciners, Brunton's, 287
—— Oxland's, 287
Calcite, 896
Calcium bromostannate, 456
—— chloroplumbate, 736
—— chlorostannate, 449
—— chlorostannite, 433
—— diborylstannate, 419
—— dihydrodeuterotetraplumbate, 700
—— dihydrodeuterotriplumbate, 700
—— dihydroproterodiplumbate, 699
—— ferrous mesozirconate, 136
—— fluostannate, 423
—— fluotitanate, 72
—— —— dihydrated, 72
—— —— trihydrated, 72
—— fluozirconate, 141
—— hemiplumbide, 614
—— hemistannide, 373
—— hemitriplumbide, 614
—— hexachloroplumbite, 730
—— hexaiododiplumbite, 777
—— isopropylstannonate, 410
—— lead orthoplumbate, 700
—— —— sulphide, 797
—— —— trioxydichloride, 743
—— metaplumbate, 698

Calcium metaplumbate, dihydrated, 698
—— —— tetrahydrated, 698
—— metatitanate, 52
—— metazirconate, 136
—— orthodiplumbate, 700
—— orthoplumbate, 699
—— —— tetrahydrated, 699
—— orthostannate, 419
—— pentitastannide, 373
—— phosphatozirconate, 165
—— plumbide, 614
—— plumbite, 668
—— polyplumbate, 699
—— potassium phosphatoplumbate, 886
—— —— phosphatostannate, 483
—— —— phosphatothorate, 253
—— —— phosphatotitanate, 97
—— silicotitanate, 54
—— α-stannate, 418
—— —— pentahydrate, 419
—— —— tetrahydrate, 419
—— —— trihydrate, 419
—— stannide, 373
—— sulphatoplumbite, 821
—— sulphatostannate, 479
—— sulphometastannate, 476
—— sulphorthostannate, 476
—— tetrachloroplumbite, 730
—— titanic sulphate, 94
—— titanium oxysulphide, 91
—— triplumbide, 614
—— tristannide, 373
—— triterotetraplumbate, 700
Caledonite, 491, 819
Calx plumbi aerata, 846
—— —— dulcis, 856
Calyptolite, 100
Canfieldite, 275, 283
Caracolite, 491
Carminite, 491
Carnallite, 896
Carnotite, 896
Carolinium, 174, 209
Caryinite, 491
Cassel's yellow, 742
Cassiterite, 394, 896
—— tantalum, 394
Cassiteros, 276, 277
Castor, 896
Catapleite, 100
Celtium, 166
Cerasite, 739
Cerite, 100
Cerium distannide, 385
—— hemistannide, 385
—— hemitristannide, 385
—— sulphatostannate, 479
—— thorium nitrate, 251
—— —— sulphate, 247
Cerous lead orthophosphate, 877
Céruse, 829
Cerussa nativa, 829
—— usta, 673
Cerussite, 491, 829
Chalcolamprite, 3, 100
Cherokine, 883
Chillagite, 491
Chiviatite, 491
Chloroplumbates, 734
Chloroplumbites, 725

Chlorospath, 740
Chlorostannates, 447
Chlorotitanates, 85
Chloroxiphite, 743
Chlorozirconates, 143
Chrome tin pink, 42
Chromite, 896
Chromium stannate, 421
Chromous hexaiodoplumbite, 778
Chrysitine, 638
Chrysitis, 644
Chrysoberyl, 896
Chrysolithos, 98
Chrystis, 638
Chubutite, 491
Chumbe bianco, 797
Cinnabaris, 673
Cirite, 896
Clarus hyalinus, 98
Clausthalite, 491, 896
Cleveite, 185, 896
Cobalt bromostannate, 456
—— chlorostannate, 450
—— ethylstannonate, 410
—— fluotitanate, 73
—— —— hexahydrated, 73
—— hexamminochlorostannite, 434
—— hexamminofluotitanate, 73
—— metatitanate, 60
—— orthostannate, 420
—— plumbite, 669
—— α-stannate, 420
—— zirconium, 117
Cobaltous hexaiodoplumbite, 779
Columbite, 100, 255, 896
Columbium zirconium, 117
Condensed oxide, 224
Copper ammonium fluotitanate, 72
—— chloroplumbite, 730
—— chlorostannate, 449
—— distannide, 351
—— fluostannate, 423
—— fluotitanate, 72
—— hemistannide, 351
—— lead aluminosulphate, 822
—— —— hexahydroxytetrasulphate, 819
—— —— hydroxychloride, 742
—— —— hydroxysulphate, 820
—— —— oxyphosphate, 877
—— —— tetrahydroxydichloride, 743
—— —— tetroxychloride, 742
—— —— tetroxydecachloride, 743
—— —— trioxydichloride, 743
—— monostannide, 351
—— nitratoplumbite, 866
—— pentahexitastannide, 351
—— pentastannide, 351
—— silver lead octoxyhenacosichloride, 743
—— tetritastannide, 351
—— tristannide, 351
—— tritaheptastannide, 351
—— tritastannide, 350
Copper-tin alloys, 347
—— —— —— aluminium alloys, 361
—— —— —— antimony alloys, 362
—— —— —— bismuth alloys, 362
—— —— —— cadmium alloys, 361
—— —— —— calcium alloys, 361
—— —— —— chromium alloys, 361
—— —— —— cobalt alloys, 362

Copper-tin alloys, iron alloys, 362
—— —— —— lead alloys, 362
—— —— —— manganese alloys, 362
—— —— —— nickel alloys, 362
—— —— —— phosphorus alloys, 362
—— —— —— sodium alloys, 361
—— —— —— vanadium alloys, 362
—— —— —— zinc alloys, 361
—— zirconate, 136
—— zirconium, 116
Corandite, 896
Corkite, 877
Corundum, 896
Cosalite, 491
Cossyrite, 3
Cotunnite, 707
Crateritis, 98
Crichtonite, 2, 57
Crispite, 2, 30, 34
Crocoite, 491
Cromfordite, 491, 852
Cryolite, 896
Cryosol, 882
Crystolite, 185
Cumengite, 742
Cupreous lead sulphide, 796
Cupric ammonium a-stannate, 418
—— metaplumbate, 698
—— octofluozirconate, 141
—— plumbite, 668
—— a-stannate, 418
—— —— tetrahydrate, 418
—— tetradecafluodizirconate, 141
Cuprite, 896
Cuprocassiterite, 283, 417, 476
Cuprodescloizite, 491
Cuprosilicotitanium, 12, 24
Cuprotitanium, 12, 20, 24
Cuprouranite, 896
Cuprous ferrous stannic sulphide, 475
—— lead sulphate, 820
—— —— sulphatocarbonate, 819
—— plumbite, 668
—— a-stannate, 417
—— stannous chlorides, 433
—— —— stannate, 418
Curite, 491
Cylindrite, 283, 491
Cyrtolite, 100, 167, 185, 896

D

Dauphinite, 30
Davidite, 2, 30
Daviesite, 740
Dechenite, 491
Delorenzite, 3, 59
Derbylite, 3
Deselvizite, 491
Dewindite, 491
Diaboleite, 743
Diabolus metallorum, 279
Diachylon, 591
Diamant brut, 98
Diamonds, Matura, 98
Diazonium hexachloroplumbates, 721
Dicksbergite, 2, 30
Didymium lead sulphate, 822

Die-casting alloys, 362
Digermane, 264
Diisopropyl stannone, 410
Diol-diplumbous bromide, 754
Dioxylite, 818
Diphosphoryl titanium decachloride, 85
Diplasites plumbicus, 681
Diplumbic acid, 685
Dipropyl stannone, 410
Disglomeration, 302
Domingite, 491
Donarium, 174
Dufrenoysite, 491
Dundasite, 855
Dürfeldite, 491
Dysanalyte, 3

E

Ecedemite, 491
Edisonite, 30
Eisenerz hexaderal, 56
Eisenrosen, 57
Ekedemite, 491
Electrotype, 362
Elpidite, 100
Embolite, 896
Embrithite, 491
Enceladite, 54
Endeolite, 100
Endlichite, 491
Epiboulangerite, 491
Epistolite, 3
Erdmannite, 100
Estano, 276
Etain, 276
Ethyl stannic bromide, 455
—— —— chloride, 446
—— —— iodide, 463
—— stannone, 410
Eucolite, 100
—— (titanite,), 3
Eudialite, 896
Eudialyte, 100
Eumanite, 31
Eusynchite, 491
Euxenerde, 99
Euxenia, 99
Euxenite, 3, 100, 185, 896
Euxenium, 99

F

Fahlun brilliants, 630
Fava, 124
Fergusonite, 100, 255, 896
—— tyrite, 185
Ferrazite, 491, 877
Ferric fluotitanate, 73
—— metatitanate, 60
—— orthotitanate, 59
Ferro-carbo-titanium, 11
Ferrosilicotitanium, 12
Ferrotitanium, 11, 24
Ferrous bromostannate, 456
—— calcium mesozirconate, 136
—— chlorostannate, 450

Ferrous fluotitanate, 73
—— hexaiodoplumbite, 779
—— lead manganese metatitanate, 56
—— metatitanate, 57
—— orthotitanate, 59
—— stannic cuprous sulphide, 475
—— uranium yttrium metatitanate, 59
Ferryl metatitanate, 60
Fiedlerite, 737
Flèches d'amour, 34
Float tin, 394
Florencite, 877
Flores jovis, 395
—— plumbi, 563, 639
—— stannic, 395
Flowers of tin, 395
Flue dust, 503
Fluopyromorphite, 882
Fluorspar, 896
Fluostannates, 422
Fluotitanates, 69
Fluotitanites, 66
Fluotitanous acid, 66
Fluozirconates, 137, 138
Franckeite, 255, 283, 491
Freieslebenite, 491
Freyalite, 185
Fume (lead furnace), 503
Furnace, blast (lead), 502
—— Flintshire, 501
—— Jumbo, 502
—— Moffat hearth, 502
—— ore hearth (lead), 502
—— Pilz, 503
—— Raschette, 502
—— reverberatory, 501
—— Rossie, 502
—— Scotch hearth, 502
—— shaft (lead), 502

G

Gadolinite, 185, 255, 896
Galena, 491, 780, 781, 896
—— blendosa, 797
Galenite, 780
Galenobismuthite, 491
Galenoceratite, 852
Galliferous zinc blende, 896
Ganomalite, 491
Garnet, black, 30
—— schörl-like, 30
Garnierite, 896
Geikielite, 3, 54
Geocronite, 491
Germanic fluoride, 268
—— iodide, 272
—— oxide, 265
—— sulphide, 274
Germanite, 255, 275
Germanites, 265
Germanium, 254
—— analytical reactions, 261
—— atomic number, 262
—— —— weight, 261
—— bromide, 271
—— carbonates, 275
—— chloride, 269

Germanium chloroform, 263, 270
—— difluoride, 268
—— diiodide, 272
—— dioxide, 265
—— discovery, 254
—— disulphide, 274
—— —— colloidal, 274
—— electronic structure, 262
—— extraction, 256
—— fluorides, 268
—— hydrides, 263
—— hydrotrichloride, 270
—— hydroxide, 265
—— iodide, 271
—— isotopes, 262
—— lead silver sulphantimonite, 255
—— monosulphide, 273
—— —— colloidal, 273
—— nitrates, 275
—— occurrence, 254
—— oxide, 265
—— oxychloride, 271
—— oxysulphide, 274
—— phosphate, 275
—— potassium sulphate, 269
—— preparation, 256
—— properties, chemical, 259
—— —— physical, 257
—— sulphates, 275
—— sulphide, 273
—— tetrabromide, 271
—— tetrachloride, 269
—— tetrafluoride, 268
—— tetrahydride, 263
—— tetraiodide, 272
Germanochloroform, 270
Germanoethane, 264
Germanoformic acid, 265
Germanomethane, 263
Germanopropane, 264
Germanous fluoride, 268
—— hydroxide, 265
—— iodide, 272
—— oxide, 265
—— phosphate, 275
—— sulphide, 273
Germanyl chloride, 271
Gold cadmium distannide, 384
—— chloroplumbite, 730
—— dicadmium stannide, 384
—— distannide, 371
—— lead sulphide, 796
—— monostannide, 370
—— mosaic, 469
—— muscovite, 469
—— purple, 418
—— tetrastannide, 371
—— tin alloys, 368
—— zirconium, 116
Goldglätte, 644
Granite, 896
Graphite metal, 362
Greenovite, 3
Grothite, 3
Grünbleierz, 882
Guarinite, 3, 100
Guitermanite, 491
Gummispath, 877
Gummite, 491
Gun metals, 347

H

Hæmatite, 896
Hafnia, 166
—— extraction, 167
Hafnium, 166
—— atomic weight, 172
—— history, 166
—— iodide, 172
—— occurrence, 166
—— oxalate, 172
—— oxychloride, 172
—— properties, 170
—— salicylate, 172
—— salts, 170
—— sulphate, 172
—— sulphide, 172
—— tetrachloride, 172
—— thorium zirconium orthosilicate, 167
Hafnyl chloride, 172
—— dihydrophosphate, 172
—— hydrophosphate, 172
—— metaphosphate, 172
Hainite, 3, 100
Hamlinite, 877
Hancockite, 491
Haplotypite, 57
Hard head, 289
Hauscolite, 797
Hedyphane, 491
Helium, 889
—— atomic weight, 947
—— electronic structure, 949
—— history, 890
—— hydride, 945
—— isotopes, 948
—— metastable, 922
—— occurrence, 892
—— preparation, 902
—— properties, chemical, 941
—— —— physical, 906
Heteromorphite, 491
Hexachlorostannites, 429
Hexahydroxyplumbic acid, 685
Hinsdalite, 491, 877, 878
Hiörtdahlite, 100
Hitchcockite, 877
Hoegbomite, 3, 57
Hokutolite, 821
Horn lead, 706, 852
Hügelite, 491
Hutchinsonite, 491
Hyacinth, 98, 100
Hyacinthus, 98
Hyalotekite, 491
Hydrates, chemical, 129
—— colloidal, 129
Hydrazine fluotitanate, 70
—— tetrachlorostannite, 432
—— trichlorostannite, 432
Hydriodotitanic acid, 89
Hydrobromoplumbic acid, 754
Hydrobromostannic acid, 456
Hydrobromotitanic acid, 88
Hydrocerussite, 491, 837
Hydrochloroplumbic acid, 720
Hydrochlorostannic acid, 439, 447
Hydrochlorotitanic acid, 85
Hydroctofluoplumbic acid, 704

Hydrodisulphatozirconylic acid, 154, 155
Hydrofluogermanic acid, 268
Hydrofluoplumbic acid, 704
Hydrofluoplumbous acid, 703
Hydrofluostannous acid, 422
Hydrofluotitanic acid, 69
Hydrofluozirconic acid, 138
Hydrohexachloroplumbic acid, 720
Hydroilmenite, 57
Hydroiodostannic acid, 463
Hydroiodostannous acid, 460
Hydropentachloroplumbic acid, 720
Hydrophosphatoplumbic acid, 886
Hydroplumbite, 491
Hydrostannous acid, 390
Hydrosulphatoplumbic acid, 823
Hydrosulphatozirconic acid, 154
Hydrotetrachlorostannous acid, 429
Hydrotitanite, 3
Hydrotrichlorostannous acid, 429
Hydrotrisulphatometaplumbic acid, 601
Hydrotrisulphatoplumbic acid, 823
Hydroxyfluopertitannic acid, 68
Hystatite, 2

I

Iglésiasite, 491, 829, 855
Iliorite, 896
Ilmenite, 2, 56, 57, 896
—— α-, 59
—— β-, 59
Ilmenorutile, 2, 30
Incandescent mantle, 213
Indiferous zinc blende, 896
Indium-lead alloys, 625
Inert gases, 889
—— —— occurrence, 892
—— —— preparation, 902
—— —— properties, physical, 906
Iodolaurionite, 767
Iodostannates, 463
Iodostannites, 460
Iodotitanates, 89
Iodyrite, 896
Iron ore, titaniferous, 2
—— zirconium, 117
Iserin, 56
Iserine, 2
Iserite, 30
—— stannic bromide, 455
—— —— chloride, 446
Isopropyl (di) stannic chloride, 446
—— stannonic acid, 410
Ivaarite, 3

J

Jacinth, 98
Jacoby metal, 362
Jacupirangite, 124
Jamesonite, 491
Jargon, 98, 100
—— de Ceylon, 98
Jargonia, 99
Jargonium, 99
Johnsonite, 491
Johnstonite, 793

Johnstrupite, 3, 100
Jordanite, 491
Jurinite, 2

K

Kainite, 896
Kalkowskite, 60
Kampylite, 491
Karyinite, 491
Kasolite, 491
Kastira, 277
Keilhauite, 3, **896**
Kentrolite, 491
Kerasine, 739, 852
Kerstenite, 491
Khespet, 277
Kibdelophane, 2, **57**
Kieserite, 896
Kilbrickenite, 491
Kilmacooite, 797
Knopite, 3, 52
Kobellite, 491
Konstrastin, 121
Krugite, 896
Krypton, 889
—— atomic weight, 947
—— electronic structure, 94**9**
—— history, 890
—— hydrate, 943
—— isotopes, 948
—— occurrence, 892
—— preparation, 902
—— properties, chemical, **941**
—— —— physical, 906
Kuprite, 349

L

Lävenite, 100
Lamp. Nernst's, 112, 120
Lamprophyllite, 3
Lanarkite, 491, 818, 854
Langbeinite, 896
Lanthanium sulphatostannate, **479**
Lapis plumbaris, 638
—— plumbarius, 781
Latten ware, 630
Laurionite, 491, **738**
Lead, 484
—— acetylpyrophosphate, **880**
—— alcohol, 509
—— allotropic, 520
—— aluminium alloys, 624
—— aluminophosphate, 877
—— amalgams, 618
—— amminoxide, 668
—— ammonium dimetaphosphate, **881**
—— —— pyrophosphate, 880
—— analytical reactions, 585
—— anorthophosphate, 879
—— antimonial, 505
—— antimonious enneaiodide, **762**
—— arsenious enneaiodide, 762
—— ash, 563, 639
—— atomic number, 602
—— —— weight, 600
—— barium orthophosphate, **876**
—— —— oxychloride, 744

Lead, barium sulphide, 797
—— -baryte, peritomous, **740**
—— bromide, 745
—— —— properties, chemical, **748**
—— —— —— physical, 746
—— bromocarbonate, 853
—— bromofluoride, 750
—— bromoiodide, 766
—— bromotriorthophosphate, **885**
—— bullion, 503, 504
—— cadmium alloys, 617
—— calcium alloys, 613
—— —— orthoplumbate, **700**
—— —— sulphide, 797
—— —— trioxydichloride, **743**
—— carbonate, 828
—— —— basic, 836
—— —— colloidal, 831
—— —— preparation, 830
—— —— properties, chemical, **833**
—— —— —— physical, 832
—— cerous orthophosphate, 877
—— chemical assay, 505
—— chloride, 706
—— —— colloidal, 708
—— —— properties, chemical, **712**
—— —— —— physical, 708
—— chlorides, 706
—— chlorobishydrophosphate, 885
—— chlorobromide, 750
—— chlorocarbonate, 852
—— chlorodiorthophosphate, **885**
—— chloroiodide, 765
—— —— dihydrate, 765
—— —— hemihydrate, **765**
—— chlorostannate, 450
—— chlorosulphate, 817
—— chlorotriorthophosphate, **883**
—— —— hydrated, 883
—— colloidal, 508
—— copper alloys, 609
—— —— aluminophosphate, 878
—— —— aluminosulphate, 822
—— —— hexahydroxytetrasulphate, 819
—— —— hydroxychloride, 742
—— —— hydroxysulphate, 820
—— —— oxyphosphate, 877
—— —— -red, 515
—— —— silver octoxyhenacosichloride, **743**
—— —— tetrahydroxydichloride, 743
—— —— tetroxychloride, 742
—— —— tetroxydecachloride, 743
—— —— trioxydichloride, 743
—— corneous, 852
—— corrosion, 565
—— —— electrolytic theory, **565**
—— —— hydrogen dioxide theory, 565
—— cupreous sulphide, 796
—— cuprous sulphate, 820
—— —— sulphatocarbonate, 819
—— decoxytetraiodide, 768
—— desilvered, 505
—— desilverization, 505
—— —— Parkes's process, 505
—— —— Pattinson's process, 505
—— —— Rozan's process, 505
—— deuterotetraphosphate, 879
—— diamminobromide, 749
—— diamminodichloride, **716**
—— diamminoiodide, 716

Lead diamminotetrachloride, 719
—— dibromoctofluoride, 750
—— dibromodiiodide, 769
—— didymium sulphate, 822
—— dihydride, 262
—— dihydroperoxide, 685
—— dihydrophosphate, 879
—— dihydroxycarbonate, 838
—— dihydroxydicarbonate, 836
—— dihydroxydisulphate, 819
—— dihydroxypentabomide, 755
—— dihydroxysulphate, 819
—— dihydroxysulphatodicarbonate, 852
—— dihydroxytetrachloride, 737
—— dihydroxytripyrophosphate, 880
—— dimetaphosphate, 881
—— —— hemitrihydrate, 881
—— dioxide, 681
—— —— colloidal, 683, 685
—— —— hydrated, 685
—— —— properties. chemical, 687
—— —— —— physical, 683
—— dioxycarbonate, 836
—— dioxydibromide, 754
—— —— dihydrated, 754
—— dioxydichloride, 739
—— dioxydihydroxide, 661
—— dioxydiiodide, 767
—— dioxydinitrate, 868
—— dioxyhenabromide, 755
—— dioxyheptabromide, 755
—— dioxyiodochloride, 768
—— dioxypentabromide, 755
—— dioxysulphate, 818
—— dioxytrimetaphosphate, 881
—— dioxytrisulphate, 819
—— disulphate, 822
—— disulphide, 794, 795
—— dodeca-tetrahenicosichloride, 736
—— dodecabromodiiodide, 766
—— double refined, 505
—— earth, 638
—— electrodeposition, 542
—— electronic structure, 602
—— enneaoxytetraiodide, 767
—— ethyl alcohol, 509
—— extraction, 497, 501
—— —— air reduction process, 496
—— —— Brittany process, 502
—— —— Corinthian process, 502
—— —— Cornish process, 502
—— —— dry process, 501
—— —— flowing furnace process, 502
—— —— French process, 502
—— —— precipitation process, 496
—— —— reduction process, 496
—— —— Silesian process, 501
—— —— wet, 504
—— —— —— chloridizing roast, 504
—— —— —— H. E. Fry's process, 504
—— ferrous manganese metatitanate, 56
—— filaments, 507
—— films, 508
—— flowers of, 563
—— fluochloride, 732
—— fluoiodide, 765
—— fluonitrate, 862
—— fluoride, 701
—— fluostannate, 424
—— fluosulphate, 817

Lead fluotitanate, 73
—— —— trihydrated, 73
—— fluotriorthophosphate, 882
—— gold alloys, 611
—— —— sulphide, 796
—— granulated, 505
—— hard, 504, 505
—— —— chemical, 505
—— hemiamminoiodide, 762
—— hemihenamminobromide, 749
—— hemihexaphosphate, 882
—— hemimercuride, 619
—— hemioxide, 636
—— hemisulphide, 780
—— hemitriamminodichloride, 716
—— hemitrimercuride, 619
—— hemitrioxide, 670
—— heptoxydichloride, 742
—— heptoxypentaiodide, 768
—— hexachlorodiiodide, 765
—— hexahydroxydinitrate, 867
—— hexahydroxydisulphate, 819
—— hexametaphosphate, 882
—— —— hydrate, 882
—— hexanitritodinitrate, 870
—— hexaphosphate, 882
—— hexasulphodichloride, 795
—— hexoxydibromide, 755
—— hexoxydichloride, 742
—— —— dihydrate, 742
—— hexoxydiiodatohexachloride, 768
—— hexoxydiiodide, 767
—— hexoxytetraiodide, 768
—— history, 484
—— horn, 707, 852
—— hydride, 562, 651
—— hydriodide, 764
—— hydrophosphate, 878
—— hydroplumbite, 662
—— hydrosol, 508
—— hydrosulphate, 812
—— hydroxide, 661
—— —— colloidal, 661
—— hydroxybromide, 754
—— hydroxychloride, 738
—— hydroxychlorocarbonate, 852
—— hydroxydioxysulphate, 818
—— hydroxyhydroplumbite, 664
—— hydroxynitrate, 868, 869
—— —— tetrahydrate, 869
—— hydroxysulphocarbonate, 848, 852
—— -indium alloys, 625
—— iodide, 757
—— —— colloidal, 758
—— —— properties, chemical, 760
—— —— —— physical, 758
—— iodocarbonate, 852
—— iodosulphate, 817
—— iodotriorthophosphate, 885
—— isobutyl alcohol, 509
—— isotopes, 603
—— liquation, 504
—— lithium alloys, 606
—— matte, 503
—— mercuride, 619
—— mercurous oxyhexanitrate, 869
—— mercury alloys, 619
—— metallic precipitation, 506
—— metaphosphate, 881
—— metaplumbate, 670

Lead metatitanate, 56
—— methyl alcohol, 509
—— monamminobromide, 750
—— monamminodichloride, 716
—— monamminoiodide, 762
—— monochloride, 706, 745
—— monohydroxide, 637
—— monoiodide, 757
—— monoxide, 638
—— —— properties, 650
—— —— —— physical, 644
—— native, 490
—— nitrate, 856
—— —— properties, chemical, 862
—— —— —— physical, 857
—— nitrates, basic, 867
—— nitratobisdihydrophosphate, 885
—— nitratorthophosphate, 885
—— nitritonitrate, 869
—— nitrosonitrate, 869
—— occurrence, 487
—— ochre, 638
—— octamminobromide, 749
—— octamminodichloride, 716
—— octamminoiodide, 761
—— octofluochloride, 732
—— octofluodiiodide, 765
—— octoxydiiodide, 768
—— oleate, 591
—— orthophosphate, 876
—— —— tetrahydrate, 876
—— —— trihydrate, 876
—— orthoplumbate, 697
—— oxide, brown, 681
—— oxides, higher, 669
—— oxybromides, 754
—— oxycarbonate, 836
—— oxychlorides, 736
—— oxydecabromide, 755
—— oxydibromide, 754
—— —— hemitrihydrate, 754
—— —— monohydrate, 754
—— —— trihydrate, 754
—— oxydichloride, 737
—— —— hemipentahydrate, 738
—— —— hemitrihydrate, 738
—— —— monohydrate, 738
—— oxydihydroxide, 661, 664
—— oxydiiodide, 766
—— —— hemihydrate, 767
—— —— monohydrate, 767
—— oxydisulphate, 819
—— (penta) oxyenneachloride, 736
—— oxyfluoride, 703
—— (tetra) oxyheptachloride, 736
—— oxyhexachloride, 736
—— (octo) oxyhexadecachloride, 736
—— oxyhexahydroxytetranitrate, 868
—— oxyiodide, 766
—— oxyorthophosphate, 875, 877
—— oxypentaiodide, 768
—— —— monohydrate, 768
—— oxysulphate, 818
—— —— hydrated, 819
—— oxysulphates, 817
—— oxytetrachloride, 737
—— —— dihydrate, 737
—— —— monohydrate, 737
—— oxytetrametaphosphate, 881
—— oxytetranitrate, 869

Lead parkesized, 505
—— pattinized, 505
—— pentamminoiodide, 761
—— pentasulphide, 794
—— pentitaheptoxide, 670
—— pentitahexoxide, 670
—— pentitoctoxide, 670
—— pentoxydichloride, 742
—— —— pentahydrate, 742
—— pentoxydiiodide, 767
—— —— heptahydrate, 767
—— pentoxydinitrate, 867
—— —— hydrate, 867
—— pentoxyorthophosphate, 875, 877
—— peroxide, 681
—— phosphate, 875
—— —— fava, 877
—— phosphatophosphates, 882
—— phosphorous enneaiodide, 762
—— physiological action, 588
—— plumbite, 662, 669
—— porous, 507
—— potassium dimetaphosphate, 881
—— —— dinitritodinitrate, 872
—— —— heptapyrophosphate, 880
—— —— octonitritotetranitrate, 872
—— —— orthophosphate, 876
—— —— pyrophosphate, 880
—— powdered, 507
—— properties, chemical, 561
—— —— physical, 515
—— purification, 504
—— —— electrolytic, 505
—— purified, 508
—— pyrolignite, 591
—— pyrophoric, 563
—— pyrophosphate, 880
—— pyroplumbite, 670
—— quadrantosulphide, 780
—— red, 672
—— sesquioxide, 670
—— sesquisulphide, 793
—— silver alloys, 610
—— —— germanium sulphantimonite, 255
—— —— sulphide, 796
—— slag, 502
—— soap, 591
—— sodium chlorophosphate, 885
—— —— dihydroxytetracarbonate, 855
—— —— hydroxychlorosulphate, 739
—— —— orthophosphate, 876
—— —— pentapyrophosphate, 880
—— —— pyrophosphate, 880
—— —— sulphide, 796
—— —— triphosphate, 882
—— soft, 505
—— softening, 504
—— spar, 829
—— spongy, 507
—— stannate, 420
—— strontium oxychloride, 744
—— subbromide, 637
—— subchloride, 637, 706, 745
—— subhydroxide, 637
—— subiodide, 637, 757
—— suboxide, 636
—— subsulphate, 803
—— subsulphide, 780
—— sulphate, 803
—— —— colloidal, 805

Lead sulphate, physical, 805
—— —— properties, chemical, 808
—— sulphates, basic, 817
—— sulphatocarbonate, 818
—— sulphatostannate, 478
—— sulphatotricarbonate, 853
—— sulphide, 779, 780
—— —— colloidal, 784
—— —— hydrated, 789
—— —— properties, chemical, 788
—— —— —— physical, 784
—— —— reduction of, 497
—— sulphoctoiodide, 794
—— sulphodibromide, 795
—— sulphodichloride, 794
—— sulphodiiodide, 795
—— sulphofluoride, 794
—— sulphohalides, 794
—— sulphometastannate, 479
—— super-refined, 505
—— supersulphuretted, 793
—— tempered, 607
—— tetrabromide, 753
—— tetrabromodiiodide, 766
—— tetrachloride, 718
—— tetrachlorodiiodide, 765
—— tetrafluoride, 704
—— tetrahydride, 262
—— tetrahydroxydinitritodinitrate, 870
—— tetraiodide, 764
—— —— pyridine, 764
—— —— quinoline, 764
—— tetrametaphosphate, 881
—— —— octohydrate, 881
—— tetramminoiodide, 761
—— tetramminotetrachloride, 719
—— tetranitrate, 857
—— tetrasulphodiiodide, 795
—— tetritantimonide, 579
—— tetritapentoxide, 669
—— tetritasulphide, 780
—— tetroxybromide, 754
—— tetroxydichloride, 742
—— —— dihydrate, 742
—— tetroxydihydroxydinitrate, 867
—— tetroxydinitrate, 867
—— tetroxysulphate, 819
—— -thallium alloys, 625
—— thallous sulphide, 797
—— -tin alloys, 626
—— —— colloidal, 627
—— transmutation to silver, 604
—— tree, 516
—— triamminobromide, 749
—— tribromoiodide, 766
—— trichloride, 718
—— trichlorobromide, 750
—— trihydroxide, 670
—— trimetaphosphate, 881
—— trioxydibromide, 755
—— trioxydichloride, 741
—— —— hemihydrate, 741
—— —— monohydrate, 741
—— —— tetrahydrate, 741
—— —— trihydrate, 741
—— trioxydiiodide, 767
—— —— dihydrate, 767
—— —— monohydrate, 767
—— trioxydinitrate, 868
—— trioxyoctohydroxyhexanitrate, 868

Lead trioxyorthophosphate, 877
—— trioxypentacarbonate, 836
—— trioxysulphate, 818
—— —— hydrated, 818
—— trisulphodichloride, 794
—— tritamercuride, 619
—— ultraphosphates, 882
—— uses, 591
—— valency, 600
—— white-, see white-lead
—— wool, 507
—— work's, 504
—— zinc alloys, 616
—— —— sulphide, 797
—— zirconate, 136
—— zirconium, 117
Leadhillite, 491, 853
Lederite, 3
Lehrbachite, 491
Lengenbachite, 491
Lepidolite, 896
Leucosphenite, 3, 54, 100
Leucoxene, 3
Lewisite, 3
Libavius' fuming spirit, 436
Ligurite, 3
Lillianite, 491
Linarite, 491, 820
Linotype metal, 362
Lipilite, 896
Liquor argenti vivi sublimati, 436
—— fumens ex stanno, 437
—— plumbi subacetatis, 591
Litharge, 639
—— flake, 639
—— levigated, 639
—— sublimed, 639
Lithium bromostannate, 456
—— chloroplumbate, 727
—— chlorostannate, 448
—— ditritastannide, 346
—— fluostannate, 423
—— fluotitanate, 70
—— fluozirconate, 139
—— hemipentastannide, 346
—— metadizirconate, 136
—— metaplumbate, 696
—— metazirconate, 135
—— octofluozirconate, 139
—— pentachlorodiplumbite, 727
—— pentaiodoplumbite, 776
—— —— pentahydrate, 776
—— —— tetrahydrate, 776
—— plumbate, 698
—— —— trihydrate, 698
—— stannate, 417
—— sulphatopertitanate, 95
—— tetraiodoplumbite, 776
—— tetritastannide, 346
—— thorium hexachloride, 235
—— —— hydroxytrichloride, 232
—— —— nitrate, 251
—— —— oxychloride, 232
—— —— pentachloride, 235
—— —— sulphate, 246
Liveingite, 491
Loranskite, 100
Lorenzenite, 3, 100
Lorettoite, 491, 742
Lossenite, 491

M

Mackintoshite, 185
Mänaken, 56
Magisterium plumbi, 706
Magnesium borotitanate, 54
—— bromostannate, 456
—— chlorostannate, 449
—— chlorostannite, 434
—— fluostannate, 424
—— fluotitanate, 72
—— —— hexahydrated, 72
—— fluozirconate, 141
—— hemiplumbide, 615
—— hemistannide, 373
—— hexabromoplumbite, 753
—— hexachloroplumbite, 731
—— hexaiodoplumbite, 778
—— —— hexadecahydrate, 778
—— metaplumbate, 700
—— metatitanate, 54
—— orthotitanate, 54
—— plumbite, 669
—— silicotitanate, 54
—— stannate (a-), 419
—— tetrachloroplumbite, 731
—— thorium hexanitrate, 251
—— titanide, 20
—— zirconate, 136
—— zirconium, 116
Magnetites titaniferous, 11
—— —— smelting, 11
Magnolia, 362
Malacone, 100, 167, 896
Manaccanite, 56
Manganese bromostannate, 456
—— chloroplumbite, 731
—— ethylstannonate, 410
—— fluostannate, 424
—— fluotitanate, 73
—— —— hexahydrated, 73
—— fluozirconate, 142
—— lead ferrous metatitanate, 56
—— metatitanate, 56
—— octofluozirconate, 142
—— orthotitanate, 56
—— plumbite, 669
—— stannate (a-), 420
Manganotitanium, 12, 24
Manganous hexaiodoplumbite, 779
Mantle, incandescent, 213
—— Welsbach's, 218
Mararosanite, 491
Marignacite, 3
Massicot, 639
Massicottite, 638
Matlockite, 491, 736, 737
Matte lead, 503
Mauzetite, 3
Maxite, 853
Melanolekite, 491
Melichrysos, 98
Mellephanite, 896
Mellonite, 729
Menacanite, 1, 3
Menaccanite, 56, 57
Menacconite, 56
Menakanite, 56
Menakeisenstein, 56
Mendipite, 491, 736, 739, 740

Meneghinite, 491
Mennige, 491
Mercuric stannate (a-), 419
—— tetrachloroplumbite, 731
Mercurous lead oxyhexanitrate, 869
—— stannate (a-), 419
Mercury bromoplumbite, 753
—— decahelide, 943
—— ethylstannonate, 410
—— hexargentodistannide, 380
—— iodoplumbite, 778
—— monohelide, 945
—— plumbite, 669
—— thorium octoiodide, 239
—— —— tetradecaiodide, 238
—— zirconium, 116
Mesothorium, 186
—— -1, 186
—— -2, 188
Metaperowskite, 53
Metaplumbic acid, 685
Metargon, 890
Metastannic acid, 406
Metasulphatoplumbic acid, 823
Metathoric acid, 224
Metatitanic acid, 40
Metazirconates, 134
Metazirconic acid, 129, 134, 148
Methyl stannic bromide, 455
—— —— chloride, 446
—— —— iodide, 463
—— stannonic acid, 410
Michaelsomite, 100
Microlite, 896
Miesite, 883
Mimetesite, 491
Mineral yellow, 742
Minium, 672, 673
—— nativum, 673
Miriquidite, 491
Mohsite, 57
Molengraaffite, 3
Moltramite, 491
Molybdæna, 638
Molybdænite, 897
Molybditis, 638
Molybdœna, 780, 781
Molybdophyllite, 491
Monazite, 100, 876
—— sand, 185
Monogermane, 263
Monoperstannic acid, 413
Mosaic gold, 469
Mosandrite, 13, 100
Mullanite, 491
Muscovite gold, 469

N

Naak, 277
Nadorite, 491
Nägeite, 167
Nagite, 100
Naga, 277
Nagyagite, 491
Narsarsukite, 3
Nasonite, 491
Needle tin ore, 394
Neon, 889

Neon, atomic disruption, 948
—— —— weight, 947
—— electronic structure, 949
—— history, 891
—— hydrate, 943
—— isotopes, 948
—— occurrence, 892
—— preparation, 902
—— properties, chemical, 941
—— —— physical, 906
Neo-thorium, 209
Neptunite, 3
Nernst's lamp, 112, 120
Nickel bromostannate, 457
—— chlorostannate, 450
—— ethylstannonate, 410
—— fluostannate, 423
—— fluotitanate, hexahydrated, 73
—— fluozirconate, 142
—— metatitanate, 60
—— octofluozirconate, 142
—— orthostannate, 420
—— plumbite, 669
—— potassium fluozirconate, 142
—— stannate (a-), 420
—— zirconium, 117
Nickelous hexaiodoplumbite, 779
Nigrine, 2, 30
Nigrum, 99
Nipponium, 177
Niton, 889
Nitrogen stannic chlorosulphide, 444
—— —— hexachlorotetrasulphide, 77
—— —— oxychloride, 445
—— —— sulphotetrachloride, 84
—— —— sulphotrichloride, 84
—— —— trioxychloride, 445
—— trihydrotrinitride, 761
Nitrosyl (di) titanium hexachloride, 84
Nivenite, 491
Noheet metal, 607
Nordenskjöldine, 283, 419
Norerde, 99
Noria, 99
Norium, 99
Nussierite, 883

O

Oceanium, 2
Ochrolite, 491
Octahedrite, 2, 30
Œrstedite, 100
Oisanite, 30
Oliveiraite, 56, 100
Opheret, 484
Orangeite, 896
Orangite, 175, 185
Ore bell-metal, 475
—— potter's, 781
—— tinder, 491
Orthite, 897
—— allanite, 185
Orthoclase, 897
Orthoplumbic acid, 685
Orthostannic acid, 408
Orthotitanic acid, 39
Orthozirconic acid, 128
Orvillite, 100

Ostranite, 100
Ostranium, 99
Oxides, condensed, 224
Oxychloroiodure de plomb, 768
Oxyfluopertitanates, 68

P

Palladium β-stannate, 420
Palmierite, 491, 821
Paracolumbite, 57
Parahelium, 922
Parailmenite, 57
Paralaurionite, 491, 739
Parastannic dichloride, 443
Parsonsite, 491
Patina, 357
—— antiqua, 357
Pavonado blanco, 797
Penfieldite, 491, 737
Pentametastannic acid, 406
Pentastannyl decahydroxide, 406
Percylite, 491
—— silver, 742
Perdistannic acid, 413
Perofskite, 52
Perovskite, 52
Perowskite, 2, 52
Perstannates, 412
Perstannic acid, 404, 412
Pertitanates, 50
Pertitanic acid, 27, 63
—— phosphate, 97
—— potassium sulphate, 65
Perzirconates, 134
Petterdite, 740
Pewter, 630
Phenacite, 897
Phœnicite, 491
Phonolite, 897
Phosgene spar, 852
Phosgenite, 491, 852
Phosphonium chlorotitanate, 85
Phosphor bronze, 347
Phosphoric titanium enneachloride, 85
Phosphorous lead enneaiodide, 762
—— titanium heptachloride, 85
—— zirconium oxyhenichloride, 145
—— —— tridecachloride, 145
Phosphoryl titanium heptachloride, 85
Picroilmenite, 1, 57
Picrotitanite, 57
Pictite, 3
Pilbarite, 491
Pink chrome-tin, 42
—— salt, 447
Piombo muriato corneo, 706
Pitchblende, 896
Plagionite, 491
Platinic perstannate, 413
—— distannyl stannate (β-), 420
—— —— stannic oxide, 393
—— —— stannate (β), 420
—— tristannyl, 393
Platinum chlorostannate, 450
—— chlorostannite, 434
Plattnerite, 681
Plomb carbonaté rhomboidal, 853

Plomb hydroalumineux, 877
—— spathique, 829
—— terreuse, 638
—— vitriol de, 803
Plumbago, 780, 781
Plumbates, 695
Plumbeine, 782
Plumbi minera spathacea, 829
Plumbic acid, 685
—— —— colloidal, 685
—— bishydrophosphate, 886
—— dihydrophosphate, 886
—— hexoxydisulphate, 823
—— iodide, 575
—— monoxysulphate, 823
—— nitrate, 857
—— orthoplumbate, 676
—— phosphates, 885
—— plumbite, 676
—— sulphate, 822
—— tetroxysulphate, 823
Plumbism, 589
Plumbites, 662, 665
Plumboaragonite, 855
Plumbobismuth glance, 491
Plumbocalcite, 835
Plumbocolumbite, 491, 897
Plumbocuprite, 796
Plumboferrite, 491
Plumboformic acid, 665
Plumboiodite, 768
Plumbojarosite, 491
Plumbonacrite, 838
Plumbo-oxichloroïoduro, 768
Plumboresinate, 877
Plumbosite, 491
Plumbostannite, 283, 491
Plumbostibnite, 491
Plumbous acid, 665
—— iodide, 757
—— metaplumbate, 671
—— nitrate, 856
—— orthophosphate, 876
Plumbum acido aereo mineralisatum, 829
—— —— vitriolico minseralisatum, 803
—— album, 276, 515
—— candidum, 276, 277, 484
—— corneum, 706
—— nativum, 490
—— nigrum, 276, 277, 484, 515
—— sulphure et argento mineralisatum, 781
—— ustum, 782
Plusinglanz, 254
Polychrom, 883
Polycrase, 4
Polycrasilites, 99
Polyhalite, 897
Polymignite, 3, 100
Polysphærite, 491, 883
Polytelite, 491
Potassium ammonium chloroplumbite, 729
—— bromoiodoplumbite, 775
—— bromoiodostannate, 463
—— bromostannate, 456
—— calcium phosphatoplumbate, 886
—— —— phosphatostannate, 483
—— —— phosphatothorate, 253
—— —— phosphatotitanate, 97
—— —— phosphatozirconate, 165
—— carbonatostannite, 480

Potassium chloroplumbate, 735
—— chlorostannate, 448
—— —— monohydrated, 449
—— chlorosulphatostannite, 478
—— chlorozirconate, 145
—— decaiodoplumbite, 774
—— decaiodotriplumbite, 774
—— deuterotriplumbate, 697
—— —— zirconium octohydroxypenta-sulphate, 159
—— dibromodiiodostannite, 461
—— dioxytetraiodotricarbonatotetraplumbite, 854
—— diplumbide, 608
—— distannide, 345
—— disulphatodiplumbite, 820
—— disulphatoplumbite, 820
—— dodecatitanate, 51
—— —— enneahydrated, 51
—— fluogermanate, 269
—— fluoplumbite, 704
—— fluostannate, 423
—— —— α-salt, 423
—— —— β-salt, 423
—— fluostannite, 422
—— fluotitanate, 71
—— —— hydrated, 71
—— fluozirconate, 140
—— germanium sulphate, 269
—— hemiplumbide, 608
—— hemistannide, 345
—— heptafluozirconate, 141
—— heptaiodoplumbite, 774
—— hexachlorostannite, 433
—— hexadecabromoplumbite, 751
—— hexafluohafniate, 171
—— hexahydroxyplatinate, 409
—— hexaiodostannite, 460
—— —— enneahydrated, 460
—— hexatitanate, 51
—— hydroctofluoplumbate, 705
—— hydrodiiodotrichlorostannite, 461
—— hydroplumbate, 666
—— hydrostannite, 391
—— hydrotriiodotrichlorostannite, 461
—— hyperoxypertitanate, 65
—— iodostannate, 463
—— isopropylstannonate, 410
—— lead dimetaphosphate, 881
—— —— dinitritodinitrate, 872
—— —— heptapyrophosphate, 880
—— —— octonitritotetranitrate, 872
—— —— orthophosphate, 876
—— —— pyrophosphate, 880
—— mesodistannate, 417
—— metaplumbate, 695
—— metatitanate, 50
—— —— tetrahydrated, 51
—— methyl stannonate, 410
—— monostannide, 345
—— nickel fluozirconate, 142
—— nitratoplumbite, 865
—— octobromodiplumbite, 752
—— octobromotriplumbite, 751
—— oxydiiodocarbonatoplumbite, 854
—— —— dihydrate, 854
—— oxyfluoperplumbate, 705
—— oxyfluopertitanate, 69
—— oxyphosphatostannate, 482
—— oxyphosphatotitanate, 96

Potassium parastannate, 417
—— paratrititanate, 51
—— paratrizirconate, 135
—— pentabromodiplumbite, 751
—— pentachlorodiplumbite, 728
—— pentafluotitanite, 66
—— pentafluozirconate, 140
—— perdistannate, 413
—— permonostannate, 413
—— pertitanic sulphate, 65
—— perzirconate, 132
—— plumbide, 608
—— plumbite, 665
—— silicozirconate, 134
—— sodium heptasulphatotetraplumbite, 821
—— stannate (α-), 414, 417
—— —— pentahydrate, 415
—— —— tetrahydrate, 415
—— —— trihydrate, 415
—— stannite, 391
—— sulphatopertitanate, 95
—— sulphatostannate, 479
—— sulphatotitanite, 93
—— sulphometastannate, 475
—— sulphorthostannate, 475
—— sulphostannite, 478
—— tetrabromoplumbite, 752
—— —— monohydrate, 752
—— tetrabromostannite, 453
—— tetrachloroplumbite, 729
—— tetrachlorostannite, 433
—— —— monohydrate, 433
—— tetraiodocarbonatoplumbite, 854
—— tetrastannide, 345
—— thorium bromide, 238
—— —— enneachloride, 235
—— —— enneafluoride, 227
—— —— henasulphate, 247
—— —— hexachloride, 235
—— —— hexafluoride, 228
—— —— hexanitrate, 251
—— —— hexasulphate, 247
—— —— hydroxychloride, 232
—— —— (di) orthophosphate, 253
—— —— orthophosphate, 252
—— —— pentacarbonate, 249
—— —— pentachloride, 235
—— —— pentafluoride, 228
—— —— pentanitrate, 251
—— —— phosphate, 253
—— —— tetrasulphate, 246
—— —— trihydrodecanitrate, 251
—— —— trisulphate, 247
—— titanic sulphate, 94
—— titanium carbonate, 96
—— titanous alum, 93
—— titanyl sulphate, 95
—— tribromoplumbite, 752
—— —— monohydrate, 752
—— —— tritahydrate, 752
—— tribromostannite, 453
—— tricarbonatodiplumbite, 854
—— trichloroplumbite, 729
—— —— tritahydrate, 729
—— trichlorostannite, 432
—— triiodoplumbite, 774
—— —— dihydrate, 774
—— —— monohydrate, 774
—— triiodostannite, 461

Potassium triphosphatostannate, 482
—— triphosphatotitanate, 96
—— trisulphatoplumbate, 823
—— trititanyl pentasulphate, 95
—— zirconate, 135
—— zirconium carbonate, 161
—— —— diorthophosphate, 164
—— (tetra) —— octohydroxypentasulphate, 159
—— —— tetrasulphate, 159
—— —— triorthophosphate, 164
—— —— trioxydisulphate, 158
—— zirconyl dihydropentafluoride, 140
—— —— (tri) tetrasulphate, 159
Potter's ore, 781
Preslite, 817
Propyl stannic bromide, 455
—— —— iodide, 463
—— stannonic acid, 410
Pseudoboleite, 491, 743
Pseudobrokite, 2, 59
—— α-, 60
—— β-, 60
Pseudocotunnia, 729
Pesudocotunnite, 491, 729
Pseudomendipite, 491
Psimythite, 852
Pufahlite, 477
Purpurea rubica, 673
Pyridine lead tetraiodide, 764
Pyrites, tin, 475
Pyrobenolite, 491
Pyrochlore, 3, 100
Pyromorphite, 883, 896
Pyrophanite, 3, 56
Pyroplumbic acid, 685

Q

Quartz, 897
Quinoline lead tetraiodide, 764
Quirogite, 491

R

Radioactivity, induced, 194
Radiothorium, 189
Radium emanation, 889
Rafaelite, 491, 739
Raspite, 491
Rathite, 49
Red-lead, 672
—— —— colloidal, 677
—— —— properties, chemical, 678
—— —— —— physical, 677
Rezbanyite, 491
Rhodonite, 897
Rhonite, 3
Riebeckite, 100
Rinkite, 3
Risörite, 3
Rock-salt, 897
Roeblingite, 491, 821
Rosenbuschite, 3, 100
Rosieresite, 878
Rubidium bromostannate, 456

Rubidium chloroplumbate, 735
—— chlorostannate, 449
—— chlorotitanite, 77
—— fluogermanate, 269
—— fluostannate, 423
—— fluotitanate, 72
—— fluozirconate, 141
—— heptafluozirconate, 141
—— hexafluoplumbate, 705
—— iodostannate, 463
—— pentabromotriplumbite, 752
—— pentachlorodiplumbite, 729
—— pentaiodostannite, 460
—— sulphatostannate, 479
—— sulphatotitanite, 93
—— tetrabromoplumbite, 752
—— tetrachloroplumbite, 730
—— —— hemihydrate, 730
—— tetraiodoplumbite, 775
—— thorium hexachloride, 235
—— —— —— enneahydrate, 235
—— —— hexanitrate, 251
—— —— octochloride, 235
—— —— pentafluoride, 228
—— —— trisulphate, 247
—— titanous alum, 95
—— —— pentachloride, 77
—— —— sulphate, 92
—— trichloroplumbite, 730
—— triiodoplumbite, 775
—— —— dihydrate, 775
—— triiodostannite, 460
—— trisulphatoplumbate, 824
—— zirconium trioxydisulphate, 158
Rutherfordite, 897
Rutile, 2, 30

S

Sacondios, 98
Sagenite, 2, 30, 34
Samarskite, 100, 185, 255, 896
Sandaraca, 672, 673
Sardinian, 803
Sartorite, 491
Saturnism, 589
Schapbachite, 491
Scheelite, 897
Schirmerite, 491
Schlorlomite, 3
Schönite, 897
Schörl, Hungarian red, 1
—— rouge, 30
Schorl indigo blue, 30
—— octahedral, 30
Schwartzembergite, 491, 768
Schwerbleierz, 681
Scoria argenti, 638
—— plumbi, 638
Selenium titanium dioxyoctochloride, 81, 85
Seligmannite, 491
Semseyite, 491
Senaite, 3, 56
Sexangulites plumbeus, 782
Shot metal, 578
Silberglötte, 644
Silex circonius, 98
Silicon bronze, 348
—— tin octofluoride, 422

Silver chloroplumbite, 730
—— dibrostannate, 449
—— copper lead octoxyhenacosichloride, 743
—— ethylstannonate, 410
—— fluostannate, 423
—— fluotitanate, 72
—— germanium lead sulphantimonite, 255
—— lead sulphide, 796
—— metaplumbate, 698
—— nitratoplumbite, 866
—— pentabromoplumbite, 753
—— pentamminotetraiodoplumbite, 777
—— percylite, 742
—— plumbite, 668
—— purple, 418
—— stannate (α-), 418
—— —— (β-), 418
—— —— heptahydrate, 418
—— —— trihydrate, 418
—— sulphatostannate, 479
—— sulphogermanate, 254, 275
—— sulphostannate, 254
—— tetraiodoplumbite, 777
—— tetritastannide, 369
—— thorium nitrate, 251
—— tin alloys, 368
—— triiodoplumbite, 777
—— tritastannide, 368
—— zirconium, 116
Sipylite, 100, 185
Smaltite, 897
Smelter's smoke, 503
Sodium barium silicotitanate, 54
—— bromostannate, 456
—— carbonatostannite, 480
—— chloropertitanate, 83
—— chloroplumbite, 727
—— chlorostannate, 448
—— chlorozirconate, 145
—— dichlorodibromostannite, 453
—— dihydrorthoplumbate, 698
—— dihydroxydichlorostannate, 448
—— dioxytetraiodotricarbonatotetraplumbite, 854
—— dipentitaplumbide, 606
—— diphosphatodistannate, 482
—— diphosphatostannate, 482
—— diplumbide, 607
—— distannide, 346
—— disulphatoplumbite, 821
—— fluoplumbite, 703
—— fluostannate, 423
—— fluotitanate, 70
—— fluozirconate, 139
—— hemipentaplumbide, 607
—— hemiplumbide, 606
—— hemistannide, 345
—— hemitriplumbide, 607
—— hexafluoplumbate, 704
—— hydrofluotitanate, 71
—— hydrometaplumbate, 697
—— hydroplumbite, 666
—— hydrostannite, 390
—— iodostannate, 463
—— iodostannite, 460
—— isopropylstannonate, 410
—— lead chlorophosphate, 885
—— —— dihydroxytetracarbonate, 855
—— —— hydroxychlorosulphate, 739

Sodium lead orthophosphate, 876
—— —— pentapyrophosphate, 880
—— —— pyrophosphate, 880
—— —— sulphide, 796
—— —— triphosphate, 882
—— mesodititanate, 52
—— mesotrititanate, 52
—— metaplumbate, 697
—— —— hexahydrate, 697
—— —— tetrahydrate, 697
—— —— trihydrate, 696
—— metatitanate, 51
—— metazirconate, 135
—— monostannide, 346
—— nitratoplumbite, 864, 866
—— orthodiplumbate, 698
—— orthoplumbate, 698
—— orthotitanate, 51
—— orthozirconate, 135
—— oxydiiodocarbonatoplumbite, 854
—— paratrititanate, 52
—— pentachlorodiplumbite, 727
—— permonostannate, 413
—— peroxyhypertitanate, 65
—— peroxypertitanate, 65
—— perzirconate, 132
—— phosphatopertitanates, 97
—— plumbide, 607
—— plumbite, 665
—— potassium heptasulphatotetraplumbite, 821
—— silicozirconate, 135
—— stannate (α-), 416
—— —— decahydrate, 416
—— —— enneahydrate, 416
—— —— henicosihydrate, 416
—— —— octohydrate, 416
—— —— tetrahydrate, 416
—— —— (β-), 417
—— stannite, 391
—— sulphatopertitanate, 95
—— sulphatoplumbite, 821
—— sulphometastannate, 475
—— sulphoplumbite, 796
—— sulphorthostannate, 474
—— tetrabromoplumbite, 753
—— tetraiodocarbonatoplumbite, 854
—— tetraiodoplumbite, 776
—— —— hexahydrate, 776
—— —— tetrahydrate, 776
—— tetritaplumbide, 606
—— tetritastannide, 345
—— thorium fluoride, 227
—— —— hexachloride, 235
—— —— hydroxytrichloride, 232
—— —— metaphosphate, 253
—— —— orthophosphate, 252
—— —— (di) orthophosphate, 253
—— —— pentacarbonate, 249
—— —— —— dihydrate, 249
—— —— —— tetrahydrate, 249
—— —— pentachloride, 235
—— —— pentanitrate, 251
—— —— pyrophosphate, 253
—— —— trisulphate, 246
—— —— —— dodecahydrate, 246
—— —— —— tetrahydrate, 246
—— titanite, 29
—— titanium phosphate, 96
—— titanous sulphate, 92

Sodium titanyl sulphate, 95
—— tribromoplumbite, 753
—— tridecafluozirconate, 140
—— triiodoplumbite, 776
—— triphosphatostannate, 483
—— triplumbide, 607
—— tritatitanate, 52
—— tritetritastannide, 345
—— zirconate, 135
—— zirconium carbonate, 161
—— —— octaorthophosphate, 164
—— —— tetraorthophosphate, 164
—— —— tetrasulphate, 159
—— —— triorthophosphate, 164
—— zirconyl (di) hexasulphate, 159
—— —— tetrasulphate, 159
Solders, 630
Solute metal, 362
Sparable tin, 394
Spatum plumbi, 829
Speculum metals, 348
Sphere, 3, 30, 54
Spinthere, 3
Spiritus argenti vivi sublimati, 436
—— fumans Libavii, 436
Spodumene, 897
Spuma argenti, 638
Stagno, 276
Stannates, 414
—— (α-), 414
—— (β-), 417
Stannic acid, 404
—— —— α-, 405
—— —— β-, 405
—— (β-) acid colloidal, 408
—— —— —— properties, 409
—— acid -colloidal, 411
—— —— —— properties, 411
—— bromide, 454
—— —— ethyl, 455
—— —— isopropyl, 455
—— —— methyl, 455
—— —— propyl, 455
—— —— tetrahydrated, 455
—— bromochlorides, 457
—— bromotrichloride, 457
—— bromotriiodide, 464
—— chloride, β-, 442
—— —— dihydrated, 437
—— —— enneahydrated, 437
—— —— ethyl, 446
—— —— isopropyl, 446
—— —— (di), 446
—— —— methyl, 446
—— —— pentahydrated, 437
—— —— properties, chemical, 448
—— —— —— physical, 457
—— —— tetrahydrated, 457
—— —— trihydrated, 437
—— chlorides, 436
—— chlorodisulphohydrate, 443
—— chloropentasulphohydrate, 443
—— chlorotetrasulphohydrate, 443
—— chlorotriiodide, 464
—— diamminobromide, 456
—— diamminochloride, 445
—— dibromodichloride, 457
—— dibromodiiodide, 464
—— dichloride (β-), 443
—— dichlorodiiodide, 463

Stannic dihydroxysulphate, 479
—— dinitrate (β-), 481
—— dinitroxylchloride, 445
—— disulphotetrachloride, 443
—— ditritaphosphinochloride, 445
—— ferrous cuprous sulphide, 475
—— fluoride, 422
—— hexamminoiodide, 463
—— hydroxide, 406, 408
—— hydroxytribromide, 455
—— iodide, 462
—— —— ethyl, 463
—— —— methyl, 463
—— —— propyl, 463
—— nitrate, 481
—— nitrogen chlorosulphide, 444
—— —— oxychloride, 445
—— —— trioxychloride, 445
—— nitroxylchloride, 445
—— octamminoiodide, 463
—— oxide, 386, 394
—— —— colloidal, 395
—— —— properties, chemical, 399
—— —— —— physical, 396
—— oxybromide, 455
—— oxychlorides, 440
—— oxydiphosphate, 482
—— oxyfluoride, 422
—— oxytrisulphide, 471
—— phosphoxylchloride, 446
—— pyrophosphate, 482
—— selenoxychloride, 444
—— sulphate, 479
—— —— dihydrated, 479
—— sulphatoplumbate, 822
—— sulphide, 469
—— —— colloidal, 470
—— —— properties, 471
—— sulphoiodide, 472
—— tetramminoiodide, 463
—— thorium tetrasulphate, 247
—— titanate, 56
—— triamminoiodide, 463
—— tribromochloride, 457
—— tribromoiodide, 464
—— trichloroiodide, 464
—— trioxide, 413
—— trioxydinitrate, 481
Stannite, 283, 394, 475
Stannites, 390
Stannoformic acid, 390
Stannones, 410
Stannosic chloride, 443
—— oxybromide, 453
—— tetrachlorodiiodide, 461
Stannostannic chloride, 443
—— oxybromide, 453
Stannous aminochloride, 430
—— and cadmium chlorides, 434
—— —— zinc chlorides, 434
—— bromide, 452
—— —— monohydrated, 453
—— bromoiodide, 461
—— chloride, 424
—— —— dihydrated, 425
—— —— monohydrated, 425
—— —— properties, chemical, 427
—— —— —— physical, 425
—— —— trihydrated, 425
—— chlorobromide, 453

Stannous chloroiodide, 460, 461
—— chloroplumbite, 732
—— cuprous chlorides, 433
—— —— stannate, 418
—— diamminobromide, 453
—— diamminoiodide, 459
—— dihydrazinochloride, 430
—— dihydrophosphate, 482
—— dioxysulphate, 478
—— enneamminobromide, 453
—— enneamminochloride, 430
—— enneamminoiodide, 459
—— hydrochloride, 428
—— hydrophosphate, 482
—— hydrosulphochloride, 466
—— hydroxide, 386
—— —— preparation, 389
—— —— properties, 389
—— iodide, 457
—— —— alkyl, 459
—— —— dihydrated, 458
—— —— monohydrate, 458
—— metaphosphate, 482
—— monamminoiodide, 459
—— nitrate, 480
—— orthophosphate, 481
—— oxide, 386
—— —— preparation, 386
—— —— properties, chemical, 389
—— —— —— physical, 387
—— oxycarbonate, 480
—— oxychloride, 428
—— oxyiodides, 459
—— oxynitrate, 480
—— oxysulphate, 478
—— pentamminobromide, 453
—— pentamminoiodide, 459
—— pentoxyhexachloride, 428
—— —— trihydrated, 428
—— pyrophosphate, 482
—— stannate, 386, 392
—— sulphate, 477
—— sulphide, 465
—— —— properties, chemical, 467
—— —— —— physical, 466
—— —— tritahydrated, 466
—— tetradecahydroxytetrachloride, 428
—— tetraiodoplumbite, 778
—— tetramminochloride, 430
—— tetramminoiodide, 459
—— tetraphosphate, 481
—— tetroxydichloride, 428
—— triamminobromide, 453
—— triamminoiodide, 459
—— trioxytetrachloride, 428
—— tristannate, 392
Stannum, 276, 277
—— calciforme, 394
—— nativum, 283
Stannyl ammonium chloride, 442
—— chloride, 442
—— heptachloride, 443
—— heptastannate, 392
—— hexastannate, 392
—— hydroxychloride, 442
—— icosistannate, 392
—— (di) platinum α-stannate, 420
Stasite, 491
Stokesite, 283
Stolzite, 491

Stream tin, 394
Strontium bromostannate, 456
—— chlorostannate, 449
—— —— tetrahydrate, 449
—— fluostannate, 423
—— fluotitanate, 72
—— —— dihydrated, 72
—— fluozirconate, 141
—— hexaiododiplumbite, 777
—— iodostannite, 460
—— isopropylstannonate, 410
—— lead oxychloride, 744
—— mesotrititanate, 54
—— metazirconate, 136
—— nitratoplumbite, 866
—— orthoplumbate, 699
—— plumbite, 668
—— stannate (α-), 419
—— sulphatostannate, 479
—— sulphometastannate, 476
—— tetrachloroplumbite, 730
—— tetrachlorostannite, 434
—— thorium orthophosphate, 252
—— titanic sulphate, 94
—— triplumbide, 614
Strüverite, 2
Sulphatotitanic acid, 92
Sulphogermanates, 274
Sulphometastannic acid, 473
Sulphorthostannic acid, 473
Sulphostannates, 473
Suroxigenation, 676
Susannite, 491, 853
Svanbergite, 877
Sylvine, 897

T

Tachyaphalite, 100
Tachyhydrite, 897
Tantalite, 255
Tantalum cassiterite, 394
—— zirconium, 117
Tarnovicite, 855
Tarnowitzite, 855
Teallite, 283, 477, 491
Tenn, 276
Terne plates, 630
Terra plumbaria citrina, 638
—— —— rubia, 638
Terrar, 121
Tertiarium, 630
Tetrachlorostannites, 429
Tetramethylarsonium iodostannate, 463
Tetraplumbic acid, 685
Thallic ammonium bromoplumbite, 753
—— —— chloroplumbite, 732
Thallium hemiplumbide, 626
—— lead alloys, 625
—— thorium carbonate, 249
—— —— enneasulphate, 247
—— —— trisulphate, 247
—— —— —— tetrahydrate, 247
—— —— trihydrate, 247
Thallous chlorostannate, 450
—— heptadecafluotrizirconate, 142
—— heptafluozirconate, 142
—— lead sulphide, 797
—— metaplumbate, 701

Thallous pentachloroplumbite, 632
—— pentachlorostannite, 434
—— pentafluozirconate, 142
—— sulphorthostannate, 476
—— thorium nitrate, 251
—— tribromoplumbite, 753
—— trichloroplumbite, 732
—— trichlorostannite, 434
—— triiodoplumbite, 778
—— zirconium enneasulphate, 166
—— —— pentasulphate, 160
—— —— tetrasulphate, 160
Thiostannates, 473
Thoria, 220
—— extraction, 178
—— purification, 181
Thorianite, 100, 176, 185, 896
Thoric acid, 224
Thorite, 175, 185
Thorium, 174
—— -A, 194
—— active deposit, 194
—— amalgam, 208
—— amminochlorides, 233
—— ammonium carbonate, 249
—— —— dodecachloride, 234
—— —— fluoride, 227
—— —— hexachloride, 234
—— —— hexanitrate, 251
—— —— hexasulphate, 246
—— —— hydronitrate, 251
—— —— pentachloride, 235
—— —— pentanitrate, 250
—— —— —— dihydrate, 251
—— —— —— pentahydrate, 250
—— —— pentasulphate, 246
—— —— tetrasulphate, 245
—— —— trisulphate, 245
—— atomic disintegration, 211
—— —— number, 211
—— —— weight, 210
—— -B, 194
—— —— hydride, 196
—— barium orthophosphate, 252
—— bromide, 236
—— bromophosphate, 252
—— -C, 196
—— —— hydride, 196
—— -C₂, 196
—— cæsium fluoride, 228
—— —— hexachloride, 235
—— —— —— dodecahydrate, 236
—— —— —— henahydrate, 235
—— —— —— octohydrate, 235
—— —— hexanitrate, 251
—— —— nitrate, 251
—— —— octochloride, 235
—— —— trisulphate, 247
—— carbonate, 248
—— cerium sulphate, 247
—— chloride, 228
—— —— dodecahydrated, 230
—— —— octohydrated, 230
—— chlorophosphate, 252
—— colloidal, 204
—— -D, 196
—— dihydropentasulphate, 245
—— dihydroperoxide, 225
—— dihydrotrisulphate, 245
—— dihydroxydibromide, 238

Thorium dihydroxydibromide, henahydrate, 238
—— —— tetrahydrate, 238
—— dihydroxydichloride, 232
—— —— octohydrated, 232
—— —— pentahydrated, 232
—— —— tetrahydrated, 232
—— diimide, 234
—— dioxide, 220
—— dipotassium orthophosphate, 253
—— disodium orthophosphate, 253
—— dodecamminochloride, 234
—— -E, 200
—— emanation, 192, 889
—— fluoride, 227
—— —— tetrahydrated, 227
—— hafnium zirconium orthosilicate, 167
—— hemiheptoxide, 225
—— hexamminochloride, 234
—— history, 174
—— hydride, 207
—— hydrocarbonate, 249
—— hydronitrate, 250
—— hydrophosphate, 253
—— hydroxide, 222
—— —— colloidal, 224
—— hydroxyhydrochlorides, 233
—— hydroxytribromide, 237
—— hydroxytrichloride, 232
—— —— henahydrated, 252
—— —— heptahydrated, 232
—— —— monohydrated, 232
—— hydroxytriiodide, 238
—— —— decahydrate, 238
—— individuality of, 209
—— iodide, 238
—— isotopes, 211
—— lead, 200
—— lithium hexachloride, 235
—— —— hydroxytrichloride, 232
—— —— nitrate, 251
—— —— oxychloride, 232
—— —— pentachloride, 235
—— —— sulphate, 246
—— magnesium hexanitrate, 251
—— mercuric octoiodide, 239
—— —— tetradecaiodide, 238
—— metacarbonate, 248
—— metahydroxide, 224
—— metanitrate, 250
—— metaoxychloride, 232
—— metaoxysulphate, 244
—— metaphosphate, 253
—— metoxide, 223
—— —— hydrochlorides of, 233
—— monohydroperoxide, 225
—— monoxide, 220
—— nitrate, 249
—— —— dodecahydrate, 249
—— —— hexahydrate, 250
—— —— pentahydrate, 250
—— —— tetrahydrate, 250
—— occurrence, 174
—— octamminochloride, 234
—— octodecamminochloride, 234
—— oxide, 220
—— —— colloidal, 224
—— oxycarbonate, 248
—— oxychloride, 231
—— oxydibromide, 237

Thorium oxyfluoride, 227
—— oxyheptasulphate, 244
—— oxynitrate, 250
—— oxysulphate, 244
—— oxysulphide, 240
—— pentatritaoxide, 220
—— peroxide, 220, 225
—— peroxychloride, 232
—— peroxysulphate, 244
—— phosphate, 252
—— potassium bromide, 238
—— —— enneachloride, 235
—— —— enneafluoride, 227
—— —— henasulphate, 247
—— —— hexachloride, 235
—— —— hexafluoride, 228
—— —— hexanitrate, 251
—— —— hexasulphate, 247
—— —— hydroxychloride, 232
—— —— orthophosphate, 252
—— —— pentacarbonate, 249
—— —— pentachloride, 235
—— —— pentafluoride, 228
—— —— pentanitrate, 251
—— —— phosphate, 253
—— —— tetrasulphate, 246
—— —— trihydrodecanitrate, 251
—— —— trisulphate, 247
—— preparation, 203
—— properties, chemical, 207
—— —— physical, 205
—— pyrophosphate, 253
—— radioactivity, 184
—— rubidium hexachloride, 235
—— —— —— enneahydrate, 235
—— —— hexanitrate, 251
—— —— octochloride, 235
—— —— pentafluoride, 228
—— —— trisulphate, 247
—— silver nitrate, 251
—— sodium fluoride, 227
—— —— hexachloride, 235
—— —— hydroxytrichloride, 232
—— —— metaphosphate, 253
—— —— orthophosphate, 252
—— —— pentachloride, 235
—— —— pentanitrate, 251
—— —— pyrophosphate, 253
—— —— trisulphate, 246
—— —— —— dodecahydrate, 246
—— —— —— tetrahydrate, 246
—— stannic tetrasulphate, 247
—— strontium orthophosphate, 252
—— sulphate, 240
—— —— dihydrated, 243
—— —— enneahydrated, 241
—— —— hemienneahydrated, 242
—— —— hexahydrated, 242
—— —— octohydrated, 242
—— —— tetrahydrated, 243
—— —— trihydrated, 243
—— sulphatometaphosphate, 253
—— sulphatostannate, 479
—— sulphide, 239
—— tetrabromide, 236
—— —— decahydrate, 237
—— —— dodecahydrate, 237
—— —— heptahydrate, 237
—— —— octohydrate, 237
—— tetrachloride dihydrated, 231

Thorium tetrachloride enneahydrated, 231
—— —— heptahydrated, 231
—— —— tetrahydrated, 231
—— tetrahydroperoxide, 225
—— tetraiodide, 238
—— —— decahydrate, 238
—— tetramide, 234
—— tetramminochloride, 234
—— tetroxydisulphide, 240
—— thallium carbonate, 249
—— —— enneasulphate, 247
—— —— nitrate, 251
—— —— trisulphate, 247
—— —— —— tetrahydrate, 247
—— —— —— trihydrate, 247
—— trialuminide, 208
—— triamminobromide, 238
—— tridecaoxycarbonate, 248
—— trioxide, 225
—— trioxycarbonate, 248
—— valency, 209
—— -X, 190
—— yttrium metatitanate, 59
—— zinc hexanitrate, 251
Thorogummite, 185
Thoron, 192, 889
Thoryl chloride, 231
—— sulphide, 240
Tigererz, 782
Tin, 276, 277
—— alloys, 344
—— analyses, 292
—— analytical reactions, 336
—— antimonide, 332
—— arsenide, 331
—— ash, 394
—— atomic number, 340
—— —— weight, 339
—— barium alloys, 372
—— bismuthide, 334
—— black, 287
—— block, 289
—— butter of, 424, 436
—— cadmium alloys, 376
—— -calcium alloys, 372
—— carbonate, 480
—— chloroform, 437
—— chrome pink, 421
—— colloidal, 292
—— concentrates, 286
—— -copper alloys (see copper-tin)
—— cupride, 351
—— diantimonide, 334
—— dihydride, 325
—— dioxide, 386, 394
—— diphosphohecachloride, 445
—— disintegration atoms, 340
—— ditritantimonide, 333
—— ditritarsenide, 331
—— electric smelting, 289
—— electronic structure, 299
—— extraction, 286, 290
—— filaments, 292
—— float, 394
—— flowers of, 394
—— fluorides, 422
—— gold alloys, 368
—— grain, 289
—— grey, 300
—— hemitriarsenide, 331

Tin hemitrioxide, 386, 392
—— hexitarsenide, 33
—— hexoxytetrachloride, 443
—— history, 278
—— hydride, 324
—— hydroxytrichloride, 442
—— indium alloys, 384
—— isotopes, 340
—— -lead alloys, 626
—— —— —— colloidal, 627
—— liquation, 289
—— lode, 286
—— -mercury alloys, 377
—— metallic precipitation, 338
—— monoarsenide, 331
—— monoxide, 386
—— nitrates, 480
—— occurrence, 280
—— ore, 394
—— —— needle, 394
—— oxychloride, 442
—— oxymuriate, 437
—— peroxide, 386
—— pest, 300
—— phosphates, 481
—— physiological action, 336
—— plumbite, 669
—— poling, 289
—— preparation, pure, 293
—— properties, chemical, 323
—— —— physical, 295
—— purification, 286
—— pyrites, 283, 475, 897
—— recovery from scraps, 291
—— reef, 286
—— refined, 289
—— refining, 289
—— —— electrical, 289
—— sesquioxide, 386, 392
—— —— hydrated, 392
—— sesquisulphide, 465, 468
—— —— hydrated, 468
—— silicon octofluoride, 422
—— silver alloys, 368
—— slip bands, 297
—— sparable, 394
—— stone, 394
—— strain disease, 202
—— stream, 394
—— strontium alloys, 372
—— sulphates, 477
—— sulphochlorides, 472
—— tetrachloride, 436
—— tetratritarsenide, 331
—— tetritoxide, 392
—— tetroxide, 386
—— -thallium alloys, 384
—— toad's eye, 394
—— tossing, 289
—— tree, 298, 338
—— trichloride, 424
—— tritatetroxide, 386
—— tritetritarsenide, 331
—— uses, 339
—— wood, 394
—— -zinc alloys, 374
—— zirconium, 117
—— —— alloys, 385
Tinder ore, 491
Titanamide, 84

Titanate, 54
Titanates, 2, 50
Titane oxyde, 30
—— —— chromifère, 31
Titaneisen, 56
—— axotome, 57
—— oxyde octahedral, 56
Titaneisenstein, 56
Titanerz, 56
Titania (see titanium dioxide)
Titanic acid, 27, 31
—— —— α-, 39
—— —— -β, 39
—— —— meta-, 40
—— —— ortho-, 39
—— alcogel, 39
—— barium sulphate, 94
—— bromide, 88
—— calcium sulphate, 94
—— etherogel, 39
—— glycerogel, 39
—— potassium sulphate, 94
—— salts, 27
—— strontium sulphate, 94
—— sulphatogel, 39
Titanite, 1, 3, 30
Titanium, 1
—— α-, 16
—— β-, 16
—— γ-, 16
—— alcoholotetrafluoride, 68
—— alloys, 22
—— amminochlorides, 83
—— ammonium carbonate, 96
—— —— oxysulphate, 95
—— amorphous, 8
—— analytical reactions, 22
—— argento-, 20
—— atomic number, 24
—— —— weight, 23
—— bromides, 87
—— bromonitride, 88
—— bromotrichloride, 88
—— calcium oxysulphide, 91
—— carbonate, 96
—— chlorides, 74
—— chloronitride, 84
—— chlorophosphate, 96
—— colloidal, 14
—— cupro-, 12, 18, 24
—— cuprosilico-, 12
—— diamminotetrafluoride, 67
—— dichloride, 74
—— dichlorodibromide, 88
—— difluoride, 66
—— dihydroxide, 28
—— dihydroxydichloride, 83
—— diiodide, 89
—— dinitrosyl hexachloride, 84
—— dioxide, 27, 31
—— —— colloidal, 39
—— —— extraction, 6
—— —— preparation, 32
—— —— properties, chemical, 41
—— —— —— physical, 33
—— dioxyoctochloride, 81
—— diphosphoryl decachloride, 85
—— discovery, 1
—— disulphate, 93
—— —— trihydrated, 93

Titanium disulphide, 90
—— disulphohydrate, 81
—— dititanite, 28
—— electronic structure, 24
—— ferro-, 11
—— ferrocarbo-, 11
—— ferrosilico-, 11
—— fluochloride, 81
—— fluorides, 66
—— hexamminotetrachloride, 84
—— hydride, 18
—— hydrotrichloride, 80
—— hydroxytribromide, 88
—— hydroxytrichloride, 83
—— iodides, 89
—— isotopes, 24
—— mangano-, 12, 24
—— monosulphate, 91
—— monosulphide, 90
—— monosulphohydrate, 81
—— monoxide, 27
—— nitrate, 96
—— nitrogen hexachlorotetrasulphide, 77
—— —— sulphotetrachloride, 84
—— —— sulphotrichloride, 84
—— occurrence, 2
—— octamminotetrabromide, 88
—— octamminotetrachloride, 84
—— oxydichloride, 82
—— oxyfluoride, 67
—— oxynitrate, 96
—— oxytrisulphate, 93
—— —— dihydrate, 94
—— —— monohydrate, 94
—— —— pentahydrate, 94
—— pentoxide, 64
—— phosphate, 96
—— phosphinotetrachloride, 85
—— phosphite, 96
—— phosphoric enneachloride, 85
—— phosphorous heptachloride, 85
—— phosphoryl heptachloride, 85
—— potassium carbonate, 96
—— preparation, 8
—— properties, chemical, 18
—— —— physical, 14
—— selenium dioxyoctachloride, 85
—— sesquichloride, 75
—— sesquioxide, 27, 28
—— sesquisulphate, 91
—— sesquisulphide, 90
—— sodium phosphate, 96
—— sulphates, 91
—— sulphatotetrachloride, 85
—— sulphides, 90
—— sulphochloride, 81, 90
—— sulphoctochloride, 84
—— tetrabromide, 88
—— —— disulphohydrate, 88
—— —— sulphohydrate, 88
—— tetrachloride, 78, 84
—— —— dihydrated, 81
—— —— pentahydrated, 81
—— —— properties, chemical, 80
—— —— —— physical, 79
—— tetrafluoride, 67
—— —— dihydrated, 67
—— tetraiodide, 89
—— tetramide, 84
—— tetramminotetrachloride, 83

Titanium tetramminotetrafluoride, 67
—— tribromide, 87
—— trichloride, 75
—— —— hexahydrated, 77
—— trifluoride, 66
—— trihydroxide, 29
—— trihydroxybromide, 88
—— trihydroxychloride, 82, 83
—— trihydroxyorthophosphate, 97
—— triiodide, 89
—— trioxide, 27
—— —— hydrated, 63
—— valency, 23
Titanoantimonites, 3
Titanochloroform, 80
Titanoferrite, 2, 57
Titanomagnetite, 27, 28
Titanomorphite, 3
Titanonium salts, 82
Titano-olivine, 54
Titanosic oxide, 28
Titanosiderum, 56
Titanosilicates, 3
Titanosulphuric acid, 92
Titanous acid, 29
—— ammonium alum, 92
—— —— sulphate, 92
—— bromide, 87
—— cæsium alum, 93
—— —— pentachloride, 77
—— chloride, 75
—— hydrosulphate, 91
—— hydroxide, 29
—— iodide, 89
—— oxide, 28
—— oxychloride, 82
—— potassium sulphate, 93
—— rubidium alum, 93
—— —— pentachloride, 77
—— —— sulphate, 92
—— sodium sulphate, 92
—— sulphate, 91
—— titanate, 30
Titanyl ammonium sulphate, 95
—— chloride, 82
—— dichloride, 82
—— dititanite, 30
—— metaphosphate, 96
—— (tri) potassium pentasulphate, 95
—— —— sulphate, 95
—— sodium sulphate, 95
—— sulphate, 93
Toad's-eye tin, 394
Topaz, 897
Tourmaline, 897
Trichlorogermane, 263
Trigermane, 264
Trigonite, 491
Triphyllen, 897
Triplumbic acid, 685
Tritomite, 100
Tscheffkinite, 3
T-siloxyd, 25
Tsumebite, 877
Tuffa, 897
Tungsten zirconium, 117
Turmali, 98
Turner's yellow, 741, 742
Type metal, 362, 580

U

Uddevallite, 57
Uguentum plumbi acetatis, 591
—— —— carbonatis, 591
—— —— iodide, 591
Uhligite, 100, 137
Uraninite, 100, 491
Uranium ferrous yttrium metatitanate, 59
Uranothorite, 175, 185

V

Vanadinite, 491
Vauquelinite, 491
Veneris crisis, 34
Venus' hair stone, 34
Verde antiquo, 357
Veronese yellow, 742
Verre de plomb, 639

W

Warwickite, 3, 54
Washingtonite, 2, 57
Wasmium, 174
Weibullite, 491
Welsbach's mantle, 218
Werkblei, 504
White-lead, 841
—— composition, 846
—— Dutch process, 842
—— electrolytic process, 846
—— French process, 845
—— G. Bischof's process, 845
—— German process, 844
—— Klangenfurth process, 844
—— mild process, 845
—— non-poisonous, 818
—— precipitation process, 845
—— properties, 847
—— quick process, 846
—— stack process, 842
—— sublimed, 818
—— Venetian process, 841
—— W. H. Rowley's process, 845
—— W. L. Matheson's process, 845
Wiikite, 100
Wilkite, 3
Wiltshireite, 491
Wöhlerite, 100
Wolframite, 897
Wood-tin, 394
Wulfenite, 491

X

Xanthitane, 3
Xenon, 889
—— atomic weight, 947
—— electronic structure, 949
—— history, 890
—— hydrate, 943
—— isotopes, 948
—— occurrence, 892
—— preparation, 902
—— properties, chemical, 941
—— —— physical, 900
Xenotime, 100, 185

Y

Yellow, Cassel's, 742
—— mineral, 742
—— Turner's, 741, 742
—— veronese, 742
Youngite, 797
Yttrium ferrous uranium metatitanate, 59
—— sulphatostannate, 479
—— thorium metatitanate, 59
Yttrocrasite, 3, 59
Yttrotitanite, 3

Z

Zerk, 98
Zinc and stannous chlorides, 434
—— blende, 255, 897
—— chloroplumbite, 731
—— chlorostannate, 449
—— ethylstannonate, 410
—— fluostannate, 424
—— fluotitanate, 73
—— —— hexahydrated, 73
—— fluozirconate, 141
—— hexaiodoplumbite, 778
—— lead sulphide, 797
—— mesopentatitanate, 56
—— metaplumbate, 701
—— metatitanate, 55
—— orthodititanate, 55
—— orthotitanate, 55
—— paratrititanate, 55
—— plumbite, 669
—— sesquititanate, 55
—— stannate, (α-), 419
—— tetritastannide, 374
—— thorium hexanitrate, 251
—— titanate, acid, 55
—— titanide, 20
—— zirconate, 136
Zinkenite, 491
Zinn, 276
Zinngraupen, 394
Zinnkies, 475
Zinnkupferglanz, 475
Zinnstein, 394
Zircon, 98, 100, 897
Zirconates, 100, 134
Zirconerde, 99
Zirconia, 124
—— extraction, 101
Zirconiferous, 896
Zirconite, 99
Zirconium, 98
—— ammonium carbonate, 161
—— —— octohydroxyhexasulphate, 159
—— —— tetrasulphate, 159
—— —— (tri) tetrasulphate, 159
—— amorphous, 110
—— analytical reaction, 118
—— atomic number, 117
—— —— weight, 118
—— bromides, 149
—— carbonate, 160
—— chlorides, 143
—— cobalt, 117
—— colloidal, 109
—— columbium, 117

Zirconium, copper, 116
—— crystalline, 110
—— decahydroxytrisulphate, 157
—— —— decahydrated, 156
—— —— dihydrated, 156
—— dichloride, 143
—— dihydride, 114
—— dihydrotrisulphate, 154
—— —— trihydrated, 154
—— dihydrotrisulphide, 154
—— —— monohydrated, 154
—— (di) dihydroxytrisulphate, 156
—— —— pentahydrated, 156
—— dioxide, 124
—— —— properties, chemical, 128
—— —— —— physical, 125
—— electronic structure, 118
—— fluorides, 137
—— gold, 116
—— graphitic, 106, 110
—— hemipentoxide, 123
—— heptoxypentasulphide, 155
—— —— dodecahydrate, 155
—— hexaiodide, 151
—— history, 98
—— hydride, 114
—— hydrophosphate, 163
—— hydroxide hydrogel, 131
—— —— hydrosol, 130
—— hydroxides, 128
—— iodides, 149
—— iron, 117
—— isotopes, 118
—— lead, 117
—— magnesium, 116
—— mercury, 116
—— monoxide, 123
—— nickel, 117
—— nitrate, 161
—— —— pentahydrated, 162
—— occurrence, 99
—— octoxytetrachloride, 147
—— oxides, 123
—— oxytrisulphate, 156
—— pentoxytrisulphate, 155
—— —— octohydrated, 155
—— peroxide, 131
—— phosphates, 163
—— phosphorus oxyhenichloride, 145
—— —— tridecachloride, 145
—— potassium carbonate, 161
—— —— diorthophosphate, 164
—— —— (di) octohydroxypentasulphate, 159
—— —— (tetra) octohydroxypentasulphate, 159
—— —— tetrasulphate, 159
—— —— triorthophosphate, 174
—— —— trioxydisulphate, 158
—— preparation, 106
—— properties, chemical, 114
—— —— physical, 110
—— pyrophosphate, 163
—— sesquioxide, 123
—— silver, 116
—— sodium carbonate, 161
—— —— octa-orthophosphate, 164
—— —— tetraorthophosphate, 164
—— —— tetrasulphate, 159
—— —— triorthophosphate, 164

Zirconium sulphate, 152
—— —— monohydrated, 153
—— —— tetrahydrated, 153
—— sulphide, 152
—— tantalum, 117
—— tetrabromide, 149
—— —— decammino-, 149
—— —— tetrammino-, 149
—— tetrachloride, 143
—— —— diammino-, 145
—— —— octammino-, 145
—— —— tetrammino-, 145
—— —— triammino-, 145
—— tetrafluoride, 137
—— —— hemipentitammino-, 138
—— —— trihydrated, 137
—— tetraiodide, 150
—— —— heptammino-, 151
—— —— hexammino-, 151
—— —— octammino-, 151
—— —— tetrammino-, 151
—— tetraoxydisulphate, 156
—— —— octohydrate, 156
—— thallous enneasulphate, 160
—— —— pentasulphate, 160
—— —— tetrasulphate, 160
—— thorium hafnium orthosilicate, 167
—— tin, 117
—— titanate, 56
—— trichloride, 143
—— trihydroxybromide, 150
—— trioxide, 123, 132
—— trioxydibromide, 150
—— —— dodecahydrated, 150
—— trioxydichloride, 147
—— —— trihydrated, 147
—— trioxysulphate, 156
—— —— octohydrate, 156
—— tungsten, 117
—— uses, 120
—— valency, 117
Zirconopyrophyllite, 136
Zirconyl, 134
—— ammonium tetrasulphate, 159
—— —— trisulphate, 159
—— bromide, 150
—— —— hemiheptahydrated, 150

Zirconyl bromide, octohydrated, 150
—— —— tetrahydrated, 150
—— carbonate, 160
—— chloride, 146
—— —— dihydrated, 146
—— —— hemiheptahydrated, 146
—— —— hexahydrated, 146
—— —— octohydrated, 146
—— —— tetrahydrated, 146
—— —— trihydrated, 146
—— diamminonitrate, 162
—— —— dihydrated, 162
—— dihydrofluoride, 138
—— —— dihydrated, 138
—— dihydrophosphate, 163
—— disulphatozirconate, 137
—— fluoride, 138
—— —— dihydrated, 138
—— hydrosulphate, 154
—— —— trihydrated, 154
—— hydroxide, 129
—— hydroxybromide, 150
—— hydroxyiodide, 151
—— hydroxynitrate, 161
—— —— dihydrated, 161
—— iodide, octohydrated, 151
—— metaphosphate, 163
—— nitrate, 161
—— —— dihydrated, 161
—— —— hemiheptanitrate, 161
—— potassium dihydropentafluoride, 140
—— pyrophosphate, 163
—— (di) sodium hexasulphate, 159
—— sulphate, 155
—— —— dihydrated, 155
—— —— monohydrated, 155
—— —— tetrahydrated, 155
—— sulphide, 152
—— (tetrahydroxy) zirconate, 130
—— —— potassium tetrasulphate, 159
—— —— sodium tetrasulphate, 159
Zirkelite, 3, 100
Zirkite, 126
Zorgite, 491
Zundererz, 491
Zurinite, 30
Zwitter, 394

END OF VOL. VII